Henry Gray

ANATOMY

OF

THE HUMAN BODY

BY

HENRY GRAY, F.R.S.

*Late Fellow of the Royal College of Surgeons; Lecturer on Anatomy at St. George's
Hospital Medical School, London*

TWENTY-SEVENTH EDITION, EDITED BY

CHARLES MAYO GOSS, M.D.

*Managing Editor of the Anatomical Record; Professor of Anatomy,
Louisiana State University School of Medicine,
New Orleans, Louisiana*

1174 Illustrations mostly in Color

LEA & FEBIGER

PHILADELPHIA

Library of Congress Catalog Card Number: 59-12082

Printed in the United States of America

HENRY GRAY, F.R.S., F.R.C.S.

THE READERS of Gray's Anatomy will be interested to learn something about the originator of this now famous book which has reached its one hundredth year of publication. Although he achieved great distinction during his short lifetime, as well as renown for his book later, astonishingly little has been recorded of the personal history of Henry Gray. He was born in 1827, probably in London. His father was private messenger to George IV and William IV. He had two brothers and one sister, but in 1908 the only surviving relative, a niece, could give no information about his life history. Nothing is known of his early schooling but it must have been of high excellence to have fitted him for the scholarly accomplishments which he achieved at an early age.

His signature appears on the pupil's book at St. George's Hospital, London, as a "perpetual student" entering on the 6th of May, 1845. He is described by those who knew him as "a most painstaking and methodical worker, and one who learned his anatomy by the slow but invaluable method of making dissections for himself." He must have had much greater brilliance than this statement would indicate because four years later, in 1849, his name appears in the Proceedings of the Royal Society with the M.R.C.S. after it, the approximate equivalent of our M.D. While still a student in 1848, he won the triennial prize of the Royal College of Surgeons for an essay entitled "The Origin, Connections and Distribution of the Nerves to the Human Eye and Its Appendages, Illustrated by Comparative Dissections of the Eye in Other Vertebrate Animals."

He was appointed for the customary year as house surgeon to St. George's Hospital in 1850. Successively thereafter he held the posts of demonstrator of anatomy, curator of the museum, and lecturer on anatomy at St. George's Hospital. In 1861 he was surgeon to St. James Infirmary and was a candidate for the post of assistant surgeon to St. George's Hospital and would certainly have been elected if he had lived. Unfortunately he was stricken by an attack of confluent smallpox, which he contracted while looking after his nephew who had fallen a victim to the same disease, and died at the early age of thirty-four. Sir Benjamin Brodie, president of the Royal Society, wrote, "I am much grieved about poor Gray. His death, just as he was on the point of obtaining the reward of his labors, is a sad event indeed . . . Gray is a great loss to the hospital and school. Who is there to take his place?"

During his lifetime he received outstanding recognition for his original investigations. That they have received so little mention since his death is as surprising as the lack of information about his life. The study of the eye which won him the Royal College of Surgeons prize was expanded into an embryological work, "On the development of the retina and optic nerve, and of the membranous labyrinth and auditory nerve," published in the Philosophical Transactions of the Royal Society in 1850. It contains the earliest description of the histogenesis of the retina. Two years later the Transactions contain another article, "On the development of the ductless glands in the chick." This must have stimulated his interest in the spleen, which he classed as a ductless gland, because he obtained an allotment of funds for further study from the annual grant placed at the disposal of the Royal Society by Parliament for the promotion of science. The result was a monograph of 380 pages, "On the Structure and Use of the Spleen," which won him the triennial

Astley Cooper Prize of £300 (about $1,500.00) in 1853. It was published by J. W. Parker and Son in 1854, but appears now to be excessively rare. Numerous "first observations" recorded in this book have escaped notice by all subsequent authors writing about the spleen. He described, among other things, the origin of the spleen from the dorsal mesogastrium ten years before Müller who is usually given credit for the discovery.

As a result of his ability and accomplishment he was made a Fellow of the Royal Society at the very young age of twenty-five. Besides Anatomy, his interests also included pathological and clinical investigation. In 1853 he had a paper in the Medico-Chirurgical Proceedings entitled, "An Account of a Dissection of an Ovarian Cyst Which Contained Brain," and in 1856 a more extensive treatise entitled, "On Myeloid and Myelo-Cystic Tumours of Bone; Their Structure, Pathology, and Mode of Diagnosis."

His crowning achievement, however, and the one which is the source of his lasting fame is the publication, "Anatomy, Descriptive and Surgical," now widely known as Gray's Anatomy.

100 YEARS OF GRAY'S ANATOMY

The first edition of Gray's Anatomy was published in London by J. W. Parker and Son in 1858 and in June of the following year in Philadelphia by Blanchard and Lea who had purchased the American rights for the book. The American edition was identical with the English, except that many typographical errors had been corrected, the index considerably improved, and the binding made more rugged. It contained xxxii + 754 pages and 363 figures. The drawings were the work of Dr. H. Van Dyke Carter of whom Gray writes in his preface, "The Author gratefully acknowledges the great services he has derived, in the execution of this work, from the assistance of his friend, Dr. H. V. Carter, late Demonstrator of Anatomy at St. George's Hospital. All the drawings, from which the engravings were made, were executed by him. In the majority of cases, they have been copied from, or corrected by, recent dissections. made jointly by the Author and Dr. Carter."

Blanchard and Lea obtained the services of Dr. R. J. Dunglison to edit the first and the next four American editions. He corrected the typographical and other small errors and improved the index but made very few alterations or additions in the text. Almost no adaptation was required because medical education in this country and in England were still much alike.

Henry Gray had just finished preparing the second edition before his untimely death, and it was brought out in 1860 in England and in 1862 in this country under the editorship of Dunglison. The next edition in America was a "New American from the 5th English Edition" in 1870 bound in either cloth or sheep. Another pause, and there appeared the "New American from the 8th English" in 1878, and "The New American from the 10th English" in 1883. Dunglison was the editor again, but a new editor, W. W. Keen, revised extensively the section on topographical anatomy at the end of the book. The next edition, a "New American from the Eleventh English" in 1887 was edited and thoroughly revised by W. W. Keen. Color was used for the first time in the chapters on blood vessels and nerves. The New American from the Thirteenth English appeared in 1893 apparently edited by Keen and others.

In 1896 the reference to the English edition was dropped and we have the Fourteenth Edition with the editors Bern B. Gallaudet, F. J. Brockway, and J. P. McMurrich. J. C. DaCosta, editor of the Sixteenth Edition in 1905, expanded the book, introducing much new material. E. A. Spitzka assisted DaCosta with the Seventeeth Edition in 1908 and edited the next two alone in 1910 and 1913. The publishers also tried a "New American from the Eighteenth English Edition" in 1913, but its sale was much smaller than that of the American edition of that year. In 1918 W. H. Lewis began his editorship, giving the book a scholarly treatment, reducing its length, improving the sections on Embryology, and generally giving a more straight-forward treatment of the various chapters. For his last edition, the Twenty-fourth in 1942, he had the assistance of six associate editors.

Beginning with the Twentieth Edition in 1918, new editions appeared at regular intervals of six years; their dates and the names of the editors are listed on page 16. The interval was changed to five years for the present edition in order to have its publication fall on the 100th year. With the 1954 edition the book has grown from 786 pages with 363 engravings to 1480 pages with 1202 engravings and the price from $7.00 to $16.00. The total number of copies printed within 100 years before this 1959 edition was 572,500, a stack of books twenty-four miles high weighing 2,000 tons.

During the last fifty years the American and English editions have tended to drift apart. Even from an early date, new American editions were less frequent than the English, and if the American editions had been numbered independently from the beginning the present edition would be the twenty-second, whereas the current English edition is the thirty-second. Somewhat more of the imprint of Henry Gray has been preserved in the American edition, in the illustrations especially, as it still has 211 of the original drawings by Carter but only some twenty-five have not been altered or redrawn in the latest English edition. Nevertheless, both books are Gray's Anatomy, both have the unmistakable stamp of their originator, and both uphold his fine tradition.

PREFACE TO TWENTY-SEVENTH EDITION.

THIS EDITION finds Gray's *Anatomy* in its hundredth year with its popularity undiminished. The book is still dominated by the genius of Henry Gray, both as an anatomist and as a teacher, and of his friend, H. Van Dyke Carter, who made the drawings in the first edition. As in the last edition, a special effort has been made to preserve the flavor of their original work where ever possible.

In the preparation of a new revision, the editor must rely heavily upon the criticisms and suggestions of his colleagues for guidance. Two opinions are continually in conflict, one demanding amplification, the other elimination. There are those who would like to have the book an encyclopedia, containing detailed information in many specialized fields of anatomy. This would produce a work well beyond the bounds of a single volume. For example, a number of requests have been made for greater emphasis on *x*-ray anatomy. It is not feasible to attempt more than the presentation of a point of view and the selected *x*-ray photographs in the second chapter accomplish this. Others have suggested that the embryology and histology be eliminated because they cannot be presented adequately and because the students must purchase separate texts for the courses dealing with them. The decision has been made to retain them, nevertheless, because the editor has found, in his discussions with medical students and other users of the book, that the brief summaries of these subjects are popular and frequently used for preliminary reading and review.

Many teachers have expressed the opinion that the chapter on the central nervous system was too extensive, especially since here again the student must obtain a separate text. In this edition, the chapter has been completely rewritten, simplified, and reduced in length by fifty pages. This was effected largely by the avoidance of repetition and by replacing illustrations of limited value with a smaller number of those with a more comprehensive purpose. Extensive cross references to the illustrations and descriptions in other parts of the book are used in place of repetition. Although the greatest emphasis is placed on morphological and structural features, function is constantly woven in and implied without attempting to turn this chapter into a complete treatise on neurology. The subject matter is confined to the facts more firmly established by clinical and experimental research; controversial matters are largely omitted. Important recent discoveries are not overlooked, however, and references to the original articles containing them have been included. It has been constantly kept in mind that this chapter should contain the basic anatomical information required by a medical student in preparation for his future work with neurological patients.

The cardiovascular system has been split into three parts; the heart, the arteries, and the veins, each with its own section on embryology. The chapter on the heart has been almost completely rewritten and many new illustrations added. The description of the early development of this organ contains new material emphasizing mammalian embryos, and the rest of the embryology is given rather full treatment in accord with the growing interest in congenital anomalies. The arteries of the upper abdomen are more fully described including important statistics on the variations.

As a result of the many past revisions, a few inconsistencies of arrangement have been left in certain chapters. The logical plan of having embryology first and histology last in the different chapters and sections has been followed throughout. The histology of all the connective tissues has been added to that of bone and moved to the end of the Osteology chapter. The histology of muscle is at the end of its chapter, that of the heart is last in its chapter, and the histology of blood vessels is combined at the end of the chapter on veins. Nervous tissue now includes the peripheral nerve endings other than special senses, and is placed at the end of the Central Nervous System chapter. Other changes in this edition include the addition of new illustrations in various parts, notably in the sections on the skin and on the liver. The "Ductless Glands" have been named the "Endocrine Glands" and their description expanded and brought up to date.

The new Paris nomenclature has been adopted throughout the book with a few unavoidable exceptions, particularly where changes would be of little significance and would involve considerable expense in relabelling figures. In the central nervous system, the terms anterior and posterior have been abandoned in favor of the more accurate dorsal, ventral, rostral, and so forth. It is inevitable that this change will be universally adopted, and it is regrettable that the International Nomenclature Commission did not eliminate the many inconsistencies, such as the ventral roots of the spinal nerves coming from anterior columns of the spinal cord.

As in the last edition, references to original articles have been included in newly written parts of the text. References at the end of a paragraph are not always used to authenticate the statements preceding them. They may refer to more detailed and extensive accounts of the same subject in which the reader can find further information. The lists of references at the ends of the chapters have been revised and brought up to date. The editor wishes that all users of the book would realize that details of anatomy not included in the text are almost always to be found in one of these references because they have been deliberately chosen with this in mind.

It is a pleasure to thank Don Alvarado for a number of new drawings. In them he has followed the highly-praised style of Van Dyke Carter of printing the labels on the structures in the drawing as much as possible. Acknowledgement is also made to Fr. Kopsch and the publishers of the Rauber-Kopsch *Anatomie des Menschen* for permission to use a number of illustrations. The latter were favored because they also make effective use of labels written on the structures in the drawings. For permission to use illustrations from their publications, grateful acknowledgement is made to: A. R. Buchanan, W. E. Le G. Clark, C. L. Davis, T. C. Kramer, W. J. S. Kreig, R. H. Licata, N. A. Michels, B. M. Patten, A. T. Rasmussen, and R. Warwick; also to J. B. Lippincott Company for figures from Villiger-Addison and from Tandler.

I am grateful to my students and to my colleagues in the Anatomists' Association for their interested suggestions and corrections, especially A. R. Buchanan and T. H. Evans; to General Troy H. Middleton, President of Louisiana State University, Professor Richard J. Russell, Dean of the Graduate School, and Doctor William W. Frye, Dean, and many other loyal friends in the School of Medicine for their interest and support; to the staff of the L.S.U. Medical Library, especially Marjorie LeDoux and Darthy Liptak, for assistance with the bibliographic references, and to the faculty and staff of the Department of Anatomy, especially Marilyn Zimny and Ruth Miller for their help and encouragement, and Victoria Page and Gloria Miller for secretarial assistance. Again, as always, it is a pleasure to thank all the people at Lea & Febiger for their encouragement, confidence, and generosity.

CHARLES M. GOSS

NEW ORLEANS, LA.

CONTENTS.

EMBRYOLOGY.

The Cell 21
Cell Division 21
The Ovum 24
   Ovulation 24
   Maturation 24
     Meiosis 25
The Spermatozon 26
Fertilization of the Ovum 27
Segmentation of the Fertilized Ovum . . 28
Implantation 30
Germ Layers 30
Development of the Embryo 32

Neural Groove and Tube 35
Primitive Segments or Somites . . . 35
Early Growth of the Embryo 35
Development of the Body Cavities . . 37
Branchial Region 39
Fetal Membranes and Placenta . . . 46
   Chorion 47
   Maternal Tissues 49
   Placenta 54
   Yolk Sac 54
   The Allantois 55
Growth of the Embryo and Fetus . . . 56

SURFACE AND TOPOGRAPHICAL ANATOMY.

The Head 61
The Neck 69
The Back 75
The Thorax 76

The Abdomen 81
The Perineum 96
The Upper Extremity 100
The Lower Extremity 110

OSTEOLOGY.

Development of the Skeleton 119

THE VERTEBRAL COLUMN.

General Characteristics of a Vertebra . . 127
The Cervical Vertebræ 128
The Thoracic Vertebræ 132
The Lumbar Vertebræ 135
The Sacral and Coccygeal Vertebræ . . 137
Ossification of the Vertebral Column . . 142
The Vertebral Column as a Whole . . 145

THE THORAX. . . . 147

The Sternum 149
The Ribs 153
The Costal Cartilages 157

THE SKULL.

The Exterior of the Skull 158
The Interior of the Skull 171
Differences in the Skull Due to Age . . 177
Sex Differences, Function and Cleft
   Palate 179
The Mandible (Lower Jaw) 179
The Hyoid Bone 185
The Cranial Bones.
   The Occipital Bone 186
   The Parietal Bone 190
   The Frontal Bone 193
   The Temporal Bone 195
   The Sphenoid Bone 204
   The Ethmoid Bone 209
   Sutural Bones 213

The Facial Bones.
   The Nasal Bone 213
   The Maxilla (Upper Jaw) 214
   The Lacrimal Bone 220
   The Zygomatic Bone 220
   The Palatine Bone 222
   The Inferior Nasal Concha . . . 225
   The Vomer 226

THE EXTREMITIES.

The Bones of the Upper Extremity
   The Clavicle 227
   The Scapula 230
   The Humerus 235
   The Radius 246
   The Ulna 247
The Hand 248
   The Carpus 248
   The Metacarpus 254
   The Phalanges of the Hand . . . 257
The Bones of the Lower Extremity.
   The Hip Bone 258
     The Ilium 258
     The Ischium 261
     The Pubis 263
     The Acetabulum 264
   The Pelvis 265
   The Femur 269
   The Patella 282
   The Tibia 283
   The Fibula 287
The Foot 289
   The Tarsus 289
   The Metatarsus 299
   The Phalanges of the Foot . . . 302

Comparison of the Bones of the Hand
   and Foot 303
The Sesamoid Bones 304

Histological Structure of Connective Tissue 305
   Cartilage 306
   Bone 310

JOINTS AND LIGAMENTS.

Development of the Joints 321
Classification of Joints 322
Structures Composing Movable Joints . 325

ARTICULATIONS OF THE TRUNK.

Articulations of the Vertebral Column . 326
  Articulations of Vertebral Bodies . 326
  Articulations of Vertebral Arches . 329
  Articulation of the Atlas with the
    Epistropheus or Axis. . . . 331
Articulations of the Vertebral Column
  with the Cranium 334
Articulation of the Mandible . . . 335
Costovertebral Articulations . . . 337
Sternocostal Articulations 341
Articulations of the Sternum . . . 343
Mechanism of the Thorax . . . 343
Articulation of the Vertebral Column with
  the Pelvis 345
Articulations of the Pelvis 345
Mechanism of the Pelvis 350

ARTICULATIONS OF THE UPPER EXTREMITY.

Sternoclavicular Articulation . . . 352

Acromioclavicular or Scapuloclavicular
  Articulation 354
The Ligaments of the Scapula . . . 355
Humeral Articulation or Shoulder-joint . 356
Elbow-joint 360
Radioulnar Articulations 364
Radiocarpal Articulation or Wrist-joint . 366
Intercarpal Articulations 369
Carpometacarpal Articulations . . . 371
Intermetacarpal Articulations . . . 372
Metacarpophalangeal Articulations . . 372
Articulations of the Digits 374

ARTICULATIONS OF THE LOWER EXTREMITY.

Coxal Articulation or Hip-joint . . . 374
The Knee-joint 380
Articulations between the Tibia and
  Fibula 388
Talocrural Articulations or Ankle-joint . 390
Intertarsal Articulations. 393
Tarsometatarsal Articulations . . . 399
Intermetatarsal Articulations . . . 400
Metatarsophalangeal Articulations. . . 401
Articulations of the Digits 401
Arches of the Foot 401

MUSCLES AND FASCIAE.

Development of the Muscles . . . 405
Arrangement of Muscles and Fasciæ . . 407
Fasciæ 407
Structure and Attachment of Muscles . 411
Muscle Action 411

THE MUSCLES AND FASCIÆ OF THE HEAD.

The Facial Muscles 413
The Muscles of Mastication . . . 422

THE MUSCLES AND FASCIÆ OF THE ANTERO-LATERAL REGION OF THE NECK.

The Superficial Cervical Muscle . . 426
The Cervical Fasciæ 426
The Lateral Cervical Muscles . . . 431
The Suprahyoid Muscles 432
The Infrahyoid Muscles 433
The Anterior Vertebral Muscles . . 436
The Lateral Vertebral Muscles . . 436

THE FASCIÆ AND MUSCLES OF THE TRUNK.

The Deep Muscles of the Back . . . 438
The Suboccipital Muscles 445
The Muscles of the Thorax 446
The Fasciæ and Muscles of the Abdomen . 453
  The Antero-lateral Muscles of the
    Abdomen. 453
  The Posterior Muscles of the
    Abdomen. 467
The Fasciæ and Muscles of the Pelvis. . 468

The Fasciæ and Muscles of the Perineum 471
  The Muscles of the Urogenital Region
    in the Male 478
  The Muscles of the Urogenital Regon
    in the Female. 480
  The Muscles of the Anal Region . . 482

THE MUSLCES AND FASCIÆ OF THE UPPER EXTREMITY.

The Muscles Connecting the Upper
  Extremity to the Vertebral Column. . 483
The Muscles Connecting the Upper Ex-
  tremity to the Anterior and Lateral
  Thoracic Walls 487
The Muscles and Fasciæ of the Shoulder . 492
The Muscles and Fasciæ of the Arm . 496
The Muscles and Fasciæ of the Forearm . 499
  The Volar Antebrachial Muscles . 500
  The Dorsal Antebrachial Muscles . 505
The Muscles and Fasciæ of the Hand . 511
  The Thenar Muscles 520
  The Hypothenar Muscles . . . 523
  The Intermediate Muscles . . . 524

THE MUSCLES AND FASCIÆ OF THE LOWER EXTREMITY.

The Muscles and Fasciæ of the Iliac
  Region 526
The Muscles and Fasciæ of the Thigh . 528
  The Anterior Femoral Muscles . . 530
  The Medial Femoral Muscles . . 533
  The Muscles of the Gluteal Region . 536

The Posterior Femoral Muscles . . 541
The Muscles and Fasciæ of the Leg . . 543
The Anterior Crural Muscles . . . 543
The Posterior Crural Muscles . . 545
The Lateral Crural Muscles . . . 550

The Fasciæ Around the Ankle 551
The Muscles and Fasciæ of the Foot . . 553
The Dorsal Muscle of the Foot . . 553
The Plantar Muscles of the Foot . . 554
Structure of Muscles 559

THE CARDIOVASCULAR SYSTEM

THE HEART

The Cardiovascular System 567
Development of the Heart 568
Peculiarities in the Vascular System of
the Fetus and Changes at Birth . 576
Anatomy of the Heart 579
The Heart Wall 579
The Pericardium 581
Component Parts of the Heart . . 583
Conduction System 594
Histology of Cardiac Muscle . . . 597
Congenital Malformations of the Heart . 598

THE ARTERIES

Collateral Circulation 603
Development of the Arteries . . . 604
The Pulmonary Trunk 611
The Aorta 613
The Ascending Aorta 613
The Arch of the Aorta 616
The Brachiocephalic Trunk . . . 617
The Arteries of the Head and Neck . . 618
The Common Carotid Artery . . . 618
The External Carotid Artery . . . 619
The Internal Carotid Artery . . . 631
The Arteries of the Brain 640

THE ARTERIES OF THE UPPER EXTREMITY

The Subclavian Artery 641
The Axilla 652
The Axillary Artery 653
The Brachial Artery 656
The Radial Artery 660
The Ulnar Artery 662

THE ARTERIES OF THE TRUNK

The Descending Aorta 666
The Abdominal Aorta 669
The Common Iliac Arteries . . . 684
The Internal Iliac Artery . . . 685
The External Iliac Artery . . . 694

THE ARTERIES OF THE LOWER EXTREMITIES

The Femoral Artery 695
The Popliteal Fossa 703
The Popliteal Artery 704
The Anterior Tibial Artery 706
The Dorsalis Pedis Artery 708
The Posterior Tibial Artery 709

THE VEINS

Development of the Veins 718
The Pulmonary Veins 723
The Systemic Veins 723
Veins of the Heart 724

THE VEINS OF THE NECK AND HEAD

The Veins of the Neck 728
The Diploic Veins 733
The Veins of the Brain 733
The Sinuses of the Dura Mater . . . 735

THE VEINS OF THE UPPER EXTREMITY AND THORAX

The Superficial Veins of the Upper
Extremity 742
The Deep Veins of the Upper Extremity . 744
The Veins of the Thorax 746
The Veins of the Vertebral Column . . 749

THE VEINS OF THE LOWER EXTREMITY, ABDOMEN AND PELVIS

The Superficial Veins of the Lower
Extremity 752
The Deep Veins of the Lower Extremity 754

THE PORTAL SYSTEM OF VEINS 762

HISTOLOGY OF THE BLOOD VESSELS

Artieris 765
Capillaries 767
Veins 768
Blood 769

THE LYMPHATIC SYSTEM.

Development of the Lymphatic Vessels . 775
Lymphatic Capillary Plexuses . . . 776
Lymphatic Vessels 779
The Lymph Nodes 780

THE THORACIC DUCT . 782

The Lymphatics of the Head, Face
and Neck 784
The Lymphatics of the Upper Extremity 792
The Lymphatics of the Lower Extremity 794

THE LYMPHATICS OF THE ABDOMEN AND PELVIS.

The Lymph Nodes and Vessels of the
Abdomen and Pelvis 796

The Lymph Nodes and Vessels of the Abdominal and Pelvic Viscera and Vessels. . 799

THE LYMPHATICS OF THE THORAX 808

Lymphatic Vessels of the Mamma . . 809

THE SPLEEN

Development. 813
Relations 813
Structure 814

THE THYMUS

Development. 816
Anatomy 817
Structure 817

THE NERVOUS SYSTEM.

Development of the Nervous System . 821

THE CENTRAL NERVOUS SYSTEM.

The Spinal Cord 836
The Medulla Oblongata 847
The Pons 859
The Cerebellum 863
The Fourth Ventricle 867
The Midbrain or Mesencephalon . . . 869
The Forebrain or Prosencephalon . . 874
    The Diencephalon 874
    The Third Ventricle 881
    The Telencephalon 882
    Structure of the Cerebral Cortex. . 887

Corpus Striatum and Basal Ganglia 898
    The Lateral Ventricle 899
    The Rhinencephalon 904
Cranial Nerve Nuclei and their Connections 910
Spinal Nerve Composition and Connections 921
Meninges of Brain and Spinal Cord . . 924
    The Cerebrospinal Fluid 928
Histology of the Nervous System . . 930
Peripheral Nerve Terminations . . . 937

THE PERIPHERAL NERVOUS SYSTEM.

CRANIAL NERVES

The Olfactory Nerve 955
The Optic Nerve 956
The Oculomotor Nerve 957
The Trochlear Nerve 960
The Trigeminal Nerve 960
    The Ophthalmic Nerve . . . 961
    The Maxillary Nerve 964
    The Mandibular Nerve . . . 968
The Abducent Nerve 973
The Facial Nerve 974
The Acoustic Nerve 981
The Glossopharyngeal Nerve . . . 981
The Vagus Nerve 986
The Accessory Nerve 994
The Hypoglossal Nerve. 995

THE SPINAL NERVES

Dorsal Primary Divisions of the Spinal
    Nerves 1001

The Cervical Nerves 1001
The Thoracic Nerves 1002
The Lumbar Nerves 1003
The Sacral and Coccygeal Nerves . . 1004
The Cervical Plexus. 1005
The Brachial Plexus 1011
Thoracic Nerves 1031
The Lumbar Nerves 1036
The Lumbar Plexus 1036
The Sacral Plexus 1045
The Pudendal Plexus 1055

THE VISCERAL NERVOUS SYSTEM

The Visceral Afferent Fibers 1057
The Autonomic or Visceral Efferent System 1060
    Parasympathetic System 1061
    The Sympathetic System 1063
    The Great Autonomic Plexuses . . 1082
    The Cardiac Plexus 1083
    The Celiac Plexus 1084
    The Pelvic Plexus 1087

THE ORGANS OF THE SENSES.

THE SPECIAL SENSES.

The Organ of Smell 1093
The Organ of Taste 1094
The Organ of Sight 1095
    The Development of the Eye. . . 1096
    The Tunics of the Eye 1099
    The Refracting Media 1112
    The Accessory Organs of the Eye . 1114
        The Ocular Muscles . . . 1114
        The Eyebrows. 1118
        The Eyelids 1118

The Tarsal Glands 1119
The Conjunctiva 1119
The Lacrimal Apparatus. . . . 1121
The Organ of Hearing 1122
    The Development of the Ear . . 1122
    The External Ear 1126
    The Middle Ear or Tympanic Cavity 1130
    The Auditory Ossicles 1136
    The Internal Ear or Labyrinth . . 1139
        The Osseous Labyrinth . . . 1140
        The Membranous Labyrinth . 1144

THE INTEGUMENT (SKIN).

The Development of the Skin 1153
The Epidermis 1153
The Corium 1155
The Cleavage Lines (Langer's) . . . 1157

The Appendages of the Skin 1158
    The Nails 1158
    Hairs 1158
    The Sebaceous Glands. 1161
    The Sudoriferous or Sweat Glands . 1163

THE RESPIRATORY SYSTEM.

The Development of the Lungs . . . 1167
The External Nose 1168
The Nasal Cavity 1170
The Accessory Sinuses of the Nose . . 1175
The Larynx 1176
   The Cartilages of the Larynx. . . 1176
   The Ligaments of the Larynx . . 1179
   Interior of the Larynx . . . 1181

Muscles of the Larynx 1185
The Trachea and Bronchi 1188
The Pleuræ 1191
The Mediastinum 1194
The Lungs 1196
   Fissures and Lobes of the lungs . . 1199
   Bronchopulmonary Segments . . 1200
   Structure of the Lungs . . . 1202

THE DIGESTIVE SYSTEM.

The Development of the Digestive Tube 1207
The Mouth 1215
   The Mouth Cavity Proper . . 1216
   The Teeth 1220
   The Tongue. 1230
   The Salivary Glands 1237
      The Parotid Gland . . . 1237
      The Submandibular Gland . 1239
      The Sublingual Gland . . 1240
The Fauces 1241
   The Palatine Tonsils 1242
   The Muscles of the Palate . . 1244
The Pharynx 1247
   The Muscles of the Pharynx . . 1249
The Esophagus 1251
The Abdomen 1253
   The Peritoneum 1258
The Stomach. 1272

The Small Intestine 1278
   The Duodenum 1278
   The Jejunum and Ileum . . . 1280
The Large Intesinte 1284
   The Cecum 1284
   The Appendix or Vermiform Process 1285
   The Colon 1287
   The Rectum 1289
The Liver 1294
   Development 1294
   Structure 1301
The Hepatic Duct 1304
   The Gall-bladder 1305
   The Cystic Duct 1306
   The Common Bile Duct . . . 1306
The Pancreas 1307
   Development 1307
   The Pancreatic Duct 1309
   Structure 1311

THE UROGENITAL SYSTEM.

DEVELOPMENT OF THE URINARY AND
GENERATIVE ORGANS

The Pronephros and Wolffman Duct . 1315
The Mesonephros, Müllerian Duct, and
   Genital Gland 1316
The Ovary 1319
The Testis 1320
The Metanephros and the Permanent
   Kidney 1322
The Urinary Bladder 1323
The External Organs of Generation . 1323
The Urethra 1324

THE URINARY ORGANS.

The Kidneys 1326
   General Structure of the Kidney . 1332
   Minute Anatomy 1334
The Ureters 1337
The Urinary Bladder 1339
The Male Urethra 1346

The Female Urethra 1348

THE MALE GENITAL ORGANS.

The Testes and Their Coverings . . . 1348
The Ductus Deferens 1358
The Seminal Vesicles 1359
The Ejaculatory Ducts 1360
The Penis 1360
The Prostate 1365
The Bulbourethral Glands 1367

THE FEMALE GENITAL ORGANS.

The Ovaries 1367
The Uterine Tube 1370
The Uterus 1372
   Supports 1376
   Structure 1377
The Vagina 1378
The External Genital Organs . . . 1379
The Mamma 1381

THE ENDOCRINE GLANDS.

The Thyroid Gland 1391
The Parathyroid Glands 1394
The Hypophysis Cerebri 1395

The Suprarenal or Adrenal Glands . 1399
Paraganglia, Glomera, and "Glands" and
   Bodies 1402

AMERICAN EDITIONS OF GRAY'S ANATOMY

Date	Edition	Editor
June 1859	First American Edition	Dr. R. J. Dunglison
February 1862	Second American Edition	Dr. R. J. Dunglison
May 1870	New Third American from Fifth English Edition	Dr. R. J. Dunglison
July 1878	New American from the Eighth English Edition	Dr. R. J. Dunglison
August 1883	New American from the Tenth English Edition	Dr. R. J. Dunglison
September 1887	New American from the Eleventh English Edition	Dr. W. W. Keen
September 1893	New American from the Thirteenth English Edition	
September 1896	Fourteenth Edition	Drs. B. Gallaudet, J. Brockway and J. McMurrich
October 1901	Fifteenth Edition	Drs. B. Gallaudet, J. Brockway and J. McMurrich
October 1905	Sixteenth Edition	Dr. J. C. DaCosta
September 1908	Seventeenth Edition	Drs. J. C. DaCosta and E. A. Spitzka
October 1910	Eighteenth Edition	Dr. E. A. Spitzka
July 1913	Nineteenth Edition	Dr. E. A. Spitzka
October 1913	New American from Eighteenth English Edition	Dr. Robert Howden
September 1918	Twentieth Edition	Dr. W. H. Lewis
August 1924	Twenty-first Edition	Dr. W. H. Lewis
August 1930	Twenty-second Edition	Dr. W. H. Lewis
July 1936	Twenty-third Edition	Dr. W. H. Lewis
May 1942	Twenty-fourth Edition	Dr. W. H. Lewis
August 1948	Twenty-fifth Edition	Dr. C. M. Goss
July 1954	Twenty-sixth Edition	Dr. C. M. Goss

ANATOMY OF THE HUMAN BODY.

INTRODUCTION.

THE word *anatomy* was used by the ancient Greeks of more than two thousand years ago to mean a dissection: (ἀνατομή) from tomé (τομή), a cutting, such as that performed by a surgeon (Hippocrates 460 B.C.), with the prefix aná (ἀνά), meaning up. Today anatomy is still closely associated in our minds with the dissection of a human cadaver, but the term was extended very early to include the whole field of knowledge dealing with the structure of living things. Even before human dissection was practiced by Herophilos and Erasistratos (300–250 B.C.), Aristotle (384–323 B.C.) dissected animals, wrote a treatise on their anatomy, and laid the groundwork for a scientific study of their form and structure. Anatomy, therefore, became the branch of knowledge concerned with **structure** or **morphology**, rather than with function or physiology, and it now applies to plants as well as animals. Our fund of anatomical information has been increased greatly during the last three or four centuries by a study of minute structure through the microscope, by following the development of the embryo, and by the addition of new and refined technical methods. The whole field of anatomy has become very large and as a result a number of subdivisions of the subject have been recognized and named, usually to correspond with a specialized interest or avenue of approach.

Human anatomy is presented from three principal points of view: (*a*) **Descriptive or Systematic Anatomy,** (*b*) **Regional or Topographical Anatomy,** and (*c*) **Applied or Practical Anatomy.** This book is primarily concerned with Systematic Anatomy, but Regional and Applied Anatomy are brought in at appropriate places.

Systematic Anatomy.—The body as a whole is composed of a number of systems whose parts are related to each other by physiological as well as anatomical considerations. Each system is composed of similar parts or tissues and assists in the performance of particular functions. Although the study of anatomy is concerned primarily with morphology, the knowledge of structure becomes understandable and of practical value only if the close association between structure and function are kept continually in mind. It is interesting in this regard that the Father of Anatomy, Vesalius, in 1543 gave his great treatise on anatomy the title "*De humani corporis fabrica,*" which is translated by some authorities as the "works" or the "workings" rather than the "architecture" of the human body.

The systems of the body are as follows:

The **Skeletal System,** a study of which is called *Osteology*, is composed of bones and cartilage, and its function is to support and protect the soft parts of the body.

The **System of Joints or Articulations** (*Arthrology*) makes the rigid segments of bone moveable, but holds them together with strong fibrous bands, the ligaments.

The **Muscles** (*Myology*) form the fleshy parts of the body and put the bones and joints into useful motion.

The **Vascular System** (*Angiology*) includes **the circulatory system** or the heart and blood vessels and the **lymphatic system** which transports the lymph and tissue fluids.

The **Nervous System** (*Neurology*) includes the **Central Nervous System,** which is composed of the brain and spinal cord, the **Peripheral Nervous System,** which is

2

composed of nerves and ganglia, and the **Sense Organs**, such as the eye and ear. Its function is to control and co-ordinate all the other organs and structures, and to relate the individual to his environment.

The **Integumentary System** is composed of the skin, hair and nails.

The **Alimentary System** is composed of the food passages and the associated digestive glands.

The **Respiratory System** is composed of the air passages and lungs.

The **Urogenital System** includes the kidneys and urinary passages and the reproductive organs in both sexes.

The **Endocrine System** includes the thyroid, suprarenal, pituitary, and other ductless glands which control certain functions of the whole body or of specific remote target organs by secreting hormones into the blood stream.

Splanchnology is the name given to the study of all the internal organs, especially those in the thorax and abdomen.

An account of the anatomy of any system would be incomplete without consideration of its microscopic anatomy and embryology, and sections dealing with them will be found in their proper places.

Microscopic Anatomy is concerned with the finer details of structure which are revealed through the microscope; that part dealing with the organs is called **organology**, with the tissues, **histology**, and with the cells, **cytology**. The study of the minute anatomy of the tissues and cells, particularly in the living state, affords a valuable opportunity to bring morphology and physiology closer together, and in some schools histology is taught as a subdivision of physiology rather than anatomy.

Embryology or **Developmental Anatomy** deals with the growth and differentiation of the organism from the single-celled ovum to birth. When applied to the life history of an individual it is called *ontogeny*. It is impossible to understand clearly all the structures found in the adult body without some knowledge of embryology. Since human embryos, particularly the younger stages, are difficult to obtain for study, a large part of our knowledge has been gained from animals, that is, from **comparative embryology**. The first chapter in this book is devoted to a brief summary of **human embryology**. The development of each system is outlined in the appropriate chapters and sections.

Comparative Anatomy deals with the structure of all living creatures, in contradistinction to human anatomy which deals only with man. A comparison of all the known animal forms, both living and fossil, indicates that they can be arranged in a scale which begins with the simplest forms and progresses through various gradations of complexity and specialization to the highest forms. The unfolding of a particular race or species is called *phylogeny*. Many of the earlier stages of development in man and other higher animals resemble the adult stages of animals lower in the scale, and hence it has been said that ontogeny repeats phylogeny. Although this is not strictly true, the study of comparative anatomy has contributed vitally to the understanding of human anatomy and physiology.

Topographical or Regional Anatomy.—Regional Anatomy is more strictly morphological than Systematic Anatomy because it deals with the structural relationships within the various parts of the body. Students in the laboratory must approach the subject of anatomy regionally because they dissect by regions rather than systems. Although the acquisition and organization of anatomical knowledge is easier for beginners if followed by systems, students in the medical fields must continually be on the alert to learn the relationship of the various parts to each other and to the surface of the body because the final purpose of their study is to visualize them in living subjects. In addition to the dissection of the body, the study of topographical anatomy is carried out by the study of **Surface Anatomy, Cross Sectional Anatomy,** and **Radiographic** or **X-ray Anatomy.**

Applied Anatomy has a number of subdivisions, and is concerned with the practical application of anatomical knowledge in some field or specialty. **Surgical Anatomy, Pathological Anatomy,** and **Radiological Anatomy** are probably the largest fields.

Physical Anthropology is closely related to Human Anatomy because it relies heavily upon anatomical studies and measurements of man and other primates, but it is a much broader science of human biology with particular emphasis on racial development, evolution, genetics, and paleontology.

Terms of Position and Direction

The Anatomical Position.—The traditional anatomical position which has long been agreed upon places the body in the erect posture with the feet together, the arms hanging at the side, and the thumbs pointing away from the body. This position is used in giving topographic relationships, especially those which are medial and lateral when referred to the limbs. The muscle actions and motions at the joints are given with reference to this position unless it is stated otherwise. It is particularly important that this position be remembered in descriptions using anterior and posterior, or the more general and ambiguous terms such as up, down, over, under, below, above, etc.

The **median plane** is a vertical plane which divides the body into right and left halves; it passes approximately through the sagittal suture of the skull, and therefore any plane parallel to it is called a **sagittal plane**. **Frontal planes** are vertical planes, also passing from head to feet, but they are at right angles to the sagittal, and since one of them passes approximately through the coronal suture of the skull, they are also called **coronal planes**. **Transverse** or **horizontal planes** cut across the body at right angles to both sagittal and frontal planes.

Ventral and dorsal refer to the front or belly and the back of the body, and are synonymous with **anterior** and **posterior**. Because of man's erect posture, this is not the same usage as that of comparative anatomy. In the hands and forearms, **palmar** or **volar** are substituted for ventral or anterior, and the sole of the foot is called **plantar** while **dorsal** is retained for the top or opposite surface of the foot.

Cephalic and **caudal** indicate the head and tail respectively, and with human subjects in the anatomical position, superior and inferior are synonymous with them, but in comparative anatomy the latter terms might be confused with dorsal and ventral when referring to four-footed beasts.

Median refers to structures in the middle line or median sagittal plane. Those nearer to the median plane are **medial,** those farther away are **lateral**. It should be noticed that the Latin word *"medius"* means middle, not medial. The Latin word for medial is *"medialis."*

Superficial and **deep** indicate the relative depth from the surface, and are preferable to over and under, and above or below, because the latter may be confused with superior and inferior.

Proximal and **distal** indicate a direction toward or away from the attached end of a limb, the origin of a structure, or the center of the body.

External and **internal** are most commonly used for describing the body wall, or the walls of cavities and hollow viscera, but they may be synonymous with superficial and deep, or with lateral and medial.

Nomenclature

Although the majority of the common anatomical names have been taken almost directly from those used by the ancient Greeks, a considerable amount of disagreement and confusion has arisen because of conflicting loyalties to teachers, schools, or national traditions. Shortly before the end of the last century, the need for a comprehensive system of nomenclature was realized, and a Commission of eminent authorities from the various countries of Europe and the United States was organized for this purpose. The system devised by this Commission was adopted by the German Anatomical Society in 1895 at their meeting in Basel, Switzerland, and it has since been called the **Basle Nomina Anatomica** or the **BNA**.

The **BNA** gives the names in Latin, which is our closest approach to an international language, and many nations, including the United States, adopted it, translating the terms into their own language whenever desirable. The French anatomists, however, did not entertain it with much enthusiasm, preferring their own quite ancient tradition. The British anatomists found many errors and inconsistencies in the **BNA** and the Anatomical Society of Great Britain and Ireland broke away and adopted a revision in 1933 which they called the **British Revision** or the **BR**. The German anatomists also felt the need for a revision, and the **Nomenklatur-Kommission report,** now known as the **NK**, was adopted by the Anatomische Gesellschaft in 1935. A later version, adopted in 1937, is known as the **Jena Nomina Anatomica** or **INA**. The British revision favors time-honored British tradition and is particularly applicable to the human body in the anatomical position. The German revisions have introduced a number of changes toward more puristic Latin usage and they attempt to establish a scientific language applicable to comparative anatomy of the vertebrates, as well as to human anatomy.

At the Fifth International Congress of Anatomists held at Oxford in 1950 a committee was appointed to attempt a new revision of anatomical names. This International Nomenclature Committee met at Paris in July, 1955 and approved the "Nomina Anatomica" which was then submitted to the Sixth International Congress of Anatomists at Paris, also in July 1955, now known as the **PNA**.

In the present edition of this book an attempt has been made to conform to this nomenclature, with one exception. In the chapter on the central nervous system the terms anterior and posterior have been replaced by ventral and dorsal unless the change seemed to cause confusion. Also, it was not deemed feasible to make all minor changes in this one edition. Since Latin is becoming unfamiliar to students, names are usually given in English with the official Latin name italicized in parenthesis. Other recognized names are also added in parenthesis.

Anatomical Eponyms, that is, designations by the names of persons, are popular among clinicians and specialists, but will be avoided in this book wherever another term is available.

REFERENCES

Nomina Anatomica (paris); PNA. 1956. Revised by the International Anatomical Nomenclature Committee, Approved in Paris, 1955. x + 51 pages. The Williams & Wilkins Co., Baltimore.

Clark, W. E. Le Gros. 1958. The Tissues of the Body, an Introduction to the Study of Anatomy. 4th Ed. xii + 415 pages. Oxford University Press, New York.

Knese, K. H. 1957. Nomina Anatomica. 5th Ed. xi + 115 pages. Georg Thieme Verlag, Stuttgart.

Pepper, O. H. Perry. 1949. Medical Etymology, the History and Derivation of Medical Terms for Students of Medicine, Dentistry and Nursing. vii + 263 pages. W. B. Saunders Co., Philadelphia.

Skinner, H. A. 1949. The Origin of Medical Terms. viii + 379 pages. The Williams & Wilkins Co., Baltimore.

Spector, William S., Editor. 1956. Handbook of Biological Data. xxxvi + 584 pages, 445 tables, appendix and index. Wright Air Development Center and W. B. Saunders Company, Philadelphia.

Triepel, Herman. 1957. Die Anatomischen Namen, ihre Ableitung und Aussprache. 25th Ed. by Robert Herrlinger. 82 pages. J. F. Bergmann, München.

EMBRYOLOGY.

THE CELL

THE adult human body is composed of several hundred trillion structural units of living material or protoplasm, called **cells,** and large amounts of **intercellular material** which is especially evident in the bones, cartilages, tendons, and ligaments. The cells can be seen only with the aid of a microscope and occur in many gradations of size, shape, and composition corresponding to their widely diversified functions. Every human individual begins his existence as a single cell, the ovum, and the embryological and later development is the result of a multiplication or increase in the number of cells through cell division, followed by growth and differentiation of the cells, and accompanied by the functional activity broadly known as metabolism. All cells are composed of two parts, the outer soft, jelly-like **cytoplasm** and an inner **nucleus.** During the interval between periodic divisions of the cell, the nucleus is called a resting nucleus; during periods of division, the nucleus goes through a series of changes called mitosis.

The **cytoplasm** of a living cell is composed of an optically homogeneous matrix (Porter, '53) with a thin outer layer, the ectoplasm, and an internal portion, the endoplasm, in which various intracellular bodies and organelles are embedded (Fig. 1, f). The external surface of the cytoplasm, the **cell membrane,** although invisible, is an important functional organ because it controls the exchange of materials between the cell and its environment by osmosis, phagocytosis, secretion, and other phenomena. The **central body** or **centrosome** lies at one side of the nucleus near the central part of the cell; the other intracellular structures are arranged around it, and it serves as a dynamic center, especially active during mitosis. **Mitochondria** are visible in living cells in the form of minute threads, rodlets, or granules; they have an internal organization revealed by the electron microscope (Palade, '52), and they are probably concerned with respiratory metabolism. **Golgi bodies** can be demonstrated in nearly all cells by special methods of preservation but are seldom identifiable as discrete structures in living cells; their composition, function, and condition in living cells are still matters of controversy. Their appearance in electron micrographs has been shown by Dalton and Felix, '54). Many cells contain granules of varied chemical composition, including secretion granules, fat droplets, fluid-filled vacuoles, and inert or ingested materials.

The **nucleus** of a living cell in the intermitotic or resting stage is a spherical or elongated body with a thin nuclear membrane and a clear, translucent internal nucleoplasm containing one to several semi-solid bodies called **nucleoli.** In nuclei which have been preserved by chemical fixation, dark masses of material called **chromatin** may be brought out by staining the nuclei with various dyes, the one most commonly used being hematoxylin. The chromatin material is invisible in living resting nuclei except possibly with phase microscopy, but during cell division it is aggregated first into threads and then into refractive bodies called **chromosomes.** The process is called **mitosis** from the Greek word mitos (μίτος) meaning thread. The chromosomes of the germ cells carry the factors for the genetic or hereditary constitution of the individual.

CELL DIVISION

The division of living cells cannot be observed with high magnifications of the microscope in the intact body. It was discovered by Harrison ('10), however, that

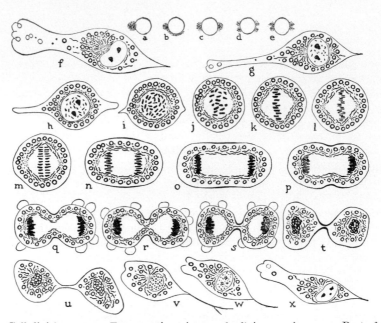

Fig. 1.—Cell division. **a–e.** From motion picture of a living monkey egg. Part of the finely granular centrosome material spreads around the nucleus to the opposite pole and there forms a second centrosome. Each centrosome divides and then unites to form a duplex centrosome. The process begins three and one-half and ends one and one-half hours before cell cleavage. **f–x.** From a living fibroblast dividing in a tissue culture. **f.** Resting stage. The centrally located centrosome is surrounded by a radial zone of mitochondria, a granular zone and a radial zone of fat globules except where interrupted by the somewhat eccentrically located nucleus and some intermingling of these intracellular bodies. A few bodies are scattered in the homogeneous ectoplasm. Ruffle pseudopodia at the tip of the advancing cell process are engulfing globules of fluid (pinocytosis). The nucleus has a thin membrane, a homogeneous nucleoplasm and two nucleoli. **g.** Beginning prophase. Chromosomes are beginning to appear as granules. Cell processes are retracting. **h.** Mid-prophase. Chromosomes are more evident in the otherwise homogeneous nucleoplasm. Cell processes are more retracted. The nucleus has become centrally located. **i.** Late prophase. Chromosomes nearly fill the nucleus. They now exhibit movements, probably passive ones. Nucleoli have split into their chromosomal elements. The nuclear membrane has disappeared. The cell has become nearly spherical. The nucleus is surrounded by an endoplasmic zone with mitochondria, granules, and fat globules and this in turn by a homogeneous zone, the ectoplasm or superficial gel layer. **j.** Transition from prophase to metaphase. The chromosomes are being pulled into the metaphase plate, presumably by invisible spindle fibers. **k.** Metaphase. The nucleus has become spindle-shaped. The chromosomes are in the equatorial plane where they slowly oscillate in short paths, presumably due to variations of the contractile tension of the spindle fibers. The clear interchromosomal material shows a relative increase over the chromosomes. **l.** Late metaphase. Each chromosome has split longitudinally into two equal parts. **m.** Early anaphase. Each group of chromosomes has begun to move toward the poles of the spindle. **n.** Late anaphase. The chromosomes have nearly reached the poles. Between the two groups of chromosomes is the homogeneous interchromosomal material, or exnuclear sap. The cell has been flattened in the equatorial region and elongated in the polar direction by the contraction of a broad thickened band of the superficial gel layer. **o.** End of anaphase. Chromosomes form small compact daughter nuclei. The cell is more flattened and elongated by the automatic contraction of a broad equatorial band of the ectoplasm or gel layer. **p.** Beginning telophase. The cleavage furrow has begun to appear due to the automatic constriction of an equatorial band of the gel layer. The endoplasmic zone is bent inward and indents the softer interchromosomal material. **q.** Early telophase. The cleavage furrow has deepened and bent the endoplasm with its intracellular bodies still farther inward. The relatively soft interchromosomal material is partially divided. The intracellular bodies retain their spacial relations in the relatively firm endoplasm. A few blebs have appeared on the surface of the cell. **r.** Mid-telophase. The constricting gel layer has bent the endoplasm inward until it meets and fuses in the equatorial region and divides the interchromosomal material into two parts. **s.** Late telophase. Continued contraction of the superficial equatorial band of the gel layer has nearly divided the endoplasm. Fat globules, granules and mitochondria that were in the equatorial region have been pressed into one or the other daughter cell. **t.** End of telophase. The daughter cells are connected by the ectoplasmic stalk. The endoplasm has been completely divided by the constriction of the equatorial band. It has mixed with the interchromosomal (exnuclear) material. The compact daughter nuclei have begun to show clear areas and to enlarge. **u.** The daughter cells have moved in opposite directions and stretched the connecting stalk. The nuclei have larger clear areas and less visible chromosome material. **v.** The connecting stalk has been pulled into a thin strand by the migration of the daughter cells in opposite directions. The visible chromosome material has been reduced to granules in the clear nucleoplasm. A nuclear membrane has developed. **w.** Some of the chromosomal granules have begun to agglutinate to form the nucleoli; the others have begun to disappear. The connecting stalk is broken. **x.** All the chromosomal granules except those which have agglutinated to form the nucleoli have disappeared into homogeneous nucleoplasm.

embryonic cells would survive and divide on glass slides if they were placed in an appropriate medium with aseptic precautions. Since that time a great many observations have been made with this method, known as *tissue culture*, on a wide range of different animal forms, including tissues from human fetuses, normal adults, and tumor growths. The following description of cell division is based upon observations of connective tissue cells or fibroblasts in cultures of tissues from chick embryos.

Mitosis or **Karyokinesis.**—An hour or two before division begins, the centrosome material is divided into two parts, placed at opposite poles of the nucleus (Fig. 1, a–e). The division is a continuous, uninterrupted process but is described in four stages as follows: (Fig. 1, f–x)

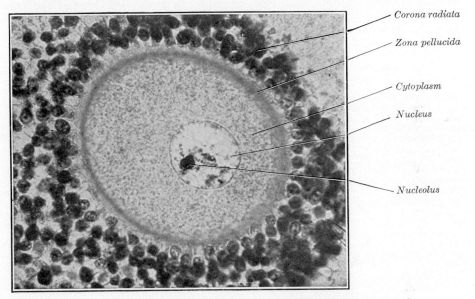

Corona radiata

Zona pellucida

Cytoplasm

Nucleus

Nucleolus

Fig. 2.—Mature human ovum. Carnegie collection.

During **prophase**, the chromatin is formed into threads and then chromosomes. The cell retracts its processes and tends to become spherical with the nucleus centrally placed and mitochondria or other intracellular bodies arranged around it. Near the end of the prophase, which takes about an hour, the nuclear membrane disappears and the chromosomes are released and move into the equatorial plane

During **metaphase**, about six minutes, the chromosomes oscillate back and forth in short paths in the equatorial region as if they were pulled first toward one pole and then toward the other by strings or fibers. These fibers are not visible in living fibroblasts (Fig. 1, k) but are visible in many kinds of cells, especially after fixation, and together with the chromosomes make up the *mitotic spindle* (Fig. 5, 6). Each chromosome splits longitudinally into two equal and similar daughter chromosomes.

During **anaphase**, about three minutes, one set of daughter chromosomes moves to each pole of the spindle, or is pulled there by contraction of the spindle fibers, and is clumped into a compact mass. As the chromosomes approach the poles, the cell becomes elongated and a groove encircles it at the equator.

During **telophase**, about three minutes, the groove sinks farther into the cell, gradually pinching it into two daughter cells which remain connected for a short time by a stalk. Each daughter cell receives approximately one-half the mitochondria, but the division of fat droplets and other intracellular bodies is more haphazard. The chromosomes lose their identity in the compact mass of the daughter nuclei.

The daughter nuclei slowly increase in size, as clear areas split the compact mass into granules, and a nuclear membrane forms. As the clear areas increase, the chromosomal granules become invisible except for those which become the nucleoli. It takes several hours for the nucleus to attain the final resting or intermitotic condition.

Amitosis or direct division of the cell has been described but probably does not occur under normal conditions. Degenerating cells may show **nuclear fragmentation** without division of the cytoplasm of the centrosome (Lewis, '47).

Binucleate cells are not uncommon, especially in certain organs, and are formed either by mitotic division of the nucleus without cleavage of the cytoplasm, or by some process not clearly understood such as fragmentation.

COMPARATIVE SIZE OF LIVING ONE-CELL TUBAL EGGS AFTER THE FORMATION OF THE PERIVITELLINE SPACE (LEWIS AND WRIGHT).

Volume and surface area of vitellus in cubic and square microns estimated by authors. ODZ: outside diameter of zona. IDZ: inside diameter of zona. DV: Diameter of vitellus in microns.

Animal.	Eggs.	Author.	ODZ.	IDZ.	DV.	Volume.*	Surface.*
Mouse	26	Lewis and Wright	113.0	87.8	71.6	192000	16100
Guinea-pig	1	Squier	121.3	96.8	84.3	314000	22300
Macaque I	1	Corner		109.0*	86.0	333000	23400
Macaque two-cell	1	Lewis and Hartman	150.0	125.0	103.0*	562000	
Macaque IV	1	Allen	178.5	138.5*	104.0	589000	34000
Human	1	Allen *et al.*	176.0*	139.0*	104.0*	589000	34000
Human (abnormal)	1	Lewis	148.0	136.0			
Rabbit	2	Gregory	174.0	126.0*			
Rabbit	9	Lewis	174.2	126.5	111.0	718000	38700
Pig	4	Heuser and Streeter	160.0	130.0	111.0	718000	38700
Cow (non-fertile)	1	Hartman and Lewis	170.0	143.0	120.0	907000	45300
Cow two-cell	1	Miller and Swett	162.5	135.0		740000	
Dog	3	Hartman	172.0	141.0	120.0	907000	45300
Sheep	6	Clark	178.0*	150.0*	133.0*	1232000	55700

* Determined or estimated from illustrations and data in articles quoted.

THE OVUM

The human ovum (Fig. 2) is a large cell, about 0.14 mm. in diameter, and contains the visible internal structures found in most cells. The nucleus with nucleolus and chromatin is known as the *germinal vesicle*. The cytoplasm contains a centrosome, mitochondria, granules, fat droplets, Golgi body, and yolk material. The ovum or **vitellus** is enclosed in a tough transparent membrane about 12μ in thickness, named the **zona pellucida**. Within the ovary, the mature ovum is contained in a spherical vesicle about 1 cm. in diameter called an **ovarian** or **Graafian follicle** (See Index). The ovum is held at one side of the follicle by a mass of follicular cells named the **cumulus oöphorus**; the follicular cells immediately around the zona pellucida are radially arranged and make up the **corona radiata** (Fig. 2). While in the ovary and at the time of ovulation, the vitellus completely fills the cavity of the zona, but it shrinks shortly after ovulation and a perivitelline space filled with clear fluid is developed.

Ovulation occurs when the mature Graafian follicle ruptures through the outer wall of the ovary and the ovum is discharged into the peritoneal cavity. Normally it is not allowed to go free in the peritoneal cavity because the fimbriated end of the uterine tube covers the point of rupture and the ovum is immediately swept into the lumen of the tube, probably by ciliary action (Rock and Hertig, '44).

Maturation of the Ovum.—Before an ovum can be fertilized it must have reached a particular stage in a process known as maturation. This involves two divisions and begins just previous to ovulation. During the first maturation division, the **primary oöcyte** divides into a large cell, the **secondary oöcyte,** and a small one known as the first **polar body.** The secondary oöcyte quickly initiates the second maturation division by forming the mitotic spindle, but it is arrested in the metaphase stage until after it escapes from the follicle and is penetrated by a spermatozoan. During the secondary maturation division, which can be completed normally only if the ovum is fertilized, a large mature ovum and a small second polar body are formed (Figs. 3, 5, 6). The first polar body may or may not divide into two smaller polar bodies.

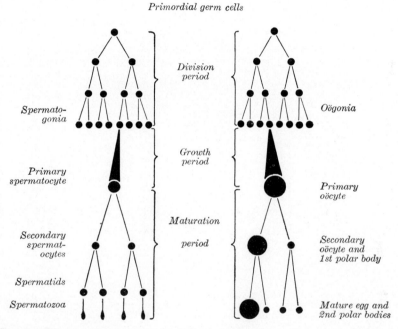

Fig. 3.—Diagram showing genesis of the sperm and of the egg. (After Boveri.)

Meiosis.—The most important part of maturation is the distribution of the **chromosomes** and their constituent carriers of heredity, the **genes.** It is generally agreed by modern investigators that the chromosome number in man is 46. The human primary oöcyte, therefore, has 23 pairs, each pair consisting of a maternal and a paternal chromosome. The random distribution of maternal and paternal chromosomes results in possible combinations for the daughter cells well in the millions. During the prophase of the first maturation division, the two chromosomes of each pair except the sex chromosomes come into close union by a process known as *synapsis* with a resulting chromosomal configuration which is not found in ordinary mitotic division and is known as a *tetrad* from its quadruplicate appearance. The individual chromosomes of the synaptic pairs do not complete their splitting into daughter chromosomes at the first maturation division. Instead, one chromosome of each pair or tetrad goes to each daughter cell, with the result that the number of chromosomes is reduced by one-half, or 23, in the secondary oöcyte.

During the second maturation division, which follows the first without a resting stage, the splitting of the chromosomes begun at the first maturation division is completed and the mature ovum and second polar body each receive 23 daughter chromosomes.

One of the 23 pairs of chromosomes is composed of **sex chromosomes** which can be identified by their size and shape as **X** and **Y chromosomes**. In all the cells of a female, including the germ cells or primary oöcytes, the sex is determined by the possession of two X-chromosomes in the sex chromosome pair. After meiosis or the reduction division, therefore, all secondary oöcytes and hence all ova will contain only X-chromosomes.

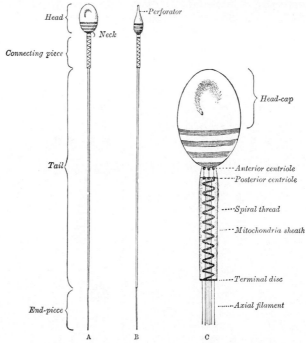

Fig. 4.—Human spermatozoön. Diagrammatic. *A*. Surface view. *B*. Profile view. In *C* the head, neck, and connecting piece are more highly magnified.

THE SPERMATOZOÖN

The spermatozoa or male germ cells are produced by the testes and are present in enormous numbers in the seminal fluid. Each human spermatozoön is a small but greatly modified cell possessing a head, a neck, a connecting piece or body, and a tail (Fig. 4).

The **head** is oval or elliptical, but flattened, so that when viewed in profile it is pear-shaped. Its anterior two-thirds are covered by a layer of modified protoplasm, which is named the head-cap. This, in some animals, *e.g.*, the salamander, is prolonged into a barbed spear-like process or perforator, which probably facilitates the entrance of the spermatozoön into the ovum. The posterior part of the head exhibits an affinity for certain reagents, and presents a transversely striated appearance, being crossed by three or four dark bands. In some animals a central rod-like filament extends forward for about two-thirds of the length of the head, while in others a rounded body is seen near its center. The head contains a mass of chromatin, and is generally regarded as the nucleus of the cell surrounded by a thin envelope.

The **neck** is less constricted in the human spermatozoön than in those of some of the lower animals. The anterior centriole, represented by two or three rounded particles, is situated at the junction of the head and neck, and behind it is a band of homogeneous substance.

The **connecting piece** or **body** is rod-like, and is limited behind by a terminal disk. The posterior centriole is placed at the junction of the body and neck, and, like the anterior, consists of two or three rounded particles. From this centriole an **axial filament**, surrounded by a sheath, runs backward through the body and **tail**. In the body the sheath of the axial filament is encircled by a spiral thread, around which is an envelope containing mitochondrial granules, and termed the mitochondrial sheath.

The tail is of great length, and consists of the axial thread or filament, surrounded by its sheath, which may contain a spiral thread or may present a striated appearance. The terminal portion or end-piece of the tail consists of the axial filament only.

The length of the human spermatozoön is between 52μ and 62μ, the head measuring 4 to 5μ, the connecting piece 6μ, and the tail from 41μ to 52μ.

By virtue of their tails, which act as propellers, the spermatozoa are capable of free movement, and unless placed in unfavorable surroundings, will retain their vitality for at least a day or two.

The spermatozoa are developed within the seminiferous tubules (see Index) of the testes, and the stages of their **maturation** are very similar to those of the maturation of the ovum. The primary germ cells undergo division and produce a number of cells called **spermatogonia,** and from these the primary spermatocytes are derived (see Index). Each **primary spermatocyte** divides into two secondary spermatocytes, and each **secondary spermatocyte** into two **spermatids** or young spermatozoa; from this it will be seen that a primary spermatocyte gives rise to four spermatozoa, each one capable of fertilizing a mature ovum (Painter '23).

During the first maturation division there is the same random distribution of the chromosomes to the secondary spermatocytes as to the secondary oöcytes and consequently the same number of equally possible combinations of the chromosomes. Since the primary spermatocyte contains, as does the primary oöcyte, 23 pairs or 46 chromosomes, there are also over 16,000,000 equally possible combinations for the spermatozoa. During the maturation divisions there is a reduction in the number of chromosomes in the spermatids similar to that in the mature egg and polar bodies. The spermatozoa thus have 23 chromosomes.

The *determination of sex* in male cells is by the possession of a Y-chromosome as well as an X-chromosome in the sex chromosome pair. At meiosis, therefore, each reduction division of a primary spermatocyte produces two secondary spermatocytes of different sex chromosome content, one having an X-chromosome and one a Y-chromosome. When these two secondary spermatocytes divide, they produce two spermatids with a Y-chromosome, and two with an X-chromosome. Unlike the oöcyte, which produces only one fertilizable ovum, each primary spermatocyte produces four equally viable spermatozoa, with those possessing X- and Y-chromosomes in equal numbers. The equal distribution of sex is maintained because every ovum contains only an X-chromosome, and it has an equal chance of being fertilized by a sperm with an X- or Y-chromosome.

FERTILIZATION OF THE OVUM

Ovulation takes place in the human ovary approximately ten to fourteen days after the onset of the preceding menstrual flow and the released ovum immediately begins its course through the uterine tube. It must be met by sperm in the ampulla of the tube within approximately six to twelve hours or it will begin to show signs of degeneration and be no longer fertilizable.

Fertilization takes place when a spermatozoön enters the ovum. Normally only one sperm takes part in the process; its entrance causes the peripheral layer of the ovum to change into the **vitelline membrane** which prevents the entrance of additional sperm. Once the spermatozoön has penetrated the ovum, the tail portion is lost, and the head and connecting piece expand into the **male pronucleus** and the centrosome. The nucleus of the ovum, known as the **female pronucleus,** and the

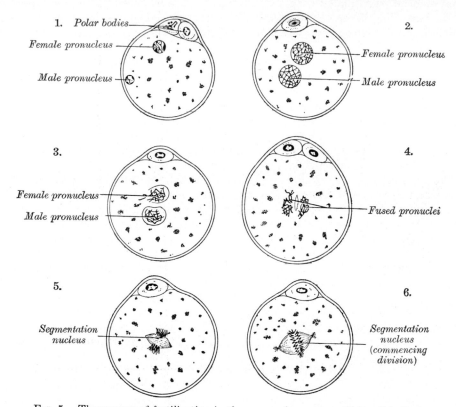

Fig. 5.—The process of fertilization in the ovum of a mouse. (After Sobotta.)

male pronucleus migrate toward each other, and, breaking down into their constituent chromosomes near the center of the cell, are combined into the new **segmentation nucleus.** The mitotic division of this nucleus and the cleavage of the cell produce the two-celled stage which is the beginning of the embryological development of the individual.

SEGMENTATION OF THE FERTILIZED OVUM

These first two cells, known as **blastomeres,** soon undergo division, and the process of cleavage continues until a grape-like cluster of daughter cells, the **morula,** has been produced. During segmentation the ovum does not enlarge; the morula is about the same size as the single-celled ovum. The exact timing is not known but probably two or three days are required for these five or six cleavage divisions, and while they are taking place the ovum makes its passage through the uterine tube.

Morula.—Although there is no visible difference between the early daughter cells, a segregation of materials and potencies takes place during cleavage which first becomes evident in the morula. Two parts become recognizable, an outer layer of cells known as the **trophoblast**, and an inner cluster of cells, known as the **inner cell mass**.

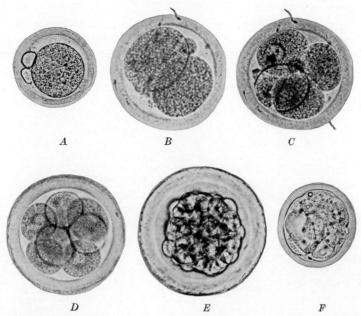

A   *B*   *C*

D   *E*   *F*

Fig. 6.—Photographs of living eggs, × 200. (*A*) Fertile one-cell mouse egg showing the zona pellucida, perivitelline space, vitellus, first and second polar bodies (Lewis and Wright). (*B*) Two-cell monkey egg. (*C*) Four-cell stage of same egg, extra sperm in zona (Lewis and Hartman). (*D*) Eight-cell rabbit egg. (*E*) Rabbit morula (Gregory). (*F*) Early blastocyst, seventy-six-hour mouse egg with a small amount of fluid.

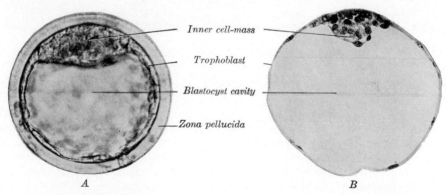

Inner cell-mass

Trophoblast

Blastocyst cavity

Zona pellucida

A   *B*

Fig. 7.—(*A*) Blastocyst, ninety-two-hour rabbit egg. Trophoblast and inner cell-mass. × 200 (Gregory.) (*B*) Blastocyst, nine-day monkey egg. Stained section. The zona has disappeared the trophoblast is thin and the inner cell-mass small. × 200. (Carnegie collection.)

The **Blastocyst** is formed by the secretion of fluid into the interior of the morula by the trophoblast, and as it enlarges into a vesicle, the trophoblast cells multiply, spread out, and become flattened against the zona pellucida which, in turn, is stretched into a thin membrane and disappears. The inner cell mass remains as a relatively small cluster of cells attached to the inner surface of the trophoblast at a region which is known as the **animal pole**. The blastocyst stage is reached soon after the ovum enters the uterus and it remains free in the uterine cavity for an estimated three to five days.

IMPLANTATION

On the seventh or eighth day after fertilization, the zona pellucida has disappeared and the blastocyst comes into direct contact with the uterine mucosa or endometrium and adheres to it. The trophoblast works its way into the endometrium by digesting the uterine tissue and on the eighth to tenth day has become a thickened invasive mass buried in the mucosa with a thin wall of blastocyst still protruding into the uterine cavity (Fig. 8).

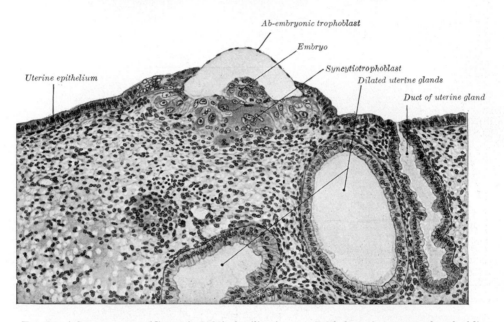

FIG. 8.—A human ovum (Carnegie 8020), fertilization age 7–7½ days, in process of embedding in the uterine mucosa. In the actual specimen the abembryonic trophoblast had collapsed on the inner cell mass, but for the purposes of clarity it is shown projecting into the uterine cavity. Drawing from a photomicrograph. × 150. (Hertig and Rock, Am. J. Obst. and Gynec., 1945.)

By the twelfth day the embryo has become completely buried and the defect in the endometrium has been closed over by the uterine epithelium (Fig. 9). The trophoblast has formed a spongy mass which has broken into the walls of some of the maternal vessels and the strands of cells are bathed in maternal blood. The trophoblast continues to grow rapidly, later combining with mesoderm to form the **chorion**, the extraembryonic membrane which protects the embryo and makes contact with the maternal blood for the absorption of oxygen and food substances, and for the elimination of waste.

Germ Layers.—While the blastocyst is becoming embedded in the uterine mucosa, the inner cell mass proliferates rapidly and within its cluster two groups of cells become distinguishable. The group nearest to the animal pole is the outer germ layer or **ectoderm**, the group protruding into the blastocyst cavity is the inner germ layer or **entoderm**. In the interior of each group, the cells pull away from each other and the area of separation quickly expands into a cavity.

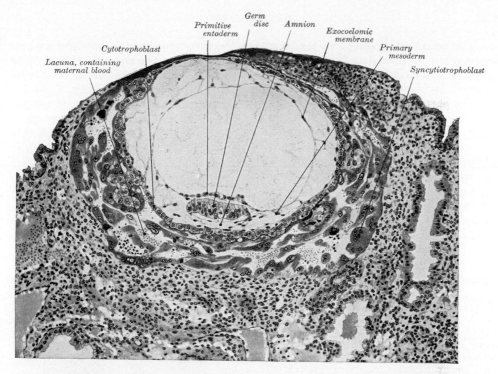

Fig. 9.—A human ovum (Carnegie 7700), fertilization age 12–12½ days, embedded in the stratum compactum of the endometrium. Drawing from a photomicrograph. × 105. (Hertig and Rock, 1941.)

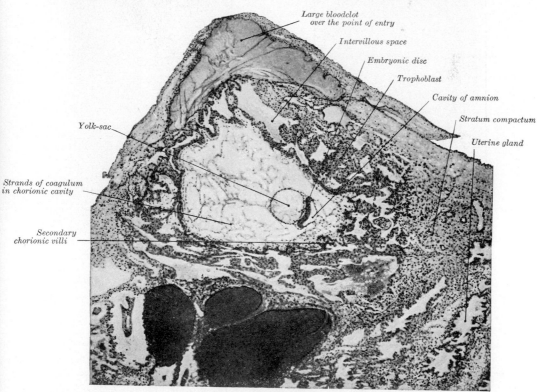

Fig. 10.—A human ovum embedded in the stratum compactum. Estimated age 13½ days. × 35. (Heuser, Hertig and Rock, 1945.)

The cells surrounding the cavity within the ectoderm stretch out into a thin-roofed vesicle known as the **amnion**, the cavity becoming the **amniotic cavity**. The cells of the entoderm stretch out into the vesicle which protrudes into the blastocyst cavity, and is known as the **yolk sac**, its cavity being the **yolk sac cavity**.

The parts of the ectoderm and entoderm which are adjacent to each other remain in close contact sharing in the formation of a thickened plate, named the **germ disc** (Fig. 9), from which the embryo proper will be developed. At about this time also, scattered cells migrate out from the border of the germ disc, forming a loose network of cellular processes which stretch across the blastocyst cavity and occupy the space between the trophoblast and the yolk sac, helping to hold the latter in place. This is the first representation of the middle germ layer or **mesoderm**, and since it occupies the blastocyst cavity rather than the germ disc it is called the **extraembryonic mesoderm**.

As the blastocyst cavity expands, the entire embryonic mass, including the yolk sac and amnion, are carried away from their close contact with the trophoblast and become suspended in the chorionic cavity by a concentration of mesoderm, the **primitive body stalk** (Fig. 36).

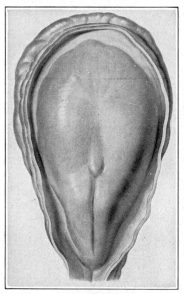

FIG. 11.—Embryonic disk of sixteen-day-old human embryo surrounded by cut edge of amnion. Body-stalk cut off at posterior end. Primitive groove overlies primitive streak. Primitive node at anterior end of primitive groove. × 50. (Heuser.)

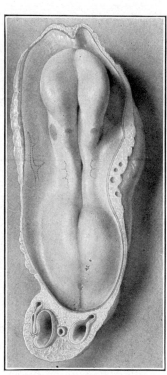

FIG. 12.—Dorsal view human embryo 1.38 mm. in length, medullary groove open, about eighteen days old. × 52.5. (Ingalls.)

THE DEVELOPMENT OF THE EMBRYO

Embryonic Disc.—As the thickened layers of the germ disc (Fig. 10) grow out into a flat oval plate, they begin the formation of the embryo proper. The narrow end of the disc (Fig. 11) is attached at the body stalk and represents the caudal end of the embryo. The median line or axis, in the caudal part of the embryonic disc, is marked by the **primitive groove**. Lying along the bottom of the primitive groove is an elongated mass of rapidly proliferating cells known as the **primitive streak**. The cells formed by this rapid proliferation spread out laterally between the ectoderm and entoderm as the **definitive mesoderm** of the embryo, part of which migrates forward as far as the cephalic portion of the embryo (Fig. 13). At the cephalic end of the primitive groove is a knot of cells, known as the **primitive node**

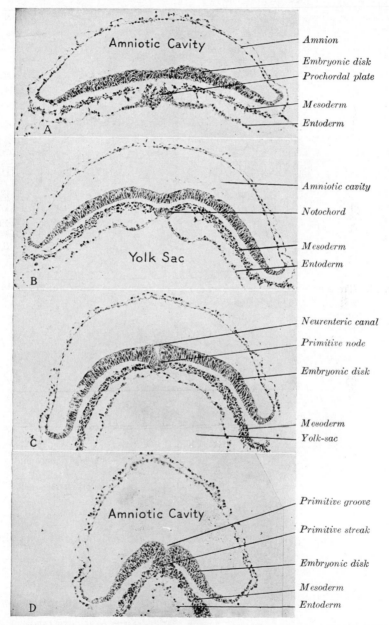

Fig. 13.—Transverse sections through presomite embryo shown in Fig. 11. (*A*) Prochordal region. (*B*) Notochordal region. (*C*) Primitive node region. (*D*) Primitive streak region. × 100. (Heuser, 1932.)

(*Hensen's node*), from which mesoderm originates also, but the latter is distinct from that produced by the primitive streak, and forms a special column of cells in the midline which becomes the **notochord**.   The primitive streak is a temporary structure corresponding to the fused lips of the *blastopore* of more primitive vertebrates, and as the embryo becomes differentiated beginning at the cephalic regions and progressing caudad, the primitive streak is pushed caudad also and finally is used up and disappears.

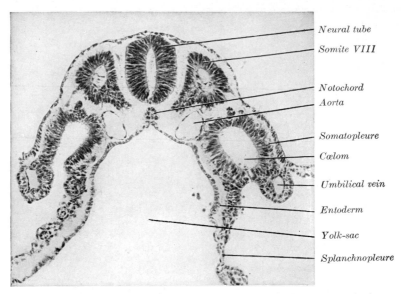

Fig. 14.—Transverse section through somites VIII (primitive segments) of the 14-somite human embryo shown in Fig. 16.   × 150.   (Heuser, 1930.)

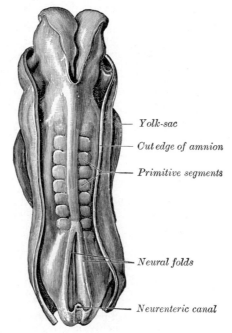

Fig. 15.—Dorsum of human embryo, 2.11 mm. in length.   (After Eternod.)

THE NEURAL GROOVE AND TUBE

From the primitive streak forward almost to the cephalic extremity of the embryonic disc, the thickened lateral ectoderm rises into rounded ridges on each side of the notochord and prochordal plate (see Fig. 13, *A* and *B*). As these ridges become more prominent they are known as the **neural folds,** and the median groove between them is the **neural groove** (Fig. 12). The lateral borders of the neural folds rise up rapidly and curve inward until they come together over the neural groove, converting it into the **neural tube** (Fig. 14). The closing of the neural tube occurs first in the region of the future hindbrain (see Fig. 15), and from there progresses both caudad and cephalad. Toward the end of the third week the cephalic opening (*anterior neuropore*) of the neural tube finally closes at the anterior end of the future brain, and forms a recess which is in contact with the overlying ectoderm. The open caudal part of the neural groove has for a time a rhomboidal outline, and is called the *sinus rhomboidalis.*

Along the prominent outer border of the neural folds, there is an abrupt transition from the thick neural primordium to the thin primitive body ectoderm. In the groove thus formed a strand of cells pushes out beside the neural tube and is known as the **neural crest** or **ganglionic ridge** (see Index). These cells migrate laterally and eventually form certain ganglionic and sheath cell components of the cranial, spinal, and sympathetic nerves.

The cephalic end of the neural tube is expanded into a large vesicle with three subdivisions which correspond to the future forebrain (prosencephalon), midbrain (mesencephalon), and hindbrain (rhombencephalon) (Fig. 19). The walls develop into the nervous tissue and neuroglia of the brain, and the cavity is modified into the cerebral ventricles. The more caudal portion of the neural tube develops into the spinal cord or medulla spinalis.

THE PRIMITIVE SEGMENTS OR SOMITES

Early in the third week, the column of mesoderm which lies along both sides of the notochord becomes organized into regularly arranged blocks of tissue, lateral to the neural groove, just under the ectoderm, and visible in the intact embryo (Fig. 15). These are the primitive segments or **somites** which are primarily responsible for the segmentation of the future skeletal, muscular, and, indirectly, nervous systems. The first somite to differentiate is in the future occipital region, and the separation of new somites progresses in a caudal direction until eventually there are 36 to 38 somites. The first occipital somite disappears at an early age (Hinsch and Hamilton, '56).

At first each somite contains a central cavity called the **myocoel,** but as the thickened walls become differentiated, this cavity loses its identity and is filled in with spindle-shaped cells. Lateral to the somites, the mesoderm stretches out between the ectoderm and entoderm as two sheets, separated by the body cavity or **coelom.** The outer sheet lies close to the ectoderm and together with it makes up the **somatopleure**; similarly the inner sheet is combined with the entoderm into the **splanchnopleure.** At the junction between the lateral mesoderm just described and the somites a strand of cells known as the **intermediate cell mass** is developed. It is the source of the future genitourinary system.

EARLY GROWTH OF THE EMBRYO

The embryo increases rapidly in size once the neural tube is established, but it does so by the overgrowth of the central region of the embryonic disc, while the margin of the disc, or line of junction between the embryo and amnion, stops growing and later even gradually becomes narrower. The constriction thus formed, corresponding in position to the future umbilicus, gradually pinches off the part of the yolk sac included in the disc so that it becomes enclosed in the embryo proper as the **primitive gut**.

The embryo grows more rapidly in length than in width, with the result that the cephalic and caudal ends push out beyond the margin of the embryonic disc, and are bent ventrally into **head** and **tail folds** (Figs. 15, 16). The head fold is the first to appear, and during its formation the pericardial cœlom (see below) and the

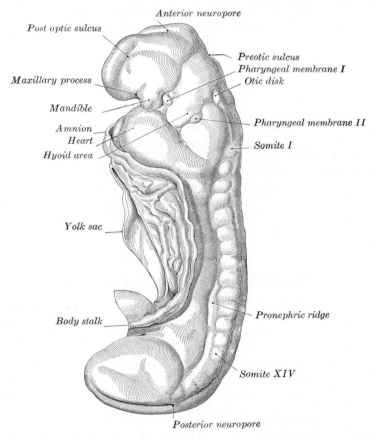

Anterior neuropore

Post optic sulcus

Preotic sulcus
Pharyngeal membrane I
Otic disk

Maxillary process

Mandible

Pharyngeal membrane II

Amnion
Heart
Hyoid area

Somite I

Yolk sac

Body stalk

Pronephric ridge

Somite XIV

Posterior neuropore

FIG. 16.—Lateral view of a 14-somite human embryo. × 50. (Heuser, 1930.)

buccopharyngeal membrane are carried around to a position ventral to the brain. The diverticulum of the primitive gut which occupies the head is known as the **foregut**, and its most cephalic extremity, the buccopharyngeal membrane, marks the location of the future opening into the mouth, the **stomodeum**. The caudal end of the embryo is at first connected to the chorion by a band of mesoderm called the **body stalk**, but with the formation of the tail fold, the body stalk is moved ventrally into the position of the umbilicus, and a diverticulum of the yolk sac called the **hindgut** is formed. For a time the opening into the yolk sac between the fore- and hindgut remains wide, but the communication is gradually reduced to a slender tube known as the **vitelline duct** or **yolk stalk** and the yolk sac itself, being rudimentary, remains a small pear-shaped sac.

DEVELOPMENT OF THE BODY CAVITIES

The Extraembryonic Coelom.—The first representation of the body cavity or coelom in the human embryo occurs very early, at a time when the amniotic cavity and yolk sac are still very small and the germ disc has just been established. The extraembryonic mesoderm, just beginning to form, spreads out in a layer over the amnion and yolk sac, and around the inner surface of the trophoblast, as well as filling in the cavity of the blastocyst with a loose meshwork (Fig. 10, labelled chorionic cavity). Between the layers of mesoderm covering the embryo and lining the blastocyst cavity, the loosely arranged mesodermal cells separate from each other and leave a space, the extraembryonic coelom (Fig. 36). The body cavity of the embryo proper is formed somewhat later and is at first independent of this extraembryonic cœlom, but, during the period when the yolk sac is being constricted at the body stalk, the two cavities become confluent for a short time (Fig. 14).

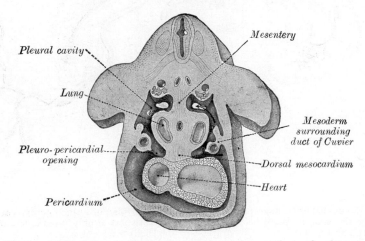

FIG. 17.—Figure obtained by combining several successive sections of a human embryo of about the fourth week. (From Kollmann.) The upper arrow is in the pleuroperitoneal opening, the lower in the pleuropericardial.

The **embryonic cœlom** originates in the mesoderm which is the earliest product of the primitive streak and occupies the most cephalic area of the embryonic disc. It begins with the formation of scattered vesicles in the layer of mesoderm at the periphery of the embryonic disc encircling the cephalic end of the neural folds. The vesicles quickly coalesce into a horseshoe-shaped cavity which is continuous across the midline in front of the forebrain but is closed caudally in the region of the early somites. This cavity is the **primitive pericardial** portion of the primitive **coelomic cavity** and it splits the mesoderm into a somatic layer next the ectoderm, and a splanchnic layer next the entoderm. The somatic mesoderm and the ectoderm form a sheet called the **somatopleure**. The splanchnic mesoderm and the entoderm are the **splanchnopleure** (Fig. 14). Between the splanchnic mesoderm and entoderm there appear scattered mesodermal cells known as **mesenchyme**, which become the primordium of the endocardium, while the compact layer of splanchnic mesoderm becomes the myocardium and epicardium, and the somatic mesoderm becomes eventually the parietal pericardium. The two lateral ends of the U-shaped cavity progress caudally, and in a short time become confluent with the extraembryonic coelom at each side of the body of the embryo. (See Heart Chapter.)

As the pericardial cavity is moved into its position ventral to the foregut by the formation of the head fold (see Fig. 38), a thick plate of splanchnic mesoderm comes to lie between the greatly enlarged heart and the constricted portion of the yolk sac. This plate is known as the **septum transversum**. Through it the vitelline veins from the yolk sac reach the heart and into it grows the diverticulum from the gut

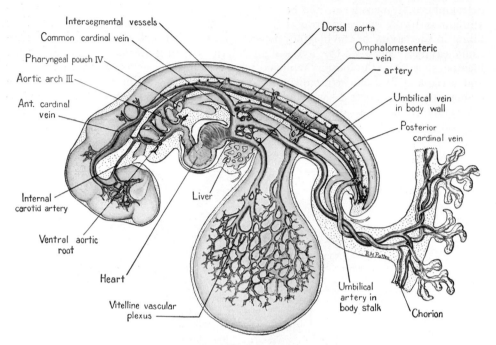

FIG. 18.—Semischematic diagram to show basic vascular plan of human embryo at end of first month. For the sake of simplicity the paired vessels are shown only on side toward observer. (Patten's Human Embryology, 1953, courtesy of the Blakiston Company.)

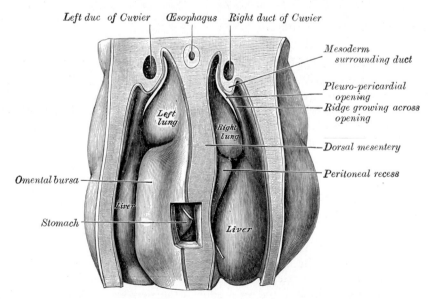

FIG. 19.—Upper part of coelom of human embryo of 6.8 mm., seen from behind. (From model by Piper.)

which forms the liver (Fig. 18). The more caudal parts of the coelom remain as narrow extensions on each side of the foregut in the region of the somites. This narrowed portion of the coelom dorsal to the septum transversum is called the **pleural canal** because a little later the diverticula from the foregut which develop into the lungs push out into this canal and expand it into the pleural cavities (Fig. 19).

At this early stage, the coelomic cavity is continuous from the pericardial cavity around the heart, through the pleural canals around the lung buds, into the peritoneal cavity in the abdomen. Later it is broken up into the pericardial, pleural, and peritoneal cavities by the formation of two septa. One septum begins as a fold of tissue from the cephalic border of the septum transversum and the lateral body wall; it protrudes into the pleural canal cephalic to the lung bud and is known as the **pleuropericardial fold**. It continues to grow out until it completely closes the canal as a septum, separating the pericardial cavity from the pleural cavities.

The second fold appears at the lower part of the septum transversum in the region where the common cardinal veins (ducts of Cuvier) open into the sinus venosus at the base of the heart. This fold, known as the **pleuroperitoneal fold,** grows dorsally from the septum transversum, and, as the growing lung buds expand the thoracic cavities at both sides of the heart, it contributes an important part of the tissue which forms the diaphragm. Eventually the diaphragm closes off the coelom and separates the pleural cavities from the peritoneal cavity.

THE BRANCHIAL REGION.

The Branchial or Visceral Arches and Pharyngeal Pouches.—In the lateral walls of the anterior part of the foregut five *pharyngeal pouches* appear (Fig. 22); each of the upper four pouches is prolonged into a dorsal and a ventral diverticulum. Over these pouches corresponding indentations of the ectoderm occur, forming what are known as the **branchial** or **outer pharyngeal grooves**. The intervening mesoderm

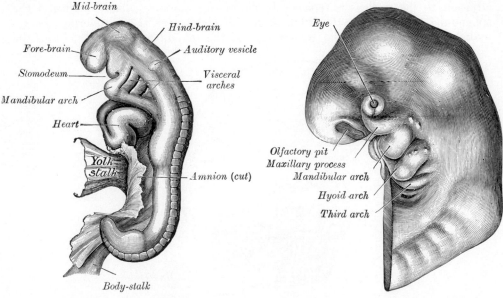

FIG. 20.—Embryo of the fourth week. (His.)

FIG. 21.—Head end of human embryo, about the end of the fourth week. (From model by Peter.)

is pressed aside and the ectoderm comes for a time into contact with the ento-dermal lining of the foregut, and the two layers unite along the floors of the grooves to form thin **closing membranes** between the foregut and the exterior. Later the mesoderm again penetrates between the entoderm and the ectoderm. In gill-bearing animals the closing membranes disappear, and the grooves become complete clefts, the **gill-clefts**, opening from the pharynx on to the exterior; perforation, however, does not occur in birds or mammals. The grooves separate a series of rounded bars or arches, the **branchial** or **visceral arches**, in which thickening of the mesoderm takes place (Figs. 20 and 21). The dorsal ends of these arches are attached to the sides of the head, while the ventral extremities ultimately meet in the middle line of the neck. In all, six arches make their appearance, but of these only the first four are visible externally. The first arch is named the

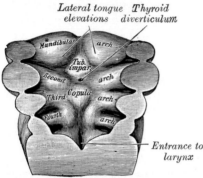

FIG. 22.—Floor of pharynx of embryo shown in Fig. 20.

mandibular, and the second the hyoid; the others have no distinctive names. The mandibular and hyoid arches are the first ones to appear and are recognizable in the 14-somite stage (Fig. 16). In each arch a cartilaginous bar, consisting of right and left halves, is developed, and with each of these there is one of the primitive aortic arches.

The **mandibular arch** lies between the first branchial groove and the stomodeum; from it are developed the lower lip, the mandible, the muscles of mastication, and the anterior part of the tongue. Its cartilaginous bar is formed by what are known as **Meckel's cartilages** (right and left) (Fig. 23); above this the

incus is developed. The dorsal end of each cartilage is connected with the ear-capsule and is ossified to form the malleus; the ventral ends meet each other in the region of the symphysis menti. Most of the cartilage disappears; the portion immediately adjacent to the malleus is replaced by fibrous membrane, which constitutes the spheno-mandibular ligament, while from the connective tissue covering the remainder of the cartilage the greater part of the mandible is ossified. From the

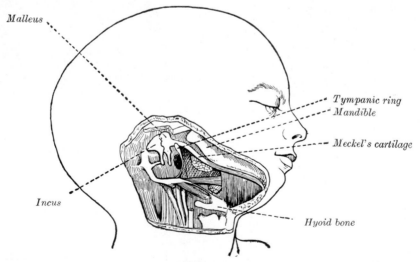

FIG. 23.—Head and neck of a human embryo eighteen weeks old, with Meckel's cartilage and hyoid bar exposed. (After Kölliker.)

dorsal ends of the mandibular arch a triangular process, the **maxillary process**, grows forward on either side and forms the cheek and lateral part of the upper lip. The **second** or **hyoid arch** assists in forming the side and front of the neck. From its cartilage are developed the styloid process, stylohyoid ligament, and lesser cornu of the hyoid bone. The stapes probably arises in the upper part of this arch. The cartilage of the **third arch** gives origin to the greater cornu of the hyoid bone. The ventral ends of the second and third arches unite with those of the opposite side, and form a transverse band, from which the body of the hyoid bone and the posterior part of the tongue are developed. The ventral portions of the cartilages of the **fourth arch** unite to form the thyroid cartilage; from the cartilages of the **fifth arch** the cricoid and arytenoid cartilages are developed. The mandibular and hyoid arches grow more rapidly than those behind them, with the result that the latter become, to a certain extent, telescoped within the former, and a deep depression, the **sinus cervicalis**, is formed on either side of the neck. This sinus is bounded in front by the hyoid arch, and behind by the thoracic wall; it is ultimately obliterated by the fusion of its walls.

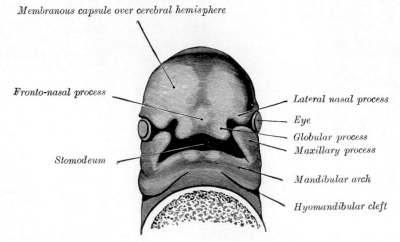

Membranous capsule over cerebral hemisphere

Fronto-nasal process

Lateral nasal process

Eye

Globular process

Maxillary process

Stomodeum

Mandibular arch

Hyomandibular cleft

FIG. 24.—Under surface of the head of a human embryo about twenty-nine days old. (After His.)

From the first branchial groove the concha auriculæ and external acoustic meatus are developed, while around the groove there appear, on the mandibular and hyoid arches, a number of swellings from which the auricula or pinna is formed. The first pharyngeal pouch is prolonged dorsally to form the auditory tube and the tympanic cavity; the closing membrane between the mandibular and hyoid arches is invaded by mesoderm, and forms the tympanic membrane. No traces of the second, third, and fourth branchial grooves persist. The inner part of the second pharyngeal pouch is named the **sinus tonsillaris**; in it the tonsil is developed, above which a trace of the sinus persists as the supratonsillar fossa. The fossa of Rosenmüller or lateral recess of the pharynx is by some regarded as a persistent part of the second pharyngeal pouch, but it is probably developed as a secondary formation. From the third pharyngeal pouch the thymus arises as an entodermal diverticulum on either side, and from the fourth pouches small diverticula project and become incorporated with the thymus, but in man these diverticula probably never form true thymus tissue. The parathyroids also arise as diverticula from the third and fourth pouches. From the fifth pouches the ultimobranchial bodies originate and are enveloped by the lateral prolongations of the median thyroid rudiment; they do not, however, form true thyroid tissue, nor are any traces of them found in the human adult (See: Development of Thyroid Gland).

The Nose and Face.—During the third week two areas of thickened ectoderm, the **olfactory areas**, appear immediately under the fore-brain in the anterior wall of the stomodeum, one on either side of a region termed the **fronto-nasal process** (Fig. 24), By the upgrowth of the surrounding parts these areas are converted into pits. the **olfactory pits**, which indent the fronto-nasal process and divide it into a **medial** and two **lateral nasal processes** (Fig. 25). The rounded lateral angles of

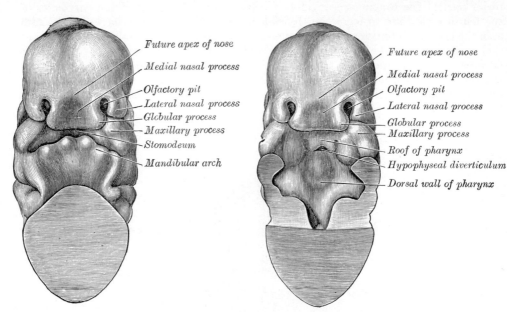

FIG. 25.—Head end of human embryo of about thirty to thirty-one days. (From model by Peters.)

FIG. 26.—Same embryo as shown in Fig. 25, with front wall of pharynx removed.

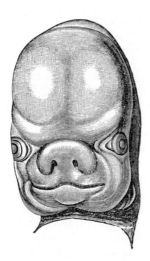

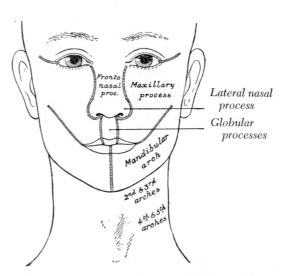

FIG. 27.—Head of a human embryo of about eight weeks, in which the nose and mouth are formed. (His.)

FIG. 28.—Diagram showing the regions of the adult face and neck related to the fronto-nasal process and the branchial arches.

the medial process constitute the **globular processes** of His. The olfactory pits form the rudiments of the nasal cavities, and from their ectodermal lining the epithelium of the nasal cavities, with the exception of that of the inferior meatuses, is derived. The globular processes are prolonged backward as plates, termed the **nasal laminæ**: these laminæ are at first some distance apart, but, gradually approach-

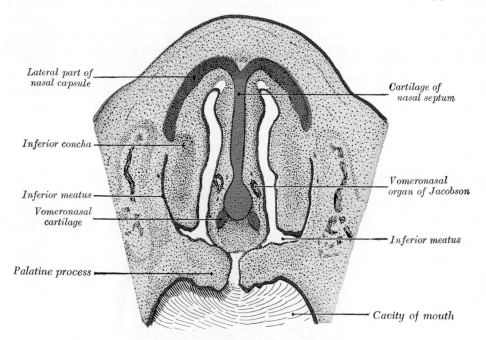

Lateral part of nasal capsule

Inferior concha

Inferior meatus

Vomeronasal cartilage

Palatine process

Cartilage of nasal septum

Vomeronasal organ of Jacobson

Inferior meatus

Cavity of mouth

FIG. 29.—Frontal section of nasal cavities of a human embryo 28 mm. long. (Kollmann.)

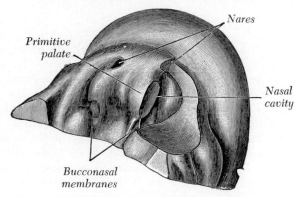

Primitive palate

Nares

Nasal cavity

Bucconasal membranes

FIG. 30.—Primitive palate of a human embryo of thirty-seven to thirty-eight days. (From model by Peters.) On the left side the lateral wall of the nasal cavity has been removed.

ing, they ultimately fuse and form the nasal septum; the processes themselves meet in the middle line, and form the premaxillæ and the philtrum or central part of the upper lip (Fig. 28). The depressed part of the medial nasal process between the globular processes forms the lower part of the nasal septum or **columella;** while above this is seen a prominent angle, which becomes the future apex (Figs. 25, 26), and still higher a flat area, the future bridge, of the nose. The lateral nasal processes form the alæ of the nose.

Continuous with the dorsal end of the mandibular arch, and growing forward from its cephalic border, is a triangular process, the **maxillary process**, the ventral extremity of which is separated from the mandibular arch by a > shaped notch (Fig. 24). The maxillary process forms the lateral wall and floor of the orbit, and in it are ossified the zygomatic bone and the greater part of the maxilla; it meets with the lateral nasal process, from which, however, it is separated for a time by a groove, the **naso-optic furrow,** that extends from the furrow encircling the eyeball to the olfactory pit. The maxillary processes ultimately fuse with the lateral nasal and globular processes, and form the lateral parts of the upper lip and the posterior boundaries of the nares (Figs. 27, 28). From the third to the fifth month the nares are filled by masses of epithelium, on the breaking down and disappearance of which the permanent openings are produced. The maxillary process also gives rise to the lower portion of the lateral wall of the nasal cavity

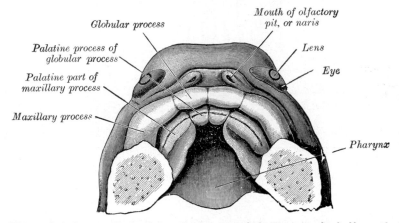

FIG. 31.—The roof of the mouth of a human embryo, aged about two and a half months, showing the mode of formation of the palate. (His.)

The roof of the nose and the remaining parts of the lateral wall,. *viz,* the ethmoidal labyrinth, the inferior nasal concha, the lateral cartilage, and the lateral crus of the alar cartilage, are developed in the lateral nasal process. By the fusion of the maxillary and nasal processes in the roof of the stomodeum the **primitive palate** (Fig. 30) is formed, and the olfactory pits extend backward above it. The posterior end of each pit is closed by an epithelial membrane, the **bucco-nasal membrane,** formed by the apposition of the nasal and stomodeal epithelium. By the rupture of these membranes the **primitive choanæ** or openings between the olfactory pits and the stomodeum are established. The floor of the nasal cavity is completed by the development of a pair of shelf-like **palatine processes** which extend medial-ward from the maxillary processes (Figs. 29 and 30); these coalesce with each other in the middle line, and constitute the entire palate, except a small part in front which is formed by the premaxillary bones. Two apertures persist for a time between the palatine processes and the premaxillæ and represent the permanent channels which in the lower animals connect the nose and mouth. The union of the parts which form the palate commences in front, the premaxillary and palatine processes joining in the eighth week, while the region of the future hard palate is completed by the ninth, and that of the soft palate by the eleventh week. By the completion of the palate the **permanent choanæ** are formed and are situated a considerable distance behind the primitive choanæ. The deformity known as cleft palate results from a non-union of the palatine processes, and that of hare-lip through a non-union of the maxillary and globular processes (see above).

The nasal cavity becomes divided by a vertical septum, which extends downward and backward from the medial nasal process and nasal laminæ, and unites below with the palatine processes. Into this septum a plate of cartilage extends from the under aspect of the ethmoid plate of the chondrocranium. The anterior part of this cartilaginous plate persists as the septal cartilage of the nose and the medial crus of the alar cartilage, but the posterior and upper parts are replaced by the vomer and perpendicular plate of the ethmoid. On either side of the nasal septum, at its lower and anterior part, the ectoderm is invaginated to form a blind pouch or diverticulum, which extends backward and upward into the nasal septum and is supported by a curved plate of cartilage. These pouches form the rudiments of the **vomero-nasal organs** of Jacobson, which open below, close to the junction of the premaxillary and maxillary bones (Fig. 29).

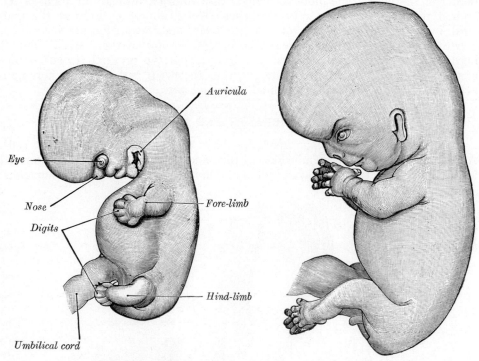

FIG. 32.—Embryo of about six weeks. (His.)

FIG. 33.—Human embryo about eight and a half weeks old. (His.)

The Limbs.—The limbs begin to make their appearance in the fourth week as small elevations or buds at the side of the trunk (Figs. 20 and 46). Unsegmented somatic mesoderm pushes into the limb buds and multiplies by division of its cells into closely packed cellular masses. The intrinsic muscles of the limbs differentiate *in situ* from the peripheral portions of this unsegmented mesoderm. The upper limb begins its differentiation in the neck region and receives its nerve supply from the fourth cervical to the second thoracic before it migrates caudally. The lower limb arises in the region from the twelfth thoracic to the fourth sacral inclusive receiving nerves from these segments before its caudal migration. The axial part of the mesoderm of the limb bud becomes condensed and converted into its cartilaginous skeleton, and by the ossification of this the bones of the limbs are formed. By the sixth week the three chief divisions of the limbs are marked off by furrows—the upper into arm, forearm, and hand; the lower into thigh, leg, and foot (Fig. 32). The limbs are at first directed backward nearly parallel to the long axis of the trunk, and each presents two surfaces and two borders. Of the surfaces, one — the future *flexor* surface of the limb—is directed ventrally; the other, the *extensor* surface, dorsally; one border, the *preaxial*, looks forward toward the cephalic end of the embryo, and the other, the *postaxial*, backward toward the caudal end. The lateral epicondyle of the humerus, the radius, and the thumb lie along the preaxial border of the upper limb; and the medial epicondyle of the femur, the tibia, and the great toe along the corresponding border of the lower limb. The preaxial part is derived from the anterior segments, the postaxial from the posterior segments of the limb-bud; and this explains, to a large extent, the innervation of the adult limb, the nerves of the more anterior segments being distributed along the preaxial (radial or tibial), and those of the more posterior along the postaxial (ulnar or fibular) border of the limb. The limbs next undergo a rotation through an angle of 90° around their long axes the rotation being effected almost entirely at the limb girdles. In the upper limb the rotation is outward and forward; in the lower limb, inward and backward. As a consequence of this rotation the preaxial (radial) border of the fore limb is directed lateralward, and the preaxial (tibial) border of the hind limb is directed medialward; thus the flexor surface of the fore limb is turned forward, and that of the hind limb backward.

FETAL MEMBRANES AND PLACENTA

In the early blastocyst stage, the trophoblast consists of a single layer of cells. As the blastocyst becomes embedded in the endometrium, two layers are formed in the trophoblast; the outer layer, rich in nuclei but with no evident cell boundaries,

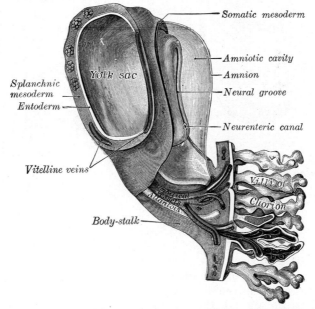

Fig. 34.—Model of human embryo 1.3 mm. long. (After Eternod.)

is called the **syncytiotrophoblast;** the inner layer is cellular and is called the **cytotrophoblast** or layer of Langhans. The trophoblast, as it invades the uterine wall, becomes converted into a thick sponge-like mass of strands and sheets with cores of cytotrophoblast and outer coverings of syncytiotrophoblast. The walls of the uterine vessels which are in the path become eroded and maternal blood seeps into the spaces between the strands of trophoblast, now called the **intervillous space.**

Chorion.—As some of the strands of trophoblast become anchored to the uterine tissue and others protrude into the intervillous space as villi, the resulting structure is known as the chorion (Figs. 10, 35). At first its internal cavity, developed from the blastocyst cavity, contains only fluid and loose strands of extraembryonic mesoderm, but later the amnion expands so rapidly that it encroaches upon the space until it comes into contact with the inner wall of the chorion and obliterates its

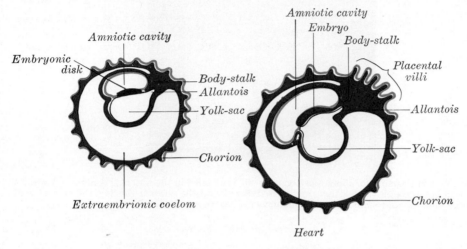

FIG. 35.—Diagram illustrating early formation of allantois and differentiation of body-stalk.

FIG. 36.—Diagram showing later stage of allantoic development with commencing constriction of the yolk-sac.

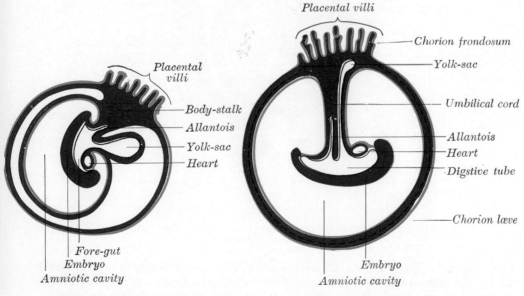

FIG. 37.—Diagram showing the expansion of amnion and constriction of the yolk-sac.

FIG. 38.—Diagram illustrating a later stage in the development of the umbilical cord.

cavity. The chorion continues to expand throughout pregnancy, however, to accommodate the fetus and serve as the outer barrier between it and the uterus.

The Chorionic Villi.—The **primary villi**, as mentioned above, develop from the solid strands of trophoblast which extend into the uterine wall and consist of an inner cluster of cytotrophoblast covered with an irregular layer of syncytiotropho-

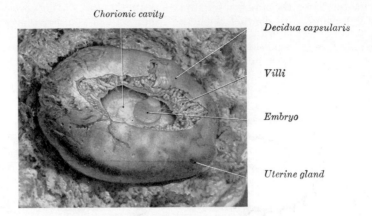

Chorionic cavity

Decidua capsularis

Villi

Embryo

Uterine gland

Fig. 39.—Human ovum, about fourteen days old, imbedded in the wall of the uterus. A window has been cut through the decidua capsularis (reflexa) and the chorion to show the embryo with its large yolk sac and amnion. × 4.5 diameter. (Carnegie collection.)

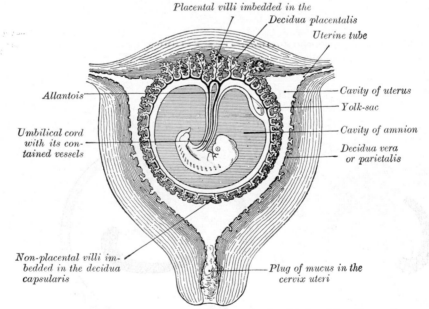

Placental villi imbedded in the
Decidua placentalis
Uterine tube

Allantois

Cavity of uterus

Yolk-sac

Umbilical cord with its contained vessels

Cavity of amnion

Decidua vera or parietalis

Non-placental villi imbedded in the decidua capsularis

Plug of mucus in the cervix uteri

Fig. 40.—Sectional plan of the gravid uterus in the third and fourth month. (Modified from Wagner.)

blast (Fig. 42). The primary villi are converted into the **secondary or true chorionic villi** by the central ingrowth of a core of mesoderm accompanied by sprouts from the umbilical vessels which have grown out into the extraembryonic mesoderm by way of the body stalk. As the chorionic villi continue to grow and ramify, the ingrowth of mesoderm and umbilical vessels keeps pace and the structural pattern is established for the exchange of substances between the fetal and maternal circulations (Fig. 43).

Until about the end of the second month, the villi sprout from the entire outer surface of the chorion and are more or less uniform in size. After this time, the villi in contact with the decidua capsularis (see below), which constitutes the greater part of the chorion, gradually atrophy, and by the fourth month scarcely a trace of them is left. The resulting smooth surface has given this part of the chorion the name **chorion laeve**. It is the non-placental part of the chorion. The villi in contact with the decidua basalis, on the other hand, increase greatly in size and complexity and this part, becoming the fetal portion of the placenta, is named the **chorion frondosum** (Fig. 38).

Maternal Tissues.—By the time the blastocyst comes into contact with the inside of the uterus, the mucous membrane or endometrium has already undergone the usual changes through which it goes during the menstrual cycle in preparation for the possible arrival of a fertilized ovum. These changes are also called premenstrual because in the event that a fertilized ovum is not implanted, the tissue is lost in the next menstrual flow. After implantation of an ovum takes place, however, the thickness and vascularity of the endometrium are greatly increased; its glands are elongated with funnel-shaped orifices at the surface, and their deeper portions are dilated into irregular, tortuous spaces. These changes are well advanced by the second month of pregnancy and the tissue between the glands has become crowded with enlarged connective tissue cells known as **decidual cells**. The endometrium

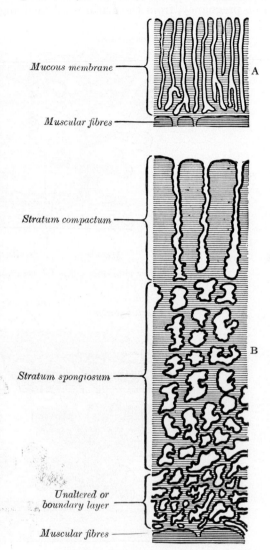

Mucous membrane

Muscular fibres

A

Stratum compactum

Stratum spongiosum

B

Unaltered or boundary layer

Muscular fibres

Fig. 41.—Diagrammatic sections of the uterine mucous membrane: *A*. The non-pregnant uterus. *B*. The pregnant uterus, showing the thickened mucous membrane and the altered condition of the uterine glands. (Kundrat and Engelmann.)

consists of the following strata (Fig. 41): (*a*) the **stratum compactum**, next the free surface, is traversed by the necks of the uterine glands and contains a rather compact layer of interglandular tissue; (*b*) the **stratum spongiosum** contains the tortuous and dilated glands and only a small amount of interglandular tissue; (*c*) the **stratum basale**, or boundary layer, next the uterine muscular wall, contains the

4

deepest parts of the uterine glands. At each menstrual flow and at the termination of pregnancy the stratum compactum and spongiosum are cast off, and together are known as the **pars functionalis.** The stratum basale remains and is the source of epithelium for the regeneration of the mucous membrane after the functional layer is lost.

The **Decidua** is the name given to the pars functionalis of the endometrium during pregnancy, from the Latin word meaning to fall away. The various parts

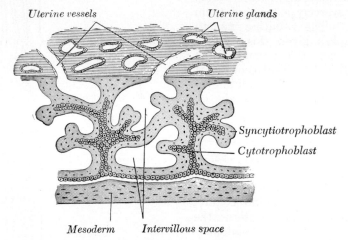

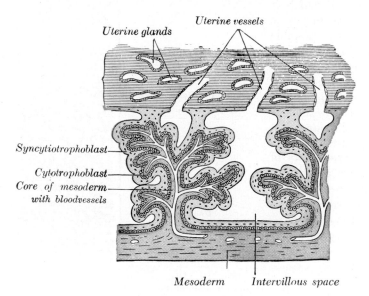

FIG. 42.—Primary chorionic villi. Diagrammatic. (Modified from Bryce.)

FIG. 43.—Secondary or true chorionic villi. Diagrammatic. (Modified from Bryce.)

of the decidua are given special names according to their relation to the embryo and fetus. The portion which closes over the embryo after it has burrowed into the uterine tissue is the **decidua capsularis** (Fig. 40); the deeper part of the endometrium between the embryo and the muscular wall of the uterus is the **decidua basalis,** or, since it is the part involved in the placenta, the **decidua placentalis;** and the part which lines the rest of the uterus is the **decidua parietalis** or the **decidua vera.**

During the growth of the embryo, the decidua capsularis is stretched out but is not broken, and it gradually fills in the cavity of the uterus until it comes in contact with the decidua vera and, by the third month, has obliterated the cavity of the uterus. By the fifth month the remnant of the capsularis has practically disappeared and during the succeeding months the decidua vera also undergoes atrophy from the increased pressure. The glands of the stratum compactum are obliterated, and in the spongiosum they are compressed into slit-like fissures with degenerated epithelium. In the stratum basale, the glandular epithelium is retained.

The **Placenta** is the highly specialized organ by means of which the fetus makes its functional contact with the uterine wall. It has a fetal and a maternal portion.

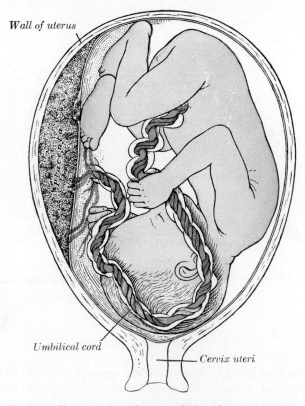

Wall of uterus

Umbilical cord

Cervix uteri

FIG. 44.—Fetus in utero, between fifth and sixth months.

The **Fetal portion** of the placenta consists of the villi of the chorion frondosum. The greatly ramified villi are suspended in the intervillous space, and are bathed in maternal blood. The branches of the umbilical arteries enter each of the villi and end in capillary plexuses, and these in turn are drained by tributaries of the umbilical vein. Within a villus, the endothelium of the blood vessels is surrounded by a thin layer of gelatinous mesodermal connective tissue and the trophoblast. During the first half of pregnancy the trophoblast consists of two layers, the deeper stratum next the connective tissue is the cellular cytotrophoblast or Langhans layer, and the superficial layer in contact with the maternal blood, the syncytiotrophoblast. After about the fifth month only a single stratum, that of the syncytiotrophoblast, is present.

Maternal Portion.—The maternal portion of the placenta is formed by the pars functionalis of the decidua placentalis. The changes involve the conversion of the greater portion of the stratum compactum and the stratum spongiosum into a **basal plate** and **placental septa** (Fig. 45), through which the uterine arteries and veins pass to and from the intervillous space. The endothelial lining of the uterine vessels ceases at the intervillous space, the latter being lined by the syncytiotrophoblast. The portions of the stratum compactum which persist in the form of septa extend from the basal plate through the thickness of the placenta and subdivide it into the **lobules** or **cotyledons** which are characteristic markings on the detached surface of the placenta seen at parturition.

The fetal blood currents pass through the blood vessels of the placental villi, the maternal blood through the intervillous space (Fig. 45). The two currents do not intermingle, being separated from each other by the delicate walls of the villi.

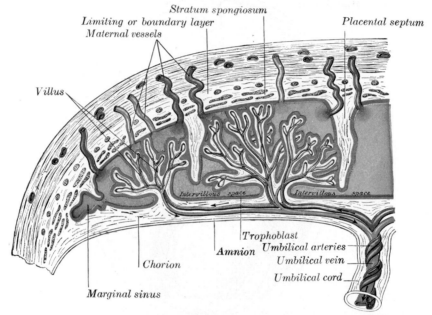

FIG. 45.—Scheme of placental circulation.

Nevertheless, the fetal blood is able to absorb, through the walls of the villi, oxygen and nutritive materials from the maternal blood, and give up to the latter its waste products. The blood, so purified, is carried back to the fetus by the umbilical vein.

The placenta is usually attached near the fundus of the uterus, and more frequently on the posterior than on the anterior wall. It may occupy a lower position, however, and, in rare cases, its site is close to the internal os or opening into the cervix, which it may occlude, giving rise to the condition known as placenta previa.

Separation of the Placenta.—After the child is born, the placenta and membranes are expelled from the uterus as the **afterbirth**. The separation of the placenta and membranes from the uterine wall takes place through the stratum spongiosum, and necessarily causes rupture of the uterine vessels. The vessels are tightly compressed and closed, however, by the firm contraction of the uterine muscular fibers, and thus postpartum hemorrhage is controlled. During the postpartum period, the epithelial lining of the uterus is restored by the proliferation and extension of the epithelium which lines the persistent portions of the uterine glands in the stratum basale of the decidua.

The expelled placenta is a discoid mass which weighs about 450 gm. and has a diameter of from 15 to 20 cm. Its average thickness is about 3 cm., but this diminishes rapidly toward the circumference of the disk, which is continuous with the membranes. Its uterine surface is divided by a series of fissures into lobules or cotyledons, the fissures containing the remains of the septa which extended between the maternal and fetal portions. Most of these septa end in irregular or pointed processes; others, especially those near the edge of the placenta, pass through its thickness and are attached to the chorion. The fetal surface of the placenta is smooth, being closely invested by the amnion. Seen through the latter, the chorion presents a mottled appearance, consisting of gray, purple, or yellowish areas. The **umbilical cord** is usually attached near the center of the placenta, but may be inserted anywhere between the center and the margin; in some cases it is inserted into the membranes, *i.e.*, the velamentous insertion. From the attachment of the cord the larger branches of the umbilical vessels radiate under the amnion, the veins being deeper and larger than the arteries. The remains of the yolk stalk and yolk sac may be observed beneath the amnion, close to the cord, the former as an attenuated thread, the latter as a minute sac.

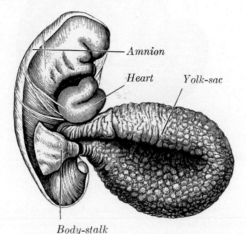

Body-stalk

Fig. 46.—Human embryo of 2.6 mm. (His.)

The Amnion—The amnion in man arises in the ectodermal part of the inner cell mass which lies next the trophoblast. Fluid is secreted within the cluster of cells, causing the formation of the amniotic cavity (Fig. 10). The ectodermal cells in contact with the entoderm are part of the embryonic disc, the other ectoderm cells enclosing the cavity are the amnion. As the amnion increases in size its cells become flat, and the outer surface is separated from the cytotrophoblast (Fig. 10) by a layer of extraembryonic mesoderm. About the fourth week, fluid (*liquor amnii*) accumulates and expands the amnion until it eventually comes into contact with the inner wall of the chorionic sac and obliterates the primitive blastocyst cavity about the end of the second month. It also grows around the body stalk and yolk sac and thus forms the covering of the umbilical cord (Figs. 36 to 39).

The liquor amnii increases in quantity up to the sixth or seventh month of pregnancy, after which it diminishes somewhat; at the end of pregnancy it amounts to about 1 liter. It allows the fetus free movement and protects it from mechanical injury during the later stages of pregnancy.

The Body Stalk and Umbilical Cord.—The inner cell mass is at first directly in contact with the trophoblast. After the development of the embryonic disk, chorionic mesoderm anchors the embryo to the inner wall of the chorion. As the embryo and the chorion grow, this mesodermal attachment becomes elongated into the body stalk (Fig. 36), which extends from the posterior end of the embryo to the chorion, and when the tail fold is formed, the attachment is moved to the midventral region of the embryo (Figs. 37 to 39), becoming the umbilical cord.

The umbilical blood vessels grow beside the allantois into the body stalk and ramify as the chorionic vessels which provide the vascular pathways to and from the embryo and the chorion. With the further development of the embryo and the expansion of the amnion, the body stalk and yolk sac are enclosed in the umbilical cord. The mesoderm of the body stalk blends with that of the yolk sac and its elongated yolk stalk, being converted into a gelatinous tissue known as *Wharton's jelly*. The vitelline vessels, together with the right umbilical vein, undergo atrophy and disappear; and thus the cord, at birth, contains a pair of umbilical arteries and one (the left) umbilical vein. It attains a length of about 50 cm.

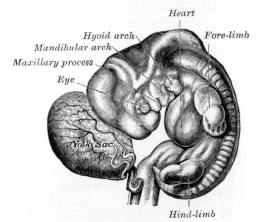

FIG. 47.—Human embryo from thirty-one to thirty-four days. (His.)

THE YOLK SAC

The yolk sac develops within the cluster of entoderm cells in the inner cell mass (Fig. 10). As it expands into a vesicle, two parts become distinguishable. The thicker part lying against the ectoderm in the embryonic disc is the future primitive gut of the embryo; the thinner expansion growing out into the cavity of the chorion is the yolk sac. The extraembryonic mesoderm on the outer surface of the entodermal yolk sac becomes a compact layer which differentiates quite early for the production of the first blood cells. During the presomite and early somite stages, the cells of this mesodermal layer proliferate rapidly, producing clusters which are known as **blood islands** and which give the yolk sac a lumpy appearance (Fig. 46). The outermost cells of the blood islands gradually become flattened into **primitive endothelium**; the inner cells become separated from each other by a small amount of primitive blood plasma, and most of them elaborate hemoglobin in their cytoplasm. The endothelial lining of the blood islands becomes continuous with similar endothelium which has been differentiating at the same time in the proximal part of the yolk sac, the yolk stalk, and the embryo proper. This primitive blood vascular system, corresponding to arteries, capillaries, and veins, completes the circuit by making connection with the developing heart, and, at about the eight somite stage, the **blood cells** in the islands are swept into the circulation by the pumping of the heart. The blood vessels of the yolk sac remain as the vitelline plexus, fed by the vitelline or omphalomesenteric artery and drained by the vitelline or omphalomesenteric vein; but in the human embryo, after it has supplied the blood cells for the beginning of circulation, the yolk sac appears to have no further function and undergoes regression.

At the end of the fourth week the yolk sac presents the appearance of a small pear-shaped vesicle (*umbilical vesicle*) opening into the digestive tube by the long narrow yolk stalk. As the amnion spreads around the body stalk and over the inner surface of the chorion, the proximal part of the yolk stalk becomes enclosed in the umbilical cord; the distal part extends to the placenta and ends in the **yolk sac vesicle** which lies between amnion and chorion either on the placenta or a short distance from it. The vesicle can be seen in the afterbirth as a small oval body whose diameter varies from 1 mm. to 5 mm. As a rule the **yolk stalk** undergoes complete obliteration during the seventh week, but occasionally it persists within the embryo, and in about 2 per cent of adult bodies is found as a diverticulum from the small intestine, *Meckel's diverticulum*, which is situated about 3 or 4 feet above the ileocolic junction and may be attached by a fibrous cord to the abdominal wall at the umbilicus.

THE ALLANTOIS

The **Allantois** (Figs. 36 to 39) arises as a tubular diverticulum from the posterior part of the yolk sac entoderm. When the hindgut is developed the allantois is carried backward with it and then opens into the terminal part of the hindgut or the cloaca. It grows out into the body stalk as a diverticulum lined by entoderm and covered by mesoderm, and with it are carried the allantoic vessels which extend into the chorionic mesoderm, eventually forming the umbilical vessels and their branches in the chorionic villi of the placenta. In reptiles, birds, and many mammals the allantois expands into a large sac, acquires an elaborate blood supply, and plays an important role in the early nutrition of the embryo. In man and other primates, however, the allantois itself remains rudimentary, but its blood vessels become functionally significant as the **umbilical vessels**.

MENSTRUAL AGE WITH MEAN SITTING HEIGHT AND WEIGHT OF FETUS. (STREETER.)

Menstrual age, weeks.	Sitting height at end of week, mm.	Increment in height.		Formalin weight, grams.	Increment in weight.	
		mm.	per cent.		grams.	per cent.
8	23	...	...	1.1		
9	31	8	26.0	2.7	1.6	59.3
10	40	9	22.5	4.6	1.9	41.3
11	50	10	20.0	7.9	3.3	41.8
12	61	11	18.0	14.2	6.3	44.4
13	74	13	17.6	26.0	11.8	45.4
14	87	13	15.0	45.0	19.0	42.2
15	101	14	14.0	72.0	27.0	37.5
16	116	15	13.0	108.0	36.0	33.3
17	130	14	10.8	150.0	42.0	28.0
18	142	12	8.4	198.0	48.0	24.2
19	153	11	7.2	253.0	55.0	21.7
20	164	11	6.7	316.0	63.0	20.0
21	175	11	6.3	385.0	69.0	18.0
22	186	11	6.0	460.0	75.0	16.3
23	197	11	5.6	542.0	82.0	15.0
24	208	11	5.3	630.0	88.0	14.0
25	218	10	4.6	723.0	93.0	13.0
26	228	10	4.4	823.0	100.0	12.2
27	238	10	4.2	930.0	107.0	11.5
28	247	9	3.6	1045.0	115.0	11.0
29	256	9	3.5	1174.0	129.0	11.0
30	265	9	3.4	1323.0	149.0	11.3
31	274	9	3.3	1492.0	169.0	11.3
32	283	9	3.1	1680.0	188.0	11.2
33	293	10	3.4	1876.0	196.0	10.4
34	302	9	3.0	2074.0	198.0	9.5
35	311	9	3.0	2274.0	200.0	8.8
36	321	10	3.1	2478.0	204.0	8.2
37	331	10	3.0	2690.0	212.0	8.0
38	341	10	3.0	2914.0	224.0	7.7
39	352	11	3.1	3150.0	236.0	7.5
40	362	10	2.8	3405.0	255.0	7.5

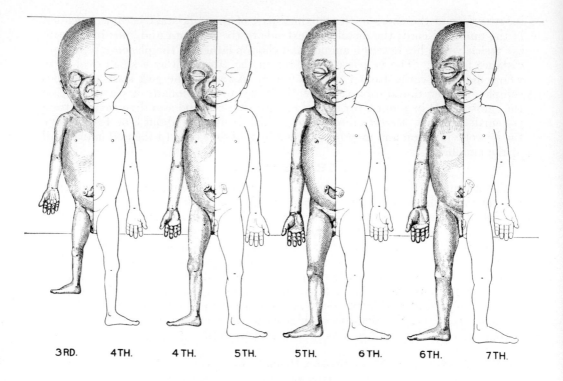

3RD.　　4TH.　　4TH.　　5TH.　　5TH.　　6TH.　　6TH.　　7TH.

THE GROWTH OF THE EMBRYO AND FETUS.

First Week.—No fertile human ova of the first week have been examined. From what we know of the monkey and other mammals it seems probable that the egg is fertilized in the upper end of the uterine tube and segments into about eight cells before it passes into the uterus at the end of the third day. In the uterus it continues to segment and develop into a blastocyst with a trophoblast and an inner cell-mass.

Second Week.—The blastocyst enlarges, loses its zona pellucida and becomes implanted in the uterine mucosa. The trophoblast, enclosing the blastocyst cavity, develops into an actively invading outer syncytiotrophoblast and inner cytotrophoblast and forms primitive chorionic villi into which first mesoderm and then blood vessels grow. The inner cell mass becomes the embryonic disc, amnion, and yolk sac. The primitive streak differentiates, and mesoderm and notochord are formed.

Third Week.—During the first part of the third week the neural folds appear (Figs 12, 34), the allantoic duct begins to develop, the yolk sac enlarges and blood vessels begin to form. Before the end of the week the neural folds begin to unite (Fig. 15). The neurenteric canal opens. The primitive segments begin to form. The changes during this week occur with great rapidity.

Fourth Week.—During the fourth week (Figs. 20, 21, 47) the neural folds close, the primitive segments increase in number, the branchial arches appear and the connection of the yolk-sac with the embryo becomes considerably narrowed so that the embryo assumes a more definite form. The limb-buds begin to show and the heart increases greatly in size, producing a prominent bulge in the branchial region.

Fifth Week.—The embryo becomes markedly curved, the head increases greatly in size and the limb-buds show segments (Fig 47). The branchial arches undergo profound changes and partly disappear. The superficial nose, eye and ear rudiments become prominent.

Sixth Week.—The curvature of the embryo is further diminished. The branchial grooves—except the first—have disappeared, and the rudiments of the fingers and toes can be recognized (Fig. 32).

Seventh and Eighth Weeks.—The flexure of the head is gradually reduced and the neck is somewhat lengthened. The upper lip is completed and the nose is more prominent. The nostrils are directed forward and the palate is not completely developed. The eyelids are present in the shape of folds above and below the eye, and the different parts of the auricula are distinguishable. By the end of the second month the fetus measures from 28 to 30 mm. in length (Fig. 33).

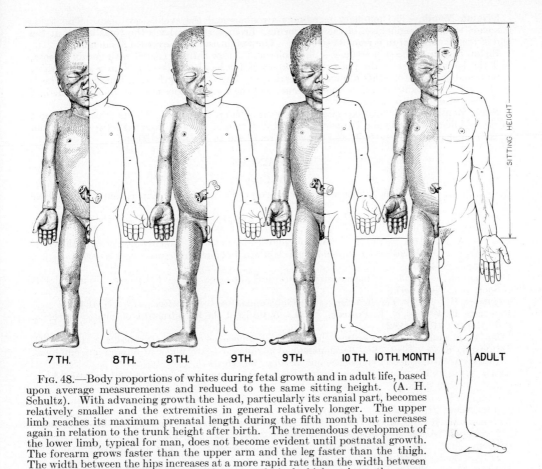

| 7 TH. | 8 TH. | 8 TH. | 9 TH. | 9 TH. | 10 TH. | 10 TH. MONTH | ADULT |

SITTING HEIGHT

FIG. 48.—Body proportions of whites during fetal growth and in adult life, based upon average measurements and reduced to the same sitting height. (A. H. Schultz). With advancing growth the head, particularly its cranial part, becomes relatively smaller and the extremities in general relatively longer. The upper limb reaches its maximum prenatal length during the fifth month but increases again in relation to the trunk height after birth. The tremendous development of the lower limb, typical for man, does not become evident until postnatal growth. The forearm grows faster than the upper arm and the leg faster than the thigh. The width between the hips increases at a more rapid rate than the width between the shoulders. In fetuses the shoulders are relatively higher above the suprasternal notch, the nipples relatively higher on the chest, and the umbilicus relatively lower on the abdominal wall than in adults. With advance in growth the breadth of the head decreases in relation to the head length, the ears become relatively larger, the eyes move closer together, the nose increases in height in relation to the face height, and decreases in width in relation to the face width.

Racial differences in body proportions develop as early as the human form can be recognized. Individual differences *i. e.*, variability, are fully as pronounced in fetal as in adult life. Asymmetries become evident long before birth.

Third Month.—The head is extended and the neck is lengthened. The eyelids meet and fuse, remaining closed until the end of the sixth month. The limbs are well-developed and nails appear on the digits. The external generative organs are so far differentiated that it is possible to distinguish the sex. By the end of this month the length of the fetus is about 7 cm., but if the legs be included it is from 9 to 10 cm.

Fourth Month.—The loop of gut which projected into the umbilical cord is withdrawn within the fetus. The hairs begin to make their appearance. There is a general increase in size so that by the end of the fourth month the fetus is from 12 to 13 cm. in length, but if the legs be included it is from 16 to 20 cm.

Fifth Month.—It is during this month that the first movements of the fetus are usually observed The eruption of hair on the head commences, and the *vernix caseosa* begins to be deposited. By the end of this month the total length of the fetus, including the legs, is from 25 to 27 cm.

Sixth Month.—The body is covered by fine hairs (*lanugo*) and the deposit of vernix caseosa is considerable. The papillæ of the skin are developed and the free border of the nail projects from the corium of the dermis. Measured from vertex to heels, the total length of the fetus at the end of this month is from 30 to 32 cm.

Seventh Month.—The pupillary membrane atrophies and the eyelids are open. The testis descends with the vaginal sac of the peritoneum. From vertex to heels the total length at the end of the seventh month is from 35 to 36 cm. The weight is a little over three pounds.

Eighth Month.—The skin assumes a pink color and is now entirely coated with vernix caseosa, and the lanugo begins to disappear. Subcutaneous fat has been developed to a considerable extent, and the fetus presents a plump appearance. The total length, *i. e.*, from head to heels at the end of the eighth month is about 40 cm., and the weight varies between four and one-half and five and one-half pounds.

Ninth Month.—The lanugo has largely disappeared from the trunk. The umbilicus is almost in the middle of the body and the testes are in the scrotum. At full time the fetus weighs from six and one-half to eight pounds, and measures from head to heels about 50 cm.

REFERENCES

The Cell

ALLEN, J. M. 1958. The influence of hormones on cell division. II. Exper. Cell Res., *14*, 142–148.

BRACHET, J. 1957. Biochemical Cytology. xi + 516 pages. Academic Press Inc., Publishers, New York.

DALTON, A. J. and M. D. FELIX. 1954. Cytologic and cytochemical characteristics of the Golgi substance of epithelial cells of the epididymis—in situ, in homogenates and after isolation. Am J. Anat., *94*, 171–207.

DANIELLI, J. F. 1953. Cytochemistry: A critical approach. ix + 139 pages. John Wiley & Sons, Inc., New York.

ELFTMAN, H. 1954. The structure of the Golgi apparatus. Anat. Rec., *118*, 147–164.

FAWCETT, D. W. and K. R. PORTER. 1954. A study of the fine structure of ciliated epithelia. J. Morph., *94*, 221–282.

FORD, C. E. and J. L. HAMERTON. 1956. The chromosomes of man. Nature, *178*, 1020–1023.

HARRISON, R. G. 1910. The development of peripheral nerve fibers in altered surroundings. Roux's Arch. f. Entwicklungsmechanik d. Org., *30*, 15–31.

LEWIS, WARREN H. 1947. Interphase (resting) nuclei, chromosomal vesicles and amitosis. Anat. Rec., *97*, 433–445.

MOORE, K. L. and M. L. BARR. 1954. Nuclear morphology, according to sex, in human tissues Acta Anat., *21*, 197–208.

MURRAY, M. R. and G. KOPECH. 1953. A Bibliography of the Research in Tissue Culture. 2 volumes. Academic Press, Inc., Publishers, New York.

PAINTER, T. S. 1923. Studies in mammalian spermatogenesis. II. The spermatogenesis of man. J. Exp. Zool., *37*, 291–336.

PALADE, G. E. 1952. The fine structure of mitochondria. Anat. Rec., *114*, 427–452.

PALADE, G. E. 1955. A small particulate component of the cytoplasm. J. Biophys. & Biochem. Cytol., *1*, 59–68.

PALAY, S. L. 1958. Frontiers in Cytology. xiv + 529 pages + 253 figures. Yale University Press, New Haven.

PORTER, K. R. 1953. Observations on a submicroscopic basophilic component of cytoplasm. J. Exp. Med., *97*, 727–750.

REED, C. I. and B. P. REED. 1948. Comparative study of human and bovine sperm by electron microscopy. Anat. Rec., *100*, 1–7.

WALLIS, T. E. 1957. Analytical Microscopy. 2nd Ed. viii + 215 pages. Little, Brown & Co., Boston.

SYMPOSIUM. 1956. Fine Structure of Cells. 321 pages. Interscience Publishers, Inc., New York.

Embryology

HAMILTON, W. J., J. D. BOYD, and H. W. MOSSMAN. 1952. Human Embryology. 2nd Ed. viii + 432 pages. The Williams & Wilkins Co., Baltimore

HINSCH, G. W. and H. L HAMILTON. 1956. The developmental fate of the first somite of the chick. Anat. Rec., *125*, 225–246.

NICHOLAS, J. S. 1954. Mechanisms affecting embryonic growth. Cold Spring Harbor Symp. on Quant. Biol., *19*, 36–40.

PATTEN, B. M. 1953. Human Embryology. 2nd Ed. xvii + 798 pages. The Blakiston Division, McGraw-Hill Book Co., Inc., New York.

VALDEZ-DAPENA, M. A. 1957. Atlas of Fetal and Neonatal Histology. ix + 200 pages. J. B. Lippincott Co., Philadelphia.

Ovulation and Fertilization

BLANDAU, R J. and D. L. ODOR. 1949. The total number of spermatozoa reaching various segments of the reproductive tract in the female albino rat at intervals after insemination. Anat Rec., *103*, 93–110.

CHANG, M. C. 1952. Fertilizability of rabbit ova and the effects of temperature in vitro on their subsequent fertilization and activation in vivo. J. Exp. Zool., *121*, 351–381.

EVERETT, J. W. 1956. The time of release of ovulating hormone from the rat hypophysis. Endocrinology, *59*, 580–585.

EVERETT, J. W. and C. H. SAWYER. 1949. A neural timing factor in the mechanism by which progesterone advances ovulation in the cyclic rat. Endocrinology, *45*, 581–595.

HARTMAN, C. G. 1936. Time of Ovulation in Women. x + 226 pages. The Williams & Wilkins Co., Baltimore.

HARTMAN, C. G. and G. W. CORNER. 1941. The first maturation division of the macaque ovum. Carnegie Contrib. to Emb., *29*, 1–6.

LEWIS, W. H. and C. G. HARTMAN. 1941. Tubal ova of the rhesus monkey. Carnegie Contrib. to Emb., *29*, 7–14.

ODOR, D. L. and R. J. BLANDAU. 1951. Observations on fertilization and the first segmentation division in rat ova. Am. J. Anat., *89*, 29–61.

ROCK, J. and A. T. HERTIG. 1944. Information regrading the time of human ovulation derived from a study of 3 unfertilized and 11 fertilized ova. Am. J. Obst. & Gynec., *47*, 343–356.

SHETTLES, L. B. 1954. Studies on living human ova. Trans. New York Acad. Sci. Ser. II, *17*, 99–102.

WOLSTENHOLME, G. E. W. 1953. Mammalian Germ Cells. xvi + 302 pages. Little Brown & Co., Boston.

IMPLANTATION, FETAL MEMBRANES AND PLACENTA

DEMPSEY, E. W. 1953. Electron microscopy of the visceral yolk-sac epithelium of the guinea pig. Am. J. Anat., *93*, 331–364.

FERM, V. H. 1956. Permeability of the rabbit blastocyst to trypan blue. Anat. Rec., *125*, 745–760.

HAMLETT, G. W. D. 1935. Delayed implantation and discontinuous development in the mammals. Quart. Rev. Biol., *10*, 432–447.

SHELESNYAK, M. C. 1956. Studies on the mechanism of the implantation of the fertilized ovum: A fertility control target. Acta Endocrinologica, Supplement, *28*, 106–113.

SINCLAIR, J. G. 1948. Significance of placental and birthweight ratios. Anat. Rec., *102*, 245–258.

WISLOCKI, G. B. and H. S. BENNETT. 1943. The histology and cytology of the human and monkey placenta with special reference to the trophoblast. Am. J. Anat., *73*, 335–450.

WISLOCKI, G. B. and E. W. DEMPSEY. 1955. Electron microscopy of the human placenta. Anat. Rec., *123*, 133–168.

EARLY HUMAN EMBRYOS

CORNER, G. W. 1929. A well-preserved human embryo of 10 somites. Carnegie Contrib. to Emb., *20*, 81–102.

GEORGE, W. C. 1942. A presomite human embryo with chorda canal and prochordal plate. Carnegie Contrib. to Emb., *30*, 1–7.

HERTIG, A. T. and J. ROCK. 1949. Two human ova of the pre-villous stage, having a developmental age of about eight and nine days respectively. Carnegie Contrib. to Emb., *33*, 169–186.

HERTIG, A. T., J. ROCK, and E. C. ADAMS. 1956. A description of 34 human ova within the first 17 days of development. Am. J. Anat., *98*, 435–494.

HERTIG, A. T., J. ROCK, E. C. ADAMS, and W. J. MULLIGAN. 1954. On the preimplantation stages of the human ovum: A description of four normal and four abnormal specimens ranging from the second to the fifth day of development. Carnegie Contrib. Embryol., *35*, 199–220.

HEUSER, C. H. 1930. A human embryo with fourteen pairs of somites. Carnegie Contrib. to Emb., *22*, 135–154.

HEUSER, C. H. 1932. A presomite human embryo with a definite chorda canal. Carnegie Contrib. to Emb., *23*, 251–267.

HEUSER, C. H., J. ROCK and A. T. HERTIG. 1945. Two human embryos showing early stages of the definitive yolk sac. Carnegie Contrib. to Emb., *31*, 85–99.

INGALLS, N. W. 1920. A human embryo at the beginning of segmentation, with special reference to the vascular system. Carnegie Contrib. to Emb., *11*, 61–90.

KINDRED, J. E. 1933. A human embryo of the presomite period from the uterine tube. Am. J. Anat., *53*, 221–242.

McKAY, D. G., E. C. ADAMS, A. T. HERTIG, and S. DANZIGER. 1955. Histochemical horizons in human embryos. I. Five millimeter embryo-Streeter horizon XIII. Anat. Rec., *122*, 125–152.

McKAY, D. G., E. C. ADAMS, A. T. HERTIG, and S. DANZIGER. 1956. Histochemical horizons in human embryos. II. Six and seven millimeter embryos-Streeter horizon XIV. Anat. Rec., *126*, 433–464.

PAYNE, F. 1925. General description of a seven somite human embryo. Carnegie Contrib. to Emb., *16*, 115–124.

Shaner, R. F.　1945.　A human embryo of two to three pairs of somites.　Canadian J. Research, Section E., *23*, 235–243.

Streeter, G. L.　1951.　Developmental horizons in human embryos.　Description of age group XIX, XX, XXI, XXII, and XXIII, being the fifth issue of a survey of the Carnegie collection. Carnegie Contrib. to Embr., *34*, 165–196.

Early Mammalian Embryos

Boving, B. G.　1956.　Rabbit blastocyst distribution.　Am. J. Anat., *98*, 403–434.

Heuser, C. H. and G. L. Streeter.　1941.　Development of the macaque embryo.　Carnegie Contrib. to Emb., *29*, 15–55.

Lewis, W. H. and C. G. Hartman.　1933.　Early cleavage stages of the egg of the monkey (Macacus rhesus).　Carnegie Contrib. to Emb. *24*, 187–201.

Experimental Embryology

Chang, M. C.　1955.　The maturation of rabbit oocytes in culture and their maturation, activation, fertilization and subsequent development in the fallopian tubes.　J. Exp. Zool., *128*, 379–406.

Duryee, W. R.　1954.　Microdissection studies on human ovarian eggs.　Trans. New York Acad. Sci. Ser. II, *17*, 103–108.

Experimental Embryology

Eastwick, H. L. and R. H. Anderson.　1944.　Studies on transplanted embryonic limbs of the chick.　II.　The development of limb primordia within the anterior chamber of the eye.　J. Morph., *75*, 1–9.

Fawcett, D. W.　1950.　The development of mouse ova under the capsule of the kidney. Anat. Rec., *108*, 71–92.

Fawcett, D. W., G. B. Wislocki, and C. M. Waldo.　1947.　The development of mouse ova in the anterior chamber of the eye and in the abdominal cavity.　Am. J. Anat., *81*, 413–444.

Flexner, J. B., C. L. Greenblatt, S. R. Cooperband, and L. B. Flexner.　1956.　Biochemical and physiological differentiation during morphogenesis.　XIX. Alkaline phosphatase and aldolase activities in the developing cerebral cortex and liver of the fetal guinea pig.　Am. J. Anat., *98*, 129–138.

Goss, C. M.　1935.　Double hearts produced experimentally in rat embryos.　J. Exp. Zool., *72*, 33–49.

Hamilton, J. B. and J. M. Wolfe.　1938.　The effect of male hormone substances upon birth and prenatal development in the rat.　Anat. Rec., *70*, 433–440.

Harrison, R. G.　1934.　Heteroplastic grafting in embryology.　Harvey Lectures, pp. 116–157.

Menkin, M. F. and J. Rock.　1948.　In vitro fertilization and cleavage of human ovarian eggs. Am. J. Obst. & Gyn., *55*, 440–452.

Rock, J. and M. F. Menkin.　1944.　In vitro fertilization and cleavage of human ovarian eggs. Science, *100*, 105–107.

Spemann, H.　1938.　Embryonic Development and Induction.　Yale Univ. Press, New Haven, xii + 401 pp.

Symposium.　1954.　The mammalian fetus:　Physiological aspects of development.　Cold Spring Harbor Symposia on Quantitative Biology, *19*, 1–225.　Long Island, New York.

Anomalies and Multiple Births

Fox, M. H. and C. M. Goss.　1956.　Experimental production of a syndrome of congenital cardiovascular defects in rats.　Anat. Rec., *124*, 189–208.

Fox, M. H. and C. M. Goss.　1957.　Experimentally produced malformations of the heart and great vessels in rat fetuses.　Atrial and caval abnormalities.　Anat. Rec., *129*, 309–332.

Fox, M. H. and C. M. Goss.　1958.　Experimentally produced malformations of the heart and great vessels in rat fetuses.　Transposition complexes and aortic arch abnormalities.　Amer. J. Anat., *102*, 65–92.

Hamlett, G. W. D. and G. B. Wislocki.　1934.　A proposed classification for types of twins in mammals.　Anat. Rec., *61*, 81–96.

Kimmel, D. L., E. K. Moyer, A. R. Peale, L. W. Winborne, and J. E. Gotwals.　1950.　A cerebral tumor containing five human fetuses.　A case of fetus in fetu. Anat. Rec., *106*, 141–165.

Nishimura, H. and K. Nakai.　1958.　Developmental anomalies in offspring of pregnant mice treated with nicotine.　Science, *127*, 877–878.

Wilson, J. G., C. B. Roth, and J. Warkany.　1953.　An analysis of the syndrome of malformations induced by maternal vitamin A deficiency.　Effects of restoration of vitamin A at various times during gestation.　Am. J. Anat., *92*, 189–218.

SURFACE AND TOPOGRAPHICAL ANATOMY.

THE HEAD.

Cranium.—The covering of the cranial part of the head is the scalp, a structure composed of the following layers: (1) skin; (2) subcutaneous tissue; (3) Occipitofrontalis muscle, including the galea aponeurotica; (4) subaponeurotic fascial cleft; and (5) pericranium or periosteum of the bones (Fig. 49). These layers are of rather uniform thickness, so that the conformation of the head is largely that of the underlying frontal, parietal, and parts of the occipital and temporal bones.

Bones.—Clearly visible landmarks are the **parietal** and **frontal eminences,** and the opening of the **external auditory meatus** of the ear. In addition, certain prominences can be recognized by palpation. In the occipital region or back of the head, the **external occipital protuberance** or **inion** is a bony prominence in the midline, at the junction of the head and neck. The **superior nuchal line** is a slight, upward curving ridge which extends laterally from the protuberance to the mastoid process of the temporal bone. The muscles of the neck stop at the superior nuchal line; above it, the cranium is covered only by scalp. The **mastoid process** projects downward and forward from behind the ear; its anterior border lies immediately behind the concha, and the apex is on a level with the lobe of the auricula.

Face.—The main contours of the face are governed by the bony landmarks, most of which are evident to the eye but which require palpation for establishment of their details (Fig. 50).

The **superciliary ridge** is the part of the frontal bone above the eye. It is marked by a depression, the supraorbital notch or foramen.

The rim of the hollow of the orbit is the **orbital margin,** formed by the frontal, zygomatic, and maxillary bones.

The **zygomatic arch** is formed by part of the frontal, zygomatic, and temporal bones.

The **superior temporal line** arches high on the parietal bone between the zygomatic process of the frontal bone and the region behind the ear.

The **mandible** can be recognized throughout most of its extent, including the prominence of the chin or mental protuberance, the angle of the jaw, the alveolar portion containing the teeth, and the condyle which articulates with the temporal bone.

The **temporomandibular joint** can be made easily recognizable by opening the jaws widely; this draws the mandible forward and a depression can be felt between the condyle of the mandible and fossa in the temporal bone, just in front of the tragus of the ear.

Some of these recognizable bony points are used in surgery and in anthropological measurements and therefore are given special names; other bony landmarks, not recognizable by observation or palpation, can be located by using the identifiable structures as points of reference.

Auricular Point.—The center of the opening of the external acoustic meatus.

(61)

Preauricular Point.—At the root of the zygomatic arch immediately in front of the external acoustic meatus.

Asterion.—A point 4 cm. behind and 12 mm. above the auricular point. It marks the meeting of the lambdoidal, occipitomastoid, and parietomastoid sutures.

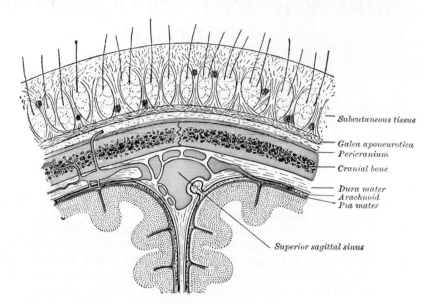

FIG. 49.—Diagrammatic section of scalp.

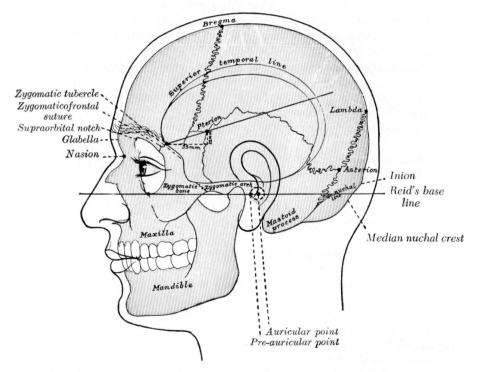

FIG. 50.—Side view of head, showing surface relations of bones.

Zygomatic Tubercle.—A prominence on the posterior margin of the zygomatic bone at the level of the lateral palpebral commissure of the eye.

Frontozygomatic Suture.—A slight depression on the posterior margin of the zygomatic bone, 1 cm. above the zygomatic tubercle.

Pterion.—A point 35 mm. behind and 12 mm. above the level of the frontozygomatic suture. It marks the point where the great wing of the sphenoid meets the sphenoidal angle of the parietal bone.

Inion.—The external occipital protuberance.

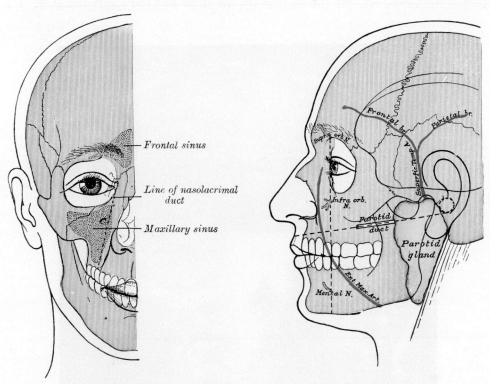

Fig. 51.—Outline of bones of face, showing position of air sinuses.

Fig. 52.—Outline of side of face, showing chief surface markings.

Lambda.—The point of meeting of the lambdoidal and sagittal sutures, about 6.5 cm. above the inion.

Bregma.—The meeting point of the coronal and sagittal sutures, at the intersection of a line drawn vertically upward from the preauricular point and the midline at the top of the head.

Lambdoidal Suture.—The upper two-thirds of a line from the mastoid process to the lambda.

Sagittal Suture.—The midline between the lambda and the bregma.

Obelion.—The point on the sagittal suture between the parietal emissary formina, a flattened area at the top of the head.

Coronal Suture.—Is approximated by a line from the bregma to the middle of the zygomatic arch.

Glabella.—A flattened triangular area between the two superciliary ridges.

Nasion.—A slight depression at the root of the nose marking the frontonasal suture.

Reid's base line passes through the inferior margin of the orbit and the auricular point.

The **fontanelles** or soft spots in the skull of a newborn infant (page 177) correspond to the above mentioned points and sutures as follows: (*a*) the anterior fontanelle, the largest, is at the bregma; (*b*) the posterior is at the lambda; (*c*) the lateral or sphenoidal fontanelle at the pterion; and (*d*) the mastoid fontanelle at the asterion.

Muscles and Soft Parts.—The *Masseter* produces the fullness of the posterior part of the cheek, between the angle of the mandible and the zygomatic arch. Its

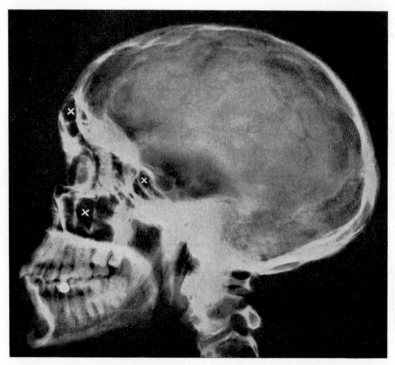

FIG. 53.—Adult skull. Lateral view. Crosses are placed on the frontal, the maxillary and the sphenoidal sinuses. Behind the last-named, the hypophyseal fossa can be identified. The dense white area below and behind the fossa is due to the petrous part of the temporal bone.

posterior border is masked by the substance of the *parotid gland*, lying over the muscle and between it and the ear (Fig. 52). The anterior border may be palpated readily when the muscle is contracted by clenching the teeth; in front of it the fullness of the cheek is produced by the *buccopharyngeal fat pad* and the *facial muscles*.

The *Temporalis* occupies the temporal fossa, extending from the hollow behind the zygomatic arch to the superior temporal line. The thick temporal fascia, covering the muscle, makes the superior border of the zygomatic arch difficult to palpate.

Arteries (Fig. 52).—The pulsations of the *superficial temporal artery* may be felt just above the zygomatic arch in front of the ear, and its frontal branch frequently is visible making its serpentine course across the temple, especially in older individuals. The *external maxillary* may be felt as it crosses the margin of the mandible at the anterior border of the Masseter; it has a tortuous course from this point upward across the face to the angle between the eye and the root of the nose.

Veins.—The facial vein crosses the margin of the mandible with the external maxillary artery, and takes a relatively straight course to the angle between the eye and nose.

Nerves.—The *supraorbital nerve* crosses the superciliary ridge through the supraorbital notch (or foramen). The *infraorbital nerve* becomes subcutaneous at the infraorbital foramen, just below the orbit. The *mental nerve* emerges from the mandible above and lateral to the mental protuberance. The *facial nerve* emerges from the substance of the anterior part of the parotid gland and spreads over the face like a fan.

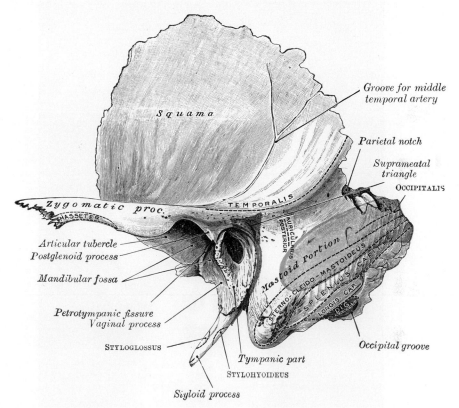

Fig. 54.—Left temporal bone showing surface markings for the tympanic antrum (red), transverse sinus (blue), and facial nerve (yellow).

Lymph nodes usually are not palpable in the head, but if enlarged, the following nodes may be felt: posterior auricular, parotid, occipital, buccal, and submaxillary.

The Eye.—The palpebral fissure, between the two lids, has as its extremities, the medial and lateral commissures. At the medial commissure are the caruncula lacrimalis, the plica semilunaris, and the puncta lacrimalia. The nasolacrimal duct runs from the puncta to an opening in the inferior meatus of the nose (*see* Sense Organ Chapter). The lacrimal sac, at the top of the duct, lies behind the medial palpebral ligament which may be felt at the medial commissure if the eyelids are drawn laterally to tighten the skin. The palpebral conjunctiva lines the lids and at the fornix conjunctivæ, it doubles back over the eyeball

5

as the bulbar conjunctiva. The colored part of the eye is covered by the transparent cornea, and through its central aperture, the pupil, the lens, the vessels of the retina, and the optic disc can be seen with an ophthalmoscope.

The Ear.—The auricula is marked by various prominences and fossæ (*see* Sense Organs). The opening of the external acoustic meatus is more fully exposed by drawing the tragus forward; the orifice is guarded by crisp hairs and contains a coating of wax, the secretion of the ceruminous glands. The interior of the meatus can be examined through a speculum or otoscope more easily if the auricula is drawn

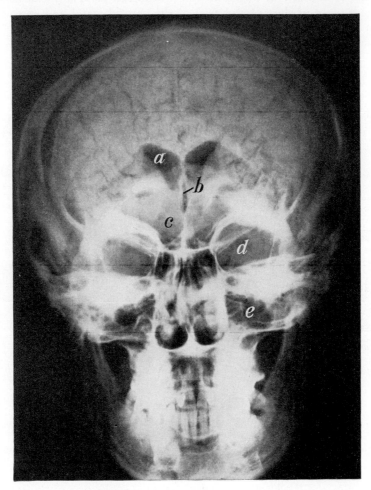

Fig. 55.—Brain ventricles injected with air. Note extension of air into sulci. *a*, Lateral ventricle; *b*, third ventricle; *c*, frontal sinus; *d*, orbit; *e*, maxillary sinus. (Department of Radiology, University of Pennsylvania.)

upward, backward, and slightly outward in order to straighten the slight curvature at the junction of the cartilaginous and bony portions of the wall. At the interior end of the meatus is the *tympanic membrane* which shows certain structures and markings when viewed with an otoscope. The *suprameatal triangle* (Fig. 54) is an important landmark for internal structures such as the tympanic antrum, facial nerve, and transverse sinus.

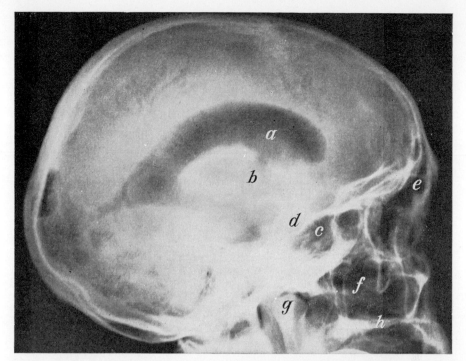

FIG. 56.—Adult head. *a*, Lateral ventricle injected with air; *b*, third ventricle, interventricular foramen mid-way between *a* and *b*; *c*, sphenoidal sinus; *d*, sella turcica; *e*, frontal sinus; *f*, maxillary sinus; *g*, condyle of mandible; *h*, hard palate. (Department of Radiology, University of Pennsylvania.)

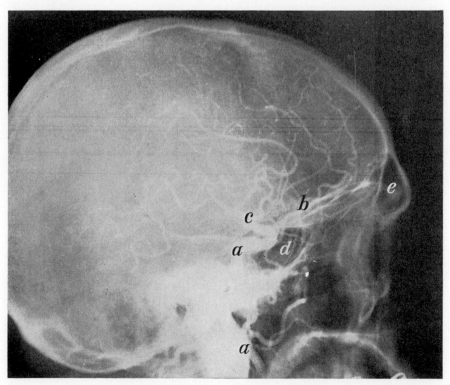

FIG. 57.—Internal carotid artery. *a*, After injection of diotrast into the common carotid artery; *b*, anterior cerebral artery; *c*, middle cerebral; *d*, sphenoidal sinus; *e*, frontal sinus. (Department of Radiology, University of Pennsylvania.)

(67)

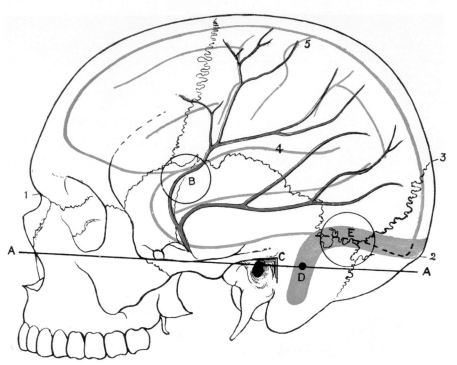

Fig. 58.—Relations of the brain and middle meningeal artery to the surface of the skull. 1. Nasion. 2. Inion. 3. Lambda. 4. Lateral cerebral fissure. 5. Central sulcus. *AA*. Reid's base line. *B*. Point for trephining the anterior branch of the middle meningeal artery. *C*. Suprameatal triangle. *D*. Sigmoid bend of the transverse sinus. *E*. Point for trephining over the straight portion of the transverse sinus, exposing dura mater of both cerebrum and cerebellum. Outline of cerebral hemisphere indicated in blue; course of middle meningeal artery in red.

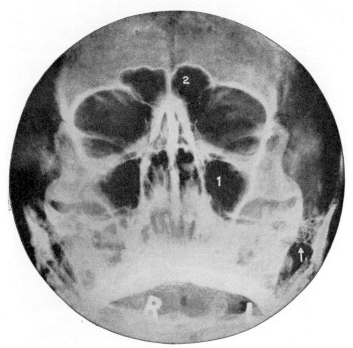

Fig. 59.—Adult skull. Frontal view. *1*, Maxillary sinus; *2*, frontal sinus. The arrow is directed towards the mastoid air-cells.

(68)

The **brain** can be placed approximately by certain external landmarks and measurements (Figs. 58, 60). The *lateral cerebral fissure* (Sylvian) can be located by a point, termed the Sylvian point, which practically corresponds to the pterion, 3.5 cm. behind and 12 mm. above the level of the frontozygomatic suture. The position of the *lateral ventricle* may be shown by an *x*-ray ventriculogram after air is injected into it (Figs. 54, 56). The branches of the *internal carotid artery* may be visualized in an *x*-ray after injection of the opaque medium diotrast (Fig. 55).

The **middle meningeal artery** lies at the level of the middle of the superior border of the zygomatic arch; its anterior branch may be reached through a trephined opening slightly anterior and below the pterion (Fig. 58). The **transverse dural sinus** may be approximated by a line through the asterion curving downward toward the mastoid process (Fig. 58).

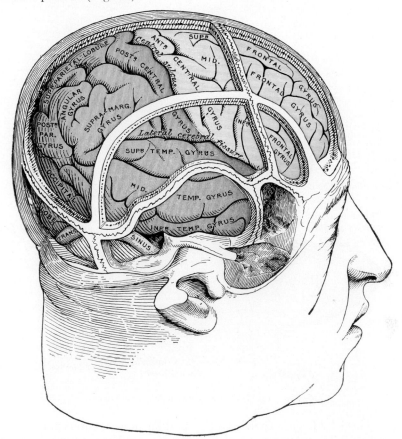

Fɪɢ. 60.—Drawing of a cast by Cunningham to illustrate the relations of the brain to the skull.

The **air sinuses** or **paranasal sinuses** vary greatly in size, shape, and position. The *frontal sinus* occupies the area in the bone deep to the medial part of the superciliary ridge. The *maxillary sinus* occupies the body of the maxilla, the area between the orbit, nasal cavity, and upper teeth (Fig. 59).

THE NECK.

Bones.—The **vertebral column** is deeply placed in the neck but certain processes can be identified by palpation. The tip of the **transverse process of the atlas** can be felt about 1 cm. below and in front of the mastoid process. The **anterior tubercle**

on the **transverse process** of the **sixth cervical vertebra** may be felt deep in the neck at the anterior border of the Sternocleidomastoideus; it has been named the **carotid** or **Chassaignac's tubercle**, and is the point of preference for compressing the common carotid artery to stop bleeding. The **hyoid bone** may be felt in the receding angle between the chin and anterior part of the neck. It is at the level of the fourth cervical vertebra and its greater cornu extends back on a level with the angle of the mandible (Figs. 61, 63).

The Larynx and Trachea.—The laryngeal prominence of the **thyroid cartilage** is visible in the midline, 1 or 2 cm. below the hyoid bone. The upper margin of the thyroid cartilage is connected with the hyoid bone by the thyrohyoid membrane, and its lower margin to the cricoid cartilage by the cricothyroid ligament. The

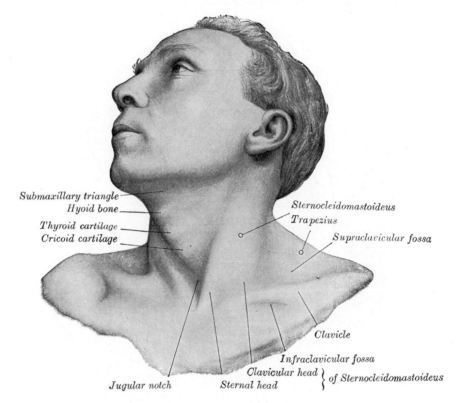

Submaxillary triangle
Hyoid bone

Thyroid cartilage
Cricoid cartilage

Sternocleidomastoideus
Trapezius

Supraclavicular fossa

Clavicle

Infraclavicular fossa
Clavicular head } *of Sternocleidomastoideus*
Jugular notch   *Sternal head*

FIG. 61.—Antero-lateral view of head and neck.

level of the vocal folds corresponds to the middle of the anterior border of the thyroid cartilage. The **cricoid cartilage** is at the level of the sixth cervical vertebra. Below it the **trachea** can be felt, but only in thin subjects can the individual rings be distinguished. As a rule there are seven or eight rings above the jugular notch of the sternum, and the isthmus of the **thyroid gland** covers the second, third, and fourth rings.

Muscles.—The **Sternocleidomastoideus** is the most prominent muscle in the neck. Its entire extent, from the mastoid process to the sternal and clavicular heads (Fig. 61) is clearly visible in most persons. The **Trapezius** forms the upper border of the shoulder, sloping upward from the point of the shoulder toward the back of the head. The **Platysma** is a very thin superficial sheet of muscle overlying the anterior neck; it can be detected only if thrown into prominence by being contracted, as it is when one attempts to relieve the pressure of a tight collar.

Triangles of the Neck.—The lack of prominent topographical features and the large number of important nerves and blood vessels contained within the neck have made it customary to subdivide this region into smaller areas. These areas, triangular in shape and related to some of the more superficial muscles, are known as the triangles of the neck (Fig. 62).

Anterior Triangle.—The anterior triangle is bounded anteriorly by the **midline**, and posteriorly by the anterior border of the **Sternocleidomastoideus;** its apex is below at the sternum, and its base is formed by the lower margin of the **body of the mandible** and an extension of this line to the mastoid process. This larger triangle is subdivided by the Digastricus above, and the superior belly of the Omohyoideus below into four smaller triangles: the inferior carotid, superior carotid, submaxillary, and suprahyoid triangles.

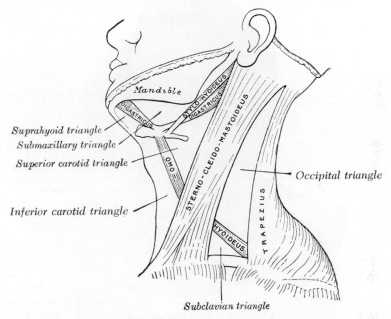

Fig. 62.—The triangles of the neck.

The **Inferior Carotid** or **Muscular Triangle** is bounded in front, by the midline of the neck; behind, by the superior belly of the Omohyoideus above, and the anterior margin of the lower part of the Sternocleidomastoideus below. In this triangle, under cover of the skin, superficial fascia, Platysma, and deep fascia, are the Sternohyoideus, Sternothyroideus, the isthmus of the thyroid gland, the larynx, and the trachea. Although not within the triangle as bounded above, the following structures can be approached surgically through the triangle by displacing the Sternocleidomastoideus laterally: the lower part of the common carotid artery in the carotid sheath with the internal jugular vein and vagus nerve, the ansa hypoglossi, the sympathetic trunk, recurrent nerve, and the esophagus.

The **Superior Carotid** or **Carotid Triangle** is bounded behind, by the Sternocleidomastoideus; below, by the superior belly of the Omohyoideus; and above, by the Stylohyoideus and posterior belly of the Digastricus. It is covered by the skin, superficial fascia, Platysma, and deep fascia, layers which contain the ramifications of the cutaneous cervical nerves and the cervical branch of the facial nerve. The floor or deepest part of the triangle is formed by the Thyrohyoideus, Hyoglossus and the Constrictores pharyngis medius and inferior. In the triangle, especially if it is enlarged by displacing the Sternocleidomastoideus backward, is the upper part of the common carotid artery which bifurcates at the level of the upper border of the thyroid cartilage into the internal and external carotids. The internal carotid is here posterior and somewhat lateral to the external and has no branches. The branches of the external carotid at the triangle are the superior thyroid, the lingual, the external maxillary, the occipital, and the ascending pharyngeal. Enclosed in a fascial membrane with the arteries, the carotid sheath, are the internal jugular vein and the vagus nerve. The tributaries of the vein correspond with the branches of the external carotid: superior thyroid, lingual, common facial, ascending pharyngeal, and sometimes the occipital. Superficial to the carotid sheath is the

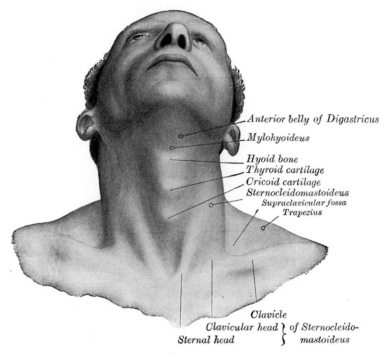

Fig. 63.—Front view of neck.

ansa hypoglossi; and deep to it or imbedded in its substance is the sympathetic trunk. The hypoglossal nerve crosses both the internal and external carotids in the upper part of the triangle, curving around the origin of the occipital artery. Between the external carotid and the pharynx, just below the hyoid bone, is the internal branch of the superior laryngeal nerve; the external branch is slightly lower. The accessory nerve may cross the uppermost corner of the triangle. The carotid sinus and carotid body lie at the level below the hyoid bone, between it and the superior border of the thyroid cartilage.

The **Submaxillary** or **Digastric Triangle** corresponds to the region of the neck immediately below the body of the mandible. It is bounded, above, by the lower border of the body of the mandible and an extension of this line to the mastoid process; below, by the posterior belly of the Digastricus and the Stylohyoideus; and in front, by the anterior belly of the Digastricus. It is covered by the skin, superficial fascia, Platysma, and deep fascia, ramifying in which are branches of the facial nerve and ascending filaments from the cervical cutaneous nerves. Its floor is formed by the Mylohyoideus and Hyoglossus. It is divided into an anterior and a posterior part by the stylomandibular ligament at the angle of the mandible. The anterior part contains the submaxillary gland, which is crossed by the anterior facial vein and external maxillary artery. Deep to the gland are the submental artery and the mylohyoid artery and nerve. The posterior part of this triangle is largely occupied by the parotid gland. If the triangle is enlarged by displacing the muscles slightly and by turning the head and raising the chin, certain deeper structures may be included. The external carotid is deep in the substance of the parotid gland, where it is superficial to the internal carotid, is crossed by the facial nerve, and gives off its posterior auricular, superficial temporal, and internal maxillary branches. The internal jugular vein and vagus nerve are still deeper, separated from the external carotid by the Styloglossus, Stylopharyngeus, and the glosso-pharyngeal nerve.

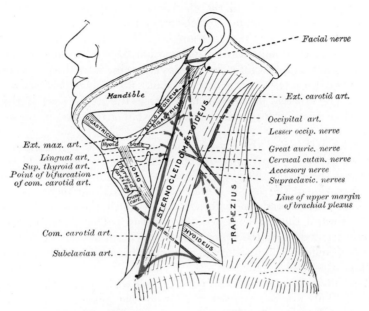

FIG. 64.—Side of neck, showing chief surface markings.

The **Suprahyoid Triangle** is bounded by the anterior belly of the Digastricus, the midline, and the body of the hyoid bone. Its floor is the Mylohyoideus. It contains one or two lymph nodes and small tributaries of the anterior jugular vein.

POSTERIOR TRIANGLE.—The posterior triangle is bounded, in front, by the **Sternocleidomastoideus;** behind, by the anterior margin of the **Trapezius;** its base is the middle third of the **clavicle**, and its apex is at the occipital bone. About 2.5 cm. above the clavicle, it is crossed obliquely by the inferior belly of the Omo-hyoideus, dividing it into an upper or occpital, and a lower or subclavian triangle.

The **Occipital Triangle** is bounded, in front, by the Sternocleidomastoideus; behind, by the Trapezius; and below, by the Omohyoideus. Its floor is formed by the Splenius capitis, Levator scapulæ, and Scalenus medius and posterior, and it is covered by the skin, superficial fascia, and deep fascia. About one-half or two-thirds of the way up, the triangle is crossed by the accessory nerve; somewhat lower the cervical cutaneous and supraclavicular nerves emerge from under the posterior border of the Sternocleidomastoideus; and the upper part of the brachial plexus crosses the lowest part of the triangle.

The **Subclavian Triangle** is bounded, above, by the inferior belly of the Omo-hyoideus; below, by the clavicle; and in front by the Sternocleidomastoideus. Its floor is formed by the first rib and the first digitation of the Serratus anterior. Its size depends upon the extent of attachment of the Sternocleidomastoideus and Trapezius to the clavicle and the position of the Omohyoideus; some of the struc-tures listed below might have to be reached by displacement of the muscles, and the triangle is increased in size by drawing the shoulder downward to lower the clavicle. It is covered by the skin, superficial fascia, Platysma, and deep fascia containing the supraclavicular nerves. In the medial part of the triangle, the third part of the subclavian artery emerges from behind the Scalenus anterior and curves down behind the clavicle. Sometimes the arch of the artery rises 4 cm. above the clavicle, and this is the most commonly chosen place for ligature. The subclavian vein usually remains down behind the clavicle, but may be found partly in the triangle. The transverse scapular vessels cross the lower part, the superficial cervical vessels the upper part of the triangle. The external jugular vein enters the anterior part of the triangle from its position on the surface of the Sterno-cleidomastoideus and empties into the subclavian vein; its tributaries, the trans-verse scapular and transverse cervical veins, make a plexus superficial to the sub-clavian artery. The brachial plexus of nerves crosses the lateral part of the triangle coming into close relationship with the subclavian artery as it passes behind the clavicle.

Arteries.—The position of the *common* and *external carotid arteries* is indicated by a line drawn from the upper part of the sternal end of the clavicle to a point midway between the tip of the mastoid process and the angle of the mandible. Above the bifurcation at the upper border of the thyroid cartilage, this line over-lies the internal carotid and the external carotid until the latter arches back-ward slightly toward the external acoustic meatus. The *main branches* of the *external carotid* originate near the tip of the greater cornu of the hyoid bone. The *subclavian artery* underlies a line arching upward from the sternoclavicular joint to the middle of the clavicle (Fig. 64).

Veins.—The *internal jugular vein* is parallel and slightly lateral to the internal carotid artery. The *external jugular* runs from the angle of the mandible to the middle of the clavicle (Fig. 64).

Nerves.—The exit of the *facial nerve* from the stylomastoid foramen is about 2.5 cm. below the surface of the skin, opposite the anterior border of the mastoid process. The *accessory nerve* is quite superficial as it crosses the posterior triangle, running downward from under the upper middle part of the posterior border of the Sternocleidomastoideus to pass under the anterior border of the Trapezius. Also emerging from under the posterior border of the Sternocleidomastoideus in this same region are the *cutaneous nerves*: the lesser occipital, the greater auricular, the cervical cutaneous, and the supraclavicular nerves. The *phrenic nerve* begins at the level of the middle of the thyroid cartilage and passes deep to and about half way between the two borders of the Sternocleidomastoideus. The upper part of the *brachial plexus* is indicated by a line from the cricoid cartilage to the middle of the clavicle. The *vagus nerve* and *sympathetic trunk* run parallel and deep to the internal carotid artery.

Lymph Nodes.—Lymph nodes may be felt between the ramus of the mandible and the Sternocleidomastoideus, along the course of the internal jugular vein at the anterior border of this muscle, and along the posterior border of the same muscle in the upper and lower portions of the posterior triangle.

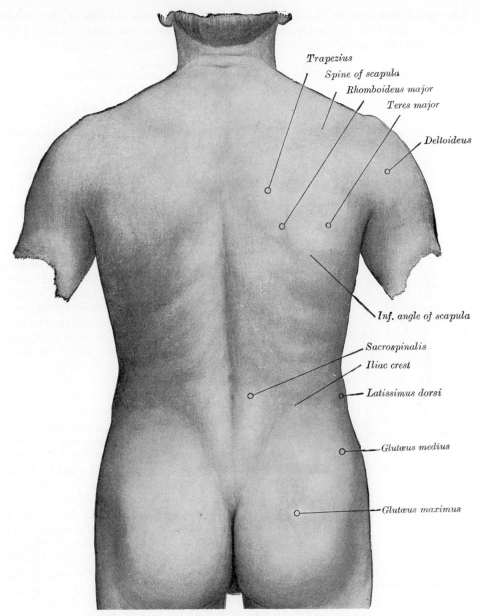

Trapezius

Spine of scapula

Rhomboideus major

Teres major

Deltoideus

Inf. angle of scapula

Sacrospinalis

Iliac crest

Latissimus dorsi

Glutæus medius

Glutæus maximus

Fig. 65.—Surface anatomy of the back.

THE BACK.

Bones.—The furrow down the middle of the back lies over the tips of the *spinous processes of the vertebræ*. The upper cervicals cannot be felt, but the seventh can be distinguished easily and is next above the more prominent *first thoracic*. Other thoracic spines can be identified by counting from these. The root of the *spine of the scapula* is on a level with the third thoracic spine, the inferior angle with the seventh. The highest point of the *crest of the ilium* is on a level with the fourth lumbar spinous process and the *posterior superior iliac spine* with that of the second sacral.

The **spinal cord** extends down to the level of the spinous process of the second lumbar vertebra (Fig. 66) in the adult body, but as far as the fourth in an infant. The **subarachnoid space**, containing the spinal fluid, extends down to the third sacral vertebra.

The **muscles** of the back are large and usually can be identified with ease in a living subject (Fig. 65).

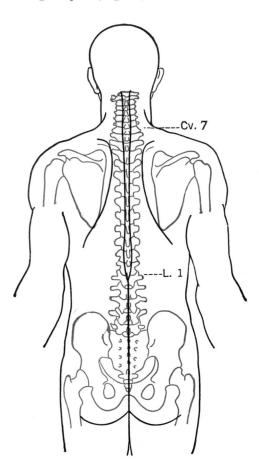

FIG. 66.—Diagram showing the relation of the spinal cord to the dorsal surface of the trunk. The bones are outlined in red.

THE THORAX.

The surface of the thorax is covered by several large muscles belonging to the musculature of the upper extremity (Fig. 74). At each side, the **axilla** or hollow of the armpit (Fig. 69) is limited by two fleshy folds; the **anterior axillary fold** is the prominence caused by the Pectoralis major, the **posterior axillary fold** is the prominence of the Latissimus dorsi. The size of the **breast** or **mamma** is subject to great variation. In most adult nulliparous females it extends vertically from the second to the sixth ribs, and transversely from the sternum to the midaxillary line. In males and nulliparous females, the **mammary papilla** or **nipple** is situated in the fourth intercostal space (Fig. 67).

Bony Landmarks.—The *sternum, ribs, scapula* and *clavicle* can be seen in many individuals and can be felt in all but the very muscular or obese subjects. The upper border of the sternum is marked by the **jugular notch**, between the sternal heads of the two Sternocleidomastoidei (Fig. 63). In the midline the sternum is subcutaneous, leaving the sternal furrow between the origins of the two Pectorales majores. The junction between the two parts of the sternum, the manubrium above and the body or gladiolus below, is marked by a well defined transverse ridge about 5 cm. below the jugular notch. This ridge, called the **sternal angle** or **angle of Louis**, is opposite the sternochondral junction of the second rib (Fig. 72). At the lower end of the body of the sternum is the infrasternal notch between the sternal attachments of the seventh costal cartilages. In the triangular depression below the notch, the epigastric fossa, the **xiphoid process** of the sternum can be felt.

The **ribs** can usually be felt at the sternum in front, at the sides, and in back as far as their angles, although they are mostly covered by muscles. The first rib is difficult to palpate because it is deep and partly hidden by the clavicle. The **second rib** is the one most reliably identified because of its attachment at the angle of Louis. The lower boundary of the thorax is formed by the xiphoid process, the cartilages of the seventh, eighth, ninth, and tenth ribs and the ends of the eleventh and twelfth cartilages (Figs. 72, 75).

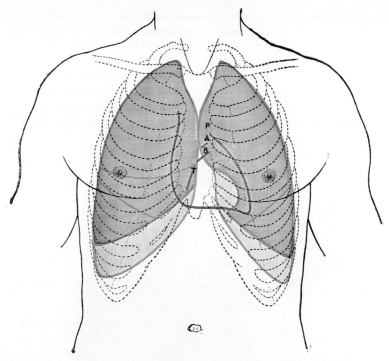

FIG. 67.—Front of thorax, showing surface relations of bones, lungs (purple), pleura (blue) and heart (red outline). *P.* Pulmonary valve. *A.* Aortic valve. *B.* Bicuspid valve. *T.* Tricuspid valve.

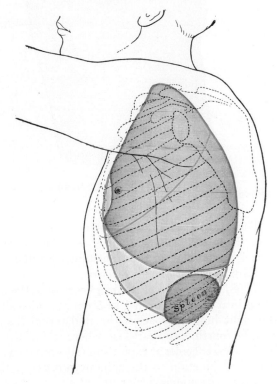

FIG. 68.—Side of thorax, showing surface markings for bones, lungs (purple), pleura (blue), and spleen (green).

Lines for Orientation (Fig. 77).—The **midsternal line** is the midline of the body over the sternum. The **midclavicular** or **mammary line** is a vertical line, parallel with the midsternal, through a point midway between the center of the jugular notch and the tip of the acromion or point of the shoulder. The **lateral sternal line** is a vertical line along the sternal margin. The **anterior** and **posterior axillary lines** are vertical lines drawn on the corresponding folds; the **midaxillary line**, half way between them, passes through the apex of the axilla. On the back, the **scapular line** is drawn vertically through the inferior angle of the Scapula (Fig. 65).

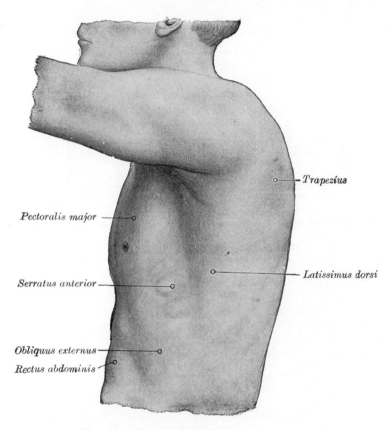

Trapezius

Pectoralis major

Latissimus dorsi

Serratus anterior

Obliquus externus

Rectus abdominis

Fig. 69.—The left side of the thorax.

Vertebral Level.—The **jugular notch** is at the same horizontal level as the lower border of the body of the second thoracic vertebra. The **sternal angle** is at the level of the fifth thoracic vertebra, and the **xiphisternal junction** at the level of the disc between the ninth and tenth thoracic vertebræ.

The Lungs (Figs. 67, 68).—The **apex of the lung** lies behind the medial third of the clavicle and extends up into the neck from 1 to 5 cm., usually about 2.5 cm. The **anterior border** of the right lung approaches the midsternal line, that of the left does likewise as far as the fourth costal cartilage where it deviates laterally because of the cardiac notch. The **lower border** at expiration follows a curving line downward from the sixth sternocostal junction to the spinous process of the tenth thoracic vertebra. This line crosses the midclavicular line at the sixth and the midaxillary line at the eighth rib. The **posterior border** is parallel with the midline, 2 to 3 cm. from it, and extends from the spinous process of the seventh cervical vertebra to that of the tenth thoracic vertebra.

The **pleura** corresponds in general with the lungs, but is more extensive. The **parietal pleuræ** of the two sides of the body come close to each other in the midline

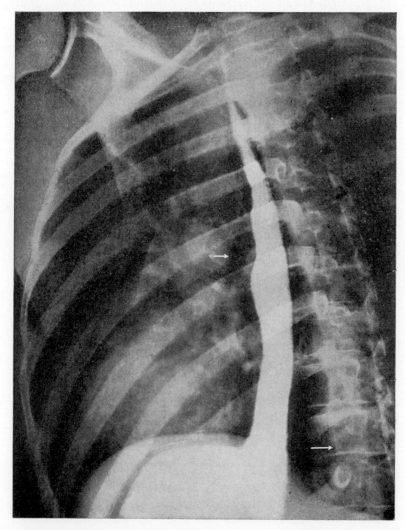

Fig. 70.—Esophagus during the passage of a barium meal. Note that in the upper part of the esophagus longitudinal folds in the mucous membrane can be identified. The upper arrow points to the shadow of the right bronchus; the lower arrow indicates the tenth thoracic vertebra. Note that the lower part of the esophagus inclines forwards away from the vertebral column.

anteriorly, at expiration, opposite the second to fourth costal cartilages. The medial 1 or 2 cm. of the pleural cavity is unoccupied by lung, the potential space being known as the **costomediastinal sinus**. The inferior limit of the pleura is 2 to 5 cm. below that of the lung at expiration, leaving the **phrenicocostal sinus** unoccupied by lung. This is a favorite place for the introduction of a needle into the pleural cavity to drain fluid. The **attachment of the diaphragm** along the costal margin is 2 or 3 cm. below the inferior limit of the pleura.

The Heart.—The **apex of the heart** usually may be felt by its pulsation in the fifth intercostal space just below the nipple or about 9 cm. to the left of the midsternal line. In an approximate projection of the heart on the anterior chest wall, the **superior border** is marked by a horizontal line at the third sternochondral attachment; the **right margin** corresponds to a vertical line drawn 2.5 cm. lateral

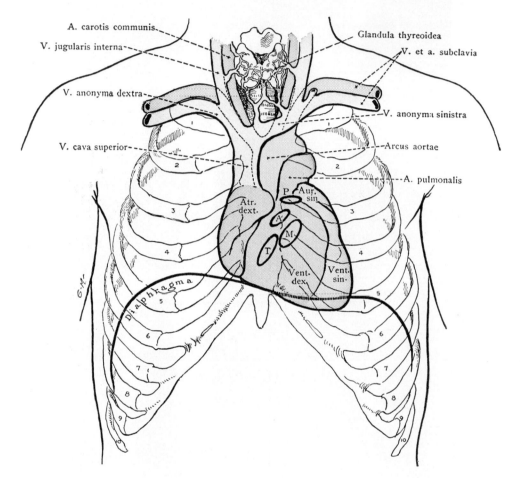

Fig. 71.—The heart and cardiac valves projected on the anterior chest wall, showing their relation to the ribs, sternum and diaphragm. (Eycleshymer and Jones.)

to the sternal margin; the **inferior or diaphragmatic margin** is marked by a line sloping slightly downward and to the left at the xiphisternal junction, and the **left border** angles upward from the apex to the second intercostal space 2.5 cm. from the sternal margin. The superior margin is also the **base of the heart** and marks the beginning of the great vessels. The position of the chambers, sulci, and valves are shown in Figure 71.

The **internal mammary vessels** run vertically 1 cm. lateral to the sternal margin as far as the sixth cartilage. The **intercostal vessels** and **nerves** generally lie along the inferior border of the rib in their intercostal spaces anteriorly and tend to lie deep to the rib posteriorly.

THE ABDOMEN.

The contours of the abdomen are established largely by the muscles, with modifications brought about by the accumulation of adipose tissue in the subcutaneous

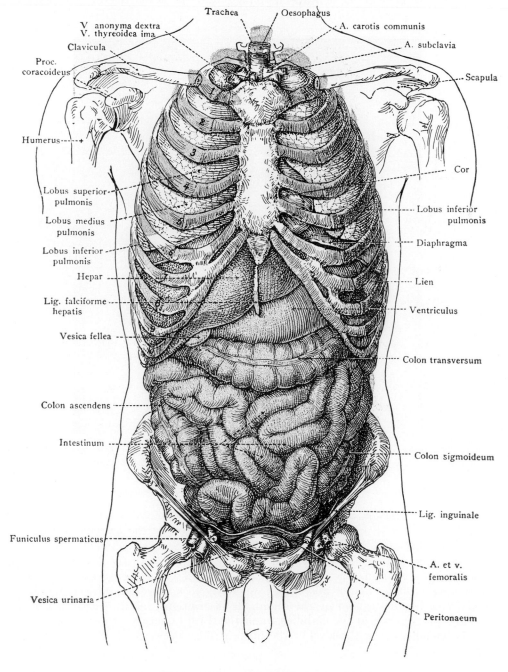

Trachea — Oesophagus
V anonyma dextra
V. thyreoidea ima
A. carotis communis
Clavicula
A. subclavia
Proc. coracoideus
Scapula
Humerus
Cor
Lobus superior pulmonis
Lobus inferior pulmonis
Lobus medius pulmonis
Diaphragma
Lobus inferior pulmonis
Hepar
Lien
Lig. falciforme hepatis
Ventriculus
Vesica fellea
Colon transversum
Colon ascendens
Intestinum
Colon sigmoideum
Lig. inguinale
Funiculus spermaticus
A. et v. femoralis
Vesica urinaria
Peritonaeum

Fig. 72.—Thoracic and abdominal viscera shown in their normal relations to the skeleton. Anterior view.   (Eycleshymer and Jones.)

layers. A groove in the midline separates the medial margin of the **Rectus abdominis** of one side from that of the other side and lies over an aponeurotic junction known as the **linea alba** (Fig. 74). The **umbilicus** interrupts the linea alba about half way between the infrasternal notch and the pubic symphysis. The lateral margin of the Rectus abdominis corresponds to another groove, the **linea semilunaris** (Fig. 90), which is not as clearly marked as the linea alba except in muscular subjects. At the level of the umbilicus, the linea semilunaris is about 7 cm. from the midline and it curves medially as it nears the pubis. Lateral to the Rectus, the **Obliquus**

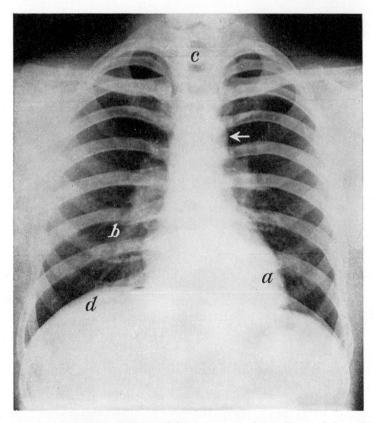

Fig. 73.—Anterior view, thorax, heart, and diaphragm. *a*, Apex of heart; *b*, bronchi; *c*, trachea; *d*, diaphragm. The arrow points to the arch of the aorta. (Department of Radiology, University of Pennsylvania.)

externus abdominis is the superficial muscle; it interdigitates with the **Serratus anterior** above, and posteriorly it is partly overlapped by the **Latissimus dorsi**. A separation between the Externus and Latissimus at their attachment to the crest of the ilium is known as the *lumbar triangle* of Petit. At the lower border of the Obliquus externus, the **inguinal ligament** lies deep to the groove of the groin. The surface of the Rectus abdominis, especially in a muscular subject, has three transverse furrows caused by the tendinous inscriptions; one is a little below the xiphoid process, one at the umbilicus, and the third in between these two.

The **umbilicus** is at the level of the fibrocartilage between the third and fourth lumbar vertebræ.

The **subcutaneous inguinal ring** (Fig. 90) is situated 1 cm. above and lateral to the pubic tubercle; the **abdominal inguinal ring** lies 1 to 2 cm. above the middle of the inguinal ligament. The position of the **inguinal canal** is indicated by a line joining these two points.

The **Bony Landmarks** of the abdomen are: above, the lower border of the thorax which has already been described, and below, the bony pelvis. The **crest** of the **ilium** may be identified by the prominent **tubercle** on the outer lip, which can be

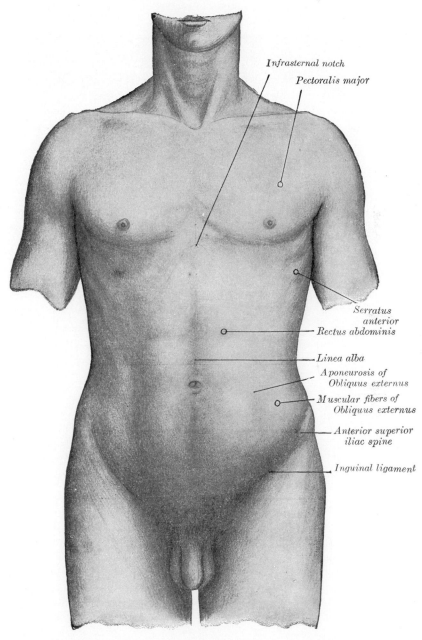

FIG. 74.—Surface anatomy of the front of the thorax and abdomen.

seen or palpated. The **anterior superior spine** of the **ilium** may be felt in the groin at the lateral end of the inguinal ligament (Fig. 74), and the **pubic tubercle** may be felt at the medial end of the ligament, a point which may also be identified as the inferior attachment of the Rectus abdominis in the region known as the **mons pubis.**

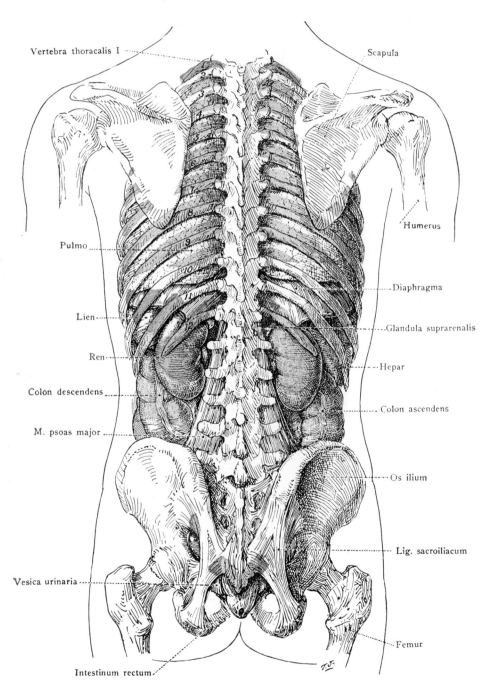

Fig. 75.—Thoracic and abdominal viscera shown in their normal relations to the skeleton. Posterior view. (Eycleshymer and Jones.)

Surface Lines.—For convenience of description and reference, the abdomen is divided into nine regions by imaginary planes, two horizontal and two sagittal, indicated by the following lines drawn on the surface of the body (Fig. 77). (1) An upper transverse, the **transpyloric**, halfway between the jugular notch and the upper border of the symphysis pubis; this cuts through the pylorus, the tips of the ninth costal cartilages and the lower border of the first lumbar vertebra; (2) a

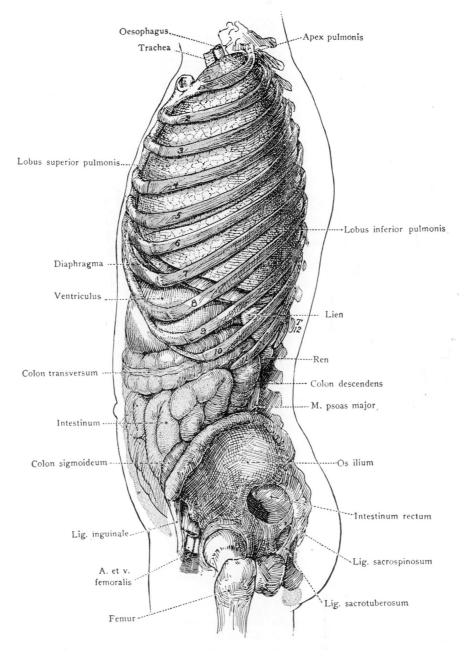

Fig. 76.—Thoracic and abdominal viscera shown in their normal relations to the skeleton, from the left side. (Eycleshymer and Jones.)

lower transverse line termed the **transtubercular,** corresponds to the iliac tubercles and cuts the body of the fifth lumbar vertebra.

By means of these horizontal planes the abdomen is divided into three zones named from above, the **subcostal, umbilical,** and **hypogastric zones.** Each of these is further subdivided into three regions by the two sagittal planes, which are indi-

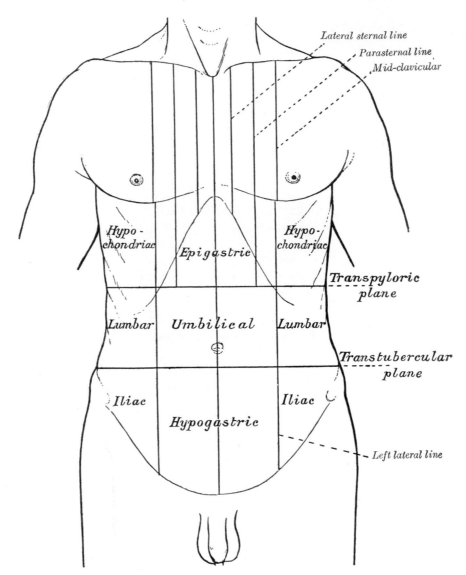

Fig. 77.—Surface lines of the front of the thorax and abdomen.

cated on the surface by a right and a left lateral line drawn vertically through points halfway between the anterior superior iliac spines and the midline. The middle region of the upper zone is called the **epigastric,** and the two lateral regions the **right** and **left hypochondriac.** The central region of the middle zone is the **umbilical,** and the two lateral regions the **right** and **left lumbar.** The middle region of the lower zone is the **hypogastric** or **pubic**, and the lateral are the **right** and **left** **iliac** or **inguinal**.

Another more simplified but quite useful subdivision of the abdomen is by two planes at right angles to each other, one corresponding to the midsagittal plane of the body, the other a transverse plane through the umbilicus. The resulting four portions are known as quadrants, the upper and lower, right and left.

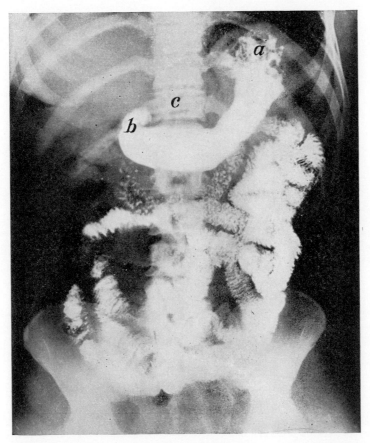

FIG. 78.—Stomach and small intestines after a barium meal. *a*, Barium has settled out of the fundus of the stomach; *b*, pylorus; *c*, thoracic vertebra XII. (Department of Radiology, University of Pennsylvania.)

Viscera.—Under normal conditions the various portions of the digestive tube cannot be identified by simple palpation. The greater part of the liver lies under cover of the ribs and cartilages, especially in the supine position, but during a deep inspiration it may be pushed out below the costal margin on the right side and be felt. Other viscera can only be palpated in emaciated subjects with lax abdominal walls, or if they are the seat of disease or tumors.

Stomach (Fig. 79).—The shape of the stomach is constantly undergoing alteration; it is affected by the particular phase of digestion, by the state of the surrounding viscera, and by the amount and character of its contents. Its position also varies with that of the body, so that it is impossible to indicate it on the surface with any degree of accuracy. The measurements given refer to a moderately filled stomach with the body in the supine position. (See Digestive Apparatus.)

The cardiac orifice is opposite the seventh left costal cartilage about 2.5 cm. from the side of the sternum; it corresponds to the level of the tenth thoracic vertebra. The pyloric orifice is on the transpyloric line about 1 cm. to the right of the midline, or alternately 5 cm. below the seventh right sternocostal articulation; it is at the level of the first lumbar vertebra.

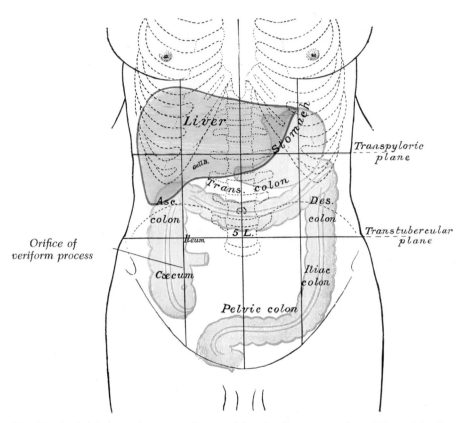

Fig. 79.—Front of abdomen, showing surface markings for liver, stomach, and large intestine.

Duodenum (Fig. 86).—The superior part is horizontal and extends from the pylorus to the right lateral line; the descending part is situated medial to the right lateral line, from the transpyloric line to a point midway between the transpyloric and transtubercular lines. The horizontal part runs with a slight upward slope from the end of the descending part to the left of the midline; the ascending part is vertical, and reaches the transpyloric line, where it ends in the duodenojejunal flexure, about 2.5 cm. to the left of the midline.

Small Intestine.—The coils of small intestine occupy most of the abdomen. Frequently the coils of the jejunum are situated on the left side, the coils of the ileum toward the right and partly within the pelvis. The end of the ileum, *i.e.*, the **ileocolic junction,** is slightly below and medial to the intersection of the right lateral and transtubercular lines.

Cecum and Vermiform Process or Appendix.—The **cecum** is in the right iliac and hypogastric regions; its position varies with its degree of distension, but a line drawn from the right anterior superior iliac spine to the upper margin of the symphysis pubis will mark approximately the middle of its lower border. The position of the base of the **appendix** is indicated by a point on the lateral line on a level with the anterior superior iliac spine (Fig. 79).

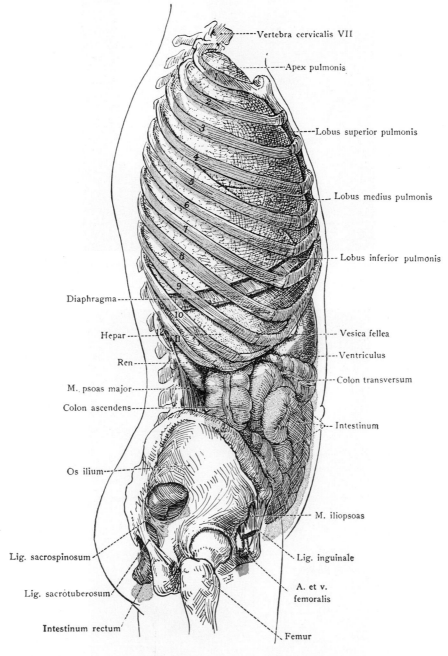

Fig. 80.—Thoracic and abdominal viscera shown in their normal relations to the skeleton, from the right side. (Eycleshymer and Jones.)

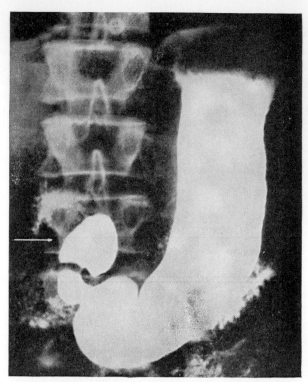

FIG. 81.—Normal stomach after a barium meal. The tone of the muscular wall is good and supports the weight of the column in the body of the organ. The arrow points to the duodenal cap, below which a gap in the barium indicates the the position of the pylorus.

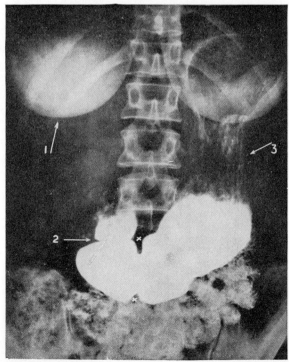

FIG. 82.—Atonic stomach after a barium meal. Note that this stomach contains the same amount of barium as the stomach in Fig. 81. Arrow *1* points to the shadow of the right breast; arrow *2*, to the pylorus; arrow *3*, to the upper part of the body of the stomach, where longitudinal folds can be seen in the mucous membrane. ✕✕ marks a wave of peristalsis.

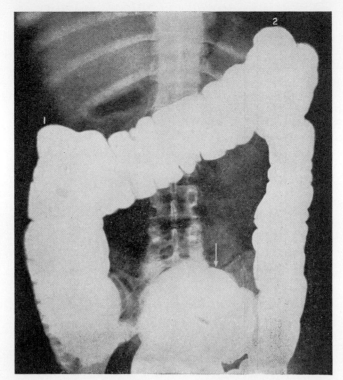

Fig. 83.—Large intestine after a barium enema. *1*, Right colic flexure; *2*, left colic flexure. The arrow points to the pelvic colon. Note the sacculations of the gut, and the different levels of the two flexures.

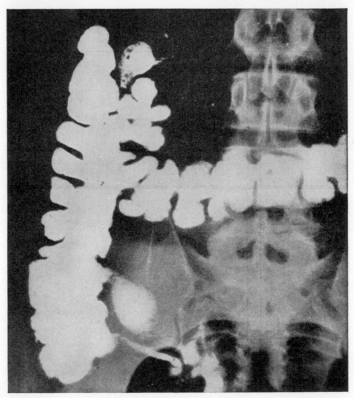

Fig. 84.—Part of the large intestine after a barium meal. Note the vermiform appendix, which passes from the medial side of the cæcum medially and slightly downwards into the true pelvis. At a slightly higher level the terminal part of the ileum can be recognized. The first part of the transverse colon runs downwards in front of, and slightly medial to, the ascending colon, before it turns to the left.

Ascending Colon.—The ascending colon passes upward through the right lumbar region, lateral to the right lateral line. The **right colic flexure** is situated in the lower and right angle of intersection of the transpyloric and right lateral lines.

Transverse Colon.—The transverse colon crosses the abdomen in the umbilical and epigastric regions, its lower border being on a level slightly above the umbilicus, its upper border just below the greater curvature of the stomach.

Descending Colon.—The **left colic flexure** is situated in the upper left angle of the intersection between the left lateral and transpyloric lines. The descending colon courses down through the left lumbar region, lateral to the left lateral line, as far as the iliac crest.

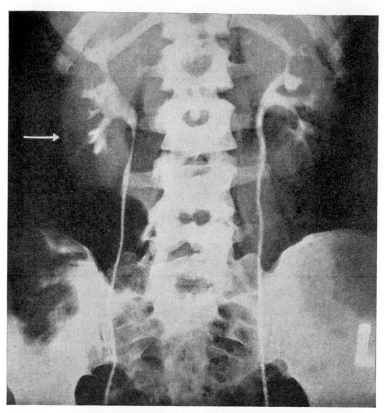

Fig. 85.—Ureters, pelves and minor calyces after intravenous injection of uroselectan. Note cupping of minor calyces; the relation of the ureter to the transverse processes of the lumbar vertebræ, and the Psoas major. The arrow points to the shadow of the right kidney. Anterior view.

Iliac Colon.—The line of the iliac colon is from the end of the descending colon to the left lateral line at the level of the anterior superior iliac spine.

Liver (Fig. 79).—The upper limit of the right lobe of the liver, in the midline, is at the level of the junction between the body of the sternum and the xiphoid process; on the right side the line must be carried upward as far as the fifth costal cartilage in the mammary line, and then downward to reach the seventh rib at the side of the thorax. The upper limit of the left lobe can be defined by continuing this line downward and to the left to the sixth costal cartilage, 5 cm. from the midline. The lower limit can be indicated by a line drawn 1 cm. below the lower margin of the thorax on the right side as far as the ninth costal cartilage, thence obliquely upward to the eighth left costal cartilage, crossing the midline just above the transpyloric plane and finally, with a slight left convexity, to the end of the line indicating the upper limit.

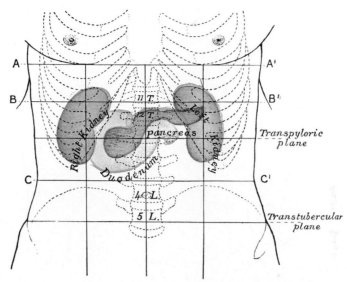

Fig. 86.—Front of abdomen, showing surface markings for duodenum, pancreas, and kidneys. *A A'*. Plane through joint between body and xiphoid process of sternum. *B B'*. Plane midway between *A A'* and transpyloric plane. *C C'*. Plane midway between transpyloric and transtubercular planes.

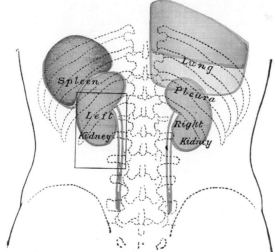

Fig. 87.—Back of lumbar region, showing surface markings for kidneys, ureters, and spleen. The lower portions of the lung and pleura are shown on the right side.

The fundus of the **gall-bladder** approaches the surface behind the anterior end of the ninth right costal cartilage close to the lateral margin of the Rectus abdominis.

Pancreas (Fig. 86).—The pancreas lies in front of the second lumbar vertebra. Its head occupies the curve of the duodenum and is therefore indicated by the same lines as that viscus; its neck corresponds to the pylorus. Its body extends along

the transpyloric line, the bulk of it lying above this line; the tail is in the left hypochondriac region slightly to the left of the lateral line and above the transpyloric line.

Spleen (Figs. 72, 75, 76).—The long axis of the spleen corresponds to that of
the tenth rib, and it is situated between the upper border of the ninth and the lower
border of the eleventh ribs. Its medial end is about 4 cm. from the midline in back,
its lateral end in the midaxillary line at the ninth intercostal space; the highest
point is at the ninth rib in the scapular line and the lowest point is at the level of
the spine of the first lumbar vertebra in the posterior axillary line. It is posterior
to the stomach more than lateral to it.

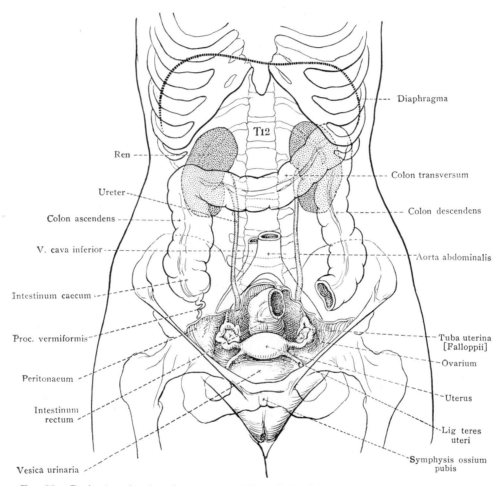

Fig. 88.—Projection showing the average position of the abdominal and pelvic viscera in the
female. Anterior view. (Eycleshymer and Jones.)

Kidneys (Figs. 86, 87).—The right kidney usually lies about 1 cm. lower than
the left, but for practical purposes similar surface markings are taken for each.

On the front of the abdomen the upper pole lies midway between the plane of
the lower end of the body of the sternum and the transpyloric plane, 5 cm. from
the midline. The lower pole is situated midway between the transpyloric and
intertubercular planes, 7 cm. from the midline. The hilum is on the transpyloric
plane, 5 cm. from the midline. Around these three points a kidney-shaped figure

4 cm. to 5 cm. broad is drawn, two-thirds of which lies medial to the lateral line. To indicate the position of the kidney from the back, the parallelogram of Morris is used; two vertical lines are drawn, the first 2.5 cm., the second 9.5 cm. from the midline; the parallelogram is completed by two horizontal lines drawn at the level of the tip of the spinous process of the eleventh thoracic and the lower border of the spinous process of the third lumbar vertebra. The hilum is 5 cm. from the midline at the level of the spinous process of the first lumbar vertebra (Fig. 87).

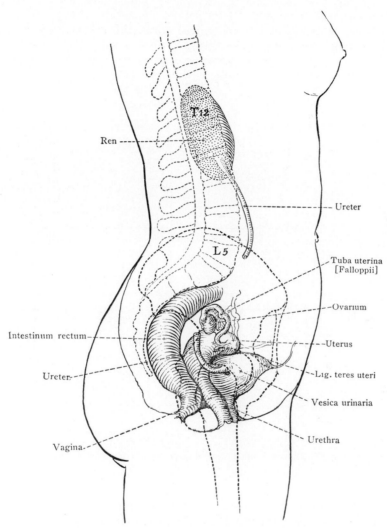

Fig. 89.—Projection showing the average position of the female pelvic organs. Lateral view. (Eycleshymer and Jones.)

Ureters.—On the front of the abdomen, the line of the ureter runs from the hilum of the kidney to the pubic tubercle; on the back, from the hilum vertically downward, passing practically through the posterior superior iliac spine (Fig. 88).

Vessels (Fig. 90).—The **inferior epigastric artery** can be marked out by a line from a point midway between the anterior superior iliac spine and the pubic symphysis to the umbilicus. This line also indicates the lateral boundary of **Hessel-**

bach's triangle (important in inguinal hernia); the other boundaries being the lateral edge of Rectus abdominis, and the medial half of the inguinal ligament. The abdominal aorta begins in the midline about 4 cm. above the transpyloric line and extends to a point 2 cm. below and to the left of the umbilicus (AA', Fig. 89). The point of termination of the abdominal aorta corresponds to the level of the fourth lumbar vertebra; a line drawn from it to a point midway between the anterior superior iliac spine and the symphysis pubis indicates the common and external iliac arteries.

Of the larger branches of the abdominal aorta, the celiac artery is 4 cm., the superior mesenteric 2 cm. above the transpyloric line; the renal arteries are 2 cm. below the same line. The inferior mesenteric artery is 4 cm. above the bifurcation of the abdominal aorta.

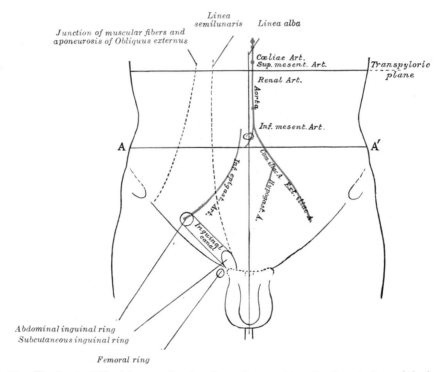

FIG. 90.—The front of the abdomen, showing the surface markings for the arteries and the inguinal canal. The line $A\ A'$ is drawn at the level of the highest points of the iliac crests.

Nerves.—The thoracic nerves on the anterior abdominal wall are represented by lines continuing those of the bony ribs. The termination of the seventh nerve is at the level of the xiphoid process, the tenth reaches the vicinity of the umbilicus, the twelfth ends about midway between the umbilicus and the upper border of the symphysis pubis. The first lumbar is parallel to the thoracic nerves; its iliohypogastric branch becomes cutaneous above the subcutaneous inguinal ring; its ilioinguinal branch at the ring.

THE PERINEUM.

A line drawn transversely across in front of the ischial tuberosities divides the perineum into a posterior or rectal, and an anterior or urogenital, triangle (see Myology). This line passes through the central point of the perineum, which is situated about 2.5 cm. in front of the center of the anal aperture, or, in the male, midway between the anus and the reflection of the skin on to the scrotum.

Rectal Examination.—A finger inserted through the anal orifice is compressed by the Sphincter ani externus, passes into the region of the Sphincter ani internus, and higher up encounters the resistance of the Puborectalis; beyond this it may reach the lowest of the transverse rectal folds. In front, the urethral bulb and membranous part of the urethra are first identified, and then about 4 cm. above the anal orifice the prostate is felt; beyond this the seminal vesicles if enlarged, and the fundus of the bladder, when distended, can be recognized. On either side is the ischiorectal fossa. Behind are the anococcygeal body, the pelvic surfaces of the coccyx and lower end of the sacrum, and the sacrospinous ligaments.

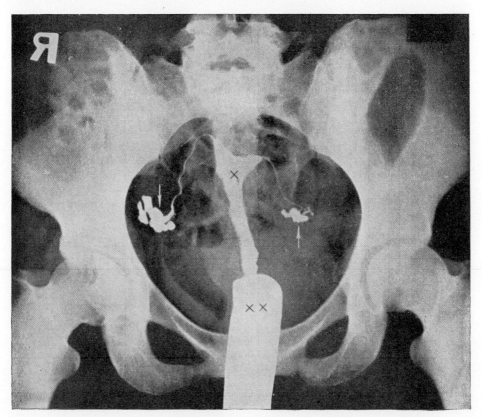

Fig. 91.—Genital tract in the female, after an injection of barium sulphate into the uterus ×, Body of uterus. Note the two cornua leading to the uterine tubes. × ×, Speculum in vagina The arrows indicate the infundibula of the uterine tubes. Some of the barium has passed through the pelvic opening of the tube into the general peritoneal cavity.

In the female the posterior wall and fornix of the vagina, and the cervix and body of the uterus can be felt in front, while somewhat laterally the ovaries can just be reached.

Male Urogenital Organs (see Urogenital System).—The **corpora cavernosa penis** can be followed backward to the crura which are attached to the sides of the pubic arch. The **glans penis,** covered by the prepuce, and the external urethral orifice can be examined, and the course of the urethra traced along the under surface of the penis to the bulb which is situated immediately in front of the central point of the perineum. Through the wall of the **scrotum** on either side the **testis** can be palpated;

7

it lies toward the back of the scrotum, and along its posterior border the **epididymis** can be felt; passing upward along the medial side of the epididymis is the **spermatic cord**, which can be traced upward to the subcutaneous inguinal ring.

Female Urogenital Organs.—In the **pudendal cleft** (see Index) between the labia minora are the openings of the **vagina** and **urethra**. In the virgin the vaginal opening is partly closed by the **hymen**—after coitus the remains of the hymen are represented by the carunculæ hymenales. Between the hymen and the frenulum of the labia is the **fossa navicularis**, while in the groove between the hymen and the labium minus, on either side, the small opening of the **greater vestibular** (*Bartholin's*) **gland** can be seen. These glands when enlarged can be felt on either side of the posterior part of the vaginal orifice.

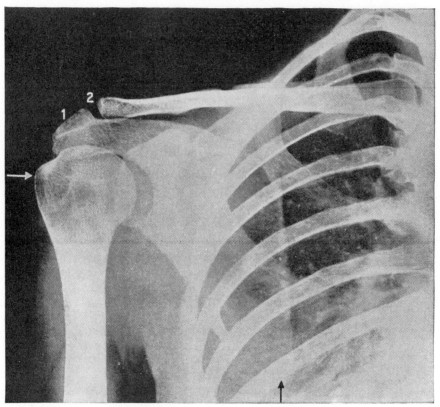

Fig. 92.—Adult shoulder. *1*, Acromion; *2*, acromio-clavicular joint. The lower arrow indicates the inferior angle of the scapula, the upper arrow the greater tuberosity. Note that the shadow of the head of the humerus overlaps the shadow of the acromial angle and a part of the glenoid cavity.

Vaginal Examination.—With the examining finger inserted into the vagina the following structures can be palpated through its wall (Fig. 89). Behind from below upward, are the **anal canal**, the **rectum**, and the **rectouterine excavation**. Projecting into the roof of the vagina is the vaginal portion of the cervix uteri with the external uterine orifice; in front of and behind the cervix the anterior and posterior **vaginal fornices** respectively can be examined. With the finger in the vagina and the other hand exerting pressure on the abdominal wall the whole of the **cervix** and **body of the uterus**, the **uterine tubes**, and the **ovaries** can be palpated. If a speculum be introduced into the vagina, the walls of the passage, the vaginal portion of the cervix, and the external uterine orifice can all be exposed for visual examination.

The external urethral orifice lies in front of the vaginal opening; the angular gap in which it is situated between the two converging labia minora is termed the **vestibule.** The urethral canal in the female is very dilatable and can be explored

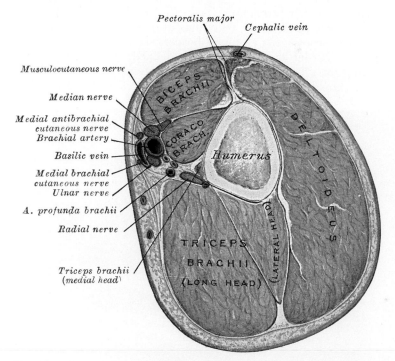

Fig. 93.—Cross section through the arm at the junction of the proximal with the intermediate one-third of the humerus.

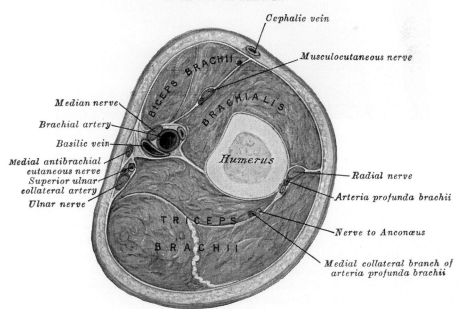

Fig. 94.—Cross section through the arm, a little below the middle of the body of the humerus.

with the finger.   About 2.5 cm. in front of the external orifice of the urethra are the **glans** and **prepuce of the clitoris,** and still farther forward is the **mons pubis.**

THE UPPER EXTREMITY.

Bones.—The **clavicle** can be felt throughout its entire length.

The only parts of the **scapula** that are truly subcutaneous are the spine and acromion, but the coracoid process, the vertebral border, the inferior angle, and to a lesser extent the axillary border can also be readily defined.   The acromion and spine are easily recognizable throughout their entire extent, forming with the clavicle the arch of the shoulder.   The acromion forms the point of the shoulder;

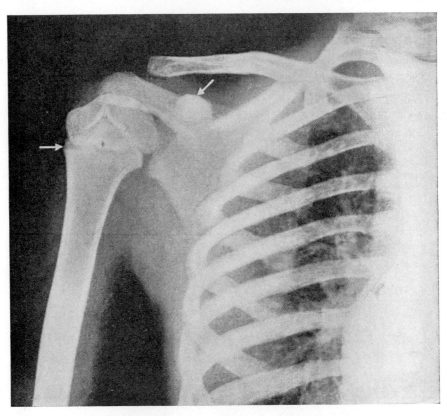

Fig. 95.—Shoulder of a child aged six years.   The upper arrow indicates the coracoid process; the lower arrow indicates the epiphyseal line.   Note that the upper end of the diaphysis is conical and projects into the center of the epiphysis.   The centers for the head of the humerus and the tuberosities have fused to form a single epiphysis.

it joins the clavicle at an acute angle—the acromial angle—slightly medial to, and behind the tip of the acromion.   The spine can be felt as a distinct ridge, marked on the surface as an oblique depression which becomes less distinct and ends in a slight dimple a little lateral to the spinous processes of the vertebræ.   The coracoid process is situated about 2 cm. below the junction of the intermediate and lateral thirds of the clavicle; it is covered by the anterior border of Deltoideus, and thus lies a little lateral to the infraclavicular fossa or depression which marks the interval between the Pectoralis major and Deltoideus.

The **humerus** is almost entirely surrounded by muscles, and the only parts which are strictly subcutaneous are small portions of the medial and lateral epicondyles;

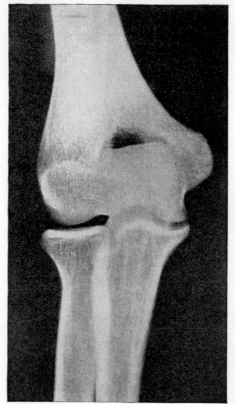

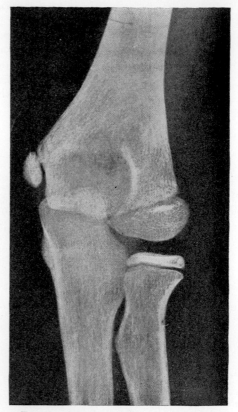

FIG. 96.—Adult elbow. Frontal view. The shadow of the olecranon extends upwards to the olecranon fossa and obscures the outline of the trochlea. The gap between the humerus and the bones of the forearm is occupied by the articular cartilage of the bones concerned.

FIG. 97.—Elbow of a child aged eleven years. Frontal view. The upper epiphysis of the radius, the epiphysis for the medial epicondyle, and the center for the capitulum and lateral part of the trochlea can be recognized without difficulty.

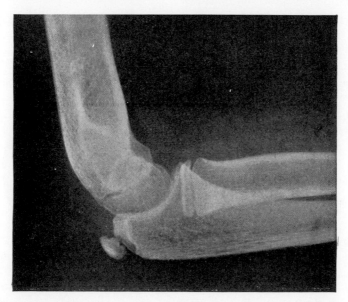

FIG. 98.—Elbow of a child aged ten years. Lateral view. The upper epiphysis of the radius, the olecranon epiphysis and the center for the capitulum and the lateral part of the trochlea can be recognized without difficulty.

(101)

in addition to these, however, the tubercles and a part of the head of the bone can be felt under the skin and muscles by which they are covered. The greater tubercle forms the most prominent bony point of the shoulder, extending beyond the acromion. On either side of the elbow-joint and just above it are the medial and lateral epicondyles. Of these, the former is the more prominent, but the medial supracondylar ridge passing upward from it is much less marked than the lateral, and as a rule is not palpable.

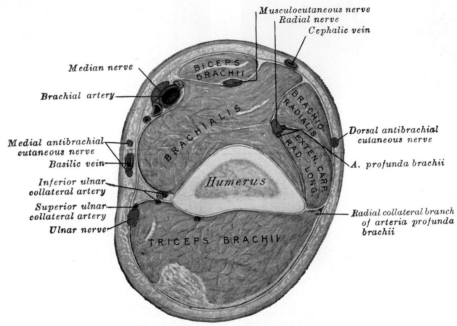

Fig. 99.—Cross section through the arm, 2 cm. proximal to the medial epicondyle of the humerus

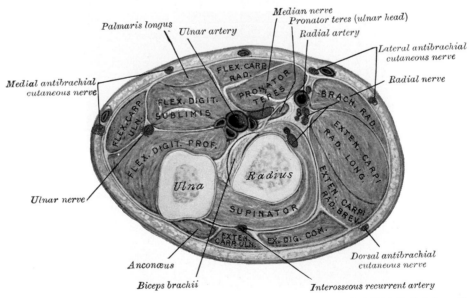

Fig. 100.—Cross section through the forearm at the level of the radial (bicipital) tuberosity.

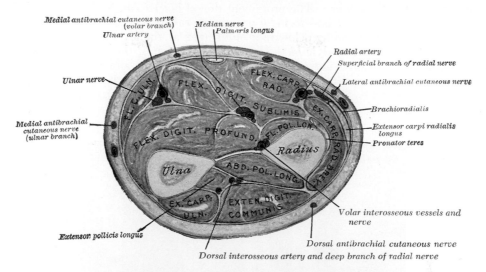

Medial antibrachial cutaneous nerve (volar branch)
Ulnar artery
Median nerve
Palmaris longus
Radial artery
Superficial branch of radial nerve
Lateral antibrachial cutaneous nerve
Ulnar nerve
Brachioradialis
Medial antibrachial cutaneous nerve (ulnar branch)
Extensor carpi radialis longus
Pronator teres
Volar interosseous vessels and nerve
Extensor pollicis longus
Dorsal antibrachial cutaneous nerve
Dorsal interosseous artery and deep branch of radial nerve

FLEX. CARP. RAD.
EX. CARP. RAD. BREV.
FL. C. ULN.
FLEX. DIGIT. SUBLIMIS
FLEX. DIGIT. PROFUND.
FL. POL. LON.
Radius
Ulna
ABD. POL. LONG.
EX. CARP. ULN.
EXTEN. DIGIT. COMMUNIS

Fig. 101.—Cross section through the middle of the forearm.

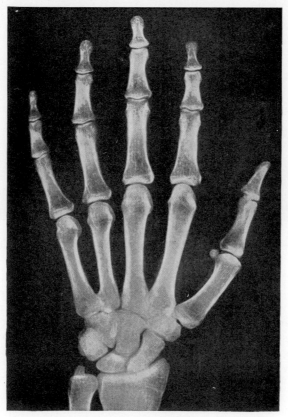

Fig. 102.—Adult hand.

The most prominent part of the **ulna**, the olecranon, can always be identified at the back of the elbow-joint.   The prominent dorsal border can be felt in its whole length and the styloid process forms a prominent tubercle continuous above with the dorsal border and ending below in a blunt apex at the level of the wrist-joint.

Below the lateral epicondyle of the humerus a portion of the head of the **radius** is palpable; its position is indicated on the surface by a little dimple, which is best seen when the arm is extended.   The upper half of the body of the bone is obscured by muscles; the lower half, though not subcutaneous, can be traced downward to a lozenge-shaped convex surface on the lateral side of the base of the styloid process.

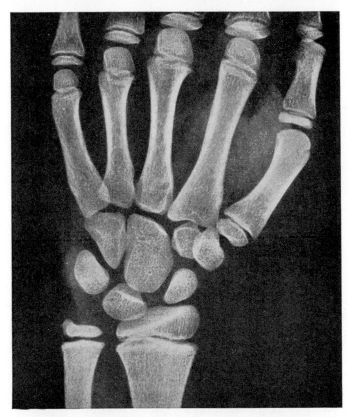

Fig. 103.—Hand and wrist of a child aged eleven years.   All the centers of ossification are present except that for the pisiform bone.   Note how the first metacarpal differs from the other metacarpal bones.

On the front of the wrist are two subcutaneous eminences, one, on the radial side, the larger and flatter, produced by the tuberosity of the **navicular** and the ridge on the **greater multangular;** the other, on the ulnar side, by the **pisiform**.   The rest of the volar surface of the bony carpus is covered by tendons and the transverse carpal ligament, and is entirely concealed, with the exception of the hamulus of the **hamate bone,** which, however, is difficult to define.   On the dorsal surface of the carpus only the **triangular bone** can be clearly made out.

Distal to the carpus the dorsal surfaces of the **metacarpal bones,** covered by the Extensor tendons are visible only in very thin hands; the dorsal surface of the fifth is, however, subcutaneous throughout almost its whole length.   The heads of the metacarpal bones can be plainly seen and felt, rounded in contour and standing out in bold relief under the skin when the fist is clenched; the head of the third is the most prominent.

The enlarged ends of the **phalanges** can be easily felt. When the digits are bent the proximal phalanges form prominences, which in the joints between the first and second phalanges are slightly hollow, but flattened and square-shaped in those between the second and third.

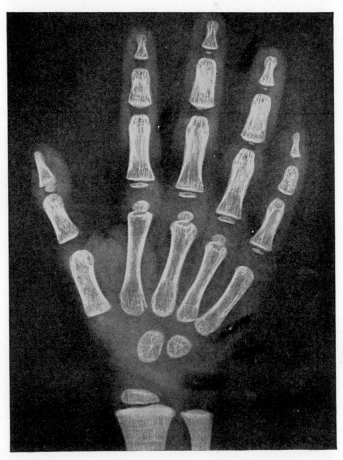

Fig. 104.—Hand and wrist of a child aged two-and-a-half years. The capitate and hamate bones are in process of ossification, but the other carpel bones are still cartilaginous. The center for the head of the ulna has not yet appeared, but the center for the lower epiphysis of the radius is present. Note the condition of the metacarpal bones and phalanges.

Articulations.—The **sternoclavicular joint** is subcutaneous, and its position is indicated by the enlarged sternal extremity of the clavicle, lateral to the long cord-like sternal head of the Sternocleidomastoideus. If this muscle be relaxed a depression between the end of the clavicle and the sternum can be felt, defining the exact position of the joint.

The position of the **acromioclavicular joint** can generally be ascertained by determining the slightly enlarged acromial end of the clavicle which projects above the level of the acromion; sometimes this enlargement is so considerable as to form a rounded eminence.

The **shoulder-joint** is deeply seated and cannot be palpated. If the forearm be slightly flexed a curved crease or fold with its convexity downward is seen in front of the elbow, extending from one epicondyle to the other; the **elbow joint** is slightly distal to the center of the fold. The position of the **radiohumeral joint** can be ascertained by feeling for a slight groove or depression between the head of the radius and the capitulum of the humerus, at the back of the elbow joint.

The position of the **proximal radioulnar joint** is marked on the surface at the back of the elbow by the dimple which indicates the position of the head of the radius. The site of the **distal radioulnar joint** can be defined by feeling for the slight groove at the back of the wrist between the prominent head of the ulna and the lower end of the radius, when the forearm is in a state of almost complete pronation.

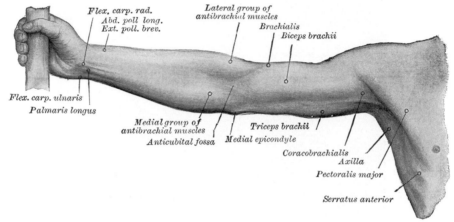

Fig. 105.—Front of right upper extremity.

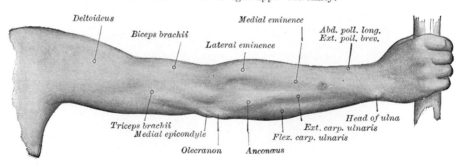

Fig. 106.—Back of right upper extremity.

Of the three transverse skin furrows on the front of the wrist, the middle corresponds fairly accurately with the **wrist joints**, while the most distal indicates the position of the **midcarpal articulation.**

The **metacarpophalangeal** and **interphalangeal joints** are readily available for surface examination; the former are situated just distal to the prominences of the knuckles, the latter are sufficiently indicated by the furrows on the volar, and the wrinkles on the dorsal surfaces.

Muscles.—The large muscles which arise on the trunk and insert on the shoulder girdle form the outer layers of muscle of the thorax; the **Pectoralis major** (Figs. 69, 74, 105), **Latissuimus dorsi** (Figs. 65, 69), and **Trapezius** (Figs. 65, 69) are easily visible in most subjects, but the **Serratus anterior** (Figs. 69, 74, 105) is mostly concealed by the scapula and the **Pectoralis minor** is completely hidden by the Pectoralis major.

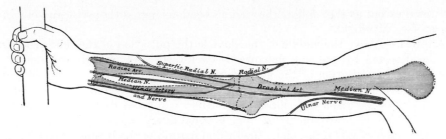

FIG. 107.—Front of right upper extremity, showing surface markings for bones, arteries, and nerves

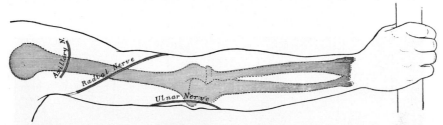

FIG. 108.—Back of right upper extremity, showing surface markings for bones and nerves.

The **Deltoideus** (Figs. 65, 106) and the **Teres major** (Fig. 65) are prominent on the shoulder. The **Biceps, Coracobrachialis,** and **Brachialis** (Fig. 105) are prominent on the anterior, and the **Triceps** (Fig. 106) on the posterior aspect of the arm. The muscles of the forearm form two groups, the flexor and pronator group arising from the medial epicondyle and making the medial group, the extensor and supinator group arising from the lateral epicondyle and making the lateral group. The tendons of insertion of many of the individual muscles can be identified at the wrist (Figs. 105, 106).

The **antecubital fossa** (Fig. 105), in front of the elbow joint, is triangular in shape, and its boundaries are the Brachioradialis, a member of the lateral group of antebrachial muscles, the Pronator teres, a member of the medial group, and the tendon of the Biceps and Brachialis above. In the fossa the brachial artery and median nerve may be palpated, and through it the median cubital vein communicates with the deeper veins.

The **Synovial Tendon Sheaths** of the palm and dorsum of the hand cannot be

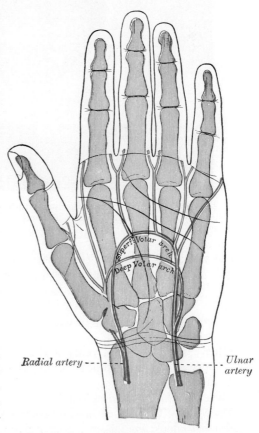

FIG. 109.—Palm of left hand, showing position of skin creases and bones, and surface markings for the volar arches.

identified except as they follow the various tendons across the wrist and out in the fingers (see Myology).

Arteries.—Above the middle of the clavicle the pulsation of the **subclavian artery** can be detected by pressing downward, backward, and medialward against the first rib. The pulsation of the **axillary artery** as it crosses the second rib can be felt below the middle of the clavicle just medial to the coracoid process; along the lateral wall of the axilla the course of the artery can be easily followed close to the medial border of Coracobrachialis. The **brachial artery** can be recognized in practically the whole of its extent, along the medial margin of the Biceps. Over the lower end of the radius, between the styloid process and Flexor carpi radialis, a portion of the **radial artery** is superficial and is used clinically for observations on the pulse.

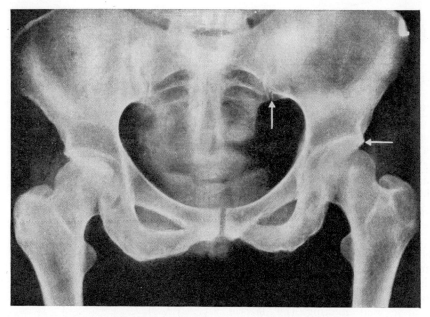

Fig. 110.—Adult pelvis. The upper arrow indicates the line of the sacro-iliac joint; the lower arrow points to the anterior inferior iliac spine.

The **superficial volar arch** (Fig. 109) can be indicated by a line starting from the radial side of the pisiform bone and curving distalward and lateralward as far as the base of the thumb, with its convexity toward the fingers. The summit of the arch is usually on a level with the ulnar border of the outstretched thumb. The **deep volar arch** is practically transverse, and is situated about 1 cm. nearer to the carpus.

Veins.—The superficial veins of the upper extremity are easily rendered visible by compressing the proximal trunks; their arrangement is described in Chapter on Veins.

Nerves.—The uppermost trunks of the **brachial plexus** are palpable for a short distance above the clavicle as they emerge from under the lateral border of Sternocleidomastoideus; the larger nerves derived from the plexus can be rolled under the finger against the lateral axillary wall but cannot be identified. The **ulnar nerve** can be detected in the groove behind the medial epicondyle of the humerus.

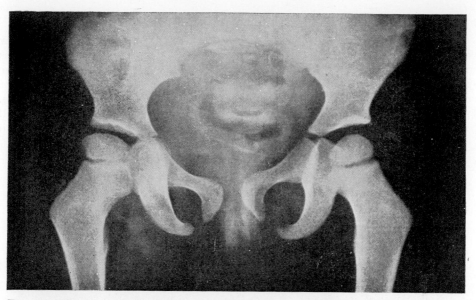

Fig. 111.—Pelvis of a child aged three-and-a-half years. The epiphysis for the head of the femur is well formed, but the center for the greater trochanter has not yet appeared. The rami of the pubis and ischium are still connected by cartilage and the triradiate cartilage in the acetabulum is wide.

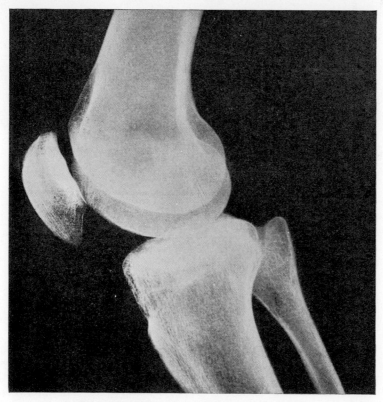

Fig. 112.—Knee of an adult. Lateral view.

THE LOWER EXTREMITY.

Bones.—The **hip bones** are largely covered with muscles, so that only at a few points do they approach the surface. In front the anterior superior iliac spine is easily recognized, and the iliac crest can be traced to the posterior superior iliac spine, the site of which is indicated by a slight depression; on the outer lip of the crest, about 5 cm. behind the anterior superior spine, is the prominent iliac tubercle. In thin subjects the pubic tubercle is very apparent, but in the obese it is obscured by the pubic fat; it can, however, be detected by following up the tendon of origin

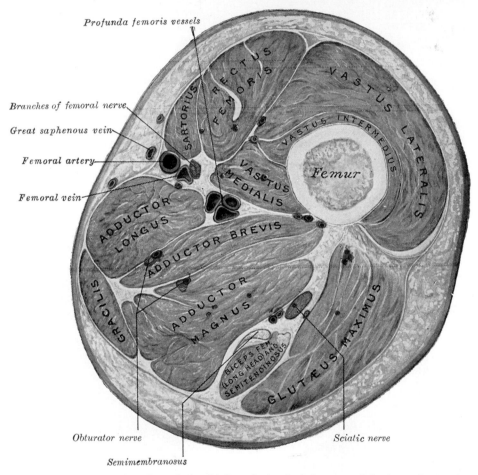

Fig. 113.—Cross section through the thigh at the level of the apex of the femoral triangle. Four-fifths of natural size.

of the Adductor longus. Another part of the bony pelvis which is accessible to touch is the ischial tuberosity, situated beneath the Glutæus maximus, and, when the hip is flexed, easily felt, as it is then uncovered by muscle.

The **femur** is enveloped by muscles, so that the only accessible parts are the lateral surface of the greater trochanter and the lower expanded end of the bone. The greater trochanter is generally indicated by a depression, owing to the thickness of the Glutæi medius and minimus which project above it. The lateral condyle is more easily felt than the medial; both epicondyles can be readily identified, and at

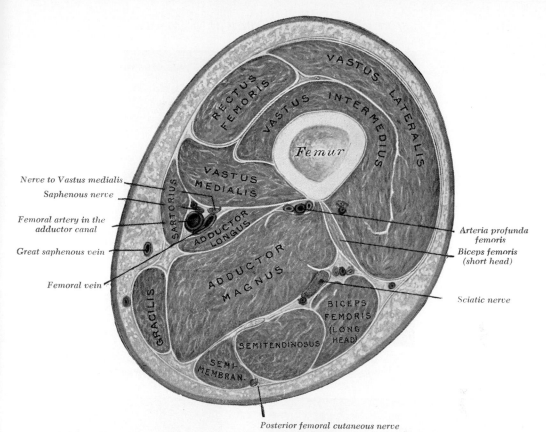

Nerve to Vastus medialis

Saphenous nerve

Femoral artery in the
adductor canal

Great saphenous vein

Femoral vein

Arteria profunda
femoris

Biceps femoris
(short head)

Sciatic nerve

Posterior femoral cutaneous nerve

FIG. 114.—Cross section through the middle of the thigh. Four-fifths of natural size.

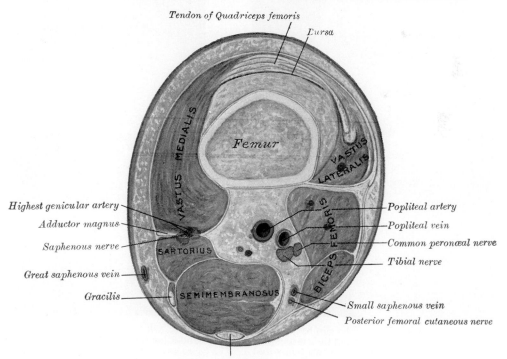

Tendon of Quadriceps femoris

Bursa

Highest genicular artery

Adductor magnus

Saphenous nerve

Great saphenous vein

Gracilis

Popliteal artery

Popliteal vein

Common peronœal nerve

Tibial nerve

Small saphenous vein

Posterior femoral cutaneous nerve

Semitendinosus

FIG. 115—Cross section through the thigh, 4 cm., proximal to the adductor tubercle of the
femur. Four-fifths of natural size.

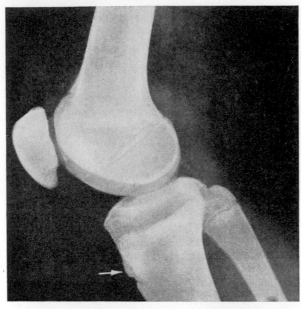

FIG. 116.—Knee of a boy aged sixteen years. Lateral view. Note that the upper epiphysis of the tibia includes the tibial tubercle, which is indicated by the arrow.

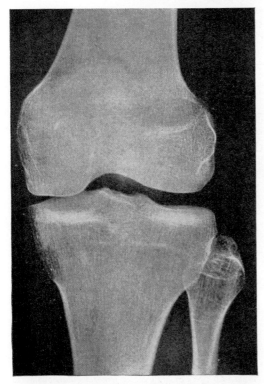

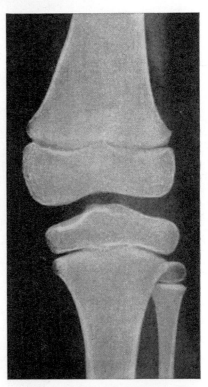

FIG. 117.—Adult knee. The gap between the lateral condyles of the femur and tibia is occupied by the articular cartilage of the two bones and the lateral semilunar cartilage.

FIG. 118.—Knee of a child aged seven-and-a-half years. Note that the styloid process of the head of the fibula and the tubercles of the intercondylar eminence of the tibia are still cartilaginous and therefore cannot be recognized.

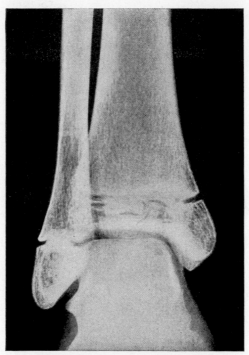

FIG. 119.—Ankle of a child aged ten years. Note that the inferior epiphyseal line of the fibula is opposite the ankle joint.

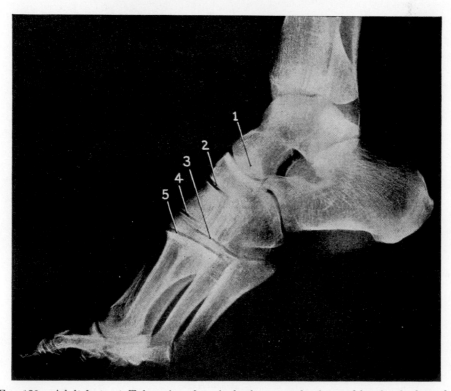

FIG. 120.—Adult foot. *1*, Tuberosity of navicular bone, partly obscured by the shadow of the head of the talus; *2*, cuneo-navicular joint; *3*, joint between metatarsal III and the lateral cuneiform bone; *4*, joint between metatarsal II and the intermediate cuneiform bone; *5*, joint between metatarsal I and the medial cuneiform bone.

8

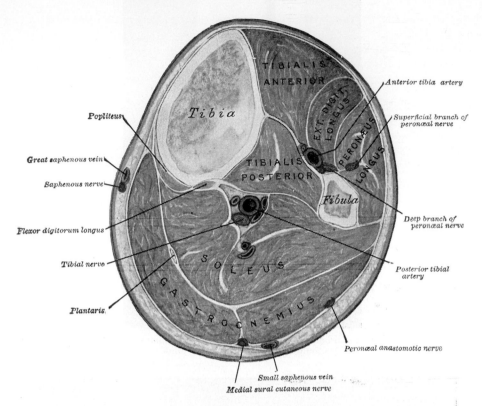

FIG. 121.—Cross section through the leg, 9 cm. distal to the knee joint.

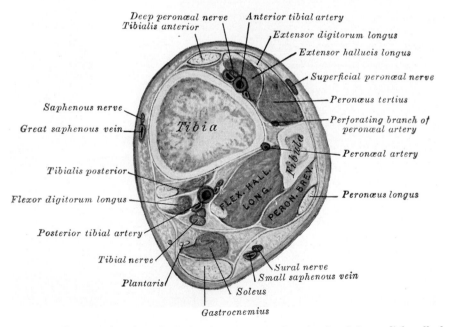

FIG. 122.—Cross section through the leg, 6 cm. proximal to the tip of the medial malleolus.

the upper part of the medial condyle the sharp adductor tubercle can be recognized without difficulty.

The anterior surface of the **patella** is subcutaneous.

A considerable portion of the **tibia** is subcutaneous. At the upper end the condyles can be felt just below the knee. In front of the upper end of the bone, between the condyles, is an oval eminence, the tuberosity, which is continuous below with the anterior crest of the bone. The medial malleolus forms a broad prominence, situated at a higher level and somewhat farther forward than the lateral malleolus.

The only subcutaneous parts of the **fibula** are the head, the lower part of the body, and the lateral malleolus. The lateral malleolus is a narrow elongated prominence, from which the lower third or half of the lateral surface of the body of the bone can be traced upward.

On the dorsum of the tarsus the individual bones cannot be distinguished, with the exception of the head of the **talus**, which forms a rounded projection in front of the ankle-joint when the foot is forcibly extended. The whole dorsal surface of the foot has a smooth convex outline, the summit of which is the ridge formed by the head of the talus, the navicular, the second cuneiform, and the second metatarsal bone. On the medial side of the foot the medial process of the tuberosity of the **calcaneus** is in front of this, and below the medial malleolus, is the sustentaculum tali. The tuberosity of the **navicular** is palpable about 2.5 to 3 cm. in front of the medial malleolus.

Farther forward, the ridge formed by the base of the **first metatarsal bone** can be obscurely

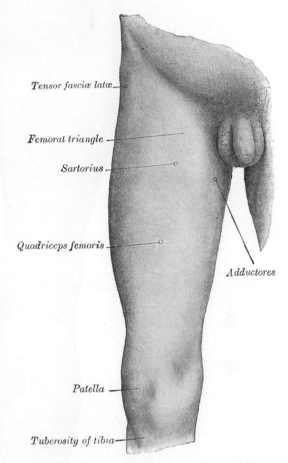

Tensor fasciæ latæ

Femoral triangle

Sartorius

Quadriceps femoris

Adductores

Patella

Tuberosity of tibia

FIG. 123.—Front and medial aspect of right thigh.

felt; beneath the base of the first phalanx is the medial sesamoid bone. On the lateral side of the foot the most posterior bony point is the lateral process of the tuberosity of the calcaneus; in front of this the greater part of the lateral surface is subcutaneous. Farther forward the base of the **fifth metatarsal bone** is prominent.

The dorsal surfaces of the **metatarsal bones** are easily defined; the plantar surfaces are obscured by muscles. The **phalanges** in their whole extent are readily palpable.

Articulations.—The **hip-joint** is deeply seated and cannot be palpated.

The interval between the tibia and femur can always be felt; if the **knee-joint** be extended this interval is on a higher level than the apex of the patella, but if the joint be slightly flexed it is directly behind the apex.

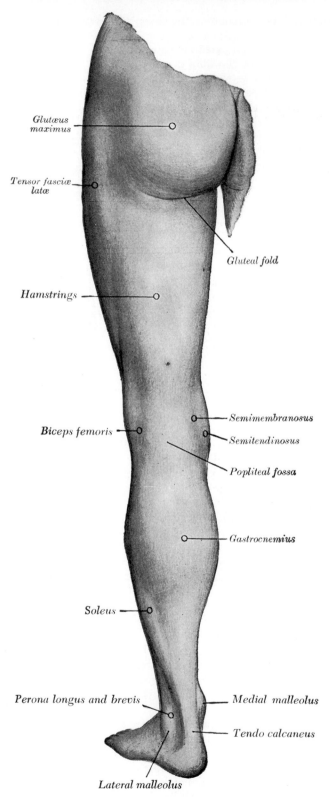

FIG. 124.—Back of left lower extremity.

The **ankle-joint** can be felt on either side of the Extensor tendons, and during extension of the joint the superior articular surface of the talus presents below the anterior border of the lower end of the tibia.

Muscles.—The prominent muscles on the anterior aspect of the thigh are the Quadriceps femoris, Sartorius and Tensor fasciæ latæ (Fig. 123). At the medial side of the thigh are the Adductors (Fig. 123), and at the back of the thigh the hamstrings, medially the Semimembranosus and Semitendinosus and laterally the Biceps femoris (Fig. 124). Above, the prominence of the buttock is caused mostly by the Glutæus maximus. At the back of the leg are the Gastrocnemius and Soleus,

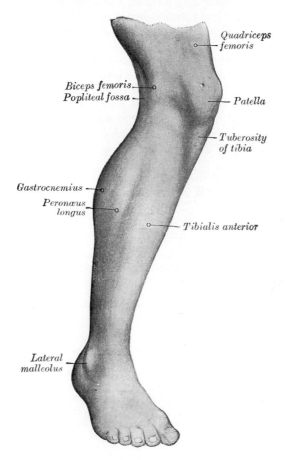

Fig. 125.—Lateral aspect of right leg.

terminating at the heel in the tendon of Achilles or tendo calcaneus (Fig. 124). On the lateral aspect of the leg, the Peronæi and Tibialis anterior can usually be recognized (Fig. 125).

The **femoral triangle** is bounded above by the inguinal ligament, laterally by the medial border of Sartorius, and medially by the medial border of Adductor longus. In the triangle is the fossa ovalis, through which the great saphenous vein dips to join the femoral; the center of this fossa is about 4 cm. below and lateral to the pubic tubercle, its vertical diameter measures about 4 cm. and its transverse about 1.5 cm. The femoral ring is about 1.25 cm. lateral to the pubic tubercle.

The **adductor canal** occupies the medial part of the middle third of the thigh; it begins at the apex of the femoral triangle and lies deep to the vertical part of Sartorius (Fig. 114).

The popliteal fossa, at the back of the knee, is bounded above by the medial and lateral hamstrings, and below by the medial and lateral heads of the Gastrocnemius. In this fossa the popliteal artery and sciatic nerve are covered only by subcutaneous tissue and fat, and through it the small saphenous vein joins the popliteal vein.

Synovial Sheaths.—The positions of the synovial sheaths around the tendons about the ankle-joints are described and illustrated in the Myology Chapter.

Arteries.—The **femoral artery** as it crosses the brim of the pelvis is readily felt; in its course down the thigh its pulsation becomes gradually more difficult of recognition. When the knee is flexed the pulsation of the **popliteal artery** can easily be detected in the popliteal fossa.

On the lower part of the front of the tibia the **anterior tibial artery** becomes superficial and can be traced over the ankle into the **dorsalis pedis**; the latter can be followed to the proximal end of the first intermetatarsal space. The pulsation of the **posterior tibial artery** becomes evident near the lower end of the back of the tibia, and is easily detected behind the medial malleolus.

Veins.—By compressing the proximal trunks, the venous arch on the dorsum of the foot, together with the great and small saphenous veins leading from it are rendered visible.

Nerves.—The only nerve of the lower extremity which can be located by palpation is the **common peroneal** as it winds around the lateral side of the neck of the fibula.

REFERENCES

BASSETT, D. L. 1954. A Stereoscopic Atlas of Human Anatomy. 5 sections with reels for use with View-Master stereoscopes and projectors. Sawyer's Inc., Portland, Oregon.

BENNINGHOFF, A. 1948–50. Lehrbuch der Anatomie des Menschen. 3rd and 4th Edition. 3 volumes. Urban & Schwarzenberg, Berlin.

JOHNSTON, T. B. 1957. A Synopsis of Regional Anatomy. 8th Edition. viii + 450 pages. Lea & Febiger, Philadelphia.

KAMPMEIER, O., A. R. COOPER, and T. F. JONES. 1957. A Frontal Section Anatomy of the Head and Neck. iii + 17 pages + 20 plates. University of Illinois Press, Urbana.

KAPLAN, E. B. 1953. Functional and Surgical Anatomy of the Hand. xvi + 288 pages. J. B. Lippincott Co., Philadelphia.

KOPSCH, F. 1955. Rauber-Kopsch Lehrbuch und Atlas der Anatomie des Menschen. 19th Ed. 2 volumes. Georg Thieme Verlag, Stuttgart.

ROGERS, L. C. 1957. Treves' Surgical Applied Anatomy. 13th Ed. x + 591 pages. Lea & Febiger, Philadelphia.

ROUVIERE, H. 1954. Anatomie Humaine—Descriptive et Toptgraphique. 7th Ed. 3 volumes. Masson et Cie, Editeurs, Paris.

TÖNDURY, G. 1951. Angewandte und topographische Anatomie. 416 pages. Georg Thieme Verlag, Stuttgart.

OSTEOLOGY.

THE general framework of the body is built up mainly of a series of bones supplemented, however, in certain regions by pieces of cartilage; the bony part of the framework constitutes the **skeleton**.

In the skeleton of the adult there are 206 distinct bones, as follows:—

Axial Skeleton	Vertebral column	26	
	Skull	22	
	Hyoid bone	1	
	Ribs and sternum	25	
		—	74
Appendicular Skeleton	Upper extremities	64	
	Lower extremities	62	
		—	126
Auditory ossicles			6
	Total		206

The patellæ are included in this enumeration, but the smaller sesamoid bones are not reckoned.

DEVELOPMENT OF THE SKELETON.

The **skeleton** is of mesodermal origin. The first indications usually appear as condensations of the mesenchyme into the membranous or blastemal rudiments in which cartilage and bone differentiate. With the exception of certain of the cranial bones the membranous rudiments are converted into cartilage which is in turn replaced by bone.

The Vertebral Column.—The notochord (Fig. 14) is a temporary structure and forms a central axis, around which the segments of the vertebral column are developed. It is derived from the entoderm, and consists of a rod of cells, which lies on the ventral aspect of the neural tube and reaches from the anterior end of the mid-brain to the extremity of the tail. On either side of it is a column of paraxial mesoderm which becomes subdivided into a number of more or less cubical segments, the **primitive segments** (Figs. 14 and 15). These are separated from one another by **intersegmental septa** and are arranged symmetrically on either side of the neural tube and notochord: to every segment a spinal nerve is distributed. At first each segment contains a central cavity, the **myocœl**, but this is soon filled with a core of angular and spindle-shaped cells. The cells of the segment become differentiated into three groups, which form respectively the cutis-plate or dermatome, the muscle-plate or myotome, and the sclerotome (Fig. 14). The **cutis-plate** is placed on the lateral and dorsal aspect of the myocœl, and from it the true skin of the corresponding segment is derived; the **muscle-plate** is situated on the medial side of the cutis-plate and furnishes the muscles of the segment. The cells of the **sclerotome** are largely derived from those forming the core of the myocœl, and lie next the notochord. Fusion of the individual sclerotomes in an antero-posterior direction soon takes place, and thus a continuous strand of cells, the **sclerotogenous layer**, is formed along the ventro-lateral aspects of the neural tube. The cells of this layer proliferate rapidly, and extending medialward surround the notochord; at the same time they grow backward on the lateral aspects of the neural tube and eventually surround it, and thus the notochord and neural tube are enveloped by a continuous sheath of mesoderm, which is termed the **membranous vertebral column.** In this mesoderm the original segments are still distinguishable, but each is now differentiated into two portions, an anterior, consisting of loosely arranged cells, and a posterior, of more condensed tissue (Fig. 126, *A* and *B*). Between the two portions the rudiment of the intervertebral fibrocartilage is laid down (Fig. 126, *C*). Cells from the posterior mass grow into the intervals between the myotomes (Fig. 126, *B* and *C*) of the corresponding and succeeding segments, and extend both dorsally and ventrally; the dorsal extensions surround the neural tube and represent the future neural arch, while the ventral extend into the body-wall as the costal processes. The hinder part of the posterior mass joins the anterior mass of the succeeding segment to form the vertebral body. Each vertebral body is therefore a composite of two segments, being formed from the posterior portion of one segment and the anterior part of that immediately behind it. The vertebral and costal arches are derivatives of the posterior part of the segment in front of the intersegmental septum with which they are associated.

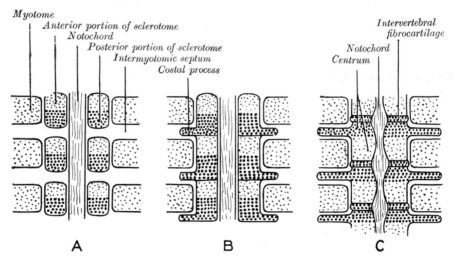

FIG. 126.—Scheme showing the manner in which each vertebral centrum is developed from portions of two adjacent segments.

This stage is succeeded by that of the **cartilaginous vertebral column.** In the fourth week two cartilaginous centers make their appearance, one on either side of the notochord; these extend around the notochord and form the body of the cartilaginous vertebra. A second pair of cartilaginous foci appear in the lateral parts of the vertebral bow, and grow backward on either side of the neural tube to form the cartilaginous vertebral arch, and a separate cartilaginous center appears for each costal process. By the eighth week the cartilaginous arch has fused with the body, and in the fourth month the two halves of the arch are joined on the dorsal aspect of the neural tube. The spinous process is developed from the junction of the two halves of the neural or vertebral arch. The transverse process grows out from the vertebral arch behind the costal process.

In the upper cervical vertebræ a band of mesodermal tissue connects the ends of the vertebral arches across the ventral surfaces of the intervertebral fibrocartilages. This is termed the **hypochordal bar** or **brace;** in all except the first it is transitory and disappears by fusing with the fibrocartilages. In the atlas, however, the entire bow persists and undergoes chondrification; it develops into the anterior arch of the bone, while the cartilage representing the body of the atlas forms the dens or odontoid process which fuses with the body of the second cervical vertebra.

The portions of the notochord which are surrounded by the bodies of the vertebræ atrophy, and ultimately disappear, while those which lie in the centers of the intervertebral fibrocartilages undergo enlargement, and persist throughout life as the central **nucleus pulposus** of the fibrocartilages.

The Ribs.—The ribs are formed from the ventral or costal processes of the primitive vertebral bows, the processes extending between the muscleplates. In the *thoracic region* of the vertebral column the costal processes grow lateralward to from a series of arches, the **primitive costal arches.** As already described, the transverse process grows out behind the vertebral end of each arch. It is at first connected to the costal process by continuous mesoderm, but this becomes differentiated later to form the costotransverse ligament; between the costal process and the tip of the transverse process the costotransverse joint is formed by absorption. The costal process becomes separated from the vertebral bow by the development of the costocentral joint. In the *cervical vertebræ* (Fig. 127) the trans-

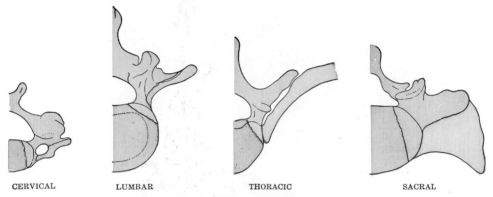

CERVICAL   LUMBAR   THORACIC   SACRAL

FIG. 127.—Diagrams showing the portions of the adult vertebræ derived respectively from the bodies, vertebral arches, and costal processes of the embryonic vertebræ. The bodies are represented in yellow, the vertebral arches in red, and the costal processes in blue.

verse process forms the posterior boundary of the foramen transversarium, while the costal process corresponding to the head and neck of the rib fuses with the body of the vertebra, and forms the anterolateral boundary of the foramen. The distal portions of the primitive costal arches remain undeveloped; occasionally the arch of the seventh cervical vertebra undergoes greater development, and by the formation of costovertebral joints is separated off as a rib. In the *lumbar region* the distal portions of the primitive costal arches fail; the proximal portions fuse with the transverse processes to form the transverse processes of descriptive anatomy. Occasionally a movable rib is developed in connection with the first lumbar vertebra. In the *sacral region* costal processes are developed only in connection with the upper three, or it may be four, vertebræ; the processes of adjacent segments fuse with one another to form the lateral parts of the sacrum. The *coccygeal vertebræ* are devoid of costal processes.

The Sternum.—The ventral ends of the ribs become united to one another by a longitudinal bar termed the **sternal plate,** and opposite the first seven pairs of ribs these sternal plates fuse in the middle line to form the manubrium and body of the sternum. The xiphoid process is formed by a backward extension of the sternal plates.

The Skull.—The first indications of the membranous skull are found in the basi-occipital and basisphenoid and about the auditory vesicles. The condensation of the mesoderm gradually extends from these areas around the brain until the latter is enclosed by the **membranous cranium.** This is incomplete in the region where the large nerves and vessels pass into or out of the cranium. Before the membranous cranium is complete, chondrification begins to show in the basioccipital. Two centers appear one on either side of the notochord near where it enters the occipital blastema or condensed mesoderm. Chondrification gradually spreads from these centers, medially around the notochord, laterally about the roots of the hypoglossal nerve, and cephalad to unite with the spreading cartilaginous center of the basi-sphenoid to form an elongated basal plate of cartilage extending from the foramen

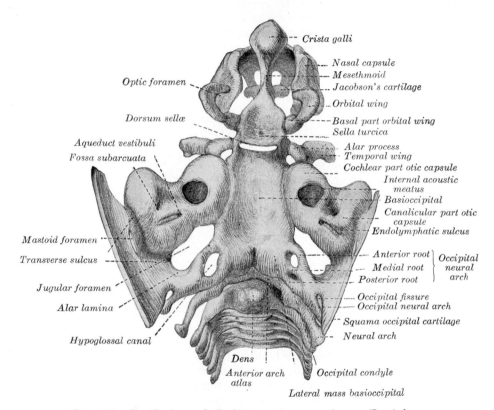

FIG. 128.—Cartilaginous skull of 21 mm. human embryo. (Lewis.)

magnum to the cephalic end of the sphenoid where it continues into the blastema of the ethmoid region which later becomes chondrified. When the auditory cap-sules begin to chondrify they are quite widely separated from the basal plate. By the time the embryo is 20 mm. in length the cochlear portion of the auditory or otic capsule is fused to the widened basal plate and the jugular foramen has become separated from the foramen lacerum (Fig. 128). From the lateral region of the occipital cartilage a broad thin plate of cartilage (tectum posterius or nuchal plate) extends around the caudal region of the brain in a complete ring (Fig. 129) forming the primitive foramen magnum. The complete **chondrocranium** is shown in Figs. 130 and 131. There are other minor cartilaginous centers which unite with main con-tinuous mass. The chondrocranium forms only a small part of the future ossified

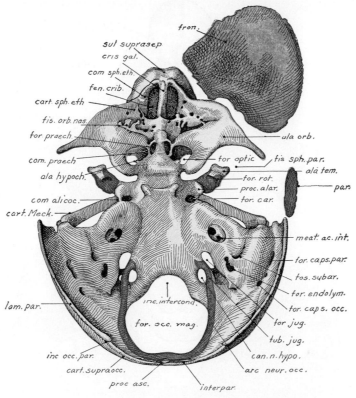

FIG. 129.—Cartilaginous skull of a 43 mm. human embryo. (Macklin.)

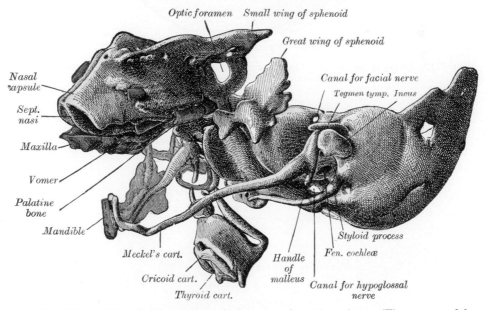

FIG. 130.—Model of the chondrocranium of a human embryo, 8 cm. long. (The same model as shown in Fig. 131 from the left side. Certain of the membrane bones of the right side are represented in yellow. (Hertwig.)

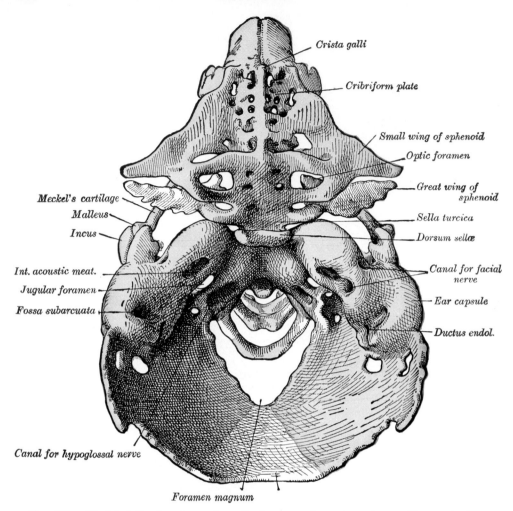

Crista galli

Cribriform plate

Small wing of sphenoid

Optic foramen

Great wing of sphenoid

Meckel's cartilage

Malleus

Incus

Sella turcica

Dorsum sellæ

Int. acoustic meat.

Jugular foramen

Fossa subarcuata

Canal for facial nerve

Ear capsule

Ductus endol.

Canal for hypoglossal nerve

Foramen magnum

FIG. 131.—Model of the chondrocranium of a human embryo, 8 cm. long. (Hertwig.) The membrane bones are not represented.

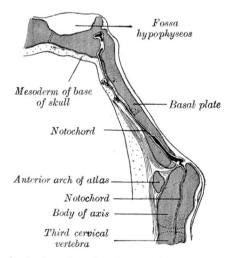

Fossa hypophyseos

Mesoderm of base of skull

Notochord

Basal plate

Anterior arch of atlas

Notochord

Body of axis

Third cervical vertebra

FIG. 132.—Sagittal section of cephalic end of notochord. (Kiebel.)

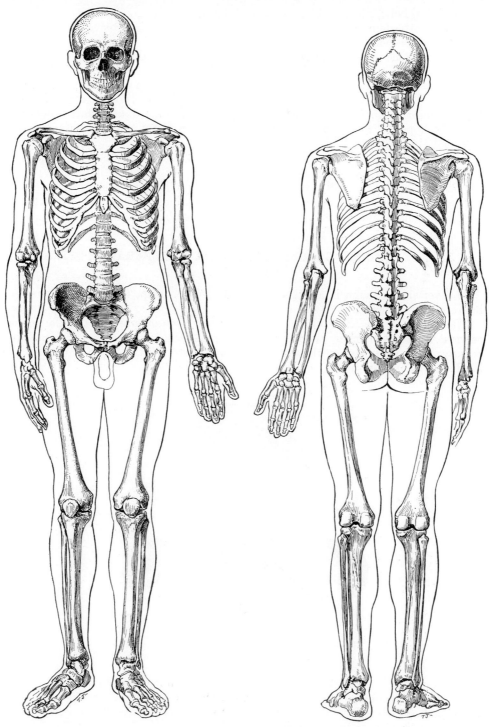

FIG. 133.—The skeleton as projected on the surface of the body viewed from in front and from behind.   (Eycleshymer and Jones.)

skull. Various centers of ossification develop in the cartilage and give rise to all of the occipital bone, except the upper part of the squama, to the petrous and mastoid portions of the temporal, to the sphenoid, except its medial pterygoid plates and part of the temporal wings, and to the ethmoid.

The **membrane bones** of the cranial vault and face ossify directly in the mesoderm of the membraneous cranium. They comprise the upper part of the occipital squama (interparietal), the squamæ and tympanic parts of the temporals, the parietals, the frontal, the vomer, the medial pterygoid plates, and the bones of the face. Some of them remain distinct throughout life, *e. g.*, parietal and frontal, while others join with the bones of the chondrocranium, *e. g.*, interparietal, squamæ of temporals, and medial pterygoid plates.

The anterior and posterior thirds of the cranial notochord become surrounded by the cartilage of the basal plate, its middle part lies between the middle part of the basal plate and the wall of the pharynx (Fig. 132). The anterior end is embedded in the basisphenoid. There are very distinct indications of an occipital vertebra at the caudal end of the occipital cartilage in embryos about 20 mm. in length.

THE VERTEBRAL COLUMN (COLUMNA VERTEBRALIS; SPINAL COLUMN).

The **vertebral column** is a flexuous and flexible column, formed of a series of bones called **vertebræ**.

The vertebræ are thirty-three in number, and are grouped under the names **cervical, thoracic, lumbar, sacral,** and **coccygeal,** according to the regions they occupy; there are seven in the cervical region, twelve in the thoracic, five in the lumbar, five in the sacral, and four in the coccygeal.

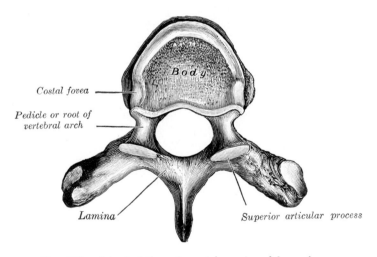

Costal fovea

Pedicle or root of vertebral arch

Body

Lamina

Superior articular process

Fig. 134.—A typical thoracic vertebra, viewed from above.

This number is sometimes increased by an additional vertebra in one region, or it may be diminished in one region, the deficiency often being supplied by an additional vertebra in another. The number of cervical vertebræ is, however, very rarely increased or diminished.

The vertebræ in the upper three regions of the column remain distinct throughout life, and are known as **true** or **movable** vertebræ; those of the sacral and coccygeal regions, on the other hand, are termed **false** or **fixed** vertebræ, because they are united with one another in the adult to form two bones—five forming the upper bone or **sacrum,** and four the terminal bone or **coccyx.**

With the exception of the first and second cervical, the true or movable vertebræ present certain common characteristics which are best studied by examining one from the middle of the thoracic region.

GENERAL CHARACTERISTICS OF A VERTEBRA.

A **typical vertebra** consists of two essential parts—viz., an anterior segment, the **body,** and a posterior part, the **vertebral** or **neural arch;** these enclose a foramen, the **vertebral foramen.** The vertebral arch consists of a pair of **pedicles** and a pair of **laminæ** and supports **seven processes**—viz., four **articular,** two **transverse,** and one **spinous.**

When the vertebræ are articulated with each other the bodies form a strong pillar for the support of the head and trunk, and the vertebral foramina constitute a canal for the protection of the spinal cord, while between every pair of vertebræ are two apertures, the **intervertebral foramina,** one on either side, for the transmission of the spinal nerves and vessels.

Body (*corpus vertebræ*).—The body is the largest part of a vertebra, and is more or less cylindrical in shape. Its upper and lower surfaces are flattened and rough, and give attachment to the intervertebral fibrocartilages, and each presents a rim around its circumference. In front, the body is convex from side to side and concave from above downward. Behind, it is flat from above downward and slightly concave from side to side. Its anterior surface presents a few small apertures, for the passage of nutrient vessels; on the posterior surface is a single large, irregular aperture, or occasionally more than one, for the exit of the basivertebral veins from the body of the vertebra.

Pedicles (*radices arci vertebræ*).—The pedicles are two short, thick processes, which project backward, one on either side, from the upper part of the body, at the junction of its posterior and lateral surfaces. The concavities above and below the pedicles are named the **vertebral notches;** and when the vertebræ are articulated, the notches of each contiguous pair of bones form the intervertebral foramina, already referred to.

Laminæ.—The laminæ are two broad plates directed backward and medialward from the pedicles. They fuse in the middle line posteriorly, and so complete the posterior boundary of the vertebral foramen. Their upper borders and the lower parts of their anterior surfaces are rough for the attachment of the ligamenta flava.

Processes.—Spinous Process (*processus spinosus*).—The spinous process is directed backward and downward from the junction of the laminæ, and serves for the attachment of muscles and ligaments.

Articular Processes.—The articular processes, two superior and two inferior, spring from the junctions of the pedicles and laminæ. The superior project upward, and their articular surfaces are directed more or less backward; the inferior project downward, and their surfaces look more or less forward. The articular surfaces are coated with hyaline cartilage.

Transverse Processes (*processus transversus*).—The transverse processes, two in number, project one at either side from the point where the lamina joins the pedicle, between the superior and inferior articular processes. They serve for the attachment of muscles and ligaments.

Structure of a Vertebra (Fig. 135).—The body is composed of cancellous tissue, covered by a thin coating of compact bone; the latter is perforated by numerous orifices, some of large size for the passage of vessels; the interior of the bone is traversed by one or two large canals, for the reception of veins, which converge toward a single large, irregular aperture, or several small apertures, at the posterior part of the body. The thin bony lamellæ of the cancellous tissue are more pronounced in lines perpendicular to the upper and lower surfaces and are developed in response to greater pressure in this direction (Fig. 135). The arch and processes projecting from it have thick coverings of compact tissue.

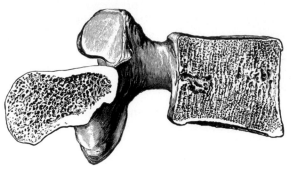

FIG. 135.—Sagittal section of a lumbar vertebra.

The Cervical Vertebræ (Vertebræ Cervicales).

The **cervical vertebræ** (Fig. 136) are the smallest of the true vertebræ, and can be readily distinguished from those of the thoracic or lumbar regions by the presence of a foramen in each transverse process. The first, second, and seventh present exceptional features and must be separately described; the following characteristics are common to the remaining four.

The **body** is small, and broader from side to side than from before backward The **anterior and posterior surfaces** are flattened and of equal depth; the former is placed on a lower level than the latter, and its inferior border is prolonged downward, so as to overlap the upper and forepart of the vertebra below. The **upper surface** is concave transversely, and presents a projecting lip on either side; the **lower surface** is concave from before backward, convex from side to side, and

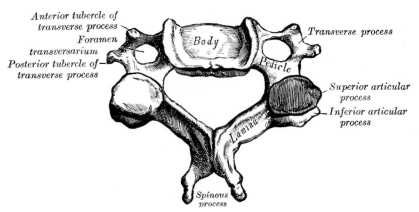

FIG. 136.—A cervical vertebra.

presents laterally shallow concavities which receive the corresponding projecting lips of the subjacent vertebra. The **pedicles** are directed lateralward and backward, and are attached to the body midway between its upper and lower borders, so that the superior vertebral notch is as deep as the inferior, but it is, at the same time, narrower. The **laminæ** are narrow, and thinner above than below; the **vertebral foramen** is large, and of a triangular form. The **spinous process** is short and bifid, the two divisions being often of unequal size. The **superior** and **inferior articular processes** on either side are fused to form an articular pillar, which projects lateralward from the junction of the pedicle and lamina. The articular facets are flat

and of an oval form: the superior look backward, upward, and slightly medialward: the inferior forward, downward, and slightly lateralward. The **transverse
processes** are each pierced by the **foramen transversarium,** which, in the upper six
vertebræ, gives passage to the vertebral artery and vein and a plexus of sympathetic nerves. Each process consists of an anterior and a posterior part. The
anterior portion is the homologue of the rib in the thoracic region, and is therefore named the **costal process** or **costal element:** it arises from the side of the body,
is directed lateralward in front of the foramen, and ends in a tubercle, the **anterior
tubercle.** The **posterior** part, the true transverse process, springs from the
vertebral arch behind the foramen, and is directed forward and lateralward; it

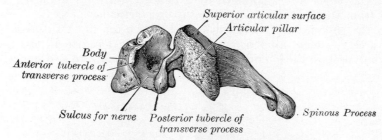

FIG. 137.—Side view of a typical cervical vertebra.

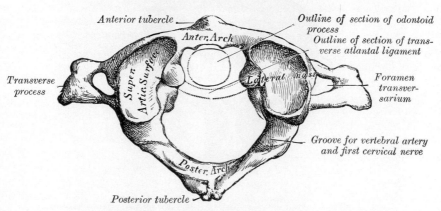

FIG. 138.—First cervical vertebra, or atlas.

ends in a flattened vertical tubercle, the **posterior tubercle.** These two parts are
joined, outside the foramen, by a bar of bone which exhibits a deep sulcus on its
upper surface for the passage of the corresponding spinal nerve. The *costal element*
of a cervical vertebra not only includes the portion which springs from the side of
the body, but the anterior and posterior tubercles and the bar of bone which
connects them (Fig. 127).

First Cervical Vertebra.—The first cervical vertebra (Fig. 138) is named the
atlas because it supports the globe of the head. Its chief peculiarity is that it has
no body, and this is due to the fact that the body of the atlas has fused with that
of the next vertebra. Its other peculiarities are that it has no spinous process,
is ring-like, and consists of an anterior and a posterior arch and two lateral masses.
The **anterior arch** forms about one-fifth of the ring: its anterior surface is convex,
and presents at its center the **anterior tubercle** for the attachment of the Longus
colli muscles; posteriorly it is concave, and marked by a smooth, oval or circular
facet (*fovea dentis*), for articulation with the odontoid process (*dens*) of the axis.

9

The upper and lower borders respectively give attachment to the anterior atlanto-occipital membrane and the anterior atlantoaxial ligament; the former connects it with the occipital bone above, and the latter with the axis below. The **posterior arch** forms about two-fifths of the circumference of the ring: it ends behind in the **posterior tubercle,** which is the rudiment of a spinous process and gives origin to the Recti capitis posteriores minores. The diminutive size of this process prevents any interference with the movements between the atlas and the skull. The posterior part of the arch presents above and behind a rounded edge for the attachment of the posterior atlantoöccipital membrane, while immediately behind each superior articular process is a groove (*sulcus arteriæ vertebralis*), sometimes converted into a foramen by a delicate bony spiculum which arches backward from the posterior end of the superior articular process. This groove represents the superior vertebral notch, and serves for the transmission of the vertebral artery, which, after ascending through the foramen in the transverse process, winds around the lateral mass in a direction backward and medialward; it

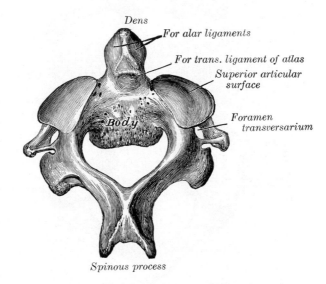

Fig. 139.—Second cervical vertebra, or epistropheus, from above.

also transmits the suboccipital (first spinal) nerve. On the under surface of the posterior arch, behind the articular facets, are two shallow grooves, the **inferior vertebral notches.** The lower border gives attachment to the posterior atlanto-axial ligament, which connects it with the axis. The **lateral masses** are the most bulky and solid parts of the atlas, in order to support the weight of the head. Each carries two articular facets, a superior and an inferior. The **superior facets** are of large size, oval, concave, and approach each other in front, but diverge behind: they are directed upward, medialward, and a little backward, each forming a cup for the corresponding condyle of the occipital bone, and are admirably adapted to the nodding movements of the head. Not infrequently they are partially subdivided by indentations which encroach upon their margins. The **inferior articular facets** are circular in form, flattened or slightly convex and directed downward and medialward, articulating with the axis, and permitting the rotatory movements of the head. Just below the medial margin of each superior facet is a small tubercle, for the attachment of the transverse atlantal ligament which stretches across the ring of the atlas and divides the vertebral foramen into two unequal parts—the anterior or smaller receiving the odontoid process of the axis, the posterior transmitting the medulla spinalis and its membranes. This part of the vertebral canal is of considerable size, much greater than is required for the accommodation of the medulla spinalis, and hence lateral displacement of the atlas may occur without compression of this structure. The **transverse processes** are large; they project lateralward and downward from the lateral masses, and serve for the attachment of muscles which assist in rotating the head. They are long, and their anterior and posterior tubercles are fused into one mass; the foramen transversarium is directed from below, upward and backward.

Second Cervical Vertebra.—The second cervical vertebra (Figs. 139 and 140) is named the **epistropheus** or **axis** because it forms the pivot upon which the first vertebra, carrying the head, rotates. The most distinctive characteristic of this bone is the strong odontoid process which rises perpendicularly from the upper surface of the body. The **body** is deeper in front than behind, and prolonged downward

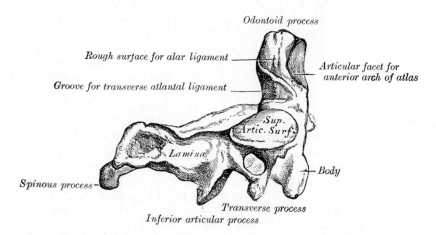

FIG. 140.—Second cervical vertebra, epistropheus, or axis, from the side.

anteriorly so as to overlap the upper and fore part of the third vertebra. It presents in front a median longitudinal ridge, separating two lateral depressions for the attachment of the Longus colli muscles. Its under surface is concave from before backward and convex from side to side. The **dens** or **odontoid process** exhibits a slight constriction or neck, where it joins the body. On its anterior surface is an oval or nearly circular facet for articulation with that on the anterior arch of the atlas. On the back of the neck, and frequently extending on to its lateral surfaces, is a shallow groove for the transverse atlantal ligament which retains the process in position. The **apex** is pointed, and gives attachment to the apical odontoid ligament; below the apex the process is somewhat enlarged, and presents on either side a rough impression for the attachment of the alar ligament; these ligaments connect the process to the occipital bone. The internal structure of the odontoid process is more compact than that of the body. The **pedicles** are broad and strong, especially in front, where they coalesce with the sides of the body and the root of the odontoid process. They are covered above by the superior articular surfaces. The **laminæ** are thick and strong, and the vertebral foramen large, but smaller than that of the atlas. The **transverse processes** are very small, and each ends in a single tubercle; each is perforated by the foramen transversarium, which is directed obliquely upward and lateralward. The **superior articular surfaces** are round, slightly convex, directed upward and lateralward, and are supported on the body, pedicles, and transverse processes. The **inferior articular surfaces** have the same direction as those of the other cervical vertebræ. The **superior vertebral notches** are very shallow, and lie behind the articular processes; the **inferior** lie in front of the articular processes, as in the other cervical vertebræ. The **spinous process** is large, very strong, deeply channelled on its under surface, and presents a bifid, tuberculated extremity.

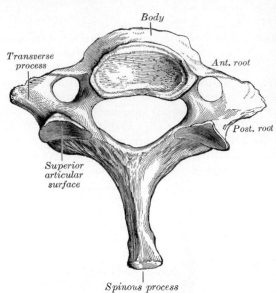

FIG. 141.—Seventh cervical vertebra.

The **Seventh Cervical Vertebra** (Fig. 141).—The most distinctive characteristic of this vertebra is the existence of a long and prominent spinous process, hence the name **vertebra prominens**. This process is thick, nearly horizontal in direction, not bifurcated, but terminating in a tubercle to which the lower end of the ligamentum nuchæ is attached. The **transverse processes** are of considerable size, their posterior roots are large and prominent, while the anterior are small and faintly marked. The foramen transversarium may be as large as that in the other cervical vertebræ, but is generally smaller on one or both sides; occasionally it is double, sometimes it is absent. On the left side it occasionally gives passage to the vertebral artery; more frequently the vertebral vein traverses it on both sides; but the usual arrangement is for both artery and vein to pass in front of the transverse process, and not through the foramen. Sometimes the anterior root of the transverse process attains a large size and exists as a separate bone, which is known as a **cervical rib**.

The Thoracic Vertebræ (Vertebræ Thoracicae).

The **thoracic vertebræ** (Fig. 142) are intermediate in size between those of the cervical and lumbar regions; they increase in size from above downward, the upper vertebræ being much smaller than those in the lower part of the region. They are distinguished by the presence of facets on the sides of the bodies for articulation with the heads of the ribs, and facets on the transverse processes of all, except the eleventh and twelfth, for articulation with the tubercles of the ribs.

The **bodies** in the middle of the thoracic region are heart-shaped, and as broad in the antero-posterior as in the transverse direction. At the ends of the thoracic region they resemble respectively those of the cervical and lumbar vertebræ. They are slightly thicker behind than in front, flat above and below, convex from side to side in front, deeply concave behind, and, slightly constricted laterally and in front. They present, on either side, two costal demi-facets, one above, near the root of the pedicle, the other below, in front of the inferior vertebral notch; these are covered with cartilage in the fresh state, and, when the vertebræ are articulated with one another, form, with the intervening intervertebral fibrocartilages, oval surfaces for the reception of the heads of the ribs. The **pedicles** are directed backward and slightly upward, and the inferior vertebral notches are of large size, and deeper than in any other region of the vertebral column. The **laminæ** are broad, thick, and imbricated—that is to say, they overlap those of subjacent vertebræ like tiles on a roof. The **vertebral foramen** is small, and of a circular form. The **spinous process** is long, triangular on coronal section, directed obliquely downward, and ends in a tuberculated extremity. These processes overlap from the fifth to the eighth, but are less oblique in direction above and below. The **superior articular processes** are thin plates of bone projecting upward from the junctions of the pedicles and laminæ; their articular facets are practically flat, and are directed backward and a little lateralward and upward. The **inferior articular processes** are fused to a considerable extent with the laminæ, and project but slightly beyond their lower borders; their facets are directed

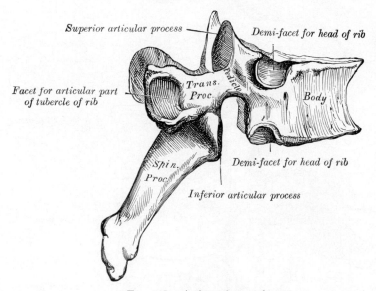

Fig. 142.—A thoracic vertebra.

forward and a little medialward and downward. The **transverse processes** arise from the arch behind the superior articular processes and pedicles; they are thick, strong, and of considerable length, directed obliquely backward and lateralward, and each ends in a clubbed extremity, on the front of which is a small, concave surface, for articulation with the tubercle of a rib.

The *first, ninth, tenth, eleventh,* and *twelfth* thoracic vertebræ present certain peculiarities, and must be specially considered (Fig. 143).

The **First Thoracic Vertebra** has, on either side of the **body,** an entire articular facet for the head of the first rib, and a demi-facet for the upper half of the head of the second rib. The body is like that of a cervical vertebra, being broad transversely; its upper surface is concave, and lipped on either side. The **superior articular surfaces** are directed upward and backward; the **spinous process** is thick, long, and almost horizontal. The **transverse processes** are long, and the upper vertebral notches are deeper than those of the other thoracic vertebræ.

The **Ninth Thoracic Vertebra** may have no demi-facets below. In some subjects however, it has two demi-facets on either side; when this occurs the tenth has only demi-facets at the upper part.

The **Tenth Thoracic Vertebra** has (except in the cases just mentioned) an entire articular facet on either side, which is placed partly on the lateral surface of the pedicle.

In the **Eleventh Thoracic Vertebra** the **body** approaches in its form and size to that of the lumbar vertebræ. The articular facets for the heads of the ribs

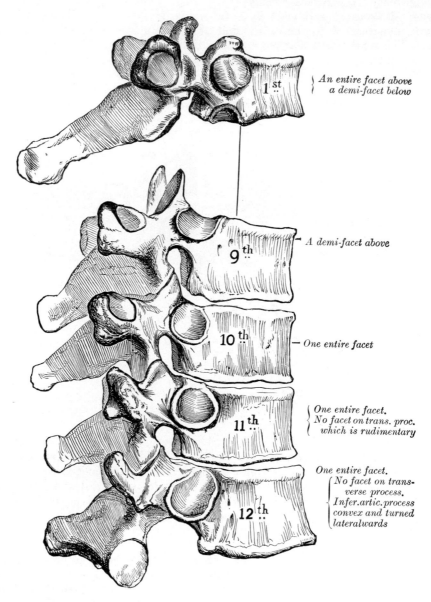

{ An entire facet above
a demi-facet below

— A demi-facet above

— One entire facet

{ One entire facet.
No facet on trans. proc.
which is rudimentary

One entire facet.
{ No facet on trans-
verse process.
Infer.artic.process
convex and turned
lateralwards

FIG. 143.—Peculiar thoracic vertebræ.

are of large size, and placed chiefly on the pedicles, which are thicker and stronger in this and the next vertebra than in any other part of the thoracic region. The **spinous process** is short, and nearly horizontal in direction. The **transverse processes** are very short, tuberculated at their extremities, and have no articular facets.

The **Twelfth Thoracic Vertebra** has the same general characteristics as the eleventh, but may be distinguished from it by its inferior articular surfaces being convex and directed lateralward, like those of the lumbar vertebræ; by the general form of the body, laminæ, and spinous process, in which it resembles the lumbar vertebræ; and by each transverse process being subdivided into three elevations, the superior, inferior, and lateral tubercles: the superior and inferior correspond to the mammillary and accessory processes of the lumbar vertebræ. Traces of similar elevations are found on the transverse processes of the tenth and eleventh thoracic vertebræ.

The Lumbar Vertebræ (Vertebræ Lumbales).

The **lumbar vertebræ** (Figs. 144 and 145) are the largest segments of the movable part of the vertebral column, and can be distinguished by the absence of a foramen in the transverse process, and by the absence of facets on the sides of the body.

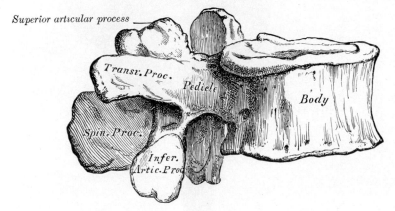

Fig. 144.—A lumbar vertebra seen from the side.

The **body** is large, wider from side to side than from before backward, and a little thicker in front than behind. It is flattened or slightly concave above and below, concave behind, and deeply constricted in front and at the sides. The **pedicles** are very strong, directed backward from the upper part of the body; consequently, the inferior vertebral notches are of considerable depth. The **laminæ** are broad, short, and strong; the **vertebral foramen** is triangular, larger than in the thoracic, but smaller than in the cervical region. The **spinous process** is thick, broad, and somewhat quadrilateral; it projects backward and ends in a rough, uneven border, thickest below where it is occasionally notched. The **superior** and **inferior articular processes** are well-defined, projecting respectively upward and downward from the junctions of pedicles and laminæ. The facets on the superior processes are concave, and look backward and medialward; those on the inferior are convex, and are directed forward and lateralward. The former are wider apart than the latter, since in the articulated column the inferior articular processes are embraced by the superior processes of the subjacent vertebra. The **transverse processes** are long, slender, and horizontal in the upper three lumbar vertebræ; they incline a little upward in the lower two. In the upper three vertebræ they arise from the junctions of the pedicles and laminæ, but in the lower two they are set farther forward and spring from the pedicles and posterior parts of the bodies. They are situated in front of the articular processes instead of behind

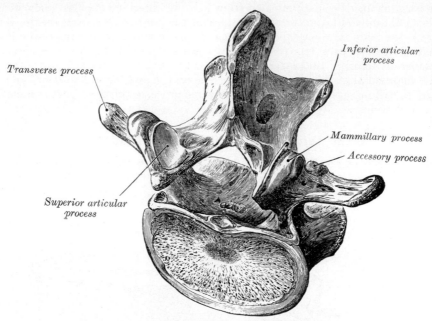

Transverse process

Inferior articular process

Mammillary process

Accessory process

Superior articular process

FIG. 145.—A lumbar vertebra from above and behind.

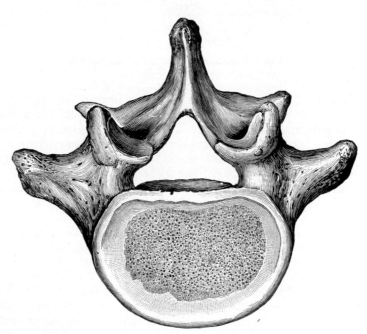

FIG. 146.—Fifth lumbar vertebra, from above.

them as in the thoracic vertebræ, and are homologous with the ribs. Of the three tubercles noticed in connection with the transverse processes of the lower thoracic vertebræ, the superior one is connected in the lumbar region with the back part of the superior articular process, and is named the **mammillary process**; the inferior is situated at the back part of the base of the transverse process, and is called the **accessory process** (Fig. 145).

The **Fifth Lumbar Vertebra** (Fig. 146) is characterized by its body being much deeper in front than behind, which accords with the prominence of the sacro-vertebral articulation; by the smaller size of its spinous process; by the wide interval between the inferior articular processes; and by the thickness of its transverse processes, which spring from the body as well as from the pedicles.

Variations.—The last **lumbar vertebra** is subject to certain defects described as bifid and separate neural arches, the latter occurring three times as frequently as the former. Both defects result in weakness of the column; the bifid arch by impairing ligamentous attachments; the separate arch through loss of bony anchorage of the column to its base.

The Sacral and Coccygeal Vertebræ.

The **sacral** and **coccygeal vertebræ** consist at an early period of life of nine separate segments which are united in the adult, so as to form two bones, five entering into the formation of the sacrum, four into that of the coccyx. Sometimes the coccyx consists of five bones; occasionally the number is reduced to three.

The Sacrum (*os sacrum*).—The sacrum is a large, triangular bone, situated in the lower part of the vertebral column and at the upper and back part of the pelvic cavity, where it is inserted like a wedge between the two hip bones; its upper part or base articulates with the last lumbar vertebra, its apex with the coccyx. It is curved upon itself and placed very obliquely, its base projecting forward and forming the **prominent sacrovertebral angle** when articulated with the last lumbar vertebra; its central part is projected backward, so as to give increased capacity to the pelvic cavity.

Pelvic Surface (*facies pelvina*).—The pelvic surface (Fig. 147) is concave from above downward, and slightly so from side to side. Its middle part is crossed by four **transverse ridges**, the positions of which correspond with the original planes of separation between the five segments of the bone. The portions of bone intervening between the ridges are the bodies of the sacral vertebræ. The body of the first segment is of large size, and in form resembles that of a lumbar vertebra; the succeeding ones diminish from above downward, are flattened from before backward, and curved so as to accommodate themselves to the form of the sacrum, being concave in front, convex behind. At the ends of the ridges are seen the **anterior sacral foramina**, four in number on either side, somewhat rounded in form, diminishing in size from above downward, and directed lateralward and forward; they give exit to the anterior divisions of the sacral nerves and entrance to the lateral sacral arteries. Lateral to these foramina are the **lateral parts of the sacrum**, each consisting of five separate segments at an early period of life; in the adult, these are blended with the bodies and with each other. Each lateral part is traversed by four broad, shallow grooves, which lodge the anterior divisions of the sacral nerves, and are separated by prominent ridges of bone which give origin to the Piriformis muscle.

If a sagittal section be made through the center of the sacrum (Fig. 151), the bodies are seen to be united at their circumferences by bone, wide intervals being left centrally, which, in the fresh state, are filled by the intervertebral fibro-cartilages. In some bones this union is more complete between the lower than the upper segments.

Dorsal Surface (*facies dorsalis*).—The dorsal surface (Fig. 148) is convex and narrower than the pelvic. In the middle line it displays a crest, the **middle sacral crest,** surmounted by three or four tubercles, the rudimentary spinous processes of the upper three or four sacral vertebræ. On either side of the middle sacral crest is a shallow groove, the **sacral groove,** which gives origin to the Multifidus, the floor of the groove being formed by the united laminæ of the corresponding vertebræ. The Sacrospinalis arises partly from the medial and lateral crests and the Latissimus dorsi partly from the medial crest. The laminæ of the fifth sacral vertebra, and sometimes those of the fourth, fail to meet behind, and thus a hiatus or deficiency occurs in the posterior wall of the sacral canal. On the lateral aspect of the sacral groove is a linear series of tubercles produced by the fusion of the articular

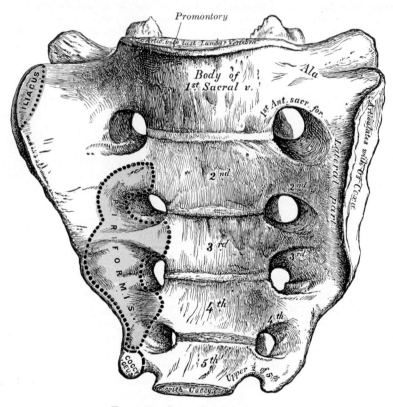

Fig. 147.—Sacrum, pelvic surface.

processes which together form the indistinct **sacral articular crests.** The articular processes of the first sacral vertebra are large and oval in shape; their facets are concave from side to side, look backward and medialward, and articulate with the facets on the inferior processes of the fifth lumbar vertebra. The tubercles which represent the inferior articular processes of the fifth sacral vertebra are prolonged downward as rounded processes, which are named the **sacral cornua,** and are connected to the cornua of the coccyx. Lateral to the articular processes are the four **posterior sacral foramina**; they are smaller in size and less regular in form than the anterior, and transmit the posterior divisions of the sacral nerves. On the lateral side of the posterior sacral foramina is a series of tubercles, which represent the transverse processes of the sacral vertebræ, and form the **lateral crests** of the sacrum.

The transverse tubercles of the first sacral vertebra are large and very distinct; they, together with the transverse tubercles of the second vertebra, give attachment to the horizontal parts of the posterior sacroiliac ligaments; those of the third vertebra give attachment to the oblique fasciculi of the posterior sacroiliac ligaments; and those of the fourth and fifth to the sacrotuberous ligaments.

Lateral Surface.--The lateral surface is broad above, but narrowed into a thin edge below. The upper half presents in front an ear-shaped surface, the **auricular surface,** covered with cartilage in the fresh state, for articulation with the ilium.

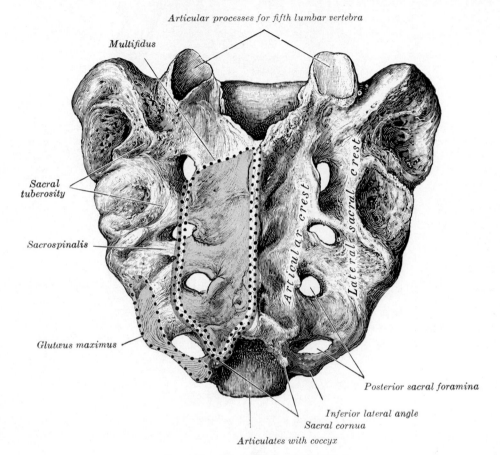

FIG. 148.—The sacrum, dorsal aspect.

Behind it is a rough surface, the **sacral tuberosity,** on which are three deep and uneven impressions, for the attachment of the posterior sacroiliac ligament. The lower half is thin, and ends in a projection called the **inferior lateral angle;** medial to this angle is a notch, which is converted into a foramen by the transverse process of the first piece of the coccyx, and transmits the anterior division of the fifth sacral nerve. The thin lower half of the lateral surface gives attachment to the sacrotuberous and sacrospinous ligaments, to some fibers of the Glutæus maximus behind, and to the Coccygeus in front.

Base (*basis oss. sacri*).—The base of the sacrum, which is broad and expanded, is directed upward and forward. In the middle is a large oval articular surface, the upper surface of the body of the first sacral vertebra, which is connected with the under surface of the body of the last lumbar vertebra by an intervertebral fibrocartilage. Behind this is the large triangular orifice of the sacral canal, which is completed by the laminæ and spinous process of the first sacral vertebra. The

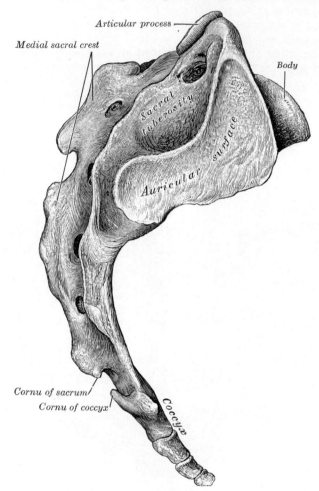

FIG. 149.—Lateral surfaces of sacrum and coccyx.

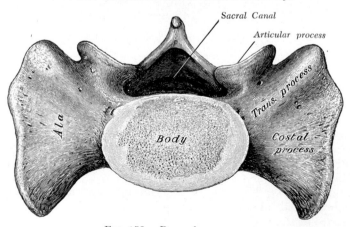

FIG. 150.—Base of sacrum.

superior articular processes project from it on either side; they are oval, concave, directed backward and medialward, like the superior articular processes of a lumbar vertebra. They are attached to the body of the first sacral vertebra and to the alæ by short thick pedicles; on the upper surface of each pedicle is a vertebral notch, which forms the lower part of the foramen between the last lumbar and first sacral vertebræ. On either side of the body is a large triangular surface, which supports the Psoas major and the lumbosacral trunk, and in the articulated pelvis is continuous with the iliac fossa. This is called the **ala**; it is slightly concave from side to side, convex from before backward, and gives attachment to a few of the fibers of the Iliacus. The posterior fourth of the ala represents the transverse process, and its anterior three-fourths the costal process of the first sacral segment.

Apex (*apex oss. sacri*).—The apex is directed downward, and presents an oval facet for articulation with the coccyx.

Vertebral Canal (*canalis sacralis; sacral canal*).—The vertebral canal (Fig. 151) runs throughout the greater part of the bone; above, it is triangular in form; below, its posterior wall is incomplete, from the non-development of the laminæ and spinous processes. It lodges the sacral nerves, and its walls are perforated by the anterior and posterior sacral foramina through which these nerves pass out.

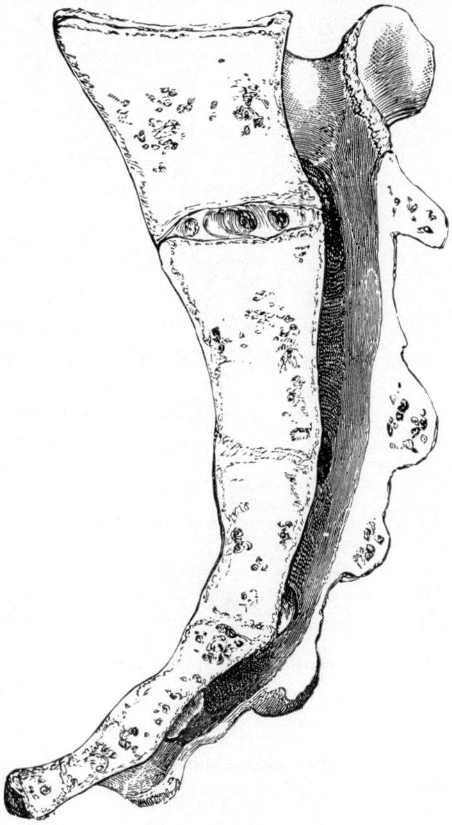

Structure.—The sacrum consists of cancellous tissue enveloped by a thin layer of compact bone.

Articulations.—The sacrum articulates with *four* bones; the last lumbar vertebra above, the coccyx below, and the hip bone on either side.

Differences in the Sacrum of the Male and Female.—In the female the sacrum is shorter and wider than in the male; the lower half forms a greater angle with the upper; the upper half is

FIG. 151.—Median sagittal section of the sacrum.

nearly straight, the lower half presenting the greatest amount of curvature. The bone is also directed more obliquely backward; this increases the size of the pelvic cavity and renders the sacrovertebral angle more prominent. In the male the curvature is more evenly distributed over the whole length of the bone, and is altogether greater than in the female.

Variations.—The sacrum, in some cases, consists of six pieces; occasionally the number is reduced to four. The bodies of the first and second vertebræ may fail to unite. Sometimes the uppermost transverse tubercles are not joined to the rest of the ala on one or both sides, or the sacral canal may be open throughout a considerable part of its length, in consequence of the imperfect development of the laminæ and spinous processes. The sacrum, also, varies considerably with respect to its degree of curvature.

The Coccyx (*os coccygis*).—The coccyx (Figs. 152 and 153) is usually formed of four rudimentary vertebræ; the number may however be increased to five or diminished to three. In each of the first three segments may be traced a rudimentary body and articular and transverse processes; the last piece (sometimes the third) is a mere nodule of bone. All the segments are destitute of pedicles, laminæ, and spinous processes. The first is the largest; it resembles the lowest sacral vertebra, and often exists as a separate piece; the last three diminish in size from above downward, and are usually fused with one another.

Surfaces.—The **anterior surface** is slightly concave, and marked with three transverse grooves which indicate the junctions of the different segments. It gives attachment to the anterior sacrococcygeal ligament and the Levatores ani, and supports part of the rectum. The **posterior surface** is convex, marked by transverse grooves similar to those on the anterior surface, and presents on either side a linear

Cornua
Rudim.
Trans.
prac.
With Sacrum
1st
COCC.V.
2nd
3rd
4th
COCCYGEUS
LEVATOR ANI

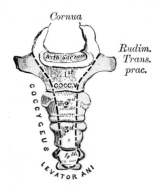

FIG. 152.—Coccyx, anterior surface.

GLUT. MAXIM.
SPHINCTER ANI
EXTERNUS

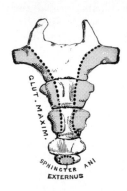

FIG. 153.—Coccyx, posterior surface.

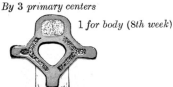

By 3 primary centers
1 for body (8th week)
1 for each vertebral arch (7th or 8th week)

FIG. 154.

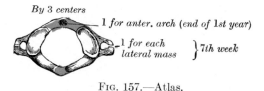

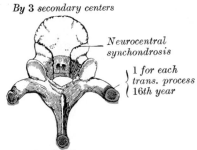

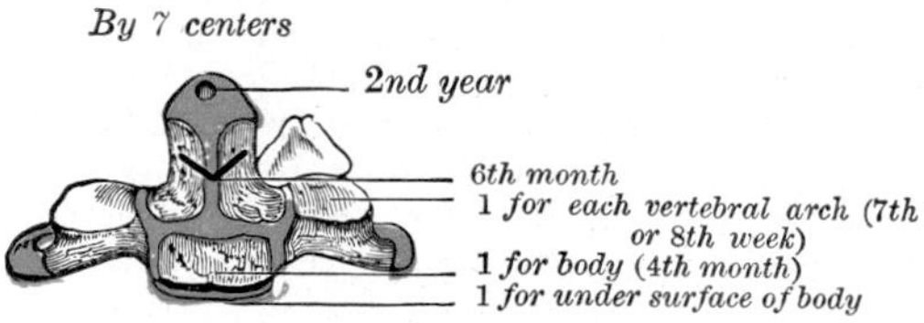

By 3 secondary centers
Neurocentral synchondrosis
1 for each trans. process 16th year
1 for spinous process (16th year)

FIG. 155.

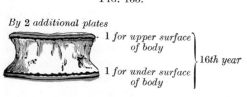

By 2 additional plates
1 for upper surface of body
1 for under surface of body
16th year

FIG. 156.

FIGS. 154–156.—Ossification of a vertebra.

By 3 centers
1 for anter. arch (end of 1st year)
1 for each lateral mass
7th week

FIG. 157.—Atlas.

By 7 centers
2nd year
6th month
1 for each vertebral arch (7th or 8th week)
1 for body (4th month)
1 for under surface of body

FIG. 158.—Axis.

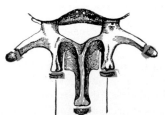

2 additional centers for mammillary processes

FIG. 159.—Lumbar vertebra.

FIGS. 157–159.—Individual peculiarities.

row of tubercles, the rudimentary articular processes of the coccygeal vertebræ. Of these, the superior pair are large, and are called the **coccygeal cornua;** they project upward, and articulate with the cornua of the sacrum, and on either side complete the foramen for the transmission of the posterior division of the fifth sacral nerve.

Borders.—The **lateral borders** are thin, and exhibit a series of small eminences, which represent the transverse processes of the coccygeal vertebræ. Of these, the first is the largest; it is flattened from before backward, and often ascends to join the lower part of the thin lateral edge of the sacrum, thus completing the foramen for the transmission of the anterior division of the fifth sacral nerve; the others diminish in size from above downward, and are often wanting. The borders of the coccyx are narrow, and give attachment on either side to the sacro-tuberous and sacrospinous ligaments, to the Coccygeus in front of the ligaments, and to the Glutæus maximus behind them.

Base.—The base presents an oval surface for articulation with the sacrum.

Apex.—The apex is rounded, and has attached to it the tendon of the Sphincter ani externus. It may be bifid, and is sometimes deflected to one or other side.

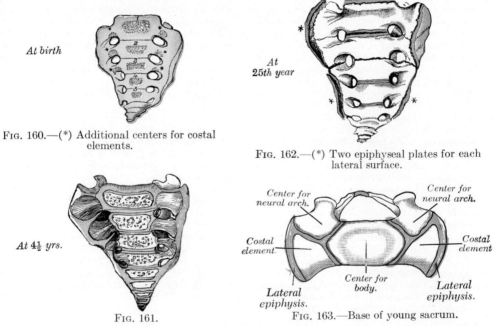

At birth

FIG. 160.—(*) Additional centers for costal elements.

At 25th year

FIG. 162.—(*) Two epiphyseal plates for each lateral surface.

At 4½ yrs.

FIG. 161.

Center for neural arch.

Center for neural arch.

Costal element

Costal element

Center for body.

Lateral epiphysis.

Lateral epiphysis.

FIG. 163.—Base of young sacrum.

FIGS. 160–163.—Ossification of the sacrum.

Ossification of the Vertebral Column.—Each cartilaginous vertebra is ossified from three primary centers (Fig. 154), two for the vertebral arch and one for the body.[1] Ossification of the vertebral arches begins in the upper cervical vertebræ about the seventh or eighth week of fetal life, and gradually extends down the column. The ossific granules first appear in the situations where the transverse processes afterward project, and spread backward to the spinous process forward into the pedicles, and lateralward into the transverse and articular processes. Ossification of the bodies begins about the eighth week in the lower thoracic region, and subsequently extends upward and downward along the column. The center for the body does not give rise to the whole of the body of the adult vertebra, the postero-lateral portions of which are ossified by extensions from the vertebral arch centers. The body of the vertebra during the first few years of life shows, therefore,

---

[1] A vertebra is occasionally found in which the body consists of two lateral portions—a condition which proves that the body is sometimes ossified from *two* primary centers, one on either side of the middle line.

two synchondroses, **neurocentral synchondroses,** traversing it along the planes of junction of the three centers (Fig. 155). In the thoracic region, the facets for the heads of the ribs lie behind the neurocentral synchondroses and are ossified from the centers for the vertebral arch. At birth the vertebra consists of three pieces, the body and the halves of the vertebral arch. During the first year the halves of the arch unite behind, union taking place first in the lumbar region and then extending upward through the thoracic and cervical regions. About the third year the bodies of the upper cervical vertebræ are joined to the arches on either side; in the lower lumbar vertebræ the union is not completed until the sixth year. Before puberty, no other changes occur, excepting a gradual increase of these primary centers, the upper and under surfaces of the bodies and the ends of the transverse and spinous processes being cartilaginous. About the sixteenth year (Fig. 155), five secondary centers appear, one for the tip of each transverse process, one for the extremity of the spinous process, one for the upper and one for the lower surface of the body (Fig. 156). These fuse with the rest of the bone about the age of twenty-five.

Exceptions to this mode of development occur in the first, second and seventh cervical vertebræ, and in the lumbar vertebræ.

Atlas.—The atlas is usually ossified from *three* centers (Fig. 157). Of these, one appears in each lateral mass about the seventh week of fetal life, and extends backward; at birth, these portions of bone are separated from one another behind by a narrow interval filled with cartilage. Between the third and fourth years they unite either directly or through the medium of a separate center developed in the cartilage. At birth, the anterior arch consists of cartilage; in this a separate center appears about the end of the first year after birth, and joins the lateral masses from the sixth to the eighth year—the lines of union extending across the anterior portions of the superior articular facets. Occasionally there is no separate center, the anterior arch being formed by the forward extension and ultimate junction of the two lateral masses; sometimes this arch is ossified from two centers, one on either side of the middle line.

Epistropheus or Axis.—The axis is ossified from *five* primary and *two* secondary centers (Fig. 158). The body and vertebral arch are ossified in the same manner as the corresponding parts in the other vertebræ, viz., one center for the body, and two for the vertebral arch. The centers for the arch appear about the seventh or eighth week of fetal life, that for the body about the fourth or fifth month. The dens or odontoid process consists originally of a continuation upward of the cartilaginous mass, in which the lower part of the body is formed. About the sixth month of fetal life, two centers make their appearance in the base of this process: they are placed laterally, and join before birth to form a conical bilobed mass deeply cleft above; the interval between the sides of the cleft and the summit of the process is formed by a wedge-shaped piece of cartilage. The base of the process is separated from the body by a cartilaginous disk, which gradually becomes ossified at its circumference, but remains cartilaginous in its center until advanced age. In this cartilage, rudiments of the lower epiphyseal lamella of the atlas and the upper epiphyseal lamella of the axis may sometimes be found. The apex of the odontoid process has a separate center which appears in the second and joins about the twelfth year; this is the upper epiphyseal lamella of the atlas. In addition to these there is a secondary center for a thin epiphyseal plate on the under surface of the body of the bone.

The Seventh Cervical Vertebra.—The anterior or costal part of the transverse process of this vertebra is sometimes ossified from a separate center which appears about the sixth month of fetal life and joins the body and posterior part of the transverse process between the fifth and sixth years. Occasionally the costal part persists as a separate piece, and, becoming lengthened lateralward and forward, constitutes what is known as a *cervical rib*. Separate ossific centers have also been found in the costal processes of the fourth, fifth, and sixth cervical vertebræ.

Lumbar Vertebræ.—The lumbar vertebræ (Fig. 159) have each *two* additional centers, for the mammillary processes. The transverse process of the first lumbar is sometimes developed as a separate piece, which may remain permanently ununited with the rest of the bone, thus forming a lumbar rib—a peculiarity, however, rarely met with.

Sacrum (Figs. 160 to 163).—The *body* of each sacral vertebra is ossified from a primary center and *two* epiphyseal plates, one for its upper and another for its under surface, while each vertebral arch is ossified from two centers.

The anterior portions of the *lateral parts* have *six* additional centers, two for each of the three vertebræ; these represent the costal elements, and make their appearance above and lateral to the anterior sacral foramina (Figs. 160, 161).

On each *lateral surface* two epiphyseal plates are developed (Figs. 162, 163): one for the auricular surface, and another for the remaining part of the thin lateral edge of the bone.

PERIODS OF OSSIFICATION.—About the eighth or ninth week of fetal life, ossification of the central part of the body of the first sacral vertebra commences, and is rapidly followed by deposit of ossific matter in the second and third: ossification does not commence in the bodies of the lower two segments until between the fifth and eighth months of fetal life. Between the sixth and eighth months ossification of the vertebral arches takes place; and about the same time the costal centers for the lateral parts make their appearance. The junctions of the vertebral arches with the bodies take place in the lower vertebræ as early as the second year, but are not effected in the uppermost until the fifth or sixth year. About the sixteenth year the epiphysial plates for the upper and under surfaces of the bodies are formed; and between the eighteenth and twentieth years, those for the lateral surfaces make their appearance. The bodies of the sacral vertebræ are, during early life, separated from each other by intervertebral fibrocartilages, but about the eighteenth year the two lowest segments become united by bone, and the process of bony union gradually extends upward, with the result that between the twenty-fifth and thirtieth years of life all the segments are united. On examining a sagittal section of the sacrum, the situations of the intervertebral fibrocartilages are indicated by a series of oval cavities (Fig. 151).

Coccyx.—The coccyx is ossified from *four* centers, one for each segment. The ossific nuclei make their appearance in the following order: in the first segment between the first and fourth years; in the second between the fifth and tenth years; in the third between the tenth and fifteenth years; in the fourth between the fourteenth and twentieth years. As age advances, the segments unite with one another, the union between the first and second segments being frequently delayed until after the age of twenty-five or thirty. At a late period of life, especially in females, the coccyx often fuses with the sacrum.

THE VERTEBRAL COLUMN AS A WHOLE.

The vertebral column is situated in the median line, as the posterior part of the trunk; its average length in the male is about 71 cm. Of this length the cervical part measures 12.5 cm., the thoracic about 28 cm., the lumbar 18 cm., and the sacrum and coccyx 12.5 cm. The female column is about 61 cm. in length.

Curves.—Viewed laterally (Fig. 164), the vertebral column presents several curves, which correspond to the different regions of the column, and are called cervical, thoracic, lumbar, and pelvic. The **cervical** curve, convex forward, begins at the apex of the odontoid process, and ends at the middle of the second thoracic vertebra; it is the least marked of all the curves. The **thoracic** curve, concave forward, begins at the middle of the second and ends at the middle of the twelfth thoracic vertebra. Its most prominent point behind corresponds to the spinous process of the seventh thoracic vertebra. The **lumbar** curve is more marked in the female than in the male; it begins at the middle of the last thoracic vertebra, and ends at the sacrovertebral angle. It is convex anteriorly, the convexity of the lower three vertebræ being much greater than that of the upper two. The **pelvic** curve begins at the sacrovertebral articulation, and ends at the point of the coccyx; its concavity is directed downward and forward. The thoracic and pelvic curves are termed primary curves, because they alone are present during fetal life. The cervical and lumbar curves are compensatory or secondary, and are developed after birth, the former when the child is able to hold up its head (at three or four months), and to sit upright (at nine months), the latter at twelve or eighteen months, when the child begins to walk.

The vertebral column has also a slight **lateral** curvature, the convexity of which is directed toward the right side. This may be produced by muscular action, most persons using the right arm in preference to the left, especially in making long-continued efforts, when the body is curved to the right side. In support of this explanation it has been found that in one or two individuals who were left-handed, the convexity was to the left side. By others this curvature is regarded as being produced by the aortic arch and upper part of the descending thoracic aorta—a view which is supported by the fact that in cases where the viscera are transposed and the aorta is on the right side, the convexity of the curve is directed to the left side.

Surfaces.—**Anterior Surface.**—When viewed from in front, the width of the bodies of the vertebræ is seen to increase from the second cervical to the first thoracic; there is then a slight diminution in the next three vertebræ; below this there is again a gradual and progressive increase in width as low as the sacrovertebral angle. From this point there is a rapid diminution, to the apex of the coccyx.

10

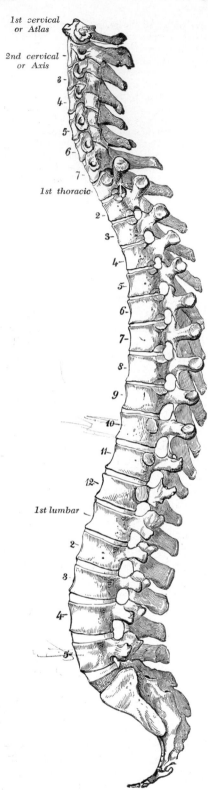

1st cervical
or Atlas

2nd cervical
or Axis

3-

4-

5-

6-

7-

1st thoracic

2-

3-

4-

5-

6-

7-

8-

9-

10-

11-

12-

1st lumbar

2-

3-

4-

5-

Fig. 164.—Lateral view of the vertebral column.

Posterior Surface.—The posterior surface of the vertebral column presents in the median line the spinous processes. In the cervical region (with the exception of the second and seventh vertebræ) these are short and horizontal, with bifid extremities. In the upper part of the thoracic region they are directed obliquely downward; in the middle they are almost vertical, and in the lower part they are nearly horizontal. In the lumbar region they are nearly horizontal. The spinous processes are separated by considerable intervals in the lumbar region, by narrower intervals in the neck, and are closely approximated in the middle of the thoracic region. Occasionally one of these processes deviates a little from the median line—a fact to be remembered in practice, as irregularities of this sort are attendant also on fractures or displacements of the vertebral column. On either side of the spinous processes is the **vertebral groove** formed by the laminæ in the cervical and lumbar regions, where it is shallow, and by the laminæ and transverse processes in the thoracic region, where it is deep and broad; these grooves lodge the deep muscles of the back. Lateral to the vertebral grooves are the articular processes, and still more laterally the transverse processes. In the thoracic region, the transverse processes stand backward, on a plane considerably behind that of the same processes in the cervical and lumbar regions. In the cervical region, the transverse processes are placed in front of the articular processes, lateral to the pedicles and between the intervertebral foramina. In the thoracic region they are posterior to the pedicles, intervertebral foramina, and articular processes. In the lumbar region they are in front of the articular processes, but behind the intervertebral foramina.

Lateral Surfaces.—The lateral surfaces are separated from the posterior surface by the articular processes in the cervical and lumbar regions, and by the transverse processes in the thoracic region. They present, in front, the sides of the bodies of the vertebræ, marked in the thoracic region by the facets for articulation with the heads of the ribs. More posteriorly are the intervertebral foramina, formed by the juxtaposition of the vertebral notches, oval in shape, smallest in the cervical and upper part of the thoracic regions, and gradually increasing in size to the last lumbar. They transmit the spinal nerves and are situated between the transverse processes in the cervical region, and in front of them in the thoracic and lumbar regions.

Vertebral Canal.—The vertebral canal follows the different curves of the column; it is large and triangular in those parts of the column which enjoy the greatest freedom of movement, viz., the cervical and lumbar regions; and is small and rounded in the thoracic region, where motion is more limited.

Abnormalities.—Occasionally the coalescence of the laminæ is not completed, and consequently a cleft is left in the arches of the vertebræ, through which a protrusion of the spinal membranes (dura mater and arachnoid), and generally of the medulla spinalis itself, takes place, constituting the malformation known as *spina bifida*. This condition is most common in the lumbosacral region, but it may occur in the thoracic or cervical region, or the arches throughout the whole length of the canal may remain incomplete.

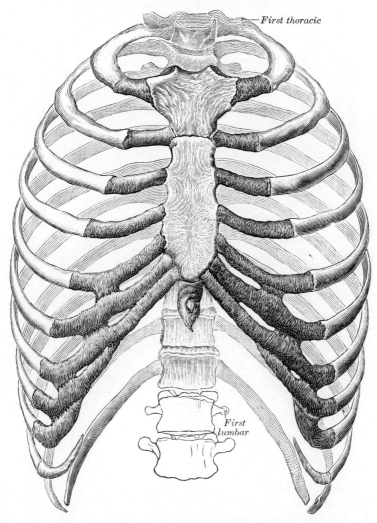

First thoracic

First lumbar

FIG. 165.—The thorax from in front. (Spalteholz.)

THE THORAX.

The skeleton of the **thorax** or **chest** (Figs. 165, 166, 167) is an osseo-cartilaginous cage, containing and protecting the principal organs of respiration and circulation.

It is conical in shape, being narrow above and broad below, flattened from before backward, and longer behind than in front. It is somewhat reniform on transverse section on account of the projection of the vertebral bodies into the cavity.

Boundaries.—The **posterior surface** is formed by the twelve thoracic vertebræ and the posterior parts of the ribs. It is convex from above downward, and presents on either side of the middle line a deep groove, in consequence of the lateral and backward direction which the ribs take from their vertebral extremities to their angles. The **anterior surface**, formed by the sternum and costal cartilages,

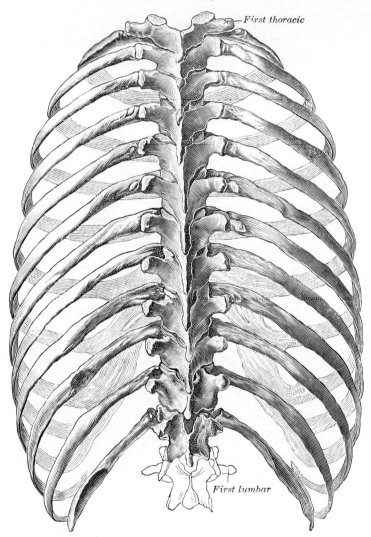

First thoracic

First lumbar

FIG. 166.—The thorax from behind. (Spalteholz.)

is flattened or slightly convex, and inclined from above downward and forward. The **lateral surfaces** are convex; they are formed by the ribs, separated from each other by the intercostal spaces, eleven in number, which are occupied by the Intercostal muscles and membranes.

The **upper opening** of the thorax is reniform in shape, being broader from side to side than from before backward. It is formed by the first thoracic vertebra behind, the upper margin of the sternum in front, and the first rib on either side. It slopes downward and forward, so that the anterior part of the opening is on a lower level than the posterior. Its antero-posterior diameter is about 5 cm., and its transverse diameter about 10 cm. The **lower opening** is formed by the twelfth thoracic vertebra behind, by the eleventh and twelfth ribs at the sides, and in front by the cartilages of the tenth, ninth, eighth, and seventh ribs, which ascend on either side and form an angle, the **subcostal angle,** into the apex of which the xiphoid process projects. The lower opening is wider transversely than from before backward, and slopes obliquely downward and backward, it is closed by the diaphragm which forms the floor of the thorax.

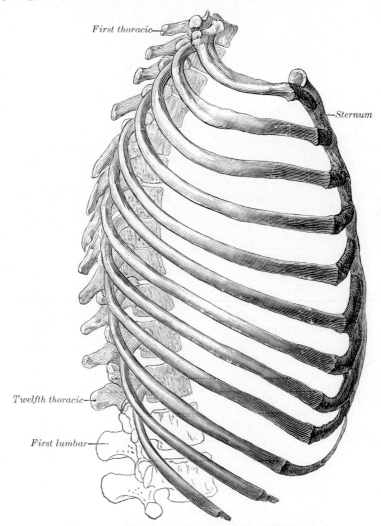

First thoracic

Sternum

Twelfth thoracic

First lumbar

Fig. 167.—The thorax from the right. (Spalteholz.)

The thorax of the female differs from that of the male as follows: 1. Its capacity is less. 2. The sternum is shorter. 3. The upper margin of the sternum is on a level with the lower part of the body of the third thoracic vertebra, whereas in the male it is on a level with the lower part of the body of the second. 4. The upper ribs are more movable, and so allow a greater enlargement of the upper part of the thorax.

The Sternum (Breast Bone).

The **sternum** (Figs. 168 to 170) is an elongated, flattened bone, forming the middle portion of the anterior wall of the thorax. Its upper end supports the clavicles, and its margins articulate with the cartilages of the first seven pairs of ribs. It consists of three parts, named from above downward, the **manubrium**, the **body** or **gladiolus**, and the **xiphoid process**; in early life the body consists of four segments or *sternebræ*. In its natural position the inclination of the bone is oblique from above, downward and forward. It is slightly convex in front and concave behind; broad above, becoming narrowed at the point where the manubrium joins

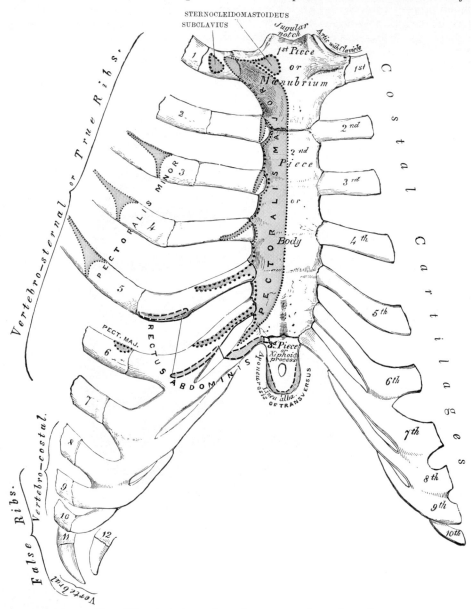

Fig. 168.—Anterior surface of sternum and costal cartilages.

the body, after which it again widens a little to below the middle of the body, and then narrows to its lower extremity. Its average length in the adult is about 17 cm., and is rather greater in the male than in the female.

Manubrium (*manubrium sterni*).—The manubrium is of a somewhat quad-rangular form, broad and thick above, narrow below at its junction with the body.

Surfaces.—Its **anterior surface**, convex from side to side, concave from above downward, is smooth, and affords attachment on either side to the sternal origins of the Pectoralis major and Sternocleidomastoideus. Sometimes the ridges limiting the attachments of these muscles are very distinct. Its **posterior surface,** concave and smooth, affords attachment on either side to the Sterno-hyoideus and Sternothyreoideus.

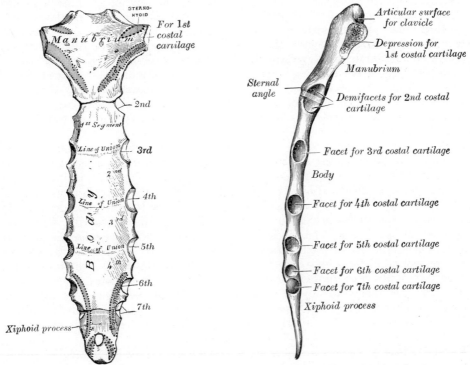

FIG. 169.—Posterior surface of sternum.   FIG. 170.—Lateral border of sternum.

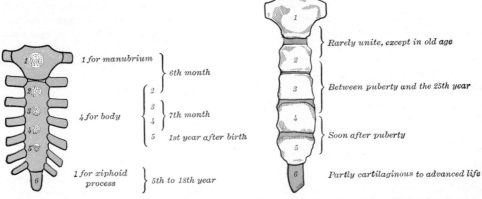

FIG. 171.—Time of appearance.   Ossification of the sternum.   FIG. 172.—Time of union.

Borders.—The **superior border** is the thickest and presents at its center the **jugular** or **presternal notch;** on either side of the notch is an oval articular surface, directed upward, backward, and lateralward, for articulation with the sternal end of the clavicle. The **inferior border,** oval and rough, is covered in a fresh state with a thin layer of cartilage, for articulation with the body. The **lateral borders** are each marked above by a depression for the first costal cartilage, and below by a small facet, which, with a similar facet on the upper angle of the body, forms a notch for the reception of the costal cartilage of the second rib. Between the depression for the first costal cartilage and the demi-facet for the second is a narrow, curved edge, which slopes from above downward and medialward.

Body (*corpus sterni; gladiolus*).—The body, considerably longer, narrower, and thinner than the manubrium, attains its greatest breadth close to the lower end.

Surfaces.—Its **anterior surface** is nearly flat, directed upward and forward, and marked by three transverse ridges which cross the bone opposite the third, fourth, and fifth articular depressions. It affords attachment on either side to the sternal origin of the Pectoralis major. At the junction of the third and fourth pieces of the body is occasionally seen an orifice, the **sternal foramen,** of varying size and form. The **posterior surface,** slightly concave, is also marked by three transverse lines, less distinct, however, than those in front; from its lower part, on either side, the Transversus thoracis takes origin.

Borders.—The **superior border** is oval and articulates with the manubrium, the junction of the two forming the **sternal angle.** The **inferior border** is narrow, and articulates with the xiphoid process. Each **lateral border** (Fig. 170), at its superior angle, has a small facet, which with a similar facet on the manubrium, forms a cavity for the cartilage of the second rib; below this are four angular depressions which receive the cartilages of the third, fourth, fifth, and sixth ribs, while the inferior angle has a small facet, which, with a corresponding one on the xiphoid process, forms a notch for the cartilage of the seventh rib. These articular depressions are separated by a series of curved interarticular intervals, which diminish in length from above downward, and correspond to the intercostal spaces. Most of the cartilages belonging to the true ribs, as will be seen from the foregoing description, articulate with the sternum at the lines of junction of its primitive component segments. This is well seen in many of the lower animals, where the parts of the bone remain ununited longer than in man.

Xiphoid Process (*processus xiphoideus; ensiform or xiphoid appendix*).—The xiphoid process is the smallest of the three pieces: it is thin and elongated, cartilaginous in structure in youth, but more or less ossified at its upper part in the adult.

Surfaces.—Its **anterior surface** affords attachment on either side to the anterior costoxiphoid ligament and a small part of the Rectus abdominis; its **posterior surface,** to the posterior costoxiphoid ligament and to some of the fibers of the diaphragm and Transversus thoracis, its **lateral borders,** to the aponeuroses of the abdominal muscles. Above, it articulates with the lower end of the body, and on the front of each superior angle presents a facet for part of the cartilage of the seventh rib; below, by its pointed extremity, it gives attachment to the linea alba. The xiphoid process varies much in form; it may be broad and thin, pointed, bifid, perforated, curved, or deflected considerably to one or other side.

Structure.—The sternum is composed of highly vascular cancellous tissue, covered by a thin layer of compact bone which is thickest in the manubrium between the articular facets for the clavicles.

Ossification.—The sternum originally consists of two cartilaginous bars, situated one on either side of the median plane and connected with the cartilages of the upper nine ribs of its own side. These two bars fuse with each other along the middle line to form the cartilaginous sternum which is ossified from *six* centers: one for the manubrium, four for the body, and one for the xiphoid process (Fig. 171). The ossific centers appear in the intervals between the articular depressions for the costal cartilages, in the following order: in the manubrium and first piece of the body, during the sixth month; in the second and third pieces of the body, during the seventh month of fetal life; in its fourth piece, during the first year after birth; and in the xiphoid process, between the fifth and eighteenth years. The centers make their appearance at the upper parts of the segments, and proceed gradually downward. To these may be added the occasional existence of two small episternal centers, which make their appearance one on either side of the jugular notch; they are probably vestiges of the episternal bone of the monotremata and lizards. Occasionally some of the segments are formed from more than one center, the number and position of which vary. Thus, the first piece may have two, three, or even six centers. When two are present, they are generally situated one above the other, the upper being the larger; the second piece has seldom more than one; the third, fourth, and fifth pieces are often formed from two centers placed laterally, the irregular union of which explains the rare occurrence of the sternal foramen, or of the vertical fissure which occasionally intersects this part of the bone constituting the malformation known as *fissura sterni;* these conditions are further explained by the manner in which the cartilaginous sternum is formed. More rarely still the upper end of the sternum may be divided by a fissure. Union of the various centers of the body begins about puberty, and proceeds from below upward (Fig. 172); by the age of twenty-five they are all united. The xiphoid process may become joined to the body before the age of thirty, but this occurs more frequently after forty; on the other hand, it sometimes remains ununited in old age. In advanced life the manubrium is occasionally joined to the body by bone. When this takes place, however, the bony tissue is generally only superficial, the central portion of the intervening cartilage remaining unossified.

Articulations.—The sternum articulates on either side with the clavicle and upper seven costal cartilages.

The Ribs (Costæ).

The **ribs** are elastic arches of bone, which form a large part of the thoracic skeleton. They are twelve in number on either side; but this number may be increased by the development of a cervical or lumbar rib, or may be diminished to eleven. The first seven are connected behind with the vertebral column, and in front, through the intervention of the costal cartilages, with the sternum (Fig. 168); they are called **true** or **vertebro-sternal ribs.**[1] The remaining five are **false ribs;** of these, the first three have their cartilages attached to the cartilage of the rib above (**vertebro-chondral**): the last two are free at their anterior extremities and are termed **floating** or **vertebral ribs.** The ribs vary in their direction, the upper ones being less oblique than the lower; the obliquity reaches its maximum at the ninth rib, and gradually decreases from that rib to the twelfth. The ribs are situated one below the other in such a manner that spaces called **intercostal spaces** are left between them. The length of each space corresponds to that of the adjacent ribs and their cartilages; the breadth is greater in front than behind, and between the upper than the lower ribs. The ribs increase in length from the first to the seventh, below which they diminish to the twelfth. In breadth they decrease from above downward; in the upper ten the greatest breadth is at the sternal extremity.

Common Characteristics of the Ribs (Figs. 173, 174).—A rib from the middle of the series should be taken in order to study the common characteristics of these bones.

Each rib has two extremities, a **posterior** or **vertebral,** and an **anterior** or **sternal,** and an intervening portion—the **body** or **shaft.**

Posterior Extremity.—The **posterior** or **vertebral extremity** presents for examination a head, neck, and tubercle.

The **head** is marked by a kidney-shaped articular surface, divided by a horizontal crest into two facets for articulation with the depression formed on the bodies of two adjacent thoracic vertebræ; the upper facet is the smaller; to the crest is attached the interarticular ligament.

The **neck** is the flattened portion which extends lateralward from the head; it is about 2.5 cm. long, and is placed in front of the transverse process of the lower of the two vertebræ with which the head articulates. Its **anterior surface** is flat and smooth, its **posterior** rough for the attachment of the ligament of the neck, and perforated by numerous foramina. Of its two borders the **superior** presents a rough crest (*crista colli costæ*) for the attachment of the anterior costotransverse ligament; its **inferior border** is rounded. On the posterior surface at the junction of the neck and body, and nearer the lower than the upper border, is an eminence

[1] Sometimes the eighth rib cartilage articulates with the sternum; this condition occurs more frequently on the right than on the left side.

—the **tubercle**; it consists of an articular and a non-articular portion. The *articular portion*, the lower and more medial of the two, presents a small, oval surface for

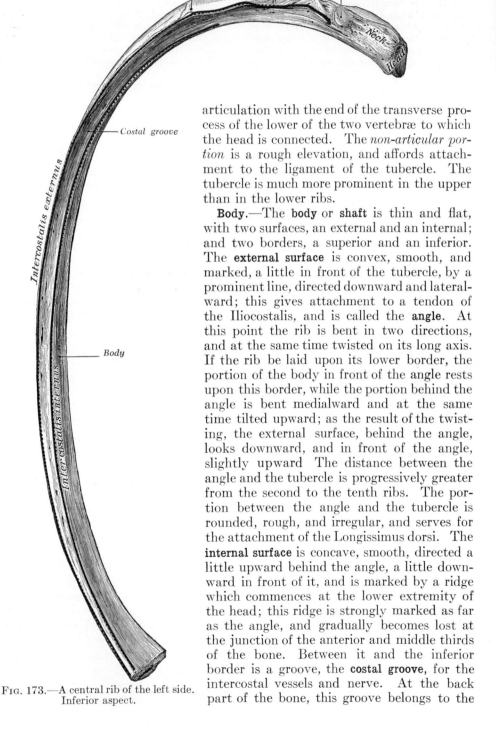

Non-articular part of tubercle

Angle

Articular part of tubercle

Neck

Head

Costal groove

Intercostalis externus

Intercostalis internus

Body

FIG. 173.—A central rib of the left side. Inferior aspect.

articulation with the end of the transverse process of the lower of the two vertebræ to which the head is connected. The *non-articular portion* is a rough elevation, and affords attachment to the ligament of the tubercle. The tubercle is much more prominent in the upper than in the lower ribs.

Body.—The **body** or **shaft** is thin and flat, with two surfaces, an external and an internal; and two borders, a superior and an inferior. The **external surface** is convex, smooth, and marked, a little in front of the tubercle, by a prominent line, directed downward and lateralward; this gives attachment to a tendon of the Iliocostalis, and is called the **angle**. At this point the rib is bent in two directions, and at the same time twisted on its long axis. If the rib be laid upon its lower border, the portion of the body in front of the angle rests upon this border, while the portion behind the angle is bent medialward and at the same time tilted upward; as the result of the twisting, the external surface, behind the angle, looks downward, and in front of the angle, slightly upward The distance between the angle and the tubercle is progressively greater from the second to the tenth ribs. The portion between the angle and the tubercle is rounded, rough, and irregular, and serves for the attachment of the Longissimus dorsi. The **internal surface** is concave, smooth, directed a little upward behind the angle, a little downward in front of it, and is marked by a ridge which commences at the lower extremity of the head; this ridge is strongly marked as far as the angle, and gradually becomes lost at the junction of the anterior and middle thirds of the bone. Between it and the inferior border is a groove, the **costal groove**, for the intercostal vessels and nerve. At the back part of the bone, this groove belongs to the inferior border, but just in front of the angle, where it is deepest and broadest, it is on the internal surface.   The superior edge of the groove is rounded and serves for the attachment of an Intercostalis internus; the inferior edge corresponds to the lower margin of the rib, and gives attachment to an Intercostalis externus. Within the groove are seen the orifices of numerous small foramina for nutrient vessels which traverse the shaft obliquely from before backward.   The **superior**

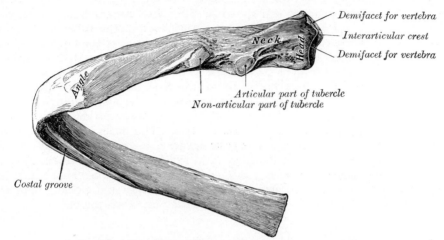

FIG. 174.—A central rib of the left side, viewed from behind.

FIG. 175.

FIG. 176

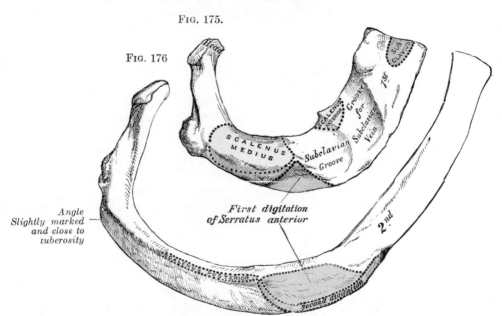

FIGS. 175 and 176.—Peculiar ribs.

border, thick and rounded, is marked by an external and an internal lip, more distinct behind than in front, which serve for the attachment of Intercostales externus and internus.   The **inferior border** is thin, and has attached to it an Intercostalis externus.

Anterior Extremity.—The **anterior** or **sternal extremity** is flattened, and presents a porous, oval, concave depression, into which the costal cartilage is received.

Peculiar Ribs.—The first, second, tenth, eleventh, and twelfth ribs present certain variations from the common characteristics described above, and require special consideration.

First Rib.—The first rib (Fig. 175) is the most curved and usually the shortest of all the ribs; it is broad and flat, its surfaces looking upward and downward, and its borders inward and outward. The **head** is small, rounded, and possesses only a single articular facet, for articulation with the body of the first thoracic vertebra. The **neck** is narrow and rounded. The **tubercle**, thick and prominent, is placed on the outer border. There is *no angle*, but at the tubercle the rib is slightly bent, with the convexity upward, so that the head of the bone is directed downward. The **upper surface** of the body is marked by two shallow grooves, separated from each other by a slight ridge prolonged internally into a tubercle, the **scalene tubercle**, for the attachment of the Scalenus anterior; the anterior groove transmits the subclavian vein, the posterior the subclavian artery and the lowest trunk of the brachial plexus. Behind the posterior groove is a rough area for the attachment of the Scalenus medius. The **under surface** is smooth, and destitute of a costal groove. The **outer border** is convex, thick, and rounded, and at its posterior part gives attachment to the first digitation of the Serratus anterior; the **inner border** is concave, thin, and sharp, and marked about its center by the scalene tubercle. The **anterior extremity** is larger and thicker than that of any of the other ribs and gives attachment to the Subclavius muscle.

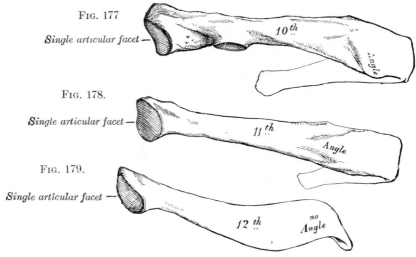

FIG. 177

Single articular facet

FIG. 178.

Single articular facet

FIG. 179.

Single articular facet

FIGS. 177 to 179.—Peculiar ribs.

Second Rib.—The second rib (Fig. 176) is much longer than the first, but has a very similar curvature. The non-articular portion of the **tubercle** is occasionally only feebly marked. The **angle** is slight, and situated close to the tubercle. The **body** is not twisted, so that both ends touch any plane surface upon which it may be laid; but there is a bend, with its convexity upward, similar to, though smaller than that found in the first rib. The body is not flattened horizontally like that of the first rib. Its **external surface** is convex, and looks upward and a little outward; near the middle of it is a rough eminence for the origin of the lower part of the first and the whole of the second digitation of the Serratus anterior; behind and above this is attached the Scalenus posterior. The **internal surface**, smooth, and concave, is directed downward and a little inward: on its posterior part there is a short costal groove.

Tenth Rib.—The tenth rib (Fig. 177) has only a single articular facet on its head.

Eleventh and Twelfth Ribs.—The eleventh and twelfth ribs (Figs. 178 and 179) have each a single articular facet on the head, which is of rather large size; they have *no necks or tubercles*, and are pointed at their anterior ends. The eleventh has a slight angle and a shallow costal groove. The twelfth has neither; it is much shorter than the eleventh, and its head is inclined slightly downward. Sometimes the twelfth rib is even shorter than the first.

Structure.—The ribs consist of highly vascular cancellous tissue, enclosed in a thin layer of compact bone.

Ossification.—Each rib, with the exception of the last two, is ossified from *four* centers; a primary center for the body, and three epiphysial centers, one for the head and one each for the articular and non-articular parts of the tubercle. The eleventh and twelfth ribs have each only *two* centers, those for the tubercles being wanting. Ossification begins near the angle toward the end of the second month of fetal life, and is seen first in the sixth and seventh ribs. The epiphyses for the head and tubercle make their appearance between the sixteenth and twentieth years, and are united to the body about the twenty-fifth year.

The Costal Cartilages (Cartilagines Costales).

The **costal cartilages** (Fig. 168) are bars of hyaline cartilage which serve to prolong the ribs forward and contribute very materially to the elasticity of the walls of the thorax. The first seven pairs are connected with the sternum; the next three are each articulated with the lower border of the cartilage of the preceding rib; the last two have pointed extremities, which end in the wall of the abdomen. Like the ribs, the costal cartilages vary in their length, breadth, and direction. They increase in length from the first to the seventh, then gradually decrease to the twelfth. Their breadth, as well as that of the intervals between them, diminishes from the first to the last. They are broad at their attachments to the ribs, and taper toward their sternal extremities, excepting the first two, which are of the same breadth throughout, and the sixth, seventh, and eighth, which are enlarged where their margins are in contact. They also vary in direction: the first descends a little, the second is horizontal, the third ascends slightly, while the others are angular, following the course of the ribs for a short distance, and then ascending to the sternum or preceding cartilage. Each costal cartilage presents two surfaces, two borders, and two extremities.

Surfaces.—The **anterior surface** is convex, and looks forward and upward: that of the first gives attachment to the costoclavicular ligament and the Subclavius muscle; those of the first six or seven at their sternal ends, to the Pectoralis major. The others are covered by, and give partial attachment to, some of the flat muscles of the abdomen. The **posterior surface** is concave, and directed backward and downward; that of the first gives attachment to the Sternothyroideus, those of the third to the sixth inclusive to the Transversus thoracis, and the six or seven inferior ones to the Transversus abdominis and the diaphragm.

Borders.—Of the two borders the **superior** is concave, the **inferior** convex; they afford attachment to the Intercostales interni: the upper border of the sixth gives attachment also to the Pectoralis major. The inferior borders of the sixth, seventh, eighth, and ninth cartilages present heel-like projections at the points of greatest convexity. These projections carry smooth oblong facets which articulate respectively with facets on slight projections from the upper borders of the seventh, eighth, ninth, and tenth cartilages.

Extremities.—The **lateral end** of each cartilage is continuous with the osseous tissue of the rib to which it belongs. The **medial end** of the first is continuous with the sternum; the medial ends of the six succeeding ones are rounded and are received into shallow concavities on the lateral margins of the sternum. The medial ends of the eighth, ninth, and tenth costal cartilages are pointed, and are connected each with the cartilage immediately above. Those of the eleventh and twelfth are pointed and free. In old age the costal cartilages are prone to undergo superficial ossification.

Cervical ribs derived from the seventh cervical vertebra (page 121) are of not infrequent occurrence, and are important clinically because they may give rise to obscure nervous or vascular symptoms. The cervical rib may be a mere epiphysis articulating only with the transverse process of the vertebra, but more commonly it consists of a defined head, neck, and tubercle, with or without a body. It extends lateralward, or forward and lateralward, into the posterior triangle of the neck, where it may terminate in a free end or may join the first thoracic rib, the first costal cartilage, or the sternum. It varies much in shape, size, direction, and mobility. If it reach far enough forward, part of the brachial plexus and the subclavian artery and vein cross over it, and are apt to suffer compression in so doing. Pressure on the artery may obstruct the circulation so much that arterial thrombosis results, causing gangrene of the finger tips. Pressure on the nerves is commoner, and affects the eighth cervical and first thoracic nerves, causing paralysis of the muscles they supply, and neuralgic pains and paresthesia in the area of skin to which they are distributed: no oculopupillary changes are to be found.

The *thorax* is frequently found to be altered in shape in certain diseases.

In *rickets*, the ends of the ribs, where they join the costal cartilages, become enlarged, giving rise to the so-called "rickety rosary," which in mild cases is only found on the internal surface of the thorax. Lateral to these enlargements the softened ribs sink in, so as to present a groove passing downward and lateralward on either side of the sternum. This bone is forced forward by the bending of the ribs, and the antero-posterior diameter of the chest is increased. The ribs affected are the second to the eighth, the lower ones being prevented from falling in by the presence of the liver, stomach, and spleen; and when the abdomen is distended, as it often is in rickets, the lower ribs may be pushed outward, causing a transverse groove (Harrison's sulcus) just above the costal arch. This deformity or forward projection of the sternum, often asymmetrical, is known as *pigeon breast*, and may be taken as evidence of active or old rickets except in cases of primary spinal curvature. In many instances it is associated in children with obstruction in the upper air passages, due to enlarged tonsils or adenoid growths. In some rickety children or adults, and also in others who give no history or further evidence of having had rickets, an opposite condition obtains. The lower part of the sternum and often the xiphoid process as well are deeply depressed backward, producing an oval hollow in the lower sternal and upper epigastric regions. This is known as *funnel breast* (German, *Trichterbrust*); it never appears to produce the least disturbance of any of the vital functions. The *phthisical chest* is often long and narrow, and with great obliquity of the ribs and projection of the scapulæ. In *pulmonary emphysema* the chest is enlarged in all its diameters, and presents on section an almost circular outline. It has received the name of the *barrel-shaped chest*. In severe cases of *lateral curvature of the vertebral column* the thorax becomes much distorted. In consequence of the rotation of the bodies of the vertebræ which takes place in this disease, the ribs opposite the convexity of the dorsal curve become extremely convex behind, being thrown out and bulging, and at the same time flattened in front, so that the two ends of the same rib are almost parallel. Coincidently with this the ribs on the opposite side, on the concavity of the curve, are sunk and depressed behind, and bulging and convex in front.

THE SKULL.

The **skull** is supported on the summit of the vertebral column, and is of an oval shape, wider behind than in front. It is composed of a series of flattened or irregular bones which, with one exception (the mandible), are immovably jointed together. It is divisible into two parts: (1) the **cranium**, which lodges and protects the brain, consists of eight bones, and (2) the **skeleton of the face,** of fourteen.

THE EXTERIOR OF THE SKULL.

Norma Verticalis.—When viewed from above the outline presented varies greatly in different skulls; in some it is more or less oval, in others more nearly circular. The surface is traversed by three sutures, viz.: (1) the **coronal sutures,** nearly transverse in direction, between the frontal and parietals; (2) the **sagittal sutures,** medially placed, between the parietal bones, and deeply serrated in its anterior two-thirds; and (3) the upper part of the **lambdoidal suture,** between the parietals and the occipital. The point of junction of the sagittal and coronal suture is named the **bregma,** that of the sagittal and lambdoid sutures, the **lambda;** they indicate respectively the positions of the anterior and posterior fontanelles in the fetal skull. On either side of the sagittal suture are the **parietal eminence** and **parietal foramen**—the latter, however, is frequently absent on one or both sides. The skull is often somewhat flattened in the neighborhood of the parietal foramina, and the term **obelion** is applied to that point of the sagittal suture which is on a level with the foramina. In front is the **glabella,** and on its lateral aspects are the **superciliary arches,** and above these the **frontal eminences.** Immediately above the glabella may be seen the remains of the **frontal suture**; in a small percentage of skulls this suture persists and extends along the middle line to the bregma. Passing backward and upward from the zygomatic processes of the frontal bone are the **temporal lines,** which mark the upper limits of the temporal fossæ. The zygomatic arches may or may not be seen projecting beyond the anterior portions of these lines.

Norma Basalis (Fig. 180).—The inferior surface of the base of the skull, exclusive of the mandible, is bounded in front by the incisor teeth in the maxillæ; behind, by the superior nuchal lines of the occipital; and laterally by the alveolar arch, the lower border of the zygomatic bone, the zygomatic arch and an imaginary line extending from it to the mastoid process and extremity of the superior nuchal line of the occipital. It is formed by the palatine processes of the maxillæ and palatine bones, the vomer, the pterygoid processes, the under surfaces of the great wings, spinous processes, and part of the body of the sphenoid, the under surfaces of the squamæ and mastoid and petrous portions of the temporals, and the under surface of the occipital bone. The anterior part or hard palate projects below the level of the rest of the surface, and is bounded in front and laterally by the alveolar arch containing the sixteen teeth of the maxillæ. Immediately behind the incisor teeth is the **incisive foramen.** In this foramen are two lateral apertures, the openings of the **incisive canals** (*foramina of Stenson*) which transmit the anterior branches of the descending palatine vessels, and the nasopalatine nerves. Occasionally two additional canals are present in the incisive foramen; they are termed the **foramina of Scarpa** and are situated in the middle line; when present they transmit the nasopalatine nerves. The vault of the hard palate is concave, uneven, perforated by numerous foramina, marked by depressions for the palatine glands, and traversed by a crucial suture formed by the junction of the four bones of which it is composed. In the young skull a suture may be seen extending on either side from the incisive foramen to the interval between the lateral incisor and canine teeth, and marking off the os incisivum or premaxillary bone. At either posterior angle of the hard palate is the **greater palatine foramen,** for the transmission of the descending palatine vessels and anterior palatine nerve; and running forward and medialward from it a groove, for the same vessels and nerve. Behind the posterior palatine foramen is the **pyramidal process of the palatine bone,** perforated by one or more **lesser palatine foramina,** and marked by the commencement of a transverse ridge, for the attachment of the tendinous expansion of the Tensor veli palatini. Projecting backward from the center of the posterior border of the hard palate is the **posterior nasal spine,** for the attachment of the Musculus uvulæ. Behind and above the hard palate are the **choanæ,** measuring about 2.5 cm. in their vertical and 1.25 cm. in their transverse diameters. They are separated from one another by the vomer, and each is bounded above by the body of the sphenoid, below by the horizontal part of the palatine bone, and laterally by the medial pterygoid plate of the sphenoid. At the superior border of the vomer may be seen the expanded alæ of this bone, receiving between them the rostrum of the sphenoid. Near the lateral margins of the alæ of the vomer, at the roots of the pterygoid processes, are the **pharyngeal canals.** The pterygoid process presents near its base the **pterygoid canal,** for the transmission of a nerve and artery. The medial pterygoid plate is long and narrow; on the lateral side of its base is the **scaphoid fossa,** for the origin of the Tensor veli palatini, and at its lower extremity the **hamulus,** around which the tendon of this muscle turns. The lateral pterygoid plate is broad; its lateral surface forms the medial boundary of the infratemporal fossa, and affords attachment to the Pterygoideus externus.

Behind the nasal cavities is the basilar portion of the occipital bone, presenting near its center the **pharyngeal tubercle** for the attachment of the fibrous raphé of the pharynx, with depressions on either side for the insertions of the Rectus capitis anterior and Longus capitis. At the base of the lateral pterygoid plate is the **foramen ovale,** for the transmission of the mandibular nerve, the accessory

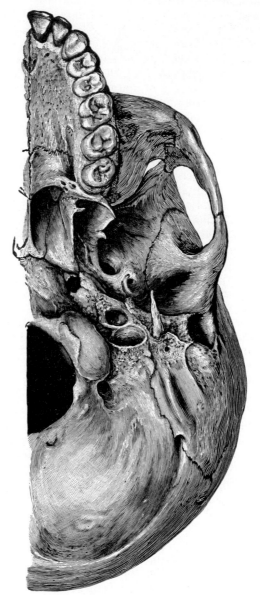

FIG. 180.—The external surface of the left half of the base of the skull. (Norma basalis.)

meningeal artery, and sometimes the lesser superficial petrosal nerve; behind this are the **foramen spinosum** which transmits the middle meningeal vessels, and the prominent **spina angularis** (*sphenoidal spine*), which gives attachment to the spheno-mandibular ligament and the Tensor veli palatini. Lateral to the spina angularis is the **mandibular fossa,** divided into two parts by the **petrotympanic fissure;** the anterior portion, concave, smooth, bounded in front by the **articular tubercle,** serves for the articulation of the condyle of the mandible; the posterior portion, rough and bounded behind by the tympanic part of the temporal, is sometimes occupied by a part of the parotid gland. Emerging from between the laminæ of the vaginal process of the tympanic part is the **styloid process**; and at the base of this process is the **stylomastoid foramen**, for the exit of the facial nerve, and

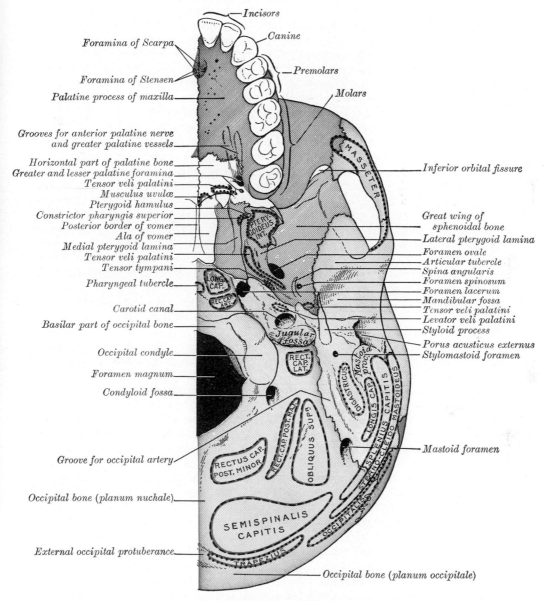

Fig. 181.—Key to Fig. 180.

entrance of the stylomastoid artery. Lateral to the stylomastoid foramen, between the tympanic part and the mastoid process, is the **tympanomastoid fissure,** for the auricular branch of the vagus. Upon the medial side of the mastoid process is the **mastoid notch** for the posterior belly of the Digastricus, and medial to the notch, the **occipital groove** for the occipital artery. At the base of the medial pterygoid

11

plate is a large and somewhat triangular aperture, the **foramen lacerum,** bounded in front by the great wing of the sphenoid, behind by the apex of the petrous portion of the temporal bone and medially by the body of the sphenoid and basilar portion of the occipital bone; it presents in front the posterior orifice of the **ptery-goid canal;** behind, the aperture of the **carotid canal.** The lower part of this opening is filled up in the fresh state by a fibrocartilaginous plate, across the upper or cerebral surface of which the internal carotid artery passes. Lateral to this aperture is a groove, the **sulcus tubæ auditivæ,** between the petrous part of the temporal and the great wing of the sphenoid. This sulcus is directed lateralward and backward from the root of the medial pterygoid plate and lodges the cartilaginous part of the auditory tube; it is continuous behind with the canal in the temporal bone which forms the bony part of the same tube. At the bottom of this sulcus is a narrow cleft, the **petrosphenoidal fissure,** which is occupied, in the fresh condition, by a plate of cartilage. Behind this fissure is the under surface of the petrous portion of the temporal bone, presenting, near its apex, the quadrilateral rough surface, part of which affords attachment to the Levator veli palatini; lateral to this surface is the orifice of the **carotid canal,** and medial to it, the depression leading to the **aquæductus cochleæ,** the former transmitting the internal carotid artery and the carotid plexus of the sympathetic, the latter serving for the passage of a vein from the cochlea. Behind the carotid canal is the **jugular foramen,** a large aperture, formed in front by the petrous portion of the temporal, and behind by the occipital; it is generally larger on the right than on the left side, and may be subdivided into three compartments. The anterior compartment transmits the inferior petrosal sinus; the intermediate, the glossopharyngeal, vagus, and accessory nerves; the posterior, the transverse sinus and some meningeal branches from the occipital and ascending pharyngeal arteries. On the ridge of bone dividing the carotid canal from the jugular foramen is the **inferior tympanic canaliculus** for the transmission of the tympanic branch of the glossopharyngeal nerve; and on the wall of the jugular foramen, near the root of the styloid process, is the **mastoid canaliculus** for the passage of the auricular branch of the vagus nerve. Extending forward from the jugular foramen to the foramen lacerum is the **petroöccipital fissure** occupied, in the fresh state, by a plate of cartilage. Behind the basilar portion of the occipital bone is the **foramen magnum,** bounded laterally by the occipital condyles, the medial sides of which are rough for the attachment of the alar ligaments. Lateral to each condyle is the **jugular process** which gives attachment to the Rectus capitis lateralis muscle and the lateral atlantoöccipital ligament. The foramen magnum transmits the medulla oblongata and its membranes, the accessory nerves, the vertebral arteries, the anterior and posterior spinal arteries, and the ligaments connecting the occipital bone with the axis. The mid-points on the anterior and posterior margins of the foramen magnum are respectively termed the **basion** and the **opisthion.** In the front of each condyle is the canal for the passage of the hypoglossal nerve and a meningeal artery. Behind each condyle is the **condyloid fossa,** perforated on one or both sides by the condyloid canal, for the transmission of a vein from the transverse sinus. Behind the foramen magnum is the **median nuchal line** ending above at the **external occipital protuberance,** while on either side are the **superior** and **inferior nuchal lines;** these, as well as the surfaces of bone between them, are rough for the attachment of the muscles which are enumerated on Figs. 181 and 203.

Norma Lateralis (Fig. 182).—When viewed from the side the skull is seen to consist of the cranium above and behind, and of the face below and in front. The cranium is somewhat ovoid in shape, but its contour varies in different cases and depends largely on the length and height of the skull and on the degree of promi-nence of the superciliary arches and frontal eminences. Entering into its formation are the frontal, the parietal, the occipital, the temporal, and the great wing of the sphenoid. These bones are joined to one another and to the zygomatic by the following **sutures**: the **zygomaticotemporal** between the zygomatic process of the temporal and the temporal process of the zygomatic; the **zygomaticofrontal** uniting the zygomatic bone with the zygomatic process of the frontal; the sutures surrounding the great wing of the sphenoid, viz., the **sphenozygomatic** in front, the **sphenofrontal** and **sphenoparietal** above, and the **sphenosquamosal** behind. The sphenoparietal suture varies in length in different skulls, and is absent in those cases where the frontal articulates with the temporal squama. The point corresponding with the posterior end of the sphenoparietal suture is named the **pterion**; it is situated about 3 cm. behind, and a little above the level of the zygomatic process of the frontal bone.

The **squamosal suture** arches backward from the pterion and connects the temporal squama with the lower border of the parietal: this suture is continuous behind with the short, nearly horizontal **parietomastoid suture**, which unites the mastoid process of the temporal with the region of the mastoid angle of the parietal. Extending from above downward and forward across the cranium are the **coronal** and **lambdoidal sutures**; the former connects the parietals with the frontal, the latter, the parietals with the occipital. The lambdoidal suture is continuous below with the **occipitomastoid suture** between the occipital and the mastoid portion of the temporal. In or near the last suture is the **mastoid foramen**, for the transmission of an emissary vein. The point of meeting of the parietomastoid, occipitomastoid, and lambdoidal sutures is known as the **asterion**. Immediately above the orbital margin is the **superciliary arch**, and, at a higher level, the **frontal eminence**. Near the center of the parietal bone is the **parietal eminence**. Posteriorly is the **external occipital protuberance**, from which the superior nuchal line may be followed forward to the mastoid process. Arching across the side of the cranium are the **temporal lines**, which mark the upper limit of the temporal fossa.

The Temporal Fossa (*fossa temporalis*).—The temporal fossa is bounded above and behind by the temporal lines, which extend from the zygomatic process of the frontal bone upward and backward across the frontal and parietal bones, and then curve downward and forward to become continuous with the supramastoid crest and the posterior root of the zygomatic arch. The point where the upper temporal line cuts the coronal suture is named the **stephanion**. The temporal fossa is bounded in *front* by the frontal and zygomatic bones, and opening on the back of the latter is the **zygomaticotemporal foramen**. *Laterally* the fossa is limited by the zygomatic arch, formed by the zygomatic and temporal bones; *below*, it is separated from the infratemporal fossa by the **infratemporal crest** on the great wing of the sphenoid, and by a ridge, continuous with this crest, which is carried backward across the temporal squama to the anterior root of the zygomatic process. In front and below, the fossa communicates with the orbital cavity through the **inferior orbital** or **sphenomaxillary fissure**. The floor of the fossa is deeply concave in front and convex behind, and is formed by the zygomatic, frontal, parietal, sphenoid, and temporal bones. It is traversed by vascular furrows; one, usually well-marked, runs upward above and in front of the external acoustic meatus, and lodges the middle temporal artery. Two others, frequently indistinct, may be observed on the anterior part of the floor, and are for the anterior and posterior deep temporal arteries. The temporal fossa contains the Temporalis muscle and its vessels and nerves, together with the zygomaticotemporal nerve.

The **zygomatic arch** is formed by the zygomatic process of the temporal and the temporal process of the zygomatic, the two being united by an oblique suture; the tendon of the Temporalis passes medial to the arch to gain insertion into the coronoid process of the mandible. The zygomatic process of the temporal arises by two roots, an anterior, directed inward in front of the mandibular fossa, where it expands to form the articular tubercle, and a posterior, which runs backward above the external acoustic meatus and is continuous with the supramastoid crest. The upper border of the arch gives attachment to the temporal fascia; the lower border and medial surface give origin to the Masseter.

Below the posterior root of the zygomatic arch is the elliptical orifice of the **external acoustic meatus**, bounded in front, below, and behind by the tympanic part of the temporal bone; to its outer margin the cartilaginous segment of the external acoustic meatus is attached. The small triangular area between the posterior root of the zygomatic arch and the postero-superior part of the orifice is termed the **suprameatal triangle**, on the anterior border of which a small spinous process, the **suprameatal spine**, is sometimes seen. Between the tympanic part and the articular tubercle is the **mandibular fossa**, divided into two parts by the

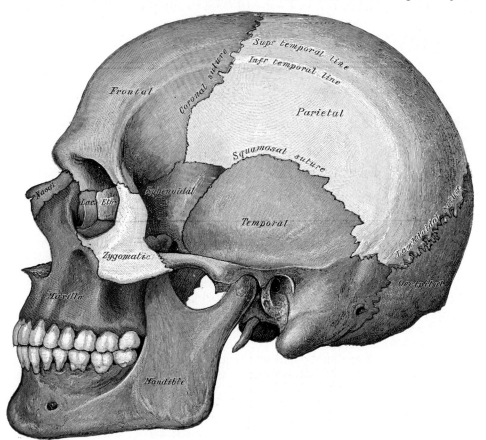

FIG. 182.—Side view of the skull.

petrotympanic fissure. The anterior and larger part of the fossa articulates with the condyle of the mandible and is limited behind by the external acoustic meatus: the posterior part sometimes lodges a portion of the parotid gland. The styloid process extends downward and forward for a variable distance from the lower part of the tympanic part, and gives attachment to the Styloglossus, Stylohyoideus, and Stylopharyngeus, and to the stylohyoid and stylomandibular ligaments. Projecting downward behind the external acoustic meatus is the mastoid process, to the outer surface of which the Sternocleidomastoideus, Splenius capitis, and Longissimus capitis are attached.

The Infratemporal Fossa (*fossa infratemporalis; zygomatic fossa*) (Fig. 183).—The infratemporal fossa is an irregularly shaped cavity, situated below and medial to the

zygomatic arch. It is bounded, in *front*, by the infratemporal surface of the maxilla and the ridge which descends from its zygomatic process; *behind*, by the articular tubercle of the temporal and the spina angularis of the sphenoid; *above*, by the great wing of the sphenoid below the infratemporal crest, and by the under surface by the temporal squama; *below*, by the alveolar border of the maxilla; *medially*, of the lateral pterygoid plate. It contains the lower part of the Temporalis, the Pterygoidei internus and externus, the internal maxillary vessels, and the mandibular and maxillary nerves. The **foramen ovale** and **foramen spinosum** open on its roof, and the **alveolar canals** on its anterior wall. At its upper and medial part are two fissures, which meet at right angles, the horizontal limb being named the inferior orbital, and the vertical one the pterygomaxillary.

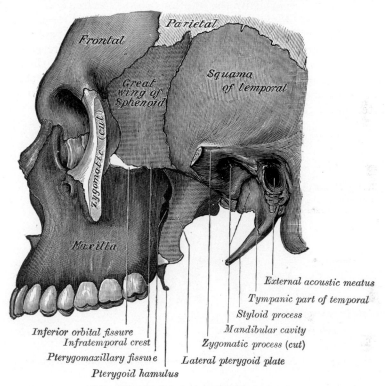

Fig. 183.—Left infratemporal fossa.

The **inferior orbital fissure** (*fissura orbitalis inferior; sphenomaxillary fissure*), horizontal in direction, opens into the lateral and back part of the orbit. It is bounded *above* by the lower border of the orbital surface of the great wing of the sphenoid; *below*, by the lateral border of the orbital surface of the maxilla and the orbital process of the palatine bone; *laterally*, by a small part of the zygomatic bone:[1] *medially*, it joins at right angles with the pterygomaxillary fissure. Through the inferior orbital fissure the orbit communicates with the temporal, infratemporal, and pterygopalatine fossæ; the fissure transmits the maxillary nerve and its zygomatic branch, the infraorbital vessels, the ascending branches from the sphenopalatine ganglion, and a vein which connects the inferior ophthalmic vein with the pterygoid venous plexus.

The **pterygomaxillary fissure** is vertical, and descends at right angles from the medial end of the preceding; it is a triangular interval, formed by the diver-

[1] Occasionally the maxilla and the sphenoid articulate with each other at the anterior extremity of this fissure; the zygomatic is then excluded from it.

gence of the maxilla from the pterygoid process of the sphenoid. It connects the infratemporal with the pterygopalatine fossa, and transmits the terminal part of the internal maxillary artery and veins.

The Pterygopalatine Fossa (*fossa pterygopalatina; sphenomaxillary fossa*).—The pterygopalatine fossa is a small, triangular space at the angle of junction of the inferior orbital and pterygomaxillary fissures, and placed beneath the apex of the orbit. It is bounded *above* by the under surface of the body of the sphenoid and by the orbital process of the palatine bone; in *front*, by the infratemporal surface of the maxilla; *behind*, by the base of the pterygoid process and lower part of the anterior surface of the great wing of the sphenoid; *medially*, by the vertical part of the palatine bone with its orbital and sphenoidal processes. This fossa communicates with the orbit by the inferior orbital fissure, with the nasal cavity by the sphenopalatine foramen, and with the infratemporal fossa by the pterygomaxillary fissure. Five foramina open into it. Of these, three are on the posterior wall, viz., the **foramen rotundum**, the **pterygoid canal**, and the **pharyngeal canal**, in this order downward and medialward. On the medial wall is the **sphenopalatine foramen,** and below is the superior orifice of the **pterygopalatine canal.** The fossa contains the maxillary nerve, the sphenopalatine ganglion, and the terminal part of the internal maxillary artery.

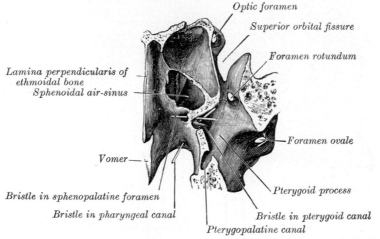

Optic foramen

Superior orbital fissure

Foramen rotundum

Lamina perpendicularis of ethmoidal bone
Sphenoidal air-sinus

Foramen ovale

Vomer

Pterygoid process

Bristle in sphenopalatine foramen

Bristle in pharyngeal canal

Bristle in pterygoid canal

Pterygopalatine canal

Fig. 184.—A section showing the posterior wall of the pterygopalatine fossa.

Norma Occipitalis.—When viewed from behind the cranium presents a more or less circular outline. In the middle line is the posterior part of the **sagittal suture** connecting the parietal bones; extending downward and lateralward from the hinder end of the sagittal suture is the deeply serrated **lambdoidal suture** joining the parietals to the occipital and continuous below with the **parietomastoid** and **occipitomastoid sutures**; it frequently contains one or more sutural bones. Near the middle of the occipital squama is the **external occipital protuberance** or **inion**, and extending lateralward from it on either side is the superior nuchal line, and above this the faintly marked highest nuchal line. The part of the squama above the inion and highest lines is named the **planum occipitale**, and is covered by the Occipitalis muscle; the part below is termed the **planum nuchale**, and is divided by the median nuchal line which runs downward and forward from the inion to the foramen magnum; this ridge gives attachment to the ligamentum nuchæ. The muscles attached to the planum nuchale are enumerated on p. 187. Below and in front are the mastoid processes, convex laterally and grooved medially by the mastoid notches. In or near the occipitomastoid suture is the **mastoid foramen** for the passage of the mastoid emissary vein.

Norma Frontalis (Fig. 186).—When viewed from the front the skull exhibits a somewhat oval outline, limited *above* by the frontal bone, *below* by the body of the mandible, and *laterally* by the zygomatic bones and the mandibular rami. The upper part, formed by the frontal squama, is smooth and convex. The lower part, made up of the bones of the face, is irregular; it is excavated laterally by the orbital cavities, and presents in the middle line the **anterior nasal aperture** leading to the nasal cavities, and below this the transverse slit between the upper and lower dental arcades. *Above*, the **frontal eminences** stand out more or less prominently, and beneath these are the **superciliary arches**, joined to one another in the middle by the **glabella**. On and above the glabella a trace of the **frontal suture** sometimes persists; beneath it is the frontonasal suture, the mid-point of which is termed the

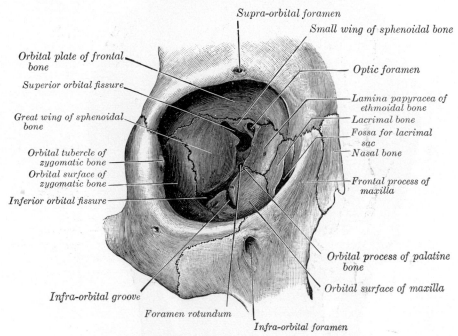

Fig. 185.—The right orbital cavity, anterior aspect.

nasion. Behind and below the frontonasal suture the frontal articulates with the frontal process of the maxilla and with the lacrimal. Arching transversely below the superciliary arches is the upper part of the margin of the orbit, thin and prominent in its lateral two-thirds, rounded in its medial third, and presenting, at the junction of these two portions, the **supraorbital notch** or **foramen** for the supraorbital nerve and vessels. The supraorbital margin ends laterally in the zygomatic process which articulates with the zygomatic bone, and from it the temporal line extends upward and backward. Below the frontonasal suture is the bridge of the nose, convex from side to side, concavo-convex from above downward, and formed by the two nasal bones supported in the middle line by the perpendicular plate of the ethmoid, and laterally by the frontal processes of the maxillæ which are prolonged upward between the nasal and lacrimal bones and form the lower and medial part of the circumference of each orbit. Below the nasal bones and between the maxillæ is the anterior aperture of the nose, pyriform in shape, with the narrow end directed upward. Laterally this opening is bounded by sharp margins, to which the lateral and alar cartilages of the nose are attached; *below*, the margins are thicker and curve medialward and forward to end in the **anterior nasal spine.** On looking into the nasal cavity, the bony septum which separates the nasal cavities presents, in front, a large triangular deficiency; this, in the fresh state, is filled up by the cartilage of the nasal septum; on the lateral wall of each nasal cavity the anterior part of the inferior nasal concha is visible. Below and lateral to the anterior nasal aperture are the anterior surfaces of the maxillæ, each perforated, near the lower margin of the orbit, by the **infraorbital foramen** for the passage of the infraorbital nerve and vessels. Below and medial to this foramen is the canine eminence separating the incisive from the canine fossa. Beneath these fossæ are the alveolar processes of the maxillæ containing the upper teeth,

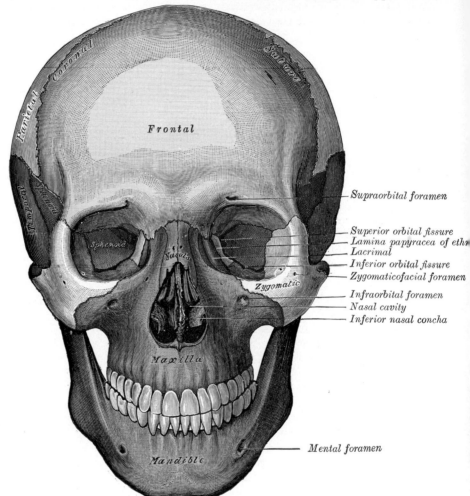

FIG. 186.—The skull from the front.

which overlap the teeth of the mandible in front. The zygomatic bone on either side forms the prominence of the cheek, the lower and lateral portion of the orbital cavity, and the anterior part of the zygomatic arch. It articulates medially with the maxilla, behind with the zygomatic process of the temporal, and above with the great wing of the sphenoid and the zygomatic process of the frontal; it is perforated by the **zygomaticofacial foramen** for the passage of the zygomaticofacial nerve. On the body of the mandible is a median ridge, indicating the position of the symphysis; this ridge divides below to enclose the mental protuberance, the lateral angles of which constitute the mental tubercles. Below the incisor teeth is the **incisive fossa,** and beneath the second premolar tooth the **mental foramen** which transmits the mental nerve and vessels. The oblique line runs upward from the mental tubercle and is continuous behind with the anterior border of the ramus. The posterior border of the ramus runs downward and forward from the condyle to the angle, which is frequently more or less everted.

The Orbits (*orbitæ*) (Fig. 185).—The orbits are two quadrilateral pyramidal cavities, situated at the upper and anterior part of the face, their bases being directed forward and lateralward, and their apices backward and medialward, so that their long axes, if continued backward, would meet over the body of the sphenoid. Each presents for examination a **roof,** a **floor,** a **medial** and a **lateral wall,** a **base,** and an **apex.**

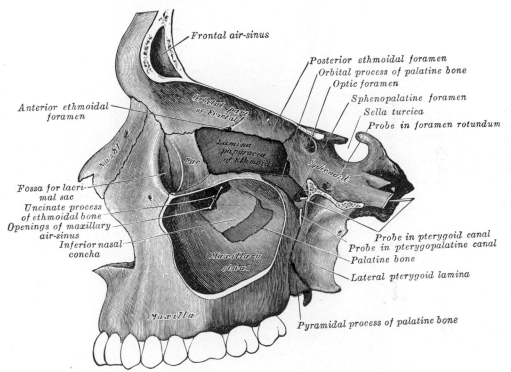

Fig. 187.—Medial wall of left orbit.

The **roof** is concave, directed downward, and slightly forward, and formed in *front* by the orbital plate of the frontal; *behind* by the small wing of the sphenoid. It presents *medially* the **trochlear fovea** for the attachment of the cartilaginous pulley of the Obliquus oculi superior; *laterally,* the **lacrimal fossa** for the lacrimal gland; and *posteriorly,* the suture between the frontal bone and the small wing of the sphenoid.

The **floor** (Fig. 187) is directed upward and lateralward, and is of less extent than the roof; it is formed chiefly by the orbital surface of the maxilla; in *front* and *laterally,* by the orbital process of the zygomatic bone, and *behind* and *medially,* to a small extent, by the orbital process of the palatine. At its medial angle is the upper opening of the nasolacrimal canal, immediately to the lateral side of which is a depression for the origin of the Obliquus oculi inferior. On its lateral part is the suture between the maxilla and zygomatic bone, and at its posterior part that between the maxilla and the orbital process of the palatine. Running forward near the middle of the floor is the **infraorbital groove,** ending in front in the infraorbital canal and transmitting the infraorbital nerve and vessels.

The **medial wall** (Fig. 188) is nearly vertical, and is formed from before backward by the frontal process of the maxilla, the lacrimal, the lamina papyracea of the ethmoid, and a small part of the body of the sphenoid in front of the optic foramen. Sometimes the sphenoidal concha forms a small part of this wall (see page 208). It exhibits three vertical sutures, viz., the lacrimomaxillary, lacrimoethmoidal, and sphenoethmoidal. In front is seen the **lacrimal groove**, which lodges the lacrimal sac, and behind the groove is the **posterior lacrimal crest**, from which the lacrimal part of the Orbicularis oculi arises. At the junction of the medial wall and the roof are the frontomaxillary, frontolacrimal, frontoethmoidal, and

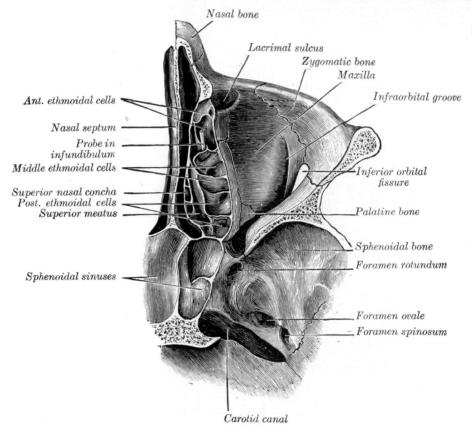

FIG. 188.—A horizontal section through the nasal and orbital cavities. Superior aspect.

sphenofrontal sutures. The point of junction of the anterior border of the lacrimal with the frontal is named the **dacryon**. In the frontoethmoidal suture are the **anterior** and **posterior ethmoidal foramina,** the former transmitting the nasociliary nerve and anterior ethmoidal vessels, the latter the posterior ethmoidal nerve and vessels.

The **lateral wall,** directed medialward and forward, is formed by the orbital process of the zygomatic and the orbital surface of the great wing of the sphenoid; these are united by the sphenozygomatic suture which terminates below at the front end of the inferior orbital fissure. On the orbital process of the zygomatic bone are the orbital tubercle (Whitnall) and the orifices of one or two canals which transmit the branches of the zygomatic nerve. Between the roof and the lateral wall, near the apex of the orbit, is the **superior orbital fissure.** Through this fissure the oculomotor, the trochlear, the ophthalmic division of the trigeminal, and the abducent nerves enter the orbital cavity, also some filaments from the cavernous plexus of the sympathetic and the orbital branches of the middle meningeal artery. Passing backward through the fissure are the ophthalmic vein and the recurrent branch from the lacrimal artery to the dura mater. The lateral wall and the floor are separated posteriorly by the **inferior orbital fissure** which transmits the maxillary nerve and its zygomatic branch, the infraorbital vessels, and the ascending branches from the sphenopalatine ganglion.

The **base** of the orbit, quadrilateral in shape, is formed *above* by the supra-orbital arch of the frontal bone, in which is the **supraorbital notch** or **foramen** for the passage of the supraorbital vessels and nerve; *below* by the zygomatic bone and maxilla, united by the zygomaticomaxillary suture; laterally by the zygomatic bone and the zygomatic process of the frontal joined by the zygomaticofrontal suture; medially by the frontal bone and the frontal process of the maxilla united by the frontomaxillary suture.

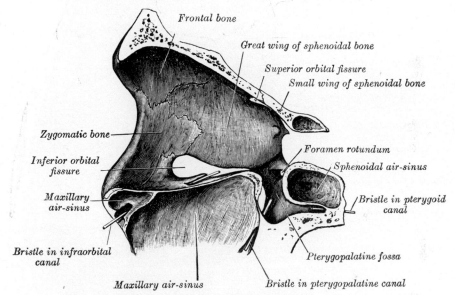

FIG. 189.—The lateral wall of the right orbit.

The **apex**, situated at the back of the orbit, corresponds to the optic foramen a short, cylindrical canal, which transmits the optic nerve and ophthalmic artery.

It will thus be seen that there are nine openings communicating with each orbit, viz., the optic foramen, superior and inferior orbital fissures, supraorbital foramen, infraorbital canal, anterior and posterior ethmoidal foramina, zygomatic foramen, and the canal for the nasolacrimal duct.

THE INTERIOR OF THE SKULL.

Inner Surface of the Skull-cap.—The inner surface of the skull-cap is concave and presents depressions for the convolutions of the cerebrum, together with numerous furrows for the lodgement of branches of the meningeal vessels. Along the middle line is a longitudinal groove, narrow in front, where it commences at the frontal crest, but broader behind; it lodges the superior sagittal sinus, and its margins afford attachment to the falx cerebri. On either side of it are several depressions for the arachnoid granulations, and at its back part, the openings of the **parietal foramina** when these are present. It is crossed, in front, by the **coronal suture,** and behind by the **lambdoidal,** while the **sagittal** lies in the medial plane between the parietal bones.

Upper Surface of the Base of the Skull (Fig. 190).—The upper surface of the
base of the skull or floor of the cranial cavity presents three fossæ, called the **anterior,
middle,** and **posterior cranial fossæ.**

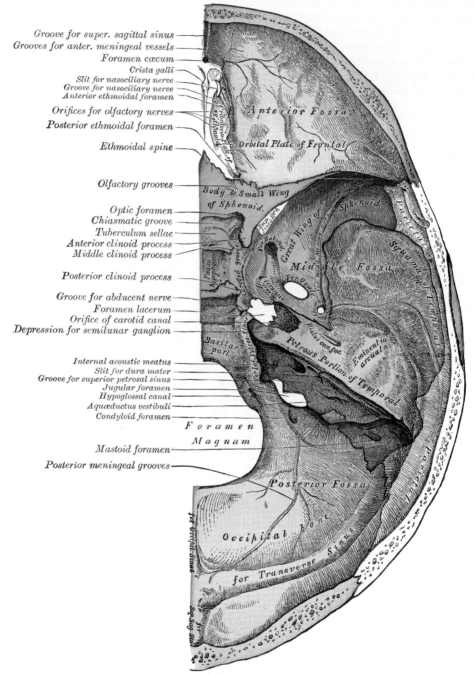

Groove for super. sagittal sinus
Grooves for anter. meningeal vessels
Foramen cæcum
Crista galli
Slit for nasociliary nerve
Groove for nasociliary nerve
Anterior ethmoidal foramen
Orifices for olfactory nerves
Posterior ethmoidal foramen
Ethmoidal spine

Olfactory grooves

Optic foramen
Chiasmatic groove
Tuberculum sellæ
Anterior clinoid process
Middle clinoid process

Posterior clinoid process

Groove for abducent nerve
Foramen lacerum
Orifice of carotid canal
Depression for semilunar ganglion

Internal acoustic meatus
Slit for dura mater
Groove for superior petrosal sinus
Jugular foramen
Hypoglossal canal
Aquæductus vestibuli
Condyloid foramen

Mastoid foramen
Posterior meningeal grooves

Anterior Fossa
Orbital Plate of Frontal
Body & Small Wing of Sphenoid
Great Wing of Sphenoid
Squama of Temporal
Middle Fossa
Eminentia arcuata
Petrous Portion of Temporal
Basilar part
Foramen Magnum
Posterior Fossa
Occipital bone
for Transverse Sinus

Fig. 190.—Base of the skull. Upper surface.

Anterior Fossa (*fossa cranii anterior*).—The floor of the anterior fossa is formed
by the orbital plates of the frontal, the cribriform plate of the ethmoid, and the
small wings and front part of the body of the sphenoid; it is limited behind by the

posterior borders of the small wings of the sphenoid and by the anterior margin of the chiasmatic groove. It is traversed by the **frontoethmoidal, sphenoethmoidal,** and **sphenofrontal sutures.** Its lateral portions roof in the orbital cavities and support the frontal lobes of the cerebrum; they are convex and marked by depressions for the brain convolutions, and grooves for branches of the meningeal vessels. The central portion corresponds with the roof of the nasal cavity, and is markedly depressed on either side of the crista galli. It presents, in and near the median line, from before backward, the commencement of the **frontal crest** for the attachment of the falx cerebri; the **foramen cecum,** between the frontal bone and the crista galli of the ethmoid, which usually transmits a small vein from the nasal cavity to the superior sagittal sinus; behind the foramen cecum, the **crista galli,** the free margin of which affords attachment to the falx cerebri; on either side of the crista galli, the **olfactory groove** formed by the cribriform plate, which supports the olfactory bulb and presents foramina for the transmission of the olfactory

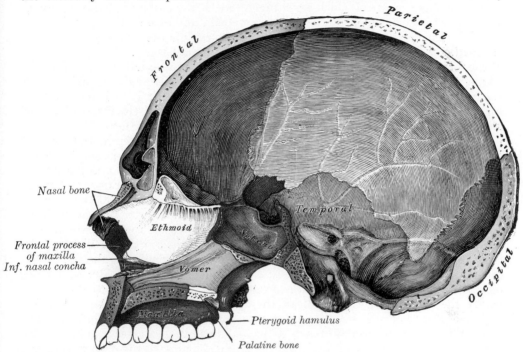

Fig. 191.—Sagittal section of skull.

nerves, and in front a slit-like opening for the nasociliary nerve. Lateral to either olfactory groove are the internal openings of the **anterior** and **posterior ethmoidal foramina;** the anterior, situated about the middle of the lateral margin of the olfactory groove, transmits the anterior ethmoidal vessels and the nasociliary nerve; the nerve runs in a groove along the lateral edge of the cribriform plate to the slit-like opening above mentioned; the posterior ethmoidal foramen opens at the back part of this margin under cover of the projecting lamina of the sphenoid, and transmits the posterior ethmoidal vessels and nerve. Farther back in the middle line is the **ethmoidal spine,** bounded behind by a slight elevation separating two shallow longitudinal grooves which support the olfactory lobes. Behind this is the anterior margin of the chiasmatic groove, running lateralward on either side to the upper margin of the optic foramen.

The Middle Fossa (*fossa cranii media*).—The middle fossa, deeper than the preceding, is narrow in the middle, and wide at the sides of the skull. It is bounded in *front* by the posterior margins of the small wings of the sphenoid, the anterior clinoid processes, and the ridge forming the anterior margin of the chiasmatic groove; *behind*, by the superior angles of the petrous portions of the temporals and the dorsum sellæ; *laterally* by the temporal squamæ, sphenoidal angles of the parietals, and great wings of the sphenoid. It is traversed by the **squamosals, sphenoparietal, sphenosquamosal,** and **sphenopetrosal sutures.**

The middle part of the fossa presents, in *front*, the **chiasmatic groove** and **tuberculum sellæ**; the chiasmatic groove ends on either side at the **optic foramen,** which transmits the optic nerve and ophthalmic artery to the orbital cavity. Behind the optic foramen the **anterior clinoid process** is directed backward and medialward and gives attachment to the tentorium cerebelli. Behind the tuberculum sellæ is a deep depression, the **sella turcica,** containing the **fossa hypophyseos,** which lodges the hypophysis, and presents on its anterior wall the **middle clinoid processes.** The sella turcica is bounded posteriorly by a quadrilateral plate of bone, the **dorsum sellæ,** the upper angles of which are surmounted by the **posterior clinoid processes:** these afford attachment to the tentorium cerebelli, and below each is a notch for the abducent nerve. On either side of the sella turcica is the **carotid groove,** which is broad, shallow, and curved somewhat like the italic letter *f*. It begins behind at the foramen lacerum, and ends on the medial side of the anterior clinoid process, where it is sometimes converted into a foramen (*carotico-clinoid*) by the union of the anterior with the middle clinoid process; posteriorly, it is bounded laterally by the **lingula.** This groove lodges the cavernous sinus and the internal carotid artery, the latter being surrounded by a plexus of sympathetic nerves.

The lateral parts of the middle fossa are of considerable depth, and support the temporal lobes of the brain. They are marked by depressions for the brain convolutions and traversed by furrows for the anterior and posterior branches of the middle meningeal vessels. These furrows begin near the foramen spinosum, and the anterior runs forward and upward to the sphenoidal angle of the parietal, where it is sometimes converted into a bony canal; the posterior runs lateralward and backward across the temporal squama and passes on to the parietal near the middle of its lower border. The following apertures are also to be seen. In front is the **superior orbital fissure,** bounded above by the small wing, below, by the great wing, and medially, by the body of the sphenoid; it is usually completed laterally by the orbital plate of the frontal bone. It transmits to the orbital cavity the oculomotor, the trochlear, the ophthalmic division of the trigeminal, and the abducent nerves, some filaments from the cavernous plexus of the sympathetic, and the orbital branch of the middle meningeal artery; and from the orbital cavity a recurrent branch from the lacrimal artery to the dura mater, and the ophthalmic veins. Behind the medial end of the superior orbital fissure is the **foramen rotundum,** for the passage of the maxillary nerve. Behind and lateral to the foramen rotundum is the **foramen ovale,** which transmits the mandibular nerve, the accessory meningeal artery, and the lesser superficial petrosal nerve.[1] Medial to the foramen ovale is the **foramen Vesalii,** which varies in size in different individuals, and is often absent; when present, it opens below at the lateral side of the scaphoid fossa, and transmits a small vein. Lateral to the foramen ovale is the **foramen spinosum,** for the passage of the middle meningeal vessels, and a recurrent branch from the mandibular nerve. Medial to the foramen ovale is the **foramen lacerum;** in the fresh state the lower part of this aperture is filled up by a layer of fibrocartilage; its upper and inner parts are crossed by the internal carotid artery surrounded by a plexus of sympathetic nerves. The nerve of the pterygoid canal and a meningeal branch from the ascending pharyngeal artery pierce the layer of fibrocartilage. On the anterior surface of the petrous portion of the temporal bone are seen the eminence caused by the projection of the superior semicircular canal; in front of and a little lateral to this a depression corresponding to the roof of the tympanic cavity; the groove leading to the **hiatus of the facial canal,** for the transmission of the greater superficial petrosal nerve and the petrosal branch of the middle meningeal artery; beneath it, the smaller groove, for the passage of the lesser superficial petrosal nerve; and, near the apex of the bone, the depression for the semilunar ganglion and the orifice of the carotid canal.

The Posterior Fossa (*fossa cranii posterior*).—The posterior fossa is the largest and deepest of the three. It is formed by the dorsum sellæ and clivus of the sphenoid, the occipital, the petrous and mastoid portions of the temporals, and the mastoid angles of the parietal bones; it is crossed by the **occipitomastoid** and the **parietomastoid sutures,** and lodges the cerebellum, pons, and medulla oblongata. It is separated from the middle fossa in and near the median line by the dorsum sellæ of the sphenoid and on either side by the superior angle of the petrous portion of the temporal bone. This angle gives attachment to the tentorium cerebelli, is grooved for the superior petrosal sinus, and presents at its medial end a notch upon which the trigeminal nerve rests. The fossa is limited behind by the grooves for the transverse sinuses. In its center is the **foramen magnum,** on either side of which is a rough tubercle for the attachment of the alar ligaments; a little above this tubercle is the canal, which transmits the hypoglossal nerve and a meningeal branch from the ascending pharyngeal artery. In front of the foramen magnum the basilar portion of the occipital and the posterior part of the body of the sphenoid form a grooved surface which supports the medulla oblongata and pons; in the young skull these bones are joined by a synchondrosis. This grooved surface is separated on either side from the petrous portion of the temporal by the **petro-occipital fissure,** which is occupied in the fresh state by a plate of cartilage; the fissure is continuous behind with the jugular foramen, and its margins are grooved for the inferior petrosal sinus. The **jugular foramen** is situated between the lateral part of the occipital and the petrous part of the temporal. The anterior portion of this foramen transmits the inferior petrosal sinus; the posterior portion, the transverse sinus and some meningeal branches from the occipital and ascending pharyngeal arteries; and the intermediate portion, the glossopharyngeal, vagus, and accessory nerves. Above the jugular foramen is the **internal acoustic meatus,** for the facial and acoustic nerves and internal auditory artery; behind and lateral to this is the slit-like opening leading into the aquæductus vestibuli, which lodges the ductus endolymphaticus; while between these, and near the superior angle of the petrous portion, is a small triangular depression, the remains of the fossa subarcuata, which lodges a process of the dura mater and occasionally transmits a small vein. Behind the foramen magnum are the **inferior occipital fossæ,** which support the hemispheres of the cerebellum, separated from one another by the **internal occipital crest,** which serves for the attachment of the falx cerebelli, and lodges the occipital sinus. The posterior fossæ are surmounted by the deep grooves for the **transverse sinuses.** Each of these channels, in its passage to the jugular foramen, grooves the occipital, the mastoid angle of the parietal, the mastoid portion of the temporal, and the jugular process of the occipital, and ends at the back part of the jugular foramen. Where this sinus grooves the mastoid portion of the temporal, the orifice of the **mastoid foramen** may be seen; and, just previous to its termination, the **condyloid canal** opens into it; neither opening is constant.

The Nasal Cavity (*cavum nasi; nasal fossa*).—The nasal cavities are two irregular spaces, situated one on either side of the middle line of the face, extending from the base of the cranium to the roof of the mouth, and separated from each other by a thin vertical septum. They open on the face through the pear-shaped **anterior nasal aperture,** and their posterior openings or **choanæ** communicate, in the fresh state, with the nasal part of the pharynx. They are much narrower above than below, and in the middle than at their anterior or posterior openings: their depth, which is considerable, is greatest in the middle. They communicate with the frontal, ethmoidal, sphenoidal, and maxillary sinuses. Each cavity is bounded by a **roof**, a **floor**, a **medial** and a **lateral wall**.

The **roof** (Figs. 192, 246) is horizontal in its central part, but slopes downward in front and behind; it is formed in *front* by the nasal bone and the spine of the frontal; in the *middle*, by the cribriform plate of the ethmoid; and *behind*, by the body of the sphenoid, the sphenoidal concha, the ala of the vomer and the sphenoidal process of the palatine bone. In the cribriform plate of the ethmoid are the foramina for the olfactory nerves, and on the posterior part of the roof is the opening into the sphenoidal sinus.

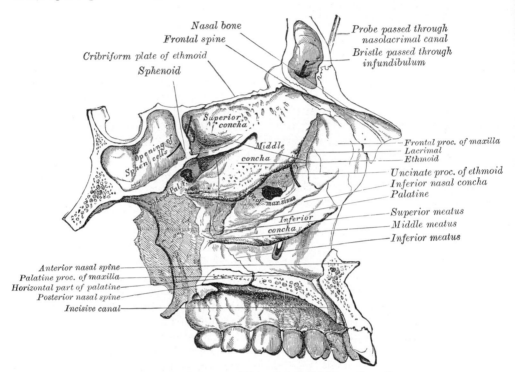

FIG. 192.—Roof, floor, and lateral wall of left nasal cavity.

The **floor** is flattened from before backward and concave from side to side. It is formed by the palatine process of the maxilla and the horizontal part of the palatine bone; near its anterior end is the opening of the incisive canal.

The **medial wall** (*septum nasi*) (Fig. 246), is frequently deflected to one or other side, more often to the left than to the right. It is formed, in *front*, by the crest of the nasal bones and frontal spine; in the *middle*, by the perpendicular plate of the ethmoid; *behind*, by the vomer and the rostrum of the sphenoid; *below*, by the crest of the maxillæ and palatine bones. It presents, in front, a large, triangular notch, which receives the cartilage of the septum; and behind, the free edge of the vomer. Its surface is marked by numerous furrows for vessels and nerves and by the grooves for the nasopalatine nerve, and is traversed by sutures connecting the bones of which it is formed.

The **lateral wall** (Fig. 192) is formed, in front, by the frontal process of the maxilla and by the lacrimal bone; in the middle, by the ethmoid, maxilla, and inferior nasal concha; behind, by the vertical plate of the palatine bone, and the medial pterygoid plate of the sphenoid. On this wall are three irregular antero-posterior passages, termed the superior, middle, and inferior meatuses of the nose. The **superior meatus**, the smallest of the three, occupies the middle third of the lateral wall. It lies between the superior and middle nasal conchæ; the **spheno-palatine foramen** opens into it behind, and the **posterior ethmoidal cells** in front. The sphenoidal sinus opens into a recess, the **sphenoethmoidal recess**, which is placed above and behind the superior concha. The **middle meatus** is situated between the middle and inferior conchæ, and extends from the anterior to the posterior end of the latter. The lateral wall of this meatus can be satisfactorily studied only after the removal of the middle concha. On it is a curved fissure, the **hiatus semilunaris**, limited below by the edge of the uncinate process of the ethmoid and above by an elevation named the **bulla ethmoidalis**; the middle ethmoidal cells are contained within this bulla and open on or near to it. Through the hiatus semilunaris the meatus communicates with a curved passage termed the **infundibulum**, which communicates in front with the anterior ethmoidal cells and in rather more than fifty per cent of skulls is continued upward as the **frontonasal duct** into the frontal air-sinus; when this continuity fails, the frontonasal duct opens directly into the anterior part of the meatus. Below the bulla ethmoidalis and hidden by the uncinate process of the ethmoid is the opening of the maxillary sinus (**ostium maxillare**); an accessory opening is frequently present above the posterior part of the inferior nasal concha. The **inferior meatus**, the largest of the three, is the space between the inferior concha and the floor of the nasal cavity. It extends almost the entire length of the lateral wall of the nose, is broader in front than behind, and presents anteriorly the lower **orifice of the nasolacrimal canal.**

The **Anterior Nasal Aperture** (Fig. 185) is a heart-shaped or pyriform opening, whose long axis is vertical, and narrow end upward; in the recent state it is much contracted by the lateral and alar cartilages of the nose. It is bounded *above* by the inferior borders of the nasal bones; *laterally* by the thin, sharp margins which separate the anterior from the nasal surfaces of the maxillæ; and *below* by the same borders, where they curve medialward to join each other at the anterior nasal spine.

The **choanæ** are each bounded *above* by the under surface of the body of the sphenoid and ala of the vomer; *below*, by the posterior border of the horizontal part of the palatine bone; *laterally*, by the medial pterygoid plate; they are separated from each other by the posterior border of the vomer.

DIFFERENCES IN THE SKULL DUE TO AGE.

At birth the skull is large in proportion to the other parts of the skeleton, but its facial portion is small, and equals only about one-eighth of the bulk of the cranium as compared with one-half in the adult. The frontal and parietal eminences are prominent, and the greatest width of the skull is at the level of the latter; on the other hand, the glabella, superciliary arches, and mastoid processes are not developed. Ossification of the skull bones is not completed, and many of them, *e. g.*, the occipital, temporals, sphenoid, frontal, and mandible, consist of more than one piece. Unossified membranous intervals, termed *fontanelles*, are seen at the angles of the parietal bones; these fontanelles are six in number: two, an anterior and a posterior, are situated in the middle line, and two, an antero-lateral and a postero-lateral, on either side.

The *anterior* or *bregmatic fontanelle* (Fig. 193) is the largest, and is placed at the junction of the sagittal, coronal, and frontal sutures; it is lozenge-shaped, and measures about 4 cm. in its antero-posterior and 2.5 cm. in its transverse diameter. The *posterior fontanelle* is triangular in form and is situated at the junction of the sagittal and lambdoidal sutures. The *lateral fontanelles* (Fig. 194) are small, irregular in shape, and correspond respectively with the sphenoidal and mastoid angles of the parietal bones. An additional fontanelle is sometimes seen in the sagittal suture at the region of the obelion. The fontanelles are usually closed by the growth and extension of the bones which surround them, but sometimes they are the sites of separate ossific centers which develop into sutural bones. The posterior and lateral fontanelles are obliterated within a month or two after birth, but the anterior is not completely closed until about the middle of the second year.

The smallness of the face at birth is mainly accounted for by the rudimentary condition of the maxillæ and mandible, the non-eruption of the teeth, and the small size of the maxillary air sinuses and nasal cavities. At birth the nasal cavities lie almost entirely between the orbits, and the lower border of the anterior nasal aperture is only a little below the level of the orbital floor. With the eruption of the deciduous teeth there is an enlargement of the face and jaws, and these changes are still more marked after the second dentition.

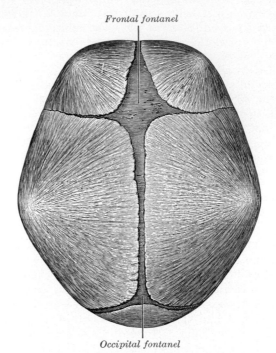

Frontal fontanel

Occipital fontanel

FIG. 193.—Skull at birth, showing frontal and occipital fontanelles.

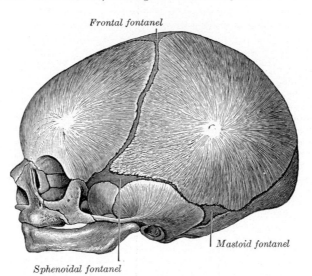

Frontal fontanel

Mastoid fontanel

Sphenoidal fontanel

FIG. 194.—Skull at birth, showing sphenoidal and mastoid fontanelles.

The skull grows rapidly from birth to the seventh year, by which time the foramen magnum and petrous parts of the temporals have reached their full size and the orbital cavities are only a little smaller than those of the adult. Growth is slow from the seventh year until the approach of puberty, when a second period of activity occurs: this results in an increase in all directions, but it is especially marked in the frontal and facial regions, where it is associated with the development of the air sinuses.

Suture closure begins at twenty-two years in the sagittal and sphenofrontal, at twenty-four years in the coronal and at twenty-six years in the lambdoid and masto-occipital. The process is most rapid from twenty-six to thirty years then slows down and may not be complete until old age. The sphenoparietal, sphenotemporal, parietomastoid and squamous begin to close at twenty-nine, thirty, thirty-seven and thirty-seven years. Closure progresses very slowly with a final burst of activity in old age. There is considerable individual variation.

The most striking feature of the old skull is the diminution in the size of the maxillæ and mandible consequent on the loss of the teeth and the absorption of the alveolar processes. This is associated with a marked reduction in the vertical measurement of the face and with an alteration in the angles of the mandible.

SEX DIFFERENCES, FUNCTION AND CLEFT PALATE.

Until the age of puberty there is little difference between the skull of the female and that of the male. The skull of an adult female is, as a rule, lighter and smaller, and its cranial capacity about 10 per cent. less, than that of the male. Its walls are thinner and its muscular ridges less strongly marked; the glabella, superciliary arches, and mastoid processes are less prominent, and the corresponding air sinuses are small or rudimentary. The upper margin of the orbit is sharp, the forehead vertical, the frontal and parietal eminences prominent, and the vault somewhat flattened. The contour of the face is more rounded, the facial bones are smoother, and the maxillæ and mandible and their contained teeth smaller. From what has been said it will be seen that more of the infantile characteristics are retained in the skull of the adult female than in that of the adult male. A well-marked male or female skull can easily be recognized as such, but in some cases the respective characteristics are so indistinct that the determination of the sex may be difficult or impossible.

The chief function of the skull is to protect the brain, and therefore those portions of the skull which are most exposed to external violence are thicker than those which are shielded from injury by overlying muscles. Thus, the skull-cap is thick and dense, whereas the temporal squamæ, being protected by the temporales muscles, and the inferior occipital fossæ, being shielded by the muscles at the back of the neck, are thin and fragile. Fracture of the skull is further prevented by its elasticity, its rounded shape, and its construction of a number of secondary elastic arches, each made up of a single bone. The manner in which vibrations are transmitted through the bones of the skull is also of importance as regards its protective mechanism, at all events as far as the base is concerned. In the vault, the bones being of a fairly equal thickness and density, vibrations are transmitted in a uniform manner in all directions, but in the base, owing to the varying thickness and density of the bones, this is not so; and therefore in this situation there are special buttresses which serve to carry the vibrations in certain definite directions. At the front of the skull, on either side, is the ridge which separates the anterior from the middle fossa of the base; and behind, the ridge or buttress which separates the middle from the posterior fossa; and if any violence is applied to the vault, the vibrations would be carried along these buttresses to the sella turcica, where they meet. This part has been termed the "center of resistance," and here there is a special protective mechanism to guard the brain. The subarachnoid cavity at the base of the brain is dilated, and the cerebrospinal fluid which fills it acts as a water cushion to shield the brain from injury. In like manner, when violence is applied to the base of the skull, as in falls upon the feet, the vibrations are carried backward through the occipital crest, and forward through the basilar part of the occipital and body of the sphenoid to the vault of the skull.

In connection with the bones of the face a common malformation is *cleft palate*. The cleft usually starts posteriorly, and its most elementary form is a bifid uvula; or the cleft may extend through the soft palate; or the posterior part or the whole of the hard palate may be involved, the cleft extending as far forward as the incisive foramen. In the severest forms, the cleft extends through the alveolus and passes between the incisive or premaxillary bone and the rest of the maxilla; that is to say, between the lateral incisor and canine teeth. In some instances, the cleft runs between the central and lateral incisor teeth; and this has induced some anatomists to believe that the premaxillary bone is developed from two centers and not from one. The cleft may affect one or both sides; if the latter, the central part is frequently displaced forward and remains united to the septum of the nose, the deficiency in the alveolus being complicated with a cleft in the lip (hare-lip).

The Mandible (Mandibula; Inferior Maxillary Bone; Lower Jaw).

The **mandible,** the largest and strongest bone of the face, serves for the reception of the lower teeth. It consists of a curved, horizontal portion, the **body,** and two perpendicular portions, the **rami,** which unite with the ends of the body nearly at right angles.

The Body (*corpus mandibulæ*).—The body is curved somewhat like a horseshoe, and has two surfaces and two borders.

Surfaces.—The **external surface** (Fig. 195) is marked in the median line by a
faint ridge, indicating the **symphysis** or line of junction of the two pieces of which
the bone is composed at an early period of life. This ridge divides below and
encloses a triangular eminence, the **mental protuberance,** the base of which is depressed in the center but raised on either side to form the **mental tubercle.** On either
side of the symphysis, just below the incisor teeth, is a depression, the **incisive
fossa,** which gives origin to the Mentalis and a small portion of the Orbicularis
oris. Below the second premolar tooth, on either side, midway between the upper
and lower borders of the body, is the **mental foramen,** for the passage of the mental
vessels and nerve. Running backward and upward from each mental tubercle
is a faint ridge, the **oblique line,** which is continuous with the anterior border of the
ramus; it affords attachment to the Quadratus labii inferioris and Triangularis;
the Platysma is attached below it.

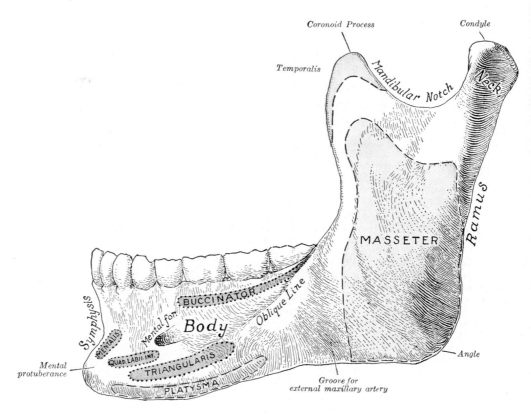

FIG. 195.—The left half of the mandible. Lateral aspect.

The **internal surface** (Fig. 196) is concave from side to side. Near the lower
part of the symphysis is a pair of laterally placed spines, termed the **mental spines,**
which give origin to the Genioglossi. Immediately below these is a second pair
of spines, or more frequently a median ridge or impression, for the origin of the
Geniohyoidei. In some cases the mental spines are fused to form a single eminence,
in others they are absent and their position is indicated merely by an irregularity
of the surface. Above the mental spines a median foramen and furrow are sometimes seen; they mark the line of union of the halves of the bone. Below the mental
spines, on either side of the middle line, is an oval depression for the attachment
of the anterior belly of the Digastricus. Extending upward and backward on either
side from the lower part of the symphysis is the **mylohyoid line,** which gives origin

to the Mylohyoideus; the posterior part of this line, near the alveolar margin, gives attachment to a small part of the Constrictor pharyngis superior, and to the pterygomandibular raphé. Above the anterior part of this line is a smooth triangular area against which the sublingual gland rests, and below the hinder part, an oval fossa for the submaxillary gland.

Borders.—The **superior** or **alveolar border**, wider behind than in front, is hollowed into cavities, for the reception of the teeth; these cavities are sixteen in number, and vary in depth and size according to the teeth which they contain. To the outer lip of the superior border, on either side, the Buccinator is attached as far forward as the first molar tooth. The **inferior border** is rounded, longer than the superior, and thicker in front than behind; at the point where it joins the lower border of the ramus a shallow groove; for the external maxillary artery, may be present.

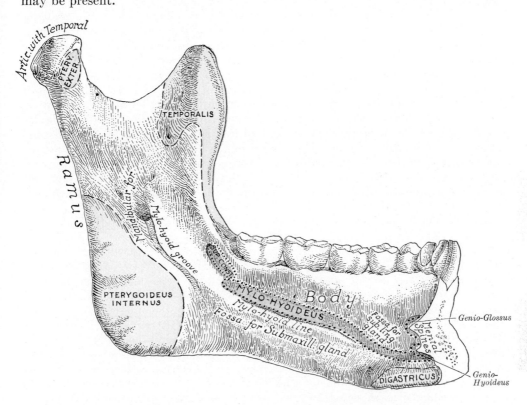

Fig. 196.—The left half of the mandible. Medial aspect.

The Ramus (*ramus mandibulæ; perpendicular portion*).—The ramus is quadrilateral in shape, and has two surfaces, four borders, and two processes.

Surfaces.—The **lateral surface** (Fig. 195) is flat and marked by oblique ridges at its lower part; it gives attachment throughout nearly the whole of its extent to the Masseter. The **medial surface** (Fig. 196) presents about its center the oblique **mandibular foramen**, for the entrance of the inferior alveolar vessels and nerve. The margin of this opening is irregular; it presents in front a prominent ridge, surmounted by a sharp spine, the **lingula mandibulæ**, which gives attachment to the sphenomandibular ligament; at its lower and back part is a notch from which the **mylohyoid groove** runs obliquely downward and forward, and lodges the mylohyoid vessels and nerve. Behind this groove is a rough surface, for the insertion of the Pterygoideus internus. The **mandibular canal** runs obliquely downward and forward in the ramus, and then horizontally forward in the body, where it is placed under the alveoli and communicates with them by small openings. On arriving at the incisor teeth, it turns back to communicate with the mental foramen, giving off two small canals which run to the cavities containing the incisor teeth. In the posterior two-thirds of the bone the canal is situated nearer the internal surface of the mandible; and in the anterior third, nearer its external surface. It contains the inferior alveolar vessels and nerve, from which branches are distributed to the teeth. The **lower border** of the ramus is thick, straight, and continuous with the inferior border of the body of the bone. At its junction with the posterior border is the **angle of the mandible**, which may be either inverted or everted and is marked by rough, oblique ridges on each side, for the attachment of the Masseter laterally, and the Pterygoideus internus medially; the stylomandibular ligament is attached to the angle between these muscles. The **anterior border** is thin above, thicker below, and continuous with the oblique line. The **posterior border** is thick, smooth, rounded, and covered by the parotid gland. The **upper border** is thin, and is surmounted by two processes, the **coronoid** in front and the **condyloid** behind, separated by a deep concavity, the **mandibular notch**.

The **Coronoid Process** (*processus coronoideus*) is a thin, triangular eminence, which is flattened from side to side and varies in shape and size. Its *anterior border* is convex and is continuous below with the anterior border of the ramus; its *posterior border* is concave and forms the anterior boundary of the mandibular notch. Its *lateral surface* is smooth, and affords insertion to the Temporalis and Masseter. Its *medial surface* gives insertion to the Temporalis, and presents a ridge which begins near the apex of the process and runs downward and forward to the inner side of the last molar tooth. Between this ridge and the anterior border is a grooved triangular area, the upper part of which gives attachment to the Temporalis, the lower part to some fibers of the Buccinator.

The **Condyloid Process** (*processus condylaris*) is thicker than the coronoid, and consists of two portions: the **condyle**, and the constricted portion which supports it, the **neck**. The **condyle** presents an articular surface for articulation with the articular disk of the temporomandibular joint; it is convex from before backward and from side to side, and extends farther on the posterior than on the anterior surface. Its long axis is directed medialward and slightly backward, and if prolonged to the middle line will meet that of the opposite condyle near the anterior margin of the foramen magnum. At the lateral extremity of the condyle is a small tubercle for the attachment of the temporomandibular ligament. The **neck** is flattened from before backward, and strengthened by ridges which descend from the forepart and sides of the condyle. Its posterior surface is convex; its anterior presents a depression for the attachment of the Pterygoideus externus.

The **mandibular notch**, separating the two processes, is a deep semilunar depression, and is crossed by the masseteric vessels and nerve.

Ossification.—The mandible is ossified in the fibrous membrane covering the outer surface of Meckel's cartilages. These cartilages form the cartilaginous bar of the mandibular arch (see p. 38), and are two in number, a right and a left. Their proximal or cranial ends are connected with the ear capsules, and their distal extremities are joined to one another at the symphysis by mesodermal tissue. They run forward immediately below the condyles and then, bending downward, lie in a groove near the lower border of the bone; in front of the canine tooth they incline upward to the symphysis. From the proximal end of each cartilage the malleus and incus, two of the bones of the middle ear, are developed; the next succeeding portion, as far as the lingula, is replaced by fibrous tissue, which persists to form the sphenomandibular ligament. Between the lingula and the canine tooth the cartilage disappears, while the portion of it below and behind the incisor teeth becomes ossified and incorporated with this part of the mandible.

Ossification takes place in the membrane covering the outer surface of the ventral end of Meckel's cartilage (Figs. 197 to 200), and each half of the bone is formed from a single center which appears, near the mental foramen, about the sixth week of fetal life By the tenth week the portion of Meckel's cartilage which lies below and behind the incisor teeth is surrounded and invaded by the membrane bone. Somewhat later, accessory nuclei of cartilage make their appearance, viz., a wedge-shaped nucleus in the condyloid process and extending downward through the ramus; a small strip along the anterior border of the coronoid process; and smaller nuclei in the front part of both alveolar walls and along the front of the lower border of the bone. These accessory nuclei possess no separate ossific centers, but are invaded by the surrounding membrane bone and undergo absorption. The inner alveolar border, usually described as arising from a

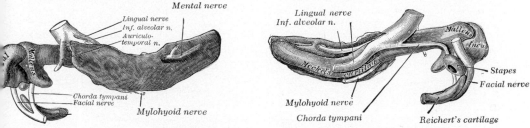

Fig. 197.—Mandible of human embryo, 24 mm. long. Outer aspect. (From model by Low.)

Fig. 198.—Mandible of human embryo 24 mm. long. Inner aspect. (From model by Low.)

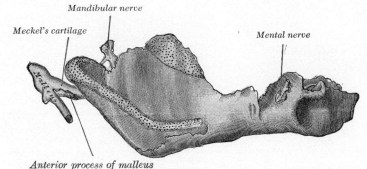

Fig. 199.—Mandible of human embryo 95 mm. long. Outer aspect. Nuclei of cartilage stippled. (From model by Low.)

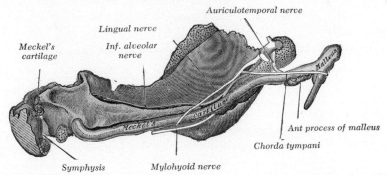

Fig. 200.—Mandible of human embryo 95 mm. long. Inner aspect. Nuclei of cartilage stippled. (From model by Low.)

separate ossific center (*splenial center*), is formed in the human mandible by an ingrowth from the main mass of the bone. At birth the bone consists of two parts, united by a fibrous symphysis, in which ossification takes place during the first year.

The foregoing description of the ossification of the mandible is based on the researches of Fawcett ('05), and differs somewhat from that usually given.

Articulations.—The mandible articulates with the *two* temporal bones.

CHANGES PRODUCED IN THE MANDIBLE BY AGE.

At birth (Fig. 201, *A*) the body of the bone is a mere shell, containing the sockets of the two incisor, the canine, and the two deciduous molar teeth, imperfectly partitioned off from one another. The mandibular canal is of large size, and runs near the lower border of the bone; the mental foramen opens beneath the socket of the first deciduous molar tooth. The angle is obtuse (175°), and the condyloid portion is nearly in line with the body. The coronoid process is of comparatively large size, and projects above the level of the condyle.

After birth (Fig. 201, *A* and *B*) the two segments of the bone become joined at the symphysis, from below upward, in the first year; but a trace of separation may be visible in the beginning of the second year, near the alveolar margin. The body becomes elongated in its whole length, but more especially behind the mental foramen, to provide space for the three additional teeth developed in this part. The depth of the body increases owing to increased growth of the alveolar part, to afford room for the roots of the teeth, and by thickening of the subdental portion which

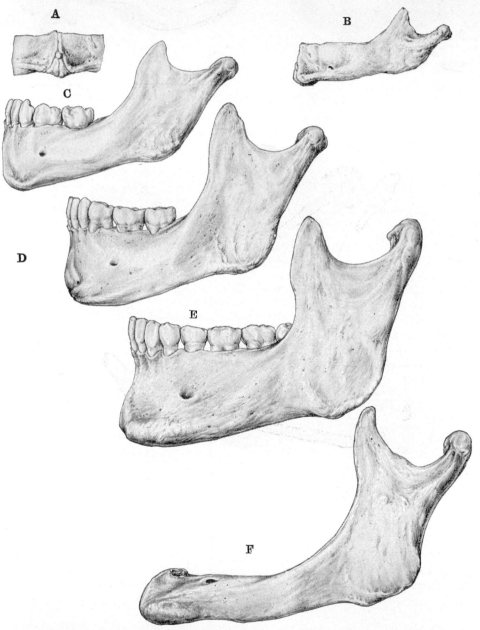

Fig. 201.—The mandible at different periods of life. *A*, at birth. Anterior aspect, showing the ossicula mentalia. *B*, at birth. Left lateral aspect. *C*, at four years. Full milk dentition. *D*, at eight years. The permanent incisor and first molar teeth have erupted; the milk molars are in process of being shed. *E*, adult. *F*, old age.

enables the jaw to withstand the powerful action of the masticatory muscles; but the alveolar portion is the deeper of the two, and, consequently, the chief part of the body lies above the oblique line. The mandibular canal, after the second dentition, is situated just above the level of the mylohyoid line; and the mental foramen occupies the position usual to it in the adult. The angle becomes less obtuse, owing to the separation of the jaws by the teeth; about the fourth year it is 140 degrees.

In the adult (Fig. 201 *E*) the alveolar and subdental portions of the body are usually of equal depth. The mental foramen opens midway between the upper and lower borders of the bone, and the mandibular canal runs nearly parallel with the mylohyoid line. The ramus is almost vertical in direction, the angle measuring from 110° to 120°.

In old age (Fig. 201 *F*) the bone becomes greatly reduced in size, for with the loss of the teeth the alveolar process is absorbed, and, consequently, the chief part of the bone is below the oblique line. The mandibular canal, with the mental foramen opening from it, is close to the alveolar border. The ramus is oblique in direction, the angle measures about 140°, and the neck of the condyle is more or less bent backward.

The Hyoid Bone (Os Hyoideum; Lingual Bone).

The **hyoid bone** is shaped like a horseshoe, and is suspended from the tips of the styloid processes of the temporal bones by the stylohyoid ligaments. It consists of five segments, viz., a **body**, two **greater cornua**, and two **lesser cornua**.

The Body or Basihyal (*corpus oss. hyoidei*).—The body or central part is of a quadrilateral form. Its **anterior surface** (Fig. 202) is convex and directed forward and upward. It is crossed in its upper half by a well-marked transverse ridge with a slight downward convexity, and in many cases a vertical median ridge divides it into two lateral halves. The portion of the vertical ridge above the transverse line is present in a majority of specimens, but the lower portion is

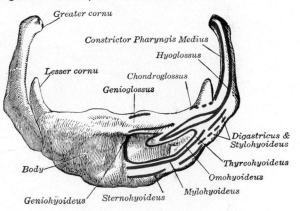

FIG. 202.—Hyoid bone. Anterior surface. Enlarged.

evident only in rare cases. The anterior surface gives insertion to the Geniohyoideus in the greater part of its extent both above and below the transverse ridge; a portion of the origin of the Hyoglossus notches the lateral margin of the Geniohyoideus attachment. Below the transverse ridge the Mylohyoideus, Sternohyoideus, and Omohyoideus are inserted. The **posterior surface** is smooth, concave, directed backward and downward, and separated from the epiglottis by the hyothyroid membrane and a quantity of loose areolar tissue; a bursa intervenes between it and the hyothyroid membrane. The **superior border** is rounded, and gives attachment to the hyothyroid membrane and some aponeurotic fibers of the Genioglossus. The **inferior border** affords insertion medially to the Sternohyoideus and laterally to the Omohyoideus and occasionally a portion of the Thyreohyoideus. It also gives attachment to the Levator glandulæ thyreoideæ, when this muscle is present. In early life the **lateral borders** are connected to the greater cornua by synchondroses; after middle life usually by bony union.

The Greater Cornua or Thyrohyals (*cornua majora*).—The greater cornua project backward from the lateral borders of the body; they are flattened from above downward and diminish in size from before backward; each ends in a tubercle to which is fixed the lateral hyothyroid ligament. The **upper surface** is rough close to its lateral border, for muscular attachments: the largest of these are the origins of the Hyoglossus and Constrictor pharyngis medius which extend along the whole length of the cornu; the Digastricus and Stylohyoideus have small insertions in front of these near the junction of the body with the cornu. To the **medial border** the hyothyroid membrane is attached, while the anterior half of the **lateral border** gives insertion to the Thyreohyoideus.

The Lesser Cornua or Ceratohyals (*cornua minora*).—The lesser cornua are two small, conical eminences, attached by their bases to the angles of junction between the body and greater cornua. They are connected to the body of the bone by fibrous tissue, and occasionally to the greater cornua by distinct diarthrodial joints, which usually persist throughout life, but occasionally become ankylosed.

The lesser cornua are situated in the line of the transverse ridge on the body and appear to be morphological continuations of it. The apex of each cornua gives attachment to the stylohyoid ligament; the Chondroglossus rises from the medial side of the base.

Ossification.—The hyoid is ossified from *six* centers: two for the body, and one for each cornu. Ossification commences in the greater cornua toward the end of fetal life, in the body shortly afterward, and in the lesser cornua during the first or second year after birth.

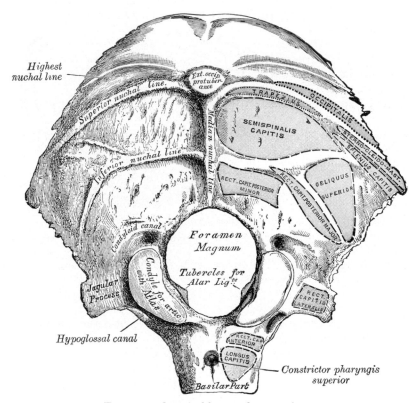

Fig. 203.—Occipital bone. Outer surface.

THE CRANIAL BONES (OSSA CRANII).

The Occipital Bone (Os Occipitale).

The **occipital bone** (Figs. 203, 204), situated at the back and lower part of the cranium, is trapezoid in shape and curved on itself. It is pierced by a large oval aperture, the **foramen magnum**, through which the cranial cavity communicates with the vertebral canal.

The curved, expanded plate behind the foramen magnum is named the **squama**;

the thick, somewhat quadrilateral piece in front of the foramen is called the **basilar part**, whilst on either side of the foramen is the **lateral portion**.

The Squama (*squama occipitalis*).—The squama, situated above and behind the foramen magnum, is curved from above downward and from side to side.

Surfaces.—The **external surface** is convex and presents midway between the summit of the bone and the foramen magnum a prominence, the **external occipital protuberance**. Extending lateralward from this on either side are two curved lines, one a little above the other. The upper, often faintly marked, is named the **highest nuchal line,** and to it the galea aponeurotica is attached. The lower is termed the **superior nuchal line.** That part of the squama which lies above the

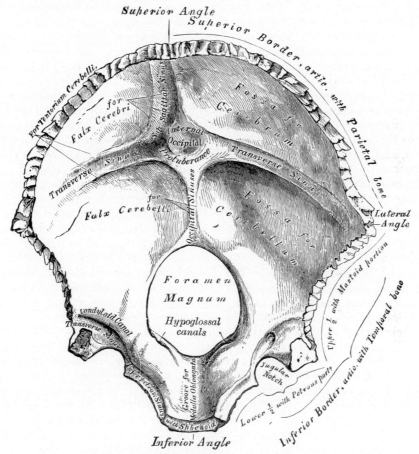

FIG. 204.—Occipital bone. Inner surface.

highest nuchal lines is named the **planum occipitale**, and is covered by the Occipitalis muscle; that below, termed the **planum nuchale**, is rough and irregular for the attachment of several muscles. From the external occipital protuberance a ridge or crest, the **median nuchal line**, often faintly marked, descends to the foramen magnum, and affords attachment to the ligamentum nuchæ; running from the middle of this line across either half of the nuchal plane is the **inferior nuchal line.** Several muscles are attached to the outer surface of the squama, thus: the superior nuchal line gives origin to the Occipitalis and Trapezius, and insertion to the Sternocleidomastoideus and Splenius capitis: into the surface between the superior and inferior nuchal lines the Semispinalis capitis and the Obliquus capitis superior are inserted, while the inferior nuchal line and the area below it receive the insertions of the Recti capitis posteriores major and minor. The posterior atlantoöccipital membrane is attached around the postero-lateral part of the foramen magnum, just outside the margin of the foramen

The **internal surface** is deeply concave and divided into four fossæ by a **cruciate eminence.** The upper two fossæ are triangular and lodge the occipital lobes of the cerebrum; the lower two are quadrilateral and accommodate the hemispheres of the cerebellum. At the point of intersection of the four divisions of the cruciate eminence is the **internal occipital protuberance.** From this protuberance the upper division of the cruciate eminence runs to the superior angle of the bone, and on one side of it (generally the right) is a deep groove, the **sagittal sulcus,** which lodges the hinder part of the superior sagittal sinus; to the margins of this sulcus the falx cerebri is attached. The lower division of the cruciate eminence is prominent, and is named the **internal occipital crest;** it bifurcates near the foramen magnum and gives attachment to the falx cerebelli; in the attached margin of this falx is the occipital sinus, which is sometimes duplicated. In the upper part of the internal occipital crest, a small depression is sometimes distinguishable; it is termed the **vermian fossa** since it is occupied by part of the vermis of the cerebellum. Transverse grooves, one on either side, extend from the internal occipital protuberance to the lateral angles of the bone; those grooves accommodate the transverse sinuses, and their prominent margins give attachment to the tentorium cerebelli. The groove on the right side is usually larger than that on the left, and is continuous with that for the superior sagittal sinus. Exceptions to this condition are, however, not infrequent; the left may be larger than the right or the two may be almost equal in size. The angle of union of the superior sagittal and transverse sinuses is named the **confluence of the sinuses** (*torcular Herophili*), and its position is indicated by a depression situated on one or other side of the protuberance.

Lateral Parts (*pars lateralis*).—The lateral parts are situated at the sides of the foramen magnum; on their under surfaces are the **condyles** for articulation with the superior facets of the atlas. The condyles are oval or reniform in shape, and their anterior extremities, directed forward and medialward, are closer together than their posterior, and encroach on the basilar portion of the bone; the posterior extremities extend back to the level of the middle of the foramen magnum. The articular surfaces of the condyles are convex from before backward and from side to side, and look downward and lateralward. To their margins are attached the capsules of the atlantoöccipital articulations, and on the medial side of each is a rough impression or tubercle for the alar ligament. At the base of either condyle the bone is tunnelled by a short canal, the **hypoglossal canal** (*anterior condyloid foramen*). This begins on the cranial surface of the bone immediately above the foramen magnum, and is directed lateralward and forward above the condyle. It may be partially or completely divided into two by a spicule of bone; it gives exit to the hypoglossal or twelfth cranial nerve, and entrance to a meningeal branch of the ascending pharyngeal artery. Behind either condyle is a depression, the **condyloid fossa,** which receives the posterior margin of the superior facet of the atlas when the head is bent backward; the floor of this fossa is sometimes perforated by the **condyloid canal,** through which an emissary vein passes from the transverse sinus. Extending lateralward from the posterior half of the condyle is a quadrilateral plate of bone, the **jugular process,** excavated in front by the **jugular notch,** which, in the articulated skull, forms the posterior part of the jugular foramen. The jugular notch may be divided into two by a bony spicule, the **intrajugular process,** which projects lateralward above the hypoglossal canal. The under surface of the jugular process is rough, and gives attachment to the Rectus capitis lateralis muscle and the lateral atlantoöccipital ligament; from this surface an eminence, the **paramastoid process,** sometimes projects downward, and may be of sufficient length to reach, and articulate with, the transverse process of the atlas. Laterally the jugular process presents a rough quadrilateral or triangular area which is joined to the jugular surface of the temporal bone by a plate of cartilage; after the age of twenty-five this plate tends to ossify.

The **upper surface** of the lateral part presents an oval eminence, the **jugular tubercle,** which overlies the hypoglossal canal and is sometimes crossed by an oblique groove for the glossopharyngeal, vagus, and accessory nerves. On the upper surface of the jugular process is a deep groove which curves medialward and forward and is continuous with the jugular notch. This groove lodges the terminal part of the transverse sinus, and opening into it, close to its medial margin, is the orifice of the condyloid canal.

Basilar Part (*pars basilaris*).—The basilar part extends forward and upward from the foramen magnum, and presents *in front* an area more or less quadrilateral in outline. In the young skull this area is rough and uneven, and is joined to the body of the sphenoid by a plate of cartilage. By the twenty-fifth year this cartilaginous plate is ossified, and the occipital and sphenoid form a continuous bone.

Surfaces.—On its **lower surface,** about 1 cm. in front of the foramen magnum, is the **pharyngeal tubercle** which gives attachment to the fibrous raphé of the pharynx. On either side of the middle line the Longus capitis and Rectus capitis anterior are inserted, and immediately in front of the foramen magnum the anterior atlantoöccipital membrane is attached.

The **upper surface** presents a broad, shallow groove which inclines upward and forward from the foramen magnum; it supports the medulla oblongata, and near the margin of the foramen magnum gives attachment to the membrana tectoria. On the lateral margins of this surface are faint grooves for the inferior petrosal sinuses.

Foramen Magnum.—The foramen magnum is a large oval aperture with its long diameter antero-posterior; it is wider behind than in front where it is encroached

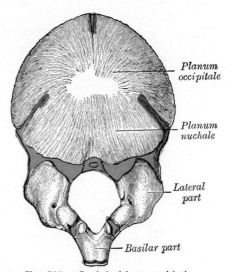

Planum occipitale

Planum nuchale

Lateral part

Basilar part

Fig 205.—Occipital bone at birth.

upon by the condyles. It transmits the medulla oblongata and its membranes, the accessory nerves, the vertebral arteries, the anterior and posterior spinal arteries, and the membrana tectoria and alar ligaments.

Angles.—The **superior angle** of the occipital bone articulates with the occipital angles of the parietal bones and, in the fetal skull, corresponds in position with the **posterior fontanelle.** The **inferior angle** is fused with the body of the sphenoid. The **lateral angles** are situated at the extremities of the grooves for the transverse sinuses: each is received into the interval between the mastoid angle of the parietal and the mastoid part of the temporal.

Borders.—The **superior borders** extend from the superior to the lateral angles: they are deeply serrated for articulation with the occipital borders of the parietals, and form by this union the **lambdoidal suture.** The **inferior borders** extend from the lateral angles to the inferior angle; the upper half of each articulates with the mastoid portion of the corresponding temporal, the lower half with the petrous part of the same bone. These two portions of the inferior border are separated from one another by the jugular process, the notch on the anterior surface of which forms the posterior part of the jugular foramen.

Structure.—The occipital, like the other cranial bones, consists of two compact lamellæ, called the *outer* and *inner tables*, between which is the cancellous tissue or diploë; the bone is especially thick at the ridges, protuberances, condyles, and anterior part of the basilar part; in the inferior fossæ it is thin, semitransparent, and destitute of diploë.

Ossification (Fig. 205).—The planum occipitale of the squama is developed in membrane, and may remain separate throughout life when it constitutes the *interparietal* bone; the rest of the bone is developed in cartilage. The number of nuclei for the planum occipitale is usually given as four, two appearing near the middle line about the second month, and two some little distance from the middle line about the third month of fetal life. The planum nuchale of the squama is ossified from two centers, which appear about the seventh week of fetal life and soon unite to form a single piece. Union of the upper and lower portions of the squama takes place in the third month of fetal life. Each of the lateral parts begins to ossify from a single center during the eighth week of the fetal life. The basilar portion is ossified from one or two centers, these appear about the sixth week of fetal life. About the fourth year the squama and the two lateral portions unite, and about the sixth year the bone consists of a single piece. Between the eighteenth and twenty-fifth years the occipital and sphenoid become united, forming a single bone.

Articulations.—The occipital articulates with *six* bones: the two parietals, the two temporals, the sphenoid, and the atlas.

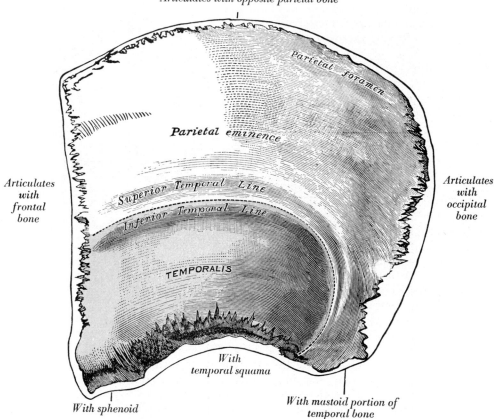

FIG. 206.—Left parietal bone. Outer surface.

The Parietal Bone (Os Parietale).

The **parietal bones** form, by their union, the sides and roof of the cranium. Each bone is irregularly quadrilateral in form, and has two surfaces, four borders, and four angles.

Surfaces.—The **external surface** (Fig. 206) is convex, smooth, and marked near the center by an eminence, the **parietal eminence** (*tuber parietale*), which indicates the point where ossification commenced. Crossing the middle of the bone in an arched direction are two curved lines, the **superior** and **inferior temporal lines;** the former gives attachment to the temporal fascia, and the latter indicates the upper limit of the muscular origin of the Temporalis. Above these lines the bone is covered by the galea aponeurotica; below them it forms part of the temporal fossa, and affords attachment to the Temporalis muscle. At the back part and close to the upper or sagittal border is the **parietal foramen**, which transmits a vein to the superior sagittal sinus, and sometimes a small branch of the occipital artery; it is not constantly present, and its size varies considerably.

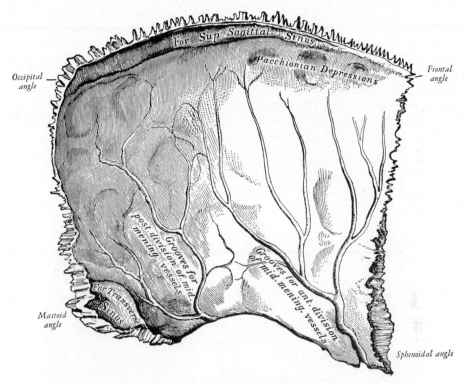

Fig. 207.—Left parietal bone. Inner surface.

The **internal surface** (Fig. 207) is concave; it presents depressions corresponding to the cerebral convolutions, and numerous furrows for the ramifications of the middle meningeal vessels; the latter run upward and backward from the sphenoidal angle, and from the central and posterior part of the squamous border. Along the upper margin is a shallow groove, which, together with that on the opposite parietal, forms a channel, the **sagittal sulcus,** for the superior sagittal sinus; the edges of the sulcus afford attachment to the falx cerebri. Near the groove are several depressions, best marked in the skulls of old persons, for the **arachnoid granulations** (*Pacchionian bodies*). In the groove is the internal opening of the parietal foramen when that aperture exists.

Borders.—The **sagittal border,** the longest and thickest, is dentated and articulates with its fellow of the opposite side, forming the sagittal suture. The **squamous border** is divided into three parts: of these, the anterior is thin and pointed, bevelled at the expense of the outer surface, and overlapped by the tip of the great wing of the sphenoid; the middle portion is arched, bevelled at the expense of the outer surface, and overlapped by the squama of the temporal; the posterior part is thick and serrated for articulation with the mastoid portion of the temporal. The **frontal border** is deeply serrated, and bevelled at the expense of the outer surface above and of the inner below; it articulates with the frontal bone, forming one-half of the **coronal suture**. The **occipital border**, deeply denticulated, articulates with the occipital, forming one-half of the **lambdoidal suture**.

Angles.—The **frontal angle** is practically a right angle, and corresponds with the point of meeting of the sagittal and coronal sutures; this point is named the **bregma**; in the fetal skull and for about a year and a half after birth this region is membranous, and is called the **anterior fontanelle**. The **sphenoidal angle**, thin and acute, is received into the interval between the frontal bone and the great wing of the sphenoid. Its inner surface is marked by a deep groove, sometimes a canal, for the anterior divisions of the middle meningeal artery. The **occipital angle** is rounded and corresponds with the point of meeting of the sagittal and lambdoidal sutures—a point which is termed the **lambda**; in the fetus this part of the skull is membranous, and is called the **posterior fontanelle**. The **mastoid angle** is truncated; it articulates with the occipital bone and with the mastoid portion of the temporal, and presents on its inner surface a broad, shallow groove which lodges part of the transverse sinus. The point of meeting of this angle with the occipital and the mastoid part of the temporal is named the **asterion**.

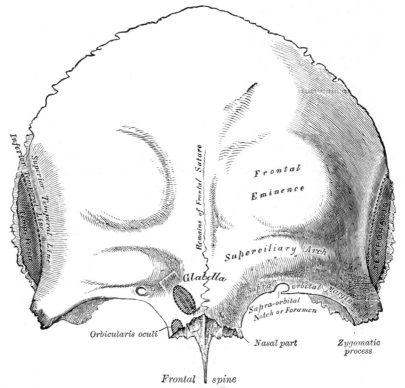

FIG. 208.—Frontal bone. Outer surface.

Ossification.—The parietal bone is ossified in membrane from a single center, which appears at the parietal eminence about the eighth week of fetal life. Ossification gradually extends in a radial manner from the center toward the margins of the bone; the angles are consequently the parts last formed, and it is here that the fontanelles exist. Occasionally the parietal bone is divided into two parts, upper and lower, by an antero-posterior suture.

Articulations.—The parietal articulates with *five* bones: the opposite parietal, the occipital, frontal, temporal, and sphenoid.

The Frontal Bone (Os Frontale).

The **frontal bone** resembles a cockle-shell in form, and consists of two portions —a **vertical** portion, the **squama**, corresponding with the region of the forehead; and an **orbital** or **horizontal** portion, which enters into the formation of the roofs of the orbital and nasal cavities.

Squama (*squama frontalis*).—Surfaces.—The **external surface** (Fig. 208) of this portion is convex and usually exhibits, in the lower part of the middle line, the remains of the **frontal** or **metopic suture**; in infancy this suture divides the bone into two, a condition which may persist throughout life. On either side of this suture, about 3 cm. above the supraorbital margin, is a rounded elevation, the **frontal eminence** (*tuber frontale*). These eminences vary in size in different individuals, are

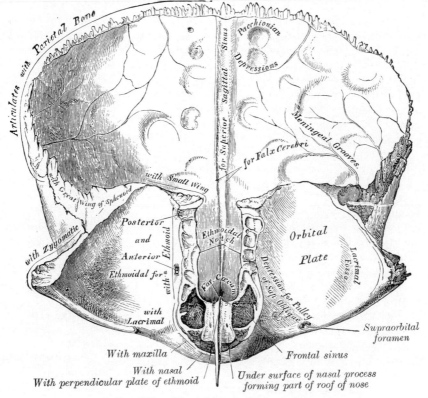

FIG. 209.—Frontal bone. Inner surface.

occasionally unsymmetrical, and are especially prominent in young skulls; the surface of the bone above them is smooth, and covered by the galea aponeurotica. Below the frontal eminences, and separated from them by a shallow groove, are two arched elevations, the **superciliary arches**; these are prominent medially, and are joined to one another by a smooth elevation named the **glabella**. They are larger in the male than in the female, and their degree of prominence depends to some extent on the size of the frontal air sinuses; prominent ridges are, however, occasionally associated with small air sinuses. Beneath each superciliary arch is a curved and prominent margin, the **supraorbital margin**, which forms the upper boundary of the base of the orbit, and separates the squama from the orbital portion of the bone. The lateral part of this margin is sharp and prominent, affording to the eye, in that situation, considerable protection from injury; the

13

medial part is rounded. At the junction of its medial and intermediate thirds is a notch, sometimes converted into a foramen, the **supraorbital notch** or **foramen,** which transmits the supraorbital vessels and nerve. A small aperture in the upper part of the notch transmits a vein from the diploë to join the supraorbital vein. The supraorbital margin ends laterally in the **zygomatic process**, which is strong and prominent, and articulates with the zygomatic bone. Running upward and backward from this process is a well-marked line, the **temporal line,** which divides into the **upper** and **lower temporal lines,** continuous, in the articulated skull, with the corresponding lines on the parietal bone. The area below and behind the temporal line forms the anterior part of the temporal fossa, and gives origin to the Temporalis muscle. Between the supraorbital margins the squama projects downward to a level below that of the zygomatic processes; this portion is known as the **nasal part** and presents a rough, uneven interval, the **nasal notch,** which articulates on either side of the middle line with the nasal bone, and laterally with the frontal process of the maxilla and with the lacrimal. The term **nasion** is applied to the middle of the frontonasal suture. From the center of the notch the **nasal process** projects downward and forward beneath the nasal bones and frontal processes of the maxillæ, and supports the bridge of the nose. The nasal process ends below in a sharp **spine,** and on either side of this is a small grooved surface which enters into the formation of the roof of the corresponding nasal cavity. The spine forms part of the septum of the nose, articulating in front with the crest of the nasal bones and behind with the perpendicular plate of the ethmoid.

The **internal surface** (Fig. 209) of the squama is concave and presents in the upper part of the middle line a vertical groove, the **sagittal sulcus,** the edges of which unite below to form a ridge, the **frontal crest;** the sulcus lodges the superior sagittal sinus, while its margins and the crest afford attachment to the falx cerebri. The crest ends below in a small notch which is converted into a foramen, the **foramen cecum,** by articulation with the ethmoid. This foramen varies in size in different subjects, and is frequently impervious; when open, it transmits a vein from the nose to the superior sagittal sinus. On either side of the middle line the bone presents depressions for the convolutions of the brain, and numerous small furrows for the anterior branches of the middle meningeal vessels. Several small, irregular fossæ may also be seen on either side of the sagittal sulcus, for the reception of the arachnoid granulations.

Orbital or **Horizontal Part** (*pars orbitalis*).—This portion consists of two thin triangular plates, the **orbital plates,** which form the vaults of the orbits, and are separated from one another by a median gap, the **ethmoidal notch.**

Surfaces.—The **inferior surface** (Fig. 209) of each orbital plate is smooth and concave, and presents, laterally, under cover of the zygomatic process, a shallow depression, the **lacrimal fossa,** for the lacrimal gland; near the nasal part is a depression, the **fovea trochlearis,** or occasionally a small **trochlear spine,** for the attachment of the cartilaginous pulley of the Obliquus oculi superior. The **superior surface** is convex, and marked by depressions for the convolutions of the frontal lobes of the brain, and faint grooves for the meningeal branches of the ethmoidal vessels.

The **ethmoidal notch** separates the two orbital plates; it is quadrilateral, and filled, in the articulated skull, by the cribriform plate of the ethmoid. The margins of the notch present several half-cells which, when united with corresponding half-cells on the upper surface of the ethmoid, complete the ethmoidal air cells. Two grooves cross these edges transversely; they are converted into the **anterior** and **posterior ethmoidal canals** by the ethmoid, and open on the medial wall of the orbit. The anterior canal transmits the nasociliary nerve and anterior ethmoidal vessels, the posterior, the posterior ethmoidal nerve and vessels. In front of the ethmoidal notch, on either side of the frontal spine, are the openings of the **frontal**

air sinuses. These are two irregular cavities, which extend backward, upward, and lateralward for a variable distance between the two tables of the skull; they are separated from one another by a thin bony septum, which often deviates to one or other side, with the result that the sinuses are rarely symmetrical. Absent at birth, they are usually fairly well-developed between the seventh and eighth years, but only reach their full size after puberty. They vary in size in different persons, and are larger in men than in women. They are lined by mucous membrane, and each communicates with the corresponding nasal cavity by means of a passage called the **frontonasal duct.**

Borders.—The **border of the squama** is thick, strongly serrated, bevelled at the expense of the inner table above, where it rests upon the parietal bones, and at the expense of the outer table on either side, where it receives the lateral pressure of those bones; this border is continued below into a triangular, rough surface, which articulates with the great wing of the sphenoid. The **posterior borders of the orbital plates** are thin and serrated, and articulate with the small wings of the sphenoid.

Structure.—The squama and the zygomatic processes are very thick, consisting of diploic tissue contained between two compact laminæ; the diploic tissue is absent in the regions occupied by the frontal air sinuses. The orbital portion is thin, translucent, and composed entirely of compact bone; hence the facility with which instruments can penetrate the cranium through this part of the orbit; when the frontal sinuses are exceptionally large they may extend backward for a considerable distance into the orbital portion, which in such cases also consists of only two tables.

Ossification (Fig. 210).—The frontal bone is ossified in membrane from *two primary* centers, one for each half, which appear toward the end of the second month of fetal life, one above each supraorbital margin. From each of these centers ossification extends upward to form the corresponding half of the squama, and backward to form the orbital plate. The spine is ossified from a pair of *secondary* centers, on either side of the middle line; similar centers appear in the nasal part and zygomatic processes. At birth the bone consists of two pieces, separated by the frontal suture, which is usually obliterated, except at its lower part, by the eighth year, but occasionally persists throughout life. It is generally maintained that the development of the frontal sinuses begins at the end of the first or beginning of the second year, but Onodi's researches indicate that development begins at birth. The sinuses are of considerable size by the seventh or eighth year, but do not attain their full proportions until after puberty.

Articulations. — The frontal articulates with *twelve* bones: the sphenoid, the ethmoid, the two parietals, the two nasals, the two maxillæ, the two lacrimals, and the two zygomatics.

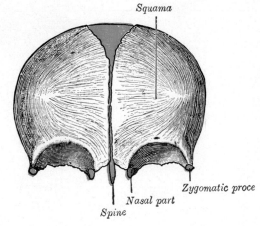

Fig. 210.—Frontal bone at birth.

The Temporal Bone (Os Temporale).

The **temporal bones** are situated at the sides and base of the skull. Each consists of five parts, viz., the **squama**, the **petrous**, **mastoid**, and **tympanic parts**, and the **styloid process**.

The Squama (*pars squamosa*).—The squama forms the anterior and upper part of the bone, and is scale-like, thin, and translucent.

Surfaces.—Its **outer surface** (Fig. 211) is smooth and convex; it affords attachment to the Temporalis muscle, and forms part of the temporal fossa; on its hinder part is a vertical groove for the middle temporal artery. A curved line, the **tem-**

poral line, or **supramastoid crest,** runs backward and upward across its posterior part; it serves for the attachment of the temporal fascia, and limits the origin of the Temporalis muscle. The boundary between the squama and the mastoid portion of the bone, as indicated by traces of the original suture, lies about 1 cm. below this line. Projecting from the lower part of the squama is a long, arched process, the **zygomatic process.** This process is at first directed lateralward, its two surfaces looking upward and downward; it then appears as if twisted inward upon itself, and runs forward, its surfaces now looking medialward and lateralward. The superior border is long, thin, and sharp, and serves for the attachment of the temporal fascia; the inferior, short, thick, and arched, has attached to it some fibers of the Masseter. The lateral surface is convex and subcutaneous; the medial is concave, and affords attachment to the Masseter. The anterior end is deeply

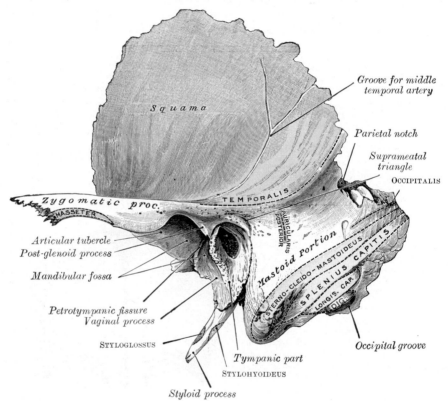

FIG. 211.—Left temporal bone. Outer surface.

serrated and articulates with the zygomatic bone. The posterior end is connected to the squama by two roots, the **anterior** and **posterior roots.** The posterior root, a prolongation of the upper border, is strongly marked; it runs backward above the external acoustic meatus, and is continuous with the temporal line. The anterior root, continuous with the lower border, is short but broad and strong; it is directed medialward and ends in a rounded eminence, the **articular tubercle** (*tuberculum articularis*). This tubercle forms the front boundary of the mandibular fossa, and in the fresh state is covered with cartilage. In front of the articular tubercle is a small triangular area which assists in forming the infratemporal fossa; this area is separated from the outer surface of the squama by a ridge which is continuous behind with the anterior root of the zygomatic process, and in front, in the articulated skull, with the infratemporal crest on the great wing of the sphenoid.

Between the posterior wall of the external acoustic meatus and the posterior root of the zygomatic process is the area called the **suprameatal triangle** (Macewen), or **mastoid fossa**, through which an instrument may be pushed into the tympanic antrum. At the junction of the anterior root with the zygomatic process is a projection for the attachment of the temporomandibular ligament; and behind the anterior root is an oval depression, forming part of the mandibular fossa, for the reception of the condyle of the mandible. The **mandibular fossa** (*glenoid fossa*) is bounded, in front, by the articular tubercle; behind, by the tympanic part of the bone, which separates it from the external acoustic meatus; it is divided into two parts by a narrow slit, the **petrotympanic fissure** (*Glaserian fissure*). The anterior part, formed by the squama, is smooth, covered in the fresh state with cartilage, and articulates with the condyle of the mandible. Behind this part

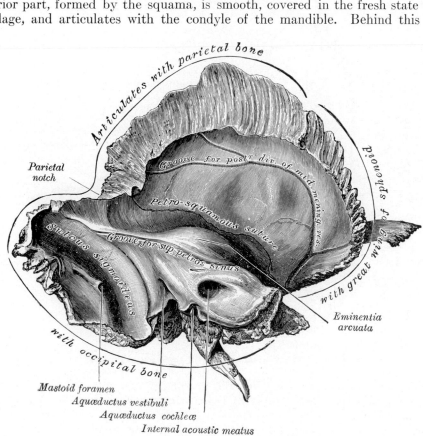

FIG. 212.—Left temporal bone. Inner surface.

of the fossa is a small conical eminence; this is the representative of a prominent tubercle which, in some mammals, descends behind the condyle of the mandible, and prevents its backward displacement. The posterior part of the mandibular fossa, formed by the tympanic part of the bone, is non-articular, and sometimes lodges a portion of the parotid gland. The petrotympanic fissure leads into the middle ear or tympanic cavity; it lodges the anterior process of the malleus, and transmits the tympanic branch of the internal maxillary artery. The chorda tympani nerve passes through a canal (*canal of Huguier*), separated from the anterior edge of the petrotympanic fissure by a thin scale of bone and situated on the lateral side of the auditory tube, in the retiring angle between the squama and the petrous portion of the temporal.

The **internal surface** of the squama (Fig. 212) is concave; it presents depressions corresponding to the convolutions of the temporal lobe of the brain, and grooves for the branches of the middle meningeal vessels.

Borders.—The **superior border** is thin, and bevelled at the expense of the internal table, so as to overlap the squamous border of the parietal bone, forming with it the squamosal suture. Posteriorly, the superior border forms an angle, the **parietal notch**, with the mastoid portion of the bone. The **antero-inferior border** is thick, serrated, and bevelled at the expense of the inner table above and of the outer below, for articulation with the great wing of the sphenoid.

Mastoid Portion (*processus mastoideus*).—The mastoid portion forms the posterior part of the bone.

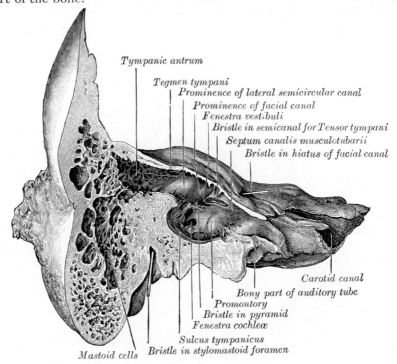

Fig. 213.—Coronal section of right temporal bone.

Surfaces.—Its **outer surface** (Fig. 211) is rough, and gives attachment to the Occipitalis and Auricularis posterior. It is perforated by numerous foramina; one of these, of large size, situated near the posterior border, is termed the **mastoid foramen**; it transmits a vein to the transverse sinus and a small branch of the occipital artery to the dura mater. The position and size of this foramen are very variable; it is not always present; sometimes it is situated in the occipital bone, or in the suture between the temporal and the occipital. The mastoid portion is continued below into a conical projection, the **mastoid process**, the size and form of which vary somewhat; it is larger in the male than in the female. This process serves for the attachment of the Sternocleidomastoideus, Splenius capitis, and Longissimus capitis. On the medial side of the process is a deep groove, the **mastoid notch** (*digastric fossa*), for the attachment of the Digastricus; medial to this is a shallow furrow, the **occipital groove**, which lodges the occipital artery.

The **inner surface** of the mastoid portion presents a deep, curved groove, the **sigmoid sulcus**, which lodges part of the transverse sinus; in it may be seen the opening of the mastoid foramen. The groove for the transverse sinus is separated from the innermost of the mastoid air cells by a very thin lamina of bone, and even this may be partly deficient.

Borders.—The **superior border** of the mastoid portion is broad and serrated, for articulation with the mastoid angle of the parietal. The **posterior border,** also serrated, articulates with the inferior border of the occipital between the lateral angle and jugular process. Anteriorly the mastoid portion is fused with the descending process of the squama above; below it enters into the formation of the external acoustic meatus and the tympanic cavity.

A section of the mastoid process (Fig. 213) shows it to be hollowed out into a number of spaces, the **mastoid cells,** which exhibit the greatest possible variety as to their size and number. At the upper and front part of the process they are large and irregular and contain air, but toward the lower part they diminish in size, while those at the apex of the process are frequently quite small and contain marrow; occasionally they are entirely absent, and the mastoid is then solid throughout. In addition to these a large irregular cavity is situated at the upper and front part of the bone. It is called the **tympanic antrum,** and must be distinguished from the mastoid cells, though it communicates with them. Like the mastoid cells it is filled with air and lined by a prolongation of the mucous membrane of the tympanic cavity, with which it communicates. The tympanic antrum is bounded above by a thin plate of bone, the **tegmen tympani,** which separates it from the middle fossa of the base of the skull; below by the mastoid process; laterally by the squama just below the temporal line, and medially by the lateral semicircular canal of the internal ear which projects into its cavity. It opens in front into that portion of the tympanic cavity which is known as the **attic** or **epitympanic recess.** The tympanic antrum is a cavity of some considerable size at the time of birth; the mastoid air cells may be regarded as diverticula from the antrum, and begin to appear at or before birth; by the fifth year they are well-marked, but their development is not completed until toward puberty.

Petrous Portion (*pars petrosa* [*pyramis*]).—The petrous portion or **pyramid** is pyramidal and is wedged in at the base of the skull between the sphenoid and occipital. Directed medialward, forward, and a little upward, it presents for examination a base, an apex, three surfaces, and three angles, and contains, in its interior, the essential parts of the organ of hearing.

Base.—The base is fused with the internal surfaces of the squama and mastoid portion.

Apex.—The apex, rough and uneven, is received into the angular interval between the posterior border of the great wing of the sphenoid and the basilar part of the occipital and sphenoid; it presents the anterior or internal orifice of the carotid canal, and forms the postero-lateral boundary of the foramen lacerum.

Surfaces.—The **anterior surface** forms the posterior part of the middle fossa of the base of the skull, and is continuous with the inner surface of the squamous portion, to which it is united by the **petrosquamous suture,** remains of which are distinct even at a late period of life. It is marked by depressions for the convolutions of the brain, and presents six points for examination: (1) near the center, an **eminence** (*eminentia arcuata*) which indicates the situation of the superior semicircular canal; (2) in front of and a little lateral to this eminence, a depression indicating the position of the tympanic cavity: here the layer of bone which separates the tympanic from the cranial cavity is extremely thin, and is known as the **tegmen tympani;** (3) a shallow groove, sometimes double, leading lateralward and backward to an oblique opening, the **hiatus of the facial canal,** for the passage of the greater superficial petrosal nerve and the petrosal branch of the middle meningeal artery; (4) lateral to the hiatus, a smaller opening, occasionally seen, for the passage of the lesser superficial petrosal nerve; (5) near the apex of the bone, the termination of the carotid canal, the wall of which in this situation is deficient in front; (6) above this canal the shallow **trigeminal impression** for the reception of the semilunar ganglion.

The **posterior surface** (Fig. 212) forms the front part of the posterior fossa of the base of the skull, and is continuous with the inner surface of the mastoid portion. Near the center is a large orifice, the **internal acoustic meatus**, the size of which varies considerably; its margins are smooth and rounded, and it leads into a short canal, about 1 cm. in length, which runs lateralward. It transmits the facial and acoustic nerves, the nervus intermedius and the internal auditory branch of the basilar artery. The lateral end of the canal is closed by a vertical plate, which is divided by a horizontal crest, the **crista falciformis**, into two unequal portions (Fig. 214). Each portion is further subdivided by a vertical ridge into an anterior and a posterior part. In the portion beneath the crista falciformis are three sets of foramina; one group, just below the posterior part of the crest, situated in the **area cribrosa media**, consists of several small openings for the nerves to the saccule; below and behind this area is the **foramen singulare**, or opening for the nerve to the posterior semicircular duct; in front of and below the first is the **tractus spiralis foraminosus**, consisting of a number of small spirally arranged openings, which encircle the **canalis centralis cochleæ**; these openings together with this central canal transmit the nerves to the cochlea. The portion above the crista falciformis presents behind, the **area cribrosa superior**, pierced by a series of small openings, for the passage of the nerves to the utricle and the superior and lateral semicircular ducts, and, in front, the **area facialis**, with one large opening, the com-

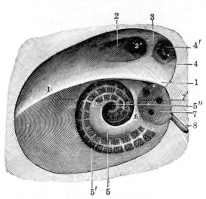

FIG. 214.—Diagrammatic view of the fundus of the right internal acoustic meatus. (Testut.) 1. Crista falciformis. 2. Area facialis, with (2') internal opening of the facial canal. 3. Ridge separating the area facialis from the area cribrosa superior. 4. Area cribrosa superior, with (4') openings for nerve filaments. 5. Anterior inferior cribriform area, with (5') the tractus spiralis foraminosus, and (5'') the canalis centralis of the cochlea. 6. Ridge separating the tractus spiralis foraminosus from the area cribrosa media. 7. Area cribrosa media, with (7') orifices for nerves to saccule. 8. Foramen singulare.

mencement of the canal for the facial nerve (**aquæductus Fallopii**). Behind the internal acoustic meatus is a small slit almost hidden by a thin plate of bone, leading to a canal, the **aquæductus vestibuli**, which transmits the ductus endolymphaticus together with a small artery and vein. Above and between these two openings is an irregular depression which lodges a process of the dura mater and transmits a small vein; in the infant this depression is represented by a large fossa, the **subarcuate fossa**, which extends backward as a blind tunnel under the superior semicircular canal.

The **inferior surface** (Fig. 215) is rough and irregular, and forms part of the exterior of the base of the skull. It presents eleven points for examination: (1) near the apex is a rough surface, quadrilateral in form, which serves partly for the attachment of the Levator veli palatini and the cartilaginous portion of the auditory tube, and partly for connection with the basilar part of the occipital bone through the intervention of some dense fibrous tissue; (2) behind this is the large circular aperture of the **carotid canal**, which ascends at first vertically, and then, making a bend, runs horizontally forward and medialward; it transmits into the cranium the internal carotid artery, and the carotid plexus of nerves; (3) medial to the opening for the carotid canal and close to its posterior border, in front of the jugular fossa, is a triangular depression; at the apex of this is a small opening, the **aquæductus cochleæ**, which lodges a tubular prolongation of the dura mater establishing a communication between the perilymphatic space and the subarachnoid space, and transmits a vein from the cochlea to join the internal jugular; (4) behind these openings is a deep depression, the **jugular fossa**, of variable depth and size in different skulls; it lodges the bulb of the internal jugular vein; (5) in the bony ridge dividing the carotid canal from the jugular fossa is the small **inferior tympanic canaliculus** for the passage of the tympanic branch of the glossopharyngeal nerve; (6) in the lateral part of the jugular fossa is the **mastoid canaliculus** for the entrance of the auricular branch of the vagus nerve; (7) behind the jugular fossa is a quadrilateral area, the **jugular surface**, covered with cartilage in the fresh state, and articulating with the jugular process of the occipital bone; (8) extending backward from the carotid canal is the **vaginal process**, a sheath-like plate of bone, which divides behind into two laminæ; the lateral lamina is continuous with the tympanic part of the bone, the medial with the lateral margin of the jugular surface; (9) between these laminæ is the **styloid process**, a sharp spine, about 2.5 cm. in length; (10) between the styloid and mastoid processes is the **stylomastoid foramen;** it is the termination of the facial canal, and transmits the facial nerve and stylomastoid artery; (11) situated between the tympanic portion and the mastoid process is the tympanomastoid fissure, for the exit of the auricular branch of the vagus nerve.

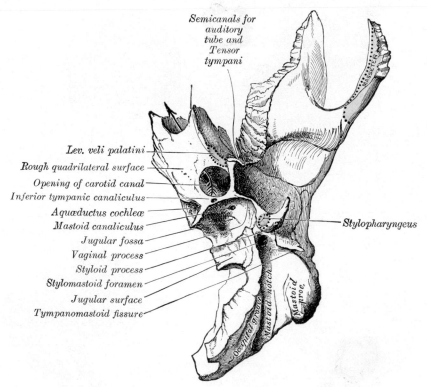

Fig. 215.—Left temporal bone. Inferior surface.

Angles.—The **superior angle**, the longest, is grooved for the superior petrosal sinus, and gives attachment to the tentorium cerebelli; at its medial extremity is a notch, in which the trigeminal nerve lies. The **posterior angle** is intermediate in length between the superior and the anterior. Its medial half is marked by a sulcus, which forms, with a corresponding sulcus on the occipital bone, the channel for the inferior petrosal sinus. Its lateral half presents an excavation —the **jugular fossa**—which, with the jugular notch on the occipital, forms the **jugular foramen**; an eminence occasionally projects from the center of the fossa, and divides the foramen into two. The **anterior angle** is joined to the squama by a suture (*petrosquamous*), the remains of which are more or less distinct; it also articulates with the sphenoid. At the angle of junction of the petrous part and the squama are two canals, one above the other, and separated by a thin plate of bone, the **septum canalis musculotubarii** (*processus cochleariformis*); both canals lead into the tympanic cavity. The upper one (*semicanalis m. tensoris tympani*) transmits the Tensor tympani, the lower one (*semicanalis tubæ auditivæ*) forms the bony part of the auditory tube.

The tympanic cavity, auditory ossicles, and internal ear, are described with the organ of hearing.

Tympanic Part (*pars tympanica*).—The tympanic part is a curved plate of bone lying below the squama and in front of the mastoid process.

Surfaces.—Its **postero-superior surface** is concave, and forms the anterior wall, the floor, and part of the posterior wall of the bony external acoustic meatus.

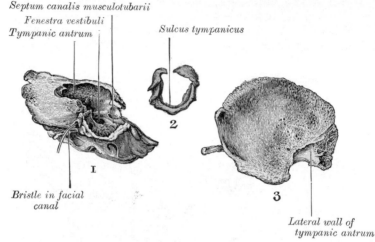

Septum canalis musculotubarii
Fenestra vestibuli
Tympanic antrum
Sulcus tympanicus

Bristle in facial canal

Lateral wall of tympanic antrum

FIG. 216.—The three principal parts of the temporal bone at birth. 1. Outer surface of petro-mastoid part. 2. Outer surface of tympanic ring. 3. Inner surface of squama.

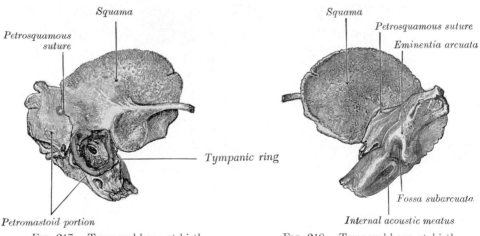

Squama
Petrosquamous suture

Squama
Petrosquamous suture
Eminentia arcuata

Tympanic ring

Petromastoid portion

Fossa subarcuata

Internal acoustic meatus

FIG. 217.—Temporal bone at birth. Outer aspect.

FIG. 218.—Temporal bone at birth. Inner aspect.

Medially, it presents a narrow furrow, the **tympanic sulcus**, for the attachment of the tympanic membrane. Its **antero-inferior surface** is quadrilateral and slightly concave; it constitutes the posterior boundary of the mandibular fossa, and is in contact with the retromandibular part of the parotid gland.

Borders.—Its **lateral border** is free and rough, and gives attachment to the cartilaginous part of the external acoustic meatus. Internally, the tympanic part is fused with the petrous portion, and appears in the retreating angle between it and the squama, where it lies below and lateral to the orifice of the auditory tube. Posteriorly, it blends with the squama and mastoid part, and forms the anterior boundary of the tympanomastoid fissure. Its **upper border** fuses laterally with the back of the postglenoid process, while medially it bounds the petrotympanic fissure. The medial part of the **lower border** is thin and sharp; its lateral part splits to enclose the root of the styloid process, and is therefore named the **vaginal process**. The central portion of the tympanic part is thin, and in a considerable percentage of skulls is perforated by a hole, the **foramen of Huschke**.

The **external acoustic meatus** is nearly 2 cm. long and is directed inward and slightly forward: at the same time it forms a slight curve, so that the floor of the canal is convex upward. In sagittal section it presents an oval or elliptical shape with the long axis directed downward and slightly backward. Its anterior wall and floor and the lower part of its posterior wall are formed by the tympanic part; the roof and upper part of the posterior wall by the squama. Its inner end is closed, in the recent state, by the tympanic membrane; the upper limit of its outer orifice is formed by the posterior root of the zygomatic process, immediately below which there is sometimes seen a small spine, the **suprameatal spine**, situated at the upper and posterior part of the orifice.

Styloid Process (*processus styloideus*).—The styloid process is slender, pointed, and of varying length; it projects downward and forward, from the under surface of the temporal bone. Its proximal part (*tympanohyal*) is ensheathed by the vaginal process of the tympanic portion, while its distal part (*stylohyal*) gives attachment to the stylohyoid and stylomandibular ligaments, and to the Styloglossus, Stylohyoideus, and Stylopharyngeus muscles. The stylohyoid ligament extends from the apex of the process to the lesser cornu of the hyoid bone, and in some instances is partially, in others completely, ossified.

Structure.—The structure of the squama is like that of the other cranial bones: the mastoid portion is spongy, and the petrous portion dense and hard.

Ossification.—The temporal bone is ossified from *eight* centers, exclusive of those for the internal ear and the tympanic ossicles, viz., one for the squama including the zygomatic process, one for the tympanic part, four for the petrous and mastoid parts, and two for the styloid process. Just before the close of fetal life (Fig. 216) the temporal bone consists of three principal parts: 1. The *squama* is ossified in membrane from a single nucleus, which appears near the root of the zygomatic process about the second month. 2. The *petromastoid* part is developed from four centers, which make their appearance in the cartilaginous ear capsule about the fifth or sixth month. One (*proötic*) appears in the neighborhood of the eminentia arcuata, spreads in front and above the internal acoustic meatus and extends to the apex of the bone; it forms part of the cochlea, vestibule, superior semicircular canal, and medial wall of the tympanic cavity. A second (*opisthotic*) appears at the promontory on the medial wall of the tympanic cavity and surrounds the fenestra cochleæ; it forms the floor of the tympanic cavity and vestibule, surrounds the carotid canal, invests the lateral and lower part of the cochlea, and spreads medially below the internal acoustic meatus. A third (*pterotic*) roofs in the tympanic cavity and antrum; while the fourth (*epiotic*) appears near the posterior semicircular canal and extends to form the mastoid process (Vrolik). 3. The *tympanic ring* is an incomplete circle, in the concavity of which is a groove, the tympanic sulcus, for the attachment of the circumference of the tympanic membrane. This ring expands to form the tympanic part, and is ossified in membrane from a single center which appears about the third month. The *styloid process* is developed from the proximal part of the cartilage of the second branchial or hyoid arch by two centers: one for the proximal part, the *tympanohyal*, appears before birth; the other, comprising the rest of the process, is named the *stylohyal*, and does not appear until after birth. The tympanic ring unites with the squama shortly before birth; the petromastoid part and squama join during the first year, and the tympanohyal portion of the styloid process about the same time (Figs. 217, 218). The stylohyal does not unite with the rest of the bone until after puberty, and in some skulls never at all.

The chief subsequent changes in the temporal bone apart from increase in size are: (1) The tympanic ring extends outward and backward to form the tympanic part. This extension does not, however, take place at an equal rate all around the circumference of the ring, but occurs most rapidly on its anterior and posterior portions, and these outgrowths meet and blend, and thus, for a time, there exists in the floor of the meatus a foramen, the *foramen of Huschke;* this foramen is usually closed about the fifth year, but may persist throughout life. (2) The mandibular fossa is at first extremely shallow, and looks lateralward as well as downward; it becomes deeper and is ultimately directed downward. Its change in direction is accounted for as follows. The part of the squama which forms the fossa lies at first below the level of the zygomatic process. As, however, the base of the skull increases in width, this lower part of the squama is directed hori-ozntally inward to contribute to the middle fossa of the skull, and its surfaces therefore come to look upward and downward; the attached portion of the zygomatic process also becomes everted, and projects like a shelf at right angles to the squama. (3) The mastoid portion is at first quite flat, and the stylomastoid foramen and rudimentary styloid process lie immediately behind the tympanic ring. With the development of the air cells the outer part of the mastoid portion grows downward and forward to form the mastoid process, and the styloid process and stylomastoid foramen now come to lie on the under surface. The descent of the foramen is necessarily accompanied by a corresponding lengthening of the facial canal. (4) The downward and forward growth of the mastoid process also pushes forward the tympanic part, so that the portion of it which formed the original floor of the meatus and contained the foramen of Huschke is ultimately found in the anterior wall. (5) The fossa subarcuata becomes filled up and almost obliterated.

Articulations.—The temporal articulates with *five* bones: occipital, parietal, sphenoid, mandible, and zygomatic.

The Sphenoid Bone (Os Sphenoidale).

The **sphenoid bone** is situated at the base of the skull in front of the temporals and basilar part of the occipital. It somewhat resembles a bat with its wings extended, and is divided into a median portion or body, two great and two small wings extending outward from the sides of the body, and two pterygoid processes which project from it below.

Body (*corpus sphenoidale*).—The body, more or less cubical in shape, is hollowed out in its interior to form two large cavities, the **sphenoidal air sinuses**, which are separated from each other by a septum.

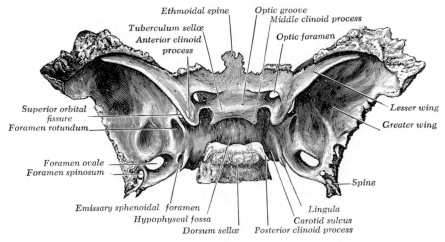

Fig. 219.—The sphenoid bone. Superior aspect.

Surfaces.—The **superior surface** of the body (Fig. 219) presents in front a prominent spine, the **ethmoidal spine,** for articulation with the cribriform plate of the ethmoid; behind this is a smooth surface slightly raised in the middle line, and grooved on either side for the olfactory lobes of the brain. This surface is bounded behind by a ridge, which forms the anterior border of a narrow, transverse groove, the **chiasmatic groove** (*optic groove*), above and behind which lies the optic chiasma; the groove ends on either side in the **optic foramen,** which transmits the optic nerve and ophthalmic artery into the orbital cavity. Behind the chiasmatic groove is an elevation, the **tuberculum sellæ;** and still more posteriorly, a deep depression, the **sella turcica,** the deepest part of which lodges the hypophysis cerebri and is known as the **fossa hypophyseos.** The anterior boundary of the sella turcica is completed by two small eminences, one on either side, called the **middle clinoid processes,** while the posterior boundary is formed by a square-shaped plate of bone, the **dorsum sellæ,** ending at its superior angles in two tubercles, the **posterior clinoid processes,** the size and form of which vary considerably in different individuals. The posterior clinoid processes deepen the sella turcica, and give attachment to the tentorium cerebelli. On either side of the dorsum sellæ is a notch for the passage of the abducent nerve, and below the notch a sharp process, the **petrosal process**, which articulates with the apex of the petrous portion of the temporal bone, and forms the medial boundary of the foramen lacerum. Behind the dorsum sellæ is a shallow depression, the **clivus**, which slopes obliquely backward, and is continuous with the groove on the basilar portion of the occipital bone; it supports the upper part of the pons.

The **lateral surfaces** of the body are united with the great wings and the medial pterygoid plates. Above the attachment of each great wing is a broad groove, curved something like the italic letter *f;* it lodges the internal carotid artery and the cavernous sinus, and is named the **carotid groove**. Along the posterior part of the lateral margin of this groove, in the angle between the body and great wing, is a ridge of bone, called the **lingula**.

The **posterior surface**, quadrilateral in form (Fig. 220), is joined, during infancy and adolescence, to the basilar part of the occipital bone by a plate of cartilage. Between the eighteenth and twenty-fifth years this becomes ossified, ossification commencing above and extending downward.

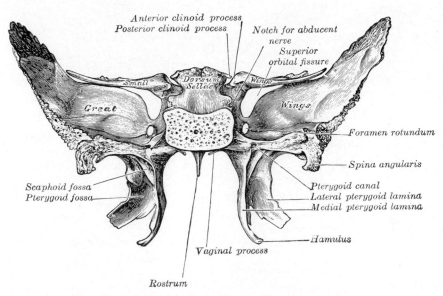

FIG. 220.—Sphenoid bone. Upper and posterior surfaces.

The **anterior surface** of the body (Fig. 221) presents, in the middle line, a vertical crest, the **sphenoidal crest**, which articulates with the perpendicular plate of the ethmoid, and forms part of the septum of the nose. On either side of the crest is an irregular opening leading into the corresponding **sphenoidal air sinus**. These sinuses are two large, irregular cavities hollowed out of the interior of the body of the bone, and separated from one another by a bony septum, which is commonly bent to one or the other side. They vary considerably in form and size, are seldom symmetrical, and are often partially subdivided by irregular bony laminæ. Occasionally, they extend into the basilar part of the occipital nearly as far as the foramen magnum. They begin to be developed before birth, and are of a considerable size by the age of six. They are partially closed, in front and below, by two thin, curved plates of bone, the **sphenoidal conchæ** (see page 214), leaving in the articulated skull a round opening at the upper part of each sinus by which it communicates with the upper and back part of the nasal cavity and occasionally with the posterior ethmoidal air cells. The lateral margin of the anterior surface is serrated, and articulates with the lamina papyracea of the ethmoid, completing the posterior ethmoidal cells; the lower margin articulates with the orbital process of the palatine bone, and the upper with the orbital plate of the frontal bone.

The **inferior surface** presents, in the middle line, a triangular spine, the **sphenoidal rostrum**, which is continuous with the sphenoidal crest on the anterior surface, and is received in a deep fissure between the alæ of the vomer. On either side of the rostrum is a projecting lamina, the **vaginal process**, directed medialward from the base of the medial pterygoid plate, with which it will be described.

The Great Wings (*alæ majores*).—The great wings, or **ali-sphenoids**, are two strong processes of bone, which arise from the sides of the body, and are curved upward, lateralward, and backward; the posterior part of each projects as a tri-angular process which fits into the angle between the squama and the petrous portion of the temporal and presents at its apex a downwardly directed process, the **spina angularis** (*sphenoidal spine*).

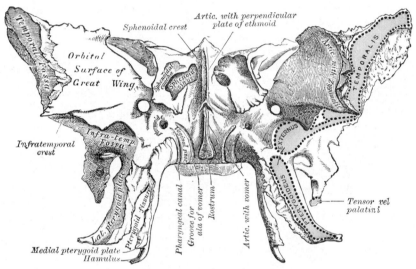

FIG. 221.—Sphenoid bone. Anterior and inferior surfaces.

Surfaces.—The **superior** or **cerebral surface** of each great wing (Fig. 183) forms part of the middle fossa of the skull; it is deeply concave, and presents depressions for the convolutions of the temporal lobe of the brain. At its anterior and medial part is a circular aperture, the **foramen rotundum,** for the transmission of the maxillary nerve. Behind and lateral to this is the **foramen ovale,** for the transmission of the mandibular nerve, the accessory meningeal artery, and sometimes the lesser superficial petrosal nerve. Medial to the foramen ovale, a small aperture, the **foramen Vesalii,** may occasionally be seen opposite the root of the pterygoid process; it opens below near the scaphoid fossa, and transmits a small vein from the cavernous sinus. Lastly, in the posterior angle, near to and in front of the spine, is a short canal, sometimes double, the **foramen spinosum,** which transmits the middle meningeal vessels and a recurrent branch from the mandibular nerve. The lesser superficial petrosal nerve sometimes passes through a special canal (*canaliculus innominatus* of Arnold) situated medial to the foramen spinosum.

The **lateral surface** (Fig. 183) is convex, and divided by a transverse ridge, the **infratemporal crest,** into two portions. The superior or temporal portion, convex from above downward, concave from before backward, forms a part of the temporal fossa, and gives attachment to the Temporalis; the inferior or infratemporal, smaller in size and concave, enters into the formation of the infratemporal fossa and, together with the infratemporal crest, affords attachment to the Pterygoideus externus. It is pierced by the foramen ovale and foramen spinosum, and at its posterior part is the spina angularis, which is frequently grooved on its medial surface for the chorda tympani nerve. To the spina angularis are attached the sphenomandibular ligament and the Tensor veli palatini. Medial to the anterior extremity of the infratemporal crest is a triangular process which serves to increase the attachment of the Pterygoideus externus; extending downward and medialward from this process on to the front part of the lateral pterygoid plate is a ridge which forms the anterior limit of the infratemporal surface, and, in the articulated skull, the posterior boundary of the pterygomaxillary fissure.

The **orbital surface** of the great wing (Fig. 221), smooth, and quadrilateral in shape, is directed forward and medialward and forms the posterior part of the lateral wall of the orbit. Its upper serrated edge articulates with the orbital plate of the frontal. Its inferior rounded border forms the postero-lateral boundary of the inferior orbital fissure. Its medial sharp margin forms the lower boundary of the superior orbital fissure and has projecting from about its center a little tubercle which gives attachment to the inferior head of the Rectus lateralis oculi; at the upper part of this margin is a notch for the transmission of a recurrent branch of the lacrimal artery. Its lateral margin is serrated and articulates with the zygomatic bone. Below the medial end of the superior orbital fissure is a grooved surface, which forms the posterior wall of the pterygopalatine fossa, and is pierced by the foramen rotundum.

Margin (Fig. 219).—Commencing from behind, that portion of the circumference of the great wing which extends from the body to the spine is irregular. Its medial half forms the anterior boundary of the foramen lacerum, and presents the posterior aperture of the pterygoid canal for the passage of the corresponding nerve and artery. Its lateral half articulates, by means of a synchondrosis, with the petrous portion of the temporal, and between the two bones on the under surface of the skull, is a furrow, the **sulcus tubæ**, for the lodgement of the cartilaginous part of the auditory tube. In front of the spine the circumference presents a concave, serrated edge, bevelled at the expense of the inner table below, and of the outer table above, for articulation with the temporal squama. At the tip of the great wing is a triangular portion, bevelled at the expense of the internal surface, for articulation with the sphenoidal angle of the parietal bone; this region is named the **pterion**. Medial to this is a triangular, serrated surface, for articulation with the frontal bone; this surface is continuous medially with the sharp edge, which forms the lower boundary of the superior orbital fissure, and laterally with the serrated margin for articulation with the zygomatic bone.

The Small Wings (*alæ minores*).—The small wings or **orbito-sphenoids** are two thin triangular plates, which arise from the upper and anterior parts of the body, and, projecting lateralward, end in sharp points (Fig. 219).

Surfaces.—The **superior surface** of each is flat, and supports part of the frontal lobe of the brain. The **inferior surface** forms the back part of the roof of the orbit, and the upper boundary of the **superior orbital fissure**. This fissure is of a triangular form, and leads from the cavity of the cranium into that of the orbit: it is bounded *medially* by the body; *above*, by the small wing; *below*, by the medial margin of the orbital surface of the great wing; and is completed *laterally* by the frontal bone. It transmits the oculomotor, trochlear, and abducent nerves, the three branches of the ophthalmic division of the trigeminal nerve, some filaments from the cavernous plexus of the sympathetic, the orbital branch of the middle meningeal artery, a recurrent branch from the lacrimal artery to the dura mater, and the ophthalmic vein.

Borders.—The **anterior border** is serrated for articulation with the frontal bone. The **posterior border**, smooth and rounded, is received into the lateral fissure of the brain; the medial end of this border forms the **anterior clinoid process**, which gives attachment to the tentorium cerebelli; it is sometimes joined to the middle clinoid process by a spicule of bone, and when this occurs the termination of the groove for the internal carotid artery is converted into a foramen (*carotico-clinoid*). The small wing is connected to the body by two roots, the upper thin and flat, the lower thick and triangular; between the two roots is the **optic foramen,** for the transmission of the optic nerve and ophthalmic artery.

Pterygoid Processes (*processus pterygoidei*).—The pterygoid processes, one on either side, descend perpendicularly from the regions where the body and great wings unite. Each process consists of a medial and a lateral plate, the upper parts of which are fused anteriorly; a vertical sulcus, the **pterygopalatine groove,** descends on the front of the line of fusion. The plates are separated below by an angular cleft, the **pterygoid fissure,** the margins of which are rough for articulation with the pyramidal process of the palatine bone. The two plates diverge behind and enclose between them a V-shaped fossa, the **pterygoid fossa,** which contains the Pterygoideus internus and Tensor veli palatini. Above this fossa is a small, oval, shallow depression, the **scaphoid fossa,** which gives origin to the Tensor veli palatini. The anterior surface of the pterygoid process is broad and triangular near its root, where it forms the posterior wall of the pterygopalatine fossa and presents the anterior orifice of the pterygoid canal.

Lateral Pterygoid Plate.—The **lateral pterygoid plate** is broad, thin, and everted; its **lateral surface** forms part of the medial wall of the infratemporal fossa, and gives attachment to the Pterygoideus externus; its **medial surface** forms part of the pterygoid fossa, and gives attachment to the Pterygoideus internus.

Medial Pterygoid Plate.—The medial pterygoid plate is narrower and longer than the lateral; it curves lateralward at its lower extremity into a hook-like process, the **pterygoid hamulus,** around which the tendon of the Tensor veli palatini glides. The **lateral surface** of this plate forms part of the pterygoid fossa, the **medial surface** constitutes the lateral boundary of the choana or posterior aperture of the corresponding nasal cavity. Superiorly the medial plate is prolonged on to the under surface of the body as a thin lamina, named the **vaginal process,** which articulates in front with the sphenoidal process of the palatine and behind this with the ala of the vomer. The angular prominence between the posterior margin of the vaginal process and the medial border of the scaphoid fossa is named the **pterygoid tubercle,** and immediately above this is the posterior opening of the pterygoid canal. On the under surface of the vaginal process is a furrow, which is converted into a canal by the sphenoidal process of the palatine bone, for the transmission of the pharyngeal branch of the internal maxillary artery and the pharyngeal nerve from the sphenopalatine ganglion. The pharyngeal aponeurosis is attached to the entire length of the posterior edge of the medial plate, and the Constrictor pharyngis superior takes origin from its lower third. Projecting backward from near the middle of the posterior edge of this plate is an angular process, the **processus tubarius,** which supports the pharyngeal end of the auditory tube. The anterior margin of the plate articulates with the posterior border of the vertical part of the palatine bone.

The Sphenoidal Conchæ (*conchæ sphenoidales; sphenoidal turbinated processes*). —The sphenoidal conchæ are two thin, curved plates, situated at the anterior and lower part of the body of the sphenoid. An aperture of variable size exists in the anterior wall of each, and through this the sphenoidal sinus opens into the nasal cavity. Each is irregular in form, and tapers to a point behind, being broader and thinner in front. Its upper surface is concave, and looks toward the cavity of the sinus; its under surface is convex, and forms part of the roof of the corresponding nasal cavity. Each bone articulates in front with the ethmoid laterally with the palatine; its pointed posterior extremity is placed above the vomer, and is received between the root of the pterygoid process laterally and the rostrum of the sphenoid medially. A small portion of the sphenoidal concha sometimes enters into the formation of the medial wall of the orbit, between the lamina papyracea of the ethmoid in front, the orbital plate of the palatine below, and the frontal bone above.

Ossification.—Until the seventh or eighth month of fetal life the body of the sphenoid consists of two parts, *viz.*, one in front of the tuberculum sellæ, the *presphenoid*, with which the small wings are continuous; the other, comprising the sella turcica and dorsum sellæ, the *postsphenoid*, with which are associated the great wings, and pterygoid process. The greater part of the bone is ossified in cartilage. There are fourteen centers in all, *six* for the prephenoid and *eight* for the postsphenoid.

Presphenoid.—About the ninth week of fetal life and ossific center appears for each of the small wings (orbitospheonids) just lateral to the optic foramen; shortly afterward two nuclei appear in the presphenoid part of the body. The sphenoidal conchæ are each developed from

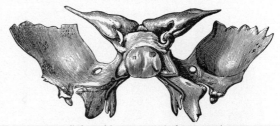

FIG. 222.—Sphenoid bone at birth. Posterior aspect.

four centers which make their appearance about the fifth month; at birth they consist of small triangular laminæ, and it is not until the third year that they become hollowed out and cone-shaped; about the fourth year they fuse with the labyrinths of the ethmoid, and between the ninth and twelfth years they unite with the sphenoid.

Postsphenoid.—The first ossific nuclei are those for the great wings (ali-sphenoids). One makes its appearance in each wing between the foramen rotundum and foramen ovale about the eighth week. The orbital plate and that part of the sphenoid which is found in the temporal fossa, as well as the lateral pterygoid plate, are ossified in membrane (Fawcett). Soon after, the centers for the postsphenoid part of the body appear, one on either side of the sella turcica, and become blended together about the middle of fetal life. Each medial pterygoid plate (with the exception of its hamulus) is ossified in membrane, and its center probably appears about the ninth or tenth week; the hamulus becomes chondrified during the third month, and almost at once undergoes ossification. The medial joins the lateral pterygoid plate about the sixth month. About the fourth month a center appears for each lingula, and speedily joins the rest of the bone.

The presphenoid is united to the postsphenoid about the eighth month, and at birth the bone is in three pieces (Fig. 222): a central, consisting of the body and small wings, and two lateral, each comprising a great wing and pterygoid process. In the first year after birth the great wings and body unite, and the small wings extend inward above the anterior part of the body, and, meeting with each other in the middle line, form an elevated smooth surface, termed the *jugum sphenoidale*. By the twenty-fifth year the sphenoid and occipital are completely fused. Between the pre- and postsphenoid there are occasionally seen the remains of a canal, the *canalis cranio-pharyngeus*, through which, in early fetal life, the hypophyseal diverticulum of the buccal ectoderm is transmitted.

The sphenoidal sinuses are present as minute cavities at the time of birth, but do not attain their full size until after puberty.

Intrinsic Ligaments of the Sphenoid.—The more important of these are: the *pterygospinous*, stretching between the spina angularis and the lateral pterygoid plate (see *cervical fascia*); the *interclinoid*, a fibrous process joining the anterior to the posterior clinoid process; and the *carotico-clinoid*, connecting the anterior to the middle clinoic process. These ligaments occasionally ossify.

Articulations.—The sphenoid articulates with *twelve* bones: four single, the vomer, ethmoid, frontal, and occipital; and four paired, the parietal, temporal, zygomatic, and palatine. It also sometimes articulates with the tuberosity of the maxilla.

The Ethmoid Bone (Os Ethmoidale).

The **ethmoid bone** is exceedingly light and spongy, and cubical in shape; it is situated at the anterior part of the base of the cranium, between the two orbits, at the roof of the nose, and contributes to each of these cavities. It consists of four parts: a **horizontal** or **cribriform plate**, forming part of the base of the cranium; a **perpendicular plate**, constituting part of the nasal septum; and two **lateral masses** or labyrinths.

14

Cribriform Plate (*lamina cribrosa; horizontal lamina*).—The cribriform plate (Fig. 223) is received into the ethmoidal notch of the frontal bone and roofs in the nasal cavities. Projecting upward from the middle line of this plate is a thick, smooth, triangular process, the **crista galli**, so called from its resemblance to a cock's comb. The long thin posterior border of the crista galli serves for the attachment of the falx cerebri. Its anterior border, short and thick, articulates with the frontal bone, and presents two small projecting **alæ**, which are received into corresponding depressions in the frontal bone and complete the foramen cecum. Its sides are smooth, and sometimes bulging from the presence of a small air sinus in the interior. On either side of the crista galli, the cribriform plate is narrow and deeply grooved; it supports the olfactory bulb and is perforated by foramina for the passage of the olfactory nerves. The foramina in the middle of the groove are small and transmit the nerves to the roof of the nasal cavity; those at the medial and lateral parts of the groove are larger—the former transmit the nerves to the upper part of the nasal septum, the latter those to the superior nasal concha. At the front part of the cribriform

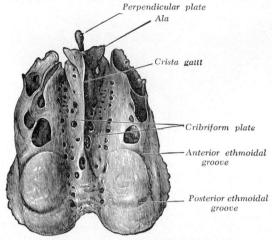

Fig. 223.—Ethmoid bone from above.

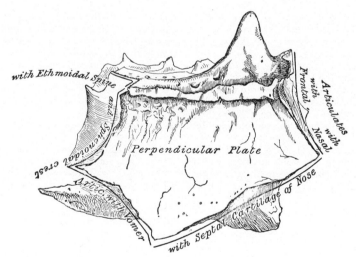

Fig. 224.—Perpendicular plate of ethmoid. Shown by removing the right labyrinth.

plate, on either side of the crista galli, is a small fissure which is occupied by a process of dura mater. Lateral to this fissure is a notch or foramen which transmits the nasociliary nerve; from this notch a groove extends backward to the anterior ethmoidal foramen.

Perpendicular Plate (*lamina perpendicularis; vertical plate*).—The perpendicular plate (Figs. 224, 225) is a thin, flattened lamina, polygonal in form, which descends from the under surface of the cribriform plate, and assists in forming the septum of the nose; it is generally deflected a little to one or other side. The **anterior border**

articulates with the spine of the frontal bone and the crest of the nasal bones. The **posterior border** articulates by its upper half with the sphenoidal crest, by its lower with the vomer. The **inferior border** is thicker than the posterior, and serves for the attachment of the septal cartilage of the nose. The surfaces of the plate are smooth, except above, where numerous grooves and canals are seen; these lead from the medial foramina on the cribriform plate and lodge filaments of the olfactory nerves.

The **Labyrinth** or **Lateral Mass** (*labyrinthus ethmoidalis*) consists of a number of thin-walled cellular cavities, the **ethmoidal cells**, arranged in three groups, *anterior*, *middle*, and *posterior*, and inter-posed between two vertical plates of bone; the lateral plate forms part of the orbit, the medial, part of the corresponding nasal cavity. In the disarticulated bone many of these cells are opened into, but when the bones are articulated, they are closed in at every part, except where they open into the nasal cavity.

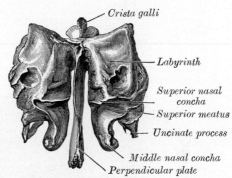

Crista galli

Labyrinth

Superior nasal concha

Superior meatus

Uncinate process

Middle nasal concha

Perpendicular plate

FIG. 225.—Ethmoid bone from behind.

Surfaces.—The **upper surface** of the laby-rinth (Fig. 223) presents a number of half-broken cells, the walls of which are completed, in the articulated skull, by the edges of the ethmoidal notch of the frontal bone. Crossing this surface are two grooves, converted into canals by articulation with the frontal; they are the **anterior** and **posterior ethmoidal canals**, and open on the inner wall of the orbit. The **posterior surface** presents large irregular cellular cavities, which are closed in by articulation with the sphenoidal concha and orbital process of the palatine. The **lateral surface** (Fig. 226) is formed of a thin, smooth, oblong plate, the **lamina papyracea** (*lamina perpendicularis*), which covers in the middle and posterior

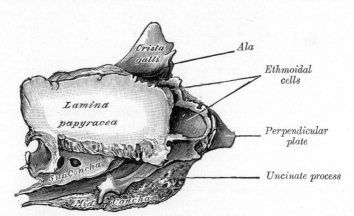

Crista galli

Ala

Ethmoidal cells

Lamina papyracea

Perpendicular plate

Sup. Concha

Uncinate process

Mid. Concha

FIG. 226.—Ethmoid bone from the right side.

ethmoidal cells and forms a large part of the medial wall of the orbit; it articulates above with the orbital plate of the frontal bone, below with the maxilla and orbital process of the palatine, in front with the lacrimal, and behind with the sphenoid.

In front of the lamina papyracea are some broken air cells which are overlapped and completed by the lacrimal bone and the frontal process of the maxilla. A curved lamina, the **uncinate process**, projects downward and backward from this part of the labyrinth; it forms a small part of the medial wall of the maxillary sinus, and articulates with the ethmoidal process of the inferior nasal concha.

The **medial surface** of the labyrinth (Fig. 227) forms part of the lateral wall of the corresponding nasal cavity. It consists of a thin lamella, which descends from the under surface of the cribriform plate, and ends below in a free, convoluted margin, the **middle nasal concha**. It is rough, and marked above by numerous grooves, directed nearly vertically downward from the cribriform plate; they lodge branches of the olfactory nerves, which are distributed to the mucous membrane covering the superior nasal concha. The back part of the surface is subdivided by a narrow oblique fissure, the **superior meatus** of the nose, bounded above

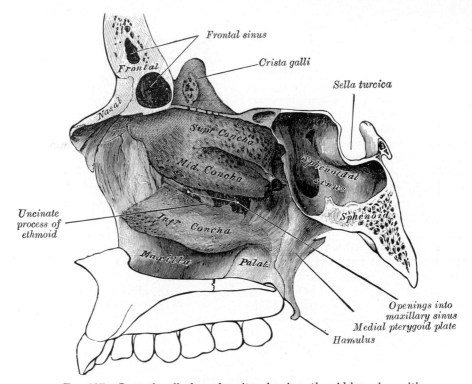

FIG. 227.—Lateral wall of nasal cavity, showing ethmoid bone in position.

by a thin, curved plate, the **superior nasal concha**; the posterior ethmoidal cells open into this meatus. Below, and in front of the superior meatus, is the convex surface of the middle nasal concha; it extends along the whole length of the medial surface of the labyrinth, and its lower margin is free and thick. The lateral surface of the middle concha is concave, and assists in forming the **middle meatus** of the nose. The middle ethmoidal cells open into the central part of this meatus, and a sinuous passage, termed the **infundibulum**, extends upward and forward through the labyrinth and communicates with the anterior ethmoidal cells, and in about 50 per cent of skulls is continued upward as the frontonasal duct into the frontal sinus.

Ossification.—The ethmoid is ossified in the cartilage of the nasal capsule by *three* centers: one for the perpendicular plate, and one for each labyrinth.

The labyrinths are first developed, ossific granules making their appearance in the region of the lamina papyracea between the fourth and fifth months of fetal life, and extending into the conchæ. At birth, the bone consists of the two labyrinths, which are small and ill-developed. During the first year after birth, the perpendicular plate and crista galli begin to ossify from a single center, and are joined to the labyrinths about the beginning of the second year. The cribriform plate is ossified partly from the perpendicular plate and partly from the labyrinths. The development of the ethmoidal cells begins during fetal life.

Articulations.—The ethmoid articulates with *thirteen* bones: two of the cranium—the frontal, and the sphenoid; and eleven of the face—the two nasals, two maxillæ, two lacrimals, two palatines, two inferior nasal conchæ, and the vomer.

Sutural Bones.—In addition to the usual centers of ossification of the cranium, others may occur in the course of the sutures, giving rise to irregular, isolated bones, termed *sutural* or *Wormian bones*. They occur most frequently in the course of the lambdoidal suture, but are occasionally seen at the fontanelles, especially the posterior. One, the *pterion ossicle*, sometimes exists between the sphenoidal angle of the parietal and the great wing of the sphenoid. They have a tendency to be more or less symmetrical on the two sides of the skull, and vary much in size. Their number is generally limited to two or three; but more than a hundred have been found in the skull of an adult hydrocephalic subject.

THE FACIAL BONES (OSSA FACIEI).

The Nasal Bones (Ossa Nasalia).

The **nasal bones** are two small oblong bones, varying in size and form in different individuals; they are placed side by side at the middle and upper part of the face, and form, by their junction, "the bridge" of the nose (Fig. 230). Each has two surfaces and four borders.

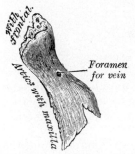

FIG. 228.—Right nasal bone. Outer surface.

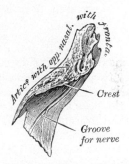

FIG. 229.—Right nasal bone. Inner surface.

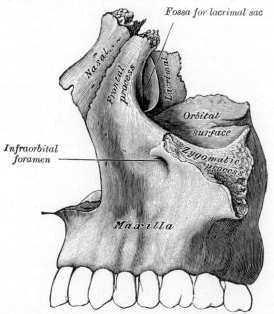

FIG. 230.—Articulation of nasal and lacrimal bones with maxilla.

Surfaces.—The **outer surface** (Fig. 228) is concavoconvex from above downward, convex from side to side; it is covered by the Procerus and Nasalis, and perforated about its center by a foramen, for the transmission of a small vein. The **inner surface** (Fig. 229) is concave from side to side, and is traversed from above downward, by a groove for the passage of a branch of the nasociliary nerve.

Borders.—The **superior border** is narrow, thick, and serrated for articulation with the nasal notch of the frontal bone. The **inferior border** is thin, and gives attachment to the lateral cartilage of the nose; near its middle is a notch which marks the end of the groove just referred to. The **lateral border** is serrated, bevelled at the expense of the inner surface above, and of the outer below, to articulate with the frontal process of the maxilla. The **medial border,** thicker above than below, articulates with its fellow of the opposite side, and is prolonged behind into a vertical crest, which forms part of the nasal septum: this crest articulates, from above downward, with the spine of the frontal, the perpendicular plate of the ethmoid, and the septal cartilage of the nose.

Ossification.—Each bone is ossified from *one* center, which appears at the beginning of the third month of fetal life in the membrane overlying the front part of the cartilaginous nasal capsule.

Articulations.—The nasal articulates with four bones: two of the cranium, the frontal and ethmoid, and two of the face, the opposite nasal and the maxilla.

The Maxilla (Upper Jaw).

The **maxillæ** are the largest bones of the face, excepting the mandible, and form, by their union, the whole of the upper jaw. Each assists in forming the boundaries of three cavities, viz., the roof of the mouth, the floor and lateral wall of the nose and the floor of the orbit; it also enters into the formation of two fossæ, the infratemporal and pterygopalatine, and two fissures, the inferior orbital and pterygomaxillary.

Each bone consists of a body and four processes—zygomatic, frontal, alveolar, and palatine.

The Body (*corpus maxillæ*).—The body is somewhat pyramidal in shape, and contains a large cavity, the **maxillary sinus** (*antrum of Highmore*). It has four surfaces—an anterior, a posterior or infratemporal, a superior or orbital, and a medial or nasal.

Surfaces.—The **anterior or facial surface** (Fig. 231) is directed forward and lateralward. It presents at its lower part a series of eminences corresponding to the positions of the roots of the teeth. Just above those of the incisor teeth is a depression, the **incisive fossa,** which gives origin to the Depressor alæ nasi; to the alveolar border below the fossa is attached a slip of the Orbicularis oris; above and a little lateral to it, the Nasalis arises. Lateral to the incisive fossa is another depression, the **canine fossa;** it is larger and deeper than the incisive fossa, and is separated from it by a vertical ridge, the **canine eminence,** corresponding to the socket of the canine tooth; the canine fossa gives origin to the Caninus. Above the fossa is the **infraorbital foramen,** the end of the infraorbital canal; it transmits the infraorbital vessels and nerve. Above the foramen is the margin of the orbit, which affords attachment to part of the Quadratus labii superioris. Medially, the anterior surface is limited by a deep concavity, the **nasal notch,** the margin of which gives attachment to the Dilatator naris posterior and ends below in a pointed process, which with its fellow of the opposite side forms the **anterior nasal spine.**

The **infratemporal surface** (Fig. 231) is convex, directed backward and lateralward, and forms part of the infratemporal fossa. It is separated from the anterior surface by the zygomatic process and by a strong ridge, extending upward from the socket of the first molar tooth. It is pierced about its center by the apertures of the **alveolar canals**, which transmit the posterior superior alveolar vessels and nerves. At the lower part of this surface is a rounded eminence, the **maxillary tuberosity,** especially prominent after the growth of the wisdom tooth; it is rough on its medial side for articulation with the pyramidal process of the palatine bone and in some cases articulates with the lateral pterygoid plate of the sphenoid. It gives origin to a few fibers of the Pterygoideus internus. Immediately above this is a smooth surface, which forms the anterior boundary of the pterygopalatine fossa, and presents a groove, for the maxillary nerve; this groove is directed lateral-ward and slightly upward, and is continuous with the infraorbital groove on the orbital surface.

The **orbital surface** (Fig. 231) is smooth and triangular, and forms the greater part of the floor of the orbit. It is bounded *medially* by an irregular margin which in front presents a notch, the **lacrimal notch;** behind this notch the margin articu-lates with the lacrimal, the lamina papyracea of the ethmoid and the orbital process of the palatine. It is bounded *behind* by a smooth rounded edge which forms the anterior margin of the inferior orbital fissure, and sometimes articulates at its lateral extremity with the orbital surface of the great wing of the sphenoid. It is limited *in front* by part of the circumference of the orbit, which is continuous medially with the frontal process, and laterally with the zyogmatic process. Near the middle of the posterior part of the orbital surface is the **infraorbital groove**, for the passage of the infraorbital vessels and nerve. The groove begins at the middle of the posterior border, where it is continuous with that near the upper edge of the infratemporal surface, and, passing forward, ends in a canal, which subdivides into two branches. One of the canals, the **infraorbital canal**, opens just below the margin of the orbit; the other, which is smaller, runs downward in the substance of the anterior wall of the maxillary sinus, and transmits the anterior superior alveolar vessels and nerve to the front teeth of the maxilla. From the back part of the infraorbital canal, a second small canal is sometimes given off; it runs downward in the lateral wall of the sinus, and conveys the middle alveolar nerve to the premolar teeth. At the medial and forepart of the orbital surface, just lateral to the lacrimal groove, is a depression, which gives origin to the Obliquus oculi inferior.

The **nasal surface** (Fig. 232) presents a large, irregular opening leading into the maxillary sinus. At the upper border of this aperture are some broken air cells, which, in the articulated skull, are closed in by the ethmoid and lacrimal bones. Below the aperture is a smooth concavity which forms part of the inferior meatus of the nasal cavity, and behind it is a rough surface for articulation with the per-pendicular part of the palatine bone; this surface is traversed by a groove, com-mencing near the middle of the posterior border and running obliquely downward and forward; the groove is converted into a canal, the **pterygopalatine canal,** by the palatine bone. In front of the opening of the sinus is a deep groove, the **lacrimal groove,** which is converted into the nasolacrimal canal, by the lacrimal bone and inferior nasal concha; this canal opens into the inferior meatus of the nose and transmits the nasolacrimal duct. More anteriorly is an oblique ridge, the **conchal crest,** for articulation with the inferior nasal concha. The shallow concavity above this ridge forms part of the atrium of the middle meatus of the nose, and that below it, part of the inferior meatus.

The Maxillary Sinus or Antrum of Highmore (*sinus maxillaris*).—The maxillary sinus is a large pyramidal cavity, within the body of the maxilla. Its walls are thin, and correspond to the nasal, orbital, anterior and infratemporal surfaces of the body of the bone. Its **nasal wall,** presents, in the disarticulated bone, a large, irregular aperture, communicating with the nasal cavity. In the articulated skull this aper-ture is much reduced in size by the following bones: the uncinate process of the ethmoid above, the ethmoidal process of the inferior nasal concha below, the vertical part of the palatine behind, and a small part of the lacrimal above and in front (Figs. 232, 233); the sinus communicates with the middle meatus of the nose, generally by two small apertures left between the above-mentioned bones. In the fresh state, usually only one small opening exists, near the upper part of the cavity; the other is closed by mucous membrane. On the **posterior wall** are the **alveolar**

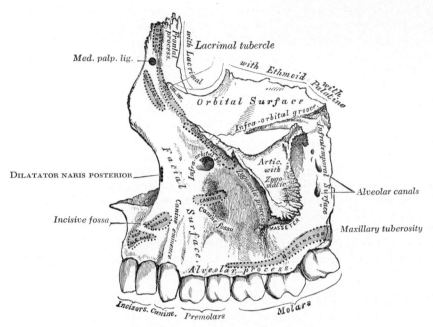

FIG. 231.—Left maxilla. Outer surface.

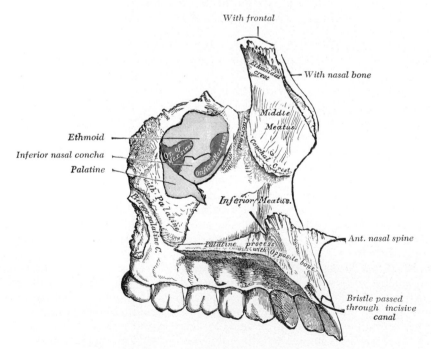

FIG. 232.—Left maxilla. Nasal surface.

canals, transmitting the posterior superior alveolar vessels and nerves to the molar teeth. The **floor** is formed by the alveolar process of the maxilla, and, if the sinus be of an average size, is on a level with the floor of the nose; if the sinus be large it reaches below this level.

Projecting into the floor of the antrum are several conical processes, corresponding to the roots of the teeth; in some cases the floor is perforated by the fangs of the teeth. The infraorbital canal usually projects into the cavity as a well-marked ridge extending from the roof to the anterior wall; additional ridges are sometimes seen in the posterior wall of the cavity, and are caused by the alveolar canals. The size of the cavity varies in different skulls, and even on the two sides of the same skull.

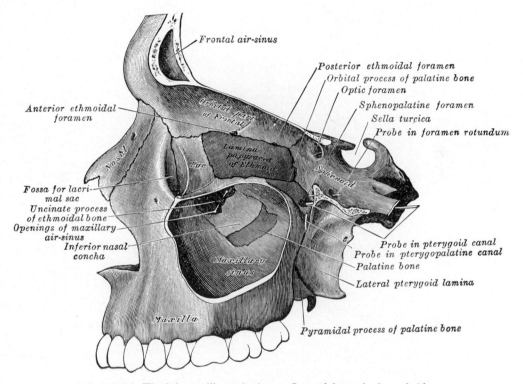

FIG. 233.—The left maxillary air-sinus. Opened from the lateral side.

The Zygomatic Process (*processus zygomaticus; malar process*).—The zygomatic process is a rough triangular eminence, situated at the angle of separation of the anterior, infratemporal and orbital surfaces. *In front* it forms part of the anterior surface; *behind,* it is concave, and forms part of the infratemporal fossa; *above,* it is rough and serrated for articulation with the zygomatic bone; while *below,* it presents the prominent arched border which marks the division between the anterior and infratemporal surfaces.

The Frontal Process (*processus frontalis; nasal process*).—The frontal process is a strong plate, which projects upward, medialward, and backward, by the side of the nose, forming part of its lateral boundary. Its *lateral surface* is smooth, continuous with the anterior surface of the body, and gives attachment to the Quadratus labii superioris, the Orbicularis oculi, and the medial palpebral ligament. Its *medial surface* forms part of the lateral wall of the nasal cavity; at its upper part is a rough, uneven area, which articulates with the ethmoid, closing in the anterior ethmoidal cells; below this is an oblique ridge, the **ethmoidal crest,** the posterior end of which articulates with the middle nasal concha, while the anterior part is termed the **agger nasi**; the crest forms the upper limit of the atrium of the middle meatus. The *upper border* articulates with the frontal bone and the *anterior* with the nasal; the *posterior border* is thick, and hollowed into a groove, which is continuous below with the lacrimal groove on the nasal surface of the body: by the articulation of the medial margin of the groove with the anterior border of the lacrimal a corresponding groove on the lacrimal is brought into continuity, and together they form the **lacrimal fossa** for the lodgement of the lacrimal sac. The lateral margin of the groove is named the **anterior lacrimal crest**, and is continuous below with the orbital margin; at its junction with the orbital surface is a small tubercle, the **lacrimal tubercle**, which serves as a guide to the position of the lacrimal sac.

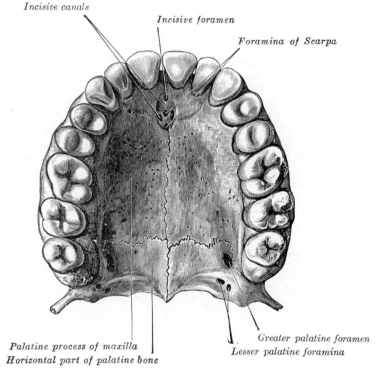

FIG. 234.—The bony palate and the alveolar arch. Inferior aspect.

The Alveolar Process (*processus alveolaris*).—The alveolar process is the thickest and most spongy part of the bone. It is broader behind than in front, and excavated into deep cavities for the reception of the teeth. These cavities are eight in number, and vary in size and depth according to the teeth they contain. That for the canine tooth is the deepest; those for the molars are the widest, and are subdivided into minor cavities by septa; those for the incisors are single, but deep and narrow. The Buccinator arises from the outer surface of this process, as far forward as the first molar tooth. When the maxillæ are articulated with each other, their alveolar processes together form the **alveolar arch**; the center of the anterior margin of this arch is named the **alveolar point**.

The Palatine Process (*processus palatinus; palatal process*).—The palatine process, thick and strong, is horizontal and projects medialward from the nasal surface of the bone. It forms a considerable part of the floor of the nose and the roof of the mouth and is much thicker in front than behind. Its *inferior surface* Fig. 234) is concave, rough and uneven, and forms, with the palatine process of the opposite bone, the anterior three-fourths of the hard plate. It is perforated by numerous foramina for the passage of the nutrient vessels; is channelled at the back part of its lateral border by a groove, sometimes a canal, for the transmission of the descending palatine vessels and the anterior palatine nerve from the spheno-palatine ganglion; and presents little depressions for the lodgement of the palatine glands. When the two maxillæ are articulated, a funnel-shaped opening, the **incisive foramen,** is seen in the middle line, immediately behind the incisor teeth. In this opening the orifices of two lateral canals are visible; they are named the **incisive canals** or **foramina of Stenson;** through each of them passes the terminal branch of the descending palatine artery and the nasopalatine nerve. Occasionally two additional canals are present in the middle line; they are termed the **foramina of Scarpa,** and when present transmit the nasopalatine nerves, the left passing through the anterior, and the right through the posterior canal. On the under surface of the palatine process, a delicate linear suture, well seen in young skulls, may sometimes be noticed extending lateralward and forward on either side from the incisive foramen to the interval between the lateral incisor and the canine tooth. The small part in front of this suture constitutes the **premaxilla** (*os incisivum*), which in most vertebrates forms an independent bone; it includes the whole thickness of the alveolus, the corresponding part of the floor of the nose and the anterior nasal spine, and contains the sockets of the incisor teeth. The *upper surface* of the palatine process is concave from side to side, smooth, and forms the greater part of the floor of the nasal cavity. It presents, close to its medial margin, the upper orifice of the incisive canal. The *lateral border* of the process is incorporated with the rest of the bone. The *medial border* is thicker in front than behind, and is raised above into a ridge, the **nasal crest,** which, with the corresponding ridge of the opposite bone, forms a groove for the reception of the vomer. The front part of this ridge rises to a considerable height, and is named the **incisor crest;** it is prolonged forward into a sharp process, which forms, together with a similar process of the opposite bone, the **anterior nasal spine.** The *posterior border* is serrated for articulation with the horizontal part of the palatine bone.

Ossification.—The maxilla is ossified in membrane. Mall ('06) and Fawcett ('11) maintain that it is ossified from *two* centers only, one for the maxilla proper and one for the premaxilla. These centers appear during the sixth week of fetal life and unite in the beginning of the third month, but the suture between the two portions persists on the palate until nearly middle life. Mall states that the frontal process is developed from both centers. The maxillary sinus appears as a shallow groove on the nasal surface of the bone about the fourth month of fetal life, but does not reach its full size until after the second dentition.

Fig. 235.—Anterior surface of maxilla at birth.   Fig. 236.—Inferior surface of maxilla at birth.

Articulations.—The maxilla articulates with *nine* bones: two of the cranium, the frontal and ethmoid, and seven of the face, viz., the nasal, zygomatic, lacrimal, inferior nasal concha, palatine, vomer, and its fellow of the opposite side. Sometimes it articulates with the orbital surface, and sometimes with the lateral pterygoid plate of the sphenoid.

CHANGES PRODUCED IN THE MAXILLA BY AGE.

At birth the transverse and antero-posterior diameters of the bone are each greater than the vertical. The frontal process is well-marked and the body of the bone consists of little more than the alveolar process, the teeth sockets reaching almost to the floor of the orbit. The maxillary sinus presents the appearance of a furrow on the lateral wall of the nose. In the adult the vertical diameter is the greatest, owing to the development of the alveolar process and the increase in size of the sinus. In old age the bone reverts in some measure to the infantile condition; its height is diminished, and after the loss of the teeth the alveolar process is absorbed, and the lower part of the bone contracted and reduced in thickness.

The Lacrimal Bone (Os Lacrimale).

The **lacrimal bone**, the smallest and most fragile bone of the face, is situated at the front part of the medial wall of the orbit (Fig. 238). It has two surfaces and four borders.

Surfaces.—The **lateral** or **orbital surface** (Fig. 237) is divided by a vertical ridge, the **posterior lacrimal crest**, into two parts. In front of this crest is a longitudinal groove, the **lacrimal sulcus** (*sulcus lacrimalis*), the inner margin of which unites with the frontal process of the maxilla, and the lacrimal fossa is thus completed. The upper part of this fossa lodges the lacrimal sac, the lower part, the nasolacrimal duct. The portion behind the crest is smooth, and forms part of the medial wall of the orbit. The crest, with a part of the orbital surface immediately behind it, gives origin to the lacrimal part of the Orbicularis oculi and ends below in a small, hook-like projection, the **lacrimal hamulus**, which articulates with the lacrimal tubercle of the maxilla, and completes the upper orifice of the lacrimal canal; it sometimes exists as a separate piece, and is then called the **lesser lacrimal bone.**

The **medial** or **nasal surface** presents a longitudinal furrow, corresponding to the crest on the lateral surface. The area in front of this furrow forms part of the middel meatus of the nose; that behind it articulates with the ethmoid, and completes some of the anterior ethmoidal cells.

Borders.—Of the *four borders* the **anterior** articulates with the frontal process of the maxilla; the **posterior** with the lamina papyracea of the ethmoid; the **superior** with the frontal bone. The **inferior** is divided by the lower edge of the posterior lacrimal crest into two parts: the posterior part articulates with the orbital plate of the maxilla; the anterior is prolonged downward as the **descending process**, which articulates with the lacrimal process of the inferior nasal concha, and assists in forming the canal for the nasolacrimal duct.

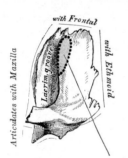

With inferior nasal concha — Lacrimal part of Orbicularis oculi

Articulates with Maxilla

Lacrim. groove

with Frontal

with Ethmoid

Fig. 237.—The left lacrimal bone. Lateral aspect. (Enlarged.)

Ossification.—The lacrimal is ossified from a single center, which appears about the twelfth week in the membrane covering the cartilaginous nasal capsule.

Articulations.—The lacrimal articulates with *four* bones: two of the cranium, the frontal and ethmoid, and two of the face, the maxilla and the inferior nasal concha.

The Zygomatic Bone (Os Zygomaticum; Malar Bone).

The **zygomatic bone** is small and quadrangular, and is situated at the upper and lateral part of the face: it forms the prominence of the cheek, part of the lateral wall and floor of the orbit, and parts of the temporal and infratemporal fossæ (Fig. 238). It presents a malar and a temporal surface; four processes, the frontosphenoidal, orbital, maxillary, and temporal; and four borders.

Surfaces.—The **malar surface** (Fig. 239) is convex and perforated near its center by a small aperture, the **zygomaticofacial foramen,** for the passage of the zygomaticofacial nerve and vessels; below this foramen is a slight elevation, which gives origin to the Zygomaticus and the Quadratus labii superioris.

The **temporal surface** (Fig. 240), directed backward and medialward, is concave, presenting medially a rough, triangular area, for articulation with the maxilla, and laterally a smooth, concave surface, the upper part of which forms the anterior boundary of the temporal fossa, the lower a part of the infratemporal fossa. Near the center of this surface is the **zygomaticotemporal foramen** for the transmission of the zygomaticotemporal nerve.

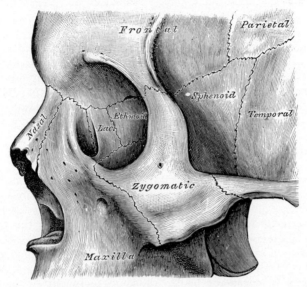

FIG. 238.—Left zygomatic bone *in situ.*

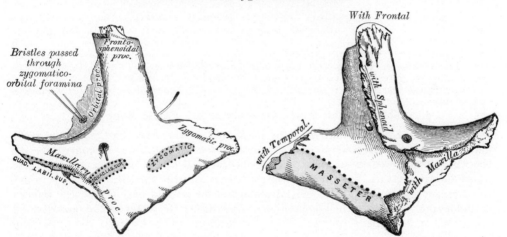

FIG. 239.—Left zygomatic bone. Malar surface.

FIG. 240.—Left zygomatic bone. Temporal surface.

Processes.—The **frontosphenoidal process** is thick and serrated, and articulates with the zygomatic process of the frontal bone. On its orbital surface, just within the orbital margin and about 11 mm. below the zygomaticofrontal suture is a tubercle of varying size and form, but present in 95 per cent of skulls (Whitnall[1]). The **orbital process** is a thick, strong plate, projecting backward and medialward from the orbital margin. Its *antero-medial surface* forms, by its junction with the orbital surface of the maxilla and with the great wing of the sphenoid, part of the floor and lateral wall of the orbit. On it are usually the orifices of two canals,

[1] Journal of Anatomy and Physiology, vol. **45.** The structures attached to this tubercle are: (1) the check ligament of the Rectus lateralis; (2) the lateral end of the aponeurosis of the Levator palpebræ superioris; (3) the suspensory ligament of the eye (Lockwood); and (4) the lateral extremities of the superior and inferior tarsi.

the **zygomaticoörbital foramina**; one of these canals opens into the temporal fossa, the other on the malar surface of the bone; the former transmits the zygomatico-temporal, the latter the zygomaticofacial nerve. Its *postero-lateral surface*, smooth and convex, forms parts of the temporal and infratemporal fossæ. Its *anterior margin*, smooth and rounded, is part of the circumference of the orbit. Its *superior margin*, rough, and directed horizontally, articulates with the frontal bone behind the zygomatic process. Its *posterior margin* is serrated for articulation, with the great wing of the sphenoid and the orbital surface of the maxilla. At the angle of junction of the sphenoidal and maxillary portions, a short, concave, non-articular part is generally seen; this forms the anterior boundary of the inferior orbital fissure: occasionally, this non-articular part is absent, the fissure then being completed by the junction of the maxilla and sphenoid, or by the interposition of a small sutural bone in the angular interval between them. The **maxillary process** presents a rough, triangular surface which articulates with the maxilla. The **temporal process**, long, narrow, and serrated, articulates with the zygomatic process of the temporal.

Borders.—The **antero-superior** or **orbital border** is smooth, concave, and forms a considerable part of the circumference of the orbit. The **antero-inferior** or **maxillary border** is rough, and bevelled at the expense of its inner table, to articulate with the maxilla; near the orbital margin it gives origin to the Quadratus labii superioris. The **postero-superior** or **temporal border,** curved like an italic letter *f,* is continuous above with the commencement of the temporal line, and below with the upper border of the zygomatic arch; the temporal fascia is attached to it. The **postero-inferior** or **zygomatic border** affords attachment by its rough edge to the Masseter.

Ossification.—The zygomatic bone is generally described as ossifying from three centers— one for the malar and two for the orbital portion; these appear about the eighth week and fuse about the fifth month of fetal life. Mall describes it as being ossified from one center which appears just beneath and to the lateral side of the orbit. After birth, the bone is sometimes divided by a horizontal suture into an upper larger, and a lower smaller division. In some quad-rumana the zygomatic bone consists of two parts, an orbital and a malar.

Articulations.—The zygomatic articulates with *four* bones: the frontal, sphenoidal, temporal, and maxilla.

The Palatine Bone (Os Palatinum; Palate Bone).

The **palatine bone** is situated at the back part of the nasal cavity between the maxilla and the pterygoid process of the sphenoid (Fig. 241). It contributes to the walls of three cavities: the floor and lateral wall of the nasal cavity, the roof of the mouth, and the floor of the orbit; it enters into the formation of three fossæ, the **pterygopalatine, pterygoid,** and **infratemporal fossæ**; and one fissure, the **inferior orbital fissure.** The palatine bone somewhat resembles the letter L, and consists of a horizontal and a vertical part and three outstanding processes—viz., the pyramidal process, which is directed backward and lateralward from the junction of the two parts, and the orbital and sphenoidal processes, which surmount the vertical part, and are separated by a deep notch, the sphenopalatine notch.

The Horizontal Part (*lamina horizontalis; horizontal plate*) (Figs. 242, 243).—The horizontal part is quadrilateral, and has two surfaces and four borders.

Surfaces.—The **superior surface,** concave from side to side, forms the back part of the floor of the nasal cavity. The **inferior surface,** slightly concave and rough, forms, with the corresponding surface of the opposite bone, the posterior fourth of the hard palate. Near its posterior margin may be seen a more or less marked transverse ridge for the attachment of part of the aponeurosis of the Tensor veli palatini.

Borders.—The **anterior border** is serrated, and articulates with the palatine process of the maxilla. The **posterior border** is concave, free. and serves for the attachment of the soft palate. Its medial end is sharp and pointed, and, when united with that of the opposite bone, forms a projecting process, the **posterior nasal spine**

for the attachment of the Musculus uvulæ. The **lateral border** is united with the lower margin of the perpendicular part, and is grooved by the lower end of the pterygopalatine canal. The **medial border,** the thickest, is serrated for articulation with its fellow of the opposite side; its superior edge is raised into a ridge, which, united with the ridge of the opposite bone, forms the **nasal crest** for articulation with the posterior part of the lower edge of the vomer.

The Vertical Part (*pars perpendicularis; perpendicular plate*) (Figs. 242, 243).—The vertical part is thin, of an oblong form, and presents two surfaces and four borders.

Surfaces.—The **nasal surface** exhibits at its lower part a broad, shallow depression, which forms part of the inferior meatus of the nose. Immediately above this is a well-marked horizontal ridge, the **conchal crest,** for articulation with the inferior nasal concha; still higher is a second broad, shallow depression, which forms part of the middle meatus, and is limited above by a horizontal crest less prominent than the inferior, the **ethmoidal crest,** for articulation with the middle nasal concha. Above the ethmoidal crest is a narrow, horizontal groove, which forms part of the superior meatus.

The **maxillary surface** is rough and irregular throughout the greater part of its extent, for articulation with the nasal surface of the maxilla; its upper and back part is smooth where it enters into the formation of the pterygopalatine fossa; it is also smooth in front, where it forms the posterior part of the medial wall of the maxillary sinus. On the posterior part of this surface is a deep vertical groove, converted into the **pterygopalatine canal,** by articulation with the maxilla; this canal transmits the descending palatine vessels, and the anterior palatine nerve.

Borders.—The **anterior border** is thin and irregular; opposite the conchal crest is a pointed, projecting lamina, the **maxillary process,** which is directed forward, and closes in the lower and back part of the opening of the maxillary sinus. The **posterior border** (Fig. 243) presents a deep groove, the edges of which are serrated for articulation with the medial pterygoid plate of the sphenoid. This border is continuous above with the sphenoidal process; below it expands into the pyramidal process. The **superior border** supports the orbital process in front and the sphenoidal process behind. These processes are separated by the **sphenopalatine notch,** which is converted into the **sphenopalatine foramen** by the under surface of the body of the sphenoid. In the articulated skull this foramen leads from the pterygopalatine fossa into the posterior part of the superior meatus of the nose, and transmits the sphenopalatine vessels and the superior nasal and nasopalatine nerves. The **inferior border** is fused with the lateral edge of the horizontal part, and immediately in front of the pyramidal process is grooved by the lower end of the pterygopalatine canal.

The Pyramidal Process or Tuberosity (*processus pyramidalis*).—The pyramidal process projects backward and lateralward from the junction of the horizontal and vertical parts, and is received into the angular interval between the lower extremities of the pterygoid plates. On its **posterior surface** is a smooth, grooved, triangular area, limited on either side by a rough articular furrow. The furrows articulate with the pterygoid plates, while the grooved intermediate area completes the lower part of the pterygoid fossa and gives origin to a few fibers of the Pterygoideus internus. The anterior part of the **lateral surface** is rough, for articulation with the tuberosity of the maxilla; its posterior part consists of a smooth triangular area which appears, in the articulated skull, between the tuberosity of the maxilla and the lower part of the lateral pterygoid plate, and completes the lower part of the infratemporal fossa. On the **base** of the pyramidal process, close to its union with the horizontal part, are the lesser palatine foramina for the transmission of the posterior and middle palatine nerves.

The Orbital Process (*processus orbitalis*).—The orbital process is placed on a higher level than the sphenoidal, and is directed upward and lateralward from the front of the vertical part, to which it is connected by a constricted neck. It presents five surfaces, which enclose an air cell. Of these surfaces, three are articular and two non-articular. The articular surfaces are: (1) the **anterior** or **maxillary,** directed forward, lateralward, and downward, of an oblong form, and rough for

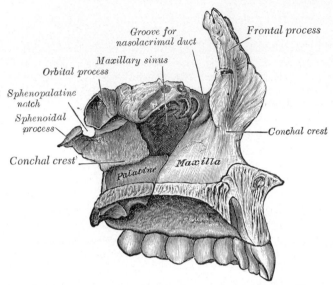

Fig. 241.—Articulation of left palatine bone with maxilla.

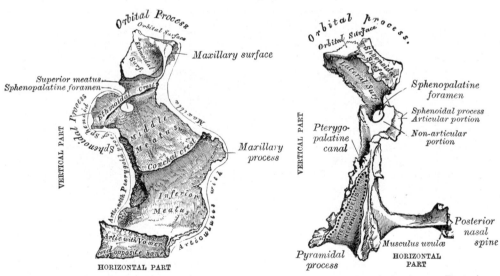

Fig. 242.—Left palatine bone. Nasal aspect. Enlarged.

Fig. 243.—Left palatine bone. Posterior aspect. Enlarged.

articulation with the maxilla; (2) the **posterior** or **sphenoidal,** directed backward, upward, and medialward; it presents the opening of the air cell, which usually communicates with the sphenoidal sinus; the margins of the opening are serrated for articulation with the sphenoidal concha; (3) the **medial** or **ethmoidal,** directed forward, articulates with the labyrinth of the ethmoid. In some cases the air cell opens on this surface of the bone and then communicates with the posterior ethmoidal cells. More rarely it opens on both surfaces, and then communicates with the posterior ethmoidal cells and the sphenoidal sinus. The non-articular surfaces are: (1) the **superior** or **orbital,** directed upward and lateralward; it is triangular in shape, and forms the back part of the floor of the orbit; and (2) the **lateral,** of an oblong form, directed toward the pterygopalatine fossa; it is separated from the orbital surface by a rounded border, which enters into the formation of the inferior orbital fissure.

The Sphenoidal Process (*processus sphenoidalis*).—The sphenoidal process is a thin, compressed plate, much smaller than the orbital, and directed upward and medialward. It presents three surfaces and two borders. The **superior surface** articulates with the root of the pterygoid process and the under surface of the sphenoidal concha, its medial border reaching as far as the ala of the vomer; it presents a groove which contributes to the formation of the pharyngeal canal. The **medial surface** is concave, and forms part of the lateral wall of the nasal cavity. The **lateral surface** is divided into an articular and a non-articular portion: the former is rough, for articulation with the medial pterygoid plate; the latter is smooth, and forms part of the pterygopalatine fossa. The **anterior border** forms the posterior boundary of the sphenopalatine notch. The **posterior border,** serrated at the expense of the outer table, articulates with the medial pterygoid plate.

The orbital and sphenoidal processes are separated from one another by the **sphenopalatine notch.** Sometimes the two processes are united above, and form between them a complete foramen (Fig. 242), or the notch may be crossed by one or more spicules of bone, giving rise to two or more foramina.

Ossification.—The palatine bone is ossified in membrane from a single center, which makes its appearance about the sixth or eighth week of fetal life at the angle of junction of the two parts of the bone. From this point ossification spreads medialward to the horizontal part, downward into the pyramidal process, and upward into the vertical part. Some authorities describe the bone as ossifying from four centers: one for the pyramidal process and portion of the vertical part behind the pterygopalatine groove; a second for the rest of the vertical and the horizontal parts; a third for the orbital, and a fourth for the sphenoidal process. At the time of birth the height of the vertical part is about equal to the transverse width of the horizontal part, whereas in the adult the former measures about twice as much as the latter.

Articulations.—The palatine articulates with *six* bones: the sphenoid, ethmoid, maxilla, inferior nasal concha, vomer, and opposite palatine.

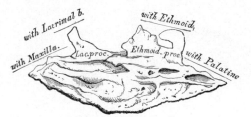

FIG. 244.—Right inferior nasal concha. Medial surface.

FIG. 245.—Right inferior nasal concha. Lateral surface.

The Inferior Nasal Concha (Concha Nasalis Inferior; Inferior Turbinated Bone).

The **inferior nasal concha** extends horizontally along the lateral wall of the nasal cavity (Fig. 227) and consists of a lamina of spongy bone, curled upon itself like a scroll. It has two surfaces, two borders, and two extremities.

The **medial surface** (Fig. 244) is convex, perforated by numerous apertures, and traversed by longitudinal grooves for the lodgement of vessels. The **lateral surface** is concave (Fig. 245), and forms part of the inferior meatus. Its **upper border** is thin, irregular, and connected to various bones along the lateral wall of the nasal cavity. It may be divided into three portions: of these, the anterior articulates with the conchal crest of the maxilla; the posterior with the conchal

15

crest of the palatine; the middle portion presents three well-marked processes, which vary much in their size and form. Of these, the anterior or **lacrimal process** is small and pointed and is situated at the junction of the anterior fourth with the posterior three-fourths of the bone: it articulates, by its apex, with the descending process of the lacrimal bone, and, by its margins, with the groove on the back of the frontal process of the maxilla, and thus assists in forming the canal for the nasolacrimal duct. Behind this process a broad, thin plate, the **ethmoidal process**, ascends to join the uncinate process of the ethmoid; from its lower border a thin lamina, the **maxillary process**, curves downward and lateralward; it articulates with the maxilla and forms a part of the medial wall of the maxillary sinus. The **inferior border** is free, thick, and cellular in structure, more especially in the middle of the bone. Both **extremities** are more or less pointed, the posterior being the more tapering.

Ossification.—The inferior nasal concha is ossified from a single center, which appears about the fifth month of fetal life in the lateral wall of the cartilaginous nasal capsule.

Articulations.—The inferior nasal concha articulates with *four* bones: the ethmoid, maxilla, lacrimal, and palatine.

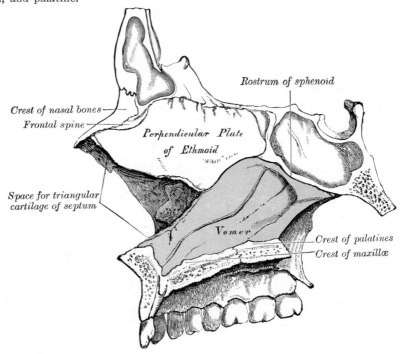

FIG. 246.—Median wall of left nasal cavity showing vomer *in situ*.

The Vomer.

The **vomer** is situated in the median plane, but its anterior portion is frequently bent to one or other side. It is thin, somewhat quadrilateral in shape, and forms the hinder and lower part of the nasal septum (Fig. 246); it has two surfaces and four borders. The **surfaces** (Fig. 247) are marked by small furrows for blood-vessels, and on each is the **nasopalatine groove**, which runs obliquely downward and forward, and lodges the nasopalatine nerve and vessels. The **superior border**, the thickest, presents a deep furrow, bounded on either side by a horizontal projecting ala of bone; the furrow receives the rostrum of the sphenoid, while the margins of the alæ articulate with the vaginal processes of the medial pterygoid plates of the sphenoid behind, and with the sphenoidal processes of the palatine bones in front. The **inferior border** articulates with the crest formed by the maxillæ and palatine bones. The **anterior border** is the longest and slopes downward and forward. Its upper half is fused with the perpendicular plate of the ethmoid; its lower half is grooved for the inferior margin of the septal cartilage of the nose. The **posterior border** is free, concave, and separates the choanæ. It is thick and bifid above, thin below.

Ossification.—At an early period the septum of the nose consists of a plate of cartilage, the *ethmovomerine cartilage*. The postero-superior part of this cartilage is ossified to form the perpendicular plate of the ethmoid; its antero-inferior portion persists as the septal cartilage, while the vomer is ossified in the membrane covering its postero-inferior part. Two ossific centers, one on either side of the middle line, appear about the eighth week of fetal life in this part of the membrane, and hence the vomer consists primarily of two lamellæ. About the third month

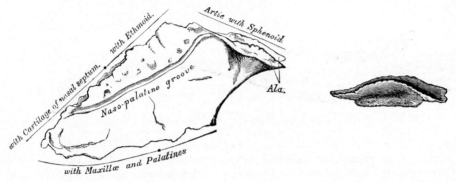

FIG. 247.—The vomer.   FIG. 248.—Vomer of infant.

these unite below, and thus a deep groove is formed in which the cartilage is lodged. As growth proceeds, the union of the lamellæ extends upward and forward, and at the same time the intervening plate of cartilage undergoes absorption. By the age of puberty the lamellæ are almost completely united to form a median plate, but evidence of the bilaminar origin of the bone is seen in the everted alæ of its upper border and the groove on its anterior margin.

Articulations.—The vomer articulates with *six* bones: two of the cranium, the sphenoid and ethmoid; and four of the face, the two maxillæ and the two palatine bones; it also articulates with the septal cartilage of the nose.

THE EXTREMITIES.

The bones by which the upper and lower limbs are attached to the trunk constitute respectively the shoulder and pelvic girdles. The **shoulder girdle** or **girdle of the superior extremity** is formed by the scapulæ and clavicles, and is imperfect in front and behind. In front, however, it is completed by the upper end of the sternum, with which the medial ends of the clavicles articulate. Behind, it is widely imperfect, the scapulæ being connected to the trunk by muscles only. The **pelvic girdle** or **girdle of the inferior extremity** is formed by the hip bones, which articulate with each other in front, at the symphysis pubis. It is imperfect behind, but the gap is filled in by the upper part of the sacrum. The pelvic girdle, with the sacrum, is a complete ring, massive and comparatively rigid, in marked contrast to the lightness and mobility of the shoulder girdle.

THE BONES OF THE UPPER EXTREMITY (OSSA EXTREMITATIS SUPERIORIS).

The Clavicle (Clavicula; Collar Bone).

The **clavicle** (Figs. 249, 250) forms the anterior portion of the shoulder girdle. It is a long bone, curved somewhat like the italic letter *f*, and placed nearly horizontally at the upper and anterior part of the thorax, immediately above the first rib. It articulates medially with the manubrium sterni, and laterally with the acromion of the scapula.[1] It presents a double curvature, the convexity being directed forward at the sternal end, and the concavity at the scapular end. Its lateral third is flattened from above downward, while its medial two-thirds is of a rounded or prismatic form.

The **upper surface** of the **lateral** third is flat, rough, and marked by impressions for the attachments of the Deltoideus in front, and the Trapezius behind; between these impressions a small portion of the bone is subcutaneous. The **under surface** is flat. At its posterior border, near the point where the prismatic joins with the flattened portion, is a rough eminence, the **coracoid tuberosity** (*conoid tubercle*); this, in the natural position of the bone, surmounts the coracoid process of the

Sternal extremity   Acromial extremity

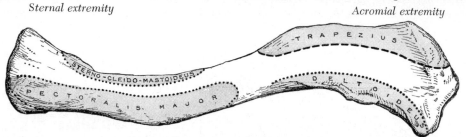

FIG. 249.—Left clavicle. Superior surface.

scapula, and gives attachment to the conoid ligament. From this tuberosity an oblique ridge, the **oblique** or **trapezoid ridge**, runs forward and lateralward, and afford attachment to the trapezoid ligament. The **anterior border** of the lateral third is concave, thin, and rough, and gives attachment to the Deltoideus. The **posterior border** is convex, rough, thicker than the anterior, and gives attachment to the Trapezius.

The medial two-thirds constitute the prismatic portion and is curved so as to be convex in front, concave behind. The **anterior border** is continuous with the anterior margin of the flat portion. Its lateral part is smooth, and corresponds to the interval between the attachments of the Pectoralis major and Deltoideus;

Articular capsule   Articular capsule

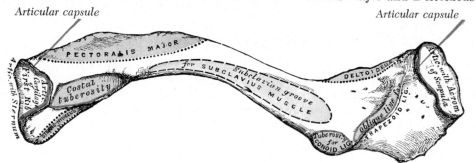

FIG. 250.—Left clavicle. Inferior surface.

its medial part forms the lower boundary of an elliptical surface for the attachment of the clavicular portion of the Pectoralis major, and approaches the posterior border of the bone. The **superior border** is continuous with the posterior margin of the flat portion, and separates the anterior from the posterior surface. Smooth and rounded laterally, it becomes rough toward the medial third for the attachment of the Sternocleidomastoideus, and ends at the upper angle of the sternal extremity. The **posterior** or **subclavian border** separates the posterior from the

---

[1] The clavicle acts especially as a fulcrum to enable the muscles to give lateral motion to the arm. It is accordingly absent in those animals whose fore-limbs are used only for progression, but is present for the most part in animals whose anterior extremities are clawed and used for prehension, though in some of them—as, for instance, in a large number of the carnivora—it is merely a rudimentary bone suspended among the muscles, and not articulating with either the scapula or sternum.

inferior surface, and extends from the coracoid tuberosity to the costal tuberosity; it forms the posterior boundary of the groove for the Subclavius, and gives attachment to a layer of cervical fascia which envelops the Omohyoideus. The **anterior surface** is included between the superior and anterior borders. Its lateral part looks upward, and is continuous with the superior surface of the flattened portion; it is smooth, convex, and nearly subcutaneous, being covered only by the Platysma. Medially it is divided by a narrow subcutaneous area into two parts: a lower, elliptical in form, and directed forward, for the attachment of the Pectoralis major; and an upper for the attachment of the Sternocleidomastoideus. The **posterior** or **cervical surface** is smooth, and looks backward toward the root of the neck. It is limited, above, by the superior border; below, by the subclavian border; medially, by the margin of the sternal extremity; and laterally, by the coracoid tuberosity. It is concave medio-laterally, and is in relation, by its lower part, with the transverse scapular vessels. This surface, at the junction of the curves of the bone, is also in relation with the brachial plexus of nerves and the subclavian vessels. It gives attachment, near the sternal extremity, to part of the Sternohyoideus; and presents, near the middle, an oblique foramen directed lateralward, which transmits the chief nutrient artery of the bone. Sometimes there are two foramina on the posterior surface, or one on the posterior and another on the inferior surface. The **inferior** or **subclavian surface** is bounded, in front, by the anterior border; behind, by the subclavian border. It is narrowed medially, but gradually increases in width laterally, and is continuous with the under surface of the flat portion. On its medial part is a broad rough surface, the **costal tuberosity** (*rhomboid impression*), rather more than 2 cm. in length, for the attachment of the costoclavicular ligament. The rest of this surface is occupied by a groove, which gives attachment to the Subclavius; the coracoclavicular fascia, which splits to enclose the muscle, is attached to the margins of the groove. Not infrequently this groove is subdivided longitudinally by a line which gives attachment to the intermuscular septum of the Subclavius.

The Sternal Extremity (*extremitas sternalis; internal extremity*).—The sternal extremity of the clavicle is triangular in form, directed medialward, and a little downward and forward; it presents an articular facet, concave from before backward, convex from above downward, which articulates with the manubrium sterni through the intervention of an articular disk. The lower part of the facet is continued on to the inferior surface of the bone as a small semi-oval area for articulation with the cartilage of the first rib. The circumference of the articular surface is rough, for the attachment of numerous ligaments; the upper angle gives attachment to the articular disk.

The Acromial Extremity (*extremitas acromialis; outer extremity*).—The acromial extremity presents a small, flattened, oval surface directed obliquely downward, for articulation with the acromion of the scapula. The circumference of the articular facet is rough, especially above, for the attachment of the acromioclavicular ligaments.

In the female, the clavicle is generally shorter, thinner, less curved, and smoother than in the male. In those persons who perform considerable manual labor it becomes thicker and more curved, and its ridges for muscular attachment are prominently marked.

Structure.—The clavicle consists of cancellous tissue, enveloped by a compact layer, which is much thicker in the intermediate part than at the extremities of the bone.

Ossification.—The clavicle begins to ossify before any other bone in the body; it is ossified from *three* centers—viz., two primary centers, a medial and a lateral, for the body, which appear during the fifth or sixth week of fetal life; and

Secondary center

Primary centers

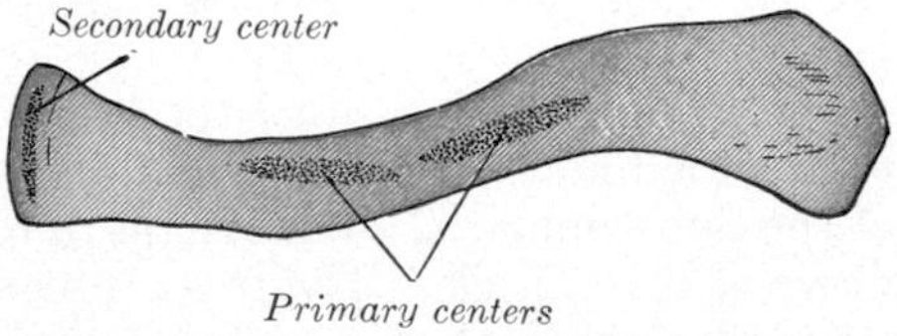

FIG. 251.—Diagram showing the three centers of ossification of the clavicle.

a secondary center for the sternal end, which appears about the eighteenth or twentieth year, and unites with the rest of the bone about the twenty-fifth year.

The Scapula (Shoulder Blade).

The **scapula** forms the posterior part of the shoulder girdle. It is a flat, triangular bone, with two surfaces, three borders, and three angles.

Surfaces.—The **costal** or **ventral surface** (Fig. 252) presents a broad concavity, the **subscapular fossa**. The medial two-thirds of the fossa are marked by several

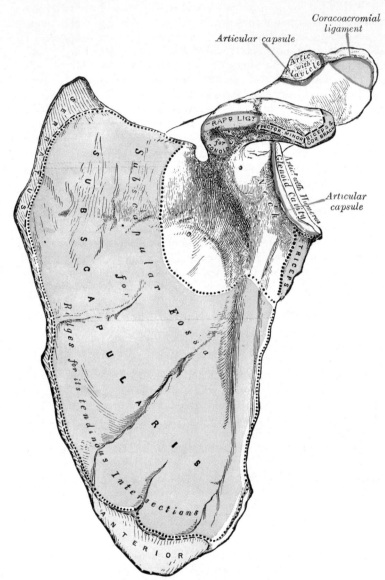

Fig. 252.—Left scapula. Costal surface.

oblique ridges, which run lateralward and upward. The ridges give attachment to the tendinous insertions, and the surfaces between them to the fleshy fibers, of the Subscapularis. The lateral third of the fossa is smooth and covered by the fibers of this muscle. The fossa is separated from the vertebral border by smooth triangular areas at the medial and inferior angles, and in the interval between these by a narrow ridge which is often deficient. These triangular areas and the intervening ridge afford attachment to the Serratus anterior. At the upper part of the fossa is a transverse depression, where the bone appears to be bent on itself along a line at right angles to and passing through the center of the glenoid cavity, forming a considerable angle, called the **subscapular angle**; this gives greater strength to the body of the bone by its arched form, while the summit of the arch serves to support the spine and acromion.

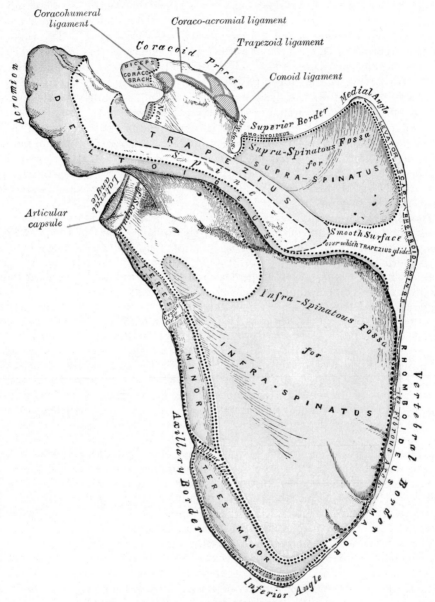

FIG. 253.—Left scapula. Dorsal surface.

The **dorsal surface** (Fig. 253) is arched from above downward, and is subdivided into two unequal parts by the spine; the portion above the spine is called the **supraspinatous fossa**, and that below it the **infraspinatous fossa**.

The **supraspinatous fossa**, the smaller of the two, is concave, smooth, and broader at its vertebral than at its humeral end; its medial two-thirds give origin to the Supraspinatus.

The **infraspinatous fossa** is much larger than the preceding; toward its vertebral margin a shallow concavity is seen at its upper part; its center presents a prominent convexity, while near the axillary border is a deep groove which runs from the upper toward the lower part. The medial two-thirds of the fossa give origin to the Infraspinatus; the lateral third is covered by this muscle.

The dorsal surface is marked near the axillary border by an elevated ridge, which runs from the lower part of the glenoid cavity, downward and backward to the vertebral border, about 2.5 cm. above the inferior angle. The ridge serves for the attachment of a fibrous septum, which separates the Infraspinatus from the Teres major and Teres minor. The surface between the ridge and the axillary border is narrow in the upper two-thirds of its extent, and is crossed near its center by a groove for the passage of the scapular circumflex vessels; it affords attachment to the Teres minor. Its lower third presents a broader, somewhat triangular surface, which gives origin to the Teres major, and over which the Latissimus dorsi glides; frequently the latter muscle takes origin by a few fibers from this part. The broad and narrow portions above alluded to are separated by an oblique line, which runs from the axillary border, downward and backward, to meet the elevated ridge: to it is attached a fibrous septum which separates the Teres muscles from each other.

The Spine (*spina scapulæ*).—The spine is a prominent plate of bone, which crosses obliquely the medial four-fifths of the dorsal surface of the scapula at its upper part, and separates the supra- from the infraspinatous fossa. It begins at the vertebral border by a smooth, triangular area over which the tendon of insertion of the lower part of the Trapezius glides, and, gradually becoming more elevated, ends in the acromion, which overhangs the shoulder-joint. The spine is triangular, and flattened from above downward, its apex being directed toward the vertebral border. It presents two surfaces and three borders. Its **superior surface** is concave; it assists in forming the supraspinatous fossa, and gives origin to part of the Supraspinatus. Its **inferior surface** forms part of the infraspinatous fossa, gives origin to a portion of the Infraspinatus, and presents near its center the orifice of a nutrient canal. Of the three borders, the **anterior** is attached to the dorsal surface of the bone; the **posterior,** or **crest of the spine,** is broad, and presents two lips and an intervening rough interval. The Trapezius is attached to the superior lip, and a rough tubercle is generally seen on that portion of the spine which receives the tendon of insertion of the lower part of this muscle. The Deltoideus is attached to the whole length of the inferior lip. The interval between the lips is subcutaneous and partly covered by the tendinous fibers of these muscles. The **lateral border,** or **base,** the shortest of the three, is slightly concave; its edge, thick and round, is continuous above with the under surface of the acromion, below with the neck of the scapula. It forms the medial boundary of the **great scapular notch,** which serves to connect the supra- and infraspinatous fossæ.

The Acromion.—The acromion forms the summit of the shoulder, and is a large, somewhat triangular or oblong process, flattened from behind forward, projecting at first lateralward, and then curving forward and upward, so as to overhang the glenoid cavity. Its **superior surface,** directed upward, backward, and lateralward, is convex, rough, and gives attachment to some fibers of the Deltoideus, and in the rest of its extent is subcutaneous. Its **inferior surface** is smooth and concave. Its **lateral border** is thick and irregular, and presents three or four tubercles for the tendinous origins of the Deltoideus. Its **medial border,** shorter than the lateral, is concave, gives attachment to a portion of the Trapezius, and presents about its center a small, oval surface for articulation with the acromial end of the clavicle.

Its **apex,** which corresponds to the point of meeting of these two borders in front, is thin, and has attached to it the coracoacromial ligament.

Borders.—Of the *three* borders of the scapula, the **superior** is the shortest and thinnest; it is concave, and extends from the medial angle to the base of the coracoid process. At its lateral part is a deep, semicircular notch, the **scapular notch,** formed partly by the base of the coracoid process. This notch is converted into a foramen by the superior transverse ligament, and serves for the passage of the suprascapular nerve; sometimes the ligament is ossified. The adjacent part of the superior border affords attachment to the Omohyoideus. The **axillary border** (*margo lateralis*) is the thickest of the three. It begins above at the lower margin of the glenoid cavity, and inclines obliquely downward and backward to the inferior angle. Immediately below the glenoid cavity is a rough impression, the **infraglenoid tuberosity,** about 2.5 cm. in length, which gives origin to the long head of the Triceps brachii; in front of this is a longitudinal groove, which extends as far as the lower third of this border, and affords origin to part of the Subscapularis. The inferior third is thin and sharp, and serves for the attachment of a few fibers of the Teres major behind, and of the Subscapularis in front. The **vertebral border**

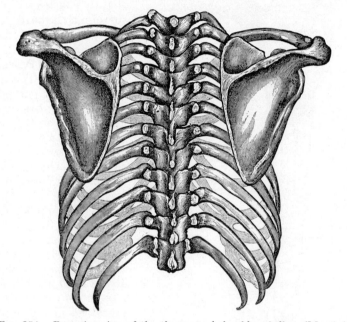

Fig. 254.—Posterior view of the thorax and shoulder girdle.   (Morris.)

(*margo medidis*) is the longest of the three, and extends from the medial to the inferior angle. It is arched, intermediate in thickness between the superior and the axillary borders, and the portion of it above the spine forms an obtuse angle with the part below. This border presents an anterior and a posterior lip, and an intermediate narrow area. The anterior lip affords attachment to the Serratus anterior; the posterior lip, to the Supraspinatus above the spine, the Infraspinatus below; the area between the two lips, to the Levator scapulæ above the triangular surface at the commencement of the spine, to the Rhomboideus minor on the edge of that surface, and to the Rhomboideus major below it; this last is attached by means of a fibrous arch, connected above to the lower part of the triangular surface at the base of the spine, and below to the lower part of the border.

Angles.—Of the *three* angles, the **medial,** formed by the junction of the superior and vertebral borders, is thin, smooth, rounded, inclined somewhat lateralward, and gives attachment to a few fibers of the Levator scapulæ. The **inferior angle,** thick and rough, is formed by the union of the vertebral and axillary borders; its dorsal surface affords attachment to the Teres major and frequently to a few fibers of the Latissimus dorsi. The **lateral angle** is the thickest part of the bone, and is sometimes called the head of the scapula. On it is a shallow pyriform, articular surface, the **glenoid cavity**, which is directed lateralward and forward and articulates with the head of the humerus; it is broader below than above and its vertical diameter is the longest. The surface is covered with cartilage in the fresh state; and its margins, slightly raised, give attachment to a fibrocartilaginous structure, the **glenoidallabrum**, which deepens the cavity. At its apex is a slight elevation, the **supraglenoid tuberosity**, to which the long head of the Biceps brachii is attached. The **neck** of the scapula is the slightly constricted portion which surrounds the head; it is more distinct below and behind than above and in front.

The Coracoid Process (*processus coracoideus*). — The coracoid process is a thick curved process attached by a broad base to the upper part of the neck of the scapula; it runs at first upward and medialward; then, becoming smaller, it changes its direction, and projects forward and lateralward. The ascending portion, flattened from before backward, presents in front a smooth concave surface, across which the Subscapularis passes. The horizontal portion is flattened from above downward; its upper surface is convex and irregular, and gives attachment to the Pectoralis minor; its under surface is smooth; its medial and lateral borders are rough; the former gives attachment to the Pectoralis minor and the latter to the coracoacromial ligament; the apex is embraced by the conjoined tendon of origin of the Coracobrachialis and short head of the Biceps brachii and gives attachment to the coraco-

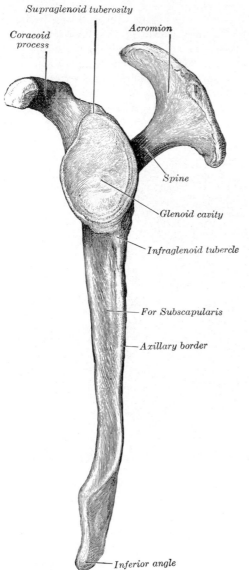

Supraglenoid tuberosity

Acromion

Coracoid process

Spine

Glenoid cavity

Infraglenoid tubercle

For Subscapularis

Axillary border

Inferior angle

FIG. 255.—Left scapula. Lateral view.

clavicular fascia. On the medial part of the root of the coracoid process is a rough impression for the attachment of the conoid ligament; and running from it obliquely forward and lateralward, on to the upper surface of the horizontal portion, is an elevated ridge for the attachment of the trapezoid ligament.

Structure.—The head, processes, and the thickened parts of the bone, contain cancellous tissue; the rest consists of a thin layer of compact tissue. The central part of the supraspinatous fossa and the upper part of the infraspinatous fossa, but especially the former, are usually so thin as to be semitransparent; occasionally the bone is found wanting in this situation, and the adjacent muscles are separated only by fibrous tissue.

Ossification (Fig. 256).—The scapula is ossified from *seven* or more centers: one for the body, two for the coracoid process, two for the acromion, one for the vertebral border, and one for the inferior angle.

Ossification of the body begins about the second month of fetal life, by the formation of an irregular quadrilateral plate of bone, immediately behind the glenoid cavity. This plate extends so as to form the chief part of the bone, the spine growing up from its dorsal surface about the third month. At birth, a large part of the scapula is osseous, but the glenoid cavity, the coracoid process, the acromion, the vertebral border, and the inferior angle are cartilaginous. From the fifteenth to the eighteenth month after birth, ossification takes place in the middle of the coracoid process, which as a rule becomes joined with the rest of the bone about the fifteenth year. Between the fourteenth and twentieth years, ossification of the remaining parts takes place in quick succession, and usually in the following order; first, in the root of the coracoid process, in the form of a broad scale; secondly, near the base of the acromion; thirdly, in the inferior angle and contiguous part of the vertebral border; fourthly, near the extremity of the acromion; fifthly, in the vertebral border. The base of the acromion is formed by an extension from the spine; the two separate nuclei of the acromion unite, and then join with the extension from the spine. The upper third of the glenoid cavity is ossified from a separate center (subcoracoid), which makes its appearance between the tenth and eleventh years and joins between the sixteenth and the eighteenth. Further, an epiphyseal plate appears for the lower part of the glenoid cavity, while the tip of the coracoid process frequently presents

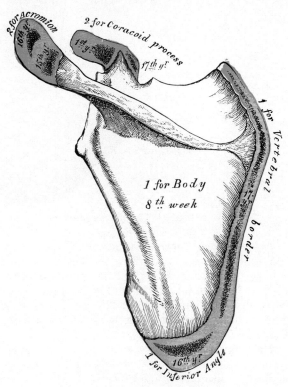

FIG. 256.—Plan of ossification of the scapula.
From seven centers.

a separate nucleus. These various epiphyses are joined to the bone by the twenty-fifth year. Failure of bony union between the acromion and spine sometimes occurs, the junction being effected by fibrous tissue, or by an imperfect articulation; in some cases of supposed fracture of the acromion with ligamentous union, it is probable that the detached segment was never united to the rest of the bone.

The Humerus (Arm Bone).

The **humerus** (Figs. 259, 260) is the longest and largest bone of the upper extremity; it is divisible into a **body** and **two extremities.**

Upper Extremity.—The upper extremity consists of a large rounded *head* joined to the body by a constricted portion called the **neck,** and two eminences, the **greater** and **lesser tubercles.**

The Head (*caput humeri*).—The head (Fig. 257), nearly hemispherical in form, is directed upward, medialward, and a little backward, and articulates with the glenoid cavity of the scapula. The circumference of its articular surface is slightly constricted and is termed the **anatomical neck,** in contradistinction to a constriction below the tubercles called the **surgical neck** which is frequently the seat of fracture. Fracture of the anatomical neck rarely occurs.

The **Anatomical Neck** (*collum anatomicum*) is obliquely directed, forming an obtuse angle with the body. It is best marked in the lower half of its circumference; in the upper half it is represented by a narrow groove separating the head from the tubercles. It affords attachment to the articular capsule of the shoulder-joint, and is perforated by numerous vascular foramina.

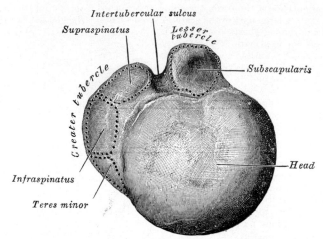

FIG. 257.—The upper end of the left humerus. Superior aspect.

The **Greater Tubercle** (*tuberculum majus; greater tuberosity*).—The greater tubercle is situated lateral to the head and lesser tubercle. Its upper surface is rounded and marked by three flat impressions: the highest of these gives insertion to the Supraspinatus; the middle to the Infraspinatus; the lowest one, and the body of the bone for about 2.5 cm. below it, to the Teres minor. The lateral surface of the greater tubercle is convex, rough, and continuous with the lateral surface of the body.

The **Lesser Tubercle** (*tuberculum minus; lesser tuberosity*).—The lesser tubercle, although smaller, is more prominent than the greater: it is situated in front, and is directed medialward and forward. Above and in front it presents an impression for the insertion of the tendon of the Subscapularis.

The tubercles are separated from each other by a deep groove, the **intertubercular groove** (*bicipital groove*), which lodges the long tendon of the Biceps brachii and transmits a branch of the anterior humeral circumflex artery to the shoulder-joint. It runs obliquely downward, and ends near the junction of the upper with the middle third of the bone. In the fresh state its upper part is covered with a thin layer of cartilage, lined by a prolongation of the synovial membrane of the shoulder-joint; its lower portion gives insertion to the tendon of the Latissimus dorsi. It is deep and narrow above, and becomes shallow and a little broader as it descends. Its lips are called, respectively, the **crests of the greater and lesser tubercles** (*bicipital ridges*), and form the upper parts of the anterior and medial borders of the body of the bone.

The **Body or Shaft** (*corpus humeri*).—The body is almost cylindrical in the upper half of its extent, prismatic and flattened below, and has three borders and three surfaces.

Borders.—The **anterior border** runs from the front of the greater tubercle above to the coronoid fossa below, separating the antero-medial from the antero-lateral surface. Its upper part is a prominent ridge, the crest of the greater tubercle; it serves for the insertion of the tendon of the Pectoralis major. About its center it forms the anterior boundary of the deltoid tuberosity; below, it is smooth and rounded, affording attachment to the Brachialis.

The **lateral border** runs from the back part of the greater tubercle to the lateral epicondyle, and separates the antero-lateral from the posterior surface. Its upper half is rounded and indistinctly marked, serving for the attachment of the lower part of the insertion of the Teres minor, and below this giving origin to the lateral head of the Triceps brachii; its center is traversed by a broad but shallow oblique depression, the **radial sulcus** (*musculospiral groove*). Its lower part forms a prominent, rough margin, a little curved from behind forward, the **lateral supracondylar ridge**, which presents an anterior lip for the origin of the Brachioradialis above, and Extensor carpi radialis longus below, a posterior lip for the Triceps brachii, and an intermediate ridge for the attachment of the lateral intermuscular septum.

The **medial border** extends from the lesser tubercle to the medial epicondyle. Its upper third consists of a prominent ridge, the **crest of the lesser tubercle,** which gives insertion to the tendon of the Teres major. About its center is a slight impression for the insertion of the Coracobrachialis, and just below this is the entrance of the nutrient canal, directed downward; sometimes there is a second nutrient canal at the commencement of the radial sulcus. The inferior third of this border is raised into a slight ridge, the **medial supracondylar ridge**, which becomes very prominent below; it presents an anterior lip for the origin of the Brachialis, a posterior lip for the medial head of the Triceps brachii, and an intermediate ridge for the attachment of the medial intermuscular septum.

Surfaces.—The **antero-lateral surface** is directed lateralward above, where it is smooth, rounded, and covered by the Deltoideus; forward and lateralward below, where it is slightly concave from above downward, and gives origin to part of the Brachialis. About the middle of this surface is a rough, triangular elevation, the **deltoid tuberosity** for the insertion of the Deltoideus; below this is the **radial sulcus**, directed obliquely from behind, forward, and downward, and transmitting the radial nerve and profunda artery.

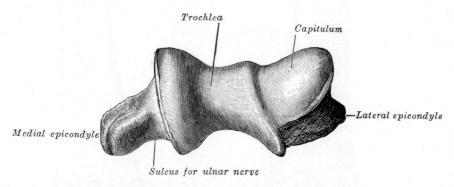

Trochlea *Capitulum*

Medial epicondyle *Lateral epicondyle*

Sulcus for ulnar nerve

Fig. 258.—The lower end of the left humerus. Inferior aspect.

The **antero-medial surface**, less extensive than the antero-lateral, is directed medialward above, forward and medialward below; its upper part is narrow, and forms the floor of the intertubercular groove which gives insertion to the tendon of the Latissimus dorsi; its middle part is slightly rough for the attachment of some of the fibers of the tendon of insertion of the Coracobrachialis; its lower part is smooth, concave from above downward, and gives origin to the Brachialis.

The **posterior surface** appears somewhat twisted, so that its upper part is

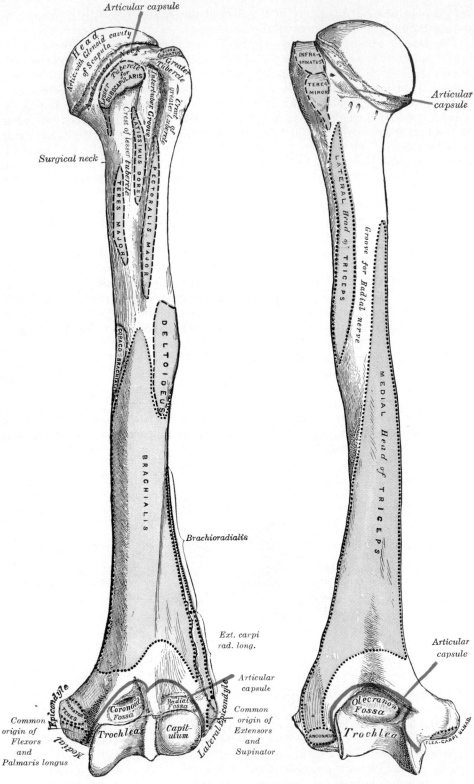

Fig. 259.—Left humerus. Anterior view. Fig. 260.—Left humerus. Posterior view.

directed a little medialward, its lower part backward and a little lateralward. Nearly the whole of this surface is covered by the lateral and medial heads of the Triceps brachii, the former arising above, the latter below the radial sulcus.

The Lower Extremity. (Fig. 258).—The lower extremity is flattened from before backward, and curved slightly forward; it ends below in a broad, articular surface, which is divided into two parts by a slight ridge. Projecting on either side are the lateral and medial epicondyles. The **articular surface** extends a little lower than the epicondyles, and is curved slightly forward; its medial extremity occupies a lower level than the lateral. The lateral portion of this surface consists of a smooth, rounded eminence, named the **capitulum of the humerus**; it articulates with the cup-shaped depression on the head of the radius, and is limited to the front and lower part of the bone. On the medial side of this eminence is a shallow groove, in which is received the medial margin of the head of the radius. Above the front part of the capitulum is a slight depression, the **radial fossa**, which receives the anterior border of the head of the radius, when the forearm is flexed. The medial portion

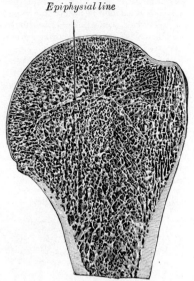

Epiphysial line

FIG. 261.—Longitudinal section of head of left humerus.

of the articular surface is named the **trochlea**, and presents a deep depression between two well-marked borders; it is convex from before backward, concave from side to side, and occupies the anterior, lower, and posterior parts of the extremity. The lateral border separates it from the groove which articulates with the margin of the head of the radius. The medial border is thicker, of greater length, and consequently more prominent, than the lateral. The grooved portion of the articular surface fits accurately within the semilunar notch of the ulna; it is broader and deeper on the posterior than on the anterior aspect of the bone, and is inclined obliquely downward and forward toward the medial side. Above the front part of the trochlea is a small depression, the **coronoid fossa**, which receives the coronoid process of the ulna during flexion of the forearm. Above the back part of the trochlea is a deep triangular depression, the **olecranon fossa**, in which the summit of the olecranon is received in extension of the forearm. These fossæ are separated from one another by a thin, transparent lamina of bone, which is sometimes perforated by a **supratrochlear foramen**; they are lined in the fresh state by the synovial membrane of the elbow-joint, and their margins afford attachment to the anterior and posterior ligaments of this articulation. The **lateral epicondyle** is a small, tuberculated eminence, curved a little forward, and giving attachment to the radial collateral ligament of the elbow-joint, and to a tendon common to the origin of the Supinator and some of the Extensor muscles. The **medial epicondyle**, larger and more prominent than the lateral, is directed a little backward; it gives attachment to the ulnar collateral ligament of the elbow-joint, to the Pronator teres, and to a common tendon of origin of most of the Flexor muscles of the forearm; the ulnar nerve runs in a groove on the back of this epicondyle. The epicondyles are continuous above with the supracondylar ridges.

Structure.—The extremities consist of cancellous tissue, covered with a thin, compact layer (Fig. 261); the body is composed of a cylinder of compact tissue, thicker at the center than toward the extremities, and contains a large medullary canal which extends along its whole length.

Ossification (Figs. 262, 263).—The humerus is ossified from *eight* centers, one for each of the following parts: the body, the head, the greater tubercle, the lesser tubercle, the capitulum, the trochlea, and one for each epicondyle. The center for the body appears near the middle of the bone in the eighth week of fetal life, and soon extends toward the extremities. At birth the humerus is ossified in nearly its whole length, only the extremities remaining cartilaginous. During the first year, sometimes before birth, ossification commences in the head of the bone, and during the third year the center for the greater tubercle, and during the fifth that for the lesser tubercle, make their appearance. By the sixth year the centers for the head and tubercules have joined, so as to form a single large epiphysis, which fuses with the body about the twentieth year. The conical shape of the proximal end of the diaphysis, where the epiphyseal cap fits over it as shown by the epiphyseal line in Figure 261, is an adult condition. In the fetus and newborn, the end of the diaphysis is flat; the conical shape is established during the first year and gradually reaches the height of the adult by the twelfth year. The lower end of the humerus is ossified as follows. At the end of the second year ossification begins in the capitulum, and extends medialward, to form the chief part of the articular end of the bone; the center for the medial part of the trochlea appears about the age of twelve. Ossification begins in the medial epicondyle about the fifth year, and in the lateral about the thirteenth or fourteenth year. About the sixteenth or seventeenth year, the lateral epicondyle and both portions of the articulating surface, having already joined, unite with the body, and at the eighteenth year the medial epicondyle becomes joined to it.

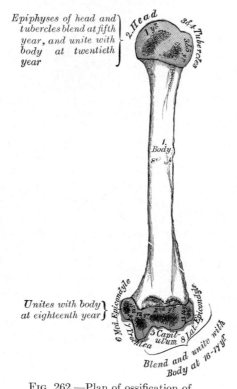

FIG. 262.—Plan of ossification of the humerus.

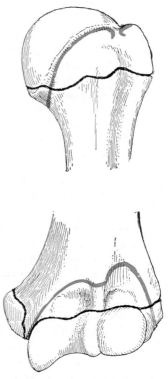

FIG. 263.—Epiphyseal lines of humerus in a young adult. Anterior aspect. The lines of attachment of the articular capsules are in blue.

Torsion of the Humerus is the term used to refer to the twisting of the bone about its longitudinal axis, that is, the change in the relation of the transverse, articular axes of the two ends of the bone to each other. This is entirely distinct and independent of the rotation of the whole limb referred to in the section on Embryology. The angle formed by the axes of the two ends of the bone is called the torsion angle. According to Evans and Krahl (1945), the angle measures 74° in the adult bone, the distal end having been twisted medially in relation to the proximal end. Two factors have been identified; a primary torsion which is hereditary and evolutionary, and a secondary which is ontogenetic. The primary torsion is found in all tetrapods, and in the evolutionary scale of mammals, the angle increases from 27° to 74°. The secondary torsion takes place at the proximal epiphyseal junction before the age of twenty, while cartilage is still present, and apparently is due to muscular pull since the lateral rotators are attached proximal and the medial rotators distal to the junction. There is no torsion in the diaphysis; the apparent twisting of this part of the bone is due to the surface markings associated with the spiral course of the radial nerve.

Variations.—A small, hook-shaped process of bone, the *supracondylar process*, varying from 2 to 20 mm. in length, is not infrequently found projecting from the antero-medial surface of the body of the humerus 5 cm. above the medial epicondyle. It is curved downward and forward, and its pointed end is connected to the medial border, just above the medial epicondyle, by a fibrous band, which gives origin to a portion of the Pronator teres; through the arch completed by this fibrous band the median nerve and brachial artery pass, when these structures deviate from their usual course. Sometimes the nerve alone is transmitted through it, or the nerve may be accompanied by the ulnar artery, in cases of high division of the brachial. A well-marked groove is usually found behind the process, in which the nerve and artery are lodged. This arch is the homologue of the *supracondyloid foramen* found in many animals, and probably serves in them to protect the nerve and artery from compression during the contraction of the muscles in this region.

The Ulna (Elbow Bone).

The **ulna** (Figs. 265, 266) is a long bone, prismatic in form, placed at the medial side of the forearm, parallel with the radius. It is divisible into a **body** and **two extremities.** Its upper extremity, of great thickness and strength, forms a large part of the elbow-joint; the bone diminishes in size from above downward, its lower extremity being very small, and excluded from the wrist-joint by the interposition of an articular disk.

The Upper Extremity (*proximal extremity*) (Fig. 264).—The upper extremity presents two curved processes, the **olecranon** and the **coronoid process**; and two concave, articular cavities, the **semilunar** and **radial notches.**

The Olecranon (*olecranon process*).—The olecranon is a large, thick, curved eminence, situated at the upper and back part of the ulna. It is bent forward at the summit so as to present a prominent lip which is received into the olecranon fossa of the humerus in extension of the forearm. Its **base** is contracted where it joins the body and the narrowest part of the upper end of the ulna. Its **posterior surface**, directed backward, is triangular, smooth, subcutaneous, and covered by a bursa. Its **superior surface** is of quadrilateral form, marked behind by a rough impression for the insertion of the Triceps brachii; and in front, near the margin, by a slight transverse groove for the attachment of part of the posterior ligament of the elbow-joint. Its **anterior surface** is smooth, concave, and forms the upper part of the semilunar notch. Its **borders** present continuations of the groove on the margin of the superior surface; they serve for the attachment of ligaments, viz., the back part of the ulnar collateral ligament medially, and the posterior ligament laterally. From the medial border a part of the Flexor carpi ulnaris arises; while to the lateral border the Anconæus is attached.

The Coronoid Process (*processus coronoideus*).— The coronoid process is a triangular eminence projecting forward from the upper and front part of the ulna. Its **base** is continuous with the body of the bone, and of considerable strength. Its **apex** is pointed, slightly curved upward, and in flexion of the

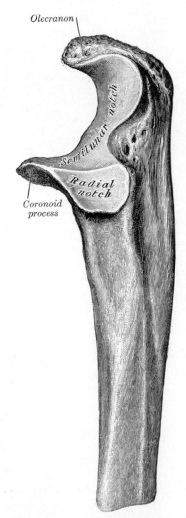

FIG. 264.—Upper extremity of left ulna. Lateral aspect.

16

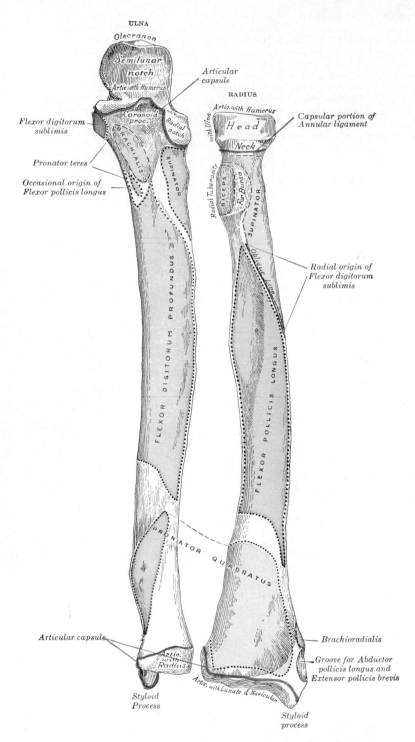

ULNA
Olecranon
Semilunar notch
Artic. with Humerus
Articular capsule
RADIUS
Artic. with Humerus
Flexor digitorum sublimis
Coronoid proc.
Radial notch
BRACHIALIS
with Ulna
Capsular portion of Annular ligament
Head
Neck
Pronator teres
SUPINATOR
Occasional origin of Flexor pollicis longus
Radial Tuberosity
BICEPS
Bursa
SUPINATOR
Radial origin of Flexor digitorum sublimis
FLEXOR DIGITORUM PROFUNDUS
Oblique Line
FLEXOR POLLICIS LONGUS
PRONATOR QUADRATUS
Articular capsule
Artic. with Radius
Brachioradialis
Groove for Abductor pollicis longus and Extensor pollicis brevis
Artic. with Lunate & Navicular
Styloid Process
Styloid process

FIG. 265.—The bones of the left forearm. Anterior aspect.

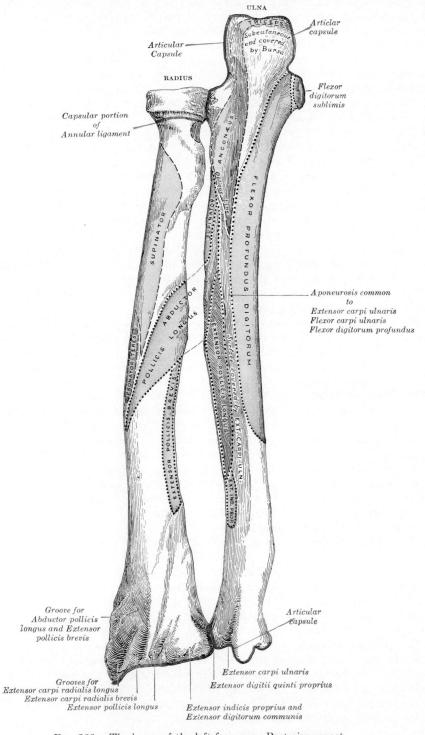

Fig. 266.—The bones of the left forearm. Posterior aspect.

forearm is received into the coronoid fossa of the humerus. Its **upper surface** is smooth, concave, and forms the lower part of the semilunar notch. Its **antero-inferior surface** is concave, and marked by a rough impression for the insertion of the Brachialis. At the junction of this surface with the front of the body is a rough eminence, the **tuberosity of the ulna,** which gives insertion to a part of the Brachialis; to the lateral border of this tuberosity the oblique cord is attached. Its **lateral surface** presents a narrow, oblong, articular depression, the **radial notch.** Its **medial surface,** by its prominent, free margin, serves for the attachment of part of the ulnar collateral ligament. At the front part of this surface is a small rounded eminence for the origin of one head of the Flexor digitorum sublimis; behind the eminence is a depression for part of the origin of the Flexor digitorum profundus; descending from the eminence is a ridge which gives origin to one head of the Pronator teres. Frequently, the Flexor pollicis longus arises from the lower part of the coronoid process by a rounded bundle of muscular fibers.

The Semilunar Notch (*incisura trochlearis; greater sigmoid cavity*).—The semilunar notch is a large depression, formed by the olecranon and the coronoid process, and serving for articulation with the trochlea of the humerus. About the middle of either side of this notch is an indentation, which contracts it somewhat, and indicates the junction of the olecranon and the coronoid process. The notch is concave from above downward, and divided into a medial and a lateral portion by a smooth ridge running from the summit of the olecranon to the tip of the coronoid process. The medial portion is the larger, and is slightly concave transversely; the lateral is convex above, slightly concave below.

The Radial Notch (*incisura radialis; lesser sigmoid cavity*).—The radial notch is a narrow, oblong, articular depression on the lateral side of the coronoid process; it receives the circumferential articular surface of the head of the radius. It is concave from before backward, and its prominent extremities serve for the attachment of the annular ligament.

The Body or Shaft (*corpus ulnæ*).—The body at its upper part is prismatic in form, and curved so as to be convex behind and lateralward; its central part is straight; its lower part is rounded, smooth, and bent a little lateralward. It tapers gradually from above downward, and has three borders and three surfaces.

Borders.—The **anterior border** (*margo anterior; volar border*) begins above at the prominent medial angle of the coronoid process, and ends below in front of the styloid process. Its upper part, well-defined, and its middle portion, smooth and rounded, give origin to the Flexor digitorum profundus; its lower fourth, called the **pronator ridge,** serves for the origin of the Pronator quadratus. This border separates the volar from the medial surface.

The **posterior border** (*margo posterior; dorsal border*) begins above at the apex of the triangular subcutaneous surface at the back part of the olecranon, and ends below at the back of the styloid process; it is well-marked in the upper three-fourths, and gives attachment to an aponeurosis which affords a common origin to the Flexor carpi ulnaris, the Extensor carpi ulnaris, and the Flexor digitorum profundus; its lower fourth is smooth and rounded. This border separates the medial from the dorsal surface.

The **interosseous crest** (*margo interossea; external or interosseous border*) begins above by the union of two lines, which converge from the extremities of the radial notch and enclose between them a triangular space for the origin of part of the Supinator; it ends below at the head of the ulna. Its upper part is sharp, its lower fourth smooth and rounded. This crest gives attachment to the interosseous membrane, and separates the volar from the dorsal surface.

Surfaces.—The **anterior surface** (*facies anterior; volar surface*), much broader above than below, is concave in its upper three-fourths, and gives origin to the Flexor digitorum profundus; its lower fourth, also concave, is covered by the Pronator quadratus. The lower fourth is separated from the remaining portion by a ridge, directed obliquely downward and medialward, which marks the extent of origin of the Pronator quadratus. At the junction of the upper with the middle third of the bone is the nutrient canal, directed obliquely upward.

The **posterior surface** (*facies dorsal; posterior surface*) directed backward and lateralward, is broad and concave above; convex and somewhat narrower in the middle; narrow, smooth, and rounded below. On its upper part is an oblique ridge, which runs from the dorsal end of the radial notch, downward to the dorsal

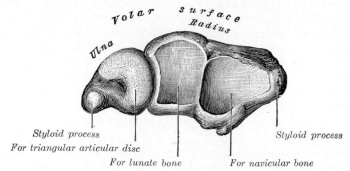

FIG. 267.—The lower ends of the left radius and ulna. Inferior aspect.

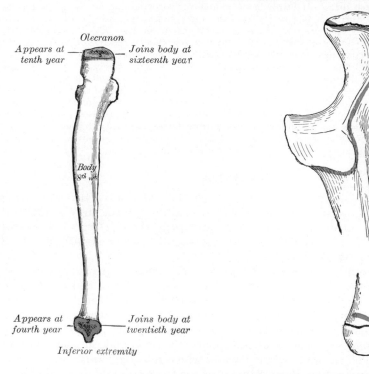

FIG. 268.—Plan of ossification of the ulna. From three centers.

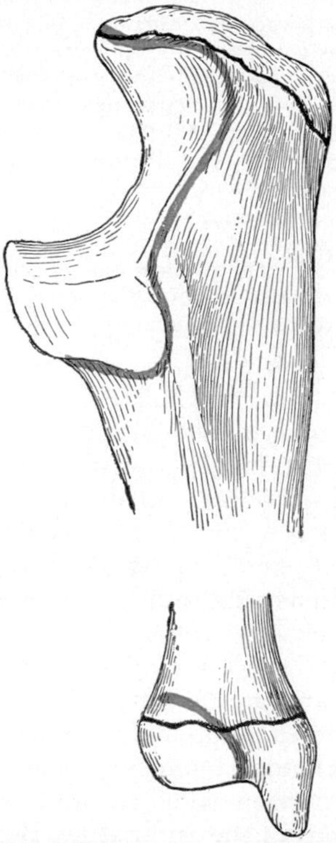

FIG. 269.—Epiphyseal lines of ulna in a young adult. Lateral aspect. The lines of attachment of the articular capsules are in blue.

border; the triangular surface above this ridge receives the insertion of the Anconæus, while the upper part of the ridge affords attachment to the Supinator. Below this the surface is subdivided by a longitudinal ridge, sometimes called the **perpendicular line**, into two parts: the medial part is smooth, and covered by the Extensor carpi ulnaris; the lateral portion, wider and rougher, gives origin from above downward to the Supinator, the Abductor pollicis longus, the Extensor pollicis longus, and the Extensor indicis proprius.

The **medial surface** (*facies medialis; internal surface*) is broad and concave above, narrow and convex below. Its upper three-fourths give origin to the Flexor digitorum profundus; its lower fourth is subcutaneous.

The Lower Extremity (*distal extremity*).—The lower extremity of the ulna is small, and presents two eminences; the lateral and larger is a rounded, articular eminence, termed the head of the ulna; the medial, narrower and more projecting, is a non-articular eminence, the styloid process. The **head** presents an articular surface, part of which, of an oval or semilunar form, is directed downward, and articulates with the upper surface of the triangular articular disk which separates it from the wrist-joint; the remaining portion, directed lateralward, is narrow, convex, and received into the ulnar notch of the radius. The **styloid process** projects from the medial and back part of the bone; it descends a little lower than the head, and its rounded end affords attachment to the ulnar collateral ligament of the wrist-joint. The head is separated from the styloid process by a depression for the attachment of the apex of the triangular articular disk, and behind, by a shallow groove for the tendon of the Extensor carpi ulnaris.

Structure.—The long, narrow medullary cavity is enclosed in a strong wall of compact tissue which is thickest along the interosseous border and dorsal surface. At the extremities the compact layer thins. The compact layer is continued onto the back of the olecranon as a plate of close spongy bone with lamellæ parallel. From the inner surface of this plate and the compact layer below it trabeculæ arch forward toward the olecranon and coronoid and cross other trabeculæ, passing backward over the medullary cavity from the upper part of the shaft below the coronoid. Below the coronoid process there is a small area of compact bone from which trabeculæ curve upward to end obliquely to the surface of the semilunar notch which is coated with a thin layer of compact bone. The trabeculæ at the lower end have a more longitudinal direction.

Ossification (Figs. 268, 269).—The ulna is ossified from *three* centers: one each for the body, the inferior extremity, and the top of the olecranon. Ossification begins near the middle of the body, about the eighth week of fetal life, and soon extends through the greater part of the bone. At birth the ends are cartilaginous. About the fourth year, a center appears in the middle of the head, and soon extends into the styloid process. About the tenth year, a center appears in the olecranon near its extremity, the chief part of this process being formed by an upward extension of the body. The upper epiphysis joins the body about the sixteenth, the lower about the twentieth year.

Articulations.—The ulna articulates with the humerus and radius.

The Radius.

The **radius** (Figs. 265, 266) is situated on the lateral side of the ulna, which exceeds it in length and size. Its upper end is small, and forms only a small part of the elbow-joint; but its lower end is large, and forms the chief part of the wrist-joint. It is a long bone, prismatic in form and slightly curved longitudinally. It has a body and two extremities.

The Upper Extremity (*proximal extremity*).—The upper extremity presents a head, neck, and tuberosity. The **head** is of a cylindrical form, and on its upper surface is a shallow cup or fovea for articulation with the capitulum of the humerus. The circumference of the head is smooth; it is broad medially where it articulates with the radial notch of the ulna, narrow in the rest of its extent, which is embraced by the annular ligament. The head is supported on a round, smooth, and constricted portion called the **neck**, on the back of which is a slight ridge for the insertion of part of the Supinator. Beneath the neck, on the medial side, is an eminence, the **radial tuberosity**; its surface is divided into a posterior, rough portion, for the insertion of the tendon of the Biceps brachii, and an anterior, smooth portion, on which a bursa is interposed between the tendon and the bone.

The Body or Shaft (*corpus radii*).—The body is prismoid in form, narrower above than below, and slightly curved, so as to be convex lateralward. It presents three borders and three surfaces.

Borders.—The **anterior border** (*margo anterior; volar border*) extends from the lower part of the tuberosity above to the anterior part of the base of the styloid process below, and separates the volar from the lateral surface. Its upper third is prominent, and from its oblique direction has received the name of the **oblique line of the radius**; it gives origin to the Flexor digitorum sublimis and Flexor pollicis longus; the surface above the line gives insertion to part of the Supinator. The middle third of the volar border is indistinct and rounded. The lower fourth is prominent, and gives insertion to the Pronator quadratus, and attachment to the dorsal carpal ligament; it ends in a small tubercle, into which the tendon of the Brachioradialis is inserted.

The **posterior border** (*margo posterior; dorsal border*) begins above at the back of the neck, and ends below at the posterior part of the base of the styloid process; it separates the posterior from the lateral surface. It is indistinct above and below, but well-marked in the middle third of the bone.

The **interosseous crest** (*margo interossea; internal or interosseous border*) begins above, at the back part of the tuberosity, and its upper part is rounded and indistinct; it becomes sharp and prominent as it descends, and at its lower part divides into two ridges which are continued to the anterior and posterior margins of the ulnar notch. To the posterior of the two ridges the lower part of the interosseous membrane is attached, while the triangular surface between the ridges gives insertion to part of the Pronator quadratus. This crest separates the volar from the dorsal surface, and gives attachment to the interosseous membrane.

Surface.—The **anterior surface** (*facies anterior; volar surface*) is concave in its upper three-fourths, and gives origin to the Flexor pollicis longus; it is broad and flat in its lower fourth, and affords insertion to the Pronator quadratus. A prominent ridge limits the insertion of the Pronator quadratus below, and between this and the inferior border is a triangular rough surface for the attachment of the volar radiocarpal ligament. At the junction of the upper and middle thirds of the volar surface is the nutrient foramen, which is directed obliquely upward.

The **posterior surface** (*facies posterior; dorsal surface*) is convex, and smooth in the upper third of its extent, and covered by the Supinator. Its middle third is broad, slightly concave, and gives origin to the Abductor pollicis longus above, and the Extensor pollicis brevis below. Its lower third is broad, convex, and covered by the tendons of the muscles which subsequently run in the grooves on the lower end of the bone.

The **lateral surface** (*facies lateralis; external surface*) is convex throughout its entire extent. Its upper third gives insertion to the Supinator. About its center is a rough ridge, for the insertion of the Pronator teres. Its lower part is narrow, and covered by the tendons of the Abductor pollicis longus and Extensor pollicis brevis.

The Lower Extremity.—The lower extremity is large, of quadrilateral form, and provided with two articular surfaces—one below, for the carpus, and another at the medial side, for the ulna The carpal articular surface is triangular, concave, smooth, and divided by a slight antero-posterior ridge into two parts. Of these, the lateral, triangular, articulates with the navicular bone; the medial, quadrilateral, with the lunate bone. The articular surface for the ulna is called the **ulnar notch** (*sigmoid cavity*) **of the radius**; it is narrow, concave, smooth, and articulates with the head of the ulna. These two articular surfaces are separated by a prominent ridge, to which the base of the triangular articular disk is attached; this disk separates the wrist-joint from the distal radioulnar articulation. This end of the bone has three non-articular surfaces—volar, dorsal, and lateral. The **anterior surface**, rough and irregular, affords attachment to the volar radiocarpal ligament. The **posterior surface** is convex, affords attachment to the dorsal radiocarpal ligament, and is marked by three grooves. Enumerated from the lateral side, the first groove is broad, but shallow, and subdivided into two by a slight ridge; the lateral of these two transmits the tendon of the Extensor carpi radialis longus, the medial the tendon of the Extensor carpi radialis brevis. The second is deep but narrow, and bounded laterally by a sharply defined ridge; it is directed obliquely from above downward and lateralward, and transmits the tendon of the Extensor pollicis longus. The third is broad, for the passage of the tendons of the Extensor indicis proprius and Extensor digitorum communis. The **lateral surface** is prolonged obliquely downward into a strong, conical projection, the **styloid process**, which gives attachment by its base to the tendon of the Brachioradialis, and by its apex to the radial collateral ligament of the wrist-joint. The lateral surface of this process is marked by a flat groove, for the tendons of the Abductor pollicis longus and Extensor pollicis brevis.

Structure.—The long narrow medullary cavity is enclosed in a strong wall of compact tissue which is thickest along the interosseous border and thinnest at the extremities except over the cup-shaped articular surface (fovea) of the head where it is thickened. The trabeculæ of the spongy tissue are somewhat arched at the upper end and pass upward from the compact layer of the shaft to the fovea capituli; they are crossed by others parallel to the surface of the fovea. The arrangement at the lower end is somewhat similar.

Ossification (Figs. 270, 271).—The radius is ossified from *three* centers: one for the body, and one for either extremity. That for the body makes its appearance near the center of the bone, during the eighth week of fetal life. About the end of the second year, ossification commences in the lower end; and at the fifth year, in the upper end. The upper epiphysis fuses with the body at the age of seventeen or eighteen years, the lower about the age of twenty. An additional center sometimes found in the radial tuberosity, appears about the fourteenth or fifteenth year.

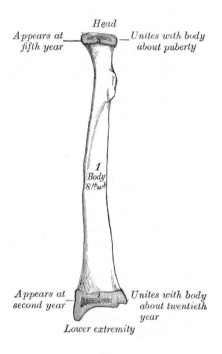

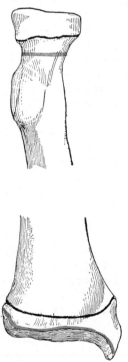

Fig. 270.—Plan of ossification of the radius. From three centers.

Fig. 271.—Epiphyseal lines of radius in a young adult. Anterior aspect. The line of attachment of the articular capsule of the wrist-joint is in blue.

THE HAND.

The skeleton of the hand (Figs. 274, 275) is subdivided into three segments: the **carpus or wrist bones**; the **metacarpus or bones of the palm**; and the **phalanges or bones of the digits.**

The Carpus (Ossa Carpi).

The **carpal bones**, eight in number, are arranged in two rows. Those of the proximal row, from the radial to the ulnar side, are named the **navicular, lunate, triangular**, and **pisiform**; those of the distal row, in the same order, are named the **greater multangular, lesser multangular, capitate**, and **hamate**.

Common Characteristics of the Carpal Bones.—Each bone (excepting the pisi-form) presents six surfaces. Of these the *volar* or *anterior* and the *dorsal* or *posterior* *surfaces* are rough, for ligamentous attachment; the dorsal surfaces being the broader, except in the navicular and lunate. The *superior* or *proximal*, and *inferior* or *distal surfaces* are articular, the superior generally convex, the inferior concave; the *medial* and *lateral surfaces* are also articular where they are in contact with contiguous bones, otherwise they are rough and tuberculated. The structure in all is similar, viz., cancellous tissue enclosed in a layer of compact bone.

Bones of the Proximal Row (*upper row*).—**The Navicular Bone** (*os scaphoideum*; *scaphoid bone*) (Fig. 272).—The navicular bone is the largest bone of the proximal

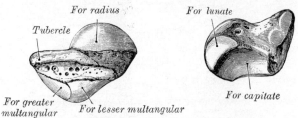

FIG. 272.—The left navicular bone.

row, and has received its name from its fancied resemblance to a boat. It is situated at the radial side of the carpus, its long axis being from above downward, lateralward, and forward. The **superior surface** is convex, smooth, of triangular shape, and artic-ulates with the lower end of the radius. The **inferior surface**, directed downward, lateralward, and backward, is also smooth, convex, and triangular, and is divided by a slight ridge into two parts, the lateral articulating with the greater multangu-lar, the medial with the lesser multangular. On the **dorsal surface** is a narrow, rough groove, which runs the entire length of the bone, and serves for the attach-ment of ligaments. The **volar surface** is concave above, and elevated at its lower and lateral part into a rounded projection, the **tubercle**, which is directed forward and gives attachment to the transverse carpal ligament and sometimes origin to a few fibers of the Abductor pollicis brevis. The **lateral surface** is rough and narrow, and gives attachment to the radial collateral ligament of the wrist. The **medial surface** presents two articular facets; of these, the superior or smaller is flattened, of semilunar form, and articulates with the lunate bone; the inferior or larger is concave, forming with the lunate a concavity for the head of the capitate bone.

Articulations.—The navicular articulates with *five* bones: the radius proximally, greater and lesser multangulars distally, and capitate and lunate medially.

The Lunate Bone (*os lunatum; semilunar bone*) (Fig. 273).—The lunate bone may be distinguished by its deep concavity and crescentic outline. It is situated in

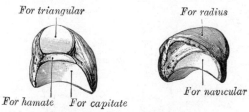

FIG. 273.—The left lunate bone.

the center of the proximal row of the carpus, between the navicular and triangular. The **superior surface**, convex and smooth, articulates with the radius. The **inferior surface** is deeply concave, and of greater extent from before backward than trans-versely: it articulates with the head of the capitate, and, by a long, narrow facet (separated by a ridge from the general surface), with the hamate. The **dorsal** and **volar surfaces** are rough, for the attachment of ligaments, the latter being the broader. The **lateral surface** presents a narrow, flattened, semilunar facet for articulation with the navicular. The **medial surface** is marked by a smooth, quadrilateral facet, for articulation with the triangular.

Articulations.—The lunate articulates with *five* bones: the radius proximally, capitate and hamate distally, navicular laterally, and triangular medially.

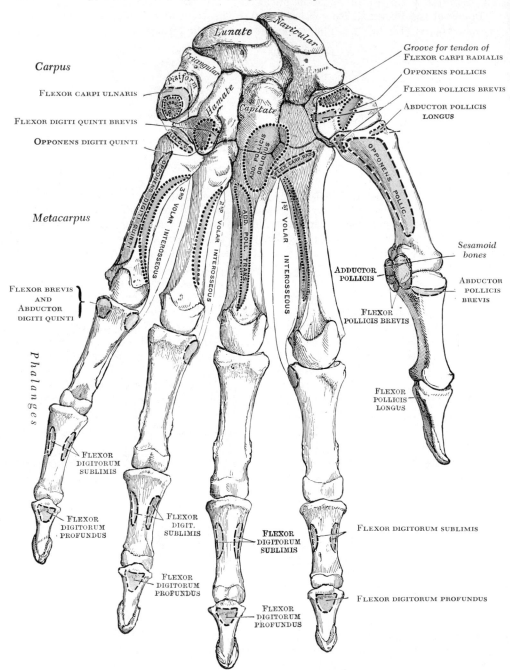

FIG. 274.—Bones of the left hand. Volar surface.

The Triangular Bone (*os triquetrum; cuneiform bone*) (Fig. 276).—The triangular bone may be distinguished by its pyramidal shape, and by an oval isolated facet for articulation with the pisiform bone. It is situated at the upper and ulnar side of the carpus. The **superior surface** presents a medial, rough, non-articular portion, and a lateral convex articular portion which articulates with the triangular articular disk of the wrist. The **inferior surface**, directed lateralward, is concave, sinuously

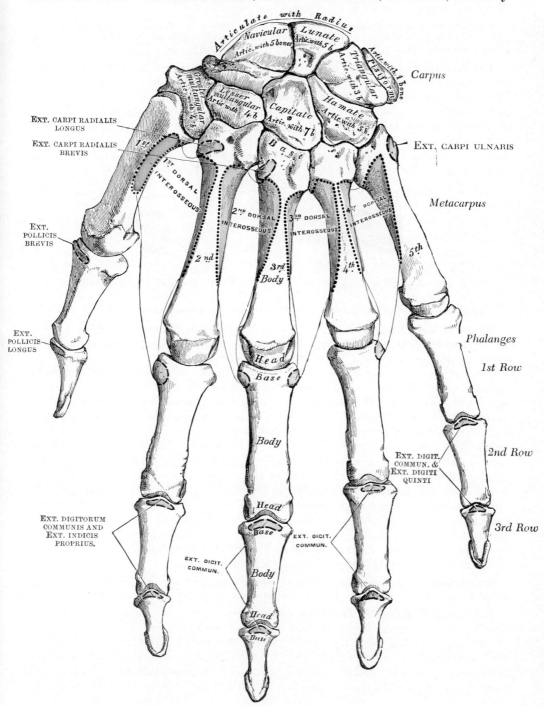

Fig. 275.—Bones of the left hand. Dorsal surface.

curved, and smooth for articulation with the hamate. The **dorsal surface** is rough for the attachment of ligaments. The **volar surface** presents, on its medial part, an oval facet, for articulation with the pisiform; its lateral part is rough for ligamentous attachment. The **lateral surface**, the base of the pyramid, is marked by a flat, quadrilateral facet, for articulation with the lunate. The **medial surface**, the summit of the pyramid, is pointed and roughened, for the attachment of the ulnar collateral ligament of the wrist.

Articulations.—The triangular articulates with *three* bones: the lunate laterally, the pisiform in front, the hamate distally; and with the triangular articular disk which separates it from the lower end of the ulna.

The Pisiform Bone (*os pisiforme*) (Fig. 277).—The pisiform bone may be known by its small size, and by its presenting a single articular facet. It is situated on a plane anterior to the other carpal bones and is spheroidal in form. Its **dorsal surface** presents a smooth, oval facet, for articulation with the triangular: this facet approaches the superior, but not the inferior border of the bone. The **volar surface** is rounded and rough, and gives attachment to the transverse carpal ligament, and to the Flexor carpi ulnaris and Abductor digiti quinti. The **lateral** and **medial surfaces** are also rough, the former being concave, the latter usually convex.

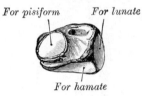

For pisiform   *For lunate*

For hamate

FIG. 276.—The left triangular bone.

For triangular

FIG. 277.—The left pisiform bone.

Articulation.—The pisiform articulates with *one* bone, the triangular.

Bones of the Distal Row (*lower row*).—**The Greater Multangular Bone** (*os trapezium*) (Fig. 278).—The greater multangular bone may be distinguished by a deep groove on its volar surface. It is situated at the radial side of the carpus, between the navicular and the first metacarpal bone. The **superior surface** is directed upward and medialward; medially it is smooth, and articulates with the navicular; laterally it is rough and continuous with the lateral surface. The **inferior surface** is oval, concave from side to side, convex from before backward, so as to form a saddle-shaped surface for articulation with the base of the first metacarpal bone. The **dorsal surface** is rough. The **volar surface** is narrow and rough. At its upper part is a deep groove, running from above obliquely downward and medialward, it transmits the tendon of the Flexor carpi radialis, and is bounded laterally by an oblique ridge. This surface gives origin to the Opponens pollicis and to the Abductor and Flexor pollicis brevis; it also affords attachment to the transverse carpal ligament. The **lateral surface** is broad and rough, for the attachment of ligaments. The **medial surface** presents two facets; the upper, large and concave, articulates with the lesser multangular; the lower, small and oval, with the base of the second metacarpal.

Articulations.—The greater multangular articulates with *four* bones: the navicular proximally the first metacarpal distally, and the lesser multangular and second metacarpal medially.

The Lesser Multangular Bone (*os trapezoideum; trapezoid bone*) (Fig. 279).— The lesser multangular is the smallest bone in the distal row. It may be known by its wedge-shaped form, the broad end of the wedge constituting the dorsal, the narrow end the volar surface; and by its having four articular facets touching each other, and separated by sharp edges. The **superior surface**, quadrilateral, smooth, and slightly concave, articulates with the navicular. The **inferior surface**

articulates with the proximal end of the second metacarpal bone; it is convex from side to side, concave from before backward and subdivided by an elevated ridge into

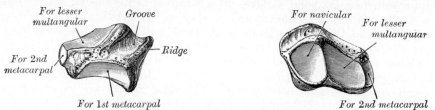

FIG. 278.—The left greater multangular bone.

two unequal facets. The **dorsal** and **volar surfaces** are rough for the attachment of ligaments, the former being the larger of the two. The **lateral surface**, convex and smooth, articulates with the greater multangular. The **medial surface** is concave and smooth in front, for articulation with the capitate; rough behind, for the attachment of an interosseous ligament.

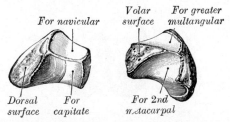

FIG. 279.—The left lesser multangular bone.

Articulations.—The lesser multangular articulates with *four* bones: the navicular proximally, second metacarpal distally, greater multangular laterally, and capitate medially.

The Capitate Bone (*os capitatum; os magnum*) (Fig. 280).—The capitate bone is the largest of the carpal bones, and occupies the center of the wrist. It presents, above, a rounded portion or head, which is received into the concavity formed by

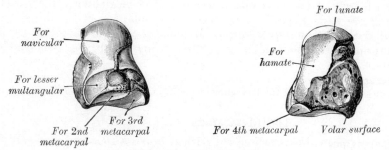

FIG. 280.—The left capitate bone.

the navicular and lunate; a constricted portion or neck; and below this, the body. The **superior surface** is round, smooth, and articulates with the lunate. The **inferior surface** is divided by two ridges into three facets, for articulation with the second, third, and fourth metacarpal bones, that for the third being the largest. The **dorsal surface** is broad and rough. The **volar surface** is narrow, rounded, and rough, for the attachment of ligaments and a part of the Adductor pollicis obliquus. The **lateral surface** articulates with the lesser multangular by a small facet at its anterior inferior angle, behind which is a rough depression for the attachment of an interosseous ligament. Above this is a deep, rough groove, forming part of the neck, and serving for the attachment of ligaments; it is bounded superiorly by a smooth, convex surface, for articulation with the navicular. The **medial surface** articulates with the hamate by a smooth, concave, oblong facet, which occupies its posterior and superior parts; it is rough in front, for the attachment of an interosseous ligament.

Articulations.—The capitate articulates with *seven* bones: the navicular and lunate proximally, the second, third, and fourth metacarpals distally, the lesser multangular on the radial side, and the hamate on the ulnar side.

The Hamate Bone (*os hamatum; unciform bone*) (Fig. 281).—The hamate bone may be readily distinguished by its wedge-shaped form, and the hook-like process which projects from its volar surface. It is situated at the medial and lower angle of the carpus, with its base downward, resting on the fourth and fifth metacarpal bones, and its apex directed upward and lateralward. The **superior surface**, the apex of the wedge, is narrow, convex, smooth, and articulates with the lunate. The **inferior surface** articulates with the fourth and fifth metacarpal bones, by concave facets which are separated by a ridge. The **dorsal surface** is triangular and rough for ligamentous attachment. The **volar surface** presents, at its lower and ulnar side, a curved, hook-like process, the **hamulus**, directed forward and lateralward. This process gives attachment, by its apex, to the transverse carpal

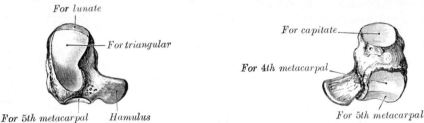

For lunate

For triangular

For capitate

For 4th metacarpal

For 5th metacarpal   *Hamulus*

For 5th metacarpal

Fig. 281.—The left hamate bone.

ligament and the Flexor carpi ulnaris; by its medial surface to the Flexor brevis and Opponens digiti quinti; its lateral side is grooved for the passage of the Flexor tendons into the palm of the hand. It is one of the four eminences on the front of the carpus to which the transverse carpal ligament of the wrist is attached; the others being the pisiform medially, the oblique ridge of the greater multangular and the tubercle of the navicular laterally. The **medial surface** articulates with the triangular bone by an oblong facet, cut obliquely from above, downward and medialward. The *lateral surface* articulates with the capitate by its upper and posterior part, the remaining portion being rough, for the attachment of ligaments.

Articulations.—The hamate articulates with *five* bones: the lunate proximally, the fourth and fifth metacarpals distally, the triangular medially, the capitate laterally.

The Metacarpus (Figs. 274, 275).

The **metacarpus** consists of five cylindrical bones which are numbered from the lateral side (*ossa metacarpalia I–V*); each consists of a body and two extremities.

Common Characteristics of the Metacarpal Bones.—The Body (*corpus; shaft*).— The body is prismoid in form, and curved, so as to be convex in the longitudinal direction behind, concave in front. It presents three surfaces: medial, lateral, and dorsal. The **medial** and **lateral surfaces** are concave, for the attachment of the Interossei, and separated from one another by a prominent anterior ridge. The **dorsal surface** presents in its distal two-thirds a smooth, triangular, flattened area which is covered in the fresh state, by the tendons of the Extensor muscles. This surface is bounded by two lines, which commence in small tubercles situated on either side of the digital extremity, and, passing upward, converge and meet some distance above the center of the bone and form a ridge which runs along the rest of the dorsal surface to the carpal extremity. This ridge separates two sloping surfaces for the attachment of the Interossei dorsales. To the tubercles on the digital extremities are attached the collateral ligaments of the metacarpophalangeal joints.

The **Base** or **Carpal Extremity** (*basis*) is of a cuboidal form, and broader behind than in front: it articulates with the carpus, and with the adjoining metacarpal bones; its **dorsal** and **volar surfaces** are rough, for the attachment of ligaments.

The **Head** or **Digital Extremity** (*capitulum*) presents an oblong surface markedly convex from before backward, less so transversely, and flattened from side to side; it articulates with the proximal phalanx. It is broader, and extends farther upward, on the volar than on the dorsal aspect, and is longer in the antero-posterior than in the transverse diameter. On either side of the head is a tubercle for the attachment of the collateral ligament of the metacarpophalangeal joint. The **dorsal surface**, broad and flat, supports the Extensor tendons; the **volar surface** is grooved in the middle line for the passage of the Flexor tendons, and marked on either side by an articular eminence continuous with the terminal articular surface.

Characteristics of the Individual Metacarpal Bones.—The **First Metacarpal Bone** (*os metacarpale I; metacarpal bone of the thumb*) (Fig. 282) is shorter and stouter than the others, diverges to a greater degree from the carpus, and its volar surface is directed toward the palm. The **body** is flattened and broad on its dorsal surface, and does not present the ridge which is found on the other metacarpal bones; its volar surface is concave from above downward. On its radial border is inserted the Opponens pollicis; its ulnar border gives origin to the lateral head of the first Interosseus dorsalis. The **base** presents a concavo-convex surface, for articulation with the greater multangular; it has no facets on its sides, but on its radial side is a tubercle for the insertion of the Abductor pollicis longus. The **head** is less convex than those of the other metacarpal bones, and is broader from side to side than from before backward. On its volar surface are two articular eminences, of which the lateral is the larger, for the two sesamoid bones in the tendons of the Flexor pollicis brevis.

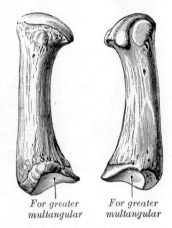

For greater multangular   For greater multangular

FIG. 282.—The first metacarpal. (Left.)

The **Second Metacarpal Bone** (*os metacarpale II; metacarpal bone of the index finger*) (Fig. 283) is the longest, and its base the largest, of the four remaining bones. Its **base** is prolonged upward and medialward, forming a prominent ridge. It presents four articular facets: three on the upper surface and one on the ulnar side. Of the facets on the upper surface the intermediate is the largest and is concave from side to side, convex from before backward for articulation with the lesser multangular; the lateral is small, flat and oval for articulation with the greater multangular; the medial, on the summit of the ridge, is long and narrow for articulation with the capitate. The facet on the ulnar side articulates with the third metacarpal. The Extensor carpi radialis longus is inserted on the dorsal surface and the Flexor carpi radialis on the volar surface of the base.

The **Third Metacarpal Bone** (*os metacarpale III; metacarpal bone of the middle finger*) (Fig. 284) is a little smaller than the second. The dorsal aspect of its **base** presents on its radial side a pyramidal eminence, the **styloid process**, which extends upward behind the capitate; immediately distal to this is a rough surface for the attachment of the Extensor carpi radialis brevis. The carpal articular facet is concave behind, flat in front, and articulates with the capitate. On the radial side is a smooth, concave facet for articulation with the second metacarpal, and on the ulnar side two small oval facets for the fourth metacarpal.

The **Fourth Metacarpal Bone** (*os metacarpale IV; metacarpal bone of the ring finger*) (Fig. 285) is shorter and smaller than the third. The **base** is small and quadrilateral; its superior surface presents two facets, a large one medially for articulation with the hamate, and a small one laterally for the capitate. On the radial side are two oval facets, for articulation with the third metacarpal; and on the ulnar side a single concave facet, for the fifth metacarpal.

The Fifth Metacarpal Bone (*os metacarpale V; metacarpal bone of the little finger*) (Fig. 286) presents on its **base** one facet on its superior surface, which is concavos convex and articulates with the hamate, and one on its radial side, which articulate- with the fourth metacarpal. On its ulnar side is a prominent tubercle for the inser-

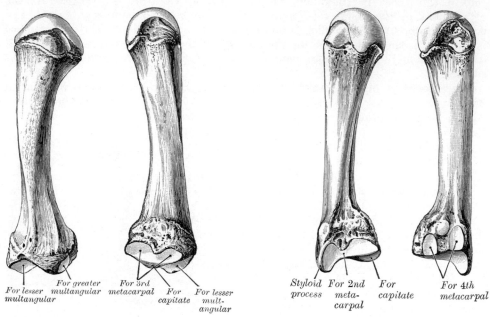

Fig. 283.—The second metacarpal. (Left.)   Fig. 284.—The third metacarpal. (Left.)

tion of the tendon of the Extensor carpi ulnaris. The dorsal surface of the body is divided by an oblique ridge, which extends from near the ulnar side of the base to the radial side of the head. The lateral part of this surface serves for the attach-

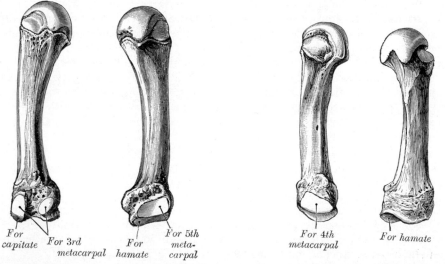

Fig. 285.—The fourth metacarpal. (Left.)   Fig. 286.—The fifth metacarpal. (Left.)

ment of the fourth Interosseus dorsalis; the medial part is smooth, triangular, and covered by the Extensor tendons of the little finger.

Articulations.—Besides their phalangeal articulations, the metacarpal bones articulate as follows: the first with the greater multangular; the second with the greater multangular, lesser multangular, capitate and third metacarpal; the third with the capitate and second and fourth metacarpals; the fourth with the capitate, hamate, and third and fifth metacarpals; and the fifth with the hamate and fourth metacarpal.

The Phalanges of the Hand (Phalanges Digitorum Manus) (Figs. 274, 275)

The **phalanges** are fourteen in number, three for each finger, and two for the thumb. Each consists of a body and two extremities. The **body** tapers from above downward, is convex posteriorly, concave in front from above downward, flat from side to side; its sides are marked by rough ridges which give attachment to the fibrous sheaths of the Flexor tendons. The **proximal extremities** of the bones of the first row present oval, concave articular surfaces, broader from side to side than from before backward. The **proximal extremity** of each of the bones of the second and third rows presents a double concavity separated by a median ridge. The **distal extremities** are smaller than the proximal, and each ends in two condyles separated by a shallow groove; the articular surface extends farther on the volar than on the dorsal surface, a condition best marked in the bones of the first row.

The **ungual phalanges** are convex on their dorsal and flat on their volar surfaces; they are recognized by their small size, and by a roughened, elevated surface of a horseshoe form on the volar surface of the distal extremity of each which serves to support the sensitive pulp of the finger.

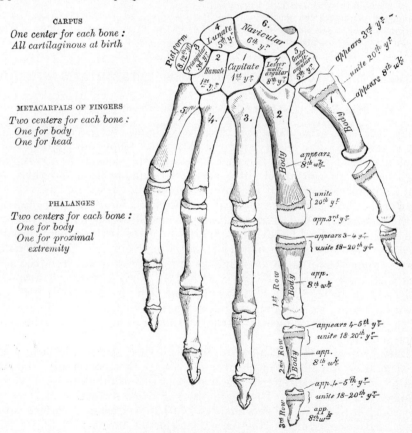

FIG. 287.—Plan of ossification of the hand.

Articulations.—In the four fingers the phalanges of the first row articulate with those of the second row and with the metacarpals; the phalanges of the second row with those of the first and third rows, and the ungual phalanges with those of the second row. In the thumb, which has only two phalanges, the first phalanx articulates by its proximal extremity with the metacarpal bone and by its distal with the ungual phalanx.

17

Ossification of the Bones of the Hand.—The **carpal bones** are each ossified from a single center, and ossification proceeds in the following order (Fig. 287): in the capitate and hamate, during the first year, the former preceding the latter; in the triangular, during the third year; in the lunate and greater multangular, during the fifth year, the former preceding the latter; in the navicular, during the sixth year; in the lesser multangular, during the eighth year; and in the pisiform, about the twelfth year. Ossification is usually bilaterally symmetrical (Pryor).

Occasionally an additional bone, the *os centrale*, is found on the back of the carpus, lying between the navicular, lesser multangular, and capitate. During the second month of fetal life it is represented by a small cartilaginous nodule, which usually fuses with the cartilaginous navicular. Sometimes the styloid process of the third metacarpal is detached and forms an additional ossicle.

The **metacarpal bones** are each ossified from *two* centers: one for the body and one for the distal extremity of each of the second, third, fourth, and fifth bones; one for the body and one for the base of the first metacarpal bone. The first metacarpal bone is therefore ossified in the same manner as the phalanges, and this has led some anatomists to regard the thumb as being made up of three phalanges, and not of a metacarpal bone and two phalanges. Ossification commences in the middle of the body about the eighth or ninth week of fetal life, the centers for the second and third metacarpals being the first, and that for the first metacarpal, the last, to appear; about the third year the distal extremities of the metacarpals of the fingers, and the base of the metacarpal of the thumb, begin to ossify; they unite with the bodies about the twentieth year.

The **phalanges** are each ossified from *two* centers: one for the body, and one for the proximal extremity. Ossification begins in the body, about the eighth week of fetal life. Ossification of the proximal extremity commences in the bones of the first row between the third and fourth years, and a year later in those of the second and third rows. The two centers become united in each row between the eighteenth and twentieth years.

In the ungual phalanges the centers for the bodies appear at the distal extremities of the phalanges, instead of at the middle of the bodies, as in the other phalanges. Moreover, of all the bones of the hand, the ungual phalanges are the first to ossify.

THE BONES OF THE LOWER EXTREMITY (OSSA EXTREMITATIS INFERIORIS).

The Hip Bone (Os Coxæ; Innominate Bone) (Fig. 288, 289).

The **hip bone** is a large, flattened, irregularly shaped bone, constricted in the center and expanded above and below. It meets its fellow on the opposite side in the middle line in front, and together they form the sides and anterior wall of the pelvic cavity. It consists of three parts, the **ilium, ischium,** and **pubis,** which are distinct from each other in the young subject, but are fused in the adult; the union of the three parts takes place in and around a large cup-shaped articular cavity, the **acetabulum,** which is situated near the middle of the outer surface of the bone. The **ilium,** so-called because it supports the flank, is the superior broad and expanded portion which extends upward from the acetabulum. The **ischium** is the lowest and strongest portion of the bone; it proceeds downward from the acetabulum, expands into a large tuberosity, and then, curving forward, forms, with the pubis, a large aperture, the **obturator foramen.** The **pubis** extends medialward and downward from the acetabulum and articulates in the middle line with the bone of the opposite side: it forms the front of the pelvis and supports the external organs of generation.

The Ilium (*os ilii*).—The ilium is divisible into two parts, the **body** and the **ala;** the separation is indicated on the internal surface by a curved line, the **arcuate line,** and on the external surface by the margin of the acetabulum.

The Body (*corpus oss. ilii*).—The body enters into the formation of the acetabulum, of which it forms rather less than two-fifths. Its **external surface** is partly articular, partly non-articular; the articular segment forms part of the lunate surface of the acetabulum, the non-articular portion contributes to the acetabular fossa. The **internal surface** of the body is part of the wall of the lesser pelvis and gives origin to some fibers of the Obturator internus. Below, it is continuous with the pelvic surfaces of the ischium and pubis, only a faint line indicating the place of union.

The Ala (*ala oss. ilii*).—The ala is the large expanded portion which bounds the greater pelvis laterally. It presents for examination two surfaces—an external and an internal—a crest, and two borders—an anterior and a posterior. The **external surface** (Fig. 288), known as the **dorsum ilii**, is directed backward and lateralward behind, and downward and lateralward in front. It is smooth, convex in front, deeply concave behind; bounded above by the crest, below by the upper border of the acetabulum, in front and behind by the anterior and posterior borders. This surface is crossed in an arched direction by three lines—the posterior, anterior, and inferior gluteal lines. The **posterior gluteal line** (*superior curved line*), the shortest of the three, begins at the crest, about 5 cm. in front of its posterior extremity; it is at first distinctly marked, but as it passes downward to the upper part of the greater sciatic notch, where it ends, it becomes less distinct, and is often altogether lost. Behind this line is a narrow semilunar surface, the upper part of which is rough and gives origin to a portion of the Glutæus maximus; the lower part is smooth and has no muscular fibers attached to it. The **anterior gluteal line** (*middle curved line*), the longest of the three, begins at the crest, about 4 cm. behind its anterior extremity, and, taking a curved direction downward and backward, ends at the upper part of the greater sciatic notch. The space between the anterior and posterior gluteal lines and the crest is concave, and gives origin to the Glutæus medius. Near the middle of this line a nutrient foramen is often seen. The **inferior gluteal line** (*inferior curved line*), the least distinct of the three, begins in front at the notch on the anterior border, and, curving backward and downward, ends near the middle of the greater sciatic notch. The surface of bone included between the anterior and inferior gluteal lines is concave from above downward, convex from before backward, and gives origin to the Glutæus minimus. Between the inferior gluteal line and the upper part of the acetabulum is a rough, shallow groove, from which the reflected tendon of the Rectus femoris arises.

The **internal surface** (Fig. 289) of the ala is bounded above by the crest, below, by the arcuate line; in front and behind, by the anterior and posterior borders. It presents a large, smooth, concave surface, called the **iliac fossa**, which gives origin to the Iliacus and is perforated at its inner part by a nutrient canal; and below this a smooth, rounded border, the **arcuate line** (iliopectineal line, Fig. 289), which runs downward, forward, and medialward. Behind the iliac fossa is a rough surface, divided into two portions, an anterior and a posterior. The **articular surface** (*auricular surface*), so called from its resemblance in shape to the ear, is coated with cartilage in the fresh state, and articulates with a similar surface on the side of the sacrum. The posterior portion, known as the **iliac tuberosity**, is elevated and rough, for the attachment of the posterior sacroiliac ligaments and for the origins of the Sacrospinalis and Multifidus. Below and in front of the auricular surface is the **preauricular sulcus**, more commonly present and better marked in the female than in the male; to it is attached the pelvic portion of the anterior sacroiliac ligament.

The **crest** of the ilium is convex in its general outline but is sinuously curved, being concave inward in front, concave outward behind. It is thinner at the center than at the extremities, and ends in the **anterior** and **posterior superior iliac spines**. The surface of the crest is broad, and divided into external and internal lips, and an intermediate line. About 5 cm. behind the anterior superior iliac spine there is a prominent tubercle on the outer lip. To the external lip are attached the Tensor fasciæ latæ, Obliquus externus abdominis, and Latissimus dorsi, and along its whole length the fascia lata; to the intermediate line the Obliquus internus abdominis; to the internal lip, the fascia iliaca, the Transversus abdominis, Quadratus lumborum, Sacrospinalis, and Iliacus.

The **anterior border** of the ala is concave. It presents two projections, separated by a notch. Of these, the uppermost, situated at the junction of the crest and anterior border, is called the **anterior superior iliac spine**; its outer border gives attachment to the fascia lata, and the Tensor fasciæ latæ, its inner border, to the Iliacus; while its extremity affords attachment to the inguinal ligament and gives origin to the Sartorius. Beneath this eminence is a notch from which the Sartorius takes origin and across which the lateral femoral cutaneous nerve passes. Below

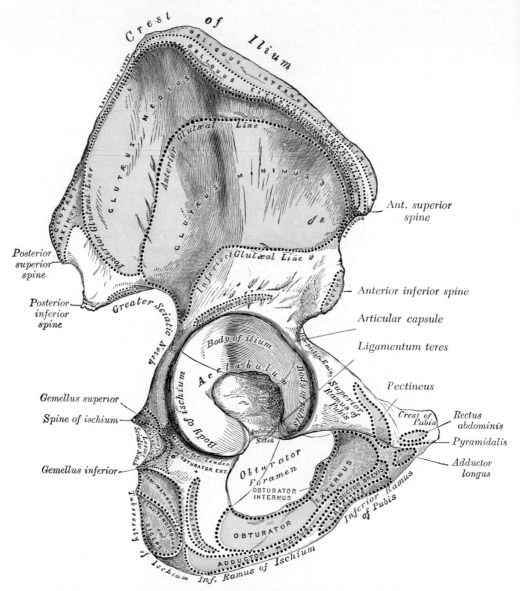

FIG. 288.—Right hip bone. External surface.

the notch is the **anterior inferior iliac spine**, which ends in the upper lip of the acetabulum; it gives attachment to the straight tendon of the Rectus femoris and to the iliofemoral ligament of the hip-joint. Medial to the anterior inferior spine is a broad, shallow groove, over which the Iliacus and Psoas major pass. This groove is bounded medially by an eminence, the **iliopectineal eminence**, which marks the point of union of the ilium and pubis.

The **posterior border** of the ala, shorter than the anterior, also presents two projections separated by a notch, the **posterior superior iliac spine** and the **posterior inferior iliac spine**. The former serves for the attachment of the oblique portion of the posterior sacroiliac ligaments and the Multifidus; the latter corresponds with the posterior extremity of the auricular surface. Below the posterior inferior spine is a deep notch, the **greater sciatic notch**.

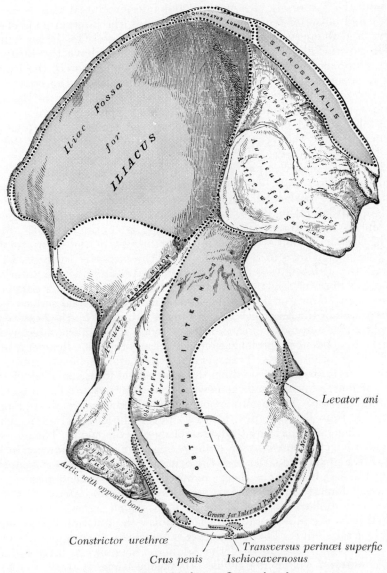

Fig. 289.—Right hip bone. Internal surface.

The **Ischium** (*os ischii*).—The ischium forms the lower and back part of the hip bone. It is divisible into three portions—a **body** and **two rami**.

The **Body** (*corpus oss. ischii*).—The body enters into and constitutes a little more than two-fifths of the acetabulum. Its **external surface** forms part of the lunate surface of the acetabulum and a portion of the acetabular fossa. Its **internal surface** is part of the wall of the lesser pelvis; it gives origin to some fibers of the

Obturator internus. Its anterior border projects as the **posterior obturator tubercle;** from its posterior border there extends backward a thin and pointed triangular eminence, the **ischial spine**, more or less elongated in different subjects. The external surface of the spine gives attachment to the Gemellus superior, its internal surface to the Coccygeus, Levator ani, and the pelvic fascia; while to the pointed extremity the sacrospinous ligament is attached. Above the spine is a large notch, the **greater sciatic notch**, converted into a foramen by the sacrospinous ligament; it transmits the Piriformis, the superior and inferior gluteal vessels and nerves, the sciatic and posterior femoral cutaneous nerves, the internal pudendal vessels, and nerve, and the nerves to the Obturator internus and Quadratus femoris. Of these, the superior gluteal vessels and nerve pass out above the Piriformis, the other structures below it. Below the spine is a smaller notch, the **lesser sciatic notch;** it is smooth, coated in the recent state with cartilage, the surface of which presents two or three ridges corresponding to the subdivisions of the tendon of the Obturator internus, which winds over it. It is converted into a foramen by the sacrotuberous and sacrospinous ligaments, and transmits the tendon of the Obturator internus, the nerve which supplies that muscle, and the internal pudendal vessels and nerve.

The Superior Ramus (*corpus oss. ischii; descending ramus*).—The superior ramus projects downward and backward from the body and presents for examination three surfaces: external, internal, and posterior. The **external surface** is quadrilateral in shape. It is bounded *above* by a groove which lodges the tendon of the Obturator externus; *below*, it is continuous with the inferior ramus; in *front* it is limited by the posterior margin of the obturator foramen; *behind*, a prominent margin separates it from the posterior surface. In front of this margin the surface gives origin to the Quadratus femoris, and anterior to this to some of the fibers of origin of the Obturator externus; the lower part of the surface gives origin to part of the Adductor magnus. The **internal surface** forms part of the bony wall of the lesser pelvis. In *front* it is limited by the posterior margin of the obturator foramen. *Below*, it is bounded by a sharp ridge which gives attachment to a falciform prolongation of the sacrotuberous ligament, and, more anteriorly, gives origin to the Transversus perinæi and Ischiocavernosus. *Posteriorly* the ramus forms a large swelling, the **tuberosity of the ischium**, which is divided into two portions: a lower, rough, somewhat triangular part, and an upper, smooth, quadrilateral portion. The lower portion is subdivided by a prominent longitudinal ridge, passing from base to apex, into two parts; the outer gives attachment to the Adductor magnus, the inner to the sacrotuberous ligament. The upper portion is subdivided into two areas by an oblique ridge, which runs downward and outward; from the upper and outer area the Semimembranosus arises; from the lower and inner, the long head of the Biceps femoris and the Semitendinosus.

The Inferior Ramus (*ramus inferior oss. ischii; ascending ramus*).—The inferior ramus is the thin, flattened part of the ischium, which ascends from the superior ramus, and joins the inferior ramus of the pubis—the junction being indicated in the adult by a raised line. The **outer surface** is uneven for the origin of the Obturator externus and some of the fibers of the Adductor magnus; its **inner surface** forms part of the anterior wall of the pelvis. Its **medial border** is thick, rough, slightly everted, forms part of the outlet of the pelvis, and presents two ridges and an intervening space. The ridges are continuous with similar ones on the inferior ramus of the pubis: to the outer is attached the deep layer of the superficial perineal fascia (*fascia of Colles*), and to the inner the inferior fascia of the urogenital diaphragm. If these two ridges be traced downward, they will be found to join with each other just behind the point of origin of the Transversus perinæi; here the two layers of fascia are inseparable behind the posterior border of the muscle. To the intervening space, just in front of the point of junction of the ridges, the

Transversus perinæi is attached, and in front of this a portion of the crus penis vel clitoridis and the Ischiocavernosus. Its **lateral border** is thin and sharp, and forms part of the medial margin of the obturator foramen.

The **Pubis** (*os pubis*).—The pubis, the anterior part of the hip bone, is divisible into a **body,** a **superior** and an **inferior ramus.**

The **Body** (*corpus oss. pubis*).—The body forms one-fifth of the acetabulum, contributing by its **external surface** both to the lunate surface and the acetabular fossa. Its **internal surface** enters into the formation of the wall of the lesser pelvis and gives origin to a portion of the Obturator internus.

The **Superior Ramus** (*ramus superior oss. pubis; ascending ramus*).—The superior ramus extends from the body to the median plane where it articulates with its fellow of the opposite side. It is conveniently described in two portions, viz., a medial flattened part and a narrow lateral prismoid portion.

The **Medial Portion** of the superior ramus, formerly described as the body of the pubis, is somewhat quadrilateral in shape, and presents for examination two surfaces and three borders. The **external surface** is rough, directed downward and outward, and serves for the origin of various muscles. The Adductor longus arises from the upper and medial angle, immediately below the crest; lower down, the Obturator externus, the Adductor brevis, and the upper part of the Gracilis take origin. The **internal surface,** convex from above downward, concave from side to side, is smooth, and forms part of the anterior wall of the pelvis. It gives origin to the Levator ani and Obturator internus, and attachment to the puboprostatic ligaments and to a few muscular fibers prolonged from the bladder. The **upper border** presents a prominent tubercle, the **pubic tubercle** (*pubic spine*), which projects forward; the inferior crus of the **subcutaneous inguinal ring** (*external abdominal ring*), and the **inguinal ligament** (*Poupart's ligament*) are attached to it. Passing upward and lateralward from the pubic tubercle is a well-defined ridge, forming a part of the **pecten pubis** which marks the brim of the lesser pelvis: to it are attached a portion of the **inguinal falx** (*conjoined tendon of Obliquus internus and Transversus*), the **lacunar ligament** (*Gimbernat's ligament*), and the **reflected inguinal ligament** (*triangular fascia*). Medial to the pubic tubercle is the **crest,** which extends from this process to the medial end of the bone. It affords attachment to the inguinal falx, and to the Rectus abdominis and Pyramidalis. The point of junction of the crest with the medial border of the bone is called the **angle;** to it, as well as to the symphysis, the superior crus of the subcutaneous inguinal ring is attached. The **medial border** is articular; it is oval, and is marked by eight or nine transverse ridges, or a series of nipple-like processes arranged in rows, separated by grooves; they serve for the attachment of a thin layer of cartilage, which intervenes between it and the interpubic fibrocartilaginous lamina. The **lateral border** presents a sharp margin, the **obturator crest,** which forms part of the circumference of the obturator foramen and affords attachment to the obturator membrane.

The **Lateral Portion** of the superior ramus has three surfaces: superior, inferior, and posterior. The **superior surface** presents the **iliopectineal line,** a continuation of the pecten pubis, already mentioned as commencing at the pubic tubercle. In front of this line, the surface of bone is triangular in form, wider laterally than medially, and is covered by the Pectineus. The surface is bounded, laterally, by a rough eminence, the **iliopectineal eminence,** which serves to indicate the point of junction of the ilium and pubis, and below by a prominent ridge which extends from the acetabular notch to the pubic tubercle. The **inferior surface** forms the upper boundary of the obturator foramen, and presents, laterally, a broad and deep, oblique groove, for the passage of the obturator vessels and nerve; and medially, a sharp margin, the **obturator crest,** forming part of the circumference of the obturator foramen, and giving attachment to the obturator membrane. The posterior surface constitutes part of the anterior boundary of the lesser pelvis. It is smooth, convex from above downward, and affords origin to some fibers of the Obturator internus.

The Inferior Ramus (*ramus inferior oss. pubis; descending ramus*).—The inferior ramus is thin and flattened. It passes lateralward and downward from the medial end of the superior ramus; it becomes narrower as it descends and joins with the inferior ramus of the ischium below the obturator foramen. Its external surface is rough, for the origin of muscles—the Gracilis along its medial border, a portion of the Obturator externus where it enters into the formation of the obturator foramen, and between these two, the Adductores brevis and magnus, the former being the more medial. The internal surface is smooth, and gives origin to the Obturator internus, and, close to the medial margin, to the Constrictor urethræ. The medial border is thick, rough, and everted, especially in females. It presents two ridges, separated by an intervening space. The ridges extend downward, and are continuous with similar ridges on the inferior ramus of the ischium; to the external is attached the fascia of Colles, and to the internal the inferior fascia of the urogenital diaphragm. The lateral border is thin and sharp, forms part of the circumference of the obturator foramen, and gives attachment to the obturator membrane.

By eight centers { *Three primary (Ilium, Ischium, and Pubis)* { *Five secondary*

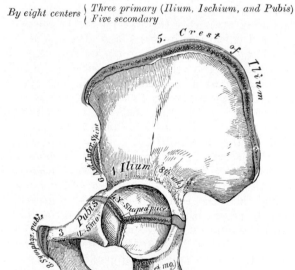

FIG. 290.—Plan of ossification of the hip bone. The three primary centers unite through a Y-shaped piece about puberty. Epiphyses appear about puberty, and unite about twenty-fifth year.

The Acetabulum (*cotyloid cavity*).—The acetabulum is a deep, cup-shaped, hemispherical depression, directed downward, lateralward, and forward. It is formed medially by the pubis, above by the ilium, laterally and below by the ischium; a little less than two-fifths is contributed by the ilium, a little more than two-fifths by the ischium, and the remaining fifth by the pubis. It is bounded by a prominent uneven rim, which is thick and strong above, and serves for the attachment of the glenoidal labrum (*cotyloid ligament*), which contracts its orifice, and deepens the surface for articulation. It presents below a deep notch, the acetabular notch, which is continuous with a circular non-articular depression, the acetabular

fossa, at the bottom of the cavity: this depression is perforated by numerous apertures, and lodges a mass of fat. The notch is converted into a foramen by the transverse ligament; through the foramen nutrient vessels and nerves enter the joint; the margins of the notch serve for the attachment of the ligamentum teres. The rest of the acetabulum is formed by a curved articular surface, the **lunate surface,** for articulation with the head of the femur.

The Obturator Foramen (*foramen obturatum; thyroid foramen*).—The obturator foramen is a large aperture, situated between the ischium and pubis. In the male it is large and of an oval form, its longest diameter slanting obliquely from before backward; in the female it is smaller, and more triangular. It is bounded by a thin, uneven margin, to which a strong membrane is attached, and presents, superiorly, a deep groove, the **obturator groove,** which runs from the pelvis obliquely medialward and downward. This groove is converted into a canal by a ligamentous band, a specialized part of the obturator membrane, attached to two tubercles: one, the **posterior obturator tubercle,** on the medial border of the ischium, just in front of the acetabular notch; the other, the **anterior obturator tubercle,** on the obturator crest of the superior ramus of the pubis. Through the canal the obturator vessels and nerve pass out of the pelvis.

Structure.—The thicker parts of the bone consist of cancellous tissue, enclosed between two layers of compact tissue; the thinner parts, as at the bottom of the acetabulum and center of the iliac fossa, are usually semitransparent, and composed entirely of compact tissue.

Ossification (Fig. 290).—The hip bone is ossified from *eight* centers: *three* primary—one each for the ilium, ischium, and pubis; and *five* secondary—one each for the crest of the ilium, the anterior inferior spine (said to occur more frequently in the male than in the female), the tuberosity of the ischium, the pubic symphysis (more frequent in the female than in the male), and one or more for the Y-shaped piece at the bottom of the acetabulum. The centers appear in the following order: in the lower part of the ilium, immediately above the greater sciatic notch, about the eighth or ninth week of fetal life; in the superior ramus of the ischium, about the third month; in the superior ramus of the pubis, between the fourth and fifth months. At birth, the three primary centers are quite separate, the crest, the bottom of the acetabulum, the ischial tuberosity and the inferior rami of the ischium and pubis being still cartilaginous. By the seventh or eighth year, the inferior rami of the pubis and ischium are almost completely united by bone. About the thirteenth or fourteenth year, the three primary centers have extended their growth into the bottom of the acetabulum, and are there separated from each other by a Y-shaped portion of cartilage, which now presents traces of ossification, often by two or more centers. One of these, the *os acetabuli,* appears about the age of twelve, between the ilium and pubis, and fuses with them about the age of eighteen; it forms the pubic part of the acetabulum. The ilium and ischium then become joined, and lastly the pubis and ischium, through the intervention of this Y-shaped portion. At about the age of puberty, ossification takes place in each of the remaining portions, and they join with the rest of the bone between the twentieth and twenty-fifth years. Separate centers are frequently found for the pubic tubercle and the ischial spine, and for the crest and angle of the pubis.

Articulations.—The hip bone articulates with its fellow of the opposite side, and with the sacrum and femur.

The Pelvis.

The **pelvis,** so called from its resemblance to a basin, is a bony ring, interposed between the movable vertebræ of the vertebral column which it supports, and the lower limbs upon which it rests; it is stronger and more massively constructed than the wall of the cranial or thoracic cavities, and is composed of four bones: the two **hip bones** laterally and in front and the **sacrum** and **coccyx** behind.

The pelvis is divided by an oblique plane passing through the prominence of the sacrum, the arcuate and pectineal lines, and the upper margin of the symphysis pubis, into the greater and the lesser pelvis. The circumference of this plane is termed the **linea terminalis** or **pelvic brim.**

The Greater or False Pelvis (*pelvis major*).—The greater pelvis is the expanded portion of the cavity situated above and in front of the pelvic brim. It is bounded on either side by the ilium; in *front* it is incomplete, presenting a wide interval between the anterior borders of the ilia, which is filled up in the fresh state by the parietes of the abdomen; behind is a deep notch on either side between the ilium and the base of the sacrum. It supports the intestines, and transmits part of their weight to the anterior wall of the abdomen.

The Lesser or True Pelvis (*pelvis minor*).—The lesser pelvis is that part of the pelvic cavity which is situated below and behind the pelvic brim. Its bony walls are more complete than those of the greater pelvis. For convenience of description, it is divided into an **inlet** bounded by the superior circumference, and **outlet** bounded by the inferior circumference, and a **cavity**.

The Superior Circumference.—The superior circumference forms the brim of the pelvis, the included space being called the **superior aperture** or **inlet** (*apertura pelvis* [*minoris*] *superior*) (Fig. 291).   It is formed laterally by the pectineal and arcuate lines, in front by the crests of the pubes, and behind by the anterior margin of the base of the sacrum and sacrovertebral angle. The superior aperture is somewhat heart-shaped, obtusely pointed in front, diverging on either side, and encroached upon behind by the projection forward of the promontory of the sacrum. It has three principal diameters: antero-posterior, transverse, and oblique. The **antero-posterior or conjugate diameter** extends from the sacrovertebral angle to the sym-

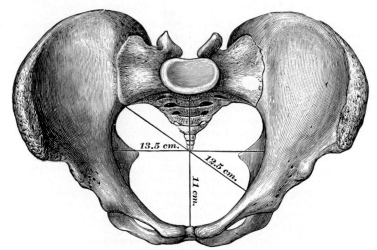

Fig. 291.—Diameters of superior aperture of lesser pelvis (female).

physis pubis; its average measurement is about 11 cm. in the female. The **transverse diameter** extends across the greatest width of the superior aperture, from the middle of the brim on one side to the same point on the opposite; its average measurement is about 13.5 cm. in the female. The **oblique diameter** extends from the iliopectineal eminence of one side to the sacroiliac articulation of the opposite side; its average measurement is about 12.5 cm. in the female.

The **cavity** of the lesser pelvis is bounded in front and below by the pubic symphysis and the superior rami of the pubes; above and behind, by the pelvic surfaces of the sacrum and coccyx, which, curving forward above and below, contract the superior and inferior apertures of the cavity; laterally, by a broad, smooth, quadrangular area of bone, corresponding to the inner surfaces of the body and superior ramus of the ischium and that part of the ilium which is below the arcuate line.   From this description it will be seen that the cavity of the lesser pelvis is a short, curved canal, considerably deeper on its posterior than on its anterior wall. It contains, in the fresh subject, the pelvic colon, rectum, bladder, and some of the organs of generation. The rectum is placed at the back of the pelvis, in the curve of the sacrum and coccyx; the bladder is in front, behind the pubic symphysis. In the female the uterus and vagina occupy the interval between these viscera.

The Lower Circumference.—The lower circumference of the pelvis is very irregular; the space enclosed by it is named the **inferior aperture** or **outlet** (*apertura pelvis [minoris] inferior*) (Fig. 292), and is bounded behind by the point of the coccyx, and laterally by the ischial tuberosities. These eminences are separated by three notches: one in front, the **pubic arch**, formed by the convergence of the inferior rami of the ischium and pubis on either side. The other notches, one on either side, are formed by the sacrum and coccyx behind, the ischium in front, and

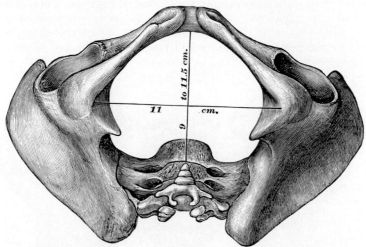

FIG. 292.—Diameters of inferior aperture of lesser pelvis (female).

the ilium above; they are called the **sciatic notches;** in the natural state they are converted into foramina by the sacrotuberous and sacrospinous ligaments. When the ligaments are *in situ*, the inferior aperture of the pelvis is lozenge-shaped, bounded, in front, by the pubic arcuate ligament and the inferior rami of the pubes and ischia; laterally, by the ischial tuberosities; and behind, by the sacrotuberous ligaments and the tip of the coccyx.

The diameters of the outlet of the pelvis are two, antero-posterior and transverse. The **antero-posterior diameter** extends from the tip of the coccyx to the lower part of the pubic symphysis; its measurement is from 9 to 11.5 cm. in the female. It varies with the length of the coccyx, and is capable of increase or diminution, on account of the mobility of that bone. The **transverse diameter**, measured between the posterior parts of the ischial tuberosities, is about 11 cm. in the female.

Axes (Fig. 293).—A line at right angles to the plane of the superior aperture at its center would, if prolonged, pass through the umbilicus above and the middle of the coccyx below; the axis of the superior aperture is therefore directed downward and backward. The axis of the inferior aperture, produced upward, would touch the base of the sacrum, and is also directed

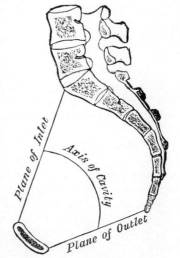

FIG. 293.—Median sagittal section of pelvis.

downward, and slightly backward. The axis of the cavity—*i. e.*, an axis at right angles to a series of planes between those of the superior and inferior apertures

—is curved like the cavity itself: this curve corresponds to the concavity of the sacrum and coccyx, the extremities being indicated by the central points of the superior and inferior apertures. A knowledge of the direction of these axes serves to explain the course of the fetus in its passage through the pelvis during parturition.

Position of the Pelvis (Fig. 293).—In the erect posture, the pelvis is placed obliquely with regard to the trunk: the plane of the superior aperture forms an angle of from 50° to 60°, and that of the inferior aperture one of about 15° with the horizontal plane. The pelvic surface of the symphysis pubis looks upward and backward, the concavity of the sacrum and coccyx downward and forward. The position of the pelvis in the erect posture may be indicated by holding it so that the anterior superior iliac spines and the front of the top of the symphysis pubis are in the same vertical plane.

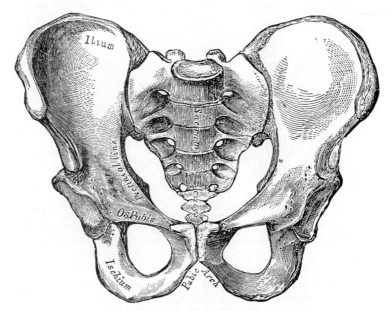

Fig. 294.—Male pelvis.

Differences between the Male and Female Pelves.—The *female* pelvis (Fig. 295) is distinguished from that of the *male* (Fig. 294) by its bones being more delicate and its depth less. The whole pelvis is less massive, and its muscular impressions are slightly marked. The ilia are less sloped, and the anterior iliac spines more widely separated; hence the greater lateral prominence of the hips. The preauricular sulcus is more commonly present and better marked. The superior aperture of the lesser pelvis is larger in the female than in the male; it is more nearly circular, and its obliquity is greater. The cavity is shallower and wider; the sacrum is shorter, wider, and its upper part is less curved; the obturator foramina are triangular in shape and smaller in size than in the male. The inferior aperture is larger and the coccyx more movable. The sciatic notches are wider and shallower, and the spines of the ischia project less inward. The acetabula are smaller and look more distinctly forward. The ischial tuberosities and the acetabula are wider apart, and the former are more everted. The pubic symphysis is less deep, and the pubic arch is wider and more rounded than in the male, where it is an angle rather than an arch.

The size of the pelvis varies not only in the two sexes, but also in different members of the same sex, and does not appear to be influenced in any way by the height of the individual. Women of short stature, as a rule, have broad pelves. Occasionally the pelvis is equally contracted in all its dimensions, so much so that all its diameters measure 12.5 mm. less than the average, and this even in well-formed women of average height. The principal divergences, however, are found at the superior aperture, and affect the relation of the antero-posterior to the transverse diameter. Thus the superior aperture may be elliptical either in a transverse or an antero-posterior direction, the transverse diameter in the former, and the antero-posterior in the latter, greatly exceeding the other diameters; in other instances it is almost circular.

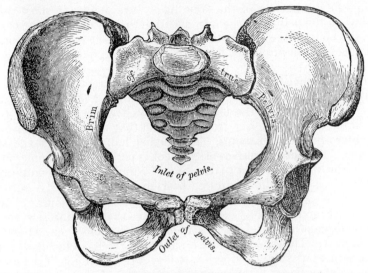

Fig. 295.—Female pelvis.

In the fetus, and for several years after birth, the pelvis is smaller in proportion than in the adult, and the projection of the sacrovertebral angle less marked. The characteristic differences between the male and female pelvis are distinctly indicated as early as the fourth month of fetal life.

The Femur (Thigh Bone).

The **femur** (Figs. 297, 298), the longest and strongest bone in the skeleton, is almost perfectly cylindrical in the greater part of its extent. In the erect posture it is not vertical, being separated above from its fellow by a considerable interval, which corresponds to the breadth of the pelvis, but inclining gradually downward and medialward, so as to approach its fellow toward its lower part, for the purpose of bringing the knee-joint near the line of gravity of the body. The degree of this inclination varies in different persons, and is greater in the female than in the male, on account of the greater breadth of the pelvis. The femur, like other long bones, is divisible into a **body** and **two extremities**.

The **Upper Extremity** (*proximal extremity*, Fig. 296).—The upper extremity presents for examination a **head**, a **neck**, a **greater** and a **lesser trochanter**.

The **Head** (*caput femoris*).—The head which is globular and forms rather more than a hemisphere, is directed upward, medialward, and a little forward, the greater part of its convexity being above and in front. Its surface is smooth, coated with cartilage in the fresh state, except over an ovoid depression, the **fovea capitis femoris**, which is situated a little below and behind the center of the head, and gives attachment to the ligamentum teres.

The Neck (*collum femoris*).—The neck is a flattened pyramidal process of bone, connecting the head with the body, and forming with the latter a wide angle opening medialward. The angle is widest in infancy, and becomes lessened during growth, so that at puberty it forms a gentle curve from the axis of the body of the bone. In the adult, the neck forms an angle of about 125° with the body, but this varies in inverse proportion to the development of the pelvis and the stature. In the female, in consequence of the increased width of the pelvis, the neck of the femur forms more nearly a right angle with the body than it does in the male. The angle decreases during the period of growth, but after full growth has been attained it does not usually undergo any change, even in old age; it varies considerably in different persons of the same age. It is smaller in short than in long bones, and when the pelvis is wide. In addition to projecting upward and medialward from the body of the femur, the neck also projects somewhat forward; the amount of this forward projection is extremely variable, but on an average is from 12° to 14°.

The neck is flattened from before backward, contracted in the middle, and broader laterally than medially. The vertical diameter of the lateral half is increased by the obliquity of the lower edge, which slopes downward to join the body at the level of the lesser trochanter, so that it measures one-third more than the antero-posterior diameter. The medial half is smaller and of a more circular shape. The **anterior surface** of the neck is perforated by numerous vascular foramina. Along the upper part of the line of junction of the anterior surface with the head is a shallow groove, best marked in elderly subjects; this groove lodges the orbicular fibers of the capsule of the hip-joint. The **posterior surface** is smooth, and is broader and more concave than the anterior: the posterior part of the capsule of the hip-joint is attached to it about 1 cm. above the intertrochanteric crest. The **superior border** is short and thick, and ends laterally at the greater trochanter; its surface is perforated by large foramina. The **inferior border**, long and narrow, curves a little backward, to end at the lesser trochanter.

The Trochanters.—The trochanters are prominent processes which afford leverage to the muscles that rotate the thigh on its axis. They are two in number, the greater and the lesser.

The **Greater Trochanter** (*trochanter major; great trochanter*) is a large, irregular, quadrilateral eminence, situated at the junction of the neck with the upper part of the body. It is directed a little lateralward and backward, and, in the adult, is about 1 cm. lower than the head. It has two surfaces and four borders. The **lateral surface**, quadrilateral in form, is broad, rough, convex, and marked by a diagonal impression, which extends from the postero-superior to the antero-inferior angle, and serves for the insertion of the tendon of the Glutæus medius. Above the impression is a triangular surface, sometimes rough for part of the tendon of the same muscle, sometimes smooth for the interposition of a bursa between the tendon and the bone. Below and behind the diagonal impression is a smooth, triangular surface, over which the tendon of the Glutæus maximus plays, a bursa being interposed. The **medial surface**, of much less extent than the lateral, presents at its base a deep depression, the **trochanteric fossa** (*digital fossa*), for the insertion of the tendon of the Obturator externus, and above and in front of this an impression for the insertion of the Obturator internus and Gemelli. The **superior border** is free; it is thick and irregular, and marked near the center by an impression for the insertion of the Piriformis. The **inferior border** corresponds to the line of junction of the base of the trochanter with the lateral surface of the body; it is marked by a rough, prominent, slightly curved ridge, which gives origin to the upper part of the Vastus lateralis. The **anterior border** is prominent and somewhat irregular; it affords insertion at its lateral part to the Glutæus minimus. The **posterior border** is very prominent and appears as a free, rounded edge which bounds the back part of the trochanteric fossa.

The **Lesser Trochanter** (*trochanter minor; small trochanter*) is a conical eminence, which varies in size in different subjects; it projects from the lower and back part of the base of the neck. From its apex three well-marked borders extend; two of these are above—a **medial** continuous with the lower border of the neck, a **lateral** with the intertrochanteric crest; the **inferior border** is continuous with the middle division of the linea aspera. The **summit** of the trochanter is rough, and gives insertion to the tendon of the Psoas major.

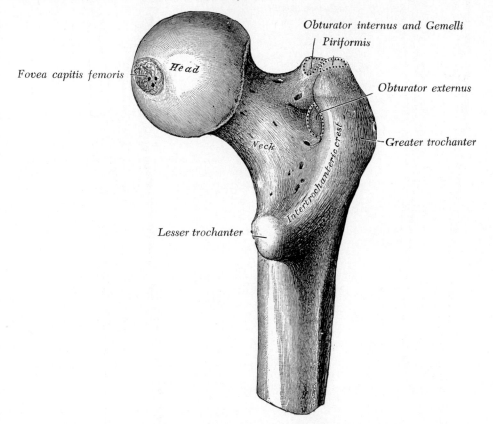

Fig. 296.—Upper extremity of right femur viewed from behind and above.

A prominence, of variable size, occurs at the junction of the upper part of the neck with the greater trochanter, and is called the **tubercle of the femur**; it is the point of meeting of five muscles: the Glutæus minimus laterally, the Vastus lateralis below, and the tendon of the Obturator internus and two Gemelli above. Running obliquely downward and medialward from the tubercle is the **intertrochanteric line** (*spiral line of the femur*); it winds around the medial side of the body of the bone, below the lesser trochanter, and ends about 5 cm. below this eminence in the linea aspera. Its upper half is rough, and affords attachment to the iliofemoral ligament of the hip-joint; its lower half is less prominent, and gives origin to the upper part of the Vastus medialis. Running obliquely downward and medialward from the summit of the greater trochanter on the posterior surface of the neck is a prominent ridge, the **intertrochanteric crest**. Its upper half forms the posterior border of the greater trochanter, and its lower half runs downward and medialward to the lesser trochanter. A slight ridge is sometimes seen com-

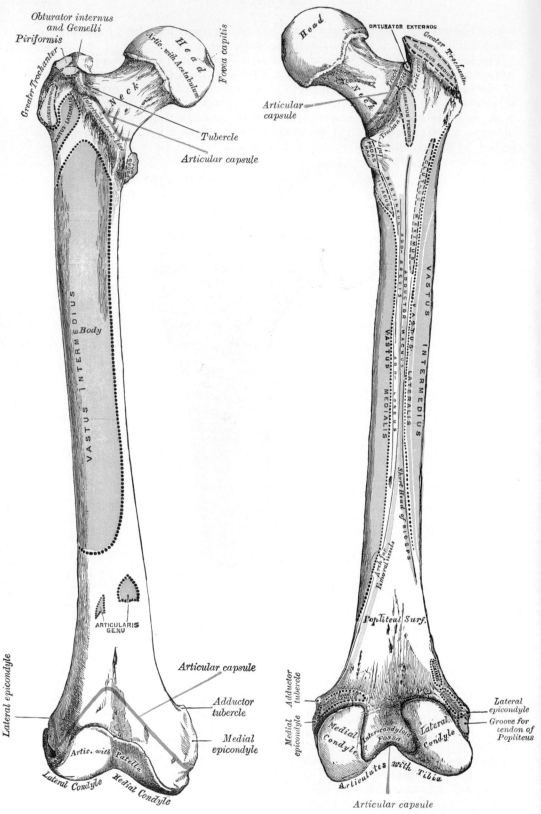

FIG. 297.—Right femur. Anterior surface.

(272)

FIG. 298.—Right femur. Posterior surface.

mencing about the middle of the intertrochanteric crest, and reaching vertically downward for about 5 cm. along the back part of the body: it is called the **linea quadrata**, and gives attachment to the Quadratus femoris and a few fibers of the Adductor magnus. Generally there is merely a slight thickening about the middle of the intertrochanteric crest, marking the attachment of the upper part of the Quadratus femoris.

The Body or Shaft (*corpus femoris*).—The body, almost cylindrical in form, is a little broader above than in the center, broadest and somewhat flattened from before backward below. It is slightly arched, so as to be convex in front, and concave behind, where it is strengthened by a prominent longitudinal ridge, the **linea aspera**. It presents for examination three borders, separating three surfaces. Of the borders, one, the linea aspera, is posterior, one is medial, and the other, lateral.

The **linea aspera** (Fig. 298) is a prominent longitudinal ridge or crest, on the middle third of the bone, presenting a medial and a lateral lip, and a narrow rough, intermediate line. Above, the linea aspera is prolonged by three ridges. The lateral ridge is very rough, and runs almost vertically upward to the base of the greater trochanter. It is termed the **gluteal tuberosity**, and gives attachment to part of the Glutæus maximus: its upper part is often elongated into a roughened crest, on which a more or less well-marked, rounded tubercle, the **third trochanter**, is occasionally developed. The intermediate ridge or **pectineal line** is continued to the base of the lesser trochanter and gives attachment to the Pectineus; the medial ridge is lost in the intertrochanteric line; between these two a portion of the Iliacus is inserted. Below, the linea aspera is prolonged into two ridges, enclosing between them a triangular area, the **popliteal surface**, upon which the popliteal artery rests. Of these two ridges, the lateral is the more prominent, and descends to the summit of the lateral condyle. The medial is less marked, especially at its upper part, where it is crossed by the femoral artery. It ends below at the summit of the medial condyle, in a small tubercle, the **adductor tubercle**, which affords insertion to the tendon of the Adductor magnus.

From the **medial lip** of the linea aspera and its prolongations above and below, the Vastus medialis arises; and from the **lateral lip** and its upward prolongation, the Vastus lateralis takes origin. The Adductor magnus is inserted into the linea aspera, and to its lateral prolongation above, and its medial prolongation below. Between the Vastus lateralis and the Adductor magnus two muscles are attached —viz., the Glutæus maximus inserted above, and the short head of the Biceps femoris arising below. Between the Adductor magnus and the Vastus medialis four muscles are inserted: the Iliacus and Pectineus above; the Adductor brevis and Adductor longus below. The linea aspera is perforated a little below its center by the nutrient canal, which is directed obliquely upward.

The other two *borders* of the femur are only slightly marked: the **lateral border** extends from the antero-inferior angle of the greater trochanter to the anterior extremity of the lateral condyle; the **medial border** from the intertrochanteric line, at a point opposite the lesser trochanter, to the anterior extremity of the medial condyle.

The **anterior surface** includes that portion of the shaft which is situated between the lateral and medial borders. It is smooth, convex, broader above and below than in the center. From the upper three-fourths of this surface the Vastus intermedius arises; the lower fourth is separated from the muscle by the intervention of the synovial membrane of the knee-joint and a bursa; from the upper part of it the Articularis genu takes origin. The **lateral surface** includes the portion between the lateral border and the linea aspera; it is continuous above with the corresponding surface of the greater trochanter, below with that of the lateral condyle: from its upper three-fourths the Vastus intermedius takes origin. The **medial surface** includes the portion between the medial border and the linea aspera; it is continu-

18

ous above with the lower border of the neck, below with the medial side of the medial condyle: it is covered by the Vastus medialis.

The Lower Extremity (*distal extremity*), (Fig. 299).—The lower extremity, larger than the upper, is somewhat cuboid in form, but its transverse diameter is greater than its antero-posterior; it consists of two oblong eminences known as the **condyles.** In front, the condyles are but slightly prominent, and are separated from one another by a smooth shallow articular depression called the **patellar surface**; behind, they project considerably, and the interval between them forms a deep notch, the **intercondyloid fossa.** The **lateral condyle** is the more prominent and is the broader both in its antero-posterior and transverse diameters, the **medial condyle** is the longer and, when the femur is held with its body perpendicular, projects to a lower level. When, however, the femur is in its natural oblique position the lower surfaces of the two condyles lie practically in the same horizontal plane. The condyles are not quite parallel with one another; the long axis of the lateral is almost directly antero-posterior, but that of the medial runs backward and medialward. Their opposed surfaces are small, rough, and concave, and form the walls of the intercondyloid fossa. This fossa is limited above by a ridge, the **intercondyloid**

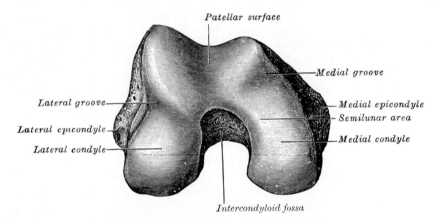

Fig. 299.—Lower extremity of right femur viewed from below.

line, and below by the central part of the posterior margin of the patellar surface. The posterior cruciate ligament of the knee-joint is attached to the lower and front part of the medial wall of the fossa and the anterior cruciate ligament to an impression on the upper and back part of its lateral wall. Each condyle is surmounted by an elevation, the epicondyle. The **medial epicondyle** is a large convex eminence to which the tibial collateral ligament of the knee-joint is attached. At its upper part is the adductor tubercle, already referred to, and behind it is a rough impression which gives origin to the medial head of the Gastrocnemius. The **lateral epicondyle.** smaller and less prominent than the medial, gives attachment to the fibular collateral ligament of the knee-joint. Directly below it is a small depression from which a smooth well-marked groove curves obliquely upward and backward to the posterior extremity of the condyle. This groove is separated from the articular surface of the condyle by a prominent lip across which a second, shallower groove runs vertically downward from the depression. In the fresh state these grooves are covered with cartilage. The Popliteus arises from the depression; its tendon lies in the oblique groove when the knee is flexed and in the vertical groove when the knee is extended. Above and behind the lateral epicondyle is an area for the origin of the lateral head of the Gastrocnemius, above and to the medial side of which the Plantaris arises.

The **articular surface** of the lower end of the femur occupies the anterior, inferior, and posterior surfaces of the condyles. Its front part is named the **patellar surface** and articulates with the patella; it presents a median groove which extends downward to the intercondyloid fossa and two convexities, the lateral of which is broader, more prominent, and extends farther upward than the medial. The lower and posterior parts of the articular surface constitute the **tibial surfaces** for articulation with the corresponding condyles of the tibia and menisci. These surfaces are separated from one another by the intercondyloid fossa and from the patellar surface by faint grooves which extend obliquely across the condyles. The lateral groove is the better marked; it runs lateralward and forward from the front part of the intercondyloid fossa, and expands to form a triangular depression. When the knee-joint is fully extended, the triangular depression rests upon the anterior portion of the lateral meniscus, and the medial part of the groove comes into contact with the medial margin of the lateral articular surface of the tibia in front of the lateral tubercle of the tibial intercondyloid eminence. The medial groove is less distinct than the lateral. It does not reach as far as the intercondyloid fossa and therefore exists only on the medial part of the condyle; it receives the anterior edge of the medial meniscus when the knee-joint is extended. Where the groove ceases laterally the patellar surface is seen to be continued backward as a semilunar area close to the anterior part of the intercondyloid fossa; this semilunar area articulates with the medial vertical facet of the patella in forced flexion of the knee-joint. The tibial surfaces of the condyles are convex from side to side and from before backward. Each presents a double curve, its posterior segment being an arc of a circle, its anterior, part of a cycloid.[1]

The Architecture of the Femur.—Koch[2] by mathematical analysis has "shown that in every part of the femur there is a remarkable adaptation of the inner structure of the bone to the mechanical requirements due to the load on the femur-head. The various parts of the femur taken together form a single mechanical structure wonderfully well-adapted for the efficient, economical transmission of the loads from the acetabulum to the tibia; a structure in which every element contributes its modicum of strength in the manner required by theoretical mechanics for maximum efficiency." "The internal structure is everywhere so formed as to provide in an efficient manner for all the internal stresses which occur due to the load on the femur-head. Throughout the femur, with the load on the femur-head, the bony material is arranged in the paths of the maximum internal stresses, which are thereby resisted with the greatest efficiency, and hence with maximum economy of material." "The conclusion is inevitable that the inner structure and outer form of the femur are governed by the conditions of maximum stress to which the bone is subjected normally by the preponderant load on the femur-head; that is, by the body weight transmitted to the femur-head through the acetabulum." "The femur obeys the mechanical laws that govern other elastic bodies under stress; the relation between the computed internal stresses due to the load on the femur-head, and the internal structure of the different portions of the femur is in very close agreement with the theoretical relations that should exist between stress and structure for maximum economy and efficiency; and, therefore, it is believed that the following laws of bone structure have been demonstrated for the femur:

"1. The inner structure and external form of human bone are closely adapted to the mechanical conditions existing at every point in the bone.

"2. The inner architecture of normal bone is determined by definite and exact requirements of mathematical and mechanical laws to produce a maximum of strength with a minimum of material."

The Inner Architecture of the Upper Femur.—"The spongy bone of the upper femur (to the lower limit of the lesser trochanter) is composed of two distinct systems of trabeculæ arranged in curved paths: one, which has its origin in the medial (inner) side of the shaft and curving upward in a fan-like radiation to the opposite side of the bone; the other, having origin in the lateral (outer) portion of the shaft and arching upward and medially to end in the upper surface of the greater trochanter, neck and head. These two systems intersect each other at right angles.

[1] A *cycloid* is a curve traced by a point in the circumference of a wheel when the wheel is rolled along in a straight line.

[2] The Laws of Bone Architecture. Am. Jour. of Anat., **21**, 1917. The following paragraphs are taken almost verbatim from Koch's article in which we have the first correct mathematical analysis of the femur in support of the theory of the functional form of bone proposed by Wolff and also by Roux.

"*A. Medial (Compressive) System of Trabeculæ.*—As the compact bone of the medial (inner) part of the shaft nears the head of the femur it gradually becomes thinner and finally reaches the articular surface of the head as a very thin layer. From a point at about the lower level of the lesser trochanter, $2\frac{1}{2}$ to 3 inches from the lower limit of the articular surface of the head, the trabeculæ branch off from the shaft in smooth curves, spreading radially to cross to the opposite side in two well-defined groups: a lower, or secondary group, and an upper, or principal group.

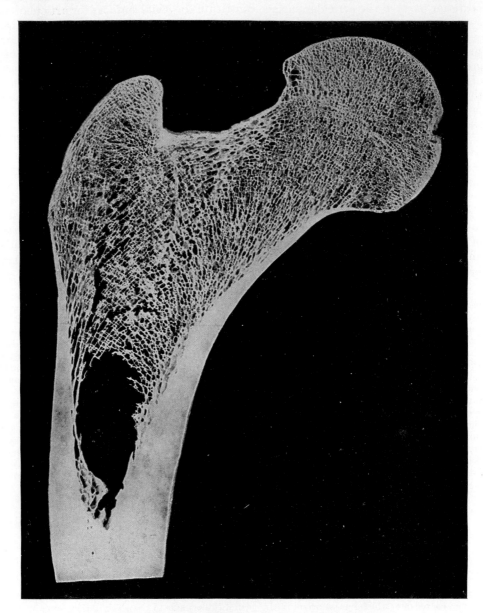

Fig. 300.—Frontal longitudinal midsection of upper femur.

"*a. The Secondary Compressive Group.*—This group of trabeculæ leaves the inner border of the shaft beginning at about the level of the lesser trochanter, and for a distance of almost 2 inches along the curving shaft, with which the separate trabeculæ make an angle of about 45 degrees. They curve outwardly and upwardly to cross in radiating smooth curves to the opposite side. The lower filaments end in the region of the greater trochanter: the adjacent filaments above these pursue a more nearly vertical course and end in the upper portion of the neck of the femur. The trabeculæ of this group are thin and with wide spaces between them. As they traverse the space between the medial and lateral surfaces of the bone they cross at right angles the system of curved trabeculæ which arise from the lateral (outer) portion of the shaft. (Figs. 300 and 301.)

"*b. The Principal Compressive Group.*—This group of trabeculæ (Figs. 303 and 305) springs from the medial portion of the shaft just above the group above-described, and spreads upward and in slightly radial smooth curved lines to reach the upper portion of the articular surface of the head of the femur. These trabeculæ are placed very closely together and are the thickest ones seen in the upper femur. They are a prolongation of the shaft from which they spring in straight lines which gradually curve to meet at right-angles the articular surface. There is no change as they cross the epiphyseal line. They also intersect at right-angles the system of lines which rise from the lateral side of the femur.

"This system of principal and secondary compressive trabeculæ corresponds in position and in curvature with the lines of maximum compressive stress, which were traced out in the mathematical analysis of this portion of the femur. (Figs. 301 and 303.)

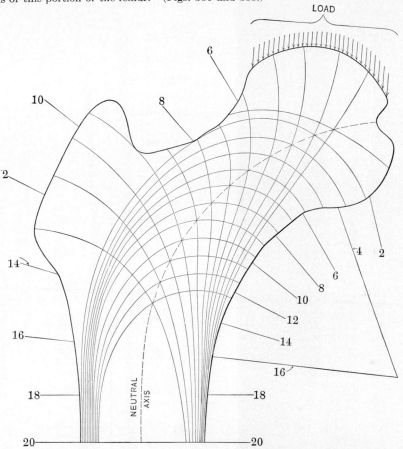

FIG. 301.—Diagram of the lines of stress in the upper femur, based upon the mathematical analysis of the right femur. These result from the combination of the different kinds of stresses at each point in the femur. (After Koch.)

"*B. Lateral (Tensile) System of Trabeculæ.*—As the compact bone of the outer portion of the shaft approaches the greater trochanter it gradually decreases in thickness. Beginning at a point about 1 inch below the level of the lower border of the greater trochanter, numerous thin trabeculæ are given off from the outer portion of the shaft. These trabeculæ lie in three distinct groups.

"*c. The Greater Trochanter Group.*—These trabeculæ rise from the outer part of the shaft just below the greater trochanter and rise in thin, curving lines to cross the region of the greater trochanter and end in its upper surface. Some of these filaments are poorly defined. This group intersects the trabeculæ of group (*a*) which rise from the opposite side. The trabeculæ of this group evidently carry small stresses, as is shown by their slenderness.

"*d. The Principal Tensile Group.*—This group springs from the outer part of the shaft immediately below group *c*, and curves convexly upward and inward in nearly parallel lines across the neck of the femur and ends in the inferior portion of the head. These trabeculæ are somewhat thinner and more widely spaced than those of the principal compressive group (*b*). All the trabeculæ of this group cross those of groups (*a*) and (*b*) at right angles. This group is the most important of the lateral system (tensile) and, as will be shown later, the greatest tensile stresses of the upper femur are carried by the trabeculæ of this group

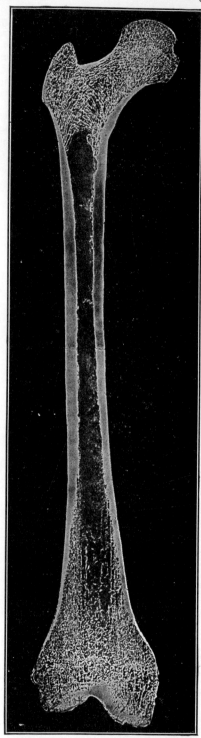

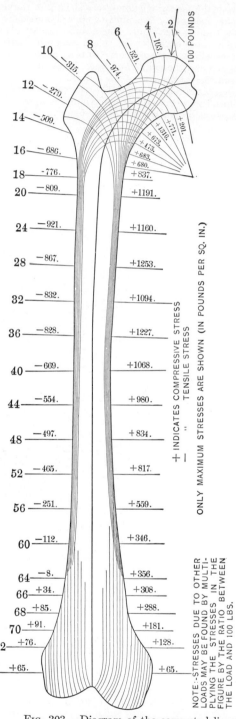

FIG. 302.—Frontal longitudinal midsection of right femur. Taken from the same subject as the one that was analyzed and shown in Figs. 303 and 304. ⅓ of natural size. (After Koch.)

FIG. 303.—Diagram of the computed lines of maximum stress in the normal femur. The section numbers 2, 4, 6, 8, etc., show the positions of the transverse sections analyzed. The amounts of the maximum tensile and compressive stress at the various sections are given for a load of 100 pounds on the femur-head. For the standing position ("at attention") these stresses are multiplied by 0.6, for walking by 1.6 and for running by 3.2. (After Koch.)

"*e. The Secondary Tensile Group.*—This group consists of the trabeculæ which spring from the outer side of the shaft and lie below those of the preceding group. They curve upward and medially across the axis of the femur and end more or less irregularly after crossing the midline, but a number of these filaments end in the medial portion of the shaft and neck. They cross at right angles the trabeculæ of group (*a*).

"In general, the trabeculæ of the tensile system are lighter in structure than those of the compressive system in corresponding positions. The significance of the difference in thickness of these two systems is that the thickness of the trabeculæ varies with the intensity of the stresses at any given point. Comparison of Fig. 300 with FIG. 301 will show that the trabeculæ of the compressive system carry heavier stresses than those of the tensile system in corresponding positions. For example, the maximum tensile stress at section 8 (Fig. 304) in the outermost fiber is 771 pounds per square inch, and at the corresponding point on the compressive side the compressive stress is 954 pounds per square inch. Similar comparisons may be made at other points, which confirm the conclusion that the thickness and closeness of spacing of the trabeculæ varies in proportion to the intensity of the stresses carried by them.

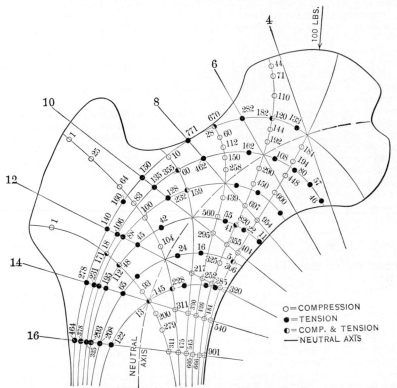

FIG. 304.—Intensity of the maximum tensile and compressive stresses in the upper femur. Computed for the load of 100 pounds on the right femur. Corresponds to the upper part of Fig. 303. (After Koch.)

"It will be seen that the trabeculæ lie exactly in the paths of the maximum tensile and compressive stresses (compare Figs. 300, 301 and 304), and hence these trabeculæ carry these stresses in the most economical manner. This is in accordance with the well-recognized principle of mechanics that the most direct manner of transmitting stress is in the direction in which the stress acts.

"Fig. 302 shows a longitudinal frontal section through the left femur, which is the mate of the right femur on which the mathematical analysis was made. In this midsection the system of tensile trabeculæ, which rises from the lateral (outer) part of the shaft and crosses over the central area to end in the medial portion of the shaft, neck and head, is clearly shown. This figure also shows the compressive system of trabeculæ which rises on the medial portion of the shaft and crosses the central area to end in the head, neck and greater trochanter. By comparing the position of these two systems of trabeculæ shown in Fig. 302 with the lines of maximum and minimum stresses shown in Figs. 301 and 303, it is seen that the tensile system of trabeculæ corresponds exactly with the position of the lines of maximum and minimum tensile stresses which were determined by mathematical analysis. In a similar manner, the compressive system of trabeculæ in Fig. 302 corresponds exactly with the lines of maximum and minimum compressive stresses computed by mathematical analysis.

"The amount of vertical shear varies almost uniformly from a maximum of 90 pounds (90 per cent. of the load on the femur-head) midway between sections 4 and 6, to a minimum of —5.7 pounds at section 18" (Fig. 304). There is a gradual diminution of the spongy bone from section 6 to section 18 parallel with the diminished intensities of the vertical shear.

1. The trabeculæ of the upper femur, as shown in frontal sections, are arranged in two general systems, compressive and tensile, which correspond in position with the lines of maximum and minimum stresses in the femur determined by the mathematical analysis of the femur as a mechanical structure.

2. The thickness and spacing of the trabeculæ vary with the intensity of the maximum stresses at various points in the upper femur, being thickest and most closely spaced in the regions where the greatest stresses occur.

3. The amount of bony material in the spongy bone of the upper femur varies in proportion to the intensity of the shearing force at the various sections.

4. The arrangement of the trabeculæ in the positions of maximum stresses is such that the greatest strength is secured with a minimum of material.

Significance of the Inner Architecture of the Shaft.—1. Economy for resisting shear. The shearing stresses are at a minimum in the shaft. "It is clear that a minimum amount of material will be required to resist the shearing stresses." As horizontal and vertical shearing stresses are most efficiently resisted by material placed near the neutral plane, in this region a minimum amount of material will be needed near the neutral axis. In the shaft there is very little if any material in the central space, practically the only material near the neutral plane being in the compact bone, but lying at a distance from the neutral axis. This conforms to the requirement of mechanics for economy, as a minimum of material is provided for resisting shearing stresses where these stresses are a minimum.

2. Economy for resisting bending moment. "The bending moment increases from a minimum at section 4 to a maximum between sections 16 and 18, then gradually decreases almost uniformly to 0 near section 75." "To resist bending moment stresses most effectively the material should be as far from the neutral axis as possible." It is evident that the hollow shaft of the femur is an efficient structure for resisting bending moment stresses, all of the material in the shaft being relatively at a considerable distance from the neutral axis. It is evident that the hollow shaft provides efficiently for resisting bending moment not only due to the load on the femur-head, but from any other loads tending to produce bending in other planes.

3. Economy for resisting axial stress.

The inner architecture of the shaft is adapted to resist in the most efficient manner the combined action of the minimal shearing forces and the axial and maximum bending stresses.

The structure of the shaft is such as to secure great strength with a relatively small amount of material.

The Distal Portion of the Femur.—In frontal section (Fig. 302) in the distal 6 inches of the femur "there are to be seen two main systems of trabeculæ, a longitudinal and a transverse system. The trabeculæ of the former rise from the inner wall of the shaft and continue in perfectly straight lines parallel to the axis of the shaft and proceed to the epiphyseal line, whence they continue in more or less curved lines to meet the articular surface of the knee-joint at right angles at every point. Near the center there are a few thin, delicate, longitudinal trabeculæ which spring from the longitudinal trabeculæ just described, to which they are joined by fine transverse filaments that lie in planes parallel to the sagittal plane.

"The trabeculæ of the transverse system are somewhat lighter in structure than those of the longitudinal system, and consist of numerous trabeculæ at right angles to the latter.

"As the distal end of the femur is approached the shaft gradually becomes thinner until the articular surface is reached, where there remains only a thin shell of compact bone. With the gradual thinning of the compact bone of the shaft, there is a simultaneous increase in the amount of the spongy bone, and a gradual flaring of the femur which gives this portion of the bone a gradually increasing gross area of cross-section.

"There is a marked thickening of the shell of bone in the region of the intercondyloid fossa where the anterior and posterior crucial ligaments are attached. This thickened area is about 0.4 inch in diameter and consists of compact bone from which a number of thick trabeculæ pass at right angles to the main longitudinal system. The inner structure of the bone is here evidently adapted to the efficient distribution of the stresses arising from this ligamentary attachment.

"Near the distal end of the femur the longitudinal trabeculæ gradually assume curved paths and end perpendicularly to the articular surface at every point. Such a structure is in accordance with the principles of mechanics, as stresses can be communicated through a frictionless joint only in a direction perpendicular to the joint surface at every point.

"With practically no increase in the amount of bony material used there is a greatly increased stability produced by the expansion of the lower femur from a hollow shaft of compact bone to a structure of much larger cross-section almost entirely composed of spongy bone.

"*Significance of the Inner Architecture of the Distal Part of the Femur.*—The function of the lower end of the femur is to transmit through a hinged joint the loads carried by the femur. For stability the width of the bearing on which the hinge action occurs should be relatively large. For economy of material the expansion of the end bearing should be as lightly constructed as is consistent with proper strength. In accordance with the principles of mechanics. . . . . ., the most efficient manner in which stresses are transmitted is by the arrangement of the resisting material in lines parallel to the direction in which the stresses occur and in the paths taken by the stresses. Theoretically the most efficient manner to attain these objects would be to prolong the innermost filaments of the bone as straight lines parallel to the longitudinal axis of the bone, and gradually to flare the outer shell of compact bone outward, and continuing to give off filaments of bone parallel to the longitudinal axis as the distal end of the femur is approached. These filaments should be well-braced transversely and each should carry its proportionate part of the total load, parallel to the longitudinal axis, transmitting it eventually to the articular surface, and in a direction perpendicular to that surface."

Referring to Fig. 302, it is seen that the large expansion of the bone is produced by the gradual transition of the hollow shaft of compact bone to cancellated bone, resulting in the production of a much larger volume. The trabeculæ are given off from the shaft in lines parallel to the longitudinal axis, and are braced transversely

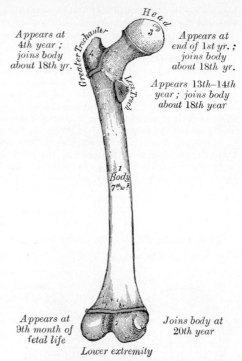

Appears at 4th year; joins body about 18th yr.

Appears at end of 1st yr.; joins body about 18th yr.

Appears 13th–14th year; joins body about 18th year

Appears at 9th month of fetal life

Joins body at 20th year

Lower extremity

Fig. 305.—Plan of ossification of the femur. From five centers.

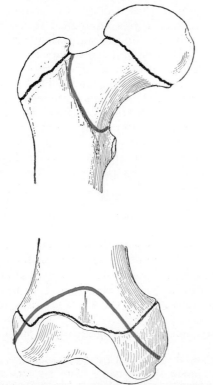

Fig. 306.—Epiphyseal lines of femur in a young adult. Anterior aspect. The lines of attachment of the articular capsules are in blue.

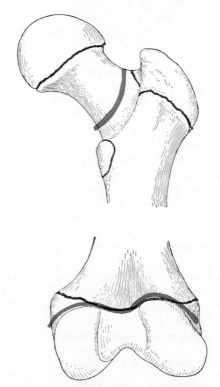

Fig. 307.—Epiphyseal lines of femur in a young adult. Posterior aspect. The lines of attachment of the articular capsules are in blue.

by two series of trabeculæ at right angles to each other, in the same manner as required theoretically for economy.

Although the action of the muscles exerts an appreciable effect on the stresses in the femur, it is relatively small and very complex to analyze and has not been considered in the above analysis.

Ossification (Figs. 305, 306, 307).—The femur is ossified from *five* centers: one for the body, one for the head, one for each trochanter, and one for the lower extremity. Of all the long bones, except the clavicle, it is the first to show traces of ossification; this commences in the middle of the body, at about the seventh week of fetal life, and rapidly extends upward and downward. The centers in the epiphyses appear in the following order: in the lower end of the bone, at the ninth month of fetal life (from this center the condyles and epicondyles are formed); in the head, at the end of the first year after birth; in the greater trochanter, during the fourth year; and in the lesser trochanter, between the thirteenth and fourteenth years. The order in which the epiphyses are joined to the body is the reverse of that of their appearance; they are not united until after puberty, the lesser trochanter being first joined, then the greater, then the head, and, lastly, the inferior extremity, which is not united until the twentieth year.

The Patella (Knee Cap).

The **patella** (Figs.308, 309) is a flat, triangular bone, situated on the front of the knee-joint. It is usually regarded as a sesamoid bone, developed in the

FIG. 308.—Right patella. Anterior surface.

FIG. 309.—Right patella. Posterior surface.

tendon of the Quadriceps femoris, and resembles these bones (1) in being developed in a tendon; (2) in its center of ossification presenting a knotty or tuberculated outline; (3) in being composed mainly of dense cancellous tissue. It serves to protect the front of the joint, and increases the leverage of the Quadriceps femoris by making it act at a greater angle. It has an anterior and a posterior surface three borders, and an apex.

Surfaces.—The **anterior surface** is convex, perforated by small apertures for the passage of nutrient vessels, and marked by numerous rough, longitudinal striæ. This surface is covered, in the recent state, by an expansion from the tendon of the Quadriceps femoris, which is continuous below with the superficial fibers of the ligamentum patellæ. It is separated from the integument by a bursa. The **posterior surface** presents above a smooth, oval, articular area, divided into two facets by a vertical ridge; the ridge corresponds to the groove on the patellar surface of the femur, and the facets to the medial and lateral parts of the same surface; the lateral facet is the broader and deeper. Below the articular surface is a rough, convex, non-articular area, the lower half of which gives attachment to the ligamentum patellæ; the upper half is separated from the head of the tibia by adipose tissue.

Borders.—The **base** or **superior border** is thick, and sloped from behind, downward, and forward: it gives attachment to that portion of the Quadriceps femoris which is derived from the Rectus femoris and Vastus intermedius. The **medial** and **lateral borders** are thinner and converge below: they give attachment to those portions of the Quadriceps femoris which are derived from the Vasti lateralis and medialis.

Apex.—The apex is pointed, and gives attachment to the ligamentum patellæ.

Structure.—The patella consists of a nearly uniform dense cancellous tissue, covered by a thin compact lamina. The cancelli immediately beneath the anterior surface are arranged parallel with it. In the rest of the bone they radiate from the articular surface toward the other parts of the bone.

Ossification.—The patella is ossified from a single center, which usually makes its appearance in the second or third year, but may be delayed until the sixth year. More rarely, the bone is developed by two centers, placed side by side. Ossification is completed about the age of puberty.

Articulation.—The patella articulates with the femur.

The Tibia (Shin Bone).

The **tibia** (Figs. 312, 313) is situated at the medial side of the leg, and, excepting the femur, is the longest bone of the skeleton. It is prismoid in form, expanded above, where it enters into the knee-joint, contracted in the lower third, and again enlarged but to a lesser extent below. In the male, its direction is vertical, and parallel with the bone of the opposite side; but in the female it has a slightly oblique direction downward and lateralward, to compensate for the greater obliquity of the femur. It has a **body** and **two extremities.**

The Upper Extremity (*proximal extremity*.)—The upper extremity is large, and expanded into two eminences, the **medial** and **lateral condyles.** The **superior articular surface** presents two smooth articular facets (Fig. 310). The medial facet, oval in shape, is slightly concave from side to side, and from before backward. The lateral,

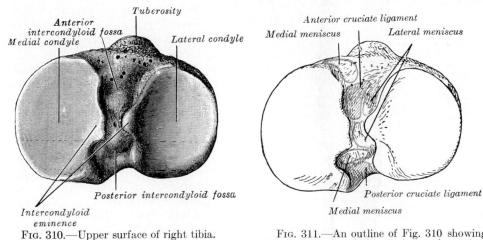

Fig. 310.—Upper surface of right tibia.

Fig. 311.—An outline of Fig. 310 showing the attachment of the menisci and cruciate ligaments.

nearly circular, is concave from side to side, but slightly convex from before backward, especially at its posterior part, where it is prolonged on to the posterior surface for a short distance. The central portions of these facets articulate with the condyles of the femur, while their peripheral portions support the menisci of the knee-joint, which here intervene between the two bones. Between the articular facets, but nearer the posterior than the anterior aspect of the bone, is the **intercondyloid eminence** (*spine of tibia*), surmounted on either side by a prominent tubercle, on to the sides of which the articular facets are prolonged; in front of and behind the intercondyloid eminence are rough depressions for the attachment of the anterior and posterior cruciate ligaments and the menisci. The **anterior surfaces** of the condyles are continuous with one another, forming a large somewhat flattened area; this area is triangular, broad above, and perforated by large vascular foramina; narrow below where it ends in a large oblong elevation, the **tuberosity of the tibia,** which gives attachment to the ligamentum patellæ; a bursa intervenes between the deep surface of the ligament and the part of the bone immediately above the tuberosity. *Posteriorly*, the condyles are separated from each other by a shallow depression, the **posterior intercondyloid fossa,** which gives attachment to part of the posterior cruciate ligament of the knee-joint. The **medial condyle** presents posteriorly a deep transverse groove, for the insertion of the tendon of

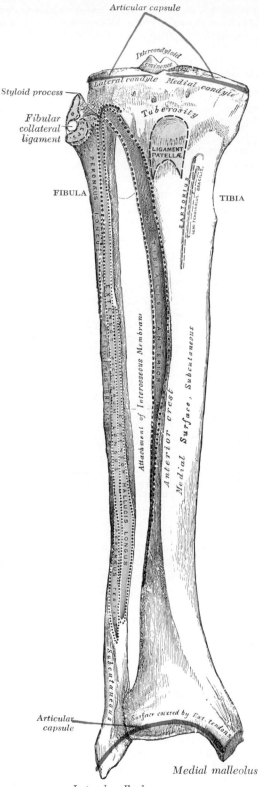

Fig. 312.—Bones of the right leg. Anterior surface.

the Semimembranosus. Its *medial surface* is convex, rough, and prominent; it gives attachment to the tibial collateral ligament. The **lateral condyle** presents posteriorly a flat articular facet, nearly circular in form, directed downward, backward, and lateralward, for articulation with the head of the fibula. Its *lateral surface* is convex, rough, and prominent in front: on it is an eminence, situated on a level with the upper border of the tuberosity and at the junction of its anterior and lateral surfaces, for the attachment of the iliotibial band. Just below this a part of the Extensor digitorum longus takes origin and a slip from the tendon of the Biceps femoris is inserted.

The Body or Shaft (*corpus tibiæ*). —The body has three borders and three surfaces.

Borders.—The **anterior crest** or **border**, the most prominent of the three, commences above at the tuberosity, and ends below at the anterior margin of the medial malleolus. It is sinuous and prominent in the upper two-thirds of its extent, but smooth and rounded below; it gives attachment to the deep fascia of the leg.

The **medial border** is smooth and rounded above and below, but more prominent in the center; it begins at the back part of the medial condyle, and ends at the posterior border of the medial malleolus; its upper part gives attachment to the tibial collateral ligament of the knee-joint to the extent of about 5 cm., and insertion to some fibers of the Popliteus; from its middle third some fibers of the Soleus and Flexor digitorum longus take origin.

The **interosseous crest** or **lateral border** is thin and prominent, especially its central part, and gives attachment to the interosseous membrane; it commences above in front of the fibular articular facet, and bifurcates below, to form the boundaries of a triangular rough surface, for the attachment of the interosseous ligament connecting the tibia and fibula.

Surfaces.—The **medial surface** is smooth, convex, and broader above than below; its upper third, directed forward and medialward, is covered by the aponeurosis derived from the tendon of the Sartorius, and by the tendons of the Gracilis and Semitendinosus, all of which are inserted nearly as far forward as the anterior crest; in the rest of its extent it is subcutaneous.

The **lateral surface** is narrower than the medial; its upper two-thirds present a shallow groove for the origin of the Tibialis anterior; its lower third is smooth, convex, curves gradually forward to the anterior aspect of the bone, and is covered by the tendons of the Tibialis anterior, Extensor hallucis longus, and Extensor digitorum longus, arranged in this order from the medial side.

The **posterior surface** (Fig. 313) presents, at its upper part, a prominent ridge, the **popliteal line,** which extends obliquely downward from the back part of the articular facet for the fibula to the medial border, at the junction of its upper and middle thirds; it marks the lower limit of the insertion of the Popliteus, serves for the attachment of the fascia covering this muscle, and gives origin to part of the Soleus, Flexor digitorum longus, and Tibialis posterior. The triangular area, above this line, gives insertion to the Popliteus. The middle third of the posterior surface is divided by a vertical ridge into two parts; the ridge begins at the popliteal line and is well-marked above, but indistinct below; the medial and broader portion gives origin to the Flexor digitorum longus, the lateral and narrower to part of the Tibialis posterior. The

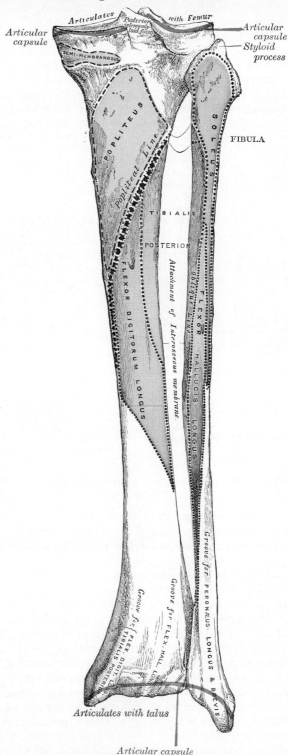

FIG. 313.—Bones of the right leg. Posterior surface.

remaining part of the posterior surface is smooth and covered by the Tibialis posterior, Flexor digitorum longus, and Flexor hallucis longus. Immediately below the popliteal line is the **nutrient foramen**, which is large and directed obliquely downward.

The Lower Extremity (*distal extremity*).—The lower extremity, much smaller than the upper, presents five surfaces; it is prolonged downward on its medial side as a strong process, the **medial malleolus**.

Surfaces.—The **inferior articular surface** is quadrilateral, and smooth for articulation with the talus. It is concave from before backward, broader in front than behind, and traversed from before backward by a slight elevation, separating two depressions. It is continuous with that on the medial malleolus.

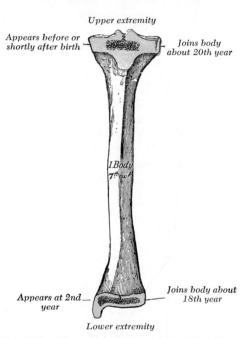

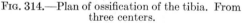

FIG. 314.—Plan of ossification of the tibia. From three centers.

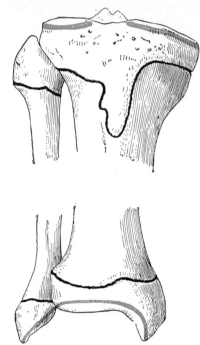

FIG. 315.—Epiphyseal lines of tibia and fibula in a young adult. Anterior aspect.

The **anterior surface** of the lower extremity is smooth and rounded above, and covered by the tendons of the Extensor muscles; its lower margin presents a rough transverse depression for the attachment of the articular capsule of the ankle-joint.

The **posterior surface** is traversed by a shallow groove directed obliquely downward and medialward, continuous with a similar groove on the posterior surface of the talus and serving for the passage of the tendon of the Flexor hallucis longus.

The **lateral surface** presents a triangular rough depression for the attachment of the inferior interosseous ligament connecting it with the fibula; the lower part of this depression is smooth, covered with cartilage in the fresh state, and articulates with the fibula. The surface is bounded by two prominent borders, continuous above with the interosseous crest; they afford attachment to the anterior and posterior ligaments of the lateral malleolus.

The **medial surface** is prolonged downward to form a strong pyramidal process, flattened from without inward—the **medial malleolus**. The *medial surface* of this process is convex and subcutaneous; its *lateral* or *articular surface* is smooth and slightly concave, and articulates with the talus; its *anterior border* is rough, for the attachment of the anterior fibers of the deltoid ligament of the ankle-joint;

its *posterior border* presents a broad groove, the **malleolar sulcus**, directed obliquely downward and medialward, and occasionally double; this sulcus lodges the tendons of the Tibialis posterior and Flexor digitorum longus. The *summit* of the medial malleolus is marked by a rough depression behind, for the attachment of the deltoid ligament.

Structure.—The structure of the tibia is like that of the other long bones. The compact wall of the body is thickest at the junction of the middle and lower thirds of the bone.

Ossification.—The tibia is ossified from *three* centers (Figs. 314, 315): one for the body and one for either extremity. Ossification begins in the center of the body, about the seventh week of fetal life, and gradually extends toward the extremities. The center for the upper epiphysis appears before or shortly after birth; it is flattened in form, and has a thin tongue-shaped process in front, which forms the tuberosity (Fig. 314); that for the lower epiphysis appears in the second year. The lower epiphysis joins the body at about the eighteenth, and the upper one joins about the twentieth year. Two additional centers occasionally exist, one for the tongue-shaped process of the upper epiphysis, which forms the tuberosity, and one for the medial malleolus.

The Fibula (Calf Bone).

The **fibula** (Figs. 312, 313) is placed on the lateral side of the tibia, with which it is connected above and below. It is the smaller of the two bones, and, in proportion to its length, the most slender of all the long bones. Its upper extremity is small, placed toward the back of the head of the tibia, below the level of the knee-joint, and excluded from the formation of this joint. Its lower extremity inclines a little forward, so as to be on a plane anterior to that of the upper end; it projects below the tibia, and forms the lateral part of the ankle-joint. The bone has a **body** and **two extremities.**

The Upper Extremity or Head (*caput fibulæ*; *proximal extremity*).—The upper extremity is of an irregular quadrate form, presenting above a flattened articular surface, directed upward, forward, and medialward, for articulation with a corresponding surface on the lateral condyle of the tibia. On the lateral side is a thick and rough prominence continued behind into a pointed eminence, the **apex** (*styloid process*), which projects upward from the posterior part of the head. The prominence, at its upper and lateral part, gives attachment to the tendon of the Biceps femoris and to the fibular collateral ligament of the knee-joint, the ligament dividing the tendon into two parts. The remaining part of the circumference of the head is rough, for the attachment of muscles and ligaments. It presents in front a tubercle for the origin of the upper and anterior fibers of the Peronæus longus, and a surface for the attachment of the anterior ligament of the head; and behind, another tubercle, for the attachment of the posterior ligament of the head and the origin of the upper fibers of the Soleus.

The Body or Shaft (*corpus fibulæ*).—The body presents four borders—the antero-lateral, the antero-medial, the postero-lateral, and the postero-medial; and four surfaces—anterior, posterior, medial, and lateral.

Borders.—The **antero-lateral border** begins above in front of the head, runs vertically downward to a little below the middle of the bone, and then curving somewhat lateralward, bifurcates so as to embrace a triangular subcutaneous surface immediately above the lateral malleolus. This border gives attachment to an intermuscular septum, which separates the Extensor muscles on the anterior surface of the leg from the Peronæi longus and brevis on the lateral surface.

The **antero-medial border**, or **interosseous crest**, is situated close to the medial side of the preceding, and runs nearly parallel with it in the upper third of its extent, but diverges from it in the lower two-thirds. It begins above just beneath the head of the bone (sometimes it is quite indistinct for about 2.5 cm. below the head), and ends at the apex of a rough triangular surface immediately above the articular facet of the lateral malleolus. It serves for the attachment of the interosseous membrane, which separates the Extensor muscles in front from the Flexor muscles behind.

The **postero-lateral border** is prominent; it begins above at the apex, and ends below in the posterior border of the lateral malleolus. It is directed lateralward above, backward in the middle of its course, backward, and a little medialward below, and gives attachment to an aponeurosis which separates the Peronæi on the lateral surface from the Flexor muscles on the posterior surface.

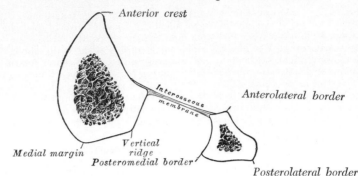

FIG. 316.—A transverse section through the right tibia and fibula, showing the attachment of the crural interosseous membrane.

The **postero-medial border,** sometimes called the **oblique line,** begins above at the medial side of the head, and ends by becoming continuous with the interosseous crest at the lower fourth of the bone. It is well-marked and prominent at the upper and middle parts of the bone. It gives attachment to an aponeurosis which separates the Tibialis posterior from the Soleus and Flexor hallucis longus.

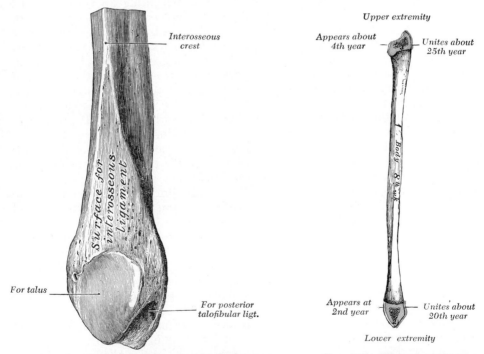

FIG. 317.—Lower extremity of right fibula. Medial aspect.

FIG. 318.—Plan of ossification of the fibula. From three centers.

Surfaces.—The **anterior surface** is the interval between the antero-lateral and antero-medial borders. It is extremely narrow and flat in the upper third of its extent; broader and grooved longitudinally in its lower third; it serves for the origin of three muscles: the Extensor digitorum longus, Extensor hallucis longus, and Peronæus tertius.

The **posterior surface** is the space included between the postero-lateral and the postero-medial borders; it is continuous below with the triangular area above the articular surface of the lateral malleolus; it is directed backward above, backward and medialward at its middle, directly medialward below. Its upper third is rough, for the origin of the Soleus; its lower part presents a triangular surface, connected to the tibia by a strong interosseous ligament; the intervening part of the surface is covered by the fibers of origin of the Flexor hallucis longus. Near the middle of this surface is the nutrient foramen, which is directed downward.

The **medial surface** is the interval included between the antero-medial and the postero-medial borders. It is grooved for the origin of the Tibialis posterior.

The **lateral surface** is the space between the antero-lateral and postero-lateral borders. It is broad, and often deeply grooved; it is directed lateralward in the upper two-thirds of its course, backward in the lower third, where it is continuous with the posterior border of the lateral malleolus. This surface gives origin to the Peronæi longus and brevis.

The Lower Extremity or Lateral Malleolus (*malleolus lateralis; distal extremity; external malleolus*).—The lower extremity is of a pyramidal form, and somewhat flattened from side to side; it descends to a lower level than the medial malleolus, The **lateral surface** is convex, subcutaneous, and continuous with the triangular, subcutaneous surface on the lateral side of the body. The **medial surface** (Fig. 328) presents in front a smooth triangular surface, convex from above downward. which articulates with a corresponding surface on the lateral side of the talus. Behind and beneath the articular surface is a rough depression, which gives attachment to the posterior talofibular ligament. The **anterior border** is thick and rough, and marked below by a depression for the attachment of the anterior talofibular ligament. The **posterior border** is broad and presents the shallow **malleolar sulcus,** for the passage of the tendons of the Peronæi longus and brevis. The **summit** is rounded, and give attachment to the calcaneofibular ligament.

Ossification.—The fibula is ossified from *three* centers (Fig. 318): one for the body, and one for either end. Ossification begins in the body about the eighth week of fetal life, and extends toward the extremities. At birth the ends are cartilaginous. Ossification commences in the lower end in the second year, and in the upper about the fourth year. The lower epiphysis, the first to ossify, unites with the body about the twentieth year; the upper epiphysis joins about the twenty-fifth year.

THE FOOT.

The skeleton of the foot (Figs. 319 and 320) consists of three parts: the **tarsus, metatarsus,** and **phalanges.**

The Tarsus (Ossa Tarsi).

The **tarsal bones** are seven in number, viz., the **calcaneus, talus, cuboid, navicular,** and the **first, second,** and **third cuneiforms.**

The **Calcaneus** (*os calcis*) (Figs. 321 to 324).—The calcaneus is the largest of the tarsal bones. It is situated at the lower and back part of the foot, serving to transmit the weight of the body to the ground, and forming a strong lever for the muscles of the calf. It is irregularly cuboidal in form, having its long axis directed forward and lateralward; it presents for examination six surfaces.

Surfaces.—The **superior surface** extends behind on to that part of the bone which projects backward to form the heel. This varies in length in different individuals, is convex from side to side, concave from before backward, and supports a mass of fat placed in front of the tendo calcaneus. In front of this area is a large usually somewhat oval-shaped facet, the **posterior articular surface,** which looks upward and forward; it is convex from behind forward, and articulates with the posterior

19

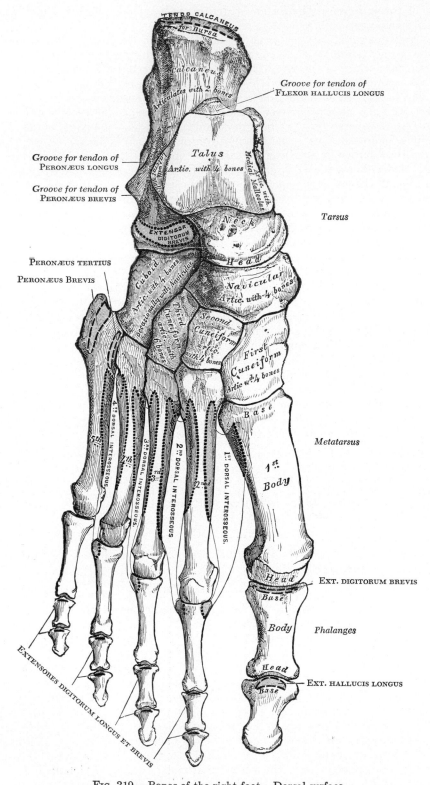

FIG. 319.—Bones of the right foot. Dorsal surface.

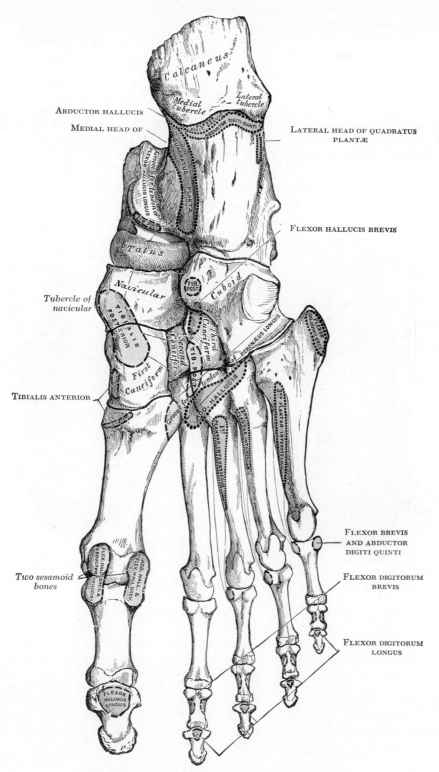

Fig. 320.—Bones of the right foot. Plantar surface.

calcaneal facet on the under surface of the talus. It is bounded anteriorly by a deep depression which is continued backward and medialward in the form of a groove, the **calcaneal sulcus**. In the articulated foot this sulcus lies below a similar one on the under surface of the talus, and the two form a canal (**sinus tarsi**) for the lodgement of the interosseous talocalcaneal ligament. In front and to the medial side of this groove is an elongated facet, concave from behind forward, and with its long axis directed forward and lateralward. This facet is frequently divided into two by a notch: of the two, the posterior, and larger is termed the **middle articular surface**; it is supported on a projecting process of bone, the **sustentaculum talare**, and articulates with the middle calcaneal facet on the under surface of the talus; the **anterior articular surface** is placed on the anterior part of the body, and articulates with the anterior calcaneal facet on the talus. The upper surface, anterior and lateral to the facets, is rough for the attachment of ligaments and for the origin of the Extensor digitorum brevis.

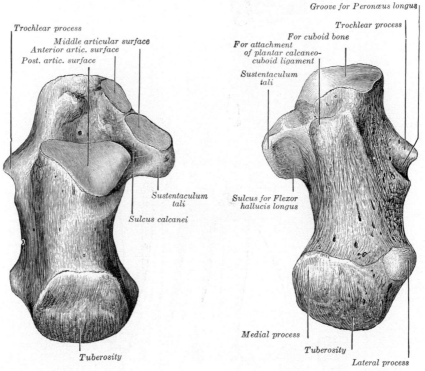

FIG. 321.—Left calcaneus, superior surface.   FIG. 322.—Left calcaneus, inferior surface.

The **inferior** or **plantar surface** is uneven, wider behind than in front, and convex from side to side; it is bounded posteriorly by a transverse elevation, the **calcaneal tuberosity**, which is depressed in the middle and prolonged at either end into a process; the **lateral process**, small, prominent, and rounded, gives origin to part of the Abductor digiti quinti; the **medial process**, broader and larger, gives attachment, by its prominent medial margin, to the Abductor hallucis, and in front to the Flexor digitorum brevis and the plantar aponeurosis; the depression between the processes gives origin to the Abductor digiti quinti. The rough surface in front of the processes gives attachment to the long plantar ligament, and to the lateral head of the Quadratus plantæ; while to a prominent tubercle nearer the anterior part of this surface, as well as to a transverse groove in front of the tubercle, is attached the plantar calcaneocuboid ligament.

The **lateral surface** is broad behind and narrow in front, flat and almost subcutaneous; near its center is a tubercle, for the attachment of the calcaneofibular ligament. At its upper and anterior part, this surface gives attachment to the lateral talocalcaneal ligament; and in front of the tubercle it presents a narrow surface marked by two oblique grooves. The grooves are separated by an elevated ridge, or tubercle, the **trochlear process** (*peroneal tubercle*), which varies much in size in different bones. The **superior groove** transmits the tendon of the Peronæus brevis; the **inferior groove**, that of the Peronæus longus.

The **medial surface** is deeply concave; it is directed obliquely downward and forward, and serves for the transmission of the plantar vessels and nerves into the sole of the foot; it affords origin to part of the Quadratus plantæ. At its upper

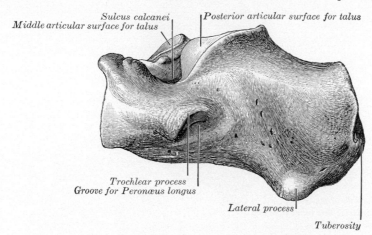

Sulcus calcanei   *Posterior articular surface for talus*
Middle articular surface for talus

Trochlear process
Groove for Peronæus longus

Lateral process

Tuberosity

FIG. 323.—Left calcaneus, lateral surface.

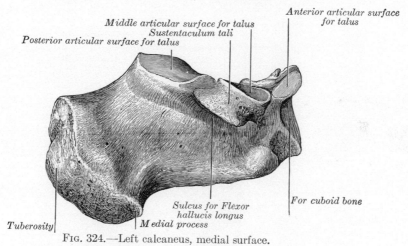

Middle articular surface for talus
Sustentaculum tali
Posterior articular surface for talus

Anterior articular surface for talus

For cuboid bone

Sulcus for Flexor hallucis longus
Tuberosity   *Medial process*

FIG. 324.—Left calcaneus, medial surface.

and forepart is a horizontal eminence, the **sustentaculum talare**, which gives attachment to a slip of the tendon of the Tibialis posterior. This eminence is concave above, and articulates with the middle calcaneal articular surface of the talus; below, it is grooved for the tendon of the Flexor hallucis longus; its anterior margin gives attachment to the plantar calcaneonavicular ligament, and its medial, to a part of the deltoid ligament of the ankle-joint.

The **anterior** or **cuboid articular surface** is of a somewhat triangular form. It is concave from above downward and lateralward, and convex in a direction at right angles to this. Its medial border gives attachment to the plantar calcaneonavicular ligament.

The **posterior surface** is prominent, convex, wider below than above, and divisible into three areas. The lowest of these is rough, and covered by the fatty and fibrous tissue of the heel; the middle, also rough, gives insertion to the tendo calcaneus and Plantaris; while the highest is smooth, and is covered by a bursa which intervenes between it and the tendo calcaneus.

Articulations.—The calcaneus articulates with two bones: the talus and cuboid.

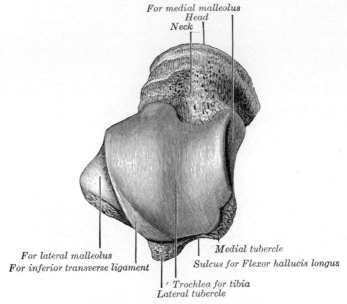

For medial malleolus
Head
Neck

For lateral malleolus
For inferior transverse ligament

Medial tubercle
Sulcus for Flexor hallucis longus

Trochlea for tibia
Lateral tubercle

Fig. 325.—Left talus, from above.

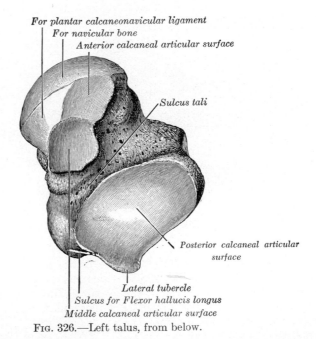

For plantar calcaneonavicular ligament
For navicular bone
Anterior calcaneal articular surface

Sulcus tali

Posterior calcaneal articular surface

Lateral tubercle
Sulcus for Flexor hallucis longus
Middle calcaneal articular surface

Fig. 326.—Left talus, from below.

The Talus (*astragalus; ankle bone*) (Figs. 325 to 328).—The talus is the second largest of the tarsal bones. It occupies the middle and upper part of the tarsus, supporting the tibia above, resting upon the calcaneus below, articulating on

either side with the malleoli, and in front with the navicular. It consists of a
body, a **neck,** and a **head**

The Body (*corpus tali*).—The **superior surface** of the body presents, behind, a
smooth trochlear surface, the **trochlea,** for articulation with the tibia. The trochlea
is broader in front than behind, convex from before backward, slightly concave
from side to side: in front it is continuous with the upper surface of the neck of
the bone.

The **inferior surface** presents two articular areas, the posterior and middle calcaneal surfaces, separated from one another by a deep groove, the **sulcus tali.**
The groove runs obliquely forward and lateralward, becoming gradually broader
and deeper in front: in the articulated foot it lies above a similar groove upon
the upper surface of the calcaneus, and forms, with it, a canal (**sinus tarsi**) filled
up in the fresh state by the interosseous talocalcaneal ligament. The **posterior
calcaneal articular surface** is large and of an oval or oblong form. It articulates

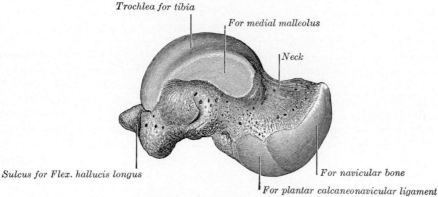

Trochlea for tibia

For medial malleolus

Neck

Sulcus for Flex. hallucis longus

For navicular bone

For plantar calcaneonavicular ligament

FIG. 327.—Left talus, medial surface.

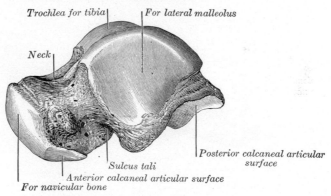

Trochlea for tibia *For lateral malleolus*

Neck

Posterior calcaneal articular surface

Sulcus tali

Anterior calcaneal articular surface

For navicular bone

FIG. 328.—Left talus, lateral surface.

with the corresponding facet on the upper surface of the calcaneus, and is deeply
concave in the direction of its long axis which runs forward and lateralward at
an angle of about 45° with the median plane of the body. The **middle calcaneal
articular surface** is small, oval in form and slightly convex; it articulates with the
upper surface of the sustentaculum tali of the calcaneus.

The **medial surface** presents at its upper part a pear-shaped articular facet for
the medial malleolus, continuous above with the trochlea; below the articular
surface is a rough depression for the attachment of the deep portion of the deltoid
ligament of the ankle-joint.

The **lateral surface** carries a large triangular facet, concave from above downward, for articulation with the lateral malleolus; its anterior half is continuous above with the trochlea; and in front of it is a rough depression for the attachment of the anterior talofibular ligament. Between the posterior half of the lateral border of the trochlea and the posterior part of the base of the fibular articular surface is a triangular facet which comes into contact with the transverse inferior tibiofibular ligament during flexion of the ankle-joint; below the base of this facet is a groove which affords attachment to the posterior talofibular ligament.

The **posterior surface** is narrow, and traversed by a groove running obliquely downward and medialward, and transmitting the tendon of the Flexor hallucis longus. Lateral to the groove is a prominent tubercle, the **posterior process,** to which the posterior talofibular ligament is attached; this process is sometimes separated from the rest of the talus, and is then known as the **os trigonum.** Medial to the groove is a second smaller tubercle.

The **Neck** (*collum tali*).—The neck is directed forward and medialward, and comprises the constricted portion of the bone between the body and the oval head. Its **upper** and **medial surfaces** are rough, for the attachment of ligaments; its **lateral surface** is concave and is continuous below with the deep groove for the interosseous talocalcaneal ligament.

The **Head** (*caput tali*).—The head looks forward and medialward; its **anterior articular** or **navicular surface** is large, oval, and convex. Its **inferior surface** has two facets, which are best seen in the fresh condition. The medial, situated in front of the middle calcaneal facet, is convex, triangular, or semi-oval in shape, and rests on the plantar calcaneonavicular ligament; the lateral, named the **anterior calcaneal articular surface,** is somewhat flattened, and articulates with the facet on the upper surface of the anterior part of the calcaneus.

Articulations.—The talus articulates with *four* bones: tibia, fibula, calcaneus, and navicular.

The **Cuboid Bone** (*os cuboideum*) (Figs. 329, 330).—The cuboid bone is placed on the lateral side of the foot, in front of the calcaneus, and behind the fourth and fifth metatarsal bones. It is of a pyramidal shape, its base being directed medialward.

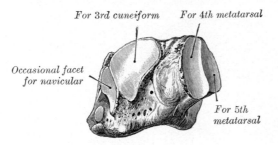

FIG. 329.—The left cuboid. Antero-medial view.

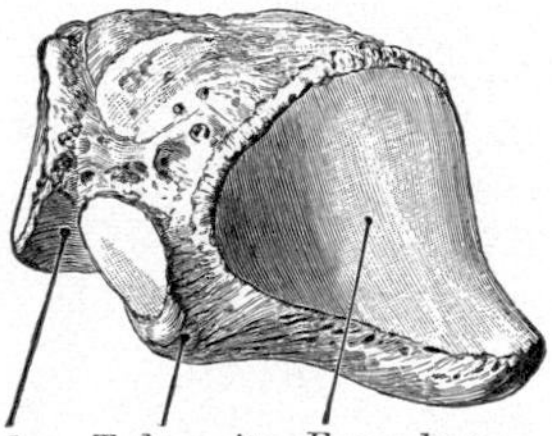

FIG. 330.—The left cuboid. Postero-lateral view.

Surfaces.—The **dorsal surface,** directed upward and lateralward, is rough, for the attachment of ligaments. The **plantar surface** presents in front a deep groove, the **peroneal sulcus,** which runs obliquely forward and medialward; it lodges the tendon of the Peronæus longus, and is bounded behind by a prominent ridge, to which the long plantar ligament is attached. The ridge ends laterally in an eminence, the **tuberosity,** the surface of which presents an oval facet; on this facet glides the sesamoid bone or cartilage frequently found in the tendon of the Peronæus longus. The surface of bone behind the groove is rough, for the attachment of the plantar calcaneocuboid ligament, a few fibers of the Flexor hallucis brevis, and a fasciculus from the tendon of the Tibialis posterior. The **lateral surface** presents a deep notch formed by the commencement of the peroneal sulcus. The

posterior surface is smooth, triangular, and concavo-convex, for articulation with the anterior surface of the calcaneus; its infero-medial angle projects backward as a process which underlies and supports the anterior end of the calcaneus. The **anterior surface,** of smaller size, but also irregularly triangular, is divided by a vertical ridge into two facets: the medial, quadrilateral in form, articulates with the fourth metatarsal; the lateral, larger and more triangular, articulates with the fifth. The **medial surface** is broad, irregularly quadrilateral, and presents at its middle and upper part a smooth oval facet, for articulation with the third cuneiform; and behind this (occasionally) a smaller facet, for articulation with the navicular; it is rough in the rest of its extent, for the attachment of strong interosseous ligaments.

Articulations.—The cuboid articulates with *four* bones: the calcaneus, third cuneiform, and fourth and fifth metatarsals; occasionally with a fifth, the navicular.

The Navicular Bone (*os naviculare pedis; scaphoid bone*) (Figs. 331, 332).—The navicular bone is situated at the medial side of the tarsus, between the talus behind and the cuneiform bones in front.

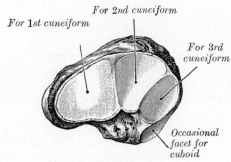

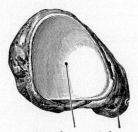

FIG. 331.—The left navicular. Antero-lateral view.

FIG. 332.—The left navicular. Postero-medial view.

Surfaces.—The **anterior surface** is convex from side to side, and subdivided by two ridges into three facets, for articulation with the three cuneiform bones. The **posterior surface** is oval, concave, broader laterally than medially, and articulates with the rounded head of the talus. The **dorsal surface** is convex from side to side, and rough for the attachment of ligaments. The **plantar surface** is irregular, and also rough for the attachment of ligaments. The **medial surface** presents a rounded tuberosity, the lower part of which gives attachment to part of the tendon of the Tibialis posterior. The **lateral surface** is rough and irregular for the attachment of ligaments, and occasionally presents a small facet for articulation with the cuboid bone.

Articulations.—The navicular articulates with *four* bones: the talus and the three cuneiforms; occasionally with a fifth, the cuboid.

The First Cuneiform Bone (*os cuneiforme mediale; internal cuneiform*) (Figs. 333, 334).—The first cuneiform bone is the largest

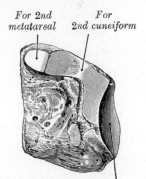

FIG. 333.—The left first cuneiform. Antero-medial view.

FIG. 334.—The left first cuneiform. Postero-lateral view.

of the three cuneiforms. It is situated at the medial side of the foot, between the navicular behind and the base of the first metatarsal in front.

Surfaces.—The **medial surface** is subcutaneous, broad, and quadrilateral; at its anterior plantar angle is a smooth oval impression, into which part of the tendon of the Tibialis anterior is inserted; in the rest of its extent it is rough for the attachment of ligaments. The **lateral surface** is concave, presenting, along its superior and posterior borders a narrow L-shaped surface, the vertical limb and posterior part of the horizontal limb of which articulate with the second cuneiform, while the anterior part of the horizontal limb articulates with the second metatarsal bone: the rest of this surface is rough for the attachment of ligaments and part of the tendon of the Peronæus longus. The **anterior surface**, kidney-shaped and much larger than the posterior, articulates with the first metatarsal bone. The **posterior surface** is triangular, concave, and articulates with the most medial and largest of the three facets on the anterior surface of the navicular. The **plantar surface** is rough, and forms the base of the wedge; at its back part is a tuberosity for the insertion of part of the tendon of the Tibialis posterior. It also gives insertion in front to part of the tendon of the Tibialis anterior. The **dorsal surface** is the narrow end of the wedge, and is directed upward and lateralward; it is rough for the attachment of ligaments.

Articulations.—The first cuneiform articulates with *four* bones: the navicular, second cuneiform, and first and second metatarsals.

The Second Cuneiform Bone (*os cuneiforme intermedium; middle cuneiform*) (Figs. 335, 336).—The second cuneiform bone, the smallest of the three, is of very regular wedge-like form, the thin end being directed downward. It is situated between the other two cuneiforms, and articulates with the navicular behind, and the second metatarsal in front.

Surfaces.—The **anterior surface**, triangular in form, and narrower than the posterior, articulates with the base of the second metatarsal bone. The **posterior surface**, also triangular, articulates with the intermediate facet on the anterior surface of the navicular. The **medial surface** carries an L-shaped articular facet, running along the superior and posterior borders, for articulation with the first cuneiform, and is rough in the rest of its extent for the attachment of ligaments. The **lateral**

For 1st cuneiform   *For navicular*

For 2nd metatarsal   *For 3rd cuneiform*

Fig. 335.—The left second cuneiform. Antero-medial view.

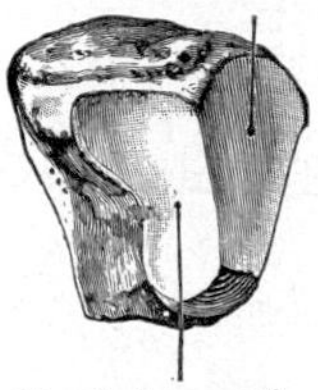

Fig. 336.—The left second cuneiform. Postero-lateral view.

surface presents posteriorly a smooth facet for articulation with the third cuneiform bone. The **dorsal surface** forms the base of the wedge; it is quadrilateral and rough for the attachment of ligaments. The **plantar surface**, sharp and tuberculated, is also rough for the attachment of ligaments, and for the insertion of a slip from the tendon of the Tibialis posterior.

Articulations.—The second cuneiform articulates with *four* bones: the navicular, first and third cuneiforms, and second metatarsal.

The Third Cuneiform Bone (*os cuneiforme laterale; external cuneiform*) (Figs. 337, 338).—The third cuneiform bone, intermediate in size between the two preceding, is wedge-shaped, the base being uppermost. It occupies the center of the front row of the tarsal bones, between the second cuneiform medially, the cuboid laterally, the navicular behind, and the third metatarsal in front.

Surfaces.—The **anterior surface**, triangular in form, articulates with the third metatarsal bone. The **posterior surface** articulates with the lateral facet on the anterior surface of the navicular, and is rough below for the attachment of ligamentous fibers. The **medial surface** presents an anterior and a posterior articular facet, separated by a rough depression: the anterior, sometimes divided, articulates with the lateral side of the base of the second metatarsal bone; the posterior skirts the posterior border, and articulates with the second cuneiform; the rough depression gives attachment to an interosseous ligament. The **lateral surface** also presents two articular facets, separated by a rough non-articular area; the anterior facet, situated at the superior angle of the bone, is small and semi-oval in shape, and articulates with the medial side of the base of the fourth metatarsal bone; the posterior and larger one is triangular or oval, and articulates with the cuboid; the rough, non-articular area serves for the attachment of an interosseous ligament. The three facets for articulation with the three metatarsal bones are continuous with one another; those for articulation with the second cuneiform and navicular are also continuous, but that for articulation with the cuboid is usually separate. The **dorsal surface** is of an oblong form, its postero-lateral angle being prolonged backward. The **plantar surface** is a rounded margin, and serves for the attachment of part of the tendon of the Tibialis posterior, part of the Flexor hallucis brevis, and ligaments.

Articulations.—The third cuneiform articulates with *six* bones: the navicular, second cuneiform, cuboid, and second, third, and fourth metatarsals.

For navicular   For 2nd cuneiform

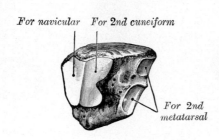

For 2nd metatarsal

FIG. 337.—The left third cuneiform. Postero-medial view.

For 4th metatarsal   For cuboid

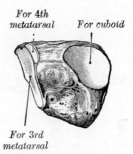

For 3rd metatarsal

FIG. 338.—The third left cuneiform. Antero-lateral view.

The Metatarsus (Fig. 319, 320).

The **metatarsus** consists of five bones which are numbered from the medial side (*ossa metatarsalia* I.–V.); each presents for examination a **body** and **two extremities.**

Common Characteristics of the Metatarsal Bones.—The body is prismoid in form, tapers gradually from the tarsal to the phalangeal extremity, and is curved longitudinally, so as to be concave below, slightly convex above. The **base** or **posterior extremity** is wedge-shaped, articulating proximally with the tarsal bones, and by its sides with the contiguous metatarsal bones: its dorsal and plantar surfaces are rough for the attachment of ligaments. The **head** or **anterior extremity** presents a convex articular surface, oblong from above downward, and extending farther backward below than above. Its sides are flattened, and on each is a depression, surmounted by a tubercle, for ligamentous attachment. Its plantar surface is grooved antero-posteriorly for the passage of the Flexor tendons, and marked on either side by an articular eminence continuous with the terminal articular surface.

Characteristics of the Individual Metatarsal Bones. — The First Metatarsal Bone (*os metatarsale I; metatarsal bone of the great toe*) (Fig. 339).—The first metatarsal bone is remarkable for its great thickness, and is the shortest of the metatarsal bones. The **body** is strong, and of well-marked prismoid form. The **base** presents, as a rule, no articular facets on its sides, but occasionally on the lateral side there is an oval facet, by which it articulates with the second metatarsal. Its proximal articular surface is of large size and kidney-shaped; its circumference is grooved, for the tarsometatarsal ligaments, and medially gives insertion to part of the tendon of the Tibialis anterior; its plantar angle presents a rough oval prominence for the insertion of the tendon of the Peronæus longus. The **head** is large; on its plantar surface are two grooved facets, on which glide sesamoid bones; the facets are separated by a smooth elevation.

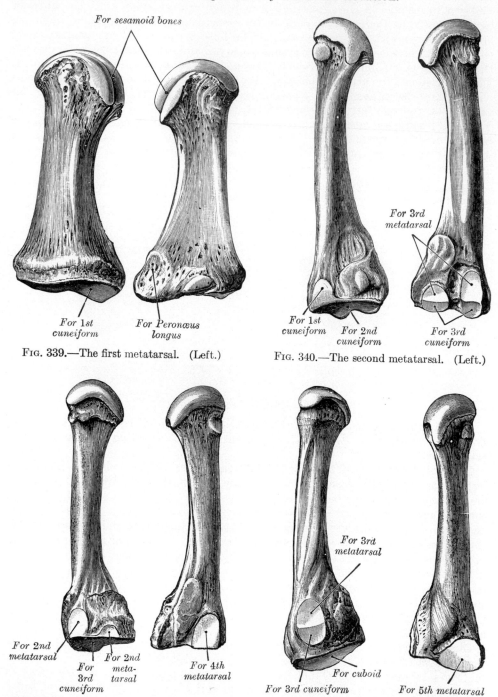

For sesamoid bones

For 1st cuneiform   *For Peronæus longus*

Fig. 339.—The first metatarsal. (Left.)

For 3rd metatarsal

For 1st cuneiform   *For 2nd cuneiform*   *For 3rd cuneiform*

Fig. 340.—The second metatarsal. (Left.)

For 2nd metatarsal   *For 3rd cuneiform*   *For 2nd metatarsal*   *For 4th metatarsal*

Fig. 341.—The third metatarsal. (Left.)

For 3rd metatarsal   *For cuboid*   *For 3rd cuneiform*   *For 5th metatarsal*

Fig. 342.—The fourth metatarsal. (Left.)

The Second Metatarsal Bone (*os metatarsale II*) (Fig. 340).—The second metatarsal bone is the longest of the metatarsal bones, being prolonged backward into the recess formed by the three cuneiform bones. Its **base** is broad above, narrow and rough below. It presents four articular surfaces: one behind, of a triangular form, for articulation with the second cuneiform; one at the upper part of its medial surface, for articulation with the first cuneiform; and two on its lateral surface, an upper and lower, separated by a rough non-articular interval. Each of these lateral articular surfaces is divided into two by a vertical ridge; the two anterior facets articulate with the third metatarsal; the two posterior (sometimes continuous) with the third cuneiform. A fifth facet is occasionally present for articulation with the first metatarsal; it is oval in shape, and is situated on the medial side of the body near the base.

The Third Metatarsal Bone (*os metatarsale III*) (Fig. 341).—The third metatarsal bone articulates proximally, by means of a triangular smooth surface, with the third cuneiform; medially, by two facets, with the second metatarsal; and laterally, by a single facet, with the fourth metatarsal. This last facet is situated at the dorsal angle of the base.

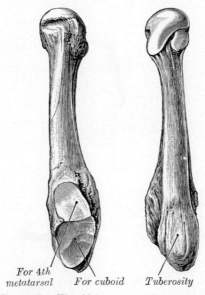

For 4th
metatarsal   For cuboid   Tuberosity
Fɪɢ. 343.—The fifth metatarsal. (Left.)

The Fourth Metatarsal Bone (*os metatarsale IV*) (Fig. 342).—The fourth metatarsal bone is smaller in size than the preceding; its **base** presents an oblique quadrilateral surface for articulation with the cuboid; a smooth facet on the medial side, divided by a ridge into an anterior portion for articulation with the third metatarsal, and a posterior portion for articulation with the third cuneiform; on the lateral side a single facet, for articulation with the fifth metatarsal.

The Fifth Metatarsal Bone (*os metatarsale V*) (Fig. 343).—The fifth metatarsal bone is recognized by a rough eminence, the **tuberosity**, on the lateral side of its base. The **base** articulates behind, by a triangular surface cut obliquely in a transverse direction, with the cuboid; and medially, with the fourth metatarsal. On the medial part of its dorsal surface is inserted the tendon of the Peronæus tertius and on the dorsal surface of the tuberosity that of the Peronæus brevis. A strong band of the plantar aponeurosis connects the projecting part of the tuberosity with the lateral process of the tuberosity of the calcaneus. The plantar surface of the base is grooved for the tendon of the Abductor digiti quinti, and gives origin to the Flexor digiti quinti brevis.

Articulations.—The base of each metatarsal bone articulates with one or more of the tarsal bones, and the head with one of the first row of phalanges. The first metatarsal articulates with the first cuneiform, the second with all three cuneiforms, the third with the third cuneiform, the fourth with the third cuneiform and the cuboid, and the fifth with the cuboid.

The Phalanges of the Foot (Phalanges Digitorum Pedis) (Fig. 319).

The **phalanges** of the foot correspond, in number and general arrangement, with those of the hand; there are two in the great toe, and three in each of the other toes. They differ from them, however, in their size, the bodies being much reduced in length, and, especially in the first row, laterally compressed.

First Row.—The **body** of each is compressed from side to side, convex above, concave below. The **base** is concave; and the **head** presents a trochlear surface for articulation with the second phalanx.

Second Row.—The phalanges of the second row are remarkably small and short, but rather broader than those of the first row.

The **ungual phalanges,** in form, resemble those of the fingers; but they are smaller and are flattened from above downward; each presents a broad base for articulation with the corresponding bone of the second row, and an expanded distal extremity for the support of the nail and end of the toe.

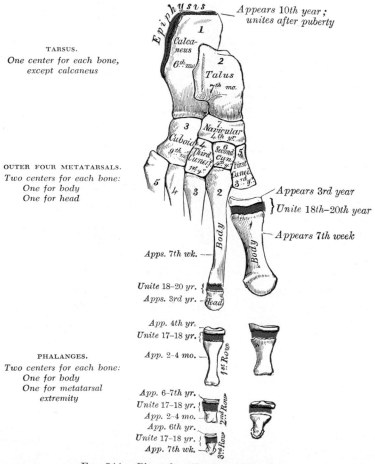

FIG. 344.—Plan of ossification of the foot.

Articulations.—In the second, third, fourth, and fifth toes the phalanges of the first row articulate behind with the metatarsal bones, and in front with the second phalanges, which in their turn articulate with the first and third: the ungual phalanges articulate with the second.

Ossification of the Bones of the Foot (Fig. 344).—The **tarsal bones** are each ossified from a *single* center, excepting the calcaneus, which has an epiphysis for its posterior extremity. The centers make their appearance in the following order: calcaneus at the sixth month of fetal life:

talus, about the seventh month; cuboid, at the ninth month; third cuneiform, during the first year; first cuneiform, in the third year; second cuneiform and navicular, in the fourth year. The epiphysis for the posterior extremity of the calcaneus appears at the tenth year, and unites with the rest of the bone soon after puberty. The posterior process of the talus is sometimes ossified from a separate center, and may remain distinct from the main mass of the bone, when it is named the *os trigonum*.

The **metatarsal bones** are each ossified from *two* centers: one for the body, and one for the head, of the second, third, fourth, and fifth metatarsals; one for the body, and one for the base, of the first metatarsal. Ossification commences in the center of the body about the ninth week, and extends toward either extremity. The center for the base of the first metatarsal appears about the third year; the centers for the heads of the other bones between the fifth and eighth years; they join the bodies between the eighteenth and twentieth years.

The **phalanges** are each ossified from *two* centers: one for the body, and one for the base. The center for the body appears about the tenth week, that for the base between the fourth and tenth years; it joins the body about the eighteenth year.

Comparison of the Bones of the Hand and Foot.

The hand and foot are constructed on somewhat similar principles, each consisting of a proximal part, the carpus or the tarsus, a middle portion, the metacarpus, or the metatarsus, and a terminal portion, the phalanges. The proximal part consists of a series of more or less cubical bones which allow a slight amount of gliding on one another and are chiefly concerned in distributing forces transmitted to or from the bones of the arm or leg. The middle part is made up of slightly movable long bones which assist the carpus or tarsus in distributing forces and also give greater breadth for the reception of such forces. The separation of the individual bones from one another allows of the attachments of the Interossei and protects the dorsi-palmar and dorsi-plantar vascular anastomoses. The terminal portion is the most movable, and its separate elements enjoy a varied range of movements, the chief of which are flexion and extension.

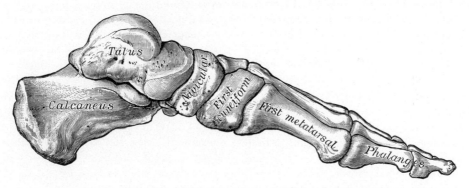

Fig. 345.—Skeleton of foot. Medial aspect.

The function of the hand and foot are, however, very different, and the general similarity between them is greatly modified to meet these requirements. Thus the foot forms a firm basis of support for the body in the erect posture, and is therefore more solidly built up and its component parts are less movable on each other than those of the hand. In the case of the phalanges the difference is readily noticeable; those of the foot are smaller and their movements are more limited than those of the hand. Very much more marked is the difference between the metacarpal bone of the thumb and the metatarsal bone of the great toe. The metacarpal bone of the thumb is constructed to permit of great mobility, is directed at an acute angle from that of the index finger, and is capable of a considerable range of movements at its articulation with the carpus. The metatarsal bone of the great toe assists in supporting the weight of the body, is constructed with great solidity, lies parallel with the other metatarsals, and has a very limited degree of mobility. The carpus is small in proportion to the rest of the hand, is placed in line with the forearm, and forms a transverse arch, the concavity of which constitutes a bed for the Flexor tendons and the palmar vessels and nerves. The tarsus forms a considerable part of the foot, and is placed at right angles to the leg, a position which is almost peculiar to man, and has relation to his erect posture. In order to allow of their supporting the weight of the body with the least expenditure of material the tarsus and a part of the metatarsus are constructed in a series of arches (Figs. 345, 346), the disposition of which will be considered after the articulations of the foot have been described.

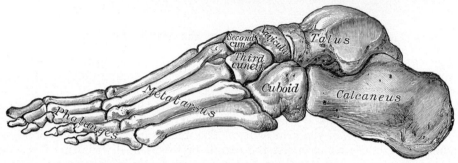

FIG. 346.—Skeleton of foot. Lateral aspect.

The Sesamoid Bones (Ossa Sesamoidea).

Sesamoid bones are small more or less rounded masses embedded in certain tendons and usually related to joint surfaces. Their functions probably are to modify pressure, to diminish friction, and occasionally to alter the direction of a muscle pull. That they are not developed to meet certain physical requirements in the adult is evidenced by the fact that they are present as cartilaginous nodules in the fetus, and in greater numbers than in the adult. They must be regarded, according to Thilenius, as integral parts of the skeleton phylogenetically inherited. Physical necessities probably come into play in selecting and in regulating the degree of development of the original cartilaginous nodules. Nevertheless, irregular nodules of bone may appear as the result of intermittent pressure in certain regions, e. g., the "rider's bone," which is occasionally developed in the Adductor muscles of the thigh.

Sesamoid bones are invested by the fibrous tissue of the tendons, except on the surfaces in contact with the parts over which they glide, where they present smooth articular facets.

In the upper extremity the sesamoid bones of the joints are found only on the palmar surface of the hand. Two, of which the medial is the the larger, are constant at the metacarpophalangeal joint of the thumb; one is frequently present in the corresponding joint of the little finger, and one (or two) in the same joint of the index finger. Sesamoid bones are also found occasionally at the metacarpophalangeal joints of the middle and ring fingers, at the interphalangeal joint of the thumb and at the distal interphalangeal joint of the index finger.

In the lower extremity the largest sesamoid bone of the joints is the patella, developed in the tendon of the Quadriceps femoris. On the plantar aspect of the foot, two, of which the medial is the larger, are always present at the metatarsophalangeal joint of the great toe; one sometimes at the metatarsophalangeal joints of the second and fifth toes, one occasionally at the corresponding joint of the third and fourth toes, and one at the interphalangeal joint of the great toe.

Sesamoid bones apart from joints are seldom found in the tendons of the upper limb; one is sometimes seen in the tendon of the Biceps brachii opposite the radial tuberosity. They are, however, present in several of the tendons of the lower limb, viz., one in the tendon of the Peronæus longus, where it glides on the cuboid; one, appearing late in life, in the tendon of the Tibialis anterior, opposite the smooth facet of the first cuneiform bone; one in the tendon of the Tibialis posterior, opposite the medial side of the head of the talus; one in the lateral head of the Gastrocnemius, behind the lateral condyle of the femur; and one in the tendon of the Psoas major, where it glides over the pubis. Sesamoid bones are found occasionally in the tendon of the Glutæus maximus, as it passes over the greater trochanter, and in the tendons which wind around the medial and lateral malleoli.

HISTOLOGICAL STRUCTURE OF CONNECTIVE TISSUES.

The connective tissues include the connecting and supporting tissues in all parts of the body except the central nervous system. Every organ has its capsule or stroma of connective tissue, and the entire body is supported by the skeleton. The muscles are particularly closely associated with the connective tissues because the latter make it possible for the muscles to perform their functions. Thus, the bones are the rigid levers, they are made movable by the joints, and the force of muscular contraction is transmitted to them by the tendons. The connective tissues are composed largely of intercellular material. They are classified according to the character of this intercellular matrix, and their particular mechanical properties are based upon it.

Bone has a tough fibrous matrix which has been made rigid by the deposit of mineral salts. It can withstand the stress of either compression or tension to a remarkable degree.

Cartilage has a firm, more or less solid, but elastic matrix which may or may not have fibers imbedded in it. It withstands compression especially well and tension to a considerable extent.

Fibrous connective tissue has many varieties which involve the relative concentrations of the different kinds of fibers and the fluid ground substance. They are: (1) dense fibrous, (a) organized or (b) unorganized; (2) loose fibrous, (a) fibroelastic, (b) fibroareolar, (c) adipose, and (d) reticular.

Dense fibrous connective tissue occurs either organized into specific organs such as the tendons, aponeuroses, and ligaments, or formed into unorganized bands and membranes of a less specific nature. The *organized fibrous connective tissues* consist of compact parallel bundles of collagenous fibers. They are pliable and inelastic, and are able to withstand great tensional but comparatively small compressional stress. An exception to the inelasticity is found in the large ligamentum nuchæ of some lower animals and the corresponding human ligamenta flava which are composed almost entirely of elastic fibers. In the *unorganized dense fibrous connective tissue* the collagenous bundles are interwoven rather than arranged into parallel bundles. Examples are the periosteum of bones, the corium of the skin, the dura mater, and many of the fascial membranes. This type of fibrous connective tissue is very strong in resisting tensional stress, and it withstands stresses in many directions instead of in one particular direction as in the case of a tendon.

Loose fibrous connective tissue is the most pervasive of all tissues, with the exception of the blood. It has a strong binding power but is very pliable and somewhat stretchable since it contains elastic fibers as well as collagenous bundles, and even the latter are loosely interwoven and easily displaced. Between the fibers there are comparatively wide interstices or *areolæ* which are filled with ground substance

20

or tissue fluid. When this tissue is comparatively strong and closely woven, as in the capsules of organs, it is called *fibro-elastic tissue*. When it is loosely woven and weak, as in the fascial clefts, it is called *fibro-areolar* or *areolar tissue*.

The most delicate connective tissue, that which surrounds individual cells, muscle fibers, or the acini of glands, is composed of very fine fibrils woven into a network, and is called **reticular tissue**. It merges into the fibro-elastic connective tissue of the capsule and stroma of the organs, wherever the smallest units of the organ are grouped into lobules, fasciculi, etc.

The specific cells of fibrous connective tissue, commonly called fibroblasts, usually are quite widely separated and distributed, but in certain parts of the body, and especially in well nourished individuals, the cells are clumped together and each contains a large vesicle of fat. Where these fat cells occur in considerable concentration, the tissue is called **adipose tissue**. Adipose tissue is commonly found as a packing or padding tissue; it fills pockets, rounds out contours, and forms soft cushions.

Tendons are white, glistening, fibrous cords, varying in length and thickness, sometimes round, sometimes flattened, of great tensile strength, flexible, and practically inelastic. They consist of white fibrous or collagenous bundles which are firmly united together and whose fibrils have a parallel course. Except where they are attached, the tendons have a sheath of delicate fibro-elastic connective tissue, and the larger ones have a stroma of thin internal septa as well. They are very sparingly supplied with bloodvessels, the smaller tendons presenting no trace of them in their interior. They are supplied with sensory nerves whose fibers have specialized terminations called the organs of Golgi and which mediate a special stereognostic sensibility.

Aponeuroses are fibrous membranes, of a pearly white color, iridescent, and glistening, which represent very much flattened tendons. They consist of closely packed, parallel, collagenous bundles, and by this characteristic may be differentiated from the fibrous membranes of fascia which have their collagenous bundles more irregularly interwoven. They are only sparingly supplied with bloodvessels.

CARTILAGE

Cartilage is a non-vascular structure which is found in various parts of the body—in adult life chiefly in the joints, in the parietes of the thorax, and in various tubes, such as the trachea and bronchi, nose, and ears, which require to be kept permanently open. In the fetus, at an early period, the greater part of the skeleton is cartilaginous; as this cartilage is afterward replaced by bone, it is called **temporary**, in contradistinction to that which remains unossified during the whole of life, and is called **permanent**.

Cartilage is divided, according to its minute structure, into **hyaline cartilage**, **white fibrocartilage**, and **yellow** or **elastic fibrocartilage**.

Hyaline Cartilage.—Hyaline cartilage consists of a gristly mass of a firm consistence, but of considerable elasticity and pearly bluish color. Except where it coats the articular ends of bones, it is covered externally by a fibrous membrane, the **perichondrium**, from the vessels of which it imbibes its nutritive fluids, being itself destitute of bloodvessels. It contains no nerves. Its intimate structure is very simple. If a thin slice be examined under the microscope, it will be found to consist of cells of a rounded or bluntly angular form, lying in groups of two or more in a granular or almost homogeneous matrix (Fig. 347). The cells, when arranged in groups of two or more, have generally straight outlines where they are in contact with each other, and in the rest of their circumference are rounded. They consist of clear translucent protoplasm in which fine interlacing filaments and minute granules are sometimes present; imbedded in this are one or two round nuclei, having the usual intranuclear network. The cells are contained in cavities in the matrix, called **cartilage lacunæ**; around these the matrix is arranged in concentric lines, as if it had been formed in successive portions around the cartilage cells. This constitutes the so-called **capsule of the space**. Each lacuna is generally occupied by a single cell, but during the division of the cells it may contain two, four, or eight cells.

The matrix is transparent and apparently without structure, or else presents a dimly granular appearance, like ground glass. Some observers have shown that the matrix of hyaline cartilage, and especially of the articular variety, after prolonged maceration, can be broken up into fine fibrils. These fibrils are probably of the same nature, chemically, as the white fibers of connective tissue. It is believed by some histologists that the matrix is permeated by a number of fine

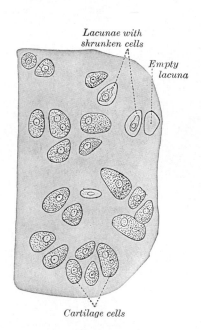

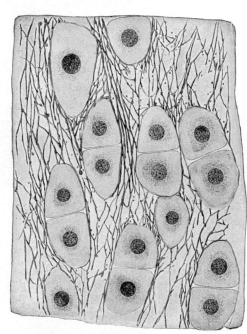

Fig. 347

Fig. 348

Fig. 347.—Hyaline cartilage, 350 ×. (Rauber-Kopsch, *Lehrbuch u. Altas d. Anatomie d. Menschen*, 19th Edition, Vol. I, courtesy of Georg Thieme Verlag, Stuttgart, 1955.)

Fig. 348.—Elastic cartilage from human ear. 1000 ×. (From Rauber-Kopsch. *Lehrbuch u. Altas d. Anatomie d. Menschen*, 19th Edition, Vol. I, courtesy of Georg Thieme Verlag, Stuttgart, 1955.)

channels, which connect the lacunæ with each other, and that these canals communicate with the lymphatics of the perichondrium, and thus the structure is permeated by a current of nutrient fluid.

Articular cartilage, costal cartilage, and **temporary cartilage** are all of the hyaline variety. They present differences in the size, shape, and arrangement of their cells.

In **Articular Cartilage** (Fig. 347), which shows no tendency to ossification, the matrix is finely granular; the cells and nuclei are small, and are disposed parallel to the surface in the superficial part, while nearer to the bone they are arranged in vertical rows. Articular cartilages have a tendency to split in a vertical direction; in disease this tendency becomes very manifest. The free surface of articular cartilage, where it is exposed to friction, is not covered by perichondrium, although a layer of connective tissue continuous with that of the synovial membrane can be traced in the adult over a small part of its circumference, and here the cartilage cells are more or less branched and pass insensibly into the branched connective tissue corpuscles of the synovial membrane. Articular cartilage forms a thin incrustation upon the joint surfaces of the bones, and its elasticity enables it to break the force of concussions, while its smoothness affords ease and freedom of movement. It varies in thickness according to the shape of the articular surface on which it lies; where this is convex the cartilage is thickest at the center, the reverse being the case on concave articular surfaces. It appears to derive its nutriment partly from the vessels of the neighboring synovial membrane and partly from those of the bone upon which it is implanted. Toynbee has shown that the minute vessels of the cancellous tissue as they approach the articular lamella dilate and form arches, and then return into the substance of the bone.

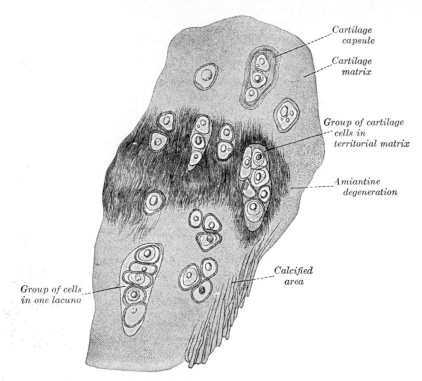

FIG. 349.—Cross section of costal cartilage from an old man. Approx. 400 ×. (From Rauber-Kopsch, *Lehrbuch u. Altas d. Anatomie d. Menschen*, 19th Edition, Vol. I, courtesy of Georg Thieme Verlag, Stuttgart, 1955.)

In **Costal Cartilage** the cells and nuclei are large, and the matrix has a tendency to fibrous striation, especially in old age (Fig. 349). In the thickest parts of the costal cartilages a few large vascular channels may be detected. This appears, at first sight, to be an exception to the statement that cartilage is a non-vascular tissue, but is not so really, for the vessels give no branches to the cartilage substance itself, and the channels may rather be looked upon as involutions of the perichondrium. The xiphoid process and the cartilages of the nose, larynx, and trachea (except the epiglottis and corniculate cartilages of the larynx, which are composed of elastic fibrocartilage) resemble the costal cartilages in microscopic characteristics. The arytenoid cartilage of the larynx shows a transition from hyaline cartilage at its base to elastic cartilage at the apex.

The hyaline cartilages, especially in adult and advanced life, are prone to calcify —that is to say, to have their matrix permeated by calcium salts without any appearance of true bone. The process of calcification, occurs frequently, in such cartilages as those of the trachea and in the costal cartilages, where it may be succeeded by conversion into true bone.

White Fibrocartilage.—White fibrocartilage consists of a mixture of white fibrous tissue and cartilaginous tissue in various proportions; to the former of these constituents it owes its flexibility and toughness, and to the latter its elasticity. When examined under the microscope it is found to be made up of fibrous connective tissue arranged in bundles, with cartilage cells between the bundles; the cells to a certain extent resemble tendon cells, but may be distinguished from them by being surrounded by a concentrically striated area of cartilage matrix and by being less flattened (Fig. 350).

The white fibrocartilages admit of arrangement into four groups—**interarticular, connecting, circumferential,** and **stratiform.**

1. The **Interarticular Fibrocartilages** (*menisci*) are flattened fibrocartilaginous plates, of a round, oval, triangular, or sickle-like form, interposed between the articular cartilages of certain joints. They are free on both surfaces, usually thinner toward the center than at the circumference, and held in position by the attachment of their margins and extremities to the surrounding ligaments. The synovial surfaces of the joints are prolonged over them. They are found in the temporomandibular, sternoclavicular, acromioclavicular, wrist, and knee joints—*i. e.*, in those joints which are most exposed to violent concussion and subject to frequent movement. Their uses are to obliterate the intervals between opposed surfaces in their various motions; to increase the depths of the articular surfaces and give ease to the gliding movements; to moderate the effects of great pressure and deaden the intensity of the shocks to which the parts may be subjected. It should be pointed out that these interarticular fibrocartilages serve an important purpose in increasing the varieties of movement in a joint. Thus in the knee joint there are two

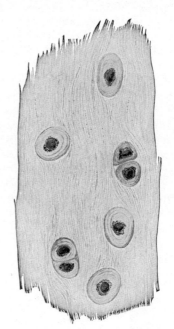

Fig. 350.—Fibrocartilage from human intervertebral disk. (From Rauber-Kopsch, *Lehrbuch u. Atlas d. Anatomie d. Menschen,* 19th Edition, Vol. I, Georg Thieme Verlag, Stuttgart, 1955.)

kinds of motion, *viz.,* angular movement and rotation, although it is a hinge joint, in which, as a rule, only one variety of motion is permitted; the former movement takes place between the condyles of the femur and the interarticular cartilages, the latter between the cartilages and the head of the tibia.

2. The **Connecting Fibrocartilages** are interposed between the bony surfaces of those joints which admit of only slight mobility, as between the bodies of the vertebræ. They form disks which are closely adherent to the opposed surfaces. Each disk is composed of concentric rings of fibrous tissue, with cartilaginous laminæ interposed, the former tissue predominating toward the circumference, the latter toward the center.

3. The **Circumferential Fibrocartilages** consist of rims of fibrocartilage, which surround the margins of some of the articular cavities, *e. g.*, the glenoidal labrum of the hip, and of the shoulder; they serve to deepen the articular cavities and to protect their edges.

4. The **Stratiform Fibrocartilages** are those which form a thin coating to osseous grooves through which the tendons of certain muscles glide. Small masses of fibro-

cartilage are also developed in the tendons of some muscles, where they glide over bones, as in the tendons of the Peronæus longus and Tibialis posterior.

The distinguishing feature of cartilage chemically is that it yields on boiling a substance called **chondrin**, very similar to gelatin, but differing from it in several of its reactions. It is now believed that chondrin is not a simple body, but a mixture of gelatin with mucinoid substances, chief among which, perhaps, is a compound termed **chondro-mucoid**.

BONE

Structure and Physical Properties.—Bone is one of the hardest structures of the animal body; it possesses also a certain degree of toughness and elasticity. Its color, in a fresh state, is pinkish-white externally, and deep red within. If one examines a section cut through a dried bone, one sees that it is composed of two kinds of osseous tissue. One is dense in texture, like ivory, and is termed compact tissue; the other consists of slender spicules, trabeculæ, and lamellæ, joined into a spongey structure which is called, from its resemblance to latticework, cancellous tissue. The compact tissue is always placed on the exterior of the bone, the cancellous in the interior. The relative quantity of these two kinds of tissue varies in different bones, and in different parts of the same bone, according as strength or lightness is requisite. Close examination of the compact tissue shows it to be extremely porous, so that the difference in structure between it and the cancellous tissue depends merely upon the different amount of solid matter, and the size and number of spaces in each; the cavities are small in the compact tissue and the solid matter between them abundant, while in the cancellous tissue the spaces are large and the solid matter is in smaller quantity (Fig. 351).

THE STRENGTH OF BONE COMPARED WITH OTHER MATERIALS

Substance.	Weight in pounds per cubic foot.	Ultimate strength. Pounds per square inch.		
		Tension.	Compression.	Shear.
Medium steel	490	65,000	60,000	40,000
Granite	170	1,500	15,000	2,000
Oak, white	46	12,500[1]	7,000[1]	4,000[2]
Compact bone (low)	119	13,200[1]	18,000[1]	11,800[2]
Compact bone (high)	. . . . . .	17,700[1]	24,000[1]	7,150[1]

[1] Indicates stresses with the grain, *i. e.*, when the load is parallel to the long axis of the material, or parallel to the direction of the fibers of the material.
[2] Indicates unit-stresses across the grain, *i. e.*, at right angles to the direction of the fibers of the material.

Bone during life is permeated by vessels, and is enclosed, except where it is coated with articular cartilage, in a fibrous membrane, the **periosteum**, by means of which many of these vessels reach the hard tissue. If the periosteum be stripped from the surface of the living bone, small bleeding points are seen which mark the entrance of the periosteal vessels; and on section during life every part of the bone exudes blood from the minute vessels which ramify in it. The interior of each of the long bones of the limbs presents a cylindrical cavity filled with marrow and lined by a vascular areolar structure, called the **endosteum**.

Periosteum.—The periosteum adheres to the surface of each of the bones in nearly every part, but not to cartilaginous extremities. When strong tendons or ligaments are attached to a bone, the periosteum is incorporated with them. It consists of two layers closely united together, the outer one formed chiefly of collagenous tissue, containing occasionally a few fat cells; the inner one, of elastic fibers of the finer kind, forming dense membranous networks, which again can be separated into several layers. In young bones the periosteum is thick and very vascular, and is intimately connected at either end of the bone with the epiphyseal cartilage, but less closely with the body of the bone, from which it is separated by a layer of soft tissue, containing a number of **osteoblasts**, by which ossification proceeds on the exterior of the young bone. Later in life the periosteum is thinner and less vascular, and the osteoblasts are converted into an epithelioid layer on the deep surface of the periosteum. The periosteum serves as a nidus for the ramification of the vessels previous to their distribution in the bone; hence the liability of bone to exfoliation or necrosis when denuded of this membrane by injury or disease. Fine nerves and lymphatics, which generally accompany the arteries, may also be demonstrated in the periosteum.

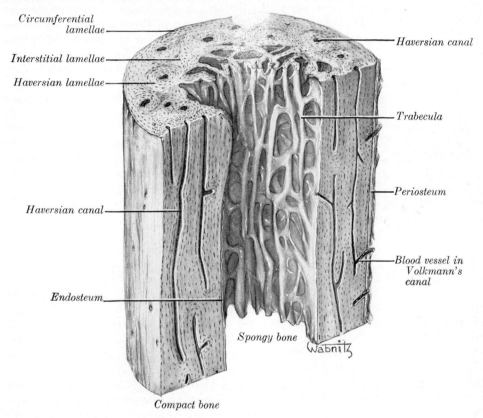

Fig. 351.—Portion of finger bone from which marrow has been removed to show spongy bone. 10 ×

Bone Marrow.—Bone marrow fills the cavities of the bones. **Yellow marrow** is found in the large cavities of the long bones. It consists for the most part of fat cells and a few primitive blood cells. It may be replaced by red marrow in anemia. **Red marrow** is the site for the production of the granular leucocytes (neutrophil, eosinophil, and basophil leucocytes) and the red blood cells (erythrocytes). It is found in the flat and short bones, the articular ends of the long bones, the bodies of the vertebræ, the cranial diploe, and the sternum and ribs. It consists, for the most part, of myeloid cells, namely, primitive blood cells, immature stages and many mature ones. Macrophages, fat cells and megakaryocytes (giant cells) are always present. Both types of marrow have a supporting connective tissue and numerous bloodvessels. Thin-walled sinusoids are supposed to connect the terminal arterioles with the veins in the red bone marrow. Great numbers of mature blood cells (both red and white) pass into the blood stream. The mechanism whereby the mature cells escape into the blood stream and immature ones are held back is not known. *Osteoclasts* large, multinucleated, protoplasmic masses, are to be found in both sorts of adult marrow, but more particularly in red marrow. They were believed to be concerned in the absorption of bone matrix, and to excavate in the bone small shallow pits or cavities, **Howship's lacunæ**, in which they are often located.

Vessels and Nerves of Bone.—The **bloodvessels** of bone are very numerous. Those of the compact tissue are derived from a close and dense network of vessels ramifying in the periosteum. From this membrane vessels pass into the minute orifices in the compact tissue, and run through the canals which traverse its substance. The cancellous tissue is supplied in a similar way, but by less numerous and larger vessels, which, perforating the outer compact tissue, are distributed to the cavities of the spongy portion of the bone. In the long bones, numerous apertures may be seen at the ends near the articular surfaces; some of these give passage to the arteries of the larger set of vessels referred to; but the most numerous and largest apertures are for some of the veins of the cancellous tissue, which emerge apart from the arteries. The marrow in the body of a long bone is supplied by one large artery (or sometimes more), which enters the bone at the nutrient foramen (situated in most cases near the center of the body), and perforates obliquely the compact structure. The *medullary* or *nutrient* artery, usually accompanied by one or two veins, sends branches upward and downward, which ramify in the marrow and give twigs to the adjoining canals. The ramifications of this vessel anastomose with

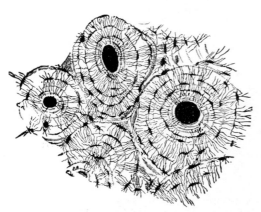

Fig. 352.—Transverse section of compact tissue bone. Magnified. (Sharpey.)

the arteries of the cancellous and compact tissues. In most of the flat, and in many of the short spongy bones, one or more large apertures are observed, which transmit to the central parts of the bone vessels corresponding to the nutrient arteries and veins. The **veins** emerge from the long bones in three places (Kölliker): (1) one or two large veins accompany the artery; (2) numerous large and small veins emerge at the articular extremities; (3) many small veins pass out of the compact substance. In the flat cranial bones the veins are large, very numerous, and run in tortuous canals in the diploic tissue, the sides of the canals being formed by thin lamellæ of bone, perforated here and there for the passage of branches from the adjacent cancelli. The same condition is also found in all cancellous tissue, the veins being enclosed and supported by osseous material, and having exceedingly thin coats. When a bone is divided, the vessels remain patulous, and do not contract in the canals in which they are contained. **Lymphatic vessels**, in addition to those found in the periosteum, have been traced by Cruikshank into the substance of bone, and Klein describes them as running in the Haversian canals. **Nerves** are distributed freely to the periosteum. and accompany the nutrient arteries into the interior of the bone. They are said by Kölliker to be most numerous in the articular extremities of the long bones, in the vertebræ, and in the larger flat bones.

Minute Anatomy.—A transverse section of dense bone may be cut with a saw and ground down until it is sufficiently thin (Figs. 352).

If this be examined with a rather low power the bone will be seen to be mapped out into a number of circular districts each consisting of a central hole surrounded by a number of concentric rings. These districts are termed **Haversian systems**;

the central hole is an **Haversian canal,** and the rings are layers of bony tissue arranged concentrically around the central canal, and termed **lamellæ.** Moreover, on closer examination it will be found that between these lamellæ, and therefore also arranged concentrically around the central canal, are a number of little dark spots, the **lacunæ,** and that these lacunæ are connected with each other and with the central Haversian canal by a number of fine dark lines, which radiate like the spokes of a wheel and are called **canaliculi.** Filling in the irregular intervals which are left between these circular systems are other lamellæ, with their lacunæ and canaliculi running in various directions, but more or less curved (Fig. 351); they are termed **interstitial lamellæ.** Again, other lamellæ, found on the surface of the bone, are arranged parallel to its circumference; they are termed **circumferential,** or by some authors **primary** or **fundamental lamellæ,** to distinguish them from those laid down around the axes of the Haversian canals, which are then termed **secondary** or **special lamellæ** (Fig. 351).

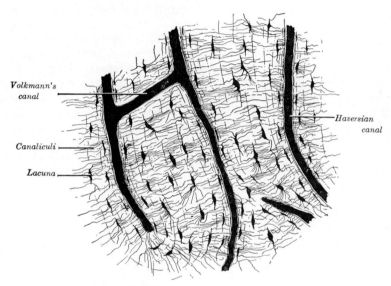

Fig. 353.—Longitudinal section of compact bone tissue. Magnified.

The **Haversian canals,** seen in a transverse section of bone as round holes at or about the center of each Haversian system, may be demonstrated to be true canals if a longitudinal section be made (Fig. 353). It will then be seen that the canals run parallel with the longitudinal axis of the bone for a short distance and then branch and communicate. They vary considerably in size, some being as much as 0.12 mm. in diameter; the average size is, however, about 0.05 mm. Near the medullary cavity the canals are larger than those near the surface of the bone. Each canal contains one or two bloodvessels, with a small quantity of delicate connective tissue and some nerve filaments. In the larger ones there are also lymphatic vessels, and cells with branching processes which communicate, through the canalculi, with the branched processes of certain bone cells in the substance of the bone. Those canals near the surface of the bone open upon it by minute orifices, and those near the medullary cavity open in the same way into this space, so that the whole of the bone is permeated by a system of bloodvessels running through the bony canals in the centers of the Haversian systems.

The **lamellæ** are thin plates of bony tissue encircling the central canal, and may be compared, for the sake of illustration, to a number of sheets of paper pasted one over another around a central hollow cylinder. After macerating a piece of bone in dilute mineral acid, these lamellæ may be stripped off in a longitudinal direction as thin films. If one of these be examined with a high power of the microscope, it will be found to be composed of a finely reticular structure, made up of very slender transparent fibers, decussating obliquely; and coalescing at the points of intersection; these fibers are composed of fine fibrils identical with those of white connective tissue. The intercellular matrix between the fibers is impregnated by calcareous deposit which the acid dissolves. In many places the various lamellæ may be seen to be held together by tapering fibers, which run obliquely through them, pinning or bolting them together; they were first described by Sharpey, and were named by him **perforating fibers.**

The **Lacunæ** are situated between the lamellæ, and consist of a number of oblong spaces. In an ordinary microscopic section, viewed by transmitted light, they appear as fusiform opaque spots. Each lacuna is occupied during life by a branched cell, termed a **bone-cell** or **bone-corpuscle,** the processes from which extend into the canaliculi (Fig. 354).

The **Canaliculi** are exceedingly minute channels, crossing the lamellæ and connecting the lacunæ with neighboring lacunæ and also with the Haversian canal. From the Haversian canal a number of canaliculi are given off, which radiate from it, and open into the first set of lacunæ between the first and second lamellæ. From these lacunæ a second set of canaliculi is given off; these run outward to the next series of lacunæ, and so on until the periphery of the Haversian system is reached; here the canaliculi given off from the last series of lacunæ do not as a rule communicate with the lacunæ of neighboring Haversian systems, but after passing outward for a short distance form loops and return to their own lacunæ. Thus every part of an Haversian system is supplied with nutrient fluids derived from the vessels in the Haversian canal and distributed through the canaliculi and lacunæ.

The **bone cells** are contained in the lacunæ, which, however, they do not completely fill. They are flattened nucleated branched cells, homologous with those of connective tissue; the branches, especially in young bones, pass into the canaliculi from the lacunæ.

In thin plates of bone (as in the walls of the spaces of cancellous tissue) the Haversian canals are absent, and the canaliculi open into the spaces of the cancellous tissue (medullary spaces), which thus have the same function as the Haversian canals.

Chemical Composition.—Bone consists of an animal and an earthy part intimately combined together.

The animal part may be obtained by immersing a bone for a considerable time in dilute mineral acid, after which process the bone comes out exactly the same shape as before, but perfectly flexible, so that a long bone (one of the ribs, for example) can easily be tied in a knot. If now a transverse section is made the same general arrangement of the Haversian canals, lamellæ, lacunæ, and canaliculi is seen.

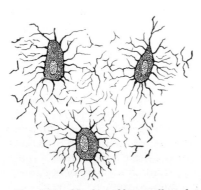

FIG. 354.—Nucleated bone cells and their processes, contained in the bone lacunæ and their canaliculi respectively. From a section through the vertebra of an adult mouse. (Klein and Noble Smith.)

The earthy part may be separately obtained by calcination, by which the animal matter is completely burnt out. The bone will still retain its original form, but it will be white and brittle, will have lost about one-third of its original weight, and will crumble down with the slightest force. The earthy matter is composed chiefly of calcium phosphate, about 58 per cent. of the weight of the bone, calcium carbonate about 7 per cent., calcium fluoride and magnesium phosphate from 1 to 2 per cent. each and sodium chloride less than 1 per cent.; they confer on bone its hardness and rigidity, while the animal matter (*ossein*) determines its tenacity.

Ossification.—Some bones are preceded by membrane, such as those forming the roof and sides of the skull; others, such as the bones of the limbs, are preceded by rods of cartilage. Hence two kinds of ossification are described: the **intra-membranous** and the **intracartilaginous.**

INTRAMEMBRANOUS OSSIFICATION.—In the case of bones which are developed in membrane, no cartilaginous mould precedes the appearance of the bony tissue. The membrane which occupies the place of the future bone is of the nature of connective tissue, and ultimately forms the periosteum; it is composed of fibers and granular cells in a matrix. The peripheral portion is more fibrous, while, in the interior the cells or *osteoblasts* predominate; the whole tissue is richly supplied with bloodvessels. At the outset of the process of bone formation a little network of spicules is noticed radiating from the point or center of ossification. These rays consist at their growing points of a network of fine clear fibers and granular corpuscles with an intervening ground substance. The fibers are termed **osteogenetic fibers,** and are made up of fine fibrils differing little from those of white fibrous tissue. The membrane soon assumes a dark and granular appearance from the deposition of calcareous granules in the fibers and in the intervening matrix, and in the calcified material some of the granular corpuscles or osteoblasts are enclosed. By the fusion of the calcareous granules the tissue again assumes a more transparent appearance, but the fibers are no longer so distinctly seen. The involved osteoblasts form the corpuscles of the future bone, the spaces in which they are enclosed constituting the lacunæ. As the osteogenetic fibers grow out to the periphery they continue to ossify, and give rise to fresh bone spicules. Thus a network of bone is formed, the meshes of which contain the bloodvessels and a delicate connective tissue crowded with osteoblasts. The bony trabeculæ thicken by the addition of fresh layers of bone formed by the osteoblasts on their surface, and the meshes are correspondingly encroached upon. Subsequently successive layers of bony tissue are deposited under the periosteum and around the larger vascular channels which become the Haversian canals, so that the bone increases much in thickness.

INTRACARTILAGINOUS OSSIFICATION.—Just before ossification begins the mass is entirely cartilaginous, and in a long bone, which may be taken as an example, the process commences in the center and proceeds toward the extremities, which for some time remain cartilaginous. Subsequently a similar process commences in one or more places in those extremities and gradually extends through them. The extremities do not, however, become joined to the body of the bone by bony tissue until growth has ceased; between the body and either extremity a layer of cartilaginous tissue termed the **epiphysial cartilage** persists for a definite period.

The first step in the ossification of the cartilage is that the cartilage cells, at the point where ossification is commencing and which is termed a **center of ossification,** enlarge and arrange themselves in rows (Fig. 355). The matrix in which they are imbedded increases in quantity, so that the cells become further separated from each other. A deposit of calcareous material now takes place in this matrix, between the rows of cells, so that they become separated from each other by longitudinal columns of calcified matrix, presenting a granular and opaque appearance. Here and there the matrix between two cells of the same row also becomes calcified, and transverse bars of calcified substance stretch across from one calcareous column to another. Thus there are longitudinal groups of the cartilage cells enclosed in oblong cavities, the walls of which are formed of calcified matrix which cuts off all nutrition from the cells; the cells, in consequence, atrophy, leaving spaces called the **primary areolæ.**

SUBPERIOSTEAL OSSIFICATION.—At the same time that this process is going on in the center of the solid bar of cartilage, certain changes are taking place on its surface. This is covered by a very vascular membrane, the **perichondrium**, entirely similar to the embryonic connective tissue already described as constituting the basis of membrane bone; on the inner surface of this—that is to say, on the surface in contact with the cartilage—are gathered the formative cells, the **osteoblasts**. By the agency of these cells a thin layer of bony tissue is formed between the perichondrium and the cartilage, by the *intramembranous* mode of ossification just described. There are then, in this first stage of ossification, two processes going on simultaneously: in the center of the cartilage the formation of a number

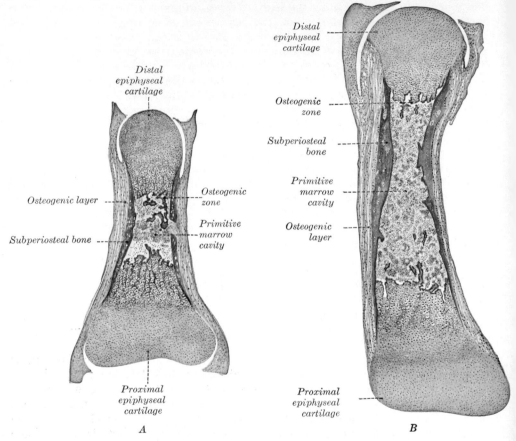

*Distal
epiphyseal
cartilage*

*Distal
epiphyseal
cartilage*

*Osteogenic
zone*

*Subperiosteal
bone*

Osteogenic layer

*Osteogenic
zone*

*Primitive
marrow
cavity*

Subperiosteal bone

*Primitive
marrow
cavity*

*Osteogenic
layer*

*Proximal
epiphyseal
cartilage*

*Proximal
epiphyseal
cartilage*

A   B

Fɪɢ. 355.—Intracartilagenous osteogenesis. Longitudinal section of *A*, middle Phalanx and *B*, proximal phalanx of 5 month human fetus. 20 ×. (From Rauber-Kopsch, *Lehrbuch u. Altas d. Anatomie d. Menschen*, 19th Edition, Vol. I, courtesy of Georg Thieme Verlag, Stuttgart, 1955.

of oblong spaces, formed of calcified matrix and containing the withered cartilage cells, and on the surface of the cartilage the formation of a layer of true membrane bone.

The second stage of the intracartilagenous ossification consists in the prolongation into the cartilage of processes of the deeper or osteogenetic layer of the perichondrium, which has now become periosteum (Fig. 355). The processes consist of bloodvessels and cells—**osteoblasts**, or **bone-formers**, and **osteoclasts**, or **bone-destroyers**. The latter are similar to the giant cells (myeloplaxes) found in marrow, and they excavate passages through the new-formed bony layer by absorption, and pass through it into the calcified matrix (Fig. 356). Wherever these processes come in contact with the calcified walls of the primary areolæ they absorb them, and thus cause a fusion of the original cavities and the formation of larger spaces,

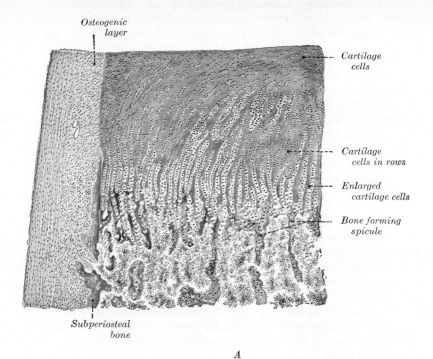

Osteogenic layer

Cartilage cells

Cartilage cells in rows

Enlarged cartilage cells

Bone forming spicule

Subperiosteal bone

A

Enlarged cartilage cells

Marrow cells

Newly formed bone

Calcified cartilage

Osteoblasts

B

Fig. 356.—*A*, Endochondral osteogenesis. Section of osteogenic zone of humerus of seven month human fetus. 40×. *B*, Enodochondral osteogenesis. Part of figure 356*A* more highly magnified. 120×. (Rauber-Kopsch, *Lehrbuch u Atlas d. Anatomie d. Menschen*, 19th Edition, Vol. I, Georg Thieme Verlag, Stuttgart, 1955.)

which are termed the **secondary areolæ** or **medullary spaces.** These secondary spaces become filled with embryonic marrow, consisting of osteoblasts and vessels, derived, in the manner described above, from the osteogenetic layer of the periosteum (Fig. 356).

Thus far there has been traced the formation of enlarged spaces (secondary areolæ), the perforated walls of which are still formed by calcified cartilage matrix, containing an embryonic marrow derived from the processes sent in from the osteogenetic layer of the periosteum, and consisting of bloodvessels and osteoblasts. The walls of these secondary areolæ are at this time of only inconsiderable thickness, but they become thickened by the deposition of layers of true bone on their surface. This process takes place in the following manner: Some of the osteoblasts of the embryonic marrow, after undergoing rapid division, arrange themselves as an epithelioid layer on the surface of the wall of the space. This layer of osteoblasts forms a bony stratum, and thus the wall of the space becomes gradually covered with a layer of true osseous substance in which some of the bone-forming cells are included as bone corpuscles. The next stage in the process consists in the removal of these primary bone spicules by the osteoclasts. One of these giant cells may be found lying in a Howship's foveola at the free end of each spicule. The removal of the primary spicules goes on *pari passu* with the formation of permanent bone by the periosteum, and in this way the medullary cavity of the body of the bone is formed.

This series of changes has been gradually proceeding toward the end of the body of the bone, so that in the ossifying bone all the changes described above may be seen in different parts, from the true bone at the center of the body to the hyaline cartilage at the extremities.

While the ossification of the cartilaginous body is extending toward the articular ends, the cartilage immediately in advance of the osseous tissue continues to grow until the length of the adult bone is reached.

During the period of growth the articular end, or epiphysis, remains for some time entirely cartilaginous, then a bony center appears, and initiates in it the process of intracartilaginous ossification; but this process never extends to any great distance. The epiphysis remains separated from the body by a narrow cartilaginous layer for a definite time. This layer ultimately ossifies, the distinction between body and epiphysis is obliterated, and the bone assumes its completed form and shape. The same remarks also apply to such processes of bone as are separately ossified, *e. g.*, the trochanters of the femur. The bones therefore continue to grow until the body has acquired its full stature. They increase in length by ossification continuing to extend behind the epiphysial cartilage, which goes on growing in advance of the ossifying process. They increase in circumference by deposition of new bone, from the deeper layer of the periosteum, on their external surface, and at the same time an absorption takes place from within, by which the medullary cavities are increased.

The permanent bone formed by the periosteum when first laid down is cancellous in structure. Later the osteoblasts contained in its spaces become arranged in the concentric layers characteristic of the Haversian systems, and are included as bone corpuscles.

The number of ossific centers varies in different bones. In most of the short bones ossification commences at a single point near the center, and proceeds toward the surface. In the long bones there is a central point of ossification for the body or diaphysis: and one or more for each extremity, the epiphysis. That for the body is the first to appear. The times of union of the epiphyses with the body vary inversely with the dates at which their ossifications began (with the exception of the fibula) and regulate the direction of the nutrient arteries of the bones. Thus, the nutrient arteries of the bones of the arm and forearm are directed toward the elbow, since the epiphyses at this joint become united to the bodies before those at the opposite extremities. In the lower limb, on the other hand, the nutrient arteries are directed away from the knee: that is, upward in the femur, downward in the tibia and fibula; and in them it is observed that the upper epiphysis of the femur, and the lower epiphyses of the tibia and fibula, unite first with the bodies. Where there is only one epiphysis, the nutrient artery is directed toward the other end of the bone; as toward the acromial end of the clavicle, toward the distal ends of the metacarpal bone of the thumb and the metatarsal bone of the great toe, and toward the proximal ends of the other metacarpal and metatarsal bones.

REFERENCES

Embryology, Ossification and Growth

Fawcett, E. 1905. Ossification of the lower jaw in man. J. Amer. Med. Assn., *45*, 696–705.

Francis, C. C. 1939. Growth of the human tibia. Am. J. Phys. Anthrop., *25*, 323–331.

Gray, D. J., E. Gardner, and R. O'Rahilly. 1957. The prenatal development of the skeleton and joints of the human hand. Am. J. Anat., *101*, 169–224.

Greulich, W. W. and S. I. Pyle. 1950. Radiographic Atlas of Skeletal Development of the Hand and Wrist. xiii + 190 pages. Stanford University Press, Stanford, California.

Lowrance, E. W. 1955. Roentgenographic record of growth of the femur of the rabbit. Growth, *19*, 247–256.

Mall, F. P. 1906. On ossification centers in human embryos less than one hundred days old. Am. J. Anat., *5*, 433–458.

Noback, C. R. 1954. The appearance of ossification centers and the fusion of bones. Am. J. Phys. Anthrop., *12*, 63–70.

Noback, C. R. 1944. The developmental anatomy of the human osseous skeleton during the embryonic, fetal and circumnatal periods. Anat. Rec., *88*, 91–125.

Noback, C. R. and G. G. Robertson. 1951. Sequences of appearance of ossification centers in the human skeleton during the first five prenatal months. Am. J. Anat., *89*, 1–28.

Pyle, S. I. and N. L. Hoerr. 1955. Radiographic Atlas of Skeletal Development of the Knee. A Standard of Reference. viii + 82 pages. Charles C Thomas, Publisher, Springfield, Illinois.

Sensenig, E. C. 1949. The early development of the human vertebral column. Carnegie Contrib. to Emb., *33*, 21–41.

Sensenig, E. C. 1957. The development of the occipital and cervical segments and their associated structures in human embryos. Carnegie Contrib. Embryol., *36*, 141–152.

Histology and Bone Formation

Arnold, J. S. and W. S. S. Jee. 1957. Bone growth and osteoclastic activity as indicated by radioautographic distribution of plutonium. Am. J. Anat., *101*, 367–418.

Barbour, E. P. 1950. A study of the structure of fresh and fossil human bone by means of the electron microscope. Am. J. Phys. Anthrop., *8*, 315–330.

Bevelander, G., and P. L. Johnson. 1950. A histochemical study of the development of membrane bone. Anat. Rec., *108*, 1–22.

Clark, E. R. and E. L. Clark. 1942. Microscopic observations on new formation of cartilage and bone in the living mammal. Am. J. Anat., *70*, 167–200.

Furuta, W. J. 1949. Demonstration of fibers in the decalcified bone matrix by enzymatic digestion. Anat. Rec., *104*, 309–317.

Gray, D. J. 1941. Length of lacunæ and number of canaliculi in bones of several mammals. Anat. Rec., *81*, 163–169.

Lacroix, P. 1951. The Organization of Bones. Trans. by S. Gilder. The Blakiston Co., Philadelphia. viii + 235 pp.

Newman, W. F., and M. W. 1958. The Chemical Dynamics of Bone Material. The University of Chicago Press, Chicago. xi + 209 pp.

Stillwell, D. L., Jr., and D. J. Gray. 1954. The microscopic structure of periosteum in areas of tendinous contact. Anat. Rec., *120*, 663–678.

Osteology and Physical Anthropology

Basmajian, J. V. 1952. The depressions for the arachnoid granulations as a criterion of age. Anat. Rec., *112*, 843–846.

Du Brul, E. L., and H. Sicher. 1954. The Adaptive Chin. Charles C Thomas, Publisher, Springfield, Illinois. ix + 97 pp.

Evans, F. G. and V. E. Krahl. 1945. The torsion of the humerus: A phylogenetic survey from fish to man. Am. J. Anat., *76*, 303–337.

Goldstein, M. S. 1957. Skeletal pathology of early Indians in Texas. Am. J. Phys. Anthrop., *15*, 299–312.

GREULICH, W. W. and S. I. PYLE. 1950. Radiographic Atlas of Skeletal Development of the Hand and Wrist. Stanford Univ. Press., Stanford. xiii + 190 pp.

HUGHES, E. S. R. and S. SUNDERLAND. 1946. The tibial tuberosity and the insertion of the ligamentum patellæ. Anat. Rec., *96*, 439–444.

KRAHL, V. E. 1948. The bicipital groove: A visible record of humeral torsion. Anat. Rec., *101*, 319–331.

KROGMAN, W. 1941. A Bibliography of Human Morphology, 1914–1939. Univ. Chicago Press, Chicago. xxxi + 385 pp.

LASKER, G. W. 1947. The effects of partial starvation on somatotype: An analysis of material from the Minnesota starvation experiment. Am. J. Phys. Anthrop., N. S., *5*, 323–341.

LOWRANCE, E. W., and H. B. LATIMER. 1957. Weights and linear measurements of 105 human skeletons from Asia. Am. J. Anat., *101*, 445–460.

MERZ, A. L., M. TROTTER, and R. R. PETERSON. 1956. Estimation of skeleton weight in the living. Am. J. Phys. Anthrop., *14*, 589–610.

SHILLER, W. R. and O. B. WISWELL. 1954. Lingual foramina of the mandible. Anat. Rec., *119*, 387–390.

WASHBURN, S. L. 1948. Sex differences in the pubic bone. Am. J. Phys. Anthrop., N. S., *6*, 199–207.

VARIATIONS AND ANOMALIES

FRANCIS, C. C. 1955. Dimensions of the cervical vertebræ. Anat. Rec., *122*, 603–610.

GRAY, D. J. 1942. Variations in human scapulæ. Am. J. Phys. Anthrop., *29*, 57–72.

LANIER, R. R., JR. 1944. Length of first, twelfth, and accessory ribs in American Whites and Negroes; their relationship to certain vertebral variations. Am. J. Phys. Anthrop., N. S., *2*, 137–146.

LANIER, R. R. 1954. Some factors to be considered in the study of lumbosacral fusion. Am. J. Phys. Anthrop., *12*, 363–372.

MOSS, M. L. 1957. Experimental alteration of sutural area morphology. Anat. Rec., *127*, 569–590.

ROCHE, M. B. and G. G. ROWE. 1952. The incidence of separate neural arch and coincident bone variations, a summary. J. Bone and Joint Surg., *34-A*, 491–494.

ROWE, G. G. 1950. Anomalous vertebræ from the lumbosacral column of man. Anat. Rec., *107*, 171–179.

ROWE, G. G. and M. B. ROCHE. 1953. The etiology of separate neural arch. J. Bone and Joint Surg., *35-A*, 102–110.

SAUNDERS, R. L. DE C. H. 1942. The os epipyramis or epitriquetrum. Anat. Rec., *84*, 17–22.

STEWART, T. D. 1954. Metamorphosis of the joints of the sternum in relation to age changes in other bones. Am. J. Phys. Anthrop., *12*, 519–536.

TEBO, H. G. and I. R. TELFORD. 1950. An analysis of the variations in position of the mental foramen. Anat. Rec., *107*, 61–66.

TROTTER, M. 1947. Variations of the sacral canal: Their significance in the administration of caudal analgesia. Current Researches in Anesthesia and Analgesia, *26*, 192–202.

TROTTER, M. and G. S. LETTERMAN. 1944. Variations of the female sacrum: Their significance in continuous caudal anesthesia. Surg., Gyn. and Obst., *78*, 419–424.

VENNING, P. 1956. Radiological studies of variations in the segmentation and ossification of the digits of the human foot. Variation in length of the digit segments correlated with difference of segementation and ossification of the toes. Am. J. Phys. Anthrop., *14*, 129–152.

EXPERIMENTAL

AVERY, G., M. CHOW, and H. HOLTZER. 1956. An experimental analysis of the development of the spinal column. V. Reactivity of chick somites. J. Exp. Zool., *132*, 409–426.

CRELIN, E. S., and M. W. BRIGHTMAN. 1957. The pelvis of the rat: Its response to estrogen and relaxin. Anat. Rec., *128*, 467–484.

EVANS, F. G. and M. LEBROW. 1952. The strength of human compact bone as revealed by engineering technics. Am. J. Surg., *83*, 326–331.

EVANS, F. G., and H. R. LISSNER. 1955. Studies on pelvic deformations and fractures. Anat. Rec., *121*, 141–166.

GILLETTE, R., D. F. MARDFIN, and I. SCHOUR. 1956. Osteogenesis in subcutaneous rib transplants between normal and *ia* rats. Am. J. Anat., *99*, 447–472.

HOROWITZ, S. L., and H. H. SHAPIRO. 1955. Modification of skull and jaw architecture following removal of the Masseter muscle in the rat. Am. J. Phys. Anthrop., *13*, 301–308.

MEDNICK, L. W., and S. L. WASHBURN. 1956. The role of the sutures in the growth of the braincase of the infant pig. Am. J. Phys. Anthrop., *14*, 175–192.

SAWIN, P. B. 1946. Morphogenic studies of the rabbit. III. Skeletal variations resulting from the interaction of gene-determined growth forces. Anat. Rec., *96*, 183–200.

JOINTS AND LIGAMENTS.

THE bones of the skeleton are joined to one another at different parts of their surfaces, and such connections are termed **Joints** or **Articulations**. Where the joints are *immovable*, as in the articulations between practically all the bones of the skull, the adjacent margins of the bones are almost in contact, being separated merely by a thin layer of fibrous membrane, named the **sutural ligament**. In certain regions at the base of the skull this fibrous membrane is replaced by a layer of cartilage. Where *slight movement* combined with great strength is required, the osseous surfaces are united by tough and elastic **fibrocartilages**, as in the joints between the vertebral bodies, and in the interpubic articulation. In the *freely movable* joints the surfaces are completely separated; the bones forming the articulation are expanded for greater convenience of mutual connection, covered by **cartilage** and enveloped by **capsules** of fibrous tissue. The cells lining the interior of the fibrous capsule form an imperfect membrane—the **synovial membrane**—which secretes a lubricating fluid. The joints are strengthened by strong fibrous bands called **ligaments**, which extend between the bones forming the joint.

DEVELOPMENT OF THE JOINTS.

The mesoderm from which the different parts of the skeleton are formed shows at first no differentiation into masses corresponding with the individual bones. Thus continuous cores of mesoderm form the axes of the limb-buds and a continuous column of mesoderm the future vertebral column. The first indications of the bones and joints are circumscribed condensations of the mesoderm; these condensed parts become chondrified and finally ossified to form the bones of the skeleton. The intervening non-condensed portions consist at first of undifferentiated mesoderm, which may develop in one of three directions. It may be converted into fibrous tissue as in the case of the skull bones, a synarthrodial joint being the result, or it may become partly cartilaginous, in which case an amphiarthrodial joint is formed. Again, it may become looser in texture and a cavity ultimately appear in its midst; the cells lining the sides of this cavity form a synovial membrane and thus a diarthrodial joint is developed.

The tissue surrounding the original mesodermal core forms fibrous sheaths for the developing bones, *i. e.*, periosteum and perichondrium, which are continued between the ends of the bones over the synovial membrane as the capsules of the joints. These capsules are not of uniform thickness, so that in them may be recognized especially strengthened bands which are described as ligaments. This, however, is not the only method of formation of ligaments. In some cases by modification of, or derivations from, the tendons surrounding the joint, additional ligamentous bands are provided to further strengthen the articulations.

In several of the movable joints the mesoderm which originally existed between the ends of the bones does not become completely absorbed—a portion of it persists and forms an articular disk. These disks may be intimately associated in their development with the muscles surrounding the joint, *e. g.*, the menisci of the knee-joint, or with cartilaginous elements, representatives of skeletal structures, which are vestigial in human anatomy, *e. g.*, the articular disk of the sternoclavicular joint.

21

CLASSIFICATION OF JOINTS.

The articulations are divided into three classes: **synarthroses** or immovable, **amphiarthroses** or slightly movable, and **diarthroses** or freely movable, joints.

Synarthroses (*juncturæ fibrosæ; immovable articulations*).—Synarthroses include all those articulations in which the surfaces of the bones are in almost direct contact, fastened together by intervening connective tissue or hyaline cartilage, and in which there is no appreciable motion, as in the joints between the bones of the skull, excepting those of the mandible. There are four varieties of synarthrosis: **sutura, schindylesis, gomphosis,** and **synchondrosis.**

Sutura.—Sutura is that form of articulation where the contiguous margins of the bones are united by a thin layer of fibrous tissue; it is met with only in the skull (Fig. 357). When the margins of the bones are connected by a series of processes, and indentations interlocked together, the articulation is termed a **true suture** (*sutura vera*); and of this there are three varieties: sutura dentata, serrata, and limbosa. The margins of the bones are not in direct contact, being separated by a thin layer of fibrous tissue, continuous externally with the pericranium, internally with the dura mater. The **sutura dentata** is so called from the tooth-like form of the projecting processes, as in the suture between the parietal bones. In the **sutura serrata** the edges of the bones are serrated like the teeth of a fine saw, as between the two portions of the frontal bone. In the **sutura limbosa**, there is besides the interlocking, a certain degree of bevelling of the articular surfaces, so that the bones overlap one another, as in the suture between the parietal and frontal bones. When the articulation is formed by roughened surfaces placed in apposition with one another, it is termed a **false suture** (*sutura notha*), of which there are two kinds: the **sutura squamosa**, formed by the overlapping of contiguous bones by broad bevelled margins, as in the squamosal suture between the temporal and parietal, and the **sutura harmonia**, where there is simple apposition of contiguous rough surfaces, as in the articulation between the maxillæ, or between the horizontal parts of the palatine bones.

Schindylesis.—Schindylesis is that form of articulation in which a thin plate of bone is received into a cleft or fissure formed by the separation of two laminæ in another bone, as in the articulation of the rostrum of the sphenoid and perpendicular plate of the ethmoid with the vomer, or in the reception of the latter in the fissure between the maxillæ and between the palatine bones.

Gomphosis.—Gomphosis is articulation by the insertion of a conical process into a socket; this is not illustrated by any articulation between bones, properly so called, but is seen in the articulations of the roots of the teeth with the alveoli of the mandible and maxillæ.

Synchondrosis.—Where the connecting medium is cartilage the joint is termed a synchondrosis (Fig. 358). This is a temporary form of joint, for the cartilage is converted into bone before adult life. Such joints are found between the epiphyses and bodies of long bones, between the occipital and the sphenoid at, and for some years after, birth, and between the petrous portion of the temporal and the jugular process of the occipital.

Amphiarthroses (*juncturæ cartiaginleæ; slightly movable articulations*).—In these articulations the contiguous bony surfaces are either connected by broad flattened disks of fibrocartilage, of a more or less complex structure, as in the articulations between the bodies of the vertebræ; or are united by an interosseous ligament, as in the inferior tibiofibular articulation. The first form is termed a **symphysis** (Fig. 359), the second a **syndesmosis.**

Diarthroses (*juncturæ synoviales; freely movable articulations*).—This class includes the greater number of the joints in the body. In a diarthrodial joint the contiguous bony surfaces are covered with articular cartilage, and connected by ligaments lined by synovial membrane (Fig. 360). The joint may be divided, completely or incompletely, by an **articular disk** or **meniscus,** the periphery of which is continuous with the fibrous capsule while its free surfaces are covered by synovial membrane (Fig. 361).

The varieties of joints in this class have been determined by the kind of motion permitted in each. There are two varieties in which the movement is uniaxial, that is to say, all movements take place around one axis. In one form, the **ginglymus,** this axis is, practically speaking, transverse; in the other, the **trochoid** or **pivot-joint,** it is longitudinal. There are two varieties where the movement is biaxial, or around two horizontal axes at right angles to each other, or at any intervening axis between the two. These are the **condyloid** and the **saddle-joint.** There is one form where the movement is polyaxial, the **enarthrosis** or **ball-and-socket joint;** and finally there are the **arthrodia** or **gliding joints.**

Ginglymus or Hinge-joint.—In this form the articular surfaces are moulded to each other in such a manner as to permit motion only in one plane, forward and backward, the extent of motion at the same time being considerable. The direction which the distal bone takes in this motion is seldom in the same plane as that of the axis of the proximal bone; there is usually a certain amount of deviation from the straight line during flexion. The articular surfaces are connected together by strong collateral ligaments, which form their chief bond of union. The best examples of ginglymus are the interphalangeal joints and the joint between the humerus and ulna; the knee- and ankle-joints are less typical, as they allow a slight degree of rotation or of side-to-side movement in certain positions of the limb.

Trochoid or Pivot-joint (*articulatio trochoidea; rotary joint*).—Where the movement is limited to rotation, the joint is formed by a pivot-like process turning within a ring, or a ring on a pivot, the ring being formed partly of bone, partly of ligament. In the proximal radioulnar articulation, the ring is formed by the radial notch of the ulna and the annular ligament; here, the head of the radius rotates within the ring. In the articulation of the odontoid process of the axis with the atlas the ring is formed in front by the anterior arch, and behind by the transverse ligament of the atlas; here, the ring rotates around the odontoid process.

Condyloid Articulation (*articulatio ellipsoidea*).—In this form of joint, an ovoid articular surface, or condyle, is received into an elliptical cavity in such a manner as to permit of flexion, extension, adduction, abduction, and circumduction, but no axial rotation. The wrist-joint is an example of this form of articulation.

Saddle Joint (*articulatio sellaris*).—In this variety the opposing surfaces are reciprocally concavo-convex. The movements are the same as in the preceding form; that is to say, flexion, extension, adduction, abduction, and circumduction are allowed; but no axial rotation. The best example of this form is the carpometacarpal joint of the thumb.

Enarthrosis (*ball-and-socket joints*).—Enarthrosis is a joint in which the distal bone is capable of motion around an indefinite number of axes, which have one common center. It is formed by the reception of a globular head into a cup-like cavity, hence the name "ball-and-socket." Examples of this form of articulation are found in the hip and shoulder.

Arthrodia (*gliding joints*) is a joint which admits of only gliding movement; it is formed by the apposition of plane surfaces, or one slightly concave, the other slightly convex, the amount of motion between them being limited by the ligaments or osseous processes surrounding the articulation. It is the form present in the joints between the articular processes of the vertebræ, the carpal joints, except that of the capitate with the navicular and lunate, and the tarsal joints with the exception of that between the talus and the navicular.

THE KINDS OF MOVEMENT ADMITTED IN JOINTS.

The movements admissible in joints may be divided into four kinds: **gliding** and **angular movements, circumduction,** and **rotation.** These movements are often, however, more or less combined in the various joints, so as to produce an infinite variety, and it is seldom that only one kind of motion is found in any particular joint.

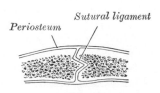

Fig. 357.—Section across the sagittal suture.

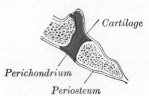

Fig. 358.—Section through occipitosphenoid synchondrosis of an infant.

Gliding Movement.—Gliding movement is the simplest kind of motion that can take place in a joint, one surface gliding or moving over another without any angular or rotatory movement. It is common to all movable joints; but in some, as in most of the articulations of the carpus and tarsus, it is the only motion permitted. This movement is not confined to plane surfaces, but may exist between any two contiguous surfaces, of whatever form.

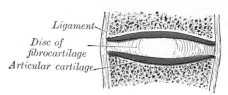

Fig. 359.—Diagrammatic section of a symphysis.

Angular movements increase or decrease the angle between two adjoining bones. Flexion and extension, abduction and adduction are the common examples.

Flexion occurs when the angle between adjoining bones is decreased as when the forearm, hand or fingers are moved forward and upward, the thigh forward and upward, the lower leg backward and upward and the foot upward. In the erect

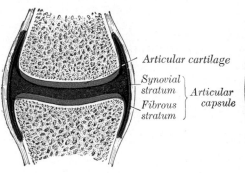

Fig. 360.—Diagrammatic section of a diarthrodial joint.

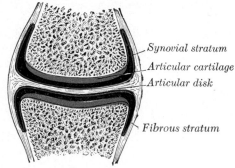

Fig. 361.—Diagrammatic section of a diarthrodial joint, with an articular disk.

posture the foot is normally in flexion. Further flexion is often designated as dorsi-flexion. When the hand is overextended or bent backward the term dorsi-flexion also applies.

Extension occurs when the angle between adjoining bones is increased, as when an arm or a leg is straightened. Extension of the foot is often designated as plantar-flexion.

Abduction occurs when an arm or a leg is moved away from the mid-sagittal plane, or when the fingers and toes are moved away from the median longitudinal axis of the hand or foot.

Adduction occurs when an arm or a leg is moved toward or beyond the mid-sagittal plane or when the fingers or toes are moved toward the median longitudinal axis of the hand or foot.

Circumduction.—Circumduction is that form of motion which takes place between the head of a bone and its articular cavity, when the bone is made to circumscribe a conical space; the base of the cone is described by the distal end of the bone, the apex is in the articular cavity; this kind of motion is best seen in the shoulder- and hip-joints.

Rotation.—Rotation is a form of movement in which a bone moves around a central axis without undergoing any displacement from this axis; the axis of rotation may lie in a separate bone, as in the case of the pivot formed by the odontoid process of the axis vertebræ around which the atlas turns; or a bone may rotate around its own longitudinal axis, as in the rotation of the humerus at the shoulder-joint; or the axis of rotation may not be quite parallel to the long axis of the bone, as in the movement of the radius on the ulna during pronation and supination of the hand, where it is represented by a line connecting the center of the head of the radius above with the center of the head of the ulna below.

In **supination** the radius and ulna are parallel, and palm faces forward or upward.

In **pronation** the radius is rotated diagonally across the ulna and the palm faces backward or downward.

STRUCTURES COMPOSING MOVEABLE JOINTS

Ligaments.—Ligaments are composed mainly of bundles of **collagenous fibers** placed parallel with, or closely interlaced with one another, and present a white, shining, silvery appearance. They are pliant and flexible, so as to allow perfect freedom of movement, but strong, tough, and inextensible, so as not to yield readily to applied force. Some ligaments consist entirely of **yellow elastic tissue,** as the ligamenta flava which connect together the laminæ of adjacent vertebræ, and the ligamentum nuchæ in the lower animals. In these cases the elasticity of the ligament is intended to act as a substitute for muscular power.

The Articular Capsules.—The articular capsules form complete envelopes for the freely movable joints. Each capsule consists of two strata—an **external** (*stratum fibrosum*) composed of white fibrous tissue, and an **internal** (*stratum synoviale*) which is a specialized layer, and is usually described separately as the synovial membrane.

The **fibrous capsule** is attached to the whole circumference of the articular end of each bone entering into the joint, and thus entirely surrounds the articulation.

The **synovial membrane** covers the inner surface of the fibrous capsule, forming a closed sac called the **synovial cavity.** It is composed of loose connective tissue, cellular in some places, fibrous in others, and it has a free surface which elaborates a thick, viscous, glairy fluid, similar to the white of an egg and termed, therefore, **synovia** or **synovial fluid.** The synovial membrane covers tendons which pass through the joint, such as the tendon of the Popliteus in the knee, and the long head of the Biceps in the shoulder. The membrane is not closely applied to the inner surface of the fibrous capsule, but is thrown into folds, fringes, or projections which are composed of connective tissue, fat, and blood vessels. These folds commonly surround the margin of the articular cartilage, filling in clefts and crevices, and in some joints, such as the knee, forming large pads of fat. The synovial cavity of a normal joint contains only enough synovial fluid to moisten and lubricate the synovial surfaces, but in an injured or inflamed joint, the fluid may accumulate in painful amounts. Part of the lining of the synovial cavity is provided by the surface of the articular cartilage which is moistened by the synovia but is not covered by the synovial membrane.

Similar to the synovial cavities of true joints are the synovial tendon sheaths and synovial bursæ which have an inner lining equivalent to the synovial membrane of a joint and are lubricated by a fluid very similar to synovial fluid.

The **Synovial Tendon Sheaths** (*vaginæ mucosæ*) facilitate the gliding of tendons which pass through fibrous and bony tunnels such as those under the transverse carpal ligament of the wrist. These sheaths are closed sacs, one layer of the synovial membrane lining the tunnel, the other reflected over the surface of the tendon.

Synovial Bursæ (*bursæ mucosæ*) are clefts in the connective tissue between muscles, tendons, ligaments, and bones. They are made into closed sacs by a synovial lining, similar to that of a true joint, which may in some cases be continuous through an opening in the wall with the lining of a joint cavity. They facilitate the gliding of muscles or tendons over bony or ligamentous prominences, and are named according to their location, subcutaneous, submuscular, and subtendinous.

Ligamentous Action of Muscles.—The movements of the different joints of a limb are combined by means of the long muscles passing over more than one joint. These, when relaxed and stretched to their greatest extent, act as elastic ligaments in restraining certain movements of one joint, except when combined with corresponding movements of the other—the latter movements being usually in the opposite direction. Thus the shortness of the hamstring muscles prevents complete flexion of the hip, unless the knee-joint is also flexed so as to bring their attachments nearer together. The uses of this arrangement are threefold: (1) It coördinates the kinds of movements which are the most habitual and necessary, and enables them to be performed with the least expenditure of power. (2) It enables the short muscles which pass over only one joint to act upon more than one. (3) It provides the joints with ligaments which, while they are of very great power in resisting movements to an extent incompatible with the mechanism of the joint, at the same time spontaneously yield when necessary.

ARTICULATIONS OF THE TRUNK.

These may be divided into the following groups, viz.:

I. Of the Vertebral Column.
II. Of the Atlas with the Axis.
III. Of the Vertebral Column with the Cranium.
IV. Of the Mandible.
V. Of the Ribs with the Vertebræ.

VI. Of the Cartilages of the Ribs with the Sternum, and with Each Other.
VII. Of the Sternum.
VIII. Of the Vertebral Column with the Pelvis.
IX. Of the Pelvis.

I. Articulations of the Vertebral Column.

The articulations of the vertebral column consist of (1) a series of amphiarthrodial joints between the vertebral bodies, and (2) a series of diarthrodial joints between the vertebral arches.

1. **Articulations of Vertebral Bodies** (*intercentral ligaments*).—The articulations between the bodies of the vertebræ are amphiarthrodial joints, and the individual vertebræ move only slightly on each other. When, however, this slight degree of movement between the pairs of bones takes place in all the joints of the vertebral column, the total range of movement is very considerable. The ligaments of these articulations are the following:

The Anterior Longitudinal.   The Posterior Longitudinal.
The Intervertebral Fibrocartilages.

The Anterior Longitudinal Ligament (*ligamentum longitudinale anterius; anterior common ligament*) (Figs. 362, 373).—The anterior longitudinal ligament is a broad and strong band of fibers, which extends along the anterior surfaces of the bodies of the vertebræ, from the axis to the sacrum. It is broader below than above, thicker in the thoracic than in the cervical and lumbar regions, and somewhat thicker opposite the bodies of the vertebræ than opposite the intervertebral fibrocartilages. It is attached, above, to the body of the axis, where it is continuous with the anterior atlantoaxial ligament, and extends down as far as the upper part of the front of the sacrum. It consists of dense longitudinal fibers, which are intimately adherent to the intervertebral fibrocartilages and the prominent margins of the vertebræ, but not to the middle parts of the bodies. In the latter situation the ligament is thick and serves to fill up the concavities on the anterior surfaces, and to make the front of the vertebral column more even. It is composed of several layers of fibers, which vary in length, but are closely interlaced with each other. The most superficial fibers are the longest and extend between four or five vertebræ. A second, subjacent set extends between two or three vertebræ; while a third set, the shortest and deepest, reaches from one vertebra to the next. At the sides of the bodies the ligament consists of a few short fibers which pass from one vertebra to the next, separated from the concavities of the vertebral bodies by oval apertures for the passage of vessels.

The Posterior Longitudinal Ligament (*ligamentum longitudinale posterius; posterior common ligament*) (Figs. 362, 363).—The posterior longitudinal ligament is situated within the vertebral canal, and extends along the posterior surfaces of the bodies of the vertebræ, from the body of the axis, where it is continuous with the membrana tectoria, to the sacrum. It is broader above than below, and thicker in the thoracic than in the cervical and lumbar regions. In the situation of the intervertebral fibrocartilages and contiguous margins of the vertebræ, where the ligament is more intimately adherent, it is broad, and in the thoracic and lumbar regions presents a series of dentations with intervening concave margins; but it is narrow and thick over the centers of the bodies, from which it is separated by the basivertebral veins. This ligament is composed of smooth, shining, longitudinal fibers, denser and more compact than those of the anterior ligament, and consists of superficial layers occupying the interval between three or four vertebræ, and deeper layers which extend between adjacent vertebræ.

The Intervertebral Disks (*disci intervertebrales; intervertebral fibrocartilages*) (Figs. 362, 374).—The intervertebral disks are interposed between the adjacent surfaces of the bodies of the vertebræ, from the axis to the sacrum, and form the chief bonds of connection between the vertebræ. They vary in shape, size, and thickness, in different parts of the vertebral column. In *shape* and *size* they correspond with the surfaces of the bodies between which they are placed, except in the cervical region, where they are slightly smaller from side to side than the corresponding bodies. In *thickness* they vary not only in the different regions of the column, but in different parts of the same disk; they are thicker in front than behind in the cervical and lumbar regions, and thus contribute to the anterior convexities of these parts of the column; while they are of nearly uniform thickness in the thoracic region, the anterior concavity of this part of the column being almost entirely owing to the shape of the vertebral bodies. The intervertebral disks constitute about one-fourth of the length of the vertebral column, exclusive of the first two vertebræ; but this amount is not equally distributed between the various bones, the cervical and lumbar portions having, in proportion to their length, a much greater amount than the thoracic region, with the result that these parts possess greater pliancy and freedom of movement. The intervertebral disks are adherent, by their surfaces, to thin layers of hyaline cartilage which cover the upper and under surfaces of the bodies of the vertebræ; in the lower cervical vertebræ, however, small joints lined by synovial membrane are occasionally present between the upper surfaces of the bodies and the margins of the disks on either side. By their circumferences the intervertebral disks are closely connected in front to the anterior, and behind to the posterior, longitudinal ligaments. In the thoracic region they are joined laterally, by means of the interarticular ligaments, to the heads of those ribs which articulate with two vertebræ.

Structure of the Intervertebral Disks.—Each is composed, at its circumference, of laminæ of fibrous tissue and fibrocartilage, forming the *annulus fibrosus;* and, at its center, of a soft, pulpy, highly elastic substance, of a yellowish color, which projects considerably above the surrounding level when the disk is divided horizontally. This pulpy substance (*nucleus pulposus*), especially well-developed in the lumbar region, is the remains of the noto-

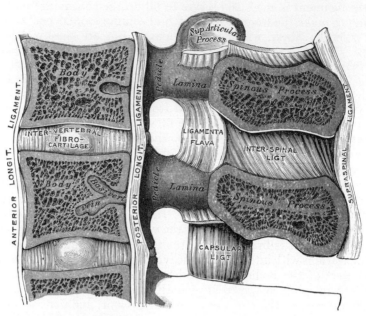

Fig. 362.—Median sagittal section of two lumbar vertebræ and their ligaments.

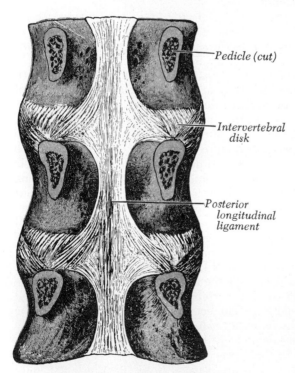

Fig. 363.—Posterior longitudinal ligament of the vertebræ in the lumbar region.

chord. The laminæ are arranged concentrically; the outermost consist of ordinary fibrous tissue, the others of white fibrocartilage. The laminæ are not quite vertical in their direction, those near the circumference being curved outward and closely approximated; while those nearest the center curve in the opposite direction, and are somewhat more widely separated. The fibers of which each lamina is composed are directed, for the most part, obliquely from above downward, the fibers of adjacent laminæ passing in opposite directions and varying in every layer; so that the fibers of one layer are directed across those of another, like the limbs of the letter X. This laminar arrangement belongs to about the outer half of each fibrocartilage. The pulpy substance presents no such arrangement, and consists of a fine fibrous matrix, containing angular cells united to form a reticular structure.

The intervertebral fibrocartilages are important shock absorbers. Under pressure the highly elastic nucleus pulposus becomes flatter and broader and pushes the more resistant fibrous laminæ outward in all directions.

2. **Articulations of Vertebral Arches.**—The joints between the articular processes of the vertebræ belong to the arthrodial variety and are enveloped by capsules lined by synovial membranes; while the laminæ, spinous and transverse processes are connected by the following ligaments: (Fig. 362).

The Ligamenta Flava.
The Supraspinal.
The Ligamentum Nuchæ
The Interspinal.
The Intertransverse.

The Articular Capsules (*capsulæ articulares; capsular ligaments*) (Fig. 362).—The articular capsules are thin and loose, and are attached to the margins of the articular processes of adjacent vertebræ. They are longer and looser in the cervical than in the thoracic and lumbar regions (Fig. 368).

The Ligamenta Flava (*ligmenta subflava*) (Fig. 364).—The ligamenta flava connect the laminæ of adjacent vertebræ, from the axis to the first segment of the sacrum. They are best seen from the interior of the vertebral canal; when looked at from the outer surface they appear short, being overlapped by the laminæ.

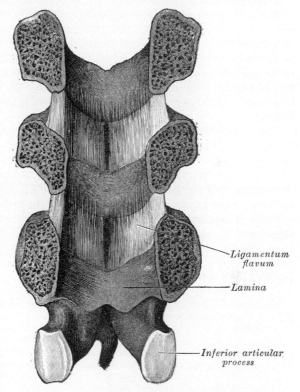

FIG. 364.—The ligamenta flava of the lumbar region. Anterior aspect.

Ligamentum flavum

Lamina

Inferior articular process

Each ligament consists of two lateral portions which commence one on either side of the roots of the articular processes, and extend backward to the point where the laminæ meet to form the spinous process; the posterior margins of the two portions are in contact and to a certain extent united, slight intervals being left for the passage of small vessels. Each consists of yellow elastic tissue, the fibers of which, almost perpendicular in direction, are attached to the anterior surface of the lamina above, some distance from its inferior margin, and to the posterior surface and upper margin of the lamina below. In the cervical region the ligaments are thin, but broad and long; they are thicker in the thoracic region and thickest in the lumbar region. Their marked elasticity serves to preserve the upright posture, and to assist the vertebral column in resuming it after flexion.

The Supraspinal Ligament (*ligamentum supraspinale; supraspinous ligament*) (Fig. 362).—The supraspinal ligament is a strong fibrous cord, which connects together the apices of the spinous processes from the seventh cervical vertebra to the sacrum; at the points of attachment to the tips of the spinous processes fibrocartilage is developed in the ligament. It is thicker and broader in the lumbar than in the thoracic region, and intimately blended, in both situations, with the neighboring fascia. The most superficial fibers of this ligament extend over three or four vertebræ; those more deeply seated pass between two or three vertebræ; while the deepest connect the spinous processes of neighboring vertebræ. Between the spinous processes it is continuous with the interspinal ligaments. It is continued upward to the external occipital protuberance and median nuchal line, as the ligamentum nuchæ.

The Ligamentum Nuchæ.—The ligamentum nuchæ is a fibrous membrane, which, in the neck, represents the supraspinal ligaments of the lower vertebræ. It extends from the external occipital protuberance and median nuchal line to the spinous process of the seventh cervical vertebra. From its anterior border a fibrous lamina is given off, which is attached to the posterior tubercle of the atlas, and to the spinous processes of the cervical vertebræ, and forms a septum between the muscles on either side of the neck. In man it is merely the rudiment of an important elastic ligament, which, in some of the lower animals, serves to sustain the weight of the head.

The Interspinal Ligaments (*ligamenta interspinalia; interspinous ligaments*) (Fig. 362).—The interspinal ligaments thin and membranous, connect adjoining spinous processes and extend from the root to the apex of each process. They meet the ligamenta flava in front and the supraspinal ligament behind. They are narrow and elongated in the thoracic region; broader, thicker, and quadrilateral in form in the lumbar region; and only slightly developed in the neck.

The Intertransverse Ligaments (*ligamenta intertransversaria*).—The intertransverse ligaments are interposed between the transverse processes. In the cervical region they consist of a few irregular, scattered fibers; in the thoracic region they are rounded cords intimately connected with the deep muscles of the back; in the lumbar region they are thin and membranous.

Movements.—The movements permitted in the vertebral column are: *flexion, extension, lateral flexion, circumduction,* and *rotation.*

In **flexion,** or movement forward, the anterior longitudinal ligment is relaxed, and the intervertebral fibrocartilages are compressed in front; while the posterior longitudinal ligament, the ligamenta flava, and the inter- and supraspinal ligaments are stretched, as well as the posterior fibers of the intervertebral fibrocartilages. The interspaces between the laminæ are widened, and the inferior articular processes glide upward, upon the superior articular processes of the subjacent vertebræ. Tension of the extensor muscles of the back is the most important factor in limiting the movement. Flexion is the most extensive of all the movements of the vertebral column, and is freest in the cervical region.

In **extension,** or movement backward, an exactly opposite disposition of the parts takes place. This movement is limited by the anterior longitudinal ligament, and by the approximation of the spinous processes. It is freest in the cervical and lumbar regions.

In **lateral flexion,** the sides of the intervertebral fibrocartilages are compressed, the extent of motion being limited by the resistance offered by the surrounding ligaments. This movement may take place in any part of the column, but is freest in the cervical and lumbar regions.

Circumduction is very limited, and is merely a succession of the preceding movements.

Rotation is produced by the twisting of the intervertebral fibrocartilages; this, although only slight between any two vertebræ, allows of a considerable extent of movement when it takes place in the whole length of the column, the front of the upper part of the column being turned to one or other side. This movement occurs to a slight extent in the cervical region, is freer in the upper part of the thoracic region, and absent in the lumbar region.

The extent and variety of the movements are influenced by the shape and direction of the articular surfaces. In the *cervical* region the upward inclination of the superior articular surfaces allows of free flexion and extension. Extension can be carried farther than flexion; at the upper end of the region it is checked by the locking of the posterior edges of the superior atlantal facets in the condyloid fossæ of the occipital bone; at the lower end it is limited by a mechanism whereby the inferior articular processes of the seventh cervical vertebra slip into grooves behind and below the superior articular processes of the first thoracic. Flexion is arrested just beyond the point where the cervical convexity is straightened; the movement is checked by the apposition of the projecting lower lips of the bodies of the vertebræ with the shelving surfaces on the bodies of the subjacent vertebræ. Lateral flexion and rotation are free in the cervical region; they are, however, always combined. The upward and medial inclinations of the superior articular surfaces impart a rotatory movement during lateral flexion, while pure rotation is prevented by the slight medial slope of these surfaces.

In the **thoracic region,** notably in its upper part, all the movements are limited in order to reduce interference with respiration to a minimum. The almost complete absence of an upward inclination of the superior articular surfaces prohibits any marked flexion, while extension is checked by the contact of the inferior articular margins with the laminæ, and the contact of the spinous processes with one another. The mechanism between the seventh cervical and the first thoracic vertebræ, which limits extension of the cervical region, will also serve to limit flexion of the thoracic region when the neck is extended. Rotation is free in the thoracic region: the superior articular processes are segments of a cylinder whose axis is in the mid-ventral line of the vertebral bodies. The direction of the articular facets would allow of free lateral flexion, but this movement is considerably limited in the upper part of the region by the resistance of the ribs and sternum.

In the **lumbar region** extension is free and wider in range than flexion. The inferior articular facets are not in close apposition with the superior facets of the subjacent vertebræ, and on this account a considerable amount of lateral flexion is permitted. For the same reason a slight amount of rotation can be carried out, but this is so soon checked by the interlocking of the articular surfaces that it is negligible.

The *principal muscles* which produce *flexion* are the Sternocleidomastoideus, Longus capitis, and Longus colli; the Scaleni; the abdominal muscles and the Psoas major. *Extension* is produced by the intrinsic muscles of the back, assisted in the neck by the Splenius, Semispinales dorsi and cervicis, and the Multifidus. *Lateral* motion is produced by the intrinsic muscles of the back by the Splenius, the Scaleni, the Quadratus lumborum, and the Psoas major, the muscles of one side only acting; and *rotation* by the action of the following muscles of one side only, viz., the Sternocleidomastoideus, the Longus capitis, the Scaleni, the Multifidus, the Semispinalis capitis, and the abdominal muscles.

II. Articulation of the Atlas with the Epistropheus or Axis (Articulatio Atlantoepistrophica).

The articulation of the atlas with the axis comprises three joints. There is a pivot articulation, **median atlanto-axial joint,** between the odontoid process of the axis and the ring formed by the anterior arch and the transverse ligament of the atlas (see Fig. 367); here there are two synovial cavities: one between the posterior surface of the anterior arch of the atlas and the front of the odontoid process; the other between the anterior surface of the ligament and the back of the process. Between the articular processes of the two bones there is on either side an arthrodial or gliding joint, **lateral atlanto-axial joint.** The ligaments are:

Two Articular Capsules.
The Anterior Atlantoaxial.

The Posterior Atlantoaxial.
The Transverse.

The **Articular Capsules** (*capsulæ articulares; capsular ligaments*).—The articular capsules are thin and loose, and connect the margins of the lateral masses of the atlas with those of the posterior articular surfaces of the axis. Each is strengthened at its posterior and medial part by an **accessory ligament,** which is attached below to the body of the axis near the base of the odontoid process, and above to the lateral mass of the atlas near the transverse ligament.

The **Anterior Atlantoaxial Ligament** (Fig. 365).—This ligament is a strong membrane, fixed, *above,* to the lower border of the anterior arch of the atlas; *below* to the front of the body of the axis. It is strengthened in the middle line by a rounded cord, which connects the tubercle on the anterior arch of the atlas to the body of the axis, and is a continuation upward of the anterior longitudinal ligament. The ligament is in relation, in front, with the Longi capitis.

The **Posterior Atlantoaxial Ligament** (Fig. 369).—This ligament is a broad, thin membrane attached, *above,* to the lower border of the posterior arch of the atlas; *below,* to the upper edges of the laminæ of the axis. It supplies the place of the ligamenta flava, and is in relation, *behind,* with the Obliqui capitis inferiores.

The **Transverse Ligament of the Atlas** (*ligamentum transversum atlantis*) (Figs. 367, 368, 369).—The transverse ligament of the atlas is a thick, strong band, which arches across the ring of the atlas, and retains the odontoid process in contact with the anterior arch. It is concave in front, convex behind, broader and thicker in the middle than at the ends, and firmly attached on either side to a small tubercle on the medial surface of the lateral mass of the atlas. As it crosses the odontoid

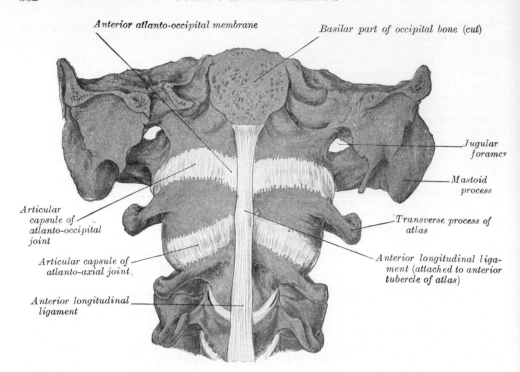

Fig. 365.—The atlantoöccipital and atlantoaxial joints.   Anterior aspect.   On each side a small occasional, synovial joint is shown between the lateral part of the upper surface of the body of the third cervical vertebra and the bevelled, inferior surface of the body of the axis.   The joint cavities have been opened.

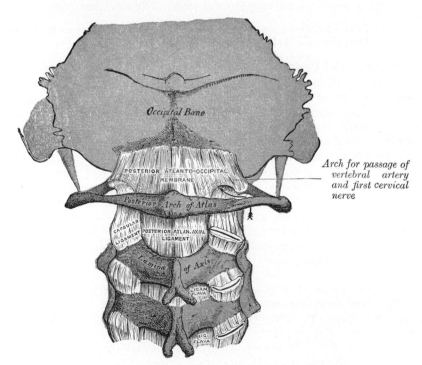

Fig. 366.—Posterior atlantoöccipital membrane and atlantoaxial ligament.

process, a small fasciculus (*crus superius*) is prolonged upward, and another (*crus inferius*) downward, from the superficial or posterior fibers of the ligament. The former is attached to the basilar part of the occipital bone, in close relation with the membrana tectoria; the latter is fixed to the posterior surface of the body

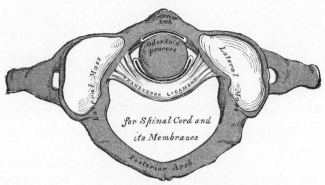

Fig. 367.—Articulation between odontoid process and atlas.

of the axis; hence, the whole ligament is named the **cruciate ligament of the atlas.** The transverse ligament divides the ring of the atlas into two unequal parts: of these, the posterior and larger serves for the transmission of the medulla spinalis and its membranes and the accessory nerves; the anterior and smaller contains

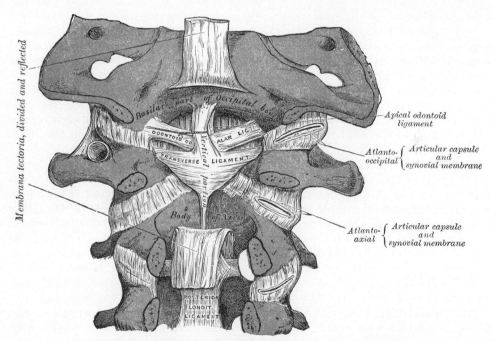

Fig. 368.—Membrana tectoria, transverse, and alar ligaments.

the odontoid process. The neck of the odontoid process is constricted where it is embraced posteriorly by the transverse ligament, so that this ligament suffices to retain the odontoid process in position after all the other ligaments have been divided.

Synovial Membranes.—There is a synovial membrane for each joint; the joint cavity between the odontoid process and the transverse ligament is often continuous with those of the atlanto-occipital articulations.

Movements.—The opposed articular surfaces of the atlas and axis are not reciprocally curved; both surfaces are convex in their long axes. When, therefore, the upper facet glides forward on the lower it also descends; the fibers of the articular capsule are relaxed in a vertical direction, and will then permit of movement in an antero-posterior direction. By this means a shorter capsule suffices and the strength of the joint is materially increased.

This joint allows the rotation of the atlas (and, with it, the skull) upon the axis, the extent of rotation being limited by the alar ligaments.

The principal muscles by which these movements are produced are the Sternocleidomastoideus and Semispinalis capitis of one side, acting with the Longus capitis, Splenius, Longissimus capitis, Rectus capitis posterior major, and Obliqui capitis superior and inferior of the other side.

III. Articulations of the Vertebral Column with the Cranium.

Articulation of the Atlas with the Occipital Bone (*articulatio atlantoöccipitalis*). —The atlanto-occipital joint of each side lies between the superior articular facet of the lateral mass of the atlas and the condyle of the occipital bone; it is condyloid in type. The articular surfaces are reciprocally curved. The ligaments connecting the bones are:

Two Articular Capsules.	The Posterior Atlantoöccipital
The Anterior Atlantoöccipital	membrane.
membrane.	Two Lateral Atlantoöccipital.

The Articular Capsules (*capsulæ articulares; capsular ligaments*).—The articular capsules surround the condyles of the occipital bone, and connect them with the articular processes of the atlas: they are thin and loose (Fig. 368).

The Anterior Atlantoöccipital Membrane (*membrana atlantoöccipitalis anterior; anterior atlantoöccipital ligament*) (Fig. 365).—The anterior atlantoöccipital membrane is broad and composed of densely woven fibers, which pass between the anterior margin of the foramen magnum above, and the upper border of the anterior arch of the atlas below; laterally, it is continuous with the articular capsules; in front, it is strengthened in the middle line by a strong, rounded cord, which connects the basilar part of the occipital bone to the tubercle on the anterior arch of the atlas. This membrane is in relation in *front* with the Recti capitis anteriores, *behind* with the alar ligaments.

The Posterior Atlantoöccipital Membrane (*membrana atlantoöccipitalis posterior; posterior atlantoöccipital ligament*) (Fig. 366).—The posterior atlantoöccipital membrane, broad but thin, is connected above, to the posterior margin of the foramen magnum; below, to the upper border of the posterior arch of the atlas. On either side this membrane is defective below, over the groove for the vertebral artery, and forms with this groove an opening for the entrance of the artery and the exit of the suboccipital nerve. The free border of the membrane, arching over the artery and nerve, is sometimes ossified. The membrane is in relation, *behind*, with the Recti capitis posteriores minores and Obliqui capitis superiores; in *front*, with the dura mater of the vertebral canal, to which it is intimately adherent.

The Lateral Ligaments.—The lateral ligaments are thickened portions of the articular capsules reinforced by bundles of fibrous tissue, and are directed obliquely upward and medialward; they are attached above to the jugular processes of the occipital bone, and below to the bases of the transverse processes of the atlas.

Synovial Membranes.—There are two synovial membranes: one lining each of the articular capsules. The joints frequently communicate with that between the posterior surface of the odontoid process and the transverse ligament of the atlas.

Movements.—The movements permitted in this joint are (*a*) flexion and extension, which give rise to the ordinary forward and backward nodding of the head, and (*b*) slight lateral motion to one or other side. *Flexion* is produced mainly by the action of the Longi capitis and Recti capitis anteriores; *extension* by the Recti capitis posteriores major and minor, the Obliquus superior, the Semispinalis capitis, Splenius capitis, Sternocleidomastoideus, and upper fibers of the Trapezius. The Recti laterales are concerned in the *lateral movement*, assisted by the Trapezius, Splenius capitis, Semispinalis capitis, and the Sternocleidomastoideus of the same side, all acting together.

Ligaments Connecting the Axis with the Occipital Bone.—

The Membrana Tectoria.   Two Alar.   The Apical Odontoid.

The Membrana Tectoria (*occipitoaxial ligament*) (Figs. 368, 369).—The membrana tectoria is situated within the vertebral canal. It is a broad, strong band which covers the odontoid process and its ligaments, and appears to be a prolongation upward of the posterior longitudinal ligament of the vertebral column. It is fixed, below, to the posterior surface of the body of the axis, and, expanding as it ascends, is attached to the basilar groove of the occipital bone, in front of the foramen magnum, where it blends with the cranial dura mater. Its anterior surface is in relation with the transverse ligament of the atlas, and its posterior surface with the dura mater.

The Alar Ligaments (*ligamenta alaria; odontoid ligaments*) (Fig. 368).—The alar ligaments are strong, rounded cords, which arise one on either side of the upper part of the odontoid process, and, passing obliquely upward and lateralward, are inserted into the rough depressions on the medial sides of the condyles of the occipital bone. In the triangular interval between these ligaments is another fibrous cord, the **apical odontoid ligament** (Fig. 369), which extends from the tip of the odontoid process to the anterior margin of the foramen magnum, being intimately blended with the deep portion of the anterior atlantoöccipital membrane and superior crus of the transverse ligament of the atlas. It is regarded as a rudimentary intervertebral fibrocartilage, and in it traces of the notochord may persist. The alar ligaments limit rotation of the cranium and therefore receive the name of **check ligaments.**

In addition to the ligaments which unite the atlas and axis to the skull, the ligamentum nuchæ (page 330) must be regarded as one of the ligaments connecting the vertebral column with the cranium.

IV. Articulation of the Mandible (Articulatio Mandibularis; Temporomandibular Articulation).

This is a ginglymo-arthrodial joint; the parts entering into its formation on either side are: the anterior part of the mandibular fossa of the temporal bone and the articular tubercle above; and the condyle of the mandible below. The ligaments of the joint are the following:

The Articular Capsule.   The Sphenomandibular.
The Temporomandibular.   The Articular Disk.
                    The Stylomandibular.

The Articular Capsule (*capsula articularis; capsular ligament*).—The articular capsule is a thin, loose envelope, attached above to the circumference of the mandibular fossa and the articular tubercle immediately in front; below, to the neck of the condyle of the mandible.

The Temporomandibular Ligament (*ligamentum laterale; external lateral ligament*) (Fig. 370).—The temporomandibular ligament consists of two short, narrow fasciculi, one in front of the other, attached, above, to the lateral surface of the zygomatic arch and to the tubercle on its lower border; below, to the lateral surface and posterior border of the neck of the mandible. It is broader above than below, and its fibers are directed obliquely downward and backward. It is covered by the parotid gland, and by the integument.

The Sphenomandibular Ligament (*ligamentum sphenomandibulare; internal lateral ligament*) (Fig. 371).—The sphenomandibular ligament is a flat, thin band which is attached above to the spina angularis of the sphenoid bone, and, becoming broader as it descends, is fixed to the lingula of the mandibular foramen. Its lateral surface is in relation, above, with the Pterygoideus externus; lower down, it is separated from the neck of the condyle by the internal maxillary vessels; still lower, the

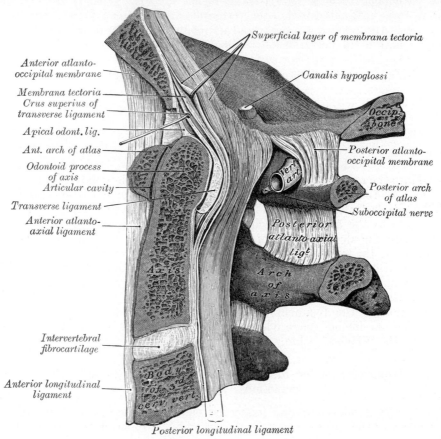

FIG. 369.—Median sagittal section through the occipital bone and first three cervical vertebræ. (Spalteholz.)

interior alveolar vessels and nerve and a lobule of the parotid gland lie between it and the ramus of the mandible. Its medial surface is in relation with the Pterygoideus internus.

The Articular Disk (*discus articularis; interarticular fibrocartilage; articular meniscus*) (Fig. 372).—The articular disk is a thin, oval plate, placed between the condyle of the mandible and the mandibular fossa. Its upper surface is concavo-convex from before backward, to accommodate itself to the form of the mandibular fossa and the articular tubercle. Its under surface, in contact with the condyle, is concave. Its circumference is connected to the articular capsule; and in front to the tendon of the Pterygoideus externus. It is thicker at its periphery, especially behind, than at its center. The fibers of which it is composed have a concentric arrangement, more apparent at the circumference than at the center.

It divides the joint into two cavities, each of which is furnished with a synovial membrane.

The Synovial Membranes.—The synovial membranes, two in number, are placed one above and the other below, the articular disk. The upper one, the larger and looser of the two, is continued from the margin of the cartilage covering the mandibular fossa and articular tubercle on to the upper surface of the disk. The lower one passes from the under surface of the disk to the neck of the condyle, being prolonged a little farther downward behind than in front. The articular disk is sometimes perforated in its center, and the two cavities then communicate with each other.

The Stylomandibular Ligament (*ligamentum stylomandibulare*); *stylomaxillary ligament* (Fig. 371).—The stylomandibular ligament is a specialized band of the cervical fascia, which extends from near the apex of the styloid process of the temporal bone to the angle and posterior border of the ramus of the mandible, between the Masseter and Pterygoideus internus. This ligament separates the parotid from the submaxillary gland, and from its deep surface some fibers of the Styloglossus take origin. Although classed among the ligaments of the temporo-mandibular joint, it can only be considered as accessory to it.

The **nerves** of the temporomandibular joint are derived from the auriculotemporal and masseteric branches of the mandibular nerve, the **arteries** from the superficial temporal branch of the external carotid.

Movements.—The movements in this articulation are the opening and closing of the jaws, protrusion of the mandible, and lateral displacement of the mandible. It must be born in mind that there are two parts to this articulation—one between the condyle and the articular disk, and the other between the disk and the mandibular fossa. When the jaws are opened and closed, motion takes place in both parts; the disk glides on the articular tubercle, and the condyle moves on the disk like a hinge, causing the mandible to rotate about a center of suspension near the angle of the mandible. This somewhat moveable center is provided by the attachment of the spheno-mandibular ligament to the lingula, and the sling formed by the Masseter and the Pterygoideus internus. When the jaws are opened, the angle of the mandible remains more or less fixed in position; the condyle glides forward as the short arm of a lever, and the chin, as the long arm of the lever, describes a wide arc. The motion between the condyle and the articular disk is largely one of accommodation to the change in position. When the jaws are closed, some of the force is applied to the condyle as a fulcrum, especially in biting with the incisors, but in chewing with the molars, the pressure comes more directly between the teeth, the condyle acting as a guide more than as a fulcrum. In protruding the mandible, both disks glide forward in the mandibular fossa, the usual rotation of opening the jaws being prevented by the synergetic action of the closing muscles. In lateral displacement of the mandible, one disk glides forward while the other remains in place. In grinding or chewing movements; there is first a lateral displacement of the mandible by a forward movement of one condyle, and then the mandible is brought back into place by the action of the closing muscles and the meshing of the teeth. The condyles may be displaced alternately, or the same one may be displaced repeatedly as in chewing with the teeth of one side.

The jaws are opened, that is, the mandible is depressed, by the Pterygoideus externus, assisted by the Digastricus, Mylohyoideus, and Geniohyoideus. The jaws are closed, that is, the mandible is elevated, by the Masseter, Pterygoideus internus, and Temporalis. It is protruded by the simultaneous action of the Pterygoidei externi of both sides and the synergetic action of the closing muscles. It is drawn backward by the posterior fibers of the Temporalis, and displaced laterally by the action of the Pterygoideus externus of one side.

V. Costovertebral Articulations (Articulationes Costovertebrales).

The articulations of the ribs with the vertebral column may be divided into two sets, one connecting the heads of the ribs with the bodies of the vertebræ, another uniting the necks and tubercles of the ribs with the transverse processes.

1. **Articulations of the Heads of the Ribs** (*articulationes capitis costæ; costocentral articulations*) (Fig. 373).—These constitute a series of gliding or arthrodial joints, and are formed by the articulation of the heads of the typical ribs with the facets on the contiguous margins of the bodies of the thoracic vertebræ and with the

22

intervertebral fibrocartilages between them; the first, tenth, eleventh, and twelfth ribs each articulate with a single vertebra. The ligaments of the joints are:

The Articular Capsule.   The Radiate.   The Intraarticular.

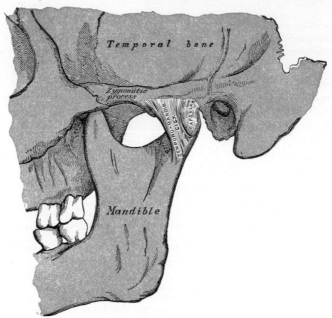

FIG. 370.—Articulation of the mandible. Lateral aspect.

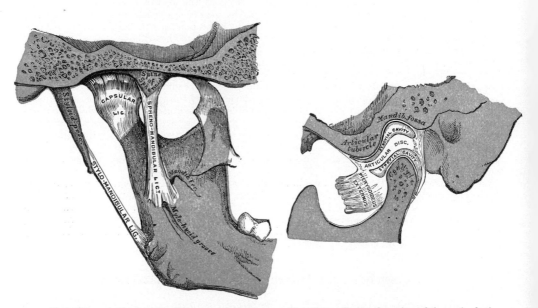

FIG. 371.—Articulation of the mandible.
Medial aspect.

FIG. 372.—Sagittal section of the articulation
of the mandible.

The Articular Capsule (*capsula articularis; capsular ligament*).—The articular capsule surrounds the joint, being composed of short, strong fibers, connecting the head of the rib with the circumference of the articular cavity formed by the intervertebral fibrocartilage and the adjacent vertebræ. It is most distinct at

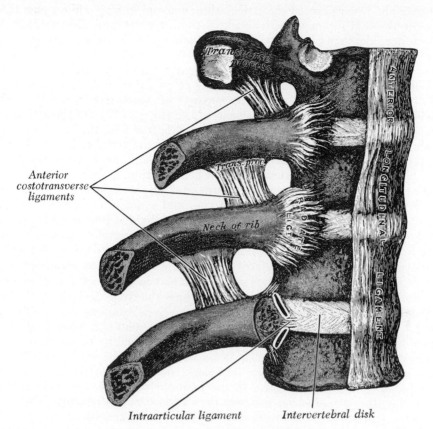

FIG. 373.—Costovertebral articulations. Anterior view.

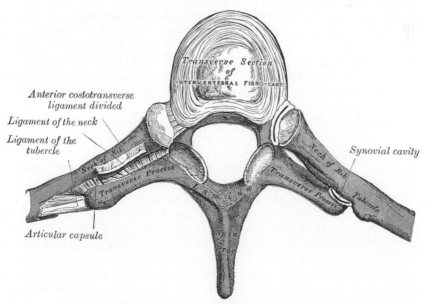

FIG. 374.—Costotransverse articulation. Seen from above.

the upper and lower parts of the articulation; some of its upper fibers pass through the intervertebral foramen to the back of the intervertebral fibrocartilage, while its posterior fibers are continuous with the ligament of the neck of the rib.

The Radiate Ligament (*ligamentum capituli costæ radiatum; anterior costoverte-bral or stellate ligament*).—The radiate ligament connects the anterior part of the head of each rib with the side of the bodies of two vertebræ, and the interverte-bral fibrocartilage between them. It consists of three flat fasciculi, which are attached to the anterior part of the head of the rib, just beyond the articular sur-face. The superior fasciculus ascends and is connected with the body of the verte-bra above; the inferior one descends to the body of the vertebra below; the middle one, the smallest and least distinct, is horizontal and is attached to the interver-tebral fibrocartilage. The radiate ligament is in relation, in *front*, with the thoracic ganglia of the sympathetic trunk, the pleura, and, on the right side, with the azygos vein; *behind*, with the interarticular ligament and synovial membranes (Fig. 373).

In the case of the first rib, this ligament is not divided into three fasciculi, but its fibers are attached to the body of the last cervical vertebra, as well as to that of the first thoracic. In the articulations of the heads of the tenth, eleventh, and twelfth ribs, each of which articulates with a single vertebra, the triradiate arrange-ment does not exist; but the fibers of the ligament in each case are connected to the vertebra above, as well as to that with which the rib articulates.

The Intraarticular Ligament (*ligamentum capitis costæ intraarticulare*).—The intra-articular ligament is situated in the interior of the joint. It consists of a short band of fibers, flattened from above downward. attached by one extremity to the crest separating the two articular facets on the head of the rib, and by the other to the intervertebral fibrocartilage; it divides the joint into two cavities. Each cavity has a synovial membrane. In the joints of the first, tenth, eleventh, and twelfth ribs, the intraarticular ligament does not exist; consequently, there is but one cavity and one synovial membrane in each of these articulations.

2. **Costotransverse Articulations** (*articulationes costotransversariæ*) (Fig. 374).—The articular portion of the tubercle of the rib forms with the articular surface on the adjacent transverse process an arthrodial joint.

In the eleventh and twelfth ribs this articulation is wanting.

The ligaments of the joint are:

The Articular Capsule.	The Posterior Costotransverse.
The Anterior Costotransverse.	The Ligament of the Neck of the Rib.

The Ligament of the Tubercle of the Rib.

The Articular Capsule (*capsula articularis; capsular ligament*).—The articular cap-sule is a thin membrane attached to the circumferences of the articular surfaces, and lined by a synovial membrane.

The Anterior Costotransverse Ligament (*ligamentum costotransversarium anterius; anterior superior ligament*).—The anterior costotransverse ligament is attached below to the sharp crest on the upper border of the neck of the rib, and passes obliquely upward and lateralward to the lower border of the transverse process immediately above. It is in relation, in front, with the intercostal vessels and nerves; its medial border is thickened and free, and bounds an aperture which transmits the posterior branches of the intercostal vessels and nerves; its lateral border is continuous with a thin aponeurosis, which covers the Intercostalis externus.

The first rib has no anterior costotransverse ligament. A band of fibers, the **lumbocostal ligament**, in series with the anterior costotransverse ligaments, con-nects the neck of the twelfth rib to the base of the transverse process of the first lumbar vertebra; it is merely a thickened portion of the lumbocostal aponeurosis or anterior layer of the lumbodorsal fascia.

The Posterior Costotransverse Ligament (*ligamentum costotransversarium posterius*). —The posterior costotransverse ligament is a feeble band which is attached below to the neck of the rib and passes upward and medialward to the base of the transverse process and lateral border of the inferior articular process of the vertebra above.

The Ligament of the Neck of the Rib (*ligamentum colli costæ; middle costotransverse or interosseous ligament*).—The ligament of the neck of the rib consists of short but strong fibers, connecting the rough surface on the back of the neck of the rib with the anterior surface of the adjacent transverse process. A rudimentary ligament may be present in the case of the eleventh and twelfth ribs.

The Ligament of the Tubercle of the Rib (*ligamentum tuberculi costæ; posterior costotransverse ligament*).—The ligament of the tubercle of the rib is a short but thick and strong fasciculus, which passes obliquely from the apex of the transverse process to the rough non-articular portion of the tubercle of the rib. The ligaments attached to the upper ribs ascend from the transverse processes; they are shorter and more oblique than those attached to the inferior ribs, which descend slightly.

Movements.—The heads of the ribs are so closely connected to the bodies of the vertebræ by the radiate and interarticular ligaments that only slight gliding movements of the articular surfaces on one another can take place. Similarly, the strong ligaments binding the necks and tubercles of the ribs to the transverse processes limit the movements of the costotransverse joints to slight gliding, the nature of which is determined by the shape and direction of the articular surfaces. In the upper six ribs the articular surfaces on the tubercles are oval in shape and convex from above downward; they fit into corresponding concavities on the *anterior surfaces* of the transverse process, so that upward and downward movements of the tubercles are associated with rotation of the rib neck on its long axis. In the seventh, eighth, ninth, and tenth ribs the articular surfaces on the tubercles are flat, and are directed obliquely downward, medialward, and backward. The surfaces with which they articulate are placed on the *upper margins* of the transverse processes; when, therefore, the tubercles are drawn up they are at the same time carried backward and medialward. The two joints, costocentral and costotransverse, move simultaneously and in the same directions, the total effect being that the neck of the rib moves as if on a single joint, of which the costocentral and costotransverse articulations form the ends. In the upper six ribs the neck of the rib moves but slightly upward and downward; its chief movement is one of rotation around its own long axis, rotation backward being associated with depression, rotation forward with elevation. In the seventh, eighth, ninth, and tenth ribs the neck of the rib moves upward, backward, and medialward, or downward, forward, and lateralward; very slight rotation accompanies these movements.

VI. Sternocostal Articulations (Articulationes Sternocostales; Costosternal Articulations) (Fig. 375).

The articulations of the cartilages of the true ribs with the sternum are arthrodial joints, with the exception of the first, in which the cartilage is directly united with the sternum, and which is, therefore, a synarthrodial articulation. The ligaments connecting them are:

The Articular Capsules. The Intra-articular Sternocostal.
The Radiate Sternocostal. The Costoxiphoid.

The Articular Capsules (*capsulæ articulares; capsular ligaments*).—The articular capsules surround the joints between the cartilages of the true ribs and the sternum. They are very thin, intimately blended with the radiate sternocostal ligaments, and strengthened at the upper and lower parts of the articulations by a few fibers, which connect the cartilages to the side of the sternum.

The Radiate Sternocostal Ligaments (*ligamenta sternocostalia radiata; chondrosternal or sternocostal ligaments*).—These ligaments consist of broad and thin membranous bands that radiate from the front and back of the sternal ends of the cartilages of the true ribs to the anterior and posterior surfaces of the sternum. They are composed of fasciculi which pass in different directions. The **superior fasciculi** ascend obliquely, the **inferior fasciculi** descend obliquely, and the **middle fasciculi** run horizontally. The superficial fibers are the longest; they intermingle with the fibers of the ligaments above and below them, with those of the opposite

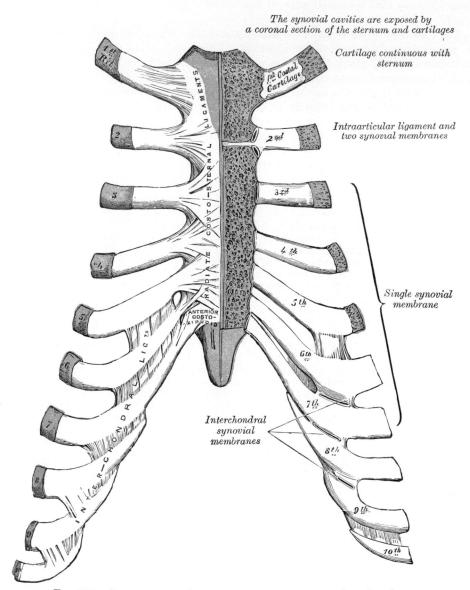

FIG. 375.—Sternocostal and interchondral articulations. Anterior view.

side, and in front with the tendinous fibers of origin of the Pectoralis major, forming a thick fibrous membrane (**membrana sterni**) which envelopes the sternum. This is more distinct at the lower than at the upper part of the bone.

The Intra-articular Sternocostal Ligament (*ligamentum sternocostale intraarticulare; interarticular chondrosternal ligament*).—This ligament is found constantly only between the second costal cartilages and the sternum. The cartilage of the *second* *rib* is connected with the sternum by means of an intra-articular ligament, attached by one end to the cartilage of the rib, and by the other to the fibrocartilage which unites the manubrium and body of the sternum. This articulation is provided with two synovial membranes. Occasionally the cartilage of the *third rib* is connected with the first and second pieces of the body of the sternum by an interarticular ligament. Still more rarely, similar ligaments are found in the other four joints of the series. In the lower two the ligament sometimes completely obliterates the cavity, so as to convert the articulation into an amphiarthrosis.

The Costoxiphoid Ligaments (*ligamenta costoxiphoidea; chondroxiphoid ligaments*). —These ligaments connect the anterior and posterior surfaces of the seventh costal cartilage, and sometimes those of the sixth, to the front and back of the xiphoid process. They vary in length and breadth in different subjects; those on the back of the joint are less distinct than those in front.

Synovial Membranes.—There is no synovial membrane between the first costal cartilage and the sternum, as this cartilage is directly continuous with the manubrium. There are two in the articulation of the second costal cartilage and generally one in each of the other joints; but those of the sixth and seventh sternocostal joints are sometimes absent; where an intra-articular ligament is present, there are two synovial cavities. After middle life the articular surfaces lose their polish, become roughened, and the synovial membranes apparently disappear. In old age, the cartilages of most of the ribs become continuous with the sternum, and the joint cavities are consequently obliterated.

Movements.—Slight gliding movements are permitted in the sternocostal articulations.

Interchondral Articulations (*articulationes interchondrales; articulations of the cartilages of the ribs with each other*) (Fig. 375).—The contiguous borders of the sixth, seventh, and eighth, and sometimes those of the ninth and tenth, costal cartilages articulate with each other by small, smooth, oblong facets. Each articulation is enclosed in a thin **articular capsule,** lined by **synovial membrane** and strengthened laterally and medially by ligamentous fibers (**interchondral ligaments**) which pass from one cartilage to the other. Sometimes the fifth costal cartilages, more rarely the ninth and tenth, articulate by their lower borders with the adjoining cartilages by small oval facets; more frequently the connection is by a few ligamentous fibers.

Costochondral Articulations.—The lateral end of each costal cartilage is received into a depression in the sternal end of the rib, and the two are held together by the periosteum.

VII. Articulations of the Sternum.

The **manubriosternal articulation.**—The manubrium is united to the body of the sternum by fibrocartilage. It occasionally ossifies in advanced life. About one-third of the fibrocartilages develop a synovial cavity. The two bones are also connected by fibrous tissue.

The **xiphisternal articulation** between the xiphoid process and the body of the sternum is cartilaginous. It is usually ossified by the fifteenth year.

Mechanism of the Thorax.—Each rib possesses its own range and variety of movements, but the movements of all are combined in the respiratory excursions of the thorax. Each rib may be regarded as a lever the fulcrum of which is situated immediately outside the costotransverse articulation, so that when the body of the rib is elevated the neck is depressed and *vice versa;* from the disproportion in length of the arms of the lever a slight movement at the vertebral end of the rib is greatly magnified at the anterior extremity.

The anterior ends of the ribs lie on a lower plane than the posterior; when therefore the body of the rib is elevated the anterior extremity is thrust also forward. Again, the middle of the body of the rib lies in a plane below that passing through the two extremities, so that when the body is elevated relatively to its ends it is at the same time carried outward from the median plane of the thorax. Further, each rib forms the segment of a curve which is greater than that of the rib immediately above, and therefore the elevation of a rib increases the transverse diameter of the thorax in the plane to which it is raised. The modifications of the rib movements at their vertebral ends have already been described (page 341). Further modifications result from the attachments of their anterior extremities, and it is convenient therefore to consider separately the movements of the ribs of the three groups—vertebrosternal, vertebrochondral, and vertebral.

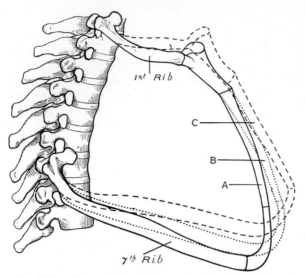

Vertebrosternal Ribs (Figs. 376, 377).—The first rib differs from the others of this group in that its attachment to the sternum is a rigid one; this is counterbalanced to some extent by the fact that its head possesses no interarticular ligament, and is therefore more movable. The first pair of ribs with the manubrium sterni move as a single piece, the anterior portion being elevated by rotatory movements at the vertebral extremities. In normal quiet respiration the movement of this arc is practically *nil;* when it does occur the anterior part is raised and carried forward, increasing the antero-posterior and transverse diameters of this region of the chest. The movement of the second rib is also slight in normal respiration, as its anterior extremity is fixed to the manubrium, and prevented therefore from moving upward. The sternocostal articulation, however, allows the middle of the body of the rib to be drawn up, and

Fig. 376.—Lateral view of first and seventh ribs in position, showing the movements of the sternum and ribs in *A*, ordinary expiration; *B*, quiet inspiration; *C*, deep inspiration.

in this way the transverse thoracic diameter is increased. Elevation of the third, fourth, fifth, and sixth ribs raises and thrusts forward their anterior extremities, the greater part of the movement being effected by the rotation of the rib neck backward. The thrust of the anterior extremities carries forward and upward the body of the sternum, which moves on the joint

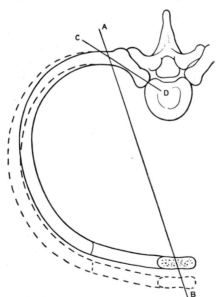

Fig. 377.—Diagram showing the axes of movement (*A B* and *C D*) of a vertebrosternal rib. The interrupted lines indicate the position of the rib in inspiration.

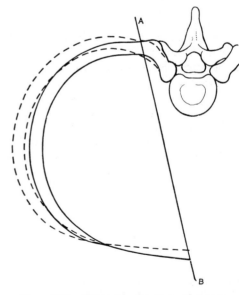

Fig. 378.—Diagram showing the axis of movement (*A B*) of a vertebrochondral rib. The interrupted lines indicate the position of the rib in inspiration.

between it and the manubrium, and thus the antero-posterior thoracic diameter is increased. This movement is, however, soon arrested, and the elevating force is then expended in raising the middle part of the body of the rib and everting its lower border; at the same time the costochondral angle is opened out. By these latter movements a considerable increase in the transverse diameter of the thorax is effected.

Vertebrochondral Ribs (Fig. 378).—The seventh rib is included with this group, as it conforms more closely to their type. While the movements of these ribs assist in enlarging the thorax for respiratory purposes, they are also concerned in increasing the upper abdominal space for viscera displaced by the action of the diaphragm. The costal cartilages articulate with one another, so that each pushes up that above it, the final thrust being directed to pushing forward and upward the lower end of the body of the sternum. The amount of elevation of the anterior extremities is limited on account of the very slight rotation of the rib neck. Elevation of the shaft is accompanied by an outward and backward movement; the outward movement everts the anterior end of the rib and opens up the subcostal angle, while the backward movement pulls back the anterior extremity and counteracts the forward thrust due to its elevation; this latter is most noticeable in the lower ribs, which are the shortest. The total result is a considerable increase in the transverse and a diminution in the median antero-posterior diameter of the upper part of the abdomen; at the same time, however, the lateral antero-posterior diameters of the abdomen are increased.

Vertebral Ribs.—Since these ribs have free anterior extremities and only costocentral articulations with no interarticular ligaments, they are capable of slight movements in all directions. When the other ribs are elevated these are depressed and fixed to form points of action for the diaphragm.

VIII. Articulation of the Vertebral Column with the Pelvis.

The ligaments connecting the fifth lumbar vertebra with the sacrum are similar to those which join the movable segments of the vertebral column with each other —viz.: 1. The continuation downward of the anterior and posterior longitudinal ligaments. 2. The intervertebral fibrocartilage, connecting the body of the fifth lumbar to that of the first sacral vertebra and forming an amphiarthrodial joint. 3. Ligamenta flava, uniting the laminæ of the fifth lumbar vertebra with those of the first sacral. 4. Capsules connecting the articular processes and forming a double arthrodia. 5. Inter- and supraspinal ligaments.

On either side an additional ligament, the **iliolumbar**, connects the pelvis with the vertebral column.

The Iliolumbar Ligament (*ligamentum iliolumbale*) (Fig. 379).—The iliolumbar ligament is attached above to the lower and front part of the transverse process of the fifth lumbar vertebra. It radiates as it passes lateralward and is attached by two main bands to the pelvis. The lower bands run to the base of the sacrum, blending with the anterior sacroiliac ligament; the upper is attached to the crest of the ilium immediately in front of the sacroiliac articulation, and is continuous above with the lumbodorsal fascia. In *front*, it is in relation with the Psoas major; *behind*, with the muscles occupying the vertebral groove; *above*, with the Quadratus lumborum.

IX. Articulations of the Pelvis.

The ligaments connecting the bones of the pelvis with each other may be divided into four groups: 1. Those connecting the sacrum and ilium. 2. Those passing between the sacrum and ischium. 3. Those uniting the sacrum and coccyx. 4. Those between the two pubic bones.

1. **Sacroiliac Articulation** (*articulatio sacroiliaca*).—The sacroiliac articulation is an amphiarthrodial joint, formed between the auricular surfaces of the sacrum and the ilium. The articular surface of each bone is covered with a thin plate of cartilage, thicker on the sacrum than on the ilium. These cartilaginous plates are in close contact with each other, and to a certain extent are united together by irregular patches of softer fibrocartilage, and at their upper and posterior part by fine interosseous fibers. In a considerable part of their extent, especially in advanced life, they are separated by a space containing a synovia-like fluid, and

hence the joint presents the characteristics of a diarthrosis. The ligaments of the joint are:

The Anterior Sacroiliac. The Posterior Sacroiliac.
The Interosseous.

The Anterior Sacroiliac Ligament (*ligamentum sacroiliacum ventralis*) (Fig. 379).—The anterior sacroiliac ligament consists of numerous thin bands, which connect the anterior surface of the lateral part of the sacrum to the margin of the auricular surface of the ilium and to the preauricular sulcus.

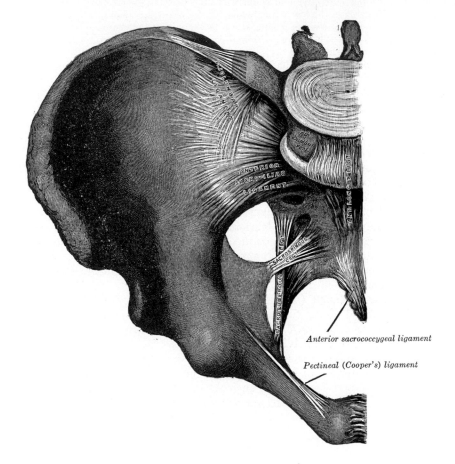

Anterior sacrococcygeal ligament

Pectineal (Cooper's) ligament

Fig. 379.—The joints and ligaments of the right side of the pelvis. Anterior superior aspect.

The Posterior Sacroiliac Ligament (*ligamentum sacroiliacum posterius*) (Fig. 380).—The posterior sacroiliac ligament is situated in a deep depression between the sacrum and ilium behind; it is strong and forms the chief bond of union between the bones. It consists of numerous fasciculi, which pass between the bones in various directions. The upper part (**short posterior sacroiliac ligament**) is nearly horizontal in direction, and passes from the first and second transverse tubercles on the back of the sacrum to the tuberosity of the ilium. The lower part (**long posterior sacroiliac ligament**) is oblique in direction; it is attached by one extremity to the third transverse tubercle of the back of the sacrum, and by the other to the posterior superior spine of the ilium, where it merges with the upper part of the sacrotuberous ligament.

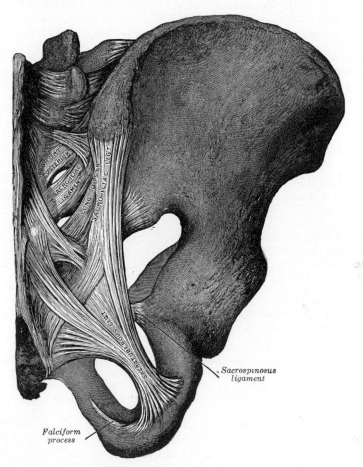

FIG. 380.—The joints and ligaments of the right side of the pelvis. Posterior aspect.

The Interosseous Sacroiliac Ligament (*ligamentum sacroiliacum interosseum*).— This ligament lies deep to the posterior ligament, and consists of a series of short, strong fibers connecting the tuberosities of the sacrum and ilium.

2. **Ligaments Connecting the Sacrum and Ischium** (Fig. 380).

The Sacrotuberous.   The Sacrospinous.

The Sacrotuberous Ligament (*ligamentum sacrotuberosum; great or posterior sacrosciatic ligament*).—The sacrotuberous ligament is situated at the lower and back part of the pelvis. It is flat, and triangular in form; narrower in the middle than at the ends; attached by its broad base to the posterior inferior spine of the ilium, to the fourth and fifth transverse tubercles of the sacrum, and to the lower part of the lateral margin of that bone and the coccyx. Passing obliquely downward, forward, and lateralward, it becomes narrow and thick, but at its insertion into the inner margin of the tuberosity of the ischium, it increases in breadth, and is prolonged forward along the inner margin of the ramus, as the **falciform process,** the free concave edge of which gives attachment to the obturator fascia; one of its surfaces is turned toward the perineum, the other toward the Obturator internus. The lower border of the ligament is directly continuous with the tendon of origin of the long head of the Biceps femoris, and by many is believed to be the proximal end of this tendon, cut off by the projection of the tuberosity of the ischium.

Relations.—The *posterior surface* of this ligament gives origin, by its whole extent, to the Glutæus maximus. Its *anterior surface* is in part united to the sacrospinous ligament. Its *upper border* forms, above, the posterior boundary of the greater sciatic foramen, and, below, the posterior boundary of the lesser sciatic foramen. Its *lower border* forms part of the boundary of the perineum. It is pierced by the coccygeal nerve and the coccygeal branch of the inferior gluteal artery.

The Sacrospinous Ligament (*ligamentum sacrospinosum; small or anterior sacrosciatic ligament*).—The sacrospinous ligament is thin, and triangular in form; it is attached by its apex to the spine of the ischium, and medially, by its broad base, to the lateral margins of the sacrum and coccyx, in front of the sacrotuberous ligament with which its fibers are intermingled.

Relations.—It is in relation, *anteriorly*, with the Coccygeus muscle, to which it is closely connected; *posteriorly*, it is covered by the sacrotuberous ligament, and crossed by the internal pudendal vessels and nerve. Its *upper border* forms the lower boundary of the greater sciatic foramen; its *lower border*, part of the margin of the lesser sciatic foramen.

These two ligaments convert the sciatic notches into foramina. The **greater sciatic foramen** as bounded, in *front* and *above*, by the posterior border of the hip bone; *behind*, by the sacrotuberous ligament; and *below*, by the sacrospinous ligament. It is partially filled up, in the recent state, by the Piriformis which leaves the pelvis through it. Above this muscle, the superior gluteal vessels and nerve emerge from the pelvis; and below it, the inferior gluteal vessels and nerve, the internal pudendal vessels and nerve, the sciatic and posterior femoral cutaneous nerves, and the nerves to the Obturator internus and Quadratus femoris make their exit from the pelvis. The **lesser sciatic foramen** is bounded, in *front*, by the tuberosity of the ischium; *above*, by the spine of the ischium and sacrospinous ligament; *behind*, by the sacrotuberous ligament. It transmits the tendon of the Obturator internus, its nerve, and the internal pudendal vessels and nerve.

3. **Sacrococcygeal Symphysis** (*symphysis sacrococcygea; articulation of the sacrum and coccyx*).—This articulation is an amphiarthrodial joint, formed between the oval surface at the apex of the sacrum, and the base of the coccyx. It is homologous with the joints between the bodies of the vertebræ, and is connected by similar ligaments. They are:

The Anterior Sacrococcygeal.   The Lateral Sacrococcygeal.
The Posterior Sacrococcygeal.   The Interposed Fibrocartilage.
                    The Interarticular.

The Anterior Sacrococcygeal Ligament (*ligamentum sacrococcygeum anterius*).—This consists of a few irregular fibers, which descend from the anterior surface of the sacrum to the front of the coccyx, blending with the periosteum.

The Posterior Sacrococcygeal Ligament (*ligamentum sacrococcygeum posterius*).—This is a flat band, which arises from the margin of the lower orifice of the sacral canal, and descends to be inserted into the posterior surface of the coccyx. This ligament completes the lower and back part of the sacral canal, and is divisible into a short deep portion and a longer superficial part. It is in relation, behind, with the Glutæus maximus.

The Lateral Sacrococcygeal Ligament (*ligamentum sacrococcygeum laterale; intertransverse ligament*).—The lateral sacrococcygeal ligament exists on either side and connects the transverse process of the coccyx to the lower lateral angle of the sacrum; it completes the foramen for the fifth sacral nerve.

A disk of **fibrocartilage** is interposed between the contiguous surfaces of the sacrum and coccyx; it differs from those between the bodies of the vertebræ in that it is thinner, and its central part is firmer in texture. It is somewhat thicker in front and behind than at the sides. Occasionally the coccyx is freely movable on the sacrum, most notably during pregnancy; in such cases a synovial membrane is present.

The **Interarticular Ligaments** are thin bands, which unite the cornua of the two bones.

The different segments of the coccyx are connected together by the extension downward of the anterior and posterior sacrococcygeal ligaments, thin annular disks of fibrocartilage being interposed between the segments. In the adult male, all the pieces become ossified together at a comparatively early period; but in the female, this does not commonly occur until a later period of life. At more advanced age the joint between the sacrum and coccyx is obliterated.

Movements.—The movements which take place between the sacrum and coccyx, and between the different pieces of the latter bone, are forward and backward; they are very limited. Their extent increases during pregnancy.

4. **The Pubic Symphysis** (*symphysis ossium pubica; articulation of the pubic bones*) (Fig. 381).—The articulation between the pubic bones is an amphiarthrodial joint, formed between the two oval articular surfaces of the bones. The ligaments of this articulation are:

The Superior Pubic.   The Arcuate Pubic.
The Interpubic Fibrocartilaginous Lamina.

The Superior Pubic Ligament (*ligamentum pubicum superius*).—The superior pubic ligament connects together the two pubic bones superiorly, extending later ally as far as the pubic tubercles.

The Arcuate Pubic Ligament (*ligamentum arcuatum pubis; inferior pubic or subpubic ligament.*—The arcuate pubic ligament is a thick, triangular arch of ligamentous fibers, connecting together the two pubic bones below, and forming the upper boundary of the pubic arch. *Above*, it is blended with the interpubic fibrocartilaginous lamina; *laterally*, it is attached to the inferior rami of the pubic bones; *below*, it is free and is separated from the fascia of the urogenital diaphragm by an opening through which the deep dorsal vein of the penis passes into the pelvis.

The Interpubic Fibrocartilaginous Lamina (*discus interpubicus; interpubic disk*).— The interpubic fibrocartilaginous lamina connects the opposed surfaces of the pubic bones. Each of these surfaces is covered by a thin layer of hyaline cartilage firmly joined to the bone by a series of nipple-like processes which accurately fit into corresponding depressions on the osseous surfaces. These opposed cartilaginous surfaces are connected together by an intermediate lamina of fibrocartilage which varies in thickness in different subjects. It often contains a cavity in its interior, probably formed by the softening and absorption of the fibrocartilage, since it rarely appears before the tenth year of life and is not lined by synovial membrane (Fig. 381). In front the lamina is strengthened by decussating fibers which pass obliquely from one bone to the other and interlace with fibers of the aponeuroses of the Oblique externi and the medial tendons of orgin of the Recti abdominis.

Mechanism of the Pelvis.—The pelvic girdle supports and protects the contained viscera and affords surfaces for the attachments of the trunk and lower limb muscles. Its most important mechanical function, however, is to transmit the weight of the trunk and upper limbs to the lower extremities.

It may be divided into two arches by a vertical plane passing through the acetabular cavities; the posterior of these arches is the one chiefly concerned in the function of transmitting the weight. Its essential parts are the upper three sacral vertebræ and two strong pillars of bone running from the sacroiliac articulations to the acetabular cavities. For the reception and diffusion of the weight each acetabular cavity is strengthened by two additional bars running toward the pubis and ischium. In order to lessen concussion in rapid changes of distribution of the weight, joints (sacroiliac articulations) are interposed between the sacrum and the iliac bones; an accessory joint (pubic symphysis) exists in the middle of the anterior arch. The sacrum forms the summit of the posterior arch; the weight transmitted falls on it at the lumbosacral articulation and, theoretically, has a component in each of two directions. One component of the force is expended in driving the sacrum downward and backward between the iliac bones, while the other thrusts the upper end of the sacrum downward and forward toward the pelvic cavity.

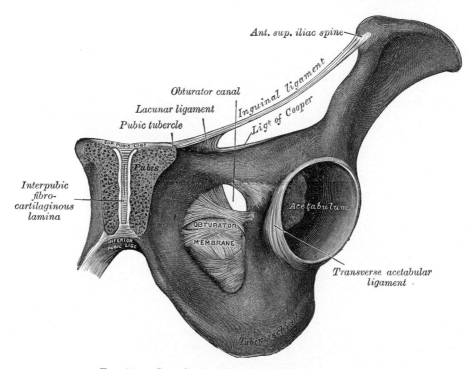

Fig. 381.—Symphysis pubis exposed by a coronal section.

The movements of the sacrum are regulated by its form. Viewed as a whole, it presents the shape of a wedge with its base upward and forward. The first component of the force is therefore acting against the resistance of the wedge, and its tendency to separate the iliac bones is resisted by the sacroiliac and iliolumbar ligaments and by the ligaments of the pubic symphysis.

If a series of coronal sections of the sacroiliac joints be made, it will be found possible to divide the articular portion of the sacrum into three segments: anterior, middle, and posterior. In the **anterior segment** (Fig. 382), which involves the first sacral vertebra, the articular surfaces show slight sinuosities and are almost parallel to one another; the distance between their dorsal margins is, however, slightly greater than that between their ventral margins. This segment therefore presents a slight wedge shape with the truncated apex downward. The **middle segment** (Fig. 383) is a narrow band across the centers of the articulations. Its dorsal width is distinctly greater than its ventral, so that the segment is more definitely wedge-shaped, the truncated apex being again directed downward. Each articular surface presents in the center a marked concavity from above downward and into this a corresponding convexity of the iliac articular surface fits, forming an interlocking mechanism. In the **posterior segment** (Fig. 384) the ventral width is greater than the dorsal, so that the wedge form is the reverse of those of the other segments—*i. e.*, the truncated apex is directed upward. The articular surfaces are only slightly concave.

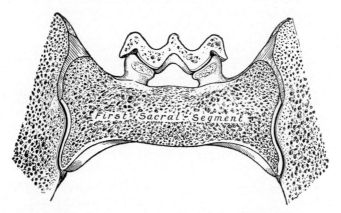

Fig. 382.—Coronal section of anterior sacral segment.

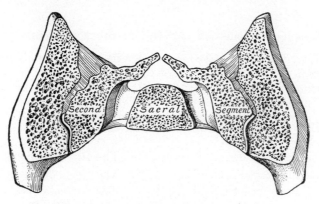

Fig. 383.—Coronal section of middle sacral segment.

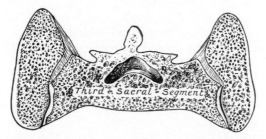

Fig. 384.—Coronal section of posterior sacral segment.

Dislocation downward and forward of the sacrum by the second component of the force applied to it is prevented therefore by the middle segment, which interposes the resistance of its wedge shape and that of the interlocking mechanism on its surfaces; a rotatory movement, however, is produced by which the anterior segment is tilted downward and the posterior upward; the axis of this rotation passes through the dorsal part of the middle segment. The movement of the anterior segment is slightly limited by its wedge form, but chiefly by the posterior and interosseous sacroiliac ligaments; that of the posterior segment is checked to a slight extent by its wedge form, but the chief limiting factors are the sacrotuberous and sacrospinous ligaments.

In all these movements the effect of the sacroiliac and iliolumbar ligaments and the ligaments of the symphysis pubis in resisting the separation of the iliac bones must be recognized.

During pregnancy the pelvic joints and ligaments are relaxed, and capable therefore of more extensive movements. When the fetus is being expelled the force is applied to the front of the sacrum. Upward dislocation is again prevented by the interlocking mechanism of the middle segment. As the fetal head passes the anterior segment the latter is carried upward, enlarging the antero-posterior diameter of the pelvic inlet; when the head reaches the posterior segment this also is pressed upward against the resistance of its wedge, the movement only being possible by the laxity of the joints and the stretching of the sacrotuberous and sacrospinous ligaments.

ARTICULATIONS OF THE UPPER EXTREMITY.

The articulations of the Upper Extremity may be arranged as follows:

I. Sternoclavicular.	VI. Wrist.
II. Acromioclavicular.	VII. Intercarpal.
III. Shoulder.	VIII. Carpometacarpal.
IV. Elbow.	IX. Intermetacarpal.
V. Radioulnar.	X. Metacarpophalangeal.

XI. Articulations of the Digits.

I. Sternoclavicular Articulation (Articulatio Sternoclavicularis) (Fig. 385).

The sternoclavicular articulation is a double arthrodial joint. The parts entering into its formation are the sternal end of the clavicle, the upper and lateral part of the manubrium sterni, and the cartilage of the first rib. The articular surface of the clavicle is much larger than that of the sternum, and is invested with a layer of fibrocartilage, which is thicker than that on the latter bone. The ligaments of this joint are:

The Articular Capsule.	The Interclavicular.
The Anterior Sternoclavicular.	The Costoclavicular.
The Posterior Sternoclavicular.	The Articular Disk.

The Articular Capsule (*capsula articularis; capsular ligament*).—The articular capsule surrounds the articulation and varies in thickness and strength. In front and behind it is of considerable thickness, and forms the anterior and posterior sternoclavicular ligaments; but above, and especially below, it is thin and partakes more of the character of areolar than of true fibrous tissue.

The Anterior Sternoclavicular Ligament (*ligamentum sternoclaviculare anterior*).— The anterior sternoclavicular ligament is a broad band of fibers, covering the anterior surface of the articulation; it is attached *above* to the upper and front part of the sternal end of the clavicle, and, passing obliquely downward and medialward, is attached below to the front of the upper part of the manubrium sterni. This ligament is covered by the sternal portion of the Sternocleidomastoideus and the integument; *behind*, it is in relation with the capsule, the articular disk, and the two synovial membranes.

The Posterior Sternoclavicular Ligament (*ligamentum sternoclaviculare posterius*).— The posterior sternoclavicular ligament is a similar band of fibers, covering the posterior surface of the articulation; it is attached above to the upper and back part of the sternal end of the clavicle, and, passing obliquely downward and medialward, is fixed below to the back of the upper part of the manubrium sterni. It is in relation, in *front*, with the articular disk and synovial membranes; *behind*, with the Sternohyoideus and Sternothyreoideus.

The Interclavicular Ligament (*ligamentum interclaviculare*).—This ligament is a flattened band, which varies considerably in form and size in different individuals, it passes in a curved direction from the upper part of the sternal end of one clavicle to that of the other, and is also attached to the upper margin of the sternum. It is in relation, in *front*, with the integument and Sternocleidomastoidei; *behind*, with the Sternothyreoidei.

The Costoclavicular Ligament (*ligamentum costoclaviculare; rhomboid ligament*).—This ligament is short, flat, strong, and rhomboid in form. Attached below to the upper and medial part of the cartilage of the first rib, it ascends obliquely backward and lateralward, and is fixed above to the costal tuberosity on the under surface of the clavicle. It is in relation, in *front*, with the tendon of origin of the Subclavius; *behind*, with the subclavian vein.

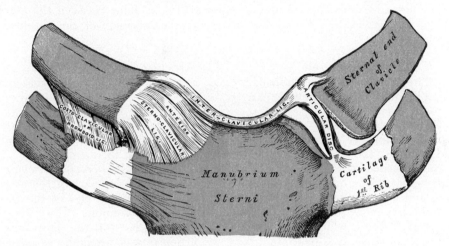

FIG. 385.—Sternoclavicular articulation. Anterior view.

The Articular Disk (*discus articularis*).—The articular disk is flat and nearly circular, interposed between the articulating surfaces of the sternum and clavicle. It is attached, *above*, to the upper and posterior border of the articular surface of the clavicle; *below*, to the cartilage of the first rib, near its junction with the sternum; and by its circumference to the interclavicular and anterior and posterior sternoclavicular ligaments. It is thicker at the circumference, especially its upper and back part, than at its center. It divides the joint into two cavities, each of which is furnished with a synovial membrane.

Synovial Membranes.—Of the two synovial membranes found in this articulation, the lateral is reflected from the sternal end of the clavicle, over the adjacent surface of the articular disk, and around the margin of the facet on the cartilage of the first rib; the medial is attached to the margin of the articular surface of the sternum and clothes the adjacent surface of the articular disk; the latter is the larger of the two.

Movements.—This articulation admits of a limited amount of motion in nearly every direction—upward, downward, backward, forward, as well as circumduction. When these movements take place in the joint, the clavicle in its motion carries the scapula with it, this bone gliding on the outer surface of the chest. This joint therefore forms the center from which all movements of the supporting arch of the shoulder originate, and is the only point of articulation of the shoulder girdle with the trunk. The movements attendant on elevation and depression of the shoulder take place between the clavicle and the articular disk, the bone rotating upon the ligament on an axis drawn from before backward through its own articular facet; when the shoulder is moved forward and backward, the clavicle, with the articular disk rolls to and fro on the articular surface of the sternum, revolving, with a sliding movement, around an axis drawn nearly vertically through the sternum; in the circumduction of the shoulder, which is compounded of

23

these two movements, the clavicle revolves upon the articular disk and the latter, with the clavicle, rolls upon the sternum. Elevation of the shoulder is limited principally by the costoclavicular ligament; depression, by the interclavicular ligament and articular disk. The muscles which *raise* the shoulder are the upper fibers of the Trapezius, the Levator scapulæ, and the clavicular head of the Sternocleidomastoideus, assisted to a certain extent by the Rhomboidei, which pull the vertebral border of the scapula backward and upward and so raise the shoulder. The *depression* of the shoulder is principally effected by gravity assisted by the Subclavius, Pectoralis minor and lower fibers of the Trapezius. The shoulder is drawn *backward* by the Rhomboidei and the middle and lower fibers of the Trapezius, and *forward* by the Serratus anterior and Pectoralis minor.

II. Acromioclavicular Articulation (Articulatio Acromioclavicularis; Scapulo-clavicular Articulation) (Fig. 386).

The acromioclavicular articulation is an arthrodial joint between the acromial end of the clavicle and the medial margin of the acromion of the scapula. Its ligaments are:

The Articular Capsule. The Articular Disk.
The Superior Acromioclavicular. The Coracoclavicular {Trapezoid and
The Inferior Acromioclavicular.   Conoid.

The Articular Capsule (*capsula articularis; capsular ligament*).—The articular capsule completely surrounds the articular margins, and is strengthened above and below by the superior and inferior acromioclavicular ligaments.

The Superior Acromioclavicular Ligament (*ligamentum acromioclaviculare*).— This ligament is a quadrilateral band, covering the superior part of the articulation, and extending between the upper part of the acromial end of the clavicle and the adjoining part of the upper surface of the acromion. It is composed of parallel fibers, which interlace with the aponeuroses of the Trapezius and Deltoideus; *below*, it is in contact with the articular disk when this is present.

The Inferior Acromioclavicular Ligament.—This ligament is somewhat thinner than the preceding; it covers the under part of the articulation, and is attached to the adjoining surfaces of the two bones. It is in relation, *above*, in rare cases with the articular disk; *below*, with the tendon of the Supraspinatus.

The Articular Disk (*discus articularis*).—The articular disk is frequently absent in this articulation. When present, it generally only partially separates the articular surfaces, and occupies the upper part of the articulation. More rarely, it completely divides the joint into two cavities.

The Synovial Membrane.—There is usually only one synovial membrane in this articulation, but when a complete articular disk is present, there are two.

The Coracoclavicular Ligament (*ligamentum coracoclaviculare*) (Fig. 386).—This ligament serves to connect the clavicle with the coracoid process of the scapula. It does not properly belong to this articulation, but is usually described with it, since it forms a most efficient means of retaining the clavicle in contact with the acromion. It consists of two fasciculi, called the **trapezoid** and **conoid ligaments**.

The Trapezoid Ligament (*ligamentum trapezoideum*), the anterior and lateral fasciculus, is broad, thin, and quadrilateral: it is placed obliquely between the coracoid process and the clavicle. It is attached, *below*, to the upper surface of the coracoid process; *above*, to the oblique ridge on the under surface of the clavicle. Its anterior border is free; its posterior border is joined with the conoid ligament, the two forming, by their junction, an angle projecting backward.

The Conoid Ligament (*ligamentum conoideum*), the posterior and medial fasciculus, is a dense band of fibers, conical in form, with its base directed upward. It is attached by its apex to a rough impression at the base of the coracoid process, medial to the trapezoid ligament; above, by its expanded base, to the coracoid tuberosity on the under surface of the clavicle, and to a line proceeding medialward from it for 1.25 cm. These ligaments are in relation, in *front*, with the Subclavius and Deltoideus; *behind*, with the Trapezius.

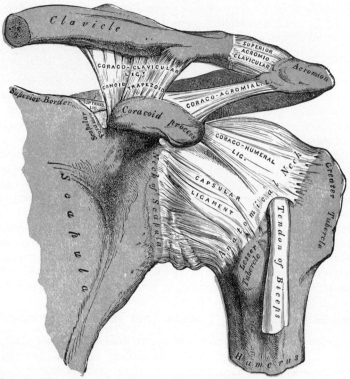

FIG. 386.—The left shoulder and acromioclavicular joints, and the proper ligaments of the scapula.

Movements.—The movements of this articulation are of two kinds: (1) a gliding motion of the articular end of the clavicle on the acromion; (2) rotation of the scapula forward and backward upon the clavicle. The extent of this rotation is limited by the two portions of the coracoclavicular ligament, the trapezoid limiting rotation forward, and the conoid backward.

The acromioclavicular joint has important functions in the movements of the upper extremity. It has been well pointed out by Humphry, that if there had been no joint between the clavicle and scapula, the circular movement of the scapula on the ribs (as in throwing the shoulders backward or forward) would have been attended with a greater alteration in the direction of the shoulder than is consistent with the free use of the arm in such positions, and it would have been impossible to give a blow straight forward with the full force of the arm; that is to say, with the combined force of the scapula, arm, and forearm. "This joint," as he happily says, "is so adjusted as to enable either bone to turn in a hinge-like manner upon a vertical axis drawn through the other, and it permits the surfaces of the scapula, like the baskets in a roundabout swing, to look the same way in every position, or nearly so." Again, when the whole arch formed by the clavicle and scapula rises and falls (in elevation or depression of the shoulder), the joint between these two bones enables the scapula still to maintain its lower part in contact with the ribs.

THE LIGAMENTS OF THE SCAPULA (Fig. 386).

Coracoacromial, Superior and Inferior Transverse.

The Coracoacromial Ligament (*ligamentum coracoacromiale*).—This ligament is a strong triangular band, extending between the coracoid process and the acromion.

It is attached, by its apex, to the summit of the acromion just in front of the articular surface for the clavicle; and by its broad base to the whole length of the lateral border of the coracoid process. This ligament, together with the coracoid process and the acromion, forms a vault for the protection of the head of the humerus. It is in relation, *above*, with the clavicle and under surface of the Deltoideus; *below*, with the tendon of the Supraspinatus, a bursa being interposed. Its lateral border is continuous with a dense lamina that passes beneath the Deltoideus upon the tendons of the Supraspinatus and Infraspinatus. The ligament is sometimes described as consisting of two marginal bands and a thinner intervening portion, the two bands being attached respectively to the apex and the base of the coracoid process, and joining together at the acromion. When the Pectoralis minor is inserted, as occasionally is the case, into the capsule of the shoulder-joint instead of into the coracoid process, it passes between these two bands, and the intervening portion of the ligament is then deficient.

The Superior Transverse Ligament (*ligamentum transversum scapulæ superius; transverse* or *suprascapular ligament*).—This ligament converts the scapular notch into a foramen. It is a thin and flat fasciculus, narrower at the middle than at the extremities, attached by one end to the base of the coracoid process, and by the other to the medial end of the scapular notch. The suprascapular nerve runs through the foramen; the transverse scapular vessels cross over the ligament. The ligament is sometimes ossified.

The Inferior Transverse Ligament (*ligamentum transversum scapulæ inferius; spinoglenoid ligament*).—This ligament is a weak membranous band, situated behind the neck of the scapula and stretching from the lateral border of the spine to the margin of the glenoid cavity. It forms an arch under which the transverse scapular vessels and suprascapular nerve enter the infraspinatous fossa.

III. Humeral Articulation or Shoulder-joint (Articulatio Humeri) (Fig. 386).

The shoulder-joint is an enarthrodial or ball-and-socket joint. The bones entering into its formation are the hemispherical head of the humerus and the shallow glenoid cavity of the scapula, an arrangement which permits of very considerable movement, while the joint itself is protected against displacement by the tendons which surround it. The ligaments do not maintain the joint surfaces in apposition, because when they alone remain the humerus can be separated to a considerable extent from the glenoid cavity; their use, therefore, is to limit the amount of movement. The joint is protected above by an arch, formed by the coracoid process, the acromion, and the coracoacromial ligament. The articular cartilage on the head of the humerus is thicker at the center than at the circumference, the reverse being the case with the articular cartilage of the glenoid cavity. The ligaments of the shoulder are:

The Articular Capsule.	The Glenohumeral.
The Coracohumeral.	The Transverse Humeral.

The Glenoidal Labrum.

The Articular Capsule (*capsula articularis; capsular ligament*) (Fig. 388).—The articular capsule completely encircles the joint, being attached, above, to the circumference of the glenoid cavity beyond the glenoidal labrum; below, to the anatomical neck of the humerus, approaching nearer to the articular cartilage above than in the rest of its extent. It is thicker above and below than elsewhere, and is so remarkably loose and lax, that it has no action in keeping the bones in contact, but allows them to be separated from each other more than 2.5 cm., an evident provision for that extreme freedom of movement which is peculiar to this articulation. It is strengthened, *above*, by the Supraspinatus; *below*, by the long head of the Triceps brachii; *behind,* by the tendons of the Infraspinatus and Teres minor; and in *front,* by the tendon of the Subscapularis. There are usually three openings in the capsule. One anteriorly, below the coracoid process, establishes a communication between the joint and a bursa beneath the tendon of the Sub-

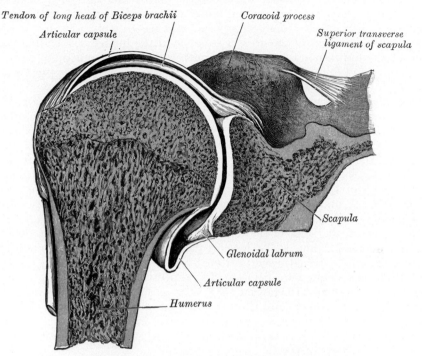

Fig. 387.—A section through the shoulder-joint.

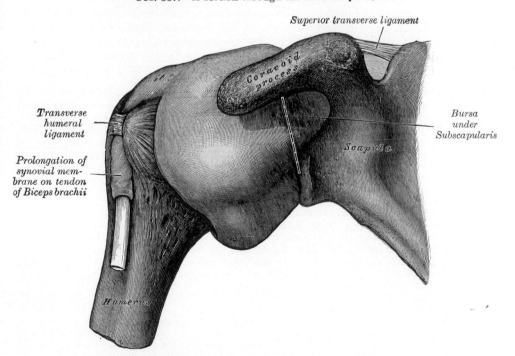

Fig. 388.—Capsule of shoulder-joint (distended). Anterior aspect.

scapularis. The second, which is not constant, is at the posterior part, where an opening sometimes exists between the joint and a bursal sac under the tendon of the Infraspinatus. The third is between the tubercles of the humerus, for the passage of the long tendon of the Biceps brachii.

The Coracohumeral Ligament (*ligamentum coracohumerale*).—This ligament is a broad band which strengthens the upper part of the capsule. It arises from the lateral border of the coracoid process, and passes obliquely downward and lateralward to the front of the greater tubercle of the humerus, blending with the tendon of the Supraspinatus. This ligament is intimately united to the capsule by its hinder and lower border; but its anterior and upper border presents a free edge, which overlaps the capsule.

Glenohumeral Ligaments.—In addition to the coracohumeral ligament, three supplemental bands, which are named the **glenohumeral ligaments**, strengthen the capsule. These may be best seen by opening the capsule at the back of the joint and removing the head of the humerus. One on the medial side of the joint passes from the medial edge of the glenoid cavity to the lower part of the lesser tubercle of the humerus. A second at the lower part of the joint extends from the under edge of the glenoid cavity to the under part of the anatomical neck of the humerus. A third at the upper part of the joint is fixed above to the apex of the glenoid cavity close to the root of the coracoid process, and passing downward along the medial edge of the tendon of the Biceps brachii, is attached below to a small depression above the lesser tubercle of the humerus. In addition to these, the capsule is strengthened in front by two bands derived from the tendons of the Pectoralis major and Teres major respectively.

The Transverse Humeral Ligament (Fig. 388) is a broad band passing from the lesser to the greater tubercle of the humerus, and always limited to that portion of the bone which lies above the epiphyseal line. It converts the intertubercula groove into a canal, and is the homologue of the strong process of bone which connects the summits of the two tubercles in the musk ox.

The Glenoidal Labrum (*labrium glenoidale; glenoid ligament*) is a fibrocartilaginous rim attached around the margin of the glenoid cavity. It is triangular on section, the base being fixed to the circumference of the cavity, while the free edge is thin and sharp. It is continuous above with the tendon of the long head of the Biceps brachii, which gives off two fasciculi to blend with the fibrous tissue of the labrum. It deepens the articular cavity, and protects the edges of the bone (Fig. 389).

Synovial Membrane.—The synovial membrane is reflected from the margin of the glenoid cavity over the labrum; it is then reflected over the inner surface of the capsule, and covers the lower part and sides of the anatomical neck of the humerus as far as the articular cartilage on the head of the bone. The tendon of the long head of the Biceps brachii passes through the capsule and is enclosed in a tubular sheath of synovial membrane, which is reflected upon it from the summit of the glenoid cavity and is continued around the tendon into the intertubercular groove as far as the surgical neck of the humerus (Fig. 388). The tendon thus traverses the articulation, but it is not contained within the synovial cavity (Fig. 387).

Bursæ.—The bursæ in the neighborhood of the shoulder-joint are the following: (1) A constant bursa is situated between the tendon of the Subscapularis muscle and the capsule; it communicates with the synovial cavity through an opening in the front of the capsule; (2) a bursa which occasionally communicates with the joint is sometimes found between the tendon of the Infraspinatus and the capsule; (3) a large bursa exists between the under surface of the Deltoideus and the capsule, but does not communicate with the joint; this bursa is prolonged under the acromion and coracoacromial ligament, and intervenes between these structures and the capsule; (4) a large bursa is situated on the summit of the acromion; (5) a bursa is frequently found between the coracoid process and the capsule; (6) a bursa exists beneath the Coracobrachialis; (7) one lies between the Teres major and the long head of the Triceps brachii; (8) one is placed in front of, and another behind, the tendon of the Latissimus dorsi.

The **muscles** in relation with the joint are, *above*, the Supraspinatus; *below*, the long head of the Triceps brachii; in *front*, the Subscapularis; *behind*, the Infraspinatus and Teres minor; *within*, the tendon of the long head of the Biceps brachii. The Deltoideus covers the articulation in front, behind, and laterally.

The **arteries** supplying the joint are articular branches of the anterior and posterior humeral circumflex, and transverse scapular.

The **nerves** are derived from the axillary and suprascapular.

Movements.—The shoulder-joint is capable of every variety of movement, flexion, extension, abduction, adduction, circumduction, and rotation. The humerus is *flexed* (drawn forward) by the Pectoralis major, anterior fibers of the Deltoideus, Coracobrachialis, and when the forearm is flexed, by the Biceps brachii; *extended* (drawn backward) by the Latissimus dorsi, Teres major, posterior fibers of the Deltoideus, and, when the forearm is extended, by the Triceps brachii; it is *abducted* by the Deltoideus and Supraspinatus; it is *adducted* by the Subscapularis, Pectoralis major, Latissimus dorsi, and Teres major, and by the weight of the limb; it is *rotated outward* by the Infraspinatus and Teres minor; and it is *rotated inward* by the Subscapularis, Latissimus dorsi, Teres major, Pectoralis major, and the anterior fibers of the Deltoideus.

The most striking peculiarities in this joint are: (1) The large size of the head of the humerus in comparison with the depth of the glenoid cavity, even when this latter is supplemented by the glenoidal labrum. (2) The looseness of the capsule of the joint. (3) The intimate connection of the capsule with the muscles attached to the head of the humerus. (4) The peculiar relation of the tendon of the long head of the Biceps brachii to the joint.

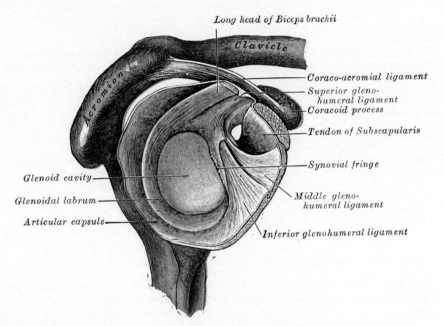

Fig. 389.—Interior of shoulder-joint. Lateral aspect.

It is in consequence of the relative sizes of the two articular surfaces, and the looseness of the articular capsule, that the joint enjoys such free movement in all directions. The arm can be carried considerably farther by the movements of the scapula, involving, of course, motion at the acromio- and sternoclavicular joints. These joints are therefore to be regarded as accessory structures to the shoulder-joint (see pages 353 and 355). The extent of the scapular movements is very considerable, especially in extreme elevation of the arm, a movement best accomplished when the arm is thrown somewhat forward and outward, because the margin of the head of the humerus is by no means a true circle; its greatest diameter is from the intertubercular groove, downward, medialward, and backward, and the greatest elevation of the arm can be obtained by rolling its articular surface in the direction of this measurement. The great width of the central portion of the humeral head also allows of very free horizontal movement when the arm is raised to a right angle, in which movement the arch formed by the acromion, the coracoid process and the coracoacromial ligament, constitutes a sort of supplemental articular cavity for the head of the bone.

The looseness of the capsule is so great that the humeral head will fall away from the scapula about 2.5 cm. when the muscles are dissected from around the joint. The articular surfaces of the two bones are held in contact, not so much by the capsule as by the surrounding muscles, an arrangement which allows very easy movement in the joint, especially when the muscles are not under tension. In all ordinary positions of the joint, the capsule is not put on the stretch, but extreme movements are checked by the tension of appropriate portions of the capsule, as well as by other ligaments and certain muscles.

The scapula is capable of being moved upward and downward, forward and backward, or, by a combination of these movements, circumducted on the wall of the chest. The muscles which *raise* the scapula are the upper fibers of the Trapezius, the Levator scapulæ, and the Rhomboidei; those which *depress* it are the lower fibers of the Trapezius, the Pectoralis minor, and, through the clavicle, the Subclavius. The scapula is drawn *backward* by the Rhomboidei and the middle and lower fibers of the Trapezius, and *forward* by the Serratus anterior and Pectoralis minor, assisted, when the arm is fixed, by the Pectoralis major. The mobility of the scapula is very considerable, and greatly assists the movements of the arm at the shoulder-joint. This mobility is of special importance in ankylosis of the shoulder-joint, the movements of this bone compensating to a very great extent for the immobility of the joint.

Raising of the arm above the head, either by carrying it forward in flexion or to the side in abduction, is brought about by the combined activity of the shoulder joint and rotation of the scapula on the chest wall. Although it has been customary to separate the movement into two parts, one, raising the arm to the horizontal, the other, from horizontal to overhead, such a distinction is artificial. During practically all of both parts of the movement, the ratio of motion in the two articulations is that of two parts glenohumeral to one part scapulothoracic. If motion in the glenohumeral articulation is destroyed by ankylosis, therefore, only one-third of the whole movement of 60° of motion will be retained in the compensatory motion of the scapulo-thoracic articulation.

The intimate union of the tendons of the Supraspinatus, Infraspinatus, Teres minor and Subscapularis with the capsule, converts these muscles into elastic and spontaneously acting ligaments of the joint.

The peculiar relations of the tendon of the long head of the Biceps brachii to the shoulder-joint appear to subserve various purposes. In the first place, by its connection with both the shoulder and elbow the muscle harmonizes the action of the two joints, and acts as an elastic ligament in all positions, in the manner previously discussed (see page 326). It strengthens the upper part of the articular cavity, and prevents the head of the humerus from being pressed up against the acromion, when the Deltoideus contracts; it thus fixes the head of the humerus as the center of motion in the glenoid cavity. By its passage along the intertubercular groove it assists in steadying the head of the humerus in the various movements of the arm. When the arm is raised from the side it assists the Supraspinatus and Infraspinatus in rotating the head of the humerus in the glenoid cavity. It also holds the head of the bone firmly in contact with the glenoid cavity, and prevents its slipping over its lower edge, or being displaced by the action of the Latissimus dorsi and Pectoralis major, as in climbing and many other movements.

IV.　Elbow-joint (Articulatio Cubiti) (Figs. 390, 391, 392).

The elbow-joint is a ginglymus or hinge-joint. The trochlea of the humerus is received into the semilunar notch of the ulna, and the capitulum of the humerus articulates with the fovea on the head of the radius. The articular surfaces are connected together by a **capsule**, which is thickened medially and laterally into the **ulnar collateral** and the **radial collateral** ligaments.

The Articular Capsule (Fig. 390).—The anterior part is a broad and thin fibrous layer covering the anterior surface of the joint. It is attached to the *front* of the medial epicondyle and to the front of the humerus immediately above the coronoid and radial fossæ; *below*, to the anterior surface of the coronoid process of the ulna and to the annular ligament (page 364), being continuous on either side with the collateral ligaments. Its superficial fibers pass obliquely from the medial epicondyle of the humerus to the annular ligament. The middle fibers, vertical in direction, pass from the upper part of the coronoid depression and become partly blended with the preceding, but are inserted mainly into the anterior surface of the coronoid process. The deep or transverse set intersects these at right angles. It is in relation, in *front*, with the Brachialis, except at its most lateral part.

The posterior part (Fig. 391), is thin and membranous, and consists of transverse and oblique fibers. *Above*, it is attached to the humerus immediately behind the capitulum and close to the medial margin of the trochlea, to the margins of the olecranon fossa, and to the back of the lateral epicondyle some little distance from the trochlea. *Below*, it is fixed to the upper and lateral margins of the olecranon, to the posterior part of the annular ligament, and to the ulna behind the radial notch. The transverse fibers form a strong band which bridges across the olecranon fossa; under

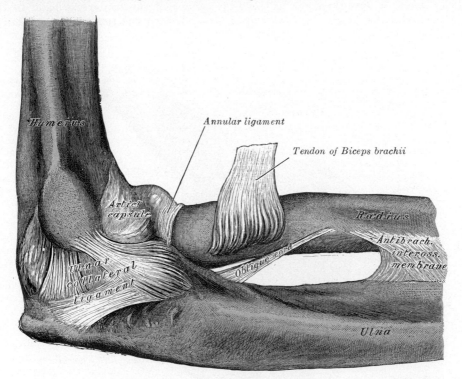

FIG. 390.—The left elbow-joint. Medial aspect.

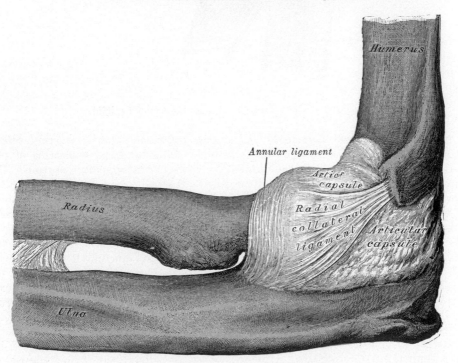

FIG. 391.—The left elbow-joint. Lateral aspect.

cover of this band a pouch of synovial membrane and a pad of fat project into the upper part of the fossa when the joint is extended. In the fat are a few scattered fibrous bundles, which pass from the deep surface of the transverse band to the upper part of the fossa. It is in relation, *behind*, with the tendon of the Triceps brachii and the Anconæus.

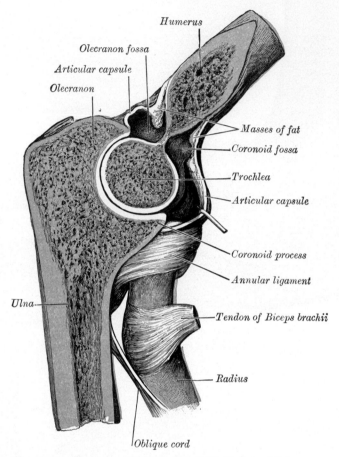

Humerus

Olecranon fossa

Articular capsule

Olecranon

Masses of fat

Coronoid fossa

Trochlea

Articular capsule

Coronoid process

Annular ligament

Ulna

Tendon of Biceps brachii

Radius

Oblique cord

Fig. 392.—Sagittal section through the left elbow-joint.

The Ulnar Collateral Ligament (*ligamentum collaterale ulnare; internal lateral ligament*) (Fig. 390).—This ligament is a thick triangular band consisting of two portions, an anterior and posterior united by a thinner intermediate portion. The **anterior portion**, directed obliquely forward, is attached, *above*, by its apex, to the front part of the medial epicondyle of the humerus; and, *below*, by its broad base to the medial margin of the coronoid process. The **posterior portion**, also of triangular form, is attached, *above*, by its apex, to the lower and back part of the medial epicondyle; *below*, to the medial margin of the olecranon. Between these two bands a few intermediate fibers descend from the medial epicondyle to blend with a *transverse band* which bridges across the notch between the olecranon and the coronoid process. This ligament is in relation with the Triceps brachii and Flexor carpi ulnaris and the ulnar nerve, and gives origin to part of the Flexor digitorum sublimis.

The Radial Collateral Ligament (*ligamentum collaterale radiale; external lateral ligament*) (Fig. 391).—This ligament is a short and narrow fibrous band, less distinct than the ulnar collateral, attached, *above*, to a depression below the lateral epicondyle of the humerus; *below*, to the annular ligament, some of its most posterior fibers passing over that ligament, to be inserted into the lateral margin of the ulna. It is intimately blended with the tendon of origin of the Supinator.

Synovial Membrane (Figs. 393, 394).—The synovial membrane is very extensive. It extends from the margin of the articular surface of the humerus, and lines the coronoid, radial and olecranon fossæ on that bone; it is reflected over the deep surface of the capsule and forms a pouch between the radial notch, the deep surface of the annular ligament, and the circumference of the head of the radius. Projecting between the radius and ulna into the cavity is a crescentic fold of synovial membrane, suggesting the division of the joint into two; one the humeroradial, the other the humeroulnar.

Between the capsule and the synovial membrane are three masses of fat: the largest, over the olecranon fossa, is pressed into the fossa by the Triceps brachii during the flexion; the second, over the coronoid fossa, and the third, over the radial fossa, are pressed by the Brachialis into their respective fossæ during extension.

The **muscles** in relation with the joint are, in *front*, the Brachialis; *behind*, the Triceps brachii and Anconæus; *laterally*, the Supinator, and the common tendon of origin of the Extensor muscles; *medially*, the common tendon of origin of the Flexor muscles, and the Flexor carpi ulnaris.

The **arteries** supplying the joint are derived from the anastomosis between the profunda and the superior and inferior ulnar collateral branches of the brachial, with the anterior, posterior, and interosseous recurrent branches of the ulnar, and the recurrent branch of the radial. These vessels form a complete anastomotic network around the joint.

The **nerves** of the joint are a twig from the ulnar, as it passes between the medial condyle and the olecranon; a filament from the musculocutaneous. and two from the median.

Movements.—The elbow-joint comprises three different portions—viz., the joint between the ulna and humerus, that between the head of the radius and the humerus, and the proximal radioulnar articulation, described below. All these articular surfaces are enveloped by a common synovial membrane, and the movements of the whole joint should be studied together. The combination of the movements of flexion and extension of the forearm with those of pronation and supination of the hand, which is ensured by the two being performed at the same joint, is essential to the accuracy of the various minute movements of the hand.

The portion of the joint between the ulna and humerus is a simple hinge-joint, and allows of movements of flexion and extension only. Owing to the obliquity of the trochlea of the humerus, this movement does not take place in the antero-posterior plane of the body of the humerus. When the forearm is extended and supinated, the axes of the arm and forearm are not in the same line; the arm forms an obtuse angle with the forearm, the hand and forearm being directed lateralward. During flexion, however, the forearm and the hand tend to approach the middle line of the body, and thus enable the hand to be easily carried to the face. The accurate adaptation of the trochlea of the humerus, with its prominences and depressions, to the semilunar notch of the ulna, prevents any lateral movement. *Flexion* is produced by the action of the Biceps brachii and Brachialis, assisted by the Brachioradialis and the muscles arising from the medial condyle of the humerus; *extension*, by the Triceps brachii and Anconæus, assisted by the Extensors of the wrist, the Extensor digitorum communis, and the Extensor digiti quinti proprius.

The joint between the head of the radius and the capitulum of the humerus is an arthrodial joint. The bony surfaces would of themselves constitute an enarthrosis and allow of movement in all directions, were it not for the annular ligament, by which the head of the radius is bound to the radial notch of the ulna, and which prevents any separation of the two bones laterally. It is to the same ligament that the head of the radius owes its security from dislocation which would otherwise tend to occur, from the shallowness of the cup-like surface on the head of the radius. In fact, but for this ligament, the tendon of the Biceps brachii would be liable to pull the head of the radius out of the joint. The head of the radius is not in complete contact with the capitulum of the humerus in all positions of the joint. The capitulum occupies only the anterior and inferior surfaces of the lower end of the humerus, so that in complete extension a part of the radial head can be plainly felt projecting at the back of the articulation. In full flexion the movement of the radial head is hampered by the compression of the surrounding soft parts, so that the freest rotatory movement of the radius on the humerus (pronation and supination) takes place in semiflexion, in which position the two articular surfaces are in most intimate contact. Flexion and extension of the elbow-joint are limited by the tension of the structures on the front and back of the joint; the limitation of flexion is also aided by the soft structures of the arm and forearm coming into contact.

In any position of flexion or extension, the radius, carrying the hand with it, can be rotated in the proximal radioulnar joint. The hand is directly articulated to the lower surface of the radius only, and the ulnar notch on the lower end of the radius travels around the lower end of the ulna. The latter bone is excluded from the wrist-joint by the articular disk. Thus, rotation of the head of the radius around an axis passing through the center of the radial head of the humerus imparts circular movement to the hand through a very considerable arc.

V. Radioulnar Articulations (Articulatio Radioulnaris).

The articulation of the radius with the ulna is effected by ligaments which connect together the extremities as well as the bodies of these bones. The ligaments may, consequently, be subdivided into three sets: 1, those of the proximal radioulnar articulation; 2, the middle radioulnar ligaments; 3, those of the distal radioulnar articulation.

Proximal Radioulnar Articulation (*articulatio radioulnaris proximalis; superior radioulnar joint*).—This articulation is a trochoid or pivot-joint between the circumference of the head of the radius and the ring formed by the radial notch of the ulna and the *annular ligament*.

The Annular Ligament (*ligamentum annulare radii; orbicular ligament*) (Fig. 395). —This ligament is a strong band of fibers, which encircles the head of the radius, and retains it in contact with the radial notch of the ulna. It forms about four-fifths of the osseo-fibrous ring, and is attached to the anterior and posterior margins of the radial notch; a few of its lower fibers are continued around below the cavity and form at this level a complete fibrous ring. Its upper border blends with the anterior and posterior ligaments of the elbow, while from its lower border a thin loose membrane passes to be attached to the neck of the radius; a thickened band which extends from the inferior border of the annular ligament below the radial notch to the neck of the radius is known as the **quadrate ligament**. The superficial surface of the annular ligament is strengthened by the radial collateral ligament of the elbow, and affords origin to part of the Supinator. Its deep surface is smooth, and lined by synovial membrane, which is continuous with that of the elbow-joint.

Movements.—The movements allowed in this articulation are limited to rotatory movements of the head of the radius within the ring formed by the annular ligament and the radial notch of the ulna; rotation forward being called *pronation;* rotation backward, *supination.* Supination is performed by the Biceps brachii and Supinator, assisted to a slight extent by the Extensor muscles of the thumb. Pronation is performed by the Pronator teres and Pronator quadratus.

Middle Radioulnar Union.—The shafts of the radius and ulna are connected by the Oblique Cord and the Interosseous Membrane.

The Oblique Cord (*chorda obliqua; oblique ligament*) (Fig. 390).—The oblique cord is a small, flattened band, extending downward and lateralward, from the lateral side of the tubercle of the ulna at the base of the coronoid process to the radius a little below the radial tuberosity. Its fibers run in the opposite direction to those of the interosseous membrane. It is sometimes wanting.

The Interosseous Membrane (*membrana interossea antebrachii*).—The interosseous membrane is a broad and thin plane of fibrous tissue descending obliquely downward and medialward, from the interosseous crest of the radius to that of the ulna; the lower part of the membrane is attached to the posterior of the two lines into which the interosseous crest of the radius divides. It is deficient above, commencing about 2.5 cm. beneath the tuberosity of the radius; is broader in the middle than at either end; and presents an oval aperture a little above its lower margin for the passage of the volar interosseous vessels to the back of the forearm. This membrane serves to connect the bones, and to increase the extent of surface for the attachment of the deep muscles. Between its upper border and the oblique cord is a gap, through which the dorsal interosseous vessels pass. Two or three fibrous bands are occasionally found on the dorsal surface of this membrane; they descend obliquely from the ulna toward the radius, and have consequently a direction contrary to that of the other fibers. The membrane is in relation, in *front*, by its upper three-fourths, with the Flexor pollicis longus on the radial side, and with the Flexor digitorum profundus on the ulnar, lying in the interval between which are the volar interosseous vessels and nerve; by its lower fourth with the Pronator quadratus; *behind*, with the Supinator, Abductor pollicis longus, Extensor pollicis

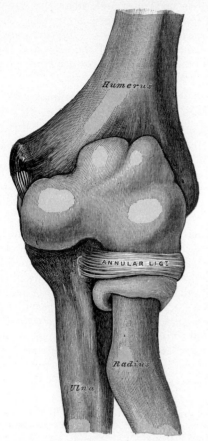

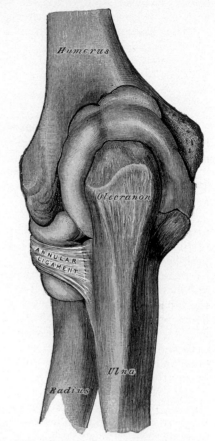

FIG. 393.—Capsule of elbow-joint (distended).
Anterior aspect.

FIG. 394.—Capsule of elbow-joint (distended).
Posterior aspect.

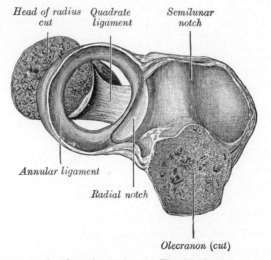

FIG. 395.—Annular ligament of radius, from above. The head of the radius has been sawn off
and the bone dislodged from the ligament.

brevis, Extensor pollicis longus, Extensor indicis proprius; and, near the wrist, with the volar interosseous artery and dorsal interosseous nerve.

Distal Radioulnar Articulation (*articulatio radioulnaris distalis; inferior radioulnar joint*).—This is a pivot-joint formed between the head of the ulna and the ulnar notch on the lower end of the radius. The articular surfaces are connected together by the following ligaments:

The Volar Radioulnar.	The Dorsal Radioulnar.

The Articular Disk.

The Volar Radioulnar Ligament (*anterior radioulnar ligament*) (Fig. 396).—This ligament is a narrow band of fibers extending from the anterior margin of the ulnar notch of the radius to the front of the head of the ulna.

The Dorsal Radioulnar Ligament (*posterior radioulnar ligament*) (Fig. 397).—This ligament extends between corresponding surfaces on the dorsal aspect of the articulation.

The Articular Disk (*discus articularis; triangular fibrocartilage*) (Fig. 398).—The articular disk is triangular in shape, and is placed transversely beneath the head of the ulna, binding the lower ends of the ulna and radius firmly together. Its periphery is thicker than its center, which is occasionally perforated. It is attached by its apex to a depression between the styloid process and the head of the ulna; and by its base, which is thin, to the prominent edge of the radius, which separates the ulnar notch from the carpal articular surface. Its margins are united to the ligaments of the wrist-joint. Its **upper surface**, smooth and concave, articulates with the head of the ulna, forming an arthrodial joint; its **under surface**, also concave and smooth, forms part of the wrist-joint and articulates with the triangular bone and medial part of the lunate. Both surfaces are clothed by synovial membrane; the upper, by that of the distal radioulnar articulation, the under, by that of the wrist.

Synovial Membrane (Fig. 398).—The synovial membrane of this articulation is extremely loose, and extends upward as a recess (*recessus sacciformis*) between the radius and the ulna.

Movements.—The movements in the distal radioulnar articulation consist of rotation of the lower end of the radius around an axis which passes through the center of the head of the ulna. When the radius rotates forward, *pronation* of the forearm and hand is the result; and when backward, *supination*. It will thus be seen that in pronation and supination the radius describes the segment of a cone, the axis of which extends from the center of the head of the radius to the middle of the head of the ulna. In this movement the head of the ulna is not stationary, but describes a curve in a direction opposite to that taken by the head of the radius. This, however, is not to be regarded as a rotation of the ulna—the curve which the head of this bone describes is due to a combined antero-posterior and rotatory movement, the former taking place almost entirely at the elbow-joint, the latter at the shoulder-joint.

VI. Radiocarpal Articulation or Wrist-joint (Articulatio Radiocarpea)
(Figs. 396, 397).

The wrist-joint is a condyloid articulation. The parts forming it are the distal end of the radius and under surface of the articular disk above; and the navicular, lunate, and triangular bones below. The articular surface of the radius and the under surface of the articular disk form together a transversely elliptical concave surface. The superior articular surfaces of the navicular, lunate, and triangular form a smooth convex surface, the **condyle**, which is received into the concavity. The joint is surrounded by a capsule and strengthened by the following ligaments:

The Volar Radiocarpal.	The Ulnar Collateral.
The Dorsal Radiocarpal.	The Radial Collateral.

The Volar Radiocarpal Ligament (*ligamentum radiocarpeum volare; anterior ligament*) (Fig. 396).—This ligament is a broad membranous band, attached above to the anterior margin of the lower end of the radius, to its styloid process, and to the front of the lower end of the ulna; its fibers pass downward and medialward to be inserted into the volar surfaces of the navicular, lunate, and triangular bones, some being continued to the capitate. In addition to this broad membrane, there is a rounded fasciculus, superficial to the rest, which reaches from the base of the styloid process of the ulna to the lunate and triangular bones. The ligament is perforated by apertures for the passage of vessels, and is in relation,

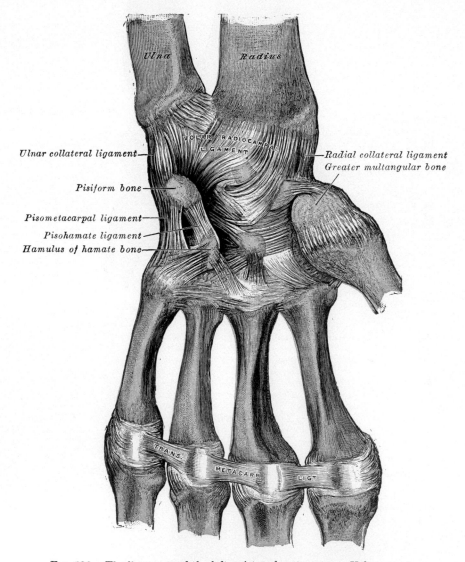

FIG. 396.—The ligaments of the left wrist and metacarpus. Volar aspect.

in *front*, with the tendons of the Flexor digitorum profundus and Flexor pollicis longus; *behind*, it is closely adherent to the anterior border of the articular disk of the distal radioulnar articulation.

The Dorsal Radiocarpal Ligament (*ligamentum radiocarpeum dorsale; posterior ligament*) (Fig. 397).—The dorsal radiocarpal ligament less thick and strong than the volar, is attached, *above*, to the posterior border of the lower end of the radius; its fibers are directed obliquely downward and medialward, and are fixed, *below*, to the dorsal surfaces of the navicular, lunate, and triangular, being continuous with those of the dorsal intercarpal ligaments. It is in relation, *behind*, with the Extensor tendons of the fingers; in *front*, it is blended with the articular disk.

The Ulnar Collateral Ligament (*ligamentum collaterale carpi ulnare; interna lateral ligament*) (Fig. 396).—The ulnar collateral ligament is a rounded cord

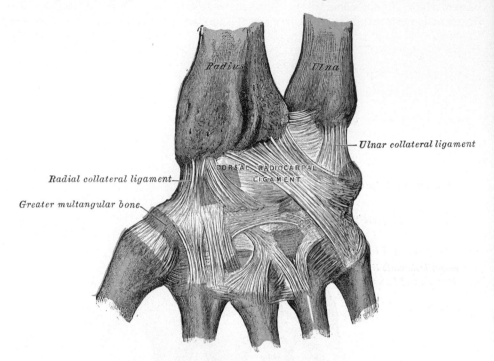

FIG. 397.—The ligaments of the left wrist. Dorsal aspect.

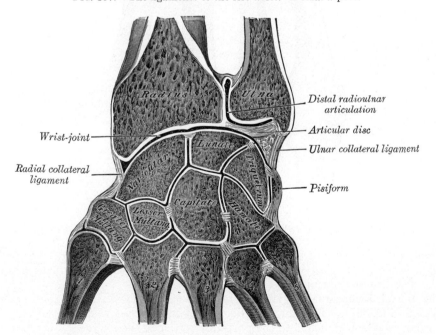

FIG. 398.—Vertical section through the articulations at the wrist, showing the synovial cavities.

attached above to the end of the styloid process of the ulna, and dividing below into two fasciculi, one of which is attached to the medial side of the triangular bone, the other to the pisiform and transverse carpal ligament.

The Radial Collateral Ligament (*ligamentum collaterale carpi radiale; external lateral ligament*) (Fig. 397).—The radial collateral ligament extends from the tip of the styloid process of the radius to the radial side of the navicular, some of its fibers being prolonged to the greater multangular bone and the transverse carpal ligament. It is in relation with the radial artery, which separates the ligament from the tendons of the Abductor pollicis longus and Extensor pollicis brevis.

Synovial Membrane (Fig. 398).—The synovial membrane lines the deep surfaces of the ligaments above described, extending from the margin of the lower end of the radius and articular disk above to the margins of the articular surfaces of the carpal bones below. It is loose and lax, and presents numerous folds, especially behind.

The wrist-joint is covered in front by the Flexor, and behind by the Extensor tendons.

The **arteries** supplying the joint are the volar and dorsal carpal branches of the radial and ulnar, the volar and dorsal metacarpals, and some ascending branches from the deep volar arch.

The **nerves** are derived from the ulnar and dorsal interosseous.

Movements.—The movements permitted in this joint are flexion, extension, abduction, adduction, and circumduction. They will be studied with those of the carpus, with which they are combined.

VII. Intercarpal Articulations (Articulationes Intercarpeæ; Articulations of the Carpus).

These articulations may be subdivided into three sets:

1. The Articulations of the Proximal Row of Carpal Bones.
2. The Articulations of the Distal Row of Carpal Bones.
3. The Articulations of the Two Rows with each Other.

Articulations of the Proximal Row of Carpal Bones.—These are arthrodial joints. The navicular, lunate, and triangular are connected by dorsal, volar, and interosseous ligaments.

The Dorsal Ligaments (*ligamenta intercarpea dorsalia*).—The dorsal ligaments, two in number, are placed transversely behind the bones of the first row; they connect the navicular and lunate, and the lunate and triangular.

The Volar ligaments (*ligamenta intercarpea palmaria palmar ligaments*).—The volar ligaments, also two, connect the navicular and lunate, and the lunate and triangular; they are less strong than the dorsal, and placed very deeply behind the Flexor tendons and the volar radiocarpal ligament.

The Interosseous Ligaments (*ligamenta intercarpea interossea*) (Fig. 398).—The interosseous ligaments are two narrow bundles, one connecting the lunate with the navicular, the other joining it to the triangular. They are on a level with the superior surfaces of these bones, and their upper surfaces are smooth, and form part of the convex articular surface of the wrist-joint.

The ligaments connecting the pisiform bone are the articular capsule and the two volar ligaments.

The **articular capsule** is a thin membrane which connects the pisiform to the triangular; it is lined by synovial membrane.

The two **volar ligaments** are strong fibrous bands; one, the **pisohamate ligament**, connects the pisiform to the hamate, the other, the **pisometacarpal ligament**, joins the pisiform to the base of the fifth metacarpal bone (Fig. 396). These ligaments are, in reality, prolongations of the tendon of the Flexor carpi ulnaris.

Articulations of the Distal Row of Carpal Bones.—These also are arthrodial joints; the bones are connected by dorsal, volar, and interosseous ligaments.

24

The Dorsal Ligaments (*ligamenta intercarpea dorsalia*).—The dorsal ligaments, three in number, extend transversely from one bone to another on the dorsal surface, connecting the greater with the lesser multangular, the lesser multangular with the capitate, and the capitate with the hamate.

The Volar Ligaments (*ligamenta intercarpea palmaria; palmar ligaments*).—The volar ligaments, also three, have a similar arrangement on the volar surface.

The Interosseous Ligaments (*ligamenta intercarpea interossea*).—The three interosseous ligaments are much thicker than those of the first row; one is placed between the capitate and the hamate, a second between the capitate and the lesser multangular, and a third between the greater and lesser multangulars. The first is much the strongest, and the third is sometimes wanting.

Articulations of the Two Rows of Carpal Bones with Each Other.—The joint between the navicular, lunate, and triangular on the one hand, and the second row of carpal bones on the other, is named the **midcarpal joint,** and is made up of three distinct portions: in the center the head of the capitate and the superior surface of the hamate articulate with the deep cup-shaped cavity formed by the navicular and lunate, and constitute a sort of ball-and-socket joint. On the radial side the greater and lesser multangulars articulate with the navicular, and on the ulnar side the hamate articulates with the triangular, forming gliding joints.

The ligaments are: volar, dorsal, ulnar and radial collateral.

The Volar Ligaments (*ligamenta intercarpea palmaria; anterior or palmar ligaments*). —The volar ligaments consist of short fibers, which pass, for the most part, from the volar surfaces of the bones of the first row to the front of the capitate.

The Dorsal Ligaments (*ligamenta intercarpea dorsalia; posterior ligaments*).— The dorsal ligaments consist of short, irregular bundles passing between the dorsal surfaces of the bones of the first and second rows.

The Collateral Ligaments (*lateral ligaments*).—The collateral ligaments are very short; one is placed on the radial, the other on the ulnar side of the carpus; the former, the stronger and more distinct, connects the navicular and greater multangular, the latter the triangular and hamate; they are continuous with the collateral ligaments of the wrist-joint. In addition to these ligaments, a slender interosseous band sometimes connects the capitate and the navicular.

Synovial Membrane.—The synovial membrane of the carpus is very extensive (Fig. 398), and bounds a synovial cavity of very irregular shape. The upper portion of the cavity intervenes between the under surfaces of the navicular, lunate, and triangular bones and the upper surfaces of the bones of the second row. It sends two prolongations upward—between the navicular and lunate, and the lunate and triangular—and three prolongations downward between the four bones of the second row. The prolongation between the greater and lesser multangulars, or that between the lesser multangular and capitate, is, owing to the absence of the interosseous ligament, often continuous with the cavity of the carpometacarpal joints, sometimes of the second, third, fourth, and fifth metacarpal bones, sometimes of the second and third only. In the latter condition the joint between the hamate and the fourth and fifth metacarpal bones has a separate synovial membrane. The synovial cavities of these joints are prolonged for a short distance between the bases of the metacarpal bones. There is a separate synovial membrane between the pisiform and triangular.

Movements.—The articulation of the hand and wrist considered as a whole involves four articular surfaces: (*a*) the inferior surfaces of the radius and articular disk; (*b*) the superior surfaces of the navicular, lunate, and triangular, the pisiform having no essential part in the movement of the hand; (*c*) the S-shaped surface formed by the inferior surfaces of the navicular, lunate, and triangular; (*d*) the reciprocal surface formed by the upper surfaces of the bones of the second row. These four surfaces form two joints: (1) a proximal, the wrist-joint proper; and (2) a distal, the mid-carpal joint.

1. The wrist-joint proper is a true condyloid articulation, and therefore all movements but rotation are permitted. Flexion and extension are the most free, and of these a greater amount of extension than of flexion is permitted, since the articulating surfaces extend farther on the dorsal than on the volar surfaces of the carpal bones. In this movement the carpal bones rotate on a transverse axis drawn between the tips of the styloid processes of the radius and ulna. A certain amount of adduction (or ulnar flexion) and abduction (or radial flexion) is also permitted. The

former is considerably greater in extent than the latter on account of the shortness of the styloid process of the ulna, abduction being soon limited by the contact of the styloid process of the radius with the greater multangular. In this movement the carpus revolves upon an antero-posterior axis drawn through the center of the wrist. Finally, circumduction is permitted by the combined and consecutive movements of adduction, extension, abduction, and flexion. No rotation is possible, but the effect of rotation is obtained by the pronation and supination of the radius on the ulna. The movement of *flexion* is performed by the Flexor carpi radialis, the Flexor carpi ulnaris, and the Palmaris longus; *extension* by the Extensores carpi radiales longus and brevis and the Extensor carpi ulnaris; *adduction* (ulnar flexion) by the Flexor carpi ulnaris and the Extensor carpi ulnaris; and *abduction* (radial flexion) by the Abductor pollicis longus, the Extensors of the thumb, and the Extensores carpi radiales longus and brevis and the Flexor carpi radialis. When the fingers are extended, flexion of the wrist is performed by the Flexores carpi radialis and ulnaris and extension is aided by the Extensor digitorum communis. When the fingers are flexed, flexion of the wrist is aided by the Flexores digitorum sublimis and profundus, and extension is performed by the Extensores carpi radiales and ulnaris.

2. The chief movements permitted in the mid-carpal joint are flexion and extension and a slight amount of rotation. In flexion and extension, which are the movements most freely enjoyed, the greater and lesser multangulars on the radial side and the hamate on the ulnar side glide forward and backward on the navicular and triangular respectively, while the head of the capitate and the superior surface of the hamate rotate in the cup-shaped cavity of the navicular and lunate. Flexion at this joint is freer than extension. A very trifling amount of rotation is also permitted, the head of the capitate rotating around a vertical axis drawn through its own center, while at the same time a slight gliding movement takes place in the lateral and medial portions of the joint.

VIII. Carpometacarpal Articulations (Articulationes Carpometacarpeæ).
(Figs. 397, 398).

Carpometacarpal Articulation of the Thumb (*articulatio carpometacarpea pollicis*). —This is a joint of reciprocal reception between the first metacarpal and the greater multangular; it enjoys great freedom of movement on account of the configuration of its articular surfaces, which are saddle-shaped. The joint is surrounded by a capsule, which is thick but loose, and passes from the circumference of the base of the metacarpal bone to the rough edge bounding the articular surface of the greater multangular; it is thickest laterally and dorsally, and is lined by synovial membrane.

Movements.—In this articulation the movements permitted are flexion and extension in the plane of the palm of the hand, abduction and adduction in a plane at right angles to the palm, circumduction, and opposition. It is by the movement of opposition that the tip of the thumb is brought into contact with the volar surfaces of the slightly flexed fingers. This movement is effected through the medium of a small sloping facet on the anterior lip of the saddle-shaped articular surface of the greater multangular. The Flexor muscles pull the corresponding part of the articular surface of the metacarpal bone on to this facet, and the movement of opposition is then carried out by the Adductors.

Flexion of this joint is produced by the Flexores pollicis longus and brevis, assisted by the Opponens pollicis and the Adductor pollicis. Extension is effected mainly by the Abductor pollicis longus, assisted by the Extensores pollicis longus and brevis. Adduction is carried out by the Adductor; abduction mainly by the Abductores pollicis longus and brevis, assisted by the Extensors.

Articulations of the Other Four Metacarpal Bones with the Carpus (*articulationes carpometacarpeæ*).—The joints between the carpus and the second, third, fourth, and fifth metacarpal bones are arthrodial. The bones are united by dorsal, volar, and interosseous ligaments.

The Dorsal Ligaments (*ligamenta carpometacarpea dorsalia*).—The dorsal ligaments, the strongest and most distinct, connect the carpal and metacarpal bones on their dorsal surfaces. The second metacarpal bone receives two fasciculi, one from the greater, the other from the lesser multangular; the third metacarpal receives two, one each from the lesser multangular and capitate; the fourth two, one each from the capitate and hamate; the fifth receives a single fasciculus from the hamate, and this is continuous with a similar ligament on the volar surface, forming an incomplete capsule.

The Volar Ligaments (*ligamenta carpometacarpea palmaria; palmar ligaments*)— The volar ligaments have a somewhat similar arrangement, with the exception of those of the third metacarpal, which are three in number: a lateral one from the greater multangular, situated superficial to the sheath of the tendon of the Flexor carpi radialis; an intermediate one from the capitate; and a medial one from the hamate.

The Interosseous Ligaments.—The interosseous ligaments consist of short, thick fibers, and are limited to one part of the carpometacarpal articulation; they connect the contiguous inferior angles of the capitate and hamate with the adjacent surfaces of the third and fourth metacarpal bones.

Synovial Membrane.—The synovial membrane is a continuation of that of the intercarpal joints. Occasionally, the joint between the hamate and the fourth and fifth metacarpal bones has a separate synovial membrane.

The synovial membranes of the wrist and carpus (Fig. 398) are thus seen to be five in number. The *first* passes from the lower end of the ulnar to the ulnar notch of the radius, and lines the upper surface of the articular disk. The *second* passes from the articular disk and the lower end of the radius above, to the bones of the first row below. The *third*, the most extensive, passes between the contiguous margins of the two rows of carpal bones, and sometimes, in the event of one of the interosseous ligaments being absent, between the bones of the second row to the carpal extremities of the second, third, fourth, and fifth metacarpal bones. The *fourth* extends from the margin of the greater multangular to the metacarpal bone of the thumb. The *fifth* runs between the adjacent margins of the triangular and pisiform bones. Occasionally the fourth and fifth carpometacarpal joints have a separate synovial membrane.

Movements.—The movements permitted in the carpometacarpal articulations of the fingers are limited to slight gliding of the articular surfaces upon each other, the extent of which varies in the different joints. The metacarpal bone of the little finger is most movable, then that of the ring finger; the metacarpal bones of the index and middle fingers are almost immovable.

IX. Intermetacarpal Articulations (Articulationes Intermetacarpeæ; Articulations of the Metacarpal Bones with Each Other).

The bases of the second, third, fourth and fifth metacarpal bones articulate with one another by small surfaces covered with cartilage, and are connected together by dorsal, volar, and interosseous ligaments.

The **dorsal** (*ligamenta basium oss. metacarp. dorsalia*) and **palmar ligaments** (*ligamenta basium oss. metacarp. palmaria; palmar ligaments*) pass transversely from one bone to another on the dorsal and volar surfaces. The **interosseous ligaments** (*ligamenta basium oss. metacarp. interossea*) connect their contiguous surfaces, just distal to their collateral articular facets.

The **synovial membrane** for these joints is continuous with that of the carpometacarpal articulations.

The Transverse Metacarpal Ligament (*ligamentum capitulorum [oss. metacarpalium transversum*) (Fig. 399).—This ligament is a narrow fibrous band, which runs across the volar surfaces of the heads of the second, third, fourth and fifth metacarpal bones, connecting them together. It is blended with the volar (glenoid) ligaments of the metacarpophalangeal articulations. Its volar surface is concave where the Flexor tendons pass over it; behind it the tendons of the Interossei pass to their insertions.

X. Metacarpophalangeal Articulations (Articulationes Metacarpophalangeæ; Metacarpophalangeal Joints) (Figs. 399, 400).

These articulations are of the condyloid kind, formed by the reception of the rounded heads of the metacarpal bones into shallow cavities on the proximal ends of the first phalanges, with the exception of that of the thumb, which presents more of the characters of a ginglymoid joint. Each joint has a volar and two collateral ligaments.

The Volar Ligaments (*glenoid ligaments of Cruveilhier; palmar or vaginal ligaments*). —The volar ligaments are thick, dense, fibrocartilaginous structures, placed upon the volar surfaces of the joints in the intervals between the collateral ligaments, to which they are connected; they are loosely united to the metacarpal bones, but are very firmly attached to the bases of the first phalanges. Their volar surfaces are intimately blended with the transverse metacarpal ligament, and present grooves for the passage of the Flexor tendons, the sheaths surrounding which are connected to the sides of the grooves. Their deep surfaces form parts of the articular facets for the heads of the metacarpal bones, and are lined by synovial membranes.

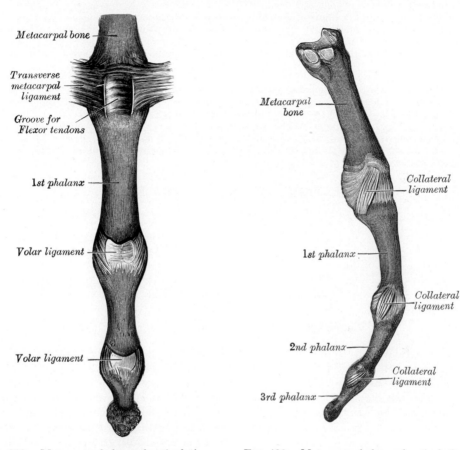

FIG. 399.—Metacarpophalangeal articulation and articulations of digit. Volar aspect.

FIG. 400.—Metacarpophalangeal articulation and articulations of digit. Ulnar aspect.

The Collateral Ligaments (*ligamenta collateralia; lateral ligaments*).—The collateral ligaments are strong, rounded cords, placed on the sides of the joints; each is attached by one extremity to the posterior tubercle and adjacent depression on the side of the head of the metacarpal bone, and by the other to the contiguous extremity of the phalanx.

The dorsal surfaces of these joints are covered by the expansions of the Extensor tendons, together with some loose areolar tissue which connects the deep surfaces of the tendons to the bones.

Movements.—The movements which occur in these joints are flexion, extension, adduction, abduction, and circumduction; the movements of abduction and adduction are very limited, and cannot be performed when the fingers are flexed.

XI. Articulations of the Digits (Articulationes Digitorum Manus; Interphalangeal Joints) (Figs. 399, 400).

The interphalangeal articulations are hinge-joints; each has a volar and two collateral ligaments. The arrangement of these ligaments is similar to those in the metacarpophalangeal articulations. The Extensor tendons supply the place of posterior ligaments.

Movements.—The only movements permitted in the interphalangeal joints are flexion and extension; these movements are more extensive between the first and second phalanges than between the second and third. The amount of flexion is very considerable, but extension is limited by the volar and collateral ligaments.

Muscles Acting on the Joints of the Digits.—Flexion of the metacarpophalangeal joints of the fingers is effected by the Flexores digitorum sublimis and profundus, Lumbricales, and Interossei, assisted in the case of the little finger by the Flexor digiti quinti brevis. Extension is produced by the Extensor digitorum communis, Extensor indicis proprius, and Extensor digiti quinti proprius.

Flexion of the interphalangeal joints of the fingers is accomplished by the Flexor digitorum profundus acting on the proximal and distal joints and by the Flexor digitorum sublimis acting on the proximal joints. Extension is effected mainly by the Lumbricales and Interossei, the long Extensors having little or no action upon these joints.

Flexion of the metacarpophalangeal joint of the thumb is effected by the Flexores pollicis longus and brevis; extension by the Extensores pollicis longus and brevis. Flexion of the interphalangeal joint is accomplished by the Flexor pollicis longus, and extension by the Extensor pollicis longus.

ARTICULATIONS OF THE LOWER EXTREMITY.

The articulations of the Lower Extremity comprise the following:

I. Hip.
II. Knee.
III. Tibiofibular.
IV. Ankle.
V. Intertarsal.
VI. Tarsometatarsal.
VII. Intermetatarsal.
VIII. Metatarsophalangeal.
IX. Articulations of the Digits.

I. Coxal Articulation or Hip-joint (Articulatio Coxæ).

This articulation is an enarthrodial or ball-and-socket joint, formed by the reception of the head of the femur into the cup-shaped cavity of the acetabulum. The articular cartilage on the head of the femur, thicker at the center than at the circumference, covers the entire surface with the exception of the fovea capitis femoris, to which the ligamentum teres is attached; that on the acetabulum forms an incomplete marginal ring, the lunate surface. Within the lunate surface there is a circular depression devoid of cartilage, occupied in the fresh state by a mass of fat, covered by synovial membrane. The ligaments of the joint are:

The Articular Capsule.
The Iliofemoral.
The Ischiofemoral
The Pubocapsular.
The Ligamentum Teres Femoris.
The Glenoidal Labrum.
The Transverse Acetabular

The Articular Capsule (*capsula articularis; capsular ligament*) (Figs. 404, 405).—The articular capsule is strong and dense. *Above*, it is attached to the margin of the acetabulum 5 to 6 mm. beyond the glenoidal labrum behind; but in *front*, it is attached to the outer margin of the labrum, and, opposite to the notch where the margin of the cavity is deficient, it is connected to the transverse ligament, and by a few fibers to the edge of the obturator foramen. It surrounds the neck of the femur, and is attached, in *front*, to the intertrochanteric line; *above*, to the base of the neck; *behind,* to the neck, about 1.25 cm. above the intertrochanteric crest; *below,* to the lower part of the neck, close to the lesser trochanter. From its femoral attachment some of the fibers are reflected upward along the neck as longitudinal bands, termed **retinacula.** The capsule is much thicker at the upper and forepart of the joint, where the greatest amount of resistance is required; behind and below, it is thin and loose. It consists of two sets of fibers, circular and longitudinal. The circular fibers, **zona orbicularis,** are most abundant at the lower and back part of the capsule (Fig. 404), and form a sling or collar around the neck of the femur. Anteriorly they blend with the deep surface of the iliofemoral ligament, and gain an attachment to the anterior inferior iliac spine. The longitudinal fibers are greatest in amount at the upper and front part of the capsule, where they are reinforced by distinct bands, or accessory ligaments, of which the

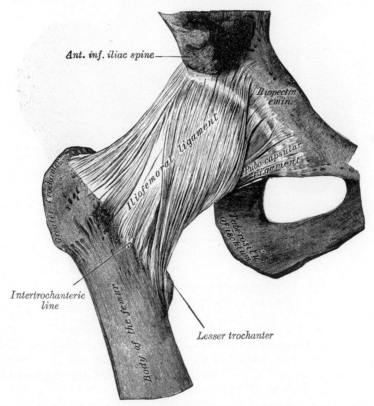

Fig. 401.—Right hip-joint from the front. (Spalteholz.)

most important is the **iliofemoral ligament.** The other accessory bands are known as the **pubocapsular** and the **ischiofemoral ligaments.** The external surface of the capsule is rough, covered by numerous muscles, and separated in front from the Psoas major and Iliacus by a bursa, which not infrequently communicates by a circular aperture with the cavity of the joint.

The Iliofemoral Ligament (*ligamentum iliofemorale; Y-ligament; ligament of Bigelow*) (Fig. 401).—The iliofemoral ligament is a band of great strength which lies in front of the joint; it is intimately connected with the capsule, and serves to strengthen it in this situation. It is attached, *above,* to the lower part of the anterior inferior iliac spine; *below,* it divides into two bands, one of which passes downward and is fixed to the lower part of the intertrochanteric line; the other is directed downward and lateralward and is attached to the upper part of the same line.   Between the two bands is a thinner part of the capsule.   In some cases there is no division, and the ligament spreads out into a flat triangular band which is attached to the whole length of the intertrochanteric line.   This ligament is frequently called the Y-shaped ligament of Bigelow; and its upper band is sometimes named the **iliotrochanteric ligament.**

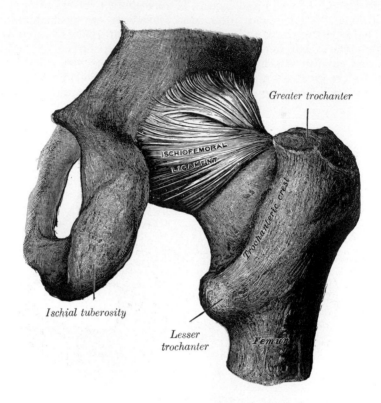

Fig. 402.—The hip-joint from behind.

The Pubocapsular Ligament (*ligamentum pubofemorale; pubofemoral ligament*).— This ligament is attached, *above*, to the obturator crest and the superior ramus of the pubis; *below*, it blends with the capsule and with the deep surface of the vertical band of the iliofemoral ligament.

The Ischiofemoral Ligament (*ligamentum ischiofemorale; ischiofemoral band; ligament of Bertin*).—The ischiofemoral ligament consists of a triangular band of strong fibers, which spring from the ischium below and behind the acetabulum, and blend with the circular fibers of the capsule (Fig. 402).

The Ligamentum Capitis Femoris (*ligamentum teres*) (Fig. 403).—The ligamentum capitis femoris is a triangular, somewhat flattened band implanted by its apex into the antero-superior part of the fovea capitis femoris; its base is attached by two bands, one into either side of the acetabular notch, and between these bony attachments it blends with the transverse ligament.   It is ensheathed by the synovial membrane, and varies greatly in strength in different subjects; occasionally only the synovial fold exists, and in rare cases even this is absent.   The ligament is made tense when the thigh is semiflexed and the limb then adducted or rotated outward; it is, on the other hand, relaxed when the limb is abducted.   It has, however, but little influence as a ligament.

The Acetabular Labrum (*labrum acetabulare; cotyloid ligament*).—The glenoidal labrum is a fibrocartilaginous rim attached to the margin of the acetabulum, the cavity of which it deepens; at the same time it protects the edge of the bone, and fills up the inequalities of its surface. It bridges over the notch as the **transverse ligament,** and thus forms a complete circle, which closely surrounds the head of the femur and assists in holding it in its place. It is triangular on section, its base being attached to the margin of the acetabulum, while its opposite edge is free and sharp. Its two surfaces are invested by synovial membrane, the external one being in contact with the capsule, the internal one being inclined inward so as to narrow the acetabulum, and embrace the cartilaginous surface of the head of the femur. It is much thicker above and behind than below and in front, and consists of compact fibers.

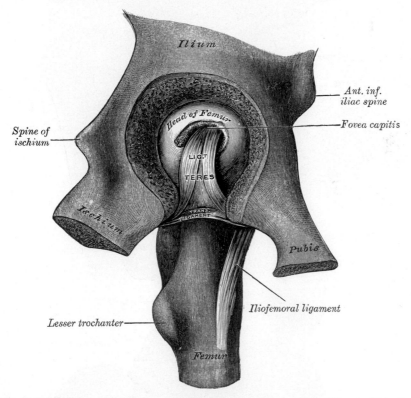

Fig. 403.—Left hip-joint, opened by removing the floor of the acetabulum from within the pelvis.

The Transverse Acetabular Ligament (*ligamentum transversum acetabuli; transverse ligament*).—This ligament is in reality a portion of the glenoidal labrum, though differing from it in having no cartilage cells among its fibers. It consists of strong, flattened fibers, which cross the acetabular notch, and convert it into a foramen through which the nutrient vessels enter the joint.

Synovial Membrane (Fig. 405).—The synovial membrane is very extensive. Commencing at the margin of the cartilaginous surface of the head of the femur, it covers the portion of the neck which is contained within the joint; from the neck it is reflected on the internal surface of the capsule, covers both surfaces of the glenoidal labrum and the mass of fat contained in the depression at the bottom of the acetabulum, and ensheathes the ligamentum teres as far as the head of the femur. The joint cavity sometimes communicates through a hole in the capsule between the vertical band of the iliofemoral ligament and the pubocapsular ligament with a bursa situated on the deep surfaces of the Psoas major and Iliacus.

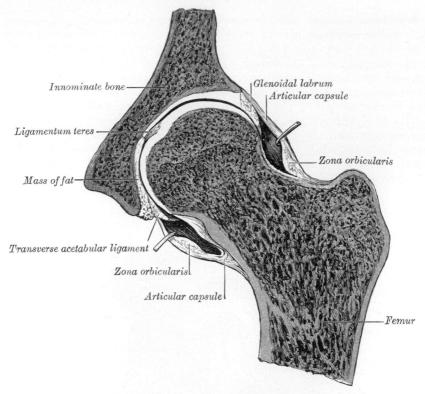

Innominate bone

Ligamentum teres

Mass of fat

Transverse acetabular ligament

Zona orbicularis

Articular capsule

Glenoidal labrum

Articular capsule

Zona orbicularis

Femur

FIG. 404.—A section through the hip-joint.

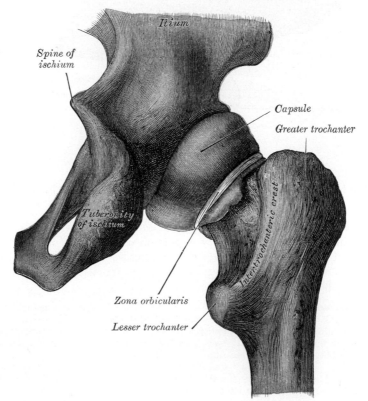

Ilium

Spine of
ischium

Tuberosity
of ischium

Capsule

Greater trochanter

Intertrochanteric crest

Zona orbicularis

Lesser trochanter

FIG. 405.—Capsule of hip-joint (distended).   Posterior aspect.

The **muscles** in relation with the joint are, in *front*, the Psoas major and Iliacus, separated from the capsule by a bursa; *above*, the reflected head of the Rectus femoris and Glutæus minimus, the latter being closely adherent to the capsule; *medially*, the Obturator externus and Pectineus; *behind*, the Piriformis, Gemellus superior, Obturator internus, Gemellus inferior, Obturator externus, and Quadratus femoris (Fig. 406).

The **arteries** supplying the joint are derived from the obturator, medial femoral circumflex, and superior and inferior gluteals.

The **nerves** are articular branches from the sacral plexus, sciatic, obturator, accessory obturator, and a filament from the branch of the femoral supplying the Rectus femoris.

Movements.—The movements of the hip are very extensive, and consist of flexion, extension, adduction, abduction, circumduction, and rotation.

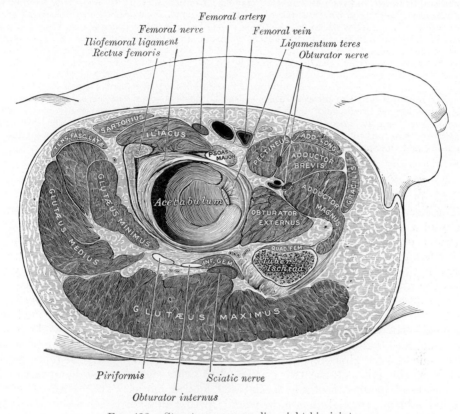

Fig. 406.—Structures surrounding right hip-joint.

The length of the neck of the femur and its inclinations to the body of the bone have the effect of converting the angular movements of flexion, extension, adduction, and abduction partially into rotatory movements in the joint. Thus when the thigh is flexed or extended, the head of the femur, on account of the *medial* inclination of the neck, rotates within the acetabulum with only a slight amount of gliding to and fro. The *forward* slope of the neck similarly affects the movements of adduction and abduction. Conversely rotation of the thigh which is permitted by the *upward* inclination of the neck, is not a simple rotation of the head of the femur in the acetabulum, but is accompanied by a certain amount of gliding.

The hip-joint presents a very striking contrast to the shoulder-joint in the much more complete mechanical arrangements for its security and for the limitation of its movements. In the shoulder, as has been seen, the head of the humerus is not adapted at all in size to the glenoid cavity, and is hardly restrained in any of its ordinary movements by the capsule. In the hip-joint, on the contrary, the head of the femur is closely fitted to the acetabulum for an area extending over nearly half a sphere, and at the margin of the bony cup it is still more closely embraced by the glenoidal labrum, so that the head of the femur is held in its place by that ligament even when the fibers of the capsule have been quite divided. The iliofemoral ligament is the strongest of all the ligaments in the body, and is put on the stretch by any attempt to extend the femur beyond a straight line with the trunk. That is to say, this ligament is the chief agent in maintaining the erect position without muscular fatigue; for a vertical line passing through the center of gravity of the trunk falls behind the centers of rotation in the hip-joints, and therefore the pelvis tends to fall backward, but is prevented by the tension of the iliofemoral ligaments. The security of the joint may be provided for also by the two bones being directly united through the ligamentum teres; but it is doubtful whether this ligament has much influence upon the mechanism of the joint. When the knee is flexed, flexion of the hip-joint is arrested by the soft parts of the thigh and abdomen being brought into contact, and when the knee is extended, by the action of the hamstring muscles; extension is checked by the tension of the iliofemoral ligament; adduction by the thighs coming into contact; adduction with flexion by the lateral band of the iliofemoral ligament and the lateral part of the capsule; abduction by the medial band of the iliofemoral ligament and the pubocapsular ligament; rotation outward by the lateral band of the iliofemoral ligament; and rotation inward by the ischiocapsular ligament and the hinder part of the capsule. The muscles which *flex* the femur on the pelvis are the Psoas major, Iliacus, Tensor fasciæ latæ, Rectus femoris, Sartorius, Pectineus, Adductors longus and brevis, and the anterior fibers of the Glutæi medius and minimus. *Extension* is mainly performed by the Glutæus maximus, assisted by the hamstring muscles and the ischial head of the Adductor magnus. The thigh is *adducted* by the Adductores magnus, longus, and brevis, the Pectineus, and the Gracilis, and *abducted* by the Glutæi medius and minimus. The muscles which *rotate* the thigh *inward* are the Glutæus minimus and the anterior fibers of the Glutæus medius, the Tensor fasciæ latæ the Adductores longus, brevis, and magnus, the Pectineus, and the Iliacus and Psoas major; while those which rotate it *outward* are the posterior fibers of the Glutæus medius, the Piriformis, Obturatores externus and internus, Gemelli superior and inferior, Quadratus femoris, Glutæus maximus, and the Sartorius.

II. The Knee-joint (Articulatio Genu).

The knee-joint was formerly described as a ginglymus or hinge-joint, but is really of a much more complicated character. It must be regarded as consisting of three articulations in one: two condyloid joints, one between each condyle of the femur and the corresponding meniscus and condyle of the tibia; and a third between the patella and the femur, partly arthrodial, but not completely so, since the articular surfaces are not mutually adapted to each other, so that the movement is not a simple gliding one. This view of the construction of the knee-joint receives confirmation from the study of the articulation in some of the lower mammals, where, corresponding to these three subdivisions, three synovial cavities are sometimes found, either entirely distinct or only connected together by small communications. This view is further rendered probable by the existence in the middle of the joint of the two cruciate ligaments, which must be regarded as the collateral ligaments of the medial and lateral joints. The existence of the patellar fold of synovial membrane would further indicate a tendency to separation of the synovial cavity into two minor sacs, one corresponding to the lateral and the other to the medial joint.

The bones are connected together by the following ligaments:

The Articular Capsule.	The Anterior Cruciate.
The Ligamentum Patellæ.	The Posterior Cruciate.
The Oblique Popliteal.	The Medial and Lateral Menisci.
The Arcuate Popliteal.	The Transverse.
The Tibial Collateral.	The Coronary.
The Fibular Collateral.	

The Articular Capsule (*capsula articularis; capsular ligament*) (Fig. 407).—The articular capsule consists of a thin, but strong, fibrous membrane which is strengthened in almost its entire extent by bands inseparably connected with it. Above and in front, beneath the tendon of the Quadriceps femoris, it is represented only by the synovial membrane. Its chief strengthening bands are derived from the fascia lata and from the tendons surrounding the joint. In front, expansions from the Vasti and from the fascia lata and its iliotibial band fill in the intervals between the anterior and collateral ligaments, constituting the **medial** and **lateral patellar retinacula.** Behind, the capsule consists of vertical fibers which arise from the condyles and from the sides of the intercondyloid fossa of the femur; the posterior part of the capsule is therefore situated on the sides of and in front of the cruciate ligaments, which are thus excluded from the joint cavity. Behind the cruciate ligaments is the oblique popliteal ligament which is augmented by fibers derived from the tendon of the Semimembranosus. Laterally, a prolongation from the iliotibial band fills in the interval between the oblique popliteal and the fibular collateral ligaments, and partly covers the latter. Medially, expansions from the Sartorius and Semimembranosus pass upward to the tibial collateral ligament and strengthen the capsule.

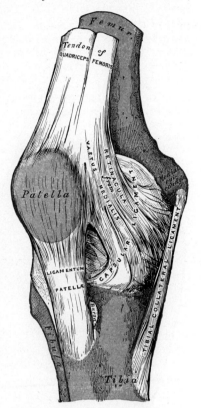

Fig. 407.—Right knee-joint. Anterior view.

The **Ligamentum Patellæ** (*anterior ligament*) (Fig. 407).—The ligamentum patellæ is the central portion of the common tendon of the Quadriceps femoris, which is continued from the patella to the tuberosity of the tibia. It is a strong, flat, ligamentous band, about 8 cm. in length, attached, *above*, to the apex and adjoining margins of the patella and the rough depression on its posterior surface; *below*, to the tuberosity of the tibia; its superficial fibers are continuous over the front of the patella with those of the tendon of the Quadriceps femoris. The medial and lateral portions of the tendon of the Quadriceps pass down on either side of the patella, to be inserted into the upper extremity of the tibia on either side of the tuberosity; these portions merge into the capsule, as stated above, forming the medial and lateral patellar retinacula. The posterior surface of the ligamentum patellæ is separated from the synovial membrane of the joint by a large infrapatellar pad of fat, and from the tibia by a bursa.

The **Oblique Popliteal Ligament** (*ligamentum popliteum obliquum; posterior ligament*) (Fig. 408).—This ligament is a broad, flat, fibrous band, formed of fasciculi separated from one another by apertures for the passage of vessels and nerves. It is attached above to the upper margin of the intercondyloid fossa and posterior surface of the femur close to the articular margins of the condyles, and below to the posterior margin of the head of the tibia. Superficial to the main part of the ligament is a strong fasciculus, derived from the tendon of the Semimembranosus and passing from the back part of the medial condyle of the tibia obliquely upward and lateralward to the back part of the lateral condyle of the femur. The oblique popliteal ligament forms part of the floor of the popliteal fossa, and the popliteal artery rests upon it.

The **Arcuate Popliteal Ligament** (Fig. 408).—This ligament arches downward from the lateral condyle of the femur to the posterior surface of the capsular ligament. It is connected to the styloid process of the head of the fibula by two converging bands.

The Tibial Collateral Ligament (*ligamentum collaterale tibiale; internal lateral liga-*
ment) (Fig. 407).—The tibial collateral is a broad, flat, membranous band, situated
nearer to the back than to the front of the joint. It is attached, *above*, to the medial
condyle of the femur immediately below the adductor tubercle; *below*, to the medial
condyle and medial surface of the body of the tibia. The fibers of the posterior
part of the ligament are short and incline backward as they descend; they are
inserted into the tibia above the groove for the Semimembranosus. The anterior
part of the ligament is a flattened band, about 10 cm. long, which inclines forward
as it descends. It is inserted into the medial surface of the body of the tibia about
2.5 cm. below the level of the condyle. It is crossed, at its lower part, by the
tendons of the Sartorius, Gracilis, and Semitendinosus, a bursa being interposed.
Its deep surface covers the inferior medial genicular vessels and nerve and the
anterior portion of the tendon of the Semimembranosus, with which it is connected
by a few fibers; it is intimately adherent to the medial meniscus.

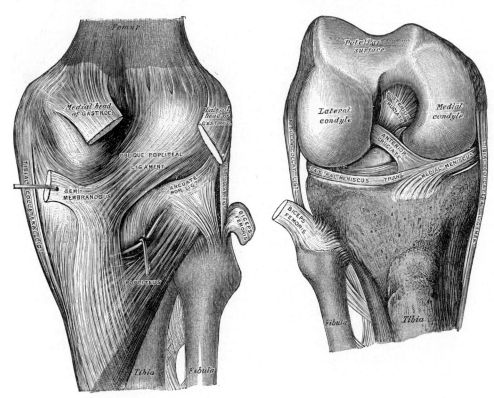

FIG. 408.—The right knee-joint. Posterior   FIG. 409.—The right knee-joint. Dissected
            aspect.   from the front.

The Fibular Collateral Ligament (*ligamentum collaterale fibulare; external lateral or*
long external lateral ligament) (Fig. 410).—The fibular collateral is a strong, rounded,
fibrous cord, attached, *above*, to the back part of the lateral condyle of the femur,
immediately above the groove for the tendon of the Popliteus; *below*, to the lateral
side of the head of the fibula, in front of the styloid process. The greater part of
its lateral surface is covered by the tendon of the Biceps femoris; the tendon,
however, divides at its insertion into two parts, which are separated by the ligament. Deep to the ligament are the tendon of the Popliteus, and the inferior
lateral genicular vessels and nerve. The ligament has no attachment to the lateral
meniscus.

An inconstant bundle of fibers, the **short fibular collateral ligament,** is placed behind and parallel with the preceding, attached, *above,* to the lower and back part of the lateral condyle of the femur; *below,* to the summit of the styloid process of the fibula. Passing deep to it are the tendon of the Popliteus, and the inferior lateral genicular vessels and nerve.

The Cruciate Ligaments (*ligamenta cruciata genu; crucial ligaments*).—The cruciate ligaments are of considerable strength, situated in the middle of the joint, nearer to its posterior than to its anterior surface. They are called *cruciate* because they cross each other somewhat like the lines of the letter X; and have received the names **anterior** and **posterior,** from the position of their attachments to the tibia.

The Anterior Cruciate Ligament (*ligamentum cruciatum anterius; external crucial ligament*) (Fig. 409) is attached to the depression in front of the intercondyloid eminence of the tibia, being blended with the anterior extremity of the lateral meniscus; it passes upward, backward, and lateralward, and is fixed into the medial and back part of the lateral condyle of the femur. (See Fig. 311).

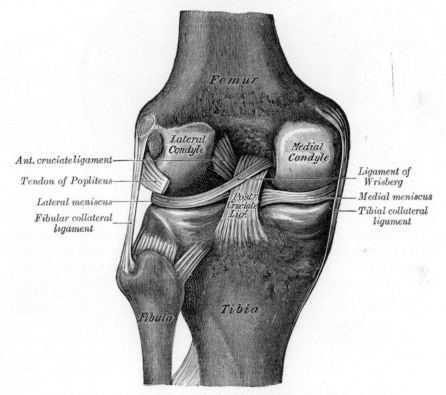

Fig. 410.—Left knee-joint from behind, showing interior ligaments.

The Posterior Cruciate Ligament (*ligamentum cruciatum posterius; internal crucial ligament*) (Fig. 410) is stronger, but shorter and less oblique in its direction, than the anterior. It is attached to the posterior intercondyloid fossa of the tibia, and to the posterior extremity of the lateral meniscus; and passes upward, forward, and medialward, to be fixed into the lateral and front part of the medial condyle of the femur. (See Fig. 311).

The Menisci (*semilunar fibrocartilages*) (Fig. 411).—The menisci are two crescentic lamellæ, which serve to deepen the surfaces of the head of the tibia for articulation with the condyles of the femur. The peripheral border of each meniscus is thick, convex, and attached to the inside of the capsule of the joint; the opposite border is thin, concave, and free. The upper surfaces of the menisci are concave, and in contact with the condyles of the femur; their lower surfaces are flat, and rest upon the head of the tibia; both surfaces are smooth, and invested by synovial membrane. Each meniscus covers approximately the peripheral two-thirds of the corresponding articular surface of the tibia.

The **medial meniscus** (*meniscus medialis; internal semilunar fibrocartilage*) is nearly semicircular in form, a little elongated from before backward, and broader behind than in front; its anterior end, thin and pointed, is attached to the anterior intercondyloid fossa of the tibia, in front of the anterior cruciate ligament; its posterior end is fixed to the posterior intercondyloid fossa of the tibia, between the attachments of the lateral meniscus and the posterior cruciate ligament.

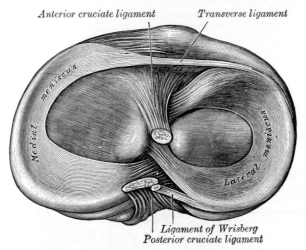

Anterior cruciate ligament　　　　Transverse ligament

Ligament of Wrisberg
Posterior cruciate ligament

Fig. 411.—Head of right tibia seen from above, showing menisci and attachments of ligaments.

The **lateral meniscus** (*meniscus lateralis; external semilunar fibrocartilage*) is nearly circular and covers a larger portion of the articular surface than the medial one. It is grooved laterally for the tendon of the Popliteus, which separates it from the fibular collateral ligament. Its anterior end is attached in front of the intercondyloid eminence of the tibia, lateral to, and behind, the anterior cruciate ligament, with which it blends; the posterior end is attached behind the intercondyloid eminence of the tibia and in front of the posterior end of the medial meniscus. The anterior attachment of the lateral meniscus is twisted on itself so that its free margin looks backward and upward, its anterior end resting on a sloping shelf of bone on the front of the lateral process of the intercondyloid eminence. Close to its posterior attachment it sends off a strong fasciculus, the **ligament of Wrisberg** (Figs. 410, 411), which passes upward and medialward, to be inserted into the medial condyle of the femur, immediately behind the attachment of the posterior cruciate ligament. Occasionally a small fasciculus passes forward to be inserted into the lateral part of the anterior cruciate ligament. The lateral meniscus gives off from its anterior convex margin a fasciculus which forms the transverse ligament.

The **Transverse Ligament** (*ligamentum transversum genus*).—The transverse ligament connects the anterior convex margin of the lateral meniscus to the anterior end of the medial meniscus; its thickness varies considerably in different subjects, and it is sometimes absent.

The **coronary ligaments** are merely portions of the capsule, which connect the periphery of each meniscus with the margin of the head of the tibia.

Synovial Membrane.—The synovial membrane of the knee-joint is the largest and most extensive in the body. Commencing at the upper border of the patella, it forms a large cul-de-sac beneath the Quadriceps femoris (Figs. 412, 413) on the lower part of the front of the femur, and frequently communicates with a bursa interposed between the tendon and the front of the femur. The pouch of synovial membrane between the Quadriceps and front of the femur is supported, during the movements of the knee, by a small muscle, the Articularis genu, which is inserted into it. On either side of the patella, the synovial membrane extends beneath the aponeuroses of the Vasti, and more especially beneath that of the Vastus medialis. Below the patella it is separated from the ligamentum patellæ by a considerable quantity of fat, known as

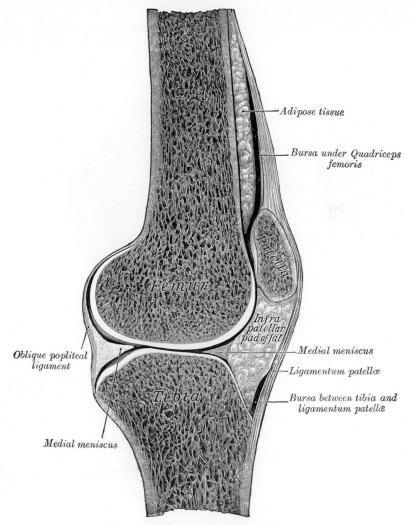

Fig. 412.—Sagittal section of right knee-joint.

the **infrapatellar pad.** From the medial and lateral borders of the articular surface of the patella, reduplications of the synovial membrane project into the interior of the joint. These form two fringe-like folds termed the **alar folds**; below, these folds converge and are continued as a single band, the **patellar fold** (*ligamentum mucosum*), to the front of the intercondyloid fossa of the femur. On either side of the joint, the synovial membrane passes downward from the femur, lining the capsule to its point of attachment to the menisci; it may then be traced over the upper surfaces of these to their free borders, and thence along their under surfaces to the tibia (Figs. 413, 414). At the back part of the lateral meniscus it forms a cul-de-sac between the groove on its surface and the tendon of the Popliteus; it is reflected across the front of the cruciate ligaments, which are therefore situated outside the synovial cavity.

25

Bursæ.—The bursæ near the knee-joint are the following: In front there are *four* bursæ: a large one is interposed between the patella and the skin, a small one between the upper part of the tibia and the ligamentum patellæ, a third between the lower part of the tuberosity of the tibia and the skin, and a fourth between the anterior surface of the lower part of the femur and the deep surface of the Quadriceps femoris, usually communicating with the knee-joint. Laterally there are four bursæ: (1) one (which sometimes communicates with the joint) between the lateral head of the Gastrocnemius and the capsule; (2) one between the fibular collateral ligament and the tendon of the Biceps; (3) one between the fibular collateral ligament and the tendon of the Popliteus (this is sometimes only an expansion from the next bursa); (4) one between the tendon of the Popliteus and the lateral condyle of the femur, usually an extension from the synovial membrane of the joint. Medially, there are five bursæ: (1) one between the medial head of the Gastrocnemius and the capsule; this sends a prolongation between the tendon of the

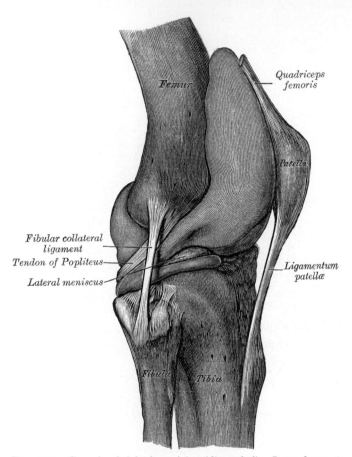

Femur

Quadriceps
femoris

Patella

Fibular collateral
ligament

Tendon of Popliteus

Lateral meniscus

Ligamentum
patellæ

Fibula   Tibia

Fig. 413.—Capsule of right knee-joint (distended). Lateral aspect.

medial head of the Gastrocnemius and the tendon of the Semimembranosus and often communicates with the joint; (2) one superficial to the tibial collateral ligament, between it and the tendons of the Sartorius, Gracilis, and Semitendinosus; (3) one deep to the tibial collateral ligament, between it and the tendon of the Semimembranosus (this is sometimes only an expansion from the next bursa); (4) one between the tendon of the Semimembranosus and the head of the tibia; (5) occasionally there is a bursa between the tendons of the Semimembranosus and Semitendinosus.

Structures Around the Joint.—In front, and at the sides, is the Quadriceps femoris; laterally the tendons of the Biceps femoris and Popliteus and the common peroneal nerve; medially, the Sartorius, Gracilis, Semitendinosus, and Semimembranosus; behind, the popliteal vessels and the tibial nerve, Popliteus, Plantaris, and medial and lateral heads of the Gastrocnemius some lymph glands, and fat.

The **arteries** supplying the joint are the highest genicular (anastomotica magna), a branch of the femoral, the genicular branches of the popliteal, the recurrent branches of the anterior tibial, and the descending branch from the lateral femoral circumflex of the profunda femoris.

The **nerves** are derived from the obturator, femoral, tibial, and common peroneal.

Movements.—The movements which take place at the knee-joint are flexion and extension, and, in certain positions of the joint, internal and external rotation. The movements of flexion and extension at this joint differ from those in a typical hinge-joint, such as the elbow, in that (*a*) the axis around which motion takes place is not a fixed one, but shifts forward during extension and backward during flexion; (*b*) the commencement of flexion and the end of extension are accompanied by rotatory movements associated with the fixation of the limb in a position of great stability. The movement from full flexion to full extension may therefore be described in three phases:

1. In the fully flexed condition the posterior parts of the femoral condyles rest on the corresponding portions of the meniscotibial surfaces, and in this position a slight amount of simple rolling movement is allowed.

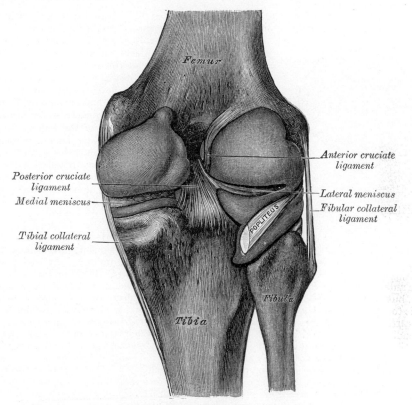

Fig. 414.—Capsule of right knee-joint (distended). Posterior aspect.

2. During the passage of the limb from the flexed to the extended position a gliding movement is superposed on the rolling, so that the axis, which at the commencement is represented by a line through the inner and outer condyles of the femur, gradually shifts forward. In this part of the movement, the posterior two-thirds of the tibial articular surfaces of the two femoral condyles are involved, and as these have similar curvatures and are parallel to one another, they move forward equally.

3. The lateral condyle of the femur is brought almost to rest by the tightening of the anterior cruciate ligament; it moves, however, slightly forward and medialward, pushing before it the anterior part of the lateral meniscus. The tibial surface on the medial condyle is prolonged farther forward than that on the lateral, and this prolongation is directed lateralward. When, therefore, the movement forward of the condyles is checked by the anterior cruciate ligament, continued muscular action causes the medial condyle, dragging with it the meniscus, to travel backward and medialward, thus producing an internal rotation of the thigh on the leg. When the position of full extension is reached the lateral part of the groove on the lateral condyle is pressed against the anterior part of the corresponding meniscus, while the medial part of the

groove rests on the articular margin in front of the lateral process of the tibial intercondyloid eminence. Into the groove on the medial condyle is fitted the anterior part of the medial meniscus, while the anterior cruciate ligament and the articular margin in front of the medial process is the tibial intercondyloid eminence are received into the forepart of the intercondyloid fossa of the femur. This third phase by which all these parts are brought into accurate apposition of known as the "screwing home," or locking movement of the joint.

The complete movement of flexion is the converse of that described above, and is therefore preceded by an external rotation of the femur which unlocks the extended joint.

The axes around which the movements of flexion and extension take place are not precisely at right angles to either bone; in flexion, the femur and tibia are in the same plane, but in extension the one bone forms an angle, opening lateralward with the other.

In addition to the rotatory movements associated with the completion of extension and the initiation of flexion, rotation inward or outward can be effected when the joint is partially flexed; these movements take place mainly between the tibia and the menisci, and are freest when the leg is bent at right angles with the thigh.

Movements of Patella.—The articular surface of the patella is indistinctly divided into seven facets—upper, middle, and lower horizontal pairs, and a medial perpendicular facet (Fig. 415).

When the knee is forcibly flexed, the medial perpendicular facet is in contact with the semilunar surface on the lateral part of the medial condyle; this semilunar surface is a prolongation backward of the medial part of the patellar surface. As the leg is carried from the flexed to the extended position, first the highest pair, then the middle pair, and lastly the lowest pair of horizontal facets is successively brought into contact with the patellar surface of the femur. In the extended position, when the Quadriceps femoris is relaxed, the patella lies loosely on the front of the lower end of the femur.

During flexion, the ligamentum patellæ is put upon the stretch, and in extreme flexion the posterior cruciate ligament, the oblique popliteal, and collateral ligaments, and, to a slight extent, the anterior cruciate ligament, are relaxed. Flexion is checked during life by the contact of the leg with the thigh. When the knee-joint is fully extended the oblique popliteal and collateral ligaments, the anterior cruciate ligament, and the posterior cruciate ligament, are rendered tense; in the act of extending the knee, the ligamentum patellæ is tightened by the Quadriceps femoris, but in full extension with the heel supported it is relaxed. Rotation inward is checked by the anterior cruciate ligament; rotation outward tends to uncross and relax the cruciate ligaments, but is checked by the tibial collateral ligament. The main function of the cruciate ligament is to act as a direct bond between the tibia and femur and to prevent the former bone from being carried too far backward or forward. They also assist the collateral ligaments in resisting any bending of the joint to either side. The menisci are intended, as it seems, to adapt the surfaces of the tibia to the shape of the femoral condyles to a certain extent, so as to fill up the intervals which would otherwise be left in the varying positions of the joint, and to obviate the jars which would be so frequently transmitted up the limb in jumping or by falls on the feet; also to permit of the two varieties of motion, flexion and extension, and rotation, as explained above. The patella is a great defence to the front of the knee-joint, and distributes upon a large and tolerably even surface, during kneeling, the pressure which would otherwise fall upon the prominent ridges of the condyles; it also affords leverage to the Quadriceps femoris.

When standing erect in the attitude of "attention," the weight of the body falls in front of a line carried across the centers of the knee-joints, and therefore tends to produce overextension of the articulations; this, however, is prevented by the tension of the anterior cruciate, oblique popliteal, and collateral ligaments.

Extension of the leg on the thigh is performed by the Quadriceps femoris; *flexion* by the Biceps femoris, Semitendinosus, and Semimembranosus, assisted by the Gracilis, Sartorius, Gastrocnemius, Popliteus, and Plantaris. *Rotation outward* is effected by the Biceps femoris, and *rotation inward* by the Popliteus, Semitendinosus, and, to a slight extent, the Semimembranosus, the Sartorius, and the Gracilis. The Popliteus comes into action especially at the commencement of the movement of flexion of the knee; by its contraction the leg is rotated inward, or, if the tibia be fixed, the thigh is rotated outward, and the knee-joint is unlocked.

III. Articulations between the Tibia and Fibula.

The tibia and fibula are connected by: (1) the Tibiofibular articulation; (2) the interosseous membrane; (3) the Tibiofibular syndesmosis.

FIG. 415.—Posterior surface of the right patella, showing diagrammatically the areas of contact with the femur in different positions of the knee.

Tibiofibular Articulation (*articulatio tibiofibularis; superior tibiofibular articulation*).—This articulation is an arthrodial joint between the lateral condyle of the tibia and the head of the fibula. The contiguous surfaces of the bones present flat, oval facets covered with cartilage and connected together by an articular capsule and by anterior and posterior ligaments.

The Articular Capsule (*capsula articularis; capsular ligament*).—The articular capsule surrounds the articulation, being attached around the margins of the articular facets on the tibia and fibula; it is much thicker in front than behind.

The Anterior Ligament (*Ligamentum capitis fibulæ anterius*).—The anterior ligament of the head of the fibula (Fig. 409) consists of two or three broad and flat bands, which pass obliquely upward from the front of the head of the fibula to the front of the lateral condyle of the tibia.

The Posterior Ligament (*lig. cap. fibulæ posterius*).—The posterior ligament of the head of the fibula (Fig. 410) is a single thick and broad band, which passes obliquely upward from the back of the head of the fibula to the back of the lateral condyle of the tibia. It is covered by the tendon of the Popliteus.

Synovial Membrane.—A synovial membrane lines the capsule; it is continuous with that of the knee-joint in occasional cases when the two joints communicate.

Interosseous Membrane (*membrana interossea cruris; middle tibiofibular ligament*).—An interosseous membrane extends between the interosseous crests of the tibia and fibula, and separates the muscles on the front from those on the back of the leg. It consists of a thin, aponeurotic lamina composed of oblique fibers, which for the most part run downward and lateralward; some few fibers, however, pass in the opposite direction. It is broader above than below. Its upper margin does not quite reach the tibiofibular joint, but presents a free concave border, above which is a large, oval aperture for the passage of the anterior tibial vessels to the front of the leg. In its lower part is an opening for the passage of the anterior peroneal vessels. It is continuous below with the interosseous ligament of the tibiofibular syndesmosis, and presents numerous perforations for the passage of small vessels. It is in relation, in *front*, with the Tibialis anterior, Extensor digitorum longus, Extensor hallucis proprius, Peronæus tertius, and the anterior tibial vessels and deep peroneal nerve; *behind*, with the Tibialis posterior and Flexor hallucis longus.

Tibiofibular Syndesmosis (*syndesmosis tibiofibularis; inferior tibiofibular articulation*).—This syndesmosis is formed by the rough, convex surface of the medial side of the lower end of the fibula, and a rough concave surface on the lateral side of the tibia. Below, to the extent of about 4 mm. these surfaces are smooth, and covered with cartilage, which is continuous with that of the ankle-joint. The ligaments are: anterior, posterior, inferior transverse, and interosseous.

The Anterior Tibiofibular Ligament (*ligamentum tibiofibulare anterius*).—The anterior ligament (Fig. 417) is a flat, triangular band of fibers, broader below than above, which extends obliquely downward and lateralward between the adjacent margins of the tibia and fibula, on the front aspect of the syndesmosis. It is in relation, in *front*, with the Peronæus tertius, the aponeurosis of the leg, and the integument; *behind*, with the interosseous ligament; and lies in contact with the cartilage covering the talus.

The Posterior Tibiofibular Ligament (*ligamentum tibiofibulare posterius*).—The posterior ligament (Fig. 417), smaller than the preceding, is disposed in a similar manner on the posterior surface of the syndesmosis.

The Inferior Transverse Ligament.—The inferior transverse ligament lies in front of the posterior ligament, and is a strong, thick band, of yellowish fibers which passes transversely across the back of the joint, from the lateral malleolus to the posterior border of the articular surface of the tibia, almost as far as its malleolar process. This ligament projects below the margin of the bones, and forms part of the articulating surface for the talus.

The Interosseous Ligament.—The interosseous ligament consists of numerous short, strong, fibrous bands, which pass between the contiguous rough surfaces of the tibia and fibula, and constitute the chief bond of union between the bones. It is continuous, above, with the interosseous membrane (Fig. 420).

Synovial Membrane.—The synovial membrane associated with the small arthrodial part of this joint is continuous with that of the ankle-joint.

IV. Talocrural Articulation or Ankle-joint (Articulatio Talocruralis; Tibiotarsal Articulation).

The ankle-joint is a ginglymus, or hinge-joint. The structures entering into its formation are the lower end of the tibia and its malleolus, the malleolus of the

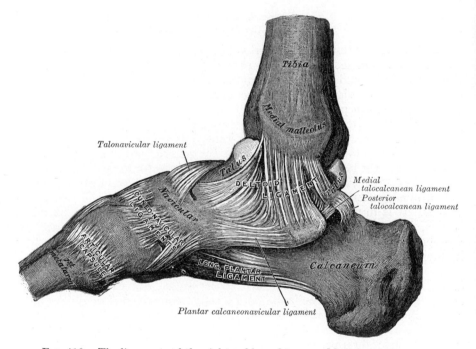

Talonavicular ligament

Medial talocalcanean ligament

Posterior talocalcanean ligament

Plantar calcaneonavicular ligament

Fig. 416.—The ligaments of the right ankle and tarsus. Medial aspect.

fibula, and the inferior transverse ligament, which together form a mortise for the reception of the upper convex surface of the talus and its medial and lateral facets. The bones are connected by the following ligaments:

The Articular Capsule.   The Anterior Talofibular.
The Deltoid.   The Posterior Talofibular.
                The Calcaneofibular.

The Articular Capsule (*capsula articularis; capsular ligament*).—The articular capsule surrounds the joints, and is attached, *above*, to the borders of the articular surfaces of the tibia and malleoli; and *below*, to the talus around its upper articular surface. The anterior part of the capsule (*anterior ligament*) is a broad, thin, membranous layer, attached, *above*, to the anterior margin of the lower end of the tibia; *below*, to the talus, in front of its superior articular surface. It is in relation, in *front*, with the Extensor tendons of the toes, the tendons of the Tibialis anterior and Peronæus tertius, and the anterior tibial vessels and deep peroneal nerve. The posterior part of the capsule (*posterior ligament*) is very thin, and consists principally of transverse fibers. It is attached, *above*, to the margin of the articular surface of the tibia, blending with the transverse ligament; *below*, to the talus behind its superior articular facet. Laterally, it is somewhat thickened, and is attached to the hollow on the medial surface of the lateral malleolus.

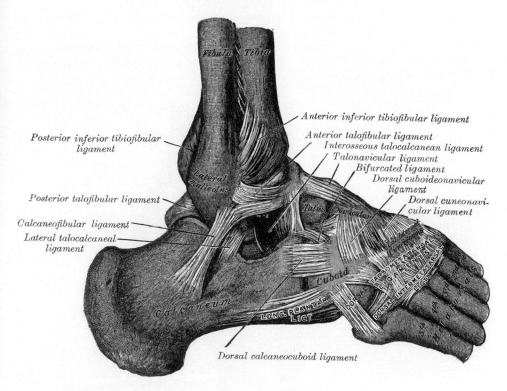

Fig. 417.—The ligaments of the right ankle and tarsus. Lateral aspect.

The Deltoid Ligament (*ligamentum deltoideum; internal lateral ligament*) (Fig. 416).—The deltoid ligament is a strong, flat, triangular band, attached, *above*, to the apex and anterior and posterior borders of the medial malleolus. It consists of two sets of fibers, superficial and deep. Of the superficial fibers the most anterior (*tibionavicular*) pass forward to be inserted into the tuberosity of the navicular bone, and immediately behind this they blend with the medial margin of the plantar calcaneonavicular ligament; the middle (*calcaneotibial*) descend almost perpendicularly to be inserted into the whole length of the sustentaculum tali of the calcaneus; the posterior fibers (*posterior talotibial*) pass backward and lateralward to be attached to the inner side of the talus, and to the prominent tubercle on its posterior surface, medial to the groove for the tendon of the Flexor hallucis longus. The deep fibers (*anterior talotibial*) are attached, *above*, to the tip of the medial malleolus, and, *below*, to the medial surface of the talus. The deltoid ligament is covered by the tendons of the Tibialis posterior and Flexor digitorum longus.

The anterior and posterior talofibular and the calcaneofibular ligaments were formerly described as the three fasciculi of the *external lateral ligament* of the ankle-joint.

The Anterior Talofibular Ligament (*ligamentum talofibulare anterius*) (Fig. 417). —The anterior talofibular ligament, the shortest of the three, passes from the anterior margin of the fibular malleolus, forward and medially, to the talus, in front of its lateral articular facet.

The Posterior Talofibular Ligament (*ligamentum talofibulare posterius*) (Fig. 418). —The posterior talofibular ligament, the strongest and most deeply seated, runs almost horizontally from the depression at the medial and back part of the fibular malleolus to a prominent tubercle on the posterior surface of the talus immediately lateral to the groove for the tendon of the Flexor hallucis longus.

The Calcaneofibular Ligament (*ligamentum calcaneofibulare*) (Fig. 417).—The calcaneofibular ligament, the longest of the three, is a narrow, rounded cord, running from the apex of the fibular malleolus downward and slightly backward to a tubercle on the lateral surface of the calcaneus. It is covered by the tendons of the Peronæi longus and brevis.

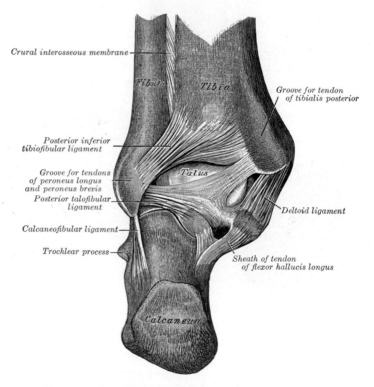

FIG. 418.—The left ankle-joint. Posterior aspect.

Synovial Membrane (Fig. 419).—The synovial membrane invests the deep surfaces of the ligaments, and sends a small process upward between the lower ends of the tibia and fibula.

Relations.—The tendons, vessels, and nerves in connection with the joint are, in *front*, from the medial side, the Tibialis anterior, Extensor hallucis proprius, anterior tibial vessels, deep peroneal nerve, Extensor digitorum longus, and Peronæus tertius; *behind*, from the medial side, the Tibialis posterior, Flexor digitorum longus, posterior tibial vessels, tibial nerve, Flexor hallucis longus; and, in the groove behind the fibular malleolus, the tendons of the Peronæi longus and brevis.

The **arteries** supplying the joint are derived from the malleolar branches of the anterior tibial and the peroneal.

The **nerves** are derived from the deep peroneal and tibial.

Movements.—When the body is in the erect position, the foot is at right angles to the leg. The movements of the joint are those of dorsiflexion and plantar flexion; dorsiflexion consists in the approximation of the dorsum of the foot to the front of the leg, while in plantar flexion the heel is drawn up and the toes pointed downward. The range of movement varies in different individuals from about 50° to 90°. The transverse axis about which movement takes place is slightly oblique. The malleoli tightly embrace the talus in all positions of the joint, so that any slight degree of side-to-side movement which may exist is simply due to stretching of the ligaments of the talofibular syndesmosis, and slight bending of the body of the fibula. The superior articular surface of the talus is broader in front than behind. In dorsiflexion, therefore, greater space is required between the two malleoli. This is obtained by a slight outward rotatory movement of the lower end of the fibula and a stretching of the ligaments of the syndesmosis; this lateral movement is facilitated by a slight gliding at the tibiofibular articulation, and possibly also by the bending of the body of the fibula. Of the ligaments, the deltoid is of very great power—so much so, that it usually resists a force which fractures the process of bone to which it is attached. Its middle portion, together with the calcaneofibular ligament, binds the bones of the leg firmly to the foot, and resists displacement in every direction. Its anterior and posterior fibers limit plantar flexion and dorsal flexion of the foot and the anterior fibers also limit abduction. The posterior talofibular ligament assists the calcaneofibular in resisting the displacement of the foot backward, and deepens the cavity for the reception of the talus. The anterior talofibular is a security against the displacement of the foot forward, and limits plantar flexion of the joint.

The movements of inversion and eversion of the foot, together with the minute changes in form by which it is applied to the ground or takes hold of an object in climbing, etc., are mainly effected in the tarsal joints; the joint which enjoys the greatest amount of motion being that between the talus and calcaneus behind and the navicular and cuboid in front. This is often called the **transverse tarsal joint,** and it can, with the subordinate joints of the tarsus, replace the ankle-joint in a great measure when the latter has become ankylosed.

Plantar flexion of the foot upon the tibia and fibula is produced by the Gastrocnemius, Soleus, Plantaris, Tibialis posterior, Poronæi longus and brevis, Flexor digitorum longus, and Flexor hallucis longus; *dorsiflexion*, by the Tibialis anterior, Peronæus tertius, Extensor digitorum longus, and Extensor hallucis longus.

V. Intertarsal Articulations (Articulationes Intertarseæ; Articulations of the Tarsus).

Subtalar Articulation (*articulatio subtalaris; talocalcaneal articulation; calcaneo-astragaloid articulation*).—The articulations between the calcaneus and talus are two in number—anterior and posterior. Of these, the anterior forms part of the talocalcaneonavicular joint, and will be described with that articulation. The posterior or talocalcaneal articulation is formed between the posterior calcaneal facet on the inferior surface of the talus, and the posterior facet on the superior surface of the calcaneus. It is an arthrodial joint, and the two bones are connected by an articular capsule and by anterior, posterior, lateral, medial, and interosseous talocalcaneal ligaments.

The Articular Capsule (*capsula articularis*).—The articular capsule envelops the joint, and consists for the most part of short fibers, which are split up into distinct slips; between these there is only a weak fibrous investment.

The Anterior Talocalcaneal Ligament (*ligamentum talocalcaneum anterius; anterior calcaneo-astragaloid ligament*) (Figs. 419, 422).—The anterior talocalcaneal ligament extends from the front and lateral surface of the neck of the talus to the superior surface of the calcaneus. It forms the posterior boundary of the talocalcaneonavicular joint, and is sometimes described as the **anterior interosseous ligament.**

The Posterior Talocalcaneal Ligament (*ligamentum talocalcaneum posterius; posterior calcaneo-astragaloid ligament*) (Fig. 416).—The posterior talocalcaneal ligament connects the lateral tubercle of the talus with the upper and medial part of the calcaneus; it is a short band, and its fibers radiate from their narrow attachment to the talus.

The Lateral Talocalcaneal Ligament (*ligamentum talocalcaneum laterale; external calcaneo-astragaloid ligament*) (Figs. 419, 422).—The lateral talocalcaneal ligament is a short, strong fasciculus, passing from the lateral surface of the talus, immediately beneath its fibular facet to the lateral surface of the calcaneus. It is placed in front of, but on a deeper plane than, the calcaneofibular ligament, with the fibers of which it is parallel.

The Medial Talocalcaneal Ligament (*ligamentum talocalcaneum mediale; internal calcaneo-astragaloid ligament*).—The medial talocalcaneal ligament connects the medial tubercle of the back of the talus with the back of the sustentaculum tali. Its fibers blend with those of the plantar calcaneonavicular ligament (Fig. 416).

The Interosseous Talocalcaneal Ligament (*ligamentum talocalcaneum interosseum*) (Figs. 420, 422).—The interosseous talocalcaneal ligament forms the chief bond of union between the bones. It is, in fact, a portion of the united capsules of the talocalcaneonavicular and the talocalcaneal joints, and consists of two partially united layers of fibers, one belonging to the former and the other to the latter joint.

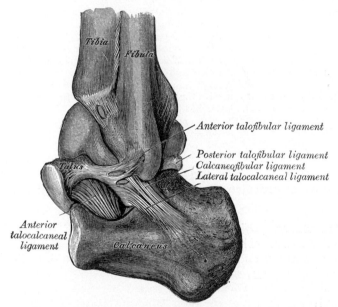

FIG. 419.—Capsule of left talocrural articulation (distended). Lateral aspect.

It is attached, *above,* to the groove between the articular facets of the under surface of the talus; *below,* to a corresponding depression on the upper surface of the calcaneus. It is very thick and strong, being at least 2.5 cm. in breadth from side to side, and serves to bind the calcaneus and talus firmly together.

Synovial Membrane (Fig. 423).—The synovial membrane lines the capsule of the joint, and is distinct from the other synovial membranes of the tarsus.

Movements.—The movements permitted between the talus and calcaneus are limited to gliding of the one bone on the other backward and forward and from side to side.

Talocalcaneonavicular Articulation (*articulatio talocalcaneonavicularis*).—This articulation is an arthrodial joint: the rounded head of the talus being received into the concavity formed by the posterior surface of the navicular, the anterior articular surface of the calcaneus, and the upper surface of the plantar calcaneonavicular ligament. There are two ligaments in this joint: the articular capsule and the dorsal talonavicular.

The Articular Capsule (*capsula articularis*).—The articular capsule is imperfectly developed except posteriorly, where it is considerably thickened and forms, with a part of the capsule of the talocalcaneal joint, the strong interosseous ligament which fills in the canal formed by the opposing grooves on the calcaneus and talus, as above mentioned.

The Dorsal Talonavicular Ligament (*ligamentum talonaviculare dorsale; superior astragalonavicular ligament*) (Fig. 416).—This ligament is a broad, thin band, which connects the neck of the talus to the dorsal surface of the navicular bone; it is covered by the Extensor tendons. The plantar calcaneonavicular supplies the place of a plantar ligament for this joint.

Synovial Membrane.—The synovial membrane lines all parts of the capsule of the joint.

Movements.—This articulation permits of a considerable range of gliding movements, and some rotation; its feeble construction allows occasionally of dislocation of the other bones of the tarsus from the talus.

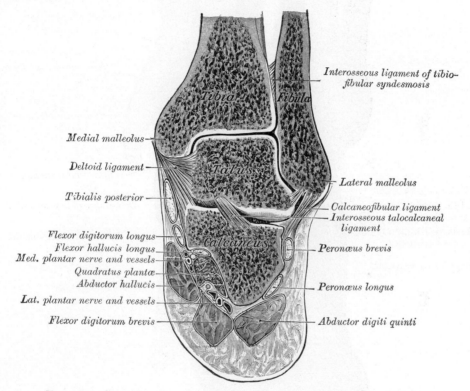

Fig. 420.—Coronal section through right talocrural and talocalcaneal joints.

Calcaneocuboid Articulation (*articulatio calcaneocuboidea; articulation of the calcaneus with the cuboid*).—The ligaments connecting the calcaneus with the cuboid are five in number, viz., the articular capsule, the dorsal calcaneocuboid, part of the bifurcated, the long plantar, and the plantar calcaneocuboid.

The Articular Capsule (*capsula articularis*).—The articular capsule is an imperfectly developed investment, containing certain strengthened bands, which form the other ligaments of the joint.

The Dorsal Calcaneocuboid Ligament (*ligamentum calcaneocuboideum dorsale; superior calcaneocuboid ligament*) (Fig. 417).—The dorsal calcaneocuboid ligament is a thin but broad fasciculus, which passes between the contiguous surfaces of the calcaneus and cuboid, on the dorsal surface of the joint.

The Bifurcated Ligament (*ligamentum bifurcatum; internal calcaneocuboid; interosseous ligament*) (Fig. 417, 422).—The bifurcated ligament is a strong band, attached behind to the deep hollow on the upper surface of the calcaneus and dividing in front in a Y-shaped manner into a calcaneocuboid and a calcaneonavicular part. The **calcaneocuboid part** is fixed to the medial side of the cuboid and forms one of the principal bonds between the first and second rows of the tarsal bones. The **calcaneonavicular part** is attached to the lateral side of the navicular.

The Long Plantar Ligament (*ligamentum plantare longum; long calcaneocuboid ligament; superficial long plantar ligament*) (Fig. 421).—The long plantar ligament is the longest of all the ligaments of the tarsus: it is attached *behind* to the plantar

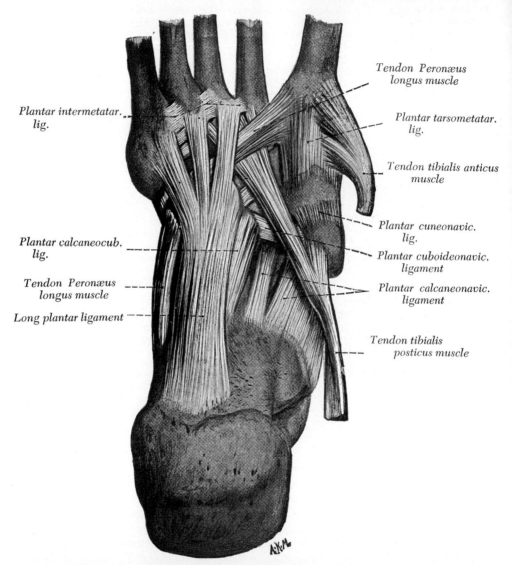

Tendon Peronæus longus muscle

Plantar intermetatar. lig.

Plantar tarsometatar. lig.

Tendon tibialis anticus muscle

Plantar cuneonavic. lig.

Plantar calcaneocub. lig.

Plantar cuboideonavic. ligament

Tendon Peronæus longus muscle

Plantar calcaneonavic. ligament

Long plantar ligament

Tendon tibialis posticus muscle

Fig. 421.—Ligaments of the sole of the foot, with the tendons of the Peronæus longus, Tibialis posterior and Tibialis anterior muscles. (Quain.)

surface of the calcaneus in front of the tuberosity, and in *front* to the tuberosity on the plantar surface of the cuboid bone, the more superficial fibers being continued forward to the bases of the third, fourth and fifth, and occasionally also the second metatarsal bones. This ligament converts the groove on the plantar surface of the cuboid into a canal for the tendon of the Peronæus longus.

The Plantar Calcaneocuboid Ligament (*ligamentum calcaneocuboideum plantare; short calcaneocuboid ligament; short plantar ligament*) (Fig. 421).—The plantar calcaneocuboid ligament lies nearer to the bones than the preceding, from which it is separated by a little areolar tissue. It is a short but wide band of great strength, and extends from the tubercle and the depression in front of it, on the forepart of the plantar surface of the calcaneus, to the plantar surface of the cuboid behind the peroneal groove.

Synovial Membrane.—The synovial membrane lines the inner surface of the capsule and is distinct from that of the other tarsal articulations (Fig. 423).

Movements.—The movements permitted between the calcaneus and cuboid are limited to slight gliding movements of the bones upon each other.

The *transverse tarsal joint* is formed by the articulation of the calcaneus with the cuboid, and the articulation of the talus with the navicular. The movement which takes place in this joint is more extensive than that in the other tarsal joints, and consists of a sort of rotation by means of which the foot may be slightly flexed or extended, the sole being at the same time carried medially (inverted) or laterally (everted).

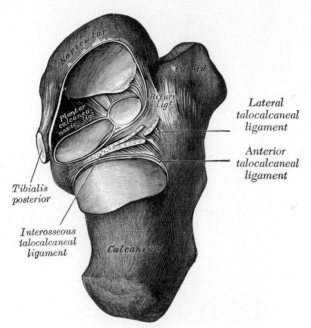

Fig. 422.—Talocalcaneal and talocalcaneonavicular articulations exposed from above by removing the talus.

The Ligaments Connecting the Calcaneus and Navicular.—Though the calcaneus and navicular do not directly articulate, they are connected by two ligaments: the calcaneonavicular part of the bifurcated, and the plantar calcaneonavicular.

The **calcaneonavicular part of the bifurcated ligament** is described on page 396.

The Plantar Calcaneonavicular Ligament (*ligamentum calcaneonaviculare plantare; inferior or internal calcaneonavicular ligament; calcaneonavicular ligament*) (Figs. 416, 421).—The plantar calcaneonavicular ligament is a broad and thick band of fibers, which connects the anterior margin of the sustentaculum tali of the calcaneus to the plantar surface of the navicular. This ligament not only serves to connect the calcaneus and navicular, but supports the head of the talus, forming part of the articular cavity in which it is received. The **dorsal surface** of the ligament presents a fibrocartilaginous facet, lined by the synovial membrane, and upon this a portion of the head of the talus rests. Its **plantar surface** is supported by the tendon of the Tibialis posterior; its **medial border** is blended with the forepart of the deltoid ligament of the ankle-joint.

The plantar calcaneonavicular ligament, by supporting the head of the talus, is principally concerned in maintaining the arch of the foot. When it yields, the head of the talus is pressed downward, medialward, and forward by the weight of the body, and the foot becomes flattened, expanded, and turned lateralward, and exhibits the condition known as *flat-foot*. This ligament contains a considerable amount of elastic fibers, so as to give elasticity to the arch and spring to the foot; hence it is sometimes called the "spring" ligament. It is supported, on its plantar surface, by the tendon of the Tibialis posterior, which spreads out at its insertion into a number of fasciculi, to be attached to most of the tarsal and metatarsal bones. This helps to prevent undue stretching of the ligament.

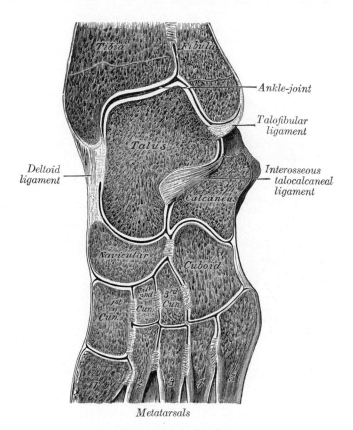

FIG. 423.—Oblique section of left intertarsal and tarsometatarsal articulations, showing the synovial cavities.

Cuneonavicular Articulation (*articulatio cuneonavicularis; articulation of the navicular with the cuneiform bones*).—The navicular is connected to the three cuneiform bones by dorsal and plantar ligaments.

The Dorsal Ligaments (*ligamenta navicularicuneiformia dorsalia*).—The dorsal ligaments are three small bundles, one attached to each of the cuneiform bones. The bundle connecting the navicular with the first cuneiform is continuous around the medial side of the articulation with the plantar ligament which unites these two bones (Figs. 416, 417).

The Plantar Ligaments (*ligamenta navicularicuneiformia plantaria*).—The plantar ligaments have a similar arrangement to the dorsal, and are strengthened by slips from the tendon of the Tibialis posterior (Fig. 421).

Synovial Membrane.—The synovial membrane of these joints is part of the great tarsal synovial membrane (Fig. 423.)

Movements.—Mere gliding movements are permitted between the navicular and cuneiform bones.

Cuboideonavicular Articulation.—The navicular bone is connected with the cuboid by dorsal, plantar, and interosseous ligaments.

The Dorsal Ligament (*ligamentum cuboideonaviculare dorsale*).—The dorsal ligament extends obliquely forward and lateralward from the navicular to the cuboid bone (Fig. 422).

The Plantar Ligament (*ligamentum cuboideonaviculare plantare*).—The plantar ligament passes nearly transversely between these two bones (Fig. 421).

The Interosseous Ligament.—The interosseous ligament consists of strong transverse fibers, and connects the rough non-articular portions of the adjacent surfaces of the two bones Fig. 423).

Synovial Membrane.—The synovial membrane of this joint is part of the great tarsal synovial membrane (Fig. 423).

Movements.—The movements permitted between the navicular and cuboid bones are limited to a slight gliding upon each other.

Intercuneiform and Cuneocuboid Articulations.—The three cuneiform bones and the cuboid are connected together by dorsal, plantar, and interosseous ligaments.

The Dorsal Ligaments (*ligamenta intercuneiformia dorsalia*).—The dorsal ligaments consist of three transverse bands: one connects the first with the second cuneiform, another the second with the third cuneiform, and another the third cuneiform with the cuboid.

The Plantar Ligaments (*ligamenta intercuneiformia plantaria*).—The plantar ligaments have a similar arrangement to the dorsal, and are strengthened by slips from the tendon of the Tibialis posterior.

The Interosseous Ligaments (*ligamenta intercuneiformia interossea*).—The interosseous ligaments consist of strong transverse fibers which pass between the rough non-articular portions of the adjacent surfaces of the bones (Fig. 423).

Synovial Membrane.—The synovial membrane of these joints is part of the great tarsal synovial membrane (Fig. 423).

Movements.—The movements permitted between these bones are limited to a slight gliding upon each other.

VI. Tarsometatarsal Articulations (Articulationes Tarsometatarseæ).

These are arthrodial joints. The bones entering into their formation are the first, second, and third cuneiforms, and the cuboid, which articulate with the bases of the metatarsal bones. The first metatarsal bone articulates with the first cuneiform; the second is deeply wedged in between the first and third cuneiforms articulating by its base with the second cuneiform; the third articulates with the third cuneiform; the fourth, with the cuboid and third cuneiform; and the fifth, with the cuboid. The bones are connected by dorsal, plantar, and interosseous ligaments.

The Dorsal Ligaments (*ligamenta tarsometatarsea dorsalia*).—The dorsal ligaments are strong, flat bands. The first metatarsal is joined to the first cuneiform by a broad, thin band; the second has three, one from each cuneiform bone; the third has one from the third cuneiform; the fourth has one from the third cuneiform and one from the cuboid; and the fifth, one from the cuboid (Figs. 416, 417).

The Plantar Ligaments (*ligamenta tarsometatarsea plantaria*).—The plantar ligaments consist of longitudinal and oblique bands, disposed with less regularity than the dorsal ligaments. Those for the first and second metatarsals are the strongest; the second and third metatarsals are joined by oblique bands to the

first cuneiform; the fourth and fifth metatarsals are connected by a few fibers
to the cuboid (Fig. 421).

The Interosseous Ligaments (*ligamenta cuneometatarsea interossea*).—The interosseous ligaments are two or three in number. The first is the strongest, and passes
from the lateral surface of the first cuneiform to the adjacent angle of the second
metatarsal. The second or middle which is the smallest and is less constant than
the others, passes from the third cuneiform to the lateral aspect of the second
metatarsal. The third connects the lateral angle of the third cuneiform with the
adjacent side of the base of the third metatarsal.

Synovial Membrane (Fig. 423).—The synovial membrane between the first cuneiform and
the first metatarsal forms a distinct sac. The synovial membrane between the second and third
cuneiforms behind, and the second and third metatarsal bones in front, is part of the great tarsal
synovial membrane. Two prolongations are sent forward from it, one between the adjacent sides
of the second and third, and another between those of the third and fourth metatarsal bones.
The synovial membrane between the cuboid and the fourth and fifth metatarsal bones forms a
distinct sac. From it a prolongation is sent forward between the fourth and fifth metatarsal bones.

Movements.—The movements permitted between the tarsal and metatarsal bones are limited
to slight gliding of the bones upon each other.

Nerve Supply.—The intertarsal and tarsometatarsal joints are supplied by the deep peroneal
nerve.

VII.　Intermetatarsal Articulations (Articulationes Intermetatarseæ).

The bases of the four lateral metatarsals are are connected by the dorsal, plantar,
and interosseous ligaments.

The first metatarsal is connected with the second by interosseous fibers only;
the fibers are weak and may be largely replaced by a bursa between indistinct
facets on the two bones.

The Dorsal Ligaments (*ligamenta basium* [*oss. metatars.*] *dorsalia*) pass transversely
between the dorsal surfaces of the bases of the adjacent metatarsal bones.

The Plantar Ligaments (*ligamenta basium* [*oss. metatars*] *plantaria*).—The plantar
ligaments have a similar arrangement to the dorsal.

The Interosseous Ligaments (*ligamenta basium* [*oss. metatars.*] *interossea*).—The
interosseous ligaments consist of strong transverse fibers which connect the rough
non-articular portions of the adjacent surfaces.

Synovial Membranes (Fig. 423).—The synovial membranes between the second and third
and the third and fourth metatarsal bones are part of the great tarsal synovial membrane; that
between the fourth and fifth is a prolongation of the synovial membrane of the cuboideometatarsal
joint.

Movements.—The movement permitted between the tarsal ends of the metatarsal bones
is limited to a slight gliding of the articular surfaces upon one another.

The heads of all the metatarsal bones are connected together by the transverse
metatarsal ligament.

The Transverse Metatarsal Ligament.—The transverse metatarsal ligament is a
narrow band which runs across and connects together the heads of all the metatarsal bones; it is blended anteriorly with the plantar (glenoid) ligaments of the
metatarsophalangeal articulations. Its plantar surface is concave where the
Flexor tendons run below it; above it the tendons of the Interossei pass to their
insertions. It differs from the transverse metacarpal ligament in that it connects
the metatarsal to the others.

The Synovial Membranes in the Tarsal and Tarsometatarsal Joints (Fig. 423).—The synovial
membranes found in the articulations of the tarsus and metatarsus are six in number: one for
the talocalcaneal articulation; a second for the talocalcaneonavicular articulation; a third for
the calcaneocuboid articulation; and a fourth for the cuneonavicular, intercuneiform, and cuneocuboid articulations, the articulations of the second and third cuneiforms with the bases of the
second and third metatarsal bones, and the adjacent surfaces of the bases of the second, third,

and fourth metatarsal bones; a fifth for the first cuneiform with the metatarsal bone of the great toe; and a sixth for the articulation of the cuboid with the fourth and fifth metatarsal bones. A small synovial cavity is sometimes found between the contiguous surfaces of the navicular and cuboid bones.

VIII.   Metatarsophalangeal Articulations (Articulationes Metatarsophalangeæ).

The metatarsophalangeal articulations are of the condyloid kind, formed by the reception of the rounded heads of the metatarsal bones in shallow cavities on the ends of the first phalanges.

The ligaments are the plantar and two collateral.

The Plantar Ligaments (*ligamenta accessoria plantaria; glenoid ligaments of Cruveilhier*).—The plantar ligaments are thick, dense, fibrous structures. They are placed on the plantar surfaces of the joints in the intervals between the collateral ligaments, to which they are connected; they are loosely united to the metatarsal bones, but very firmly to the bases of the first phalanges. Their plantar surfaces are intimately blended with the transverse metatarsal ligament, and grooved for the passage of the Flexor tendons, the sheaths surrounding which are connected to the sides of the grooves. Their deep surfaces form part of the articular facets for the heads of the metatarsal bones, and are lined by synovial membrane.

The Collateral Ligaments (*ligamenta collateralia; lateral ligaments*).—The collateral ligaments are strong, rounded cords, placed one on either side of each joint, and attached, by one end, to the posterior tubercle on the side of the head of the metatarsal bone, and, by the other, to the contiguous extremity of the phalanx.

The place of **dorsal ligaments** is supplied by the Extensor tendons on the dorsal surfaces of the joints.

Movements.—The movements permitted in the metatarsophalangeal articulations are flexion extension, abduction, and adduction.

IX   Articulations of the Digits (Articulationes Digitorum Pedis; Articulations of the Phalanges).

The interphalangeal articulations are ginglymoid joints, and each has a plantar and two collateral ligaments.

The arrangement of these ligaments is similar to that in the metatarsophalangeal articulations: the Extensor tendons supply the places of dorsal ligaments.

Movements.—The only movements permitted in the joints of the digits are flexion and extension; these movements are more extensive between the first and second phalanges than between the second and third. The amount of flexion is very considerable, but extension is limited by the plantar and collateral ligaments.

Arches of the Foot.

The **longitudinal arch** is formed by the seven tarsal and the five metatarsal bones (Figs. 345, 346) and the ligaments which bind them together. The multiplicity of parts gives resiliency. The arch rests posteriorly on the calcaneal tuberosity and anteriorly on the heads of the five metatarsals. In the standing position, 25 per cent of the body weight is distributed to each calcaneum and 25 per cent to the heads of the five metatarsals of each foot, in proportion of about 1 part for metatarsal I to 2.5 parts for metatarsals II to V. The greater part of the tension stress on the longitudinal arch is borne by the plantar ligaments (Fig. 421). Only about 15 to 20 per cent of the stress is borne by the tibialis posterior and the peroneal muscles. When the body is raised on the ball of one foot, the stress on the arch is increased four times.

26

In addition to the longitudinal arch the foot presents a series of **transverse arches.** At the posterior part of the metatarsus and the anterior part of the tarsus the arches are complete, but in the middle of the tarsus they present more the characters of half-domes the concavities of which are directed downward and medialward, so that when the medial borders of the feet are placed in apposition a complete tarsal dome is formed. The transverse arches are strengthened by the interosseous, plantar, and dorsal ligaments, by the short muscles of the first and fifth toes (especially the transverse head of the Adductor hallucis), and by the Peronæus longus, whose tendon stretches across between the piers of the arches.

REFERENCES

EMBRYOLOGY AND HISTOLOGY

CAMERON, D. A. and R. A. ROBINSON. 1958. Electron microscopy of epiphyseal and articular cartilage matrix in the femur of the newborn infant. J. Bone and Joint Surg., *40-A*, 163–170.

COHEN, J. and W. H. HARRIS. 1958. The three-dimensional anatomy of haversian systems. J. Bone and Joint Surg., *40-A*, 419–434.

COVENTRY, M. B., R. K. GHORMLEY, and J. W. KERNOHAN. 1945. The intervertebral disc; its microscopic anatomy and pathology. J. Bone and Joint Surg., *27*, 105–112, 233–247, and 460–474.

DAVIES, D. V. 1946. The lymphatics of the synovial membrane. J. Anat., *80*, 21–23.

GARDNER, E. and D. J. GRAY. 1950. Prenatal development of the human hip joint. Am. J. Anat., *87*, 163–211.

GARDNER, E. and D. J. GRAY. 1953. Prenatal development of the human shoulder and acromio-clavicular joints. Am. J. Anat., *92*, 219–276.

GRAY, D. J. and E. GARDNER. 1950. Prenatal development of the human knee and superior tibiofibular joints. Am. J. Anat., *86*, 235–287.

GRAY, D. J. and E. GARDNER. 1951. Prenatal development of the human elbow joint. Am. J. Anat., *88*, 429–469.

HAINES, R. W. 1947. The development of joints. J. Anat., *81*, 33–55.

RUTH, E. B. 1946. A note on the fibrillar structure of hyaline cartilage. Anat. Rec., *96*, 93–99.

STRAYER, L. M., JR. 1943. The embryology of the human hip joint. Yale J. Biol. and Med., *16*, 13–26.

PHYSIOLOGY AND GENERAL

BAUER, W., M. W. ROPES, and H. WAINE. 1940. The physiology of articular structures. Physiol. Rev., *20*, 272–312.

CORBIN, K. B. and J. C. HINSEY. 1939. Influence of the nervous system on bone and joints. Anat. Rec., *75*, 307–317

DE GARIS, C. F. 1942. Movable joints and joint movements. J. Internat. Coll. Surgeons, *5*, 380–388.

MORTON, D. J. 1952. Human Locomotion and Body Form. Williams & Wilkins Co., Baltimore, xii + 285 pp.

TEMPOROMANDIBULAR JOINT

ANGEL, J. L. 1948. Factors in temporomandibular joint form. Am. J. Anat., *83*, 223–246.

ASHTON, E. H. and S. ZUCKERMAN. 1954. The anatomy of the articular fossa (fossa mandibularis) in man and apes. Am. J. Phys. Anthrop., n.s. *12*, 29–62.

HOROWITZ, S. L. and H. H. SHAPIRO. 1955. Modification of skull and jaw architecture following removal of the Masseter muscle in the rat. Am. J. Phys. Anthrop., n.s. *13*, 301–308.

SARNAT, B. G., EDITOR. 1951. The Temporomandibular Joint. Charles C Thomas, Springfield. xviii + 148 pp.

SHAPIRO, H. H. and R. C. TRUEX. 1943. The temporomandibular joint and the auditory function. J. Am. Dental Assn., *30*, 1147–1168.

STEIN, M. R. 1939. The "mandibular sling." Dental Survey, *15*, 883–887.

JOINTS OF AXIAL SKELETON

FRANCIS, C. C. 1955. Variations in the articular facets of the cervical vertebræ. Anat. Rec., *122*, 589–602.

GRAY, D. J. and E. D. GARDNER. 1943. The human sternochondral joints. Anat. Rec., *87*, 235–253.

SCHUNKE, G. B. 1938. The anatomy and development of the sacro-iliac joint in man. Anat. Rec., *72*, 313–331.

SPURLING, R. G. 1956. Lesions of the Cervical Intervertebral Disc. Charles C Thomas, Springfield. xi + 134 pp.

TROTTER, M. 1940. A common anatomical variation in the sacro-iliac region. J. Bone and Joint Surg., *22*, 293–299.

SHOULDER JOINT

DE PALMA, A. F. 1957. Degenerative Changes in the Sternoclavicular and Acromioclavicular Joints in Various Decades. Charles C Thomas, Springfield. xii + 178 pp.

GARDNER, E. 1948. The innervation of the shoulder joint. Anat. Rec., *102*, 1–18.

INMAN, V. T., J. B. DEC. M. SAUNDERS, and L. C. ABBOTT. 1944. Observations on the function of the shoulder joint. J. Bone and Joint Surg., *26*, 1–30.

KAPLAN, E. B. 1943. The coraco-humeral ligament of the human shoulder. Bull. Hosp. Joint Dis., *4*, 62–65.

LAING, P. G. 1956. The arterial supply of the adult humerus. J. Bone and Joint Surg., *38-A*, 1105–1116.

MOSELEY, H. F. 1952. Ruptures of the Rotator Cuff. Charles C Thomas, Springfield. xii + 90 pp.

ELBOW, WRIST AND HAND

GARDNER, E. 1948. The innervation of the elbow joint. Anat. Rec., *102*, 161–174.

KELIKIAN, H. and A. DOUMANIAN. 1957. Congenital anomalies of the hand. J. Bone and Joint Surg., *39-A*, 1002–1019, 1949–1266.

LANDSMEER, J. M. F. 1955. Anatomical and functional investigations on the articulation of the human fingers. Acta Anat., *25*, Suppl. 24 = 2, 1–69.

ROSTON, J. B. and R. W. HAINES. 1947. Cracking in the metacarpo-phalangeal joint. J. Anat., *81*, 165–173.

SMITH, R. D. and G. R. HOLCOMB. 1958. Articular surface interrelationships in finger joints. Acta Anat., *32*, 217–229.

HIP JOINT

BUCHANAN, A. R. and B. E. ROBINSON. 1946. The position of the external hip joint in the above-the-knee prosthesis with pelvic suspension. J. Bone and Joint Surg., *28*, 71–80.

GARDNER, E. 1948. The innervation of the hip joint. Anat. Rec., *101*, 353–371.

HART, V. L. 1952. Congenital Dysplasia of the Hip Joint and Sequelæ in the Newborn and Early Postnatal Life. Charles C Thomas, Springfield. xv + 187 pp.

KNEE JOINT

ABBOTT, L. C. and W. F. CARPENTER. 1945. Surgical approaches to the knee joint. J. Bone and Joint Surg., *27*, 277–310.

BRANTIGAN, O. C. and A. F. VOSHELL. 1946. Ligaments of the knee joint: the relationship of the ligament of Humphry to the ligament of Wrisberg. J. Bone and Joint Surg., *28*, 66–67.

CHARLES, C. M. 1935. On the menisci of the knee joint in American whites and negroes Anat. Rec., *63*, 355–364.

GARDNER, E. 1948. The innervation of the knee joint. Anat. Rec., *101*, 109–130.

LACHMANN, E. 1937. The roentgen anatomy of the knee joint: An experimental analysis. Radiology, *29*, 455–471.

ANKLE JOINT AND FOOT

MANTER, J. T. 1946. Distribution of compression forces in the joints of the human foot. Anat. Rec., *96*, 313–321.

MORTON, D. J. 1935. The Human Foot: Its Evolution, Physiology and Functional Disorders. Columbia Univ. Press, New York. xiii + 244 pp.

BURSÆ

BLACK, B. M. 1934. The prenatal incidence, structure and development cf some human synovial bursæ. Anat. Rec., *60*, 333–355.

SCHNEIDER, C. L. 1943. Trabeculæ traversing human bursæ. Anat. Rec., *87*, 151–163.

MUSCLES AND FASCIÆ.

THE muscles are the organs of voluntary motion, and by their contraction, move the various parts of the body. The energy of their contraction is made mechanically effective by means of the tendons, aponeuroses, and fasciæ which secure the ends of the muscles and control the direction of their pull. They form the dark, reddish masses that are popularly known as flesh, and account for approximately 40 per cent of the body weight. They vary greatly in size. The Gastrocnemius forms the bulk of the calf of the leg; the Sartorius is nearly 2 feet in length, and the Stapedius, a tiny muscle of the middle ear, weighs 0.1 gm. and is 2 to 3 mm. in length. In addition to these muscles, which are properly called **voluntary, skeletal,** or **striated muscles,** there are other muscular tissues which are not under voluntary control, such as the cardiac muscle of the heart and the smooth muscle of the intestines. They are described in chapters dealing with the viscera.

DEVELOPMENT OF THE MUSCLES.

Both the cross striated and smooth muscles, with the exception of a few that are of ectodermal origin, arise from the mesoderm. The intrinsic muscles of the trunk are derived from the myotomes while the muscles of the head and limbs differentiate directly from the mesoderm.

The Myotomic Muscles.—The intrinsic muscles of the trunk which are derived directly from the myotomes are conveniently treated in two groups, the deep muscles of the back and the thoracoabdominal muscles.

The deep muscles of the back extend from the sacral to the occipital region and vary much in length and size. They act chiefly on the vertebral column. The shorter muscles, such as the Interspinales, Intertransversarii, the deeper layers of the Multifidus, the Rotatores, Levatores costarum, Obliquus capitis inferior, Obliquus capitis superior and Rectus capitis posterior minor which extend between adjoining vertebræ, retain the primitive segmentation of the myotomes. Other muscles, such as the Splenius capitis, Splenius cervicis, Sacrospinalis, Semispinalis, Multifidus, Iliocostalis, Longissimus, Spinales, Semispinales, and Rectus capitis posterior major, which extend over several vertebræ, are formed by the fusion of successive myotomes and the splitting into longitudinal columns.

The fascia lumbodorsalis develops between the true myotomic muscles and the more superficial ones which migrate over the back such as the Trapezius, Rhomboideus, and Latissimus.

The anterior vertebral muscles, the Longus colli, Longus capitis, Rectus capitis anterior and Rectus capitis lateralis are derived from the ventral part of the cervical myotomes as are probably also the Scaleni.

The thoracoabdominal muscles arise through the ventral extension of the thoracic myotomes into the body wall. This process takes place coincidently with the ventral extension of the ribs. In the thoracic region the primitive myotomic segments still persist as the intercostal muscles, but over the abdomen these ventral myotomic processes fuse into a sheet which splits in various ways to form the Rectus, the Obliquus externus and internus, and the Transversalis. Such muscles as the Pectoralis major and minor and the Serratus anterior do not belong to the above group.

The Ventrolateral Muscles of the Neck.—The intrinsic muscles of the tongue, the Infrahyoid muscles and the diaphragm are derived from a more or less continuous premuscle mass which extends on each side from the tongue into the lateral region of the upper half of the neck and into it early extend the hypoglossal and branches of the upper cervical nerves. The two halves which form the Infrahyoid muscles and the diaphragm are at first widely separated from each other by the heart. As the latter descends into the thorax the diaphragmatic portion of each lateral mass is carried with its nerve down into the thorax and the laterally placed Infrahyoid muscles move toward the midventral line of the neck.

Muscles of the Shoulder Girdle and Arm.—The Trapezius and Sternocleidomastoideus arise from a common premuscle mass in the occipital region just caudal to the last branchial arch; as the mass increases in size it spreads downward to the shoulder girdle to which it later becomes attached. It also spreads backward and downward to the spinous processes, gaining attachment at a still later period.

The Levator scapulæ, Serratus anterior and the Rhomboids arise from premuscle tissue in the lower cervical region and undergo extensive migration.

The Latissimus dorsi and Teres major are associated in their origin from the premuscle sheath of the arm as are also the two Pectoral muscles when the arm bud lies in the lower cervical region.

The intrinsic muscles of the arm develop *in situ* from the mesoderm of the arm bud and probably do not receive cells or buds from the myotomes. The nerves enter the arm bud when it still lies in the cervical region and as the arm shifts caudally over the thorax the lower cervical nerves which unite to form the brachial plexus, acquire a caudal direction.

The Muscles of the Leg.—The muscles of the leg like those of the arm develop *in situ* from the mesoderm of the leg bud, the myotomes apparently taking no part in their formation.

The Muscles of the Head.—The muscles of the orbit arise from the mesoderm over the dorsal and caudal sides of the optic stalk.

The muscles of mastication arise from the mesoderm of the mandibular arch. The mandibular division of the trigeminal nerve enters this premuscle mass before it splits into the Temporal, Masseter and Pterygoideus.

The facial muscles (muscles of expression) arise from the mesoderm of the hyoid arch. The facial nerve enters this mass before it begins to split, and as the muscle mass spreads out over the face and head and neck it splits more or less incompletely into the various muscles.

The early differentiation of the muscular system apparently goes on independently of the nervous system and only later does it appear that muscles are dependent on the functional stimuli of the nerves for their continued existence and growth. Although the nervous system does not influence muscle differentiation, the nerves, owing to their early attachments to the muscle rudiments, are in a general way indicators of the position of origin of many of the muscles and likewise in many instances the nerves indicate the paths along which the developing muscles have migrated during development. The muscle of the diaphragm, for example, has its origin in the region of the fourth and fifth cervical segments. The phrenic nerve enters the muscle mass while the latter is in this region and is drawn out as the diaphragm migrates through the thorax. The Trapezius and Sternocleidomastoideus arise in the lateral occipital region as a common muscle mass, into which at a very early period the nervus accessorius extends and as the muscle mass migrates and extends caudally the nerve is carried with it. The Pectoralis major and minor arise in the cervical region, receive their nerves while in this position and as the muscle mass migrates and extends caudally over the thorax the nerves are carried along. The Latissimus dorsi and Serratus anterior are excellent examples of migrating muscles whose nerve supply indicates their origin in the cervical region. The Rectus abdominis and the other abdominal muscles migrate or shift from a lateral to a ventrolateral or abdominal position, carrying with them the nerves.

The facial nerve, which early enters the common facial muscle mass of the second branchial or hyoid arch, is dragged about with the muscle as it spreads over the head and face and neck, and as the muscle splits into the various muscles of expression, the nerve is correspondingly split. The mandibular division of the trigeminal nerve enters at an early time the muscle mass in the mandibular arch and as this mass splits and migrates apart to form the muscles of mastication the nerve splits into its various branches.

The nerve supply then serves as a key to the common origin of certain groups of muscles. The muscles supplied by the oculomotor nerve arise from a single mass in the eye region; the lingual muscles arise from a common mass supplied by the hypoglossal nerve.

ARRANGEMENT OF MUSCLES AND FASCIÆ

A number of non-contractile connective tissue elements are necessary for the organization of the contractile elements of muscle, the muscle fibers, into effective mechanical instruments. Thus the fibers are bound together into fasciculi by the fibroelastic perimysium, the ends of the muscle are attached to the bones by tendons and aponeuroses, and the whole muscle is held in its proper place by connective tissue sheets called fasciæ.

FASCIÆ

The dissectable, fibrous connective tissues of the body, other than the specifically organized structures, tendons, aponeuroses, and ligaments, are called fasciæ. This same term is used also in a more restricted sense to indicate local connective tissue membranes which enclose a part of the body, or invest muscles or other structures. Although the term will be used most commonly with its restricted meaning of fibrous membranes, it is essential that the concept be borne in mind that the latter are part of the general connective tissues. This allows one to regard all the fascial structures as a part of a functional as well as morphological system in which the connective tissue varies in thickness, in density, in accumulation of fat, and in relative amounts of collagenous fibers, elastic fibers, and tissue fluid according to local requirements.

The entire fascial system is made up of three subdivisions: the **superficial fascia**, the **deep fascia**, and the **subserous fascia**. The deep fascia is the principal somatic fascia which invests and penetrates between the structures which form the body wall and appendages. It is the most extensive of the three and calls for the major part of our attention. The superficial fascia is the subcutaneous layer which intervenes between the deep fascia and the skin. The subserous fascia lies within the body cavities; it forms the fibrous layer of the serous membranes (pleura, pericardium, and peritoneum), covers and supports the viscera, and attaches the parietal layer of the serous membranes to the deep fascia of the internal surface of the body wall.

The **Superficial Fascia** (*tela subcutanea*) is continuous over the entire body between the skin and the deep fascial investment of the specialized structures of the body, such as muscles. It is composed of two layers. The outer one, often called the *panniculus adiposus*, normally contains an accumulation of fat. The latter may be several centimeters thick, or it may, in emaciated individuals, be almost entirely lacking. The inner layer is a thin membrane which ordinarily has no fat and has a generous amount of elastic tissue. The two layers are quite adherent in most regions but they can be separated by careful dissection, particularly in the lower anterior abdominal wall. Between the two layers lie the superficial arteries, veins, nerves, and lymphatics, the mammary glands, most of the facial muscles, the platysma, and one or two other muscles.

The superficial fascia in many parts of the body glides freely over the deep fascia, producing the characteristic movability of the skin in an area like the back of the hand. In these areas, the two fasciæ can be dissected apart easily by a probing finger or blunt instrument. They are separated, in other words, by a fascial cleft. At certain other points on the body surface, especially over bony prominences, the two fasciæ are closely adherent. They retain their individuality even here, however, and do not become continuous with each other.

The **deep fascia** is represented characteristically by the gray felt-like membranes immediately covering the muscles. It comprises a rather intricate series of sheets and bands which hold the muscles and other structures in their proper relative positions, separating them from each other for independent function as well as joining them together into an integrated whole. The intrinsic connective tissue of the capsules or stroma of these structures is not included in this fascia. In the case of a muscle, the epimysium may be fused with the overlying fascia and lose its identity, as in the Triceps, or it may be separated from the fascia by a cleft and retain its individuality, as in the Biceps.

The membranes of the deep fascia are organized into a continuous or never ending system. The periosteum of the bones (and perichondrium of cartilage), and the ligaments may assist in establishing this continuity. The membranes split, on occasion, in order to surround (invest) muscles or other structures and unite again into single sheets. These phenomena of splitting and fusing are important because it is by their means that any sheet of fascia can be traced to any other sheet and can be shown to make eventual attachment to the skeleton.

The deep fascia, although a continuous system, may be subdivided for the purpose of description into three parts. First, the **outer investing layer** (*Deep Subcutaneous System of Gallaudet*) is an extensive sheet which covers the trunk, neck, limbs, and part of the head, and lies just under the subcutaneous superficial fascia. Second, in the trunk there is another extensive sheet, the **internal investing layer** (*Deep Subserous System of Gallaudet*), which covers the internal surface of the body wall, that is, it lines the thoracic and abdominal cavities and, in turn, is covered internally by the Subserous Fascia (see below). The third portion comprises the manifold **intermediate membranes** which are derived from the two investing layers by splitting and attachment, and which lie between the muscles and other structures throughout the body.

The mechanical function of fascia is particularly well developed in the deep fascia and is responsible for its many local variations and specializations. A membrane may be thickened, either for strength or padding; it may be fused with another membrane or split into several sheets; it may be separated from another membrane by a plane of cleavage; or it may combine with other membranes to form compartments for groups of muscles. These specializations will be described in greater detail.

The thickening of a membrane for greater strength, especially if it receives the direct pull of a muscle, is by the addition of parallel bundles of collagenous fibers which impart to it the white, glistening appearance of an aponeurosis. A membrane of this type may lie between the origins of two muscles whose fibers pull in approximately the same direction, as, for example, the forearm muscles originating on the epicondyles of the humerus, in which case it is called an intermuscular septum. Such a strengthened membrane may cover a muscle and be used by it for a surface of attachment as in the case of the outer investing layer of the forearm. An extreme instance is that of the fascia lata of the thigh, whose iliotibial band is in fact the principal tendon of insertion for the Gluteus maximus and the Tensor fasciæ latæ muscles. This aponeurotic function of fascia has led to some confusion. Certain fibrous membranes retain the name fascia when they are actually aponeuroses and, conversely, some authors, particularly the French, are inclined to call even the unspecialized membranes aponeuroses.

A band of fascia may act as a ligament. This is the case with the greatly strengthened portion of the clavipectoral fascia, the costocoracoid membrane, which, by its attachment to the coracoid process and ribs, serves as a ligament for the articulations of the clavicle. Another important specialization is shown by the annular ligaments and retinacula at the wrist and ankle which provide tunnels for the long tendons of the hand and foot.

Lamination of a fascial membrane is found where there is a thickening without a corresponding increase in strength. The membrane splits into two leaves which are separated by a pad of connective tissue containing fat and an occasional bloodvessel or lymph node. An example of this is the lamination of the outer cervical fascia above the sternum which is ambiguously called the suprasternal (Burns') space.

A **fascial compartment** is a portion of the body which is walled off by fascial membranes. Characteristically, it contains a muscle or a group of muscles but in some instances other structures are included. A typical example is offered by the flexor and extensor compartments of the arm, where the substance of the arm, enclosed by brachial fascia, is divided into the two compartments by the medial and lateral intermuscular septa. In many descriptions of fascia, such compartments are ambiguously called spaces or potential spaces. For example, the mediastinum is frequently called a "space" containing the heart, great vessels, esophagus, etc., whereas in reality it is a compartment enclosed by mediastinal fascia. Any "potential space" must be sought in the area of cleavage which separates the parietal pericardium from the sternum except at the pericardiosternal ligaments. Another confusing use of the word space was mentioned in the preceding paragraph, that is, to refer to a lamination and thickening of a fascial membrane.

The **fascial cleft** is an important specialization which is greatly in need of emphasis. It is a place of cleavage which separates two contiguous fascial surfaces. It may be described also as a stratum rich in fluid but poor in traversing fibers which allows two fascial surfaces to move more or less freely over each other and makes them easy to separate in dissection. The degree of separation may vary from an almost complete detachment to a comparatively strong adhesion, depending on the need for motion between the parts. The cleft between the superficial fascia and the deep fascia has already been mentioned. The cleft between a muscle and an overlying, restraining fascial membrane, like the Biceps and brachial fascia, is actually between the epimysium of the muscle and the true fascial sheet. The cleft between two adjacent muscles is likely to be between the simple epimysium of each muscle, but the latter may, in some instances, be thickened into a true fascial sheet.

A **bursa** represents the final step in the development of an efficient device for freedom of motion between contiguous connective tissue surfaces. It is a relatively small, circumscribed area in which all traversing fibers have been lost. The result is a pocket of complete separation, the lining of which provides two opposed, lubricated surfaces similar to the synovial membranes of a joint. Characteristically, a bursa is found where a tendon glides directly over the periosteum of a bone. The **synovial tendon sheaths** of the hand and foot are specialized bursæ.

Just as there are adaptations for separation of membranes, there are adaptations for attachment. Fascial membranes may fuse with each other, as in the case of the outer investing and middle cervical fasciæ near the hyoid bone. They may attach to bones, as the clavipectoral fasciæ to the clavicle. The attachment in some instances is very secure, in others it is separable by dissection. The relation between two contiguous fascial membranes, therefore, may vary from the complete separation at a bursa, or the functional separation of a fascial cleft, through progressive degrees of adhesion and attachment up to complete fusion.

The names of particular parts of the fascia are derived most commonly and most appropriately from the regions of the body which they occupy or the structures which they cover. For example, the brachial fascia encloses the arm and the deltoid fascia covers the Deltoideus muscle. Some fasciæ have descriptive names, such as the fascia lata from its broad extent on the thigh or the fascia cribrosa from its many holes. A few are named from their attachments, for example, the fascia clavipectoralis or coracoclavicularis.

Eponyms which are taken from the names of persons who first described or emphasized particular portions or concepts of fascia are used very commonly by authors of clinical treatises. In most instances such nomenclature is of doubtful value anatomically, but is worthy of preservation because it emphasizes the importance of a certain fascia in operative procedures or in pathological processes such as the spread of infection. The identification of any specific fascial membrane is intrinsically difficult because the fascia has the same histological structure as the ligament, aponeurosis, and periosteum to which it may be attached, and the continuity of the whole system makes the setting of exact boundaries and limitations a matter of arbitrary definition.

The **Subserous** or **Visceral Fascia** (*tela subserosa*; *superficial subserous fascia of Gallaudet*) lies between the internal investing layer of deep fascia and the serous membranes lining the body cavities, in much the same way as the subcutaneous superficial fascia lies between the skin and the deep fascia. It is very thin in some areas, as between the pleura and the chest wall. It is thick in other areas and, except in emaciated individuals, forms a pad of adipose tissue like that surrounding the kidney. It is not separable into outer and inner layers, as is the superficial fascia, but it may be irregularly laminated in the adipose accumulations, especially in well nourished individuals. As a general rule, only the fascia of the parietal serous membrane is given in a description, but it should be remembered that this parietal layer is continuous with the visceral layer carried over to the organs at the reflections of the serous membranes and at the mesenteries.

A cleft of variable prominence separates the subserous fascia from the deep fascia as it does in the case of the subcutaneous and deep fasciæ. It allows a considerable amount of sliding motion between the two fasciæ and makes it possible to dissect them apart. Where both fasciæ are thin and delicate, it is difficult to identify and separate them.

Complications and problems of identification and naming of fasciæ arise in the regions where internal structures penetrate the wall of the body cavity. For example, the rectum penetrates the pelvic diaphragm, the spermatic cord penetrates the abdominal wall through the inguinal canal, and the trachea and esophagus leave the thoracic cavity to enter the neck, and, in so doing, they introduce transitions between the subserous, deep, and superficial fasciæ.

Careful study of the fascia has been made, for the most part, in restricted areas instead of throughout the body as a complete system. Interest has stemmed from its obvious importance in surgery and pathology. It is logical, however, to weave the fascia into a functional system. Its function is predominantly mechanical in the normal body, except for the activity of the various types of cells which are visitors within its meshes and which are beyond the scope of this discussion. The understanding and learning of the fasciæ are much easier on the basis of this mechanical function than on the basis of surgical and pathological importance, and the latter becomes easily comprehensible only with the knowledge of function as a background. One very important mechanical function must not be overlooked even if it is seldom mentioned, namely, that of supporting and carrying the blood-vessels, nerves and lymphatics.

Although much advantage might be gained by presenting the fasciæ in a separate chapter, it has been decided to retain the usual method of describing them with the muscles. Should the reader desire a systematic treatment of the fasciæ, he may obtain it by leafing through the pages of the chapter on muscles, reading only the sections on fascia. A study of the muscles or other structures in a particular region is recommended as a preliminary to the reading of the description of the fascia.

STRUCTURE AND ATTACHMENT OF MUSCLES

The tendons and aponeuroses are parts of the muscles. They are included in the description of a muscle as the ultimate attachment, that is, the origin and insertion of the muscle are the terminal attachments of the tendon or aponeurosis to a bone. not the attachment of the contractile fibers to the tendon.

The **arrangement of the fasciculi**, and the manner in which they approach the tendons has many variations. In some muscles, the fasciculi are parallel with the longitudinal axis and terminate at either end in flat tendons. In others, the fasciculi converge, like the plumes of a feather, to one side of a tendon which runs the entire length of a muscle, forming a **penniform** muscle like the Semimembranosus. If they converge to both sides of a tendon, as in the Rectus femoris, they are called **bipenniform,** or if they converge to several tendons, as in the Deltoideus, they are called **multipenniform**. The fasciculi may converge from a broad surface to a narrow tendinous point, as in the Temporalis, and be called **radiated**.

This arrangement of fasciculi is correlated with the power of the muscles. Those with comparatively few fasciculi, extending the length of the muscle, have a greater range of motion but not as much power. Penniform muscles, with a large number of fasciculi distributed along their tendons, have greater power but smaller range of motion.

The names of the muscles have been derived from: (*a*) their situation, as the Brachialis, Pectoralis, Supraspinatus; (*b*) their direction, as the Rectus, Obliquus, and Transversus abdominis; (*c*) their action, as Flexors, Extensors; (*d*) their shape, as the Deltoideus, Trapezius, Rhomboideus; (*e*) the number of divisions, as the Biceps, Triceps, Quadriceps; (*f*) their points of attachment, as the Sternocleido-mastoideus, Omohyoideus.

Origin and Insertion of Muscles.—The attachment of the two ends of a muscle are called the origin and the insertion. In the text it is customary to describe the muscle as *arising* from the origin and *inserting* at the insertion. The origin is the more fixed and proximal end, the insertion the more movable and distal end. For example, the Pectoralis major arises or has its origin from the ribs and clavicle, and its insertion is into the humerus. If the individual were climbing a tree, however, the origin and insertion might seem to be reversed, and the hand be more fixed and the body more movable. The designations of the origins and insertions in the following descriptions are more or less arbitrary, therefore, and a matter of convention among anatomists.

Illustrations of areas of attachment of the muscles are given with the descriptions of the bones and should be consulted constantly. The origins are marked in red, the insertions in blue.

MUSCLE ACTION

When a muscle contracts, it acts upon movable parts to bring about certain movements. These actions of the muscle should be studied from three points of view: (*a*) *individual action,* (*b*) *group actions,* and (*c*) *action correlated with the nerve supply.* The individual action is closely associated with the anatomy of a muscle because mechanically, the action is the direct result of the attachment of its two ends. It is not necessarily true, however, that the action in the living body is the same as that deduced from observing its attachments, nor even from pulling on it in a dead subject, because incidental actions may not be utilized or may even be suppressed in the living body. A knowledge of individual action is of practical value to a surgeon in the diagnosis and treatment of displacements due to fractures. Group actions are related to the functions as well as the anatomy of the muscles. It is seldom possible for a person to make a single muscle contract at will. In other words, the movements, not the muscles, are represented in the central nervous system. A muscle may be associated with one group for one action and a different group for another, possibly even antagonistic action. A correlation of the knowledge of the action with the nerve supply is of practical value in the diagnosis of lesions of the peripheral and central nervous system, and in the treatment of such lesions. Frequently there is a correspondence between groups of muscles arranged according to nerve supply and those arranged according to common actions.

Practically every muscle acting upon a joint is matched by another muscle which has an opposite action. Each muscle of such a pair is the **antagonist** of the other, for example, the Biceps brachii, a flexor, and the Triceps, an extensor, are antagonists at the elbow. The performance of most movements requires the combined action of a number of muscles; those which act directly to bring about the desired movement are called the **prime movers**; those which act to hold the part of the body in an appropriate position are called **fixation muscles**. It happens frequently that the prime movers have actions other than the one desired, in which case the antagonists of the undesired action come into play; these are the **synergists**. For example, in closing the fist, the prime movers are the Flexores digitorum sublimis and profundus, the Flexor pollicis longus, and the small muscles of the thumb; the fixation muscles are the Triceps, Biceps, Brachialis, and the muscles about the shoulder which hold the arm in position; the synergetic muscles are the Extensores carpi radialis and ulnaris, which prevent flexion of the wrist. In some instances, when an act is performed with extreme force, muscles which are not required for a moderate performance come to the assistance of the prime movers, and these are known as *emergency muscles*. For example, the flexors of the fingers may flex the wrist in emergency. A further point which must be borne in mind is that the force of gravity may be the prime mover, in which case, the antagonists of the muscles which might be expected to be the prime movers are the muscles which act, and they do so to retard and control the movement caused by gravity.

Individual muscles cannot always be treated as single mechanical units, with regard to their actions. Different parts of the same muscle may have different and even antagonistic actions; for example, the anterior part of the Deltoideus flexes, but the posterior portion extends the arm. Two adjacent muscles like the Infraspinatus and the Teres minor, on the other hand, may have the same action.

No study of muscles is complete without observations of the muscles in their normal positions in the living body. It is recommended that students find an opportunity to make this study. The surface markings associated with the muscles are illustrated in the second chapter of the book.

THE MUSCLES AND FASCIÆ OF THE HEAD.

The muscles of the head may be arranged in groups, of which the following two will be described in this chapter:

I. The Facial Muscles.   II. The Muscles of Mastication.

In addition to these two groups, other muscles occupying positions in the head are described in other, more appropriate parts of the book: (1) The Ocular Muscles; (2) The Muscles of the Auditory Ossicles; (3) The Muscles of the Tongue; and (4) The Muscles of the Pharynx.

I. THE FACIAL MUSCLES.

The **facial muscles** (*muscles of expression*) are cutaneous muscles, lying within the layers of the superficial fascia. In general, they arise, either from fascia or from the bones of the face, and insert into the skin. The individual muscles seldom remain separate and distinct throughout their length because of a tendency to merge with their neighbors at their terminations or attachments. They may be grouped into: (1) the muscles of the scalp; (2) the extrinsic muscles of the ear; (3) the muscles of the eyelid; (4) the muscles of the nose; (5) the muscles of the mouth. An additional muscle, the Platysma, really belongs to the facial group but will be described with the muscles of the neck.

1. The Muscles and Fasciæ of the Scalp.

Epicranius.   Occipitofrontalis.   Temporoparietalis.

The **superficial fascia** (*tela subcutanea*) of the head invests the facial muscles and carries the superficial blood vessels and nerves. It varies considerably in thickness and texture in different areas but everywhere has an abundant blood and nerve supply. Above the superior nuchal and temporal lines, and anterior to the Masseter muscle there is no deep fascia underlying it other than the periosteum of the bones. Under the scalp, the superficial fascia is very thick and tough, and over the cranial vault, the muscular stratum is represented by the broad epicranial aponeurosis or galea aponeurotica. A fascial cleft, such as that commonly found under the superficial fascia in the rest of the body, is very prominent in this region and separates the galea from the pericranium or cranial periosteum. It accounts for the movability of the scalp and makes possible the sudden accumulation of large amounts of blood in the hematomas following blows upon the head. Over the forehead, the superficial layers of the fascia are much thinner than in the scalp and the skin is closely attached to the underlying Frontalis. Over the eyelids, it is devoid of fat and is composed of a loose areolar tissue which is easily distended and infiltrated with tissue fluid in edema, or blood in ecchymosis or hemorrhage. On the cheeks and lips, it contains a considerable amount of fat and is tougher and more fibrous, especially in men. The superficial fascia is reduced over the cartilages of the nose and external ear, the skin being closely bound to the underlying perichondrium. The superficial fascia of the face is directly continuous over the mandible with that of the neck, and that of the scalp merges posteriorly with the similar fibrous layer of the back of the neck.

The skin of the scalp is thicker than in any other part of the body. The hair follicles are closely set together, have numerous sebaceous glands, and extend deeply into the superficial fascia. The subcutaneous fat is broken up into granular lobules, and is mattressed into a firm layer by the many fibrous bands which secure the skin to the deeper layers of the superficial fascia.

The **Epicranius** (Fig. 424) is a broad muscular and tendinous layer which covers the top and sides of the skull, from the occipital bone to the eyebrow. It consists

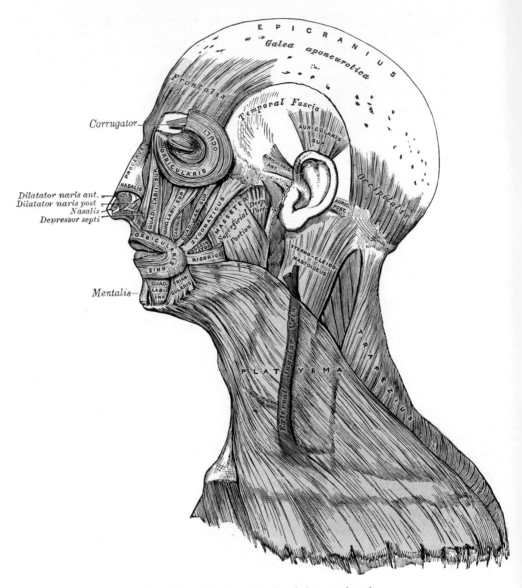

Fig. 424.—Muscles of the head, face, and neck.

of thin, broad, muscular bellies, connected by an extensive intermediate aponeurosis, the galea aponeurotica. The **occipital belly** (*Venter occipitalis; Occipitalis*), quadrilateral in form, *arises* by short tendinous fibers from the lateral two-thirds of the superior nuchal line of the occipital bone, and from the mastoid part of the temporal. The muscular fasciculi ascend in a parallel course toward the vertex and *end* in the galea aponeurotica. Between the muscles of the two sides there is a considerable, though variable, interval which is occupied by a prolongation of the galea. The **frontal belly** (*Venter frontalis; Frontalis*), also quadrilateral in form, is broader than the occipital belly and its fasciculi are longer, finer and paler in color. It has no bony attachments. Its medial fibers are continuous with those of the Procerus; its intermediate fibers blend with the Corrugator and Orbicularis oculi; and its lateral fibers are blended with the latter muscle also, over the zygomatic process of the frontal bone. From these *attachments* the fibers are directed upward, and join the galea aponeurotica below the coronal suture. The medial margins of the muscles of the two sides are joined together for some distance above the root of the nose.

The **Temporoparietalis** is newly designated in the PNA. It takes the place of the broad very thin sheet formerly named the Auricularis superior and Auricularis anterior which are so labelled in Figure 424. It *arises* from the temporal fascia above and anterior to the ear. It is divided into three parts which spread out like a fan over the temporal fascia, a temporal part anteriorly, a parietal part superiorly, with a triangular part between. It *inserts* into the lateral border of the galea aponeurotica. The Auriculares anterior and superior are still recognized in the PNA but refer to small inconstant muscle bellies more closely associated with the auricula.

The **galea aponeurotica** (*epicranial aponeurosis*) covers the upper part of the cranium between the frontal and occipital bellies of the Occipitofrontalis. In addition to its attachment to these muscle bellies, it is attached behind, in the interval between the two Occipitales, to the external occipital protuberance and the highest nuchal line of the occipital bone. In front, it forms a short, narrow prolongation between the two Frontales. On either side, it receives the insertion of the Temporoparietalis; at this point it loses its aponeurotic character, and is continuous over the temporal fascia with a layer of laminated areolar tissue. It is closely connected to the integument by the firm, dense, adipose layer of superficial fascia and is separated from the pericranium by the fascial cleft which allows the aponeurosis, carrying with it the integument, to move through a considerable distance.

Action.—The occipital and frontal bellies of the Occipitofrontalis acting together draw the scalp back raising the eyebrows and wrinkling the forehead as in an expression of surprise. The frontal bellies acting alone raise the eyebrows, either on one or both sides. The Temporoparietalis tightens the scalp and draws back the skin of the temples to combine with the Occipitofrontalis in wrinkling the forehead and widening the eyes in an expression of fright or horror. The Temporoparietalis raises the auricula.

Nerves.—The frontal belly and the Temporoparietalis are supplied by the temporal branches, and the occipital belly by the posterior auricular branch of the facial nerve.

Variations.—Both frontal and occipital bellies may vary considerably in size and in extent; either may be absent; the muscles of the two sides may fuse in the middle line; the frontal bellies may interdigitate across the line; the occipital belly may fuse with the Auricularis posterior.

A thin muscular slip, the **Transversus nuchæ** or **Occipitalis minor**, is present in 25 per cent of the bodies; it arises from the external occipital protuberance or from the superior nuchal line, either superficial or deep to the Trapezius; it is frequently inserted with the Auricularis posterior, but may join the posterior edge of the Sternocleidomastoideus.

2. The Extrinsic Muscles of the Ear.

The **Auricularis anterior** (*Attrahens aurem*) (Fig. 424), is thin, pale, delicate, and indistinct. It *arises* from the anterior portion of the fascia in the temporal area, and its fibers converge to be *inserted* into a projection on the front of the helix.

The **Auricularis superior** (*Attolens aurem*) (Fig. 424) is thin and fan-shaped. Its fibers *arise* from the fascia of the temporal area, and converge to be *inserted* by a thin flattened tendon into the upper part of the cranial surface of the auricula.

The **Auricularis posterior** (*Retrahens aurem*) (Fig. 424) consists of two or three fleshy fasciculi which *arise* from the mastoid portion of the temporal bone by short aponeurotic fibers. They are *inserted* into the lower part of the cranial surface of the concha (See Transversus nuchæ above).

Actions.—The Auricularis anterior draws the auricula forward and upward, the Auricularis superior draws it upward, and the posterior draws it backward. In man these muscles seem to act more in conjunction with the Occipitofrontalis to move the scalp than to move the auricula, but in some individuals they can be used to execute voluntary movements of the auricula.

Nerves.—The Auriculares anterior and superior are supplied by the temporal branches, the Auricularis posterior by the posterior auricular branch of the facial nerve.

Variations.—The auricular muscles vary greatly in thickness and extent or rarely may be absent.

3. The Muscles of the Eyelids.

Levator palpebræ superioris.
Orbicularis oculi.
Corrugator.

The Levator palpebræ superioris is described with the Anatomy of the Eye.

The **Orbicularis oculi** (*Orbicularis palpebrarum*) (Fig. 425) *arises* from the nasal part of the frontal bone, from the frontal process of the maxilla in front of the lacrimal groove, and from the anterior surface and borders of a short fibrous band the **medial palpebral ligament**. From this origin, the fibers are directed lateral-ward, forming a broad and thin layer, which occupies the eyelids or palpebræ,

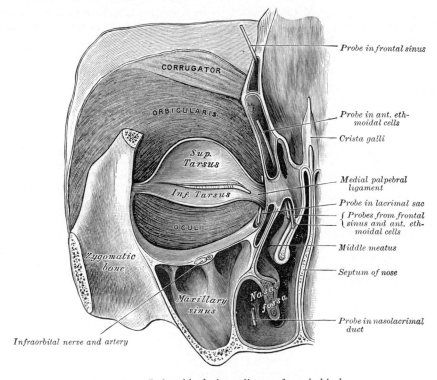

FIG. 425.—Left orbicularis oculi, seen from behind.

surrounds the circumference of the orbit, and spreads over the temple, and down-ward on the cheek. The **palpebral portion** of the muscle is thin and pale; it *arises* from the bifurcation of the medial palpebral ligament, forms a series of concentric curves, and is *inserted* into the lateral palpebral raphé. The **orbital portion** is thicker and of a reddish color; its fibers form a complete ellipse without interruption at the lateral palpebral commissure; the upper fibers of this portion blend with the Frontalis and Corrugator. The **lacrimal part** (*Tensor tarsi*) is a small, thin muscle, about 6 mm. in breadth and 12 mm. in length, situated behind the medial palpebral ligament and lacrimal sac (Fig. 425). It *arises* from the posterior crest and adjacent part of the orbital surface of the lacrimal bone, and passing behind the lacrimal sac, divides into two slips, upper and lower, which are *inserted* into the superior and inferior tarsi medial to the puncta lacrimalia; occasionally it is very indistinct.

The **medial palpebral ligament** (*tendo oculi*), about 4 mm. in length and 2 mm. in breadth, is attached to the frontal process of the maxilla in front of the lacrimal groove. Crossing the lacrimal sac, it divides into two parts, upper and lower, each attached to the medial end of the corresponding tarsus. As the ligament crosses the lacrimal sac, a strong aponeurotic lamina is given off from its posterior surface; this expands over the sac, and is attached to the posterior lacrimal crest.

The **lateral palpebral raphé** is a much weaker structure than the medial palpebral ligament. It is attached to the margin of the frontosphenoidal process of the zygomatic bone, and passes medialward to the lateral commissure of the eyelids, where it divides into two slips, which are attached to the margins of the respective tarsi.

The **Corrugator** (*Corrugator supercilii*) is a small, narrow, pyramidal muscle, placed at the medial end of the eyebrow, beneath the Frontalis and Orbicularis oculi. It *arises* from the medial end of the superciliary arch; and its fibers pass upward and lateralward, between the palpebral and orbital portions of the Orbicularis oculi, and are *inserted* into the deep surface of the skin, above the middle of the orbital arch.

Actions.—The Orbicularis oculi is the sphincter muscle of the eyelids. The palpebral portion closes the lids gently, as in blinking or in sleep; the orbital portion is used as well in stronger closing, like winking with one eye. When the entire muscle is brought into action, the skin of the forehead, temple, and cheek is drawn toward the medial angle of the orbit, and the eyelids are firmly closed, as in photophobia. The skin thus drawn upon is thrown into folds, especially radiating from the lateral angle of the eyelids; these folds become permanent in old age, and form the so-called "crows' feet." The Levator palpebræ superioris is the direct antagonist of this muscle; it raises the upper eyelid and exposes the front of the bulb of the eye. Each time the eyelids are closed through the action of the Orbicularis, the medial palpebral ligament is tightened, the wall of the lacrimal sac is thus drawn lateralward and forward, so that a vacuum is made in it, and the tears are sucked along the lacrimal canals into it. The lacrimal part of the Orbicularis oculi draws the eyelids and the ends of the lacrimal canals medialward and compresses them against the surface of the globe of the eye, thus placing them in the most favorable situation for receiving the tears; it also compresses the lacrimal sac. The Corrugator draws the eyebrow downward and medialward, producing the vertical wrinkles of the forehead. It is the "frowning" muscle, and may be regarded as the principal muscle in the expression of suffering.

Nerves.—Nerves from the temporal and zygomatic branches of the facial nerve.

Variations.—The Orbicularis varies in extent and may be fused with neighboring muscles.

4. The Muscles of the Nose (Fig. 424).

Procerus.   Depressor septi.
Nasalis.   Dilatator naris posterior.
                     Dilatator naris anterior.

The **Procerus** (*Pyramidalis nasi*) is a small pyramidal slip *arising* by tendinous fibers from the fascia covering the lower part of the nasal bone and upper part of the lateral nasal cartilage; it is *inserted* into the skin over the lower part of the forehead between the two eyebrows, its fibers decussating with those of the Frontalis.

The **Nasalis** (*Compressor naris*) consists of two parts, transverse and alar. The **transverse part** *arises* from the maxilla, above and lateral to the incisive fossa; its fibers proceed upward and medialward, expanding into a thin aponeurosis which is continuous on the bridge of the nose with that of the muscle of the opposite side, and with the aponeurosis of the Procerus. The **alar part** is attached by

27

one end to the greater alar cartilage, and by the other to the integument at the point of the nose.

The **Depressor septi** (*Depressor alæ nasi*) *arises* from the incisive fossa of the maxilla; its fibers ascend to be *inserted* into the septum and back part of the ala of the nose. It lies between the mucous membrane and muscular structure of the lip.

The **Dilatator naris posterior** is placed partly beneath the Quadratus labii superioris. It *arises* from the margin of the nasal notch of the maxilla, and from the lesser alar cartilages, and is *inserted* into the skin near the margin of the nostril.

The **Dilatator naris anterior** is a delicate fasciculus, passing from the greater alar cartilage to the integument near the margin of the nostril; it is situated in front of the preceding.

Actions.—The Procerus draws down the medial angle of the eyebrows and produces transverse wrinkles over the bridge of the nose. The two Dilatatores enlarge the aperture of the nares. Their action in ordinary breathing is to resist the tendency of the nostrils to close from atmospheric pressure, but in difficult breathing, as well as in some emotions, such as anger, they contract strongly. The Depressor septi is a direct antagonist of the other muscles of the nose, drawing the ala of the nose downward, and thereby constricting the aperture of the nares. The Nasalis depresses the cartilaginous part of the nose and draws the ala toward the septum.

Nerves.—Nerves from the buccal branches of the facial nerve.

Variations.—These muscles vary in size and strength or may be absent.

5. The Muscles of the Mouth (Fig. 424).

Levator labii superioris.	Depressor labii inferioris.
Levator labii superioris alaeque nasi.	Depressor anguli oris.
Levator anguli oris.	Mentalis.
Zygomaticus major.	Transversus menti.
Zygomaticus minor.	Orbicularis oris.
Risorius.	Buccinator.

The **Levator labii superioris** (*Quadratus labii superioris, infraorbital head*) has a rather broad *origin* from the lower margin of the orbit immediately above the infraorbital foramen, some of its fibers being attached to the maxilla, others to the zygomatic bone. Its fibers converge to be *inserted* into the muscular substance of the upper lip between the Levator anguli oris and the Levator labii superioris alaeque nasi.

The **Levator labii superioris alaeque nasi** (*Quadratus labii superioris, angular head*) *arises* by a pointed extremity from the upper part of the frontal process of the maxilla and passing obliquely downward and lateralward divides into two slips. One of these is *inserted* into the greater alar cartilage and skin of the nose; the other is prolonged into the upper lip, blending with the Levator labii superioris.

The **Zygomaticus minor** (*Quadratus labii superioris, zygomatic head*) *arises* from the malar surface of the zygomatic bone immediately behind the zygomatico-maxillary suture and passes downward and medialward as a narrow slip to be *inserted* into the upper lip between the Levator labii superioris and the Zygomaticus major.

The **Levator anguli oris** (*Caninus*) *arises* from the canine fossa, immediately below the infraorbital foramen; its fibers are *inserted* into the angle of the mouth, intermingling with those of the Zygomaticus major, Depressor anguli oris, and Orbicularis oris.

The **Zygomaticus major** (*Zygomaticus*) *arises* from the zygomatic bone, in front of the zygomaticotemporal suture, and descending obliquely with a medial inclination, is *inserted* into the angle of the mouth, where it blends with the fibers of the Levator and Depressor anguli oris and Orbicularis oris.

Actions.—The Levator labii superioris is the proper elevator of the upper lip, carrying it at the same time a little forward. The Levator labii superioris alaeque nasi also dilates the naris, and together with the former and the Zygomaticus minor forms the nasolabial furrow which is deepened in expressions of sadness. When these three muscles act in conjunction with the Levator anguli oris the furrow is deepened into an expression of contempt or disdain. The Zygomaticus major draws the angle of the mouth upward and backward in laughing.

Nerves.—Nerves from the buccal branches of the facial nerve.

Variations.—These muscles, especially the Zygomatic minor vary in extent and the degree of fusion with each other or with neighboring muscles.

The **Risorius** *arises* in the fascia over the Masseter and, passing horizontally forward, superficial to the Platysma, is *inserted* into the skin at the angle of the mouth (Fig. 424).

The **Depressor labii inferirios** (*Quadratus labii inferioris; Quadratus menti*) is a small quadrilateral muscle. It *arises* from the oblique line of the mandible, between the symphysis and the mental foramen, and passes upward and medialward, to be *inserted* into the integument of the lower lip, its fibers blending with the Orbicularis oris, and with those of its fellow of the opposite side. At its origin it is continuous with the fibers of the Platysma. Much yellow fat is intermingled with the fibers of this muscle.

The **Depressor anguli oris** (*Triangularis*) *arises* from the oblique line of the mandible, whence its fibers converge, to be *inserted*, by a narrow fasciculus, into the angle of the mouth. At its origin it is continuous with the Platysma, and at its insertion with the Orbicularis oris and Risorius; some of its fibers are directly continuous with those of the Levator anguli oris.

The **Mentalis** (*Levator menti*) is a small conical fasciculus, situated at the side of the frenulum of the lower lip. It *arises* from the incisive fossa of the mandible, and descends to be *inserted* into the integument of the chin.

The **Transversus menti,** found in more than half the bodies, is a small muscle which crosses the midline just under the chin. It is frequently continuous with the Triangularis.

Actions.—The Risorius retracts the angle of the mouth. The Depressor labii inferioris draws the lower lip directly downward and a little lateralward, as in the expression of irony. The Depressor anguli oris depresses the angle of the mouth, being the antagonist of the Levator anguli oris and Zygomaticus major; acting with the Levator, it draws the angle of the mouth medialward. The Mentalis raises and protrudes the lower lip, and at the same time wrinkles the skin of the chin, expressing doubt or disdain. The Platysma acts with this group, retracting and depressing the angle of the mouth.

Nerves.—Nerves from the mandibular and buccal branches of the facial nerve.

Variations.—The Risorius varies greatly; it may be absent, doubled, greatly enlarged, or blended with the Platysma. The Depressor labii inferioris is continuous with the Platysma to a greater or lesser extent. The Mentalis varies in size and connection with the Platysma. The Depressor anguli oris may be in two or three separate parts; its anterior fibers may cross under the chin to join the Transversus menti.

The **Orbicularis oris** (Fig. 426) is not a simple sphincter muscle like the Orbicularis oculi; it consists of numerous strata of muscular fibers surrounding the orifice of the mouth but having different direction. It consists partly of fibers derived from the other facial muscles which are inserted into the lips, and partly of fibers proper to the lips. Of the former, a considerable number are derived from the Buccinator and form the deeper stratum of the Orbicularis. Some of the Buccinator fibers—namely, those near the middle of the muscle—decussate at the angle of the mouth, those arising from the maxilla passing to the lower lip, and those from the mandible to the upper lip. The uppermost and lowermost fibers of the Buccinator pass across the lips from side to side without decussation. Superficial to this stratum is a second, formed on either side by the Caninus and Triangularis, which cross each other at the angle of the mouth; those from the Caninus passing to the lower lip, and those from the Triangularis to the upper lip, along which they run, to be inserted into the skin near the median line. In addition to these there are fibers from the Quadratus labii superioris, the Zygomaticus, and the Quadratus labii inferioris; these intermingle with the transverse fibers above described, and have principally an oblique direction. The proper fibers of the lips are oblique, and pass from the under surface of the skin to the mucous membrane, through the thickness of the lip. Finally there are fibers by which the muscle is connected with the maxillæ and the septum of the nose above and with the mandible below. In the upper lip these consist of two bands, lateral and medial, on either side of the middle line; the **lateral band** (*m. incisivus labii superioris*) *arises* from the alveolar border of the maxilla, opposite the lateral incisor tooth, and arching lateralward is continuous with the other muscles at the angle of the mouth; the **medial band** (*m. nasolabialis*) connects the upper lip to the back of the septum of the nose. The interval between the two medial bands corresponds

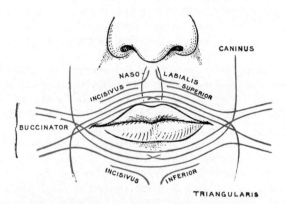

Fig. 426.—Scheme showing arrangement of fibers of Orbicularis oris.

with the depression, called the **philtrum**, seen on the lip beneath the septum of the nose. The additional fibers for the lower lip constitute a slip (*m. incisivus labii inferioris*) on either side of the middle line; this arises from the mandible, lateral to the Mentalis, and intermingles with the other muscles at the angle of the mouth.

Actions.—The Orbicularis oris in its ordinary action effects the direct closure of the lips; by its deep fibers, assisted by the oblique ones, it closely applies the lips to the alveolar arch. The superficial part, consisting principally of the decussating fibers, brings the lips together and also protrudes them forward.

Nerves.—The buccal branches of the facial nerve.

The **Buccinator** (Fig. 427) is the principal muscle of the cheek and forms the lateral wall of the oral cavity. It lies deeper than the other facial muscles, is quadrilateral in form, and occupies the interval between the maxilla and mandible, lateral to the teeth. It *arises* from the outer surfaces of the alveolar processes of the maxilla above and mandible below, alongside of the three molar teeth, and in between, from the pterygomandibular raphé, a tendinous inscription giving origin to both the Buccinator and the Constrictor pharyngis superior. The fibers of the upper and lower portions follow a slightly converging course forward, and *insert* by blending with the deeper stratum of muscle fibers in the corresponding lips. The fibers of the central portion converge toward the angle of the mouth and decussate, those from above becoming continuous with the Orbicularis oris of the lower lip, those from below with that of the upper lip. The superficial surface of the Buccinator is covered by the buccopharyngeal fascia and the buccal fat pad; the deep surface is in relation with the buccal glands and mucous membrane of the mouth. It is pierced by the duct of the parotid gland opposite the upper second molar tooth.

Action.—The Buccinator compresses the cheek and is, therefore, an important accessory muscle of mastication, holding the food under the immediate pressure of the teeth. When the cheeks have been distended with air, the Buccinators compress it and tend to force it out between the lips as in blowing a trumpet (Latin buccinator, a trumpet player).

Nerve.—The motor fibers to the Buccinator come from the facial nerve through its buccal branches. The buccinator nerve (from the trigeminal) is sensory only, in this area.

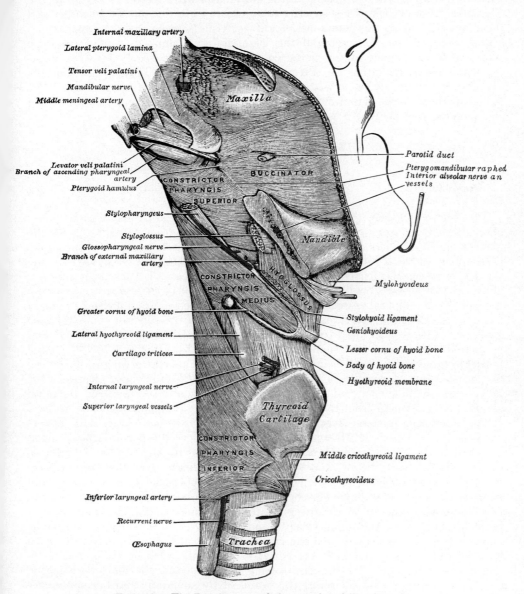

Fig. 427.—The Buccinator and the muscles of the pharynx.

The **Pterygomandibular Raphé** (*pterygomandibular ligament*) (Fig. 427) is a tendinous inscription between the Buccinator and the Constrictor pharyngis superior which gives origin to the middle portion of both muscles. Except for this tendinous interruption, the Constrictor, Buccinator and Orbicularis oris would form a continuous sphincter-like band of muscle. The raphé is held in place by its attachment superiorly to the pterygoid hamulus and inferiorly to the posterior end of the mylohyoid line of the mandible. Its relations are the same as those of the two muscles, its medial surface being covered by the mucous membrane of the mouth and its lateral surface being separated from the ramus of the mandible by a quantity of adipose tissue, the buccal fat pad.

Buccal Fat Pad (*corpus adiposum buccæ, suctorial pad*), a circumscribed or encapsulated mass of fat, lies superficial to the Buccinator at the anterior border of the Masseter. A well defined fascial cleft separates it from the superficial fascia and facial muscles. From this main mass of adipose tissue, narrow prolongations extend deeply between the Masseter and the Temporalis and upward under the deep temporal fascia. Some of the tissue continues still more deeply into the infratemporal fossa, separating the Pterygoideus externus and Temporalis from the maxilla, and filling in between the various structures and the bony fossæ. The mass superficial to the Buccinator is particularly prominent in infants, and is called the suctorial pad because it is supposed to assist in the act of sucking.

II. THE MUSCLES OF MASTICATION.

Temporalis.	Pterygoideus internus.
Masseter.	Pterygoideus externus.

The **Temporal Fascia** (*fascia temporalis*) (Fig. 430) is a strong, fibrous sheet, aponeurotic in appearance, which covers the Temporalis and is used by it for the attachment of its fibers. It is the most cranial extension of the deep fascia; above it, the deep fascia is represented only by the pericranium. It is covered by the superficial fascia which includes the Galea aponeurotica and Auricularis superior above, the Orbicularis oculi anteriorly, and just in front of the ear it is crossed by the superficial temporal vessels and auriculotemporal nerve. Its uppermost portion is a thin, single sheet, attached to the entire extent of the superior temporal line. Its lower portion, near the attachment to the zygomatic arch, is thickened and laminated. The inner leaf (*lamina profunda*) ends by attaching to the medial border of the arch; the outer leaf (*lamina superficialis*), after attaching to the lateral border, continues downward below the arch as the masseteric fascia. Between the leaves is a small quantity of fat, the orbital branch of the superficial temporal artery, and a filament from the zygomatic branch of the maxillary nerve.

The **Parotideomasseteric Fascia** (*fascia parotideomasseterica*) (Fig. 430) covers the lateral surface of the Masseter and splits to enclose the parotid gland. It is attached to the zygomatic arch above, is continuous with the suprahyoid portion of the cervical fascia below, and with the cervical fascia over the Sternocleidomastoideus posteriorly. The sheet which covers the superficial surface of the gland is fused with dense and tough superficial fascia, is intimately mingled with its capsule, and sends numerous irregular septa into its substance so that this gland cannot be shelled out, as can the submaxillary gland. The layer on the deep surface of the gland follows this surface behind the ramus of the mandible and there fuses with the fascia of the posterior belly of the Digastricus into a strong band, the stylomandibular ligament. The fascia covering the Masseter, the **masseteric fascia**, terminates anteriorly by encircling the ramus of the mandible and becoming continuous with the fascia of the Pterygoideus medialis deep to the bone. The masseteric fascia is attached to the border of the mandible inferiorly and posteriorly, completing a compartment which encloses the muscle except at its upper, deep portion where there is a communication with the tissue spaces about the insertion of the Temporalis.

The **pterygoid fascia** invests the Pterygoideus medialis and lateralis muscles. It is continuous below, at the angle of the mandible, with the masseteric and investing cervical fascias where the latter are attached to the bone. In this region also, it is continuous with the thickened band known as the stylomandibular ligament. It extends upward and forward along the deep surface of the Pterygoideus medialis to be attached with the origin of the muscle to the pterygoid process of the sphenoid bone. This sheet of fascia is attached to the mandible at both the borders of the inferior half of the muscle, but as the muscle angles away from the mandible toward its origin, the fascia wraps around the muscle forming a sheet on its superficial surface. This superficial sheet, continuing upward, splits to invest the Pterygoideus lateralis and is attached to the skull with the origin of this muscle. The fascia between the two Pterygoidei is attached to the skull along a line extending from the lateral pterygoid plate to the spina angularis of the sphenoid

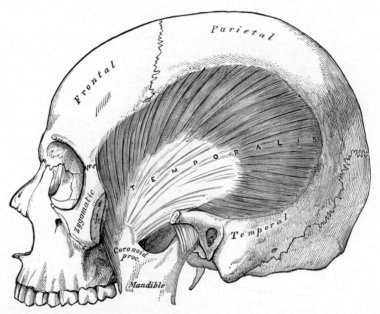

Fig. 428.—The Temporalis; the zygomatic arch and Masseter have been removed.

bone. The part attached to the spina angularis is thickened into a strong band which is attached below to the lingula of the mandible, forming the sphenomandibular ligament (page 336). Another band, the **pterygospinous ligament**, extends from the spine, between the two Pterygoidei, to the posterior margin of the lateral pterygoid plate. Occasionally this band is ossified, creating, between its upper border and the skull, a **pterygospinous foramen** which transmits the branches of the mandibular division of the trigeminal nerve to the muscles of mastication. Between the sphenomandibular ligament and the neck of the mandible, there is an interval which affords a passage for the internal maxillary vessels into the infratemporal fossa. The fascia on the surface of the Pterygoideus lateralis is in relation with the pterygoid plexus of veins. Deep to the pterygoid and deep temporal fasciæ the layer of soft adipose tissue which is an extension of the buccal fat pad separates these fasciæ from the buccopharyngeal fascia and neighboring structures.

The masticator compartment contains the four muscles of mastication and the ramus and posterior part of the body of the mandible. It is enclosed superficially by the masseteric and temporal fasciæ and deeply by the pterygoid and deep temporal fasciæ.

The **Temporalis** (*Temporal muscle*) (Fig. 428) is a broad, radiating muscle, situated at the side of the head. It *arises* from the whole of the temporal fossa and from the deep surface of the temporal fascia. Its fibers converge as they descend, and end in a tendon, which passes deep to the zygomatic arch and is *inserted* into the medial surface, apex, and anterior border of the coronoid process, and the anterior border of the ramus of the mandible nearly as far forward as the last molar tooth.

Action.—Closes the jaws. The posterior portion retracts the mandible.

Nerves.—Anterior and posterior deep temporal nerves from the mandibular division of the trigeminal nerve.

The **Masseter** (Fig. 424) is a thick, somewhat quadrilateral muscle, consisting of two portions, superficial and deep. The *superficial portion*, the larger, *arises* by a thick, tendinous aponeurosis from the zygomatic process of the maxilla, and

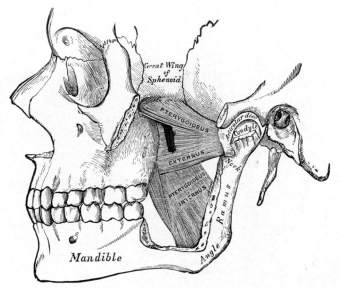

FIG. 429.—The Pterygoidei; the zygomatic arch and a portion of the ramus of the mandible have been removed.

from the anterior two-thirds of the lower border of the zygomatic arch: its fibers pass downward and backward, to be *inserted* into the angle and lower half of the lateral surface of the ramus of the mandible. The *deep portion* is much smaller, and more muscular in texture; it *arises* from the posterior third of the lower border and from the whole of the medial surface of the zygomatic arch; its fibers pass downward and forward, to be *inserted* into the upper half of the ramus and the lateral surface of the coronoid process of the mandible. The deep portion of the muscle is partly concealed, in front, by the superficial portion; behind, it is covered by the parotid gland. The fibers of the two portions are continuous at their insertion.

Action.—Closes the jaws.

Nerve.—The masseteric nerve from the mandibular division of the trigeminal nerve.

The **Pterygoideus medialis** (*Internal pterygoid muscle*) (Fig. 429) is a thick, quadrilateral muscle occupying a position on the inside of the ramus of the mandible similar to that of the Masseter on the outside. It *arises* from the medial surface of the lateral pterygoid plate and the grooved surface of the pyramidal process of the palatine bone; it has a second slip of origin from the lateral surfaces of the pyramidal process of the palatine and tuberosity of the maxilla. The second slip lies superficial to the Pterygoideus lateralis while the main mass of the muscle lies deep. Its fibers pass downward, lateralward, and backward, and are *inserted*, by a strong tendinous lamina, into the lower and back part of the medial surface of the ramus and angle of the mandible, as high as the mandibular foramen. The upper portion of the muscle is separated from the mandible by the sphenomandibular ligament, the internal maxillary vessels, the inferior alveolar vessels and nerve, and the lingual nerve. The medial surface of the muscle is closely related to the Tensor veli palatini above and to the Constrictor pharyngis superior lower down.

Action.—Closes the jaws.
Nerve.—The medial pterygoid nerve from the mandibular division of the trigeminal nerve.

The **Mandibular Sling.**—The Masseter and the Pterygoideus internus are so placed that they suspend the angle of the mandible in a sling. They form a functional articulation between the mandible and the maxilla, with the temporomandibular joint acting as a guide, in a fashion similar to the articulation between the scapula and the thorax, with the clavicle as a guide. When the mouth is opened and closed, the mandible moves about a center of rotation established by the attachment of the sling and the sphenomandibular ligament.

The **Pterygoideus lateralis** (*External pterygoid muscle*) (Fig. 429) is a short, thick muscle, somewhat conical in form, which extends almost horizontally between the infratemporal fossa and the condyle of the mandible. It *arises* by two heads; an **upper** from the lower part of the lateral surface of the great wing of the sphenoid and from the infratemporal crest; a **lower** from the lateral surface of the lateral pterygoid plate. Its fibers pass horizontally backward and lateralward, to be *inserted* into a depression in front of the neck of the condyle of the mandible, and into the front margin of the articular disk of the temporomandibular articulation.

Action.—Opens the jaws; protrudes the mandible; moves mandible from side to side.
Nerve.—The lateral pterygoid nerve from the mandibular division of the trigeminal nerve.
Group Actions.—The Temporalis, Masseter and Pterygoideus medialis close the jaws. Biting with the incisor teeth is performed by the Masseter and Pterygoideus medialis primarily, to some extent by the anterior portion of the Temporalis. Biting or chewing with the molars calls all three into maximal action. Opening of the jaws is performed primarily by the Pterygoideus lateralis pulling forward on the condyle and rotating the mandible about the center of rotation near the angle (see page 337). It is assisted, at the beginning of the action, by the Mylohyoideus, Digastricus, and Geniohyoideus. When the mouth is opened against great resistance, in addition to the above, the infrahyoid muscles act to fix the hyoid, and other suprahyoid muscles probably come into action. The Platysma is practically without action unless the corners of the mouth are widely drawn back. The Pterygoideus lateralis protrudes the jaw when accompanied by appropriate synergetic action of the closing muscles. The Pterygoideus medialis assists in this action only as a synergist, along with the other closing muscles, when they prevent the rotation which opens the jaws widely. If the Pterygoideus lateralis of one side acts, the corresponding side of the mandible is drawn forward while the opposite condyle remains comparatively fixed, and side-to-side movements, such as those occurring in the triturition of food, take place. The mandible is retracted by the posterior fibers of the Temporalis.

THE FASCIÆ AND MUSCLES OF THE ANTERO-LATERAL REGION OF THE NECK.

The antero-lateral muscles of the neck may be arranged into the following groups:

I. Superficial Cervical.
II. Lateral Cervical.
III. Suprahyoid.

IV. Infrahyoid.
V. Anterior Vertebral.
VI. Lateral Vertebral.

I. THE SUPERFICIAL CERVICAL MUSCLE.

Platysma.

The **Superficial Fascia** *lamina superficialis; tela subcutanea*) in the anterior and lateral regions of the neck is thinner and less dense than the facial portion with which it is continuous over the border of the mandible and the parotid gland. It has imbedded in its deeper layers the fibers of the Platysma muscle, and it is separated from the deep fascia by a distinct fascial cleft which facilitates the action of the muscle and increases the movability of the skin in this region. It is continuous over the clavicle with the superficial fascia of the pectoral and deltoid regions. Posteriorly, it is continuous with the superficial fascia of the back of the neck which is thick, tough, fibrous, and adherent to the deep fascia.

The **Platysma** (Fig. 424) is a broad sheet *arising* from the fascia covering the upper parts of the Pectoralis major and Deltoideus; its fibers cross the clavicle, and proceed obliquely upward and medialward along the side of the neck. The anterior fibers interlace, below and behind the symphysis menti, with the fibers of the muscle of the opposite side; the posterior fibers cross the mandible, some being inserted into the bone below the oblique line, others into the skin and subcutaneous tissue of the lower part of the face, many of these fibers blending with the muscles about the angle and lower part of the mouth. Sometimes fibers can be traced to the Zygomaticus, or to the margin of the Orbicularis oculi. Beneath the Platysma, the external jugular vein descends from the angle of the mandible to the clavicle.

Action.—Draws the outer part of the lower lip downward and backward, widening the aperture at the corners of the mouth as in an expression of horror, and assists in opening the jaws when the mouth is opened as above. When all its fibers act maximally, it pulls the skin up from the clavicular region, increasing the diameter of the neck and relieving the pressure of a tight collar.

Nerve.—The cervical branch of the facial nerve.

Variations.—The platysma may be composed of delicate, pale, scattered fasciculi, or may form a broad layer of robust, dark fasciculi; it may be deficient or reach well below the clavicle; it may extend into the face for a very short distance or may continue as high as the zygoma or the ear. Decussation of fasciculi in the middle line anteriorly is common. The muscle may be absent.

The **Occipitalis minor** may extend, as a more or less independent band, from the fascia over the Trapezius to the fascia over the insertion of the Sternocleidomastoideus.

CERVICAL FASCIÆ

The **Fascia Cervicalis** (*deep cervical fascia*) (Fig. 430) forms important transitions and connections, as might be expected, because the neck itself is a connecting structure, joining the head with the thorax and making many contributions to the upper limb. Its components are complex and form various compartments and fascial clefts which are of major surgical interest because of these associations.

Cervical Triangles.—Two triangular areas are formed in the neck by the oblique course of the Sternocleidomastoideus muscle. The **Anterior Triangle** is bounded by the middle line anteriorly, the Sternocleidomastoideus laterally, and the body of the mandible superiorly. The **Posterior Triangle** is bounded by the clavicle below, and by the adjacent borders of the Sternocleidomastoideus and Trapezius above.

The **Fascia Colli** may be divided, first, according to area, into suprahyoid and infrahyoid portions. Both of these, in turn, may be subdivided into smaller portions for the purpose of description. The suprahyoid subdivisions are: (1) the investing fascia, and (2) the deeper portion which is associated with the mandible and the floor of the mouth. The infrahyoid may be subdivided into: (1) the investing fascia; (2) the prevertebral fascia; (3) the middle cervical fascia; (4) the visceral fascia, and (5) the carotid sheath.

Fascia of the Suprahyoid Region.—Since the suprahyoid region is as much a part of the head as of the neck, it will be necessary to include descriptions of certain head fasciæ for the sake of clarity and continuity. It is convenient and logical, moreover, to look upon the fascia of the head as the cranial portion of the cervical fascia, and trace them both to the same superior termination and attachment.

The **investing fascia of the suprahyoid region** (Fig. 432) extends upward from its attachment to the hyoid bone and is attached to the whole length of the inferior border of the mandible. It covers the anterior belly of the Digastricus, is adherent to its sheath, and is continuous across the middle line. More laterally, it splits to enclose the submaxillary gland in a sheath which is separated from the intrinsic capsule of the gland by a fascial cleft. The sheet on the deep surface of the gland

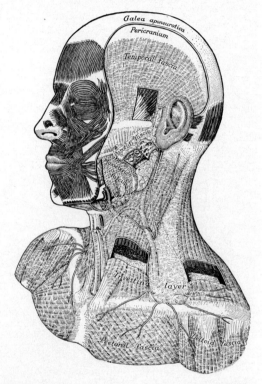

Fig. 430.—The external investing layer of deep fascia of the head and neck.

lies over the Stylohyoideus and the intermediate tendon of the Digastricus, and, by a fusion with their fascial covering, forms a band which is carried up to the styloid process, prolonging the lower boundary of the suprahyoid compartment posteriorly from the hyoid bone. The sheets of the superficial and deep surfaces of the submaxillary gland come together for a short distance near the angle of the mandible and separate again to ensheath the parotid gland. The external layer of the parotid portion extends upward over the angle of the mandible as the parotideo-masseteric fascia and attaches to the zygomatic arch. It is closely adherent to the capsule of the gland which cannot, therefore, be shelled out readily, as is the case with the submaxillary gland. The fascia at the posterior border of the parotid gland is very tough where the superficial layer joins the deeper layer. It splits again to enclose the Sternocleidomastoideus, is attached to the mastoid process of the temporal bone, and is then continuous with the fascia of the back of the neck.

The deeper layers of fascia in the anterior portion of the suprahyoid region form individual sheaths for the muscles and are attached to the hyoid bone, below, and to the mandible, the styloid process, or the tongue, above. More laterally, the portion of the investing layer between the submaxillary and parotid glands, extends deeply to fuse with the fascia of the posterior belly of the Digastricus. The result is a strong band which continues upward between the deep surface of the parotid and the posterior belly of the Digastricus; it is attached, above, to the styloid process and below, to the angle of the mandible, and is known as the stylomandibular ligament.

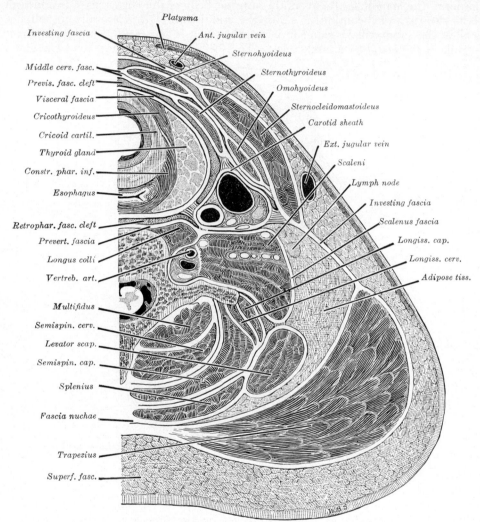

Fig. 431.—Section of the neck at about the level of the sixth cervical vertebra. Showing the arrangement of the fascia colli.

The suprahyoid compartment is closed by the attachment of the investing fascia to the border of the mandible above and to the hyoid bone below. It is continuous across the middle line anteriorly and reaches up to the floor of the mouth in the region of the sublingual gland and tongue. The fascial clefts between structures in this compartment are continuous posteriorly into the fascial cleft which lies superficial to the buccopharyngeal fascia (the lateral pharyngeal cleft) and into the region of the deep extensions of the buccal fat pad. The fascial clefts in the floor of the mouth and about the sublingual gland communicate with the cleft surrounding the submaxillary gland by extending around the posterior border of the Mylohyoideus.

The **fascia of the infrahyoid region** includes most of what is commonly called the deep cervical fascia (fascia colli).

The **investing layer of cervical fascia** (Fig. 430) in the infrahyoid region is not sharply marked off from the investing fascia of adjacent regions with which it is continuous, and the fascia of one side is continuous across the middle line with the fascia of the other side. It splits into two sheets to invest the two prominent

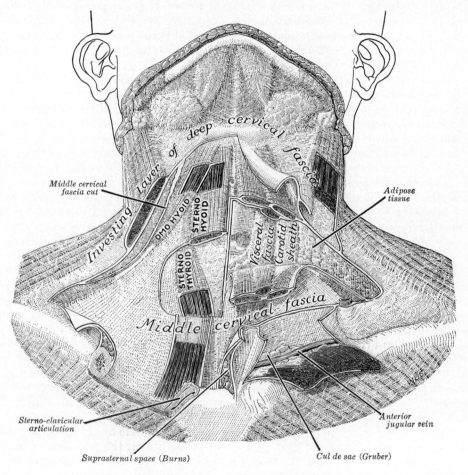

Fig. 432.—The middle cervical fascia.

superficial muscles, the Sternocleidomastoideus and the Trapezius, but it covers the anterior and posterior triangles as a single sheet except just above the sternum. It is continuous, superiorly, with the fascia of the suprahyoid region, and inferiorly, with the pectoral and deltoid fasciæ. It has bony attachments superiorly, inferiorly, and posteriorly. The anterior portion of its superior attachment is to the hyoid bone; the lateral and posterior portion is to the mandible, mastoid process, and superior nuchal line through its continuity with the suprahyoid and posterior cervical fasciæ. Through its continuity with the posterior cervical fascia also, it is attached posteriorly to the spinous process of the seventh cervical vertebra and the ligamentum nuchæ. The inferior attachment is to the acromion, the clavicle, and the manubrium sterni. Extending upward from the manubrial attachment between the sternal origins of the Sternocleidomastoidei for 3 or 4 cm., there is a thickening due to lamination. The outer lamina is attached to the anterior border of the manubrium, the inner lamina to the posterior border and the inter-clavicular ligament. The shallow interval between the two laminæ, mostly filled with fat, is called the **suprasternal space** (*Space of Burns*) (Fig. 432.) It contains the lower portions of the anterior jugular veins and their transverse connecting branch (arcus venosus), the sternal heads of the Sternocleidomastoidei, and some-times a lymph node. The anterior jugulars, in order to reach the external jugulars, traverse extensions of the laminated interval which are prolonged laterally behind the heads of the Sternocleidomastoidei (*cul de sac of Gruber*) (Fig. 432). The external and anterior jugular veins, through most of their course in the neck, appear to lie between the superficial and deep fasciæ but actually are imbedded in the superficial surface of the investing sheet.

The **prevertebral fascia** (Figs. 431, 436) is the anterior portion of a larger complex, the vertebral fascia, which encloses the vertebral column and its muscles. The cervical portion of the prevertebral fascia is part of a larger sheet which goes by that name and which lies on the anterior surface of the vertebral column from the skull to the coccyx. In the neck, it extends laterally across the anterior surface of the Longus colli and capitis, and the Rectus capitis anterior and lateralis muscles, and is then secured to the tips of the transverse processes. From this attachment, it is continuous laterally with the fascia which covers the Levator scapulæ and Splenius, and completes the enclosure of the vertebral compartment posteriorly by attaching to the spinous processes of the vertebræ. Below, it extends over the superficial surface of the Scalenus anterior, medius, and posterior muscles to become continuous with the fascia of the thoracic wall. The fascia on the deep surface of the scalenus group of muscles forms part of a conical, fibrous dome, called **Sibson's fascia**, which arches over the cupula of the lung. It varies considerably in its thick-ness and composition; it is reinforced frequently by fibrous bands, and, in some cases, by muscle fibers, the latter being called the **Scalenus minimus**. It is attached to the transverse process of the seventh cervical vertebra and to the medial border of the first rib, and merges with the carotid sheath where the latter is pierced by the subclavian artery. Below the first rib it becomes continuous with the endo-thoracic fascia. As the spinal nerves emerge from between the Scalenus medius and anterior muscles, on their way to the brachial plexus, they are covered by a prolongation from the scalenus portion of the prevertebral fascia. This prolongation encloses the nerves and the subclavian artery and vein and extends under the clavicle into the axilla as the axillary sheath.

The prevertebral fascia is separated from the visceral fascia by the **retropharyngeal fascial cleft** (*retropharyngeal space*). In the lateral region, the prevertebral fascia is adherent to the investing fascia of the neck under the Sternocleidomastoideus and superiorly in the Posterior Triangle. In the lower part of the Posterior Triangle a considerable pad of adipose tissue occupies the interval between the prevertebral and investing sheets and surrounds the axillary sheath as it passes under the clavicle.

The **middle cervical fascia** (Fig. 432) invests the two layers of infrahyoid muscles and has, therefore, a superficial, a deep, and a middle sheet. Above, all three sheets are attached to the hyoid bone and the outer sheet is also fused with the external investing fascia for a short distance below the bone. At the lateral border of the Omohyoideus, the superficial and deep sheets come together and are fused to the deep surface of the investing membrane of the neck. No independent representation of this fascia, therefore, is found in the posterior triangle above the Omohyoideus. Below, all three layers are attached to the posterior surface of the sternum along with the muscles they invest. In the supraclavicular region, the fascia is securely fastened to the clavicle and is looped over the inferior belly of the Omohyoideus like a sleeve with the medial part thickened into a pulley for the intermediate tendon. Under cover of the Sternocleidomastoideus, the lateral border of the fascia is attached to the carotid sheath. A fascial cleft separates the deep surface of the fascia from the underlying visceral fascia, especially inferior to the thyroid cartilage.

The **cervical visceral fascia** (*lamina pretrachialis*) (Fig. 431) is a roughly tubular prolongation of the visceral fascia of the mediastinum. It forms a compartment enclosing the esophagus and trachea as they enter the neck from the thorax, and farther superiorly, the pharynx, larynx, and thyroid gland. It extends superiorly into the head and is attached to the base of the skull at the pharyngeal tubercle, with the Constrictor pharyngis superior and the pharyngeal aponeurosis, and to the pterygoid hamulus and the mandible with the pterygomandibular raphe. The portion covering the Constrictor superior continues anteriorly over the Buccinator and is called the **buccopharyngeal fascia**. That covering the Constrictor medius is continuous anteriorly with the fascia over the Hyoglossus and Genioglossus, and with them, is attached to the hyoid bone.

A **perivisceral fascial cleft** (Fig. 431) almost completely surrounds the visceral fascia and separates it from the middle cervical fascia antero-laterally, from the carotid sheath laterally, and from the prevertebral fascia posteriorly, leaving the enclosed esophagus and pharynx relatively free for the movement of swallowing. Postero-laterally, however, the visceral fascia has a narrow attachment along its whole length to the tips of the transverse processes, at which point, it is fused also with the carotid sheath and prevertebral fascia. This attachment subdivides the entire perivisceral fascial cleft into anterior and posterior portions. The anterior portion, sometimes named the **previsceral cleft**, is in relation to that part of the visceral fascia frequently called the **pretracheal fascia**, that is, the part covering the trachea, larynx, and thyroid gland. The posterior portion of the cleft, between the pharynx and the prevertebral fascia, is called the retropharyngeal cleft (see above) and is of surgical importance because of its continuation downward behind the esophagus into the thorax.

The **carotid sheath** (*vagina carotica*) (Fig. 431) forms a tubular investment for the carotid artery, internal jugular vein and vagus nerve. It is attached medially to the visceral fascia by means of a sheet, the **alar fascia**, which is fused with the latter along the posterior middle line of the pharynx from the skull to the level of the seventh cervical vertebra. The sheath is attached posteriorly to the prevertebral fascia along the line of the tips of the transverse processes. Laterally, it is fused with the investing fascia on the deep surface of the Sternocleidomastoideus, and anteriorly, it is fused with the middle cervical fascia along the lateral border of the Sterno-thyroideus. In the upper part of the neck the sheath is fused with the fascia of the Stylohyoideus and posterior belly of the Digastricus as it passes deep to them and finally is fastened to the skull with its enclosed structures. In the root of the neck the sheath is adherent to the sternum and first rib, fuses with the scalenus fascia, and finally becomes continuous with the fibrous pericardium. The cervical sympathetic trunk is imbedded in the fascia of the posterior wall of the sheath and is not actually within the sheath.

II. THE LATERAL CERVICAL MUSCLES.

Trapezius and Sternocleidomastoideus.

The Trapezius is described on page 484.

The **Sternocleidomastoideus** (*Sternomastoid muscle*) (Fig. 433) passes obliquely across the side of the neck. It is thick and narrow at its central part, but broader and thinner at either end. It *arises* from the sternum and clavicle by two heads.

The **medial** or **sternal head** is a rounded fasciculus, tendinous in front, fleshy behind, which *arises* from the upper part of the anterior surface of the manubrium sterni, and is directed upward, lateralward, and backward. The **lateral** or **clavicular head** composed of fleshy and aponeurotic fibers, *arises* from the superior border and anterior surface of the medial third of the clavicle; it is directed almost vertically upward. The two heads are separated from one another at their origins by a triangular interval, but gradually blend, below the middle of the neck, into a thick, rounded muscle which is *inserted*, by a strong tendon, into the lateral surface of the mastoid process, from its apex to its superior border, and by a thin aponeurosis into the lateral half of the superior nuchal line of the occipital bone.

Action.—The muscle of one side bends the cervical vertebral column laterally, drawing the head toward the shoulder of the same side, and at the same time rotates it, pointing the chin upward, and to the opposite side. Both muscles acting together flex the vertebral column, bringing the head forward and at the same time elevating the chin.

Nerves.—The spinal part of the accessory nerve and branches from the anterior rami of the second and third cervical nerves.

Variations.—The Sternocleidomastoideus varies much in the extent of its origin from the clavicle: in some cases the clavicular head may be as narrow as the sternal; in others it may be as much as 7.5 cm. in breadth. When the clavicular origin is broad, it is occasionally subdivided into several slips, separated by narrow intervals. More rarely, the adjoining margins of the Sternocleidomastoideus and Trapezius have been found in contact. The *Supraclavicularis muscle* arises from the manubrium behind the Sternocleidomastoideus and passes behind the Sternocleidomastoideus to the upper surface of the clavicle.

III. THE SUPRAHYOID MUSCLES (Figs. 433, 434).

Digastricus.	Mylohyoideus.
Stylohyoideus.	Geniohyoideus.

The **Digastricus** (*Digastric muscle*) consists of two fleshy bellies united by an intermediate rounded tendon. It lies below the body of the mandible, and extends, in a curved form, from the mastoid process to the symphysis menti. The **posterior belly**, longer than the anterior, *arises* from the mastoid notch of the temporal bone and passes downward and forward. The **anterior belly** *arises* from a depression on the inner side of the lower border of the mandible, close to the symphysis, and passes downward and backward. The two bellies end in an intermediate tendon which perforates the Stylohyoideus muscle, and is held in connection with the side of the body and the greater cornu of the hyoid bone by a fibrous loop, which is sometimes lined by a mucous sheath. A broad aponeurotic layer is given off from the tendon of the Digastricus on either side, to be attached to the body and greater cornu of the hyoid bone; this is termed the **suprahyoid aponeurosis**.

Action.—Raises the hyoid bone; assists in opening the jaws. The anterior belly draws the hyoid forward, the posterior backward.

Nerve.—Anterior belly by the mylohyoid nerve from the inferior alveolar branch of the mandibular division of the trigeminal; posterior belly by a branch of the facial nerve.

Variations are numerous. The posterior belly may arise partly or entirely from the styloid process, or be connected by a slip to the middle or inferior constrictor; the anterior belly may be double or extra slips from this belly may pass to the jaw or Mylohyoideus or decussate with a similar slip on opposite side; anterior belly may be absent and posterior belly inserted into the middle of the jaw or hyoid bone. The tendon may pass in front, more rarely behind the Stylohyoideus. The *Mentohyoideus muscle* passes from the body of hyoid bone to chin.

The Digastricus divides the anterior triangle of the neck into three smaller triangles (1) the **submaxillary triangle**, bounded above by the lower border of the body of the mandible, and a line drawn from its angle to the Sternocleidomastoideus, below by the posterior belly of the Digastricus and the Stylohyoideus, in front by the anterior belly of the Digastricus; (2) the **carotid triangle**, bounded above by the posterior belly of the Digastricus and Stylohyoideus, behind by the Sternocleidomastoideus, below by the Omohyoideus; (3) the **suprahyoid** or **submental triangle**, bounded laterally by the anterior belly of the Digastricus, medially by the middle line of the neck from the hyoid bone to the symphysis menti, and inferiorly by the body of the hyoid bone.

The **Stylohyoideus** (*Stylohyoid muscle*) is a slender muscle, lying in front of, and above, the posterior belly of the Digastricus. It *arises* from the back and lateral surface of the styloid process, near the base; and, passing downward and forward, is *inserted* into the body of the hyoid bone, at its junction with the greater cornu, and just above the Omohyoideus. It is perforated, near its insertion, by the tendon of the Digastricus.

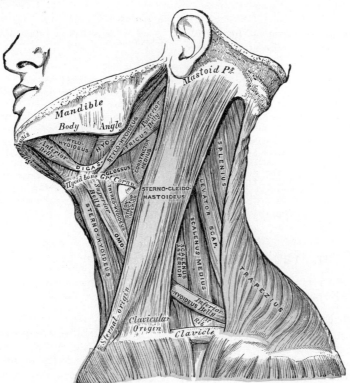

Fig. 433.—Muscles of the neck. Lateral view.

Action.—Draws the hyoid bone upward and backward.
Nerve.—A branch of the facial nerve.
Variations.—It may be absent or doubled, lie beneath the carotid artery, or be inserted into the Omohyoideus, Thyreohyoideus, or Mylohyoideus.

The **Stylohyoid Ligament** (*ligamentum stylohyoideum*).—In connection with the Stylohyoideus muscle a ligamentous band, the **stylohyoid ligament**, may be described. It is a fibrous cord, which is attached to the tip of the styloid process of the temporal and the lesser cornu of the hyoid bone. It frequently contains a little cartilage in its center, is often partially ossified, and in many animals forms a distinct bone, the **epihyal**.

The **Mylohyoideus** (*Mylohyoid muscle*), flat and triangular, is situated immediately above the anterior belly of the Digastricus, and forms, with its fellow of the opposite side, a muscular floor for the cavity of the mouth. It *arises* from the whole length of the mylohyoid line of the mandible, extending from the symphysis in front to the last molar tooth behind. The posterior fibers pass medialward and slightly downward, to be *inserted* into the body of the hyoid bone. The middle and anterior fibers are *inserted* into a median fibrous raphé extending from the symphysis menti to the hyoid bone, where they join at an angle with the fibers of the opposite muscle. This median raphé is sometimes wanting; the fibers of the two muscles are then continuous.

28

Action.—Raises the hyoid bone and tongue.

Nerve.—The mylohyoid nerve from the inferior alveolar branch of the mandibular division of the trigeminal nerve.

Variations.—It may be united to or replaced by the anterior belly of the Digastricus; accessory slips to other hyoid muscles are frequent.

The **Geniohyoideus** (*Geniohyoid muscle*) is a narrow muscle, situated above the medial border of the Mylohyoideus. It *arises* from the inferior mental spine on the back of the symphysis menti, and runs backward and slightly downward, to be *inserted* into the anterior surface of the body of the hyoid bone; it lies in contact with its fellow of the opposite side.

Action.—Draws the hyoid bone and tongue forward.

Nerve.—A branch of the first cervical nerve, through the hypoglossal nerve.

Variations.—It may be blended with the one on opposite side or double; slips to greater cornu of hyoid bone and Genioglossus occur.

Group Actions.—These muscles perform two very important actions. During deglutition, they raise the hyoid bone, and with it the base of the tongue; when the hyoid bone is fixed by its depressors and those of the larynx, they depress the mandible. During the first act of deglutition, when the mass of food is being driven from the mouth into the pharynx, the hyoid bone and with it the tongue, is carried upward and forward by the anterior bellies of the Digastrici, the Mylohyoidei, and Geniohyoidei. In the second act, when the mass is passing through the pharynx, the direct elevation of the hyoid bone takes place by the combined action of all the muscles; and after the food has passed, the hyoid bone is carried upward and backward by the posterior bellies of the Digastrici and the Stylohyoidei, which assist in preventing the return of the food into the mouth.

IV. THE INFRAHYOID MUSCLES (Figs. 433, 434).

Sternohyoideus.   Thyreohyoideus.
Sternothyreoideus.   Omohyoideus.

The **Sternohyoideus** (*Sternohyoid muscle*) is a thin, narrow muscle, which *arises* from the posterior surface of the medial end of the clavicle, the posterior sternoclavicular ligament, and the upper and posterior part of the manubrium sterni. Passing upward and medialward, it is *inserted*, by short, tendinous fibers, into the lower border of the body of the hyoid bone. Below, this muscle is separated from its fellow by a considerable interval; but the two muscles come into contact with one another in the middle of their course, and from this upward, lie side by side. It sometimes presents, immediately above its origin, a transverse tendinous inscription.

Action.—Draws the hyoid bone downward.

Nerve.—Branch of the ansa hypoglossi containing fibers from the first three cervical nerves.

Variations.—Doubling; accessory slips (Cleidohyoideus); absence.

The **Sternothyreoideus** (*Sternothyroid muscle*) is shorter and wider than the preceding muscle, beneath which it is situated. It *arises* from the posterior surface of the manubrium sterni, below the origin of the Sternohyoideus, and from the edge of the cartilage of the first rib, and sometimes that of the second rib, it is *inserted* into the oblique line on the lamina of the thyroid cartilage. This muscle is in close contact with its fellow at the lower part of the neck, but diverges somewhat as it ascends; it is occasionally traversed by a transverse or oblique tendinous inscription.

Action.—Draws the thyroid cartilage downward.

Nerve.—Branch of the ansa hypoglossi containing fibers from the first three cervical nerves.

Variations.—Doubling; absence; accessory slips to Thyreohyoideus, Inferior constrictor, or carotid sheath.

The **Thyreohyoideus** (*Thyrohyoid muscle*) is a small, quadrilateral muscle appearing like an upward continuation of the Sternothyreoideus. It *arises* from the oblique line on the lamina of the thyroid cartilage, and is *inserted* into the lower border of the greater cornu of the hyoid bone.

Action.—Draws the hyoid bone downward, or if the latter is fixed, draws the thyroid cartilage upward.

Nerve.—Fibers from the first and second cervical nerves by way of a communication to the hypoglossal nerve and through its descendens hypoglossi branch.

The **Omohyoideus** (*Omohyoid muscle*) consists of two fleshy bellies united by a central tendon. It *arises* from the upper border of the scapula, and occasionally from the superior transverse ligament which crosses the scapular notch, its extent of attachment to the scapula varying from a few millimetres to 2.5 cm. From

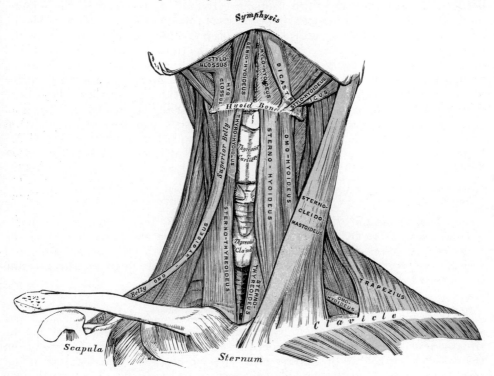

FIG. 434.—Muscles of the neck. Anterior view.

this origin, the **inferior belly** forms a flat, narrow fasciculus, which inclines forward and slightly upward across the lower part of the neck, being bound down to the clavicle by a fibrous expansion; it then passes behind the Sternocleidomastoideus, becomes tendinous and changes its direction, forming an obtuse angle. It ends in the **superior belly,** which passes almost vertically upward, close to the lateral border of the Sternohyoideus, to be inserted into the lower border of the body of the hyoid bone, lateral to the insertion of the Sternohyoideus. The central tendon of this muscle varies much in length and form, and is held in position by a process of the deep cervical fascia, which sheaths it, and is prolonged down to be attached to the clavicle and first rib; it is by this means that the angular form of the muscle is maintained.

Action.—Draws the hyoid bone downward.

Nerves.—Branches of the ansa hypoglossi containing fibers from the first three cervical nerves.

Variations.—Doubling; absence; origin from clavicle; absence or doubling of either belly.

The inferior belly of the Omohyoideus divides the posterior triangle of the neck into an upper or **occipital triangle** and a lower or **subclavian triangle,** while its superior belly divides the anterior triangle into an upper or **carotid triangle** and a lower or **muscular triangle.**

Group Actions.—These muscles depress the larynx and hyoid, after they have been drawn up with the pharynx in the act of deglutition. The Omohyoidei not only depress the hyoid bone, but carry it backward and to one or the other side. They are concerned especially in prolonged inspiratory efforts; for by rendering the lower part of the cervical fascia tense they lessen the inward suction of the soft parts, which would otherwise compress the great vessels and the apices of the lungs.

V. THE ANTERIOR VERTEBRAL MUSCLES (Fig. 435).

Longus colli.   Rectus capitis anterior.
Longus capitis.   Rectus capitis lateralis.

The **Longus colli** is situated on the anterior surface of the vertebral column, between the atlas and the third thoracic vertebra. It is broad in the middle, narrow and pointed at either end, and consists of three portions, a superior oblique, an inferior oblique, and a vertical. The **superior oblique portion** *arises* from the anterior tubercles of the transverse processes of the third, fourth, and fifth cervical vertebræ; and, ascending obliquely with a medial inclination, is *inserted* by a narrow tendon into the tubercle on the anterior arch of the atlas. The **inferior oblique portion,** the smallest part of the muscle, *arises* from the front of the bodies of the first two or three thoracic vertebræ; and, ascending obliquely in a lateral direction, is *inserted* into the anterior tubercles of the transverse processes of the fifth and sixth cervical vertebræ. The **vertical portion** *arises*, below, from the front of the bodies of the upper three thoracic and lower three cervical vertebræ, and is *inserted* into the front of the bodies of the second, third, and fourth cervical vertebræ.

Action.—Flexes the neck and slightly rotates the cervical portion of the vertebral column.
Nerve.—Branches from the second to the seventh cervical nerves.

The **Longus capitis** (*Rectus capitis anticus major*), broad and thick above, narrow below, *arises* by four tendinous slips, from the anterior tubercles of the transverse processes of the third, fourth, fifth, and sixth cervical vertebræ, and ascends, converging toward its fellow of the opposite side, to be *inserted* into the inferior surface of the basilar part of the occipital bone.

Action.—Flexes the head.
Nerve.—Branches from the first, second, and third cervical nerves.

The **Rectus capitis anterior** (*Rectus capitis anticus minor*) is a short, flat muscle, situated immediately behind the upper part of the Longus capitis. It *arises* from the anterior surface of the lateral mass of the atlas, and from the root of its transverse process, and passing obliquely upward and medialward, is *inserted* into the inferior surface of the basilar part of the occipital bone immediately in front of the foramen magnum.

Action.—Flexes the head.
Nerve.—Branches of the loop between the first and second cervical nerves.

The **Rectus capitis lateralis,** a short, flat muscle, *arises* from the upper surface of the transverse process of the atlas, and is *inserted* into the under surface of the jugular process of the occipital bone.

Action.—Bends the head laterally.
Nerve.—Branches of the loop between the first and second cervical nerves.
Group Actions.—The Longus capitis and Rectus anterior are the direct antagonists of the muscles at the back of the neck, serving to restore the head to its natural position after it has been drawn backward. These muscles also flex the head, and from their obliquity, rotate it, so as to turn the face to one or the other side. The Rectus lateralis, acting on one side, bends the head laterally.

VI.   THE LATERAL VERTEBRAL MUSCLES (Fig. 435).

Scalenus anterior.   Scalenus medius.
                          Scalenus posterior.

The **Scalenus anterior** (*Scalenus anticus*) lies deeply at the side of the neck, behind the Sternocleidomastoideus. It *arises* from the anterior tubercles of the transverse processes of the third, fourth, fifth, and sixth cervical vertebræ, and descending, almost vertically, is *inserted* by a narrow, flat tendon into the scalene tubercle on the inner border of the first rib, and into the ridge on the upper surface of the rib in front of the subclavian groove.

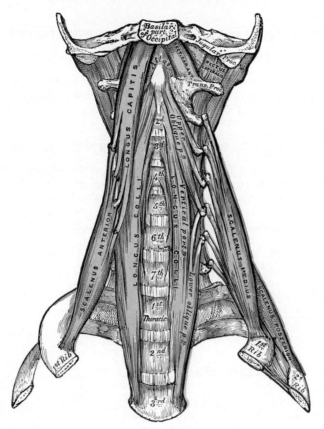

FIG. 435.—The anterior vertebral muscles.

The **Scalenus medius,** the largest and longest of the three Scaleni, *arises* from the posterior tubercles of the transverse processes of the lower six cervical vertebræ, and descending along the side of the vertebral column, is *inserted* by a broad attachment into the upper surface of the first rib, between the tubercle and the subclavian groove.

Action.—Raise the first rib; bend and slightly rotate the neck.
Nerves.—Branches of the lower cervical nerves.

The **Scalenus posterior** (*Scalenus posticus*), the smallest and most deeply seated of the three Scaleni, *arises*, by two or three separate tendons, from the posterior tubercles of the transverse processes of the lower two or three cervical vertebræ, and is *inserted* by a thin tendon into the outer surface of the second rib, behind the attachment of the Serratus anterior. It is occasionally blended with the Scalenus medius.

Action.—Raises the second rib; bends and slightly rotates the neck.
Nerve.—Branches of ventral primary divisions of last three cervical nerves.

Group Actions.—When the Scaleni act from above, they elevate the first and second ribs, and are, therefore, inspiratory muscles. Acting from below, they bend the vertebral column to one or other side; if the muscles of both sides act, the vertebral column is slightly flexed.

Variations.—The Scaleni muscles vary considerably in their attachments and in the arrangement of their fibers. A slip from the Scalenus anticus may pass behind the subclavian artery. The Scalenus posticus may be absent or extend to the third rib. The *Scalenus pleuralis muscle scalenus minimus* extends from the transverse process of the seventh cervical vertebra to the fascia supporting the dome of the pleura and inner border of first rib.

THE FASCIÆ AND MUSCLES OF THE TRUNK.

The muscles of the trunk may be arranged in six groups:

I. Deep Muscles of the Back.　　　　IV. Muscles of the Abdomen.
II. Suboccipital Muscles.　　　　　　V. Muscles of the Pelvis.
III. Muscles of the Thorax.　　　　　VI. Muscles of the Perineum.

I. THE DEEP MUSCLES OF THE BACK (Fig. 437).

The deep or intrinsic muscles of the back consist of a complex, serially arranged group of muscles, extending from the pelvis to the skull, which may be looked upon as a single muscle functionally, the extensor of the vertebral column. Two subgroups may be identified: (*A*) A superficial stratum with fasciculi mainly crossing laterally as they ascend may be called the transverso-costal group:

Splenius capitis.　　　　　　　　　　　　　Splenius cervicis
　　Sacrospinalis (Iliocostalis, Longissimus, Spinalis)

(*B*) The deeper stratum has fasciculi coursing mainly upward and medially, and may be called the transverso-spinal group:

Semispinalis.　　　　Rotatores.　　　　Interspinales.
Multifidus.　　　　　　　　　　　　　Intertransversarii.

The **Nuchal Fascia** (*fascia nuchæ*) (Fig. 431) is the cervical portion of the more extensive vertebral fascia and is continuous below with the lumbodorsal fascia. It covers the Splenius capitis and cervicis, and near the skull, the upper portion of the Semispinalis capitis. With these muscles, it is attached to the skull just below the superior nuchal line, the ligamentum nuchæ, and the spinous processes of the seventh cervical and upper six thoracic vertebræ. In the upper part of the neck it is more or less adherent to the fascia of the under surface of the Trapezius. Lower, a distinct fascial cleft separates it from the fascia of the Serratus posterior superior and Rhomboidei.

The deeper muscles of the neck are enclosed by fascial septa which form compartments for each muscle. A fascial cleft separates the Splenius from the Semispinalis capitis. A considerable layer of adipose tissue and a fascial cleft intervene between the latter and the Semispinalis cervicis. In this adipose layer are found the deep cervical bloodvessels. The fascia covering the Semispinalis cervicis continues upward from the atlas to form the thick adherent covering of the suboccipital muscles. The fasciæ of the several muscles which attach to the transverse processes of the cervical vertebræ are either fused or continuous, the scalenus fascia becoming continuous with the splenius and serratus posterior superior fascia under cover of the Levator scapulæ.

Lumbodorsal Fascia (*fascia thoracolumbalis*) (Figs. 436, 445, 455).—The name lumbodorsal fascia is given to a rather varied fascial complex. It is, in general terms, the subdivision of the vertebral fascia which forms the sheath of the Sacrospinalis muscle. It should be looked upon primarily as an intermediate stratum, derived from the fascia of the trunk deep to the large limb muscles. It becomes part of the investing fascia of the body, however, in the lower half of the trunk, because in that region the aponeurosis of the Latissimus dorsi is incorporated in it. Above, it is continuous with the fascia nuchæ. Medially, it is attached to the spines of the vertebræ, the supraspinal ligaments, and the medial crest of the sacrum; below, to the iliac crests and lateral crests of the sacrum. Laterally, in the thorax, it is attached to the angles of the ribs and intercostal fascia, and in the lumbar

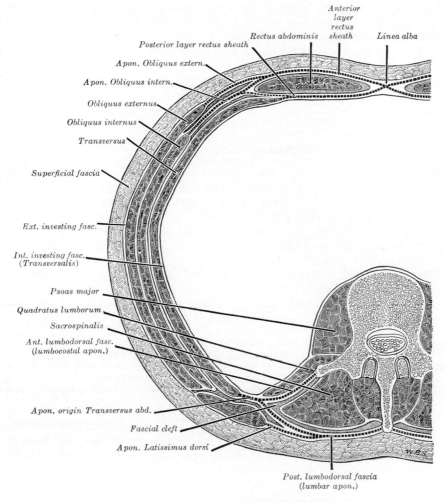

Fig. 436.—Fasciæ and aponeuroses of abdominal wall in cross-section through third lumbar vertebra. Semidiagrammatic.

region, it is continuous with the aponeurosis of origin of the Transversus abdominis muscle. In the upper part of the thorax, where it is covered by the Rhomboidei, it is thin, gray, and transparent. It retains this consistency also under the fleshy fibers of the upper part of the Latissimus dorsi. More caudally, it is a thick, white, glistening sheet which serves as the origin of the Latissimus and is called the lumbar aponeurosis. Caudal to the twelfth rib, since it can no longer attach to the ribs, the line of attachment along the lateral border of the Sacrospinalis, becomes a line of fusion between the fascia covering the dorsal surface of this muscle (**the posterior layer of the lumbodorsal fascia**) and the fascia on the deep surface of the muscle (**the anterior layer of the lumbodorsal fascia**). From this fusion, the fascia extends laterally as a single sheet, the aponeurosis of origin of the Transversus abdominis muscle. This portion of the fascia may be described in another way. The aponeurosis of origin of the Transversus abdominis, in seeking to attach to the vertebræ, meets interference at the lateral border of the Sacrospinalis and splits, therefore, to enclose the latter in a superficial and deep sheet. The superficial sheet, the **lumbar aponeurosis** or lumbodorsal fascia (posterior layer), extends over the dorsal surface of the Sacrospinalis and attaches to the spines. The deep sheet, the **lumbocostal aponeurosis** (anterior layer of the lumbodorsal fascia), extends over the deep surface of the Sacrospinalis and attaches to the transverse processes. The lumbocostal aponeurosis is a strong sheet reaching from the lower border of the twelfth rib to the crest of the ilium. Its fiber bundles radiate out from attachments to the tips of the transverse processes of the lumbar vertebræ. It lies deep to the Sacrospinalis, and superficial to the Quadratus lumborum and Psoas major muscles. The upper portion, attached to the twelfth rib and the transverse process of the first lumbar vertebra, is more specifically named the **lumbocostal ligament**.

A. Transverso-costal Muscles.

The **Splenius capitis** (Fig. 455) *arises* from the lower half of the ligamentum nuchæ, from the spinous process of the seventh cervical vertebra, and from the spinous processes of the upper three or four thoracic vertebræ. The fibers of the muscle are directed upward and lateralward and are *inserted* into the rough surface on the occipital bone just below the lateral third of the superior nuchal line, and, under cover of the Sternocleidomastoideus, into the mastoid process of the temporal bone.

The **Splenius cervicis** (*Splenius colli*) (Fig. 455) *arises* by a narrow tendinous band from the spinous processes of the third to the sixth thoracic vertebræ; it is *inserted*, by tendinous fasciculi, into the posterior tubercles of the transverse processes of the upper two or three cervical vertebræ.

Action.—Draw the head and neck backward and laterally, and rotate them, turning the face toward the same side. Both sides acting together extend the head and neck.

Nerves.—Lateral branches of the dorsal primary divisions of the middle and lower cervical nerves.

Variations.—The origin is frequently moved up or down one or two vertebræ. Accessory slips are occasionally found.

The **Sacrospinalis** (*Erector spinæ*) (Fig. 437), and its prolongations in the thoracic and cervical regions, lie in the groove on the side of the vertebral column. They are covered in the lumbar and thoracic regions by the lumbodorsal fascia, and in the cervical region by the nuchal fascia. This large muscular and tendinous mass varies in size and structure at different parts of the vertebral column. In the sacral region it is narrow and pointed, and at its origin chiefly tendinous in structure. In the lumbar region it is larger, and forms a thick fleshy mass which, in its upward course, is subdivided into three columns; these gradually diminish in size as they ascend to be inserted into the vertebræ and ribs.

The Sacrospinalis *arises* from the anterior surface of a broad and thick tendon, which is attached to the middle crest of the sacrum, to the spinous processes of the lumbar and the eleventh and twelfth thoracic vertebræ, and the supraspinal ligament, to the back part of the inner lip of the iliac crests and to the lateral crests of the sacrum, where it blends with the sacrotuberous and posterior sacro-iliac ligaments. Some of its fibers are continuous with the fibers of origin of the Glutæus maximus. The muscular fibers form a large fleshy mass which splits, in the upper lumbar region into three columns, viz., a lateral, the **Iliocostalis**, an

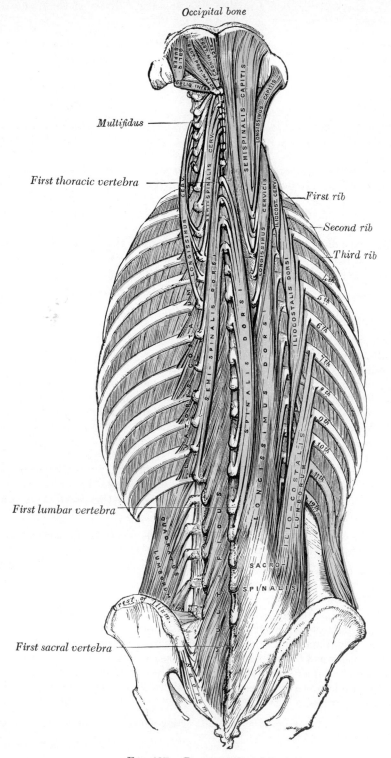

Occipital bone

Multifidus

First thoracic vertebra

First rib

Second rib

Third rib

First lumbar vertebra

First sacral vertebra

FIG. 437.—Deep muscles of the back.

intermediate, the **Longissimus**, and a medial, the **Spinalis.**   Each of these consists from below upward, of three parts, as follows (Fig. 437):

Lateral Column.	*Intermediate Column.*	*Medial Column.*
Iliocostalis.	Longissimus.	Spinalis.
I. lumborum.	L. thoracis.	S. thoracis
I. thoracis.	L. cervicis.	S. cervicis.
I. cervicis.	L. capitis.	S. capitis.

The **Iliocostalis lumborum** (*Iliocostalis muscle; Sacrolumbalis muscle*) is *inserted,* by six or seven flattened tendons, into the inferior borders of the angles of the lower six or seven ribs.

The **Iliocostalis thoracis** (*Musculus accessorius*) *arises* by flattened tendons from the upper borders of the angles of the lower six ribs medial to the tendons of insertion of the Iliocostalis lumborum; these become muscular, and are *inserted* into the upper borders of the angles of the upper six ribs and into the back of the transverse process of the seventh cervical vertebra.

The **Iliocostalis cervicis** (*Cervicalis ascendens*) *arises* from the angles of the third, fourth, fifth, and sixth ribs, and is *inserted* into the posterior tubercles of the transverse processes of the fourth, fifth, and sixth cervical vertebræ.

Action.—Extend the vertebral column and bend it to one side; lumborum and dorsi draw the ribs downward.

Nerve.—Branches of the dorsal primary divisions of the spinal nerves.

The **Longissimus thoracis** is the intermediate and largest of the continuations of the Sacrospinalis.   In the lumbar region, where it is as yet blended with the Iliocostalis lumborum and Spinalis, some of its fibers are attached to the whole length of the posterior surfaces of the transverse processes and the accessory processes of the lumbar vertebræ, and to the anterior layer of the lumbodorsal fascia (lumbocostal aponeurosis).   In the thoracic region it is *inserted,* by rounded tendons, into the tips of the transverse processes of all the thoracic vertebræ, and by fleshy processes into the lower nine or ten ribs between their tubercles and angles.

The **Longissimus cervicis** (*Transversalis cervicis*), situated medial to the Longissimus thoracis, *arises* by long thin tendons from the summits of the transverse processes of the upper four or five thoracic vertebræ, and is *inserted* by similar tendons into the posterior tubercles of the transverse processes of the cervical vertebræ from the second to the sixth inclusive.

Action.—Extend the vertebral column and bend it to one side; draw the ribs downward.

Nerve.—Branches of the dorsal primary divisions of the spinal nerves.

The **Longissimus capitis** (*Trachelomastoid muscle*) lies medial to the Longissimus cervicis, between it and the Semispinalis capitis.   It *arises* by tendons from the transverse processes of the upper four or five thoracic vertebræ along with the cervicis, and the articular processes of the lower three or four cervical vertebræ, and is *inserted* into the posterior margin of the mastoid process, beneath the Splenius capitis and Sternocleidomastoideus.   In the upper part of the neck, where the capitis and cervicis diverge toward their insertions, the Longissimus mass is crossed by the Splenius cervicis.   The latter's insertion separates that of the L. capitis from that of the L. cervicis, and where it crosses them, their muscular fasciculi are replaced by a tendinous inscription.

Action.—Extends the head; the muscle of one side acting alone bends the head to the same side and rotates the face toward that side.

Nerve.—Branches of the dorsal primary divisions of the middle and lower cervical nerves.

The **Spinalis thoracis,** the medial continuation of the Sacrospinalis, is scarcely separable as a distinct muscle.   It is situated at the medial side of the Longissimus thoracis, and is intimately blended with it; it *arises* by three or four tendons from the spinous processes of the first two lumbar and the last two thoracic vertebræ: these, uniting, form a small muscle which is *inserted* by separate tendons into the spinous processes of the upper thoracic vertebræ, the number varying from four to eight. It is intimately united with the Semispinalis dorsi, situated beneath it.

The **Spinalis cervicis** (*Spinalis colli*) is an inconstant muscle, which *arises* from the lower part of the ligamentum nuchæ, the spinous process of the seventh cervical, and sometimes from the spinous processes of the first and second thoracic vertebræ, and is *inserted* into the spinous process of the axis, and occasionally into the spinous processes of the two vertebræ below it.

The **Spinalis capitis** (*Biventer cervicis*) is usually inseparably connected with the Semispinalis capitis (see below).

Action.—Extend the vertebral column.
Nerve.—Branches of the dorsal primary divisions of the spinal nerves.

B. Transverso-spinal Muscles. (m. *transverso-spinalis*) (Fig. 437)

The **Semispinalis thoracis** consists of thin, narrow, fleshy fasciculi, interposed between tendons of considerable length. It *arises* by a series of small tendons from the transverse processes of the sixth to the tenth thoracic vertebræ, and is *inserted*, by tendons, into the spinous processes of the upper four thoracic and lower two cervical vertebræ.

The **Semispinalis cervicis** (*Semispinalis colli*), thicker than the preceding, *arises* by a series of tendinous and fleshy fibers from the transverse processes of the upper five or six thoracic vertebræ, and is inserted into the cervical spinous processes, from the axis to the fifth inclusive. The fasciculus connected with the axis is the largest, and is chiefly muscular in structure.

Action.—Extend the vertebral column and rotate it toward the opposite side.
Nerve.—Branches of the dorsal primary divisions of the spinal nerves.

The **Semispinalis capitis** (*Complexus*) is situated at the upper and back part of the neck, beneath the Splenius, and medial to the Longissimus cervicis and capitis. It *arises* by a series of tendons from the tips of the transverse processes of the upper six or seven thoracic and the seventh cervical vertebræ, and from the articular processes of the three cervical above this. The tendons, uniting, form a broad muscle, which passes upward, and is *inserted* between the superior and inferior nuchal lines of the occipital bone. The medial part, usually more or less distinct from the remainder of the muscle, is frequently termed the **Spinalis capitis**; it is also named the **Biventer cervicis** since it is traversed by an imperfect tendinous inscription.

Action.—Extends the head and rotates it toward the opposite side.
Nerve.—Branches of the dorsal primary divisions of the cervical nerves.

The **Multifidus** (*Multifidus spinæ*) (Fig. 437) consists of a number of fleshy and tendinous fasciculi, which fill up the groove on either side of the spinous processes of the vertebræ, from the sacrum to the axis. In the sacral region, these fasciculi *arise* from the back of the sacrum, as low as the fourth sacral foramen, from the aponeurosis of origin of the Sacrospinalis, from the medial surface of the posterior superior iliac spine, and from the posterior sacroiliac ligaments; in the lumbar region, from all the mammillary processes; in the thoracic region, from all the transverse processes; and in the cervical region, from the articular processes of the lower four vertebræ. Each fasciculus ascends obliquely, crossing over from two to four vertebræ in its course toward the middle line, and is inserted into the spinous process of one of the vertebræ, from the last lumbar to the axis. The fasciculi vary in length and depth of position; the longest and most superficial pass from one vertebra to the fifth above; those somewhat deeper are shorter and cross three vertebræ; the deepest and shortest cross two. The Rotatores longi (see below) are sometimes included in the Multifidus.

Action.—Extends the vertebral column and rotates it toward the opposite side.
Nerve.—Branches of the dorsal primary divisions of the spinal nerves.

The **Rotatores** (*Rotatores spinæ*) are a series of small muscles which form the deepest layer in the groove between the spinous and transverse processes. They lie beneath the Multifidus and cannot be distinguished readily from its deepest fibers. They are found along the entire length of the vertebral column from the sacrum to the axis. They arise from the transverse process of one vertebra and insert at the base of the spinous process of the vertebra above. The **Rotatores longi** cross one vertebra in their oblique course. The **Rotatores breves** insert in the next succeeding vertebra and run in an almost horizontal direction.

Action.—Extend the vertebral column and rotate it toward the opposite side.
Nerve.—Branches of the dorsal primary divisions of the spinal nerves.

The **Interspinales** are short muscular fasciculi, placed in pairs between the spinous processes of the contiguous vertebræ, one on either side of the interspinal ligament. In the *cervical region* they are most distinct, and consist of six pairs, the first being situated between the axis and third vertebra, and the last between the seventh cervical and the first thoracic. They are small narrow bundles, attached, above and below, to the apices of the spinous processes. In the *thoracic region*, they are found between the first and second vertebræ, and sometimes between the second and third, and between the eleventh and twelfth. In the *lumbar region* there are four pairs in the intervals between the five lumbar vertebræ. There is also occasionally one between the last thoracic and first lumbar, and one between the fifth lumbar and the sacrum.

Action.—Extend the vertebral column.
Nerves.—Branches of the dorsal primary divisions of the spinal nerves.

The **Extensor coccygis** is a slender muscular fasciculus, which is not always present; it extends over the lower part of the posterior surface of the sacrum and coccyx. It *arises* by tendinous fibers from the last segment of the sacrum, or first piece of the coccyx, and passes downward to be *inserted* into the lower part of the coccyx. It is a rudiment of the Extensor muscle of the caudal vertebræ of the lower animals.

The **Intertransversarii** (*Intertransversales*) are small muscles placed between the transverse processes of the vertebræ. In the *cervical region* they are best developed, consisting of rounded muscular and tendinous fasciculi, and are placed in pairs, passing between the anterior and the posterior tubercles respectively of the transverse processes of two contiguous vertebræ, and separated from one another by an anterior primary division of the cervical nerve, which lies in the groove between them. The muscles connecting the anterior tubercles are termed the **Intertransversarii anteriores**; those between the posterior tubercles, the **Intertransversarii posteriores**. There are seven pairs of these muscles, the first pair being between the atlas and axis, and the last pair between the seventh cervical and first thoracic vertebræ. In the *thoracic region* they are present between the transverse processes of the lower three thoracic vertebræ, and between the transverse processes of the last thoracic and the first lumbar. In the *lumbar region* they are arranged in pairs, on either side of the vertebral column, one set occupying the entire interspace between the transverse processes of the lumbar vertebræ, the **Intertransversarii laterales**; the other set, **Intertransversarii mediales**, passing from the accessory process of one vertebra to the mammillary of the vertebra below.

Action.—Bend the vertebral column laterally.
Nerve.—The anteriores, posteriores, and laterales by branches of the ventral primary divisions of the spinal nerves; the mediales by branches of the dorsal primary divisions.

II. THE SUBOCCIPITAL MUSCLES (Figs. 437, 438).

Rectus capitis posterior major.	Obliquus capitis inferior.
Rectus capitis posterior minor.	Obliquus capitis superior.

The **Rectus capitis posterior major** (*Rectus capitis posticus major*) *arises* by a pointed tendon from the spinous process of the axis, and, becoming broader as it ascends, is *inserted* into the lateral part of the inferior nuchal line of the occipital bone and the surface of the bone immediately below the line. As the muscles of the two sides pass upward and lateralward, they leave between them a triangular space, in which the Recti capitis posteriores minores are seen.

Action.—Extends the head and rotates it to the same side.
Nerve.—A branch of the posterior ramus of the suboccipital nerve.

The **Rectus capitis posterior minor** (*Rectus capitis posticus minor*) *arises* by a narrow pointed tendon from the tubercle on the posterior arch of the atlas, and, widening as it ascends, is *inserted* into the medial part of the inferior nuchal line of the occipital bone and the surface between it and the foramen magnum.

Action.—Extends the head.
Nerve.—A branch of the dorsal primary division of the suboccipital nerve.

The **Obliquus capitis inferior** (*Obliquus inferior*), the larger of the two Oblique muscles, *arises* from the apex of the spinous process of the axis, and passes lateralward and slightly upward, to be *inserted* into the lower and back part of the transverse process of the atlas.

Action.—Rotates the atlas, turning the face toward the same side.
Nerve.—A branch of the dorsal primary division of the suboccipital nerve.

The **Obliquus capitis superior** (*Obliquus superior*), narrow below, wide and expanded above, *arises* by tendinous fibers from the upper surface of the transverse process of the atlas, joining with the insertion of the preceding. It passes upward and medialward, and is *inserted* into the occipital bone, between the superior and inferior nuchal lines, lateral to the Semispinalis capitis.

Action.—Extends the head and bends it laterally.
Nerve.—A branch of the dorsal primary division of the suboccipital nerve.

The Suboccipital Triangle.—Between the Obliqui and the Rectus capitis posterior major is the **suboccipital triangle.** It is bounded, *above* and *medially*, by the Rectus capitis posterior major; *above* and *laterally*, by the Obliquus capitis superior; *below* and *laterally*, by the Obliquus capitis inferior. It is covered by a layer of dense fibro-fatty tissue, situated beneath the Semispinalis capitis. The floor is formed by the posterior occipito-atlantal membrane, and the posterior arch of the atlas. In the deep groove on the upper surface of the posterior arch of the atlas are the vertebral artery and the first cervical or suboccipital nerve. (Fig. 446.)

Group Actions.—The Sacrospinalis and its upward continuations and the Spinales maintain the vertebral column in the erect posture; they also serve to bend the trunk backward when it is required to counterbalance the influence of any weight at the front of the body—as, for instance, when a heavy weight is suspended from the neck, or when there is any great abdominal distension, as in pregnancy or dropsy; the peculiar gait under such circumstances depends upon the vertebral column being drawn backward, by the counterbalancing action of the Sacrospinales. The muscles which form the continuation of the Sacrospinales on to the head and neck steady those parts and fix them in the upright position. If the Iliocostalis lumborum and Longissimus dorsi of one side act, they serve to draw down the chest and vertebral column to the corresponding side. The Iliocostales cervicis, taking their fixed points from the cervical vertebræ, elevate those ribs to which they are attached; taking their fixed points from the ribs, both muscles help to extend the neck; while one muscle bends the neck to its own side. The Multifidus acts successively upon the different parts of the column; thus, the sacrum furnishes a fixed point from which the fasciculi of this muscle act upon the lumbar region; which in turn becomes the fixed point for the fasciculi moving the thoracic region, and so on throughout the entire length of the column. The Multifidus also serves to rotate the column, so that the front of the trunk is turned to the side opposite to that from which the muscle acts, this muscle being assisted in its action by the Obliquus externus abdominis.

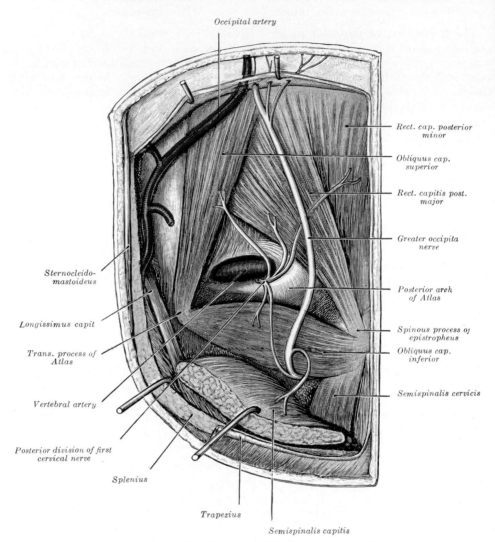

Occipital artery

Rect. cap. posterior minor

Obliquus cap. superior

Rect. capitis post. major

Greater occipita nerve

Posterior arch of Atlas

Spinous process oj epistropheus

Obliquus cap. inferior

Semispinalis cervicis

Sternocleido-mastoideus

Longissimus capit

Trans. process of Atlas

Vertebral artery

Posterior division of first cervical nerve

Splenius

Trapezius

Semispinalis capitis

Fig. 438.—The left suboccipital triangle and muscles.

III. THE MUSCLES OF THE THORAX.

Intercostales externi.
Intercostales interni.
Subcostales.
Transversus thoracis.

Levatores costarum.
Serratus posterior superior.
Serratus posterior inferior.
Diaphragm.

Fascia.—The superficial fascia (tela subcutanea) and the outer layers of deep fascia of the thorax are described with the pectoral region (page 487) and back (page 483). The thoracic cage proper, composed of ribs and intercostal muscles, is covered inside and outside by thin membranes of deep fascia. The outer membrane is the external intercostal fascia, the inner one is the endothoracic fascia.

The **External Intercostal Fascia** covers the external surface of the Intercostales externi, the anterior intercostal membranes and the intervening surfaces of the ribs, costal cartilages and sternum. Above, it is continuous with the scalenus fascia; below, with the fascia between the external and internal oblique muscles of the abdomen. Posteriorly, it splits at the border of the Sacrospinalis into an outer membrane, the lumbodorsal fascia, and an inner membrane which continues on the surface of the Intercostales externi and Levatores costarum and forms an intermuscular septum between these muscles and the Sacrospinalis.

Between the Intercostales externi and interni is a thin layer of fascia to which both muscles are adherent.

The **Endothoracic Fascia** (*fascia endothoracica*) is the internal investing fascia, that is, the deep fascia which lines the inside of the thoracic cavity. It covers the internal surface of the Intercostales interni and intervening ribs, the Subcostales, Transversus thoracis, and Diaphragm, and posteriorly, it includes the thoracic portion of the prevertebral fascia which covers the bodies of the vertebræ and intervertebral discs. It is continuous, above, with the cervical prevertebral fascia, with the scalenus fascia (Sibson's) along the inner border of the first rib, and, behind the sternum, with the middle cervical fascia. It covers the entire thoracic surface of the diaphragm and is continuous with the internal investing fascia of the abdominal cavity (transversalis fascia, endoabdominal fascia) behind the diaphragm at the lumbocostal arches and through the aortic hiatus.

The **Subserous Fascia** (*visceral fascia*) (page 410) intervenes between the endo-thoracic fascia and the pleura, and provides the connective tissue investment for the mediastinal structures. It is more fully described with the lungs.

The **Intercostales** (*Intercostal muscles*) (Fig. 443) are two thin planes of muscular and tendinous fibers occupying each of the intercostal spaces. They are named **external** and **internal** from their surface relations—the external being superficial to the internal.

The **Intercostales externi** (*External intercostals*) are *eleven* in number on either side. They extend from the tubercles of the ribs behind, to the cartilages of the ribs in front, where they end in thin membranes, the **anterior intercostal membranes**, which are continued forward to the sternum. Each *arises* from the lower border of a rib, and is *inserted* into the upper border of the rib below. In the two lower spaces they extend to the ends of the cartilages, and in the upper two or three spaces they do not quite reach the ends of the ribs. They are thicker than the Intercostales interni, and their fibers are directed obliquely downward and lateral-ward on the back of the thorax, and downward, forward, and medialward on the front.

Action.—Draw adjacent ribs together. With the first rib fixed by the Scaleni, they lift the ribs, increasing the volume of the thoracic cavity.

Nerves.—Intercostal nerves.

Variations.—Continuation with the Obliquus externus or Serratus anterior: A *Supracostalis muscle*, from the anterior end of the first rib down to the second, third or fourth ribs occasionally occurs.

The **Intercostales interni** (*Internal intercostals*) are also *eleven* in number on either side. They commence anteriorly at the sternum, in the interspaces between the cartilages of the true ribs, and at the anterior extremities of the cartilages of the false ribs, and extend backward as far as the angles of the ribs, whence they are continued to the vertebral column by thin aponeuroses, the **posterior intercostal membranes**. Each *arises* from the ridge on the inner surface of a rib, as well as from the corresponding costal cartilage, and is *inserted* into the upper border of the rib below. Their fibers are also directed obliquely, but pass in a direction opposite to those of the Intercostales externi.

The **Subcostales** (*Intracostales*) consist of muscular and aponeurotic fasciculi, which are usually well-developed only in the lower part of the thorax; each *arises* from the inner surface of one rib near its angle, and is *inserted* into the inner surface of the second or third rib below. Their fibers run in the same direction as those of the Intercostales interni.

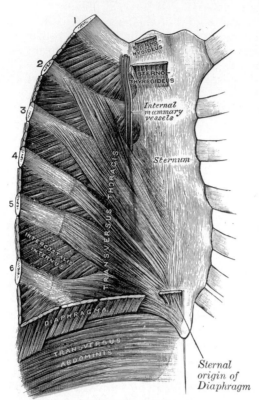

FIG. 439.—Posterior surface of sternum and costal cartilages, showing Transversus thoracis.

Action.—Draw adjacent ribs together. With the last rib fixed by the Quadratus lumborum, they lower the ribs, decreasing the volume of the thoracic cavity.

Nerves.—Intercostal nerves.

The **Transversus thoracis** (*Triangularis sterni*) is a thin plane of muscular and tendinous fibers, situated upon the inner surface of the front wall of the chest (Fig. 439). It *arises* on either side from the lower third of the posterior surface of the body of the sternum, from the posterior surface of the xiphoid process, and from the sternal ends of the costal cartilages of the lower three or four true ribs. Its fibers diverge upward and lateralward, to be *inserted* by slips into the lower borders and inner surfaces of the costal cartilages of the second, third, fourth, fifth, and sixth ribs. The lowest fibers of this muscle are horizontal in their direction, and are continuous with those of the Transversus abdominis; the intermediate fibers are oblique, while the highest are almost vertical. This muscle varies in its attachments, not only in different subjects, but on opposite sides of the same subject.

Action.—Draws the anterior portion of the ribs downward, decreasing the thoracic cavity.
Nerve. — Branches of the intercostal nerves.

The **Levatores costarum** (Fig. 437), *twelve* in number on either side, are small tendinous and fleshy bundles, which *arise* from the ends of the transverse processes of the seventh cervical and upper eleven thoracic vertebræ; they pass obliquely downward and lateralward, like the fibers of the Intercostales externi, and each is *inserted* into the outer surface of the rib immediately below the vertebra from which it takes origin, between the tubercle and the angle (**Levatores costarum breves**). Each of the four lower muscles divides into two fasciculi, one of which is inserted as above described; the other passes down to the second rib below its origin (**Levatores costarum longi**).

Action.—Raise the ribs, increasing the thoracic cavity; extend the vertebral column, bend it laterally and rotate it slightly toward the opposite side.
Nerves.—Branches of the intercostal nerves.

The **Serratus posterior superior** (*Serratus posticus superior*) is a thin, quadrilateral muscle, situated at the upper and back part of the thorax. It *arises* by a thin and broad aponeurosis from the lower part of the ligamentum nuchae, from the spinous processes of the seventh cervical and upper two or three thoracic vertebræ and from the supraspinal ligament. Inclining downward and lateralward it becomes muscular, and is *inserted*, by four fleshy digitations, into the upper borders of the second, third, fourth, and fifth ribs, a little beyond their angles.

Action.—Raises the ribs to which it is attached, increasing the thoracic cavity.
Nerve.—Branches of the ventral primary divisions of the upper four thoracic nerves.
Variations.—Increase or decrease in size and number of slips or entire absence.

The **Serratus posterior inferior** (*Serratus posticus inferior*) (Fig. 455) is situated at the junction of the thoracic and lumbar regions: it is of an irregularly quadrilateral form, broader than the preceding, and separated from it by a wide interval. It *arises* by a thin aponeurosis from the spinous processes of the lower two thoracic and upper two or three lumbar vertebræ, and from the supraspinal ligament.

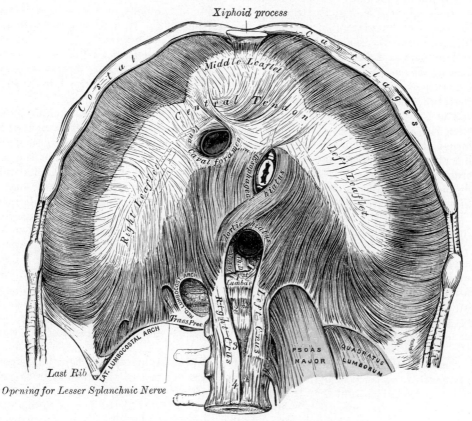

FIG. 440.—The diaphragm. Under surface.

Passing obliquely upward and lateralward, it becomes fleshy, and divides into four flat digitations, which are *inserted* into the inferior borders of the lower four ribs, a little beyond their angles. The thin aponeurosis of origin is intimately blended with the lumbodorsal fascia, and aponeurosis of the Latissimus dorsi.

Action.—Draws the ribs to which it is attached outward and downward, counter-acting the inward pull of the Diaphragm.
Nerve.—Branches of the ventral primary divisions of the ninth to twelfth thoracic nerves.
Variations.—Increase or decrease in size and number of slips or entire absence.

The **Diaphragm** (Fig. 440) is a dome-shaped musculofibrous septum which separates the thoracic from the abdominal cavity, its convex upper surface forming the floor of the former, and its concave under surface the roof of the latter. Its

29

peripheral part consists of muscular fibers which take origin from the circumference of the thoracic outlet and converge to be *inserted* into a central tendon.

The muscular fibers may be grouped according to their origins into three parts — sternal, costal, and lumbar. The **sternal part** *arises* by two fleshy slips from the back of the xiphoid process; the **costal part** from the inner surfaces of the cartilages and adjacent portions of the lower six ribs on either side, interdigitating with the Transversus abdominis; and the **lumbar part** from aponeurotic arches, named the lumbocostal arches, and from the lumbar vertebræ by two pillars or **crura**. There are two lumbocostal arches, a medial and a lateral, on either side.

The **Medial Lumbocostal Arch** (*arcus lumbocostalis medialis* [*Halleri*]; *internal arcuate ligament*) is a tendinous arch in the fascia covering the upper part of the Psoas major; medially, it is continuous with the lateral tendinous margin of the corresponding crus, and is attached to the side of the body of the first or second lumbar vertebra; laterally, it is fixed to the front of the transverse process of the first and, sometimes also, to that of the second lumbar vertebra.

The **Lateral Lumbocostal Arch** (*arcus lumbocostalis lateralis* [*Halleri*]; *external arcuate ligament*) arches across the upper part of the Quadratus lumborum, and is attached, medially, to the front of the transverse process of the first lumbar vertebra, and, laterally, to the tip and lower margin of the twelfth rib.

The Crura.—At their origins the crura are tendinous in structure, and blend with the anterior longitudinal ligament of the vertebral column. The **right crus**, larger and longer than the left, *arises* from the anterior surfaces of the bodies and intervertebral fibrocartilages of the upper three lumbar vertebræ, while the **left crus** *arises* from the corresponding parts of the upper two only. The medial tendinous margins of the crura pass forward and medialward, and meet in the middle line to form an arch across the front of the aorta; this arch is often poorly defined.

From this series of origins the fibers of the diaphragm converge to be inserted into the central tendon. The fibers arising from the xiphoid process are very short, and occasionally aponeurotic; those from the medial and lateral lumbocostal arches, and more especially those from the ribs and their cartilages, are longer, and describe marked curves as they ascend and converge to their insertion. The fibers of the crura diverge as they ascend, the most lateral being directed upward and lateralward to the central tendon. The medial fibers of the right crus ascend on the left side of the esophageal hiatus, and occasionally a fasciculus of the left crus crosses the aorta and runs obliquely through the fibers of the right crus toward the vena caval foramen.

The Central Tendon.—The central tendon of the diaphragm is a thin but strong aponeurosis situated near the center of the vault formed by the muscle, but somewhat closer to the front than to the back of the thorax, so that the posterior muscular fibers are the longer. It is situated immediately below the pericardium, with which it is partially blended. It is shaped somewhat like a trefoil leaf, consisting of three divisions or leaflets separated from one another by slight indentations. The right leaflet is the largest, the middle, directed toward the xiphoid process, the next in size, and the left the smallest. In structure the tendon is composed of several planes of fibers, which intersect one another at various angles and unite into straight or curved bundles—an arrangement which gives it additional strength.

Openings in the Diaphragm.—The diaphragm is pierced by a series of apertures to permit of the passage of structures between the thorax and abdomen. Three large openings—the **aortic**, the **esophageal**, and the **vena caval**—and a series of smaller ones are described.

The **aortic hiatus** is the lowest and most posterior of the large apertures; it lies at the level of the twelfth thoracic vertebra. Strictly speaking, it is not an aperture in the diaphragm but an osseoaponeurotic opening between it and the vertebral column, and therefore behind the diaphragm; occasionally some tendinous fibers prolonged across the bodies of the vertebræ from the medial parts of the lower ends of the crura pass behind the aorta, and thus convert the hiatus into a fibrous ring. The hiatus is situated slightly to the left of the middle line, and is bounded in front by the crura, and behind by the body of the first lumbar vertebra. Through it pass the aorta, the azygos vein, and the thoracic duct; occasionally the azygos vein is transmitted through the right crus.

The **esophageal hiatus** is situated in the muscular part of the diaphragm at the level of the tenth thoracic vertebra, and is elliptical in shape. It is placed above, in front, and a little to the left of the aortic hiatus, and transmits the esophagus, the vagus nerves, and some small esophageal bloodvessels.

The **vena caval foramen** is the highest of the three, and is situated about the level of the fibrocartilage between the eighth and ninth thoracic vertebræ. It is quadrilateral in form, and is placed at the junction of the right and middle leaflets of the central tendon, so that its margins are tendinous. It transmits the inferior vena cava, the wall of which is adherent to the margins of the opening, and some branches of the right phrenic nerve.

Of the **lesser apertures,** two in the right crus transmit the greater and lesser right splanchnic nerves; three in the left crus give passage to the greater and lesser left splanchnic nerves and the hemiazygos vein. The gangliated trunks of the sympathetic usually enter the abdominal cavity behind the diaphragm, under the medial lumbocostal arches.

On either side two small intervals exist at which the muscular fibers of the diaphragm are deficient and are replaced by areolar tissue. One between the sternal and costal parts transmits the superior epigastric branch of the internal mammary artery and some lymphatics from the abdominal wall and convex surface of the liver. The other, between the fibers springing from the medial and lateral lumbocostal arches, is less constant; when this interval exists, the upper and back part of the kidney is separated from the pleura by areolar tissue only.

Action.—Draws the central tendon downward. This action has two effects: (*a*) it tends to increase the volume and decrease the pressure within the thoracic cavity, and (*b*) it tends to decrease the volume and increase the pressure within the abdominal cavity. During inspiration, the lowering of the diaphragm decreases the pressure within the thorax, and air is forced into the lungs through the open larynx and trachea by the pressure of the atmosphere. At the same time, the descending diaphragm presses against the abdominal viscera, forcing them downward against the passive resistance of the abdominal and pelvic muscles, and causing the anterior abdominal wall to protrude slightly. The pressure within the abdominal cavity is greatly increased when the abdominal muscles and the diaphragm contract actively at the same time, and this increase in pressure tends to make the abdominal viscera discharge their contents as in micturition, defecation, emesis, and parturition. The portion of the diaphragm about the esophageal hiatus is supposed to have a sphincteric action on the esophagus.

Nerve.—The phrenic nerve from the cervical plexus, containing mainly fibers from the fourth, but also some from the third and fifth cervical nerves.

Variations.—The sternal portion of the muscle is sometimes wanting and more rarely defects occur in the lateral part of the central tendon or adjoining muscle fibers.

The **Movements of Respiration** are inspiration, caused by an increase in the thoracic cavity, and expiration, caused by a decrease in the cavity. The increase in the volume of the cavity is the result of muscular action and is brought about in two ways: (*a*) by the descent of the diaphragm from contraction of its muscle, and (*b*) by the expansion of the thoracic wall through the action of certain muscles on the ribs, sternum, and vertebral column. The decrease in volume with expiration may be passive, due to the elastic recoil of the thoracic wall and the tissues of the lungs and bronchi. The decrease may also be the result of muscular action, in which case, (*a*) the abdominal muscles force the diaphragm upward by increasing the abdominal pressure, and (*b*) the thoracic wall is contracted by the action of certain muscles on the ribs and vertebral column.

Quiet Inspiration.—The diaphragm contracts, increasing the vertical diameter of the thoracic cavity. The first and second ribs remain fixed by the inertia and resistance of the cervical structures, and the remaining ribs, except the last two, are brought upward toward them by the contraction of the Intercostales externi. The upward motion of the ribs, due to their position and to the obliquity of their axis of rotation, enlarges the antero-posterior and transverse diameters of the thorax according to the movements described on page 343.

Traditionally, there are two types of quiet inspiration, diaphragmatic and costal, but under normal conditions there is a mixture of both types, although one or the other may show decided predominance in individual cases. Diaphragmatic breathing is also called abdominal because the visible result of contraction of the diaphragm is protrusion of the abdominal wall. To contrast with this, costal breathing is also called thoracic breathing. Costal breathing predominates in recumbency and it is said to be more frequent in women, while diaphragmatic is more frequent in men.

Quiet Expiration.—The normal resting position of the thorax is that found at the end of a quiet expiration. This position is restored without muscular effort after a quiet inspiration by the recoil of the structures which were displaced by the inspiratory act. The displacement of the anterior abdominal wall is overcome by the tonus of the abdominal muscles. The ribs are restored from their displacement by the elasticity of the ligaments and cartilages which hold them in place. The extensive network of elastic fibers which permeates the pulmonary tissue retracts the lungs wherever possible, and the bronchial tree, which has been elongated by the descent of the diaphragm, helps to draw the latter back up by its elastic recoil.

Deep Inspiration.—All the actions of quiet inspiration are increased in extent. In addition, the first two ribs are raised by the Scaleni and the Sternocleidomastoideus, and the remaining ribs are raised more forcibly by the additional action of the Levatores costarum and the Serratus posterior superior. The ribs are raised still farther by a straightening of the vertebral column through contraction of the Sacrospinalis. After the abdominal viscera have been forced downward by the diaphragm to a considerable extent, the abdominal muscles offer increased resistance, and the viscera may then act as a point of fixation for the diaphragm so that its further contraction raises the ribs.

Forced Inspiration.—In patients with great air hunger, all the muscles of the body seem to combine and coördinate to assist in breathing. The Levator scapulæ, the Trapezius, and the Rhomboidei elevate and fix the scapula which is then used as an origin by the Pectoralis minor to draw the ribs upward. If the patient further fixes the shoulder girdle by grasping the back of a chair or end of the bed, the Pectoralis major and the Serratus anterior will also raise the ribs.

Forced Expiration.—In forced expiration, muscles are called into play. The last two ribs are pulled downward and fixed by the Quadratus lumborum, and the other ribs are drawn downward toward them by the Intercostales interni and the Serrati posteriores inferiores. The muscles of the abdominal wall, by pressing on the abdominal viscera, force the diaphragm upward, and the same muscles, by flexing the vertebral column, assist in lowering the ribs.

Position of the Diaphragm.—The height of the diaphragm is constantly varying during respiration; it also varies with the degree of distension of the stomach and intestines and with the size of the liver. After a forced expiration the right cupola is on a level in front with the fourth costal cartilage, at the side with the fifth, sixth, and seventh ribs, and behind with the eighth rib; the left cupola is a little lower than the right. The absolute range of movement between deep inspiration and deep expiration averages in the male and female 30 mm. on the right side and 28 mm. on the left; in quiet respiration the average movement is 12.5 mm. on the right side and 12 mm. on the left.

Radiography shows that the height of the diaphragm in the thorax varies considerably with the position of the body. It stands highest when the body is horizontal and the patient on his back, and in this position it performs the largest respiratory excursions with normal breathing. When the body is erect the dome of the diaphragm falls, and its respiratory movements become smaller. The dome falls still lower when the sitting posture is assumed, and in this position its respiratory excursions are smallest. These facts may, perhaps, explain why it is that patients suffering from severe dyspnœa are most comfortable and least short of breath when they sit up. When the body is horizontal and the patient on his side, the two halves of the diaphragm do not behave alike. The uppermost half sinks to a level lower even than when the patient sits, and moves little with respiration; the lower half rises higher in the thorax than it does when the patient is supine, and its respiratory excursions are much increased. In unilateral disease of the pleura or lungs analogous interference with the position or movement of the diaphragm can generally be observed radiographically.

It appears that the position of the diaphragm in the thorax depends upon three main factors, viz.: (1) the elastic retraction of the lung tissue, tending to pull it upward; (2) the pressure exerted on its under surface by the viscera; this naturally tends to be a negative pressure, or downward suction, when the patient sits or stands, and positive, or an upward pressure, when he reclines; (3) the intra-abdominal tension due to the abdominal muscles. These are in a state of contraction in the standing position and not in the sitting; hence the diaphragm, when the patient stands, is pushed up higher than when he sits.

The following figures represent the average changes which occur during deepest possible respiration. The manubrium sterni moves 30 mm. in an upward and 14 mm. in a forward direction; the width of the subcostal angle, at a level of 30 mm. below the articulation between the body of the sternum and the xiphoid process, is increased by 26 mm.; the umbilicus is retracted and drawn upward for a distance of 13 mm.

IV. THE FASCIÆ AND MUSCLES OF THE ABDOMEN.

The muscles of the abdomen may be divided into two groups: (1) the **antero-lateral muscles**; (2) the **posterior muscles**.

1. The Antero-lateral Muscles of the Abdomen.

Obliquus externus abdominis.   Transversus abdominis.
Obliquus internus abdominis.   Rectus abdominis.
Pyramidalis.

The **Superficial Fascia** (*tela subcutanea*) (Fig. 442) of the anterior abdominal wall is soft and movable, and likely to contain fat. It is continuous, above, with the superficial fascia of the thorax; below, with that of the thigh and external genitalia; and laterally, it gradually becomes tougher and more resistant as it changes into the fascia of the back. In the lower portion, below the umbilicus, its superficial and deep layers are unusually distinct and can be separated easily by dissection. This unaccustomed divisibility and certain other peculiar features have been emphasized by giving the two layers in this region special names, Camper's fascia and Scarpa's fascia.

The **superficial layer of the superficial fascia** (*Camper's fascia*) is a genuine panniculus adiposus. It may be several centimeters thick in obese individuals, in which case it is likely to be irregularly divisible into laminæ. It is continuous over the inguinal ligament with the similar and corresponding layer of the thigh. In the male, as it continues down on the penis and scrotum, it loses its fat and, fusing with the deep layer, assists in the formation of the special fascia of these organs called the dartos. In the female, it retains some of the adipose tissue as it is continued into the labia majora. In both sexes, it is prolonged backward in the groove between the external genitalia and the thigh and is there continuous with the superficial layer of the superficial fascia of the perineum and medial surface of the thigh.

The **deep layer of the superficial fascia** (*Scarpa's fascia*) is a membranous sheet which usually contains no adipose tissue. It is composed, in considerable part, of yellow elastic fibers, and probably corresponds to the tunica abdominalis, an elastic layer which contributes to the support of the viscera and inguinal mammæ in some lower mammals. It forms a continuous sheet across the middle line, and is attached to the linea alba as it passes across it. Above and laterally, it loses its identity as a special layer in the superficial fascia of the upper abdomen and back. Below, it passes over the inguinal ligament and is securely attached either to the ligament itself or to the fascia lata just beyond it. Inferior to the ligament, the corresponding layer is called the fascia cribrosa as it covers and fills in the fossa ovalis (saphenous opening). At the medial end of the inguinal ligament, it passes over the external inguinal ring without being attached and continues into the penis and scrotum. It continues along the groove between the scrotum (labium majus) and thigh into the perineum where it is called the fascia of Colles. As the superficial fascia comes to lie under the skin of the scrotum and penis, its two layers are fused into a single tunic called the dartos. Here the superficial layer loses its fat and acquires a layer of scattered smooth muscle cells which attach to the skin and throw it into folds or rugæ. In the middle line, over the symphysis pubis, it is thickened by the addition of numerous, closely set, strong bands which extend down to the dorsum and sides of the penis forming the **ligamentum fundiforme penis**.

The fascial cleft which separates Scarpa's from the deep fascia over the lower portion of the aponeurosis of the Obliquus externus is quite definite and of considerable clinical interest because of its continuity with a similar cleft in the perineum. It is limited upward, toward the umbilicus, by an adhesion of Scarpa's fascia to the deep fascia, and laterally, by the former's closer attachment over the muscular portion of the external oblique. It is limited, downward and laterally, by a firm attachment either to the inguinal ligament or to the fascia lata just below it. Over the medial portion of the inguinal ligament and the external inguinal ring, however, the two fasciæ are not attached, so that the cleft follows along the narrow groove between the scrotum (labium) and thigh, and is continuous with the cleft between Colles' fascia and the external perineal fascia. From this groove, it is continuous medially with the cleft under the very movable dartos of the scrotum and penis, but it is abruptly limited laterally by an attachment to the deep fascia over the pubic ramus where the adductor muscles of the medial side of the thigh originate. In obese individuals there may be accumulations of adipose tissue between the cleft and the deep surface of Scarpa's fascia. The superficial inferior epigastric and circumflex iliac blood-vessels lie between Camper's and Scarpa's fasciæ but are attached to the superficial surface of Scarpa's layer.

Deep Fascia (*Fascia innominata*; *Gallaudet's fascia*).—The **outer investing layer** of deep fascia is easily identified in the lateral portion of the anterior abdominal wall where it covers the fleshy fibers of the Obliquus externus abdominis. It is continuous with the fascia of the Latissimus dorsi and Pectoralis major. More medially, over the aponeurosis of the Obliquus externus, it is so firmly adherent that it may escape recognition. Its presence is easily demonstrated in dissection, however, by scraping it back until the glistening fibers of the aponeurosis beneath are revealed. Above, it covers the upper end of the rectus sheath and is continuous with the pectoral fascia. Below, it is firmly attached to the inguinal ligament and joins the deep fascia emerging from under that ligament to become the fascia lata of the thigh. It covers the external inguinal ring as a distinct and separate layer, and there, reinforced by the fascia of the inner surface of the aponeurosis, gives rise to a tubular prolongation, the external spermatic (intercrural) fascia, which is the coat of the spermatic cord and testis just deep to the dartos. Near the middle line, it is attached to the pubic bone and is then continuous with deep fascia investing the penis. Over the lower end of the linea alba it is thickened into a strong, fibrous triangle, the **suspensory ligament of the penis**, which attaches the dorsum of the penis to the symphysis and arcuate pubic ligament. At the medial end of the inguinal ligament and lowest medial portion of the aponeurosis of the external oblique, it is attached to the pubic ramus and arcuate pubic ligament and is then continuous posteriorly, over the Ischiocavernosus muscle, with the external perineal fascia. Laterally in this region, beyond its attachment to the ramus, it is continuous with the fascia covering the adductor muscles of the medial side of the thigh.

The **Obliquus externus abdominis** (*External or descending oblique muscle*) (Fig. 441), situated on the lateral and anterior parts of the abdomen, is the largest and the most superficial of the three flat muscles in this region. It is broad, thin, and irregularly quadrilateral, its muscular portion occupying the side, its aponeurosis the anterior wall of the abdomen. It *arises*, by eight fleshy digitations, from the external surfaces and inferior borders of the lower eight ribs; these digitations are arranged in an oblique line which runs downward and backward, the upper ones being attached close to the cartilages of the corresponding ribs, the lowest to the apex of the cartilage of the last rib, the intermediate ones to the ribs at some distance from their cartilages. The five superior serrations increase in size from above downward, and are received between corresponding processes of the Serratus anterior; the three lower ones diminish in size from above downward and receive between them corresponding processes from the Latissimus dorsi. The muscular fasciculi from the last two ribs pass nearly vertically downward and are *inserted* into the anterior half of the outer lip of the iliac crest; the rest of the fasciculi, directed downward and forward, terminate in the broad abdominal aponeurosis by means of which most of the muscle reaches its final *insertion*, the linea alba.

Action.—Compresses the abdominal contents, assisting in micturition, defecation, emesis, parturition, and forced expiration. Both sides acting together flex the vertebral column, drawing the pubis toward the xiphoid process. One side alone bends the vertebral column laterally and rotates it, bringing the shoulder of the same side forward.

Nerve.—Branches of the eighth to twelfth intercostal, and the iliohypogastric and ilioinguinal nerves.

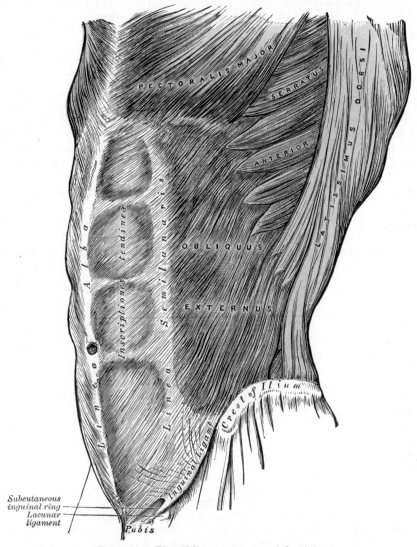

Fig. 441.—The Obliquus externus abdominis.

The **aponeurosis of the Obliquus externus abdominis** (Figs. 441, 442) is a strong membrane whose tendinous bundles continue, for the most part, in the direction of the muscular fasciculi, downward and medialward. It covers the entire front of the abdomen, lying superficial to the Rectus abdominis and helping to form its sheath. The fibers of the two sides interlace in the middle line to form the linea alba, the real insertion of the muscle, which extends from the xiphoid process to the symphysis pubis. The uppermost part of the aponeurosis serves as the origin for the lower fibers of the Pectoralis major. The lowermost portion ends in a very strong, thickened, free border which gives up its function as the tendon for the muscle and becomes, instead, a ligament attached to the anterior superior spine of the ilium at one end and to the pubic tubercle at the other. This is the **inguinal ligament**. Near its medial end, the free border is curled under like a sling to support the spermatic cord. Its attachment to the pubic bone is fanned out along the pectineal line beyond the pubic tubercle, leaving a crescentic free border which is called the **lacunar ligament**. Some of these fibers, after curling under and attaching to the bone, double back upward behind the main aponeurosis in a triangular sheet called the **reflected inguinal ligament**. The tendinous bundles of the aponeurosis just above the inguinal ligament separate from each other near the pubis to leave a narrow triangular opening which is called the **subcutaneous inguinal ring**, and which gives passage to the spermatic cord (round ligament in the female). Lateral to this opening, the aponeurosis contains, in addition to the bundles running in the usual direction, some scattered, transverse, reinforcing bundles which sweep medialward and upward in curved lines from the inguinal ligament. These are called **intercrural fibers**. In the above description, the aponeurosis has been treated as if it belonged solely to the Obliquus externus. This is advantageous for the presentation of the subcutaneous inguinal ring and associated structures, but it gives an incomplete picture because the aponeurosis serves also as the insertion of the Obliquus internus and Transversus, and it forms the sheath of the Rectus abdominis.

The **Inguinal Ligament** (*ligamentum inguinale; Poupart's ligament*) (Figs. 381, 442).—The inguinal ligament is the thickened lower border of the aponeurosis of the Obliquus externus. It extends from the anterior superior iliac spine to the pubic tubercle in a curved line with its convexity downward. It is attached securely to the fascia lata by means of its own fascia, the fascia innominata, and its lateral third is attached also to the fused transversalis and iliac fasciæ, as the latter emerge from under the ligament on the surface of the Iliacus muscle. Medial to its attachment to the iliac fascia, it arches over the femoral vessels as they enter the thigh. In the formation of the inguinal ligament, the aponeurosis folds or curves inward from the surface, especially toward the medial attachment, and forms a narrow sling for the support of the spermatic cord. The attachment of the incurved portion doubles back like the letter U, following along the pectineal line of the superior ramus of the pubis as a strong band called Cooper's ligament and leaving a crescentic free border with the concavity facing laterally. This crescentic fold is called the lacunar ligament.

The **Lacunar Ligament** (*ligamentum lacunare* [*Gimbernati*]; *Gimbernat's ligament*) (Fig. 381).—The lacunar ligament is the medial end of the inguinal ligament which is rolled under the spermatic cord and is attached along the pectineal line just lateral to the pubic tubercle. When it is viewed through the subcutaneous inguinal ring, after the spermatic cord has been removed, it appears to be a triangular fibrous membrane, about 1.25 cm. long, with a crescentic base, concave laterally, and with an apex medially at the pubic tubercle. It lies almost horizontally, in the erect posture, with the spermatic cord resting on its superior surface. Against its concave lateral border lies the medial wall of the femoral canal.

The **Reflected Inguinal Ligament** (*ligamentum inguinale reflexum* [*Collesi*]; *triangular fascia*) (Fig. 444).—The reflected inguinal ligament is a triangular, tendinous sheet 2 or 3 cm. wide extending from the medial part of the inguinal ring to the linea alba. The fibers are attached to the pectineal line along with the lacunar ligament, or they may seem to be a continuation of that ligament; they course upward and medially, behind or deep to the main aponeurosis of the external oblique, and interlace with the fibers of the latter in the linea alba. The ligament may be independent, but more often it is fused either with the aponeurosis of the external oblique or with the falx inguinalis which lies deep to it. Frequently it seems to be entirely lacking.

The **Subcutaneous Inguinal Ring** (*anulus inguinalis superficialis; superficial or external inguinal ring; external abdominal ring*) (Fig. 442).—The subcutaneous inguinal ring is the opening in the aponeurosis of the Obliquus externus abdominis just above and lateral to the pubis, through which the spermatic cord (round

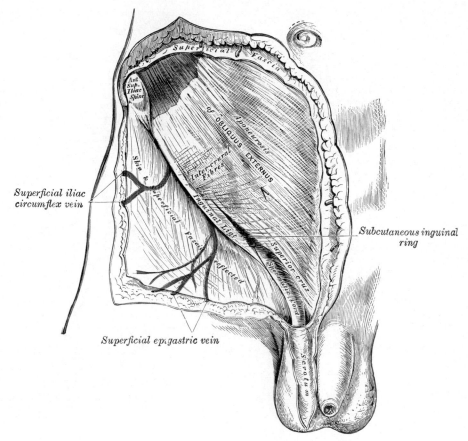

FIG. 442.—The subcutaneous inguinal ring.

ligament of the uterus) passes. It is a narrow triangle, pointing upward and laterally in the direction of the fibers of the aponeurosis. Its base is at the crest of the pubis; the sides are the margins of the opening in the aponeurosis and are called the crura of the ring. The **lateral (inferior) crus** (*external pillar*) is the stronger and is formed by the portion of the inguinal ligament which is attached to the pubic tubercle; it is curved and turned under into a narrow sling upon which the spermatic cord rests. The **medial (superior) crus** (*internal pillar*), thin and flat, is merely the part of the aponeurosis next to the opening and is not marked off except as it is attached to the front of the symphysis pubis. The triangular opening in the aponeurosis is converted by fascia into an oval ring, 2.5 cm. long and 1.25 cm. wide. The fascia of the superficial surface of the aponeurosis, called the fascia innominata by Gallaudet, fuses with the fascia of the deep surface and fills in the angular, lateral portion of the opening. A tubular prolongation of this fascia is continued down into the scrotum, enclosing the spermatic cord and testis in a sheath called the external spermatic fascia (intercrural or intercolumnar fascia). This intercrural fascia, so named because it occupies the space between the crura of the ring, is not to be confused with the intercrural fibers which are a part of the aponeurosis itself and reinforce the latter above the ring. The subcutaneous inguinal ring gives passage to the ilioinguinal nerve as well as to the spermatic cord or round ligament; it is larger in men than in women because of the greater size of the spermatic cord.

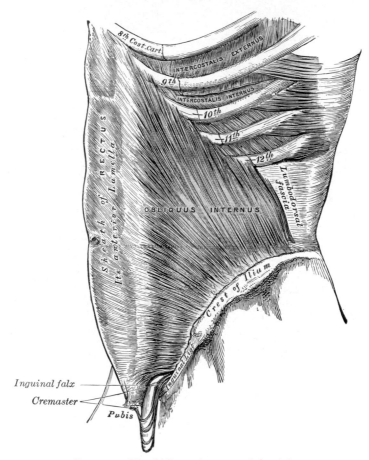

Fig. 443.—The Obliquus internus abdominis.

The Pectineal Ligament (*Cooper's Ligament*) (Fig. 381) is a narrow band of strong aponeurotic fibers which continues laterally from the lacunar ligament along the pectineal line of the pubis. It is firmly attached to the bone along this line and its medial end is continuous with the lacunar ligament. It diminishes in size gradually toward its lateral extremity at the iliopectineal eminence. It is aponeurotic rather than fascial in origin, and to it are attached parts of the iliopectineal, pectineal, and transversalis fasciæ. It forms the posterior or deep boundary of the lacuna vasorum through which the femoral vessels pass under the inguinal ligament.

The **Obliquus internus abdominis** (*Internal or ascending oblique muscle*) (Fig. 443), situated in the lateral and anterior part of the abdominal wall, is of an irregularly quadrilateral form, and is smaller and thinner than the Obliquus externus under which it lies. It *arises* by fleshy fibers from the lateral half of the inguinal ligament and the nearby iliac fascia, from the anterior two-thirds of the middle lip of the iliac crest, and from the lower portion of the lumbar aponeurosis (posterior layer of the lumbodorsal fascia) near the crest. The posterior fasciculi pass almost vertically upward to be *inserted* into the inferior borders of the cartilages of the lower three or four ribs by fleshy digitations which appear to be continuations of the internal intercostal muscles. The remainder of the fasciculi which arise from the iliac crest diverge as they spread over the side of the abdomen and terminate in the region of the linea semilunaris, in an aponeurosis which fuses with the aponeuroses of the externus and the transversus at a variable distance from the middle line. By means of the aponeurosis the muscle makes its final *insertion* into the linea alba. The fibers of the aponeurosis assist in the formation of the rectus sheath, some passing anterior and some posterior to the latter muscle. The fasciculi arising from the inguinal ligament are less compact and paler than the rest, and descending, form an arch over the spermatic cord (round ligament). They terminate in a tendinous sheet, which they share with the Transversus, and which is not fused with the aponeurosis of the externus but is independently inserted into the pubis and medial part of the pectineal line behind the lacunar ligament, forming what is known as the *falx inguinalis*.

Action.—Compresses the abdominal contents, assisting in micturition, defecation, emesis, parturition, and forced expiration. Both sides acting together flex the vertebral column, drawing the costal cartilages downward toward the pubis. One side acting alone bends the vertebral column laterally and rotates it, bringing the shoulder of the opposite side forward.

Nerves.—Branches of the eighth to twelfth intercostal, and the iliohypogastric and ilioinguinal nerves.

Variations.—Occasionally, tendinous inscriptions occur from the tips of the tenth or eleventh cartilages or even from the ninth; an additional slip to the ninth cartilage is sometimes found; paration between iliac and inguinal parts may occur.

The **Cremaster** (Fig. 444) is a thin muscular layer whose fasciculi are separate and spread out over the spermatic cord in a series of loops. It *arises* from the middle of the inguinal ligament as a continuation of the Obliquus internus, and is *inserted* by a small pointed tendon into the tubercle and crest of the pubis and into the front of the sheath of the Rectus abdominis. The fasciculi form a compact layer as they lie within the inguinal canal, but after they pass out of the subcutaneous inguinal ring they form a series of loops, the longest of which extend down as far as the testis and are attached to the tunica vaginalis. The interval between the loops is occupied by fascia which is a fused continuation of the fasciæ of the deep and superficial surfaces of the Obliquus internus and which may be called the cremasteric fascia. The muscular loops and the fascia together make up a single layer which forms the middle tunic of the spermatic cord.

Action.—Draws the testis up toward the subcutaneous inguinal ring.

Nerve.—The external spermatic branch of the genitofemoral nerve.

The **Transversus abdominis** (*Transversalis muscle*) (Fig. 445), so called from the direction of its fibers, is the internal of the flat muscles of the abdomen, being placed immediately beneath the Obliquus internus. It *arises* by fleshy fibers from the lateral third of the inguinal ligament, from the anterior three-fourths of the inner lip of the iliac crest, from the lumbodorsal fascia, and from the inner surface of the cartilages of the lower six ribs. The origin from the ribs is by means of digitations which are separated from similar digitations of the Diaphragm (Fig. 439) by a narrow fibrous raphé; viewed from the interior of the abdomen, the two muscles appear to be components of a single stratum of muscle. The fasciculi of the Transversus, except the lowermost, pass horizontally forward, and terminate in an aponeurosis which fuses with the aponeurosis of the Obliquus internus, and joins the aponeurosis of the opposite side to form the *insertion* of the muscle into the linea alba. The aponeurosis assists in the formation of the sheath of the Rectus as follows: the upper portion passes entirely behind the Rectus; a portion extending for a variable distance below the umbilicus splits and interdigitates with the aponeurosis of the Obliquus internus contributing to both the anterior and posterior layers of the sheath; and the lowest part, below the linea semicircularis, a curved fibrous border approximately half way between the umbilicus and the pubis, passes entirely in front of the Rectus. The fasciculi of the lowest portion of the muscle pass downward as well as forward, *terminating* in the falx inguinalis along with the lowest fasciculi of the Obliquus internus. The muscle ends inferiorly in a free border which forms an arch extending from the lateral part of the inguinal ligament to the pubis, a short distance above the abdominal inguinal ring and spermatic cord.

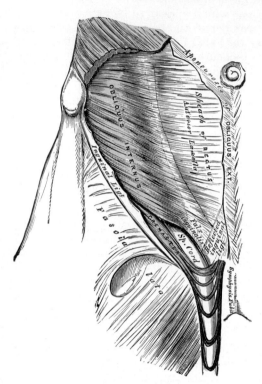

FIG. 444.—The Cremaster.

Action.—Constricts the abdomen, compressing the contents and assisting in micturition, defecation, emesis, parturition, and forced expiration.

Nerve.—Branches of the seventh to twelfth intercostal, and the iliohypogastric and ilioinguinal nerves.

Variations.—It may be more or less fused with the Obliquus internus or absent. The spermatic cord may pierce its lower border. Slender muscle slips from the iliopectineal line to transversalis fascia, the aponeurosis of the Transversus abdominis, or the outer end of the linea semicircularis and other slender slips are occasionally found.

The **Inguinal Falx** (*falx inguinalis*; *tendo conjunctivus*; *conjoined tendon of Internal oblique and Transversalis muscles*) (Figs. 444, 446, 447) is the lower terminal portion of the common aponeurosis of the Obliquus internus and Transversus abdominis muscles. It is inserted into the crest of the pubis and pectineal line immediately behind the subcutaneous inguinal ring, giving strength to a potentially weak point in the anterior abdominal wall. There is a wide variation in its width, strength, composition, and degree of union with neighboring aponeurotic and fascial structures. It may be narrow with a high arch, scarcely reaching the lateral part of the external inguinal ring, or it may be a broad, strong band, arching close to the inguinal ligament, and greatly reinforcing the abdominal wall in the region of the ring. In many cases it could be called the conjoined muscle instead of the conjoined tendon because the muscular fasciculi continue almost to the pubis. Not infrequently it is intimately fused with the reflected inguinal ligament which lies between it and the aponeurosis of the Obliquus externus. It may be reinforced on its deep surface by a fascial expansion of the Rectus tendon, **Henle's ligament.**

The **Rectus abdominis** (Fig. 445) is a long flat muscle, which extends along the whole length of the front of the abdomen, and is separated from its fellow of the opposite side by the linea alba. It is much broader, but thinner, above than below, and *arises* by two tendons; the lateral or larger is attached to the crest of the pubis, the medial interlaces with its fellow of the opposite side, and is connected with the ligaments covering the front of the symphysis pubis. The muscle is *inserted* by three portions of unequal size into the cartilages of the fifth, sixth, and seventh ribs. The upper portion, attached principally to the cartilage of the fifth rib, usually has some fibers of insertion into the anterior extremity of the rib itself. Some fibers are occasionally connected with the costoxiphoid ligaments, and the side of the xiphoid process.

The Rectus is crossed by fibrous bands, three in number, which are named the **tendinous intersections**; one is usually situated opposite the umbilicus, one at the extremity of the xiphoid process, and the third about midway between the xiphoid process and the umbilicus. These inscriptions pass transversely or obliquely across the muscle in a zigzag course; they rarely extend completely through its substance and may pass only halfway across it; they are intimately adherent in front to the sheath of the muscle. Sometimes one or two additional inscriptions, generally incomplete, are present below the umbilicus.

Action.—Flexes the vertebral column, particularly the lumbar portion, drawing the sternum toward the pubis; tenses the anterior abdominal wall, and assists in compressing the abdominal contents.

Nerves.—Branches of the seventh to twelfth intercostal nerves; the seventh supplies the portion above the first tendinous inscription, the eighth the portion between the first and second inscriptions, and the ninth the portion between the lower two inscriptions.

Variations.—The Rectus may insert as high as the fourth or third rib or may fail to reach the fifth. Fibers may spring from the lower part of the linea alba. Both the aponeurotic composition and the position of the linea semicircularis vary considerably.

The **sheath of the Rectus abdominis** (*vagina m. recti abdominis*) (Fig. 443, 445).— The Rectus abdominis is enclosed in a sheath which holds it in position but does not restrict its motion during contraction because it is separated from the muscle by a fascial cleft. The sheath is formed by the aponeuroses of the Obliquus externus, Obliquus internus, and Transversus which preserve their identity in some regions, but fuse or interlace in others. At the lateral border of the Rectus, they form two membranes, the anterior and posterior lamellæ of the sheath. The aponeurosis of the externus keeps its position anterior to the Rectus throughout its entire length, but fuses with that of the internus at a variable distance from the middle line. The line of fusion is close to the linea alba at the pubis and below the umbilicus, and gradually angles outward and upward, but remains medial to the lateral border of the Rectus. Thus a surgical incision over the Rectus, below the umbilicus, will go through the aponeuroses of the externus and internus as separate layers before it reaches the Rectus muscle itself. The aponeurosis of the internus, above the umbilicus, splits into two lamellæ, one of which passes anterior to the Rectus and fuses with the externus as just described; the other passes posterior to the Rectus and fuses with the aponeurosis of the Transversus to form the posterior lamella of the sheath. Above the costal margin, to which the internus is attached, the costal cartilages and xiphoid process of the sternum take the place of the aponeurotic sheath, posteriorly. The posterior lamella of the internus aponeurosis is attached to the cartilages; the anterior lamella ends abruptly in a fibrous band similar to the linea semicircularis, the Rectus above this point being covered only by the externus aponeurosis. The aponeurosis of the Transversus, above the umbilicus, passes entirely posterior to the Rectus and fuses with the internus as just described. Below the umbilicus, the behavior of the aponeuroses is more complicated and more variable. At an inconstant distance above the pubis, usually about half way, the contribution of the aponeuroses to the posterior lamella of the sheath ceases abruptly in a curved line, the **semicircular line of Douglas**. Below this line all the aponeurotic fibers of all three muscles pass anterior to the Rectus. Between the umbilicus and the semicircular line, the aponeuroses of the internus and Transversus fuse and interdigitate, and tendinous bundles from both may pass either anterior or posterior to the Rectus. Usually a short distance above the linea semicircularis, the internus terminates its contribution to the posterior lamella and the Transversus only remains; hence, in the majority of instances, the linea is formed by the fibers of the Transversus alone. Below the linea, the sheath is formed by a portion of the endoabdominal or transversalis fascia. This portion of the sheath is occasionally

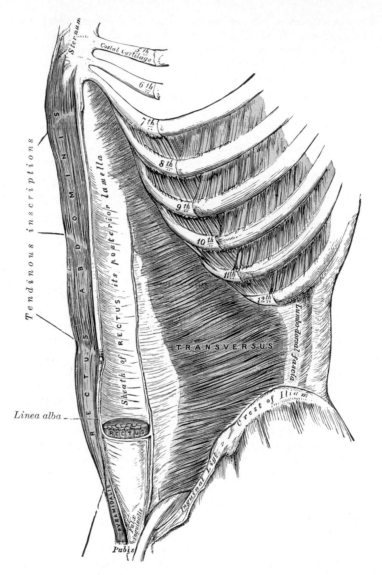

Fig. 445.—The Transversus abdominis, Rectus abdominis, and Pyramidalis.

reinforced by scattered tendinous bundles from the Transversus and by thickened laminæ of the subserous fascia. The sheath contains, besides the Rectus muscle, the Pyramidalis muscle, the superior and inferior epigastric arteries and veins, and branches of the intercostal nerves.

The **Pyramidalis** (Fig. 445) is a small triangular muscle, placed at the lower part of the abdomen, in front of the Rectus, and contained in the sheath of that muscle. It *arises* by tendinous fibers from the front of the pubis and the anterior pubic ligament; the fleshy portion of the muscle passes upward, diminishing in size as it ascends, and ends by a pointed extremity which is *inserted* into the linea alba, midway between the umbilicus and pubis.

Action.—Tenses the linea alba.

Nerve.—Branch of the twelfth thoracic nerve.

Variations.—The Pyramidalis is wanting in 10 per cent, the lower end of the Rectus then becomes proportionately large. It may vary from 1.5 to 12 cm. in length, averaging 6.8 cm.; it is occasionally double on one or both sides, and the two sides may be unequal.

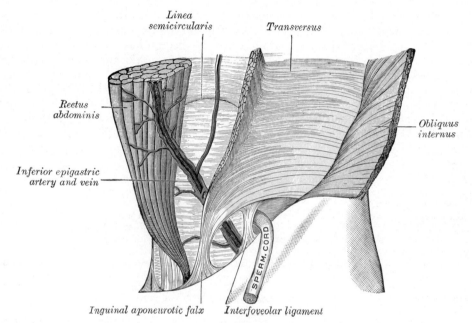

Linea semicircularis   *Transversus*

Rectus abdominis   *Obliquus internus*

Inferior epigastric artery and vein

SPERM. CORD

Inguinal aponeurotic falx   *Interfoveolar ligament*

Fig. 446.—The interfoveolar ligament, seen from in front. (Modified from Braune.)

The **Linea alba** (Fig. 441) is the name given to the portion of the anterior abdominal aponeurosis or Rectus sheath in the middle line. It represents the insertion of the Obliquus externus and internus and the Transversus by the fusion of their aponeuroses with those of the opposite side; the fibers interlace and the three aponeuroses are fused into a single tendinous band which extends from the xiphoid process to the symphysis pubis. It is broader above, where the Recti are separated from each other by a considerable interval; a surgical incision above the umbilicus in the middle line will go through the linea as a single aponeurotic layer. It is narrower below, where the Recti are more closely placed; a surgical incision in the middle line below the umbilicus seldom follows the linea and will, in consequence, go through the anterior and posterior lamellæ of the Rectus sheath as individual layers. The lower end of the linea alba has a double attachment; the superficial one passes in front of the medial heads of the Recti to the symphysis pubis; the deeper one spreads out into a triangular sheet behind the Recti, attaches to the posterior lip of the crest of the pubis, and is named the **adminiculum lineæ albæ**. The umbilicus, which is an aperture for the passage of the umbilical vessels in the fetus, is closed in the adult and has the form of a hard fibrous ring or plate of scar tissue within the linea alba.

The **Linea Semicircularis** (*semicircular line or fold of Douglas*) (Fig. 446) is a curved tendinous band, with convexity upward, in the posterior lamella of the

Rectus sheath below the umbilicus. It marks the lower limit of the aponeurotic portion of the posterior lamella, the latter being composed of transversalis fascia below the line. Its origin from the lateral border of the sheath may be from 4 to 13 cm., average 8 cm., from the pubis; its arched course may be horizontal or upward, but is most frequently downward; its insertion is into the linea alba, or occasionally as far down as the pubic crest. The tendinous bundles of the linea semicircularis are usually derived from the aponeurosis of the Transversus abdominis, but may be from the Obliquus internus, or from an interlacing of fibers from both the Transversus and the internus. A secondary linea may be found above the primary one, especially in those instances which have the primary linea formed by the Transversus, in which case the secondary is formed by the Obliquus internus.

The **Linea Semilunaris** (Fig. 441) is a slightly curved line on the anterior abdominal wall running approximately parallel with the median line, and lying about half way between the latter and the side of the body. It marks the lateral border of the Rectus abdominis, and can be seen as a shallow groove in the living subject, when that muscle is tensed. The abdominal wall is thin, particularly along the lower part of this line, where it is composed only of the aponeuroses of the Obliqui and Transversus, and their fasciæ. At its upper end, it is thicker where the muscular fasciculi of the Transversus extend under the Rectus for a variable distance.

Group Actions.—If pelvis and thorax are fixed, the abdominal muscles compress the abdominal viscera by constricting the cavity of the abdomen, in which action they are materially assisted by the descent of the diaphragm. By these means assistance is given in expelling the feces from the rectum, the urine from the bladder, the fetus from the uterus, and the contents of the stomach in vomiting.

If the pelvis and vertebral column be fixed, these muscles compress the lower part of the thorax, materially assisting expiration. If the pelvis alone be fixed, the thorax is bent directly forward, when the muscles of both sides act; when the muscles of only one side contract, the trunk is bent toward that side and rotated toward the opposite side.

If the thorax be fixed, the muscles, acting together, draw the pelvis upward, as in climbing; or, acting singly, they draw the pelvis upward, and bend the vertebral column to one side or the other. The Recti, acting from below, depress the thorax, and consequently flex the vertebral column; when acting from above, they flex the pelvis upon the vertebral column.

The **Transversalis Fascia** (*endoabdominal fascia*).—The **internal investing layer** of deep fascia which lines the entire wall of the abdomen is now generally called the Transversalis Fascia. It may even include the pelvic portion of this internal layer. Formerly, the name was applied only to the deep fascia covering the internal surface of the Transversus (Transversalis) abdominis muscle, but, because this muscle occupies a large proportion of the surface of the abdominal cavity, the name has gradually become adopted for the entire internal sheet. Various subdivisions of it are still referred to by their more specific designations; for example, the names iliac, psoas, or obturator fascia are used for the portions covering these muscles. This internal fascia is of great surgical interest and is extremely complex; in different areas it covers muscles, aponeuroses, bones, and ligaments; it may be very thin and adherent in one place or thickened and independent in another; it gives rise to specialized structures, such as tubular investments, and from it are derived certain components of important extra-abdominal fasciæ. It is a gray, felt-like membrane, sometimes transparent, sometimes thickened into strong bands, but seldom aponeurotic in appearance, and, except in obese individuals, contains no fat. Between this membrane and the peritoneum there is a layer of subserous fascia which may contain fat.

The definitive part of the transversalis fascia, that covering the internal surface of the muscular portion of the Transversus muscle, is readily identified by dissection. Over the aponeurosis of this muscle, however, it is thin and so closely adherent that only with difficulty can it be dissected free. Upward from the muscular portion of the Transversus, the fascia continues onto the diaphragm and covers its entire abdominal surface. It is thin and adherent over the muscular portion as well as over the central tendon. Ventrally, the fascia over the Transversus aponeurosis of one side is continuous across the middle line with that of the other side. Dorsally, as it leaves the muscular fasciculi of the Transversus, it continues for a short distance over the aponeurosis of origin of this muscle and then covers the Quadratus lumborum and Psoas muscles. From the Psoas it covers the crura of the diaphragm, the bodies and discs of the lumbar vertebræ, and is then continuous with the fascia of the Psoas of the other side. As the dorsal origin of the diaphragm crosses the Quadratus and Psoas, the fascia is thickened into the strong, fibrous lumbocostal arches. Downward from the muscular portion of the Transversus and the Quadratus lumborum, the fascia is attached to the bone along the crest of the ilium and continues into the greater pelvis on the surface of the Iliacus muscle. It is continuous, from the Iliacus and Psoas muscles, with the pelvic fascia which is described in the section dealing with the muscles of that region. The fascia on the internal surface of the anterior wall below the umbilicus requires an especially detailed description.

In a medial direction from the muscular fasciculi of the Transversus, the transversalis fascia below the umbilicus continues on the aponeurosis toward the middle line. The portion below the linea semicircularis, however, splits at the lateral border of the Rectus into two sheets; the thin anterior sheet continues on the aponeurosis and passes with it anterior to the Rectus; a thick posterior sheet forms the posterior lamina of the Rectus sheath and represents the internal investing or endoabdominal fascia in this area. Lateral to the lower part of the Rectus, the transversalis fascia continues downward on the Transversus aponeurosis to its lower limit, covering there the falx inguinalis, and passing over the free border of the Transversus aponeurosis as it forms an arch extending from the crest of the pubic bone to the lateral part of the inguinal ligament. The fascial membranes on both the deep and superficial surfaces of the Transversus fuse into a single sheet at this free border, providing a reinforced transversalis to bridge the interval between the arch and the inguinal ligament.

At a point just above the middle of the inguinal ligament, a tubular prolongation of this reinforced fascia is carried outward on the ductus deferens and internal spermatic vessels as they leave the abdominal cavity. This tubular investment is the inner coat of the spermatic cord and testis and is known as the internal spermatic or infundibuliform fascia. The ductus and vessels leave the abdominal cavity at a point which is called the abdominal or internal inguinal ring and they follow an oblique course through the abdominal wall in a tunnel called the inguinal canal. The lateral part of this canal, that is, before it has begun to penetrate the internal oblique muscle, has transversalis fascia for its posterior wall. The fascia is loosely attached to the inguinal ligament and has two thickenings near the ring, one extending upward is called the interfoveolar ligament, one extending downward is called the deep crural arch.

The **Interfoveolar Ligament** (*Hesselbach's ligament*) (Fig. 446) forms a crescentic medial boundary for the internal inguinal ring. It may be poorly defined or it may be a strong band whose fibers fan out medially as it follows the upward course of the deep inferior epigastric artery. It forms a slight ridge, not always visible but usually palpable from the interior of the abdominal cavity, which extends upward from the middle of the inguinal ligament, dividing the shallow fossa above the ligament into two parts, a **medial** and a **lateral inguinal fovea**. The internal inguinal ring, through which the ductus deferens leaves the abdominal cavity, is in the lateral fovea and it is here that the sac of an indirect inguinal hernia penetrates the abdominal wall. In the medial fovea, a triangular area is marked out by the inguinal ligament, the lateral boundary of the Rectus abdominis, and the

30

inferior deep epigastric artery. This is *Hesselbach's triangle* and is the site of a direct inguinal hernia.

The **Deep Crural Arch** (*iliopubic tract*) is the downward extension of the transversalis fascia from the region of the internal inguinal ring. It arches across the external iliac vessels as they pass under the inguinal ligament and marks the transition from transversalis fascia to femoral sheath. Laterally, it is attached to the iliac fascia where the latter gives origin to the lower fibers of the Transversus muscle. Medially, it follows the downward curve of the lacunar ligament. It may be a strong band or it may be poorly defined and appear to be merely the proximal part of the femoral sheath.

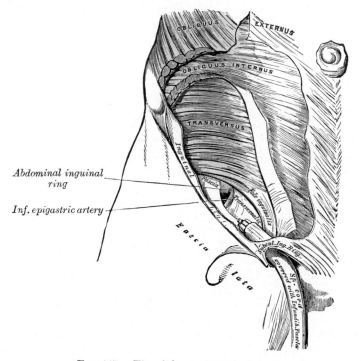

Abdominal inguinal ring

Inf. epigastric artery

FIG. 447.—The abdominal inguinal ring.

The **Abdominal Inguinal Ring** (*annulus inguinalis profundus; internal or deep inguinal ring*) (Figs. 447, 589) is the name given to the interruption in the transversalis fascia where the spermatic cord (round ligament in the female) penetrates the anterior abdominal wall, carrying with it a sleeve-like investment of the transversalis fascia called the internal spermatic fascia. It is situated midway between the anterior superior iliac spine and the symphysis pubis, and about 1.25 cm. above the inguinal ligament (Fig. 447). It is of an oval form, the long axis of the oval being vertical. It varies in size, fitting rather closely about the penetrating structures unless it has been distended by the sac of an indirect inguinal hernia. It is bounded, above, by the arched lower margin of the Transversus abdominis; medially, by the interfoveolar ligament accompanying the inferior deep epigastric vessels, and below, by the iliopubic tract.

The **Inguinal Canal** (*canalis inguinalis; spermatic canal*) is the tunnel in the lower anterior abdominal wall through which the spermatic cord (round ligament in the female) passes. Its internal (lateral) end is at the abdominal inguinal ring; its external (medial) end is at the subcutaneous inguinal ring. It is about 4 cm. long and takes an oblique course parallel with and a little above the inguinal ligament. It is bounded superficially by the skin, superficial fascia, aponeurosis of the Obliquus externus, and, in its lateral third, by the Obliquus internus; deeply, from medial to lateral ends, by the reflected inguinal ligament, the inguinal falx, the transversalis fascia, subserous fascia and peritoneum; proximally, by the arched fibers of the Obliquus internus and Transversus; distally, by the inguinal ligament, and at its medial end, the lacunar ligament. Through it pass the spermatic cord (round ligament), the ilioinguinal nerve, the internal spermatic vessels, and the Cremaster muscle.

Subserous Fascia (*subperitoneal fascia, superficial subserous fascia* [*Gallaudet*], *extraperitoneal connective tissue*).—Intervening between the internal investing layer of deep fascia of the abdominal wall and the peritoneum is the fibro-elastic connective tissue which supports the peritoneum. This subserous fascia resembles the subcutaneous superficial fascia in that it supports a free surface epithelial layer, it commonly contains adipose tissue in varying thicknesses, and it is frequently separated from the deep fascia by a fascial cleft. Not only does it have a parietal portion supporting the peritoneum of the abdominal wall, but it has a visceral portion which continues out over the viscera at the peritoneal reflections, and which accompanies the bloodvessels into the mesenteries. The subserous fascia has localized thickenings and accumulations of fat which are associated with the particular requirements of the different regions; these are described in the chapters dealing with the viscera.

The subserous fascia in the pelvis is uninterruptedly continuous with that of the abdomen. It is described in the chapter dealing with the pelvic viscera.

2. The Posterior Muscles of the Abdomen.

Psoas major.	Iliacus.
Psoas minor.	Quadratus lumborum.

The Psoas major, the Psoas minor, and the Iliacus, with the fasciæ covering them, will be described with the muscles of the lower extremity.

Fascia Covering the Quadratus Lumborum.—The transversalis (internal investing, endoabdominal) fascia covers the lateral portion of the Quadratus lumborum on its ventral surface. Since the medial portion of the muscle is overlapped by the Psoas, the fascia continues medially between the muscles and is attached to the bases of the transverse processes of the lumbar vertebræ. Its superior portion is thickened into a strong band, called the lateral lumbocostal arch (see Diaphragm), which is attached to the transverse process of the first lumbar vertebra, and the apex and lower border of the last rib. Inferiorly, the fascia is attached to the crest of the ilium, and is then continuous with the iliac fascia. At the lateral border of the muscle, the fascia fuses with the combined fascia and aponeurosis of origin of the Transversus. The latter, extending medially from this point of fusion, covers the dorsal surface of the Quadratus. The more medial portion of this aponeurotic sheet lies between the Quadratus and the Sacrospinalis and is named the lumbocostal aponeurosis (anterior layer of the lumbodorsal fascia).

The **Quadratus lumborum** (Fig. 437, page 441) is irregularly quadrilateral in shape, and broader below than above. It *arises* by aponeurotic fibers from the iliolumbar ligament and the adjacent portion of the iliac crest for about 5 cm., and is *inserted* into the lower border of the last rib for about half its length, and by four small tendons into the apices of the transverse processes of the upper four lumbar vertebræ. Occasionally a second portion of this muscle is found in front of the preceding. It *arises* from the upper borders of the transverse processes of the lower three or four lumbar vertebræ, and is *inserted* into the lower margin of the last rib. In front of the Quadratus lumborum are the colon, the kidney, the

Psoas major and minor, and the diaphragm; between the fascia and the muscle are the twelfth thoracic, ilioinguinal, and iliohypogastric nerves.

Action.—Draws the last rib toward the pelvis and flexes the lumbar vertebral column laterally toward the side of the muscle acting. Fixes the last two ribs in forced expiration.

Nerves.—Branches of the twelfth thoracic and first lumbar nerves.

Variations.—The number of attachments to the vertebræ and the extent of its attachment to the last rib vary.

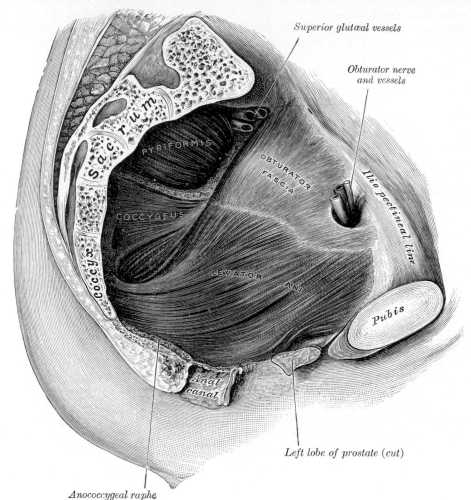

Fig. 448.—Left Levator ani from within.

V. THE MUSCLES AND FASCIÆ OF THE PELVIS.

Levator ani.   Obturator internus.
Coccygeus.   Piriformis.

The muscles within the pelvis may be divided into two groups: (1) the true pelvic muscles, the Levator ani and Coccygeus; (2) the muscles of the lower limb which originate within the pelvis and thus form part of the pelvic wall, the Obturator internus and the Piriformis. The muscles of the second group will be described later with the muscles of the lower limb, but their fasciæ will be considered here because they form an important part of the pelvic fascia.

The **Pelvic Diaphragm** (*diaphragma pelvis*) is composed of the Levator ani and Coccygeus muscles together with the fasciæ covering their internal and external surfaces. It stretches across the pelvic cavity like a hammock. It is the most inferior portion of the body wall, closing the abdominopelvic cavity, restraining the abdominal contents, and giving support to the pelvic viscera. It is pierced by the anal canal, the urethra, and the vagina, and is reinforced in the perineum by the special muscles and fasciæ associated with these structures. The pelvic diaphragm and the structures of the perineum are intimately associated both structurally and functionally and an accurate knowledge of one cannot be obtained without study of the other.

The **Levator ani** (Fig. 448) is a broad, thin muscle forming the hammock-like floor of the pelvis. Although the muscles of the two sides are separated from each other anteriorly, and are inserted into a raphé posteriorly, they function as a single sheet across the middle line forming the principal part of the pelvic diaphragm. It *arises*, anteriorly, from the inner surface of the superior ramus of the pubis lateral to the symphysis; posteriorly, from the inner surface of the spine of the ischium; and between these two points, from the *arcus tendineus musculi levatoris ani*. The latter is a thickened band of the obturator fascia attached posteriorly to the spine of the ischium and anteriorly to the pubic bone at the anterior margin of the obturator membrane. The fasciculi pass posteriorly and medially in the floor of the pelvis and are *inserted* into the side of the last two segments of the coccyx, the anococcygeal raphé, the Sphincter ani externus, and the central tendinous point of the perineum. The *anococcygeal raphé* is the narrow fibrous band extending from the coccyx to the posterior margin of the anus where the muscles of the two sides join each other in the middle line.

The Levator ani generally shows a separation into two parts, more distinct in lower mammals than in man, the Pubococcygeus and the Iliococcygeus.

The **Pubococcygeus** arises from the dorsal surface of the pubis along an oblique line extending from the lower part of the symphysis to the obturator canal. The muscular fasciculi pass posteriorly, more or less parallel with the middle line, and terminate by joining the fibers from the other side. The lateral margin of the muscle may be separated from the Iliococcygeus by a narrow interval or it may be overlapped by the latter muscle. The medial margin is separated from the muscle of the other side by an interval known as the genital hiatus which allows the passage of the urethra, vagina, and rectum. The most anterior fasciculi, which are also the most medial, pass in close relation to the prostate and insert into the central tendinous point just in front of the anus. This portion has been called the *Levator prostatæ*. In the female, this anterior portion has a similar relationship to the vagina. The majority of the fasciculi pass horizontally backward beside the anal canal, the superficial ones joining the anococcygeal raphé, the deeper ones joining the muscle of the other side to form a loop or sling about the rectum. This portion is called the *Puborectalis muscle*.

The **Iliococcygeus** arises from the arcus tendineus m. levatoris ani and the spine of the ischium, and inserts into the last two segments of the coccyx and the anococcygeal raphé. Its fasciculi pass medially as well as downward and backward which helps to distinguish them from the fasciculi of the Pubococcygeus.

Action.—Supports and slightly raises the pelvic floor, resisting increased intra-abdominal pressure, as during forced expiration. The Pubococcygeus draws the anus toward the pubis and constricts it.

Nerve.—Branches of the pudendal plexus, containing fibers from the fourth, sometimes also the third or fifth sacral nerves.

Variations.—The degree of distinctness of the Pubococcygeus and Iliococcygeus varies; the latter may be replaced by fibrous tissue.

The **Coccygeus** (Fig. 448) is situated behind the preceding. It is a triangular plane of muscular and tendinous fibers, *arising* by its apex from the spine of the ischium and sacrospinous ligament, and *inserted* by its base into the margin of the coccyx and into the side of the lowest piece of the sacrum. It assists the Levator ani and Piriformis in closing in the back part of the outlet of the pelvis.

Action.—Draws the coccyx forward, supporting the pelvic floor against intra-abdominal pressure.

Nerve.—Branches of the pudendal plexus, containing fibers from the fourth and fifth sacral nerves.

Variations.—The iliosacralis is an occasional band of muscle, ventral to the Coccygeus, attached to the iliopectineal line and the lateral border of the sacrum.

The **Sacrococcygeus ventralis** is a muscular or tendinous slip from the lower sacral vertebræ to the coccyx, representing the vestige of the Depressor caudæ of lower mammals.

The **Sacrococcygeus dorsalis** is a slip from the dorsal aspect of the sacrum to the coccyx.

Pelvic Fascia (*fascia pelvis*).—The **internal investing fascia of the pelvis** covers the Levator ani and Coccygeus and the intrapelvic portions of the Obturator internus and Piriformis muscles. It belongs to the same category of fascia as the endo-abdominal or transversalis and is directly continuous with the latter over the brim of the lesser pelvis where it is attached to or fused with the periosteum of the symphysis and superior ramus of the pubis, the ilium along the arcuate or ilio-pectineal line, and the promontory of the sacrum. From these attachments, it sweeps downward and across the middle line, attaching to the anococcygeal raphé posteriorly and blending with the fasciæ of the anal canal and urogenital structures anteriorly. Although it is a continuous sheet, for convenience in description it is divided into (1) piriformis fascia, (2) obturator fascia and (3) supra-anal fascia.

The **fascia of the Piriformis** is very thin and is attached to the front of the sacrum and the sides of the greater sciatic foramen; it is prolonged outward through the greater sciatic foramen, joins the fascia of the external surface of the muscle at its lower border, and, becoming extrapelvic, forms part of the deep gluteal fascia. At its sacral attachment around the margins of the anterior sacral foramina it comes into intimate association with and ensheathes the nerves emerging from these foramina. Hence the sacral nerves are frequently described as lying behind the fascia. The internal iliac vessels and their branches, on the other hand, lie in the subperitoneal tissue in front of the fascia, and the branches to the gluteal region emerge in special sheaths of this tissue, above and below the Piriformis muscle.

Obturator Fascia (*fascia obturatoria*) (Fig. 448).—The fascia covering the Obtur-ator internus muscle is partly intrapelvic and partly extrapelvic. This condition can best be understood if the intrapelvic portion is pictured as having incorporated in it the aponeurosis of origin of the Levator ani. It is as if the Levator had at one time been attached to the pelvic brim above the Obturator (a condition found in lower primates) but had slipped downward for a variable distance, usually about half the length of the muscle. At this point, the origin of the Levator is visible as a thickened band called the **arcus tendineus musculi levatoris ani.** Posteriorly, the arcus always ends by attaching to the spine of the ischium; anteriorly, it varies, but usually attaches to the anterior margin of the obturator membrane or the pubic bone medial to it. Since the Levator closes the aperture of the pelvis, the arcus marks the boundary between the intra- and extrapelvic portions of the obturator fascia. The intrapelvic portion usually is not aponeurotic in appearance and may be quite thin except at the arcus tendineus. Anteriorly, the obturator fascia is attached to the upper border of the obturator membrane or the pubic bone just in front of the obturator canal. It forms a tubular investment for the obturator nerve and vessels as they leave the pelvis through the obturator canal. Above, its attachment to the bone gradually angles upward from the obturator membrane until it reaches the iliopectineal line near the sacroiliac articulation. Posteriorly, it is attached to the margin of the greater sciatic notch down to the spine of the ischium. At the arcus tendineus of the Levator ani, the obturator fascia splits into three sheets; the outer one continues as the extrapelvic obturator fascia, the other two cover the external and internal surfaces of the pelvic diaphragm. The extrapelvic portion of the obturator fascia follows the muscle downward into the ischiorectal fossa and will be described with the perineum.

The **Supra-anal Fascia** (*fascia diaphragmatis pelvis superior*) (Fig. 449) covers the internal surface of the Levator ani and Coccygeus muscles. Anteriorly, above

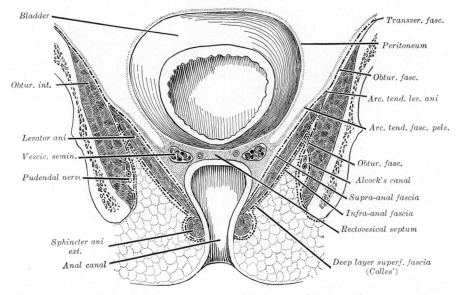

Fig. 449.—Fasciæ of pelvis and anal region of perineum. Diagram of coronal section.

the Pubococcygeus part of the Levator, it is attached to the pubic bone. Laterally, above the Iliococcygeus, it is continuous with the intrapelvic obturator fascia at the arcus tendineus of the Levator ani. Posteriorly, it covers the Coccygeus and becomes continuous with the fascia of the Piriformis. Behind the rectum, the fascia of the two sides is continuous across the middle line over the anococcygeal raphé. In front of the rectum, in the genital hiatus where the medial borders of the Pubococcygei of the two sides do not meet, the supra-anal fascia joins the infra-anal fascia to assist in the formation of the deep layer of the urogenital diaphragm. (See perineum).

Subserous Fascia (*tela subserosa*) (Fig. 450).—The subserous fascia of the pelvis not only covers the parietal wall and the viscera, but also acts as a padding tissue for the viscera in the lower part of the pelvis. It forms important ligaments, folds, and bands which are described in the chapter dealing with the pelvic viscera.

VI. THE FASCIÆ AND MUSCLES OF THE PERINEUM.

The perineum corresponds to the outlet of the pelvis. Its deep boundaries are—in *front*, the pubic arch and the arcuate ligament of the pubis; *behind*, the tip of the coccyx; and on either side the inferior rami of the pubis and ischium, and the sacrotuberous ligament. The space is somewhat lozenge-shaped and is limited on the surface of the body by the scrotum in front, by the buttocks behind, and laterally by the medial side of the thigh. A line drawn transversely across in front of the ischial tuberosities divides the space into two portions. The posterior contains the termination of the anal canal and is known as the **anal region**; the anterior, which contains the external urogenital organs, is termed the **urogenital region.**

The Superficial Fascia (*tela subcutanea, fascia superficialis perinei*).—The superficial fascia of the perineum is divisible into two layers, superficial and deep, which are similar to and continuous with the corresponding layers of the anterior abdom-

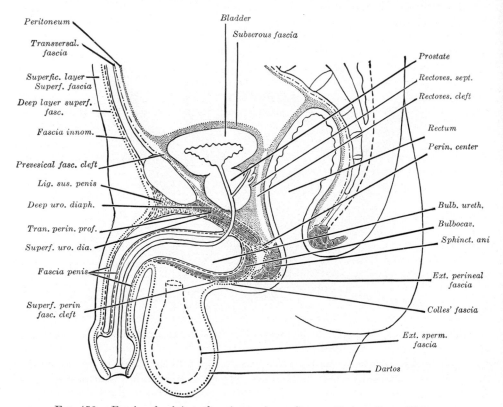

Fig. 450.—Fasciæ of pelvis and perineum in median sagittal section. Diagram.

inal wall. The deep layer is called the fascia of Colles instead of Scarpa. The superficial layer, corresponding to Camper's fascia, usually is not specifically named, although it has been called Cruveilhier's fascia.

The **superficial layer of superficial fascia** in the anterior part of the perineum, that is, over the urogenital region, contains a considerable amount of adipose tissue and is likely to be irregularly laminated. Anteriorly, in the groove between the scrotum and the thigh, it is directly continuous with the corresponding layer (Camper's fascia) on the anterior abdominal wall. More medially, it is combined with the deep layer into the dartos tunic of the scrotum in the male, while in the female, it forms the greater part of the labium majus. Laterally, it is continuous with the superficial layer of the thigh. Posteriorly, it becomes the superficial layer of the anal region.

The superficial layer in the anal region is greatly thickened into a mass of fat which occupies the ischiorectal fossa. It is continuous posteriorly with the superficial fascia of the gluteal region and posterior thigh. Over the ischial tuberosities, the fibrous tissue is increased in amount, forming a tough pad.

Ischiorectal Fossa (*fossa ischiorectalis*) (Fig. 451).—The fossa is somewhat prismatic, in the shape of a wedge, with its base at the perineum and its apex deep in the pelvis where the Levator ani and Obturator internus come together. It is bounded medially, by the infra-anal fascia covering the Levator ani and Sphincter ani externus; laterally, by the obturator fascia over the extrapelvic portion of the Obturator internus, and by the tuberosity of the ischium; anteriorly, by the posterior borders of the Transversus perinæi superficialis and profundus; posteriorly, by the fascia over the Glutæus maximus and the sacrotuberous ligament. The superficial boundary is the skin, and the fossa is occupied by a mass of adipose tissue belonging to the superficial layer of the superficial fascia. The superficial and deep layers of the superficial fascia are not separable in the fossa and both are securely attached to the deep fascia covering the entire surface of the fossa. The posterior portion of the Transversus perinæi profundus is separated from the Levator ani for a short distance, so that the ischiorectal mass of fat has an *anterior process* which projects under the posterior border of the Transversus muscles. The adipose tissue is traversed by fibrous bands and incomplete septa. It is crossed transversely by the inferior hemorrhoidal vessels and nerves; at the back part are the perineal and perforating cutaneous branches of the pudendal plexus; while from the forepart, the posterior scrotal (or labial) vessels and nerves emerge. The internal pudendal vessels and pudendal nerve lie deep to the obturator fascia on the lateral wall of the fossa in a special reduplication of the fascia known as Alcock's canal.

Deep Layer of Superficial Fascia of Perineum (*Colles' fascia*) (Figs. 450, 451, 452).—The deep layer of superficial fascia in the urogenital region of the perineum is a distinctive structure. It is a strong membrane but does not have the white glistening appearance of an aponeurosis. It has a slightly yellow color due to its content of elastic fibers and is smooth in texture, its fibrous nature not being detectable with the naked eye. This characteristic texture is of assistance frequently in differentiating it from the deep fascia in the region. Anteriorly, it is directly continuous with the deep layer of superficial abdominal fascia (Scarpa's fascia) in the groove between the scrotum (labium) and thigh. More medially, it joins the superficial layer in the formation of the **dartos tunic** of the scrotum. In the middle line, it is attached to the superficial fascia along the raphé and continues anteriorly into the **septum of the scrotum**. Laterally, it is firmly adherent to the medial surface of the thigh along the ischiopubic ramus at the origin of the adductor muscles. In the anterior part of this area, it is continuous with the fascia cribrosa which covers the fossa ovalis (saphenous opening). Posteriorly, it dips inward toward the ischiorectal fossa around the posterior border of the Transversus perinæi superficialis and becomes firmly attached to the deep fascia along the posterior border of the Transversus perinæi profundus. It is attached also, with all the other layers, to the central tendinous point of the perineum. There is a distinct fascial cleft between it (Colles' fascia) and the external perineal fascia (deep fascia) (Figs. 450, 452) over the Bulbocavernosus, Ischiocavernosus, and Transversus perinæi superficialis muscles. This **superficial perineal cleft** is continuous with the cleft under Scarpa's fascia on the anterior abdominal wall but is closed off laterally and posteriorly by the attachments described above.

In the anal region, the deep layer of the superficial fascia is adherent both to the superficial layer and to the deep fascia. From its attachment to the posterior border of the Transversus perinæi profundus mentioned above, it continues deeply into the ischiorectal fossa in close apposition to the infra-anal fascia on the Levator ani muscle. At the origin of this muscle, it folds back sharply over the extrapelvic portion of the obturator fascia. Posteriorly, it leaves the ischiorectal fossa along the border of the gluteal region and posterior thigh.

Deep Fascia.—The deep fascia of the perineum consists of the obturator fascia, the infra-anal fascia, and the fasciæ over two groups of small muscles which are associated with the urogenital organs and occupy a position superficial to the pelvic diaphragm in the urogenital region of the perineum. The phenomena of splitting,

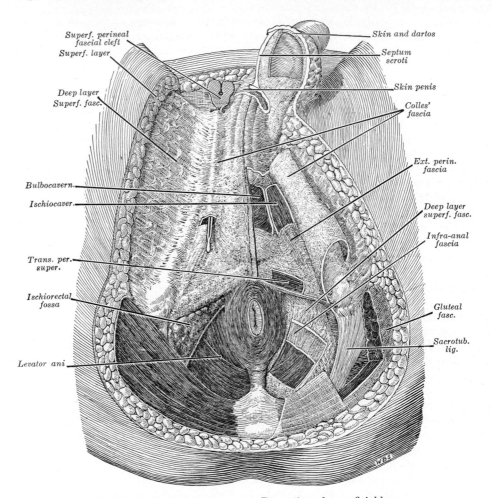

Fig. 451.—Fasciæ of perineum. Dissection of superficial layers.

fusion, and cleavage are prominent features of the fascia in this region. The clinical interest and importance of these fasciæ have made them the subject of numerous treatises in which the various parts are segregated and given special names. In the following description these parts will be considered individually but an attempt will be made to correlate the diverse terminology into a consistent description. A certain amount of repetition will be unavoidable.

Obturator Fascia (*fascia obturatoria*) (Fig. 450).—The fascia covering the extra-pelvic portion of the Obturator internus forms the lateral wall of the ischiorectal fossa, and is, therefore, a portion of the external investing layer of deep fascia of the body. Above, it meets the infra-anal fascia at a sharp angle in the deepest part of the fossa. Its inferior portion, extending from the lesser sciatic foramen to the ischial tuberosity, is thickened and splits to enclose the pudendal nerve and internal pudendal vessels in a fibrous tunnel called **Alcock's canal**. Anteriorly, it is attached to the ischiopubic ramus, and the fibrous sheath of Alcock's canal merges with the external perineal fascia and the superficial fascia of the urogenital diaphragm where branches of the nerve and vessels enter the superficial and deep perineal compartments described below.

The **Infra-anal Fascia** (*fascia diaphragmatis pelvis inferior*) (Fig. 450).—The infra-anal fascia is the deep fascia of the superficial (inferior, external) surface of the Levator ani and Coccygeus muscles. It is adherent to the muscle throughout. Above, the portion on the Iliococcygeus is continuous with the extra-pelvic obturator fascia at the arcus tendineus of the Levator ani; the portion over the Pubococcygeus is attached to the ischiopubic ramus and the pubic bone at the origin of the muscle. Between the medial borders of the two Pubococcygei, it joins the supra-anal fascia to form a thick sheet in the genital hiatus. Behind the rectum, it is continuous from side to side over the anococcygeal raphé where it is firmly attached. More posteriorly and laterally, it bridges the slight interval between the Levator ani and Coccygeus, and then binds the latter muscle to the lower edge of the sacrospinous ligament. From this ligament, it passes outward from the ischiorectal fossa along the overhanging lower border of the Glutæus maximus where it becomes continuous with the gluteal fascia. In the region of the anus, it invests the Sphincter ani externus and just anterior to the anus, it is firmly attached to the other perineal layers at the central tendinous point.

If the infra-anal fascia is traced forward from the ischiorectal fossa, it will be seen to split into three sheets at a transverse line connecting the anterior extremities of the ischial tuberosities. The deepest of the three continues on the surface of the Levator ani, and, lying between this muscle and the Transversus perinæi profundus, it is called the deep layer of the urogenital diaphragm. This is the sheet which joins the supra-anal fascia in the genital hiatus to form the thick membrane which binds the two medial borders of the Pubococcygei together. The middle sheet covers the superficial surface of the Transversus profundus and is called the superficial layer of the urogenital diaphragm. The most superficial of the three sheets curves outward around the posterior border of the Transversus perinæi superficialis and is the external perineal fascia.

The **Urogenital Diaphragm** (*diaphragma urogenitale*).—The Transversus perinæi profundus muscle is covered internally and externally by fascial membranes which are called respectively the deep and superficial layers of the urogenital diaphragm. The muscle and the two fasciæ taken together constitute the urogenital diaphragm. According to this, it is synonymous with the deep perineal compartment (pouch, interspace) and its contents, which will be described below. The urogenital diaphragm, as it has just been defined, is assisted in its rôle of a supporting structure by the portion of the Levator ani over which it lies and by the superficial perineal muscles and their fasciæ.

The **Genital Hiatus** is the interval in the middle line between the medial borders of the two Pubococcygeus portions of the Levator ani muscle. It is through this hiatus that the urethra passes in both sexes and the vagina in the female. It is filled in by fibrous tissue derived from the fascia of the Levator ani (the supra-anal and infra-anal fasciæ) and the deep layer of the urogenital diaphragm.

The **Deep** (*superior; internal*) **Layer of the Urogenital Diaphragm** (*fascia diaphragmatis urogenitalis superior*) is a flat triangular membrane stretching across the interval between the ischiopubic rami. It lies between the Transversus perinæi profundus and the Pubococcygeus portions of the Levator ani and represents, therefore, the fused fascial membranes of both these muscles. It represents also, in the genital hiatus between the medial borders of the two Pubococcygei, a fusion with still a third membrane, the supra-anal fascia. It is securely attached to the symphysis pubis anteriorly and joins the other perineal layers in the central tendinous point posteriorly. Laterally, it is attached to the medial borders of the ischiopubic rami along with the superficial layer of the diaphragm and there it is continuous with the obturator fascia. The middle portion, which occupies the genital hiatus, is thickened to fill in the gap between the two Pubococcygei and bind their medial borders together. It is pierced by the urethra and the vagina and blends with their walls as they pass through. The prostate gland rests on its pelvic surface and the connective tissue of the inferior portion of the gland's capsule blends with it intimately. The attachment of the fascia to the pubic bone and the blending with the prostatic capsule make the anterior part of the fascia a true **ligament of the prostate.** The tissue attachments may form three strands, a **middle puboprostatic**

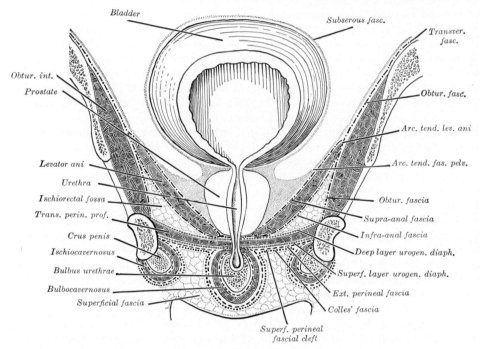

FIG. 452.—Fasciæ of pelvis and urogenital region of perineum. Diagram of coronal section.

ligament to the symphysis and two **lateral puboprostatic ligaments** to the pubic bone at the points where the anterior ends of the arcus tendinei of the Levatores ani are attached. At the posterior border of the deep Transversus, it is fused with the superficial layer of the urogenital diaphragm, closing the deep perineal compartment.

The **Superficial** (*inferior, external*) **Layer of the Urogenital Diaphragm** (*fascia diaphragmatis urogenitalis inferior*) (Figs. 450, 452) is a flat triangular membrane which, like the preceding, bridges the angular interval between the ischiopubic rami. It is attached laterally to the medial borders of the rami from the arcuate pubic ligament to the ischial tuberosities. Along these same borders, the deep layer of the diaphragm is attached more deeply and the crura of the penis more superficially. The middle portion of the fascia is pierced by the urethra and vagina and blends with their walls. It is perforated also by the arteries to the bulb, the ducts of the bulbourethral glands, the deep arteries of the penis, and the dorsal arteries and nerves of the penis. The part posterior to the urethra blends with the fascia of the bulb and, because of its attachment to the rami laterally, is sometimes called the **ligament of the bulb.** At these lateral attachments, the fascia blends with that of the crura also. The part anterior to the urethra arches across the sub-pubic angle and is sometimes called the **ligmæntum transversum pelvis.** The latter is separated from the symphysis and arcuate pubic ligament by an opening for the passage of the dorsal vein of the penis. At the posterior border of the deep Transversus muscle, the superficial and deep layers of the diaphragm fuse into a single layer and blend with the infra-anal fascia of the ischiorectal fossa.

The **External Perineal Fascia** (*inferior perineal fascia of Gallaudet*) (Figs. 451, 452) is the external investing fascia, that is, the most superficial layer of the deep fascia in the urogenital region of the perineum. It covers approximately the same tri-angular area as the preceding but it is not flat because it must accommodate itself to the contours of the superficial perineal muscles. It is attached laterally to the ischiopubic ramus at the outer border of the Ischiocavernosus. From this attach-ment it passes anteriorly along the groove between the scrotum and thigh, there becoming continuous with the external oblique fascia (fascia innominata) of the anterior abdominal wall and, more laterally, with the fascia lata of the medial surface of the thigh. It invests the Ischiocavernosus and Bulbocavernosus muscles and, in the interval between them, dips down to the level of the superficial layer of the urogenital diaphragm for a short distance and is there adherent to it. It follows the muscles just mentioned forward to the root of the penis and, at their insertion, it joins the fascia of the crura and bulb to become the **deep fascia of the penis** (*Buck's fascia*). Posteriorly, the fascia invests the Transversus perinæi superficialis. It passes deeply around the posterior border of this muscle into the ischiorectal fossa until it meets the deep Transversus where the two Transversi are in contact with each other. Here it fuses with the fascia of the urogenital diaphragm, and with it blends into the single layer of infra-anal fascia in the ischio-rectal fossa. The fusion of this fascia with the fascia of the urogenital diaphragm posteriorly, its attachment to the ischiopubic rami laterally, and its fusion with the fascia of the penis anteriorly make it the superficial layer of a closed compart-ment, the superficial perineal compartment (pouch, interspace). The deep layer of the compartment is the superficial layer of the urogenital diaphragm. The fascial cleft which is superficial to the external perineal fascia, that is, which lies between it and Colles' fascia, should not be included in the compartment.

The **Perineal Center** is often called the **central tendinous point** (Fig. 450) in the male and often simply the perineum in the female. It is the mass of tissue in the middle line between the anus and the bulb in the male and between the anus and vagina in the female. It is approximately 2 cm. in width and depth in the male and about twice this dimension in the female. It is composed predominantly of fibrous tissue since it represents the fusion of the following: infra-anal fascia (deep layer of the urogenital diaphragm), superficial layer of the urogenital diaphragm, external perineal fascia, and Colles' fascia. It contains a few muscular fibers also, principally from the Pubococcygeus and Sphincter ani externus, and it has attached to it besides these two muscles, the Transversus perinæi profundus and superficialis, and the Bulbocavernosus. It is directly continuous anteriorly with the fibrous tissue which fills in the genital hiatus between the two Pubococcygei. It is con-tinuous deeply into the pelvis with the rectoprostatic and rectovesical septum in the male and the rectovaginal septum in the female. It is the time honored route of approach to the bladder and prostate from the perineum and it is the site of the perineal tears which are frequently a result of child bearing.

The **Triangular Ligament** is a name frequently given to the urogenital diaphragm, that is, the Transversus perinæi profundus and its superficial and deep fascial membranes. The name is less commonly used for the superficial fascia of the uro-genital diaphragm alone, without the muscle or the other fascia.

The **Deep Perineal Compartment** (*deep perineal pouch; deep perineal interspace*) is formed by the deep and superficial layers of the urogenital diaphragm. The compartment and its contents, therefore, form the urogenital diaphragm. The compartment is principally occupied by the Transversus perinæi profundus but contains also: the Sphincter urethræ membranaceæ and the membranous portion of the urethra; the bulbourethral glands (vestibular glands in the female) and their ducts; the internal pudendal vessels; the deep dorsal vein of the penis, and the dorsal nerve of the penis. The internal pudendal artery enters the compartment posteriorly and its branches to the bulb, to the urethra, the deep and the dorsal arteries of the penis, pierce the superficial fascia of the urogenital diaphragm to reach their destination.

The **Superficial Perineal Compartment** (*pouch; interspace*) is bounded by the superficial layer of the urogenital diaphragm and the external perineal fascia. It contains the Bulbocavernosus, Ischiocavernosus, and Transversus perinæi superficialis muscles, and is traversed by the perineal vessels and nerve. The usual description of this compartment, in which Colles' fascia forms the superficial boundary, is erroneous. The superficial boundary is a layer of deep fascia, the external investing perineal fascia (inferior perineal fascia, Gallaudet). There is a distinct **superficial perineal fascial cleft** between the latter and Colles' fascia (Figs. 450, 452).

Clinical Considerations.—The fascial cleft between the external perineal fascia and Colles' fascia has long been included erroneously in the superficial perineal pouch. When extravasated urine or hemorrhage finds its way into the tissue under Colles' fascia, it is not in the pouch but in the fascial cleft superficial to it. If it were in the pouch, it would infiltrate the superficial muscles and be restricted in its spread to the area covered by these muscles. Clinical experience has shown that it actually does spread along the groove between the scrotum and thigh to the anterior abdominal wall in the fascial cleft under Scarpa's fascia and into the scrotum and penis in the fascial cleft under the dartos. The spread is restricted posteriorly by the termination of the fascial cleft where Colles' fascia is attached to the infra-anal fascia at the posterior border of the Transversus perinæi profundus muscle, and laterally where it is attached to the fascia lata.

The muscles of the perineum may be divided into two groups:

1. Those of the urogenital region: A, In the male; B, In the female.
2. Those of the anal region.

1. A. The Muscles of the Urogenital Region in the Male (Fig. 453).

Superficial Group:
Transversus perinæi superficialis.
Bulbocavernosus.
Ischiocavernosus.

Deep Group:
Transversus perinæi profundus.
Sphincter urethræ membranaceæ.

The **Transversus perinæi superficialis** (*Transversus perinæi; Superficial transverse perineal muscle*) is a narrow muscular slip, which passes more or less transversely across the perineal space in front of the anus. It *arises* by tendinous fibers from the inner and forepart of the tuberosity of the ischium, and, running medialward, is inserted into the central tendinous point of the perineum, joining in this situation with the muscle of the opposite side, with the Sphincter ani externus behind, and with the Bulbocavernosus in front. In some cases, the fibers of the deeper layer of the Sphincter ani externus decussate in front of the anus and are continued into this muscle. Occasionally it gives off fibers, which join with the Bulbocavernosus of the same side.

Actions.—The simultaneous contraction of the two muscles serves to fix the central tendinous point of the perineum.

Variations are numerous. It may be absent or double, or insert into Bulbocavernosus or External sphincter.

The **Bulbocavernosus** (*Ejaculator urinæ; Accelerator urinæ*) is placed in the middle line of the perineum, in front of the anus. It consists of two symmetrical parts, united along the median line by a tendinous raphé. It *arises* from the cen-

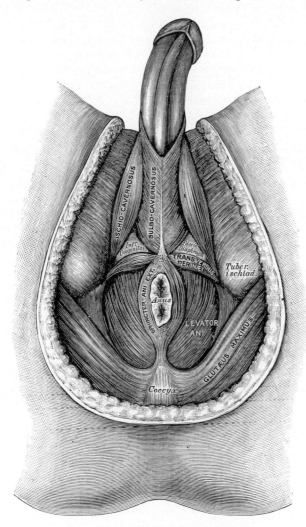

Fig. 453.—Muscles of male perineum.

tral tendinous point of the perineum and from the median raphé in front. Its fibers diverge like the barbs of a feather; the most posterior form a thin layer, which is lost on the superficial fascia of the urogenital diaphragm; the middle fibers encircle the bulk and adjacent parts of the corpus cavernosum urethræ, and join with the fibers of the opposite side, on the upper part of the corpus cavernosum urethræ, in a strong aponeurosis; the anterior fibers spread out over the side of the corpus cavernosum penis to be inserted partly into that body, anterior to the Ischiocavernosus, occasionally extending to the pubis, and partly ending in a tendinous expansion which covers the dorsal vessels of the penis. The latter fibers are best seen by dividing the muscle longitudinally, and reflecting it from the surface of the corpus cavernosum urethræ.

Actions.—This muscle serves to empty the canal of the urethra, after the bladder has expelled its contents; during the greater part of the act of micturition its fibers are relaxed, and it only comes into action at the end of the process. The middle fibers are supposed by Krause to assist in the erection of the corpus cavernosum urethræ, by compressing the erectile tissue of the bulb. The anterior fibers, according to Tyrrel, also contribute to the erection of the penis by compressing the deep dorsal vein of the penis as they are inserted into, and continuous with, the fascia of the penis.

The **Ischiocavernosus** (*Erector penis*) covers the crus penis. It is an elongated muscle, broader in the middle than at either end, and situated on the lateral boundary of the perineum. It *arises* by tendinous and fleshy fibers from the inner surface of the tuberosity of the ischium, behind the crus penis; and from the rami of the pubis and ischium on either side of the crus. From these points, fleshy fibers proceed, and end in an aponeurosis which is *inserted* into the sides and under surface of the crus penis.

Action.—The Ischiocavernosus compresses the crus penis, and retards the return of the blood through the veins, and thus serves to maintain the organ erect.

The **Transversus perinæi profundus** *arises* from the inferior rami of the ischium and runs to the median line, where it interlaces in a tendinous raphé with its fellow of the opposite side. It lies in the same plane as the Sphincter urethræ membranaceæ; formerly the two muscles were described together as the **Constrictor urethræ.**

The **Sphincter urethræ membranaceæ** surrounds the whole length of the membranous portion of the urethra, and is enclosed in the fasciæ of the urogenital diaphragm. Its *external* fibers *arise* from the junction of the inferior rami of the pubis and ischium to the extent of 1.25 to 2 cm., and from the neighboring fasciæ. They arch across the front of the urethra and bulbourethral glands, pass around the urethra, and behind it unite with the muscle of the opposite side, by means of a tendinous raphé. Its *innermost* fibers form a continuous circular investment for the membranous urethra.

Actions.—The muscles of both sides act together as a sphincter, compressing the membranous portion of the urethra. During the transmission of fluids they, like the Bulbocavernosus, are relaxed, and only come into action at the end of the process to eject the last drops of the fluid.

Nerve Supply.—The perineal branch of the pudendal nerve supplies this group of muscles.

1. B. The Muscles of the Urogenital Region in the Female (Fig. 454).

Transversus perinæi superficialis.   Ischiocavernosus.
Bulbocavernosus.   Transversus perinæi profundus.
                    Sphincter urethræ membranaceæ.

The **Transversus perinæi superficialis** (*Transversus perinæi; Superficial transverse perineal muscle*) in the female is a narrow muscular slip, which *arises* by a small tendon from the inner and forepart of the tuberosity of the ischium, and is inserted into the central tendinous point of the perineum, joining in this situation with the muscle of the opposite side, the Sphincter ani externus behind, and the Bulbocavernosus in front.

Action.—The simultaneous contraction of the two muscles serves to fix the central tendinous point of the perineum.

The **Bulbocavernosus** (*Sphincter vaginæ*) surrounds the orifice of the vagina. It covers the lateral parts of the vestibular bulbs, and is attached posteriorly to the central tendinous point of the perineum, where it blends with the Sphincter ani externus. Its fibers pass forward on either side of the vagina to be inserted into the corpora cavernosa clitoridis, a fasciculus crossing over the body of the organ so as to compress the deep dorsal vein.

Actions.—The Bulbocavernosus diminishes the orifice of the vagina. The anterior fibers contribute to the erection of the clitoris, as they are inserted into and are continuous with the fascia of the clitoris, compressing the deep dorsal vein during the contraction of the muscle.

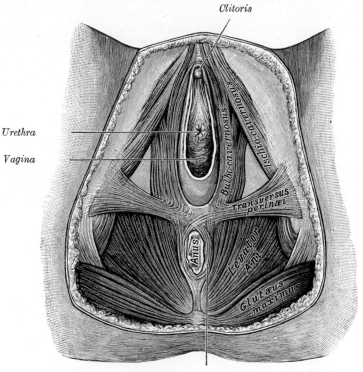

FIG. 454.—Muscles of the female perineum. (Modified from a drawing by Peter Thompson.)

The **Ischiocavernosus** (*Erector clitoridis*) is smaller than the corresponding muscle in the male. It covers the unattached surface of the crus clitoridis. It is an elongated muscle, broader at the middle than at either end, and situated on the side of the lateral boundary of the perineum. It *arises* by tendinous and fleshy fibers from the inner surface of the tuberosity of the ischium, behind the crus clitoridis; from the surface of the crus; and from the adjacent portion of the ramus of the ischium. From these points fleshy fibers succeed, and end in an aponeurosis, which is inserted into the sides and under surface of the crus clitoridis.

Actions.—The Ischiocavernosus compresses the crus clitoridis and retards the return of blood through the veins, and thus serves to maintain the organ erect.

The **fascia of the urogenital diaphragm** in the female is not so strong as in the male. It is attached to the pubic arch, its apex being connected with the arcuate pubic ligament. It is divided in the middle line by the aperture of the vagina, with the external coat of which it becomes blended, and in front of this is perforated by the urethra. Its posterior border is continuous, as in the male, with the deep layer of the superficial fascia around the Transversus perinæi superficialis.

Like the corresponding fascia in the male, it consists of two layers, between which are to be found the following structures: the deep dorsal vein of the clitoris, a portion of the urethra and the Constrictor urethrae muscle, the larger vestibular

31

glands and their ducts; the internal pudendal vessels and the dorsal nerves of the clitoris; the arteries and nerves of the bulbi vestibuli, and a plexus of veins.

The **Transversus perinæi profundus** *arises* from the inferior rami of the ischium and runs across to the side of the vagina. The Sphincter urethræ membranaceæ (*Constrictor urethræ*), like the corresponding muscle on the male, consists of external and internal fibers. The *external* fibers arise on either side from the margin of the inferior ramus of the pubis. They are directed across the pubic arch in front of the urethra, and pass around it to blend with the muscular fibers of the opposite side, between the urethra and vagina. The *innermost* fibers encircle the lower end of the urethra.

Nerve Supply.—The muscles of this group are supplied by the perineal branch of the pudendal.

2. The Muscles of the Anal Region.

Corrugator cutis ani.   Sphincter ani externus.   Sphincter ani internus.

The Corrugator Cutis Ani.—Around the anus is a thin stratum of involuntary muscular fiber, which radiates from the orifice. *Medially* the fibers fade off into the submucous tissue, while *laterally* they blend with the true skin. By its contraction it raises the skin into ridges around the margin of the anus.

The **Sphincter ani externus** (*External sphincter ani*) (Fig. 454) is a flat plane of muscular fibers, elliptical in shape and intimately adherent to the integument surrounding the margin of the anus. It measures about 8 to 10 cm. in length, from its anterior to its posterior extremity, and is about 2.5 cm. broad opposite the anus. It consists of two strata, superficial and deep. The *superficial*, constituting the main portion of the muscle, arises from a narrow tendinous band, the **anococcygeal raphé**, which stretches from the tip of the coccyx to the posterior margin of the anus; it forms two flattened planes of muscular tissue, which encircle the anus and meet in front to be inserted into the central tendinous point of the perineum, joining with the Transversus perinæi superficialis, the Levator ani, and the Bulbocavernosus. The *deeper portion* forms a complete sphincter to the anal canal. Its fibers surround the canal, closely applied to the Sphincter ani internus, and in front blend with the other muscles at the central point of the perineum. In a considerable proportion of cases the fibers decussate in front of the anus, and are continuous with the Transversi perinæi superficiales. Posteriorly, they are not attached to the coccyx, but are continuous with those of the opposite side behind the anal canal. The upper edge of the muscle is ill-defined, since fibers are given off from it to join the Levator ani.

Actions.—The action of this muscle is peculiar. (1) It is, like other muscles, always in a state of tonic contraction, and having no antagonistic muscle it keeps the anal canal and orifice closed. (2) It can be put into a condition of greater contraction under the influence of the will, so as more firmly to occlude the anal aperture, in expiratory efforts unconnected with defecation. (3) Taking its fixed point at the coccyx, it helps to fix the central point of the perineum, so that the Bulbocavernosus may act from this fixed point.

Nerve Supply.—A branch from the fourth sacral and twigs from the inferior hemorrhoidal branch of the pudendal supply the muscle.

The **Sphincter ani internus** (*Internal sphincter ani*) is a muscular ring which surrounds about 2.5 cm. of the anal canal; its inferior border is in contact with, but quite separate from, the Sphincter ani externus. It is about 5 mm. thick, and is formed by an aggregation of the involuntary circular fibers of the intestine. Its lower border is about 6 mm. from the orifice of the anus.

Actions.—Its action is entirely involuntary. It helps the Sphincter ani externus to occlude the anal aperture and aids in the expulsion of the feces.

THE MUSCLES AND FASCIÆ OF THE UPPER EXTREMITY.

The muscles of the upper extremity are divisible into groups, corresponding with the different regions of the limb.

I. Muscles Connecting the Upper Extremity to the Vertebral Column.
II. Muscles Connecting the Upper Extremity to the Anterior and Lateral Thoracic Walls.
III. Muscles of the Shoulder.
IV. Muscles of the Arm.
V. Muscles of the Forearm.
VI. Muscles of the Hand.

I. THE MUSCLES CONNECTING THE UPPER EXTREMITY TO THE VERTEBRAL COLUMN.

Trapezius.
Latissimus dorsi.
Levator scapulæ.
Rhomboideus major.
Rhomboideus minor.

The **Superficial Fascia** (*tela subcutanea*) of the back is a thick fibrous and fatty layer which extends from the scalp to the gluteal region as a comparatively uniform sheet. At the sides of the neck and trunk, it gradually changes into the thinner or softer fascia of the ventral regions. The dermal fibrous layer is thick, and is bound down to the deeper layers by numerous heavy bands and septa which divide the fat into small granular lobules, and mattress the entire layer into a tough, resilient pad. The fascial cleft, usually present between the superficial and deep fascia, is lacking in the dorsal area, making the superficial fascia firmer and less movable than in the ventral area.

Deep Fascia.—The **investing layer of deep fascia** is attached in the middle line to the ligamentum nuchæ, the supraspinal ligament, and to the spinous processes of all vertebræ caudal to the sixth cervical. It splits to enclose the Trapezius and the fleshy portion of the Latissimus dorsi, but in the neck, it covers the posterior triangle as a single layer, and there becomes continuous with the anterior cervical fascia. It is attached, over the shoulder, to the acromion and spine of the scapula, and is then continuous with the deltoid fascia. Laterally from the Latissimus, it is continuous with the axillary fascia and the fascia covering the Obliquus abdominis externus. Over the fleshy portions of the Trapezius and Latissimus, it is gray and felt-like, but strong and adherent both to the superficial fascia and to the muscles. In the triangular area between the Trapezius, Deltoideus, and Latissimus it is white and glistening, forming the aponeurosis of the Infraspinatus. In the lumbar region it is greatly strengthened by having incorporated in it the aponeurosis of origin of the Latissimus dorsi. This portion is called the lumbar aponeurosis or the posterior layer of the lumbodorsal fascia (page 440).

The fascia of the deep surface of the Trapezius is thickened by an accumulation of adipose tissue similar to that under the Pectoralis major. It contains the branches of the superficial cervical and transverse cervical arteries, and the accessory nerve. It is separated from the underlying structures by a distinct fascial cleft. The fascia of the deep surface of the fleshy portion of the Latissimus is similar to that of the Trapezius, but over the aponeurosis it loses its identity as a separate layer, and is fused with the lumbodorsal fascia.

The Rhomboidei and the Levator scapulæ are enclosed in their own proper fascial sheaths which are attached to the vertebræ and to the vertebral border of the scapula. The fascia of the superficial surface, after attaching to the border of the scapula, continues laterally as the supra and infraspinatus fasciæ. That of the deep surface continues laterally on the deep surface of the Serratus anterior. A distinct fascial cleft separates both superficial and deep surfaces of the Rhomboidei

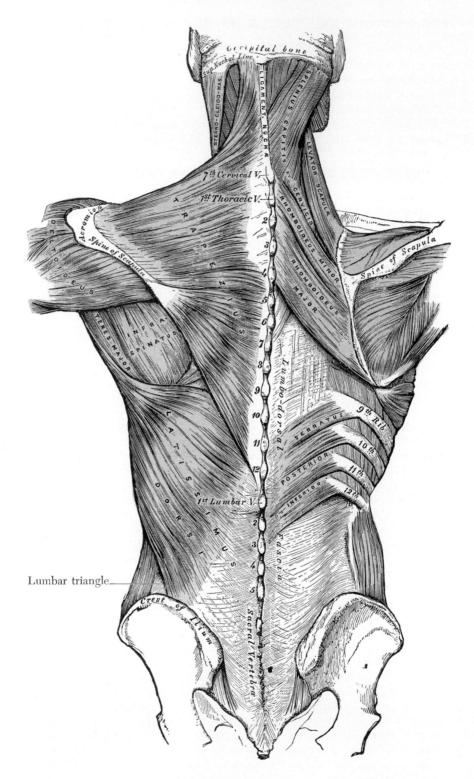

Fig. 455.—Muscles connecting the upper extremity to the vertebral column.

from contiguous structures. The fascia of the Levator is more adherent to surrounding structures and is continuous with the scalenus fascia in the posterior
triangle of the neck. In the interval between the superior and the inferior Serrati
posteriores, it is possible to dissect out a thin membrane which lies in the same
plane as these muscles, but distinct from the fascia of the underlying Sacrospinalis
and the overlying Latissimus and Rhomboidei. This may represent the vestige
of a continuous Serratus muscle like that found in some lower animals.

The **Trapezius** (Fig. 455) is a flat, triangular muscle, covering the upper and
back part of the neck and shoulders. It *arises* from the external occipital protuberance and the medial third of the superior nuchal line of the occipital bone, from
the ligamentum nuchæ, the spinous process of the seventh cervical, and the spinous
processes of all the thoracic vertebræ, and from the corresponding portion of the
supraspinal ligament. From this origin, the superior fibers proceed downward
and lateralward, the inferior upward and lateralward, and the middle horizontally;
the superior fibers are *inserted* into the posterior border of the lateral third of the
clavicle; the middle fibers into the medial margin of the acromion, and into the superior lip of the posterior border of the spine of the scapula; the inferior fibers converge near the scapula, and end in an aponeurosis, which glides over the smooth
triangular surface on the medial end of the spine, to be inserted into a tubercle
at the apex of this smooth triangular surface. At its occipital origin, the Trapezius
is connected to the bone by a thin fibrous lamina, firmly adherent to the skin.
At the middle it is connected to the spinous processes by a broad semi-elliptical
aponeurosis, which reaches from the sixth cervical to the third thoracic vertebra,
and forms, with that of the opposite muscle, a tendinous ellipse. The rest of the
muscle arises by numerous short tendinous fibers. The two Trapezius muscles
together resemble a trapezium, or diamond-shaped quadrangle: two angles corresponding to the shoulders; a third to the occipital protuberance; and the fourth
to the spinous process of the twelfth thoracic vertebra.

Action.—All parts, acting together, rotate the scapula, raising the point of the shoulder in full
abduction and flexion of the arm. They also adduct the scapula, that is, draw it medially toward
the vertebral column. The upper part acting alone, draws the scapula upward, bracing the shoulder. The lower part acting alone, draws the scapula downward. The upper part of one side draws
the head toward the same side, and turns the face to the opposite side; both sides together draw
the head directly backward.

Nerve.—The spinal accessory (spinal part of eleventh cranial) nerve and branches from the
ventral primary divisions of the third and fourth cervical nerves.

Variations.—The attachments to the thoracic vertebræ are often reduced, the lower ones being
absent. The occipital attachment may be small or wanting. The clavicular attachment may be
reduced, but is more often increased, and may cover the posterior triangle. The cervical and
thoracic portions may be separate. The muscles of the two sides are seldom symmetrical, and
complete absence has been described. Aberrant bundles are not uncommon.

The **Latissimus dorsi** (Fig. 455) is a large triangular muscle which covers the
lumbar and lower half of the posterior thoracic region. Its *origin* is principally in
a broad aponeurosis, the lumbar aponeurosis (posterior layer of the lumbodorsal
fascia, see page 440), by means of which it is attached to the spinous processes of
the lower six thoracic, the lumbar, and the sacral vertebræ, to the supraspinal
ligament, and to the posterior part of the crest of the ilium. It also *arises* by muscular fasciculi from the external lip of the crest of the ilium lateral to the margin
of the Sacrospinalis, and from the lower three or four ribs by fleshy digitations which
are interposed between similar processes of the Obliquus externus abdominis
(Fig. 441). From this extensive origin, the fasciculi converge toward the shoulder;
those of the upper part are almost horizontal, and, as they pass over the inferior
angle of the scapula, are joined by additional fasciculi arising from this bone.
The muscle curves around the lower border of the Teres major, and is twisted
upon itself, so that the superior fibers become at first posterior and then inferior,

and the vertical fibers at first anterior and then superior. It ends in a quadrilateral tendon, about 7 cm. long, which passes in front of the tendon of the Teres major, and is *inserted* into the bottom of the intertubercular groove of the humerus; its insertion extends higher on the humerus than that of the tendon of the Pectoralis major. The lower border of its tendon is united with that of the Teres major, the surfaces of the two being separated near their insertions by a bursa; another bursa is sometimes interposed between the muscle and the inferior angle of the scapula. The tendon of the muscle gives off an expansion to the deep fascia of the arm.

Action.—Extends, adducts, and rotates the arm medially; draws the shoulder downward and backward.

Nerve.—The thoracodorsal (long subscapular) nerve from the brachial plexus, containing fibers from the sixth, seventh and eighth cervical nerves.

Variations.—The number of thoracic vertebræ to which it is attached varies from four to seven or eight; the number of costal attachments varies; muscle fibers may or may not reach the crest of the ilium.

A muscular slip, the **axillary arch,** varying from 7 to 10 cm. in length, and from 5 to 15 mm. in breadth, occasionally springs from the upper edge of the Latissimus dorsi about the middle of the posterior fold of the axilla, and crosses the axilla in front of the axillary vessels and nerves, to join the under surface of the tendon of the Pectoralis major, the Coracobrachialis, or the fascia over the Biceps brachii. This axillary arch crosses the axillary artery, just above the spot usually selected for the application of a ligature, and may mislead the surgeon during the operation. It is present in about 7 per cent. of subjects and may be easily recognized by the transverse direction of its fibers.

A fibrous slip usually passes from the lower border of the tendon of the Latissimus dorsi, near its insertion, to the long head of the Triceps brachii. This is occasionally muscular, and is the representative of the *Dorsoepitrochlearis brachii* of apes.

The **lumbar triangle of Petit** is a small triangular interval which separates the lateral margin of the lower portion of the Latissimus dorsi from the Obliquus externus abdominis just above the ilium. The base of the triangle is the iliac crest, and its floor is the Obliquus internus abdominis.

The **triangle of auscultation** is a triangle associated with the upper portion of the Latissimus. It is bounded above by the Trapezius, below by the Latissimus dorsi, and laterally by the vertebral border of the scapula. The floor is partly formed by the Rhomboideus major. If the scapula is drawn forward by folding the arms across the chest, and the trunk bent forward, parts of the sixth and seventh ribs and their interspace become subcutaneous and accessible for auscultation.

The **Rhomboideus major** (Fig. 455) *arises* by tendinous fibers from the spinous processes of the second, third, fourth, and fifth thoracic vertebræ and the supraspinal ligament, and is *inserted* into a narrow tendinous arch, attached above to the lower part of the triangular surface at the root of the spine of the scapula; below to the inferior angle, the arch being connected to the vertebral border by a thin membrane. When the arch extends, as it occasionally does, only a short distance, the muscular fibers are inserted directly into the scapula.

The **Rhomboideus minor** (Fig. 455) arises from the lower part of the ligamentum nuchæ and from the spinous processes of the seventh cervical and first thoracic vertebræ. It is *inserted* into the base of the triangular smooth surface at the root of the spine of the scapula, and is usually separated from the Rhomboideus major by a slight interval, but the adjacent margins of the two muscles are occasionally united.

Action.—Adduct the scapula, that is, draw it medially toward the vertebral column, at the same time supporting it and drawing it slightly upward. The lower part of the major rotates the scapula to depress the lateral angle, assisting in adduction of the arm.

Nerve.—The dorsal scapular nerve from the brachial plexus, containing fibers from the fifth cervical nerve.

Variations.—The vertebral and scapular attachments of the two muscles vary in extent. A small slip from the scapula to the occipital bone close to the minor occasionally occurs, the *Rhomboideus occipitalis muscle.*

The **Levator scapulæ** (*Levator anguli scapulæ*) (Fig. 455) is situated at the back and side of the neck. It *arises* by tendinous slips from the transverse processes of the atlas and axis and from the posterior tubercles of the transverse processes of the third and fourth cervical vertebræ. It is *inserted* into the vertebral border of the scapula, between the medial angle and the triangular smooth surface at the root of the spine.

Action.—Raises the scapula, tending to draw it medialward and rotate it to lower the lateral angle. With the scapula fixed, it bends the neck laterally and rotates it slightly toward the same side.

Nerves.—Branches of the third and fourth cervical nerves from the cervical plexus, and frequently the lower portion by a branch of the dorsal scapular nerve containing fibers from the fifth cervical nerve.

Variations.—The number of vertebral attachments varies; a slip may extend to the occipital or mastoid, to the Trapezius, Scalene or Serratus anterior, or to the first or second rib. The muscle may be subdivided into several distinct parts from origin to insertion. *Levator claviculæ* from the transverse processes of one or two upper cervical vertebræ to the outer end of the clavicle corresponds to a muscle of lower animals. More or less union with the Serratus anterior.

II. THE MUSCLES CONNECTING THE UPPER EXTREMITY TO THE ANTERIOR AND LATERAL THORACIC WALLS.

Pectoralis major.   Subclavius.
Pectoralis minor.   Serratus anterior.

The **superficial fascia** (*tela subcutanea*) of the pectoral region is continuous with that of the neck and upper limb above, the abdomen below, and the axilla laterally. The fasciculi of the Platysma muscle extend down from the neck for a variable distance between its superficial and deep layers. In the female, the adipose tissue is increased and molded into a rounded mass which gives the bulk and form to the mamma. The parenchyma of the mammary gland is imbedded in this fat. The connective tissue stroma, distributed between the lobes of the gland, is thickened into fibrous bands, called **ligamenta suspensoria** or **Cooper's ligaments**, which secure the skin to the deep layer of the superficial fascia. A fascial cleft separates the superficial fascia from the deep fascia. Through these fascial structures, a carcinoma may make its presence known either by pulling on Cooper's ligaments and dimpling the skin like an orange peel, or by interfering with the normal movability of the gland through adhesions between the superficial and deep fasciæ.

Pectoral Fascia (*fascia pectoralis*) (Fig. 456).—The pectoral fascia is a membranous sheet of deep fascia which consists of the external investing fascia over the Pectoralis major, and a deeper layer enclosing its under surface. It is more or less adherent throughout and attached, with the origin of the muscle, to the clavicle and sternum, and with the insertion, to the humerus. The external layer is continuous medially, across the middle line, with the pectoral fascia of the other side; superiorly and laterally, with the brachial fascia which covers the Coracobrachialis and Biceps; and inferiorly, with the axillary, thoracic, and abdominal investing fasciæ. At the lower sternocostal and abdominal origins of the muscle, it is aponeurotic and is blended with the sheath of the Rectus abdominis. The deeper layer, covering the deep surface of the muscle and adherent to it, is thickened by a considerable pad of fat in which the thoracoacromial bloodvessels and anterior thoracic nerves are imbedded. A definite fascial cleft separates this layer from the underlying clavipectoral fascia. The external and the deeper layers come together at both borders of the muscle, forming a closed compartment. At the superior border, the fascia separates again to enclose the Deltoideus; at the inferior border, however, a single sheet is formed which becomes immediately the axillary fascia.

The **Clavipectoral Fascia** (*fascia coracoclavicularis*) (Fig. 456) is an intermediate stratum of deep fascia which lies between the Pectoralis major and the thoracic wall. It invests the Pectoralis minor and Subclavius, and extends from the clavicle to the axillary fascia. Its attachment to the clavicle is by means of two membranes which lie superficial and deep to the Subclavius, and which are separated from each other by the insertion of the muscle. The two sheets form a compartment for the muscle by fusing, at its inferior border, into a single sheet which stretches across the interval between the Subclavius and the Pectoralis minor. The portion superficial to the Subclavius is greatly strengthened by the addition of fibrous bundles which continue laterally beyond the muscle, and attach to the coracoid process, forming the **costocoracoid ligament.** This strong band, attached to the coracoid process, the clavicle, and the first rib, serves as an important ligament for the clavicular articulations. From its attachment to the coracoid process, the fascia passes downward as a thin sheet, investing the Pectoralis minor on both its sur-

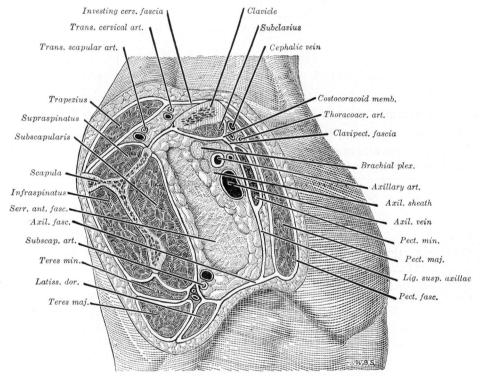

FIG. 456.—Fasciæ of axillary and pectoral regions in sagittal section.

faces, and attaching to the ribs with the origin of the latter muscle. Between the ribs it is continuous with the external intercostal fascia. At the superior border of the Pectoralis minor, the two layers investing the muscle fuse into the single sheet which bridges the triangular interval between the Pectoralis minor and Subclavius. This single sheet is thin, below the ligament, and has one or more holes or defects through which pass the thoracoacromial artery and vein, the cephalic vein, and the lateral anterior thoracic nerve. The portion of the fascia between the upper border of the Pectoralis minor and the clavicle, including the costocoracoid ligament, has been named the **fascia coracoclavicularis.** At the inferior or lateral border of the Pectoralis minor, the two layers combine again into a single sheet which passes into the axilla, and fuses with the deep surface of the axillary fascia a short distance from the lateral border of the Pectoralis major. The axillary sheath, enclosing the axillary vessels and nerves of the brachial plexus, passes under the lateral portion of the clavipectoral fascia, but is partially separated from it by some of the adipose tissue of the deep axillary fossa.

Axillary Fascia (*fascia axillaris*) (Fig. 456).—The portion of the investing fascia which crosses the interval between the lateral borders of the Pectoralis major and Latissimus dorsi dips inward to form the hollow of the armpit. It is adherent to the superficial fascia, and there are openings through which the adipose tissue of the latter is continuous with that in the deeper axillary fossa. It is continuous with the pectoral, latissimus, serratus, and brachial fasciæ. Fused with its deep surface,

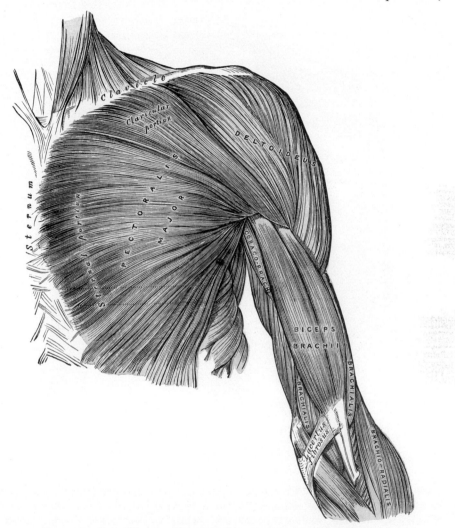

FIG. 457.—Superficial muscles of the chest and front of the arm.

in the hollow of the armpit, is the termination of the clavipectoral fascia which has continued laterally from the Pectoralis minor. The latter fascia has been named the **suspensory ligament of the axilla** because it is believed that the hollow, seen when the arm is abducted, is produced mainly by the traction of this fascia on the axillary floor.

The **axilla** (Fig. 458, "Axillary Space"), in anatomical usage comprises more than the externally visible armpit. It includes the fossa between the medial side of the arm and the lateral surface of the chest wall, inside or deep to the axillary investing layer described above. It is commonly called a space, but should be recognized as a pyramidal compartment filled with adipose tissue, vessels, nerves, and lymph nodes. The walls of the fossa are formed by the fascial coverings of the following muscles: anteriorly, the Pectoralis major and minor; posteriorly, the Latissimus dorsi, Teres major, and Subscapularis; medially, the Serratus anterior; laterally, the Coracobrachialis and Biceps. At the apex of the fossa, between the first rib, clavicle, and base of the coracoid process, the adipose padding tissue is continuous with the mass of similar tissue in the posterior triangle of the

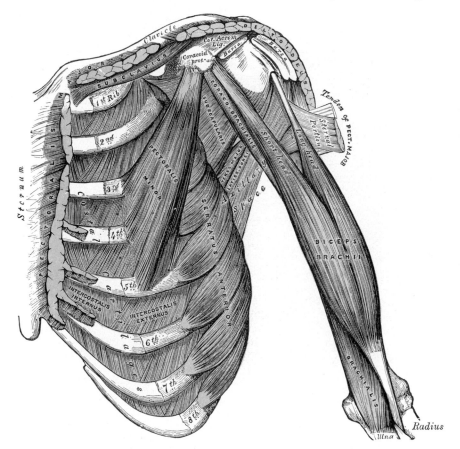

FIG. 458.—Deep muscles of the chest and front of the arm, with the boundaries of the axilla.

neck. At the apex also, the fascia of the first two ribs and first intercostal space is continuous with the scalenus fascia. In this region, the latter fascia gives a tubular investment, called the **axillary sheath,** to the large vessels and nerves of the arm. The sheath is partially adherent to the clavipectoral fascia on the deep surface of the Subclavius and Pectoralis minor as it passes under them, and then, after traversing the lateral wall of the axilla along the Coracobrachialis, it becomes fused with the anterior surface of the medial intermuscular septum of the arm.

The **Pectoralis major** (Fig. 457) is a thick, fan-shaped muscle, situated at the upper and forepart of the chest. It *arises* from the anterior surface of the sternal half of the clavicle; from half the breadth of the anterior surface of the sternum, as low down as the attachment of the cartilage of the sixth or seventh rib; from the cartilages of all the true ribs, with the exception, frequently, of the first or seventh, or both, and from the aponeurosis of the Obliquus externus abdominis. From this extensive origin the fibers converge toward their insertion; those arising from the clavicle pass obliquely downward and lateralward, and are usually separated from the rest by a slight interval; those from the lower part of the sternum, and the cartilages of the lower true ribs, run upward and lateralward; while the middle fibers pass horizontally. They all end in a flat tendon, about 5 cm. broad, which is *inserted* into the crest of the greater tubercle of the humerus. This tendon consists of two laminæ, placed one in front of the other, and usually blended together below. The anterior lamina, the thicker, receives the clavicular and the uppermost sternal fibers; they are inserted in the same order as that in which they arise: that is to say, the most lateral of the clavicular fibers are inserted at the upper part of the anterior lamina; the uppermost sternal fibers pass down to the lower part of the lamina which extends as low as the tendon of the Deltoideus and joins with it. The posterior lamina of the tendon receives the attachment of the greater part of the sternal portion and the deep fibers, *i. e.,* those from the costal cartilages. These deep fibers, and particularly those from the lower costal cartilages, ascend the higher, turning backward successively behind the superficial and upper ones, so that the tendon appears to be twisted. The posterior lamina reaches higher on the humerus than the anterior one, and from it an expansion is given off which covers the intertubercular groove and blends with the capsule of the shoulder-joint. From the deepest fibers of this lamina at its insertion an expansion is given off which lines the intertubercular groove, while from the lower border of the tendon a third expansion passes downward to the fascia of the arm.

Action.—Flexes, adducts, and rotates the arm medially. The clavicular portion draws the arm or the shoulder, if the arm is at the side, upward, forward, and medialward; the sternocostal portion draws the arm or shoulder forward, medialward, and downward.

Nerves.—Medial and lateral anterior thoracic nerves from the brachial plexus, containing fibers from the fifth, sixth, seventh, eighth cervical, and first thoracic nerves.

Variations.—The more frequent variations are greater or less extent of attachment to the ribs and sternum, varying size of the abdominal part or its absence, greater or less extent of separation of sternocostal and clavicular parts, fusion of clavicular part with deltoid, decussation in front of the sternum. Deficiency or absence of the sternocostal part is not uncommon. Absence of the clavicular part is less frequent. Rarely the whole muscle is wanting.

Costocoracoideus is a muscular band occasionally found arising from the ribs or aponeurosis of the External oblique between the Pectoralis major and Latissimus dorsi and inserted into the coracoid process.

Chondro-epitrochlearis is a muscular slip occasionally found arising from the costal cartilages or from the aponeurosis of the External oblique below the Pectoralis major or from the Pectoralis major itself. The insertion is variable on the inner side of the arm to fascia, intermuscular septum or internal condyle.

Sternalis, in front of the sternal end of the Pectoralis major parallel to the margin of the sternum. It is supplied by the anterior thoracic nerves and is probably a misplaced part of the pectoralis.

The **Pectoralis minor** (Fig. 458) is a thin, triangular muscle, situated at the upper part of the thorax, beneath the Pectoralis major. It *arises* from the upper margins and outer surfaces of the third, fourth, and fifth ribs, near their cartilages, and from the aponeuroses covering the Intercostales; the fibers pass upward and lateralward and converge to form a flat tendon, which is inserted into the medial border and upper surface of the coracoid process of the scapula.

Action.—Draws the scapula forward and downward, and rotates it to lower the lateral angle, as in adduction of the arm. Raises the third, fourth, and fifth ribs in forced inspiration, the scapula being fixed by the Levator scapulæ.

Nerve.—The medial anterior thoracic nerve from the brachial plexus, containing fibers from the eighth cervical and first thoracic nerves.

Variations.—Origin from second, third and fourth or fifth ribs. The tendon of insertion may extend over the coracoid process to the greater tubercle. May be split into several parts. Absence rare.

Pectoralis minimus, first rib-cartilage to coracoid process. Rare.

The **Subclavius** (Fig. 458) is a small cylindrical muscle, placed between the clavicle and the first rib. It *arises* by a short, thick tendon from the first rib and its cartilage at their junction, in front of the costoclavicular ligament; the fleshy fibers proceed obliquely upward and lateralward, to be *inserted* into the groove on the under surface of the clavicle between the costoclavicular and conoid ligaments.

Actions.—Draws the shoulder forward and downward.

Nerve.—A special nerve from the lateral trunk of the brachial plexus containing fibers from the fifth and sixth cervical nerves.

Variations.—Insertion into coracoid process instead of clavicle or into both clavicle and coracoid process. *Sternoscapular* fasciculus to the upper border of scapula. *Sternoclavicularis* from manubrium to clavicle between Pectoralis major and coracoclavicular fascia.

The **Serratus anterior** (*Serratus magnus*) (Fig. 458) is a thin muscular sheet, situated between the ribs and the scapula at the upper and lateral part of the chest. It *arises* by fleshy digitations from the outer surfaces and superior borders of the upper eight or nine ribs, and from the aponeuroses covering the intervening Intercostales. Each digitation (except the first) arises from the corresponding rib; the first springs from the first and second ribs; and from the fascia covering the first intercostal space. From this extensive attachment the fibers pass backward, closely applied to the chest-wall, and reach the vertebral border of the scapula, and are inserted into its ventral surface in the following manner. The first digitation is *inserted* into a triangular area on the ventral surface of the medial angle. The next two digitations spread out to form a thin, triangular sheet, the base of which is directed backward and is inserted into nearly the whole length of the ventral surface of the vertebral border. The lower five or six digitations converge to form a fan-shaped mass, the apex of which is inserted, by muscular and tendinous fibers, into a triangular impression on the ventral surface of the inferior angle. The lower four slips interdigitate at their origins with the upper five slips of the Obliquus externus abdominis.

Action.—Rotates the scapula, raising the point of the shoulder as in full flexion and'abduction of the arm. Draws the scapula forward as in the act of pushing. The upper digitation may draw the scapula downward and forward; the lower digitations draw the scapula downward.

Nerve.—The long thoracic nerve from the brachial plexus, containing fibers from the fifth, sixth, and seventh cervical nerves.

Variations.—Attachment to tenth rib. Absence of attachments to first rib, to one or more of the lower ribs. Division into three parts; absence or defect of middle part. Union with Levator scapulæ, External intercostals or External oblique.

III. THE MUSCLES AND FASCIÆ OF THE SHOULDER.

Deltoideus.	Infraspinatus.
Subscapularis.	Teres minor.
Supraspinatus.	Teres major.

Deltoid Fascia.—The deltoid portion of the investing fascia covers the Deltoideus. Above, it is attached to the clavicle, acromion, and spine of the scapula. Below, it is continuous with the brachial fascia. In front, it bridges the narrow triangular interval between the adjacent borders of the Deltoideus and the Pectoralis major. In this interval, called Mohrenheim's triangle, the fascia is thick but is pierced by the cephalic vein and deltoid branch of the thoracoacromial artery. The deltoid fascia is stronger posteriorly, and continues into the Infraspinatus fascia. Along both borders of the Deltoideus, the investing layer joins the fascia of the deep surface to form a closed compartment. Both layers are adherent to the muscle. The deep layer may contain adipose tissue, and is separated by a distinct fascial cleft from the underlying humerus, subdeltoid bursa, shoulder joint, and associated tendons and ligaments.

The **Deltoideus** (*Deltoid muscle*) (Fig. 457) is a large, thick, triangular muscle, which covers the shoulder-joint in front, behind, and laterally. It *arises* from the anterior border and upper surface of the lateral third of the clavicle; from the lateral margin and upper surface of the acromion, and from the lower lip of the posterior border of the spine of the scapula, as far back as the triangular surface at its medial end. From this extensive origin the fibers converge toward their insertion, the middle passing vertically, the anterior obliquely backward and lateralward, the posterior obliquely forward and lateralward; they unite in a thick tendon, which is *inserted* into the deltoid prominence on the middle of the lateral side of the body of the humerus. At its insertion the muscle gives off an expansion to the deep fascia of the arm. This muscle is remarkably coarse in texture, and the arrangement of its fibers is somewhat peculiar; the central portion of the muscle—that is to say, the part arising from the acromion—consists of oblique fibers; these arise in a bipenniform manner from the sides of the tendinous intersections, generally four in number, which are attached above to the acromion and pass downward parallel to one another in the substance of the muscle. The oblique fibers thus formed are inserted into similar tendinous intersections, generally three in number, which pass upward from the insertion of the muscle and alternate with the descending septa. The portions of the muscle arising from the clavicle and spine of the scapula are not arranged in this manner, but are inserted into the margins of the inferior tendon.

Action.—As a whole abducts the arm. The clavicular and adjacent part of the acromial portions flex the arm; the spinous and adjacent part of the acromial portions extend the arm. The most ventral portion rotates the arm medially, the most dorsal portion laterally.

Nerve.—The axillary nerve from the brachial plexus, containing fibers from the fifth and sixth cervical nerves.

Variations.—Large variations uncommon. More or less splitting common. Continuation into the Trapezius; fusion with the Pectoralis major; additional slips from the vertebral border of the scapula, infraspinous fascia and axillary border of scapula not uncommon. Insertion varies in extent or rarely is prolonged to origin of Brachioradialis.

Subscapular Fascia (*fascia subscapularis*).—The subscapular fascia is a thin membrane attached to the entire circumference of the subscapular fossa, and affording attachment by its deep surface to some of the fibers of the Subscapularis.

The **Subscapularis** (Fig. 458) is a large triangular muscle which fills the subscapular fossa, and *arises* from its medial two-thirds and from the lower two-thirds of the groove on the axillary border of the bone. Some fibers *arise* from tendinous laminæ which intersect the muscle and are attached to ridges on the bone; others from an aponeurosis, which separates the muscle from the Teres major and the long head of the Triceps brachii. The fibers pass lateralward, and, gradually converging, end in a tendon which is *inserted* into the lesser tubercle of the humerus and the front of the capsule of the shoulder-joint. The tendon of the muscle is separated from the neck of the scapula by a large bursa, which communicates with the cavity of the shoulder-joint through an aperture in the capsule.

Action.—Rotates the arm medially. It assists in both flexion and extension, and abduction and adduction, depending on the position of the arm. Draws the humerus toward the glenoid fossa strengthening the shoulder joint.

Nerves.—The upper and lower subscapular nerves from the brachial plexus, containing fibers from the fifth and sixth cervical nerves.

Supraspinatous Fascia (*fascia supraspinata*).—The supraspinatous fascia completes the osseofibrous case in which the Supraspinatus muscle is contained; it affords attachment, by its deep surface, to some of the fibers of the muscle. It is thick medially, but thinner laterally under the coracoacromial ligament.

The **Supraspinatus** (Fig. 459) occupies the whole of the supraspinatous fossa, *arising* from its medial two-thirds, and from the strong supraspinatous fascia. The muscular fibers converge to a tendon, which crosses the upper part of the shoulder-joint, and is *inserted* into the highest of the three impressions on the greater tubercle of the humerus; the tendon is intimately adherent to the tendon of the Infraspinatus and to the capsule of the shoulder-joint.

Action.—Abducts the arm. Draws the humerus toward the glenoid fossa, strengthening the shoulder joint. It is a weak lateral rotator and flexor.

Nerve.—Branches of the suprascapular nerve from the brachial plexus, containing fibers from the fifth cervical nerve.

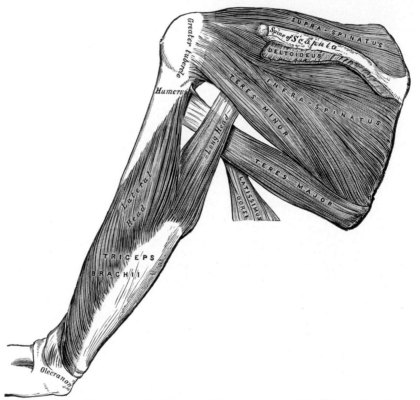

FIG. 459.—Muscles on the dorsum of the scapula, and the Triceps brachii.

Infraspinatous Fascia (*fascia infraspinata*).—The infraspinatous fascia is a dense fibrous membrane, covering the Infraspinatus muscle and fixed to the circumference of the infraspinatous fossa; it affords attachment, by its deep surface, to some fibers of that muscle. It is intimately attached to the deltoid fascia along the overlapping border of the Deltoideus.

The **Infraspinatus** (Fig. 459) is a thick triangular muscle, which occupies the chief part of the infraspinatous fossa; it *arises* by fleshy fibers from its medial two-thirds, and by tendinous fibers from the ridges on its surface; it also arises from the infraspinatous fascia which covers it, and separates it from the Teres major and minor. The fibers converge to a tendon, which glides over the lateral border of the spine of the scapula, and, passing across the posterior part of the capsule of the shoulder-joint, is *inserted* into the middle impression on the greater tubercle of the humerus, where it is fused with its neighbors. The tendon of this muscle is sometimes separated from the capsule of the shoulder-joint by a bursa, which may communicate with the joint cavity.

Action.—Rotates the arm laterally. The upper part abducts, the lower part adducts. Draws the humerus toward the glenoid fossa, strengthening the shoulder joint.

Nerve.—The suprascapular nerve from the brachial plexus, containing fibers from the fifth and sixth cervical nerves.

The **Teres minor** (Fig. 459) is a narrow, elongated muscle, which *arises* from the dorsal surface of the axillary border of the scapula for the upper two-thirds of its extent, and from two aponeurotic laminæ, one of which separates it from the Infraspinatus, the other from the Teres major. Its fibers run obliquely upward and lateralward; the upper ones end in a tendon which is *inserted* into the lowest of the three impressions on the greater tubercle of the humerus; the lowest fibers are *inserted* directly into the humerus immediately below this impression. The tendon of this muscle passes across, and is united with, the posterior part of the capsule of the shoulder-joint.

Action.—Rotates the arm laterally and weakly adducts it. Draws the humerus toward the glenoid fossa, strengthening the shoulder joint.

Nerve.—A branch of the axillary nerve, containing fibers from the fifth cervical.

Variations.—It is sometimes inseparable from the Infraspinatus.

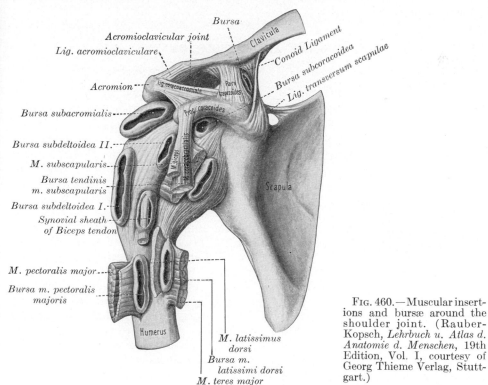

FIG. 460.—Muscular insertions and bursæ around the shoulder joint. (Rauber-Kopsch, *Lehrbuch u. Atlas d. Anatomie d. Menschen*, 19th Edition, Vol. I, courtesy of Georg Thieme Verlag, Stuttgart.)

The **Teres major** (Fig. 459) is a thick but somewhat flattened muscle, which *arises* from the oval area on the dorsal surface of the inferior angle of the scapula, and from the fibrous septa interposed between the muscle and the Teres minor and Infraspinatus; the fibers are directed upward and lateralward, and end in a flat tendon, about 5 cm. long, which is *inserted* into the crest of the lesser tubercle of the humerus. The tendon, at its insertion, lies behind that of the Latissimus dorsi, from which it is separated by a bursa, the two tendons being, however, united along their lower borders for a short distance.

Action.—Adducts, extends, and rotates the arm medially.

Nerve.—A branch of the lower subscapular nerve from the brachial plexus, containing fibers from the fifth and sixth cervical nerves.

Group Action of Muscles About the Shoulder.—Flexion of the arm is brought about by the anterior part of the Deltoideus, Coracobrachialis, and short head of the Biceps, acting on the shoulder joint and by the Trapezius and Serratus anterior rotating the scapula on the chest wall to raise the point of the shoulder. The clavicular part of the Pectoralis major also acts until the arm is raised above the shoulder. Extension of the arm is brought about by the Latissimus dorsi, acting on both the shoulder joint and the scapula, and it is strongly assisted by the lower part of the Pectoralis major except in hyperextension. The Teres major, posterior Deltoideus, and long head of the Triceps act on the shoulder joint, and the scapula is rotated downward by the Pectoralis minor, and drawn backward by the Rhomboidei and Trapezius. The arm is abducted by the Deltoideus and Supraspinatus, acting on the shoulder joint and by the Trapezius and Serratus anterior rotating the scapula to raise the shoulder. The arm is adducted by the Pectoralis major and Latissimus dorsi, by the Coracobrachialis and Teres major acting on the shoulder joint, by the Pectoralis minor rotating the scapula downward, and by the lower portion of the Trapezius drawing the scapula downward. Medial rotation is brought about primarily by the Subscapularis and Teres major when it is performed as a voluntary act, but the Pectoralis major and Latissimus dorsi have strong medial rotating power incidental to their contraction. Lateral rotation is brought about by the Infraspinatus and Teres minor. Independent movements of the scapula are elevation by the Levator scapulæ and upper part of the Trapezius; depression by the Pectoralis minor, lower Trapezius and lower Serratus anterior; drawing it forward (abduction of scapula) by the Serratus anterior, as in pushing; drawing it backward (adduction of scapula) by the Rhomboidei and Trapezius.

IV. THE MUSCLES AND FASCIÆ OF THE ARM.

Coracobrachialis.

Biceps brachii.

Brachialis.

Triceps brachii.

Brachial Fascia (*fascia brachii; deep fascia of the arm*) (Fig. 461).—The portion of the investing fascia which covers the arm is a strong membrane but is not, for the most part, distinctly aponeurotic. It is continuous above with the deltoid, pectoral, and axillary fasciæ; it is attached below to the epicondyles of the humerus and the olecranon, and is then continuous with the antebrachial fascia. Beginning at the attachment to the epicondyles and prolonged upward into the arm are two intermuscular septa, medial and lateral, which divide the arm into flexor and extensor compartments. The **lateral intermuscular septum** (*septum intermusculare* [*humeri*] *laterale*) is attached along the lateral supracondylar ridge and is fused with the under surface of the investing brachial fascia. Its lower extremity is the lateral epicondyle, its upper, the insertion of the Deltoideus where it continues into the deltoid fascia. Its dorsal surface is used by the Triceps for the origin of some of its fibers; the ventral surface by the Brachialis, Brachioradialis, and Extensor carpi radialis longus. Its lower portion is pierced by the radial nerve and the radial collateral branch of the profunda artery. The **medial intermuscular septum** (*septum intermusculare* [*humeri*] *mediale*) is attached to the medial supracondylar ridge and extends from the medial epicondyle, below, to the Teres major and Latissimus dorsi insertions, above. Some of the fibers of the Triceps originate on its dorsal surface and some of the Brachialis on its ventral surface. It is pierced, near the epicondyle, by the ulnar nerve and superior ulnar collateral artery. The medial septum appears very much thicker than the lateral because the axillary sheath, containing the main vessels and nerves of the arm, blends with its ventral surface, and the nerves and vessels continue this close association down to the elbow. The two intermuscular septa and the investing fascia of the posterior aspect of the arm form the posterior or extensor compartment which contains the Triceps, radial nerve, and profunda artery. The anterior or flexor compartment contains the Biceps, Brachialis, part of the Coracobrachialis, the brachial vessels, and the median and ulnar nerves. The relationship of the investing fascia to the muscles is different on the dorsal and ventral aspects of the arm. That over the Triceps is adherent to the muscle and is used in part for its origin. That over the Biceps is separated from the muscle by a distinct fascial cleft which is continued around the deep surface of the muscle, also separating it from the Brachialis. The ventral investing fascia, medially, just below the middle of the arm, is pierced by the basilic vein.

The **Coracobrachialis** (Fig. 458), the smallest of the three muscles in this region, is situated at the upper and medial part of the arm. It *arises* from the apex of the coracoid process, in common with the short head of the Biceps brachii, and from the intermuscular septum between the two muscles; it is *inserted* by means of a flat tendon into an impression at the middle of the medial surface and border of the body of the humerus between the origins of the Triceps brachii and Brachialis. It is perforated by the musculocutaneous nerve.

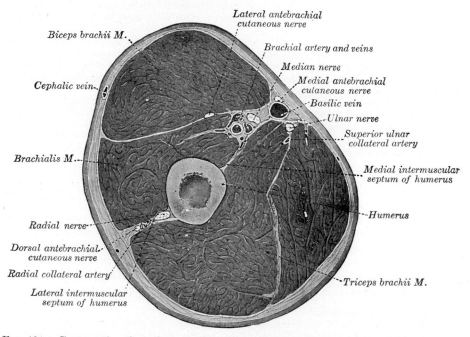

FIG. 461.—Cross-section through the middle of upper arm. (Eycleshymer and Schoemaker.)

Action.—Flexes and adducts the arm.

Nerve.—A branch of the musculocutaneous nerve, containing fibers from the sixth and seventh cervical nerves.

Variations.—A bony head may reach the medial epicondyle; a short head more rarely found may insert into the lesser tubercle.

The **Biceps brachii** (*Biceps; Biceps flexor cubiti*) (Fig. 458) is a long fusiform muscle, placed on the front of the arm, and *arising* by two heads, from which circumstance it has received its name. The **short head** *arises* by a thick flattened tendon from the apex of the coracoid process, in common with the Coracobrachialis. The **long head** *arises* from the supraglenoid tuberosity at the upper margin of the glenoid cavity, and is continuous with the glenoidal labrum. This tendon, enclosed in a special sheath of the synovial membrane of the shoulder-joint, arches over the head of the humerus; it emerges from the capsule through an opening close to the humeral attachment of the ligament, and descends in the intertubercular groove; it is retained in the groove by the transverse humeral ligament and by a fibrous prolongation from the tendon of the Pectoralis major. Each tendon is succeeded by an elongated muscular belly, and the two bellies, although closely applied to each other, can readily be separated until within about 7.5 cm. of the elbow-joint. Here they end in a flattened tendon, which is inserted into the rough posterior portion of the tuberosity of the radius, a bursa being interposed between the tendon and the front part of the tuberosity. As the tendon of the muscle approaches the radius it is twisted upon itself, so that its anterior surface becomes lateral and is applied to the tuberosity of the radius at its insertion. Opposite the bend of the elbow the tendon gives off, from its medial side, a broad aponeurosis, the **aponeurosis m. bicipitis brachii** (*lacertus fibrosus; bicipital fascia*) which passes obliquely downward and medialward across the brachial artery, and is continuous with the deep fascia covering the origins of the Flexor muscles of the forearm (Fig. 457).

Action.—Flexes the arm, flexes the forearm, and supinates the hand. The long head draws the humerus toward the glenoid fossa, strengthening the shoulder joint.

Nerves.—Branches of the musculocutaneous nerve, containing fibers from the fifth and sixth cervical nerves.

Variations.—A third head (10 per cent.) to the Biceps brachii is occasionally found, arising at the upper and medial part of the Brachialis, with the fibers of which it is continuous, and inserted into the lacertus fibrosus and medial side of the tendon of the muscle. In most cases this additional slip lies behind the brachial artery in its course down the arm. In some instances the third head consists of two slips, which pass down, one in front of and the other behind the artery, concealing the vessel in the lower half of the arm. More rarely a fourth head occurs arising from the outer side of the humerus, from the intertubercular groove, or from the greater tubercle. Other heads are occasionally found. Slips sometimes pass from the inner border of the muscle over the brachial artery to the medial intermuscular septum, or the medial epicondyle; more rarely to the Pronator teres or Brachialis. The long head may be absent or arise from the intertubercular groove.

The **Brachialis** (*Brachialis anticus*) (Fig. 458) covers the front of the elbow-joint and the lower half of the humerus. It *arises* from the lower half of the front of the humerus, commencing above at the insertion of the Deltoideus, which it embraces by two angular processes. Its origin extends below to within 2.5 cm. of the margin of the articular surface. It also arises from the intermuscular septa, but more extensively from the medial than the lateral; it is separated from the lateral below by the Brachioradialis and Extensor carpi radialis longus. Its fibers converge to a thick tendon, which is *inserted* into the tuberosity of the ulna and the rough depression on the anterior surface of the coronoid process.

Action.—Flexes the forearm.

Nerve.—A branch of the musculocutaneous nerve, containing fibers from the fifth and sixth cervical nerves; usually an additional small branch of the radial and occasionally of the median nerve.

Variations.—Occasionally doubled; additional slips to the Supinator, Pronator teres, Biceps, acertus fibrosus, or radius are more rarely found.

The **Triceps brachii** (*Triceps; Triceps extensor cubiti*) (Fig. 459) is situated on the back of the arm, extending the entire length of the dorsal surface of the humerus. It is of large size, and arises by three heads (long, lateral, and medial), hence its name.

The **long head** *arises* by a flattened tendon from the infraglenoid tuberosity of the scapula, being blended at its upper part with the capsule of the shoulder-joint; the muscular fibers pass downward between the two other heads of the muscle, and join with them in the tendon of insertion.

The **lateral head** *arises* from the posterior surface of the body of the humerus, between the insertion of the Teres minor and the upper part of the groove for the radial nerve, and from the lateral border of the humerus and the lateral intermuscular septum; the fibers from this origin converge toward the tendon of insertion.

The **medial head**, which really should be called the **deep head**, *arises* from the posterior surface of the body of the humerus, below the groove for the radial nerve; it is narrow and pointed above, and extends from the insertion of the Teres major to within 2.5 cm. of the trochlea: it also arises from the medial border of the humerus and from the back of the whole length of the medial intermuscular septum. Some of the fibers are directed downward to the olecranon, while others converge to the tendon of insertion.

The **tendon of the Triceps brachii** begins about the middle of the muscle: it consists of two aponeurotic laminæ, one of which is subcutaneous and covers the back of the lower half of the muscle; the other is more deeply seated in the substance of the muscle. After receiving the attachment of the muscular fibers, the two lamellæ join together above the elbow, and are inserted, for the most part, into the posterior portion of the upper surface of the olecranon; a band of fibers is, however, continued downward, on the lateral side, over the Anconæus, to blend with the deep fascia of the forearm.

The long head of the Triceps brachii descends between the Teres minor and Teres major, dividing the triangular space between these two muscles and the humerus into two smaller spaces, one triangular, the other quadrangular (Fig. 459). The triangular space contains the scapular circumflex vessels; it is bounded by the Teres minor above, the Teres major below, and the scapular head of the Triceps laterally. The quadrangular space transmits the posterior humeral circumflex vessels and the axillary nerve; it is bounded by the Teres minor and capsule of the shoulder-joint above, the Teres major below, the long head of the Triceps brachii medially, and the humerus laterally.

Action.—Extends the forearm. The long head extends and adducts the arm.

Nerves.—Branches of the radial nerve, containing fibers from the seventh and eighth cervical nerves.

Variations.—A fourth head from the inner part of the humerus; a slip between Triceps and Latissimus dorsi corresponding to the *Dorso-epitrochlearis*.

The **Subanconaeus** (*m. articularis cubiti*) is the name given to a few fibers which spring from the deep surface of the lower part of the Triceps brachii, and are inserted into the posterior ligament and synovial membrane of the elbow-joint.

Group Actions.—Flexion at the elbow is brought about by the Brachialis, a pure flexor, by the Biceps which also has strong Supinating action, and by the Brachioradialis, also a pure flexor. In spite of its old name, Supinator longus, the Brachioradialis does not assist in voluntary supination or pronation; it may have incidental action in restoring the forearm to the middle position from the extreme of either one. The Pronator teres contracts, but its action may be synergetic to counteract the supination of the Biceps. Other forearm muscles may be used in very strong flexion or in cases of paralysis, provided the proper position of pronation or supination is first obtained. Extension of the elbow is performed by the Triceps and Anconæus.

V. THE MUSCLES AND FASCIÆ OF THE FOREARM.

Antebrachial Fascia (*fascia antebrachii; deep fascia of the forearm*) (Fig. 465).—The portion of the investing fascia which covers the upper forearm is a strong aponeurotic sheet, closely adherent to the underlying muscles. Above, it is continuous with the brachial fascia and is attached to the epicondyles of the humerus and the olecranon. Below, it is attached to the distal portions of the radius and ulna and is continued into the fascia of the hand. It is attached to the dorsal border of the ulna through most of its length, closing off the flexor and extensor compartments of the forearm. In the proximal two-thirds of the forearm, the underlying muscles utilize the deep surface of the investing fascia for attachment of their fibers, and the area for attachment is increased further by the strong intermuscular septa which extend deeply toward the bones, between the adjacent muscles. The volar fascia is visibly thickened by collagenous bundles, derived from the tendon of the biceps, which fan out medially to form the aponeurosis of the Biceps brachii muscle. The dorsal portion is thickened, even more than the volar, by bundles from the Triceps tendon. Near the distal ends of the radius and ulna, the fascia is abruptly thickened by the addition of prominent, annular, collagenous bundles which form the volar and dorsal carpal ligaments. In the distal third of the forearm, the muscles and tendons are separated from the over-lying fascia and from each other by fascial clefts. The antebrachial fascia is pierced in several places by vessels and nerves, the largest aperture being for the branch of the median cubital vein which communicates with the deep veins in the ante-cubital fossa. The radius, ulna, and interossous membrane form a septum dividing the forearm into dorsal or extensor and volar or flexor compartments.

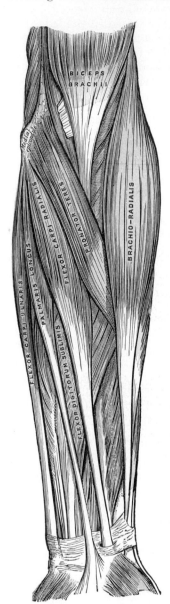

Fig. 462.— Volar aspect of left forearm. Superficial muscles.

In the **dorsal compartment**, a fascial cleft separates the superficial from the deep muscles, especially near the wrist, but it is closed medially and laterally, not communicating with other clefts. In the **volar compartment**, the fascial cleft is more extensive and may communicate with the fascial clefts of the palm. It is especially evident between the surface of the Pronator quadratus and the overlying muscles and tendons, and is here called the **volar interosseous cleft**. It continues proximally between the Flexores profundus and sublimis and may follow along the ulnar vessels and nerve to the antecubital fossa. At the wrist it is in contact with the proximal end of the flexor tendon sheaths (radial and ulnar bursæ) and may continue distally under these sheaths into the middle palmar cleft.

The antebrachial or forearm muscles may be divided into a **volar** and a **dorsal group**.

1. The Volar Antebrachial Muscles.

These muscles are divided for convenience of description into two groups, superficial and deep.

The Superficial Group (Fig. 462).

Pronator teres. Palmaris longus.
Flexor carpi radialis. Flexor carpi ulnaris.
Flexor digitorum sublimis.

The muscles of this group take origin from the medial epicondyle of the humerus by a common tendon; they receive additional fibers from the deep fascia of the forearm near the elbow, and from the septa which pass from this fascia between the individual muscles.

The **Pronator teres** has two heads of origin— humeral and ulnar. The **humeral head**, the larger and more superficial, *arises* immediately above the medial epicondyle, and from the tendon common to the origin of the other muscles; also from the intermuscular septum between it and the Flexor carpi radialis and from the antebrachial fascia. The **ulnar head** is a thin fasciculus, which *arises* from the medial side of the coronoid process of the ulna, and joins the preceding at an acute angle. The median nerve enters the forearm between the two heads of the muscle, and is separated from the ulnar artery by the ulnar head. The muscle passes obliquely across the forearm, and ends in a flat tendon, which is *inserted* into a rough impression at the middle of the lateral surface of the body of the radius. The lateral border of the muscle forms the medial boundary of a triangular hollow, the antecubital fossa, situated in front of the elbow-joint and containing the brachial artery, median nerve, and tendon of the Biceps brachii.

Action.—Pronates the hand.

Nerve.—A branch of the median nerve, containing fibers from the sixth and seventh cervical nerves.

Variations.—Absence of ulnar head; additional slips from the medial intermuscular septum, from the Biceps and from the Brachialis anterior occasionally occur.

The **Flexor carpi radialis** lies on the medial side of the preceding muscle. It *arises* from the medial epicondyle by the common tendon; from the fascia of the forearm; and from the intermuscular septa between it and the Pronator teres laterally, the Palmaris longus medially, and the Flexor digitorum sublimis beneath. Slender and aponeurotic in structure at its commencement, it increases in size, and ends in a tendon which forms rather more than the lower half of its length. This tendon passes through a canal in the lateral part of the transverse carpal ligament and runs through a groove on the greater multangular bone; the groove is converted into a canal by fibrous tissue, and lined by a synovial sheath. The tendon is inserted into the base of the second metacarpal bone, and sends a slip to the base of the third metacarpal bone. The radial artery, in the lower part of the forearm, lies between the tendon of this muscle and the Brachioradialis.

Action.—Flexes the hand and helps to abduct it.

Nerve.—A branch of the median nerve, containing fibers from the sixth and seventh cervical nerves.

Variations.—Slips from the tendon of the Biceps, the lacertus fibrosus, the coronoid, and the radius have been found. Its insertion often varies and may be mostly into the annular ligament, the trapezium, or the fourth metacarpal as well as the second or third. The muscle may be absent.

The **Palmaris longus** is a slender, fusiform muscle, lying on the medial side of the preceding. It *arises* from the medial epicondyle of the humerus by the common tendon, from the intermuscular septa between it and the adjacent muscles, and from the antebrachial fascia. It ends in a slender, flattened tendon, which passes over the upper part of the transverse carpal ligament, and is *inserted* into the central part of the transverse carpal ligament and into the palmar aponeurosis, frequently sending a tendinous slip to the short muscles of the thumb.

Action.—Flexes the hand.

Nerve.—A branch of the median nerve, containing fibers from the sixth and seventh cervical nerves.

Variations.—One of the most variable muscles in the body. This muscle is often absent (about 10 per cent.), and is subject to many variations; it may be tendinous above and muscular below; or it may be muscular in the center with a tendon above and below; or it may present two muscular bundles with a central tendon; or finally it may consist solely of a tendinous band. The muscle may be double. Slips of origin from the coronoid process or from the radius have been seen. Partial or complete insertion into the fascia of the forearm, into the tendon of the Flexor carpi ulnaris and pisiform bone, into the navicular, and into the muscles of the little finger have been observed.

The **Flexor carpi ulnaris** lies along the ulnar side of the forearm. It *arises* by two heads, humeral and ulnar, connected by a tendinous arch, beneath which the ulnar nerve and posterior ulnar recurrent artery pass. The **humeral head** *arises* from the medial epicondyle of the humerus by the common tendon; the **ulnar head** *arises* from the medial margin of the olecranon and from the upper two-thirds of the dorsal border of the ulna by an aponeurosis, common to it and the Extensor carpi ulnaris and Flexor digitorum profundus; and from the intermuscular septum between it and the Flexor digitorum sublimis. The fibers end in a tendon, which occupies the anterior part of the lower half of the muscle and is *inserted* into the pisiform bone, and is prolonged from this to the hamate and fifth metacarpal bones by the pisohamate and pisometacarpal ligaments; it is also attached by a few fibers to the transverse carpal ligament. The ulnar vessels and nerve lie on the lateral side of the tendon of this muscle, in the lower two-thirds of the forearm.

Action.—Flexes and adducts the hand.

Nerve.—A branch of the ulnar nerve, containing fibers from the eighth cervical and first thoracic nerves.

Variations.—Slips of origin from the coronoid. The _Epitrochleo-anconæus_, a small muscle often present runs from the back of the inner condyle to the olecranon, over the ulnar nerve.

The **Flexor digitorum superficialis** (_flexor digitorum sublimis_ Fig. 462) is placed beneath the previous muscle; it is the largest of the muscles of the superficial group, and arises by three heads—humeral, ulnar, and radial. The **humeral head** _arises_ from the medial epicondyle of the humerus by the common tendon, from the ulnar collateral ligament of the elbow-joint, and from the intermuscular septa between it and the preceding muscles. The **ulnar head** _arises_ from the medial side of the coronoid process, above the ulnar origin of the Pronator teres (see Fig. 265, page 242). The **radial head** _arises_ from the oblique line of the radius, extending from the radial tuberosity to the insertion of the Pronator teres. The muscle speedily separates into two planes of muscular fibers, superficial and deep: the superficial plane divides into two parts which end in tendons for the middle and ring fingers; the deep plane gives off a muscular slip to join the portion of the superficial plane which is associated with the tendon of the ring finger, and then divides into two parts, which end in tendons for the index and little fingers. As the four tendons thus formed pass beneath the transverse carpal ligament into the palm of the hand, they are arranged in pairs, the superficial pair going to the middle and ring fingers, the deep pair to the index and little fingers. The tendons diverge from one another in the palm and form dorsal relations to the superficial volar arch and digital branches of the median and ulnar nerves. Opposite the bases of the first phalanges each tendon divides into two slips to allow of the passage of the corresponding tendon of the Flexor digitorum profundus; the two slips then reunite and form a grooved channel for the reception of the accompanying tendon of the Flexor digitorum profundus. Finally the tendon divides and is inserted into the sides of the second phalanx about its middle.

Action.—Flexes the second phalanx of each finger; by continued action, flexes the first phalanx and hand.

Nerves.—Branches of the median nerve, containing fibers from the seventh and eighth cervical and first thoracic nerves.

Variations.—Absence of radial head, of little finger portion; accessory slips from ulnar tuberosity to the index and middle finger portions; from the inner head to the Flexor profundus; from the ulnar or annular ligament to the little finger.

The Deep Group (Fig. 463).

Flexor digitorum profundus.   Flexor pollicis longus.
Pronator quadratus.

The **Flexor digitorum profundus** is situated on the ulnar side of the forearm, immediately beneath the superficial Flexors. It _arises_ from the upper three-fourths of the volar and medial surfaces of the body of the ulna, embracing the insertion of the Brachialis above, and extending below to within a short distance of the Pronator quadratus. It also arises from a depression on the medial side of the coronoid process; by an aponeurosis from the upper three-fourths of the dorsal border of the ulna, in common with the Flexor and Extensor carpi ulnaris; and from the ulnar half of the interosseous membrane. The muscle ends in four tendons which run under the transverse carpal ligament dorsal to the tendons of the Flexor digitorum sublimis. Opposite the first phalanges the tendons pass through the openings in the tendons of the Flexor digitorum sublimis, and are finally _inserted_ into the bases of the last phalanges. The portion of the muscle for the index finger is usually distinct throughout, but the tendons for the middle, ring, and little fingers are connected together by areolar tissue and tendinous slips, as far as the palm of the hand.

Distal to the metacarpophalangeal joints, the tendons of the Flexores digitorum sublimis and profundus lie in strong ligamentous tunnels, the digital **fibrous tendon sheaths** (page 515 and Fig. 469). Each tunnel is lined by the **synovial tendon sheath,** a lubricated layer which is reflected on the contained tendons. Within each digital sheath, the tendons of the sublimis and profundus are connected to each other and to the phalanges by tendinous bands called **vincula tendinum** (Fig. 464). There are two types of vincula: (*a*) the **vincula brevia**, which are two in number in each finger, are fan-shaped expansions near the termination of the tendons, one connecting the sublimis tendon to the front of the proximal interphalangeal joint and the head of the first phalanx, and the other connecting the profundus tendon to the front of the second interphalangeal joint and the head of the second phalanx; (*b*) the **vincula longa** are slender, independent bands which are found in two positions: one pair of them in each finger connects the under surface of the profundus tendon to the subjacent sublimis tendon after the former has passed through the split in the latter; another pair, or a single band, connects the sublimis tendon to the proximal end of the first phalanx.

Action.—Flexes the terminal phalanx of each finger; by continued action flexes the other phalanges and to some extent the hand.

Nerves.—A branch of the volar interosseous nerve from the median and a branch of the ulnar, containing fibers from the eighth cervical and first thoracic nerves.

Variations.—The index finger portion may arise partly from the upper part of the radius. Slips from the inner head of the Flexor sublimis, medial epicondyle, or the coronoid are found. Connection with the Flexor pollicis longus.

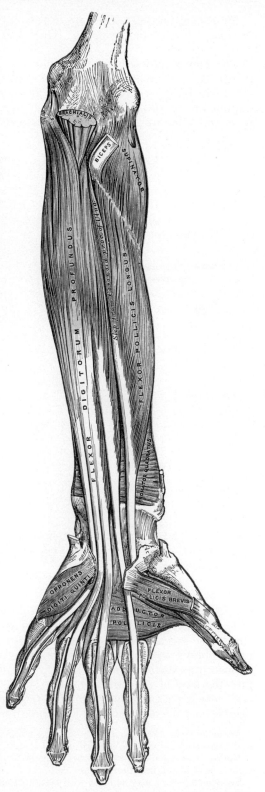

FIG. 463.—Front of the left forearm. Deep muscles.

Four small muscles, the Lumbricales, are connected with the tendons of the Flexor profundus in the palm. They will be described with the muscles of the hand (page 524).

The **Flexor pollicis longus** is situated on the radial side of the forearm, lying in the same plane as the preceding. It *arises* from the grooved volar surface of the body of the radius, extending from immediately below the tuberosity and oblique line to within a short distance of the Pronator quadratus. It *arises* also from the adjacent part of the interosseous membrane, and generally by a fleshy

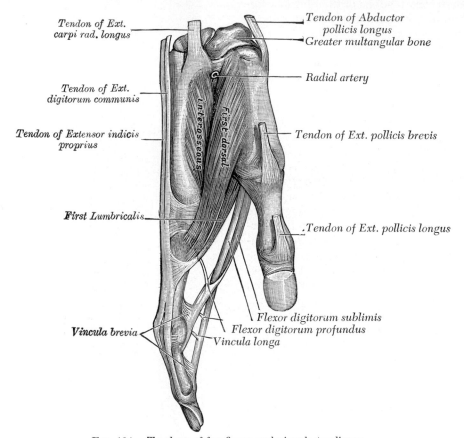

Fig. 464.—Tendons of forefinger and vincula tendinum.

slip from the medial border of the coronoid process, or from the medial epicondyle of the humerus. The fibers end in a flattened tendon, which passes beneath the transverse carpal ligament, is then lodged between the lateral head of the Flexor pollicis brevis and the oblique part of the Adductor pollicis, and, entering an osseo-aponeurotic canal similar to those for the Flexor tendons of the fingers, is *inserted* into the base of the distal phalanx of the thumb. The volar interosseous nerve and vessels pass downward on the front of the interosseous membrane between the Flexor pollicis longus and Flexor digitorum profundus.

Action.—Flexes the second phalanx of the thumb; by continued action, flexes the first phalanx, and flexes and adducts the metacarpal.

Nerve.—A branch of the volar interosseous nerve from the median, containing fibers from the eighth cervical and first thoracic nerves.

Variations.—Slips may connect with Flexor sublimis, or Profundus, or Pronator teres. An additional tendon to the index finger is sometimes found.

The **Pronator quadratus** is a small, flat, quadrilateral muscle, extending across the front of the lower parts of the radius and ulna. It *arises* from the pronator ridge on the lower part of the volar surface of the body of the ulna; from the medial part of the volar surface of the lower fourth of the ulna; and from a strong aponeurosis which covers the medial third of the muscle. The fibers pass lateralward and slightly downward, to be inserted into the lower fourth of the lateral border and the volar surface of the body of the radius. The deeper fibers of the muscle are inserted into the triangular area above the ulnar notch of the radius—an attachment comparable with the origin of the Supinator from the triangular area below the radial notch of the ulna.

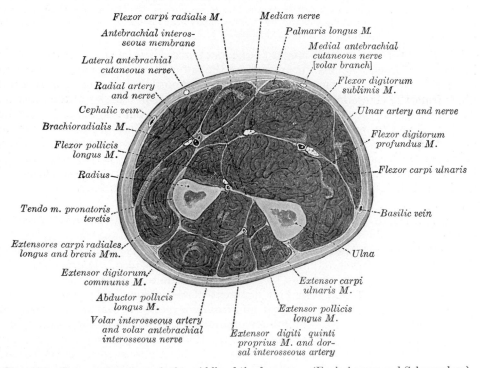

Flexor carpi radialis M.
Antebrachial interosseous membrane
Lateral antebrachial cutaneous nerve
Radial artery and nerve
Cephalic vein
Brachioradialis M.
Flexor pollicis longus M.
Radius
Tendo m. pronatoris teretis
Extensores carpi radiales longus and brevis Mm.
Extensor digitorum communis M.
Abductor pollicis longus M.
Volar interosseous artery and volar antebrachial interosseous nerve

Median nerve
Palmaris longus M.
Medial antebrachial cutaneous nerve [volar branch]
Flexor digitorum sublimis M.
Ulnar artery and nerve
Flexor digitorum profundus M.
Flexor carpi ulnaris
Basilic vein
Ulna
Extensor carpi ulnaris M.
Extensor pollicis longus M.
Extensor digiti quinti proprius M. and dorsal interosseous artery

Fig. 465.—Cross-section through the middle of the forearm. (Eycleshymer and Schoemaker.)

Action.—Pronates the hand.

Nerve.—A branch of the volar interosseous nerve from the median, containing fibers from the eighth cervical and first thoracic nerves.

Variations.—Rarely absent; split into two or three layers; increased attachment upward or downward.

2. The Dorsal Antebrachial Muscles.

These muscles are divided for convenience of description into two groups, superficial and deep.

The Superficial Group (Fig. 466).

Brachioradialis.
Extensor carpi radialis longus.
Extensor carpi radialis brevis.

Extensor digitorum communis.
Extensor digiti quinti proprius.
Extensor carpi ulnaris.

Anconæus.

The **Brachioradialis** (*Supinator longus*) is the most superficial muscle on the radial side of the forearm. It *arises* from the upper two-thirds of the lateral supracondylar ridge of the humerus, and from the lateral intermuscular septum, being limited above by the groove for the radial nerve. Interposed between it and the Brachialis are the radial nerve and the anastomosis between the radial collateral branch of the profunda artery and the radial recurrent. The fibers end above the middle of the forearm in a flat tendon, which is *inserted* into the lateral side of the base of the styloid process of the radius. The tendon is crossed near its insertion by the tendons of the Abductor pollicis longus and Extensor pollicis brevis; on its ulnar side is the radial artery.

Action.—Flexes the forearm.

Nerve.—A branch of the radial nerve, containing fibers from the fifth and sixth cervical nerves.

Variations.—Fusion with the Brachialis; tendon of insertion may be divided into two or three slips; insertion partial or complete into the middle of the radius, fasciculi to the tendon of the Biceps, the tuberosity or oblique line of the radius; slips to the Extensor carpi radialis longus or Abductor pollicis longus; absence; rarely doubled.

The **Extensor carpi radialis longus** (*Extensor carpi radialis longior*) is placed partly beneath the Brachioradialis. It *arises* from the lower third of the lateral supracondylar ridge of the humerus, from the lateral intermuscular septum, and by a few fibers from the common tendon of origin of the Extensor muscles of the forearm. The fibers end at the upper third of the forearm in a flat tendon, which runs along the lateral border of the radius, beneath the Abductor pollicis longus and Extensor pollicis brevis; it then passes beneath the dorsal carpal ligament, where it lies in a groove on the back of the radius common to it and the Extensor carpi radialis brevis, immediately behind the styloid process. It is *inserted* into the dorsal surface of the base of the second metacarpal bone, on its radial side (Fig. 464).

Action.—Extends and abducts the hand.

Nerve.—A branch of the radial nerve, containing fibers from the sixth and seventh cervical nerves.

The **Extensor carpi radialis brevis** (*Extensor carpi radialis brevior*) is shorter and thicker than the preceding muscle, beneath which it is placed. It *arises* from the lateral epicondyle of the humerus, by a tendon common to it and the three following muscles; from the radial collateral ligament of the elbow-joint; from a strong aponeurosis which covers its surface; and from the intermuscular septa between it and the adjacent muscles. The fibers end about the middle of the forearm in a flat tendon, which is closely connected with that of the preceding muscle, and accompanies it to the wrist; it passes beneath the Abductor pollicis longus and Extensor pollicis brevis, then beneath the dorsal carpal ligament, and is *inserted* into the dorsal surface of the base of the third metacarpal bone on its radial side. Under the dorsal carpal ligament the tendon lies on the back of the radius in a shallow groove, to the ulnar side of that which lodges the tendon of the Extensor carpi radialis longus, and separated from it by a faint ridge.

The tendons of the two preceding muscles pass through the same compartment of the dorsal carpal ligament in a single synovial sheath.

Action.—Extends and may abduct the hand.

Nerve.—A branch of the radial nerve, containing fibers from the sixth and seventh cervical nerves.

Variations.—Either muscle may split into two or three tendons of insertion to the second and third or even the fourth metacarpal. The two muscles may unite into a single belly with two tendons. Cross slips between the two muscles may occur. The *Extensor carpi radialis intermedius* rarely arises as a distinct muscle from the humerus, but is not uncommon as an accessory slip from one or both muscles to the second or third or both metacarpals. The *Extensor carpi radialis accessorius* is occasionally found arising from the humerus with or below the Extensor carpi radialis longus and inserted into the first metacarpal, the Abductor pollicis brevis, the First dorsal interosseus, or elsewhere.

The **Extensor digitorum communis** *arises* from the lateral epicondyle of the humerus, by the common tendon; from the intermuscular septa between it and the adjacent muscles, and from the ante-brachial fascia. It divides below into four tendons, which pass, together with that of the Extensor indicis proprius, through a separate compartment of the dorsal carpal ligament, within a synovial sheath. The tendons then diverge on the back of the hand, and are *inserted* into the second and third phalanges of the fingers in the following manner. Opposite the metacarpophalangeal articulation each tendon is bound by fasciculi to the collateral ligaments and serves as the dorsal ligament of this joint; after having crossed the joint, it spreads out into a broad aponeurosis, which covers the dorsal surface of the first phalanx and is reinforced, in this situation, by the tendons of the Interossei and Lumbricales. Opposite the first interphalangeal joint this aponeurosis divides into three slips; an intermediate and two collateral: the former is inserted into the base of the second phalanx; and the two collateral, which are continued onward along the sides of the second phalanx, unite by their contiguous margins, and are *inserted* into the dorsal surface of the last phalanx. As the tendons cross the interphalangeal joints, they furnish them with dorsal ligaments. The tendon to the index finger is accompanied by the Extensor indicis proprius, which lies on its ulnar side. On the back of the hand, the tendons to the middle, ring, and little fingers are connected by obliquely placed bands (connexus intertendineus). Occasionally the first tendon is connected to the second by a thin transverse band.

Action.—Extends the phalanges, and by continued action, extends the wrist.

Nerve.—A branch of the deep radial nerve, containing fibers from the sixth, seventh, and eighth cervical nerves.

Variations.—An increase or decrease in the number of tendons is common; an additional slip to the thumb is sometimes present.

The **Extensor digiti minimi** (*Extensor digiti quinti proprius*) is a slender muscle placed on the medial side of the Extensor digitorum communis, with which it is generally connected. It

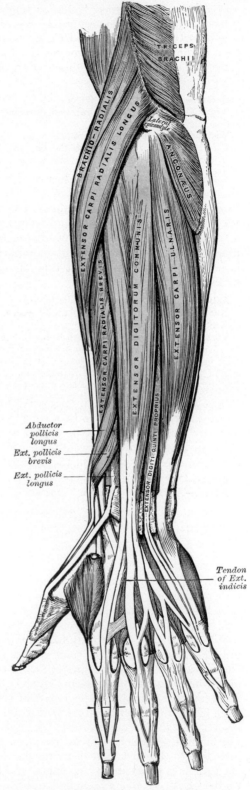

Fig. 466.—Posterior surface of the forearm. Superficial muscles.

arises from the common Extensor tendon by a thin tendinous slip, from the intermuscular septa between it and the adjacent muscles. Its tendon runs through a compartment of the dorsal carpal ligament behind the distal radio-ulnar joint, then divides into two as it crosses the hand, and finally joins the expansion of the Extensor digitorum communis tendon on the dorsum of the first phalanx of the little finger.

Action.—Extends the little finger.

Nerve.—A branch of the deep radial nerve, containing fibers from the sixth, seventh, and eighth cervical nerves.

Variations.—An additional fibrous slip from the lateral epicondyle; the tendon of insertion may not divide or may send a slip to the ring finger. Absence of muscle rare; fusion of the belly with the Extensor digitorum communis not uncommon.

The **Extensor carpi ulnaris** lies on the ulnar side of the forearm. It *arises* from the lateral epicondyle of the humerus, by the common tendon; by an aponeurosis from the dorsal border of the ulna in common with the Flexor carpi ulnaris and the Flexor digitorum profundus; and from the deep fascia of the forearm. It ends in a tendon, which runs in a groove between the head and the styloid process of the ulna, passing through a separate compartment of the dorsal carpal ligament, and is *inserted* into the prominent tubercle on the ulnar side of the base of the fifth metacarpal bone.

Action.—Extends and adducts the hand.

Nerve.—A branch of the deep radial nerve, containing fibers from the sixth, seventh, and eighth cervical nerves.

Variations.—Doubling; reduction to tendinous band; insertion partially into fourth metacarpal. In many cases (52 per cent.) a slip is continued from the insertion of the tendon anteriorly over the Opponens digit quinti, to the fascia covering that muscle, the metacarpal bone, the capsule of the metacarpophalangeal articulation, or the first phalanx of the little finger. This slip may be replaced by a muscular fasciculus arising from or near the pisiform.

The **Anconaeus** is a small triangular muscle which is placed on the back of the elbow-joint, and appears to be a continuation of the Triceps brachii. It *arises* by a separate tendon from the back part of the lateral epicondyle of the humerus; its fibers diverge and are *inserted* into the side of the olecranon, and upper fourth of the dorsal surface of the body of the ulna.

Action.—Extends the forearm.

Nerve.—A branch of radial nerve, containing fibers from the seventh and eighth cervical nerves.

The Deep Group (Fig. 468).

Supinator.	Extensor pollicis longus.
Abductor pollicis longus.	Extensor indicis proprius.
Extensor pollicis brevis.	

The **Supinator** (*Supinator brevis*) (Fig. 467) is a broad muscle, curved around the upper third of the radius. It consists of two planes of fibers, between which the deep branch of the radial nerve lies. The two planes *arise* in common—the superficial one by tendinous and the deeper by muscular fibers—from the lateral epicondyle of the humerus; from the radial collateral ligament of the elbow-joint, and the annular ligament; from the ridge on the ulna, which runs obliquely downward from the dorsal end of the radial notch; from the triangular depression below the notch; and from a tendinous expansion which covers the surface of the muscle. The superficial fibers surround the upper part of the radius, and are inserted into the lateral edge of the radial tuberosity and the oblique line of the radius, as low down as the insertion of the Pronator teres. The upper fibers of the deeper plane form a sling-like fasciculus, which encircles the neck of the radius above the tuberosity and is attached to the back part of its medial surface; the greater part of this portion of the muscle is inserted into the dorsal and lateral surfaces of the body of the radius, midway between the oblique line and the head of the bone.

Action.—Supinates the hand.

Nerve.—A branch of the deep radial nerve, containing fibers from the sixth cervical nerve.

The **Abductor pollicis longus** (*Extensor ossis metacarpi pollicis*) lies immediately below the Supinator and is sometimes united with it. It *arises* from the lateral part of the dorsal surface of the body of the ulna below the insertion of the Anconæus, from the interosseous membrane, and from the middle third of the dorsal surface of the body of the radius. Passing obliquely downward and lateralward, it ends in a tendon, which runs through a groove on the lateral side of the lower end of the radius, accompanied by the tendon of the Extensor pollicis brevis, and is *inserted* into the radial side of the base of the first metacarpal bone (Fig. 464). It usually gives off two slips near its insertion: one to the greater multangular bone and the other to blend with the origin of the Abductor pollicis brevis.

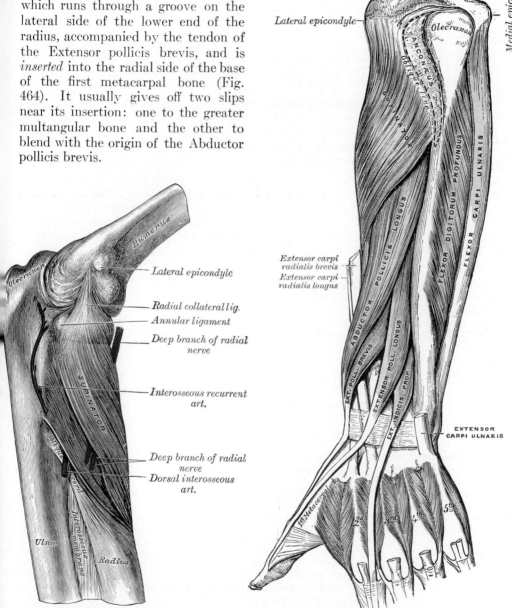

Fig. 467.—The Supinator.

Fig. 468.—Posterior surface of the forearm. Deep muscles.

Action.—Abducts the thumb and, by continued action, the wrist.

Nerve.—A branch of the deep radial nerve, containing fibers from the sixth and seventh cervical nerves.

Variations.—More or less doubling of muscle and tendon with insertion of the extra tendon into the first metacarpal, the greater multangular, or into the Abductor pollicis brevis or Opponens pollicis.

The **Extensor pollicis brevis** (*Extensor primi internodii pollicis*) (Fig. 468) lies on the medial side of, and is closely connected with, the Abductor pollicis longus. It *arises* from the dorsal surface of the body of the radius below that muscle, and from the interosseous membrane. Its direction is similar to that of the Abductor pollicis longus, its tendon passing through the same groove on the lateral side of the lower end of the radius, to be *inserted* into the base of the first phalanx of the thumb (Fig. 464).

Action.—Extends the first phalanx of the thumb and, by continued action, abducts the hand.

Nerve.—A branch of the deep radial nerve, containing fibers from the sixth and seventh cervical nerves.

Variations.—Absence; fusion of tendon with that of the Extensor pollicis longus.

The **Extensor pollicis longus** (*Extensor secundi internodii pollicis*) is much larger than the preceding muscle, the origin of which it partly covers. It *arises* from the lateral part of the middle third of the dorsal surface of the body of the ulna below the origin of the Abductor pollicis longus, and from the interosseous membrane. It ends in a tendon, which passes through a separate compartment in the dorsal carpal ligament, lying in a narrow, oblique groove on the back of the lower end of the radius. It then crosses obliquely the tendons of the Extensores carpi radiales longus and brevis, and is separated from the Extensor brevis pollicis by a triangular interval (the anatomical snuff-box), in which the radial artery is found; and is finally *inserted* into the base of the last phalanx of the thumb. The radial artery is crossed by the tendons of the Abductor pollicis longus and of the Extensores pollicis longus and brevis.

Action.—Extends the second phalanx of the thumb and, by continued action, abducts the hand.

Nerve.—A branch of the deep radial nerve, containing fibers from the sixth, seventh, and eighth cervical nerves.

The **Extensor indicis** (*Extensor indicis proprius*) is a narrow, elongated muscle, placed medial to, and parallel with, the preceding. It *arises*, from the dorsal surface of the body of the ulna below the origin of the Extensor pollicis longus, and from the interosseous membrane. Its tendon passes under the dorsal carpal ligament in the same compartment as that which transmits the tendons of the Extensor digitorum communis, and opposite the head of the second metacarpal bone, joins the ulnar side of the tendon of the Extensor digitorum communis which belongs to the index finger. (Fig. 468)

Action.—Extends and to some extent adducts the index finger.

Nerve.—A branch of the deep radial nerve, containing fibers from the sixth, seventh, and eighth cervical nerves.

Variations.—Doubling; the ulnar part may pass beneath the dorsal carpal ligament with the Extensor digitorum communis; a slip from the tendon may pass to the index finger.

Group Actions.—Flexion at the wrist is brought about by the Flexor carpi ulnaris, Flexor carpi radialis, and Palmaris longus. The Flexores digitorum sublimis and profundus are not used in voluntary flexion at the wrist unless they are prevented from flexing the fingers. The extensors of the wrist are the Extensores carpi radialis longus and brevis, and the Extensor carpi ulnaris. The Extensor digitorum communis may act if the fingers are prevented from extending. Abduction (radial flexion) at the wrist is performed by the Flexor carpi radialis, Extensores carpi radialis longus and brevis, and Abductor pollicis longus. Adduction (ulnar flexion) at the wrist is performed by the Flexor carpi ulnaris and Extensor carpi ulnaris. Pronation of the hand is brought about by the Pronator teres and Pronator quadratus. Supination is performed by the Biceps and the Supinator. Group actions of muscles inserting on the digits are presented after the description of the muscles of the hand.

VI. THE MUSCLES AND FASCIÆ OF THE HAND.

The muscles of the hand are subdivided into three groups: (1) those of the thumb, which occupy the radial side and produce the **thenar eminence**; (2) those of the little finger, which occupy the ulnar side and give rise to the **hypothenar eminence**; (3) those in the middle of the palm and between the metacarpal bones.

Superficial Fascia (*tela subcutanea*).—The superficial fascia of the volar surface of the forearm changes its character abruptly at the distal crease of the wrist from a delicate movable tissue into the tough cushion which covers the palm and palmar surface of the digits. The latter contains a considerable amount of fat, but cannot be separated readily into superficial and deep layers. The adipose tissue is permeated by strong fibrous bands and septa which break it up into small granular lobules and bind it securely to the deep fascia. The dermis is very compact, and not only protects the underlying structures, but also offers resistance to the progress of infectious processes seeking to point toward the surface; at the same time, the vertical direction of the fibrous bands tends to guide the spread of the infection into deeper layers. The superficial fascia is adherent to the deep fascia over the entire palm, but the union is especially strong at the skin creases of the wrist, the major creases of the palm, and the creases of the digits. At the medial and lateral borders of the hand and digits, the fascia changes its character rather abruptly as it becomes continuous with the corresponding layer of the dorsum.

The superficial fascia of the dorsum of the hand and digits is delicate and movable, like that of the forearm with which it is continuous. Its two layers can be identified; the superficial one is thin but may contain a small amount of fat; the deep one is a definite fibrous sheet and supports the superficial veins and cutaneous nerves. It is separated from the deep fascia by a distinct fascial cleft, the dorsal subcutaneous cleft (described below), which imparts the characteristic movability to the skin of the back of the hand.

Deep Fascia of the Wrist.—The antebrachial fascia at the wrist is thickened into an annular band or cuff which holds the tendons of the forearm muscles close against the wrist. For convenience in description, it is divided into two parts, the volar carpal ligament and the dorsal carpal ligament. An additional band, the transverse carpal ligament, is distal to the volar carpal ligament and lies at a slightly deeper level. It is not strictly a fascial derivative, coming rather from the tendons and ligaments of the carpus, but it will be described here because of its close association with the fascia.

The **Volar Carpal Ligament** (*ligamentum carpi volare*) (Fig. 475), not to be confused with the transverse carpal ligament described below, is the distal portion of the investing antebrachial fascia which is abruptly thickened at the wrist by the addition of strong transverse collagenous bundles. It is attached medially and laterally to the styloid processes of the ulna and radius and under it lie the tendons of the flexor muscles. Its distal border is difficult to determine because it merges with the transverse carpal ligament, except where the ulnar artery emerges from under the volar carpal to lie superficial to the transverse carpal ligament.

The relations of the flexor tendons to each other and to the nerves and blood-vessels in the wrist are of great surgical interest because they are frequently severed in industrial injuries and must be sutured back into place. These relations are quite constant unless actual muscular variations or anomalies occur, and are shown in Figure 472.

Transverse Carpal Ligament (*retinaculum flexorum; anterior annular ligament*) (Figs. 469, 475).—The transverse carpal ligament is a thick fibrous band which arches over the deep groove on the volar surface of the carpal bones, forming a tunnel through which the long flexor tendons and the median nerve pass. It is attached, medially, to the pisiform and the hamulus of the hamate, and laterally, to the tuberosity of the navicular, and the medial part of the volar surface and ridge of the greater multangular. Its proximal border is partly merged with the distal border of the volar carpal ligament, but the latter belongs to a definitely different and more superficial stratum, and is separated from it by the ulnar artery and nerve. It is attached to the palmar aponeurosis, which lies superficial to it, and

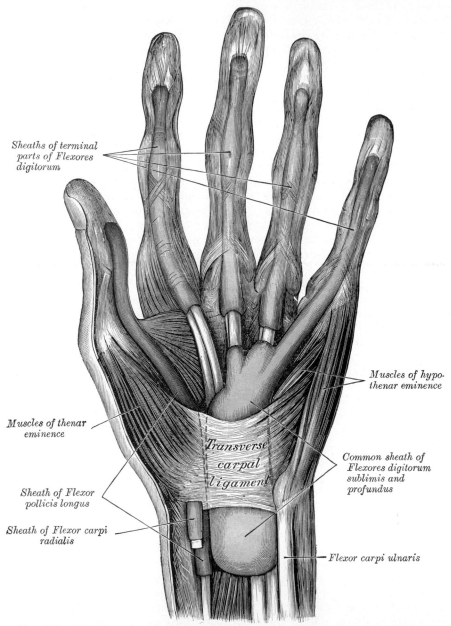

Sheaths of terminal parts of Flexores digitorum

Muscles of hypo-thenar eminence

Muscles of thenar eminence

Transverse carpal ligament

Common sheath of Flexores digitorum sublimis and profundus

Sheath of Flexor pollicis longus

Sheath of Flexor carpi radialis

Flexor carpi ulnaris

Fig. 469.—The synovial sheaths of the tendons on the front of the wrist and digits.

contributes oblique crossed fibers to the deep surface of the aponeurosis. It is attached to the greater multangular in two parts, one on either side of the groove in which the tendon of the Flexor carpi radialis lies. The Flexor carpi ulnaris, at its insertion, contributes tendinous fibers to the ligament and the short muscles of the thumb and little finger arise from it to a large extent.

The **Synovial Sheaths of the Flexor Tendons at the Wrist** (Fig. 469).—As the tendons pass under the transverse carpal ligament, they are enclosed in two specialized synovial sacs; the larger one, for all the tendons of the Flexores digitorum sublimis and profundus, is called the **ulnar bursa**; the smaller one, for the Flexor

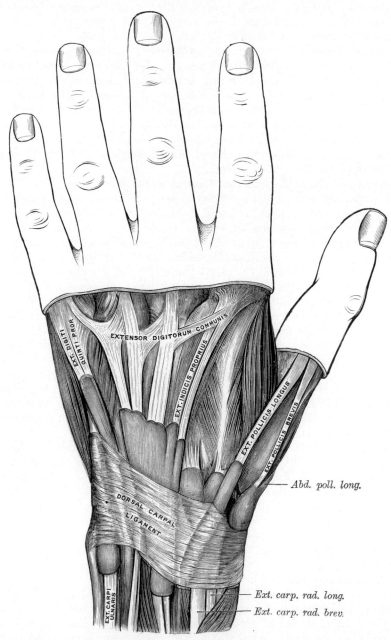

FIG. 470.—The synovial sheaths of the tendons on the back of the wrist.

pollicis longus, is called the **radial bursa**. They extend proximally into the forearm for about 2.5 cm. beyond the transverse carpal ligament. The radial bursa extends distally to the terminal phalanx of the thumb where the Flexor pollicis longus inserts. The ulnar bursa continues distally beyond the middle of the palm as the digital

33

sheath for the little finger, but it is greatly reduced in diameter at the middle of the metacarpal bones by the formation of terminal diverticula about the tendons of the second, third, and fourth digits. The tendons to the second, third, and fourth digits, therefore, are without synovial sheaths for a short distance in the middle of the palm, but they have independent digital sheaths beginning proximally over the heads of their metacarpal bones and continuing distally to the terminal phalanges, where the profundus inserts.

Dorsal Carpal Ligament (*retinaculum extensorum; posterior annular ligament*) (Figs. 468, 470).—The dorsal carpal ligament, under which the extensor tendons lie, is the distal portion of the investing antebrachial fascia which is thickened abruptly by the addition of transverse collagenous bundles. The latter take a somewhat oblique course, extending distalward as they cross from the radial to the ulnar side. The ligament is attached, medially, to the styloid process of the ulna, and to the triangular and pisiform bones, and laterally, to the lateral margin of the radius. Between these medial and lateral borders, it is attached to the ridges on the dorsal surface of the radius.

The **Synovial Sheaths of the Extensor Tendons at the Wrist** (Fig. 470).—Between the dorsal carpal ligament and the carpal bones, six tunnels are formed for the passage of tendons, each tunnel having a separate synovial sheath. One is found in each of the following positions (Fig. 472): (1) on the lateral side of the styloid process of the radius, for the tendons of the Abductor pollicis longus and Extensor pollicis brevis; (2) dorsal to the styloid process, for the tendons of the Extensores carpi radialis longus and brevis; (3) about the middle of the dorsal surface of the radius, for the tendon of the Extensor pollicis longus; (4) more medially, for the tendons of the Extensor digitorum communis and Extensor indicis proprius; (5) opposite the interval between the radius and ulna, for the Extensor digiti quinti proprius; (6) between the head and styloid process of the ulna, for the tendon of the Extensor carpi ulnaris. The sheaths lining these tunnels all begin proximal to the dorsal carpal ligament; those for the tendons of the Abductor pollicis longus, Extensor pollicis brevis, Extensores carpi radialis, and Extensor carpi ulnaris stop immediately proximal to the bases of the metacarpal bones, while the sheaths for the Extensor digitorum communis, Extensor indicis proprius, and Extensor digiti quinti proprius are prolonged to the junction of the proximal and intermediate thirds of the metacarpus.

Deep Fascia of the Palm.—The investing layer of deep fascia in the palm is continuous with the antebrachial fascia which is represented, in the wrist, by the volar carpal ligament. It is continuous also with the fascia of the dorsum at the borders of the hand, attaching to the fifth metacarpal bone medially, and the first and second metacarpal bones laterally, as it passes over them. The thenar fascia, over the muscular eminence at the radial side of the hand, and the hypothenar fascia, over the eminence of the ulnar side, are similar in texture to the antebrachial fascia, but that in the central part of the palm is greatly strengthened into what is called the palmar aponeurosis.

Palmar Aponeurosis (Fig. 471).—The Palmar aponeurosis is made up of two components: (*a*) a thick superficial stratum of longitudinal bundles which are the direct continuation of the tendon of the Palmaris longus, and (*b*) a thinner deep stratum of transverse fibers which is continuous with the volar carpal ligament. The two strata are intimately fused and partly interwoven. The deeper portion is securely attached to the transverse carpal ligament and the latter may contribute obliquely running fibers to the aponeurosis. The longitudinal bundles of the superficial stratum form a uniform layer in the proximal part of the palm, but distally, they fan out and are segregated into divergent bands which extend toward the bases of the digits, covering the long flexor tendons. The four bands to the fingers are heavier and more constant than the one to the thumb. Each of these bands has a double termination, the superficial part attaching to the skin, and the deeper part ending in the flexor tendon sheath. The most superficial fibers attach to the skin at the distal crease of the palm; other superficial fibers terminate at the crease at the base of the digit. The deeper portion of each band contributes to the fibrous tendon sheath in two ways: some of the fibers continue distally into the digit, assisting in the formation of the digital sheath; the greater number of fibers, however, form two arching ligamentous bands, on each side of the tendon, which

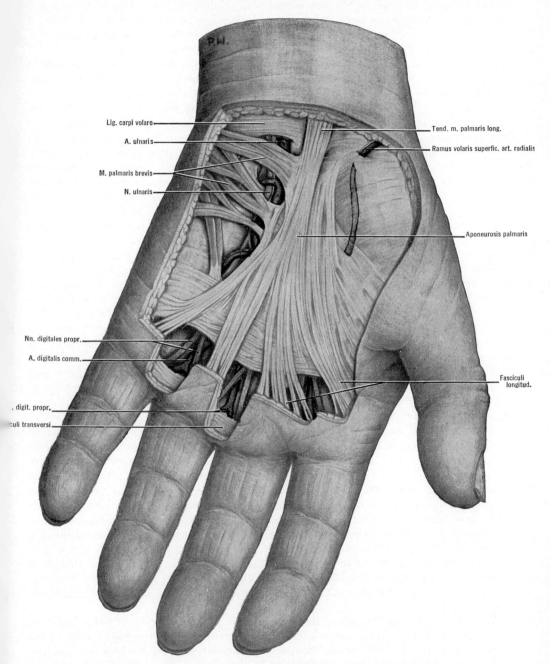

Fig. 471.—Superficial dissection of the palm of the hand. (Töndury, Angewandte und topographische Anatomie, courtesy of Georg Thieme Verlag.)

penetrate deeply toward the metacarpal bone. They attach to the bone and send fibers to the transverse metacarpal ligament, thus completing the formation of the tunnel which lies on the head of the metacarpal bone. In the central part of the palm, as the longitudinal bands diverge and separate from each other, the intervals between them are occupied by transverse fibers which represent the distal thickening of the deeper stratum of the aponeurosis. These transverse fibers, making up what is called the **superficial transverse metacarpal ligament**, extend as far distally as the heads of the metacarpal bones, but from here to the webs between the digits, the intervals are not covered by aponeurosis. In this distal, uncovered portion, therefore, the digital vessels and nerves, and the tendons of the Lumbricales are more readily accessible to the surgeon. The intervals are closed distally by other transverse fibers which occupy and support the webs between the digits and which are variously named the **fasciculi transversi**, the **superficial transverse ligament of the fingers**, the **interdigital ligament**, and the **ligamentum natatorium**. They attach to the digital sheaths at the bases of the first phalanges and merge into the fibrous septa of the sides of the fingers known as the **cutaneous ligaments of the phalanges**. The digital vessels and nerves enter the digits deep to the fasciculi transversi and lie against the cutaneous ligaments of the phalanges in their course toward the ends of the fingers. As mentioned above, the band of longitudinal fibers from the palmar aponeurosis which extends toward the thumb is not as robust as the other four. Some of its fibers attach to the longitudinal crease of the palm, many of them fuse with the fascia of the thenar eminence, and a comparatively small number assist in the formation of the sheath for the Flexor pollicis longus tendon. When the Palmaris longus is absent, a condition which occurs in 13 per cent of the hands, the attachment of the palmar aponeurosis to the transverse carpal ligament is strengthened to compensate for the loss of continuity with the Palmaris tendon. The Palmaris brevis is a small but constant muscle which lies superficial to the hypothenar fascia; it has its origin at the ulnar border of the palmar aponeurosis and inserts into the skin of the ulnar border of the palm. The palmar aponeurosis is fused, at its radial border, with the fascial membrane of the thenar eminence, and from this line of union, a membrane is continued deeply into the palm and is attached to the first metacarpal bone, forming the **thenar septum**. Similarly, the aponeurosis is fused with the hypothenar fascia, and from this union a septum is continued deeply to the fifth metacarpal, forming the **hypothenar septum**. These two septa divide the palm into three compartments: a thenar, a hypothenar, and a central compartment (see below).

Digital Tendon Sheaths.—The tendons of the Flexores digitorum sublimis and profundus are held in position along the digits by strong fibrous tunnels (Fig. 475). The tunnels or canals are formed by the volar surfaces of the phalanges and by strong collagenous bands which arch over the tendons and are attached to the margins of the phalanges on either side. Opposite the middle of the proximal and second phalanges, the bands (*digital vaginal ligaments*) are very strong and their fibers are transverse. Opposite the joints they are much thinner, and consist of annular and cruciate ligamentous fibers. At their proximal ends, the digital sheaths merge with the deeper parts of the palmar aponeurosis. Within each of the five fibrous digital sheaths, there is a synovial tendon sheath; that for the thumb is continuous with the radial bursa; that for the little finger with the ulnar bursa; those for the other three fingers are closed proximally at the metacarpophalangeal joints (Fig. 469).

Deep Fascia of the Dorsum of the Hand.—The investing layer of deep fascia of the dorsum of the hand is directly continuous with the antebrachial fascia which is thickened at the wrist by the addition of annular collagenous bundles into the dorsal carpal ligament. It is continuous, at the medial side of the hand, with the hypothenar fascia, after being attached to the dorsum of the fifth metacarpal bone.

At the lateral border of the hand, it is continuous with the fascia over the first Interosseus dorsalis, after being attached to the dorsum of the second metacarpal bone and with the thenar fascia, after being attached to the first metacarpal bone. The investing fascia forms the superficial boundary of a flat compartment which contains the tendons of the extensors of the digits.

The fascia of the dorsum of the thumb corresponds to that of the hand proper whose investing and subaponeurotic fasciæ fuse into a single layer at its lateral border. This single layer, after being attached to the dorsum of the second metacarpal bone, continues laterally over the first Interosseus dorsalis, in the web between the thumb and the index finger, and is attached to the ulnar border of the first metacarpal bone. It separates again into two layers which form a compartment for the extensor tendons of the thumb, and then, reunited into a single sheet, attaches to the radial border of the first metacarpal, where it becomes continuous with the thenar fascia.

Fascial Compartments of the Hand.—The **thenar compartment** (not to be confused with the thenar fascial cleft or space) occupies the thenar eminence of the palm and contains the short muscles of the thumb with the exception of the Adductores. The boundary is formed by the investing layer of deep fascia and its inward continuation, the thenar septum, which lies between the Adductores and the Flexor brevis. The compartment is closed by the attachment of this fascia proximally, to the carpal bones and transverse carpal ligament; distally, to the first phalanx at the insertion of the enclosed muscles; dorsally, along the subcutaneous border of the first metacarpal bone, and ventrally, by the attachment of the thenar septum along the Adductores. In addition to the Abductor brevis, the Flexor brevis and the Opponens, the compartment contains the first metacarpal bone, the superficial volar branch of the radial artery, and a portion of the tendon of the Flexor pollicis longus enclosed in the radial bursa. Within the compartment, the muscles are enclosed in their individual fascial sheaths, and for the most part, are separated from each other by fascial clefts, but these clefts do not communicate with each other nor with the major fascial clefts of the palm.

The **hypothenar compartment** occupies the hypothenar eminence and contains the short muscles of the little finger. It is enclosed by the hypothenar investing fascia and the hypothenar septum which lies between the Flexor digiti quinti brevis and the third Interosseus volaris. The fascia forms a closed compartment by attaching along the fifth metacarpal bone on both the dorsal and volar aspects of the muscles which it surrounds. Within the compartment, the individual muscles are enclosed in fascial sheaths of their own and are separated from each other by fascial clefts, but these clefts do not communicate with each other nor with the major fascial cleft of the palm.

The **central compartment** is bounded, medially and laterally, by the thenar and hypothenar fascial septa; superficially, by the palmar aponeurosis; and deeply, by a fascial membrane which covers the deep surface of the long flexor tendon mass. It contains the Flexores digitorum sublimis and profundus tendons, the Lumbricales, the superficial volar arch, the palmar branch of the medial nerve, and the superficial branch of the ulnar nerve. The compartment is narrow proximally, but widens distally as the tendons diverge toward their fingers. It is closed proximally, as far as fascial attachments are concerned, but the tendon sheaths within it extend back into the forearm, and its tissues merge distally with those of the webs and digits.

The **Interosseus-adductor Compartment.**—The compartments of the palm are separated from the dorsal portion of the hand by a septum which is made up principally of the Interossei and the Adductores pollicis, and which may be called accordingly, the interosseus-adductor compartment. It is enclosed by two fascial membranes which are continuous with each other around its medial and lateral borders. The membrane on the dorsal surface, called the **dorsal interosseous fascia**, covers and is adherent to the dorsal surfaces of the second to fifth metacarpal bones and the intervening dorsal Interossei. The palmar surface is covered by the **volar interosseous fascia** in the ulnar half, and by the fascia of the Adductores in the radial half. The compartment is closed by the attachment of these membranes at the origins of the muscles, proximally, and at their insertions, distally. It con-

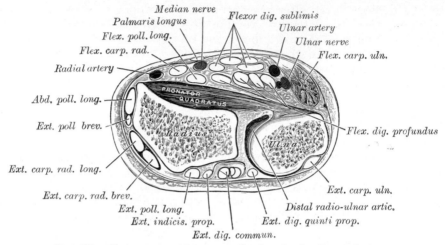

FIG. 472.—Transverse section across distal ends of radius and ulna.

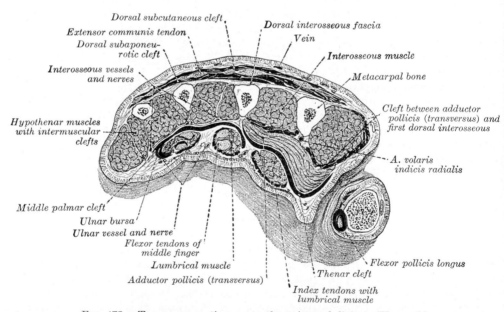

FIG. 473.—Transverse section across the wrist and digits. (Kanavel.)

tains the second, third, fourth, and fifth metacarpal bones, all the Interossei, the Adductores transversus and obliquus, the deep volar arch, and the deep branch of the ulnar nerve. The Adductores and the Interossei have been placed in the same rather than in separate compartments because the entire muscle mass lies deep to the palmar compartments (Fig. 473) and is separated from them by the major fascial cleft of the palm. A fascial cleft may separate the two Adductores from each other and from the first dorsal Interosseus, and these clefts may communicate with the thenar cleft or with the tissue spaces of the web between the thumb and index finger.

The **dorsal tendon compartment** is enclosed, superficially, by the investing fascia, and deeply, by a membrane of fascia covering the deep surface of the extensor tendon mass called the **dorsal subaponeurotic fascia**. The compartment is closed at the sides of the hand by the fusion of the two membranes into a single sheet where both are attached to the dorsum of the second and fifth metacarpal bones. It is closed distally by the fusion of the two layers at the webs between the fingers and their attachment to the joint capsules and tendinous expansions of the digits. It is closed proximally by the fusion with the tendon sheaths which pass under the dorsal carpal ligament. The compartment is separated from the superficial fascia by the subcutaneous fascial cleft, and from the dorsal interosseus fascia by the subaponeurotic fascial cleft.

Fascial Clefts (*fascial spaces*) **of the Palm** (Fig. 473).—The term fascial cleft is preferable to fascial space because the latter quite frequently leads to ambiguity and the former agrees with the description in other parts of this book (see pages 408–409). Fascial clefts are planes of cleavage between fascial membranes and should not be confused with fascial compartments which are enclosures formed by fascial membranes and contain muscles, bones, or other structures. Fascial clefts may occur inside of compartments or may lie between compartments.

The major fascial cleft of the palm lies between the fascia covering the deep surface of the long flexor tendon mass and the fascia covering the Adductores and the Interossei of the medial portion of the hand; that is, it lies between the central palmar compartment and the interosseus adductor compartment. Delicate membranous septa of variable number and extent attach to the metacarpal bones distally, and extend toward the wrist, producing more or less complete subdivisions of the cleft. The septum which is attached to the middle metacarpal bone is more constant and better developed than the rest and is commonly described as subdividing the cleft into two parts, the middle palmar cleft and the thenar cleft (Kanavel, '42).

The **middle palmar cleft** (*middle palmar space*) is triangular in shape and separates the deep surface of the long flexor tendons from the Interossei in the central part of the palm. It lies between the volar interosseous fascia and the fascia covering the deep surface of the long flexor tendon compartment. The cleft may be closed at the wrist by adhesion between the fascial membranes at the transverse carpal ligament, or it may be continued proximally, deep to the ulnar bursa, and communicate with the anterior interosseous cleft of the forearm. It is closed, medially, by the attachment of the hypothenar septum to the fifth metacarpal bone, and laterally, from the thenar cleft by a transparent fibrous membrane which is attached along the middle metacarpal bone. This membrane, instead of attaching to the flexor tendon mass directly over the middle metacarpal, takes an oblique course toward the region of the second metacarpal, causing the middle palmar cleft to extend into the radial portion of the palm so that it overlaps the thenar cleft to some extent. The membrane between the middle palmar and the thenar cleft may be incomplete proximally, allowing the two clefts to communicate with each other. Closely associated with the middle palmar cleft, acting as diverticula, are the clefts surrounding the second, third, and fourth Lumbricales, called the **lumbrical canals**.

The **thenar cleft** (*thenar space*) (Fig. 473) overlies the volar surface of the Adductores pollicis. It is bounded, medially, by the membrane which is attached to the middle metacarpal bone and which separates it from the middle palmar cleft; laterally, by the thenar septum and the first metacarpal bone; proximally, by the transverse carpal ligament, and distally, by the extent of the Adductor transversus.

The thenar cleft is commonly continuous with the cleft between the two Adductores and between the latter and the first dorsal Interosseus. It may communicate with the middle palmar cleft, proximally, and it usually has a diverticulum extending along the first Lumbricalis, the lumbrical canal.

The **lumbrical canals** are the tubular fascial clefts which separate the Lumbricales from the denser connective tissue which surrounds them. These clefts are closely associated with, or act as diverticula for, the major fascial clefts of the palm in the following way: the cleft of the first lumbrical with the thenar cleft, that of the second, third, and fourth with the middle palmar cleft.

Smaller independent fascial clefts are found between the individual muscles of the thenar and hypothenar groups. A cleft of variable extent may be found superficial to the palmar aponeurosis, lying between it and the superficial fascia in the center of the palm.

The **dorsal subcutaneous cleft** (*dorsal subcutaneous fascial space*) (Fig. 473) separates the superficial fascia from the deep fascia. It extends distally out into the fingers and proximally into the forearm. It is closed at the borders of the hand by the attachment of the superficial fascia to the deep fascia of the palm, and it has no communication with the dorsal subaponeurotic cleft.

The **dorsal subaponeurotic fascial cleft** (*dorsal subaponeurotic fascial space*) (Fig. 473) separates the dorsal subaponeurotic fascia from the dorsal interosseus fascia. It is closed at the sides of the hand by the fusion of the two membranes near their attachment to the second and the fifth metacarpal bones. It is closed distally by the fusion of the two layers and their union with the joint capsules and extensor expansions of the digits. Proximally, it is obliterated by the attachment of the tendon sheaths to the bones and ligaments of the wrist. This cleft does not communicate with the dorsal subcutaneous cleft, nor with the palmar clefts, and it does not pass from the hand into the forearm.

Variations.—The flexor tendons to the index finger and the first Lumbricalis may be enclosed in a separate compartment. In this case, there are two membranes attached to the middle metacarpal bone. One has the usual position, extending obliquely toward the radial side of the hand and overlying the thenar cleft; the other extends directly toward the deep surface of the flexor tendon mass and attaches along the flexors to the middle finger. The index compartment is bounded by these two membranes and the palmar aponeurosis. The portion of the middle palmar cleft which usually lies superficial to the thenar cleft is within the index compartment, and the lumbrical canal for this finger leads into this cleft rather than the thenar cleft.

Surgical Considerations.—An understanding of the relationship of the fascial clefts to each other and to the tendon sheaths may best be reached by a brief review of the probable spread of an infective process, independent of the participation of the bloodvessels or lymphatics.

A subcutaneous abscess on the dorsum of the hand or in the webs could be expected to point at the surface locally because of the softness of the tissues; in the palm, it might reach the surface or spread to the webs, but would not be likely to penetrate the palmar aponeurosis. An abscess of the index finger, after penetrating to the deeper tissues might progress proximally until it arrived in the lumbrical canal, and through this path, reach the thenar cleft. From the other three fingers, it might reach the middle palmar cleft by a similar path. It might progress from either of these deep palmar clefts to the other, or, if the swelling and edema would permit, it might reach the cleft of the forearm. An infection involving a digital flexor tendon sheath, if it occurred in the little finger or the thumb, would quickly follow the sheath into the ulnar or radial bursæ, and after a period of time, the latter could rupture into the volar fascial cleft of the forearm. If the infection were in the index finger, the tendon sheath might be expected to rupture into the thenar cleft; if in the middle or fourth finger, it would rupture into the middle palmar cleft. An infection of the dorsal subcutaneous cleft could be expected to reach the surface locally. An infection in the dorsal subaponeurotic cleft would be expected to spread throughout the entire cleft, and then eventually rupture into the webs or at the sides of the hand.

1. The Thenar Muscles (Figs. 474, 475).

Abductor pollicis brevis.   Flexor pollicis brevis.
Opponens pollicis.   Adductor pollicis (obliquus).
                    Adductor pollicis (transversus).

The **Abductor pollicis brevis** (*Abductor pollicis*) is a thin, flat muscle, placed most superficially in the thenar region. It *arises* from the transverse carpal ligament, the tuberosity of the navicular, and the ridge of the greater multangular, frequently by two distinct slips. Running lateralward and distalward, it is *inserted* by a thin, flat tendon into the radial side of the base of the first phalanx of the thumb and the capsule of the metacarpophalangeal articulation.

Action.—Abducts the thumb, that is, draws it away in a plane at right angles to that of the palm of the hand.

Nerve.—A branch of the median nerve, containing fibers from the sixth and seventh cervical nerves.

The **Opponens pollicis** is a small, triangular muscle, placed beneath the preceding. It *arises* from the ridge on the greater multangular and from the transverse carpal ligament, passes distalward and lateralward, and is *inserted* into the whole length of the metacarpal bone of the thumb on its radial side.

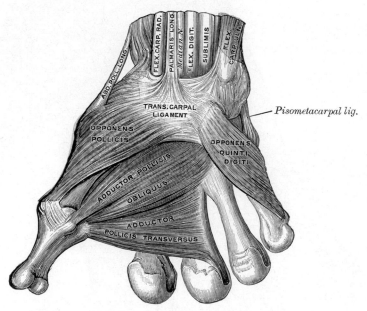

Fig. 474.—The muscles of the thumb.

Action.—Abducts, flexes, and rotates the metacarpal of the thumb, bringing the thumb out in front of the palm to face the fingers.

Nerve.—A branch of the median nerve, containing fibers from the sixth and seventh cervical nerves.

The **Flexor pollicis brevis** consists of two portions, lateral and medial. The **lateral** and more **superficial portion** *arises* from the lower border of the transverse carpal ligament and the lower part of the ridge on the greater multangular bone; it passes along the radial side of the tendon of the Flexor pollicis longus, and, becoming tendinous, is *inserted* into the radial side of the base of the first phalanx of the thumb; in its tendon of insertion there is a sesamoid bone. The **medial** and **deeper portion** of the muscle is very small, and *arises* from the ulnar side of the first metacarpal bone between the Adductor pollicis (obliquus) and the lateral head of the first Interosseous dorsalis, and is *inserted* into the ulnar side of the base of the first phalanx with the Adductor pollicis (obliquus). The medial part of the Flexor brevis pollicis is sometimes described as the **first Interosseous palmaris**.

Action.—Flexes and adducts the thumb.

Nerve.—The lateral portion, a branch of the median nerve, containing fibers from the sixth and seventh cervical nerves; the medial portion, a nerve from the deep branch of the ulnar nerve, containing fibers from the eighth cervical and first thoracic nerves.

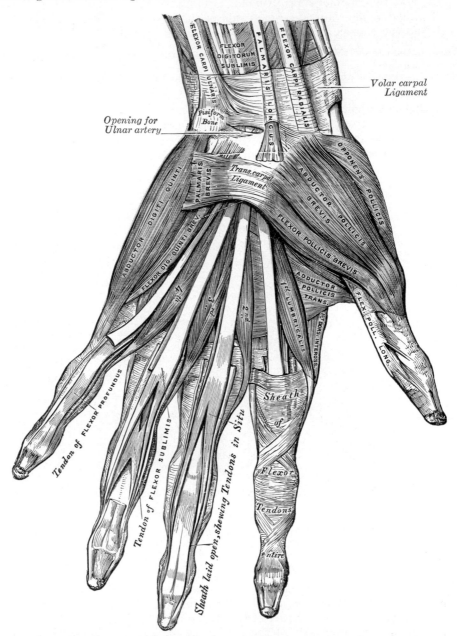

FIG. 475.—The muscles of the left hand. Palmar surface.

The **Adductor pollicis, caput obliquus** (*Adductor obliquus pollicis*) *arises* by several slips from the capitate bone, the bases of the second and third metacarpals, the intercarpal ligaments, and the sheath of the tendon of the Flexor carpi radialis. From this origin the greater number of fibers pass obliquely distalward and converge to a tendon, which, uniting with the tendons of the medial portion of the

Flexor pollicis brevis and the transverse part of the Adductor, is *inserted* into the ulnar side of the base of the first phalanx of the thumb, a sesamoid bone being present in the tendon. A considerable fasciculus, however, passes more obliquely beneath the tendon of the Flexor pollicis longus to join the lateral portion of the Flexor brevis and the Abductor pollicis brevis.

The **Adductor pollicis, caput tranversus** (*Adductor transversus pollicis*) (Fig. 474) is the most deeply seated of this group of muscles. It is of a triangular form arising by a broad base from the distal two-thirds of the volar surface of the third metacarpal bone; the fibers converge, to be *inserted* with the medial part of the Flexor pollicis brevis and the Adductor pollicis (obliquus) into the ulnar side of the base of the first phalanx of the thumb.

Action.—Adducts, that is, brings the thumb toward the palm.

Nerve.—A branch of the deep palmar branch of the ulnar, containing fibers from the eighth cervical and first thoracic nerves.

Variations.—The Abductor pollicis brevis is often divided into an outer and an inner part; accessory slips from the tendon of the Abductor pollicis longus or Palmaris longus, more rarely from the Extensor carpi radialis longus, from the styloid process or Opponens pollicis or from the skin over the thenar eminence. The deep head of the Flexor pollicis brevis may be absent or enlarged. The two adductors vary in their relative extent and in the closeness of their connection. The Adductor obliquus may receive a slip from the transverse metacarpal ligament.

2. The Hypothenar Muscles (Figs. 474, 475).

Palmaris brevis.	Flexor digiti quinti brevis.
Abductor digiti quinti.	Opponens digiti quinti.

The **Palmaris brevis** is a thin, quadrilateral muscle, placed beneath the integument of the ulnar side of the hand. It *arises* by tendinous fasciculi from the transverse carpal ligament and palmar aponeurosis; the fleshy fibers are *inserted* into the skin on the ulnar border of the palm of the hand.

Action.—Draws the skin at the ulnar side of the palm toward the middle of the palm, increasing the height of the hypothenar eminence, as in clenching the fist. Holds the hypothenar subcutaneous pad in place, as in catching a ball.

Nerve.—A branch of the ulnar nerve, containing fibers from the eighth cervical nerve.

The **Abductor digiti quinti** (*Abductor minimi digiti*) is situated on the ulnar border of the palm of the hand. It *arises* from the pisiform bone and from the tendon of the Flexor carpi ulnaris, and ends in a flat tendon, which divides into two slips; one is *inserted* into the ulnar side of the base of the first phalanx of the little finger; the other into the ulnar border of the aponeurosis of the Extensor digiti quinti proprius.

Action.—Abducts the little finger and flexes its proximal phalanx.

Nerve.—A branch of the ulnar nerve, containing fibers from the eight cervical and first thoracic nerves.

The **Flexor digiti quinti brevis** (*Flexor brevis minimi digiti*) lies on the same plane as the preceding muscle, on its radial side. It *arises* from the convex surface of the hamulus of the hamate bone, and the volar surface of the transverse carpal ligament, and is *inserted* into the ulnar side of the base of the first phalanx of the little finger. It is separated from the Abductor, at its origin, by the deep branches of the ulnar artery and nerve. This muscle is sometimes wanting; the Abductor is then, usually, of large size.

Action.—Flexes the little finger.

Nerve.—A branch of the ulnar nerve, containing fibers from the eighth cervical and first thoracic nerves.

The **Opponens digiti quinti** (*Opponens minimi digiti*) (Fig. 474) is of a triangular form, and placed immediately beneath the preceding muscles. It *arises* from the convexity of the hamulus of the hamate bone, and contiguous portion of the transverse carpal ligament; it is inserted into the whole length of the metacarpal bone of the little finger, along its ulnar margin.

Action.—Abducts, flexes, and rotates the fifth metacarpal in bringing the little finger out to face the thumb.

Nerve.—A branch of the ulnar nerve, containing fibers from the eighth cervical and first thoracic nerves.

Variations.—The Palmaris brevis varies greatly in size. The Abductor digiti quinti may be divided into two or three slips or united with the Flexor digiti quinti brevis. Accessory head from the tendon of the Flexor carpi ulnaris, the transverse carpal ligament, the fascia of the forearm or the tendon of the Palmaris longus. A portion of the muscle may insert into the metacarpal, or separate slips the *Pisimetacarpus*, *Pisiuncinatus* or the *Pisiannularis* muscle may exist.

3. The Intermediate Muscles.

Lumbricales.　　　　　　　　　　　　　　　　Interossei.

The **Lumbricales** (Fig. 475) are four small fleshy fasciculi, associated with the tendons of the Flexor digitorum profundus. The first and second *arise* from the radial sides and volar surfaces of the tendons of the index and middle fingers respectively; the third, from the contiguous sides of the tendons of the middle and ring fingers; and the fourth, from the contiguous sides of the tendons of the ring and little fingers. Each passes to the radial side of the corresponding finger, and opposite the metacarpophalangeal articulation is *inserted* into the tendinous expansion of the Extensor digitorum communis covering the dorsal aspect of the finger.

Action.—Flex the metacarpophalangeal joints and extend the two distal phalanges.

Nerves.—The first and second Lumbricales by branches of the third and fourth digital branches of the median nerve, containing fibers from the sixth and seventh cervical nerves. The third and fourth by branches of the deep palmar branch of the ulnar, containing fibers from the eighth cervical nerve. The third Lumbrical may receive twigs from both nerves or all its fibers from the median nerve.

Variations.—The Lumbricales vary in number from two to five or six and there is considerable variation in insertions.

The **Interossei** (Figs. 476, 477) are so named from occupying the intervals between the metacarpal bones, and are divided into two sets, a dorsal and a volar.

The **Interossei dorsales** (*Dorsal interossei*) are *four* in number, and occupy the intervals between the metacarpal bones. They are bipenniform muscles, each *arising* by two heads from the adjacent sides of the metacarpal bones, but more extensively from the metacarpal bone of the finger into which the muscle is inserted. They are inserted into the bases of the first phalanges and into the aponeuroses of the tendons of the Extensor digitorum communis. Between the double origin of each of these muscles is a narrow triangular interval; through the first of these the radial artery passes; through each of the other three a perforating branch from the deep volar arch is transmitted.

The **first** or **Abductor indicis** is larger than the others. It is flat, triangular in form, and *arises* by two heads, separated by a fibrous arch for the passage of the radial artery from the dorsum to the palm of the hand. The lateral head *arises* from the proximal half of the ulnar border of the first metacarpal bone; the medial head, from almost the entire length of the radial border of the second metacarpal bone; the tendon is inserted into the radial side of the index finger. The **second** and **third** are inserted into the middle finger, the former into its radial, the latter into its ulnar side. The **fourth** is inserted into the ulnar side of the ring finger.

Action.—Abduct the fingers from an imaginary line drawn through the axis of the midde finger; flex the metacarpophalangeal joint and extend the two distal phalanges.

Nerves.—Branches from the deep palmar branch of the ulnar, containing fibers from the eighth cervical and first thoracic nerves.

The **Interossei volares** (*Palmar interossei*), three in number, are smaller than the Interossei dorsales, and placed upon the volar surfaces of the metacarpal bones, rather than between them. Each *arises* from the entire length of the metacarpal bone of one finger, and is *inserted* into the side of the base of the first phalanx and aponeurotic expansion of the Extensor communis tendon to the same finger.

The **first** *arises* from the ulnar side of the second metacarpal bone, and is *inserted* into the same side of the first phalanx of the index finger. The **second** *arises* from the radial side of the fourth metacarpal bone, and is *inserted* into the same side of the ring finger. The **third** *arises* from the radial side of the fifth metacarpal bone, and is *inserted* into the same side of the little finger. From this account it may be seen that each finger is provided with two Interossei, with the exception of the little finger, in which the Abductor takes the place of one of the pair.

As already mentioned (p. 521), the medial head of the Flexor pollicis brevis is sometimes described as the **Interosseus palmaris primus.**

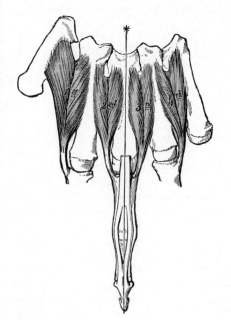
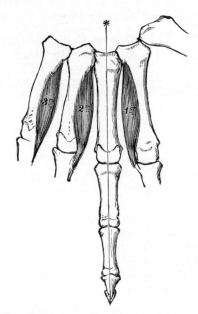

FIG. 476.—The Interossei dorsales of left hand.   FIG.477. —The Interossei volares of left hand.

Action.—Adduct the fingers toward an imaginary line through the axis of the middle finger. flex the metacarpophalangeal joint and extend the two distal phalanges.

Nerves.—Branches from the deep palmar branch of the ulnar, containing fibers from the eighth cervical and first thoracic nerves.

Group Actions.—Flexion of the fingers in grasping an object is performed by the Flexores digitorum sublimis and profundus. The wrist extensors contract synergetically to prevent flexion of the wrist. The characteristic action of the profundus, to flex the terminal phalanx, can be carried out independently as a freak by some individuals. The action of both muscles on the two terminal phalanges can be performed independently of the proximal phalanx by calling into play the synergetic action of the Extensor digitorum communis on the proximal phalanx. Flexion of the proximal phalanx at the same time as extension of the two distal joints is performed by the Interossei dorsales and volares, and the Lumbricales.

Extension of the proximal phalanges is performed by the Extensor digitorum communis, Extensor indicis proprius, and Extensor digiti quinti proprius. The wrist flexors contract synergetically to prevent extension at the wrist. The long extensors have a weak action on the two terminal joints, and must be assisted in this action by the Lumbricales and the Interossei.

Abduction of the fingers is performed by the Interossei dorsales and the Abductor digiti quinti, considering the axis of the middle finger as the center of the hand. Full abduction can be carried out only if the fingers are extended, because of restrictions in the joints. Adduction of the fingers is performed by the Interossei volares, and can be performed with the fingers either flexed or extended.

The thumb is so placed that its plane of flexion and extension is at right angles to that of the fingers. Flexion and extension of the thumb, therefore, are in the same plane as abduction and adduction of the fingers; abduction and adduction of the thumb are in the same plane as flexion and extension of the fingers. Flexion of the distal phalanx is performed by the Flexor pollicis longus; of the proximal phalanx alone by the Flexor pollicis brevis. Extension of the distal phalanx is performed by the Extensor pollicis longus, the proximal phalanx by the Extensor pollicis brevis. Abduction of the thumb is by the Abductores pollicis longus and brevis; adduction by the Adductor pollicis. It is seldom that extension or abduction are performed independently of each other, most normal activity being a mixture of the two movements. When the thumb is used in grasping, first, as a preliminary, it is abducted by the Abductores, and rotated by the Opponens so that its palmar surface faces the palm of the hand, and then finally, the actual grasping is performed largely by the Flexor pollicis longus.

THE MUSCLES AND FASCIÆ OF THE LOWER EXTREMITY.

The muscles of the lower extremity are subdivided into groups corresponding with the different regions of the limb.

I. Muscles of the Iliac Region.　　III. Muscles of the Leg.
II. Muscles of the Thigh.　　　　IV. Muscles of the Foot.

THE MUSCLES AND FASCIÆ OF THE ILIAC REGION (Fig. 478).

Psoas major.　　　　　Psoas minor.　　　　　Iliacus.

The fascia covering the intra-abdominal surface of the Iliacus and Psoas is part of the endo-abdominal or internal investing layer of deep fascia, but, as it follows these muscles under the inguinal ligament out into the thigh, it becomes continuous with the fascia lata which is a portion of the external investing fascia. In this way, it forms an important direct continuity between the internal and the external investing layers of deep fascia. The endo-abdominal portion of this fascia is covered internally by subserous fascia.

Iliac Fascia (*fascia iliaca*).—The endo-abdominal portion of the iliac fascia is attached at its cephalic limit to the entire length of the inner lip of the crest of the ilium, along with the muscle. Above that, it is continuous with the definitive transversalis fascia except near the vertebral column where it is continuous with the quadratus lumborum fascia. It is continuous medially, with the psoas fascia, and, after attaching to the arcuate line of the ilium, it is continued down into the lesser pelvis as the obturator internus fascia. At the inguinal ligament, it meets and fuses with the transversalis fascia of the lateral portion of the anterior abdominal wall to form a single sheet which follows the surface of the Iliacus under the ligament out into the thigh. It is securely attached to the ligament, as it passes under it, and at this point the origins of the Obliquus internus and Transversus abdominis are attached to the iliac fascia as well as to the inguinal ligament. In the thigh, it becomes continuous with the part of the fascia lata over the Sartorius, laterally, and with the iliopectineal fascia, medially.

Psoas Fascia.—The cephalic extremity of the psoas fascia is intimately blended with the medial lumbocostal arch of the Diaphragm, which stretches from the bodies to the transverse processes of the first or second lumbar vertebræ. It is attached, medially, by a series of arched processes to the intervertebral fibro-cartilages and prominent margins of the vertebræ, and to the upper part of the sacrum. The intervals left between these arched processes and the constricted bodies of the vertebræ transmit the lumbar arteries and veins, and the filaments of the sympathetic trunk. It is continuous laterally with the quadratus lumborum and iliac fasciæ. At the inguinal ligament and in the thigh, the psoas and iliac fasciæ combine to make up part of a complex called the iliopectineal fascia.

Iliopectineal Fascia (*fascia iliopectinea*).—The iliopectineal fascia is made up of three interconnected portions: (*a*) the fascia covering the femoral portions of the Iliacus and Psoas; (*b*) the fascia over the proximal portion of the Pectineus, and (*c*) a thickened band which dips down between the Psoas and the femoral vessels as they pass under the inguinal ligament. The fascia as a whole is continuous, under the inguinal ligament, with the endo-abdominal iliac, psoas, and transversalis fasciæ. Parts (*a*) and (*b*) together form a sheet which is the floor of the femoral (Scarpa's) triangle. At the junction of the iliopsoas and pectineal portions of this fascia, there is a firm attachment to the iliopectineal eminence of the ilium and to the pubocapsular ligament of the hip joint. From the attachment to the iliopectineal eminence, the fascia passes outward as a thickened band (*c*, above) between the Psoas and the femoral vessels toward the inguinal ligament to which it becomes attached (Fig. 384). This band divides the interval beneath the inguinal ligament, that is, between the ligament and the pelvic bone, into two parts known as the lacuna musculorum and the lacuna vasorum. The **lacuna musculorum** contains the Iliacus and Psoas, and the femoral nerve. The **lacuna vasorum** contains the femoral artery and vein, and the femoral canal (page 696).

The **Iliopsoas** is frequently regarded as a single muscle but it is here divided into its two parts, the Psoas major and the Iliacus, for convenience of description.

The **Psoas major** (*Psoas magnus*) (Fig. 478) is a long fusiform muscle placed on the side of the lumbar region of the vertebral column and brim of the lesser pelvis. It *arises* (1) from the anterior surfaces of the bases and lower borders of the transverse processes of all the lumbar vertebræ; (2) from the sides of the bodies and the corresponding intervertebral fibrocartilages of the last thoracic and all the lumbar vertebræ by five slips, each of which is attached to the adjacent upper and lower margins of two vertebræ, and to the intervertebral fibrocartilage; (3) from a series of tendinous arches which extend across the constricted parts of the bodies of the lumbar vertebræ between the previous slips; the lumbar arteries and veins, and filaments from the sympathetic trunk pass beneath these tendinous arches. The muscle proceeds downward across the brim of the lesser pelvis, and diminishing gradually in size, passes beneath the inguinal ligament and

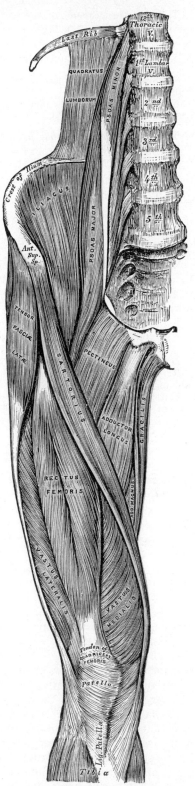

FIG. 478.—Muscles of the iliac and anterior femoral regions.

in front of the capsule of the hip-joint and ends in a tendon which also receives nearly the whole of the fibers of the Iliacus and is *inserted* into the lesser trochanter of the femur. A large bursa which may communicate with the cavity of the hip-joint, separates the tendon from the pubis and the capsule of the joint.

Action.—Flexes the thigh and rotates it medially; flexes the lumbar vertebral column and bends it laterally.

Nerves.—Branches of the lumbar plexus, containing fibers from the second and third lumbar nerves.

The **Psoas minor** (*Psoas parvus*) is a long slender muscle, placed in front of the Psoas major. It *arises* from the sides of the bodies of the twelfth thoracic and first lumbar vertebræ and from the fibrocartilage between them. It ends in a long flat tendon which is *inserted* into the pectineal line and iliopectineal eminence, and, by its lateral border, into the iliac fascia. This muscle is often absent.

Action.—Flexes the pelvis and lumbar vertebral column.

Nerve.—A branch of the first lumbar nerve.

The **Iliacus** is a flat, triangular muscle, which fills the iliac fossa. It *arises* from the upper two-thirds of this fossa, and from the inner lip of the iliac crest; behind, from the anterior sacroiliac and the iliolumbar ligaments, and base of the sacrum; in front, it reaches as far as the anterior superior and anterior inferior iliac spines, and the notch between them. The fibers converge to be inserted into the lateral side of the tendon of the Psoas major, some of them being prolonged on to the body of the femur for about 2.5 cm. below and in front of the lesser trochanter.

Action.—Flexes the thigh and rotates it medially.

Nerves.—Branches of the femoral nerve, containing fibers from the second and third lumbar nerves.

Variations.—The *Iliacus minor* or *Iliocapsularis*, a small detached part of the Iliacus is frequently present. It arises from the anterior inferior spine of the ilium and is inserted into the lower part of the intertrochanteric line of the femur or into the iliofemoral ligament.

II. THE MUSCLES AND FASCIÆ OF THE THIGH.

Superficial Fascia (*tela subcutanea*).—The superficial fascia forms a prominent layer over the entire thigh. It usually contains a considerable amount of fat, but it varies in thickness in different regions. It is continuous with the superficial fascia of the abdomen, the leg, and, over the gluteal region, with the back. It may be separated into a superficial fatty layer and a deep membranous layer between which are found the superficial vessels and nerves, the superficial inguinal lymph nodes, and the great saphenous vein. In well-nourished individuals, the adipose tissue of the superficial layer is usually divided into two or three subsidiary layers by fibrous membranes which are associated with the emergence of the superficial nerves. The deep or fibrous layer is adherent to the fascia lata a little below the inguinal ligament and along the upper medial portion of the thigh. It is attached to the margin of the fossa ovalis (saphenous opening), and fills the opening itself with an irregular layer of spongy tissue, called the **fascia cribrosa** (Fig. 627) because it is pierced by numerous openings for the passage of the saphenous vein and other blood and lymphatic vessels.

A large subcutaneous bursa is found in the superficial fascia over the patella.

Fascia Lata (Fig. 479).—The external investing fascia of the thigh is named fascia lata from its broad extent. Its thick, lateral portion is commonly taken to be typical of its texture, but it is thin in some areas where it has not been reinforced by fibrous contributions from the tendons. Proximally, it is continuous with the external abdominal and lumbodorsal fasciæ after being attached to the pelvic bone and inguinal ligament; distally it is continuous with the fascia of the leg.

The *medial portion* lies over the Adductor group of muscles and is thin, grey, and not aponeurotic. It is attached to the ischial tuberosity and ischiopubic ramus, and beyond this is continuous with the external perineal fascia. At the knee it is thick and aponeurotic, having been strengthened by fibers from the tendon of the Sartorius. The *anterior portion* is attached to the pubic tubercle, inguinal ligament, and anterior superior iliac spine. Just distal to the lateral half of the inguinal ligament, it is a single sheet formed by the fusion of three abdominal fasciæ. Of these, the most superficial is the external fascia over the aponeurosis of the Obliquus

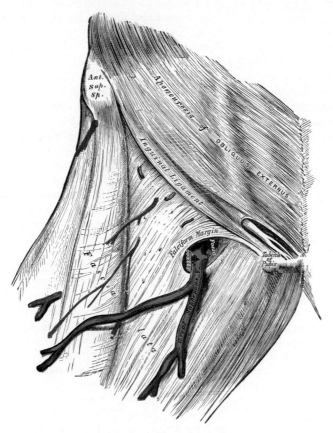

Fig. 479.—The fossa ovalis.

externus (fascia innominata) which passes superficial to the inguinal ligament; the middle one is the transversalis fascia of the anterior abdominal wall which passes under the inguinal ligament; the internal one also passes under the inguinal ligament and is the continuation of the iliac fascia. Distal to the medial half of the inguinal ligament, the middle and internal layers just mentioned fail to join the fascia lata at the ligament and continue into the thigh as the anterior and posterior portions of the femoral sheath. The fascia lata in this medial region over the femoral vessels is thickened and laminated and has an opening through it, called the fossa ovalis (see below), for the passage of the great saphenous vein. The outer lamina is attached to the pubic tubercle along with the inguinal ligament; it has a free falciform margin which crosses the proximal end of the great saphenous vein and spirals outward, downward, and behind the vein to join the deep lamina medial to the vein. The two laminæ are separated by a pad of adipose tissue. The anterior portion of the fascia lata is thicker than the medial, but is truly aponeurotic only

34

near the knee where it is reinforced by fibers from the tendons of the Vasti. It is separated from the underlying Sartorius and Quadriceps by a fascial space, except near the knee. The *lateral portion* is a thick strong aponeurosis, containing the tendinous fibers of insertion of the Glutæus maximus and the Tensor fasciæ latæ. It is attached proximally to the crest of the ilium and the back of the sacrum. Between the iliac crest and the superior border of the Glutæus maximus, it is thickened by vertical tendinous bundles and is known as the **gluteal aponeurosis** (Fig. 483) which is used by the Glutæus medius for part of its origin. At the border of the maximus it splits to enclose the muscle; the external layer of this **gluteal fascia** is thin, is closely bound to the superficial fascia and the muscle, and sends septa down between large bundles of the muscle. In the region over the great trochanter, the muscular fasciculi end in a broad tendon which is imbedded in the fascia lata and is called the **iliotibial band** (*tractus iliotibialis*). Below the anterior part of the iliac crest, the fascia splits to enclose the Tensor fasciæ latæ which is inserted into the iliotibial band below the maximus. The iliotibial band is separated from the underlying Vastus lateralis by a distinct fascial cleft. It is inserted into the tibia and is blended with fibrous expansions from the Vastus lateralis and Biceps femoris. The *posterior portion* of the fascia lata is formed proximally by the union of the two layers of fascia enclosing the Glutæus maximus at its inferior border. It covers the hamstring muscles and the popliteal fossa.

Two strong intermuscular septa (Fig. 480) connect the deep surface of the fascia lata with the linea aspera of the femur. The **lateral intermuscular septum** is the stronger; it separates the Vastus lateralis from the Biceps femoris and is used by both muscles for the attachment of their fibers. It extends from the insertion of the Glutæus maximus to the lateral condyle. The **medial intermuscular septum** lies between the Vastus medialis and the Adductores and Pectineus. Its outer portion near the fascia lata, splits to enclose the Sartorius and contributes to the formation of the adductor canal (Hunter's canal) about the femoral vessels.

The **Fossa Ovalis** (*hiatus saphenus*) (Fig. 479) is an oval aperture in the fascia lata in the proximal part of the thigh, a little below the medial end of the inguinal ligament. The great saphenous vein passes through it just before it joins the femoral vein. The fascia lata in this part of the thigh is thickened by lamination into two leaves separated by fat. The superficial leaf is attached to the inguinal ligament and pubic tubercle. It ends abruptly in a free border, the **falciform margin of the fossa,** which forms a spiral of one turn beginning at the pubic tubercle, coursing at first in a lateral direction superficial to the vein, then down along the vein and back medially under the vein. Medial to the vein the superficial leaf merges with the deep leaf. The proximal and lateral part of the falciform margin is called the **cornu superius,** the medial and distal part the **cornu inferius.** The deep leaf is formed by the pectineal, iliopectineal, and iliac fasciæ. The fossa ovalis is filled in and covered over by a thickened pad derived from the deep layer of superficial fascia, called the fascia cribrosa.

1. **The Anterior Femoral Muscles** (Fig. 478).

Sartorius.

Quadriceps femoris.
{
Rectus femoris.
Vastus lateralis.
Vastus medialis.
Vastus intermedius.

Articularis genus.

The **Sartorius,** the longest muscle in the body, is narrow and ribbon-like; it *arises* by tendinous fibers from the anterior superior iliac spine and the upper half of the notch below it. It passes obliquely across the upper and anterior part of the thigh, from the lateral to the medial side of the limb, then descends vertically, as far as the medial side of the knee, passing behind the medial condyle of the femur. It ends in a tendon which curves obliquely forward and expands into a broad aponeurosis, which is *inserted*, in front of the Gracilis and Semitendinosus, into the upper part of the medial surface of the body of the tibia, nearly as far forward as the anterior crest. The upper part of the aponeurosis is curved backward over the upper edge of the tendon of the Gracilis so as to be inserted behind it. An offset,

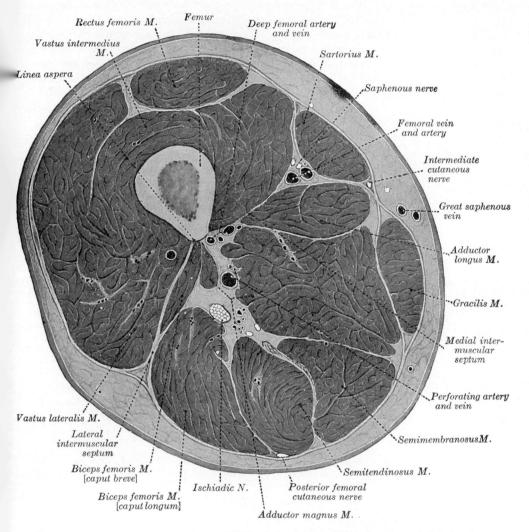

Fig. 480.—Cross-section through the middle of the thigh. (Eycleshymer and Schoemaker.)

from its upper margin, blends with the capsule of the knee-joint, and another from its lower border, with the fascia on the medial side of the leg.

Action.—Flexes the thigh and rotates it laterally. Flexes the leg and, after it is flexed, rotates it slightly medially.

Nerves.—Branches, usually two in number, from the femoral nerve containing fibers from the second and third lumbar nerves. The first branch is distributed to the proximal portion of the muscle and arises in common with the intermediate anterior cutaneous nerve; the second branch is distributed to the distal portion.

Variations.—Slips of origin from the outer end of the inguinal ligament, the notch of the ilium the ilio-pectineal line or the pubis occur. The muscle may be split into two parts, and one part may be inserted into the fascia lata, the femur, the ligament of the patella or the tendon of the Semitendinosus. The tendon of insertion may end in the fascia lata, the capsule of the knee-joint, or the fascia of the leg. The muscle may be absent.

The **Quadriceps femoris** (*Quadriceps extensor*) includes the four remaining muscles on the front of the thigh. It is the great extensor muscle of the leg, forming a large fleshy mass which covers the front and sides of the femur. It is subdivided into separate portions, which have received distinctive names. One occupying the middle of the thigh, and connected above with the ilium, is called from its straight course the **Rectus femoris**. The other three lie in immediate connection with the body of the femur, which they cover from the trochanters to the condyles. The portion on the lateral side of the femur is termed the **Vastus lateralis**; that covering the medial side, the **Vastus medialis**; and that in front, the **Vastus intermedius** (Fig. 478).

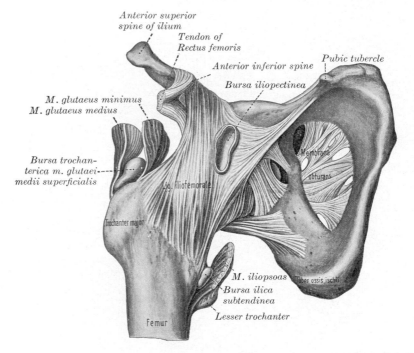

FIG. 481.—Muscular insertions and bursae around the hip joint (*Rauber-Kopsch, Lehrbuch u. Atlas d. Anatomie d. Menchen*, 19th Edition, Vol. I, courtesy of Georg Thieme Verlag Stuttgart, 1955).

The **Rectus femoris** is situated in the middle of the front of the thigh; it is fusiform in shape, and its superficial fibers are arranged in a bipenniform manner, the deep fibers running straight down to the deep aponeurosis. It *arises* by two tendons: one, the anterior or straight, from the anterior inferior iliac spine; the other, the posterior or reflected, from a groove above the brim of the acetabulum. The two unite at an acute angle, and spread into an aponeurosis which is prolonged downward on the anterior surface of the muscle, and from this the muscular fibers arise. The muscle ends in a broad and thick aponeurosis which occupies the lower two-thirds of its posterior surface, and, gradually becoming narrowed into a flattened tendon, is *inserted* into the base of the patella.

The **Vastus lateralis** (*Vastus externus*) is the largest part of the Quadriceps femoris. It *arises* by a broad aponeurosis, which is attached to the upper part of

the intertrochanteric line, to the anterior and inferior borders of the greater trochanter, to the lateral lip of the gluteal tuberosity, and to the upper half of the
lateral lip of the linea aspera; this aponeurosis covers the upper three-fourths of
the muscle, and from its deep surface many fibers take origin. A few additional
fibers arise from the tendon of the Glutæus maximus, and from the lateral intermuscular septum between the Vastus lateralis and short head of the Biceps femoris.
The fibers form a large fleshy mass, which is attached to a strong aponeurosis,
placed on the deep surface of the lower part of the muscle; this aponeurosis becomes
contracted and thickened into a flat tendon inserted into the lateral border of the
patella, blending with the Quadriceps femoris tendon, and giving an expansion to
the capsule of the knee-joint.

The Vastus medialis and Vastus intermedius appear to be inseparably united,
but when the Rectus femoris has been reflected a narrow interval will be observed
extending upward from the medial border of the patella between the two muscles,
and the separation may be continued as far as the lower part of the intertrochanteric line, where, however, the two muscles are frequently continuous.

The **Vastus medialis** (*Vastus internus*) *arises* from the lower half of the intertrochanteric line, the medial lip of the linea aspera, the upper part of the medial
supracondylar line, the tendons of the Adductor longus and the Adductor magnus
and the medial intermuscular septum. Its fibers are directed downward and forward, and are chiefly attached to an aponeurosis which lies on the deep surface
of the muscle and is *inserted* into the medial border of the patella and the Quadriceps femoris tendon, an expansion being sent to the capsule of the knee-joint.

The **Vastus intermedius** (*Crureus*) *arises* from the front and lateral surfaces of the
body of the femur in its upper two-thirds and from the lower part of the lateral
intermuscular septum. Its fibers end in a superficial aponeurosis, which forms
the deep part of the Quadriceps femoris tendon.

The **tendons** of the different portions of the Quadriceps unite at the lower part of the thigh,
so as to form a single strong tendon, which is inserted into the base of the patella, some few fibers
passing over it to blend with the ligmentum patellæ. More properly, the patella may be regarded
as a sesamoid bone, developed in the tendon of the Quadriceps; and the ligamentum patellæ,
which is continued from the apex of the patella to the tuberosity of the tibia, as the proper tendon
of insertion of the muscle, the medial and lateral patellar retinacula (see p. 318) being expansions from its borders. A bursa, which usually communicates with the cavity of the knee-joint,
is situated between the femur and the portion of the Quadriceps tendon above the patella; another
is interposed between the tendon and the upper part of the front of the tibia; and a third, the
prepatellar bursa, is placed over the patella itself.

Action.—The entire Quadriceps extends the leg. The Rectus femoris also flexes the thigh.

Nerves.—Branches of the femoral nerve containing fibers from the second, third, and fourth
lumbar nerves.

The **Articularis genus** (*Subcrureus*) is a small muscle, usually distinct from the
Vastus intermedius, but occasionally blended with it; it *arises* from the anterior
surface of the lower part of the body of the femur, and is inserted into the upper
part of the synovial membrane of the knee-joint. It sometimes consists of several
separate muscular bundles.

Action.—Draws the articular capsule upward.
Nerve.—A branch of the nerve to the Vastus intermedius.

2. The Medial Femoral Muscles.

Gracilis.	Adductor longus.	Adductor magnus.
Pectineus.	Adductor brevis.	

The **Gracilis** (Fig. 478) is the most superficial muscle on the medial side of the
thigh. It is thin and flattened, broad above, narrow and tapering below. It

arises by a thin aponeurosis from the anterior margins of the lower half of the symphysis pubis and the upper half of the pubic arch. The fibers run vertically downward, and end in a rounded tendon, which passes behind the medial condyle of the femur, curves around the medial condyle of the tibia, where it becomes flattened, and is *inserted* into the upper part of the medial surface of the body of the tibia, below the condyle. A few of the fibers of the lower part of the tendon are prolonged into the deep fascia of the leg. At its insertion the tendon is situated immediately above that of the Semitendinosus, and its upper edge is overlapped by the tendon of the Sartorius, with which it is in part blended. It is separated from the tibial collateral ligament of the knee-joint, by a bursa common to it and the tendon of the Semitendinosus.

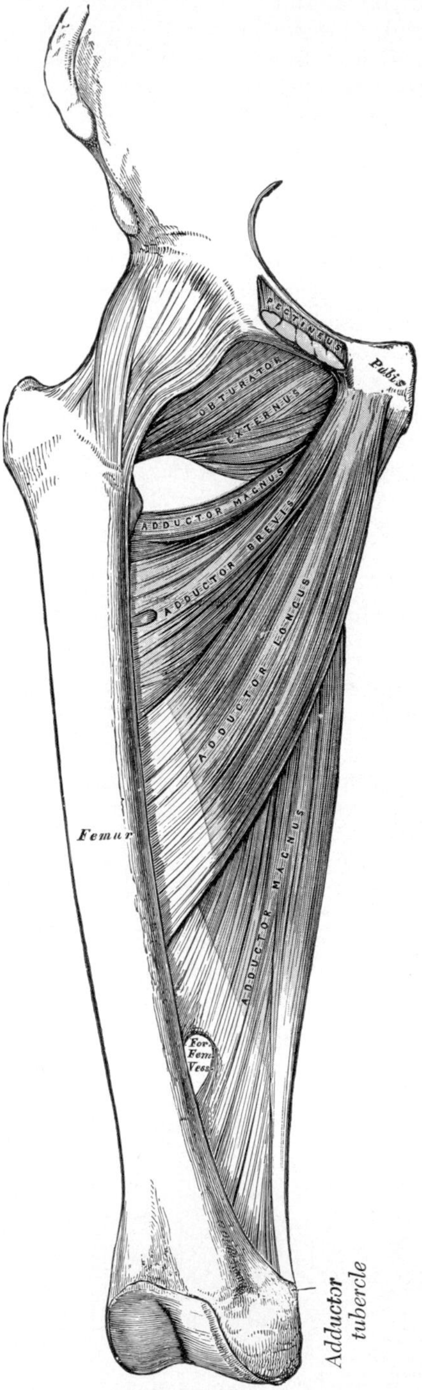

Action.—Adducts the thigh. Flexes the leg, and after it is flexed, assists in its medial rotation.

Nerve.—A branch of the anterior division of the obturator nerve containing fibers from the third and fourth lumbar nerves.

The **Pectineus** (Fig. 478) is a flat, quadrangular muscle, situated at the anterior part of the upper and medial aspect of the thigh. It *arises* from the pectineal line, and to a slight extent from the surface of bone in front of it, between the iliopectineal eminence and tubercle of the pubis, and from the fascia covering the anterior surface of the muscle; the fibers pass downward, backward, and lateralward, to be inserted into a rough line leading from the lesser trochanter to the linea aspera.

Action.—Flexes and adducts the thigh, and rotates it medially.

Nerve.—Usually a branch of the femoral nerve containing fibers from the second, third, and fourth lumbar nerves. When an accessory obturator is present, one of its branches is distributed to the Pectineus. It may receive a branch from the obturator nerve.

Variations.—The Pectineus may consist of two incompletely separated strata; the lateral or dorsal stratum is supplied by a branch of the femoral nerve or the accessory obturator if present; the medial or ventral stratum, when present, is supplied by the obturator nerve. The muscle may be attached to or inserted into the capsule of the hip joint.

The **Adductor longus** (Fig. 482), the most superficial of the three Adductores, is a triangular muscle, lying in the same plane as the Pectineus. It *arises* by a flat, narrow tendon, from the front of the pubis, at the angle of junction of the crest with the sym-

FIG. 482.—Deep muscles of the medial femoral region.

physis; and soon expands into a broad fleshy belly. This passes downward, backward, and lateralward, and is *inserted*, by an aponeurosis, into the linea aspera, between the Vastus medialis and the Adductor magnus, with both of which it is usually blended.

Action.—Adducts, flexes, and tends to rotate the thigh medially.

Nerve.—A branch of the anterior division of the obturator nerve containing fibers from the third and fourth lumbar nerves.

Variations.—The Adductor longus may be double, may extend to the knee, or be more or less united with the Pectineus.

The **Adductor brevis** (Fig. 482) is situated immediately behind the two preceding muscles. It is somewhat triangular in form, and *arises* by a narrow origin from the outer surface of the inferior ramus of the pubis, between the Gracilis and Obturator externus. Its fibers, passing backward, lateralward, and downward, are *inserted*, by an aponeurosis, into the line leading from the lesser trochanter to the linea aspera and into the upper part of the linea aspera, immediately behind the Pectineus and upper part of the Adductor longus.

Action.—Adducts, flexes, and tends to rotate the thigh medially.

Nerve.—A branch of the obturator nerve, usually from its anterior division, containing fibers from the third and fourth lumbar nerves.

Variations.—The Adductor brevis may be divided into two or three parts, or it may be united with the Adductor magnus.

The **Adductor magnus** (Fig. 482) is a large triangular muscle, situated on the medial side of the thigh. It *arises* from a small part of the inferior ramus of the pubis, from the inferior ramus of the ischium, and from the outer margin of the inferior part of the tuberosity of the ischium. Those fibers which arise from the ramus of the pubis are short, horizontal in direction, and are inserted into the rough line leading from the greater trochanter to the linea aspera, medial to the Glutæus maximus; those from the ramus of the ischium are directed downward and lateralward with different degrees of obliquity, to be *inserted*, by means of a broad aponeurosis, into the linea aspera and the upper part of its medial prolongation below. The medial portion of the muscle, composed principally of the fibers arising from the tuberosity of the ischium, forms a thick fleshy mass consisting of coarse bundles which descend almost vertically, and end about the lower third of the thigh in a rounded tendon which is inserted into the adductor tubercle on the medial condyle of the femur, and is connected by a fibrous expansion to the line leading upward from the tubercle to the linea aspera. At the *insertion* of the muscle, there is a series of osseoaponeurotic openings, formed by tendinous arches attached to the bone. The upper four openings are small, and give passage to the perforating branches of the profunda femoris artery. The lowest is of large size, *hiatus tendineus*, and transmits the femoral vessels to the popliteal fossa.

Action.—The entire muscle adducts the thigh powerfully. The upper portion rotates the thigh medially and flexes it; the lower portion extends it powerfully and rotates it laterally.

Nerves.—Branches of the posterior division of the obturator nerve containing fibers from the third and fourth lumbar nerves, and in addition a branch from the sciatic nerve.

Variations.—The Adductor magnus is composed of three superimposed portions, the superior is frequently distinct but the middle and inferior are usually fused. The ischiocondylar or inferior portion is derived from the flexor or hamstring muscles of lower forms and is the portion supplied by the sciatic nerve. The magnus may be fused with the Quadratus femoris, or with either the Adductor longus or brevis.

The **Adductor minimus** is the name given to the superior portion of the Adductor magnus when it forms a distinct muscle.

3. The Muscles of the Gluteal Region (Figs. 483, 484).

Glutæus maximus.	Obturator internus.
Glutæus medius.	Gemellus superior.
Glutæus minimus.	Gemellus inferior.
Tensor fasciæ latæ.	Quadratus femoris.
Piriformis.	Obturator externus.

The **Glutæus maximus,** the most superficial muscle in the gluteal region, is a broad and thick fleshy mass of a quadrilateral shape, and forms the prominence of the nates. Its large size is one of the most characteristic features of the muscular system in man, connected as it is with the power he has of maintaining the trunk

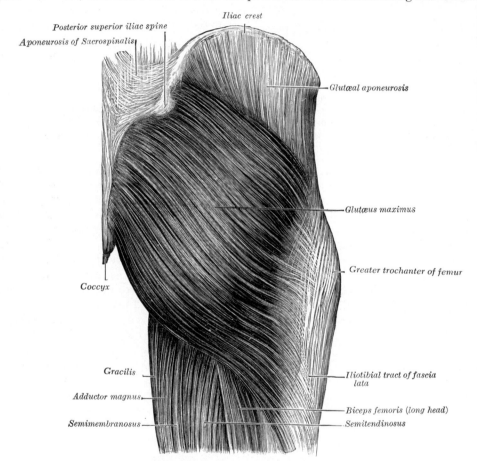

FIG. 483.—The right Glutæus maximus muscle.

in the erect posture. The muscle is remarkably coarse in structure, being made up of fasciculi lying parallel with one another and collected together into large bundles separated by fibrous septa. It *arises* from the posterior gluteal line of the ilium, and the rough portion of bone including the crest, immediately above and behind it; from the posterior surface of the lower part of the sacrum and the side of the coccyx; from the aponeurosis of the Sacrospinalis, the sacrotuberous ligament, and the fascia (gluteal aponeurosis) covering the Glutæus medius. The fibers are directed obliquely downward and lateralward; those forming the upper and larger portion of the muscle, together with the superficial fibers of the lower portion, end in a thick tendinous lamina, which passes across the greater trochanter, and is *inserted* into the iliotibial band of the fascia lata; the deeper fibers of the lower portion of the muscle are inserted into the gluteal tuberosity between the Vastus lateralis and Adductor magnus.

Action.—Extends and laterally rotates the thigh. Through the iliotibial band, it braces the knee when the latter is fully extended.

Nerve.—The inferior gluteal nerve, containing fibers from the fifth lumbar and first and second sacral nerves.

Bursæ.—Three **bursæ** are usually found in relation with the deep surface of this muscle. One of these, of large size, and generally multilocular, separates it from the greater trochanter; a second, often wanting, is situated on the tuberosity of the ischium; a third is found between the tendon of the muscle and that of the Vastus lateralis.

The **Glutæus medius** is a broad, thick, radiating muscle, situated on the outer surface of the pelvis. Its posterior third is covered by the Glutæus maximus, its anterior two-thirds by the gluteal aponeurosis, which separates it from the superficial fascia and integument. It *arises* from the outer surface of the ilium between the iliac crest and posterior gluteal line above, and the anterior gluteal line below; it also *arises* from the gluteal aponeurosis covering its outer surface. The fibers converge to a strong flattened tendon, which is *inserted* into the oblique ridge which runs downward and forward on the lateral surface of the greater trochanter. A bursa separates the tendon of the muscle from the surface of the trochanter over which it glides.

Action.—Abducts the thigh and rotates it medially. The anterior portion flexes and rotates medially; the posterior portion extends and rotates laterally.

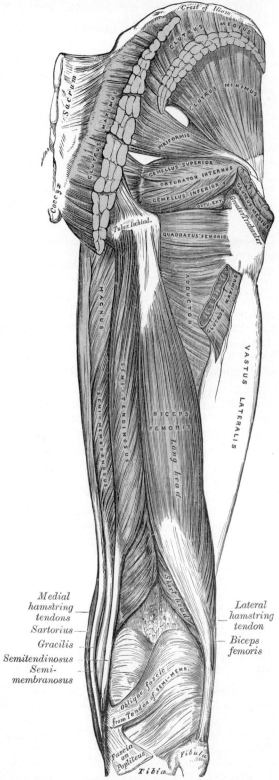

Fig. 484.—Muscles of the gluteal and posterior femoral regions.

Nerve.—Branches of the superior gluteal nerve, containing fibers from the fourth and fifth lumbar and first sacral nerves.

Variations.—The posterior border may be more or less closely united to the Piriformis, or some of the fibers end on its tendon.

The **Glutæus minimus** (Fig. 484) the smallest of the three Glutæi, is placed immediately beneath the preceding. It is fan-shaped, *arising* from the outer surface of the ilium, between the anterior and inferior gluteal lines, and behind, from the margin of the greater sciatic notch. The fibers converge to the deep surface of a radiated aponeurosis, and this ends in a tendon which is inserted into an impression on the anterior border of the greater trochanter, and gives an expansion to the capsule of the hip-joint. A bursa is interposed between the tendon and the greater trochanter. Between the Glutæus medius and Glutæus minimus are the deep branches of the superior gluteal vessels and the superior gluteal nerve. The deep surface of the Glutæus minimus is in relation with the reflected tendon of the Rectus femoris and the capsule of the hip-joint.

Action.—Rotates the thigh medially, abducts it, and to some extent, flexes it.

Nerve.—Branch of the superior gluteal nerve, containing fibers from the fourth and fifth lumbar and first sacral nerves.

Variations.—The muscle may be divided into an anterior and a posterior part, or it may send slips to the Piriformis, the Gemellus superior or the outer part of the origin of the Vastus lateralis.

The **Tensor fasciæ latæ** (*Tensor fasciæ femoris*) (Fig. 478) *arises* from the anterior part of the outer lip of the iliac crest; from the outer surface of the anterior superior iliac spine, and part of the outer border of the notch below it, between the Glutæus medius and Sartorius; and from the deep surface of the fascia lata. It is *inserted* between the two layers of the iliotibial band of the fascia lata about the junction of the middle and upper thirds of the thigh.

Action.—Flexes the thigh and, to some extent, rotates it medially.

Nerve.—A branch of the superior gluteal nerve to the Glutæus minimus, containing fibers from the fourth and fifth lumbar and first sacral nerves.

The **Piriformis** is a flat muscle, pyramidal in shape, lying almost parallel with the posterior margin of the Glutæus medius. It is situated partly within the pelvis against its posterior wall, and partly at the back of the hip-joint. It *arises* from the front of the sacrum by three fleshy digitations, attached to the portions of bone between the first, second, third, and fourth anterior sacral foramina, and to the grooves leading from the foramina: a few fibers also arise from the margin of the greater sciatic foramen, and from the anterior surface of the sacrotuberous ligament. The muscle passes out of the pelvis through the greater sciatic foramen, the upper part of which it fills, and is *inserted* by a rounded tendon into the upper border of the greater trochanter behind, but often partly blended with, the common tendon of the Obturator internus and Gemelli (Fig. 484.)

Action.—Rotates the thigh laterally, abducts and, to some extent, extends it.

Nerve.—One or two branches from the second sacral or the first and second sacral nerves.

Variations.—It is frequently pierced by the common peroneal nerve and thus divided more or less into two parts. It may be united with the Glutæus medius, or send fibers to the Glutæus minimus or receive fibers from the Gemellus superior. It may have only one or two sacral attachments or be inserted into the capsule of the hip-joint. It may be absent.

Obturator Membrane (Fig. 381, page 350).—The obturator membrane is a thin fibrous sheet, which almost completely closes the obturator foramen. Its fibers are arranged in interlacing bundles mainly transverse in direction; the uppermost bundle is attached to the obturator tubercles and completes the obturator canal for the passage of the obturator vessels and nerve. The membrane is attached to the sharp margin of the obturator foramen except at its lower lateral angle, where it is fixed to the pelvic surface of the inferior ramus of the ischium, *i. e.*, within the margin. The two obturator muscles arise partly from the opposite surfaces of this membrane.

The **Obturator internus** (Fig. 485) is situated partly within the lesser pelvis, and partly at the back of the hip-joint. It *arises* from the inner surface of the antero-lateral wall of the pelvis, where it surrounds the greater part of the obturator foramen, being attached to the inferior rami of the pubis and ischium, and at the side to the inner surface of the hip bone below and behind the pelvic brim, reaching from the

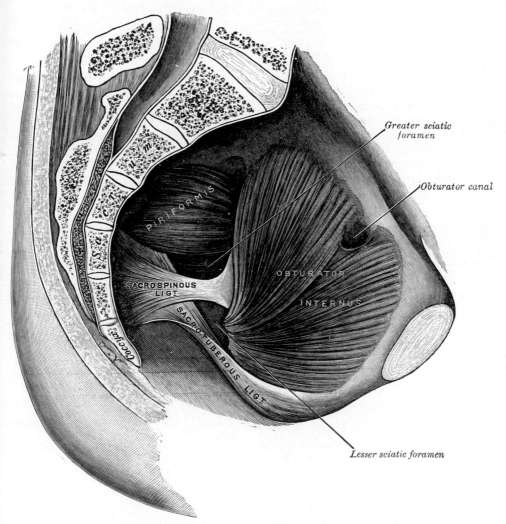

FIG. 485.—The left Obturator internus. Pelvic aspect.

upper part of the greater sciatic foramen above and behind to the obturator foramen below and in front. It also arises from the pelvic surface of the obturator membrane except in the posterior part, from the tendinous arch which completes the canal for the passage of the obturator vessels and nerve, and to a slight extent from the obturator fascia, which covers the muscle. The fibers converge rapidly toward the lesser sciatic foramen, and end in four or five tendinous bands, which are found on the deep surface of the muscle; these bands are reflected at a right angle over the grooved surface of the ischium between its spine and tuberosity. This bony

surface is covered by smooth cartilage, which is separated from the tendon by a
bursa, and presents one or more ridges corresponding with the furrows between
the tendinous bands. These bands leave the pelvis through the lesser sciatic foramen and unite into a single flattened tendon, which passes horizontally across the
capsule of the hip-joint, and, after receiving the attachments of the Gemelli, is
inserted into the forepart of the medial surface of the greater trochanter above
the trochanteric fossa. A bursa, narrow and elongated in form, is usually found
between the tendon and the capsule of the hip-joint; it occasionally communicates
with the bursa between the tendon and the ischium.

Action.—Rotates the thigh laterally; extends and abducts when the thigh is flexed.

Nerves.—A special nerve from the sacral plexus, containing fibers from the lumbosacral trunk
(fifth lumbar), and first and second sacral nerves.

The **Gemelli** are two small muscular fasciculi, accessories to the tendon of the
Obturator internus which is received into a groove between them (Fig. 484).

The **Gemellus superior**, the smaller of the two, *arises* from the outer surface of
the spine of the ischium, blends with the upper part of the tendon of the Obturator
internus, and is *inserted* with it into the medial surface of the greater trochanter.

The **Gemellus inferior** *arises* from the upper part of the tuberosity of the ischium,
immediately below the groove for the Obturator internus tendon. It blends with
the lower part of the tendon of the Obturator internus, and is *inserted* with it
into the medial surface of the greater trochanter.

Action.—Rotate the thigh laterally.

Nerves.—A branch of the nerve to the Obturator internus supplies the superior; a branch of
the nerve to the Quadratus femoris supplies the inferior.

Variations.—The Gemelli vary in size; the superior is smaller and is more frequently absent.
The inferior is more frequently bound intimately to the Obturator internus. The superior may be
fused with the Piriformis or Glutæus minimus, the inferior with the Quadratus femoris.

The **Quadratus femoris** (Fig. 484) is a flat, quadrilateral muscle; between the
Gemellus inferior and the upper margin of the Adductor magnus; it is separated
from the latter by the terminal branches of the medial femoral circumflex vessels.
It *arises* from the upper part of the external border of the tuberosity of the ischium,
and is *inserted* into the upper part of the linea quadrata—that is, the line which
extends vertically downward from the intertrochanteric crest. A bursa is often
found between the front of this muscle and the lesser trochanter.

Action.—Rotates the thigh laterally.

Nerve.—A special branch from the sacral plexus, containing fibers from the lumbosacral trunk
(fourth and fifth lumbar) and first sacral nerves.

Variations.—Absence of the Quadratus femoris has been reported in 1 or 2 per cent, but this
may be apparent only, because it is fused either with the Gemellus inferior or the Adductor
magnus. It may be double at its insertion, the posterior part having the usual attachment to the
femur, the anterior part attaching to the intertrochanteric crest.

The **Obturator externus** (Fig. 486) is a flat, triangular muscle, which covers
the outer surface of the anterior wall of the pelvis. It *arises* from the margin
of bone immediately around the medial side of the obturator foramen, viz., from
the rami of the pubis, and the inferior ramus of the ischium; it also arises from the
medial two-thirds of the outer surface of the obturator membrane, and from the
tendinous arch which completes the canal for the passage of the obturator vessels
and nerves. The fibers springing from the pubic arch extend on to the inner surface of the bone, where they obtain a narrow origin between the margin of the
foramen and the attachment of the obturator membrane. The fibers converge
and pass backward, lateralward, and upward, and end in a tendon which runs
across the back of the neck of the femur and lower part of the capsule of the hip-
joint and is *inserted* into the trochanteric fossa of the femur. The obturator vessels

lie between the muscle and the obturator membrane; the anterior branch of the obturator nerve reaches the thigh by passing in front of the muscle, and the posterior branch by piercing it.

Action.—Rotates the thigh laterally.

Nerve.—A branch of the obturator nerve, containing fibers from the third and fourth lumbar nerves.

Group Action of Muscles About the Hip Joint.—Extension of the thigh is performed by the Glutæus maximus and Adductor magnus, the former is most powerful in a position of lateral rotation, the latter in medial rotation. The Glutæus medius acts synergetically to neutralize the adduction of the magnus and the lateral rotation of the maximus. The hamstring muscles extend the thigh, but are used for this action only if it accompanies flexion of the leg.

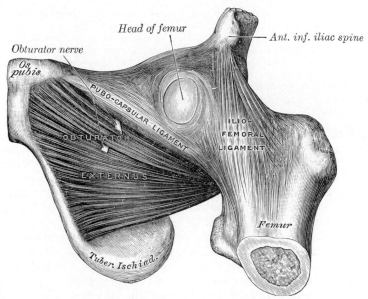

FIG. 486.—The Obturator externus.

Flexion of the thigh is performed by the Iliopsoas, Tensor fasciæ latæ, Pectineus, and Sartorius. The action is initiated by the Tensor, Pectineus, and Sartorius; stronger and final action is by the Iliopsoas; the Adductor longus assists. Positions of medial or lateral rotation have only slight effect. The Rectus femoris flexes, but only if the muscle is acting as an extensor at the knee.

Abduction of the thigh is performed by the Glutæus medius and minimus, the latter especially in a position of medial rotation. Adduction is performed by the Adductores magnus, longus, brevis, and the Gracilis.

Lateral rotation of the thigh is performed by the Obturator externus and internus, Gemelli Piriformis, and Quadratus femoris. Other muscles, such as the Glutæus maximus, have incidental power for lateral rotation but are not used for pure rotatory action. Medial rotation is performed by the Glutæus minimus and anterior Glutæus medius. The Tensor fasciæ latæ, the Adductores and Iliopsoas have incidental power for this action.

4. The Posterior Femoral Muscles (Hamstring Muscles) (Fig. 484).

The **Biceps femoris** (*Biceps*) is situated on the posterior and lateral aspect of the thigh. It has two heads of origin; one, the **long head**, *arises* from the lower and inner impression on the back part of the tuberosity of the ischium, by a tendon common to it and the Semitendinosus, and from the lower part of the sacrotuberous ligament; the other, the **short head**, *arises* from the lateral lip of the linea aspera, between the Adductor magnus and Vastus lateralis, extending up almost as high as the insertion of the Glutæus maximus; from the lateral prolongation of the linea aspera to within 5 cm. of the lateral condyle; and from the lateral inter-muscular septum. The fibers of the long head form a fusiform belly, which passes obliquely downward and lateralward across the sciatic nerve to end in an aponeu-rosis which covers the posterior surface of the muscle, and receives the fibers of the short head; this aponeurosis becomes gradually contracted into a tendon, which is *inserted* into the lateral side of the head of the fibula, and by a small slip into the lateral condyle of the tibia. At its insertion the tendon divides into two portions, which embrace the fibular collateral ligament of the knee-joint. From the posterior border of the tendon a thin expansion is given off to the fascia of the leg. The tendon of insertion of this muscle forms the lateral hamstring: the common peroneal nerve descends along its medial border.

Action.—Flexes the leg, and after it is flexed, rotates it laterally. The long head extends the thigh and tends to rotate it laterally.

Nerves.—The long head is supplied by branches, usually two, from the tibial portion of the sciatic nerve, containing fibers from the first three sacral nerves. The nerve to the short head comes from the peroneal portion and contains fibers from the fifth lumbar and first two sacral nerves.

Variations.—The short head may be absent; additional heads may arise from the ischial tuberosity, the linea aspera, the medial supracondylar ridge of the femur or from various other parts. A slip may pass to the Gastrocnemius.

The **Semitendinosus**, remarkable for the great length of its tendon of insertion, is situated at the posterior and medial aspect of the thigh. It *arises* from the lower and medial impression on the tuberosity of the ischium, by a tendon common to it and the long head of the Biceps femoris; it also arises from an aponeurosis which connects the adjacent surfaces of the two muscles to the extent of about 7.5 cm. from their origin. The muscle is fusiform and ends a little below the middle of the thigh in a long round tendon which lies along the medial side of the popliteal fossa; it then curves around the medial condyle of the tibia and passes over the tibial collateral ligament of the knee-joint, from which it is separated by a bursa, and is *inserted* into the upper part of the medial surface of the body of the tibia, nearly as far forward as its anterior crest. At its insertion it gives off from its lower border a prolongation to the deep fascia of the leg and lies behind the tendon of the Sartorius, and below that of the Gracilis, to which it is united. A tendinous intersection is usually observed about the middle of the muscle.

Action.—Flexes the leg, and, after it is flexed, rotates it medially; extends the thigh.

Nerves.—Usually two branches of the tibial portion of the sciatic, containing fibers from the fifth lumbar and first two sacral nerves.

The **Semimembranosus**, so called from its membranous tendon of origin, is situ-ated at the back and medial side of the thigh. It *arises* by a thick tendon from the upper and outer impression on the tuberosity of the ischium, above and lateral to the Biceps femoris and Semitendinosus. The tendon of origin expands into an aponeurosis, which covers the upper part of the anterior surface of the muscle; from this aponeurosis muscular fibers arise, and converge to another aponeurosis which covers the lower part of the posterior surface of the muscle and contracts into the tendon of insertion. It is *inserted* mainly into the horizontal groove on the posterior medial aspect of the medial condyle of the tibia. The tendon of insertion gives off certain fibrous expansions: one, of considerable size, passes upward and lateralward to be *inserte*d into the back part of the lateral condyle of the femur, forming part of the oblique popliteal ligament of the knee-joint; a second is continued downward to the fascia which covers the Popliteus muscle; while a few fibers join the tibial collateral ligament of the joint and the fascia of the leg. The muscle overlaps the upper part of the popliteal vessels.

Action.—Flexes the leg, and, after it is flexed, tends to rotate it medially. Extends the thigh.

Nerve.—Several branches from the tibial portion of the sciatic nerve, containing fibers from the fifth lumbar and first two sacral nerves.

Variations.—It may be reduced or absent, or double, arising mainly from the sacrotuberous ligament and giving a slip to the femur or Adductor magnus.

The tendons of insertion of the two preceding muscles form the medial hamstrings.

Group Actions at the Knee.—Extension of the leg is performed by the Quadriceps femoris; *i. e.*, the Rectus femoris, Vastus lateralis, Vastus medialis, and Vastus intermedius. Flexion is performed by the hamstring muscles; *i. e.*, the Biceps femoris, Semitendinosus, and Semimembranosus, and by the Popliteus. The Sartorius and Gracilis act in full flexion and against resistance. The Gastrocnemius has flexing action but is used more as a protective agent to prevent hyperextension. Lateral rotation of the flexed knee is performed by the Biceps femoris; medial rotation by the Popliteus and, to a lesser extent, by the medial hamstrings.

III. THE MUSCLES AND FASCIÆ OF THE LEG.

The muscles of the leg may be divided into three groups: anterior, posterior, and lateral.

1. The Anterior Crural Muscles (Fig. 487).

Deep Fascia (*fascia cruris*).—The deep fascia of the leg forms a complete investment to the muscles, and is fused with the periosteum over the subcutaneous surfaces of the bones. It is continuous *above* with the fascia lata, and is attached around the knee to the patella, the ligamentum patellæ, the tuberosity and condyles of the tibia, and the head of the fibula. *Behind*, it forms the popliteal fascia, covering in the popliteal fossa; here it is strengthened by transverse fibers, and perforated by the small saphenous vein. It receives an expansion from the tendon of the Biceps femoris laterally, and from the tendons of the Sartorius, Gracilis, Semitendinosus, and Semimembranosus medially; in *front*, it blends with the periosteum covering the subcutaneous surface of the tibia, and with that covering the head and malleolus of the fibula; below, it is continuous with the transverse crural and laciniate ligaments. It is thick and dense in the upper and anterior part of the leg, and gives attachment, by its deep surface, to the Tibialis anterior and Extensor digitorum longus; but thinner behind, where it covers the Gastrocnemius and Soleus. It gives off from its deep surface, on the lateral side of the leg, two strong intermuscular septa, the **anterior** and **posterior peroneal septa**, which enclose the Peronæi longus and brevis, and separate them from the muscles of the anterior and posterior crural regions, and several more slender processes which enclose the individual muscles in each region. A broad transverse intermuscular septum, called the **deep transverse fascia of the leg**, intervenes between the superficial and deep posterior crural muscles.

The **Tibialis anterior** (*Tibialis anticus*) is situated on the lateral side of the tibia; it is thick and fleshy above, tendinous below. It *arises* from the lateral condyle and upper half or two-thirds of the lateral surface of the body of the tibia; from the adjoining part of the interosseous membrane; from the deep surface of the fascia; and from the intermuscular septum between it and the Extensor digitorum longus. The fibers run vertically downward, and end in a tendon, which is apparent on the anterior surface of the muscle at the lower third of the leg. After passing through the most medial compartments of the transverse and cruciate crural ligaments, it is *inserted* into the medial and under surface of the first cuneiform bone, and the base of the first metatarsal bone. This muscle overlaps the anterior tibial vessels and deep peroneal nerve in the upper part of the leg.

Action.—Dorsally flexes and supinates (adducts and inverts) the foot.

Nerve.—Branch of the deep peroneal nerve, containing fibers from the fourth and fifth lumbar and first sacral nerves.

Variations.—A deep portion of the muscle is rarely inserted into the talus, or a tendinous slip may pass to the head of the first metatarsal bone or the base of the first phalanx of the great toe.

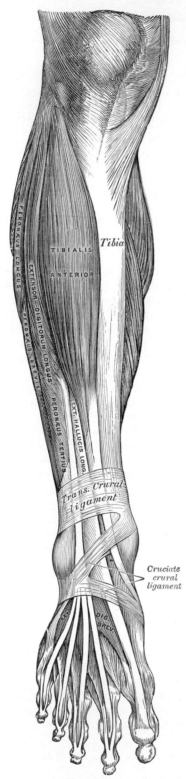

The *Tibiofascialis anterior*, a small muscle from the lower part of the tibia to the transverse or cruciate crural ligaments or deep fascia.

The **Extensor hallucis longus** (*Extensor proprius hallucis*) is a thin muscle, situated between the Tibialis anterior and the Extensor digitorum longus. It *arises* from the anterior surface of the fibula for about the middle two-fourths of its extent, medial to the origin of the Extensor digitorum longus; it also *arises* from the interosseous membrane to a similar extent. The anterior tibial vessels and deep peroneal nerve lie between it and the Tibialis anterior. The fibers pass downward, and end in a tendon, which occupies the anterior border of the muscle, passes through a distinct compartment in the cruciate crural ligament, crosses from the lateral to the medial side of the anterior tibial vessels near the bend of the ankle, and is *inserted* into the base of the distal phalanx of the great toe. Opposite the metatarsophalangeal articulation, the tendon gives off a thin prolongation on either side, to cover the surface of the joint. An expansion from the medial side of the tendon is usually inserted into the base of the proximal phalanx.

Action.—Extends proximal phalanx of great toe. Dorsally flexes and supinates the foot.

Nerve.—Branch of the deep peroneal nerve, containing fibers from the fourth and fifth lumbar and first sacral nerves.

Variations.—Occasionally united at its origin with the Extensor digitorum longus. *Extensor ossis metatarsi hallucis*, a small muscle, sometimes found as a slip from the Extensor hallucis longus, or from the Tibialis anterior, or from the Extensor digitorum longus, or as a distinct muscle; it traverses the same compartment of the transverse ligament with the Extensor hallucis longus.

The **Extensor digitorum longus** is a penniform muscle, situated at the lateral part of the front of the leg. It *arises* from the lateral condyle of the tibia; from the upper three-fourths of the anterior surface of the body of the fibula; from the upper part of the interosseous membrane; from the deep surface of the fascia; and from the intermuscular septa between it and the Tibialis anterior on the medial, and the Peronæi on the lateral side. Between it and the Tibialis anterior are the upper portions of the anterior tibial vessels and deep peroneal nerve. The tendon passes under the transverse and cruciate crural ligaments in company with the Peronæus tertius, and divides into four slips, which run forward on the dorsum of the foot, and are *inserted* into the second and third phalanges of the four lesser toes. The tendons to

FIG. 487.—Muscles of the front of the leg.

the second, third, and fourth toes are each joined, opposite the metatarso-phalangeal articulation, on the lateral side by a tendon of the Extensor digitorum brevis. The tendons are inserted in the following manner: each receives a fibrous expansion from the Interossei and Lumbricalis, and then spreads out into a broad aponeurosis, which covers the dorsal surface of the first phalanx: this aponeurosis, at the articulation of the first with the second phalanx, divides into three slips— an intermediate, which is inserted into the base of the second phalanx; and two collateral slips, which, after uniting on the dorsal surface of the second phalanx, are continued onward, to be inserted into the base of the third phalanx.

Action.—Extends the proximal phalanges of the four small toes. Dorsally flexes and pronates the foot.

Nerve.—Branches of the deep peroneal nerve, containing fibers from the fourth and fifth lumbar and first sacral nerves.

Variations.—This muscle varies considerably in the modes of origin and the arrangement of its various tendons. The tendons to the second and fifth toes may be found doubled, or extra slips are given off from one or more tendons to their corresponding metatarsal bones, or to the short extensor, or to one of the interosseous muscles. A slip to the great toe from the innermost tendon has been found.

The **Peronæus tertius** is a part of the Extensor digitorum longus, and might be described as its fifth tendon. The fibers belonging to this tendon *arise* from the lower third or more of the anterior surface of the fibula; from the lower part of the interosseous membrane; and from an intermuscular septum between it and the Peronæus brevis. The tendon, after passing under the transverse and cruciate crural ligaments in the same canal as the Extensor digitorum longus, is *inserted* into the dorsal surface of the base of the metatarsal bone of the little toe (Fig. 490).

Action.—Dorsally flexes and pronates the foot.

Nerve.—Branch of the deep peroneal nerve, containing fibers from the fourth and fifth lumbar and first sacral nerves.

2. The Posterior Crural Muscles.

The muscles of the back of the leg are subdivided into two groups—superficial and deep. Those of the superficial group constitute a powerful muscular mass, forming the calf of the leg. Their large size is one of the most characteristic features of the muscular apparatus in man, and bears a direct relation to his erect posture and his mode of locomotion.

The Superficial Group (Fig. 488).

Gastrocnemius.   Soleus.   Plantaris.

The **Gastrocnemius** is the most superficial muscle, and forms the greater part of the calf. It *arises* by two heads, which are connected to the condyles of the femur by strong, flat tendons. The **medial** and **larger head** takes its origin from a depression at the upper and back part of the medial condyle and from the adjacent part of the femur. The **lateral head** *arises* from an impression on the side of the lateral condyle and from the posterior surface of the femur immediately above the lateral part of the condyle. Both heads, also, *arise* from the subjacent part of the capsule of the knee. Each tendon spreads out into an aponeurosis, which covers the posterior surface of that portion of the muscle to which it belongs. From the anterior surfaces of these tendinous expansions, muscular fibers are given off; those of the medial head being thicker and extending lower than those of the lateral. The fibers unite at an angle in the middle line of the muscle in a tendinous raphé, which expands into a broad aponeurosis on the anterior surface of the muscle, and into this the remaining fibers are inserted. The aponeurosis, gradually contracting, unites with the tendon of the Soleus, and forms with it the tendo calcaneus.

35

Action.—Plantar flexes the foot (points the toe); flexes the leg; tends to supinate the foot.
Nerves.—Branches of the tibial nerve, containing fibers from the first and second sacral nerves.
Variations.—Absence of the outer head or of the entire muscle. Extra slips from the popliteal surface of the femur.

The **Soleus** is a broad flat muscle situated immediately in front of the Gastrocnemius. It *arises* by tendinous fibers from the back of the head of the fibula, and from the upper third of the posterior surface of the body of the bone; from the popliteal line, and the middle third of the medial border of the tibia; some fibers also arise from a tendinous arch placed between the tibial and fibular origins of the muscle, in front of which the popliteal vessels and tibial nerve run. The fibers end in an aponeurosis which covers the posterior surface of the muscle, and, gradually becoming thicker and narrower, joins with the tendon of the Gastrocnemius, and forms with it the tendo calcaneus.

Action.—Plantar flexes the foot.
Nerve.—Branch of the tibialis, containing fibers from the first and second sacral nerves.
Variations.—Accessory head to its lower and inner part usually ending in the tendo calcaneus, or the calcaneus, or the laciniate ligament.

The Gastrocnemius and Soleus together form a muscular mass which is occasionally described as the **Triceps suræ**: its tendon of insertion is the tendo calcaneus.

Tendo Calcaneus (*tendo Achillis*).—The tendo calcaneus, the common tendon of the Gastrocnemius and Soleus, is the thickest and strongest in the body. It is about 15 cm. long, and begins near the middle of the leg, but receives fleshy fibers on its anterior surface, almost to its lower end. Gradually becoming contracted below, it is inserted into the middle part of the posterior surface of the calcaneus, a bursa being interposed between the tendon and the upper part of this surface. The tendon spreads out somewhat at its lower end, so that its narrowest part is about 4 cm. above its insertion. It is covered by the fascia and the integument, and is separated from the deep muscles and vessels by a considerable interval filled up with areolar and adipose tissue. Along its lateral side, but superficial to it, is the small saphenous vein.

The **Plantaris** is placed between the Gastrocnemius and Soleus. It *arises* from the lower part of the lateral prolongation of the linea aspera, and from the oblique popliteal ligament of the knee-joint. It forms a small fusiform belly, from 7 to 10 cm. long, ending in a long slender tendon which crosses obliquely between the two muscles of the calf, and runs along the medial border of the tendo calcaneus, to be *inserted* with it into the posterior part of the calcaneus. This muscle is sometimes double, and at other times wanting. Occasionally, its tendon is lost in the laciniate ligament, or in the fascia of the leg.

Action.—Plantar flexes the foot; flexes the leg.
Nerve.—Branch of the tibial nerve, containing fibers from the fourth and fifth lumbar and first sacral nerves.

The Deep Group (Fig. 489).

Popliteus.	Flexor digitorum longus.
Flexor hallucis longus.	Tibialis posterior.

Deep Transverse Fascia.—The deep transverse fascia of the leg is a transversely placed, intermuscular septum, between the superficial and deep muscles of the back of the leg. At the sides it is connected to the margins of the tibia and fibula. *Above*, where it covers the Popliteus, it is thick and dense, and receives an expansion from the tendon of the Semimembranosus; it is thinner in the middle of the leg; but *below*, where it covers the tendons passing behind the malleoli, it is thickened and continuous with the laciniate ligament.

The **Popliteus** is a thin, flat, triangular muscle, which forms the lower part of the floor of the popliteal fossa. It *arises* by a strong tendon about 2.5 cm. long, from a depression at the anterior part of the groove on the lateral condyle of the femur, and to a small extent from the oblique popliteal ligament of the knee-joint; and is *inserted* into the medial two-thirds of the triangular surface above the pop-

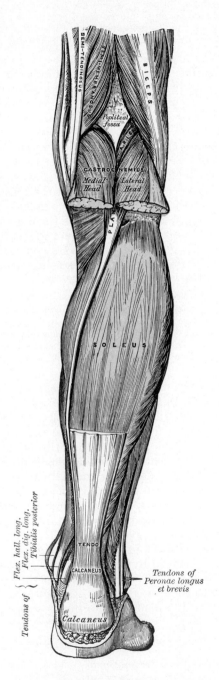

FIG. 488.—Muscles of the back of the leg. Superficial layer.

FIG. 489.—Muscles of the back of the leg. Deep layer.

liteal line on the posterior surface of the body of the tibia, and into the tendinous expansion covering the surface of the muscle.

Action.—Flexes the leg and rotates it medially.

Nerve.—Branch of the tibial nerve, containing fibers from the fourth and fifth lumbar and first sacral nerves.

Variations.—Additional head from the sesamoid bone in the outer head of the Gastrocnemius. *Popliteus minor*, rare, origin from femur on the inner side of the Plantaris, insertion into the posterior ligament of the knee-joint. *Peroneotibialis*, 14 per cent., origin inner side of the head of the fibula, insertion into the upper end of the oblique line of the tibia, it lies beneath the Popliteus.

The **Flexor hallucis longus** is situated on the fibular side of the leg. It *arises* from the inferior two-thirds of the posterior surface of the body of the fibula, with the exception of 2.5 cm. at its lowest part; from the lower part of the interosseous membrane; from an intermuscular septum between it and the Peronæi, laterally, and from the fascia covering the Tibialis posterior, medially. The fibers pass obliquely downward and backward, and end in a tendon which occupies nearly the whole length of the posterior surface of the muscle. This tendon lies in a groove which crosses the posterior surface of the lower end of the tibia, the posterior surface of the talus, and the under surface of the sustentaculum tali of the calcaneus; in the sole of the foot it runs forward between the two heads of the Flexor hallucis brevis, and is *inserted* into the base of the last phalanx of the great toe. The grooves on the talus and calcaneus, which contain the tendon of the muscle, are converted by tendinous fibers into distinct canals, lined by a synovial sheath. As the tendon passes forward in the sole of the foot, it is situated above, and crosses from the lateral to the medial side of the tendon of the Flexor digitorum longus, to which it is connected by a fibrous slip.

Action.—Flexes second phalanx of great toe. Plantar flexes and supinates the foot.

Nerve.—Branch of the tibial nerve, containing fibers from the fifth lumbar and first and second sacral nerves.

Variations.—Usually a slip runs to the Flexor digitorum and frequently an additional slip runs from the Flexor digitorum to the Flexor hallucis. *Peroneocalcaneus internus*, rare, origin below or outside the Flexor hallucis from the back of the fibula, passes over the sustentaculum tali with the Flexor hallucis and is inserted into the calcaneum.

The **Flexor digitorum longus** is situated on the tibial side of the leg. At its origin it is thin and pointed, but it gradually increases in size as it descends. It *arises* from the posterior surface of the body of the tibia, from immediately below the popliteal line to within 7 or 8 cm. of its lower extremity, medial to the tibial origin of the Tibialis posterior; it also *arises* from the fascia covering the Tibialis posterior. The fibers end in a tendon, which runs nearly the whole length of the posterior surface of the muscle. This tendon passes behind the medial malleolus, in a groove, common to it and the Tibialis posterior, but separated from the latter by a fibrous septum, each tendon being contained in a special compartment lined by a separate synovial sheath. It passes obliquely forward and lateralward, superficial to the deltoid ligament of the ankle-joint, into the sole of the foot (Fig. 492), where it crosses below the tendon of the Flexor hallucis longus, and receives from it a strong tendinous slip. It then expands and is joined by the Quadratus plantæ, and finally divides into four tendons, which are *inserted* into the bases of the last phalanges of the second, third, fourth, and fifth toes, each tendon passing through an opening in the corresponding tendon of the Flexor digitorum brevis opposite the base of the first phalanx.

Action.—Flexes the terminal phalanges of the four small toes. Plantar flexes and supinates the foot.

Nerve.—Branch of the tibial nerve, containing fibers from the fifth lumbar and first sacral, nerves.

Variations.—*Flexor accessorius longus digitorum*, not infrequent, origin from fibula, or tibia, or the deep fascia and ending in a tendon which, after passing beneath the laciniate ligament joins the tendon of the long flexor or the Quadratus plantæ.

The **Tibialis posterior** (*Tibialis posticus*) lies between the two preceding muscles, and is the most deeply seated of the muscles on the back of the leg. It begins above by two pointed processes, separated by an angular interval through which the anterior tibial vessels pass forward to the front of the leg. It *arises* from the whole of the posterior surface of the interosseous membrane, excepting its lowest part; from the lateral portion of the posterior surface of the body of the tibia,

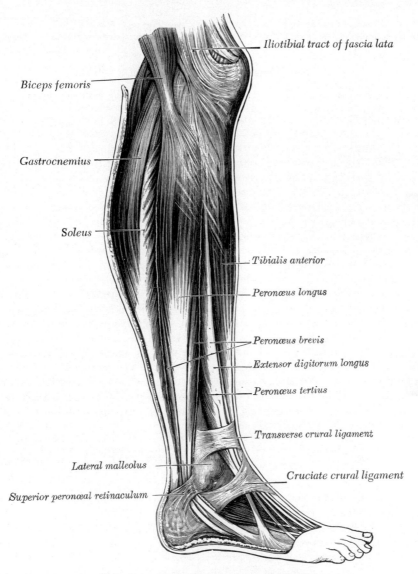

FIG. 490.—The right lateral crural muscles.

between the commencement of the popliteal line above and the junction of the middle and lower thirds of the body below; and from the upper two-thirds of the medial surface of the fibula; some fibers also arise from the deep transverse fascia, and from the intermuscular septa separating it from the adjacent muscles. In the lower fourth of the leg its tendon passes in front of that of the Flexor digitorum longus and lies with it in a groove behind the medial malleolus, but enclosed in a separate sheath; it next passes under the laciniate and over the deltoid ligament into the foot, and then beneath the plantar calcaneonavicular ligament. The tendon contains a sesamoid fibrocartilage, as it runs under the plantar calcaneo-navicular ligament. It is *inserted* into the tuberosity of the navicular bone, and gives off fibrous expansions, one of which passes backward to the sustentaculum tali of the calcaneus, others forward and lateralward to the three cuneiforms, the cuboid, and the bases of the second, third, and fourth metatarsal bones.

Action.—Supinates (adducts and inverts), and plantar flexes the foot.
Nerve.—Branch of the tibial nerve, containing fibers from the fifth lumbar and first sacral nerves.

3. The Lateral Crural Muscles (Fig. 490).

Peronæus longus   Peronæus brevis.

The **Peronæus longus** is situated at the upper part of the lateral side of the leg, and is the more superficial of the two muscles. It *arises* from the head and upper two-thirds of the lateral surface of the body of the fibula, from the deep surface of the fascia, and from the intermuscular septa between it and the muscles on the front and back of the leg; occasionally also by a few fibers from the lateral condyle of the tibia. Between its attachments to the head and to the body of the fibula there is a gap through which the common peroneal nerve passes to the front of the leg. It ends in a long tendon, which runs behind the lateral malleolus, in a groove common to it and the tendon of the Peronæus brevis, behind which it lies; the groove is converted into a canal by the superior peroneal retinaculum, and the tendons in it are contained in a common synovial sheath. The tendon then extends obliquely forward across the lateral side of the calcaneus, below the trochlear process, and the tendon of the Peronæus brevis, and under cover of the inferior peroneal retinaculum. It crosses the lateral side of the cuboid, and then runs on the under surface of that bone in a groove which is converted into a canal by the long plantar ligament; the tendon then crosses the sole of the foot obliquely, and is inserted into the lateral side of the base of the first metatarsal bone and the lateral side of the first cuneiform. Occasionally it sends a slip to the base of the second metatarsal bone. The tendon changes its direction at two points: first, behind the lateral malleolus; secondly, on the cuboid bone; in both of these situations the tendon is thickened, and, in the latter, a sesamoid fibrocartilage (sometimes a bone), is usually developed in its substance.

Action.—Pronates (abducts and everts) and plantar flexes the foot.
Nerve.—Branch of the superficial peroneal nerve, containing fibers from the fourth and fifth lumbar and first sacral nerves.

The **Peronæus brevis** lies under cover of the Peronæus longus, and is a shorter and smaller muscle. It *arises* from the lower two-thirds of the lateral surface of the body of the fibula; medial to the Peronæus longus; and from the intermuscular septa separating it from the adjacent muscles on the front and back of the leg. The fibers pass vertically downward, and end in a tendon which runs behind the lateral malleolus along with but in front of that of the preceding muscle, the two tendons being enclosed in the same compartment, and lubricated by a common synovial sheath. It then runs forward on the lateral side of the calcaneus, above the trochlear process and the tendon of the Peronæus longus, and is *inserted* into the tuberosity at the base of the fifth metatarsal bone, on its lateral side.

On the lateral surface of the calcaneus the tendons of the Peronæi longus and brevis occupy separate osseoaponeurotic canals formed by the calcaneus and the peroneal retinacula; each tendon is enveloped by a forward prolongation of the common synovial sheath.

Action.—Pronates (everts and abducts) and plantar flexes the foot.

Nerve.—Branch of the superficial peroneal nerve, containing fibers from the fourth and fifth lumbar and first sacral nerves.

Variations.—Fusion of the two peronæi is rare. A slip from the Peronæus longus to the base of the third, fourth or fifth metatarsal bone, or to the Adductor hallucis is occasionally seen.

Peronæus accessorius, origin from the fibula between the longus and brevis, joins the tendon of the longus in the sole of the foot.

Peronæus quinti digiti, rare, origin lower fourth of the fibula under the brevis, insertion into the Extensor aponeurosis of the little toe. More common as a slip of the tendon of the Peronæus brevis.

Peronæus quartus, 13 per cent. (Gruber), origin back of fibula between the brevis and the Flexor hallucis, insertion into the peroneal spine of the calcaneum, (*peroneocalcaneus externum*), or less frequently into the tuberosity of the cuboid (*peroneocuboideus*).

Group Actions at the Ankle.—Plantar flexion of the foot is brought about by the Gastrocnemius and Soleus, the Plantaris, the Peronæi longus and brevis, and the Tibialis posterior. The Peronæi and Tibialis posterior act alone if there is no resistance to be overcome. The Flexores digitorum and hallucis come into action to meet great resistance. The Gastrocnemius supinating and the Peronæi pronating are synergetic.

Dorsal flexion of the foot is performed by the Tibialis anterior, Extensores digitorum and hallucis longi, and Peronæus tertius. The Peronæus brevis acts synergetically along with the Extensor digitorum and Peronæus tertius to neutralize the inversion of the Tibialis anterior and Extensor hallucis.

Supination of the Foot (combined adduction and inversion).—The Tibiales anterior and posterior are the principal supinators. The posterior adducts more powerfully, the anterior inverts more powerfully. The Gastrocnemius tends to supinate and acts synergetically against the dorsal flexion of the Tibialis anterior.

Pronation of the foot (combined abduction and eversion) is performed by the Peronæi. The Peronæus brevis abducts more strongly and acts slightly before the longus; the longus everts more strongly. The Peronæus tertius acts when it is present. The Extensor digitorum longus acts as an emergency muscle.

THE FASCIA AROUND THE ANKLE.

Fibrous bands, or thickened portions of the fascia, bind down the tendons in front of and behind the ankle in their passage to the foot. They comprise three ligaments, viz., the **transverse crural**, the **cruciate crural** and the **laciniate**; and the **superior and inferior peroneal retinacula.**

Transverse Crural Ligament (*ligamentum transversum cruris; upper part of anterior annular ligament*) (Fig. 491).—The transverse crural ligament binds down the tendons of Extensor digitorum longus, Extensor hallucis longus, Peronæus tertius, and Tibialis anterior as they descend on the front of the tibia and fibula; under it are found also the anterior tibial vessels and deep peroneal nerve. It is attached laterally to the lower end of the fibula, and medially to the tibia; above it is continuous with the fascia of the leg.

Cruciate Crural Ligament (*ligamentum cruciatum cruris; lower part of anterior annular ligament*) (Figs. 491, 492).—The cruciate crural ligament is a Y-shaped band placed in front of the ankle-joint, the stem of the Y being attached laterally to the upper surface of the calcaneus, in front of the depression for the interosseous talocalcanean ligament; it is directed medialward as a double layer, one lamina passing in front of, and the other behind, the tendons of the Peronæus tertius and Extensor digitorum longus. At the medial border of the latter tendon these two layers join together, forming a compartment in which the tendons are enclosed. From the medial extremity of this sheath the two limbs of the Y diverge: one is directed upward and medialward, to be attached to the tibial malleolus, passing over the Extensor hallucis longus and the vessels and nerves, but enclosing the Tibialis anterior by a splitting of its fibers. The other limb extends downward and medialward, to be attached to the border of the plantar aponeurosis, and passes over the tendons of the Extensor hallucis longus and Tibialis anterior and also the vessels and nerves.

Laciniate Ligament (*ligamentum laciniatum; internal annular ligament*).—The laciniate ligament is a strong fibrous band, extending from the tibial malleolus above to the margin of the calcaneus below, converting a series of bony grooves in this situation into canals for the passage of the tendons of the Flexor muscles and the posterior tibial vessels and tibial nerve into the sole of the foot. It is continuous by its upper border with the deep fascia of the leg, and by its lower border with the plantar aponeurosis and the fibers of origin of the Abductor

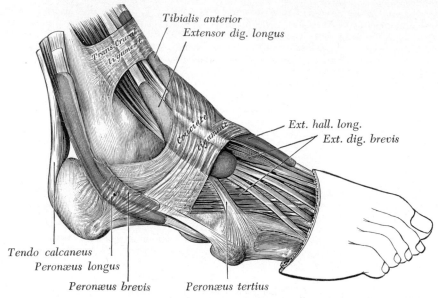

Fig. 491.—The synovial sheaths of the tendons around the ankle. Lateral aspect.

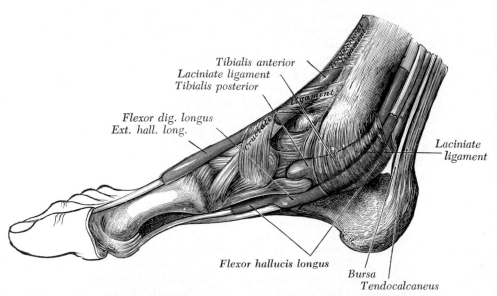

Fig. 492.—The synovial sheaths of the tendons around the ankle. Medial aspect.

hallucis muscle. Enumerated from the medial side, the four canals which it forms transmit the tendon of the Tibialis posterior; the tendon of the Flexor digitorum longus; the posterior tibial vessels and tibial nerve, which run through a broad space beneath the ligament; and lastly, in a canal formed partly by the talus, the tendon of the Flexor hallucis longus (Fig. 492).

Peroneal Retinacula.— The peroneal retinacula are fibrous bands which bind down the tendons of the Peronæi longus and brevis as they run across the lateral side of the ankle. The fibers of the **superior retinaculum** (*external annular ligament*) are attached *above* to the lateral malleolus and *below* to the lateral surface of the calcaneus. The fibers of the **inferior retinaculum** are continuous in *front* with those of the cruciate crural ligament; *behind* they are attached to the lateral surface of the calcaneus; some of the fibers are fixed to the peroneal trochlea, forming a septum between the tendons of the Peronæi longus and brevis.

The Synovial Sheaths of the Tendons Around the Ankle.— All the tendons crossing the ankle-joint are enclosed for part of their length in synovial sheaths which have an almost uniform length of about 8 cm. each. On the *front* of the ankle (Fig. 491) the sheath for the Tibialis anterior extends from the upper margin of the transverse crural ligament to the interval between the diverging limbs of the cruciate ligament; those for the Extensor digitorum longus and Extensor hallucis longus reach upward to just above the level of the tips of the malleoli, the former being the higher. The sheath of the Extensor hallucis longus is prolonged on to the base of the first metatarsal bone, while that of the Extensor digitorum longus reaches only to the level of the base of the fifth metatarsal. On the *medial side* of the ankle (Fig. 492) the sheath for the Tibialis posterior extends highest up—to about 4 cm. above the tip of the malleolus—while below it just stops short of the tuberosity of the navicular. The sheath for the Flexor hallucis longus reaches up to the level of the tip of the malleolus, while that for the Flexor digitorum longus is slightly higher; the former is continued to the base of the first metatarsal, but the latter stops opposite the first cuneiform bone.

On the *lateral side* of the ankle (Fig. 491) a sheath which is single for the greater part of its extent encloses the Peronæi longus and brevis. It extends upward for about 4 cm. above the tip of the malleolus and downward and forward for about the same distance.

IV. THE MUSCLES AND FASCIÆ OF THE FOOT.

1. The Dorsal Muscle of the Foot.

The **fascia** on the dorsum of the foot is a thin membranous layer, continuous above with the transverse and cruciate crural ligaments; on either side it blends with the plantar aponeurosis; anteriorly it forms a sheath for the tendons on the dorsum of the foot.

The **Extensor digitorum brevis** (Fig. 491) is a broad, thin muscle, which *arises* from the forepart of the upper and lateral surfaces of the calcaneus, in front of the groove for the Peronæus brevis; from the lateral talocalcaneal ligament; and from the common limb of the cruciate crural ligament. It passes obliquely across the dorsum of the foot, and ends in four tendons. The most medial, which is the largest, is *inserted* into the dorsal surface of the base of the first phalanx of the great toe, crossing the dorsalis pedis artery; it is frequently described as a separate muscle—the **Extensor hallucis brevis.** The other three are *inserted* into the lateral sides of the tendons of the Extensor digitorum longus of the second, third, and fourth toes.

Action.—Extends the proximal phalanges of the great and the adjacent three small toes.

Nerve.—Branch of the deep peroneal nerve, containing fibers from fifth lumbar and first sacral nerves.

Variations.—Accessory slips of origin from the talus and navicular, or from the external cuneiform and third metatarsal bones to the second slip of the muscle, and one from the cuboid to the third slip have been observed. The tendons vary in number and position; they may be reduced to two, or one of them may be doubled, or an additional slip may pass to the little toe. A super-

numerary slip ending on one of the metatarsophalangeal articulations, or joining a dorsal interosseous muscle is not uncommon. Deep slips between this muscle and the Dorsal interossei occur.

2. The Plantar Muscles of the Foot.

Plantar Aponeurosis (*aponeurosis plantaris; plantar fascia*).—The plantar aponeurosis is of great strength, and consists of pearly white glistening fibers, disposed,
for the most part, longitudinally: it is divided into central, lateral, and medial
portions.

The **central portion,** the thickest, is narrow behind and *attached* to the medial
process of the tuberosity of the calcaneus, posterior to the origin of the Flexor
digitorum brevis; and becoming broader and thinner in front, divides near the
heads of the metatarsal bones into five processes, one for each of the toes. Each
of these processes divides opposite the metatarsophalangeal articulation into two
strata, superficial and deep. The superficial stratum is *inserted* into the skin of
the transverse sulcus which separates the toes from the sole. The deeper stratum
divides into two slips which embrace the side of the Flexor tendons of the toes,
and blend with the sheaths of the tendons, and with the transverse metatarsal
ligament, thus forming a series of arches through which the tendons of the short
and long Flexors pass to the toes. The intervals left between the five processes
allow the digital vessels and nerves and the tendons of the Lumbricales to become
superficial. At the point of division of the aponeurosis, numerous transverse
fasciculi are superadded; these serve to increase the strength of the aponeurosis
at this part by binding the processes together, and connecting them with the integument. The central portion of the plantar aponeurosis is continuous with the lateral
and medial portions and sends upward into the foot, at the lines of junction, two
strong vertical intermuscular septa, broader in front than behind, which separate
the intermediate from the lateral and medial plantar groups of muscles; from these
again are derived thinner transverse septa which separate the various layers of
muscles in this region. The upper surface of this aponeurosis gives origin behind
to the Flexor digitorum brevis.

The lateral and medial portions of the plantar aponeurosis are thinner than
the central piece, and cover the sides of the sole of the foot.

The **lateral portion** covers the under surface of the Abductor digiti quinti; it is
thin in front and thick behind, where it forms a strong band between the lateral
process of the tuberosity of the calcaneus and the base of the fifth metatarsal bone;
it is continuous medially with the central portion of the plantar aponeurosis, and
laterally with the dorsal fascia.

The **medial portion** is thin, and covers the under surface of the Abductor hallucis;
it is *attached* behind to the laciniate ligament, and is continuous around the side
of the foot with the dorsal fascia, and laterally with the central portion of the plantar
aponeurosis.

The muscles in the plantar region of the foot may be divided into three groups,
in a similar manner to those in the hand. Those of the medial plantar region
are connected with the great toe, and corrrespond with those of the thumb; those
of the lateral plantar region are connected with the little toe, and correspond with
those of the little finger; and those of the intermediate plantar region are connected
with the tendons intervening between the two former groups. But in order to
facilitate the description of these muscles, it is more convenient to divide them into
four layers, in the order in which they are successively exposed.

The First Layer (Fig. 493).

Abductor hallucis.	Flexor digitorum brevis.

Abductor digiti quinti.

The **Abductor hallucis** lies along the medial border of the foot and covers the origins of the plantar vessels and nerves. It *arises* from the medial process of the tuberosity of the calcaneus, from the laciniate ligament, from the plantar aponeurosis, and from the intermuscular septum between it and the Flexor digitorum brevis. The fibers end in a tendon, which is *inserted*, together with the medial tendon of the Flexor hallucis brevis, into the tibial side of the base of the first phalanx of the great toe.

Action.—Abducts the great toe.

Nerve.—Branch of the medial plantar nerve, containing fibers from the fourth and fifth lumbar nerves.

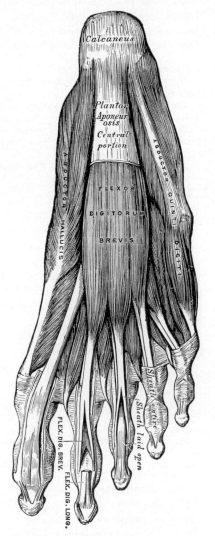

FIG. 493.—Muscles of the sole of the foot. First layer.

The **Flexor digitorum brevis** lies in the middle of the sole of the foot, immediately above the central part of the plantar aponeurosis, with which it is firmly united. Its deep surface is separated from the lateral plantar vessels and nerves by a thin layer of fascia. It *arises* by a narrow tendon, from the medial process of the tuberosity of the calcaneus, from the central part of the plantar aponeurosis, and from the intermuscular septa between it and the adjacent muscles. It passes forward, and divides into four tendons, one for each of the four lesser toes. Opposite the bases of the first phalanges, each tendon divides into two slips, to allow of the passage of the corresponding tendon of the Flexor digitorum longus; the two portions of the tendon then unite and form a grooved channel for the reception of the accompanying long Flexor tendon. Finally, it divides a second time, and is *inserted* into the sides of the second phalanx about its middle. The mode of division of the tendons of the Flexor digitorum brevis, and of their insertion into the phalanges, is analogous to that of the tendons of the Flexor digitorum sublimis in the hand.

Action.—Flexes the second phalanges of the four small toes.

Nerve.—Branch of the medial plantar nerve, containing fibers from the fourth and fifth lumbar nerves.

Variations.—Slip to the little toe frequently wanting, 23 per cent; or it may be replaced by a small fusiform muscle arising from the long flexor tendon or from the Quadratus plantæ.

Fibrous Sheaths of the Flexor Tendons.—The terminal portions of the tendons of the long and short Flexor muscles are contained in osseoaponeurotic canals similar in their arrangement to those in the fingers. These canals are formed above by the phalanges and below by fibrous bands, which arch across the tendons, and are attached on either side to the margins of the phalanges. Opposite the bodies of the proximal and second phalanges the fibrous bands are strong, and the fibers are transverse; but opposite the joints they are much thinner, and the fibers are directed obliquely. Each canal contains a synovial sheath, which is reflected on the contained tendons.

The **Abductor digiti quinti** (*Abductor minimi digiti*) lies along the lateral border of the foot, and is in relation by its medial margin with the lateral plantar vessels and nerves. It *arises,* by a broad origin, from the lateral process of the tuberosity of the calcaneus, from the under surface of the calcaneus between the two processes of the tuberosity, from the forepart of the medial process, from the plantar aponeurosis, and from the intermuscular septum between it and the Flexor digitorum brevis. Its tendon, after gliding over a smooth facet on the under surface of the base of the fifth metatarsal bone, is *inserted,* with the Flexor digiti quinti brevis, into the fibular side of the base of the first phalanx of the fifth toe.

Action.—Abducts the small toe.

Nerve.—Branch of the lateral plantar nerve, containing fibers from the first and second sacral nerves.

Variations.—Slips of origin from the tuberosity at the base of the fifth metatarsal. *Abductor ossis metatarsi quinti*, origin external tubercle of the calcaneus, insertion into tuberosity of the fifth metatarsal bone in common with or beneath the outer margin of the plantar fascia.

The Second Layer (Fig. 494).

Quadratus plantæ.   Lumbricales.

The **Quadratus plantæ** (*Flexor accessorius*) is separated from the muscles of the first layer by the lateral plantar vessels and nerve. It *arises* by two heads, which are separated from each other by the long plantar ligament: the **medial or larger head** is muscular, and is attached to the medial concave surface of the calcaneus, below the groove which lodges the tendon of the Flexor hallucis longus; the **lateral head**, flat and tendinous, *arises* from the lateral border of the inferior surface of the calcaneus, in front of the lateral process of its tuberosity, and from the long plantar ligament. The two portions join at an acute angle, and end in a flattened band which is *inserted* into the lateral margin and upper and under surfaces of the tendon of the Flexor digitorum longus, forming a kind of groove, in which the tendon is lodged. It usually sends slips to those tendons of the Flexor digitorum longus which pass to the second, third, and fourth toes.

Action.—Flexes the terminal phalanges of the four small toes.

Nerve.—Branch of the lateral plantar nerve, containing fibers from the first and second sacral nerves.

Variations.—Lateral head often wanting; entire muscle absent. Variation in the number of digital tendons to which fibers can be traced. Most frequent offsets are sent to the second, third and fourth toes; in many cases to the fifth as well; occasionally to two toes only.

The **Lumbricales** are four small muscles, accessory to the tendons of the Flexor digitorum longus and numbered from the medial side of the foot; they *arise* from these tendons, as far back as their angles of division, each springing from two tendons, except the first. The muscles end in tendons, which pass forward on the medial sides of the four lesser toes, and are *inserted* into the expansions of the tendons of the Extensor digitorum longus on the dorsal surfaces of the first phalanges.

Action.—Flex the proximal phalanges and extend the two distal phalanges of the four small toes.

Nerves.—The first Lumbricalis by a branch of the medial plantar nerve, containing fibers from the fourth and fifth lumbar nerves; the other three Lumbricales by branches of the lateral plantar nerve containing fibers from the first and second sacral nerves.

Variations.—Absence of one or more; doubling of the third or fourth. Insertion partly or wholly into the first phalanges.

The Third Layer (Fig. 495).

Flexor hallucis brevis.   Adductor hallucis.
Flexor digiti quinti brevis.

The **Flexor hallucis brevis** *arises*, by a pointed tendinous process, from the medial part of the under surface of the cuboid bone, from the contiguous portion of the third cuneiform, and from the prolongation of the tendon of the Tibialis posterior

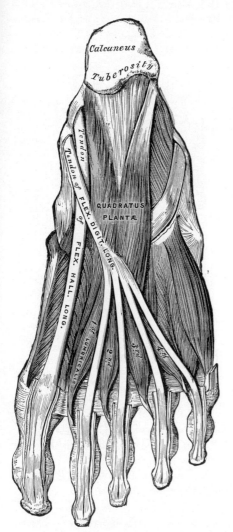

FIG. 494.—Muscles of the sole of the foot.
Second layer.

FIG. 495.—Muscles of the sole of the foot.
Third layer.

which is attached to that bone. It divides in front into two portions, which are inserted into the medial and lateral sides of the base of the first phalanx of the great toe, a sesamoid bone being present in each tendon at its insertion. The **medial portion** is blended with the Abductor hallucis previous to its insertion; the **lateral portion** with the Adductor hallucis; the tendon of the Flexor hallucis longus lies in a groove between them; the lateral portion is sometimes described as the **first Interosseous plantaris**.

Action.—Flexes the proximal phalanx of the great toe.

Nerve.—Branch of the medial plantar nerve, containing fibers from the fourth and fifth lumbar and first sacral nerves.

Variations.—Origin subject to considerable variation; it often receives fibers from the calcaneus or long plantar ligament. Attachment to the cuboid sometimes wanting. Slip to first phalanx of the second toe.

The **Adductor hallucis** (*Adductor obliquus hallucis*) *arises* by two heads—oblique and transverse. The **oblique head** is a large, thick, fleshy mass, crossing the foot obliquely and occupying the hollow space under the first, second, third, and fourth metatarsal bones. It *arises* from the bases of the second, third, and fourth metatarsal bones, and from the sheath of the tendon of the Peronæus longus, and is *inserted*, together with the lateral portion of the Flexor hallucis brevis, into the lateral side of the base of the first phalanx of the great toe. The **transverse head**

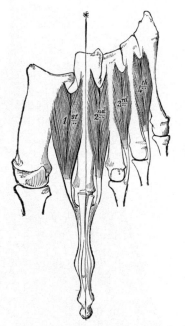

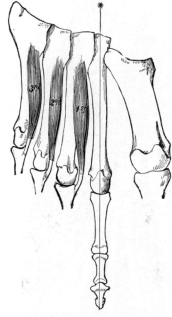

FIG. 496.—The Interossei dorsales. Left foot.   FIG. 497.—The Interossei plantares. Left foot

(*Transversus pedis*) is a narrow, flat fasciculus which *arises* from the plantar metatarsophalangeal ligaments of the third, fourth, and fifth toes (sometimes only from the third and fourth), and from the transverse ligament of the metatarsus. It is *inserted* into the lateral side of the base of the first phalanx of the great toe, its fibers blending with the tendon of insertion of the oblique head.

Action.—Adducts the great toe.

Nerve.—Branch of the lateral plantar nerve, containing fibers from the first and second sacral nerves.

Variations.—Slips to the base of the first phalanx of the second toe. *Opponens hallucis*, occasional slips from the adductor to the metatarsal bone of the great toe.

The Abductor, Flexor brevis, and Adductor of the great toe, like the similar muscles of the thumb, give off, at their insertions, fibrous expansions to blend with the tendons of the Extensor hallucis longus.

The **Flexor digiti quinti brevis** (*Flexor brevis minimi digiti*) lies under the metatarsal bone of the little toe, and resembles one of the Interossei. It *arises* from the base of the fifth metatarsal bone, and from the sheath of the Peronæus longus; its tendon is *inserted* into the lateral side of the base of the first phalanx of the fifth toe. Occasionally a few of the deeper fibers are inserted into the lateral part of the distal half of the fifth metatarsal bone; these are described by some as a distinct muscle, the **Opponens digiti quinti.**

Action.—Flexes the proximal phalanx of the small toe.

Nerve.—Branch of the lateral plantar nerve, containing fibers from the first and second sacral nerves.

The Fourth Layer.

Interossei.

The **Interossei** in the foot are similar to those in the hand, with this exception, that they are grouped around the middle line of the *second* digit, instead of that of the *third*. They are seven in number, and consist of two groups, dorsal and plantar.

The **Interossei dorsales** (*Dorsal interossei*) (Fig. 496), *four* in number, are situated between the metatarsal bones. They are bipenniform muscles, each *arising* by two heads from the adjacent sides of the metatarsal bones between which it is placed; their tendons are *inserted* into the bases of the first phalanges, and into the aponeurosis of the tendons of the Extensor digitorum longus. In the angular interval left between the heads of each of the three lateral muscles, one of the perforating arteries passes to the dorsum of the foot; through the space between the heads of the first muscle the deep plantar branch of the dorsalis pedis artery enters the sole of the foot. The first is *inserted* into the medial side of the second toe; the other three are *inserted* into the lateral sides of the second, third, and fourth toes.

Action.—Abduct the toes from the longitudinal axis of the second toe. Flex the proximal and extend the distal phalanges.

Nerves.—Branches of the lateral plantar nerve, containing fibers from the first and second sacral nerves.

The **Interossei plantares** (*Plantar interossei*) (Fig. 497), *three* in number, lie beneath rather than between the metatarsal bones, and each is connected with but one metatarsal bone. They *arise* from the bases and medial sides of the bodies of the third, fourth, and fifth metatarsal bones, and are *inserted* into the medial sides of the bases of the first phalanges of the same toes, and into the aponeuroses of the tendons of the Extensor digitorum longus.

Action.—Adduct the toes toward the axis of the second toe. Flex the proximal and extend the distal phalanges.

Nerve.—Branches of the lateral plantar nerve, containing fibers from the first and second sacral nerves.

Group Actions of Foot Muscles.—Flexion of the distal phalanges of the four small toes is performed by the Flexor digitorum longus and the Quadratus plantæ. The latter is really a part of the long flexor correcting the direction of its pull. Flexion of the second phalanges is by the Flexor digitorum brevis. Flexion of the proximal phalanges is by the Interossei and Lumbricales, with added strength given to the small toe by its Flexor brevis and Abductor. Flexion of the second phalanx of the great toe is performed by the Flexor hallucis longus; of the proximal phalanx by the Flexor hallucis brevis, Abductor hallucis, and Adductor hallucis.

Extension of the distal phalanges of all toes is performed by the Interossei, Lumbricales, Abductor digiti quinti, and Abductor hallucis. Extension of all toes is performed by the Extensor digitorum longus, Extensor hallucis longus, and Extensor digitorum brevis.

Abduction and adduction of the toes is toward the longitudinal axis of the second digit, rather than the third as in the hand. The abductors are the Interossei dorsales, Abductor hallucis, and Abductor digiti quinti. The adductors are the Interossei plantares and Adductor hallucis.

STRUCTURE OF MUSCLES.

The **skeletal** or **voluntary** muscles are called **striated muscles** because they consist of long thread-like fibers which, under the microscope, are seen to be crossed by

regularly placed, parallel, transverse bands or cross-striations. The smallest independent units of the tissue are the muscle fibers.   They are just within the limit of
visibility with the naked eye, measuring from 0.01 to 0.1 mm. in diameter, and
form 1 mm. to 12 cm. in length. They are cylindrical unless crowded against each
other, and have either blunt or tapering ends. They do not divide or anastomose,
but may occasionally be split for a short distance near their terminations. The
maximum length of fiber, except in very long muscles, is approximately 10 cm., and
if the muscular fasciculi are of this length or shorter, the majority of fibers extend
from one tendon to the other. If the fasciculi are longer, however, the fibers have

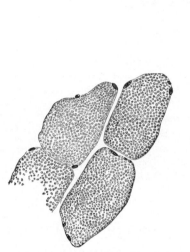

Fig. 498.—Transverse section of human
striped muscle fibers.   × 255.

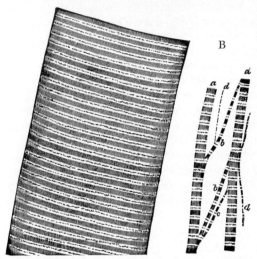

Fig. 499.—A, Portion of a medium-sized human
muscular fiber. Magnified nearly 800 diameters.
B, Separated bundles of fibrils, equally magnified.
a, a, Larger, b, b, smaller collections. c. Still
smaller. d, d, The smallest which could be
detached.

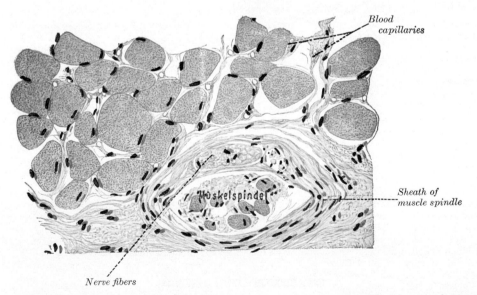

Fig. 500.—Cross section of part of a lumbrical muscle from a human hand showing muscle fibers,
endomysium, blood capillaries, and a muscle spindle.   Approximately 400 ×. (Rauber-Kopsch,
Lehrbuch u. Atlas d. Anatomie d. Menschen, 19th Ed. Vol. I, courtesy of Georg Thieme Verlag.)

one termination at a tendon and the other within the muscle, or in the case of a very long muscle like the Sartorius, both terminations may be within the muscle.

Each **muscle fiber** is a multinucleated cell. It has an outer membrane called the **sarcolemma** within which lie the nuclei and the contractile, cross-striated substance. The **nuclei** are flat oval discs, and usually are closely applied to the inner surface of the sarcolemma in adult human fibers. They are irregularly placed throughout

FIG. 501.—Attachment of a muscle fiber from the Flexor digitorum superficialis of a monkey. Reticular connective tissue fibrils are blackened with Masson's silver stain. Photograph. Magnified 900 × (Goss).

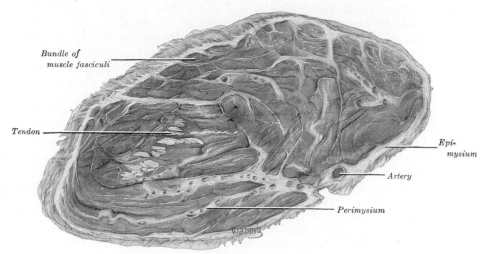

FIG. 502.—Cross section of Sartorius from dissected cadaver. × 4.

the length of the fiber, and vary in number according to the size of the fiber, several hundred occurring in a larger one. About each nucleus there is a small amount of **cytoplasm** which may contain mitochondria and a Golgi body.

The **cross-striated substance** is composed of a cytoplasmic matrix, the **sarcoplasm,** within which the long filamentous **myofibrillæ** are embedded and more or less evenly distributed across the fiber. The fibrillæ impart to the fiber a fine longitudinal marking or striation which is less regular and distinct than the cross-striation. They are usually 0.002 mm. or less in diameter in human muscle. The cross-striated appearance is due to the fact that the myofibrillæ are made up of

36

alternating birefringent and monorefringent segments which are evenly spaced at intervals of approximately 0.003 mm., unless the fiber is distorted by contraction. During contraction the cross stripes become narrower or crowded together, and when the fiber is stretched they become wider or farther apart. The cross-striations have been given various names and designations, and have been used, along with other lines, bands, discs, and membranes, as the basis for many diverse theories of muscular contraction.

The sarcoplasm contains numerous granular bodies called *sarcosomes*, as well as tiny *droplets of fat*, scattered among the myofibrillæ. The fat droplets may be abundant in well nourished individuals. Glycogen may appear to be concentrated in the sarcosomes in fixed and stained material, but in the living fiber it is diffusely distributed. The relative amount of sarcoplasm and myofibrillæ varies in individual fibers. Those with a greater concentration of fibrillæ are pale in appearance in the fresh condition; those with more sarcoplasm are darker. These **light and dark fibers** are intermingled in most human muscles, and are not as sharply demarcated as in animals or birds with light and dark flesh.

Most muscles are connected with bones, cartilages, or ligaments, and usually through the intervention of tendons or aponeuroses. The latter may be long, or the muscle may seem to connect directly with the bone or cartilage. Muscles may also attach to the skin (facial muscles), a mucous membrane (tongue), a fibrous plate (ocular muscles), or form circular bands (sphincter muscles).

The **attachment of the ends of the muscle fibers** is the same in principle whether the fasciculi end in a tendon or are connected directly with bones or cartilage. Each muscle fiber has a distinct termination which is rounded, conical, or truncated, and is covered by sarcolemma. The reticular fibrillæ of the endomysium become thickened and are closely adherent to the end of the fiber as they pass over it, and they continue on beyond it into the tendon, where they become the actual substance of the tendon (Fig. 501). In muscles which appear to attach directly to bones, cartilages, or other structures, the reticular endomysium becomes continuous with the periosteum, or other fibrous layer in the same manner as with a tendon. When the muscle fibers terminate within instead of at the end of a fasciculus, as in long muscles, the ends may be either blunt or long and tapering, and they are secured in place by the merging of their terminal reticular endomysium with the endomysium of neighboring fibers.

The muscle, considered as a contractile organ, has a parenchyma composed of muscle fibers, and an intrinsic **connective tissue stroma**. Each fiber is surrounded by a very delicate, close-meshed network of reticular connective tissue fibrillæ. This net, together with a few collagenous and elastic fibers which bind contiguous muscle fibers together, is known as the **endomysium**. Groups of a dozen or more fibers are brought together into bundles or **fasciculi** and enclosed by a thin lamella of collagenous and elastic fibers known as the perimysium. The **perimysium** also includes all the connective tissue which binds the fasciculi into larger groups and forms fibrous septa throughout the muscle. The concentration of connective tissue which envelopes the entire muscle is known as the **epimysium** (Fig. 502). It should not be confused with the definitive fascial membranes described on page 407. It may be well developed, or quite delicate, as it is where the muscle glides freely under a strong fascial sheet, or it may lose its identity and become fused with a fascial membrane if the latter is used by the muscle fibers for their attachment.

The attachments of the two ends of a muscle are called the **origin** and the **insertion**. The origin is the more fixed and proximal end, the insertion the more movable and distal end. For example, the Pectoralis major arises or has its origin from the ribs

Vessels and Nerves of Striated Muscle.—The **capillaries** of striped muscle are very abundant, and form a sort of rectangular network, the branches of which run longitudinally in the endomysium between the muscular fibers, and are joined at short intervals by transverse anastomosing branches. The larger vascular channels, arteries and veins are found only in the perimysium, between the muscular fasciculi. **Nerves** are profusely distributed to striped muscle. For mode of termination see section on Neurology. The existence of **lymphatic vessels** in striped muscle has not been ascertained, though they have been found in tendons and in the sheaths of the muscles.

REFERENCES

HISTOLOGY AND EMBRYOLOGY OF MUSCLES

BENNETT, H. S. and K. R. PORTER. 1953. An electron microscope study of sectioned breast muscle of the domestic fowl. Am. J. Anat., *93*, 61–106.

COMER, R. D. 1956. An experimental study of the "laws" of muscle and tendon growth. Anat. Rec., *125*, 665–682.

GAY, A. J., JR. and T. E. HUNT. 1954. Reuniting of skeletal muscle fibers after transection. Anat. Rec., *120*, 853–872.

GOSS, C. M. 1944. The attachment of skeletal muscle fibers. Am. J. Anat., *74*, 259–290.

KANN, F. 1957. Über Dicke und Zahl der Muskefasern auf verschiedenen Querschnitthöhen der Musculus sartorius beim Menschen. Acta Anat., *30*, 351–357.

SMITH, R. D. 1950. Studies on rigor mortis. I. Observations on the microscopic and submicroscopic structure. Anat. Rec., *108*, 185–206.

SUNDERLAND, S. and L. J. RAY. 1950. Denervation changes in mammalian striated muscle. J. Neurol., Neurosurg., & Psychiat. *13*, 159–177.

SWIGART, R. H. and W. L. WILLIAMS. 1954. Histochemical composition and vital staining of denervated skeletal muscle of the mouse. Anat. Rec., *120*, 449–468.

WELLS, L. J. 1954. Development of the human diaphragm and pleural sacs. Carnegie Contrib. to Embryol., *35*, 107–134.

MYOLOGY AND VARIATIONS

ANSON, B. J., L. E. BEATON, and C. B. McVAY. 1938. The pyramidalis muscle. Anat. Rec., *72*, 405–411.

ASHLEY, G. T. 1952. The manner of insertion of the pectoralis major muscle in man. Anat. Rec., *113*, 301–307.

BABA, M. A. 1954. The accessory tendon of the abductor pollicis longus muscle. Anat. Rec., *119*, 541–548.

BEATON, L. E. and B. J. ANSON. 1937. The relation of the sciatic nerve and of its subdivisions to the piriformis muscle. Anat. Rec., *70*, 1–5.

BEATON, L. E. and B. J. ANSON. 1942. Variations in the origin of the m. trapezius. Anat. Rec., *83*, 41–46.

CAULDWELL, E. W., B. J. ANSON, and R. R. WRIGHT. 1943. The extensor indicis proprius muscle. Quart. Bull., Northwestern Univ. M. School, *17*, 267–279.

DYKES, J. and B. J. ANSON. 1944. The accessory tendon of the flexor pollicis longus muscle. Anat. Rec., *90*, 83–87.

GEORGE, R. 1953. Co-incidence of Palmaris longus and Plantaris muscles. Anat. Rec., *116*, 521–524.

GRAY, D. J. 1945. Some anomalous hamstring muscles. Anat. Rec., *91*, 33–38.

GREIG, H. W., B. J. ANSON and J. M. Budinger. 1952. Variations in the form and attachments of the biceps brachii muscle. Quart. Bull., Northwestern Univ. M. School, *26*, 241–244.

LANDSMEER, J. M. F. 1949. The anatomy of the dorsal aponeurosis of the human finger and its functional significance. Anat. Rec., *104*, 31–44.

MANTER, J. T. 1945. Variations of the interosseous muscles of the human foot. Anat. Rec., *93*, 117–124.

MILLER, R. A. 1952. The musculature of Pan paniscus. Am. J. Anat., *91*, 183–232.

REIMANN, A. F., E. H. DASELER, B. J. ANSON, and L. E. BEATON. 1944. The palmaris longus muscle and tendon. A study of 1600 extremities. Anat. Rec., *89*, 495–505.

SEIB, G. A. 1938. The m. pectoralis minor in American whites and American negroes. Am. J. Phys. Anthrop., *23*, 389–419.

SRĚÝ, Z. and J. KRÁLÍK. 1957. Über den Muskelbau des Hiatusteiles des Zwerchfells. Acta Anat., *31*, 136–150.

STEIN, A. H., JR. 1951. Variations of the tendons of insertion of the abductor pollicis longus and the extensor pollicis brevis. Anat. Rec., *110*, 49–55.

STRAUS, W. L., JR. 1942. The homologies of the forearm flexors: Urodeles, lizards, mammals. Am. J. Anat., *70*, 281–316.

WRIGHT, R. R., W. GREIG, and B. J. ANSON   1946.   Accessory tendinous (peroneal) origin of the first dorsal interosseous muscle. A study of 125 specimens of lower extremity. Quart. Bull., Northwestern M. School, *20*, 339–341.

INNERVATION OF MUSCLES

MARKEE, J. E., W. B. STANTON, and R. N. WRENN.   1952.   The intramuscular distribution of the nerves to the muscles of the inferior extremity. Anat. Rec., *112*, 457.
SUNDERLAND, S.   1945.   The innervation of the flexor digitorum profundus and lumbrical muscles. Anat. Rec., *93*, 317–321.
SUNDERLAND, S.   1946.   The innervation of the first dorsal interosseous muscle of the hand. Anat. Rec., *95*, 7–10.
TELFORD, I. R.   1941.   Loss of nerve endings in degenerated skeletal muscles of young vitamin E deficient rats. Anat. Rec., *81*, 171–181.

MUSCLE ACTIONS AND PHYSIOLOGY

BASMAJIAN, J. V.   1957.   Electromyography of two-joint muscles. Anat. Rec., *129*, 371–380.
BASMAJIAN, J. V. and A. LATIF.   1957.   Integrated actions and functions of the chief flexors of the elbow. J. Bone & Joint Surg., *39A*, 1106–1118.
DEMPSTER, W. T. and J. C. FINERTY.   1947.   Relative activity of wrist moving muscles in static support of the wrist joint: An electromyographic study. Am. J. Physiol., *150*, 596–606.
HOYLE, G.   1957.   Comparative Physiology of the Nervous Control of Muscular Contraction. Cambridge University Press, Cambridge and New York. viii + 147 pp.
LANZ, T. VON, and A. HENNIG.   1957.   Rollwirkungen des Musculus adductor magnus am durchschnittlich geformten Schenkelbein. Acta Anat., *30*, 420–429.
SULLIVAN, W. E., O. A. MORTENSEN, M. Miles, and L. S. GREENE.   1950.   Electromyographic studies of M. biceps brachii during normal voluntary movement at the elbow. Anat. Rec., *107*, 243–251.
SUNDERLAND, S.   1945.   The actions of the extensor digitorum communis, interosseous and lumbrical muscles. Am. J. Anat., *77*, 189–217.
WEBER, H. H.   1958.   The Motility of Muscle and Cells. Harvard University Press, Cambridge. vii + 69 pp.

EXPERIMENTAL

EASTLICK, H. L.   1943.   Studies on transplanted embryonic limbs of the chick. I. The development of muscle in nerveless and in innervated grafts. J. Exp. Zool., *93*, 27–49.
HALL, E. K.   1950.   Experimental modifications of muscle development in Amblystoma punctatum. J. Exp. Zool., *113*, 355–377.
POGOGEFF, I. A. and M. R. MURRAY.   1946.   Form and behavior of adult mammalian skeletal muscle in vitro. Anat. Rec., *95*, 321–335.
SZEPSENWOL, J.   1946.   A comparison of growth, differentiation, activity and action currents of heart and skeletal muscle in tissue culture. Anat. Rec., *95*, 125–146.

TENDON SHEATHS AND TENDONS

GRODINSKY, M.   1930.   A study of the tendon sheaths of the foot and their relation to infection. Surg., Gyn. and Obst., *51*, 460–468.
KANAVEL, A. B.   1939.   Infections of the Hand. Lea & Febiger, Phila., 7th Ed., 503 pp.
KAPLAN, E. B.   1945.   Surgical anatomy of the flexor tendons of the wrist. J. Bone & Joint Surg., *27*, 368–372.

FASCIÆ

GENERAL AND COMPREHENSIVE

GALLAUDET, B. B.   1931.   A Description of the Planes of Fascia of the Human Body. Columbia U. Press, N. Y., v + 75 pp.
SINGER, E.   1935.   Fasciæ of the Human Body and Their Relation to the Organs They Envelop. William Wood, Baltimore, ix + 105 pp.

HEAD, NECK AND THORAX

GRODINSKY, M. and E. A. HOLYOKE.   1938.   The fasciæ and fascial spaces of the head, neck and adjacent regions. Am. J. Anat., *63*, 367–408.

LEE, F. C. 1941. Description of a fascia situated between the serratus anterior muscle and the thorax. Anat. Rec., *81*, 35–41.

LEE, F. C. 1944. Note on a fascia underneath the pectoralis major muscle. Anat. Rec., *90*, 45–49.

UPPER LIMB

CONGDON, E. D. and H. S. FISH. 1953. The chief insertion of the bicipital aponeurosis is on the ulna. A study of collagenous bundle patterns of antebrachial fascia and bicipital aponeurosis. Anat. Rec., *116*, 395–408.

GRAYSON, J. 1941. The cutaneous ligaments of the digits. J. Anat., *75*, 164–165.

GRODINSKY, M. and E. A. HOLYOKE. 1941. The fasciæ and fascial spaces of the palm. Anat. Rec., *79*, 435–451.

JONES, F. W. 1942. The Principles of Anatomy as Seen in the Hand. Williams & Wilkins, Baltimore. 2nd ed., x + 417 pp.

KAPLAN, E. B. 1938. The palmar fascia in connection with Dupuytren's contracture. Surgery, *4*, 415–422.

KAPLAN, E. B. 1953. Functional and Surgical Anatomy of the Hand. J. B. Lippincott Co., Philadelphia. xvi + 288 pp.

LARSEN, R. D. and J. L. POSCH. 1958. Dupuytren's Contracture. J. Bone & Joint Surg., *40-A*, 773–792.

ABDOMINAL WALL, INGUINAL REGION, AND PELVIS

ANSON, B. J., E. H. MORGAN, and C. B. McVAY. 1949. The anatomy of the hernial regions. I. Inguinal hernia. Surg., Gyn. and Obst., *89*, 417–423.

CHOUKE, K. S. 1935. The constitution of the sheath of the rectus abdominis muscle. Anat. Rec., *61*, 341–349.

COLE, A. E. 1941. A working model to demonstrate the anatomical relationships of inguinal herniæ. Anat. Rec., *79*, 53–56.

CHANDLER, S. B. 1950. Studies on the inguinal region. III. The inguinal canal. Anat. Rec., *107*, 93–102.

CONGDON, E. D., R. BLUMBERG, and W. HENRY. 1942. Fasciæ of fusion and elements of fused enteric mesenteries in the human adult. Am. J. Anat., *70*, 251–279.

CONGDON, E. D. and J. N. EDSON. 1941. The cone of renal fascia in the adult white male. Anat. Rec., *80*, 289–313.

CONGDON, E. D., J. N. EDSON, and S. YANITELLI. 1946. Gross structure of the subcutaneous layer of the anterior and lateral trunk in the male. Am. J. Anat., *79*, 399–429.

COOPER, G. W. 1952. Fascial variants of the trigonum lumbale (Petiti). Anat. Rec., *114*, 1–7.

HAYES, M. A. 1950. Abdominopelvic fasciæ. Am. J. Anat., *87*, 119–161.

MARTIN, C. P. 1942. A note on the renal fascia. J. Anat., *77*, 101–103.

McVAY, C. B. and B. J. ANSON. 1940. Composition of the rectus sheath. Anat. Rec., *77*, 213–225.

MILLER, R. A. 1947. The inguinal canal of primates. Am. J. Anat., *80*, 117–142.

RIVES, J. D. and D. D. BAKER. 1942. Anatomy of the attachments of the diaphragm: Their relation to the problems of the surgery of diaphragmatic hernia. Ann. Surg., *115*, 745–755.

TOBIN, C. E. 1944. The renal fascia and its relation to the transversalis fascia. Anat. Rec., *89*, 295–311.

TOBIN, C. E. and J. A. BENJAMIN. 1949. Anatomic and clinical re-evaluation of Camper's, Scarpa's, and Colles' fasciæ. Surg., Gyn. and Obst., *88*, 545–559.

TOBIN, C. E., J. A. BENJAMIN, and J. C. WELLS. 1946. Continuity of the fasciæ lining the abdomen, pelvis, and spermatic cord. Surg., Gyn. and Obst., *83*, 575–596.

LOWER LIMB

ANSON, B. J. and C. B. McVAY. 1938. The fossa ovalis, and related blood vessels. Anat. Rec. *72*, 399–404.

BELLOCQ, P. and P. MEYER. 1957. Contribution a l'étude de l'aponévrose dorsale du pied (Fascia dorsalis pedis, P. N. A.). Acta Anat., *30*, 67–80.

GRODINSKY, M. 1929. A study of the fascial spaces of the foot and their bearing on infections. Surg., Gyn. and Obst., *49*, 737–751.

KAPLAN, E. B. 1958. The iliotibial tract. Clinical and morphological significance. J. Bone & Joint Surg., *40A*, 817–832.

PELVIS AND PERINEUM

DAVIES, J. W. 1934. The pelvic outlet—its practical application. Surg., Gyn. and Obst., *58*, 70–78.

McVay, C. B. and B. J. Anson. 1940. Aponeurotic and fascial continuities in the abdomen, pelvis and thigh. Anat. Rec., *76*, 213–231.

Miller, R. A. 1945. The ischial callosities of primates. Am. J. Anat., *76*, 67–91.

Tobin, C. E. and J. A. Benjamin. 1944. Anatomical study and clinical consideration of the fasciæ limiting urinary extravasation from the penile urethra. Surg., Gyn. and Obst., *79*, 195–204.

Tobin, C. E. and J. A. Benjamin. 1945. Anatomical and surgical restudy of Denonvilliers' fascia. Surg., Gyn. and Obst., *80*, 373–388.

Washburn, S. L. 1957. Ischial callosities as sleeping adaptations. Am. J. Phys. Anthrop., *15*, 269–276.

Wesson, M. B. 1953. What are Buck's and Colles' fasciæ? J. Urol., *70*, 503–511.

THE HEART.

THE CARDIOVASCULAR SYSTEM

The system of vessels through which the blood circulates is composed of the heart, the arteries, the veins, and the capillaries. The **heart**, by its rhythmic contraction, propels the blood through the vessels of all parts of the body. The vessels conducting blood away from the heart are the **arteries**. They ramify greatly, becoming progressively smaller, and end in minute vessels, the **arterioles**. From these vessels the blood is able to carry out its nutrient and absorbing functions by passing through a network of microscopic channels, called **capillaries**, whose walls are very thin and therefore allow the blood to exchange substances with the tissues. From the capillaries, the blood is collected into **venules**; then through **veins** of progressively greater diameter it reaches the heart again. This passage of the blood through the heart and blood vessels is termed the **circulation of the blood**.

The powerful pumping portions of the heart are the two **ventricles**, right and left, separated by a muscular septum. The thick walled ventricles are made to function efficiently by being quickly and forcibly filled with blood by the contraction of the **atria**, also a right and left to correspond with the ventricles. As the blood is returned to the heart through the veins of the body, it enters the **right atrium** and is forced into the **right ventricle**. From here it is pumped into the capillaries of the lungs through the pulmonary arteries and there is refreshed by giving up carbon dioxide and absorbing oxygen. It is returned by the pulmonary vein to the **left atrium** which forces it into the **left ventricle**. The left ventricle propels the blood through the aorta and systemic arteries, through the capillaries, and back to the heart again through the veins. The circulation through the **right side of the heart** and the lungs is known as the **lesser** or **pulmonary circulation**. The circulation through the **left heart** and **systemic arteries** and **veins** is known as the **systemic circulation**.

Although the circuit away from the heart and back again characteristically involves only one set of capillaries, an exception is found in the vessels of the abdominal organs. The blood supplied to the spleen, pancreas, stomach, and intestines by the systemic arteries is collected into a large vein, the **portal vein**, which enters the liver and ramifies within it. As the blood passes through the capillary-like **sinusoids**, it exchanges nutrient materials with the liver cells, and is then collected into the hepatic veins which empty into the large systemic vena cava inferior just before it opens into the right atrium. This is known as the **portal circulation**.

The description of the cardiovascular system is divided into three parts for convenience in description, but all parts are, of course, completely dependent upon each other functionally. The three sections deal with the heart, the arteries, and the veins. The capillaries are of more or less uniform structure throughout the body and belong to the subject of histology.

A time-honored division of the subject of Anatomy is that of the Vascular System. Its study is called **angiology** (*angiologia*). It includes two groups of vessels, the blood vascular system and the lymphatic system. Although the lymphatic system drains into the veins, making the two systems interdependent, there are sufficient differences morphologically and functionally to make separate treatment advisable. The lymphatic system is described in the chapter following the cardiovascular system.

DEVELOPMENT OF THE HEART

The first **primordium** of the **vascular system** can be recognized very soon after the first appearance of the **coelom** or body cavity within the embryo. The latter occurs on about the twentieth day, at a time when the mesoderm has been formed by the primitive streak but before it has been organized into the primitive segments or somites (see Chapter 1). This first cœlom is a U-shaped cavity encircling the cephalic end of the neural folds (Fig. 507). It is the **primordium of the pericardial**

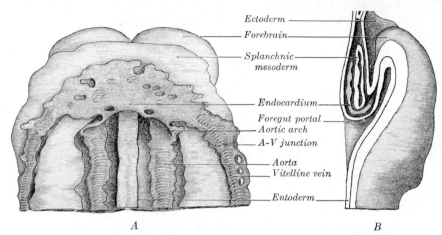

FIG. 503.—Embryo rat with 3 somites. *A*, Ventral view with entoderm removed. Lumen of heart and vessels is incomplete. *B*, Median sagittal section of same embryo   Drawings of wax reconstruction made at 400× magnification.

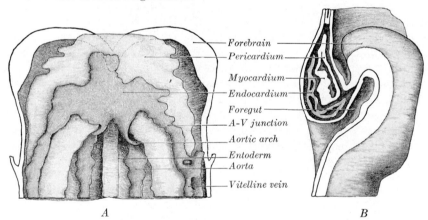

FIG. 504.—Embryo rat with 4 somites   *A*, Ventral view with entoderm removed.   Compare endocardium with that in Figure 503. *B*, Median sagittal section of same embryo.

cavity. Its outer layer, the **somatic mesoderm**, will become the parietal pericardium; its inner layer, the **splanchnic mesoderm**, will develop into the myocardium and epicardium. Scattered cells of mesodermal origin, called **mesenchyme** (*mesenchyma*), migrate between the compact laminæ of the splanchnic mesoderm and the entoderm. This mesenchyme proliferates rapidly and forms into strands and sheets which are the **primordium of the endocardium**.

The earliest stages of development of the human heart are very imperfectly known because of the scarcity of human embryos of this age. It is necessary, therefore, to fill in the gaps with information obtained from lower forms. The chick embryo has been a favorite object for these pioneering studies because of its ready accessibility, but the available human embryos have shown that their development follows the pattern of other mammals rather than that of birds. Thus the ventricle of the early mammalian heart is at first more saccular than tubular, and although it absorbs the two lateral tubes, it is differentiated primarily from tissue already present in the median region, not formed by the coalescence of two independent lateral parts, as in the chick. The following account of this early period is based on numerous rat embryos (Goss '52), both living and preserved, which have been used to elucidate the unknown period between an early human embryo containing the earliest stage of the pericardial cavity (Fig. 507) and another human embryo with

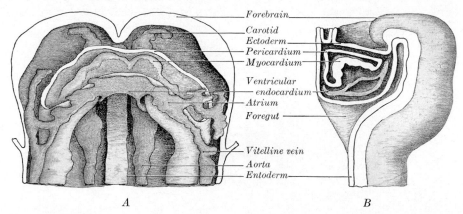

A B

FIG. 505.—Embryo rat with 5 somites. *A*, Ventral view with entoderm removed. Ventral part of pericardium cut away to show myocardium. Dotted line indicates extent of endocardium inside ventricle. *B*, Median sagittal section of same embryo. Compare with Figures 504 and 505.

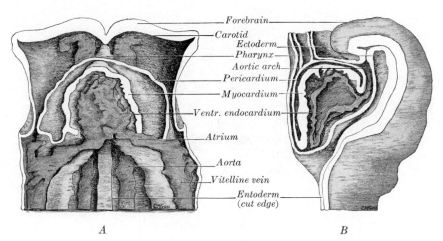

A B

FIG. 506.—Embryo rat with 6 somites. *A*, Ventral view with entoderm removed. Ventral part of pericardium and myocardium also removed to show endocardium. *B*, Median sagittal section of same embryo.

a rather well developed bent tubular heart (Fig. 508) (Davis '27). It is convenient to use the number of the somites as an index of the stage of development because (*a*) they can be counted accurately, (*b*) they retain a relatively stable relationship to the rest of the embryo, and (*c*) the passage of time can be estimated since each new somite between the third and tenth requires three or four hours for its appearance.

By the time the embryo has acquired its **first three somites** or primitive body segments and before the neural folds have closed into the neural tube, the **endocardial mesenchyme** has spread out in a thin sheet across the midline in the cephalic portion of the embryo (Fig. 503). It also extends down on each side of the still

shallow foregut invagination and a lumen has begun to form in these lateral extensions. The splanchnic mesoderm becomes thickened where it is in contact with the
endocardium and is thus identifiable as the **primordium of the myocardium**. The
myocardial layer is also deeply grooved along the lateral endocardial tubes. Thus,
the two lateral endocardial tubes with their partial cloak of myocardium constitute
the **primitive lateral hearts** where the first contractions occur. The site of the future
atrioventricular junction is marked by a constriction of the lumen of the lateral
tube slightly caudal to the level of the foregut portal.

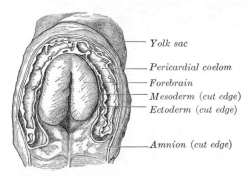

Yolk sac

Pericardial coelom

Forebrain

Mesoderm (cut edge)

Ectoderm (cut edge)

Amnion (cut edge)

Fig. 507.—Human embryo with first somite forming, 1.5 mm. in length. Dorsal view with
amnion removed and ectoderm and mesoderm cut away to show pericardial cavity. Carnegie
collection No. 5080. (Redrawn from Davis '27, courtesy Carnegie Institution.)

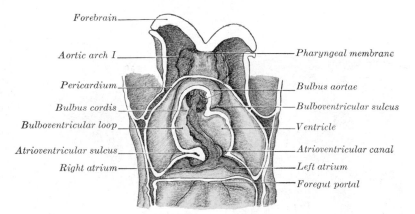

Forebrain

Aortic arch I

Pericardium

Bulbus cordis

Bulboventricular loop

Atrioventricular sulcus

Right atrium

Pharyngeal membrane

Bulbus aortae

Bulboventricular sulcus

Ventricle

Atrioventricular canal

Left atrium

Foregut portal

Fig. 508.—Human embryo with 8 somites, 2 mm. in length. Ventral view of plaster model of
heart and pericardial region. Pericardial wall and myocardium removed to expose endocardium.
(Redrawn from Davis '27. Courtesy of Carnegie Institution.)

The **median sheet of mesenchyme** is quickly differentiated into endocardium by
having the lumen extend into it from the lateral tubes. At the same time, the sheet
appears to pull in its outlying parts in much the same manner as an amœba with-
draws its pseudopodia. The result is a sac rather than a tube, which, with its
adjacent myocardial mesoderm, constitutes the **primitive ventricle**. As the endocardial sac expands, it sinks deeply into a pocket in the mesoderm. The pericardial
cavity enlarges to accommodate this growth and in a **four somite embryo** the entire
cardiac complex bulges ventrally at the foregut portal (Fig. 504).

Up to this time the myocardium has been entirely dorsal to the endocardium.
The rapid expansion of the pericardial cavity in a ventral direction allows the
myocardium to protrude ventrally over the endocardial sac, until, in a **five somite
embryo,** the heart lies in a plane at right angles to the axis of the embryo with the

arterial end more dorsally placed and the venous end more ventrally placed (Fig. 505).

By a continued rapid growth, the ventricular myocardium extends over the entire ventral surface of the endocardium (Fig. 506). In a **six somite embryo** it encloses the endocardium except for a narrow interval along the midline dorsally. This change allows the heart to assume a more tubular shape with cephalic and caudal extremities. It never quite reaches the stage of a straight tube, as in lower forms, however. The opening of the aortic sac is always dorsal rather than cephalic to the heart and the whole tube maintains a curvature with ventral convexity. The

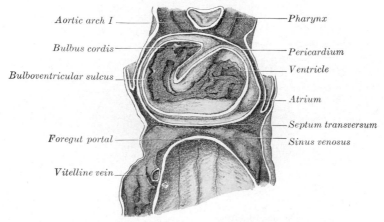

FIG. 509.—Human embryo with 11–12 somites, 3.09 mm. in length. Ventral view of plaster model of heart and pericardial region. Pericardial wall and myocardium removed to expose endocardium. (Redrawn from Davis '27. Courtesy of Carnegie Institution.)

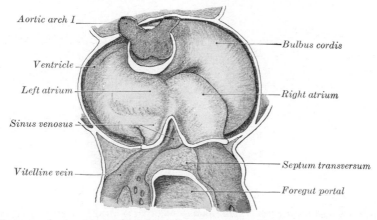

FIG. 510.—Human embryo with 20 somites, 3.01 mm. in length. Dorsal view of plaster model of heart. (Redrawn from Davis '27. Courtesy of Carnegie Institution.)

result is the marked ventral protrusion of the cardiac complex which is characteristic of early mammalian embryos. When the embryo has acquired **seven somites**, the myocardium completely surrounds the endocardium. The middle portion of the tubular ventricle becomes free and only the ends are attached, the arterial end by its continuity with the aortic sac and first aortic arches and the venous end by the atria and vitelline veins.

The length of the tubular heart increases much more rapidly than the longitudinal extent of the pericardium. The tube therefore continues to bend, this time in a loop with convexity to the right (**bulboventricular loop**) (Fig. 508).   The resulting groove on the left side is called the **bulboventricular sulcus** and establishes a subdivision of the tube into the **bulbus cordis** or **conus** and the **primitive ventricle**.   The ventricular portion increases rapidly in all diameters, protruding ventrally and causing another bend at the atrioventricular junction.   The opening of the atrium becomes narrowed into the **atrioventricular canal**, entering the ventricle dorsally and from the left.   The pericardial cavity expands out over the two lateral portions of the atrium which are then brought closer together and a constriction is formed between the veins and the atrium (Fig. 509).

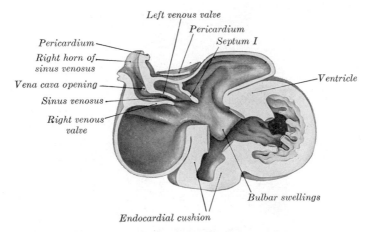

FIG. 511.—Model of heart of 6.5 mm. human embryo, interior of lower half seen from above. (From J. Tandler, 1912, courtesy of J. B. Lippincott Company).

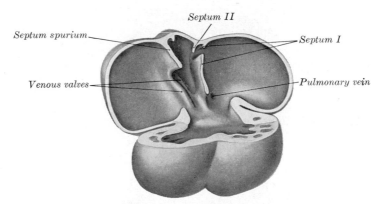

FIG. 512.—Model of heart of 9 mm. human embryo, ventral view of interior of atria. (From J. Tandler, 1912, courtesy of J. B. Lippincott Company.)

The proximal portions of the veins become part of a common chamber and are called the right and left **horns of the sinus venosus**.   The umbilical and common cardinal veins (from the embryo proper) have joined the vitelline veins just before they enter the sinus horns.   The continued bending of the bulbo-ventricular loop folds the conus against the atrium on the dorsal and cephalic aspect of the heart. The conus has remained a relatively narrow tube and as it now presses against the median region of the atrium, the lateral portions bulge out on each side.   The resulting two expansions of the atrium are the **primitive right** and **left atria** (Fig. 515). They represent the first division of the heart into its permanent right and left sides.

The tissue between the pericardial cavity and the foregut portal becomes thickened into a mass called the **septum transversum** (Fig. 510). As the liver cords grow into the septum there is a reorganization of the veins. The right vein gradually takes over the drainage of blood from the vitelline, umbilical, and posterior cardinal circulations of both sides and is thus the **precursor of the inferior vena cava.** The resultant enlargement of the right horn of the sinus venosus shifts the sinoatrial opening to the right. The right anterior cardinal vein also becomes dominant and shifts the opening somewhat cephalad (Fig. 604).

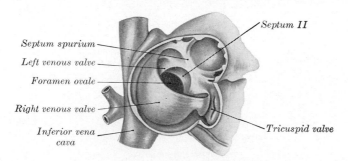

Fig. 513.—Interior of right atrium of reconstruction of heart of 25 mm. human embryo. (R. H. Licata, Am. J. Anat., *94*, 80, 1954, courtesy of Wistar Press.)

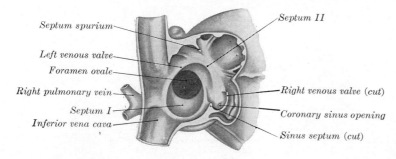

Fig. 514.—Interior of right atrium of same heart as in Figure 513 with right venous valve removed. (R. H. Licata, Am J. Anat., *94*, 80, 1954, courtesy of Wistar Press.)

In the narrow part of the atrium between the two expansions to the right and left of the conus, a fold of endocardial tissue grows toward the atrioventricular opening. This is known as **septum I** or the **septum primum.** The shifting of the sinoatrial opening to the right, already mentioned, places this opening to the right of the newly forming septum (Fig. 511). As the septum primum progresses toward the ventricles, two swellings appear in the wall of the atrioventricular canal. They soon join across the opening, making a division into a right and left atrioventricular opening. This is the **septum intermedium.** The narrowing open space between the advancing septum primum and the septum intermedium is the **ostium I** or **ostium primum** (Fig. 512). Before the septum primum completely closes this opening between the two atria, which would shut off all flow of blood between them, the substance of the septum near its attachment to the cephalic part of the atrial wall is thinned out and breaks through. This forms **ostium II** or the **ostium secundum** (Fig. 512) (Tandler '13).

In the right atrium, a new partition now grows down from the cephalic and ventral part of the atrial wall toward the venous opening so as to cover the new opening in septum I. This is **septum II** or **septum secundum** (Fig 513). Its growth ceases before it is complete, leaving an opening called the **foramen ovale,** and its cresentic border persists as the limbus fossæ ovalis, seen in the adult right atrium (Fig. 524). After septum I has joined with the septum intermedium its remaining part becomes thinned out and acts as a flap over the foramen ovale below the crescentic edge of septum II (**valve of the foramen ovale**). After birth, when the foramen ovale is no longer functional, this flap becomes adherent to the limbus and seals the opening. During this development the **pulmonary veins** grow out from the left atrium but they are of insignificant size because of the non-functioning condition of the lungs. The left heart, therefore, receives the bulk of its blood through the foramen ovale rather than from these veins.

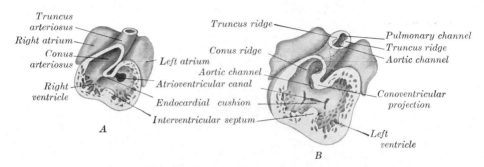

FIG. 515.—The conus and ventricle of the hearts of human embryos opened to show stages in the partitioning into pulmonary and aortic outlets. Semischematic drawings. *A*, 4–5 mm. embryo; *B*, 8.8 mm. embryo. (T. C. Kramer, Am. J. Anat., *71*, 359, 1942, courtesy of Wistar Press.)

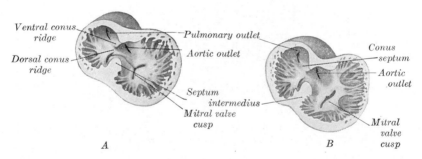

FIG. 516.—Ventral views of reconstructions of hearts of human embryos opened to show partitioning of ventricles and formation of interventricular septum. *A*, 13 mm., Carnegie Embryological Collection No. 841; *B*, 14.5 mm., modified from Tandler ('12). (From T. C. Kramer, Am. J. Anat., *71*, 361, 1942, courtesy Wistar Press).

While the interatrial septa are forming, the slit-like opening of the sinus venosus into the right atrium is guarded by two valves, the **right** and **left venous valves** (*valvulæ renosæ*; *sinus folds*) (Fig. 511). Above the opening, the two venous valves unite into a single fold, the **septum spurium**, which is a prominent feature at this stage but is of no significance for the eventual partitioning of the heart.

As the atrium increases in size it absorbs the sinus venosus into its walls. The upper part of the sinus then becomes the opening for the **superior vena cava**. The inferior part becomes divided by the further growth of the right venous valve into two openings, the **inferior vena cava** and the **coronary sinus**. The left venous valve disappears except for the lower part which is absorbed into the septum secundum. The upper part of the right venous valve and the septum spurium almost disappear but are retained in the adult heart as the crista terminalis. The lower part of the right valve persists and is divided into two parts by the growth of a transverse fold, the **sinus septum** (Fig. 514). The right upper part becomes the **valve of the inferior**

vena cava. The lower left part becomes the **valve of the coronary sinus.** Of the horns of the sinus venosus, the right becomes much more prominent since it furnishes the inferior and superior venæ cavæ. The left horn remains small, receiving only the left common cardinal vein. The left anterior cardinal dwindles into the **oblique vein** (Fig. 549) and the **vestigial fold of Marshall.** The left common cardinal also loses its connection with the body wall and becomes the **coronary sinus,** draining blood only from the substance of the heart.

The primitive ventricle becomes divided by the growth of the **septum inferius** or **interventricular septum.** It grows up from the most prominent part of the ventricular wall, its position on the surface of the heart being indicated by a furrow. Its dorsal part grows more rapidly than the ventral and fuses with the dorsal part of the septum intermedium. The opening between the two ventricles remains for some time but is ultimately closed by the fusion of the interventricular and aortic septa (Fig. 515).

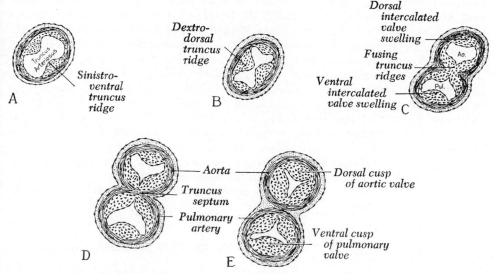

Fig. 517.—Schematic diagrams of the partitioning of the truncus arteriosus and the origin of the aortic and pulmonary semilunar valves. (Kramer, 1942, Am. J. Anat., *71*, 354.)

The conus, as mentioned above, was at first separated from the ventricle by a deep fold, the bulboventricular sulcus. This fold gradually recedes until the conus and ventricle open freely into each other. This has the effect of allowing the aortic sac or the truncus aortæ to open directly into the ventricle and it comes to lie in line with the path of the growing interventricular septum (Fig. 516). The portion of the ventricular wall which had been the conus remains to the right of the interventricular septum and becomes a part of the adult right ventricle (Kramer '42).

The **truncus arteriosus** or **primitive ascending aorta** has at this time developed both its fourth and its pulmonary pairs of arches. The partitioning of the truncus into the **aorta** and **pulmonary trunk** begins by the growth of two **endothelial cushions** in the region of the fourth pair of arches. The growth of these cushions toward the conus makes a pair of spiral ridges (Fig. 516). As the tops of these ridges grow together, partitioning off the truncus, there is a separation of the aortic from the pulmonary trunk. The right ventricle becomes connected with the pulmonary arches which go to the lungs. The left ventricle becomes connected with the fourth arch which forms the aorta.

At the junction of the conus and truncus, the endocardial cushions develop special swellings which become the **semilunar valves**. Two of the valve cusps in each vessel are formed from tissue of the ridges which partition the truncus and they retain this association of position throughout the subsequent rotation and twisting of these vessels (Kerr and Goss '56). The third cusp in each vessel develops independently from dorsal and ventral intercalated swellings (Fig. 517, 528) (Kramer '42).

Beginning of Contraction.—The first contractions of the heart have not been observed in human embryos but it can be assumed that they follow the same sequence as in other mammals. In an embryo with three somites (Fig. 504), two lateral heart tubes are recognizable. On the ventricular side of a slight constriction which marks the future atrioventricular junction, a small group of cells in the splanchnic mesoderm begin contracting with a regular rhythm. In a rat embryo, the left lateral heart initiates the contraction at a rate of 20 to 30 per minute (Goss '38). A few hours later the right heart commences with a slower rate and a regular rhythm independent of the left side. As the contraction involves the median portion of the ventricle, the rate increases gradually, the left side acting as pacemaker. By the time the rate has reached 90 per minute, a small part of the atrium adjacent to the A–V junction has begun contraction and acts as the pacemaker, but with a distinct interval between the atrial and ventricular contraction (Goss '42b).

Beginning of Circulation.—The primitive heart continues to contract while it is enlarging and differentiating after the three somite stage, but is ineffective for circulation until the embryo has eight or nine somites (Fig. 508), a period of fifteen to twenty hours. At this time the atrium is well established, the ventricle is an effective muscular pump, the cells in the blood islands of the yolk sac have acquired hemoglobin, and a continuous lumen has been established through the aortæ, umbilical and omphalomesenteric arteries, yolk sac and placental capillaries, and back through the corresponding veins to the heart (Goss '42a).

The development of the arteries and veins is described at the beginning of the corresponding chapters.

PECULIARITIES IN THE VASCULAR SYSTEM OF THE FETUS.

The chief peculiarities of the fetal heart are the direct communication between the atria through the foramen ovale, and the large size of the valve of the inferior vena cava. Among other peculiarities the following may be noted. (1) In early fetal life the heart lies immediately below the mandibular arch and is relatively large in size. As development proceeds it is gradually drawn within the thorax, but at first it lies in the middle line; toward the end of pregnancy it gradually becomes oblique in direction. (2) For a time the atrial portion exceeds the ventricular in size, and the walls of the ventricles are of equal thickness: toward the end of fetal life the ventricular portion becomes the larger and the wall of the left ventricle exceeds that of the right in thickness. (3) Its size is large as compared with that of the rest of the body, the proportion at the second month being 1 to 50, and at birth, 1 to 120, while in the adult the average is about 1 to 160.

The **foramen ovale**, situated at the lower part of the atrial septum, forms a free communication between the atria until the end of fetal life. A septum (*septum secundum*) grows down from the upper wall of the atrium to the right of the primary septum in which the foramen ovale is situated; shortly after birth it fuses with the primary septum and the foramen ovale is obliterated.

The **valve of the inferior vena cava** serves to direct the blood from that vessel through the foramen ovale into the left atrium.

The peculiarities in the arterial system of the fetus are the communication between the pulmonary artery and the aorta by means of the ductus arteriosus, and the continuation of the hypogastric arteries as the umbilical arteries to the placenta.

The **ductus arteriosus** is a short tube, about 1.25 cm. in length at birth, and 4.4 mm. in diameter. In the early condition it forms the continuation of the pulmonary artery, and opens into the aorta, just beyond the origin of the left subclavian artery; and so conducts the greater amount of the blood from the right ventricle into the aorta. When the branches of the pulmonary artery have become larger relatively to the ductus arteriosus, the latter is chiefly connected to the left pulmonary artery.

The **hypogastric arteries** run along the sides of the bladder and thence upward on the back of the anterior abdominal wall to the umbilicus; here they pass out of the abdomen and are continued as the **umbilical arteries** in the umbilical cord to the placenta. They convey the fetal blood to the placenta.

The peculiarities in the venous system of the fetus are the communications established between the placenta and the liver and portal vein, through the umbilical vein; and between the umbilical vein and the inferior vena cava through the ductus venosus.

Fetal Circulation (Fig. 518).—The fetal blood is returned from the placenta to the fetus by the umbilical vein. This vein enters the abdomen at the umbilicus, and passes upward along the free margin of the falciform ligament of the liver to the under surface of that organ, where it gives off two or three branches, one of large size to the left lobe, and others to the lobus quadratus and lobus caudatus. At the **porta hepatis** (*transverse fissure of the liver*) it divides into two branches: of these, the larger is joined by the portal vein, and enters the right lobe; the smaller is continued upward, under the name of the **ductus venosus**, and joins the inferior vena cava. The blood, therefore, which traverses the umbilical vein, passes to the inferior vena cava in three different ways. A considerable quantity circulates through the liver with the portal venous blood, before entering the inferior vena cava by the hepatic veins; some enters the liver directly, and is carried to the inferior vena cava by the hepatic veins; the remainder passes directly into the inferior vena cava through the ductus venosus.

In the inferior vena cava, the blood carried by the ductus venosus and hepatic veins becomes mixed with that returning from the lower extremities and abdominal wall. It enters the right atrium, and, guided by the valve of the inferior vena cava, passes through the foramen ovale into the left atrium, where it mixes with a small quantity of blood returned from the lungs by the pulmonary veins. From the left atrium it passes into the left ventricle; and from the left ventricle into the aorta, by means of which it is distributed almost entirely to the head and upper extremities, a small quantity being probably carried into the descending aorta. From the head and upper extremities the blood is returned by the superior vena cava to the right atrium, where it mixes with a small portion of the blood from the inferior vena cava. From the right atrium it descends into the right ventricle, and thence passes into the pulmonary artery. The lungs of the fetus being inactive, only a small quantity of the blood of the pulmonary artery is distributed to them by the right and left pulmonary arteries, and returned by the pulmonary veins to the left atrium: the greater part passes through the ductus arteriosus into the aorta, where it mixes with a small quantity of the blood transmitted by the left ventricle into the aorta. Through this vessel it descends, and is in part distributed to the lower extremities and the viscera of the abdomen and pelvis, but the greater amount is conveyed by the umbilical arteries to the placenta.

From the preceding account of the circulation of the blood in the fetus the following facts will be evident: (1) The placenta serves the purposes of nutrition and excretion, receiving the impure blood from the fetus, and returning it purified and charged with additional nutritive material. (2) Nearly all the blood of the

37

umbilical vein traverses the liver before entering the inferior vena cava; hence the large size of the liver, especially at an early period of fetal life. (3) The right atrium is the point of meeting of a double current, the blood in the inferior vena cava being guided by the valve of this vessel into the left atrium, while that in the superior vena cava descends into the right ventricle. At an early period of fetal life it is highly probable that the two streams are quite distinct; for the inferior vena cava opens almost directly into the left atrium, and the valve of the inferior vena cava would exclude the current from the right ventricle. At a later

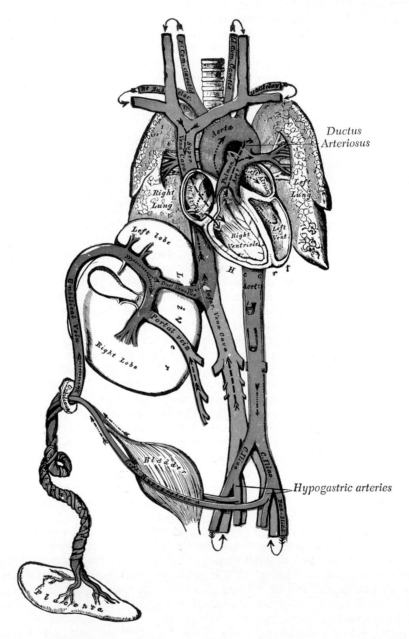

FIG. 518.—Plan of the fetal circulation. In this plan the figured arrows represent the kind of blood, as well as the direction which it takes in the vessels. Thus—arterial blood is figured >------->-; venous blood, >− − − >; mixed (arterial and venous) blood, >−−--− >.

period, as the separation between the two atria becomes more distinct, it seems probable that some mixture of the two streams must take place. (4) The pure blood carried from the placenta to the fetus by the umbilical vein, mixed with the blood from the portal vein and inferior vena cava, passes almost directly to the arch of the aorta, and is distributed by the branches of that vessel to the head and upper extremities. (5) The blood contained in the descending aorta, chiefly derived from that which has already circulated through the head and limbs, together with a small quantity from the left ventricle, is distributed to the abdomen and lower extremities.

Changes in the Vascular System at Birth.—At birth, when respiration is established, an increased amount of blood from the pulmonary artery passes through the lungs, and the placental circulation is cut off. The foramen ovale gradually decreases in size during the first month, but a small opening usually persists until the last third of the first year and often later; the valvular fold above mentioned adheres to the margin of the foramen for the greater part of its circumference, but a slit-like opening is left between the two atria above, and this sometimes persists.

The **ductus arteriosus** begins to contract immediately after respiration is established, and its lumen slowly becomes obliterated; it ultimately degenerates into an impervious cord, the **ligamentum arteriosum,** which connects the left pulmonary artery to the arch of the aorta. (Figs. 522 and 523.)

Of the **hypogastric arteries,** the parts extending from the sides of the bladder to the umbilicus become obliterated between the second and fifth days after birth, and project as fibrous cords, the **lateral umbilical ligaments,** toward the abdominal cavity, carrying on them folds of peritoneum. (Fig. 580.)

The **umbilical vein** and **ductus venosus** are obliterated between the first and fifth days after birth; the former becomes the ligamentum teres, the latter the ligamentum venosum, of the liver. The hepatic half of the ductus venosus may remain open, receive tributaries from the liver and thus function as a hepatic vein in the adult.

THE HEART

The heart (*cor*) is a hollow muscular organ shaped like a blunt cone about the size of the fist of the same individual. It rests on the diaphragm between the lower part of the two lungs. It is enclosed in a special membrane, the pericardium, and occupies a topographical compartment of the thorax known as the **middle mediastinum** (Fig. 545). Its position relative to the chest wall is shown diagrammatically in Figure 71 and the position and extent of the cardiac shadow in an x-ray plate are shown in Figure 73. It is covered ventrally by the sternum and adjoining parts of the third to sixth costal cartilages. The apex of the cone points downward, forward, and to the left, about two-thirds of the whole organ being to the left of the median plane.

Size.—The heart, in the adult, measures about 12 cm. in length, 8 to 9 cm. in breadth at the broadest part, and 6 cm. in thickness. Its weight, in the male, varies from 280 to 340 grams; in the female, from 230 to 280 grams. The heart frequently continues to increase in weight and size up to an advanced period of life; this increase may be pathological.

The Heart Wall.—The wall of the heart is composed of three layers, an outer epicardium, a middle myocardium, and an inner endocardium. The surface layer of the **epicardium** is the **serous membrane** or **visceral pericardium.** This is a single sheet of squamous mesothelial cells resting on a lamina propria of delicate connective tissue. Between the serous coat and the myocardium is a layer of heavier fibroelastic connective tissue. The latter is interspersed with **adipose tissue** which fills in the crevices and sulci to give the heart a smooth, rounded contour. The larger blood vessels and the nerves are contained in this layer also. The dark reddish color of the myocardium is visible through the epicardium except where fat has accumulated. The amount of fat varies greatly; it is seldom absent except in emaciated individuals and may almost completely obscure the myocardium in the very obese.

The **myocardium** is composed of layers and bundles of cardiac muscle with a minimum of other tissue except for the blood vessels. It is described in detail in a later section.

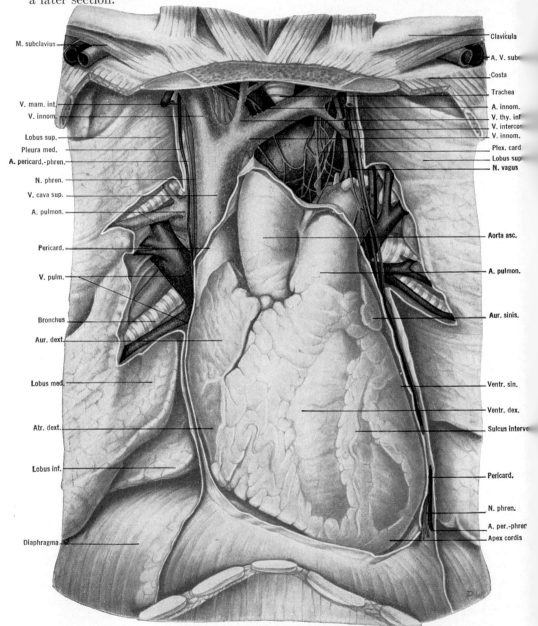

Fig. 519.—The sternocostal surface of the heart and great vessels after removal of the pericardium, with the structures at the roots of the lungs exposed. (Töndury: Angewandte und Topographische Anatomie, courtesy of Georg Thieme Verlag.)

The **endocardium** is the interior lining of the heart. Its surface layer is composed of squamous endothelial cells and is continuous with the endothelial lining of the blood vessels. The connective tissue is quite thin and transparent over the muscular walls of the ventricles but is thickened in the atria and at the attachments of the valves. It contains small blood vessels, parts of the specialized conduction system, and a few bundles of smooth muscle.

Although the heart is freely movable and unattached to the surrounding organs, it is maintained in its proper position in the thorax by continuity with the great blood vessels and by an enclosing membranous sac, the pericardium (Fig. 519).

THE PERICARDIUM

The pericardium includes two quite different components, the serous membrane and the fibrous sac. The **serous pericardium** lines the inside of the fibrous sac and covers the outside of the heart. Its characteristics are such that it provides these two structures with smooth and glistening surfaces, completely free and movable although in contact with each other. The serous layer of the heart itself is called the visceral pericardium or the epicardium. It covers the atria and ventricles and extends beyond them out on the great vessels for two or three centimeters (see Fig. 519). The serous layer lining the fibrous sac is called the parietal pericardium. The two parts of the serous layer are continuous with each other and the point at which the visceral layer ends and folds back on itself to become the parietal layer is called the **reflection of the pericardium.**

The pericardial cavity.—In a healthy state, the two serous membranes are closely apposed to each other, separated only by enough serous or watery fluid to make their surfaces slippery. This allows the heart to move easily during its contraction in systole and its relaxation in diastole. Since the two surfaces are not attached, there is a potential space between them called the pericardial cavity. After injury or due to disease, fluid may exude into the cavity causing a wide separation between the heart and the outer pericardium.

The extension of the epicardium on the great vessels is in the form of two tubular prolongations. One encloses the aorta and pulmonary artery and is called the **arterial mesocardium.** The other encloses the venæ cavæ and the pulmonary veins and is called the **venous mesocardium.** The reflection of the venous mesocardium forms a U-shaped cul-de-sac in the dorsal wall of the pericardial cavity known as the **oblique pericardial sinus.** Between the arterial mesocardium and the venous mesocardium is a pericardium-lined passage named the **transverse pericardial sinus** (Fig. 520).

The **fibrous pericardium** forms a flask-like sac the neck of which is closed by its attachment to the great vessels just beyond the reflection of the serous pericardium (Fig. 519). It is a tough membrane, much thicker than the parietal pleura. Its outer surface is adherent in varying degrees to all the structures surrounding it. It is attached ventrally to the manubrium of the sternum by a fibrous condensation, the **superior pericardiosternal ligament,** and to the Xiphoid process by the **inferior pericardiosternal ligament.** The fibrous tissue intervening between the sac and the vertebral column is the **pericardiovertebral ligament.** The sac is securely attached to the central tendon and muscular part of the left side of the dome of the diaphragm. A thickening of this fibrous attachment in the area of the inferior vena cava has been called the **pericardiophrenic ligament.**

The **ligament of the left vena cava** (*vestigial fold of Marshall*) is a triangular fold covered with serous pericardium stretching from the left pulmonary artery to the atrial wall or the subjacent pulmonary vein. It is formed by the remanent of the proximal part of the left superior vena cava (left anterior cardinal vein and left duct of Cuvier) which becomes obliterated during fetal life. If well developed, it may remain as a fibrous band stretching from the highest left intercostal vein to a small vein draining into the coronary sinus, the **oblique vein of the left atrium** (*oblique vein of Marshall*) (Fig. 549).

The lateral parts of the outer surface of the pericardial sac, *i.e.*, the mediastinal surfaces, are apposed to the mediastinal parietal pleura. The two membranes are adherent but not fused and the phrenic nerve with its accompanying blood vessels is held between them as it traverses the thorax. Because of the rounded contour of the heart, the pleural cavity thus partly encircles the pericardial sac extending

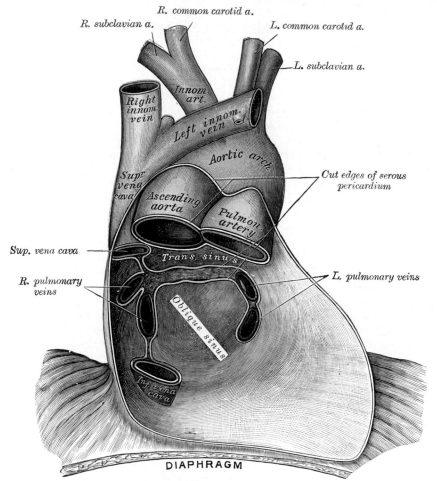

Fig. 520.—Posterior wall of the pericardial sac, showing the lines of reflection of the serous pericardium on the great vessels.

ventrally between it and the chest wall except for a small triangular area on the left side (Figs. 67, 72, 545). This area corresponds to the lower portion of the body of the sternum and the medial ends of the left fourth and fifth costal cartilages. In percussion of the chest for physical diagnosis the triangle is called the area of absolute dullness because no lung is present to give it resonance. It is also important clinically as the area through which a needle can be introduced into the pericardial cavity for removal of excess fluid, without traversing the pleural cavity or lungs. The dorsal surface of the sac is in relation to the bronchi, esophagus, and descending thoracic aorta. The caudal surface is attached to the dome of the diaphragm. The cephalic ventral surface may be in contact with the thymus in a child.

COMPONENT PARTS OF THE HEART

The heart consists of four chambers: two larger ventricles with thick muscular walls making up the bulk of the organ and two smaller atria with thin muscular walls. The septum which separates the ventricles also extends between the atria, subdividing the whole heart into what are called **left** (Latin-sinister) and **right**

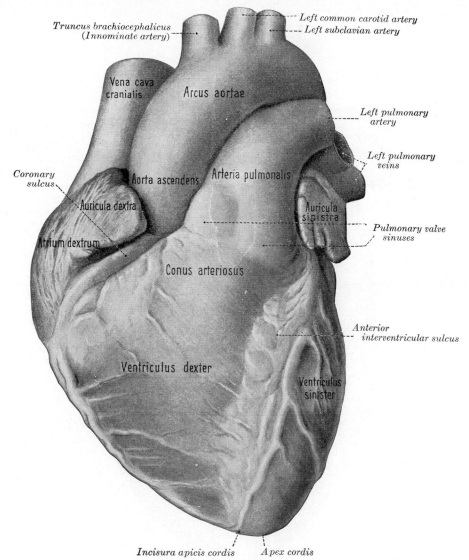

Fig. 521.—Heart. Sternocostal surface, ventral aspect. (Rauber-Kopsch, Lehrbuch u. Atlas d. Anatomie d. Menschen, 19th edition, courtesy of Georg Thieme Verlag, Stuttgart, 1955.)

(Latin-dexter) **halves** or **sides** of the heart. As they lie in the body, however, the right side is mostly ventral or anterior and the left side largely dorsal or posterior.

On the surface of the heart, the **coronary sulcus** (*sulcus coronarius*) (Fig. 521; 522) encircles the heart between the ventricles, which are toward the apex, and the atria, which are at the base. The sulcus is occupied by the arterial and venous vessels supplying the heart. Its ventral part is not visible because it is covered over by the conus arteriosus. The line of separation between the two ventricles is marked by the **anterior longitudinal sulcus** (*sulcus interventricularis anterior*) on the sternocostal surface and by the **posterior longitudinal sulcus** (*sulcus interventricularis posterior*) on the diaphragmatic surface, the two grooves becoming continuous near the apex in the **incisura apicis cordis**.

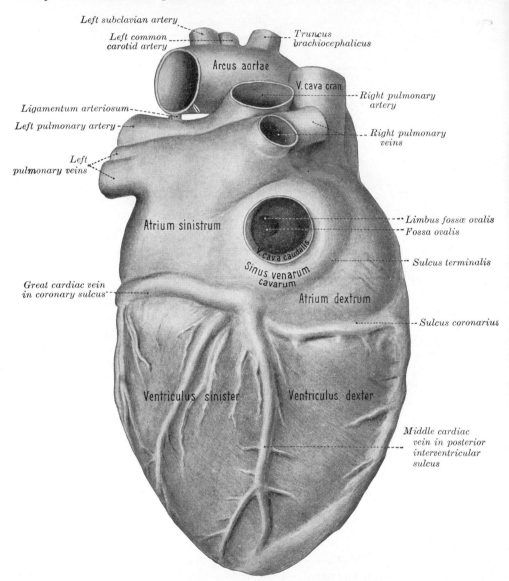

Fig. 522.—Heart. Diaphragmatic surface, inferior aspect. (Rauber-Kopsch, Lehrbuch u. Atlas d. Anatomie de Menschen, 19th edition, courtesy of Georg Thieme Verlag, Stuttgart, 1955.)

The **Apex of the Heart** (*apex cordis*) points downward, forward and to the left. Although its position changes continually during life the tip remains close to the following point under usual circumstances: deep to the left fifth intercostal space, 8 or 9 cm. from the midsternal line, or about 4 cm. below and 2 cm. medial to the left nipple. It is overlapped by an extension of the pleura and lungs as well as by the structures of the anterior thoracic wall.

The **Base of the Heart** (*basis cordis*) (Fig. 523) is more difficult to visualize than the apex but represents the base of the blunt cone which is the heart. Since it is opposite the apex, it faces to the right, upward, and toward the back. It involves mainly the left atrium, part of the right atrium, and the proximal parts of the great vessels. Its superior boundary is at the bifurcation of the pulmonary artery, its inferior at the coronary sulcus, its right side the sulcus terminalis and its left the oblique vein of the left atrium. The descending thoracic aorta, the esophagus, and the thoracic duct intervene between it and the bodies of the fifth to eighth thoracic vertebræ.

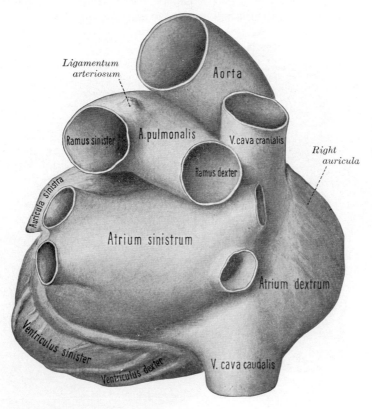

Fig. 523.—Base of the heart, dorsal or posterior aspect. (From Rauber-Kopsch, *Lehrbuch u. Altas d. Anatomie d. Menschen*, 19th Edition, Vol. I, courtesy of Georg Thieme Verlag, Stuttgart, 1955.)

The **Sternocostal Surface** (*facies sternocostalis*) (Fig. 521) is occupied by the right atrium and especially its auricula at the right, and the right ventricle with a small part of the left ventricle at the left. It is crossed obliquely downward by the coronary sulcus and by the anterior longitudinal or interventricular sulcus.

The **Diaphragmatic Surface** (*facies diaphragmatica*) (Fig. 522) is somewhat flattened from its contact with the diaphragm in a preserved cadaver. It involves the two ventricles, the left slightly more than the right, and is crossed obliquely by the posterior longitudinal sulcus. It is marked off from the base of the heart by the coronary sulcus.

The **Right Margin of the Heart** (*margo dexter*), longer than the left, describes an arc from the superior vena cava to the apex. Its upper part is along the right atrium, its lower part along the right ventricle. The ventricular part is almost horizontal, running along the line of attachment of the diaphram to the anterior chest wall.

It tends to be thin and sharp and is called the **acute margin**. The atrial portion is almost vertical and is situated deep to the third to fifth costal cartilages 1.25 cm. to the right of the margin of the sternum.

The **Left Margin** (*obtuse margin*) is formed mainly by the left ventricle and to a small extent by the left atrium. It extends obliquely downward to the apex from a point 2.5 cm. from the sternal margin in the second left interspace, describing a curve with convexity to the left.

Right Atrium (*atrium dextrum*; *right auricle*) (Fig. 524).—The right atrium appears somewhat larger and its wall, 2 mm. in thickness, somewhat thinner than the left. It has a capacity of about 57 ml. It consists of two parts: (*a*) a principal cavity or the sinus venarum and (*b*) a hollow appendage, the auricula.

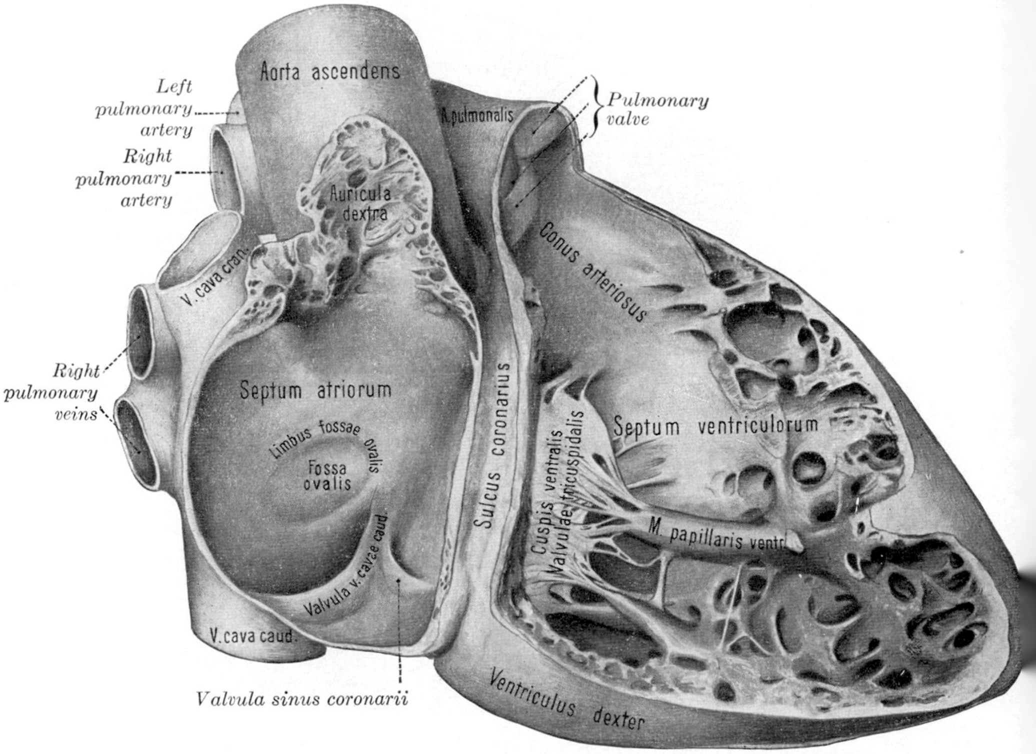

Fig. 524.—Interior of right atrium and right ventricle of heart after removal of sternocostal wall. (From Rauber-Kopsch, Lehrbuch u. Atlas d. Anatomie d. Menschen, 19th Edition, Vol. I, courtesy of Georg Thieme Verlag).

(*a*) The **Sinus Venarum** (*sinus venarum cavarum*) is the part of the cavity between the two venæ cavæ and the atrioventricular opening. Its wall merges with the two cavæ and the interior surface is quite smooth except for certain rudimentary structures described below.

(*b*) The **Right Auricula** (*auricula dextra*; *right auricular appendage*), shaped something like a dog's ear, is a blind pouch extending upward between the superior vena cava and the right ventricle. Its junction with the sinus venarum is marked on the outside by a groove, the **sulcus terminalis** (Fig. 522), which corresponds to a ridge on the inside, the **crista terminalis**. The internal surface of the auricula has the muscular bundles raised into distinctive parallel ridges resembling the teeth of a comb and named, therefore, the **musculi pectinati**.

The interior of the right atrium presents the following openings and parts for examination (Fig. 524).

The **superior vena cava** (*v.c. cranialis*) opens into the upper and posterior part of the sinus venarum. Its orifice faces downward and foreward so that the blood entering the atrium through it is directed toward the atrioventricular opening. It returns the blood from the upper half of the body. There is no valve at its opening.

The **inferior vena cava** (*v.c. caudalis*) opens into the lowest part of the sinus venarum near the interatrial septum. It returns blood from the lower half of the body. Its orifice is larger than that of the superior vena cava and faces upward and backward, toward the fossa ovalis. A rudimentary valve extends upward on the septum from the opening.

The **valve of the inferior vena cava** (*valvula venæ cavæ inferioris*; *Eustachian valve*) (Fig. 524) is a single crescentic fold attached along the ventral and left margin of the orifice of the inferior vena cava. Its concave free margin ends in two cornua of which the left is continuous with the ventral margin of the limbus fossæ ovalis, and the right spreads out on the atrial wall. The valve is composed of a fold of the membranous lining of the atrium containing a few muscular fibers. In the fetus the valve is more prominent and tends to direct the blood from the inferior cava through the then patent foramen ovale into the left atrium. In the adult it is usually rudimentary and has little if any functional significance. It may be thin and fenestrated, very small, or even entirely obliterated.

The **coronary sinus** (*sinus coronarius*) (Fig. 524) opens into the right atrium between the inferior vena cava and the atrioventricular foramen. It returns the blood from the substance of the heart itself and has a valve at its orifice. The **valve of the coronary sinus** (*valvula sinus coronarii*; *Thebesian valve*) is a single semicircular fold of the lining membrane of the atrium attached to the right and inferior lips of the orifice of the coronary sinus. It may be cribriform or double and is seldom effective for more than partial closure of the orifice during contraction of the atrium.

The **foramina venarum minimarum** are the openings of small veins (*venæ cordis minimæ*; *Thebesian veins*) which empty their blood directly into the cavity of the atrium. A few larger ones can usually be seen in the septal wall. They were used by the ancients to explain passage of blood from one side of the heart to the other before Harvey (1610 A.D.) discovered the circulation of the blood.

The right atrioventricular opening is the large oval aperture of communication between the atrium and the ventricle. It is described with the right ventricle.

The **interatrial septum** forms the dorsal wall of the right atrium. It contains rudimentary structures which were of significance in the fetus. The **fossa ovalis** (Fig. 524) is an oval depression in the septal wall and corresponds to the foramen ovale of the fetal heart. It lies within a triangle established by the openings of the two venæ cavæ and the coronary sinus. The **limbus fossæ ovalis** is the prominent oval margin of the fossa which persists in the adult. It is distinct above and at the sides but is deficient below. Frequently the upper part of the limbus does not fuse with the left leaf of the septum, leaving a slit-like opening in the septum through which a probe may be passed into the left atrium. This is spoken of as probe patency of the foramen and is found in 20 to 25 per cent of all hearts. Larger openings are not uncommon also but these defects of the interatrial septum are seldom of functional significance.

The **intervenous tubercle** (*tubercle of Lower*) is a small raised area in the septal wall of the right atrium between the fossa ovalis and the orifice of the superior vena cava. It is more distinct in the hearts of certain quadrupeds than in man and was supposed by Richard Lower (1631-1691) to direct the blood from the superior cava into the atrioventricular opening. It is now of historical interest only.

Right Ventricle (*ventriculus dexter*) (Fig. 524).—The right ventricle occupies a large part of the ventral or sternocostal surface of the heart. Its right boundary is the coronary sulcus, its left the anterior longitudinal sulcus. Superiorly, the part of it named the **conus arteriosus** joins the pulmonary trunk. Inferiorly its wall forms the acute margin of the heart and extends around to the diaphragmatic surface for some distance. Its wall is about one-third as thick as that of the left ventricle; it is thickest near the base of the heart and gradually becomes thinner toward the

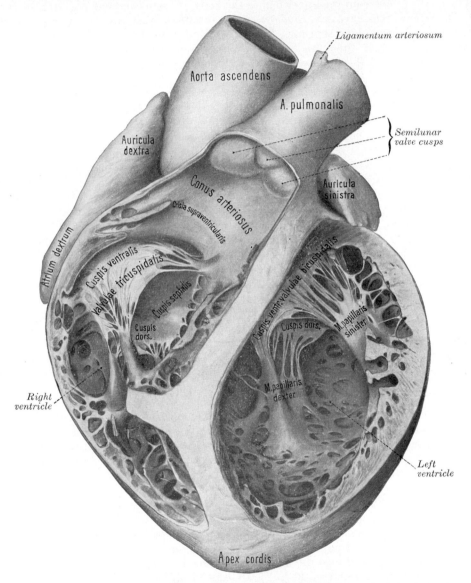

Fig. 525.—Interior of right and left ventricles of heart to show atrioventricular valves. (From Rauber-Kopsch, Lehrbuch u. Atlas d. Anatomie d. Menschen, 19th Edition, Vol. I, courtesy of Georg Thieme Verlag, Stuttgart, 1955).

apex. Its capacity is the same as that of the left ventricle, about 85 ml. (Latimer '53).

The interior of the right ventricle presents the following openings and parts for examination (Fig. 525):

The **right atrioventricular orifice** is an oval aperture about 4 cm. in diameter. It is surrounded by a strong fibrous ring and is guarded by the tricuspid valve.

The **right atrioventricular** or **tricuspid valve** (Fig. 526) surrounds the orifice with a thin apron which projects into the ventricle in three leaflets or cusps. The **anterior** or **infundibular cusp** (*cuspus ventralis*) is attached to the ventral wall in the region of the conus arteriosus (*infundibulum*). The **posterior** or **marginal cusp** (*cuspus dorsalis*) is attached to the part of the ventricle which curves around from the sternocostal to the diaphragmatic surface forming the acute margin of the heart. The **medial** or **septal cusp** (*cuspus septalis*) is attached to the septal wall of the ventricle. The cusps are of unequal size, and small intercalated leaflets may occur between them. The anterior is the largest, the marginal the smallest. The leaflets are composed of strong fibrous tissue, thick in the central part, thin and translucent

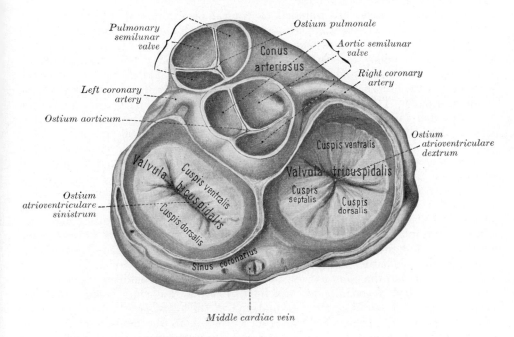

FIG. 526.—Openings and valves of the heart in closed position. Viewed from above after removal of atria and arterial trunks. (From Rauber-Kopsch, Lehrbuch u. Atlas d. Anatomie d. Menschen, 19th Edition, Vol. I, courtesy of Georg Thieme Verlag Stuttgart, 1955.)

near the margin. They are roughly triangular in shape, the bases attached to the fibrous ring and the apices projecting into the ventricular cavity. The atrial surface of the leaflets is smoothly covered by the atrial endocardial membrane but the ventricular surface is irregular and the free border presents a ragged edge for the attachment of the chordæ tendineæ. In order to make the valve as a whole competent to withstand the back pressure and prevent regurgitation of blood into the atrium during ventricular systole, the cusps are held in place by the chordæ tendineæ and papillary muscles.

The **chordæ tendineæ** are delicate but strong fibrous cords. They are attached to the apices, margins, and ventricular surfaces of the valve cusps and are anchored in the muscular wall. They number about twenty and are of different length and thickness. The majority are attached to projections of the trabeculæ called papillary muscles.

The **trabeculæ carneæ** (*columna carneæ*) are irregular bundles and bands of muscle which project from the inner surface of the ventricle except in the conus arteriosus. They are of three types, some are ridges along the wall, others extend across the lumen for short distances and are covered on all sides by endocardium, and still others form the special structures, papillary muscles, described below. The surface of the conus is quite smooth and its limit is marked by a ridge of muscular tissue, the **crista supraventricularis** (Fig. 525), which extends across the dorsal wall toward the pulmonary trunk from the attachment of the ventral cusp at the atrioventricular ring. The **moderator band** is a stout bundle of muscle in the central or apical part of the right ventricle. It crosses the lumen from the base of the anterior papillary muscle to the septum opposite. It is of variable size and constancy in the human heart but is more prominent in some larger mammals where it is supposed to resist over distention of the ventricle. When present it usually contains a branch of the atrioventricular conduction bundle.

The **papillary muscles** are rounded or conical projections of muscle to whose apices the chordæ tendineæ are attached. Although their size and number are somewhat variable, the two principal ones are named anterior and posterior. The main anterior papillary muscle (m. pap. ventralis, Fig. 524), the larger, protrudes partly from the ventral and partly from the septal wall. Its chordæ tendineæ are attached to the anterior and posterior cusps. Frequently it provides part of the moderator band. The posterior papillary muscle is in several parts arising from the posterior wall and is attached to the chordæ tendineæ of the posterior and septal cusps. A small anterior papillary muscle arising near the septal end of the crista supraventricularis, called the papillary muscle of the conus, is attached to the anterior and septal cusps. Other small papillary muscles are attached to individual chordæ tenidineæ.

The **orifice of the pulmonary trunk** is a circular opening at the summit of the conus arteriosus. It is close to the ventricular septum, above and to the left of the atrioventricular opening. The **pulmonary valve** consists of three **semilunar cusps** formed by duplicatures of the endocardial lining and reinforced by fibrous tissue (*cf.* 527). They are attached by a curved margin with convexity toward the ventricle, the free border toward the vessel. Behind each cusp (*velum*) is a pocket called the **sinus** and the point at which the attachments of two adjacent cusps come together is called a **commissure**. Each cusp has a thickened **nodule** (*nodulus*; *corpus Arantii*) at center of the free margin. A thickened band curves in an arc with convexity toward the vessel wall from the nodule to the commissure of attachment. The part of the valve between these arcs and the free margin is thin or even fenestrated and from its crescentic shape is called a **lunula**. The line of contact between the cusps, when the valve is closed, is not at the free margin but by the nodule and lunulæ.

The **Left Atrium** (*atrium sinistrum*; *left auricle*) (Fig. 531) is rather smaller than the right and its wall is thicker, measuring about 3 mm. It forms a large part of the surface at the base and upper dorsal part of the heart. Its separation from the right atrium is not identifiable on the dorsal surface except in a distended heart but the aorta and pulmonary trunk lie between them on the ventral surface. It consists of two parts, (*a*) a principal cavity and (*b*) an auricula.

(*a*) The **principal cavity** contains the openings of the four pulmonary veins, two on each side. They are not guarded by valves. Frequently the two left veins have a common opening. The left atrioventricular opening is rather smaller than the right, and is guarded by the mitral valve. The surface of the principal cavity is smooth. The interatrial septum contains a depression which is bounded below by a crescentic ridge. This is the edge of the **valve of the foramen ovale** (*valvula foraminis ovalis*) the remnant of the septum primum which was fused over the opening of the foramen ovale at birth.

(*b*) The **left auricula** (*auricula sinistra*; *left auricular appendage*) is somewhat constricted at its junction with the principal cavity. It is longer, narrower, and more curved than the right, and its margins are more deeply indented. It curves ventrally around the base of the pulmonary trunk, only its tip being visible on the sternocostal aspect of the heart (Fig. 521). It lies over the beginning of the left coronary artery. Its interior is marked by the muscular ridges of musculi pectinati.

Left Ventricle (*ventriculus sinister*) (Fig. 525).—The left ventricle occupies a small part of the sternocostal and about half of the diaphragmatic surface of the heart. Its tip forms the apex of the heart. The left ventricle is longer and more conical in shape than the right and its walls are about three times as thick. In a cross section its cavity is oval or circular in outline. The interior presents two openings, the atrioventricular guarded by the mitral valve, and the aortic guarded by the aortic valve.

The **left atrioventricular opening** (*mitral orifice*) is somewhat smaller than the right. It is encircled by a dense fibrous ring. The **bicuspid** or **mitral valve** (*valvula bicuspidalis* [*mitralis*]) (Fig. 526) surrounds the opening and extends down into the left ventricle in two valve cusps of unequal size. The larger is placed ventrally

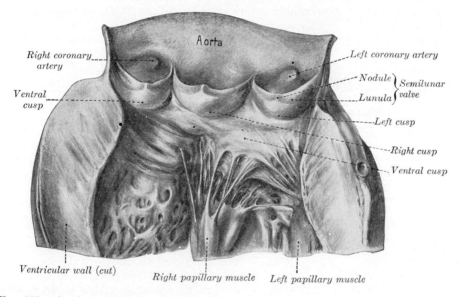

FIG. 527.—Aortic opening spread out to show semilunar valve and part of bicuspid valve. (From Rauber-Kopsch, *Lehrbuch u. Atlas d. Anatomie d. Menschen*, 19th Edition, Vol. 1, courtesy of Georg Thieme Verlag, Stuttgart, 1955.)

and to the right, adjacent to the aortic opening, and is called the ventral, anterior, or aortic cusp. The smaller is the dorsal or posterior cusp. Two smaller cusps are usually found at the angles of junction between the main cusps. The chordæ tendineæ are thicker, stronger, and less numerous than in the right ventricle (Fig. 525).

The **trabeculæ carneæ** are similar to those of the right ventricle but are more numerous and more densely packed, especially at the apex and on the dorsal wall. There are two **papillary muscles,** one attached to the ventral and one to the dorsal wall. They are of large size and end in rounded extremities to which the chordæ tendineæ are attached. The chordæ from each papillary muscle go to both cusps of the valve.

The **aortic opening** is a circular aperture ventral and to the right of the atrioventricular orifice. It is guarded by the **aortic semilunar valves.** The portion of the ventricle immediately below the aortic orifice is termed the aortic vestibule and has fibrous instead of muscular walls.

The **aortic valve** (Fig. 527) is composed of three semilunar cusps, similar to those of the pulmonary valve but larger, thicker, and stronger. The lunulæ are more distinct and the noduli or corpora Arantii are thicker and more prominent. Between the cusps and the aortic wall there are dilated pockets called the **aortic sinuses** (*sinuses of Valsalva*). From two of these sinuses the coronary arteries take origin.

The naming of the different cusps and sinuses of the aortic valve presents a problem. As the heart is situated in the body, one of the valves is anterior and the other two right and left posterior (see Fig. 526). When the heart is removed from the body, as it is at a necropsy, the heart may be held so that the septum is in the middle and the two ventricles exactly right and left. In this position, the aorta has a posterior and right and left anterior cusps. Another nomenclature which is independent of the position of the heart is based on the origin of the coronary arteries. On this basis there are right and left coronary cusps and a non-coronary cusp. Recently another terminology has been suggested which has the same advantage as the use of the coronary arteries but in addition it names the cusps of the

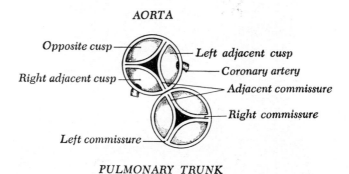

AORTA

Opposite cusp — Left adjacent cusp — Coronary artery — Right adjacent cusp — Adjacent commissure — Right commissure — Left commissure —

PULMONARY TRUNK

Fɪɢ. 528.—Names of aortic and pulmonary semilunar valve cusps with reference to the adjacent commissures. The examiner holds the specimen so that he looks from the lumen toward the adjacent commissure in naming the valves of either artery. (Kerr and Goss '56.)

pulmonary valve and is also useful even when there are anomalies of the coronary arteries. In this nomenclature advantage is taken of the embryological development of the aortic septum by division of the truncus arteriosus into the aorta and pulmonary trunk. Two adjacent cusps of both arteries are formed from the aortic septum, causing the commissure between the cusps of the two vessels to be almost exactly opposite. Thus the aortic and pulmonary valves can both be identified as a **right** and **left adjacent** and an **opposite cusps** (Fig. 528). (Kerr and Goss '56.)

The **interventricular septum** has an oblique position. It has a curvature with convexity to the right, thus completing the oval of the thick left ventricle and encroaching on the cavity of the right ventricle. Its margins correspond to the ventral and dorsal longitudinal sulci. The greater part of it is thick and muscular and is called the **muscular interventricular** septum. The upper part adjoining the atrial septum is thinner and fibrous and is called the **membranous interventricular septum** (Fig. 530). This is the last part of the septum to close in embryological development and is the usual site of the defect in a condition known as *patent interventricular septum.*

The fibrous rings which encircle the atrioventricular and arterial orifices merge with the septum membranaceum and compose a resistant core sometimes called the **skeleton of the heart.** (Fig. 529). In the heart of a large animal such as the ox, it may contain cartilage and bone. Between the right margin of the **left atrioventricular ring,** and **aortic ring** and the **right atrioventricular ring,** the dense tissue forms a triangular mass, the **right fibrous trigone** (*trigonum fibrosum dextrum*). This mass is also the basal thickening of the membranous septum. A fibrous band from the right trigonum and right atrioventricular ring to the posterior side of the conus and anterior

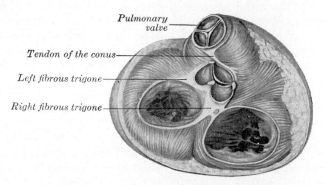

Pulmonary valve

Tendon of the conus

Left fibrous trigone

Right fibrous trigone

FIG. 529.—The fibrous skeleton of the heart. The atria have been removed and the heart is viewed toward the ventricles. (Redrawn from Tandler '13, Courtesy of Gustav Fischer Verlag.)

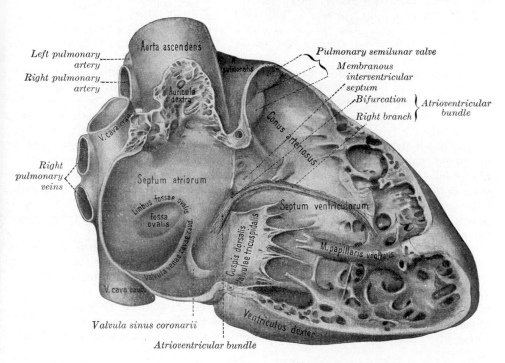

Left pulmonary artery
Right pulmonary artery
Aorta ascendens
pulmonalis
Auricula dextra
V. cava cranialis
Right pulmonary veins
Septum atriorum
Limbus fossae ovalis
fossa ovalis
Valvula venae cavae caud.
V. cava caud.
Valvula sinus coronarii
Atrioventricular bundle
Pulmonary semilunar valve
Membranous interventricular septum
Bifurcation
Right branch
Atrioventricular bundle
Conus arteriosus
Septum ventriculorum
Cuspis dorsalis valvulae tricuspidalis
M. papillaris ventralis
Ventriculus dexter

FIG. 530.—Conduction system of heart. Interior of right side of heart exposed, atrioventricular bundle (bundle of His) anf right bundle branch in red. (From Rauber-Kopsch, Lehrbuch u. Atlas d. Anatomie d. Menschen, 19th Edition, Vol. I, courtesy of Georg Thieme Verlag, Stuttgart, 1955.)

aspect of the aortic ring is called the **tendon of the conus.** A smaller trigone, the **trigonum fibrosum sinistrum** lies between the aortic and left atrioventricular rings. The atrioventricular rings and the trigones separate the muscular walls of the atria from those of the ventricles. The bundles of muscular fibers of both chambers, however, use the fibrous tissue for the attachment of their origins and insertions.

The **muscular structure of the heart** consists of bands of fibers, which present an exceedingly intricate interlacement. They comprise (*a*) the fibers of the atria, (*b*) the fibers of the ventricles, and (*c*) the atrioventricular bundle of His.

The principal **muscle bundles of the atria** radiate from one central area which surrounds the orifice of the superior vena cava and is for the most part buried in the anterior part of the atrial septum; in front and to the right of the orifice of the vena cava it comes to the external surface. The portion that appears in the groove between the vena cava and the right atrium has been designated the **sinoatrial node;** it is the seat of impulse formation for the atria in the normally beating heart. The portion that is buried in the atrial septum has been named the **septal raphé** by Papez. It provides an apparent mechanical support for many of the larger muscle bundles of both atria. The fibers of the sinoatrial node resemble those of the atrioventricular node. With the exception of the interatrial bundle, which connects the anterior surfaces of the two atria, the various muscle bundles are confined to their respective atria. These bundles radiate from either side of the septal raphé, which lies in front of the oval fossa, into the walls of the atria, the sinous venosus and the superior vena cava. There are about fifteen muscle bundles which make up the walls of the two atria. They merge into one another more or less.

The **muscle bundles of the ventricles** probably all arise from the tendinous structures at the base, converge in spiral courses toward the apex for varying distances and then turn spirally upward to be inserted on the opposite side of these same tendinous structures. The superficial fibers pass to the vortex at the apex of the left ventricle before they turn upward while the deep ones turn upward at varying distances without reaching the apex.

The **superficial bulbospiral bundle** arises from the conus, left side of the aortic septum, aortic ring and left atrioventricular ring, passes apicalward and somewhat toward the right to the posterior horn of the vortex of the left ventricle. At their origin the fibers form a broad thin sheet that becomes thick and narrow at the apex where the bundle twists on itself and continues upward in a spiral manner on the inner surface of the left ventricle, spreading out into a thin sheet that is inserted on the opposite side of the tendinous structures from which it arose. These fibers make nearly a double circle around the heart somewhat like a figure 8 that is open at the top. As the fibers pass toward the apex they lie superficial to the deep bulbospiral bundle and as they pass upward from the apex they partly blend and partly pass on the inner side of it in directions nearly at right angles to their superficial fibers.

The **deep bulbospiral bundle** arises immediately beneath the superficial bundle from the left side of the left ostia. The fibers pass downward to the right and enter the septum through the posterior longitudinal sulcus. They then encircle the left ventricle without reaching the apex after turning upon themselves on the apical side of the ring and blend with the fibers of the superficial bundle as they pass spirally upward to be inserted on the opposite sides of the fibrous rings of the left side. These fibers likewise seem to form an open figure 8 with both loops of about the same size.

The **deep sinospiral bundle** is more especially concerned with the right ventricle although its fibers communicate freely with the papillary muscles of both ventricles. Its fibers arise from the posterior part of the left ostium and pass diagonally into the deeper layer of the wall of the right ventricle where they turn upward to the conus and membranous septum. Some probably pass through the right vortex.

The **interventricular bundles** are represented in part by the longitudinal bundle of the right ventricle which passes through the septum and must be cut in order to unroll the heart, and by the interpapillary bands.

Conduction System of the Heart.—The parts of the conduction system are the sinoatrial node, the atrioventricular node, the atrioventricular bundle, and the terminal conducting fibers or Purkinje fibers. Although they differ from each other somewhat, all are composed of modified cardiac muscle and have the power of spontaneous rhythmicity and conduction more highly developed than the rest of the heart. Both the ventricles and the atria have an innate power of spontaneous contractility within their muscular tissue which is independent of any nervous influence. The conduction system, however, initiates and superimposes a rhythm with a rapid rate which it transmits to all parts of the heart and one which can be regulated by the nervous system.

The **sinoatrial node** (*S–A node; sinus node; node of Kieth and Flack*) is a small knot of modified heart muscle situated in the crista terminalis at the junction of the superior vena cava and right atrium. It receives its name from the fact that

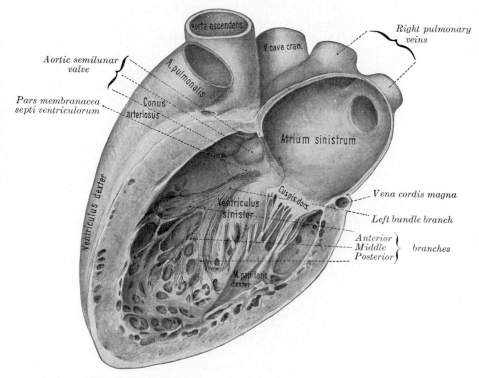

Fig. 531.—Conduction system of heart. Interior of left side exposed, left bundle branch in red. (From Rauber-Kopsch, Lehrbuch u. Atlas d. Anatomie d. Menschen, 19th Edition, Vol. I, courtesy of Georg Thieme Verlag, Stuttgart, 1955.)

this area is developed from the margin of the sinus venosus in the embryo. It is not visible in gross dissections but can be recognized on microscopic examination by certain histological peculiarities. The contraction of the heart is initiated by this node and it is therefore called the "pacemaker" of the heart. A special bundle for the conduction of the impulse from this node to the ventricle has not been identified morphologically. The fibers of the node merge with the atrial musculature which alone appears to be responsible for conducting the impulse to the atrioventricular node.

Thr **atrioventricular node** (*A–V node; node of Tawara*) (Fig. 530) lies near the orifice of the coronary sinus in the septal wall of the right atrium. It is of small size and not being encapsulated by connective tissue can seldom be recognized except by its connection with the A–V bundle.

The **atrioventricular bundle** (*bundle of His*) (Fig. 530) begins at the A–V node and follows along the membranous septum toward the left atrioventricular opening a distance of 1 or 2 cm. At about the middle of the septum, it splits into right and left branches which straddle the summit of the muscular part of the ventricular septum. The **right bundle branch** continues under the endocardium toward the apex spreading to all parts of the right ventricle. It breaks up into small bundles of what are called the terminal conducting fibers or Purkinje fibers which become continuous with the muscle of the right ventricle. A large bundle may pass along the moderator band, if this is present, to reach the opposite wall of the ventricle.

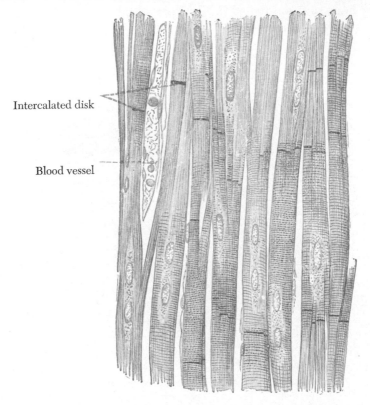

Intercalated disk

Blood vessel

Fig. 532.—Longitudinal section of human cardiac muscle fibers, approximately 400 × magnification. (From Rauber-Kopsch, Lehrbuch u. Atlas d. Anatomie d. Menschen, 19th Edition, Vol. I, courtesy of Georg Thieme Verlag, Stuttgart, 1955.)

The **left bundle branch** (Fig. 531) penetrates the fibrous septum and comes to lie just under the endocardium of the left ventricle. It fans out on the septal wall more quickly than the right bundle and breaks up into bundles of the terminal conducting fibers of Purkinje which are distributed throughout the left ventricle.

The two bundle branches are surrounded by more or less distinct connective tissue sheaths and may be visible, therefore, in gross examination of the heart. They are more easily seen in a fresh specimen than in a preserved one, and the left branch frequently shows more clearly than the right. The bundle and branches may be demonstrated by injecting India ink into the connective tissue sheath of a fresh specimen, a procedure which is particularly effective with a sheep or ox heart.

The **terminal conducting fibers** or **Purkinje fibers** are different histologically from the nodal fibers but they merge with the nodal tissue of the one hand and with the regular heart muscle on the other. They can only be identified with the aid of a

SHANER, R. F. 1954. Malformations of the truncus arteriosus in pig embryos. Anat. Rec., *118*, 539–560.

TANDLER, J. 1912. The development of the heart. In: Manual of Human Embryology by Keibel and Mall. J. B. Lippincott Company, Philadelphia, *2*, 534–570.

EXPERIMENTAL EMBRYOLOGY

ARMSTRONG, P. B. 1935. The role of the nerves in the action of acetylcholine on the embryonic heart. J. Physiol. (Lond.), *84*, 20–32.

BACON, R. L. 1945. Self-differentiation and induction in the heart of Amblystoma. J. Exp. Zool., *98*, 87–125.

COPENHAVER, W. M. 1945. Heteroplastic transplantation of the sinus venosus between two species of Amblystoma. J. Exp. Zool., *100*, 203–216.

FALES, D. E. 1946. A study of double hearts produced experimentally in embryos of Amblystoma punctatum. J. Exp. Zool., *101*, 281–298.

GOSS, C. M. 1935. Double hearts produced experimentally in rat embryos. J. Exp. Zool., *72*, 33–49.

HALL, E. K. 1957. Acetylcholine and epinephrine effects on the embryonic rat heart. J. Cell and Comp. Physiol., *49*, 187–200.

HALL, E. K. 1951. Intrinsic contractility in the embryonic rat heart. Anat. Rec., *111*, 381–400.

PAFF, G. H. 1936. Transplantation of sino-atrium to conus in the embryonic heart in vitro. Amer. J. Physiol., *117*, 313–317.

PATTEN, B. M., T. C. KRAMER and A. BARRY. 1948. Valvular action in the embryonic chick heart by localized apposition of endocardial masses. Anat. Rec., *102*, 299–311.

CHANGES IN CIRCULATION AT BIRTH

BARRON, D. H. 1944. The changes in the fetal circulation at birth. Physiol. Rev., *24*, 277–296.

EVERETT, N. B. and R. J. JOHNSON. 1951. A physiological and anatomical study of the closure of the ductus arteriosus in the dog. Anat. Rec., *110*, 103–111.

EVERETT, N. B. and B. S. SIMMONS. 1954. The magnitude of increase in the pulmonary blood volume of the postnatal guinea pig. Anat. Rec., *119*, 429–434.

KENNEDY, J. A. and S. L. CLARK. 1941. Observations on the ductus arteriosus of the guinea pig in relation to its method of closure. Anat. Rec., *79*, 349–372.

HISTOLOGY

BACON, R. L. 1948. Changes with age in the reticular fibers of the myocardium of the mouse. Amer. J. Anat., *82*, 469–496.

COPENHAVER, W. M. and R. C. TRUEX. 1952. Histology of the atrial portion of the cardiac conduction system in man and other mammals. Anat. Rec., *114*, 601–625.

GOSS, C. M. 1933. Further observations on the differentiation of cardiac muscle in tissue cultures. Arch. f. exper. Zellforsch., *14*, 175–201.

GOSS, C. M. 1941. Activity of heart muscle from rat embryos, grown in tissue culture. Anat. Rec., *81*, 144.

HIBBS, R. G. 1956. Electron microscopy of developing cardiac muscle in chick embryos. Amer. J. Anat., *99*, 17–52.

SINCLAIR, J. G. 1957. Synchronous mitosis on a cardiac infarct. Tex. Rep. on Biol. and Med., *15*, 347–352.

TRUEX, R. C. and W. M. COPENHAVER. 1947. Histology of the moderator band in man and other mammals with special reference to the conduction system. Amer. J. Anat., *80*, 173–201.

GROSS AND COMPARATIVE ANATOMY

HILL, W. C. O. 1936. Studies on the cardiac anatomy of the elephant. I. The coronary blood vessels. J. Anat. (Lond.), *70*, 386–404.

KEEN, E. N. and R. H. GOETZ. 1957. Cardiovascular anatomy of a foetal giraffe. Acta Anat., (Basel), *31*, 562–571.

KERR, A., JR. and C. M. GOSS. 1956. Retention of embryonic relationship of aortic and pulmonary valve cusps and a suggested nomenclature. Anat. Rec., *125*, 777–782.

LATIMER, H. B. 1953. The weight and thickness of the ventricular walls in the human heart. Anat. Rec., *117*, 713–724.

RUSTED, I. E., C. H. SCHEIFLEY and J. E. EDWARDS. 1952. Studies of the mitral valve. I. Anatomic features of the normal mitral valve and associated structures. Circulation, *6*, 825–831.

TANDLER, J. 1913. Anatomie des Herzens. In von Bardelebens Handbuch der Anatomie des Menschen. Gustav Fischer, Jena, viii + 292 pp.

TRUEX, R. C. and L. J. WARSHAW. 1942. The incidence and size of the moderator band in man and in mammals. Anat. Rec., *82*, 361–372.

WILLIUS, F. A. and T. J. DRY. 1948. A History of the Heart and the Circulation. W. B. Saunders Company, Philadelphia, xvii + 456 pp.

WRIGHT, R. R., B. J. ANSON and H. C. CLEVELAND. 1948. The vestigial valves and the interatrial foramen of the adult human heart. Anat. Rec., *100*, 331–355.

ANOMALIES AND VARIATIONS

BARRETT, O., JR. and W. J. WALKER. 1958. Tetralogy of Fallot with absent left pulmonary artery: Report of a case with anomalous development of the right hilar vasculature and nonfunctioning right lung. Amer. Heart J., *55*, 356–359.

COBB, W. M. 1944. Apical pericardial adhesion resembling the reptilian gubernaculum cordis. Anat. Rec., *89*, 87–91.

FOX, M. H. and C. M. GOSS. 1956. Experimental production of a syndrome of congenital cardiovascular defects in rats. Anat. Rec., *124*, 189–208.

FOX, M. H. and C. M. GOSS. 1957. Experimentally produced malformations of the heart and great vessels in rat fetuses. Atrial and caval abnormalities. Anat. Rec., *129*, 309–332.

GILBERT, E. F., K. NISHIMURA and B. G. WEDUM. 1958. Congenital malformations of the heart associated with splenic agenesis. Circulation, *17*, 72–86.

GOULD, S. E. 1953. Pathology of the Heart. Charles C Thomas, Springfield, xiii + 1023 pp.

LEV, M. 1953. Autopsy Diagnosis of Congenitally Malformed Hearts. Charles C Thomas, Springfield, xiv + 194 pp.

MAYER, F. E., A. S. NADAS, and P. A. ONGLEY. 1957. Ebstein's anomaly: Presentation of ten cases. Circulation, *16*, 1057–1069.

REEMTSMA, K. and W. M. COPENHAVER. 1958. Anatomic studies of the cardiac conduction system in congenital malformations of the heart. Circulation, *17*, 271–276.

SHANER, R. F. 1949. Malformation of the atrio-ventricular endocardial cushions of the embryo pig and its relation to defects of the conus and truncus arteriosus. Amer. J. Anat., *84*, 431–455.

SINCLAIR, J. G. 1944. A five-chambered human heart. Anat. Rec., *90*, 41–43.

SUNDERLAND, S. and R. J. WRIGHT-SMITH. 1944. Congenital pericardial defects. Brit. Heart J., *6*, 167–175.

PHYSIOLOGY AND CONDUCTION

BAIRD, J. A. and J. S. ROBB. 1950. Study, reconstruction and gross dissection of the atrioventricular conducting system of the dog heart. Anat. Rec., *108*, 747–764.

BRANDT, W. 1957. The closing mechanism of the tricuspidal valve in the human heart. Acta Anat., *30*, 128–132.

EDWARDS, J. E. 1957. Functional pathology of the pulmonary vascular tree in congenital cardiac disease. Circulation, *15*, 164–196.

ERICKSON, E. E. and M. LEV. 1952. Aging changes in the human atrioventricular node, bundle, and bundle branches. J. Gerontol., *7*, 1–12.

STOTLER, W. A. and R. A. McMAHON. 1947. The innervation and structure of the conductive system of the human heart. J. Comp. Neurol. *87*, 57–71.

TRUEX, R. C., J. L. CURRY, and M. Q. SMYTHE. 1954. Visualization of the Purkinje network of the beef heart. Anat. Rec., *118*, 723–736.

WALLS, E. W. 1947. The development of the specialized conducting tissue of the human heart. J. Anat. (Lond.), *81*, 93–110.

WIDRAN, J. and M. LEV. 1951. The dissection of the atrioventricular node, bundle and bundle branches in the human heart. Circulation, *4*, 863–867.

WHITE, P. D. 1957. The evolution of our knowledge about the heart and its diseases since 1628. Circulation, *15*, 915–923.

For additional references on innervation of the heart see Autonomic Nervous System.

BLOOD AND NERVE SUPPLY

CHASE, R. E. and C. F. DEGARIS. 1939. Arteriæ coronariæ (cordis) in the higher primates. Amer. J. Phys. Anthrop., *24*, 427–448.

GROSS, L. and M. A. KUGEL. 1933. The arterial blood vascular distribution to the left and right ventricles of the human heart. Amer. Heart J., *9*, 165–177.

JAMES, T. N. and G. E. BURCH. 1958. The atrial coronary arteries in man. Circulation, *17*, 90–98.

JAMES, T. N. and G. E. BURCH. 1958. Blood supply of the human interventricular septum. Circulation, *17*, 391–396.

Truex, R. C. and A. W. Angulo. 1952. Comparative study of the arterial and venous systems of the ventricular myocardium with special reference to the coronary sinus. Anat. Rec., *113*, 467–491.

Surgery of Heart and Great Vessels

Blalock, A. 1947. The technique of creation of artificial ductus arteriosus in the treatment of pulmonic stenosis. J. Thoracic Surg., *16*, 244–254.

Burdette, W. J. 1949. Removal of the auricular appendage in the dog. Surg. Gynec. Obstet., *89*, 623–628.

Effler, D. B., L. K. Groves, W. V. Martinez and W. J. Kolff. 1958. Open-heart surgery for mitral insufficiency. J. Thorac. Surg., *36*, 665–676.

Gross, R. E. 1947. Complete division for the patent ductus arteriosus. J. Thoracic Surg., *16*, 314–322.

Glover, R. P. and J. C. Davila. 1957. Surgical treatment of mitral insufficiency by total circumferential "purse-string" suture of the mitral ring. Circulation, *15*, 661–681.

James, T. N. and G. E. Burch. 1958. Topography of the human coronary arteries in relation to cardiac surgery. J. Thorac. Surg., *36*, 656–664.

Kirklin, J. W., H. G. Harshbarger, D. E. Donald and J. E. Edwards. 1957. Surgical correction of ventricular septal defect: Anatomic and technical considerations. J. Thorac. Surg., *33*, 45–59.

Walker, W. J., D. A. Cooley, D. G. McNamara and R. H. Moser. 1958. Corrected transposition of the great vessels, atrioventricular heart block, and ventricular septal defect. A clinical triad. Circulation, *17*, 249–254.

THE ARTERIES.

THE systemic arteries are distributed like the branches of a greatly ramified tree to the various parts of the body. They are found in all the tissues except the nails, epidermis, cornea, mucous membranes, and cartilage.

The branchings of the arteries follow different patterns. A short trunk may subdivide into several branches at the same point, for example in the celiac or thyrocervical trunk. Several branches may be given off in succession and the main trunk continue, as in the arteries to the limbs. The division may be dichotomous as at the bifurcation of the abdominal aorta into the common iliac arteries.

Although the branch of an artery is smaller than its trunk, the combined cross sectional area of the two resulting arteries is greater than that of the parent trunk before the division. Thus the combined cross sectional area of all the arterial branches greatly exceeds that of the aorta.

Throughout the body generally the larger arterial branches pursue a fairly straight course, but in certain situations they are tortuous. Thus the facial artery in its course over the face, and the arteries of the lips, are extremely tortuous, accommodating themselves to the movements of the parts. The uterine arteries are also tortuous, accommodating themselves to the increase of size which the uterus undergoes during pregnancy. Thus the larger arteries occupy the more protected situations such as along the flexor surface of the limbs where they are less exposed to injury.

Anastomosis of Arteries.—The branches of the arteries in many parts of the body open into branches of other arteries of a similar size in what are called anastomoses, instead of terminating only in capillaries. Anastomosis takes place between larger arteries forming arches such as those in the palm of the hand, the arcades of the intestines, or the circle of Willis at the base of the brain (Figs. 560, 567, 576). More frequently the anastomosis is between smaller arteries, one millimeter or less in diameter. The latter are quite numerous about the joints and between the terminal branches of the arterial trunks supplying adjacent areas of the body. They form a definite pattern of connections between neighboring arteries but in any one body all the different anastomoses which are described will not be equally well developed nor will they be easily demonstrable by dissection.

Collateral Circulation.—It is frequently necessary for a surgeon to tie off or ligate an artery in order to prevent excessive bleeding. In one part of the artery the anastomoses with branches of adjacent arteries may be more numerous than in another part and the surgeon will endeavor to place his ligature where advantage can be taken of the most numerous or effective anastomoses. The supply of blood to the distal part of an artery which has been interrupted through its anastomoses is called collateral circulation. This may take place through anastomoses with branches of the proximal part of the same artery or with branches of a large neighboring artery. In some areas the collateral circulation is very free, as it would be if either the radial or ulnar artery were ligated. In other places the collateral circulation might be carried by very small arteries only. If the part of the body involved can be put at rest, a trickle of blood through small anastomosing channels will keep the tissues alive until the anastomoses expand. The arteries retain their power of growth throughout life and a small anastomosing artery may enlarge into a main trunk, completely restoring the circulation to the part, if time is allowed for this growth to take place.

(603)

With the arteries in certain parts of the body, anastomoses are very limited or lacking. These are called end arteries. When such an artery is blocked by thrombosis or embolism, the tissues in that area are left without blood supply and the resulting condition is called an infarct.

Development of the Arteries.—The primordium of the aorta appears in the very early embryo at about the same time as the heart (Fig. 503). Two strands of cells arch dorsally from the endocardial mesenchyme, pass on each side of the foregut invagination, and turn caudalward along the neural groove. The strands beside the foregut are the primordia of the first aortic arches and their continuations are the dorsal aortæ. The latter acquire isolated stretches of lumen at the same time

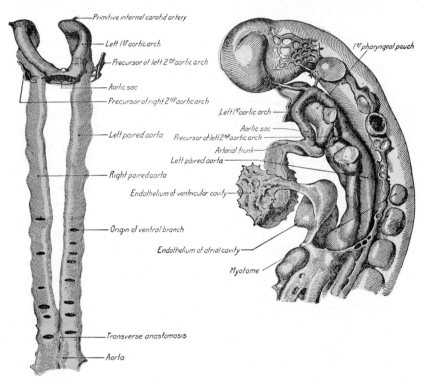

Fig. 534   Fig. 535

Figs. 534 and 535.—Ventral and lateral views of the cranial portion of the arterial system of a 3 mm. human embryo. The first aortic arch is at its maximum development and the dorsal and ventral outgrowths, which are to aid in the formation of the second arch are just appearing. (Congdon, 1922.)

as the lateral hearts, *i.e.*, in embryos with three somites. The arches become patent sometime later, at seven or eight somites, just before circulation begins. The umbilical arteries also probably arise from mesenchyme, independently, but after these main channels have become connected and the circulation is established, no further growth appears to be by local differentiation from the mesenchyme.

The circulation becomes functional when the first blood cells are washed out of the blood islands of the yolk sac at about the stage of nine somites (Goss '42). At this time the heart is contracting vigorously, capillaries have connected the aortæ with the blood islands which, in turn, drain into the vitelline veins, and the blood cells have elaborated hemoglobin. The umbilical arteries and veins also have become connected and oxygenation of the blood takes place in the primitive placenta. From this time forward, the circulatory system develops by (*a*) budding from existing trunks, (*b*) formation of new capillary networks, and (*c*) selection of parts of the network as arteries and veins. As the bulk of an embryonic part increases in size the capillaries are lengthened. This soon reaches a maximum and the hemodynamic forces select certain channels for arterioles and arteries or others for venules and veins. Later the pattern of the arteries and veins changes continually according to the growth requirements of the embryo. Not only do some vessels grow larger but well established vessels may be superceded by others more favorably placed and in consequence either regress or disappear.

The **first aortic arch** functions until the neural tube is closed and the pharynx begins to differentiate into pouches (Figs. 534 and 535). As the second pharyngeal pouch forms, a sprout from the aortic sac joins the dorsal aorta passing between the first and second pouches. The first aortic arch diminishes as this second arch

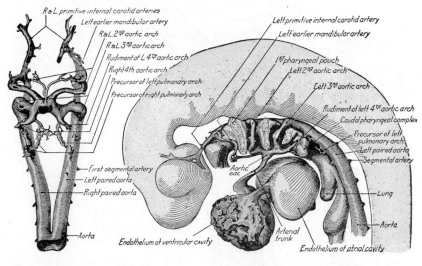

Fig. 536   Fig. 537

Figs. 536 and 537.—Ventral and lateral views of an embryo 4 mm. in length, in which the first arch has gone, the second is much reduced, and the third well developed. Dorsal and ventral outgrowths for the fourth and probably the pulmonary arch (fifth) are present. (Congdon.)

develops and the third, fourth, and sixth (pulmonary) arches are formed in a similar manner and disappear or become modified into various adult structures. The fifth arch is never more than a questionable rudiment in the human embryo.

By the time the embryo is 4 mm. in length, the first arch has about disappeared, the second arch has formed, reached its maximum development and diminished in size, and the third arch is well developed (Figs. 536 and 537). Sprouts may be present for the fourth and pulmonary arches. In a 5 mm. embryo the third and fourth arches have reached a maximum and the dorsal and ventral sprouts of the pulmonary arches are nearly joined (Figs. 539 and 540). The pulmonary arches are usually complete in a 6 mm. embryo. The right one soon begins to regress and has disappeared in a 12 to 13 mm. embryo. The third arches also have become incomplete at this time (Figs. 541, 542, and 543).

Aortic Arches.—Although the aortic arches do not persist as such, remnants of them remain as important parts of the arterial system (Fig. 538). The **first arch,**

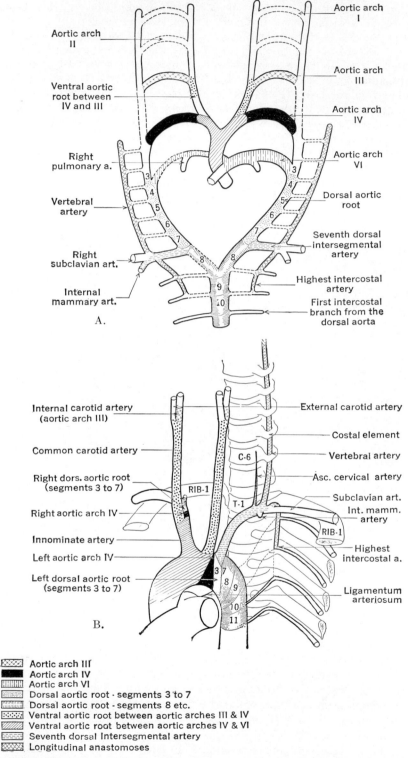

Aortic arch II

Aortic arch I

Ventral aortic root between IV and III

Aortic arch III

Right pulmonary a.

Aortic arch IV

Vertebral artery

Aortic arch VI

Right subclavian art.

Dorsal aortic root

Internal mammary art.

Seventh dorsal intersegmental artery

A.

Highest intercostal artery

First intercostal branch from the dorsal aorta

Internal carotid artery (aortic arch III)

External carotid artery

Common carotid artery

Costal element

Right dors. aortic root (segments 3 to 7)

Vertebral artery

Right aortic arch IV

Asc. cervical artery

Innominate artery

Subclavian art.

Left aortic arch IV

Int. mamm. artery

Left dorsal aortic root (segments 3 to 7)

Highest intercostal a.

B.

Ligamentum arteriosum

Aortic arch III
Aortic arch IV
Aortic arch VI
Dorsal aortic root · segments 3 to 7
Dorsal aortic root · segments 8 etc.
Ventral aortic root between aortic arches III & IV
Ventral aortic root between aortic arches IV & VI
Seventh dorsal Intersegmental artery
Longitudinal anastomoses

FIG. 538.—A, Schematic diagram indicating the various components of the embryonic aortic arch complex in the human embryo. Those components which do not normally persist in the adult are indicated by broken outlines. B, Adult aorta as seen from the left ventral aspect. (From the original of Figs. 1 and 3, Alexander Barry, Anat. Rec. *111*, 222, 1951.)

even at the very earliest stages, has an extension into the region of the forebrain, the primordium of the *internal carotid artery* (Fig. 537). The arch disappears and the primitive carotid becomes a cephalic continuation of the dorsal aorta. The **second arch** also disappears early but its dorsal end gives rise to the *stapedial artery* which atrophies in man but persists in some mammals. It passes through the ring of the stapes and divides into supraorbital, infraorbital, and mandibular branches which follow the three divisions of the trigeminal nerve. The infraorbital and mandibular arise from a common stem, the terminal part of which anastomoses with the external carotid. On the obliteration of the stapedial artery this anastomo-

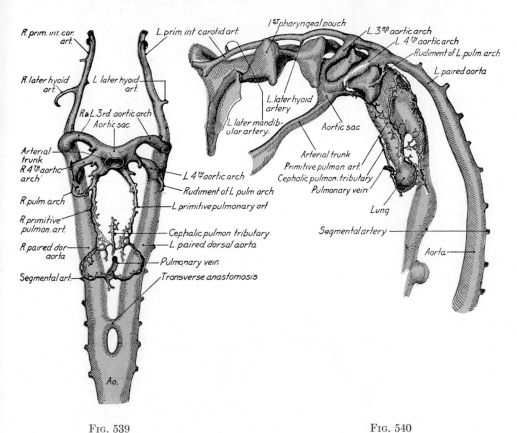

Fig. 539   Fig. 540

FIGS. 539 and 540.—Ventral and lateral views of a 5 mm. embryo. The third and fourth arches are in a condition of maximum development, the dorsal and ventral sprouts for the pulmonary arches have nearly met. The primitive pulmonary arches are already of considerable length. (Congdon, 1922)

sis enlarges and forms the **internal maxillary artery,** and the branches of the stapedial artery are now branches of this vessel. The common stem of the infraorbital and mandibular branches passes between the two roots of the auriculotemporal nerve and becomes the middle meningeal artery; the original supraorbital branch of the stapedial is represented by the orbital twigs of the middle meningeal. The **third arch** provides the *common carotid artery* and is therefore named the carotid arch. Its proximal segment connected with the aortic sac persists as the common carotid and gives rise to the external carotid (Fig. 543). The arch itself persists, keeping its connection with the cephalic extension of the dorsal aorta but losing its connection with the caudal extension toward the fourth arch. The left **fourth arch** persists

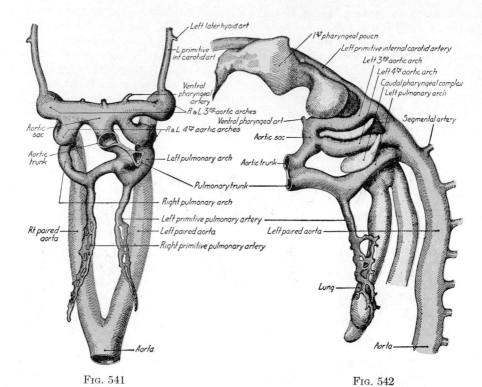

FIG. 541   FIG. 542

FIGS. 541 and 542.—Ventral and lateral views of an 11 mm. embryo. The pulmonary arches are complete and the right is already regressing. The third arch is bent cranially at its dorsal end. (Congdon.)

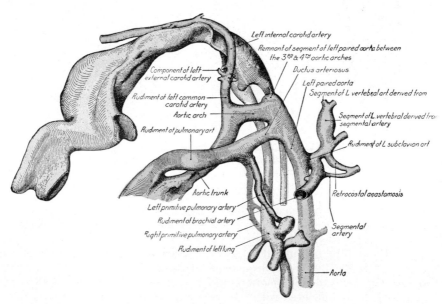

FIG. 543.—Lateral view of a 14 mm. embryo. The last indications of the aortic arch system are just disappearing. (Congdon.)

and provides the basis for the adult *aortic arch* between the aortic sac and the ductus arteriosus. The right fourth arch persists as the proximal part of the right subclavian artery. The right **pulmonary arch** disappears. The left pulmonary arch remains continuous with the pulmonary part of the truncus arteriosus as the *pulmonary trunk*. It gives rise to the pulmonary arteries and its distal segment persists as the **ductus arteriosus** until after birth at which time it contracts and gradually becomes fibrosed into the ligamentum arteriosum (Fig. 522).

Dorsal Aortæ.—The two dorsal aortæ remain separate for a short time, but come together at about the 3 mm. stage to form a single trunk caudal to the eighth or ninth somites. The segment of the aorta between the third and fourth arches disappears on both sides. The left dorsal aorta becomes the descending aorta continuing caudally from the left fourth arch. The right dorsal aorta retains its continuity with the left fourth arch and becomes the right subclavian artery as far as the seventh intersegmental artery. It disappears between this point and the original junction with the left dorsal aorta. The **aortic isthmus** is the part of the aorta between the origin of the left subclavian and the attachment of the ductus arteriosus.

The changes in the location of the heart during development produce certain changes in the aortic arches. The heart originally lies ventral to the most cephalic part of the pharynx. It later recedes into the thorax, drawing the aortic arches with it. On the right side the fourth arch recedes to the root of the neck, on the left it is withdrawn into the thorax. The recurrent laryngeal nerves of the vagus originally pass caudal to the pulmonary arches. When the heart recedes the nerves are pulled down by these arches. On the right side the pulmonary arch disappears allowing the nerve to slip up to the next arch, *i.e.*, the fourth, and it thus loops around the adult right subclavian artery. On the left side the pulmonary arch becomes the ductus arteriosus and the left recurrent nerve in the adult loops around the ligamentum arteriosum and that part of the aorta to which the latter is attached.

The Subclavian and Vertebral Arteries.—Segmental arteries arise from the primitive dorsal aortæ and anastomose between successive segments (Fig. 538). The seventh segmental artery is of special interest, since it forms the lower end of the vertebral artery and, when the forelimb bud appears, sends a branch to it (the subclavian artery). From the seventh segmental arteries the entire left subclavian and the greater part of the right subclavian are formed. The second pair of segmental arteries accompany the hypoglossal nerves to the brain and are named the *hypoglossal arteries*. Each sends forward a branch which forms the cerebral part of the **vertebral artery** and anastomoses with the posterior branch of the internal carotid. The two vertebrals unite on the ventral surface of the hindbrain to form the basilar artery. Later the hypoglossal artery atrophies and the vertebral is connected with the first segmental artery. The cervical part of the vertebral is developed from a longitudinal anastomosis between the first seven segmental arteries, so that the seventh of these ultimately becomes the source of the artery. As a result of the growth of the upper limb, the subclavian artery increases greatly in size and the vertebral then appears to spring from it.

Recent observations show that several segmental arteries contribute branches to the upper limb bud and form in it a free capillary anastomosis. Of these branches, only one, that derived from the **seventh segmental artery**, persists to form the **subclavian artery.** The subclavian artery is prolonged into the limb under the names of the axillary and brachial arteries and these together constitute the arterial stem for the upper arm, the direct continuation of this stem in the forearm is the palmar interosseous artery. A branch which accompanies the median nerve soon increases in size and forms the main vessel (median artery) of the forearm, while the palmar interosseous diminishes. Later the radial and ulnar arteries are devel-

39

oped as branches of the brachial part of the stem and coincidently with their enlargement the median artery recedes; occasionally it persists as a vessel of some considerable size and then accompanies the median nerve into the palm of the hand.

Descending Aorta.—The segmental arteries caudal to the seventh grow out into the body wall and retain their segmental character to become the intercostal and lumbar arteries. In the early embryo, paired ventral branches of the aorta grow out on the yolk sac as the omphalomesenteric arteries. At its caudal end the ventral branches accompanying the allantois become the umbilical arteries. As the gut develops, a number of ventral branches grow into it. At first they are paired

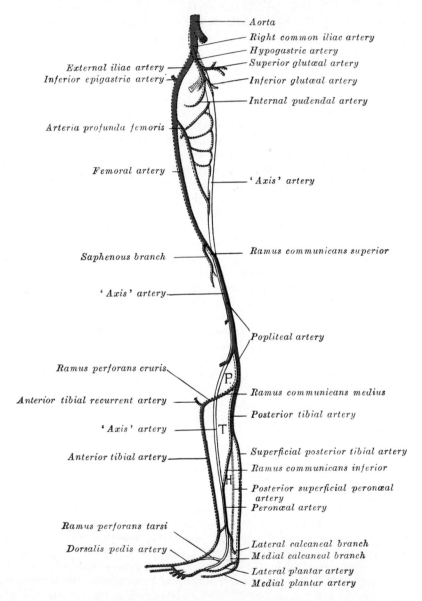

Aorta

Right common iliac artery

Hypogastric artery

Superior glutæal artery

External iliac artery

Inferior epigastric artery

Inferior glutæal artery

Internal pudendal artery

Arteria profunda femoris

Femoral artery

'Axis' artery

Saphenous branch

Ramus communicans superior

'Axis' artery

Popliteal artery

Ramus perforans cruris

Anterior tibial recurrent artery

Ramus communicans medius

Posterior tibial artery

'Axis' artery

Anterior tibial artery

Superficial posterior tibial artery

Ramus communicans inferior

Posterior superficial peronæal artery

Peronæal artery

Ramus perforans tarsi

Dorsalis pedis artery

Lateral calcaneal branch

Medial calcaneal branch

Lateral plantar artery

Medial plantar artery

FIG. 544.—A diagram to illustrate the general development of the arteries of the lower limb. The letter *P* indicates the position of the Popliteus; *T*, that of the Tibialis posterior; *H*, that of the Flexor hallucis longus. (H. D. Senior, 1919.)

but with the formation of a mesentery the pairs fuse into single stems. These ventral branches are irregularly spaced and by a process of shifting along a rich anastomosis the three main trunks, the celiac, the superior, and the inferior mesenteric, are finally selected. Lateral branches of the aorta grow into the mesonephros and the long course of the testicular and ovarian arteries is the result of the caudal migration of the gonads after their arteries had become established. Later similar lateral branches grow into the kidneys and suprarenal glands.

According to Senior (Fig. 544) the primary arterial trunk or "axis" **artery of the embryonic lower limb** arises from the dorsal root of the umbilical artery, and courses along the posterior surface of the thigh, knee and leg. The femoral artery springs from the external iliac and forms a new channel along the ventral side of the thigh to its communication with the axis artery above the knee. As this channel increases in size, that part of the axis artery proximal to the communication disappears, except its upper end which persists as the inferior gluteal artery. Two other segments of the axial artery persist; one forms the proximal part of the popliteal artery, and the other forms a part of the peroneal artery.

THE PULMONARY TRUNK

The **pulmonary trunk** (*truncus pulmonis; pulmonary artery*) (Figs. 545, 546) conveys the blood which has given up oxygen, *i.e.*, venous blood, from the heart to the lungs. It is a short, wide vessel, about 5 cm. in length and 3 cm. in diameter, arising from the conus of the right ventricle. It ascends obliquely, angling dorsalward and passes at first ventral and then to the left of the ascending aorta. Near the under surface of the aortic arch at about the level of the fibrocartilage between the fifth and sixth thoracic vertebræ it divides into right and left branches of nearly equal size.

Relations.—This entire vessel is contained within the pericardium. It is enclosed with the ascending aorta in a single tube of the visceral layer of the serous pericardium, which is continued upward upon them from the base of the heart. The fibrous layer of the pericardium is gradually lost upon the external coats of the two branches of the artery. In *front*, the pulmonary artery is separated from the anterior end of the second left intercostal space by the pleura and left lung, in addition to the pericardium; at first it is anterior to the ascending aorta, and higher up lies in front of the left atrium on a plane posterior to the ascending aorta. On *either side* of its origin is the auricula of the corresponding atrium and a coronary artery, the left coronary artery passing, in the first part of its course, behind the vessel. The superficial part of the cardiac plexus lies above its bifurcation, between it and the arch of the aorta.

The **right branch of the pulmonary artery** (*ramus dexter a. pulmonalis*), longer and larger than the left, runs horizontally to the right, behind the ascending aorta and superior vena cava and in front of the right bronchus, to the root of the right lung, where it divides into two branches. The lower and larger of these goes to the middle and lower lobes; the upper and smaller is distributed to the upper lobe.

The **left branch of the pulmonary artery** (*ramus sinister a. pulmonalis*), shorter and somewhat smaller than the right, passes horizontally in front of the descending aorta and left bronchus to the root of the left lung, where it divides into two branches, one for each lobe of the lung.

Above, it is connected to the concavity of the aortic arch by the **ligamentum arteriosum**, on the left of which is the left recurrent nerve, and on the right the superficial part of the cardiac plexus. *Below*, it is joined to the upper left pulmonary vein by the ligament of the left vena cava.

The terminal branches of the pulmonary arteries will be described with the lungs.

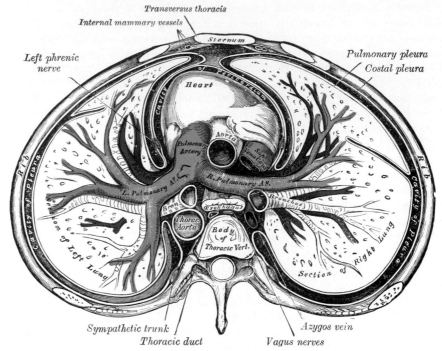

FIG. 545.—Transverse section of thorax, showing relations of pulmonary artery.

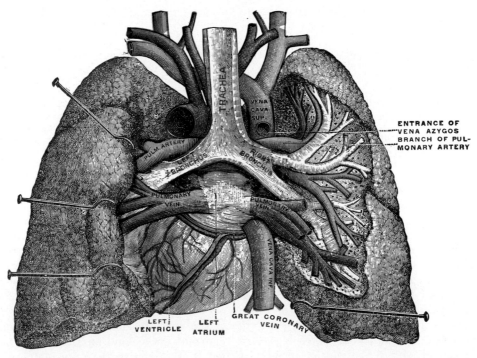

FIG. 546.—Pulmonary vessels, seen in a dorsal view of the heart and lungs. The lungs have been pulled away from the median line, and a part of the right lung has been cut away to display the air-ducts and bloodvessels.

THE AORTA

The aorta is the main trunk of the systemic arteries. At its commencement from the aortic opening of the left ventricle it is about 3 cm. in diameter. It ascends toward the neck for a short distance then bends to the left and dorsalward over the root of the left lung. It descends within the thorax on the left side of the vertebral column and passes through the aortic hiatus of the diaphragm into the abdominal cavity. Opposite the lower border of the fourth lumbar vertebra, considerably diminished in size (about 1.75 cm. in diameter) it bifurcates into the two common iliac arteries. The parts of the aorta are the **ascending aorta**, the **arch of the aorta**, and the **thoracic** and **abdominal portions** of the **descending aorta**.

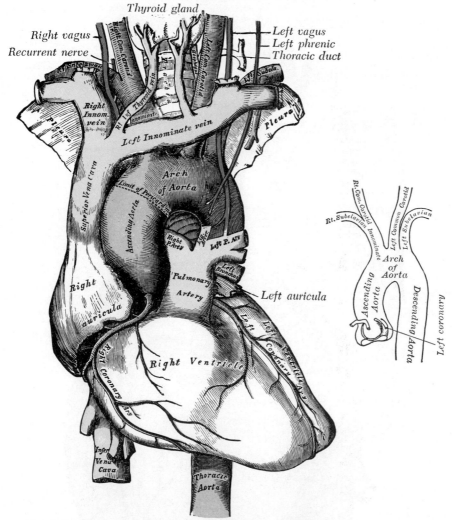

Fig. 547.—The arch of the aorta, and its branches. (Insert: Plan of the branches.)

THE ASCENDING AORTA

The **ascending aorta** (*aorta ascendens*) (Fig. 547) is about 5 cm. in length. It is covered by the visceral pericardium which encloses it in a common sheath with the pulmonary trunk. It commences at the semilunar valve, on a level with the lower border of the third costal cartilage behind the left half of the sternum. It curves obliquely upward, anteriorly, and to the right, in the direction of the heart's axis, as high as the upper border of the second right costal cartilage, and lying about 6 cm. behind the posterior surface of the sternum. At its origin, opposite the segments of the aortic valve, are three small dilatations called the **aortic sinuses.** At the union of the ascending aorta with the aortic arch the caliber of the vessel is increased by a bulging of its right wall, and on transverse section presents a somewhat oval figure.

Relations.—The ascending aorta is covered at its commencement by the trunk of the pulmonary artery and the right auricula, and, higher up, is separated from the sternum by the pericardium, the right pleura, the anterior margin of the right lung, some loose areolar tissue, and the remains of the thymus; *posteriorly,* it rests upon the left atrium and right pulmonary artery. On the *right side,* it is in relation with the superior vena cava and right atrium, the former lying partly behind it; on the *left side,* with the pulmonary trunk.

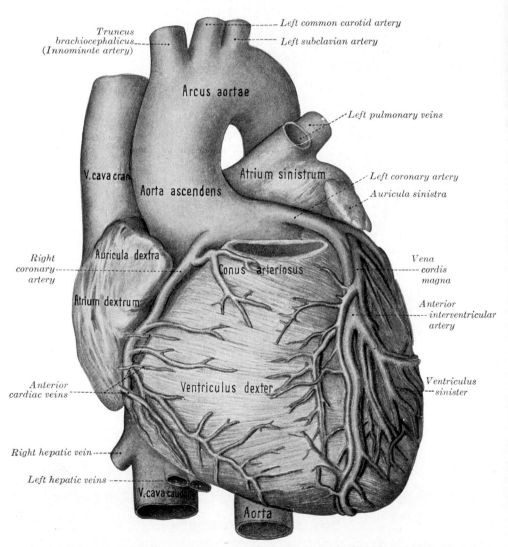

Fig. 548.—The coronary blood vessels of the sternocostal aspect of the heart. The pulmonary trunk and pulmonary valve have been removed. (Rauber-Kopsch, *Lehrbuch u. Atlas d. Anatomie d. Menschen,* 19th Edition, Vol. I, courtesy of Georg Thieme Verlag, Stuttgart, 1955.)

Branches of the ascending aorta are the right and left coronary arteries.

The **right coronary artery** (*a. coronaria dextra*) (Fig. 548, 549) arises in the right adjacent (Fig. 528) or right anterior aortic sinus (of Valsalva). It passes to the right and downward between the conus arteriosus and right auricula into the coronary sulcus. It follows the sulcus first to the right around the right margin of

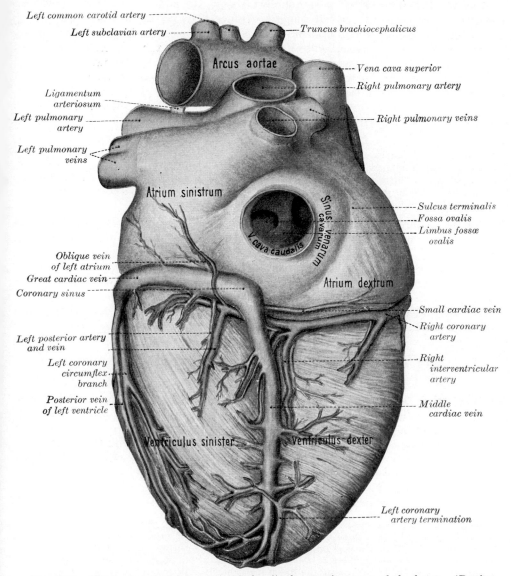

Left common carotid artery

Left subclavian artery

Arcus aortae

Truncus brachiocephalicus

Vena cava superior

Right pulmonary artery

Ligamentum arteriosum

Left pulmonary artery

Right pulmonary veins

Left pulmonary veins

Atrium sinistrum

Sinus venarum cavarum

V. cava caudalis

Sulcus terminalis

Fossa ovalis

Limbus fossæ ovalis

Oblique vein of left atrium

Great cardiac vein

Coronary sinus

Atrium dextrum

Small cardiac vein

Right coronary artery

Left posterior artery and vein

Left coronary circumflex branch

Posterior vein of left ventricle

Right interventricular artery

Middle cardiac vein

Ventriculus sinister

Ventriculus dexter

Left coronary artery termination

Fig. 549.—The coronary blood vessels of the diaphragmatic aspect of the heart. (Rauber-Kopsch, *Lerbuch u. Atlas d. Anatomie d. Menschen*, 19th Edition, Vol. I, courtesy of Georg Thieme, Verlag, Stuttgart, 1955.)

the heart and then to the left on the diaphragmatic surface, ending in two or three branches beyond the interventricular sulcus. The **posterior descending branch** (*ramus interventricularis posterior*) runs down the sulcus two thirds of the way to the apex supplying branches to both ventricles. The large **marginal branch** arises at the right margin and follows the acute margin, terminating near the apex on the posterior surface of the right ventricle and supplying both anterior and posterior surfaces of the right ventricle. It supplies small branches to the right atrium, one of which passes between the right atrium and superior vena cava to supply the *sinoatrial node.* (Gross '21).

The **left coronary artery** (*a. coronaria sinistra*) (Fig. 548, 549) arises in the left adjacent (Fig. 528) or left posterior aortic sinus (of Valsalva) and after a short course under cover of the left auricula bifurcates into the anterior descending branch and the circumflex branch. The **anterior descending branch** (*ramus interventricularis anterior*) passes ventrally to the left between the pulmonary trunk and the left auricula to the anterior interventricular sulcus which it follows to the apex, supplying branches to both ventricles. The **circumflex branch** (*r. circumflexus*) follows the left part of the coronary sulcus running first to the left and then to the right reaching nearly as far as the posterior interventricular sulcus. It supplies branches to the left atrium and ventricle.

Variations.—The left coronary artery or its descending branch may arise from the left pulmonary artery, supplying the left ventricle. This anomaly can be diagnosed clinically and usually leads to death in infancy. Rarely both coronaries arise from the pulmonary artery.

Single coronary arteries have been described, the left coronary may be a branch of the right or both arteries may arise in the same aortic sinus. There may be three coronary arteries, the accessory supplying part of the branches of either artery.

Three **patterns of distribution** of the coronary arteries have been described (Schlesinger '40). In half the hearts, the right coronary predominates, in a third, they are equally balanced and in the rest, the left coronary predominates. The sinoatrial node is supplied by a branch of the right coronary in 70 per cent, by the left in 25 per cent, by both in 7 per cent. The *atrioventricular node* is supplied by the right in 92 per cent. The *right bundle branch* generally is supplied by the anterior descending branch of the left coronary; the *left bundle branch* by septal branches of the left and small vessels from the right coronary artery (Gregg '50).

THE ARCH OF THE AORTA (ARCUS AORTÆ; TRANSVERSE AORTA) (Fig. 547).

The **arch of the aorta** begins at the level of the upper border of the second sternocostal articulation of the right side, and runs at first upward, backward, and to the left in front of the trachea; it is then directed backward on the left side of the trachea and finally passes downward on the left side of the body of the fourth thoracic vertebra, at the lower border of which it becomes continuous with the descending aorta. It thus forms two curvatures: one with its convexity upward, the other with its convexity forward and to the left. Its upper border is usually about 2.5 cm. below the superior border of the manubrium sterni.

Relations.—The arch of the aorta is covered *anteriorly* by the pleuræ and anterior margins of the lungs, and by the remains of the thymus. As the vessel runs backward its *left* side is in contact with the left lung and pleura. Passing downward on the left side of this part of the arch are four nerves; in order from before backward these are, the left phrenic, the lower of the superior cardiac branches of the left vagus, the superior cardiac branch of the left sympathetic, and the trunk of the left vagus. As the last nerve crosses the arch it gives off its recurrent branch, which hooks around below the vessel and then passes upward on its right side. The highest left intercostal vein runs obliquely upward and forward on the left side of the arch, between the phrenic and vagus nerves. On the *right* are the deep part of the cardiac plexus, the left recurrent nerve, the esophagus, and the thoracic duct; the trachea lies behind and to the right of the vessel. *Above* are the innominate, left common carotid, and left subclavian arteries, which arise from the convexity of the arch and are crossed close to their origins by the left innominate vein. *Below* are the bifurcation of the pulmonary artery, the left bronchus, the ligamentum arteriosum, the superficial part of the cardiac plexus, and the left recurrent nerve. As already stated, the ligamentum arteriosum connects the commencement of the left pulmonary artery to the aortic arch.

Between the origin of the left subclavian artery and the attachment of the ductus arteriosus the lumen of the fetal aorta is considerably narrowed, forming what is termed the **aortic isthmus,** while immediately beyond the ductus arteriosus the vessel presents a fusiform dilation which His has named the **aortic spindle**—the point of junction of the two parts being marked in the concavity of the arch by an indentation or angle. These conditions persist, to some extent, in the adult, where His found that the average diameter of the spindle exceeded that of the isthmus by 3 mm.

Variations.—The height to which the aorta rises in the thorax is usually about 2.5 cm. below the upper border of the sternum; but it may ascend nearly to the top of the bone. Occasionally it is found 4 cm., more rarely from 5 to 8 cm. below this point. Sometimes the aorta arches over the root of the right lung (right aortic arch) instead of over that of the left, and passes down on the right side of the vertebral column. a condition which is found in birds. In such cases all the thoracic and abdominal viscera are transposed. Less frequently the aorta, after arching over the root of the right lung, is directed to its usual position on the left side of the vertebral column; this peculiarity is not accompanied by transposition of the viscera. The aorta occasionally divides, as in some quadrupeds, into an ascending and a descending trunk, the former of which is directed vertically upward, and subdivides into three branches, to supply the head and upper extremities. Sometimes the aorta subdivides near its origin into two branches, which soon reunite. In one of these cases the esophagus and trachea were found to pass through the interval between the two branches; this is the normal condition of the vessel in the reptilia.

Branches (Figs. 520, 547).—The branches given off from the arch of the aorta are three in number: the **innominate,** the **left common carotid,** and the **left subclavian,** in 83 to 94 per cent. of cadavers, according to various reports.

Variations.—The branches, instead of arising from the highest part of the arch, may spring from the commencement of the arch or upper part of the ascending aorta; or the distance between them at their origins may be increased or diminished, the most frequent change in this respect being the approximation of the left carotid toward the innominate artery.

The *number* of the primary branches may be reduced to one, or more commonly two; the left carotid arising from the innominate artery; or (more rarely) the carotid and subclavian arteries of the left side arising from a left innominate artery. But the number may be increased to four, from the right carotid and subclavian arteries arising directly from the aorta, the innominate being absent. In most of these latter cases the right subclavian has been found to arise from the left end of the arch; in other cases it is the second or third branch given off, instead of the first. Another common form in which there are four primary branches is that in which the left vertebral artery arises from the arch of the aorta between the left carotid and subclavian arteries. Lastly, the number of trunks from the arch may be increased to five or six; in these instances, the external and internal carotids arise separately from the arch, the common carotid being absent on one or both sides. In some few cases six branches have been found, and this condition is associated with the origin of both vertebral arteries from the arch.

When the aorta arches over to the right side, the three branches have a reverse arrangement; the innominate artery is a left one, and the right carotid and subclavian arise separately. In other cases, where the aorta takes its usual course, the two carotids may be joined in a common trunk, and the subclavians arise separately from the arch, the right subclavian generally arising from the left end.

In some instances other arteries spring from the arch of the aorta. Of these the most common are the bronchial, one or both, and the thyreoidea ima; but the internal mammary and the inferior thyroid have been seen to arise from this vessel.

The Brachiocephalic Trunk (A. Anonyma).

The **brachiocephalic trunk** (*Innominate artery*) (Fig. 547) is the largest branch of the arch of the aorta, and is from 4 to 5 cm. in length. It *arises*, on a level with the upper border of the second right costal cartilage, from the commencement of the arch of the aorta, on a plane anterior to the origin of the left carotid; it ascends obliquely upward, backward, and to the right to the level of the upper border of the right sternoclavicular articulation, where it divides into the right common carotid and right subclavian arteries.

Relations.—*Anteriorly,* it is separated from the manubrium sterni by the Sternohyoideus and Sternothyreoideus, the remains of the thymus, the left brachiocephalic and right inferior thyroid veins which cross its root, and sometimes the superior cardiac branches of the right vagus. *Poste-*

rior to it is the trachea, which it crosses obliquely. On the *right side* are the right brachiocephalic vein, the superior vena cava, the right phrenic nerve, and the pleura; and on the *left side*, the remains of the thymus, the origin of the left common carotid artery, the inferior thyroid veins, and the trachea.

Branches.—The brachiocephalic trunk usually gives off no branches; but occasionally a small branch, the **thyreoidea ima**, arises from it. Sometimes it gives off a **thymic** or **bronchial branch.**

The **thyreoidea ima** (*a. thyreoidea ima*) ascends in front of the trachea to the lower part of the thyroid gland, which it supplies. It varies greatly in size, and appears to compensate for deficiency or absence of one of the other thyroid vessels. It occasionally arises from the aorta, the right common carotid, the subclavian or the internal mammary.

Variations.—The brachiocephalic trunk sometimes divides above the level of the sternoclavicular joint; less frequently below it. It may be absent, the right subclavian and the right common carotid then arising directly from the aorta. When the aortic arch is on the right side, the brachiocephalic is directed to the left side of the neck.

THE ARTERIES OF THE HEAD AND NECK.

The principal arteries of supply to the head and neck are the two **common carotids**; each divides into two branches, viz., (1) the **external carotid**, supplying the exterior of the head, the face, and the greater part of the neck; (2) the **internal carotid**, supplying to a great extent the parts within the cranial and orbital cavities.

THE COMMON CAROTID ARTERY (A. CAROTIS COMMUNIS).

The **common carotid arteries** differ in length and in their mode of origin. The *right* begins at the bifurcation of the brachiocephalic trunk behind the sternoclavicular joint and is confined to the neck. The *left* springs from the highest part of the arch of the aorta to the left of, and on a plane posterior to the brachiocephalic trunk, and therefore consists of a thoracic and a cervical portion.

The **thoracic portion of the left common carotid artery** ascends from the arch of the aorta through the superior mediastinum to the level of the left sternoclavicular joint, where it is continuous with the cervical portion.

Relations.—*In front*, it is separated from the manubrium sterni by the Sternohyoideus and Sternothyreoideus, the anterior portions of the left pleura and lung, the left innominate vein, and the remains of the thymus; *behind*, it lies on the trachea, esophagus, left recurrent nerve, and thoracic duct. To its *right side* below is the innominate artery, and above, the trachea, the inferior thyroid veins, and the remains of the thymus; to its *left side* are the left vagus and phrenic nerves, left pleura, and lung. The left subclavian artery is posterior and slightly lateral to it.

The **cervical portions** of the common carotids resemble each other so closely that one description will apply to both (Fig. 550). Each vessel passes obliquely upward, from behind the sternoclavicular articulation, to the level of the upper border of the thyroid cartilage, where it divides into the external and internal carotid arteries.

At the lower part of the neck the two common carotid arteries are separated by a very narrow interval which contains the trachea; but at the upper part, the thyroid gland, the larynx and pharynx project forward between the two vessels. The common carotid artery is contained in a sheath, which is derived from the deep cervical fascia and encloses also the internal jugular vein and vagus nerve, the vein lying lateral to the artery, and the nerve between the artery and vein, on a plane posterior to both. On opening the sheath, each of these three structures is seen to have a separate fibrous investment.

Relations.—At the lower part of the neck, the common carotid artery is very deep, being *covered by* the integument, superficial fascia, Platysma, and deep cervical fascia, the Sterno-cleidomastoideus, Sternohyoideus, Sternothyreoideus, and Omohyoideus; in the upper part of its course it is more superficial, being covered merely by the integument, the superficial fascia, Platysma, deep cervical fascia, and medial margin of the Sternocleidomastoideus. When the latter muscle is drawn backward, the artery is seen to be contained in a triangular space, the **carotid triangle,** bounded behind by the Sternocleidomastoideus, above by the Stylohyoideus and posterior belly of the Digastricus, and below by the superior belly of the Omohyoideus. This part of the artery is crossed obliquely, from its medial to its lateral side, by the sterno-cleidomastoid branch of the superior thyroid artery; it is also crossed by the superior and middle thyroid veins which end in the internal jugular. Usually superficial to its sheath, but occasionally contained within it, are the nerves descendens hypoglossi, descendens cervicalis, and their connecting loop, the ansa hypoglossi. The superior thyroid vein crosses the artery near its termination, and the middle thyroid vein a little below the level of the cricoid cartilage; the anterior jugular vein crosses the artery just above the clavicle, but is separated from it by the Sterno-hyoideus and Sternothyreoideus. *Behind,* the artery is separated from the transverse processes of the cervical vertebræ by the Longus colli and Longus capitis, the sympathetic trunk being interposed between it and the muscles. The inferior thyroid artery crosses behind the lower part of the vessel. *Medially,* it is in relation with the esophagus, trachea, and thyroid gland (which overlaps it), the inferior thyroid artery and recurrent nerve being interposed; higher up, with the larynx and pharynx. *Lateral* to the artery are the internal jugular vein and vagus nerve.

At the lower part of the neck, the right recurrent nerve crosses obliquely behind the artery; the right internal jugular vein diverges from the artery, but the left approaches and often overlaps the lower part of the artery.

The **carotid body** lies deep to the bifurcation of the common carotid artery or somewhat between the two branches. It is a small oval body, 2 to 5 mm. in diameter, with a characteristic structure composed of epithelioid cells, abundant nerve fibers, and a delicate fibrous capsule (Figs. 798, 799). It is a part of the visceral afferent system of the body, containing chemoreceptor endings which probably respond to changes in the oxygen content of the blood. It is probably supplied by branches of the vagus nerve.

The **carotid sinus** is described with the internal carotid artery.

Variations.—The *right common carotid* may arise above the level of the upper border of the sternoclavicular articulation; this variation occurs in about 12 per cent of cases. In other cases the artery may arise as a separate branch from the arch of the aorta, or in conjunction with the left carotid. The *left common carotid* varies in its origin more than the right. In the majority of abnormal cases it arises with the brachiocephalic trunk; if that artery is absent, the two carotids may arise by a single trunk. In the majority of abnormal cases the point of division occurs higher than usual, the artery dividing opposite or even above the hyoid bone; more rarely, it occurs below, opposite the middle of the larynx, or the lower border of the cricoid cartilage. Very rarely, the common carotid ascends in the neck without any subdivision, either the external or the internal carotid being wanting; and in a few cases the common carotid has been found to be absent, the external and internal carotids arising directly from the arch of the aorta.

The common carotid usually gives off no branch previous to its bifurcation, but it occasionally gives origin to the superior thyroid or its laryngeal branch, the ascending pharyngeal, the inferior thyroid, or, more rarely, the vertebral artery.

Collateral Circulation.—After ligature of the common carotid, the collateral circulation can be perfectly established, by the free communication which exists between the carotid arteries of opposite sides, both without and within the cranium, and by enlargement of the branches of the subclavian artery on the side corresponding to that on which the vessel has been tied. The chief communications outside the skull take place between the superior and inferior thyroid arteries, and the profunda cervicis and ramus descendens of the occipital; the vertebral supplies blood to the branches of the internal carotid within the cranium.

The External Carotid Artery (A. Carotis Externa) (Fig. 550).

The **external carotid artery** begins opposite the upper border of the thyroid cartilage, and curving slightly passes upward and forward, and then inclines backward to the space behind the neck of the mandible, where it divides into the superficial temporal and internal maxillary arteries. It rapidly diminishes in size in its course up the neck, owing to the number and large size of the branches given off from it. In the child, it is somewhat smaller than the internal carotid; but in the adult, the two vessels are of nearly equal size. At its origin, this artery is more superficial, and placed nearer the mid-line than the internal carotid, and is contained within the carotid triangle.

Relations.—The external carotid artery is *covered by* the skin, superficial fascia, Platysma, deep fascia, and anterior margin of the Sternocleidomastoideus; it is crossed by the hypoglossal nerve, by the lingual, ranine, common facial, and superior thyroid veins; and by the Digastricus and Stylohyoideus; higher up it passes deeply into the substance of the parotid gland, where it lies deep to the facial nerve and the junction of the temporal and internal maxillary veins. *Medial* to it are the hyoid bone, the wall of the pharynx, the superior laryngeal nerve, and a portion of the parotid gland. *Lateral* to it, in the lower part of its course, is the internal carotid artery. *Posterior* to it, near its origin, is the superior laryngeal nerve; and higher up, it is separated from the internal carotid by the Styloglossus and Stylopharyngeus, the glossopharyngeal nerve, the pharyngeal branch of the vagus, and part of the parotid gland.

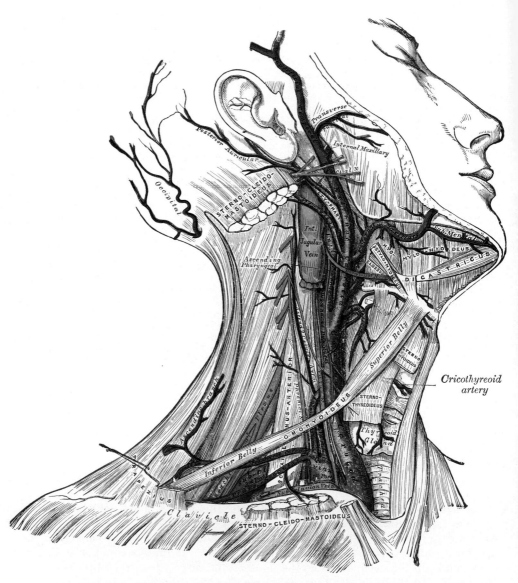

Fig. 550.—Superficial dissection of the right side of the neck, showing the carotid and subclavian arteries.

Branches.—The branches of the external carotid artery may be divided into four sets.

Anterior.	*Posterior.*	*Ascending.*	*Terminal.*
Superior Thyroid.	Occipital.	Ascending	Superficial Temporal.
Lingual.	Posterior Auricular.	Pharyngeal.	Maxillary.
Facial			

1. The **superior thyroid artery** (*a. thyreoidea superior*) (Fig. 550) *arises* from the external carotid artery just below the level of the greater cornu of the hyoid bone and ends in the thyroid gland. In 16 per cent of cases, the superior thyroid arises from the common carotid.

Relations.—From its origin under the anterior border of the Sternocleidomastoideus it runs upward and forward for a short distance in the carotid triangle, where it is covered by the skin, Platysma, and fascia; it then arches downward beneath the Omohyoideus, Sternohyoideus, and Sternothyreoideus. To its medial side are the Constrictor pharyngis inferior and the external branch of the superior laryngeal nerve.

Branches.—It distributes twigs to the adjacent muscles, and usually two main branches to the thyroid gland; one, the larger, supplies principally the anterior surface; on the isthmus of the gland it anastomoses with the corresponding artery of the opposite side; a second branch descends on the posterior surface of the gland and anastomoses with the inferior thyroid artery.

Besides the arteries distributed to the muscles and to the thyroid gland, the branches of the superior thyroid are:

Hyoid.	Superior Laryngeal.
Sternocleidomastoid.	Cricothyroid.

The **Hyoid Branch** (*ramus infrahyoideus; infrahyoid branch*) is small and runs along the lower border of the hyoid bone beneath the Thyreohyoideus and anastomoses with the vessel of the opposite side.

The **Sternocleidomastoid Branch** (*ramus sternocleidomastoideus; sternomastoid branch*) runs downward and lateralward across the sheath of the common carotid artery, and supplies the Sternocleidomastoideus and neighboring muscles and integument; it frequently *arises* as a separate branch from the external carotid.

The **Superior Laryngeal Artery** (*a. laryngea superior*), larger than either of the preceding, accompanies the internal laryngeal branch of the superior laryngeal nerve, beneath the Thyreohyoideus; it pierces the hyothyroid membrane, and supplies the muscles, mucous membrane, and glands of the larynx, anastomosing with the branch from the opposite side. It sometimes (13 per cent) arises separately from the external carotid.

The **Cricothyroid Branch** (*ramus cricothyreoideus*) is small and runs transversely across the cricothyroid membrane, communicating with the artery of the opposite side.

2. The **lingual artery** (*a. lingualis*) (Fig. 554) *arises* from the external carotid opposite the tip of the greater cornu of the hyoid bone, and between the superior thyroid and external maxillary arteries; it first runs obliquely upward and medialward above the greater cornu of the hyoid bone, then curves downward and forward, forming a loop which is crossed by the hypoglossal nerve, and passing beneath the Digastricus and Stylohyoideus it runs horizontally forward, beneath the Hyoglossus, and finally, ascending almost perpendicularly to the tongue, turns forward on its lower surface as far as the tip, under the name of the **profunda linguæ**.

Relations.—Its first, or oblique, portion is superficial, and is contained within the carotid triangle; it rests upon the Constrictor pharyngis medius, and is covered by the Platysma and the fascia of the neck. Its second, or curved, portion also lies upon the Constrictor pharyngis medius, being covered at first by the tendon of the Digastricus and by the Stylohyoideus, and afterward by the Hyoglossus. Its third, or horizontal, portion lies between the Hyoglossus and Genioglossus. The fourth, or terminal part, under the name of the **profunda linguæ** (*ranine artery*) runs along the under surface of the tongue to its tip; here it is superficial, being covered only by the mucous membrane; above it is the Longitudinalis inferior, and on the medial side the Genioglossus. The hypoglossal nerve crosses the first part of the lingual artery, but is separated from the second part by the Hyoglossus.

Branches.—The branches of the lingual artery are:

Hyoid.   Sublingual.

Dorsales linguæ.   Profunda linguæ.

The **Hyoid Branch** (*ramus suprahyoideus; suprahyoid branch*) runs along the upper border of the hyoid bone, supplying the muscles attached to it and anastomosing with its fellow of the opposite side.

The **Dorsal Lingual Arteries** (*a. dorsales linguæ; rami dorsales linguæ*) consist usually of two or three small branches which *arise* beneath the Hyoglossus; they ascend to the back part of the dorsum of the tongue, and supply the mucous membrane in this situation, the glossopalatine arch, the tonsil, soft palate, and epiglottis; anastomosing with the vessels of the opposite side.

The **Sublingual Artery** (*a. sublingualis*) *arises* at the anterior margin of the Hyoglossus, and runs forward between the Genioglossus and Mylohyoideus to the sublingual gland. It supplies the gland and gives branches to the Mylohyoideus and neighboring muscles, and to the mucous membrane of the mouth and gums. One branch runs behind the alveolar process of the mandible in the substance of the gum to anastomose with a similar artery from the other side; another pierces the Mylohyoideus and anastomoses with the submental branch of the external maxillary artery.

The **Deep Lingual Artery** (*a. profunda linguæ; ranine artery*) is the terminal portion of the lingual artery; it pursues a tortuous course, running along the under surface of the tongue, below the Longitudinalis inferior, and above the mucous membrane; it lies on the lateral side of the Genioglossus, accompanied by the lingual nerve. It anastomoses with the artery of the opposite side at the tip of the tongue.

3. The **facial or external maxillary artery** (*a. facialis*) (Fig. 551), *arises* in the the carotid triangle a little above the lingual artery and, sheltered by the ramus of the mandible, passes obliquely up beneath the Digastricus and Stylohyoideus, over which it arches to enter a groove on the posterior surface of the submaxillary gland. It then curves upward over the body of the mandible at the antero-inferior angle of the Masseter; passes forward and upward across the cheek to the angle of the mouth, then ascends along the side of the nose, and ends at the medial commissure of the eye, under the name of the **angular artery**. This vessel, both in the neck and on the face, is remarkably tortuous: in the neck, to accommodate itself to the movements of the pharynx in deglutition; and in the face, to the movements of the mandible, lips, and cheeks.

Relations.—*In the neck*, its origin is superficial, being covered by the integument, Platysma, and fascia; it then passes beneath the Digastricus and Stylohyoideus muscles and part of the submaxillary gland, and frequently beneath the hypoglossal nerve. It lies upon the Constrictores pharyngis medius and superior, the latter of which separates it, at the summit of its arch, from the lower and back part of the tonsil. *On the face*, where it passes over the body of the mandible, it is comparatively superficial, lying immediately beneath the Platysma. In its course over the face, it is covered by the integument, the fat of the cheek, and, near the angle of the mouth, by the Platysma, Risorius, and Zygomaticus. It rests on the Buccinator and Caninus, and passes either over or under the infraorbital head of the Quadratus labii superioris. The anterior facial vein lies lateral to the artery, and takes a more direct course across the face, where it is separated from the artery by a considerable interval. In the neck it lies superficial to the artery. The branches of the facial nerve cross the artery from behind forward.

Branches.—The branches of the artery may be divided into two sets: those given off in the neck (*cervical*), and those on the face (*facial*).

Cervical Branches.	*Facial Branches.*
Ascending Palatine.	Inferior Labial.
Tonsillar.	Superior Labial.
Glandular.	Lateral Nasal.
Submental.	Angular.
Muscular.	Muscular.

The **Ascending Palatine Artery** (*a. palatina ascendens*) (Fig. 554) *arises* close to the origin of the external maxillary artery and passes up between the Styloglossus and Stylopharyngeus to the side of the pharynx, along which it is continued between the Constrictor pharyngis superior and the Pterygoideus internus to near the base of the skull. It divides near the Levator veli palatini into two branches: one follows the course of this muscle, and, winding over the upper border of the Constrictor pharyngis superior, supplies the soft palate and the palatine glands, anastomosing with its fellow of the opposite side and with the descending palatine branch of the internal maxillary artery; the other pierces the Constrictor pharyngis superior and supplies the palatine tonsil and auditory tube, anastomosing with the tonsillar and ascending pharyngeal arteries.

The **Tonsillar Branch** (*ramus tonsillaris*) (Fig. 554) ascends between the Pterygoideus internus and Styloglossus, and then along the side of the pharynx, perforating the Constrictor pharyngis superior, to ramify in the substance of the palatine tonsil and root of the tongue.

The **Glandular Branches** (*rami glandulares; submaxillary branches*) consist of three or four large vessels, which supply the submaxillary gland, some being prolonged to the neighboring muscles, lymph glands, and integument.

The **Submental Artery** (*a. submentalis*) the largest of the cervical branches, is given off from the facial artery just as that vessel quits the submaxillary gland: it runs forward upon the Mylohyoideus, just below the body of the mandible, and beneath the Digastricus. It supplies the surrounding muscles, and anastomoses with the sublingual artery and with the mylohyoid branch of the inferior alveolar; at the symphysis menti it turns upward over the border of the mandible and divides into a superficial and a deep branch. The superficial branch passes between the integument and Quadratus labii inferioris, and anastomoses with the inferior labial artery; the deep branch runs between the muscle and the bone, supplies the lip, and anastomoses with the inferior labial and mental arteries.

The **Inferior Labial Artery** (*a. labialis inferior*) *arises* near the angle of the mouth; it passes upward and forward beneath the Triangularis and, penetrating the Orbicularis oris, runs a tortuous course along the edge of the lower lip between this muscle and the mucous membrane. It supplies the labial glands, the mucous membrane, and the muscles of the lower lip; and anastomoses with the artery of the opposite side, and with the mental branch of the inferior alveolar artery.

The **Superior Labial Artery** (*a. labialis superior*), larger and more tortuous than the inferior, follows a similar course along the edge of the upper lip, lying between the mucous membrane and the Orbicularis oris, anastomosing with the artery of the opposite side. It supplies the upper lip, and gives off two or three vessels which ascend to the nose; a **septal branch** ramifies on the nasal septum as far as the point of the nose, and an **alar branch** supplies the ala of the nose.

The **Lateral Nasal** branch is derived from the external maxillary as that vessel ascends along the side of the nose. It supplies the ala and dorsum of the nose, anastomosing with its fellow, with the septal and alar branches, with the dorsal nasal branch of the ophthalmic, and with the infraorbital branch of the internal maxillary.

The **Angular Artery** (*a. angularis*) is the terminal part of the external maxillary; it ascends to the medial angle of the orbit, imbedded in the fibers of the angular head of the Quadratus labii superioris, and accompanied by the angular vein.

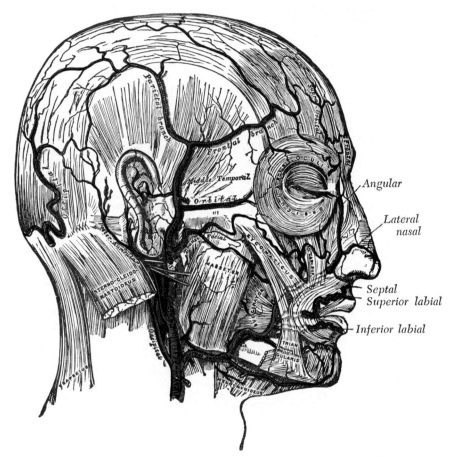

Fig. 551.—The arteries of the face and scalp. The muscular tissue of the lips has been cut away, in order to show the course of the labial arteries.

On the cheek it distributes branches which anastomose with the infraorbital; after supplying the lacrimal sac and Orbicularis oculi, it ends by anastomosing with the dorsal nasal branch of the ophthalmic artery.

The **Muscular Branches** in the neck are distributed to the Pterygoideus internus and Stylohyoideus, and on the face to the Masseter and Buccinator. The anastomoses of the external maxillary artery are very numerous, not only with the vessel of the opposite side, but, *in the neck*, with the sublingual branch of the lingual, with the ascending pharyngeal, and by its ascending palatine and tonsillar branches with the palatine branch of the internal maxillary; *on the face*, with the mental branch of the inferior alveolar as it emerges from the mental foramen, with the transverse facial branch of the superficial temporal, with the infraorbital branch of the internal maxillary, and with the dorsal nasal branch of the ophthalmic.

Variations.—The facial artery not infrequently arises in common with the lingual. It varies in size and in the extent to which it supplies the face; it occasionally ends as the submental, and not infrequently extends only as high as the angle of the mouth or nose. The deficiency is then compensated for by enlargement of one of the neighboring arteries.

4. The **occipital artery** (*a. occipitalis*) (Fig. 551) *arises* from the posterior part of the external carotid, opposite the external maxillary, near the lower margin of the posterior belly of the Digastricus, and ends in the posterior part of the scalp.

Course and Relations.—At its origin, it is covered by the posterior belly of the Digastricus and the Stylohyoideus, and the hypoglossal nerve winds around it from behind forward; higher up, it crosses the internal carotid artery, the internal jugular vein, and the vagus and accessory nerves. It next ascends to the interval between the transverse process of the atlas and the mastoid process of the temporal bone, and passes horizontally backward, grooving the surface of the latter bone, being covered by the Sternocleidomastoideus, Splenius capitis, Longissimus capitis, and Digastricus, and resting upon the Rectus capitis lateralis, the Obliquus superior, and Semispinalis capitis. It then changes its course and runs vertically upward, pierces the fascia connecting the cranial attachment of the Trapezius with the Sternocleidomastoideus, and ascends in a tortuous course in the superficial fascia of the scalp, where it divides into numerous branches, which reach as high as the vertex of the skull and anastomose with the posterior auricular and superficial temporal arteries. Its terminal portion is accompanied by the greater occipital nerve.

Branches.—The branches of the occipital artery are:

Muscular. Sternocleidomastoid. Auricular.
  Meningeal. Descending.

The **Muscular Branches** (*rami musculares*) supply the Digastricus, Stylohyoideus, Splenius, and Longissimus capitis.

The **Sternocleidomastoid Artery** (*a. sternocleidomastoidea; sternomastoid artery*) generally *arises* from the occipital close to its commencement, but sometimes springs directly from the external carotid. It passes downward and backward over the hypoglossal nerve, and enters the substance of the muscle, in company with the accessory nerve.

The **Auricular Branch** (*ramus auricularis*) supplies the back of the concha and frequently gives off a branch, which enters the skull through the mastoid foramen and supplies the dura mater, the diploë, and the mastoid cells; this latter branch sometimes arises from the occipital artery, and is then known as the **mastoid branch**.

The **Meningeal Branch** (*ramus meningeus; dural branch*) ascends with the internal jugular vein, and enters the skull through the jugular foramen and condyloid canal, to supply the dura mater in the posterior fossa.

The **Descending Branch** (*ramus descendens; arteria princeps cervicis*) (Fig. 554), the largest branch of the occipital, descends on the back of the neck, and divides into a superficial and deep portion. The superficial portion runs beneath the Splenius, giving off branches which pierce that muscle to supply the Trapezius and anastomose with the ascending branch of the transverse cervical: the deep portion runs down between the Semispinales capitis and cervicis, and anastomoses with the vertebral and with the a. profunda cervicalis, a branch of the costocervical trunk. The anastomosis between these vessels assists in establishing the collateral circulation after ligature of the common carotid or subclavian artery.

The terminal branches of the occipital artery are distributed to the back of the head: they are very tortuous, and lie between the integument and Occipitalis, anastomosing with the artery of the opposite side and with the posterior auricular

40

and temporal arteries, and supplying the Occipitalis, the integument, and pericranium. One of the terminal branches may give off a meningeal twig which passes through the parietal foramen.

5. The **posterior auricular artery** (*a. auricularis posterior*) (Fig. 551) is small and *arises* from the external carotid, above the Digastricus and Stylohyoideus, opposite the apex of the styloid process. It ascends, under cover of the parotid gland, on the styloid process of the temporal bone, to the groove between the cartilage of the ear and the mastoid process, immediately above which it divides into its auricular and occipital branches.

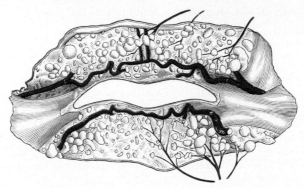

Fig. 552.—The labial arteries, the glands of the lips, and the nerves of the right side seen from the posterior surface after removal of the mucous membrane. (Poirier and Charpy.)

Branches.—Besides several small branches to the Digastricus, Stylohyoideus, and Sternocleidomastoideus, and to the parotid gland, this vessel gives off three branches:

Stylomastoid. Auricular. Occipital.

The **Stylomastoid Artery** (*a. stylomastoidea*) enters the stylomastoid foramen and supplies the tympanic cavity, the tympanic antrum and mastoid cells, and the semicircular canals. In the young subject a branch from this vessel forms, with the anterior tympanic artery from the internal maxillary, a vascular circle, which surrounds the tympanic membrane, and from which delicate vessels ramify on that membrane. It anastomoses with the superficial petrosal branch of the middle meningeal artery by a twig which enters the hiatus canalis facialis.

The **Auricular Branch** (*ramus auricularis*) ascends behind the ear, beneath the Auricularis posterior, and is distributed to the back of the auricula, upon which it ramifies minutely, some branches curving around the margin of the cartilage, others perforating it, to supply the anterior surface. It anastomoses with the parietal and anterior auricular branches of the superficial temporal.

The **Occipital Branch** (*ramus occipitalis*) passes backward, over the Sternocleidomastoideus, to the scalp above and behind the ear. It supplies the Occipitalis and the scalp in this situation and anastomoses with the occipital artery.

6. The **ascending pharyngeal artery** (*a. pharyngea ascendens*) (Fig. 554), the smallest branch of the external carotid, is a long, slender vessel, deeply seated in the neck, beneath the other branches of the external carotid and under the Stylopharyngeus. It *arises* from the back part of the external carotid, near the commencement of that vessel, and ascends vertically between the internal carotid and the side of the pharynx, anterior to the Longus capitis, to the under surface of the base of the skull. In 14 per cent. of cases it arises from the occipital artery.

Branches.—Its branches are:

Pharyngeal.   Prevertebral.
Palatine.   Inferior Tympanic.
                  Posterior Meningeal.

The **Pharyngeal Branches** (*rami pharyngei*) are three or four in number. Two of these descend to supply the Constrictores pharyngis medius and inferior and the Stylopharyngeus, ramifying in their substance and in the mucous membrane lining them.

The **Palatine Branch** varies in size, and may take the place of the ascending palatine branch of the external maxillary artery, when that vessel is small. It passes inward upon the Constrictor pharyngis superior, sends ramifications to the soft palate and tonsil, and supplies a branch to the auditory tube.

The **Prevertebral Branches** are numerous small vessels, which supply the Longi capitis and colli, the sympathetic trunk, the hypoglossal and vagus nerves, and the lymph glands; they anastomose with the ascending cervical artery.

The **Inferior Tympanic Artery** (*a. tympanica inferior*) is a small branch which passes through a minute foramen in the petrous portion of the temporal bone, in company with the tympanic branch of the glossopharyngeal nerve, to supply the medial wall of the tympanic cavity and anastomose with the other tympanic arteries.

The **Meningeal Branches** are several small vessels, which supply the dura mater. One, the **posterior meningeal**, enters the cranium through the jugular foramen; a second passes through the foramen lacerum; and occasionally a third through the canal for the hypoglossal nerve.

7. The **superficial temporal artery** (*a. temporalis superficialis*) (Fig. 551), the smaller of the two terminal branches of the external carotid, appears, from its direction, to be the continuation of that vessel. It begins in the substance of the parotid gland, behind the neck of the mandible, and crosses over the posterior root of the zygomatic process of the temporal bone; about 5 cm. above this process it divides into two branches, a frontal and a parietal.

Relations.—As it crosses the zygomatic process, it is covered by the Auricularis anterior muscle, and by a dense fascia; it is crossed by the temporal and zygomatic branches of the facial nerve and one or two veins, and is accompanied by the auriculotemporal nerve, which lies immediately behind it. Just above the zygomatic process and in front of the auricle, the superficial temporal artery is quite superficial, being covered only by skin and fascia, and can easily be felt pulsating. This artery is often used for determining the pulse, particularly by anesthetists.

Branches.—Besides some twigs to the parotid gland, to the temporomandibular joint, and to the Masseter muscle, its branches are:

Transverse Facial.   Anterior Auricular.
Middle Temporal.   Frontal.
                  Parietal.

The **Transverse Facial Artery** (*a. transversa faciei*) is given off from the superficial temporal before that vessel quits the parotid gland; running forward through the substance of the gland, it passes transversely across the side of the face, between the parotid duct and the lower border of the zygomatic arch, and divides into numerous branches, which supply the parotid gland and duct, the Masseter, and the integument, and anastomose with the external maxillary, masseteric, buccinator, and infraorbital arteries. This vessel rests on the Masseter, and is accompanied by one or two branches of the facial nerve.

The **Middle Temporal Artery** (*a. temporalis media*) *arises* immediately above the zygomatic arch, and, perforating the temporal fascia, gives branches to the Temporalis, anastomosing with the deep temporal branches of the internal maxillary. It occasionally gives off a **zygomaticoörbital branch**, which runs along the upper border of the zygomatic arch, between the two layers of the temporal fascia, to the lateral angle of the orbit. This branch, which may arise directly from the superficial temporal artery, supplies the Orbicularis oculi, and anastomoses with the lacrimal and palpebral branches of the ophthalmic artery.

The **Anterior Auricular Branches** (*rami auriculares anteriores*) are distributed to the anterior portion of the auricula, the lobule, and part of the external meatus, anastomosing with the posterior auricular.

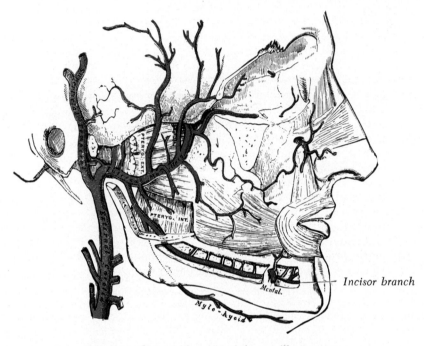

Fig. 553.—Plan of branches of the maxillary artery.

The **Frontal Branch** (*ramus frontalis; anterior temporal*) runs tortuously upward and forward to the forehead, supplying the muscles, integument, and pericranium in this region, and anastomosing with the supraorbital and frontal arteries.

The **Parietal Branch** (*ramus parietalis; posterior temporal*) larger than the frontal, curves upward and backward on the side of the head, lying superficial to the temporal fascia, and anastomosing with its fellow of the opposite side, and with the posterior auricular and occipital arteries.

8. The **maxillary artery** (*a. maxillaris; internal maxillary artery*) (Fig. 553), the larger of the two terminal branches of the external carotid, *arises* behind the neck of the mandible, and is at first imbedded in the substance of the parotid gland; it passes forward between the ramus of the mandible and the sphenomandibular ligament, and then runs, either superficial or deep to the Pterygoideus externus, to the pterygopalatine fossa. It supplies the deep structures of the face, and may be divided into **mandibular, pterygoid,** and **pterygopalatine portions.**

The **first** or **mandibular portion** passes horizontally forward, between the ramus of the mandible and the sphenomandibular ligament, where it lies parallel to and a little below the auriculotemporal nerve; it crosses the inferior alveolar nerve, and runs along the lower border of the Pterygoideus externus.

The **second** or **pterygoid portion** runs obliquely forward and upward under cover of the ramus of the mandible and insertion of the Temporalis, on the superficial (very frequently on the deep) surface of the Pterygoideus externus; it then passes between the two heads of origin of this muscle and enters the fossa.

The **third** or **pterygopalatine portion** lies in the pterygopalatine fossa lateral to the sphenopalatine ganglion.

The branches of this vessel may be divided into three groups (Fig. 553), corresponding to its three divisions.

Branches of the First or Mandibular Portions.—

Anterior Tympanic.	Middle Meningeal.
Deep Auricular.	Accessory Meningeal.

Inferior Alveolar.

The **Anterior Tympanic Artery** (*a. tympanica anterior; tympanic artery*) passes upward behind the temporomandibular articulation, enters the tympanic cavity through the petrotympanic fissure, and ramifies upon the tympanic membrane, forming a vascular circle around the membrane with the stylomastoid branch of the posterior auricular, and anastomosing with the artery of the pterygoid canal and with the caroticotympanic branch from the internal carotid.

The **Deep Auricular Artery** (*a. auricularis profunda*) often *arises* in common with the preceding. It ascends in the substance of the parotid gland, behind the temporomandibular articulation, pierces the cartilaginous or bony wall of the external acoustic meatus, and supplies its cuticular lining and the outer surface of the tympanic membrane. It gives a branch to the temporomandibular joint.

The **Middle Meningeal Artery** (*a. meningea media; medidural artery*) is the largest of the arteries which supply the dura mater. It ascends between the spheno-mandibular ligament and the Pterygoideus externus, and between the two roots of the auriculotemporal nerve to the foramen spinosum of the sphenoid bone, through which it enters the cranium; it then runs forward in a groove on the great wing of the sphenoid bone, and divides into two branches, anterior and posterior. The **anterior branch**, the larger, crosses the great wing of the sphenoid, reaches the groove, or canal, in the sphenoidal angle of the parietal bone, and then divides into branches which spread out between the dura mater and internal surface of the cranium, some passing upward as far as the vertex, and others backward to the occipital region. The **posterior branch** curves backward on the squama of the temporal bone, and, reaching the parietal some distance in front of its mastoid angle, divides into branches which supply the posterior part of the dura mater and cranium. The branches of the middle meningeal artery are distributed partly to the dura mater, but chiefly to the bones; they anastomose with the arteries of the opposite side, and with the anterior and posterior meningeal.

The middle meningeal, on entering the cranium, gives off the following branches: (1) Numerous small vessels supply the semilunar ganglion and the dura mater nearby. (2) A **superficial petrosal** branch enters the hiatus of the facial canal, supplies the facial nerve, and anastomoses with the stylomastoid branch of the posterior auricular artery. (3) A **superior tympanic artery** runs in the canal for the Tensor tympani, and supplies this muscle and the lining membrane of the canal. (4) **Orbital branches** pass through the superior orbital fissure or through separate canals in the great wing of the sphenoid, to anastomose with the lacrimal or other branches of the ophthalmic artery. (5) **Temporal branches** pass through foramina in the great wing of the sphenoid, and anastomose in the temporal fossa with the deep temporal arteries.

The **Accessory Meningeal Branch** (*ramus meningeus accessorius; small meningeal or parvidural branch*) is sometimes derived from the preceding. It enters the skull through the foramen ovale, and supplies the semilunar ganglion and dura mater.

The **Inferior Alveolar Artery** (*a. alveolaris inferior; inferior dental artery*) descends with the inferior alveolar nerve to the mandibular foramen on the medial surface of the ramus of the mandible. It runs along the mandibular canal in the substance of the bone, accompanied by the nerve, and opposite the first premolar tooth divides into two branches, incisor and mental. The **incisor branch** is continued forward beneath the incisor teeth as far as the mid-line, where it anastomoses with the artery of the opposite side; the **mental branch** emerges with the nerve from the mental foramen, supplies the chin, and anastomoses with the submental and inferior labial arteries. Near its origin the inferior alveolar artery gives off a **lingual branch** which descends with the lingual nerve and supplies the mucous membrane of the mouth. As the inferior alveolar artery enters the foramen, it gives off a **mylohyoid branch** which runs in the mylohyoid groove, and ramifies on the under surface of the Mylohyoideus. The inferior alveolar artery and its incisor branch, during their course through the substance of the bone, give off a few twigs which are lost in the cancellous tissue, and a series of branches which correspond in number to the roots of the teeth: these enter the minute apertures at the extremities of the roots, and supply the pulp of the teeth.

Branches of the Second or Pterygoid Portion.—

Deep Temporal.	Masseteric.
Pterygoid.	Buccal.

The **Deep Temporal Branches,** two in number, **anterior** and **posterior,** ascend between the Temporalis and the pericranium; they supply the muscle, and anastomose with the middle temporal artery; the anterior communicates with the lacrimal artery by means of small branches which perforate the zygomatic bone and great wing of the sphenoid.

The **Pterygoid Branches** (*rami pterygoidei*), irregular in number and origin, supply the Pterygoidei.

The **Masseteric Artery** (*a. masseterica*) is small and passes lateralward through the mandibular notch to the deep surface of the Masseter. It supplies the muscle, and anastomoses with the masseteric branches of the external maxillary and with the transverse facial artery.

The **Buccal Artery** (*a. buccis; buccinator artery*) is small and runs obliquely forward, between the Pterygoideus internus and the insertion of the Temporalis, to the outer surface of the Buccinator, to which it is distributed, anastomosing with branches of the external maxillary and with the infraorbital.

Branches of the Third or Pterygopalatine Portion.—

Posterior Superior Alveolar.	Artery of the Pterygoid Canal.
Infraorbital.	Pharyngeal.
Greater Palatine.	Sphenopalatine.

The **Posterior Superior Alveolar Artery** (*a. alveolaris superior posterior; alveolar or posterior dental artery*) is given off from the internal maxillary, frequently in conjunction with the infraorbital, just as the trunk of the vessel is passing into the pterygopalatine fossa. Descending upon the tuberosity of the maxilla, it divides into numerous branches, some of which enter the alveolar canals, to supply the molar and premolar teeth and the lining of the maxillary sinus, while others continue forward on the alveolar process to supply the gums.

The **Infraorbital Artery** (*a. infraorbitalis*) appears, from its direction, to be the continuation of the trunk of the internal maxillary, but often *arises* in conjunction with the posterior superior alveolar. It runs along the infraorbital groove and canal with the infraorbital nerve, and emerges on the face through the infraorbital foramen, beneath the infraorbital head of the Quadratus labii superioris. While in the canal, it gives off (*a*) **orbital branches** which assist in supplying the Rectus inferior and Obliquus inferior and the lacrimal sac, and (*b*) **anterior superior alveolar branches** which descend through the anterior alveolar canals to supply the upper incisor and canine teeth and the mucous membrane of the maxillary sinus. On the face, some branches pass upward to the medial angle of the orbit and the lacrimal sac, anastomosing with the angular branch of the external maxillary artery; others run toward the nose, anastomosing with the dorsal nasal branch of the ophthalmic; and others descend between the Quadratus labii superioris and the Caninus, and anastomose with the external maxillary, transverse facial, and buccinator arteries. The four remaining branches *arise* from that portion of the internal maxillary which is contained in the pterygopalatine fossa.

The **Greater Palatine Artery** (*a. palatina descendens*) descends through the pterygopalatine canal with the greater palatine branch of the sphenopalatine nerve, and, emerging from the greater palatine foramen, runs forward in a groove on the medial side of the alveolar border of the hard palate to the incisive canal; the terminal branch of the artery passes upward through this canal to anastomose with the sphenopalatine artery. Branches are distributed to the gums, the palatine glands, and the mucous membrane of the roof of the mouth; while in the pterygopalatine canal it gives off twigs which descend in the lesser palatine canals to supply the soft palate and palatine tonsil, anastomosing with the ascending palatine artery.

The **Artery of the Pterygoid Canal** (*a. canalis pterygoidei; Vidian artery*) passes backward along the pterygoid canal with the corresponding nerve. It is distributed to the upper part of the pharynx and to the auditory tube, sending into the tympanic cavity a small branch which anastomoses with the other tympanic arteries.

The **Pharyngeal Branch** is very small; it runs backward through the pharyngeal canal with the pharyngeal nerve, and is distributed to the upper part of the pharynx and to the auditory tube.

The **Sphenopalatine Artery** (*a. sphenopalatina; nasopalatine artery*) passes through the sphenopalatine foramen into the cavity of the nose, at the back part of the superior meatus. Here it gives off its **posterior lateral nasal branches** which spread forward over the conchæ and meatuses, anastomose with the ethmoidal arteries and the nasal branches of the greater palatine, and assist in supplying the frontal, maxillary, ethmoidal, and sphenoidal sinuses. Crossing the under surface of the sphenoid, the sphenopalatine artery ends on the nasal septum as the **posterior septal branches**; these anastomose with the ethmoidal arteries and the septal branch of the superior labial; one branch descends in a groove on the vomer to the incisive canal and anastomoses with the greater palatine artery.

The Internal Carotid Artery (**A. Carotis Interna**) (Fig. 554).

The **internal carotid artery** supplies the anterior part of the brain, the eye and its appendages, and sends branches to the forehead and nose. Its size, in the adult, is equal to that of the external carotid, though, in the child, it is larger than that vessel. It is remarkable for the number of curvatures that it presents in different parts of its course. It occasionally has one or two flexures near the base of the skull, while in its passage through the carotid canal and along the side of the body of the sphenoid bone it describes a double curvature and resembles the italic letter *S*.

The Carotid Sinus.—The carotid sinus, a slight dilatation of the terminal portion of the common carotid artery and of the internal carotid artery at its origin from the common carotid, or a dilatation 1 cm. in length of the internal carotid only, is an important organ for the regulation of systemic blood pressure. Special nervous end-organs in its modified wall respond to increase and to decrease in blood pressure and through a reflex arc, probably via the carotid branch of the glossopharyngeal nerve, convey stimuli to the medulla which result in increasing or decreasing the rate of the heart beat.

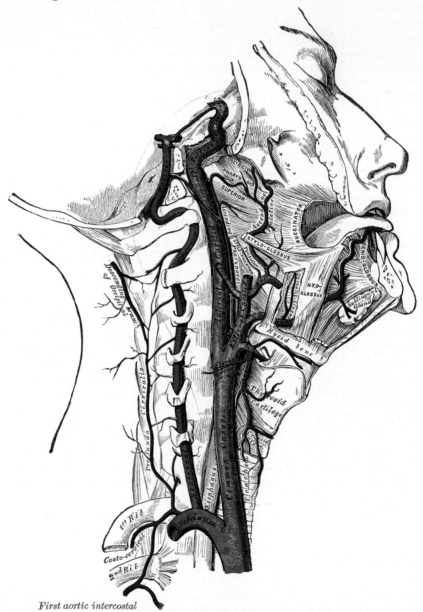

Fig. 554.—The internal carotid and vertebral arteries. Right side.

Course and Relations.—In considering the course and relations of this vessel it may be divided into four portions: **cervical, petrous, cavernous,** and **cerebral.**

Cervical Portion.—This portion of the internal carotid begins at the bifurcation of the common carotid, opposite the upper border of the thyroid cartilage, and runs perpendicularly upward, in front of the transverse processes of the upper three cervical vertebræ, to the carotid canal in the petrous portion of the temporal bone. It is comparatively superficial at its commencement, where it is contained in the carotid triangle, and lies behind and lateral to the external carotid, overlapped by the Sternocleidomastoideus, and covered by the deep fascia, Platysma, and integument: it then passes beneath the parotid gland, being crossed by the hypoglossal nerve, the Digastricus and Stylohyoideus, and the occipital and posterior auricular arteries. Higher up, it is separated from the external carotid by the Styloglossus and Stylopharyngeus, the tip of the styloid process and the stylohyoid ligament, the glossopharyngeal nerve and the pharyngeal branch of the vagus. It is in relation, *behind*, with the Longus capitis, the superior cervical ganglion of the sympathetic trunk, and the superior laryngeal nerve; *laterally*, with the internal jugular vein and vagus nerve, the nerve lying on a plane posterior to the artery; *medially*, with the pharynx, superior laryngeal nerve, and ascending pharyngeal artery. At the base of the skull the glossopharyngeal, vagus, accessory, and hypoglossal nerves lie between the artery and the internal jugular vein.

Petrous Portion.—When the internal carotid artery enters the canal in the petrous portion of the temporal bone, it first ascends a short distance, then curves forward and medialward, and again ascends as it leaves the canal to enter the cavity of the skull between the lingula and petrosal process of the sphenoid. The artery lies at first in front of the cochlea and tympanic cavity; from the latter cavity it is separated by a thin, bony lamella, which is cribriform in the young subject, and often partly absorbed in old age. Farther forward it is separated from the semilunar ganglion by a thin plate of bone, which forms the floor of the fossa for the ganglion and the roof of the horizontal portion of the canal. Frequently this bony plate is more or less deficient, and then the ganglion is separated from the artery by fibrous membrane. The artery is separated from the bony wall of the carotid canal by a prolongation of dura mater, and is surrounded by a number of small veins and by filaments of the carotid plexus, derived from the ascending branch of the superior cervical ganglion of the sympathetic trunk.

Cavernous Portion.—In this part of its course, the artery is situated between the layers of the dura mater forming the cavernous sinus, but covered by the lining membrane of the sinus. It at first ascends toward the posterior clinoid process, then passes forward by the side of the body of the sphenoid bone, and again curves upward on the medial side of the anterior clinoid process, and perforates the dura mater forming the roof of the sinus. This portion of the artery is surrounded by filaments of the sympathetic nerve, and on its lateral side is the abducent nerve.

Cerebral Portion.—Having perforated the dura mater on the medial side of the anterior clinoid process, the internal carotid passes between the optic and oculomotor nerves to the anterior perforated substance at the medial extremity of the lateral cerebral fissure, where it gives off its terminal or cerebral branches.

Variations.—The length of the internal carotid varies according to the length of the neck, and also according to the point of bifurcation of the common carotid. It arises sometimes from the arch of the aorta. The course of the artery, instead of being straight, may be very tortuous. A few instances are recorded in which this vessel was altogether absent; in one of these the common carotid passed up the neck, and gave off the usual branches of the external carotid; the cranial portion of the internal carotid was replaced by two branches of the internal maxillary, which entered the skull through the foramen rotundum and foramen ovale, and joined to form a single vessel.

Branches.—The cervical portion of the internal carotid gives off no branches. Those from the other portions are:

From the Petrous Portion	Caroticotympanic. Artery of the Pterygoid Canal.
From the Cavernous Portion	Cavernous. Hypophyseal. Semilunar. Anterior Meningeal. Ophthalmic.
From the Cerebral Portion	Anterior Cerebral. Middle Cerebral. Posterior Communicating. Choroidal.

1. The **caroticotympanic branch** (*ramus caroticotympanicus; tympanic branch*) is small; it enters the tympanic cavity through a minute foramen in the carotid canal, and anostomoses with the anterior tympanic branch of the internal maxillary, and with the stylomastoid artery.

2. The **artery of the pterygoid canal** (*a. canalis pterygoidei* [*Vidii*]; *Vidian artery*) is a small, inconstant branch which passes into the pterygoid canal and anastomoses with a branch of the internal maxillary artery.

3. The **cavernous branches** are numerous small vessels which supply the hypophysis, the semilunar ganglion, and the walls of the cavernous and inferior petrosal sinuses.   Some of them anastomose with branches of the middle meningeal.

4. The **hypophyseal branches** are one or two minute vessels supplying the hypophysis.

5. The **semilunar branches** are small vessels to the semilunar ganglion.

6. The **anterior meningeal branch** (*a. meningea anterior*) is a small branch which passes over the small wing of the sphenoid to supply the dura mater of the anterior cranial fossa; it anastomoses with the meningeal branch from the posterior ethmoidal artery.

7. The **ophthalmic artery** (*a. ophthalmica*) (Fig. 555) *arises* from the internal carotid, just as that vessel is emerging from the cavernous sinus, on the medial side of the anterior clinoid process, and enters the orbital cavity through the optic foramen, below and lateral to the optic nerve.   It then passes over the nerve to reach the medial wall of the orbit, and thence horizontally forward, beneath the lower border of the Obliquus superior, and divides it into two terminal branches, the **frontal** and **dorsal nasal**.   As the artery crosses the optic nerve it is accompanied by the nasociliary nerve, and is separated from the frontal nerve by the Rectus superior and Levator palpebræ superioris.   The artery runs below, rather than above, the optic nerve in 15 per cent. of cases.

Branches.—The branches of the ophthalmic artery may be divided into an **orbital group**, distributed to the orbit and surrounding parts; and an **ocular group**, to the muscles and bulb of the eye.

Orbital Group.	*Ocular Group.*
Lacrimal.	Central Artery of the Retina.
Supraorbital.	Short Posterior Ciliary.
Posterior Ethmoidal.	Long Posterior Ciliary.
Anterior Ethmoidal.	Anterior Ciliary.
Medial Palpebral.	Muscular.
Frontal.	
Dorsal Nasal.	

The **Lacrimal Artery** (*a. lacrimalis*) *arises* close to the optic foramen, not infrequently before it enters the orbit, and is one of the largest branches derived from the ophthalmic.   It accompanies the lacrimal nerve along the upper border of the Rectus lateralis, and supplies the lacrimal gland.   Its terminal branches, escaping from the gland, are distributed to the eyelids and conjunctiva: of those supplying the eyelids, two are of considerable size and are named the **lateral palpebral arteries**; they run medialward in the upper and lower lids respectively and anastomose with the medial palpebral arteries, forming an arterial circle in this situation.   The lacrimal artery gives off one or two **zygomatic branches**, one of which passes through the zygomatico-temporal foramen, to reach the temporal fossa, and anastomoses with the deep temporal arteries; another appears on the cheek through the zygomatico-facial foramen, and anastomoses with the transverse facial.   A **recurrent branch** passes backward through the lateral part of the superior orbital fissure to the dura mater, and anastomoses with a branch of the middle meningeal artery. The lacrimal artery is sometimes derived from one of the anterior branches of the middle meningeal artery.

The **Supraorbital Artery** (*a. supraorbitalis*) springs from the ophthalmic as that vessel is crossing over the optic nerve.   It passes upward on the medial borders of the Rectus superior and Levator palpebræ, and meeting the supraorbital nerve, accompanies it between the periosteum and Levator palpebræ to the supraorbital foramen; passing through this it divides into a superficial and a deep branch, which supply the integument, the muscles, and the pericranium of the forehead, anastomosing with the frontal, the frontal branch of the superficial temporal, and the artery of the opposite side. This artery in the orbit supplies the Rectus superior and the Levator palpebræ, and sends a branch across the pulley of the Obliquus superior, to supply the parts at the medial palpebral commissure. At the supraorbital foramen it frequently transmits a branch to the diploë.

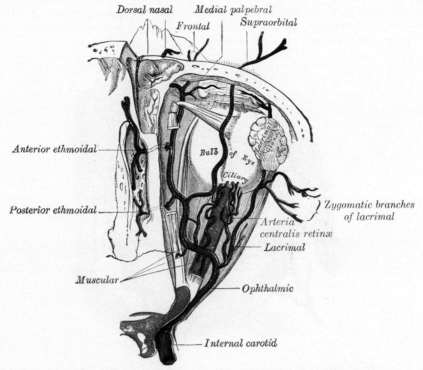

Fig. 555.—The ophthalmic artery and its branches.

The **Ethmoidal Arteries** are two in number: **posterior** and **anterior**. The **posterior ethmoidal artery**, the smaller, passes through the posterior ethmoidal canal, supplies the posterior ethmoidal cells, and, entering the cranium, gives off a meningeal branch to the dura mater, and nasal branches which descend into the nasal cavity through apertures in the cribriform plate, anastomosing with branches of the sphenopalatine. The **anterior ethmoidal artery** accompanies the nasociliary nerve through the anterior ethmoidal canal, supplies the anterior and middle ethmoidal cells and frontal sinus, and, entering the cranium, gives off a meningeal branch to the dura mater, and nasal branches; these latter descend into the nasal cavity through the slit by the side of the crista galli, and, running along the groove on the inner surface of the nasal bone, supply branches to the lateral wall and septum of the nose, and a terminal branch which appears on the dorsum of the nose between the nasal bone and the lateral cartilage.

The **Medial Palpebral Arteries** (*aa. palpebrales mediales; internal palpebral arteries*), two in number, **superior** and **inferior**, *arise* from the ophthalmic, opposite the pulley of the Obliquus superior; they leave the orbit to encircle the eyelids near their free margins, forming a superior and an inferior arch, between the

Orbicularis oculi and the tarsi. The **superior palpebral** anastomoses, at the lateral angle of the orbit, with the zygomaticoörbital branch of the temporal artery and with the upper of the two lateral palpebral branches from the lacrimal artery; the **inferior palpebral** anastomoses, at the lateral angle of the orbit, with the lower of the two lateral palpebral branches from the lacrimal and with the transverse facial artery, and, at the medial part of the lid, with a branch from the angular artery. From this last anastomoses a branch passes to the nasolacrimal duct, ramifying in its mucous membrane, as far as the inferior meatus of the nasal cavity.

The **Frontal Artery** (*a. frontalis*), one of the terminal branches of the ophthalmic, leaves the orbit at its medial angle with the supratrochlear nerve, and, ascending on the forehead, supplies the integument, muscles, and pericranium, anastomosing with the supraorbital artery, and with the artery of the opposite side.

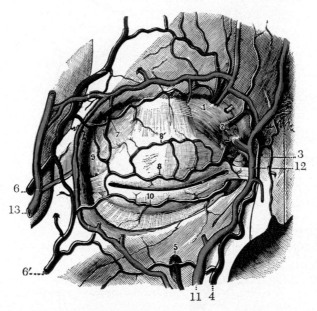

Fig. 556.—Bloodvessels of the eyelids, front view. 1, supraorbital artery and vein; 2, nasal artery; 3, angular artery, the terminal branch of 4, the facial artery; 5, infraorbital artery; 6, anterior branch of the superficial temporal artery; 6', malar branch of the transverse artery of the face; 7, lacrimal artery; 8, superior palpebral artery with 8', its external arch; 9, anastomoses of the superior palpebral with the superficial temporal and lacrimal; 10, inferior palpebral artery; 11, facial vein; 12, angular vein; 13, branch of the superficial temporal vein. (Testut.)

The **Dorsal Nasal Artery** (*a. dorsalis nasi; nasal artery*), the other terminal branch of the ophthalmic, emerges from the orbit above the medial palpebral ligament, and, after giving a twig to the upper part of the lacrimal sac, divides into two branches, one of which crosses the root of the nose, and anastomoses with the angular artery, the other runs along the dorsum of the nose, supplies its outer surface; and anastomoses with the artery of the opposite side, and with the lateral nasal branch of the external maxillary.

The **Central Artery of the Retina** (*a. centralis retinæ*) is the first and one of the smallest branches of the ophthalmic artery. It runs for a short distance within the dural sheath of the optic nerve, but about 1.25 cm. behind the eyeball it pierces the nerve obliquely, and runs forward in the center of its substance to the retina. Its mode of distribution will be described with the anatomy of the eye. It may be a branch of the lacrimal artery (Fig. 555). There is an arteria cilio-retinalis in 13 per cent. of cases (Adachi).

The **Ciliary Arteries** (*aa. ciliares*) are divisible into three groups, the long and short, the posterior, and the anterior. The **short posterior ciliary arteries**, from six to twelve in number, arise from the ophthalmic, or its branches: they pass forward around the optic nerve to the posterior part of the eyeball, pierce the sclera around the entrance of the nerve, and supply the choroid and ciliary processes. The **long posterior ciliary arteries**, two in number, pierce the posterior part of the sclera at some little distance from the optic nerve, and run forward, along either side of the eyeball, between the sclera and choroid, to the ciliary muscle, where they divide into two branches; these form an arterial circle, the **circulus arteriosus major**, around the circumference of the iris, from which numerous converging branches run, in the substance of the iris, to its pupillary margin, where they form a second arterial circle, the **circulus arteriosus minor**. The **anterior ciliary arteries** are derived from the muscular branches; they run to the front of the eyeball in company with the tendons of the Recti, form a vascular zone beneath the conjunctiva, and then pierce the sclera a short distance from the cornea and end in the circulus arteriosus major.

The **Muscular Branches**, (*rami musculares*), two in number, **superior and inferior**, frequently spring from a common trunk. The **superior**, often wanting, supplies the Levator palpebræ superioris, Rectus superior, and Obliquus superior. The **inferior**, more commonly present, passes forward between the optic nerve and Rectus inferior, and is distributed to the Recti lateralis, medialis, and inferior, and the Obliquus inferior. This vessel gives off most of the anterior ciliary arteries. Additional muscular branches are given off from the lacrimal and supraorbital arteries, or from the trunk of the ophthalmic.

8. The **anterior cerebral artery** (*a. cerebri anterior*) (Figs. 557, 559, 560) *arises* from the internal carotid, at the medial extremity of the lateral cerebral fissure. It passes forward and medialward across the anterior perforated substance, above the optic nerve, to the commencement of the longitudinal fissure. Here it comes into close relationship with the opposite artery, to which it is connected by a short trunk, the **anterior communicating artery**. From this point the two vessels run side by side in the longitudinal fissure, curve around the genu of the corpus callosum, and, turning backward, continue along the upper surface of the corpus callosum to its posterior part, where they end by anastomosing with the posterior cerebral arteries.

Branches.—In its first part the anterior cerebral artery gives off twigs which pierce the anterior perforated substance and the lamina terminalis, and supply the rostrum of the corpus callosum and the septum pellucidum. A larger branch, phylogenetically one of the oldest of the cerebral arteries, takes a recurrent course laterally over the anterior perforated substance (recurrent branch of the anterior cerebral artery, Shellshear; medial striate artery, Abbie). This medial striate artery supplies the lower anterior portion of the basal nuclei, *i. e.*, the lower part of the head of the caudate nucleus, the lower part of the frontal pole of the putamen, the frontal pole of the globus pallidus, and the anterior limb of the internal capsule up to the dorsal limit of the globus pallidus. The inferior or orbital branches of the anterior cerebral artery are distributed to the orbital surface of the frontal lobe, where they supply the olfactory lobe, gyrus rectus, and internal orbital gyrus. The anterior or prefrontal branches supply a part of the superior frontal gyrus, and send twigs over the edge of the hemisphere to the superior and middle frontal gyri and upper part of the anterior central gyrus. The **middle branches** supply the corpus callosum, the cingulate gyrus, the medial surface of the superior frontal gyrus, and the upper part of the anterior central gyrus. The **posterior branches** supply the precuneus and adjacent lateral surface of the hemisphere.

The **Anterior Communicating Artery** (*a. communicans anterior*) connects the two anterior cerebral arteries across the commencement of the longitudinal fissure. Sometimes this vessel is wanting, the two arteries joining to form a single trunk, which afterward divides; or it may be wholly, or partially, divided into two. Its length averages about 4 mm., but varies greatly. It gives off some antero-medial branches.

9. The **middle cerebral artery** (*a. cerebri media*) (Figs. 557, 558), the largest branch of the internal carotid, runs at first lateralward in the lateral cerebral or Sylvian fissure and then backward and upward on the surface of the insula, where it divides into a number of branches which are distributed to the lateral surface of the cerebral hemisphere.

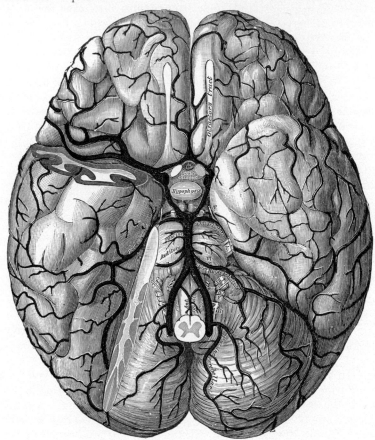

Fig. 557.—The arteries of the base of the brain. The temporal pole of the cerebrum and a portion of the cerebellar hemisphere have been removed on the right side.

Branches.—At its commencement the middle cerebral artery gives off the lateral striate arteries which supply the basal nuclei, *i. e.*, the whole of the putamen except the lower anterior pole, the upper part of the head and the whole of the body of the caudate nucleus, the lateral part of the globus pallidus, and the capsula interna above the level of the globus pallidus. It is not possible to distinguish among the branches of the lateral striate arteries any individual artery such as the "lenticulo-striate" artery of Duret or the "artery of cerebral hemorrhage" of Charcot. The thalamus is nowhere supplied by branches of the middle cerebral artery. Branches supplying cortical areas may be designated as follows: An inferior lateral frontal branch supplies the inferior frontal gyrus (Broca's convolution) and the lateral part of the orbital surface of the frontal lobe. An ascending frontal branch supplies the anterior central gyrus. An ascending parietal branch is distributed to the posterior central gyrus and the lower part of the superior parietal lobule.

A parietotemporal branch supplies the supramarginal and angular gyri, and the posterior parts of the superior and middle temporal gyri. Temporal branches, two or three in number, are distributed to the lateral surface of the temporal lobe.

10. The **posterior communicating artery** (*a. communicans posterior*) (Fig. 560) runs backward from the internal carotid, and anastomoses with the posterior cerebral, a branch of the basilar. It varies in size, being sometimes small, and occasionally so large that the posterior cerebral may be considered as arising from the internal carotid rather than from the basilar. It is frequently larger on one side than on the other. Branches of the posterior communicating artery enter

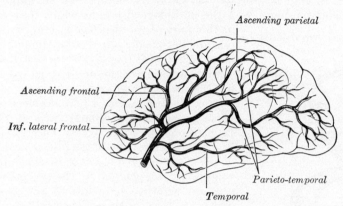

Fig. 558.—Branches of the middle cerebral artery to the lateral surface of the cerebral hemisphere. (Modified after Foix.)

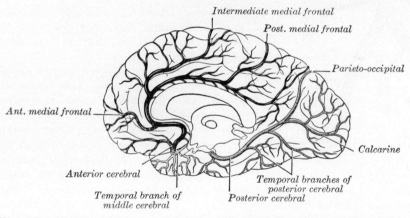

Fig. 559.—Medial surface of cerebral hemisphere, showing areas supplied by cerebral arteries.

the base of the brain between the infundibulum and the optic tract, and supply the genu and about the anterior one-third of the posterior limb of the internal capsule. There are also branches to the anterior one-third of the thalamus (exclusive of the anterior nucleus) and to the walls of the third ventricle.

11. The **anterior choroidal artery** (*a. chorioidea; choroid artery*) is, next to the middle cerebral artery, the most important source of supply to the internal capsule. The artery arises from the internal carotid near the origin of the posterior communicating artery, and takes its course along the optic tract, and around the cerebral peduncle as far as the lateral geniculate body, where its main branches turn to enter the choroid plexus of the inferior horn of the lateral ventricle. In its

course it gives branches to the optic tract, the cerebral peduncle, and the base of the brain. These branches terminate in the lateral geniculate body, the tail of the caudate nucleus, and the posterior two-thirds of the posterior limb of the internal capsule as far as the dorsal limit of the globus pallidus. The infralenticular and retrolenticular portions of the internal capsule are also vascularized by branches of the anterior choroidal artery.

THE ARTERIES OF THE BRAIN.

Since the mode of distribution of the vessels of the brain has an important bearing upon a considerable number of the pathological lesions which may occur in this part of the nervous system, it is important to consider a little more in detail the manner in which the vessels are distributed.

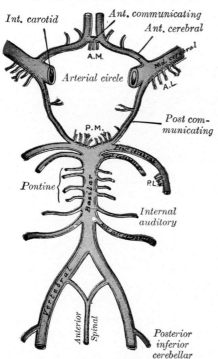

FIG. 560.—Diagram of the arterial circulation at the base of the brain. *A.L.* Antero-lateral. *A.M.* Antero-medial. *P.L.* Postero-lateral. *P.M.* Postero-medial ganglionic branches.

The cerebral arteries are derived from the internal carotid and vertebral, which at the base of the brain form a remarkable anastomosis known as the **arterial circle of Willis**. It is formed in front by the anterior cerebral arteries, branches of the internal carotid, which are connected together by the anterior communicating; behind by the two posterior cerebral arteries, branches of the basilar, which are connected on either side with the internal carotid by the posterior communicating (Figs. 557, 560). The parts of the brain included within this arterial circle are the lamina terminalis, the optic chiasma, the infundibulum, the tuber cinereum, the corpora mammillaria, and the posterior perforated substance.

The three trunks which together supply each cerebral hemisphere arise from the arterial circle of Willis. From its anterior part proceed the two anterior cerebrals, from its antero-lateral parts the middle cerebrals, and from its posterior part the posterior cerebrals. Each of these principal arteries gives origin to the numerous vessels which supply the brain substance. They contribute to a continuous complex network of capillaries, which is of different density in various parts of the central nervous system, probably in conjunction with the varying requirements of the different structures. Thus the gray matter of the brain has a much denser capillary bed than the white matter. The arteries on the surface of the brain anastomose freely, but within the central nervous system arterial anastomoses are rare. There is no evidence for the existence of arterio-venous anastomoses either in the pia or within the central nervous system. While true anatomical end-arteries exist in certain mammals, in man end- or terminal arteries do not exist in a strict anatomical sense, *i. e.*, there are no arteries which have no connections with neighboring vessels. However, the lack of sufficiently large and numerous anastomoses, and the high vulnerability of the nervous tissue in case of lack of oxygen, when an artery is occluded, greatly reduces the chances that an efficient collateral circulation might take care of the needs of the ischemic area. This ischemic area corresponds in its extent to the area of supply of the occluded vessel.

The arteries of the brain may, therefore, be considered as functional end- or terminal arteries, though anatomically they are not strictly what Cohnheim designated as terminal arteries.

THE ARTERIES OF THE UPPER EXTREMITY.

The artery which supplies the upper extremity continues as a single trunk from its commencement down to the elbow; but different portions of it have received different names, according to the regions through which they pass. That part of the vessel which extends from its origin to the outer border of the first rib is termed the **subclavian**; beyond this point to the lower border of the axilla it is named the **axillary**; and from the lower margin of the axillary space to the bend of the elbow it is termed **brachial**; here the trunk ends by dividing into two branches the **radial** and **ulnar**.

THE SUBCLAVIAN ARTERY (A. SUBCLAVIA) (Fig. 561).

On the right side the **subclavian artery** *arises* from the innominate artery behind the right sternoclavicular articulation; on the left side it springs from the arch of the aorta. The two vessels, therefore, in the first part of their course, differ in length, direction, and relation with neighboring structures.

In order to facilitate the description, each subclavian artery is divided into three parts. The first portion extends from the origin of the vessel to the medial border of the Scalenus anterior; the second lies behind this muscle; and the third extends from the lateral margin of the muscle to the outer border of the first rib, where it becomes the axillary artery. The first portions of the two vessels require separate descriptions; the second and third parts of the two arteries are practically alike.

First Part of the Right Subclavian Artery (Figs. 550, 554).—The first part of the right subclavian artery *arises* from the innominate artery, behind the upper part of the right sternoclavicular articulation, and passes upward and lateralward to the medial margin of the Scalenus anterior. It ascends a little above the clavicle, the extent to which it does so varying in different cases.

Relations.—It is covered, *in front*, by the integument, superficial fascia, Platysma, deep fascia, the clavicular origin of the Sternocleidomastoideus, the Sternohyoideus, and Sternothyreoideus, and another layer of the deep fascia. It is crossed by the internal jugular and vertebral veins, by the vagus nerve and the cardiac branches of the vagus and sympathetic, and by the subclavian loop of the sympathetic trunk which forms a ring around the vessel. The anterior jugular vein is directed lateralward in front of the artery, but is separated from it by the Sternohyoideus and Sternothyreoideus. *Below and behind* the artery is the pleura, which separates it from the apex of the lung; *behind* is the sympathetic trunk, the Longus colli and the first thoracic vertebra. The right recurrent nerve winds around the lower and back part of the vessel.

First Part of the Left Subclavian Artery (Fig. 561).—The first part of the left subclavian artery *arises* from the arch of the aorta, behind the left common carotid, and at the level of the fourth thoracic vertebra; it ascends in the superior mediastinal cavity to the root of the neck and then arches lateralward to the medial border of the Scalenus anterior.

Relations.—It is in relation, *in front*, with the vagus, cardiac, and phrenic nerves, which lie parallel with it, the left common carotid artery, left internal jugular and vertebral veins, and the commencement of the left innominate vein, and is covered by the Sternothyreoideus, Sternohyoideus, and Sternocleidomastoideus; *behind*, it is in relation with the esophagus, thoracic duct, left recurrent nerve, inferior cervical ganglion of the sympathetic trunk, and Longus colli; higher up, however, the esophagus and thoracic duct lie to its right side; the latter ultimately arching over the vessel to join the angle of union between the subclavian and internal jugular veins. *Medial* to it are the esophagus, trachea, thoracic duct, and left recurrent nerve; *lateral* to it, the left pleura and lung.

Second and Third Parts of the Subclavian Artery (Fig. 561).—The second portion of the subclavian artery lies behind the Scalenus anterior; it is very short and forms the highest part of the arch described by the vessel.

Relations.—It is covered. *in front*, by the skin, superficial fascia, Platysma, deep cervical fascia, Sternocleidomastoideus, and Scalenus anterior. On the right side of the neck the phrenic nerve is separated from the second part of the artery by the Scalenus anterior, while on the left side it crosses the first part of the artery close to the medial edge of the muscle. *Behind* the vessel are the pleura and the Scalenus medius; *above*, the brachial plexus of nerves; *below*, the pleura. The subclavian vein lies below and in front of the artery, separated from it by the Scalenus anterior.

The **third portion** of the subclavian artery runs downward and lateralward from the lateral margin of the Scalenus anterior to the outer border of the first rib, where it becomes the axillary artery. This is the most superficial portion of the vessel, and is contained in the subclavian triangle.

Relations.—It is covered, *in front*, by the skin, the superficial fascia, the Platysma, the supraclavicular nerves, and the deep cervical fascia. The external jugular vein crosses its medial part and receives the transverse scapular, transverse cervical, and anterior jugular veins, which frequently form a plexus in front of the artery. Behind the veins, the nerve to the Subclavius descends in front of the artery. The terminal part of the artery lies behind the clavicle and the Subclavius and is crossed by the transverse scapular vessels. The subclavian vein is in front of and at a slightly lower level than the artery. *Behind*, it lies on the lowest trunk of the brachial plexus, which intervenes between it and the Scalenus medius. *Above* and to its *lateral* side are the upper trunks of the brachial plexus and the Omohyoideus. *Below*, it rests on the upper surface of the first rib.

Variations.—The subclavian arteries vary in their origin, their course, and the height to which they rise in the neck.

The origin of the right subclavian from the innominate takes place, in some cases, above the sternoclavicular articulation, and occasionally, but less frequently, below that joint. The artery may arise as a separate trunk from the arch of the aorta, and in such cases it may be either the first, second, third, or even the last branch derived from that vessel; in the majority, however, it is the first or last, rarely the second or third. When it is the first branch, it occupies the ordinary position of the innominate artery; when the second or third, it gains its usual position by passing behind the right carotid; and when the last branch, it arises from the left extremity of the arch, and passes obliquely toward the right side, usually behind the trachea, esophagus, and right carotid, sometimes between the esophagus and trachea, to the upper border of the first rib, whence it follows its ordinary course. In very rare instances, this vessel arises from the thoracic aorta, as low down as the fourth thoracic vertebra. Occasionally, it perforates the Scalenus anterior; more rarely it passes in front of that muscle. Sometimes the subclavian vein passes with the artery behind the Scalenus anterior. The artery may ascend as high as 4 cm. above the clavicle, or any intermediate point between this and the upper border of the bone, the right subclavian usually ascending higher than the left.

The left subclavian is occasionally joined at its origin with the left carotid.

The left subclavian artery is more deeply placed than the right in the first part of its course, and, as a rule, does not reach quite as high a level in the neck. The posterior border of the Sternocleidomastoideus corresponds pretty closely to the lateral border of the Scalenus anterior, so that the third portion of the artery, the part most accessible for operation, lies immediately lateral to the posterior border of the Sternocleidomastoideus.

Collateral Circulation.—After ligature of the third part of the subclavian artery, the collateral circulation is established mainly by anastomoses between the transverse scapular, the descending ramus of the transverse cervical artery, and the subscapular artery, also by an anastomosis between branches of the internal mammary and lateral thoracic and subscapular arteries.

Branches.—The branches of the subclavian artery are:

Vertebral.	Internal mammary.
Thyrocervical.	Costocervical.
Transverse cervical.	

The first four branches generally arise from the first portion on the left side, but the costocervical trunk springs more frequently from the second portion on the right side. On both sides the first three branches arise close together at the medial border of the Scalenus anterior, leaving, in the majority of cases, a free interval of from 1.25 to 2.5 cm. between the commencement of the artery and the origin of the nearest branch. The transverse cervical is much less constant than the other branches, and when present is the only branch of the third portion of the artery.

1. The **Vertebral Artery** (*a. vertebralis*) (Fig. 554), is the first branch of the subclavian, and *arises* from the upper and back part of the first portion of the vessel. It is surrounded by a plexus of nerve fibers derived from the inferior cervical ganglion of the sympathetic trunk, and ascends through the foramina in the transverse processes of the upper six cervical vertebræ; it then winds behind the superior articular process of the atlas and, entering the skull through the foramen magnum, unites, at the lower border of the pons, with the vessel of the opposite side to form the basilar artery.

Relations.—The vertebral artery may be divided into four parts: The **first part** runs upward and backward between the Longus colli and the Scalenus anterior. In front of it are the internal jugular and vertebral veins, and it is crossed by the inferior thyroid artery; the left vertebral is crossed by the thoracic duct also. Behind it are the transverse process of the seventh cervical vertebra, the sympathetic trunk and its inferior cervical ganglion. The **second part** runs upward through the foramina in the transverse processes of the upper six cervical vertebræ, and is surrounded by branches from the inferior cervical sympathetic ganglion and by a plexus of veins which unite to form the vertebral vein at the lower part of the neck. It is situated in front of the trunks of the cervical nerves, and pursues an almost vertical course as far as the transverse process of the axis, above which it runs upward and lateralward to the foramen in the transverse process of the atlas. The **third part** issues from the latter foramen on the medial side of the Rectus capitis lateralis, and curves backward behind the superior articular process of the atlas, the anterior ramus of the first cervical nerve being on its medial side; it then lies in the groove on the upper surface of the posterior arch of the atlas, and enters the vertebral canal by passing beneath the posterior atlantoöccipital membrane. This part of the artery is covered by the Semispinalis capitis and is contained in the **suboccipital triangle**—a triangular space bounded by the Rectus capitis posterior major, the Obliquus superior, and the Obliquus inferior. The first cervical or suboccipital nerve lies between the artery and the posterior arch of the atlas. The **fourth part** pierces the dura mater and inclines medialward to the front of the medulla oblongata; it is placed between the hypoglossal nerve and the anterior root of the first cervical nerve and beneath the first digitation of the ligamentum denticulatum. At the lower border of the pons it unites with the vessel of the opposite side to form the basilar artery.

Branches.—The branches of the vertebral artery may be divided into two sets: those given off in the neck, and those within the cranium.

Cervical Branches.	*Cranial Branches.*
Spinal.	Meningeal.
Muscular.	Posterior Spinal.
	Anterior Spinal.
	Posterior Inferior Cerebellar.
	Medullary.

Spinal Branches (*rami spinales*) enter the vertebral canal through the intervertebral foramina, and each divides into two branches. Of these, one passes along the roots of the nerves to supply the medulla spinalis and its membranes, anastomosing with the other arteries of the medulla spinalis; the other divides into an ascending and a descending branch, which unite with similar branches from the arteries above and below, so that two lateral anastomotic chains are formed on the posterior surfaces of the bodies of the vertebræ, near the attachment of the pedicles. From these anastomotic chains branches are supplied to the periosteum and the bodies of the vertebræ, and others form communications with similar branches from the opposite side; from these communications small twigs arise which join similar branches above and below, to form a central anastomotic chain on the posterior surface of the bodies of the vertebræ.

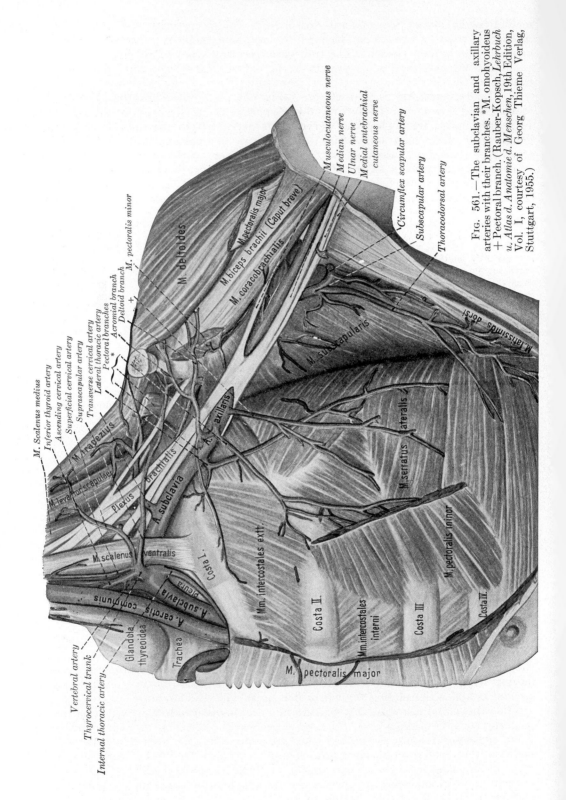

Fig. 561.—The subclavian and axillary arteries with their branches. *M. omohyoideus + Pectoral branch. (Rauber-Kopsch, *Lehrbuch u. Atlas d. Anatomie d. Menschen*, 19th Edition, Vol. I, courtesy of Georg Thieme Verlag, Stuttgart, 1955.)

Labels (clockwise / around figure):

Musculocutaneous nerve
Median nerve
Ulnar nerve
Medial antebrachial cutaneous nerve
Circumflex scapular artery
Subscapular artery
Thoracodorsal artery

M. pectoralis major
M. biceps brachii (Caput breve)
M. coracobrachialis
M. deltoides
M. pectoralis minor
Deltoid branch
Acromial branch
Pectoral branches
Lateral thoracic artery
Transverse cervical artery
Suprascapular artery
Superficial cervical artery
Ascending cervical artery
Inferior thyroid artery
M. Scalenus medius

M. trapezius
M. levator scapulae
Plexus
A. brachialis
A. axillaris
A. subclavia
M. scalenus ventralis
A. subclavia
A. carotis communis
Costa I.
Pleura
Trachea
Glandula thyreoidea
Internal thoracic artery
Thyrocervical trunk
Vertebral artery

M. subscapularis
M. latissimus dorsi
M. serratus lateralis
Mm. intercostales ext!!
Mm. intercostales interni
Costa II.
Costa III.
Costa IV.
M. pectoralis minor
M. pectoralis major

Muscular Branches are given off to the deep muscles of the neck, where the vertebral artery curves around the articular process of the atlas. They anastomose with the occipital, and with the ascending and deep cervical arteries.

The **Meningeal Branch** (*ramus meningeus; posterior meningeal branch*) springs from the vertebral at the level of the foramen magnum, ramifies between the bone and dura mater in the cerebellar fossa, and supplies the falx cerebelli. It is frequently represented by one or two small branches.

The **Posterior Spinal Artery** (*a. spinalis posterior; dorsal spinal artery*) arises from the vertebral, at the side of the medulla oblongata; passing backward, it descends on this structure, lying in front of the posterior roots of the spinal nerves, and is reinforced by a succession of small branches, which enter the vertebral canal through the intervertebral foramina; by means of these it is continued to the lower part of the medulla spinalis, and to the cauda equina. Branches from the posterior spinal arteries from a free anastomosis around the posterior roots of the spinal nerves, and communicate, by means of very tortuous transverse branches, with the vessels of the opposite side. Close to its origin each gives off an ascending branch, which ends at the side of the fourth ventricle.

The **Anterior Spinal Artery** (*a. spinalis anterior; ventral spinal artery*) is a small branch, which *arises* near the termination of the vertebral, and, descending in front of the medulla oblongata, unites with its fellow of the opposite side at the level of the foramen magnum. One of these vessels is usually larger than the other, but occasionally they are about equal in size. The single trunk, thus formed, descends on the front of the medulla spinalis, and is reinforced by a succession of small branches which enter the vertebral canal through the intervertebral foramina; these branches are derived from the vertebral and the ascending cervical of the inferior thyroid in the neck; from the intercostals in the thorax; and from the lumbar, iliolumbar, and lateral sacral arteries in the abdomen and pelvis. They unite, by means of ascending and descending branches, to form a single anterior median artery, which extends as far as the lower part of the medulla spinalis, and is continued as a slender twig on the filum terminale. This vessel is placed in the pia mater along the anterior median fissure; it supplies that membrane, and the substance of the medulla spinalis, and sends off branches at its lower part to be distributed to the cauda equina.

The **Posterior Inferior Cerebellar Artery** (*a. cerebelli inferior posterior*) (Fig. 557), the largest branch of the vertebral, winds backward around the upper part of the medulla oblongata, passing between the origins of the vagus and accessory nerves, over the inferior peduncle to the under surface of the cerebellum, where it divides into two branches. The **medial branch** is continued backward to the notch between the two hemispheres of the cerebellum; while the **lateral** supplies the under surface of the cerebellum, as far as its lateral border, where it anastomoses with the anterior inferior cerebellar and the superior cerebellar branches of the basilar artery. Branches from this artery supply the choroid plexus of the fourth ventricle.

The **Medullary Arteries** (*bulbar arteries*) are several minute vessels which spring from the vertebral and its branches and are distributed to the medulla oblongata.

The **Basilar Artery** (*a. basilaris*) (Fig. 560), so named from its position at the base of the skull, is a single trunk formed by the junction of the two vertebral arteries: it extends from the lower to the upper border of the pons, lying in its median groove, under cover of the arachnoid. It ends by dividing into the two posterior cerebral arteries.

Its **branches,** on either side, are the following:

Pontine. Anterior Inferior Cerebellar.
Internal Auditory. Superior Cerebellar.
Posterior Cerebral.

The **pontine branches** (*rami ad pontem; transverse branches*) are a number of small vessels which come off at right angles from either side of the basilar artery and supply the pons and adjacent parts of the brain.

The **internal auditory artery** (*a. auditiva interna; auditory artery*), a long slender branch, *arises* from near the middle of the artery; it accompanies the acoustic nerve through the internal acoustic meatus, and is distributed to the internal ear. It often (60 per cent, Stopford) arises from the anterior inferior cerebellar artery.

The **anterior inferior cerebellar artery** (*a. cerebelli inferior anterior*) passes backward to be distributed to the anterior part of the under surface of the cerebellum, anastomosing with the posterior inferior cerebellar branch of the vertebral.

The **superior cerebellar artery** (*a. cerebelli superior*) *arises* near the termination of the basilar. It passes lateralward, immediately below the oculomotor nerve, which separates it from the posterior cerebral artery, winds around the cerebral peduncle, close to the trochlear nerve, and, arriving at the upper surface of the cerebellum, divides into branches which ramify in the pia mater and anastomose with those of the inferior cerebellar arteries. Several branches go to the pineal body, the anterior medullary velum, and the tela chorioidea of the third ventricle.

The **posterior cerebral artery** (*a. cerebri posterior*) (Figs. 557, 559, 560) is larger than the preceding, from which it is separated near its origin by the oculomotor nerve. Passing lateralward, parallel to the superior cerebellar artery, and receiving the posterior communicating from the internal carotid, it winds around the cerebral peduncle, and reaches the tentorial surface of the occipital lobe of the cerebrum, where it breaks up into branches for the supply of the temporal and occipital lobes. It may be a branch of the internal carotid, in as many as 7 per cent of cases.

The **branches** of the posterior cerebral artery are as follows:

Posterior-medial Central.	Anterior Temporal.
Posterior Choroidal.	Posterior Temporal.
Postero-lateral Central.	Calcarine.
Parietoöccipital.	

The **postero-medial branches** (Fig. 560) are a group of small arteries which arise at the commencement of the posterior cerebral artery. These, with similar branches from the posterior communicating, pierce the posterior perforated substance, and supply the medial surfaces of the thalami and the walls of the third ventricle. The **posterior choroidal branches** run forward beneath the splenium of the corpus callosum, and supply the tela chorioidea of the third ventricle and the choroid plexus. The **postero-lateral branches** are small arteries which arise from the posterior cerebral artery after it has turned around the cerebral peduncle; they supply the posterior portion of the thalamus. The **anterior temporal branches** are distributed to the uncus and the anterior part of the fusiform gyrus; the **posterior temporal,** to the fusiform and the inferior temporal gyri; the **calcarine,** to the cuneus and gyrus lingualis and the back part of the convex surface of the occipital lobe; and the parietoöccipital, to the cuneus and the precuneus.

2. The **Thyrocervical Trunk** (*truncus thyreocervicalis; thyroid axis*) (Fig. 561) is short and thick; it *arises* from the front of the first portion of the subclavian artery, close to the medial border of the Scalenus anterior, and divides almost immediately into two constant branches, (*a*) the **inferior thyroid** and (*b*) the **suprascapular,** and a third branch which is variable and may be named (*c*) the **transverse cervical** or **superficial cervical** depending on its distribution.

(*a*) The **Inferior Thyroid Artery** (*a. thyreoidea inferior*) passes upward, in front of the vertebral artery and Longus colli; then turns medialward behind the carotid sheath and its contents, and also behind the sympathetic trunk, the middle cervical ganglion resting upon the vessel. Reaching the lower border of the thyroid gland it divides into two branches, which supply the postero-inferior parts of the gland, and anastomose with the superior thyroid, and with the corresponding artery of the opposite side. The recurrent nerve passes upward generally behind, but occasionally in front, of the artery.

The **branches** of the inferior thyroid are:

Inferior Laryngeal.	Esophageal.
Tracheal.	Ascending Cervical.
Muscular.	

The **inferior laryngeal artery** (*a. laryngea inferior*) ascends upon the trachea to the back part of the larynx under cover of the Constrictor pharyngis inferior, in company with the recurrent nerve, and supplies the muscles and mucous membrane of this part, anastomosing with the branch from the opposite side, and with the superior laryngeal branch of the superior thyroid artery.

The **tracheal branches** (*rami tracheales*) are distributed upon the trachea, and anastomose below with the bronchial arteries.

The **esophageal branches** (*rami oesophagei*) supply the esophagus, and anastomose with the esophageal branches of the aorta.

The **ascending cervical artery** (*a. cervicalis ascendens*) is a small branch which *arises* from the inferior thyroid as that vessel passes behind the carotid sheath, it runs up on the anterior tubercles of the transverse processes of the cervical vertebræ in the interval between the Scalenus anterior and Longus capitis. To the muscles of the neck it gives twigs which anastomose with branches of the vertebral, sending one or two spinal branches into the vertebral canal through the intervertebral foramina to be distributed to the medulla spinalis and its membranes, and to the bodies of the vertebræ, in the same manner as the spinal branches from the vertebral. It anastomoses with the ascending pharyngeal and occipital arteries.

The **muscular branches** supply the depressors of the hyoid bone, and the Longus colli, Scalenus anterior, and Constrictor pharyngis inferior.

(*b*) The **Suprascapular Artery** (*a. suprascapularis; transverse scapular artery*) passes at first downward and lateralward across the Scalenus anterior and phrenic nerve, being covered by the Sternocleidomastoideus; it then crosses the subclavian artery and the brachial plexus, and runs behind and parallel with the clavicle and Subclavius, and beneath the inferior belly of the Omohyoideus, to the superior border of the scapula; it passes over the superior transverse ligament of the scapula which separates it from the suprascapular nerve, and enters the supraspinous fossa (Fig. 562). In this situation it lies close to the bone, and ramifies between it and the Supraspinatus, to which it supplies branches. It then descends behind the neck of the scapula, through the great scapular notch and under cover of the inferior transverse ligament, to reach the infraspinous fossa, where it anastomoses with the scapular circumflex and the descending scapular arteries. Besides distributing branches to the Sternocleidomastoideus, Subclavius, and neighboring muscles, it gives off a **suprasternal branch**, which crosses over the sternal end of the clavicle to the skin of the upper part of the chest; and an **acromial branch**, which pierces the Trapezius and supplies the skin over the acromion, anastomosing with the thoracoacromial artery. As the artery passes over the superior transverse ligament of the scapula, it sends a branch into the subscapular fossa, where it ramifies beneath the Subscapularis, and anastomoses with the subscapular artery and descending scapular arteries. It also sends articular branches to the acromioclavicular and shoulder-joints, and a nutrient artery to the clavicle.

(*c*) The **Transverse Cervical Artery** (*a. transversa colli*) (Fig. 562) may be complete from its thyrocervical origin, but with about equal frequency one of its main branches arises independently from the third part of the subclavian artery. When it is incomplete it is named the superficial cervical and is described separately below under that name. The transverse cervical artery passes laterally across the posterior cervical triangle in a position somewhat cephalic and dorsal to the suprascapular artery. Medially it crosses superficial to the Scalenus anterior and phrenic nerve and lies deep to the Sternocleidomastoideus. Laterally it crosses the trunks of the brachial plexus covered only by the Platysma, investing layer of deep fascia, and the inferior belly of the Omohyoideus. At the anterior margin of the Trapezius it divides into an ascending branch, named the superficial branch (ramus superficialis) and a descending branch, named the deep branch (ramus profundus).

The **superficial branch** (*ramus superficialis; ascending branch*) (Fig. 562) lies against the under surface of the Trapezius and is the principal blood supply of that muscle. One branch ascends along the anterior border of the Trapezius, distributing branches to it and to neighboring muscles and anastomosing with the superficial part of the descending branch of the occipital artery. A descending branch accompanies the accessory nerve on the deep surface of the Trapezius, supplying the muscle.

The **deep branch** (*ramus profundus; descending branch*) (Fig. 562) gives branches to the Levator scapulæ and neighboring deep cervical muscles. Passing deep to the Levator it reaches the superior angle of the scapula and passes down along the medial border to the inferior angle, lying deep to the Rhomboidei and accompanying the dorsoscapular nerve. It supplies muscular branches to the Rhomboidei, Serratus posterior superior, Subscapularis, Supra and Infraspinatus, and other neighboring muscles. These branches anastomose with the suprascapular, subscapular and circumflex scapular arteries.

The **Superficial Cervical Artery** (*PNA-Var. a. cervicalis superficialis*) corresponds to the transverse cervical, superficial branch, arising from the thyrocervical trunk without sharing its origin with the deep branch. It passes laterally across the posterior triangle of the neck, at first deep to the Sternocleidomastoideus and superficial to the Scalenus anterior and phrenic nerve, then upward across the trunks of the brachial plexus to the anterior border of the Trapezius. Here it divides into an ascending branch and a descending branch. The ascending branch supplies the upper part of the Trapezius and neighboring muscles and anastomoses with the superficial descending branch of the occipital artery. The descending branch lies against the deep surface of the trapezius, supplying it with branches and accompanying the accessory nerve.

The **Descending Scapular Artery** (*PNA-Var. a. scapularis descendens*; *transverse cervical artery*; *dorsal scapular artery*) (Fig. 562) corresponds to the deep branch of the transverse cervical except that it has an independent origin from the subclavian artery instead of from the thyrocervical trunk. The two origins occur with about equal frequency. The descending scapular has its origin from the third (or sometimes the second) part of the subclavian artery. It passes upward for a short distance, then loops around the brachial plexus, frequently passing between the anterior and posterior divisions of the upper trunk. It courses downward toward the scapula and at the border of the Levator scapulæ divides into an ascending and a descending branch. The ascending branch (*ramus ascendens*) supplies the Levator scapulæ and neighboring deep cervical muscles. The descending branch (*posterior scapular artery*; *ramus descendens*) (Fig. 562) usually double, passes beneath the Levator scapulæ to the superior angle of the scapula, and then descends anterior to the Rhomboidei along the vertebral border of the bone as far as the inferior angle. The medial division is accompanied by the dorsal scapular nerve. The lateral division lies on the costal surface of the Serratus anterior muscle and is usually larger than the medial division. The descending branch supplies the

Rhomboidei, Latissimus dorsi and Trapezius, and anastomoses with the supra-scapular and subscapular arteries, and with the posterior branches of some of the intercostal arteries (Huelke '58).

3. The **Internal Thoracic Artery** (*a. thoracica interna; internal mammary artery*) (Fig. 563) *arises* from the under surface of the first portion of the subclavian

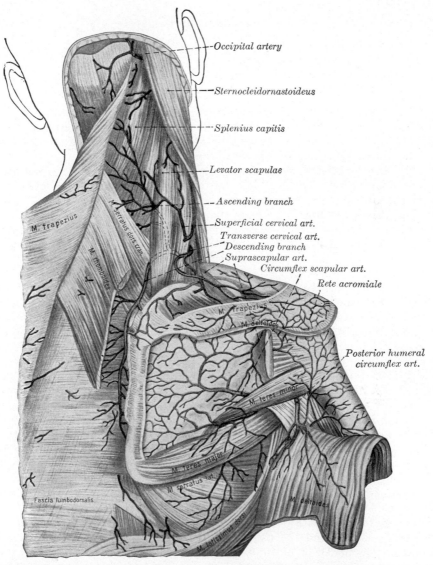

Fig. 562.—The arteries of the dorsal aspect of the shoulder and neck. (After Tiedmann, from Rauber-Kopsch, *Lehrbuch u. Atlas d. Anatomie d. Menschen,* 19th Edition, Vol. I, courtesy of Georg Thieme Verlag, Stuttgart, 1955.)

opposite the thryocervical trunk. It descends behind the cartilages of the upper six ribs at a distance of about 1.25 cm. from the margin of the sternum, and at the level of the sixth intercostal space divides into the **musculophrenic** and **superior epigastric** arteries.

Relations.—It is directed at first downward, forward, and medialward behind the sternal end of the clavicle, the subclavian and internal jugular veins, and the first costal cartilage, and passes forward close to the lateral side of the innominate vein. As it enters the thorax the phrenic nerve crosses from its lateral to its medial side. Below the first costal cartilage it descends almost vertically to its point of bifurcation. It is covered in front by the cartilages of the upper six ribs and the intervening Intercostales interni and anterior intercostal membranes, and is crossed by the terminal portions of the upper six intercostal nerves. It rests on the pleura, as far as the third costal cartilage; below this level, upon the Transversus thoracis. It is accompanied by a pair of veins; these unite above to form a single vessel, which runs medial to the artery and ends in the corresponding innominate vein.

Branches.—The branches of the internal thoracic are:

a. Pericardiacophrenic.	*e.* Intercostal.
b. Anterior Mediastinal.	*f.* Perforating.
c. Pericardial.	*g.* Musculophrenic.
d. Sternal.	*h.* Superior Epigastric.

a) The **Pericardiacophrenic Artery** (*a. pericardiacophrenica; a. comes nervi phrenici*) is a long slender branch, which accompanies the phrenic nerve, between the pleura and pericardium, to the diaphragm, to which it is distributed; it anastomoses with the musculophrenic and inferior phrenic arteries.

b) The **Anterior Mediastinal Arteries** (*aa. mediastinales anteriores; mediastinal arteries*) are small vessels, distributed to the areolar tissue and lymph glands in the anterior mediastinal cavity, and to the remains of the thymus.

c) The **Pericardial Branches** supply the upper part of the anterior surface of the pericardium; the lower part receives branches from the musculophrenic artery.

d) The **Sternal Branches** (*rami sternales*) are distributed to the Transversus thoracis, and to the posterior surface of the sternum.

The anterior mediastinal, pericardial, and sternal branches, together with some twigs from the pericardiacophrenic, anastomose with branches from the intercostal and bronchial arteries, and form a **subpleural mediastinal plexus.**

e) The **Intercostal Branches** (*rami intercostales; anterior intercostal arteries*) supply the upper five or six intercostal spaces. Two in number in each space, these small vessels pass lateralward, one lying near the lower margin of the rib above, and the other near the upper margin of the rib below, and anastomose with the intercostal arteries from the aorta. They are at first situated between the pleura and the Intercostales interni, and then between the Intercostales interni and externi. They supply the Intercostales and, by branches which perforate the Intercostales externi, the Pectorales and the mamma.

f) The **Perforating Branches** (*rami perforantes*) pierce the chest wall in the first five or six intercostal spaces. They pass forward through the internal intercostal muscles and the Pectoralis major, and curving lateralward, supply the Pectoralis major and the integument. Those which correspond to the second, third, and fourth spaces give branches to the mamma in the female, and during lactation are of large size.

g) The **Musculophrenic Artery** (*a. musculophrenica*) is directed obliquely downward and lateralward, behind the cartilages of the false ribs; it perforates the diaphragm at the eighth or ninth costal cartilage, and ends, considerably reduced in size, opposite the last intercostal space. It gives off intercostal branches to the seventh, eighth, and ninth intercostal spaces; these diminish in size as the spaces decrease in length, and are distributed in a manner precisely similar to the intercostals from the internal mammary. The musculophrenic also gives branches to the lower part of the pericardium, and others which run backward to the diaphragm, and downward to the abdominal muscles.

h) The **Superior Epigastric Artery** (*a. epigastrica superior*) continues in the original direction of the internal mammary; it descends through the interval between the costal and sternal attachments of the diaphragm, and enters the sheath of the

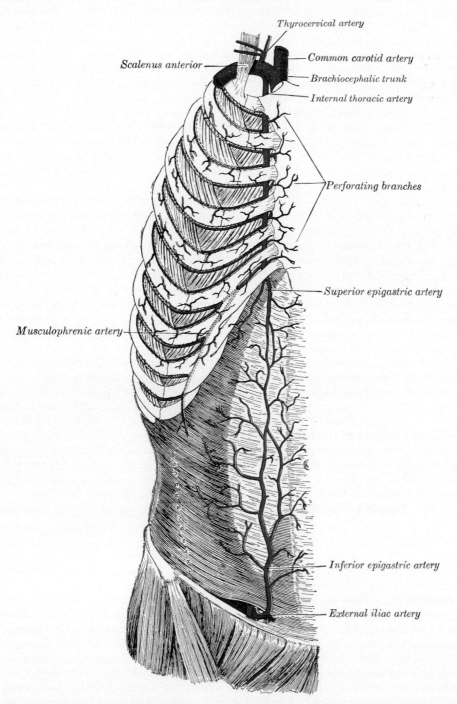

Thyrocervical artery

Common carotid artery

Scalenus anterior

Brachiocephalic trunk

Internal thoracic artery

Perforating branches

Superior epigastric artery

Musculophrenic artery

Inferior epigastric artery

External iliac artery

Fig. 563.—The internal thoracic artery and its branches. The intercostal branches lie at first between the pleura and the internal intercostal muscles, then between the internal and external intercostal muscles. (The figure does not indicate these relationships.)

Rectus abdominis, at first lying behind the muscle, and then perforating and supplying it, and anastomosing with the inferior epigastric artery from the external iliac. Branches perforate the anterior wall of the sheath of the Rectus, and supply the other muscles of the abdomen and the integument, and a small branch passes in front of the xiphoid process and anastomoses with the artery of the opposite side. It also gives some twigs to the diaphragm, while from the artery of the right side small branches extend into the falciform ligament of the liver and anastomose with the hepatic artery.

4. The **Costocervical Trunk** (*truncus costocervicalis; superior intercostal artery*), absent in 10 per cent. of cadavers (Fig. 554), *arises* from the upper and back part of the subclavian artery, behind the Scalenus anterior on the right side, and medial to that muscle on the left side. Passing backward, it gives off the **profunda cervicalis**, and, continuing as the **highest intercostal artery**, descends behind the pleura in front of the necks of the first and second ribs, and anastomoses with the first aortic intercostal. As it crosses the neck of the first rib it lies medial to the anterior division of the first thoracic nerve, and lateral to the first thoracic ganglion of the sympathetic trunk.

In the first intercostal space, it gives off a branch which is distributed in a manner similar to the distribution of the aortic intercostals. The branch for the second intercostal space usually joins with one from the highest aortic intercostal artery. This branch is not constant, but is more commonly found on the right side; when absent, its place is supplied by an intercostal branch from the aorta. Each intercostal gives off a posterior branch which goes to the posterior vertebral muscles, and sends a small spinal branch through the corresponding intervertebral foramen to the medulla spinalis and its membranes.

The **Profunda Cervicalis** (*a. cervicalis profunda; deep cervical branch*) *arises*, in most cases, from the costocervical trunk, and is analogous to the posterior branch of an aortic intercostal artery: occasionally it is a separate branch from the subclavian artery. Passing backward, above the eighth cervical nerve and between the transverse process of the seventh cervical vertebra and the neck of the first rib, it runs up the back of the neck, between the Semispinales capitis and colli, as high as the axis vertebra, supplying these and adjacent muscles, and anastomosing with the deep division of the descending branch of the occipital, and with branches of the vertebral. It gives off a spinal twig which enters the canal through the intervertebral foramen between the seventh cervical and first thoracic vertebræ.

5. The **Transverse Cervical Artery** (see Descending Scapular Artery, page 648).

THE AXILLA.

The axilla occupies a pyramidal space between the upper lateral part of the chest and the medial side of the arm (see p. 489).

Boundaries.—The *apex*, which is directed upward toward the root of the neck, corresponds to the interval between the outer border of the first rib, the superior border of the scapula, and the posterior surface of the clavicle, and through it the axillary vessels and nerves pass. The *base*, directed downward, is broad at the chest but narrow and pointed at the arm; it is formed by the integument and a thick layer of fascia, the **axillary fascia**, extending between the lower border of the Pectoralis major in front, and the lower border of the Latissimus dorsi behind. The *anterior wall* is formed by the Pectorales major and minor, the former covering the whole of this wall, the latter only its central part. The space between the upper border of the Pectoralis minor and the clavicle is occupied by the coracoclavicular fascia. The *posterior wall*, which extends somewhat lower than the anterior, is formed by the Subscapularis above, the Teres major and Latissimus dorsi below.

On the *medial side* are the first four ribs with their corresponding Intercostales, and part of the Serratus anterior. On the *lateral side*, where the anterior and posterior walls converge, the space is narrow, and bounded by the humerus, the Coracobrachialis, and the Biceps brachii.

Contents.—It contains the axillary vessels, and the brachial plexus of nerves, with their branches, some branches of the intercostal nerves, and a large number of lymph glands, together with a quantity of fat and loose areolar tissue. The axillary artery and vein, with the brachial plexus of nerves, extend obliquely along the lateral boundary of the axilla, from its apex to its base, and are placed much nearer to the anterior than to the posterior wall, the vein lying to the thoracic side of the artery and partially concealing it. At the forepart of the axilla, in contact with the Pectorales, are the thoracic branches of the axillary artery, and along the lower margin of the Pectoralis minor the lateral thoracic artery extends to the side of the chest. At the back, in contact with the lower margin of the Subscapularis, are the subscapular vessels and nerves; winding around the lateral border of this muscle are the scapular circumflex vessels; and, close to the neck of the humerus, the posterior humeral circumflex vessels and the axillary nerve curve backward to the shoulder. Along the medial or thoracic side no vessel of any importance exists, the upper part of the space being crossed merely by a few small branches from the highest thoracic artery. There are some important nerves, however, in this situation, viz., the long thoracic nerve, descending on the surface of the Serratus anterior, to which it is distributed; and the intercostobrachial nerve, perforating the upper and anterior part of this wall, and passing across the axilla to the medial side of the arm.

The position and arrangement of the lymph nodes are described in the section on Lymphatics.

The Axillary Artery (A. Axillaris) (Fig. 561).

The **axillary artery,** the continuation of the subclavian, commences at the outer border of the first rib, and ends at the lower border of the tendon of the Teres major, where it takes the name of brachial. Its direction varies with the position of the limb; thus the vessel is nearly straight when the arm is directed at right angles with the trunk, concave upward when the arm is elevated above this, and convex upward and lateralward when the arm lies by the side. At its origin the artery is very deeply situated, but near its termination is superficial, being covered only by the skin and fascia. To facilitate the description of the vessel it is divided into three portions; the first part lies proximal, the second deep, and the third distal to the Pectoralis minor. Its branches are subject to great variation.

Relations.—The **first portion** of the axillary artery is covered *anteriorly* by the clavicular portion of the Pectoralis major and the coracoclavicular fascia, and is crossed by the lateral anterior thoracic nerve, and the thoracoacromial and cephalic veins; *posterior* to it are the first intercostal space, the corresponding Intercostalis externus, the first and second digitations of the Serratus anterior, and the long thoracic and medial anterior thoracic nerves, and the medial cord of the brachial plexus; on its *lateral side* is the brachial plexus, from which it is separated by a little areolar tissue; on its *medial*, or thoracic side, is the axillary vein which overlaps the artery. It is enclosed, together with the axillary vein and the brachial plexus, in a fibrous sheath —the **axillary sheath**—continuous above with the deep cervical fascia.

The **second portion** of the axillary artery is covered, *anteriorly*, by the Pectorales major and minor; posterior to it are the posterior cord of the brachial plexus, and some areolar tissue which intervenes between it and the Subscapularis; on the *medial side* is the axillary vein, separated from the artery by the medial cord of the brachial plexus and the medial anterior thoracic nerve; on the *lateral side* is the lateral cord of the brachial plexus. The brachial plexus thus surrounds the artery on three sides, and separates it from direct contact with the vein and adjacent muscles.

The **third portion** of the axillary artery extends from the lower border of the Pectoralis minor to the lower border of the tendon of the Teres major. *In front*, it is covered by the lower part of the Pectoralis major above, but only by the integument and fascia below; *behind*, it is in relation with the lower part of the Subscapularis, and the tendons of the Latissimus dorsi and Teres major; on its *lateral side* is the Coracobrachialis, and on its *medial* or thoracic side, the axillary vein. The nerves of the brachial plexus bear the following relations to this part of the artery: on the *lateral side* are the lateral head and the trunk of the median, and the musculocutaneous for a short distance; on the *medial side* the ulnar (between the vein and artery) and medial brachial cutaneous (to the medial side of the vein); *in front* are the medial head of the median and the medial antebrachial cutaneous, and *behind*, the radial and axillary, the latter only as far as the lower border of the Subscapularis.

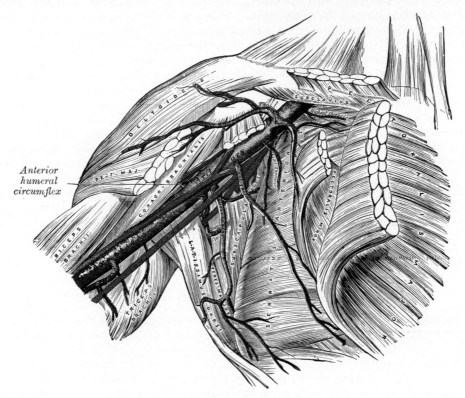

FIG. 564.—The axillary artery and its branches.

Collateral Circulation after Ligature of the Axillary Artery.—If the artery be tied above the origin of the thoracoacromial, the collateral circulation will be carried on by the same branches as after the ligature of the third part of the subclavian; if at a lower point, between the thoracoacromial and the subscapular, the latter vessel, by its free anastomosis with the transverse scapular and transverse cervical branches of the subclavian, will become the chief agent in carrying on the circulation; the lateral thoracic, if it be below the ligature, will materially contribute by its anastomoses with the intercostal and internal mammary arteries. If the point included in the ligature is below the origin of the subscapular artery, it will probably also be below the origins of the two humeral circumflex arteries. The chief agents in restoring the circulation will then be the subscapular and the two humeral circumflex arteries anastomosing with the a. profunda brachii.

Branches.—The branches of the axillary are:

From first part, Highest Thoracic.   *From second part* {Thoracoacromial.
                                                            {Lateral Thoracic.

                    From third part {Subscapular.
                                      {Posterior Humeral Circumflex.
                                      {Anterior Humeral Circumflex.

1. The **Highest Thoracic Artery** (*a. thoracalis suprema; superior thoracic artery*) is a small vessel, which may *arise* from the thoracoacromial or may be absent. Running forward and medialward along the upper border of the Pectoralis minor, it passes between it and the Pectoralis major to the side of the chest. It supplies branches to these muscles, and to the parietes of the thorax, and anastomoses with the internal mammary and intercostal arteries.

2. The **Thoracoacromial Artery** (*a. thoracoacromialis; acromiothoracic artery; thoracic axis*) is a short trunk, which *arises* from the forepart of the axillary artery, its origin being generally overlapped by the upper edge of the Pectoralis minor. Projecting forward to the upper border of this muscle, it pierces the coracoclavicular fascia and divides into four branches—pectoral, acromial, clavicular, and deltoid. The **pectoral branch** descends between the two Pectorales, and is distributed to them and to the mamma, anastomosing with the intercostal branches of the internal mammary and with the lateral thoracic. The **acromial branch** runs lateralward over the coracoid process and under the Deltoideus, to which it gives branches; it then pierces that muscle and ends on the acromion in an arterial network formed by branches from the transverse scapular, thoracoacromial, and posterior humeral circumflex arteries. The **clavicular branch** runs upward and medialward to the sternoclavicular joint, supplying this articulation, and the Subclavius. The **deltoid** (*humeral*) **branch**, often arising with the acromial, crosses over the Pectoralis minor and passes in the same groove as the cephalic vein, between the Pectoralis major and Deltoideus, and gives branches to both muscles.

3. The **Lateral Thoracic Artery** (*a. thoracalis lateralis; long thoracic artery; external mammary artery*) follows the lower border of the Pectoralis minor to the side of the chest, supplying the Serratus anterior and the Pectoralis, and sending branches across the axilla to the axillary glands and Subscapularis; it anastomoses with the internal mammary, subscapular, and intercostal arteries, and with the pectoral branch of the thoracoacromial. In the female it supplies an **external mammary branch** which turns around the free edge of the Pectoralis major and supplies the mamma. The lateral thoracic artery is often (60 per cent.) a branch either of the thoracoacromial artery or of the subscapular artery. It comes directly from the axillary only in about 30 per cent. of cases.

4. The **Subscapular Artery** (*a. subscapularis*) (Fig. 562), the largest branch of the axillary artery, arises at the distal border of the Subscapularis and after a short course, about 4 cm., divides into (*a*) the circumflex scapular and (*b*) thoracodorsal arteries (Fig. 561).

(*a*) The **Scapular Circumflex Artery** (*a. circumflexa scapulae*) (Fig. 565) is generally larger than the thoracodorsal artery. It curves around the lateral border of the scapula, traversing the triangular space between the Teres major, the Subscapularis, and the long head of the Triceps (Fig. 565). It enters the infraspinous fossa between the Teres minor and the scapula, remaining close to the bone. It supplies branches to the Infraspinatus and anastomoses with the suprascapular and descending scapular arteries. In the triangular space it gives a branch to the Subscapularis and a considerable branch continues along the lateral border of the scapula between the Teres major and minor, supplying these muscles and anastomosing with the descending scapular at the inferior angle of the scapula. It also supplies branches to the long head of the Triceps and the Deltoideus.

(*b*) The **Thoracodorsal Artery** (*a. thoracodorsalis*) (Fig. 561) is the continuation of the subscapular artery through the posterior portion of the axilla along the anterior border of the Latissimus dorsi in company with the thoracodorsal nerve. It gives branches to the Subscapularis, is the principal supply of the Latissimus, and anastomoses with the circumflex scapular and descending scapular arteries. One or two sizable branches cross the axilla to supply the Serratus anterior and intercostal muscles, anastomosing with intercostal, lateral thoracic, and thoraco-acromial branches. When the lateral thoracic artery is small or lacking this branch may take its place.

5. The **Posterior Humeral Circumflex Artery** (*a. circumflexa humeri posterior; posterior circumflex artery*) (Fig. 565) *arises* from the axillary artery at the lower border of the Subscapularis, and runs backward with the axillary nerve through the quadrangular space bounded by the Subscapularis and Teres minor above, the Teres major below, the long head of the Triceps brachii medially, and the surgical neck of the humerus laterally. It winds around the neck of the humerus and is distributed to the Deltoideus and shoulder-joint, anastomosing with the anterior humeral circumflex and profunda brachii.

6. The **Anterior Humeral Circumflex Artery** (*a. circumflexa humeri anterior; anterior circumflex artery*) (Fig. 564), considerably smaller than the posterior, *arises* nearly opposite it, from the lateral side of the axillary artery. It runs horizontally, beneath the Coracobrachialis and short head of the Biceps brachii, in front of the neck of the humerus. On reaching the intertubercular sulcus, it gives off a branch which ascends in the sulcus to supply the head of the humerus and the shoulder-joint. The trunk of the vessel is then continued onward beneath the long head of the Biceps brachii and the Deltoideus, and anastomoses with the posterior humeral circumflex artery. The anterior humeral circumflex artery often arises in common with the posterior humeral circumflex, or may be represented by three or four very small branches.

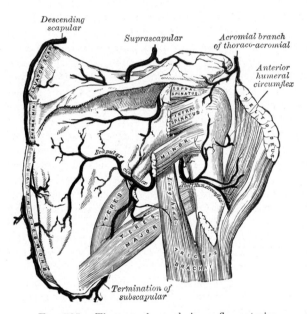

FIG. 565.—The scapular and circumflex arteries.

The Brachial Artery (A. Brachialis) (Fig. 566).

The **brachial artery** commences at the lower margin of the tendon of the Teres major, and, passing down the arm, ends about 1 cm. below the bend of the elbow, where it divides into the **radial** and **ulnar arteries**. At first the brachial artery lies medial to the humerus; but as it runs down the arm it gradually gets in front of the bone, and at the bend of the elbow it lies midway between its two epicondyles.

Relations.—The artery is superficial throughout its entire extent, being covered, *in front*, by the integument and the superficial and deep fasciæ; the lacertus fibrosus (*bicipital fascia*) lies in front of it opposite the elbow and separates it from the vena mediana cubiti; the median nerve crosses from its lateral to its medial side opposite the insertion of the Coracobrachialis. *Behind*, it is separated from the long head of the Triceps brachii by the radial nerve and a. profunda brachii. It then lies upon the medial head of the Triceps brachii, next upon the insertion of the Coracobrachialis, and lastly on the Brachialis. *Laterally*, it is in relation above with the median nerve and the Coracobrachialis, below with the Biceps brachii, the two muscles overlapping the artery to a considerable extent. *Medially*, its upper half is in relation with the medial antebrachial cutaneous and ulnar nerves, its lower half with the median nerve. The basilic vein lies on its medial side, but is separated from it in the lower part of the arm by the deep fascia. The artery is accompanied by two venæ comitantes, which lie in close contact with it, and are connected together at intervals by short transverse branches.

The **Antecubital Fossa.**—At the bend of the elbow the brachial artery sinks deeply into a triangular interval, the **antecubital fossa**. The base of the triangle is directed upward, and is represented by a line connecting the two epicondyles of the humerus; the sides are formed by the medial edge of the Brachioradialis and the lateral margin of the Pronator teres; the floor is formed by the Brachialis and Supinator. This space contains the brachial artery, with its accompanying veins; the radial and ulnar arteries; the median nerve; and the tendon of the Biceps brachii. The brachial artery occupies the middle of the space, and divides opposite the neck of the radius into the radial and ulnar arteries; it is covered, *in front*, by the integument, the superficial fascia, and the vena mediana cubiti, the last being separated from the artery by the lacertus fibrosus. *Behind* it is the Brachialis which separates it from the elbow-joint. The median nerve lies close to the medial side of the artery, above, but is separated from it below by the ulnar head of the Pronator teres. The tendon of the Biceps brachii lies to the lateral side of the artery.

The radial nerve lies normally just outside the fossa between the Supinator and the Brachioradialis, but may be exposed through the fossa by drawing the Brachioradialis laterally.

Variations of the Brachial Artery.—The brachial artery, accompanied by the median nerve may leave the medial border of the Biceps brachii, and descend toward the medial epicondyle of the humerus; in such cases it usually passes behind the *supracondylar process* of the humerus, from which a fibrous arch is thrown over the artery; it then runs beneath or through the substance of the Pronator teres, to the bend of the elbow. This variation bears considerable analogy with the normal condition of the artery in some of the carnivora; it has been referred to in the description of the humerus (p. 189).

A frequent variation is the superficial brachial artery, which may continue into the forearm to form a superficial antebrachial artery. The superficial brachial may rejoin the brachial distally. Frequently the brachial artery divides at a higher level than usual, and the vessels concerned in this high division are three, *viz.*, radial, ulnar, and interosseous. Most frequently the radial is given off high up, the other limb of the bifurcation consisting of the ulnar and interosseous; in some instances the ulnar arises above the ordinary level, and the radial and interosseous form the other limb of the division; occasionally the interosseous arises high up.

Sometimes, long slender vessels, *vasa aberrantia*, connect the brachial or the axillary artery with one of the arteries of the forearm, or branches from them. These vessels usually join the radial.

Collateral Circulation.—After the application of a ligature to the brachial artery in the upper third of the arm, the circulation is carried on by branches from the humeral circumflex and subscapular arteries anastomosing with ascending branches from the profunda brachii. If the artery be tied *below* the origin of the profunda brachii and superior ulnar collateral, the circulation is maintained by the branches of these two arteries anastomosing with the inferior ulnar collateral, the radial and ulnar recurrents, and the dorsal interosseous.

Branches.—The branches of the brachial artery are:

Profunda Brachii.	Superior Ulnar Collateral.
Nutrient.	Inferior Ulnar Collateral.
	Muscular.

1. The **deep brachial artery** (*a. profunda brachii; superior profunda artery*), the largest branch, *arises* from the medial and back part of the brachial, just below the lower border of the Teres major. It passes deeply into the arm between the long and lateral heads of the Triceps brachii and then accompanies the radial nerve in the spiral groove between the lateral and medial heads of the Triceps, on the posterior aspect of the humerus, and terminates by dividing into the radial collateral

42

and the middle collateral branches. It gives muscular branches to the Deltoideus and to the other muscles between which it lies. An occasional **nutrient artery** enters the humerus posterior to the deltoid tuberosity. The **ascending branch** (*ramus deltoideus*) runs proximally between the long and lateral heads of the Triceps to anastomose with the posterior humeral circumflex artery. The **radial collateral branch,** frequently described as the terminal portion of the profunda, continues with the radial nerve into the forearm. It lies deep to the lateral head of the Triceps until it reaches the lateral supracondylar ridge where it pierces the lateral intermuscular septum, descends between the Brachioradialis and the Brachialis to the volar aspect of the lateral epicondyle, and ends by anastomosing with the radial recurrent artery. Just before it pierces the intermuscular septum, it gives off a branch which descends to the posterior aspect of the lateral epicondyle and there joins the anastomosis about the olecranon. The **middle collateral** branch enters the substance of the long and medial heads of the Triceps and descends along the posterior aspect of the humerus to the elbow where it anastomoses with the interosseous recurrent and joins the anastomosis about the olecranon.

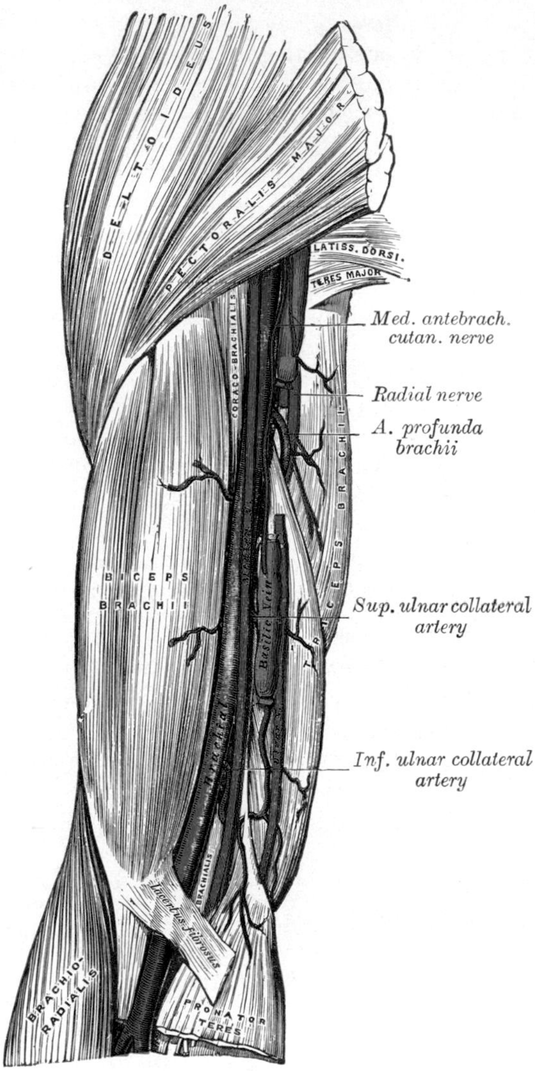

Fig. 566.—The brachial artery.

2. The **Nutrient Artery** (*a. nutricia humeri*) of the body of the humerus arises about the middle of the arm and enters the nutrient canal near the insertion of the Coracobrachialis.

3. The **Superior Ulnar Collateral Artery** (*a. collateralis ulnaris superior; inferior profunda artery*), of small size, *arises* from the brachial a little below the middle of the arm; it frequently springs from the upper part of the a. profunda brachii. It pierces the medial intermuscular septum, and descends on the surface of the medial head of the Triceps brachii to the space between the medial epicondyle and olecranon, accompanied by the ulnar nerve, and ends under the Flexor carpi ulnaris by anastomosing with the posterior ulnar recurrent, and inferior ulnar collateral. It sometimes sends a branch in front of the medial epicondyle, to anastomose with the anterior ulnar recurrent.

4. The **Inferior Ulnar Collateral Artery** (*a. collateralis ulnaris inferior; anastomotica magna artery*) *arises* about 5 cm. above the elbow. It passes medialward upon the Brachialis, and piercing the medial intermuscular septum, winds around the back of the humerus between the Triceps brachii and the bone, forming, by its junction with the profunda brachii, an arch above the olecranon fossa. As the vessel lies on the Brachialis, it gives off branches which ascend to join the superior ulnar collateral: others descend in front of the medial epicondyle, to anastomose with the anterior ulnar recurrent. Behind the medial epicondyle a branch anastomoses with the superior ulnar collateral and posterior ulnar recurrent arteries.

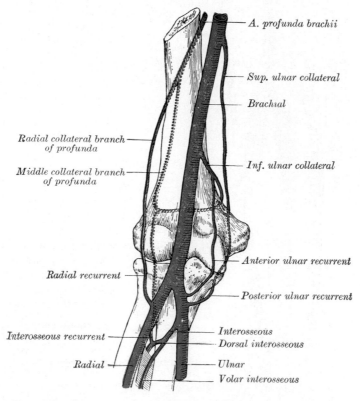

A. profunda brachii

Sup. ulnar collateral

Brachial

Radial collateral branch of profunda

Middle collateral branch of profunda

Inf. ulnar collateral

Radial recurrent

Anterior ulnar recurrent

Posterior ulnar recurrent

Interosseous recurrent

Interosseous

Dorsal interosseous

Radial

Ulnar

Volar interosseous

Fig. 567.—Diagram of the anastomosis around the elbow-joint.

5. The **muscular branches** (*rami musculares*), three or four in number, are distributed to the Coracobrachialis, Biceps brachii, and Brachialis.

The Anastomosis Around the Elbow-joint (Fig. 567).—The vessels engaged in this anastomosis may be conveniently divided into those *in front* of and those *behind* the medial and lateral epicondyles of the humerus. The branches anastomosing *in front* of the medial epicondyle are: the anterior branch of the inferior ulnar collateral, the anterior ulnar recurrent, and the anterior branch of the superior ulnar collateral. Those *behind* the medial epicondyle are: the inferior ulnar collateral, the posterior ulnar recurrent, and the posterior branch of the superior ulnar collateral. The branches anastomosing *in front* of the lateral epicondyle are: the radial recurrent and the radial collateral branch of the profunda brachii. Those *behind* the lateral epicondyle (perhaps better described as situated between the lateral epicondyle and the olecranon) are: the inferior ulnar collateral the interosseous recurrent, and the middle collateral branch of the profunda brachii. There is also an arch of anastomosis above the olecranon, formed by the interosseous recurrent joining with the inferior ulnar collateral and posterior ulnar recurrent (Fig. 567).

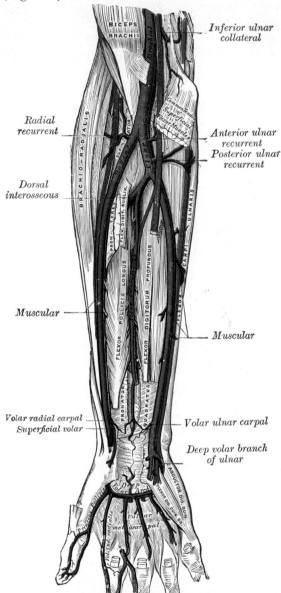

FIG. 568.—Ulnar and radial arteries. Deep view.

The Radial Artery (A. Radialis)
(Fig. 568).

The radial artery appears, from its direction, to be a continuation of the brachial, but it is smaller in caliber than the ulnar. It commences at the bifurcation of the brachial, just below the bend of the elbow, and passes along the radial side of the forearm to the wrist. It then winds backward, around the lateral side of the carpus, beneath the tendons of the Abductor pollicis longus and Extensores pollicis longus and brevis to the upper end of the space between the metacarpal bones of the thumb and index finger. Finally it passes forward between the two heads of the first Interosseous dorsalis, into the palm of the hand, where it crosses the metacarpal bones and at the ulnar side of the hand unites with the deep volar branch of the ulnar artery to form the deep palmar arch.

Relations.—(a) *In the forearm* the artery extends from the neck of the radius to the forepart of the styloid process, being placed to the medial side of the body of the bone above, and in front of it below. Its upper part is overlapped by the fleshy belly of the Brachioradialis; the rest of the artery is superficial, being covered by the integument and the superficial and deep fasciæ. In its course downward, it lies upon the tendon of the Biceps brachii, the Supinator, the Pronator teres, the radial origin of the Flexor digitorum sublimis, the Flexor pollicis longus, the Pronator quadratus, and the lower end of the radius. In the upper third of its course it lies between the Brachioradialis and the Pronator teres; in the lower two-thirds, between the tendons of the Brachioradialis and Flexor carpi radialis. The superficial branch of the radial nerve is close to the lateral side of the artery in the middle third of its course; and some filaments of the lateral antebrachial cutaneous nerve run along the lower part of the artery as it winds around the wrist. The vessel is accompanied by a pair of venæ comitantes throughout its whole course.

(b) *At the wrist* the artery reaches the back of the carpus by passing between the radial collateral ligament of the wrist and the tendons of the Abductor pollicis longus and Extensor pollicis brevis. It then descends on the navicular and greater multangular bones, and before disappearing between the heads of the first Interosseus dorsalis is crossed by the tendon of the Extensor pollicis longus. In the interval between the two Extensores pollicis it is crossed by the digital rami of the superficial branch of the radial nerve which go to the thumb and index finger.

(*c*) *In the hand*, it passes from the upper end of the first interosseous space, between the heads of the first Interosseus dorsalis, transversely across the palm between the Adductor pollicis obliquus and Adductor pollicis transversus, but sometimes piercing the latter muscle, to the base of the metacarpal bone of the little finger, where it anastomoses with the deep palmar branch from the ulnar artery, completing the **deep palmar arch** (Fig. 568).

Variations.—The origin of the radial artery is, in nearly one case in eight, higher than usual. In the forearm it deviates less frequently from its normal position than the ulnar. It has been found lying on the deep fascia instead of beneath it. It has also been observed on the surface of the Brachioradialis, instead of under its medial border; and in turning around the wrist, it has been seen lying on, instead of beneath, the Extensor tendons of the thumb. A large *median* artery may replace the radial in the formation of the palmar arches.

Branches.—The branches of the radial artery may be divided into three groups, corresponding with the three regions in which the vessel is situated.

In the Forearm	*At the Wrist.*	*In the Hand.*
Radial Recurrent.	Dorsal Carpal.	Princeps Pollicis.
Muscular.	First Dorsal Metacarpal.	Palmar Indicis Radialis.
Palmar Carpal		Palmar Metacarpal.
Superficial Palmar		Perforating.
		Recurrent.

The **radial recurrent artery** (*a. recurrens radialis*) *arises* immediately below the elbow. It ascends between the branches of the radial nerve, lying on the Supinator and then between the Brachioradialis and Brachialis, supplying these muscles and the elbow-joint, and anastomosing with the radial collateral branch of the profunda brachii.

The **muscular branches** (*rami musculares*) are distributed to the muscles on the radial side of the forearm.

The **palmar carpal branch** (*ramus carpeus palmaris; anterior radial carpal artery*) is a small vessel which *arises* near the lower border of the Pronator quadratus, and, running across the front of the carpus, anastomoses with the palmar carpal branch of the ulnar artery. This anastomosis is joined by a branch from the palmar interosseous above, and by recurrent branches from the deep palmar arch below, thus forming a **palmar carpal net-work** which supplies the articulations of the wrist.

The **superficial palmar branch** (*ramus palmaris superficialis; superficialis volae artery*) *arises* from the radial artery, where this vessel is about to wind around the lateral side of the wrist. Running forward, it passes through, occasionally over, the muscles of the ball of the thumb, which it supplies, and sometimes anastomoses with the terminal portion of the ulnar artery, completing the **superficial palmar arch.** This vessel varies considerably in size: usually it is very small, and ends in the muscles of the thumb; sometimes it is as large as the continuation of the radial.

The **dorsal carpal branch** (*ramus carpeus dorsalis; posterior radial carpal artery*) is a small vessel which *arises* beneath the Extensor tendons of the thumb; crossing the carpus transversely toward the medial border of the hand, it anastomoses with the dorsal carpal branch of the ulnar and with the palmar and dorsal interosseous arteries to form a **dorsal carpal network.** From this network are given off three slender **dorsal metacarpal arteries,** which run downward on the second, third, and fourth Interossei dorsales and bifurcate into the dorsal digital branches for the supply of the adjacent sides of the middle, ring, and little fingers respectively, communicating with the proper palmar digital branches of the superficial palmar arch. Near their origins they anastomose with the deep palmar arch by the **superior perforating arteries,** and near their points of bifurcation with the common palmar digital vessels of the superficial palmar arch by the **inferior perforating arteries.**

The **first dorsal metacarpal** *arises* just before the radial artery passes between the two heads of the first Interosseous dorsalis and divides almost immediately into two branches which supply the adjacent sides of the thumb and index finger; the radial side of the thumb receives a branch directly from the radial artery.

The **arteria princeps pollicis** *arises* from the radial just as it turns medialward to the deep part of the hand; it descends between the first Interosseous dorsalis and Adductor pollicis obliquus, along the ulnar side of the metacarpal bone of the thumb to the base of the first phalanx, where it lies beneath the tendon of the Flexor pollicis longus and divides into two branches. These make their appearance between the medial and lateral insertions of the Adductor pollicis obliquus, and run along the sides of the thumb, forming on the palmar surface of the last phalanx an arch, from which branches are distributed to the integument and subcutaneous tissue of the thumb (Fig. 568).

The **arteria radialis indicis** *arises* close to the preceding, descends between the first Interosseus dorsalis and Adductor pollicis transversus, and runs along the radial side of the index finger to its extremity, where it anastomoses with the proper digital artery, supplying the ulnar side of the finger. At the lower border of the Adductor pollicis transversus this vessel anastomoses with the princeps pollicis, and gives a communicating branch to the superficial palmar arch. The a. princeps pollicis and a. palmaris indicis radialis may spring from a common trunk termed the **first volar metacarpal artery.**

The **deep palmar arch** (*arcus palmaris profundus*) (Fig. 568) is formed by the anastomosis of the terminal part of the radial artery with the deep palmar branch of the ulnar. It lies upon the carpal extremities on the metacarpal bones and on the Interossei, being covered by the Adductor pollicis obliquus, the Flexor tendons of the fingers, and the Lumbricales. The deep palmar arch lies deep to the ulnar nerve in 63 per cent of cases; superficial, that is to say palmar to the ulnar nerve, in 34 per cent of cases. It is occasionally (2.5 per cent) double and encircles the ulnar nerve.

The **palmar metacarpal arteries** (*aa. metacarpeae palmares; palmar interosseous arteries*), three or four in number, arise from the convexity of the deep palmar arch; they run distally upon the Interossei, and anastomose at the clefts of the fingers with the common digital branches of the superficial palmar arch.

The **perforating branches** (*rami perforantes*), three in number, pass backward from the deep palmar arch, through the second, third, and fourth interosseous spaces and between the heads of the corresponding Interossei dorsales, to anastomose with the dorsal metacarpal arteries.

The **recurrent branches** *arise* from the concavity of the deep palmar arch. They ascend in front of the wrist, supply the intercarpal articulations, and end in the palmar carpal network.

The Ulnar Artery (A. Ulnaris) (Fig. 568).

The **ulnar artery,** the larger of the two terminal branches of the brachial, begins a little below the bend of the elbow, and, passing obliquely downward, reaches the ulnar side of the forearm at a point about midway between the elbow and the wrist. It then runs along the ulnar border to the wrist, crosses the transverse carpal ligament on the radial side of the pisiform bone, and immediately beyond this bone divides into two branches, which enter into the formation of the superficial and deep palmar arches.

Relations.—(*a*) *In the forearm.*—In its *upper half,* it is deeply seated, being covered by the Pronator teres, Flexor carpi radialis, Palmaris longus, and Flexor digitorum sublimis; it lies upon the Brachialis and Flexor digitorum profundus. The median nerve is in relation with the medial side of the artery for about 2.5 cm. and then crosses the vessel, being separated from it by the ulnar head of the Pronator teres. In the *lower half* of the forearm it lies upon the Flexor digitorum profundus, being covered by the integument and the superficial and deep fasciæ, and placed between the Flexor carpi ulnaris and Flexor digitorum sublimis. It is accompanied by two venæ comitantes, and is overlapped in its middle third by the Flexor carpi ulnaris; the ulnar nerve lies on the medial side of the lower two-thirds of the artery, and the palmar cutaneous branch of the nerve descends on the lower part of the vessel to the palm of the hand.

(*b*) *At the wrist* (Fig. 569) the ulnar artery is covered by the integument and the palmar carpal ligament, and lies upon the transverse carpal ligament. On its medial side is the pisiform bone, and, somewhat behind the artery, the ulnar nerve.

Variations.—The ulnar artery varies in its origin in the proportion of about one in thirteen cases; it may arise about 5 to 7 cm. below the elbow, but frequently higher. Variations in the position of this vessel are more common than in the radial. When its origin is normal, the course of the vessel is rarely changed. When it arises high up, it is almost invariably superficial to the Flexor muscles in the forearm, lying commonly beneath the fascia, more rarely between the fascia and integument. In a few cases, its position was subcutaneous in the upper part of the forearm, and subaponeurotic in the lower part.

Branches.—The branches of the ulnar artery may be arranged in the following groups:

In the Forearm {
Anterior Recurrent.
Posterior Recurrent.
Common Interosseous.
Muscular.
}

At the Wrist {
Palmar Carpal.
Dorsal Carpal.
}

In the Hand {
Deep Palmar.
Superficial Palmar Arch.
}

The **anterior ulnar recurrent artery** (*a. recurrens ulnaris anterior*) *arises* immediately below the elbow-joint, runs upward between the Brachialis and Pronator teres, supplies twigs to those muscles, and, in front of the medial epicondyle, anastomoses with the superior and inferior ulnar collateral arteries.

The **posterior ulnar recurrent artery** (*a. recurrens ulnaris posterior*) is much larger, and *arises* somewhat lower than the preceding. It passes backward and medial-ward on the Flexor digitorum profundus, behind the Flexor digitorum sublimis, and ascends behind the medial epicondyle of the humerus. Between this process and the olecranon, it lies beneath the Flexor carpi ulnaris, and ascending between the

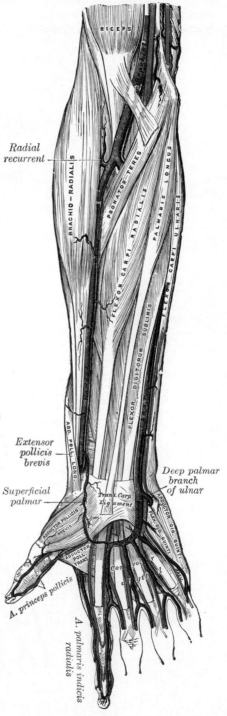

Fig. 569.—The radial and ulnar arteries.

heads of that muscle, in relation with the ulnar nerve, it supplies the neighboring muscles and the elbow-joint, and anastomoses with the superior and inferior ulnar collateral and the interosseous recurrent arteries (Fig. 567).

The **common interosseous artery** (*a. interossea communis*) (Fig. 568), about 1 cm. in length, *arises* immediately below the tuberosity of the radius, and, passing backward to the upper border of the interosseous membrane, divides into two branches, the **volar** and **dorsal interosseous arteries**.

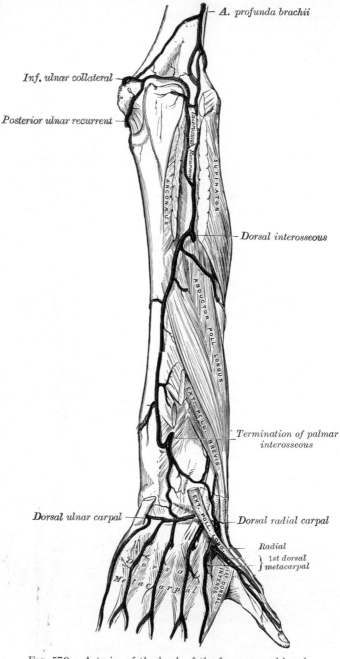

FIG. 570.—Arteries of the back of the forearm and hand.

The **Palmar Interosseous Artery** (*a. interossea palmaris; volar interosseous artery*) (Fig. 568), passes down the forearm on the palmar surface of the interosseous membrane. It is accompanied by the palmar interosseous branch of the median nerve, and overlapped by the contiguous margins of the Flexor digitorum profundus and Flexor pollicis longus, giving off **muscular branches**, and the **nutrient arteries** of the radius and ulna. At the upper border of the Pronator quadratus it pierces the interosseous membrane and reaches the back of the forearm, where it anastomoses with the dorsal interosseous artery (Fig. 570). It then descends, in company with the terminal portion of the dorsal interosseous nerve, to the back of the wrist to join the dorsal carpal net-work. The palmar interosseous artery gives off a slender branch, the **arteria mediana**, which accompanies the median nerve, and gives offsets to its substance; this artery is sometimes much enlarged, and runs with the nerve into the palm of the hand. Before it pierces the interosseous membrane the palmar interosseous sends a branch downward behind the Pronator quadratus to join the palmar carpal network.

The **Dorsal Interosseous Artery** (*a. interossea dorsalis; posterior interosseous artery*) (Fig. 570) passes backward either over or between the oblique cord and the upper border of the interosseous membrane. It appears between the contiguous borders of the Supinator and the Abductor pollicis longus, and runs down the back of the forearm between the superficial and deep layers of muscles, to both of which it distributes branches. Upon the Abductor pollicis longus and the Extensor pollicis brevis, it is accompanied by the dorsal interosseous nerve. At the lower part of the forearm it anastomoses with the termination of the volar interosseous artery, and with the dorsal carpal network. It gives off, near its origin, the **interosseous recurrent artery**, which ascends to the interval between the lateral epicondyle and olecranon, on or through the fibers of the Supinator, but beneath the Anconæus, and anastomoses with the middle collateral branch of the profunda brachii, the posterior ulnar recurrent and the inferior ulnar collateral.

The **muscular branches** (*rami musculares*) are distributed to the muscles along the ulnar side of the forearm.

The **palmar carpal branch** (*ramus carpeus palmaris; anterior ulnar carpal artery*) is a small vessel which crosses the front of the carpus beneath the tendons of the Flexor digitorum profundus, and anastomoses with the corresponding branch of the radial artery.

The **dorsal carpal branch** (*ramus carpeus dorsalis; posterior ulnar carpal artery*) *arises* immediately above the pisiform bone, and winds backward beneath the tendon of the Flexor carpi ulnaris; it passes across the dorsal surface of the carpus beneath the Extensor tendons, to anastomose with a corresponding branch of the radial artery. Immediately after its origin, it gives off a small branch, which runs along the ulnar side of the fifth metacarpal bone, and supplies the ulnar side of the dorsal surface of the little finger.

The **deep palmar branch** (*ramus palmaris profundus; profunda branch*) (Fig. 569) passes between the Abductor digiti quinti and Flexor digiti quinti brevis and through the origin of the Opponens digiti quinti; it anastomoses with the radial artery, and completes the deep palmar arch (Fig. 568).

The **superficial palmar arch** (*arcus palmaris superficialis; superficial volar arch*) (Fig. 569) is formed by the ulnar artery, and is usually completed by a branch from the a. palmaris indicis radialis, but sometimes by the superficial palmar, the median, or by a branch from the a. princeps pollicis of the radial artery. The arch curves across the palm, its convexity downward (Fig. 569).

Relations.—The superficial palmar arch is covered by the skin, the Palmaris brevis, and the palmar aponeurosis. It lies upon the transverse carpal ligament, the Flexor digiti quinti brevis and Opponens digiti quinti, the tendons of the Flexor digitorum sublimis, the Lumbricales, and the divisions of the median and ulnar nerves.

Three **Common Palmar Digital Arteries** (*aa. digitales palmares communes*; *palmar digital arteries*) (Fig. 569) *arise* from the convexity of the arch and proceed downward on the second, third, and fourth Lumbricales. Each receives the corresponding volar metacarpal artery and then divides into a pair of **proper palmar digital arteries** (*aa. digitales palmar propriae*; *collateral digital arteries*) which run along the contiguous sides of the index, middle, ring, and little fingers, behind the corresponding digital nerves; they anastomose freely in the subcutaneous tissue of the finger tips and by smaller branches near the interphalangeal joints. Each gives off a couple of dorsal branches which anastomose with the dorsal digital arteries, and supply the soft parts on the back of the second and third phalanges, including the matrix of the finger-nail. The proper palmar digital artery for medial side of the little finger springs from the ulnar artery under cover of the Palmaris brevis.

THE ARTERIES OF THE TRUNK.

THE DESCENDING AORTA.

The **descending aorta** is divided into two portions, the **thoracic** and **abdominal**, in correspondence with the two great cavities of the trunk in which it is situated

The Thoracic Aorta (Aorta Thoracica) (Fig. 571).

The **thoracic aorta** is contained in the posterior mediastinal cavity. It begins at the lower border of the fourth thoracic vertebra where it is continuous with the aortic arch, and ends in front of the lower border of the twelfth at the aortic hiatus in the diaphragm. At its commencement, it is situated on the left of the vertebral column; it approaches the median line as it descends; and, at its termination, lies directly in front of the column. The vessel describes a curve which is concave forward, and as the branches given off from it are small, its diminution in size is inconsiderable.

Relations.—It is in relation, *anteriorly*, from above downward, with the root of the left lung, the pericardium, the esophagus, and the diaphragm; *posteriorly*, with the vertebral column and the hemiazygos veins; on the *right side*, with the azygos vein and thoracic duct; on the *left side*, with the left pleura and lung. The esophagus, with its accompanying plexus of nerves, lies on the right side of the aorta above; but at the lower part of the thorax it is placed in front of the aorta, and, close to the diaphragm, is situated on its left side.

Branches of the Thoracic Aorta.—

Visceral	Pericardial. Bronchial. Esophageal. Mediastinal.	*Parietal*	Intercostal. Subcostal. Superior Phrenic.

The **pericardial branches** (*rami pericardiaci*) consist of a few small vessels which are distributed to the posterior surface of the pericardium.

The **bronchial arteries** (*aa. bronchiales*) vary in number, size, and origin. There is as a rule only one **right bronchial artery**, which *arises* from the first aortic intercostal, or from the upper left bronchial artery. The **left bronchial arteries** are usually two in number, and *arise* from the thoracic aorta. The upper left bronchial arises opposite the fifth thoracic vertebra, the lower just below the level of the left bronchus. Each vessel runs on the back part of its bronchus, dividing and subdividing along the bronchial tubes, supplying them, the areolar tissue of the lungs, the bronchial lymph glands, and the esophagus.

The **esophageal arteries** (*aa. aesophageae*) four or five in number, *arise* from the front of the aorta, and pass obliquely downward to the esophagus, forming a chain of anastomoses along that tube, anastomosing with the esophageal branches of the inferior thyroid arteries above, and with ascending branches from the left inferior phrenic and left gastric arteries below.

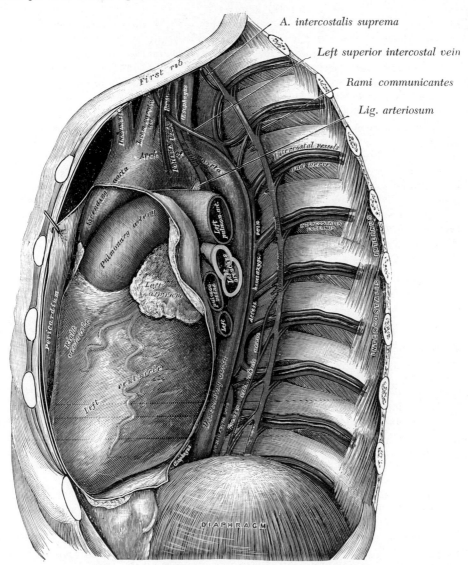

Fig. 571.—The heart and the thoracic aorta. Left lateral aspect.

The **mediastinal branches** (*rami mediastinales*) are numerous small vessels which supply the lymph glands and loose areolar tissue in the posterior mediastinum.

Intercostal arteries (*aa. intercostales posteriores*).—There are usually nine pairs of aortic intercostal arteries. They *arise* from the back of the aorta, and are distributed to the lower nine intercostal spaces, the first two spaces being supplied by the highest intercostal artery, a branch of the costocervical trunk of the subclavian. The **right** aortic intercostals are longer than the left, on account of the position of the aorta on the left side of the vertebral column; they pass across the vertebræ behind the esophagus, thoracic duct, and vena azygos, and are covered by the right lung and pleura. The **left** aortic intercostals run backward on the sides of the vertebræ and are covered by the left lung and pleura; the upper two vessels are crossed by the highest left intercostal vein, the lower vessels by the hemiazygos veins. The further course of the intercostal arteries is practically the same on both sides. Opposite the heads of the ribs the sympathetic trunk passes downward in front of them, and the splanchnic nerves also descend in front by the lower arteries. Each artery then divides into an **anterior** and a **posterior ramus.**

The **anterior ramus** crosses the corresponding intercostal space obliquely toward the angle of the upper rib, and thence is continued forward in the costal groove. It is placed at first between the pleura and the posterior intercostal membrane, then it pierces this membrane, and lies between it and the Intercostalis externus as far as the angle of the rib; from this onward it runs between the Intercostalis externus and Intercostalis internus, and anastomoses in front with the intercostal branch of the internal mammary or the musculophrenic. Each artery is accompanied by a vein and a nerve, the former being above and the latter below the artery, except in the upper spaces, where the nerve is at first above the artery. The first aortic intercostal artery anastomoses with the intercostal branch of the costocervical trunk, and may form the chief supply of the second intercostal space. The lower two intercostal arteries are continued anteriorly from the intercostal spaces into the abdominal wall, and anastomose with the subcostal, superior epigastric, and lumbar arteries.

Branches.—The anterior rami give off the following branches:

Collateral Intercostal.	Lateral Cutaneous.
Muscular.	Mammary.

The **collateral intercostal branch** comes off from the intercostal artery near the angle of the rib, and descends to the upper border of the rib below, along which it courses to anastomose with the intercostal branch of the internal mammary.

Muscular branches are given to the Intercostales and Pectorales and to the Serratus anterior; they anastomose with the highest and lateral thoracic branches of the axillary artery.

The **lateral cutaneous branches** accompany the lateral cutaneous branches of the thoracic nerves.

Mammary branches are given off by the vessels in the third, fourth, and fifth spaces. They supply the mamma, and increase considerably in size during the period of lactation.

The **posterior ramus** runs backward through a space which is bounded above and below by the necks of the ribs, medially by the body of a vertebra, and laterally by an anterior costotransverse ligament. It gives off a **spinal branch** which enters the vertebral canal through the intervertebral foramen and is distributed to the medulla spinalis and its membranes and the vertebræ. It then courses over the transverse process with the posterior division of the thoracic nerve, supplies branches to the muscles of the back and cutaneous branches which accompany the corresponding cutaneous branches of the posterior division of the nerve.

The **subcostal arteries**, so named because they lie below the last ribs, constitute the lowest pair of branches derived from the thoracic aorta, and are in series with the intercostal arteries. Each passes along the lower border of the twelfth rib behind the kidney and in front of the Quadratus lumborum muscle, and is accompanied by the twelfth thoracic nerve. It then pierces the posterior aponeurosis of the Transversus abdominis, and, passing forward between this muscle and the Obliquus internus, anastomoses with the superior epigastric, lower intercostal, and lumbar arteries. Each subcostal artery gives off a posterior branch which has a distribution similar to that of the posterior ramus of an intercostal artery.

The **superior phrenic branches** are small and *arise* from the lower part of the thoracic aorta; they are distributed to the posterior part of the upper surface of the diaphragm, and anastomose with the musculophrenic and pericardiacophrenic arteries.

A small **aberrant artery** is sometimes found *arising* from the right side of the thoracic aorta near the origin of the right bronchial. It passes upward and to the right behind the trachea and the esophagus, and may anastomose with the highest right intercostal artery. It represents the remains of the right dorsal aorta, and in a small proportion of cases is enlarged to form the first part of the right subclavian artery.

The Abdominal Aorta (Aorta Abdominalis) (Fig. 572).

The **abdominal aorta** begins at the aortic hiatus of the diaphragm, in front of the lower border of the body of the last thoracic vertebra, and, descending in front of the vertebral column, ends on the body of the fourth lumbar vertebra, commonly a little to the left of the mid-line, by dividing into the two common iliac arteries. It diminishes rapidly in size, in consequence of the many large branches which it gives off. As it lies upon the bodies of the vertebræ, the curve which it describes is convex forward, the summit of the convexity corresponding to the third lumbar vertebra.

Relations.—The abdominal aorta is covered, *anteriorly*, by the lesser omentum and stomach, behind which are the branches of the celiac artery and the celiac plexus; below these, by the lienal vein, the pancreas, the left renal vein, the inferior part of the duodenum, the mesentery, and aortic plexus. *Posteriorly*, it is separated from the lumbar vertebræ and intervertebral fibrocartilages by the anterior longitudinal ligament and left lumbar veins. On the *right side* it is in relation above with the azygos vein, cisterna chyli, thoracic duct, and the right crus of the diaphragm—the last separating it from the upper part of the inferior vena cava, and from the right celiac ganglion; the inferior vena cava is in contact with the aorta below. On the *left side* are the left crus of the diaphragm, the left celiac ganglion, the ascending part of the duodenum, and some coils of the small intestine.

Collateral Circulation.—The collateral circulation would be carried on by the anastomoses between the internal mammary and the inferior epigastric; by the free communication between the superior and inferior mesenterics, if the ligature were placed between these vessels; or by the anastomosis between the inferior mesenteric and the internal pudendal, when (as is more common) the point of ligature is below the origin of the inferior mesenteric; and possibly by the anastomoses of the lumbar arteries with the branches of the hypogastric.

Branches.—The branches of the abdominal aorta may be divided into three sets: visceral, parietal, and terminal.

Visceral Branches.	*Parietal Branches.*
A. Celiac.	*H.* Inferior Phrenics.
B. Superior Mesenteric.	*I.* Lumbars.
C. Inferior Mesenteric.	*J.* Middle Sacral.
D. Middle Suprarenals.	
E. Renals.	
F. Testicular	*Terminal Branches.*
G. Ovarian.	*K.* Common Iliacs.

Of the visceral branches, the celiac artery and the superior and inferior mesenteric arteries are unpaired, while the suprarenals, renals, testicular, and ovarian are paired. Of the parietal branches the phrenics and lumbars are paired; the middle sacral is unpaired. The terminal branches are paired.

A. The **Celiac Artery** (*truncus coeliacus; celiac axis*) (Figs. 573, 574), a thick trunk, 7 to 20 mm in diameter, arises from the aorta just below the aortic hiatus

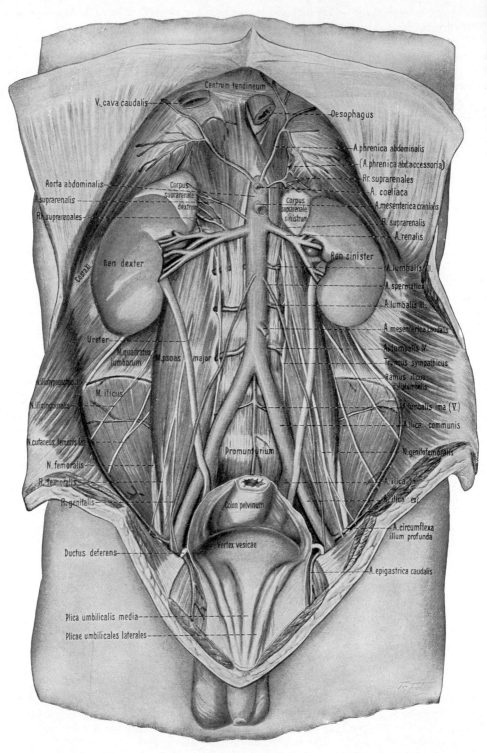

FIG. 572.—Abdominal aorta and its principal branches. (From Rauber-Kopsch, *Lehrbuch u. Atlas d. Anatomie d. Menschen*, 19th Edition, Vol. I, courtesy of Georg Thieme Verlag, Stuttgart, 1955.)

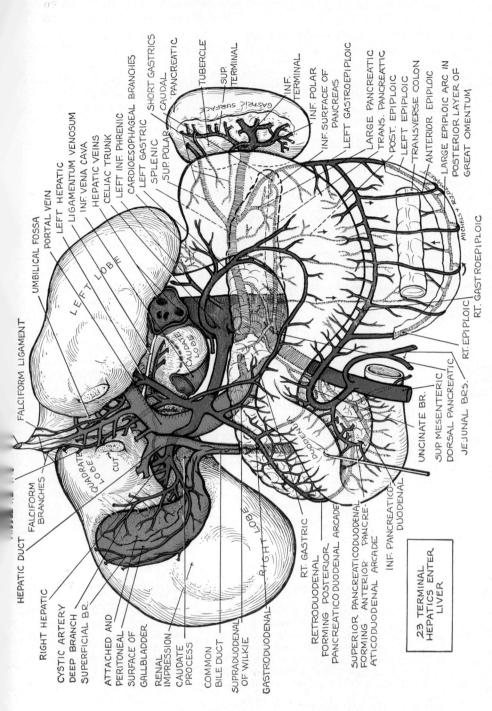

HEPATIC DUCT

FALCIFORM LIGAMENT

UMBILICAL FOSSA

PORTAL VEIN

LEFT HEPATIC

LIGAMENTUM VENOSUM

INF. VENA CAVA

HEPATIC VEINS

CELIAC TRUNK

LEFT INF. PHRENIC

CARDIOESOPHAGEAL BRANCHES

LEFT GASTRIC

SPLENIC

SUP. POLAR

CAUDAL

SHORT GASTRICS

CAUDAL PANCREATIC

TUBERCLE

SUP. TERMINAL

INF. TERMINAL

INF. POLAR

INF. SURFACE OF PANCREAS

LEFT GASTROEPIPLOIC

LARGE PANCREATIC

TRANS. PANCREATIC

POST. EPIPLOIC

LEFT EPIPLOIC

TRANSVERSE COLON

ANTERIOR EPIPLOIC

LARGE EPIPLOIC ARC IN POSTERIOR LAYER OF GREAT OMENTUM

RT. GASTROEPIPLOIC

RT. EPIPLOIC

RT. EPIPLOIC

SUP. MESENTERIC

DORSAL PANCREATIC

JEJUNAL BRS.

UNCINATE BR.

INF. PANCREATICODUODENAL

SUPERIOR PANCREATICODUODENAL FORMING ANTERIOR PANCRE-ATICODUODENAL ARCADE

RETRODUODENAL FORMING POSTERIOR PANCREATICODUODENAL ARCADE

RT. GASTRIC

GASTRODUODENAL

SUPRADUODENAL OF WILKIE

COMMON BILE DUCT

CAUDATE PROCESS

RENAL IMPRESSION

ATTACHED AND PERITONEAL SURFACE OF GALLBLADDER

SUPERFICIAL BR.

DEEP BRANCH

CYSTIC ARTERY

RIGHT HEPATIC

FALCIFORM BRANCHES

LEFT LOBE

QUADRATE LOBE

CAUDATE LOBE

CUT

RIGHT LOBE

DUODENUM

GASTRIC SURFACE

MICHELS + 230

23 TERMINAL HEPATICS ENTER LIVER

Fig. 573.—Typical pattern of the blood supply of the upper abdominal organs. Complete hepatolienogastric celiac trunk with left gastric as its first branch. (Michels, *Blood Supply and Anatomy of the Upper Abdominal Organs*, 1955, courtesy of J. B. Lippincott Company.)

of the diaphragm.   After a short course, 8 to 40 mm, it usually divides into three large branches, (1) the left gastric, (2) the common hepatic and (3) the splenic. It is covered by the peritoneum of the dorsal wall of the lesser sac (omental bursa). On its right side are the right celiac ganglion and the cardiac end of the stomach. A short distance caudal to it, commonly 1 to 6 mm, the aorta gives origin to the superior mesenteric artery.

Variations.—The most constant feature of this artery is the variability of its branching and the routes by which blood reaches the organs which it principally supplies, according to Michels ('53) whose descriptions and statistics are followed in this account.   The stomach, liver, pancreas, duodenum, and spleen are the names of these organs and they can conveniently be used to designate the important variations.

A *gastrohepatosplenic trunk* has the classical branches: a left gastric, a common hepatic, and a splenic artery.   This is the usual variety (89 per cent).   It is complete, that is, it gives origin to all its expected branches in 64.5 per cent and in the remainder there are supernumerary or accessory branches.

A *hepatosplenic trunk* (3.5 per cent) has hepatic and splenic arteries but the left gastric arises independently from the aorta or from the hepatic or splenic arteries.

A *gastrosplenic trunk* (5.5 per cent) has the left gastric and splenic arteries but the hepatic arises from the aorta or from the superior mesenteric artery.

A *hepatogastric trunk* (1.5 per cent) has the left gastric and hepatic arteries but the splenic arises from the aorta or from the superior mesenteric artery.

In rare instances the celiac trunk and superior mesenteric arteries are combined.

1. The **Left Gastric Artery** (*arteria gastrica sinistra*) is most commonly the first branch of the celiac trunk, arising near its middle part.   It is much larger (4–5 mm in diameter) than the right gastric artery.   Frequently (25 per cent) it arises from the termination of the celiac trunk together with the hepatic and splenic arteries, forming a tripod.   It is covered by that part of the parietal peritoneum of the posterior abdominal wall which forms the posterior layer of the lesser sac (omental bursa).   It runs ventrally, upward and to the left in a gentle curve, raising a crescentic ridge of peritoneum, the left gastropancreatic plica, and reaches the anterior wall of the lesser sac near the cardiac end of the stomach, accompanied by the coronary vein.   Here it reverses its direction and lying between the two leaves of the lesser omentum bifurcates into two main branches.

The **anterior branch** is distributed to the anterior surface of the stomach in two or three subdivisions.

The **posterior branch** runs along the lesser curvature of the stomach, giving branches to the posterior surface of this organ and usually anastomosing with the right gastric artery.

A **cardioesophageal branch** arises before the bifurcation and is distributed to the cardia and esophagus in one to three subdivisions.

Variations.—The left gastric artery was a branch of the aorta in 2.5 per cent, of a gastrosplenic trunk in 4.5 per cent, and a hepatogastric trunk in 1.5 per cent.   An accessory left gastric arose from the splenic in 6 per cent, the left hepatic in 3 per cent and from the celiac in 2 per cent (200 bodies, Michels '53).

An **aberrant left hepatic artery** is given off just proximal to the bend and bifurcation in 23 per cent, half of which (11.5 per cent) replace the left hepatic entirely and half are accessory. It may be 3 to 5 mm in diameter.   It runs upward about 6 cm to near the esophagus, lying between the two layers of the lesser omentum; it crosses the caudate lobe and enters the liver substance at the fissure for the ligamentum venosum.   Because of this frequent origin of the left hepatic, the left gastric was named the gastrohepatic artery by Haller (1756).

The inferior phrenics may arise from the left gastric.

2. The **Common Hepatic Artery** (*arteria hepatica commonis*) (Fig. 574) arising from the celiac trunk is usually smaller (7 to 8 mm) than the splenic artery.   Its first part is horizontal, running from left to right along the upper border of the head of the pancreas to the pylorus or first part of the duodenum.   Behind the

duodenum it gives off the gastroduodenal and turns upward as the vertical portion. It is covered by the peritoneum of the posterior wall of the lesser sac (omental bursa) which is raised thereby into the right hepatopancreatic fold. It then passes through the hepatoduodenal ligament (lesser omentum) to the porta hepatis. As it lies between the two layers of the lesser omentum, it is ventral to the epiploic foramen having the common bile duct to its right and the portal vein dorsal to it. At a variable distance from the liver it gives rise to three terminal branches, right, left, and middle hepatic arteries.

Variations.—Of 200 bodies, 41.5 per cent had one or more aberrant hepatic arteries, 50.5 per cent had none; several bodies had 2 and a few 3 aberrants. The common hepatic arose from the aorta in 3, from the superior mesenteric in 5, and the left gastric in 1 (Michels '53).

Branches.—(a) Gastroduodenal, (b) Right gastric, (c) Right hepatic, (d) Left hepatic, (e) Middle hepatic.

(a) The **gastroduodenal artery** (*arteria gastroduodenalis*) (Fig. 573) arises from the common hepatic trunk, usually about halfway between the celiac origin and its division into the hepatic branches. At first it is to the left of the common bile duct, then crosses either dorsal or ventral to it and descends behind the first part of the duodenum to the lower border of the pylorus where it divides into the right gastro-epiploic and superior pancreaticoduodenal arteries.

Variations.—The gastroduodenal artery arose from the left hepatic artery (11 per cent), the right hepatic (7 per cent), the middle hepatic (1 per cent), a replaced hepatic trunk (3.5 per cent) or from the celiac or superior mesenteric arteries.

Branches.—1. Retroduodenal, 2. Right Gastroepiploic, 3. Superior pancreaticoduodenal.

1. The **Retroduodenal Artery** is the first branch of the gastroduodenal. It arises above the duodenum, runs dorsal to it along the left side of the common bile duct, crosses ventral to the supraduodenal portion of the duct and forms the U-shaped dorsal pancreaticoduodenal arcade. The arcade supplies branches to all four parts of the duodenum and the head of the pancreas, and anastomoses with a posterior branch of the inferior pancreaticoduodenal from the superior mesenteric artery. The retroduodenal supplies branches to the bile duct, the first part of the duodenum and the head of the pancreas.

Variations.—The retroduodenal artery arose from the common hepatic in 4 per cent, right hepatic in 2 per cent, aberrant right hepatic 3 per cent, and was absent in 1 per cent.
The **supraduodenal artery** was identified in all but 6 per cent as a branch to the upper part of the first portion of the duodenum; it arose from the retroduodenal in 50 per cent, from the gastroduodenal in 25 per cent and the remainder from proper hepatic branches.

2. The **Right Gastroepiploic Artery** (*arteria gastro-epiploica dextra*) (Fig. 574) is the larger of the two terminal branches of the gastroduodenal and is much larger than the left gastroepiploic artery. It passes from right to left at a variable distance from the curvature of the stomach. It lies between the two layers of the gastrocolic ligament or the anterior two layers of the greater omentum when these are not adherent to the colon. It gives off a large ascending **pyloric branch** near its origin, and at its termination anastomoses with the left gastroepiploic artery. It supplies a number of ascending branches to the stomach and descending branches to the greater omentum. The **long anterior epiploic branches** extend around the free border of the omentum and in the posterior layer of the omentum may anastomose with other gastric, with colic, or with pancreatic arteries.

3. The **Superior Pancreaticoduodenal Artery** (*arteria pancreaticoduodenalis superior*) (Fig. 575) arises from the gastroduodenal artery as the latter passes behind

43

the first part of the duodenum. It makes a loop on the anterior surface of the pancreas, runs along the groove between the pancreas and the descending portion of the duodenum, sinks into the substance of the pancreas, and behind the head of the pancreas anastomoses with the inferior pancreaticoduodenal artery, a branch of the superior mesenteric artery. The loop supplies branches to the anterior surface of all three parts of the duodenum. The **anterior pancreaticoduodenal arcade** formed by the anastomosis of the superior and inferior arteries supplies numerous branches to the pancreas and duodenum.

(*b*) The **Right Gastric Artery** (*arteria gastrica dextra*) (Fig. 573) is much smaller and less constant than the left gastric. It arises from the common hepatic between the gastroduodenal and proper hepatic arteries and passes between the layers of the lesser omentum to the pylorus, which it supplies with branches. It runs to the left along the lesser curvature of the stomach supplying an extensive area with anterior and posterior branches and anastomoses with the posterior branch of the left gastric artery.

Variations.—The right gastric arose from the common hepatic in 40 per cent, the left hepatic in 40.5 per cent, the right hepatic in 5.5 per cent, the middle hapatic in 5 per cent, the gastroduodenal in 8 per cent.

(*c*) The **Right Hepatic Artery** (*arteria hepatica propria, ramus dexter*) (Fig. 573) usually lies ventral to the portal vein and crosses dorsal to the hepatic duct to enter the cystic triangle. It gives off the cystic artery and divides into two main branches before entering the right lobe of the liver.

Variations.—Of 200 bodies, 52 had aberrant right hepatic arteries, 36 replacing the usual artery and 16 accessory to it. The most frequent source was the superior mesenteric artery (Michels '53).

The **cystic artery** (*arteria cystica*) (Fig. 574) arises from the right hepatic artery to the right of the hepatic duct in the triangle bounded by the cystic duct, hepatic duct, and the liver (**cystic triangle** of Calot). At the gall bladder it divides into a superficial branch which supplies the free surface and a deep branch which supplies the embedded surface of the gall bladder. The branches anastomose and supply twigs to the adjacent liver substance.

Variations.—The cystic artery had a single origin in 75 per cent, double in 25 per cent. In 18 per cent the cystic artery arose to the left of the hepatic duct, not in the cystic triangle, and had to cross the duct to reach the gall bladder. In 5 per cent its origin was from an artery other than the right hepatic. In most of the double cystic arteries, both superficial and deep arose in the cystic triangle; the superficial was more variable than the deep, originating from the right hepatic to the left of the duct or from another artery.

(*d*) The **Left Hepatic Artery** (*arteria hepatica propria, ramus sinistra*) (Fig. 573) usually divides into two branches, an upper and a lower, supplying twigs to the capsule of the liver and the caudate lobe before entering the substance of the left lobe.

Variations.—Of 200 bodies, 54 had aberrant left hepatic arteries, 31 replacing the usual artery and 23 accessory. The majority of these arose from the left gastric artery.

(*e*) The **middle hepatic artery** enters the fossa for the round ligament and accompanies the middle hepatic duct to the quadrate lobe. It is the principal supply for this lobe and sends twigs to the round ligament and sometimes to the left lobe. It arises from the right hepatic in 45 per cent, left 45 per cent and from other sources in 10 per cent.

3. The **Splenic** or **Lienal Artery** (*a. lienalis*), the largest branch of the celiac, passes horizontally to the left along the pancreas to reach the spleen. It varies

from 8 to 32 cm. in length and is usually tortuous. The *first part*, before it reaches the pancreas, is a short arc, swinging to the right and downward, then across the aorta to the cephalic border of the pancreas. The *second part* lies in a groove on the dorsal cephalic surface of the body of the pancreas. It is the most tortuous part, being undulating and having one or more loops or coils, but seldom is it far from the pancreas. The *third part* leaves the upper border to cross the ventral surface of the pancreas obliquely and in most subjects divides into its superior and inferior terminal arteries. The *fourth part* is between the tail of the pancreas and the hilum of the spleen, and, as just mentioned, in the majority of individuals is represented by terminal arteries (Michels '42) (Fig. 575).

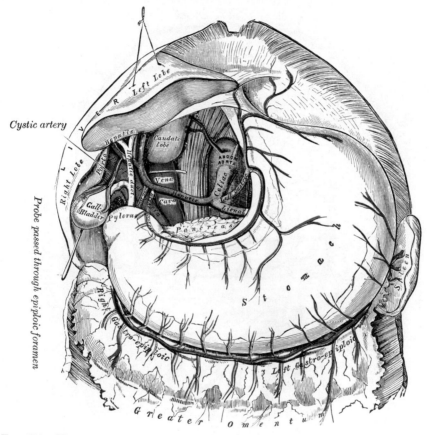

FIG. 574.—The celiac artery and its branches; the liver has been raised, and the lesser omentum and anterior layer of the greater omentum removed.

The splenic artery is covered by the peritoneum of the dorsal wall of the omental bursa (lesser sac) and lies, therefore, dorsal to the stomach. Its fourth part crosses ventral to the cephalic part of the left kidney and enters the hilum by passing in the substance of the phrenicolienal or lienorenal ligaments. Its **branches** are:

Pancreatic.   Left Gastroepiploic.   Short Gastric.   Splenic.

(*a*) **Pancreatic branches.**—In addition to numerous twiglike branches to the pancreas, the splenic artery gives rise to three larger branches: 1. The dorsal pancreatic, 2. pancreatica magna, and 3. caudæ pancreatis (Fig. 573).

1. The **dorsal pancreatic artery** typically arises from the first part of the splenic, but it commonly has other origins. It gives a number of twigs to the neck and body of the pancreas. It has two small right branches, one curving forward along the head of the pancreas supplying it and anastomosing with the gastroduodenal or its branches, the other supplies the uncinate process by plexiform branches and anastomoses with the inferior pancreaticoduodenal artery. A branch often runs caudally to below the pancreas and anastomoses with superior mesenteric branches. The main left branch is of considerable size and becomes the transverse pancreatic artery.

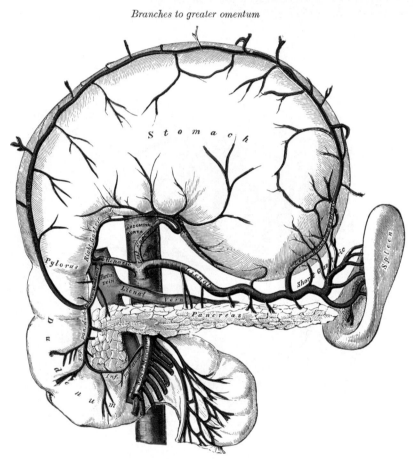

Branches to greater omentum

F IG. 575.—The celiac artery and its branches; the stomach has been raised and the peritoneum removed.

The **transverse pancreatic artery** takes a course to the left for about two-thirds of the length of the dorsal caudal surface of the pancreas and enters the substance of the gland to anastomose with other pancreatic branches from the splenic artery. It runs parallel with the pancreatic duct for some distance supplying it and neighboring gland with branches. It has long and short branches which descend in the posterior layer of the great omentum as the posterior epiploic arteries which anastomose with the anterior epiploics of the gastroepiploic arcade.

Variations.—The dorsal pancreatic arose from the splenic artery in 39 per cent, the celiac in 22 per cent, the hepatics in 19 per cent, the superior mesenteric in 14 per cent, and the gastroduodenal in 2 per cent in 200 bodies (Michels '53). The **descending branch** of the dorsal pancreatic may be quite large and supply the middle colic artery.

2. The **arteria pancreatica magna** arises from the second part of the splenic artery. It is the largest pancreatic branch (2 to 4 mm diameter) and branching to right and left anastomoses with other pancreatic arteries.

3. The **arteria caudæ pancreatis** arises from the third part of the splenic artery or one of its terminal branches. It supplies branches to the tail of the pancreas, anastomoses with the magna and dorsal pancreatics and supplies an accessory spleen when one is present.

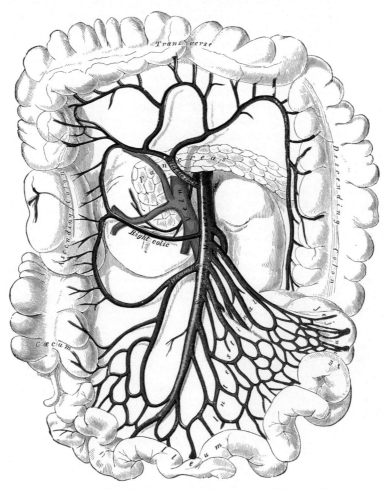

Fig. 576.—The superior mesenteric artery and its branches.

The **left gastroepiploic artery** (*a. gastroepiploica sinistra*), the largest branch, comes from the third part of the splenic artery or from its inferior terminal artery. It reaches the stomach through the pancreaticolienal and gastrolienal ligaments and courses along the greater curvature of the stomach from left to right within the anterior part of the great omentum. Its branches are distributed to both surfaces of the stomach and to the greater omentum through which it anastomoses with the middle colic artery.

The **short gastric arteries** (*aa. gastricæ breves*; *vasa brevia*) consist of from five to seven small branches, which *arise* from the end of the lienal artery, and from its terminal divisions. They pass from left to right, between the layers of the gastrolienal ligament, and are distributed to the greater curvature of the stomach. anastomosing with branches of the left gastric and left gastroepiploic arteries.

Splenic Branches.—The splenic artery divides about 3.5 cm. from the spleen into a superior and an inferior terminal branch. These terminal branches may divide into a number or a few branches before entering the spleen, and there may be an intermediate terminal branch. The branching of the inferior terminal is more complicated than the superior, and it may give origin to the left gastroepiploic and inferior polar arteries. Arteries to the poles of the spleen are of frequent occurrence. The superior polar usually has its origin from the main splenic artery and may come from the celiac axis. Inferior polar arteries are more frequent than superior and arise from the left gastroepiploic most frequently, but may come from the splenic or inferior terminal branches. Cross anastomoses between the larger branches at the hilum are common (Michels '42).

B. The **Superior Mesenteric Artery** (*a. mesenterica superior*) (Fig. 576) is a large vessel which supplies the whole length of the small intestine, except the superior part of the duodenum; it also supplies the cecum and the ascending part of the colon and about one-half of the transverse part of the colon. It arises from the front of the aorta, about 1.25 cm. below the celiac artery, at the level of the first lumbar vertebra, and is crossed at its origin by the lienal vein and the neck of the pancreas. It passes downward and forward, anterior to the processus uncinatus of the head of the pancreas and inferior part of the duodenum, and descends between the layers of the mesentery to the right iliac fossa, where, considerably diminished in size, it anastomoses with one of its own branches, viz., the ileocolic. In its course it crosses in front of the inferior vena cava, the right ureter and Psoas major, and forms an arch, the convexity of which is directed forward and downward to the left side, the concavity backward and upward to the right. It is accompanied by the superior mesenteric vein, which lies to its right side, and it is surrounded by the superior mesenteric plexus of nerves. Occasionally it arises from the aorta by a common trunk with the coeliac axis.

Branches.—Its branches are:

Inferior Pancreaticoduodenal.	Ileocolic.
Intestinal.	Right Colic.
Middle Colic.	

The **Inferior Pancreaticoduodenal Artery** (*a. pancreaticoduodenalis inferior*) is given off from the superior mesenteric or from its first intestinal branch, opposite the upper border of the inferior part of the duodenum. It courses to the right between the head of the pancreas and duodenum, and then ascends to anastomose with the superior pancreaticoduodenal artery. It distributes branches to the head of the pancreas and to the descending and inferior parts of the duodenum.

The **Intestinal Arteries** (*aa. intestinales; vasa intestini tenuis*) *arise* from the convex side of the superior mesenteric artery, are usually from twelve to fifteen in number, and are distributed to the jejunum and ileum. They run nearly parallel with one another between the layers of the mesentery, each vessel dividing into two branches, which unite with adjacent branches, forming a series of arches, the convexities of which are directed toward the intestine (Fig. 577). From this first set of arches branches arise, which unite with similar branches from above and below, thus forming a second series of arches; from the lower branches of the artery, a third, a fourth, or even a fifth series of arches may be formed, diminishing in size the nearer they approach the intestine. In the short, upper part of the mesentery only one set of arches exists, but as the depth of the mesentery increases, second, third, fourth, or even fifth groups are developed. From the terminal arches numerous small straight vessels arise which encircle the intestine, upon which they are distributed, ramifying between its coats. From the intestinal arteries small branches are given off to the lymph glands and other structures between the layers of the mesentery.

The **Ileocolic Artery** (*a. ileocolica*) is the lowest branch arising from the concavity of the superior mesenteric artery. It passes downward and to the right behind the peritoneum toward the right iliac fossa, where it divides into a superior and an inferior branch; the inferior anastomoses with the end of the superior mesenteric artery, the superior with the right colic artery.

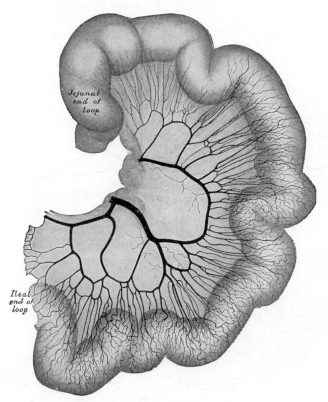

FIG. 577.—Loop of small intestine showing distribution of intestinal arteries. (From a preparation by Mr. Hamilton Drummond.) The vessels were injected while the gut was *in situ;* the gut was then removed, and an *x*-ray photograph taken.

The inferior branch of the ileocolic runs toward the upper border of the ileocolic junction and supplies the following branches (Fig. 578): (*a*) **colic**, which pass upward on the ascending colon; (*b*) **anterior** and **posterior cecal**, which are distributed to the front and back of the cecum; (*c*) an **appendicular artery**, which descends behind the termination of the ileum and enters the mesenteriole of the vermiform process; it runs near the free margin of this mesenteriole and ends in branches which supply the vermiform process; and (*d*) **ileal**, which run upward and to the left on the lower part of the ileum, and anastomose with the termination of the superior mesenteric.

The **Right Colic Artery** (*a. colica dextra*) *arises* from about the middle of the concavity of the superior mesenteric artery, or from a stem common to it and the ileocolic. It passes to the right behind the peritoneum, and in front of the right internal spermatic or ovarian vessels, the right ureter and the Psoas major, toward the middle of the ascending colon; sometimes the vessel lies at a higher level, and crosses the descending part of the duodenum and the lower end of the right kidney.   At the colon it divides into a descending branch, which anastomoses with the ileocolic, and an ascending branch, which anastomoses with the middle colic. These branches form arches, from the convexity of which vessels are distributed to the ascending colon.

The **Middle Colic Artery** (*a. colica media*) *arises* from the superior mesenteric just below the pancreas and, passing downward and forward between the layers of the transverse mesocolon, divides into two branches, right and left; the former anastomoses with the right colic; the latter with the left colic, a branch of the inferior mesenteric.   The arches thus formed are placed about two fingers' breadth from the transverse colon, to which they distribute branches.

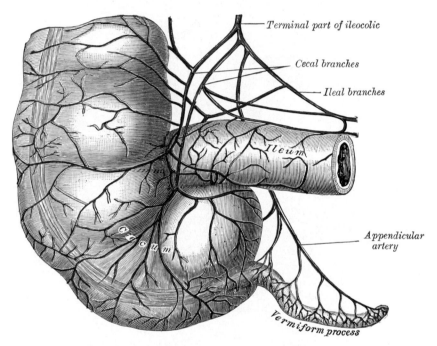

FIG. 578.—Arteries of cecum and vermiform process.

C. The **Inferior Mesenteric Artery** (*a. mesenterica inferior*) (Fig. 579) supplies the left half of the transverse part of the colon, the whole of the descending and iliac parts of the colon, the sigmoid colon, and the greater part of the rectum.   It is smaller than the superior mesenteric, and *arises* from the aorta, about 3 or 4 cm. above its division into the common iliacs and close to the lower border of the inferior part of the duodenum, at the level of the middle of the third lumbar vertebra.   It passes downward posterior to the peritoneum, lying at first anterior to and then on the left side of the aorta.   It crosses the left common iliac artery and is continued into the lesser pelvis under the name of the **superior hemorrhoidal artery,** which descends between the two layers of the sigmoid mesocolon and ends on the upper part of the rectum.

Branches.—Its branches are:

Left Colic.   Sigmoid.   Superior Hemorrhoidal.

The **Left Colic Artery** (*a. colica sinistra*) runs to the left behind the peritoneum and in front of the Psoas major, and after a short, but variable, course divides into an ascending and a descending branch; the stem of the artery or its branches cross the left ureter and left internal spermatic vessels. The ascending branch crosses in front of the left kidney and ends, between the two layers of the transverse mesocolon, by anastomosing with the middle colic artery; the descending branch anastomoses with the highest sigmoid artery. From the arches formed by these anastomoses branches are distributed to the descending colon and the left part of the transverse colon.

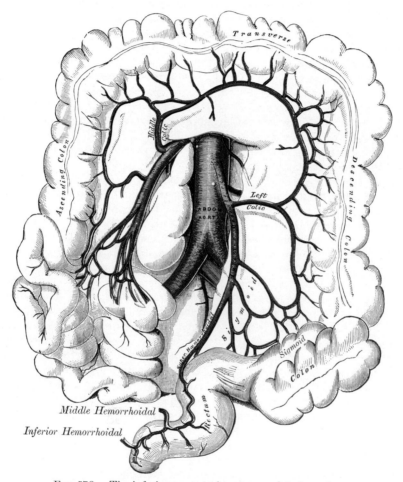

Fig. 579.—The inferior mesenteric artery and its branches.

The **Sigmoid Arteries** (*aa. sigmoideæ*) (Fig. 579), two or three in number, run obliquely downward and to the left behind the peritoneum and in front of the Psoas major, ureter, and internal spermatic vessels. Their branches supply the lower part of the descending colon, the iliac colon, and the sigmoid or pelvic colon; anastomosing above with the left colic, and below with the superior hemorrhoidal artery.

The **Superior Hemorrhoidal Artery** (*a. rectalis superior*) (Fig. 579), the continuation of the inferior mesenteric, descends into the pelvis between the layers of the mesentery of the sigmoid colon, crossing, in its course, the left common iliac vessels. It divides, opposite the third sacral vertebra, into two branches, which descend one on either side of the rectum, and about 10 or 12 cm. from the anus break up into several small branches. These pierce the muscular coat of the bowel and run downward, as straight vessels, placed at regular intervals from each other in the wall of the gut between its muscular and mucous coats, to the level of the Sphincter ani internus; here they form a series of loops around the lower end of the rectum, and communicate with the middle hemorrhoidal branches of the hypogastric, and with the inferior hemorrhoidal branches of the internal pudendal.

D. The **Middle Suprarenal Arteries** (*aa. suprarenales mediae*; *middle capsular arteries*; *suprarenal arteries*) are two small vessels which *arise*, one from either side of the aorta, opposite the superior mesenteric artery. They pass lateralward and slightly upward, over the crura of the diaphragm, to the suprarenal glands, where they anastomose with suprarenal branches of the inferior phrenic and renal arteries. In the fetus these arteries are of large size.

E. The **Renal Arteries** (*aa. renales*) (Fig. 572) are two large trunks, which *arise* from the side of the aorta, immediately below the superior mesenteric artery, at the level of the disk between the first and second lumbar vertebræ. Each is directed across the crus of the diaphragm, so as to form nearly a right angle with the aorta. The right is longer than the left, on account of the position of the aorta; it passes behind the inferior vena cava, the right renal vein, the head of the pancreas, and the descending part of the duodenum. The left is somewhat higher than the right; it lies behind the left renal vein, the body of the pancreas and the lienal vein, and is crossed by the inferior mesenteric vein. Before reaching the hilum of the kidney, each artery divides into four or five branches; the greater number of these lie between the renal vein and ureter, the vein being in front, the ureter behind, with one or more branches usually behind the ureter. Each vessel gives off some small **inferior suprarenal branches** to the suprarenal gland, the ureter, and the surrounding cellular tissue and muscles. One or two accessory renal arteries are frequently found (23 per cent), more especially on the left side. They usually arise from the aorta, and may come off above or below the main artery, the former being the more common position. Instead of entering the kidney at the hilum, they usually pierce the upper or lower part of the organ.

F. The **Testicular Arteries** (*aa. testiculares; internal spermatic arteries*) (Fig. 572) are distributed to the testes. They are two slender vessels of considerable length, and *arise* from the front of the aorta a little below the renal arteries. Each passes obliquely downward and lateralward behind the peritoneum, resting on the Psoas major, the right spermatic lying in front of the inferior vena cava and behind the middle colic and ileocolic arteries and the terminal part of the ileum, the left behind the left colic and sigmoid arteries and the iliac colon. Each crosses obliquely over the ureter and the lower part of the external iliac artery to reach the abdominal inguinal ring, through which it passes, and accompanies the other constituents of the spermatic cord along the inguinal canal to the scrotum, where it becomes tortuous, and divides into several branches. Two or three of these accompany the ductus, and supply the epididymis, anastomosing with the artery of the ductus deferens; others pierce the back part of the tunica albuginea, and supply the substance of the testis. The internal spermatic artery supplies one or two small branches to the ureter, and in the inguinal canal gives one or two twigs to the Cremaster.

G. The **Ovarian Arteries** (*aa. avaricae*) are the arteries in the female corresponding to the internal spermatic in the male. They supply the ovaries, are shorter than the internal spermatics, and do not pass out of the abdominal cavity. The origin and course of the first part of each artery are the same as those of the internal spermatic, but on arriving at the upper opening of the lesser pelvis the ovarian artery passes inward, between the two layers of the ovariopelvic ligament and of the broad ligament of the uterus, to be distributed to the ovary. Small branches are given to the ureter and the uterine tube, and one passes on to the side of the uterus, and unites with the uterine artery. Other offsets are continued on the round ligament of the uterus, through the inguinal canal, to the integument of the labium majus and groin.

At an early period of fetal life, when the testes or ovaries lie by the side of the vertebral column, below the kidneys, the internal spermatic or ovarian arteries are short; but with the descent of these organs into the scrotum or lesser pelvis, the arteries are gradually lengthened.

H. The **Phrenic Arteries** (*aa. phrenicae, inferior phrenic arteries*) (Fig. 572) are two small vessels, which supply the diaphragm but present much variety in their origin. They may *arise* separately from the front of the aorta, immediately above the celiac artery or from one of the renal arteries, or by a common trunk, which may spring either from the aorta or from the celiac artery. They diverge from one another across the crura of the diaphragm, and then run obliquely upward and lateralward upon its under surface. The left phrenic passes behind the esophagus, and runs forward on the left side of the esophageal hiatus. The right phrenic passes behind the inferior vena cava, and along the right side of the foramen which transmits that vein. Near the back part of the central tendon each vessel divides into a medial and a lateral branch. The **medial branch** curves forward, and anastomoses with its fellow of the opposite side, and with the musculophrenic and pericardiaco-phrenic arteries. The **lateral branch** passes toward the side of the thorax, and anastomoses with the lower intercostal arteries, and with the musculophrenic. The lateral branch of the right phrenic gives off a few vessels to the inferior vena cava; and the left one, some branches to the esophagus. Each vessel gives off **superior suprarenal branches** to the suprarenal gland of its own side. The spleen and the liver also receive a few twigs from the left and right vessels respectively.

I. The **Lumbar Arteries** (*aa. lumbales*) are in series with the intercostals. They are usually four in number on either side, and *arise* from the back of the aorta, opposite the bodies of the upper four lumbar vertebræ. A fifth pair, small in size, is occasionally present arising from the middle sacral artery. The lumbar arteries run lateralward and backward on the bodies of the lumbar vertebræ, behind the sympathetic trunk, to the intervals between the adjacent transverse processes, and are then continued into the abdominal wall. The arteries of the right side pass behind the inferior vena cava, and the upper two on each side run behind the corresponding crus of the diaphragm. The arteries of both sides pass beneath the tendinous arches which give origin to the Psoas major, and are then continued behind this muscle and the lumbar plexus. They now cross the Quadratus lumborum, the upper three arteries running behind, the last usually in front of the muscle. At the lateral border of the Quadratus lumborum they pierce the posterior aponeurosis of the Transversus abdominis and are carried forward between this muscle and the Obliquus internus. They anastomose with the lower intercostal, the subcostal, the iliolumbar, the deep iliac circumflex, and the inferior epigastric arteries.

Branches.—In the interval between the adjacent transverse processes each lumbar artery gives off a **posterior ramus** which is continued backward between the transverse processes and is distributed to the muscles and skin of the back; it furnishes a **spinal branch** which enters the vertebral canal and is distributed in a manner similar to the spinal branches of the posterior rami of the intercostal arteries (page 668). **Muscular branches** are supplied from each lumbar artery and from its posterior ramus to the neighboring muscles.

J. The **Middle Sacral Artery** (*a. sacralis mediana*) (Fig. 581) is a small vessel, which *arises* from the back of the aorta, a little above its bifurcation. It descends in the mid-line in front of the fourth and fifth lumbar vertebræ, the sacrum and coccyx, and ends in the glomus coccygeum (*coccygeal gland*). From it, minute branches are said to pass to the posterior surface of the rectum. On the last lumbar vertebra it anastomoses with the lumbar branch of the iliolumbar artery; in front of the sacrum it anastomoses with the lateral sacral arteries, and sends offsets into the anterior sacral foramina. It is crossed by the left common iliac vein, and is accompanied by a pair of venæ comitantes; these unite to form a single vessel, which opens into the left common iliac vein.

THE COMMON ILIAC ARTERIES (AA. ILIACÆ COMMUNES) (Figs. 572, 581).

The abdominal aorta divides on the left side of the body of the fourth lumbar vertebra into the two **common iliac arteries**, each about 5 cm. in length. They diverge from the end of the aorta, pass downward and lateralward, and divide, opposite the intervertebral fibrocartilage between the last lumbar vertebra and the sacrum, into two branches, the **external** and **internal iliac arteries**; the former supplies the lower extremity; the latter, the viscera and parietes of the pelvis.

The **right common iliac artery** (Fig. 580) is usually somewhat longer than the left, and passes more obliquely across the body of the last lumbar vertebra. *In front* of it are the peritoneum, the small intestines, branches of the sympathetic nerves, and, at its point of division, the ureter. *Behind*, it is separated from the bodies of the fourth and fifth lumbar vertebræ, and the intervening fibrocartilage, by the terminations of the two common iliac veins and the commencement of the inferior vena cava. *Laterally*, it is in relation, above, with the inferior vena cava and the right common iliac vein; and, below, with the Psoas major. *Medial* to it, above, is the left common iliac vein.

The **left common iliac artery** is in relation, *in front*, with the peritoneum, the small intestines, branches of the sympathetic nerves, and the superior hemorrhoidal artery; and is crossed at its point of bifurcation by the ureter. It rests on the bodies of the fourth and fifth lumbar vertebræ, and the intervening fibrocartilage. The left common iliac vein lies partly *medial* to, and partly behind the artery; *laterally*, the artery is in relation with the Psoas major.

Branches.—The common iliac arteries give off small branches to the peritoneum, Psoas major, ureters, and the surrounding areolar tissue, and occasionally give origin to the iliolumbar, or accessory renal arteries.

Variations.—The *point of origin* varies according to the bifurcation of the aorta. In three-fourths of a large number of cases, the aorta bifurcated either upon the fourth lumbar vertebra, or upon the fibrocartilage between it and the fifth; the bifurcation being, in one case out of nine, below, and in one out of eleven, above this point. In about 80 per cent. of the cases the aorta bifurcated within 1.25 cm. above or below the level of the crest of the ilium; more frequently below than above.

The *point of division* varies greatly. In two-thirds of a large number of cases it was between the last lumbar vertebra and the upper border of the sacrum; being above that point in one case out of eight, and below it in one case out of six. The left common iliac artery divides lower down more frequently than the right.

The *relative lengths*, also, of the two common iliac arteries vary. The right common iliac was the longer in sixty-three cases; the left in fifty-two; while they were equal in fifty-three. The length of the arteries varied, in five-sevenths of the cases examined, from 3.5 to 7.5 cm.; in about half of the remaining cases the artery was longer, and in the other half, shorter; the minimum length being less than 1.25 cm., the maximum, 11 cm. In rare instances, the right common iliac has been found wanting, the external and internal iliac arising directly from the aorta.

Collateral Circulation.—The principal agents in carrying on the collateral circulation after the application of a ligature to the common iliac are: the anastomoses of the hemorrhoidal branches of the internal iliac with the superior hemorrhoidal from the inferior mesenteric; of the uterine, ovarian, and vesical arteries of the opposite sides; of the lateral sacral with the middle sacral artery; of the inferior epigastric with the internal mammary, inferior intercostal, and lumbar arteries; of the deep iliac circumflex with the lumbar arteries; of the iliolumbar with the last lumbar artery; of the obturator artery, by means of its pubic branch, with the vessel of the opposite side and with the inferior epigastric.

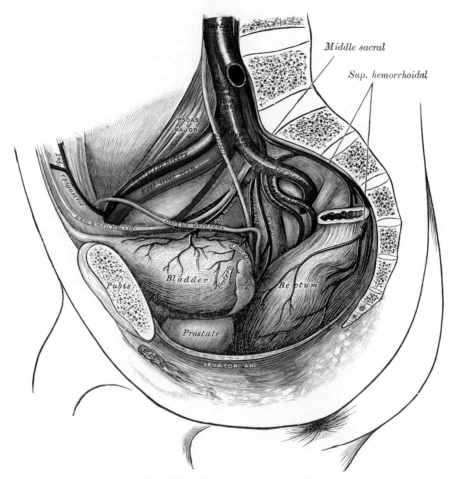

Fig. 580.—The arteries of the pelvis.

The Internal Iliac Artery

The **internal iliac or hypogastric artery** (*a. iliac interna*) (Figs. 580, 581) supplies the walls and viscera of the pelvis, the buttock, the generative organs, and the medial side of the thigh. It is a short, thick vessel, smaller than the external iliac, and about 4 cm. in length. It *arises* at the bifurcation of the common iliac, opposite the lumbosacral articulation, and passing downward to the upper margin of the greater sciatic foramen, divides into anterior and posterior branches.

Relations.—It is in relation *in front* with the ureter; *behind*, with the internal iliac vein, the lumbosacral trunk, and the Piriformis muscle; *laterally*, near its origin, with the external iliac vein, which lies between it and the Psoas major muscle; lower down, with the obturator nerve.

In the fetus, the internal iliac artery is twice as large as the external iliac, and is the direct continuation of the common iliac. It ascends along the side of the bladder, and runs upward on the back of the anterior wall of the abdomen to the umbilicus, converging toward its fellow of the opposite side. Having passed through the umbilical opening, the two arteries, now termed **umbilical**, enter the umbilical cord, where they are coiled around the umbilical vein, and ultimately ramify in the placenta.

At birth, when the placental circulation ceases, the pelvic portion only of the artery remains patent and constitutes the internal iliac and the first part of the superior vesical artery of the adult; the remainder of the vessel is converted into a solid fibrous cord, the **lateral umbilical ligament** (*obliterated hypogastric artery*) which extends from the pelvis to the umbilicus.

Variations.—The branches of the internal iliac artery are subject to great variation. Any two of the following branches, the superior gluteal, the inferior gluteal, or the internal pudendal, may have a common trunk. The iliolumbar occasionally arises from the common iliac. The obturator artery may arise either from the anterior trunk or posterior trunk of the hypogastric. The branches to be described fit the majority of cases, according to Poirier and Charpy.

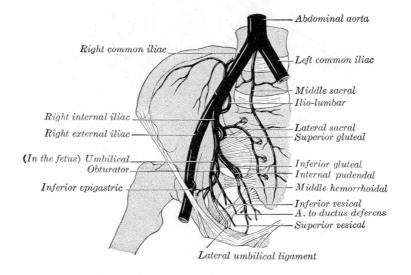

Fig. 581.—The internal iliac artery and its branches.

Collateral Circulation.—The circulation after ligature of the internal iliac artery is carried on by the anastomoses of the uterine and ovarian arteries; of the vesical arteries of the two sides; of the hemorrhoidal branches of the internal iliac with those from the inferior mesenteric; of the obturator artery, by means of its pubic branch, with the vessel of the opposite side, and with the inferior epigastric and medial femoral circumflex; of the circumflex and perforating branches of the profunda femoris with the inferior gluteal; of the superior gluteal with the posterior branches of the lateral sacral arteries; of the iliolumbar with the last lumbar; of the lateral sacral with the middle sacral; and of the iliac circumflex with the iliolumbar and superior gluteal.

Branches.—The branches of the internal iliac artery are:

Anterior Branches	*Posterior Branches*
Superior Vesical.	Iliolumbar.
Middle Vesical.	Lateral Sacral.
Inferior Vesical.	Superior Gluteal.
Middle Hemorrhoidal.	
Obturator.	
Internal Pudendal.	
Inferior Gluteal.	
Uterine ⎫ *In the Female.*	
Vaginal ⎭	

The **superior vesical artery** (*a. vesicalis superior*) supplies numerous branches to the upper part of the bladder. From one of these a slender vessel, the **artery to the ductus deferens,** takes origin and accompanies the duct in its course to the testis, where it anastomoses with the internal spermatic artery. Other branches supply the ureter. The first part of the superior vesical artery represents the terminal section of the previous portion of the fetal hypogastric artery.

The **middle vesical artery** (*a. vesicalis medialis*), usually a branch of the superior, is distributed to the fundus of the bladder and the vesiculæ seminales.

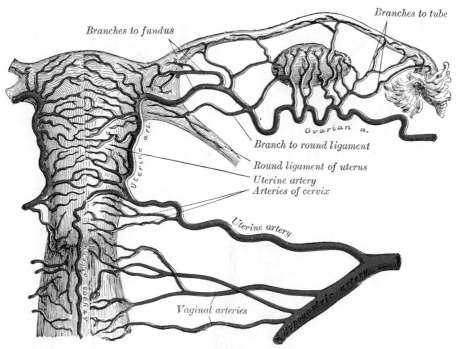

Branches to tube

Branches to fundus

Ovarian a.

Branch to round ligament

Round ligament of uterus
Uterine artery
Arteries of cervix

Uterine art.

Uterine artery

hypogastric artery

Vaginal arteries

hypogastric artery

FIG. 582.—The arteries of the internal organs of generation of the female, seen from behind. (After Hyrtl.)

The **inferior vesical artery** (*a. vesicalis inferior*) frequently *arises* in common with the middle hemorrhoidal, and is distributed to the fundus of the bladder, the prostate, and the vesiculæ seminales. The branches to the prostate communicate with the corresponding vessels of the opposite side.

The **middle hemorrhoidal artery** (*a. rectalis media*) usually *arises* with the preceding vessel. It is distributed to the rectum, anastomosing with the inferior vesical and with the superior and inferior hemorrhoidal arteries. It gives offsets to the vesiculæ seminales and prostate.

The **uterine artery** (*a. uterina*) (Fig. 582) springs from the anterior division of the internal iliac and runs medialward on the Levator ani and toward the cervix uteri; about 2 cm. from the cervix it crosses above and in front of the ureter, to which it supplies a small branch. Reaching the side of the uterus it ascends in a tortuous manner between the two layers of the broad ligament to the junction of the uterine tube and uterus. It then runs lateralward toward the hilus of the ovary, and ends by joining with the ovarian artery. It supplies branches to the cervix uteri and others which descend on the vagina; the latter anastomose with branches of the vaginal arteries and form with them two median longitudinal vessels—the **azygos arteries of the vagina**—one of which runs down in front of and the other behind the vagina. It supplies numerous branches to the body of the uterus, and from its terminal portion twigs are distributed to the uterine tube and the round ligament of the uterus.

The **vaginal artery** (*a. vaginalis*) usually corresponds to the inferior vesical in the male; it descends upon the vagina, supplying its mucous membrane, and sends branches to the bulb of the vestibule, the fundus of the bladder, and the contiguous part of the rectum. It assists in forming the azygos arteries of the vagina, and is frequently represented by two or three branches.

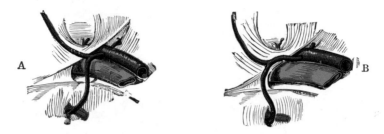

Fig. 583.—Variations in origin and course of obturator artery.

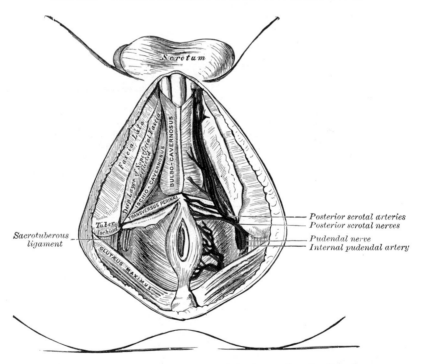

Fig. 584.—The superficial branches of the internal pudendal artery.

The **obturator artery** (*a. obturatoria*) passes forward and downward on the lateral wall of the pelvis, to the upper part of the obturator foramen, and, escaping from the pelvic cavity through the obturator canal, it divides into an **anterior** and a **posterior branch**. In the pelvic cavity this vessel is in relation, laterally, with the obturator fascia; medially, with the ureter, ductus deferens, and peritoneum; while a little below it is the obturator nerve.

Branches.—*Inside the pelvis* the obturator artery gives off **iliac branches** to the iliac fossa, which supply the bone and the Iliacus, and anastomose with the ilio-lumbar artery; a **vesical branch,** which runs backward to supply the bladder; and a **pubic branch,** which is given off from the vessel just before it leaves the pelvic cavity. The pubic branch ascends upon the back of the pubis, communicating with the opposite corresponding vessel, and with the inferior epigastric artery.

Outside the pelvis, the obturator artery divides at the upper margin of the obtur-ator foramen, into an anterior and a posterior branch which encircle the foramen under cover of the Obturator externus.

The **anterior branch** runs forward on the outer surface of the obturator mem-brane curving downward along the anterior margin of the foramen. It distributes branches to the Obturator externus, Pectineus, Adductores, and Gracilis, anasto-mosing with the posterior branch and with the medial femoral circumflex artery.

The **posterior branch** follows the posterior margin of the foramen and divides into two branches. One runs anteriorly on the inferior ramus of the ischium where it anastomoses with the anterior branch of the obturator. The other branch gives twigs to the muscles attached to the ischial tuberosity and anastomoses with the inferior gluteal. It also supplies an articular branch which enters the hip-joint through the acetabular notch, ramifies in the fat at the bottom of the acetabulum and sends a twig along the ligamentum teres to the head of the femur.

Variations.—The obturator artery sometimes arises from the main stem or from the posterior trunk of the internal iliac, or it may spring from the superior gluteal artery. It arises in common with the inferior gluteal in 24 per cent of cases (Lipschütz). Various authors describe the obturator as arising in from 13 per cent to 28 per cent of cases from the inferior epigastric or even from the external iliac; in this case it descends almost vertically to the upper part of the obturator foramen. This origin represents the enlargement of the anastomosis that is normally present. The artery in this course usually lies in contact with the external iliac vein, and on the lateral side of the femoral ring (Fig. 583 A); in such cases it would not be endangered in the operation for strangulated femoral hernia. Occasionally, however, it curves along the free margin of the lacunar ligament (Fig. 583 B), and if in such circumstances a femoral hernia occurred, the vessel would almost completely encircle the neck of the hernial sac, and would be in great danger of being wounded if an operation were performed for strangulation.

The **internal pudendal artery** (*a. pudenda interna; internal pudic artery*) is the smaller of the two terminal branches of the anterior trunk of the internal iliac, and supplies the external organs of generation. Though the course of the artery is the same in the two sexes, the vessel is smaller in the female than in the male, and the distribution of its branches somewhat different. The description of its arrange-ment in the male will first be given, and subsequently the differences which it presents in the female will be mentioned.

The **internal pudendal artery in the male** passes downward and outward to the lower border of the greater sciatic foramen, and emerges from the pelvis between the Piriformis and Coccygeus; it then crosses the ischial spine, and enters the peri-neum through the lesser sciatic foramen. The artery now crosses the Obturator internus, along the lateral wall of the ischiorectal fossa, being situated about 4 cm. above the lower margin of the ischial tuberosity. It gradually approaches the margin of the inferior ramus of the ischium and passes forward between the two layers of the fascia of the urogenital diaphragm; it then runs forward along the medial margin of the inferior ramus of the pubis, and about 1.25 cm. behind the pubic arcuate ligament it divides into the **dorsal and deep arteries of the penis,** but it may pierce the superficial fascia of the urogenital diaphragm before doing so.

Relations.—Within the pelvis, it lies in front of the Piriformis muscle, the sacral plexus of nerves, and the inferior gluteal artery. Crossing the ischial spine, it is covered by the Glutæus maximus and overlapped by the sacrotuberous ligament. Here the pudendal nerve lies to the medial side and the nerve to the Obturator internus to the lateral side. In the perineum it lies

44

on the lateral wall of the ischiorectal fossa, in a canal (*Alcock's canal*) formed by the splitting of the obturator fascia. It is accompanied by a pair of venæ comitantes and the pudendal nerve.

Variations.—The internal pudendal artery is sometimes smaller than usual, or fails to give off one or two of its usual branches; in such cases the deficiency is supplied by branches derived from an additional vessel, the **accessory pudendal,** which generally arises from the internal pudendal artery before its exit from the greater sciatic foramen. It passes forward along the lower part of the bladder and across the side of the prostate to the root of the penis, where it perforates the urogenital diaphragm, and gives off the branches usually derived from the internal pudendal artery. The deficiency most frequently met with is that in which the internal pudendal ends as the artery of the urethral bulb, the dorsal and deep arteries of the penis being derived from the accessory pudendal. The internal pudendal artery may also end as the perineal, the artery of the urethral bulb being derived, with the other two branches, from the accessory vessel. Occasionally the accessory pudendal artery is derived from one of the other branches of the hypogastric artery, most frequently the inferior vesical or the obturator.

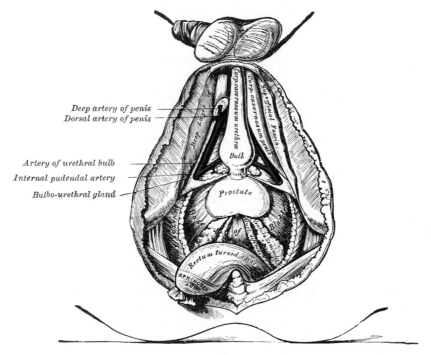

Fig. 585.—The deeper branches of the internal pudendal artery.

Branches.—The branches of the internal pudendal artery (Figs. 584, 585) are:

Muscular.
Inferior Hemorrhoidal.
Perineal.

Artery of the Urethral Bulb.
Urethral.
Deep Artery of the Penis.

Dorsal Artery of the Penis.

The **Muscular Branches** consist of two sets: one given off in the pelvis; the other as the vessel crosses the ischial spine. The former consists of several small offset which supply the Levator ani, the Obturator internus, the Piriformis, and the Coccygeus. The branches given off outside the pelvis are distributed to the adjacent parts of the Glutæus maximus and external rotator muscles. They anastomose with branches of the inferior gluteal artery.

The **Inferior Hemorrhoidal Artery** (*a. rectalis inferior*) *arises* from the internal pudendal as it passes above the ischial tuberosity. Piercing the wall of Alcock's canal it divides into two or three branches which cross the ischiorectal fossa, and are distributed to the muscles and integument of the anal region, and send offshoots around the lower edge of the Glutæus maximus to the skin of the buttock. They anastomose with the corresponding vessels of the opposite side, with the superior and middle hemorrhoidal, and with the perineal artery.

The **Perineal Artery** (*a. perinei; superficial perineal artery*) *arises* from the internal pudendal, in front of the preceding branches, and turns upward, crossing either over or under the Transverus perinæi superficialis, and runs forward, parallel to the pubic arch, in the interspace between the Bulbocavernosus and Ischiocavernosus, both of which it supplies, and finally divides into several **posterior scrotal branches** which are distributed to the skin and dartos tunic of the scrotum. As it crosses the Transversus perinæi superficialis it gives off the **transverse perineal artery** which runs transversely on the cutaneous surface of the muscle, and anastomoses with the corresponding vessel of the opposite side and with the perineal and inferior hemorrhoidal arteries. It supplies the Transversus perinæi superficialis and the structures between the anus and the urethral bulb.

The **Artery of the Urethral Bulb** (*a. bulbi penis*) is a short vessel of large caliber which *arises* from the internal pudendal between the two layers of fascia of the urogenital diaphragm; it passes medialward, pierces the inferior fascia of the urogenital diaphragm, and gives off branches which ramify in the bulb of the urethra and in the posterior part of the corpus cavernosum urethræ. It gives off a small branch to the bulbo-urethral gland.

The **Urethral Artery** (*a. urethralis*) *arises* a short distance in front of the artery of the urethral bulb. It runs forward and medialward, pierces the inferior fascia of the urogenital diaphragm and enters the corpus cavernosum urethræ, in which it is continued forward to the glans penis.

The **Deep Artery of the Penis** (*a. profunda penis; artery to the corpus cavernosum*), one of the terminal branches of the internal pudendal, *arises* from that vessel while it is situated between the two fasciæ of the urogenital diaphragm; it pierces the superficial layer, and, entering the crus penis obliquely, runs forward in the center of the corpus cavernosum penis, to which its branches are distributed.

The **Dorsal Artery of the Penis** (*a. dorsalis penis*) ascends between the crus penis and the pubic symphysis, and, piercing the superficial fascia of the urogenital diaphragm, passes between the two layers of the suspensory ligament of the penis, and runs forward on the dorsum of the penis to the glans, where it divides into two branches, which supply the glans and prepuce. On the penis, it lies between the dorsal nerve and deep dorsal vein, the former being on its lateral side. It supplies the integument and fibrous sheath of the corpus cavernosum penis, sending branches through the sheath to anastomose with the preceding vessel.

The **internal pudendal artery in the female** is smaller than in the male. Its origin and course are similar, and there is considerable analogy in the distribution of its branches. The perineal artery supplies the labia pudendi; the artery of the bulb supplies the bulbus vestibuli and the erectile tissue of the vagina; the deep artery of the clitoris supplies the corpus cavernosum clitoridis; and the dorsal artery of the clitoris supplies the dorsum of that organ, and ends in the glans and prepuce of the clitoris.

The **inferior gluteal artery** (*a. glutæa inferior; sciatic artery*) (Fig. 586), the larger of the two terminal branches of the anterior trunk of the hypogastric, is distributed chiefly to the buttocks and back of the thigh. It passes posteriorly between the first and second sacral nerves, or between the second and third sacral nerves, and then descends between the piriformis and coccygeus muscles through the lower part of the sciatic foramen to the gluteal region. It then descends in the interval between the greater trochanter of the femur and tuberosity of the ischium, accompanied by the sciatic and posterior femoral cutaneous nerves and covered by the Glutæus maximus, is continued down the back of the thigh, supplying the skin, and anastomosing with branches of the perforating arteries.

Inside the pelvis it distributes branches to the Piriformis, Coccygeus, and Levator ani; some branches which supply the fat around the rectum, and occasionally take the place of the middle hemorrhoidal artery; and vesical branches to the fundus of the bladder, vesiculæ seminales, and prostate. *Outside the pelvis* it gives off the following branches:

Muscular.	Anastomotic.
Coccygeal.	Articular.
Comitans Nervi Ischiadici.	Cutaneous.

The **Muscular Branches** supply the Glutæus maximus, anastomosing with the superior gluteal artery in the substance of the muscle; the external rotators, anastomosing with the internal pudendal artery; and the muscles attached to the tuberosity of the ischium, anastomosing with the posterior branch of the obturator and the medial femoral circumflex arteries.

The **Coccygeal Branches** run medialward, pierce the sacrotuberous ligament, and supply the Glutæus maximus, the integument, and other structures on the back of the coccyx.

The **Arteria Comitans Nervi Ischiadici** is a long, slender vessel, which accompanies the sciatic nerve for a short distance; it then penetrates it, and runs in its substance to the lower part of the thigh.

The **Anastomotic** is directed downward across the external rotators, and assists in forming the so-called **crucial anastomosis** by joining with the first perforating and medial and lateral femoral circumflex arteries.

The **Articular Branch**, generally derived from the anastomotic, is distributed to the capsule of the hip-joint.

The **Cutaneous Branches** are distributed to the skin of the buttock and back of the thigh.

The **iliolumbar artery** (*a. iliolumbalis*), a branch of the posterior trunk of the internal iliac, turns upward behind the obturator nerve and the external iliac vessels, to the medial border of the Psoas major, behind which it divides into a lumbar and an iliac branch.

The **Lumbar Branch** (*ramus lumbalis*) supplies the Psoas major and Quadratus lumborum, anastomoses with the last lumbar artery, and sends a small **spinal branch** through the intervertebral foramen between the last lumbar vertebra and the sacrum, into the vertebral canal, to supply the cauda equina.

The **Iliac Branch** (*ramus iliacus*) descends to supply the Iliacus; some offsets, running between the muscle and the bone, anastomose with the iliac branches of the obturator; one of these enters an oblique canal to supply the bone, while others run along the crest of the ilium, distributing branches to the gluteal and abdominal muscles, and anastomosing in their course with the superior gluteal, iliac circumflex, and lateral femoral circumflex arteries.

The **lateral sacral arteries** (*aa. sacrales laterales*) (Fig. 580) *arise* from the posterior division of the hypogastric; there are usually two, a **superior** and an **inferior.**

The **superior,** of large size, passes medialward, and, after anastomosing with branches from the middle sacral, enters the first or second anterior sacral foramen, supplies branches to the contents of the sacral canal, and, escaping by the corresponding posterior sacral foramen, is distributed to the skin and muscles on the dorsum of the sacrum, anastomosing with the superior gluteal.

The **inferior** runs obliquely across the front of the Piriformis and the sacral nerves to the medial side of the anterior sacral foramina, descends on the front of the sacrum, and anastomoses over the coccyx with the middle sacral and opposite the lateral sacral artery. In its course it gives off branches, which enter the anterior sacral foramina; these, after supplying the contents of the sacral canal, emerge by the posterior sacral foramina, and are distributed to the muscles and skin on the dorsal surface of the sacrum, anastomosing with the gluteal arteries.

The **superior gluteal artery** (*a. glutæa superior; gluteal artery*) (Fig. 586) is the largest branch of the internal iliac, and appears to be the continuation of the posterior division of that vessel. It is a short artery which runs backward between the lumbosacral trunk and the first sacral nerve, and, passing out of the pelvis above the upper border of the Piriformis, immediately divides into a **superficial** and a **deep branch**. Within the pelvis it gives off a few branches to the Iliacus, Piriformis, and Obturator internus, and before quitting that cavity, a nutrient artery which enters the ilium.

The **superficial branch** enters the deep surface of the Glutæus maximus, and divides into numerous branches, some of which supply the muscle and anastomose with the inferior gluteal, while others perforate its tendinous origin, and supply the integument covering the posterior surface of the sacrum, anastomosing with the posterior branches of the lateral sacral arteries.

The **deep branch** lies under the Glutæus medius and almost immediately subdivides into two. Of these, the **superior division**, continuing the original course of the vessel, passes along the upper border of the Glutæus minimus to the anterior superior spine of the ilium, anastomosing with the deep iliac circumflex artery and the ascending branch of the lateral femoral circumflex artery. The **inferior division** crosses the Glutæus minimus obliquely to the greater trochanter, distributing branches to the Glutæi and anastomoses with the lateral femoral circumflex artery. Some branches pierce the Glutæus minimus and supply the hip-joint.

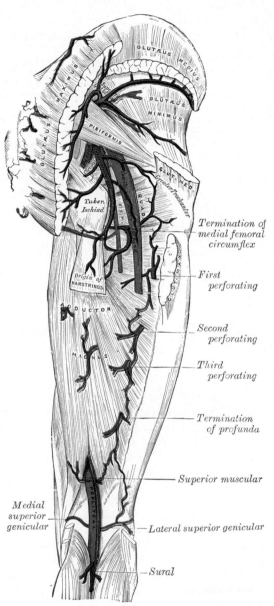

Fig. 586.—The arteries of the gluteal and posterior femoral regions.

The External Iliac Artery (A. Iliaca Externa) (Fig. 580).

The **external iliac artery** is larger than the internal iliac, and passes obliquely downward and lateralward along the medial border of the Psoas major, from the bifurcation of the common iliac to a point beneath the inguinal ligament, midway between the anterior superior spine of the ilium and the symphysis pubis, where it enters the thigh and becomes the femoral artery.

Relations.—*In front and medially*, the artery is in relation with the peritoneum, subperitoneal areolar tissue, the termination of the ileum and frequently the vermiform process on the right side, and, on the left, the sigmoid colon and a thin layer of fascia, derived from the iliac fascia, which surrounds the artery and vein. In the female it is crossed at its origin by the ovarian vessels, and occasionally by the ureter. The internal spermatic vessels lie for some distance upon it near its termination, and it is crossed in this situation by the external spermatic branch of the genitofemoral nerve and the deep iliac circumflex vein; the ductus deferens in the male, and the round ligament of the uterus in the female, curve down across its medial side. *Behind*, it is in relation with the medial border of the Psoas major, from which it is separated by the iliac fascia. At the upper part of its course, the external iliac vein lies partly behind it, but lower down lies entirely to its medial side. *Laterally*, it rests against the Psoas major, from which it is separated by the iliac fascia. Numerous lymphatic vessels and lymph glands lie on the front and on the medial side of the vessel.

Collateral Circulation.—The principal anastomoses in carrying on the collateral circulation, after the application of a ligature to the external iliac, are: the iliolumbar with the iliac circumflex; the superior gluteal with the lateral femoral circumflex; the obturator with the medial femoral circumflex; the inferior gluteal with the first perforating and circumflex branches of the profunda artery; and the internal pudendal with the external pudendal. When the obturator arises from the inferior epigastric, it is supplied with blood by branches, from either the internal iliac, the lateral sacral, or the internal pudendal. The inferior epigastric receives its supply from the internal mammary and lower intercostal arteries, and from the internal iliac by the anastomoses of its branches with the obturator.

Branches.—Besides several small branches to the Psoas major and the neighboring lymph glands, the external iliac gives off two branches of considerable size:

Inferior Epigastric.   Deep Iliac Circumflex.

The **inferior epigastric artery** (*a. epigastrica inferior; deep epigastric artery*) (Fig. 589) *arises* from the external iliac, immediately above the inguinal ligament. It curves forward in the subperitoneal tissue, and then ascends obliquely along the medial margin of the abdominal inguinal ring; continuing its course upward, it pierces the transversalis fascia, and, passing in front of the linea semicircularis, ascends between the Rectus abdominis and the posterior lamella of its sheath. It finally divides into numerous branches, which anastomose, above the umbilicus, with the superior epigastric branch of the internal mammary and with the lower intercostal arteries (Fig. 563). As the inferior epigastric artery passes obliquely upward from its origin it lies along the lower and medial margins of the abdominal inguinal ring, and behind the commencement of the spermatic cord. The ductus deferens, as it leaves the spermatic cord in the male, or the round ligament of the uterus in the female, winds around the lateral and posterior aspects of the artery.

Branches.—The branches of the vessel are: the **cremasteric artery** (*external spermatic artery*), which accompanies the spermatic cord, and supplies the Cremaster and other coverings of the cord, anastomosing with the internal spermatic artery (in the female it is very small and accompanies the round ligament); a **pubic branch** which runs along the inguinal ligament, and then descends along the medial margin of the femoral ring to the back of the pubis, and there anastomoses with the pubic branch of the obturator artery; **muscular branches**, some of which are distributed to the abdominal muscles and peritoneum, anastomosing with the iliac circumflex and lumbar arteries; branches which perforate the tendon of the Obliquus externus, and supply the integument, anastomosing with branches of the superficial epigastric.

Variations.—The origin of the inferior epigastric may take place from any part of the external iliac between the inguinal ligament and a point 6 cm. above it; or it may arise below this ligament, from the femoral. It frequently springs from the external iliac, by a common trunk with the obturator. Sometimes it arises from the obturator, the latter vessel being furnished by the hypogastric, or it may be formed of two branches, one derived from the external iliac, the other from the hypogastric.

The **deep iliac circumflex artery** (*a. circumflexa ilii profunda*) *arises* from the lateral aspect of the external iliac nearly opposite the inferior epigastric artery. It ascends obliquely lateralward behind the inguinal ligament, contained in a fibrous sheath formed by the junction of the transversalis fascia and iliac fascia, to the anterior superior iliac spine, where it anastomoses with the ascending branch of the lateral femoral circumflex artery. It then pierces the transversalis fascia and passes along the inner lip of the crest of the ilium to about its middle, where it perforates the Transversus, and runs backward between that muscle and the Obliquus internus, to anastomose with the iliolumbar and superior gluteal arteries. Opposite the anterior superior spine of the ilium it gives off a large branch, which ascends between the Obliquus internus and Transversus muscles, supplying them, and anastomosing with the lumbar and inferior epigastric arteries.

THE ARTERIES OF THE LOWER EXTREMITY.

The artery which supplies the greater part of the lower extremity is the direct continuation of the external iliac. It runs as a single trunk from the inguinal ligament to the lower border of the Popliteus, where it divides into two branches, the **anterior** and **posterior tibial**. The upper part of the main trunk is named the **femoral**, the lower part the **popliteal**.

THE FEMORAL ARTERY (A. FEMORALIS) (Figs. 587, 592).

The **femoral artery** begins immediately behind the inguinal ligament, midway between the anterior superior spine of the ilium and the symphysis pubis, and passes down the front and medial side of the thigh. It ends at the junction of the middle with the lower third of the thigh, where it passes through an opening in the Adductor magnus to become the popliteal artery. The vessel, at the upper part of the thigh, lies in front of the hip-joint; in the lower part of its course it lies to the medial side of the body of the femur, and between these two parts, where it crosses the angle between the head and body, the vessel is some distance from the bone. The first 4 cm. of the vessel is enclosed, together with the femoral vein, in a fibrous sheath—the **femoral sheath**. In the upper third of the thigh the femoral artery is contained in the **femoral triangle** (*Scarpa's triangle*), and in the middle third of the thigh, in the **adductor canal** (*Hunter's canal*).

The **femoral sheath** (*crural sheath*) (Figs. 587, 588) is formed by a prolongation downward, behind the inguinal ligament, of the fasciæ which line the abdomen, the transversalis fascia being continued down in front of the femoral vessels and the iliac fascia behind them. The sheath assumes the form of a short funnel, the wide end of which is directed upward, while the lower, narrow end fuses with the fascial investment of the vessels, about 4 cm. below the inguinal ligament. It is strengthened in front by a band termed the **deep crural arch** (page 466). The lateral wall of the sheath is vertical and is perforated by the lumboinguinal nerve; the medial wall is directed obliquely downward and lateralward, and is pierced by the great saphenous vein and by some lymphatic vessels. The sheath is divided by two vertical partitions which stretch between its anterior and posterior walls. The lateral compartment contains the femoral artery, and the intermediate the femoral vein, while the medial and smallest compartment is named the **femoral canal,** and contains some lymphatic vessels and a lymph node imbedded in a small amount of areolar tissue. The femoral canal is conical and measures about 1.25 cm. in length. Its base, directed upward and named the **femoral ring,** is oval in form, its long diameter being directed transversely and measuring about 1.25 cm. The

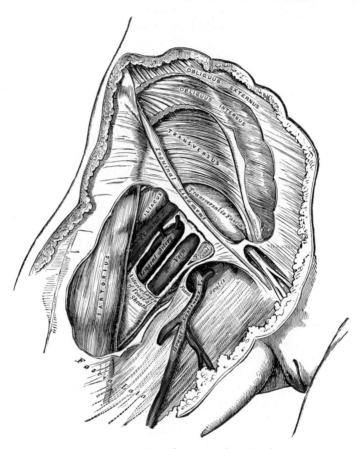

Fig. 587.—Femoral sheath laid open to show its three compartments.

femoral ring (Figs. 588, 589) is bounded in *front* by the inguinal ligament, *behind* by the Pectineus covered by the pectineal fascia, *medially* by the crescentic base of the lacunar ligament, and *laterally* by the fibrous septum on the medial side of the femoral vein. The spermatic cord in the male and the round ligament of the uterus in the female lie immediately above the anterior margin of the ring, while the inferior epigastric vessels are close to its upper and lateral angle. The femoral ring is closed by a somewhat condensed portion of the extraperitoneal fatty tissue, named the **septum femorale** (*crural septum*), the abdominal surface of which supports a small lymph gland and is covered by the parietal layer of the peritoneum. The septum femorale is pierced by numerous lymphatic vessels passing from the deep inguinal to the external iliac lymph nodes. The parietal peritoneum above it presents a slight depression named the **femoral fossa.**

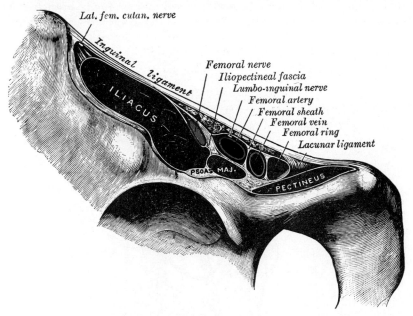

Fig. 588.—Structures passing behind the inguinal ligament.

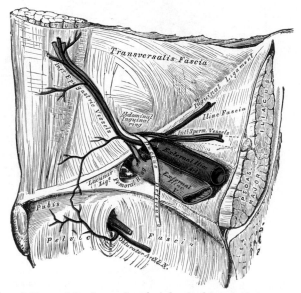

Fig. 589.—The relations of the femoral and abdominal inguinal rings, seen from within the abdomen. Right side.

The **femoral triangle** (*trigonum femorale; Scarpa's triangle*) (Fig. 591) corresponds to the depression seen immediately below the fold of the groin. Its apex is directed downward, and the sides are formed laterally by the Sartorius, medially by the Adductor longus, and above by the inguinal ligament. The floor of the space is formed from its lateral to its medial side by the Iliacus, Psoas major, Pectineus, and in some cases a small part of the Adductor brevis; it is divided into two nearly equal parts by the femoral vessels, which extend from near the middle of its base to its apex: the artery giving off its superficial and profunda branches, the vein receiving the deep femoral and great saphenous tributaries. On the lateral side of the femoral artery is the femoral nerve with its branches. Besides the vessels and nerves, this space contains some fat and lymphatics.

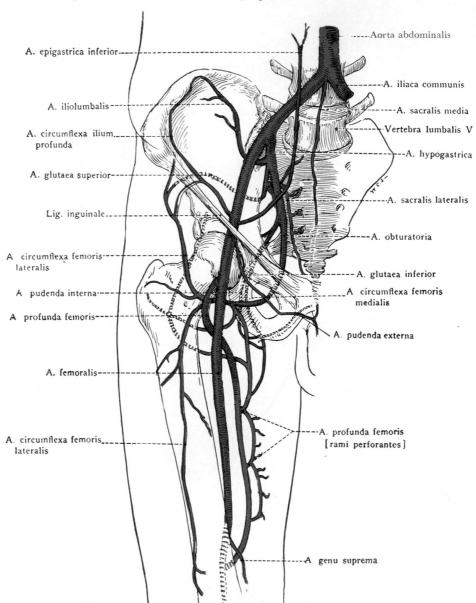

A. epigastrica inferior

A. iliolumbalis

A. circumflexa ilium profunda

A. glutaea superior

Lig. inguinale

A circumflexa femoris lateralis

A pudenda interna

A profunda femoris

A. femoralis

A. circumflexa femoris lateralis

Aorta abdominalis

A. iliaca communis

A. sacralis media

Vertebra lumbalis V

A. hypogastrica

A. sacralis lateralis

A. obturatoria

A. glutaea inferior

A circumflexa femoris medialis

A. pudenda externa

A. profunda femoris [rami perforantes]

A genu suprema

FIG. 590.—Collateral circulation about the hip and the upper part of the right thigh. (Eycleshymer and Jones.)

The **adductor canal** (*canalis adductorius; Hunter's canal*) is an aponeurotic tunnel in the middle third of the thigh, extending from the apex of the femoral triangle to the opening in the Adductor magnus. It is bounded, in front and laterally, by the Vastus medialis; behind by the Adductores longus and magnus; and is covered by a strong aponeurosis which extends from the Vastus medialis, across the femoral vessels to the Adductores longus and magnus; lying on the aponeurosis is the Sartorius muscle. The canal contains the femoral artery and vein, and the saphenous nerve.

Relations of the Femoral Artery.—In the *femoral triangle* (Fig. 591) the artery is superficial, *In front* of it are the skin and superficial fascia, the superficial subinguinal lymph glands, the superficial iliac circumflex vein, the superficial layer of the fascia lata and the anterior part of the femoral sheath. The lumboinguinal nerve courses for a short distance within the lateral compartment of the femoral sheath, and lies at first in front and then lateral to the artery. Near the apex of the femoral triangle the medial branch of the anterior femoral cutaneous nerve crosses the artery from its lateral to its medial side.

Behind the artery are the posterior part of the femoral sheath, the pectineal fascia, the medial part of the tendon of the Psoas major, the Pectineus and the Adductor longus. The artery is separated from the capsule of the hip-joint by the tendon of the Psoas major, from the Pectineus by the femoral vein and profunda vessels, and from the Adductor longus by the femoral vein. The nerve to the Pectineus passes medialward behind the artery. On the *lateral* side of the artery, but separated from it by some fibers of the Psoas major, is the femoral nerve. The femoral vein is on the medial side of the upper part of the artery, but is behind the vessel in the lower part of the femoral triangle.

In the *adductor canal* (Fig. 592) the femoral artery is more deeply situated, being covered by the integument, the superficial and deep fasciæ, the Sartorius and the fibrous roof of the canal; the saphenous nerve crosses from its lateral to its medial side. Behind the artery are the Adductores longus and magnus; in front and lateral to it is the Vastus medialis. The femoral vein lies posterior to the upper part, and lateral to the lower part of the artery.

Variations.—Several cases are recorded in which the femoral artery divided into two trunks below the origin of the profunda, and became reunited near the opening in the Adductor magnus, so as to form a single popliteal artery. One occurred in a patient who was operated upon for popliteal aneurism. A few cases have been recorded in which the femoral artery was absent, its place being supplied by the inferior gluteal artery which accompanied the sciatic nerve to the popliteal fossa. The external iliac in these cases was small, and terminated in the profunda. The femoral vein is occasionally placed along the medial side of the artery throughout the entire extent of the femoral triangle; or it may be split so that a large vein is placed on either side of the artery for a greater or lesser distance.

Collateral Circulation.—After ligature of the femoral artery, the main channels for carrying on the circulation are the anastomoses between—(1) the superior and inferior gluteal branches of the hypogastric with the medial and lateral femoral circumflex and first perforating branches of the profunda femoris; (2) the obturator branch of the hypogastric with the medial femoral circumflex of the profunda; (3) the internal pudendal of the hypogastric with the superficial and deep external pudendal of the femoral; (4) the deep iliac circumflex of the external iliac with the lateral femoral circumflex of the profunda and the superficial iliac circumflex of the femoral, and (5) the inferior gluteal of the hypogastric with the perforating branches of the profunda.

Branches.—The branches of the femoral artery are:

Superficial Epigastric.	Deep External Pudendal.
Superficial Iliac Circumflex.	Muscular.
Superficial External Pudendal.	Profunda Femoris.
Highest Genicular.	

The **superficial epigastric artery** (*a. epigastrica superficialis*) *arises* from the front of the femoral artery about 1 cm. below the inguinal ligament, and, passing through the femoral sheath and the fascia cribrosa, turns upward in front of the inguinal ligament, and ascends between the two layers of the superficial fascia of the abdominal wall nearly to the umbilicus. It distributes branches to the superficial subinguinal lymph glands, the superficial fascia, and the integument; it anastomoses with branches of the inferior epigastric, and with its fellow opposite.

The **superficial iliac circumflex artery** (*a. circumflexa ilii superficialis*), smallest of the cutaneous branches, *arises* close to the preceding, and, piercing the fascia lata, runs lateralward, parallel with the inguinal ligament, to the crest of the ilium; it divides into branches which supply the integument of the groin, and the superficial subinguinal lymph glands, anastomosing with the deep iliac circumflex, superior gluteal and lateral femoral circumflex arteries.

The **superficial external pudendal artery** (*a. pudenda externa superficialis; superficial external pudic artery*) *arises* from the medial side of the femoral artery, close to the preceding vessels, and, after piercing the femoral sheath and fascia cribrosa, courses medialward, across the spermatic cord (or round ligament in the female), to be distributed to the integument on the lower part of the abdomen, the penis and scrotum in the male, and the labium majus in the female, anastomosing with branches of the internal pudendal.

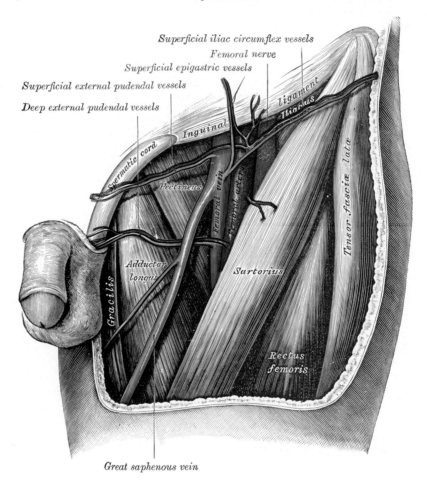

Fig. 591.—The left femoral triangle.

The **deep external pudendal artery** (*a. pudenda externa profunda; deep external pudic artery*), more deeply seated than the preceding, passes medialward across the Pectineus and the Adductor longus muscles; it is covered by the fascia lata, which it pierces at the medial side of the thigh, and is distributed, in the male, to the integument of the scrotum and perineum, in the female to the labium majus; its branches anastomose with the scrotal (or labial) branches of the perineal artery.

Muscular branches (*rami musculares*) are supplied by the femoral artery to the Sartorius, Vastus medialis, and Adductores.

The **profunda femoris artery** (*a. profunda femoris; deep femoral artery*) (Fig. 592) is a large vessel *arising* from the lateral and back part of the femoral artery, from 2 to 5 cm. below the inguinal ligament. At first it lies lateral to the femoral artery; it then runs behind it and the femoral vein to the medial side of the femur,

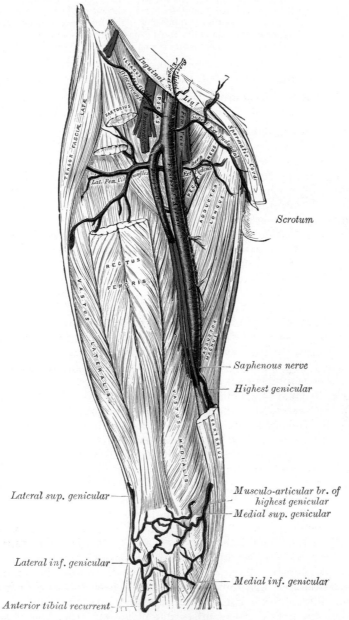

Fig. 592.—The femoral artery.

and, passing downward behind the Adductor longus, ends at the lower third of the thigh in a small branch, which pierces the Adductor magnus, and is distributed on the back of the thigh to the hamstring muscles. The terminal part of the profunda is sometimes named the **fourth perforating artery.**

Relations.—*Behind it*, from above downward, are the Iliacus, Pectineus, Adductor brevis, and Adductor magnus. *In front* it is separated from the femoral artery by the femoral and profunda veins above and by the Adductor longus below. *Laterally*, the origin of the Vastus medialis intervenes between it and the femur.

Variations.—This vessel sometimes arises from the medial side, and, more rarely, from the back of the femoral artery; but a more important peculiarity, from a surgical point of view, is that relating to the height at which the vessel arises. In three-fourths of a large number of cases it arose from 2.25 to 5 cm. below the inguinal ligament; in a few cases the distance was less than 2.25 cm.; more rarely, opposite the ligament; and in one case above the inguinal ligament, from the external iliac. Occasionally the distance between the origin of the vessel and the inguinal ligament exceeds 5 cm.

Branches.—The profunda gives off the following branches: (Fig. 590)

Medial Femoral Circumflex.   Perforating.
Lateral Femoral Circumflex.   Muscular.

The **Medial Femoral Circumflex Artery** (*a. circumflexa femoris medialis; internal circumflex artery*) *arises* from the medial aspect of the profunda, and winds around the medial side of the femur, passing first between the Pectineus and Psoas major, and then between the Obturator externus and the Adductor brevis. At the upper border of the Adductor brevis it gives off two branches: one goes to the Adductores, the Gracilis, and Obturator externus, and anastomoses with the obturator artery; the other descends beneath the Adductor brevis, to supply it and the Adductor magnus; the continuation of the vessel passes backward and divides into superficial, deep, and acetabular branches. The **superficial branch** appears between the Quadratus femoris and upper border of the Adductor magnus, and anastomoses with the inferior gluteal, lateral femoral circumflex, and first perforating arteries (*crucial anastomosis*). The **deep branch** runs obliquely upward upon the tendon of the Obturator externus and in front of the Quadratus femoris toward the trochanteric fossa, where it anastomoses with twigs from the gluteal arteries. The **acetabular branch** *arises* opposite the acetabular notch and enters the hip-joint beneath the transverse ligament in company with an articular branch from the obturator artery; it supplies the fat in the bottom of the acetabulum, and continues along the round ligament to the head of the femur.

The **Lateral Femoral Circumflex Artery** (*a. circumflexa femoris lateralis; external circumflex artery*) *arises* from the lateral side of the profunda, passes horizontally between the divisions of the femoral nerve, and behind the Sartorius and Rectus femoris, and divides into ascending, transverse, and descending branches. The **ascending branch** passes upward, beneath the Tensor fasciæ latæ, to the lateral aspect of the hip, and anastomoses with the terminal branches of the superior gluteal and deep iliac circumflex arteries. The **descending branch** runs downward, behind the Rectus femoris, upon the Vastus lateralis, to which it gives offsets; one long branch descends in the muscle as far as the knee, and anastomoses with the superior lateral genicular branch of the popliteal artery. It is accompanied by the branch of the femoral nerve to the Vastus lateralis. The **transverse branch,** the smallest branch if present, but often absent, passes lateralward over the Vastus intermedius, pierces the Vastus lateralis, and winds around the femur, just below the greater trochanter, anastomosing on the back of the thigh with the medial femoral circumflex, inferior gluteal, and first perforating arteries.

The medial circumflex artery arises independently from the femoral in from 19 to 26.5 per cent. of cases, according to various authors. The lateral circumflex artery arises independently from the femoral as frequently as 18 per cent. of the time. The two circumflex arteries may arise by a common trunk from the profunda femoris.

The **Perforating Arteries** (Fig. 594), usually three in number, are so named because they perforate the tendon of the Adductor magnus to reach the back of the thigh.

They pass backward close to the linea aspera of the femur under cover of small tendinous arches in the muscle. The first is given off above the Adductor brevis, the second in front of that muscle, and the third immediately below it.

The **first perforating artery** (*a. perforans prima*) passes backward between the Pectineus and Adductor brevis (sometimes perforating the latter); it pierces the Adductor magnus close to the linea aspera. It gives branches to the Adductores brevis and magnus, Biceps femoris, and Glutæus maximus, and anastomoses with the inferior gluteal, medial and lateral femoral circumflex and second perforating arteries. (Fig. 590)

The **second perforating artery** (*a. perforans secunda*), larger than the first, pierces the tendons of the Adductores brevis and magnus, and divides into ascending and descending branches, which supply the posterior femoral muscles, anastomosing with the first and third perforating. The second artery frequently *arises* in common with the first. The **nutrient artery** of the femur is usually given off from the second perforating artery; when two nutrient arteries exist, they usually spring from the first and third perforating vessels.

The **third perforating artery** (*a. perforans tertia*) is given off below the Adductor brevis; it pierces the Adductor magnus, and divides into branches which supply the posterior femoral muscles; anastomosing above with the higher perforating arteries, and below with the terminal branches of the profunda and the muscular branches of the popliteal. The nutrient artery of the femur may arise from this branch. The termination of the profunda artery, already described, is sometimes termed the **fourth perforating artery**.

Numerous **muscular branches** *arise* from the profunda; some of these end in the Adductores, others pierce the Adductor magnus, give branches to the hamstrings, and anastomose with the medial femoral circumflex artery and with the superior muscular branches of the popliteal.

The **descending genicular artery** (*a. genu descendens; highest genicular artery; anastomotica magna artery*) (Fig. 592) *arises* from the femoral just before it passes through the opening in the tendon of the Adductor magnus, and immediately divides into a saphenous and a musculo-articular branch. The **saphenous branch** pierces the aponeurotic covering of the adductor canal, and accompanies the saphenous nerve to the medial side of the knee. It passes between the Sartorius and Gracilis, and, piercing the fascia lata, is distributed to the integument of the upper and medial part of the leg, anastomosing with the medial inferior genicular artery. The **musculo-articular branch** descends in the substance of the Vastus medialis, and in front of the tendon of the Adductor magnus, to the medial side of the knee, where it anastomoses with the medial superior genicular artery and anterior recurrent tibial artery. A branch from this vessel crosses above the patellar surface of the femur, forming an anastomotic arch with the lateral superior genicular artery, and supplying branches to the knee-joint.

THE POPLITEAL FOSSA (Fig. 593).

Boundaries.—The **popliteal fossa** or **space** is a lozenge-shaped space, at the back of the knee-joint. Laterally it is bounded by the Biceps femoris above, and by the Plantaris and the lateral head of the Gastrocnemius below; medially it is limited by the Semitendinosus and Semimembranosus above, and by the medial head of the Gastrocnemius below. The floor is formed by the popliteal surface of the femur, the oblique popliteal ligament of the knee-joint, the upper end of the tibia, and the fascia covering the Popliteus; the fossa is covered by the fascia lata.

Contents.—The popliteal fossa contains the popliteal vessels, the tibial and the common peroneal nerves, the termination of the small saphenous vein, the lower part of the posterior femoral cutaneous nerve, the articular branch from the obturator nerve, a few small lymph nodes, and a considerable amount of fat. The tibial nerve descends through the middle of the fossa, lying under the deep fascia and crossing the vessels posteriorly from the lateral to the medial side. The common peroneal nerve descends on the lateral side of the upper part of the fossa, close to the tendon of the Biceps femoris. On the floor of the fossa are the popliteal vessels, the vein being superficial to the artery and united to it by dense areolar tissue; the vein is a thick-walled vessel, at first lateral to the artery, and then crossing it posteriorly to gain its medial side below; sometimes it is double, the artery lying between the two veins, which are usually connected by short transverse branches. The articular branch from the obturator nerve descends upon the artery to the knee-joint. The popliteal lymph nodes, six or seven in number, are imbedded in the fat; one lies beneath the popliteal fascia near the termination of the external saphenous vein, another between the popliteal artery and the back of the knee-joint, while others are placed alongside the popliteal vessel. Arising from the artery, and passing off from it at right angles, are its genicular branches.

The Popliteal Artery (A. Poplitea) (Fig. 593).

The **popliteal artery** is the continuation of the femoral, and courses through the popliteal fossa. It extends from the opening in the Adductor magnus, at the junction of the middle and lower thirds of the thigh, downward and lateralward to the intercondyloid fossa of the femur, and then vertically downward to the lower border of the Popliteus, where it divides into **anterior** and **posterior tibial arteries.**

Relations.—In *front* of the artery from above downward are the popliteal surface of the femur (which is separated from the vessel by some fat), the back of the knee-joint, and the fascia covering the Popliteus. *Behind*, it is overlapped by the Semimembranosus above, and is covered by the Gastrocnemius and Plantaris below. In the middle part of its course the artery is separated from the integument and fasciæ by a quantity of fat, and is crossed from the lateral to the medial side by the tibial nerve and the popliteal vein, the vein being between the nerve and the artery and closely adherent to the latter. On its *lateral* side, above, are the Biceps femoris, the tibial nerve, the popliteal vein, and the lateral condyle of the femur; below, the Plantaris

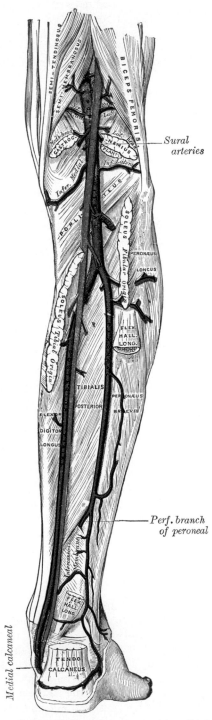

Fig. 593.—The popliteal, posterior tibial, and peroneal arteries.

and the lateral head of the Gastrocnemius. On its *medial* side, above, are the Semimembranosus and the medial condyle of the femur; below, the tibial nerve, the popliteal vein, and the medial head of the Gastrocnemius. The relations of the popliteal lymph nodes to the artery are described above.

Variations in Point of Division.—Occasionally the popliteal artery divides into its terminal branches opposite the knee-joint. The anterior tibial under these circumstances usually passes in front of the Popliteus.

Unusual Branches.—The artery sometimes divides into the anterior tibial and peroneal, the posterior tibial being wanting, or very small. Occasionally it divides into three branches, the anterior and posterior tibial, and peroneal.

Branches.—The branches of the popliteal artery are:

Muscular { Superior / Sural.	Lateral Superior Genicular.
	Middle Genicular.
Cutaneous.	Medial Inferior Genicular.
Medial Superior Genicular	Lateral Inferior Genicular.

The two or three **superior muscular branches** *arise* from the upper part of the artery, and are distributed to the lower parts of the Adductor magnus and hamstring muscles, anastomosing with the endings of the profunda femoris.

The **sural arteries** (*aa. surales; inferior muscular arteries*) are two large branches, which are distributed to the Gastrocnemius, Soleus, and Plantaris. They *arise* from the popliteal artery opposite the knee-joint.

The **cutaneous branches** *arise* either from the popliteal artery or from some of its branches; they descend between the two heads of the Gastrocnemius, and, piercing the deep fascia, are distributed to the skin of the back of the leg. One branch usually accompanies the small saphenous vein.

The **superior genicular arteries** (*aa. genus superiores; superior articular arteries*) (Figs. 593, 594), two in number, *arise* one on either side of the popliteal, and wind around the femur immediately above its condyles to the front of the knee-joint. The **medial superior genicular** runs in front of the Semimembranosus and Semitendinosus, above the medial head of the Gastrocnemius, and passes beneath the tendon of the Adductor magnus. It divides into two branches, one of which supplies the Vastus medialis, anastomosing with the highest genicular and medial inferior genicular arteries; the other ramifies close to the surface of the femur, supplying it and the knee-joint, and anastomosing with the lateral superior genicular artery. The medial superior genicular artery is frequently of small size, a condition, which is associated with an increase in the size of the highest genicular. The **lateral superior genicular** passes above the lateral condyle of the femur, beneath the tendon of the Biceps femoris, and divides into a superficial and a deep branch; the superficial branch supplies the Vastus lateralis, and anastomoses with the descending branch of the lateral femoral circumflex and the lateral inferior genicular arteries; the deep branch supplies the lower part of the femur and knee-joint, and forms an anastomotic arch across the front of the bone with the highest genicular and the medial inferior genicular arteries.

The **middle genicular artery** (*a. genus media; azygos articular artery*) is a small branch, *arising* opposite the back of the knee-joint. It pierces the oblique popliteal ligament, and supplies the ligaments and synovial membrane in the interior of the articulation.

The **inferior genicular arteries** (*aa. genus inferiores; inferior articular arteries*) (Figs. 593, 594), two in number, *arise* from the popliteal beneath the Gastrocnemius. The **medial inferior genicular** first descends along the upper margin of the Popliteus, to which it gives branches; it then passes below the medial condyle of the tibia, beneath the tibial collateral ligament, at the anterior border of which it ascends to the front and medial side of the joint, to supply the upper end of the tibia and the

45

articulation of the knee, anastomosing with the lateral inferior and medial superior genicular arteries. The **lateral inferior genicular** runs lateralward above the head of the fibula to the front of the knee-joint, passing beneath the lateral head of the Gastrocnemius, the fibular collateral ligament, and the tendon of the Biceps femoris. It ends by dividing into branches, which anastomose with the medial inferior and lateral superior genicular arteries, and with the anterior recurrent tibial artery.

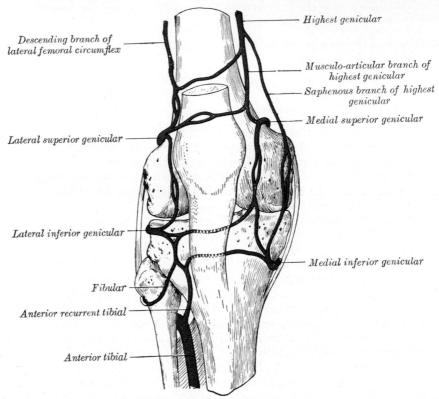

Fig. 594.—Circumpatellar anastomosis.

The **Anastomosis Around the Knee-joint** (Fig. 594).—Around and above the patella, and on the contiguous ends of the femur and tibia, is an intricate net-work of vessels forming a superficial and a deep plexus. The **superficial plexus** is situated in the superficial fascia around the patella, and forms three well-defined arches: one, above the upper border of the patella, in the loose connective tissue over the Quadriceps femoris; the other two, below the level of the patella, are situated in the fat behind the ligamentum patellæ. The **deep plexus,** which forms a close net-work of vessels, lies on the lower end of the femur and upper end of the tibia around their articular surfaces, and sends numerous offsets into the interior of the joint. The arteries which form this plexus are the two medial and the two lateral genicular branches of the popliteal, the highest genicular, the descending branch of the lateral femoral circumflex, and the anterior recurrent tibial.

The Anterior Tibial Artery (A. Tibialis Anterior) (Fig. 595).

The **anterior tibial artery** commences at the bifurcation of the popliteal, at the lower border of the Popliteus, passes forward between the two heads of the Tibialis posterior, and through the aperture above the upper border of the interosseous membrane, to the deep part of the front of the leg: it here lies close to the medial side of the neck of the fibula. It then descends on the anterior surface of the interosseous membrane, gradually approaching the tibia; at the lower part of the leg it lies on this bone, and then on the front of the ankle-joint, where it is more superficial, and becomes the **dorsalis pedis.**

Relations.—In the upper two-thirds of its extent, the anterior tibial artery rests upon the interosseous membrane; in the lower third, upon the front of the tibia, and the anterior ligament of the ankle-joint. In the upper third of its course, it lies between the Tibialis anterior and Extensor digitorum longus; in the middle third between the Tibialis anterior and Extensor hallucis longus. At the ankle it is crossed from the lateral to the medial side by the tendon of the Extensor hallucis longus, lying between it and the first tendon of the Extensor digitorum longus. It is covered in the upper two-thirds by the muscles which lie on either side of it, and by the deep fascia; in the lower third, by the integument and fascia, and the transverse and cruciate crural ligaments.

The anterior tibial artery is accompanied by a pair of venæ comitantes which lie one on either side of the artery; the deep peroneal nerve, coursing around the lateral side of the neck of the fibula, comes into relation with the lateral side of the artery shortly after it has reached the front of the leg; about the middle of the leg the nerve is in front of the artery; at the lower part it is generally again on the lateral side.

Variations.—This vessel may be diminished in size, may be deficient to a greater or less extent or may be entirely wanting, its place being supplied by perforating branches from the posterior tibial, or by the perforating branch of the peroneal artery. The artery occasionally deviates toward the fibular side of the leg, regaining its usual position at the front of the ankle. In rare instances the vessel has been found to approach the surface in the middle of the leg, being covered merely by the integument and fascia below that point.

Branches.—The branches of the anterior tibial artery are:

Posterior Tibial Recurrent.
Fibular.
Anterior Tibial Recurrent.
Muscular.
Anterior Medial Malleolar.
Anterior Lateral Malleolar.

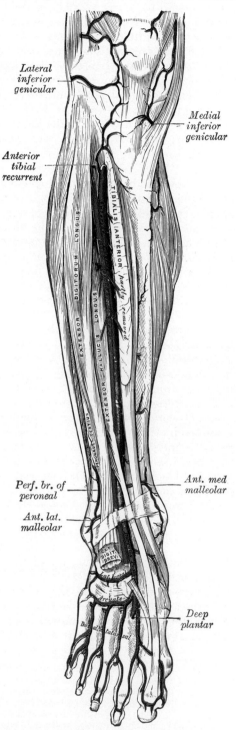

Fig. 595.—Anterior tibial and dorsalis pedis arteries.

The **posterior tibial recurrent artery** (*a. recurrens tibialis posterior*) an inconstant branch, is given off from the anterior tibial before that vessel passes through the interosseous space. It ascends in front of the Popliteus, which it supplies, and anastomoses with the inferior genicular branches of the popliteal artery, giving an offset to the tibiofibular joint.

The **fibular artery** is sometimes derived from the anterior tibial, sometimes from the posterior tibial. It passes lateralward, around the neck of the fibula, through the Soleus, which it supplies, and ends in the substance of the Peroneus longus.

The **anterior tibial recurrent artery** (*a. recurrens tibialis anterior*) *arises* from the anterior tibial, as soon as that vessel has passed through the interosseous space; it ascends in the Tibialis anterior, ramifies on the front and sides of the knee-joint, and assists in the formation of the patellar plexus by anastomosing with the genicular branches of the popliteal, and with the highest genicular artery.

The **muscular branches** (*rami musculares*) are numerous; they are distributed to the muscles which lie on either side of the vessel, some piercing the deep fascia to supply the integument, others passing through the interosseous membrane, and anastomosing with branches of the posterior tibial and peroneal arteries.

The **anterior medial malleolar artery** (*a. malleolaris anterior medialis; internal malleolar artery*) *arises* about 5 cm. above the ankle-joint, and passes behind the tendons of the Extensor hallucis longus and Tibialis anterior, to the medial side of the ankle, upon which it ramifies, anastomosing with branches of the posterior tibial and medial plantar arteries and with the medial calcaneal from the posterior tibial.

The **anterior lateral malleolar artery** (*a. malleolaris anterior lateralis; external malleolar artery*) passes beneath the tendons of the Extensor digitorum longus and Peronæus tertius and supplies the lateral side of the ankle, anastomosing with the perforating branch of the peroneal artery, and with ascending twigs from the lateral tarsal artery.

The arteries around the ankle-joint anastomose freely with one another and form net-works below the corresponding malleoli. The **medial malleolar net-work** is formed by the anterior medial malleolar branch of the anterior tibial, the medial tarsal branches of the dorsalis pedis, the posterior medial malleolar and medial calcaneal branches of the posterior tibial and branches from the medial plantar artery. The **lateral malleolar net-work** is formed by the anterior lateral malleolar branch of the anterior tibial, the lateral tarsal branch of the dorsalis pedis, the perforating and the lateral calcaneal branches of the peroneal, and twigs from the lateral plantar artery. The anterior medial and anterior lateral malleolar arteries often branch from the dorsalis pedis.

The Dorsalis Pedis Artery (A. Dorsalis Pedis) (Fig. 595).

The **arteria dorsalis pedis**, the continuation of the anterior tibial, passes forward from the ankle-joint along the tibial side of the dorsum of the foot to the proximal part of the first intermetatarsal space, where it divides into two branches, the **first dorsal metatarsal** and the **deep plantar.**

Relations.—This vessel, in its course forward, rests upon the front of the articular capsule of the ankle-joint, the talus, navicular, and second cuneiform bones, and the ligaments connecting them, being covered by the integument, fascia and cruciate ligament, and crossed near its termination by the first tendon of the Extensor digitorum brevis On its *tibial side* is the tendon of the Extensor hallucis longus; on its *fibular side*, the first tendon of the Extensor digitorum longus, and the termination of the deep peroneal nerve It is accompanied by two veins.

Variations.—The dorsal artery of the foot may be larger than usual, to compensate for a deficient plantar artery; or its terminal branches to the toes may be absent, the toes then being supplied by the medial plantar; or its place may be taken by a large perforating branch of the peroneal artery, in 3 per cent. of bodies. It frequently curves lateralward, lying lateral to the line between the middle of the ankle and the back part of the first interosseous space. In 12 per cent of bodies the dorsalis pedis is so small that it may be spoken of as absent.

Branches.—The branches of the arteria dorsalis pedis are:

Lateral Tarsal.   Arcuate.
Medial Tarsal.   First Dorsal Metatarsal.
                         Deep Plantar.

The **lateral tarsal artery** (*a. tarsea lateralis; tarsal artery*) *arises* from the dorsalis pedis, as that vessel crosses the navicular bone; it passes in an arched direction lateralward, lying upon the tarsal bones, and covered by the Extensor digitorum brevis; it supplies this muscle and the articulations of the tarsus, and anastomoses with branches of the arcuate, anterior lateral malleolar and lateral plantar arteries, and with the perforating branch of the peroneal artery.

The **medial tarsal arteries** (*aa. tarseæ mediales*) are two or three small branches which ramify on the medial border of the foot and join the medial malleolar network.

The **arcuate artery** (*a. arcuata; metatarsal artery*) *arises* a little anterior to the lateral tarsal artery; it passes lateralward, over the bases of the metatarsal bones, beneath the tendons of the Extensor digitorum brevis, its direction being influenced by its point of origin; and it anastomoses with the lateral tarsal and lateral plantar arteries. This vessel gives off the **second, third,** and **fourth dorsal metatarsal arteries,** which run forward upon the corresponding Interossei dorsales; in the clefts between the toes, each divides into two dorsal digital branches for the adjoining toes. At the proximal parts of the interosseous spaces these vessels receive the posterior perforating branches from the plantar arch, and at the distal parts of the spaces they are joined by the anterior perforating branches, from the plantar metatarsal arteries. The fourth dorsal metatarsal artery gives off a branch which supplies the lateral side of the fifth toe. The arcuate artery is a vessel of significant size in only 50 per cent. of bodies.

The **first dorsal metatarsal artery** (*a. dorsalis hallucis*) runs forward on the first Interosseous dorsalis, and at the cleft between the first and second toes divides into two branches, one of which passes beneath the tendon of the Extensor hallucis longus, and is distributed to the medial border of the great toe; the other bifurcates to supply the adjoining sides of the great and second toes.

The **deep plantar artery** (*ramus plantaris profundus; communicating artery*) descends into the sole of the foot, between the two heads of the first Interosseous dorsalis, and unites with the termination of the lateral plantar artery, to complete the plantar arch. It sends a branch along the medial side of the great toe, and continues forward along the first interosseous space as the **first plantar metatarsal artery,** which bifurcates for the supply of the adjacent sides of the first and second toes.

The Posterior Tibial Artery (**A. Tibialis Posterior**) (Fig. 593).

The **posterior tibial artery** begins at the lower border of the Popliteus, opposite the interval between the tibia and fibula; it extends obliquely downward, and, as it descends, it approaches the tibial side of the leg, lying behind the tibia, and in the lower part of its course is situated midway between the medial malleolus and the medial process of the calcaneal tuberosity. Here it divides beneath the origin of the Abductor hallucis into the **medial** and **lateral plantar arteries.**

Relations.—The posterior tibial artery lies successively upon the Tibialis posterior, the Flexor digitorum longus, the tibia, and the back of the ankle-joint. It is covered by the deep transverse fascia of the leg, which separates it above from the Gastrocnemius and Soleus; at its termination it is covered by the Abductor hallucis. In the lower third of the leg, where it is more superficial, it is covered only by the integument and fascia, and runs parallel with the medial border of the tendo calcaneus. It is accompanied by two veins, and by the tibial nerve, which lies at first to the medial side of the artery, but soon crosses it posteriorly, and is in the greater part of its course on its lateral side.

Behind the medial malleolus, the tendons, bloodvessels, and nerve are arranged, under cover of the laciniate ligament, in the following order from the medial to the lateral side: (1) the tendons of the Tibialis posterior and Flexor digitorum longus, lying in the same groove, behind the malleolus, the former being the more medial. Next is the posterior tibial artery, with a vein on either side of it; and lateral to the vessels is the tibial nerve; about 1.25 cm. nearer the heel is the tendon of the Flexor hallucis longus.

Variations in Size.—The posterior tibial is not infrequently smaller than usual, or absent, its place being supplied by a large peroneal artery, which either joins the small posterior tibial artery, or continues alone to the sole of the foot.

Branches.—The branches of the posterior tibial artery are:

Peroneal.	Posterior Medial Malleolar.
Nutrient.	Communicating.
Muscular.	Medial Calcaneal.

The **peroneal artery** (*a. peronœa*) is deeply seated on the back of the fibular side of the leg. It *arises* from the posterior tibial, about 2.5 cm. below the lower border of the Popliteus, passes obliquely toward the fibula, and then descends along the medial side of that bone, contained in a fibrous canal between the Tibialis posterior and the Flexor hallucis longus, or in the substance of the latter muscle. It then runs behind the tibiofibular syndesmosis and divides into lateral calcaneal branches which ramify on the lateral and posterior surfaces of the calcaneus.

It is covered, in the *upper* part of its course, by the Soleus and deep transverse fascia of the leg; *below*, by the Flexor hallucis longus.

Peculiarities in Origin.—The peroneal artery may arise 7 or 8 cm. below the Popliteus, or from the posterior tibial high up, or even from the popliteal.

Its size is more frequently increased than diminished; and then it either reinforces the posterior tibial by its junction with it, or altogether takes the place of the posterior tibial in the lower part of the leg and foot, the latter vessel only existing as a short muscular branch. In those rare cases where the peroneal artery is smaller than usual, a branch from the posterior tibial supplies its place; and a branch from the anterior tibial compensates for the diminished anterior peroneal artery. In one case the peroneal artery was entirely wanting.

Branches.—The branches of the peroneal are:

Muscular.	Perforating.
Nutrient (Tibial and Fibular).	Communicating.
Lateral Calcaneal.	

The **muscular branches** of the peroneal artery go to the Soleus, Tibialis posterior, Flexor hallucis longus, and Peronei.

The **nutrient artery** (*a. nutricia fibulæ*) is directed downward into the fibula.

The **perforating branch** (*ramus perforans; anterior peroneal artery*) pierces the interosseous membrane, about 5 cm. above the lateral malleolus, to reach the front of the leg, where it anastomoses with the anterior lateral malleolar; it then passes down in front of the tibiofibular syndesmosis, gives branches to the tarsus, and anastomoses with the lateral tarsal. The perforating branch is sometimes enlarged (3 per cent. of cases), and takes the place of the dorsalis pedis artery. In 50 per cent. of bodies, it anastomoses with a lateral branch of the anterior tibial, proximal to the anterior lateral malleolar.

The **communicating branch** (*ramus communicans*) is given off from the peroneal about 2.5 cm. from its lower end, and joins the communicating branch of the posterior tibial.

The **lateral calcaneal** (*ramus calcaneus lateralis; external calcaneal*) are the terminal branches of the peroneal artery; they pass to the lateral side of the heel, and communicate with the lateral malleolar and, on the back of the heel, with the medial calcaneal arteries.

The **nutrient artery** (*a. nutricia tibiæ*) of the tibia *arises* from the posterior tibial, near its origin, and after supplying a few muscular branches enters the nutrient canal of the bone, which it traverses obliquely from above downward. This is the largest nutrient artery of bone in the body.

The **muscular branches** of the posterior tibial are distributed to the Soleus and deep muscles along the back of the leg.

The **posterior medial malleolar artery** (*a. malleolaris posterior medialis; internal malleolar artery*) is a small branch which winds around the tibial malleolus and ends in the medial malleolar net-work.

The **communicating branch** (*ramus communicans*) runs transversely across the back of the tibia, about 5 cm. above its lower end, beneath the Flexor hallucis longus, and joins the communicating branch of the peroneal.

The **medial calcaneal** (*rami calcanei mediales; internal calcaneal*) are several large arteries which *arise* from the posterior tibial just before its division; they pierce the laciniate ligament and are distributed to the fat and integument behind the tendo calcaneus and about the heel, and to the muscles on the tibial side of the sole, anastomosing with the peroneal and medial malleolar and, on the back of the heel, with the lateral calcaneal arteries.

The **medial plantar artery** (*a. plantaris medialis; internal plantar artery*) (Figs. 596 and 597), much smaller than the lateral, passes forward along the medial side of the foot. It is at first situated above the Abductor hallucis, and then between it and the Flexor digitorum brevis, both of which it supplies. At the base of the first metatarsal bone, where it is much diminished in size, it passes along the medial border of the first toe, anastomosing with the first dorsal metatarsal artery. Small superficial digital branches accompany the digital branches of the medial plantar nerve and join the plantar metatarsal arteries of the first three spaces.

The **lateral plantar artery** (*a. plantaris lateralis; external plantar artery*), much larger than the medial, passes obliquely lateralward and forward to the base of the fifth metatarsal bone. It then turns medialward to the interval between the bases of the first and second metatarsal bones, where it unites with the deep plantar branch of the dorsalis pedis artery, thus completing the **plantar arch.** As this artery passes lateralward, it is first placed between the calcaneus and Abductor hallucis, and then between the Flexor digitorum brevis and Quadratus plantæ; as it runs forward to the base of the little toe it lies more superficially between the Flexor digitorum brevis and Abductor digiti quinti, covered by the plantar aponeurosis and integument. The remaining portion of the vessel is deeply situated; it extends from the base of the fifth metatarsal bone to the proximal part of the first interosseous space, and forms the plantar arch; it is convex forward, lies below the bases of the second, third, and fourth metatarsal bones and the corresponding Interossei, and upon the oblique part of the Adductor hallucis.

Branches.—The plantar arch, besides distributing numerous branches to the muscles, integument, and fasciæ in the sole, gives off the following branches:

Perforating.   Plantar Metatarsal.

The **Perforating Branches** (*rami perforantes*) are *three* in number; they ascend through the proximal parts of the second, third, and fourth interosseous spaces, between the heads of the Interossei dorsales, and anastomose with the dorsal metatarsal arteries.

The **Plantar Metatarsal Arteries** (*aa. metatarseæ plantares; digital branches*) are *four* in number, and run forward between the metatarsal bones and in contact with the Interossei. Each divides into a pair of plantar digital arteries which supply the adjacent sides of the toes. Near their points of division each sends upward an **anterior perforating branch** to join the corresponding dorsal metatarsal artery.

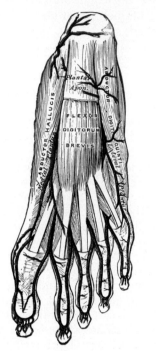

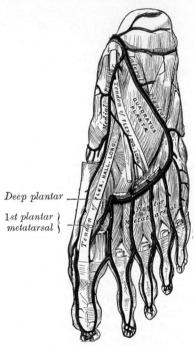

FIG. 596.—The plantar arteries. Superficial view.　　FIG. 597.—The plantar arteries. Deep view.

The **first plantar metatarsal artery** (*arteria princeps hallucis*) springs from the junction between the lateral plantar and deep plantar arteries and sends a digital branch to the medial side of the first toe. The digital branch for the lateral side of the fifth toe arises from the lateral plantar artery near the base of the fifth metatarsal bone.

Histology.—The histology of arteries, veins, and blood is described at the end of the Chapter on Veins.

REFERENCES

Embryology

Auër, J. 1948. The development of the human pulmonary vein and its major variations. Anat. Rec., *101*, 581–594.

Congdon, E. D. 1922. Transformation of the aortic arch system during the development of the human embryo. Carnegie Contrib. to Emb., *14*, 47–110.

Goldsmith, J. B. and H. W. Butler. 1937. The development of the cardiac-coronary circulatory system. Amer. J. Anat., *60*, 185–202.

Morris, E. D. and D. B. Moffat. 1956. Abnormal origin of the basilar artery from the cervical part of the internal carotid and its embryological significance. Anat. Rec., *125*, 701–712.

Noback, G. J. and I. Rehman. 1941. The ductus arteriosus in the human fetus and newborn infant. Anat. Rec., *81*, 505–528.

Padget, D. H. 1948. The development of the cranial arteries in the human embryo. Carnegie Contrib. to Emb., *32*, 205–261.

PADGET, D. H. 1954. Designation of the embryonic intersegmental arteries in reference to the vertebral artery and subclavian stem. Anat. Rec., *119*, 349–356.

SENIOR, H. D. 1919. The development of the arteries of the human lower extremity. Amer. J. Anat., *25*, 55–95.

AORTA AND AORTIC ARCH DERIVATIVES

BARRY, A. 1951. The aortic arch derivatives in the human adult. Anat. Rec., *111*, 221–238.

DE GARIS, C. F. 1938. Branches of the aortic arch in 153 rhesus monkeys, (second series). Anat. Rec., *70*, 251–262.

DE GARIS, C. F. 1941. The aortic arch in primates. Amer. J. phys. Anthrop., *28*, 41–74.

FOX, M. H. and C. M. GOSS. 1958. Experimentally produced malformations of the heart and great vessels in rat fetuses. Transposition complexes and aortic arch abnormalities. Amer. J. Anat., *102*, 65–92.

LIECHTY, J. D., T. W. SHIELDS and B. J. ANSON. 1957. Variations pertaining to the aortic arches and their branches. Quart. Bull. Northw. Univ. med. Sch., *31*, 136–143.

McDONALD, J. J. and B. J. ANSON. 1940. Variations in the origin of arteries derived from the aortic arch, in American whites and negroes. Amer. J. phys. Anthrop., *27*, 91–108.

POYNTER, C. W. M. 1923. Congenital anomalies of the arteries and veins of the human body with bibliography. Neb. Univ. Studies, *22*, 1–106.

SAWIN, P. B. and H. W. EDMONDS. 1949. Morphogenetic studies of the rabbit. VII. Aortic arch variations in relation to regionally specific growth differences. Anat. Rec., *105*, 377–398.

SHANER, R. F. 1956. The persisting right sixth aortic arch of mammals, with a note on fetal coarctation. Anat. Rec., *125*, 171–184.

SINCLAIR, J. G. and N. D. SCHOFIELD. 1944. Anomalies of the cardio-pulmonary circuit compensated without a ductus arteriosus. Anat. Rec., *90*, 209–216.

STEBBINS, T. A. 1949. A report of a case of an anomalous right subclavian artery in man with a rare arrangement of the associated arteries. Anat. Rec., *103*, 139–150.

WOODBURNE, R. T. 1951. A case of right aortic arch and associated venous anomalies. Anat. Rec., *111*, 617–628.

CORONARY ARTERIES

BOAS, E. P. and N. F. BOAS. 1949. Coronary Artery Disease. The Year Book Publishers, Chicago. 399 pp.

CHANDER, S. and I. JIT. 1957. Single coronary artery. J. anat. Soc. India, *6*, 116–118.

CHASE, R. E. 1938. The coronary arteries in 266 hearts of rhesus monkey. Amer. J. phys. Anthrop., *23*, 299–320.

CHASE, R. E. and C. F. DE GARIS. 1939. Arteriæ coronariæ (cordis) in the higher primates. Amer. J. phys. Anthrop., *24*, 427–448.

ESSENBERG, J. M. 1950. An anomalous left coronary artery in a human fetus: Its passage through the left atrium and possible discharge into the right atrium. Anat. Rec., *108*, 709–722.

GREGG, D. E. 1950. Coronary Circulation in Health and Disease. Lea & Febiger, Philadelphia. 227 pp.

GROSS, L. 1921. The Blood Supply to the Heart in its Anatomical and Clinical Aspects. Paul B. Hoeber, New York. xvi + 171 pp.

GROSS, L. and M. A. KUGEL. 1933. The arterial blood vascular distribution to the left and right ventricles of the human heart. Amer. Heart J., *9*, 165–177.

GROSS ANATOMY AND VARIATIONS

ANSON, B. J. and E. W. CAULDWELL. 1947. The pararenal vascular system. Quart. Bull. Northw. Univ. med. Sch., *21*, 320–328.

BELL, R. H., L. L. SWIGART and B. J. ANSON. 1950. The relation of the vertebral artery to the cervical vertebræ. Quart. Bull. Northw. Univ. med. Sch., *24*, 184–185.

CARR, B. W., W. E. BISHOP and B. J. ANSON. 1942. Mammary arteries. Quart. Bull. Northw. Univ. med. Sch., *16*, 150–154.

CAULDWELL, E. W. and B. J. ANSON. 1943. The visceral branches of the abdominal aorta: Topographical relationships. Amer. J. Anat., *73*, 27–58.

EDWARDS, L. F. 1941. The retroduodenal artery. Anat. Rec., *81*, 351–355.

GREIG, H. W., B. J. ANSON and S. S. COLEMAN. 1951. The inferior phrenic artery. Quart. Bull. Northw. Univ. med. Sch., *25*, 345–350.

HUBER, J. F. 1941. The arterial network supplying the dorsum of the foot. Anat. Rec., *80*, 373–391.

HUELKE, D. F. 1958. A study of the transverse cervical and dorsal scapular arteries. Anat. Rec., *132*.

KROPP, B. N. 1951. The lateral costal branch of the internal mammary artery. J. thorac. Surg., *21*, 412–425.

LASKER, G. W., D. L. OPDYKE and H. MILLER. 1951. The position of the internal maxillary artery and its questionable relation to the cephalic index. Anat. Rec., *109*, 119–126.

MCAFEE, D. K., B. J. ANSON and J. J. MCDONALD. 1953. Variation in the point of bifurcation of the common carotid artery. Quart. Bull. Northw. Univ. med. Sch., *27*, 226–229.

MCCORMACK, L. J., E. W. CAULDWELL and B. J. ANSON. 1953. Brachial and antebrachial arterial patterns. A study of 750 extremities. Surg. Gynec. Obstet., *96*, 43–54.

MICHELS, N. A. 1942. The variational anatomy of the spleen and spenic artery. Amer. J. Anat., *70*, 21–72.

MICHELS, N. A. 1955. Blood Supply and Anatomy of the Upper Abdominal Organs, with a Descriptive Atlas. J. B. Lippincott Co., Philadelphia. xiv + 581 pages.

MILLER, R. A. 1939. Observations upon the arrangement of the axillary artery and brachial plexus. Amer. J. Anat., *64*, 143–163.

PICK, JOSEPH. 1958. The innervation of the arteries in the upper limb of man. Anat. Rec., *130*, 103-124.

PICK, J. W., B. J. ANSON and F. L. ASHLEY. 1942. The origin of the obturator artery. Amer. J. Anat., *70*, 317–343.

TOBIN, C. E. 1952. The bronchial arteries and their connections with other vessels in the human lung. Surg. Gynec. Obstet., *95*, 741–750.

WEATHERSBY, H. T. 1955. The artery of the index finger. Anat. Rec., *122*, 57–64.

VANN, H. M. 1943. A note on the formation of the plantar arterial arch of the human foot. Anat. Rec., *85*, 269–275.

WOODBURNE, R. T. and L. L. OLSEN. 1951. The arteries of the pancreas. Anat. Rec., *111*, 255–270.

ANOMALIES

ALLAN, F. D. 1952. An accessory or superficial inferior thyroid artery in a full term infant. Anat. Rec., *112*, 539–542.

CLAUSEN, H. J. 1955. An unusual variation in origin of the hepatic and splenic arteries. Anat. Rec., *123*, 335–340.

CRELIN, E. S., JR. 1948. An unusual anomalous blood vessel connecting the renal and internal spermatic arteries. Anat. Rec., *102*, 205–212.

EVANS, T. H. 1956. Carotid canal anomaly: Other instances of absent internal carotid artery. Med. Times, *84*, 1069–1072.

LEE, I. N. 1955. Anomalous relationship of the inferior thyroid artery. Anat. Rec., *122*, 499–506.

LOW, F. N. 1946. An anomalous middle meningeal artery. Anat. Rec., *95*, 347–352.

MAIER, H. C. 1954. Absence or hypoplasia of a pulmonary artery with anomalous systemic arteries to the lung. J. thorac. Surg., *28*, 145–160.

MCKIM, J. S. and F. W. WIGLESWORTH. 1954. Absence of the left pulmonary artery. A report of six cases with autopsy findings in three. Amer. Heart J., *47*, 845–859.

MICHELS, N. A. 1953. Variational anatomy of the hepatic, cystic, and retroduodenal arteries. A.M.A. Arch. Surg., *66*, 20–32.

O'RAHILLY, R., H. DEBSON and T. S. KING. 1950. Subclavian origin of bronchial arteries. Anat. Rec., *108*, 227–238.

POYNTER, C. W. M. 1916. Arterial anomalies pertaining to the aortic arches and the branches arising from them. Neb. Univ. Studies, *16*, 229–345.

WEATHERSBY, H. T. 1956. Unusual variation of the ulnar artery. Anat. Rec., *124*, 245–248.

COMPARATIVE ANATOMY AND PHYSICAL ANTHROPOLOGY

ADAMS, W. E. 1955. The carotid sinus complex, "parathyroid" III and thymoparathyroid bodies, with special reference to the Australian opossum, Trichosurus vulpecula. Amer. J Anat., *97*, 1–58.

ADAMS, W. E. 1957. On the possible homologies of the occipital artery in mammals, with some remarks on the phylogeny and certain anomalies of the subclavian and carotid arteries. Acta anat. (Basel), *29*, 90–113.

ASHLEY, F. L. and B. J. ANSON. 1941. The hypogastric artery in American whites and negroes. Amer. J. phys. Anthrop., *28*, 381–396.

CHASE, R. E. and C. F. DE GARIS. 1948. The subclavian and axillary arteries in Macacus rhesus, compared with man. Amer. J. phys. Anthrop., N. S., *6*, 85–109.

MING-TZU, P. 1940. The origin of branches of the axillary artery in the Chinese. Amer. J. phys. Anthrop., *27*, 269–280.

READ, W. T. and M. TROTTER. 1941. The origins of transverse cervical and of transverse scapular arteries in American whites and negroes. Amer. J. phys. Anthrop., *28*, 239–247.

RONSTROM, G. N. 1947. Incidence of single and multiple renal arteries in negroes. Amer. J. phys. Anthrop., N. S., *5*, 485–490.

SCHARRER, E. 1940. Arteries and veins in the mammalian brain. Anat. Rec., *78*, 173–196.

TROTTER, M. 1940. The level of termination of the popliteal artery in the white and the negro. Amer. J. phys. Anthrop., *27*, 109–118.

ARTERIO-VENOUS ANASTOMOSES

CLARA, M. 1956. Die arterio-venosen Anastomosen, Anatomie, Biologie, Pathologie. 2nd edition. Springer-Verlag, Wien. vii + 315 pp. 101 figures.

PRICHARD, M. M. L. and P. M. DANIEL. 1954. Arterio-venous anastomoses in the tongue of the sheep and the goat. Amer. J. Anat., *95*, 203–226.

COLLATERAL CIRCULATION

GAYLIN, G. J. 1939. Collateral circulation following an obstruction of the abdominal aorta. Anat. Rec., *75*, 405–408.

MICHELS, N. A. 1953. Collateral arterial pathways to the liver after ligation of the hepatic artery and removal of the celiac axis. Cancer, *6*, 708–724.

QUIRING, D. P. 1949. Collateral Circulation (Anatomical Aspects). Lea & Febiger, Philadelphia. 142 pp.

SURGERY AND PATHOLOGY

BLALOCK, A. 1946. Operative closure of patent ductus arteriosus. Surg. Gynec. Obstet., *82*, 113–114.

DE BAKEY, M. E., E. S. CRAWFORD, O. CREECH, JR., and D. A. COOLEY. 1957. Arterial homografts for peripheral arteriosclerotic occlusive disease. Circulation, *15*, 21–30.

FENN, W. E. and J. E. MUSGROVE. 1958. Common iliac artery aneurysm in a boy six years of age. Ann. Surg., *147*, 109–111.

GROSS, R. E. and P. F. WARE. 1946. The surgical significance of aortic arch anomalies. Surg. Gynec. Obstet., *83*, 435–448.

LEMMON, W. M. and C. P. BAILEY. 1958 A new classification for coarctations of the aorta. J. thorac. Surg., *35*, 291–297.

PERKINS, R. and T. ELCHOS. 1958. Stab wound of the aortic arch. Ann. Surg., *147*, 83–86.

SLAGER, R. F. and K. P. KLASSEN. 1958. Anomalous right subclavian artery arising distal to a coarctation of the aorta. Ann. Surg., *147*, 93–97.

THE VEINS.

THE **Veins** convey the blood from the capillaries to the heart. They consist of two distinct sets of vessels, the **pulmonary** and **systemic**. The **Pulmonary Veins**, unlike other veins, contain oxygenated blood, which they return from the lungs to the left atrium of the heart. The **Systemic Veins** return the oxygen-depleted or venous blood from the body generally to the right atrium of the heart.

The **Portal Vein**, a subdivision of the systemic venous system, is confined to the abdominal cavity, and returns the venous blood from the spleen and the viscera of digestion to the liver. This vessel ramifies in the substance of the liver and there breaks up into a minute network of capillary-like vessels, from which the blood is conveyed by the hepatic veins to the inferior vena cava.

The veins commence by minute plexuses which receive the blood from the capillaries. The branches arising from these plexuses unite together into trunks, and these, in their passage toward the heart, constantly increase in size as they receive tributaries, or join other veins. The veins are larger and altogether more numerous than the arteries; hence, the entire capacity of the venous system is much greater than that of the arterial; the capacity of the pulmonary veins, however, only slightly exceeds that of the pulmonary arteries. The veins are cylindrical like the arteries; their walls, however, are thin and they collapse when the vessels are empty, and the uniformity of their surfaces is interrupted at intervals by slight constrictions, which indicate the existence of valves in their interior. They communicate very freely with one another, especially in certain regions of the body; and these communications exist between the larger trunks as well as between the smaller branches. Thus, between the venous sinuses of the cranium, and between the veins of the neck, where obstruction would be attended with imminent danger to the cerebral venous system, large and frequent anastomoses are found. The same free communication exists between the veins throughout the whole extent of the vertebral canal, and between the veins composing the various venous plexuses in the abdomen and pelvis, *e. g.*, the spermatic, uterine, vesical, and pudendal.

The systemic venous channels are subdivided into three sets, viz., **superficial** and **deep veins**, and **venous sinuses**.

The **Superficial Veins** (*cutaneous veins*) are found between the layers of the superficial fascia immediately beneath the skin; they return the blood from these structures, and communicate with the deep veins by perforating the deep fascia.

The **Deep Veins** accompany the arteries, and are usually enclosed in the same sheaths with those vessels. With the smaller arteries—as the radial, ulnar, brachial, tibial, peroneal—they exist generally in pairs, one lying on each side of the vessel, and are called **venæ comitantes**. The larger arteries—such as the axillary, subclavian, popliteal, and femoral—have usually only one accompanying vein. In certain organs of the body, however, the deep veins do not accompany the arteries; for instance, the veins in the skull and vertebral canal, the hepatic veins in the liver, and the larger veins returning blood from the bones.

Venous Sinuses, found only in the interior of the skull, consist of canals formed by separation of the two layers of the dura mater; their outer coat consists of fibrous tissue, their inner of an endothelial layer continuous with the lining of the veins.

DEVELOPMENT OF THE VEINS

The Parietal Veins.—The first veins from the body of embryo to appear are two short transverse veins, the **common cardinal veins** (*ducts of Cuvier*) which open into the right and left horns of the sinus venosus. Each of these veins receives a vein from the cephalic and caudal portions of the embryo (Fig. 598). The cephalic tributaries, called the **anterior cardinal veins** (*precardinal veins*), return blood from head and soon become the primitive jugular veins (Fig. 599). The caudal tributaries, called the **posterior cardinal veins** (*postcardinal veins*) return blood from the parietes of the trunk, from the mesonephroi (Wolffian bodies), and from the lower limb buds. This primitive double (right and left) plan of veins is converted into the single caval systems by the formation of a series of transverse connecting veins.

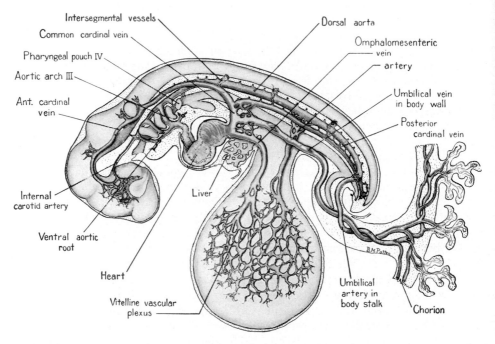

Fig. 598.—Semischematic diagram to show basic vascular plan of human embryo at end of first month. For the sake of simplicity the paired vessels are shown only on side toward observer. (Patten's Human Embryology, 1953, courtesy of The Blakiston Company.)

Inferior Vena Cava.—The blood from the lower limbs is collected by the right and left iliac veins which, in the earlier stages of development, open into the corresponding right and left posterior cardinal veins. Later, a transverse connection, the **left common iliac vein,** is developed between the caudal parts of the two posterior cardinals (Fig. 601) and through this the blood is carried into the right posterior cardinal vein. The portion of the left posterior cardinal caudal to the left renal vein atrophies and disappears up to the point of entrance of the left testicular vein. The portion above the left renal vein persists as the **hemiazygos, accessory hemiazygos,** and lower portion of the **highest left intercostal vein.** The right posterior cardinal vein forms a large venous trunk, lying along the posterior abdominal wall, which forms the lower part of the inferior vena cava up to the level of the renal veins. Above the level of the renal veins the right posterior cardinal vein remains close to the vertebral column and persists as the **azygos vein.** The hemiazygos vein becomes connected with the azygos by the formation of a transverse branch ventral to the vertebral column (Figs. 601, 602).

The further development of the inferior vena cava is associated with the formation of two additional veins, the **subcardinal veins** (Figs. 599, 600) which are parallel with and ventral to the posterior cardinal veins. They arise as longitudinal anastomosing channels which link up the tributaries from the mesentery to the posterior

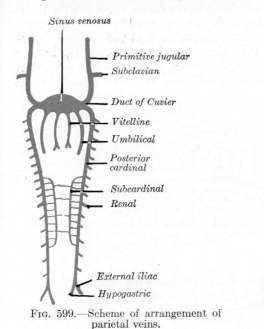

FIG. 599.—Scheme of arrangement of parietal veins.

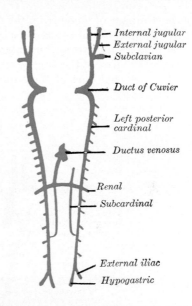

FIG. 600.—Scheme showing early stages of development of the inferior vena cava.

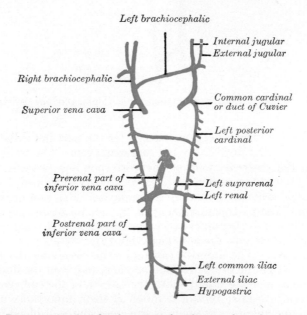

FIG. 601.—Diagram showing development of main cross branches between jugulars and between cardinals.

cardinal veins. The two subcardinals are for a time connected by several cross branches lying ventral to the aorta, but one of these transverse channels only persists. At the same level a cross connection is established between the posterior cardinals and subcardinals of the two sides (Fig. 600). The right subcardinal caudal to this cross connection disappears, whereas the part cephalic to it, the prerenal portion, forms a connection with the ductus venosus at the point of opening of the hepatic veins. Another pair of longitudinal veins is formed at a later period, dorsal to the posterior cardinal veins. These are the **supracardinals** which gradually take over the drainage of blood from the region caudal to the renal veins. The prerenal part of the subcardinal communicates with the supracardinal and enlarges rapidly, thus forming a single trunk, the **inferior vena cava** (Fig. 601). It consists, therefore, of the proximal part of the ductus venosus, the prerenal part of the right subcardinal vein, the postrenal part of the supracardinal vein, and the cross branch between these two veins.

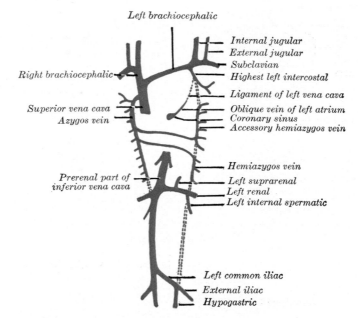

Left brachiocephalic

Internal jugular
External jugular
Subclavian
Right brachiocephalic
Highest left intercostal

Ligament of left vena cava

Superior vena cava
Azygos vein
Oblique vein of left atrium
Coronary sinus
Accessory hemiazygos vein

Hemiazygos vein
Prerenal part of inferior vena cava
Left suprarenal
Left renal
Left internal spermatic

Left common iliac
External iliac
Hypogastric

FIG. 602.—Diagram showing completion of development of the parietal veins.

The left subcardinal vein disappears except for the part immediately cephalic to the renal vein which is retained as the **left suprarenal vein.** The testicular or ovarian vein opens into the postrenal part of the corresponding posterior cardinal vein. This portion of the right posterior cardinal, as already explained, forms the caudal part of the inferior vena cava, so that the **right testicular vein** opens directly into the inferior cava. The postrenal segment of the left posterior cardinal disappears, with the exception of the portion between the testicular and renal vein, so that the **left testicular vein** drains into the left renal vein (Fig. 602).

Superior Vena Cava.—The anterior cardinal veins receiving the blood from the head and brain through the primitive jugular veins and from the limb buds through the subclavian veins increase rapidly with the growth of the embryo. As described above, the posterior cardinal veins lose much of their importance and become the azygos veins, leaving anterior cardinals as the chief source of blood for the common cardinals. The latter gradually assume an almost vertical course when the heart is brought down into the thorax. The common cardinals are originally of the same diameter and are frequently termed the **right** and **left superior venæ cavæ**. Later a transverse connecting vein, the **left brachiocephalic** or **innominate vein**, conveys the blood from the left side into the right superior vena cava (Figs. 601, 602). The right anterior cardinal between the azygos vein and the union with the left brachiocephalic becomes the upper part of the **adult superior vena cava**. The lower part of the superior cava, that is, the part between the azygos vein and the heart,

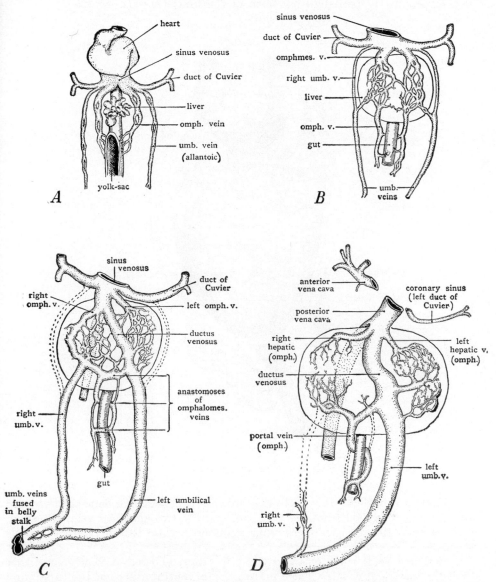

Fig. 603.—Diagrams showing development of portal circulation from omphalomesenteric veins, and changes by which blood returning from placenta by way of umbilical veins is rerouted through liver. *A*, Based on conditions in pig embryos of 3-4 mm.—applicable to human embryos of fourth week. *B*, Based on pig embryos of about 6 mm.—applicable to human embryos of fifth week. *C*, Based on pig embryos of 8-9 mm.— applicable to human embryos early in sixth week. *D*, Based on pig embryos of 20 mm. and above—applicable to human embryos of seven weeks and older. (By permission from *Human Embryology*, 2nd Edition by B. M. Patten. Copyright, 1953, The Blakiston Div., McGraw-Hill Book Co.)

46

is formed by the right common cardinal vein. The left anterior cardinal vein caudal to the transverse left brachiocephalic and the common cardinal of that side regress; the brachiocephalic part becoming the **vestigial fold of Marshall** and the common cardinal the **oblique vein of the left atrium** (*oblique vein of Marshall*) (Fig. 602). Both right and left superior venæ caval are present in some animals, and occasionally are found in adult human beings. The oblique vein of the left atrium passes downward across the dorsal surface of the left atrium to open into the **coronary sinus** which represents the persistent left horn of the sinus venosus.

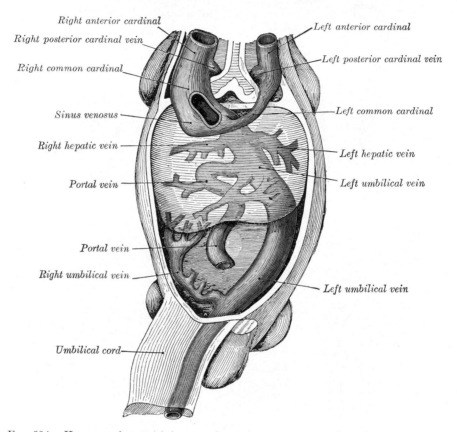

FIG. 604.—Human embryo with heart and anterior body-wall removed to show the sinus venosus and its tributaries. (After His.)

The Visceral Veins.—The visceral veins are the two **vitelline** or **omphalomesenteric veins** bringing the blood from the yolk-sac, and the two **umbilical veins** returning the blood from the placenta; these four veins open close together into the sinus venosus.

The **Vitelline Veins** run upward at first in front, and subsequently on either side of the intestinal canal. They unite on the ventral aspect of the canal, and beyond this are connected to one another by two anastomotic branches, one on the dorsal, and the other on the ventral aspect of the duodenal portion of the intestine, which is thus encircled by two venous rings (Fig. 603); into the middle or dorsal anastomosis the superior mesenteric vein opens. The portions of the veins above the upper ring become interrupted by the developing liver and broken up by it into a plexus of small capillary-like vessels termed **sinusoids** (Minot). The branches conveying the blood to this plexus are named the **venæ advehentes,** and become the branches of the portal vein; while the vessels draining the plexus into the sinus venosus are termed the **venæ revehentes,** and form the future hepatic veins (Figs. 603, 604). Ultimately the left vena revehens no longer communicates directly with the sinus venosus, but opens into the right vena revehens. The persistent part of the upper venous ring, above the opening of the superior mesenteric vein, forms the trunk of the portal vein.

The two **Umbilical Veins** fuse early to form a single trunk in the body-stalk, but remain separate within the embryo and pass forward to the sinus venosus in the side walls of the body. Like the vitelline veins, their direct connection with the sinus venosus becomes interrupted by the developing liver, and thus at this stage all the blood from the yolk-sac and placenta passes through the substance of the liver before it reaches the heart. The right umbilical and right vitelline veins shrivel and disappear; the left umbilical, on the other hand, becomes enlarged and opens into the upper venous ring of the vitelline veins. With the atrophy of the yolk-sac the left vitelline vein also undergoes atrophy and disappears. Finally a direct branch is established between this ring and the right hepatic vein; this branch is named the **ductus venosus,** and, enlarging rapidly, it forms a wide channel through which most of the blood, returned from the placenta, is carried direct to the heart without passing through the liver. A small proportion of the blood from the placenta is, however, conveyed from the left umbilical vein to the liver through the left vena advehens. The left umbilical vein and the ductus venosus undergo atrophy and obliteration after birth, and form respectively the ligamentum teres and ligamentum venosum of the liver.

THE PULMONARY VEINS (VENÆ PULMONALES).

The **pulmonary veins** return the oxygenated blood from the lungs to the left atrium of the heart. They are four in number, two from each lung, and are destitute of valves. They commence in a capillary net-work upon the walls of the air sacs, where they are continuous with the capillary ramifications of the pulmonary artery, and, joining together, form one vessel for each lobule. These vessels uniting successively, form a single trunk for each lobe, three for the right, and two for the left lung. The vein from the middle lobe of the right lung generally unites with that from the upper lobe, so that ultimately two trunks from each lung are formed; they perforate the fibrous layer of the pericardium and open separately into the upper and back part of the left atrium. Occasionally the three veins on the right side remain separate. Not infrequently the two left pulmonary veins end by a common opening.

At the root of the lung, the superior pulmonary vein lies in front of and a little below the pulmonary artery; the inferior is situated at the lowest part of the hilum of the lung and on a plane posterior to the upper vein. Behind the pulmonary artery is the bronchus (Figs. 545, 546).

Within the pericardium, their anterior surfaces are invested by its serous layer.

The right pulmonary veins pass behind the right atrium and superior vena cava; the left in front of the descending thoracic aorta.

THE SYSTEMIC VEINS.

The **systemic veins** may be arranged into three groups: (1) The **veins of the heart.** (2) The veins of the **upper extremities, head, neck,** and **thorax,** which end in the superior vena cava. (3) The veins of the **lower extremities, abdomen,** and **pelvis,** which end in the inferior vena cava.

THE VEINS OF THE HEART (VV. Cordis) (Figs. 548, 549, 605).

Coronary Sinus (*sinus coronarius*).—Most of the veins of the heart open into the coronary sinus. This is a wide venous channel about 2.25 cm. in length situated in the posterior part of the coronary sulcus, and covered by muscular fibers from the left atrium. It ends in the right atrium between the opening of the inferior vena cava and the atrioventricular aperture, its orifice being guarded by an incompetent semilunar valve, the **valve of the coronary sinus** (*valve of Thebesius*).

Tributaries.—Its tributaries are the great, small, and middle cardiac veins, the posterior vein of the left ventricle, and the oblique vein of the left atrium, all of which, except the last, are provided with valves at their orifices.

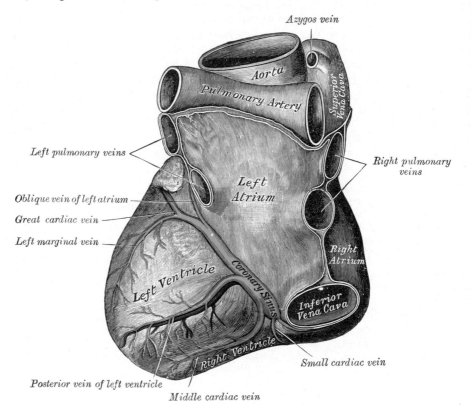

FIG. 605.—Base and diaphragmatic surface of heart.

1. The **Great Cardiac Vein** (*v. cordis magna*; *left coronary vein*) begins at the apex of the heart and ascends along the anterior longitudinal sulcus to the base of the ventricles. It then curves to the left in the coronary sulcus, and reaching the back of the heart, opens into the left extremity of the coronary sinus. It receives tributaries from the left atrium and from both ventricles: one, the **left marginal vein**, is of considerable size, and ascends along the left margin of the heart.

2. The **Small Cardiac Vein** (*v. cordis parva; right coronary vein*) runs in the coronary sulcus between the right atrium and ventricle, and opens into the right extremity of the coronary sinus. It receives blood from the back of the right atrium and ventricle; the **right marginal vein** ascends along the right margin of the heart and joins it in the coronary sulcus, or opens directly into the right atrium.

3. The **Middle Cardiac Vein** (*v. cordis media*) commences at the apex of the heart, ascends in the posterior longitudinal sulcus, and ends in the coronary sinus near its right extremity.

4. The **Posterior Vein of the Left Ventricle** (*v. posterior ventriculi sinistri*) runs on the diaphragmatic surface of the left ventricle to the coronary sinus, but may end in the great cardiac vein.

5. The **Oblique Vein of the Left Atrium** (*v. obliqua atrii sinistri* [*Marshalli*]; *oblique vein of Marshall*) is a small vessel which descends obliquely on the back of the left atrium and ends in the coronary sinus near its left extremity; it is continuous above with the **ligament of the left vena cava** (*lig. venæ cavæ sinistræ; vestigial fold of Marshall*), and the two structures form the remnant of the left Cuvierian duct.

The following cardiac veins do not end in the coronary sinus: (1) the **anterior cardiac veins**, comprising three or four small vessels which collect blood from the front of the right ventricle and open into the right atrium; the right marginal vein frequently opens into the right atrium, and is therefore sometimes regarded as belonging to this group; (2) the **smallest cardiac veins** (*veins of Thebesius*), consisting of a number of minute veins which arise in the muscular wall of the heart; the majority open into the atria, but a few end in the ventricles.

THE VEINS OF THE HEAD AND NECK.

The veins of the head and neck may be subdivided into three groups: (1) The **veins of the exterior of the head and face**. (2) The **veins of the neck**. (3) The **diploic veins**, the **veins of the brain**, and the **venous sinuses of the dura mater**.

The Veins of the Exterior of the Head and Face (Fig. 606).

The veins of the exterior of the head and face are:

Frontal.	Superficial Temporal.
Supraorbital.	Internal Maxillary.
Angular.	Posterior Facial.
Anterior Facial.	Posterior Auricular.
Occipital.	

The **frontal vein** (*v. frontalis*) *begins* on the forehead in a venous plexus which communicates with the frontal branches of the superficial temporal vein. The veins converge to form a single trunk, which runs downward near the middle line of the forehead parallel with the vein of the opposite side. The two veins are joined, at the root of the nose, by a transverse branch, called the **nasal arch**, which receives some small veins from the dorsum of the nose. At the root of the nose the veins diverge, and, each at the medial angle of the orbit, joins the **supraorbital vein**, to form the **angular vein**. Occasionally the frontal veins join to form a single trunk, which bifurcates at the root of the nose into the two angular veins.

The **supraorbital vein** (*v. supraorbitalis*) *begins* on the forehead where it communicates with the frontal branch of the superficial temporal vein. It runs downward superficial to the Frontalis muscle, and joins the frontal vein at the medial angle of the orbit to form the **angular vein**. Previous to its junction with the frontal vein, it sends through the supraorbital notch into the orbit a branch which communicates with the ophthalmic vein; as this vessel passes through the notch, it receives the frontal diploic vein through a foramen at the bottom of the notch.

The **angular vein** (*v. angularis*) *formed* by the junction of the frontal and supraorbital veins, runs obliquely downward, on the side of the root of the nose, to the level of the lower margin of the orbit, where it becomes the anterior facial vein.

It receives the veins of the ala nasi, and communicates with the superior ophthalmic vein through the nasofrontal vein, thus establishing an important anastomosis between the anterior facial vein and the cavernous sinus.

The **anterior facial vein** (*v. facialis anterior; facial vein*) *commences* at the side of the root of the nose, and is a direct continuation of the angular vein. It lies behind the external maxillary (facial) artery and follows a less tortuous course. It runs obliquely downward and backward, beneath the Zygomaticus and zygo-

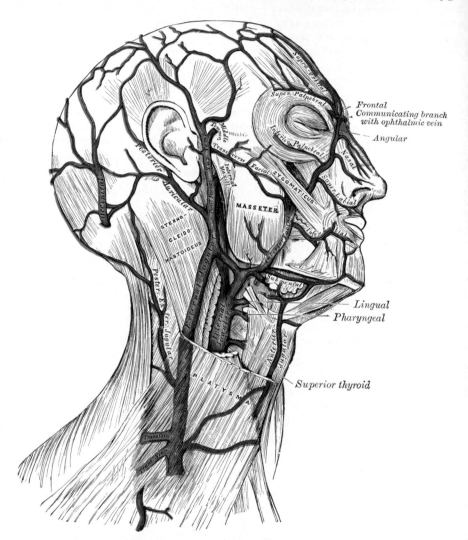

FIG. 606.—Veins of the head and neck.

matic head of the Quadratus labii superioris, descends along the anterior border and then on the superficial surface of the Masseter, crosses over the body of the mandible, and passes obliquely backward, beneath the Platysma and cervical fascia, superficial to the submaxillary gland, the Digastricus and Stylohyoideus. It unites with the posterior facial vein to form the **common facial vein**, which crosses the external carotid artery and enters the internal jugular vein at a variable point below the hyoid bone. From near its termination a communicating branch often runs down the anterior border of the Sternocleidomastoideus to join the lower part of the anterior jugular vein. The facial vein has no valves, and its walls are not so flaccid as most superficial veins.

Tributaries.—The anterior facial vein receives a branch of considerable size, the **deep facial vein**, from the pterygoid venous plexus. It is also joined by the superior and inferior palpebral, the superior and inferior labial, the buccinator and the masseteric veins. Below the mandible it receives the submental, palatine, and submaxillary veins, and, generally, the vena comitans of the hypoglossal nerve.

The **superficial temporal vein** (*v. temporalis superficialis*) *begins* on the side and vertex of the skull in a plexus which communicates with the frontal and supra-orbital veins, with the corresponding vein of the opposite side, and with the posterior auricular and occipital veins. From this net-work frontal and parietal branches arise, and unite above the zygomatic arch to form the trunk of the vein, which is joined in this situation by the **middle temporal vein**, from the substance of the Temporalis. It then crosses the posterior root of the zygomatic arch, enters the substance of the parotid gland, and unites with the internal maxillary vein to form the **posterior facial vein**.

Tributaries.—The superficial temporal vein receives in its course some parotid veins, articular veins from the temporomandibular joint, anterior auricular veins from the auricula, and the **transverse facial** from the side of the face. The middle temporal vein receives the **orbital vein**, which is formed by some lateral palpebral branches, and passes backward between the layers of the temporal fascia to join the superficial temporal vein.

The **pterygoid plexus** (*plexus pterygoideus*) (Fig. 617) is of considerable size, and is situated between the Temporalis and Pterygoideus externus, and partly between the two Pterygoidei. It receives tributaries corresponding with the branches of the internal maxillary artery. Thus it receives the sphenopalatine, the middle meningeal, the deep temporal, the pterygoid, masseteric, buccinator, alveolar, and some palatine veins, and a branch which communicates with the ophthalmic vein through the inferior orbital fissure. This plexus communicates freely with the anterior facial vein; it also communicates with the cavernous sinus, by branches through the foramen Vesalii, foramen ovale, and foramen lacerum.

The **internal maxillary vein** (*v. maxillaris interna*) is a short trunk which accompanies the first part of the internal maxillary artery. It is *formed* by a confluence of the veins of the pterygoid plexus, and passes backward between the sphenomandibular ligament and the neck of the mandible, and unites with the temporal vein to form the posterior facial vein (Fig. 617, not labelled).

The **posterior facial vein** (*v. facialis posterior; temporomaxillary vein*), *formed* by the union of the superficial temporal and internal maxillary veins, descends in the substance of the parotid gland, superficial to the external carotid artery but beneath the facial nerve, between the ramus of the mandible and the Sternocleidomastoideus muscle. It divides into two branches, an **anterior**, which passes forward and unites with the anterior facial vein to form the common facial vein and a **posterior**, which, joined by the posterior auricular vein, becomes the external jugular vein.

The **posterior auricular vein** (*v. auricularis posterior*) *begins* upon the side of the head, in a plexus which communicates with the tributaries of the occipital, and superficial temporal veins. It descends behind the auricula, and joins the posterior division of the posterior facial vein to form the external jugular. It receives the stylomastoid vein, and some tributaries from the cranial surface of the auricula.

The **occipital vein** (*v. occipitalis*) *begins* in a plexus at the back part of the vertex of the skull, From the plexus emerges a single vessel, which pierces the cranial attachment of the Trapezius and, dipping into the suboccipital triangle, joins the deep cervical and vertebral veins. Occasionally it follows the course of the occipital artery and ends in the internal jugular; in other instances, it joins the posterior auricular and through it opens into the external jugular. The parietal emissary vein connects it with the superior sagittal sinus; and as it passes across the mastoid portion of the temporal bone, it receives the mastoid emissary vein which connects it with the transverse sinus. The occipital diploic vein sometimes joins it.

The Veins of the Neck (Fig. 607).

The veins of the neck, which return the blood from the head and face, are:

External Jugular.	Anterior Jugular.
Posterior External Jugular.	Internal Jugular.
Vertebral.	

The **external jugular vein** (*v. jugularis externa*) receives the greater part of the blood from the exterior of the cranium and the deep parts of the face, being formed by the junction of the posterior division of the posterior facial with the posterior auricular vein. It commences in the substance of the parotid gland, on a level with the angle of the mandible, and runs perpendicularly down the neck, in the direction of a line drawn from the angle of the mandible to the middle of the clavicle at the posterior border of the Sternocleidomastoideus. In its course it crosses the Sternocleidomastoideus obliquely, and in the subclavian triangle perforates the deep fascia, and ends in the subclavian vein, lateral to or in front of the Scalenus anterior. It is separated from the Sternocleidomastoideus by the investing layer of the deep cervical fascia, and is covered by the Platysma, the superficial fascia, and the integument; it crosses the cutaneous cervical nerve, and its upper half runs parallel with the great auricular nerve. The external jugular vein varies in size, bearing an inverse proportion to the other veins of the neck, it is occasionally double. It is provided with two pairs of valves, the lower pair being placed at its entrance into the subclavian vein, the upper in most cases about 4 cm. above the clavicle. The portion of vein between the two sets of valves is often dilated, and is termed the **sinus**. These valves do not prevent the regurgitation of the blood, or the passage of injection from below upward.

Tributaries.—This vein receives the occipital occasionally, the posterior external jugular, and, near its termination, the transverse cervical, transverse scapular, and anterior jugular veins; in the substance of the parotid, a large branch of communication from the internal jugular joins it.

The **posterior external jugular vein** (*v. jugularis posterior*) *begins* in the occipital region and returns the blood from the skin and superficial muscles in the upper and back part of the neck, lying between the Splenius and Trapezius. It runs down the back part of the neck, and opens into the external jugular vein just below the middle of its course.

The **anterior jugular vein** (*v. jugularis anterior*) *begins* near the hyoid bone by the confluence of several superficial veins from the submaxillary region. It descends between the median line and the anterior border of the Sternocleidomastoideus, and, at the lower part of the neck, passes beneath that muscle to open into the termination of the external jugular, or, in some instances, into the subclavian vein (Figs. 606, 607). It varies considerably in size, bearing usually an inverse proportion to the external jugular; most frequently there are two anterior jugulars, a right and left; but sometimes only one. Its tributaries are some laryngeal veins, and occasionally a small thyroid vein. Just above the sternum the two anterior jugular veins communicate by a transverse trunk, the **venous jugular arch**, which receives tributaries from the inferior thyroid veins; each also communicates with the internal jugular. There are no valves in this vein.

The **internal jugular vein** (*v. jugularis interna*) collects the blood from the brain, from the superficial parts of the face, and from the neck. It is directly continuous with the transverse sinus, and begins in the posterior compartment of the jugular foramen, at the base of the skull. At its origin it is somewhat dilated, and this dilatation is called the **superior bulb**. It runs down the side of the neck in a vertical direction, lying at first lateral to the internal carotid artery, and then lateral

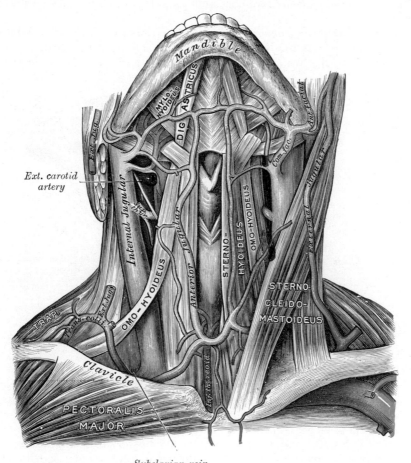

Subclavian vein

FIG. 607.—The veins of the neck, viewed from in front. (Spalteholz.)

to the common carotid, and at the root of the neck unites with the subclavian vein to form the innominate vein; a little above its termination is a second dilatation, the **inferior bulb**. Above, it lies upon the Rectus capitis lateralis, behind the internal carotid artery and the nerves passing through the jugular foramen; lower down, the vein and artery lie upon the same plane, the glossopharyngeal and hypoglossal nerves passing forward between them; the vagus descends between and behind the vein and the artery in the same sheath, and the accessory runs obliquely backward, superficial or deep to the vein. At the root of the neck the right internal jugular vein is placed at a little distance from the common carotid artery, and crosses the first part of the subclavian artery, while the left internal jugular vein usually overlaps the common carotid artery. The left vein is generally smaller than the right, and each contains a pair of valves, which are placed about 2.5 cm. above the termination of the vessel.

Tributaries.—This vein receives in its course the inferior petrosal sinus, the common facial, lingual, pharyngeal, superior and middle thyroid veins, and sometimes the occipital. The thoracic duct on the left side and the right lymphatic duct on the right side open into the angle of union of the internal jugular and subclavian veins.

The **Inferior Petrosal Sinus** (*sinus petrosus inferior*) *leaves* the skull through the anterior part of the jugular foramen, and joins the superior bulb of the internal jugular vein.

The **Lingual Veins** (*vv. linguales*) *begin* on the dorsum, sides, and under surface of the tongue, and, passing backward along the course of the lingual artery, end in the internal jugular vein. The vena comitans of the hypoglossal nerve (**ranine**

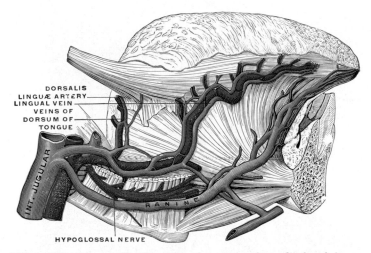

DORSALIS
LINGUÆ ARTERY
LINGUAL VEIN
VEINS OF
DORSUM OF
TONGUE

INT. JUGULAR

RANINE

HYPOGLOSSAL NERVE

Fig. 608.—Veins of the tongue. The hypoglossal nerve has been displaced downward in this preparation. (Testut after Hirschfeld.)

vein), a branch of considerable size, begins below the tip of the tongue, and may join the lingual; generally, however, it passes backward on the Hyoglossus, and joins the common facial.

The **Pharyngeal Veins** (*vv. pharyngeæ*) *begin* in the **pharyngeal plexus** on the outer surface of the pharynx, and, after receiving some posterior meningeal veins and the vein of the pterygoid canal, end in the internal jugular. They occasionally open into the facial, lingual, or superior thyroid vein.

The **Superior Thyroid Vein** (*v. thyreoidea superioris*) (Fig. 609) *begins* in the substance and on the surface of the thyroid gland, by tributaries corresponding with the branches of the superior thyroid artery, and ends in the upper part of the internal jugular vein. It receives the superior laryngeal and cricothyroid veins.

The **Middle Thyroid Vein** (Fig. 611) collects the blood from the lower part of the thyroid gland, and after being joined by some veins from the larynx and trachea, ends in the lower part of the internal jugular vein.

The **common facial** and **occipital veins** have been described.

The **vertebral vein** (*v. vertebralis*) is formed in the suboccipital triangle, from numerous small tributaries which spring from the internal vertebral venous plexuses and issue from the vertebral canal above the posterior arch of the atlas. They unite with small veins from the deep muscles at the upper part of the back of the neck, and form a vessel which enters the foramen in the transverse process of the atlas, and descends, forming a dense plexus around the vertebral artery, in the canal formed by the foramina transversaria of the cervical vertebræ. This plexus ends in a single trunk, which emerges from the foramen transversarium of the sixth cervical vertebra, and opens at the root of the neck into the back part of the innominate vein near its origin, its mouth being guarded by a pair of valves. On the right side, it crosses the first part of the subclavian artery.

Tributaries.—The vertebral vein communicates with the transverse sinus by a vein which passes through the condyloid canal, when that canal exists. It receives branches from the occipital vein and from the prevertebral muscles, from

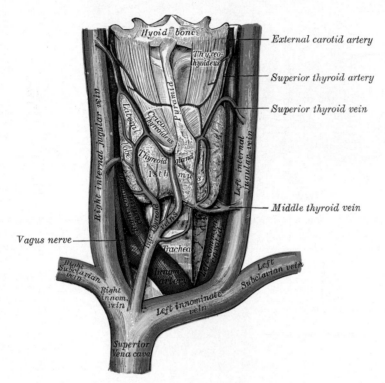

FIG. 609.—The veins of the thyroid gland.

the internal and external vertebral venous plexuses, from the anterior vertebral and the deep cervical veins; close to its termination it is sometimes joined by the first intercostal vein.

The **Anterior Vertebral Vein** *commences* in a plexus around the transverse processes of the upper cervical vertebræ, descends in company with the ascending cervical artery between the Scalenus anterior and Longus capitis muscles, and opens into the terminal part of the vertebral vein.

The **Deep Cervical Vein** (*v. cervicalis profunda; posterior vertebral or posterior deep cervical vein*) accompanies its artery between the Semispinales capitis and colli. It *begins* in the suboccipital region by communicating branches from the occipital vein and by small veins from the deep muscles at the back of the neck. It receives tributaries from the plexuses around the spinous processes of the cervical vertebræ, and terminates in the lower part of the vertebral vein.

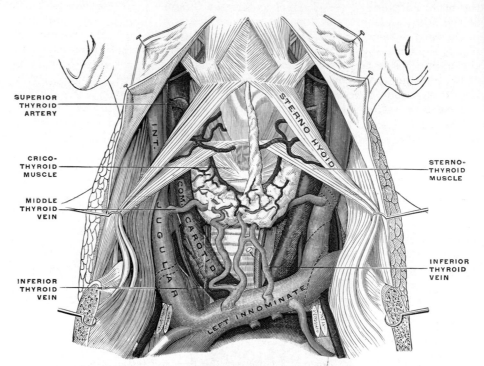

SUPERIOR
THYROID
ARTERY

CRICO-
THYROID
MUSCLE

MIDDLE
THYROID
VEIN

INFERIOR
THYROID
VEIN

STERNO-HYOID

INT.

COM. CAROTID

JUGULAR

LEFT INNOMINATE

STERNO-
THYROID
MUSCLE

INFERIOR
THYROID
VEIN

FIG. 610.—The middle and inferior thyroid veins.   (Poirier and Charpy.)

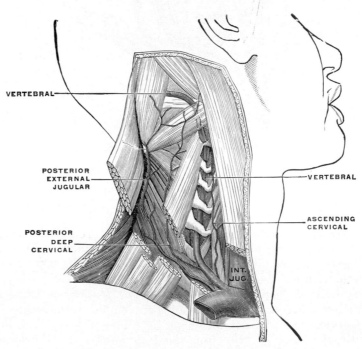

VERTEBRAL

POSTERIOR
EXTERNAL
JUGULAR

POSTERIOR
DEEP
CERVICAL

VERTEBRAL

ASCENDING
CERVICAL

INT.
JUG.

FIG. 611.—The vertebral vein.   (Poirier and Charpy.)

The Diploic Veins (Venæ Diploicæ) (Fig. 612).

The **diploic veins** occupy channels in the diploë of the cranial bones. They are large and exhibit at irregular intervals pouch-like dilatations; their walls are thin, and formed of endothelium resting upon a layer of elastic tissue.

So long as the cranial bones are separable from one another, these veins are confined to particular bones; but when the sutures are obliterated, they unite with each other, and increase in size. They communicate with the meningeal veins and the sinuses of the dura mater, and with the veins of the pericranium. They consist of (1) the **frontal**, which opens into the supraorbital vein and the superior sagittal sinus; (2) the **anterior temporal**, which, confined chiefly to the

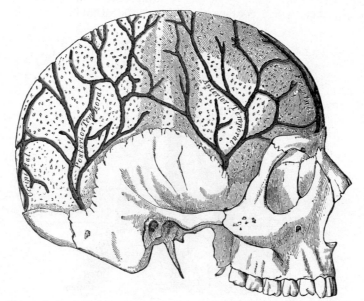

FIG. 612.—Veins of the diploë as displayed by the removal of the outer table of the skull.

frontal bone, opens into the sphenoparietal sinus and into one of the deep temporal veins, through an aperture in the great wing of the sphenoid; (3) the **posterior temporal**, which is in the parietal bone, and ends in the transverse sinus, through an aperture at the mastoid angle of the parietal bone or through the mastoid foramen; and (4) the **occipital**, the largest of the four, which is confined to the occipital bone, and opens either externally into the occipital vein, or internally into the transverse sinus or into the confluence of the sinuses (*torcular Herophili*).

The Veins of the Brain.

The veins of the brain possess no valves, and their walls, owing to the absence of muscular tissue, are extremely thin. They pierce the arachnoid membrane and the inner or meningeal layer of the dura mater, and open into the cranial venous sinuses. They may be divided into two sets, **cerebral** and **cerebellar**.

The **cerebral veins** (*vv. cerebri*) are divisible into external and internal groups according as they drain the outer surfaces or the inner parts of the hemispheres.

The **external veins** are the superior, inferior, and middle cerebral.

The **Superior Cerebral Veins** (*vv. cerebri superiores*), eight to twelve in number, drain the superior, lateral, and medial surfaces of the hemispheres, most of them being lodged in the sulci between the gyri, while some run across the gyri. They open into the superior sagittal sinus; the anterior vein runs nearly at right angles to the sinus; the posterior and larger veins are directed obliquely forward and open into the sinus in a direction more or less opposed to the current of the blood contained within it.

The **Middle Cerebral Vein** (*v. cerebri media; superficial Sylvian vein*) *begins* on the lateral surface of the hemisphere, and, running along the lateral cerebral fissure, ends in the cavernous or the sphenoparietal sinus. It is connected (*a*) with the superior sagittal sinus by the **great anastomotic vein of Trolard**, which opens into one of the superior cerebral veins; (*b*) with the transverse sinus by the **posterior anastomotic vein of Labbé**, which courses over the temporal lobe.

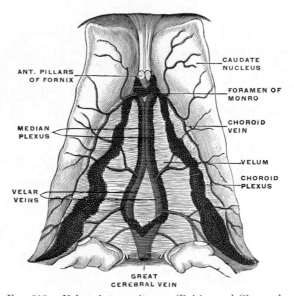

FIG. 613.—Velum interpositum. (Poirier and Charpy.)

The **Inferior Cerebral Veins** (*vv. cerebri inferiores*), of small size, drain the under surfaces of the hemispheres. Those on the orbital surface of the frontal lobe join the superior cerebral veins, and through these open into the superior sagittal sinus; those of the temporal lobe anastomose with the middle cerebral and basal veins, and join the cavernous, sphenoparietal, and superior petrosal sinuses.

The **basal vein** is formed at the anterior perforated substance by the union of (*a*) a small **anterior cerebral vein** which accompanies the anterior cerebral artery, (*b*) the **deep middle cerebral vein** (*deep Sylvian vein*), which receives tributaries from the insula and neighboring gyri, and runs in the lower part of the lateral cerebral fissure, and (*c*) the **inferior striate veins**, which leave the corpus striatum through the anterior perforated substance. The basal vein passes backward around the cerebral peduncle, and ends in the internal cerebral vein (*vein of Galen*); it receives tributaries from the interpeduncular fossa, the inferior horn of the lateral ventricle, the hippocampal gyrus, and the mid-brain.

The **Internal Cerebral Veins** (*vv. cerebri internæ; veins of Galen; deep cerebral veins*) drain the deep parts of the hemisphere and are two in number; each is formed near the interventricular foramen by the union of the **terminal** and **choroid veins**.

They run backward parallel with one another, between the layers of the tela chorioidea of the third ventricle, and beneath the splenium of the corpus callosum, where they unite to form a short trunk, the **great cerebral vein**; just before their union each receives the corresponding basal vein.

The **terminal vein** (*v. terminalis; vena corporis striati*) *commences* in the groove between the corpus striatum and thalamus, receives numerous veins from both of these parts, and unites behind the crus fornicis with the choroid vein, to form one of the internal cerebral veins. The **choroid vein** runs along the whole length of the choroid plexus, and receives veins from the hippocampus, the fornix, and the corpus callosum.

The **Great Cerebral Vein** (*v. cerebri magna* [*Galeni*]; *great vein of Galen*) (Fig. 613), formed by the union of the two internal cerebral veins, is a short median trunk which curves backward and upward around the splenium of the corpus callosum and ends in the anterior extremity of the straight sinus. (Fig. 615)

The **cerebellar veins** are placed on the surface of the cerebellum, and are disposed in two sets, superior and inferior. The **superior cerebellar veins** (*vv. cerebelli superiores*) pass partly forward and medialward, across the superior vermis, to end in the straight sinus and the internal cerebral veins, partly lateralward to the transverse and superior petrosal sinuses. The **inferior cerebellar veins** (*vv. cerebelli inferiores*) of large size, end in the transverse, superior petrosal, and occipital sinuses.

The Sinuses of the Dura Mater (Sinus Duræ Matris). Ophthalmic Veins and Emissary Veins.

The **sinuses of the dura mater** are venous channels which drain the blood from the brain; they are devoid of valves, and are situated between the two layers of the dura mater and lined by endothelium continuous with that which lines the veins. They may be divided into two groups: (1) a **postero-superior**, at the upper and back part of the skull, and (2) an **antero-inferior**, at the base of the skull.

The postero-superior group comprises the

Superior Sagittal.	Straight.
Inferior Sagittal.	Two Transverse.
Occipital.	

The **superior sagittal sinus** (*sinus sagittalis superior; superior longitudinal sinus*) (Figs. 615, 616) occupies the attached or convex margin of the falx cerebri. Commencing at the foramen cæcum, through which it receives a vein from the nasal cavity, it runs from before backward, grooving the inner surface of the frontal, the adjacent margins of the two parietals, and the superior division of the cruciate eminence of the occipital; near the internal occipital protuberance it deviates to one or other side (usually the right), and is continued as the corresponding transverse sinus. It is triangular in section, narrow in front, and gradually increases in size as it passes backward. Its inner surface presents the openings of the superior cerebral veins, which run, for the most part, obliquely forward, and open chiefly at the back part of the sinus, their orifices being concealed by fibrous folds; numerous fibrous bands (*chordæ Willisii*) extend transversely across the inferior angle of the sinus; and, lastly, small openings communicate with irregularly shaped venous spaces (*venous lacunæ*) in the dura mater near the sinus. There are usually three lacunæ on either side of the sinus: a small frontal, a large parietal, and an occipital, intermediate in size between the other two. Most of the cerebral veins from the outer surface of the hemisphere open into these lacunæ, and numerous **arachnoid granulations** (*Pacchionian bodies*) project into them from below. The superior sagittal sinus receives the superior cerebral veins, veins from the diploë and dura

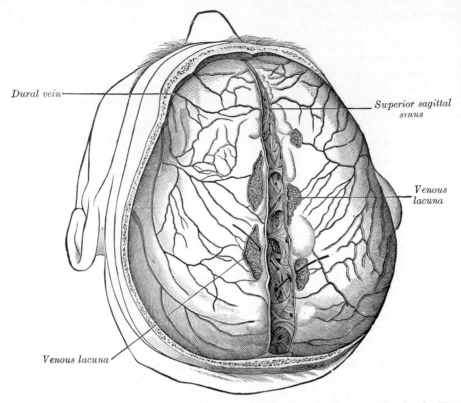

Fig. 614.—Superior sagittal sinus laid open after removal of the skull cap. The chordæ Willisi are clearly seen. The venous lacunæ are also well shown; from two of them probes are passed into the superior sagittal sinus. (Poirier and Charpy.)

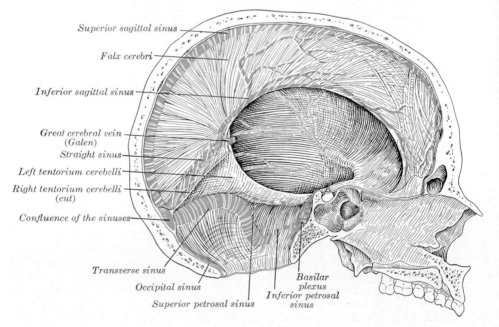

Fig. 615.—Sagittal section of the skull, showing the sinuses of the dura.

mater, and, near the posterior extremity of the sagittal suture, veins from the pericranium, which pass through the parietal foramina.

Numerous communications exist between this sinus and the veins of the nose, scalp, and diploë.

The **inferior sagittal sinus** (*sinus sagittalis inferior; inferior longitudinal sinus*) (Fig. 616) is contained in the posterior half or two-thirds of the free margin of the falx cerebri. It is of a cylindrical form, increases in size as it passes backward, and ends in the straight sinus. It receives several veins from the falx cerebri, and occasionally a few from the medial surfaces of the hemispheres.

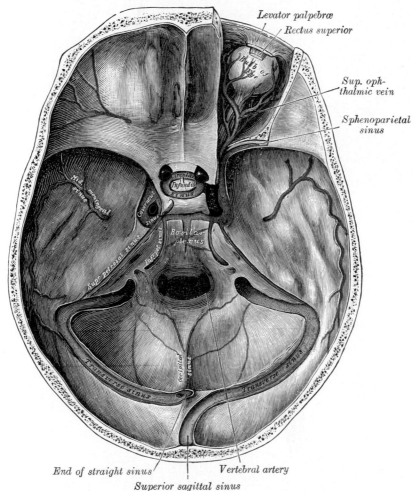

Fig. 616.—The sinuses at the base of the skull.

The **straight sinus** (*sinus rectus; tentorial sinus*) (Fig. 615) is situated at the line of junction of the falx cerebri with the tentorium cerebelli. It is triangular in section, increases in size as it proceeds backward, and runs downward and backward from the end of the inferior sagittal sinus to the transverse sinus of the opposite side to that into which the superior sagittal sinus is prolonged. Its terminal part communicates by a cross branch with the confluence of the sinuses. Besides the inferior sagittal sinus, it receives the great cerebral vein (*great vein of Galen*) and the superior cerebellar veins. A few transverse bands cross its interior.

47

The **transverse sinuses** (*sinus transversus; lateral sinuses*) (Fig. 616) are of large size and begin at the internal occipital protuberance; one, generally the right, being the direct continuation of the superior sagittal sinus, the other of the straight sinus. Each transverse sinus passes lateralward and forward, describing a slight curve with its convexity upward, to the base of the petrous portion of the temporal bone, and lies, in this part of its course, in the attached margin of the tentorium cerebelli; it then leaves the tentorium and curves downward and

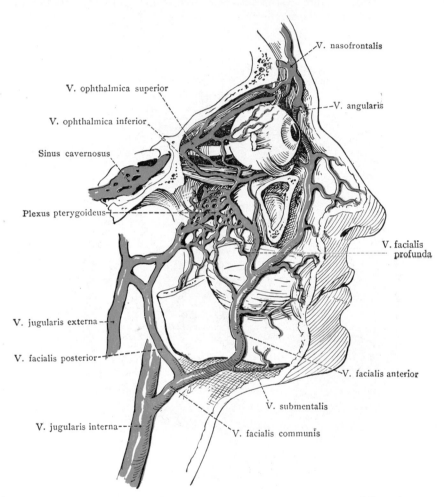

Fig. 617.—Principal veins of face and orbit. (Eycleshymer and Jones.)

medialward to reach the jugular foramen, where it ends in the internal jugular vein. In its course it rests upon the squama of the occipital, the mastoid angle of the parietal, the mastoid part of the temporal, and, just before its termination, the jugular process of the occipital; the portion which occupies the groove on the mastoid part of the temporal is sometimes termed the **sigmoid sinus**. The transverse sinuses are frequently of unequal size, that formed by the superior sagittal sinus being the larger; they increase in size as they proceed from behind forward. On transverse section the horizontal portion exhibits a prismatic, the curved portion a semicylindrical form. They receive the blood from the superior petrosal sinuses at the base of the petrous portion of the temporal bone; they communicate with the veins of the pericranium by means of the mastoid and condyloid emissary veins; and they receive some of the inferior cerebral and inferior cerebellar veins, and some veins from the diploë. The **petrosquamous sinus**, when present, runs backward along the junction of the squama and petrous portion of the temporal, and opens into the transverse sinus.

The **occipital sinus** (*sinus occipitalis*) (Fig. 616) is the smallest of the cranial sinuses. It is situated in the attached margin of the falx cerebelli, and is generally single, but occasionally there are two. It commences around the margin of the foramen magnum by several small venous channels, one of which joins the terminal part of the transverse sinus; it communicates with the posterior internal vertebral venous plexuses and ends in the confluence of the sinuses.

The **Confluence of the Sinuses** (*confluens sinuum; torcular Herophili* (Fig. 615) is the dilated junction of three tributary sinuses, the superior sagittal, the straight, and the occipital with the two large transverse sinuses. The direction of currents within the confluence is such that the right transverse sinus usually receives the greater part of its blood from the superior sagittal sinus and the left from the straight sinus.

The anterior-inferior group of sinuses comprises the

Two Cavernous.	Two Superior Petrosal.
Two Intercavernous.	Two Inferior Petrosal.

Basilar Plexus.

The **cavernous sinuses** (*sinus cavernosus*) (Figs. 616, 618) are so named because they present a reticulated structure, due to their being traversed by numerous interlacing filaments. They are of irregular form, larger behind than in front, and are placed one on either side of the body of the sphenoid bone, extending from the superior orbital fissure to the apex of the petrous portion of the temporal bone. Each opens behind into the petrosal sinuses. On the medial wall of each sinus is the internal carotid artery, accompanied by filaments of the carotid plexus; near the artery is the abducent nerve; on the lateral wall are the oculomotor and trochlear nerves, and the ophthalmic and maxillary divisions of the trigeminal nerve (Fig. 618). These structures are separated from the blood flowing along the sinus by the lining membrane of the sinus. The cavernous sinus receives the superior ophthalmic vein through the superior orbital fissure, some of the cerebral veins, and also the small **sphenoparietal sinus**, which courses along the under surface of the small wing of the sphenoid. It communicates with the transverse sinus by means of the superior petrosal sinus; with the internal jugular vein through the inferior petrosal sinus and a plexus of veins on the internal carotid artery; with the pterygoid venous plexus through the foramen Vesalii, foramen ovale, and foramen lacerum, and with the angular vein through the ophthalmic vein. The two sinuses also communicate with each other by means of the anterior and posterior intercavernous sinuses.

The **ophthalmic veins** (Fig. 617), **superior** and **inferior**, are devoid of valves.

The **Superior Ophthalmic Vein** (*v. ophthalmica superior*) begins at the inner angle of the orbit in a vein named the **nasofrontal** which communicates anteriorly with the angular vein; it pursues the same course as the ophthalmic artery, and receives tributaries corresponding to the branches of that vessel. Forming a short single trunk, it passes between the two heads of the Rectus lateralis and through the medial part of the superior orbital fissure, and ends in the cavernous sinus.

The **Inferior Ophthalmic Vein** (*v. ophthalmica inferior*) begins in a venous net-work at the forepart of the floor and medial wall of the orbit; it receives some veins from the Rectus inferior, Obliquus inferior, lacrimal sac and eyelids, runs backward in the lower part of the orbit and divides into two branches. One of these passes through the inferior orbital fissure and joins the pterygoid venous plexus, while the other enters the cranium through the superior orbital fissure and ends in the cavernous sinus, either by a separate opening, or more frequently in common with the superior ophthalmic vein.

The **intercavernous sinuses** (*sinus intercavernosi*) (Fig. 616) are two in number, an anterior and a posterior, and connect the two cavernous sinuses across the midline. The **anterior** passes in front of the hypophysis cerebri, the **posterior** behind it, and they form with the cavernous sinuses a venous circle (**circular sinus**) around the hypophysis. The anterior one is usually the larger of the two, and one or other is occasionally absent.

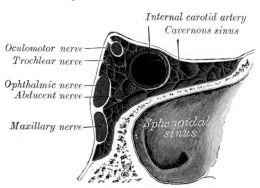

Internal carotid artery
Cavernous sinus

Oculomotor nerve
Trochlear nerve

Ophthalmic nerve
Abducent nerve

Maxillary nerve

Sphenoidal sinus

FIG. 618.—Oblique section through the cavernous sinus.

The **superior petrosal sinus** (*sinus petrosus superior*) (Fig. 616) small and narrow, connects the cavernous with the transverse sinus. It runs lateralward and backward, from the posterior end of the cavernous sinus, over the trigeminal nerve, and lies in the attached margin of the tentorium cerebelli and in the superior petrosal sulcus of the temporal bone; it joins the transverse sinus where the latter curves downward on the inner surface of the mastoid part of the temporal. It receives cerebellar and inferior cerebral veins, and veins from the tympanic cavity.

The **inferior petrosal sinus** (*sinus petrosus inferior*) (Fig. 616) is situated in the inferior petrosal sulcus formed by the junction of the petrous part of the temporal with the basilar part of the occipital. It begins in the postero-inferior part of the cavernous sinus, and, passing through the anterior part of the jugular foramen, ends in the superior bulb of the internal jugular vein. The inferior petrosal sinus receives the internal auditory veins and also veins from the medulla oblongata, pons, and under surface of the cerebellum.

The exact relation of the parts to one another in the jugular foramen is as follows: the inferior petrosal sinus lies medially and anteriorly with the meningeal branch of the ascending pharyngeal artery, and is directed obliquely downward and backward; the transverse sinus is situated at the lateral and back part of the foramen with a meningeal branch of the occipital artery, and between the two sinuses are the glossopharyngeal, vagus, and accessory nerves. These three sets of structures are divided from each other by two processes of fibrous tissue. The junction of the inferior petrosal sinus with the internal jugular vein takes place on the lateral aspect of the nerves.

The **basilar plexus** (*plexus basilaris; transverse or basilar sinus*) (Fig. 616) consists of several interlacing venous channels between the layers of the dura mater over the basilar part of the occipital bone, and serves to connect the two inferior petrosal sinuses. It communicates with the anterior vertebral venous plexus.

Emissary Veins (*venæ emissariæ*). (Fig. 619)—The emissary veins pass through the cranial wall and establish communication between the sinuses inside the skull and the veins external to it. Some are always present, others only occasionally. The principal emissary veins are the following: (1) A mastoid emissary vein, usually present, runs through the mastoid foramen and unites the transverse sinus with the posterior auricular or with the occipital vein. (2) A parietal emissary vein passes through the parietal foramen and connects the superior sagittal sinus with the veins of the scalp. (3) A net-work of minute veins (*rete canalis hypoglossi*) traverses the hypoglossal canal and joins the transverse sinus with the vertebral

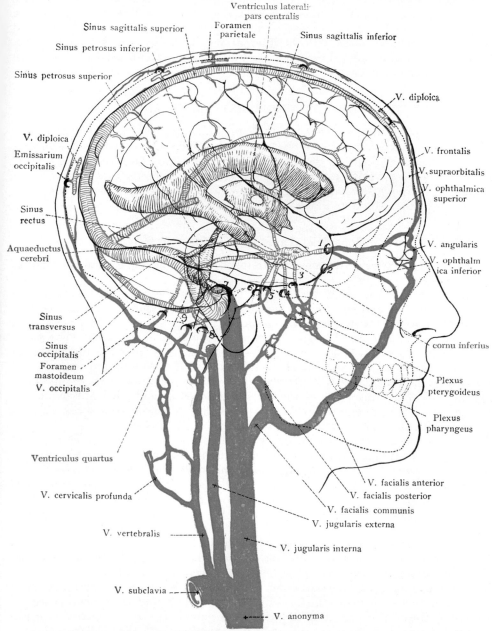

Ventriculus lateralis
pars centralis

Sinus sagittalis superior

Foramen
parietale

Sinus sagittalis inferior

Sinus petrosus inferior

Sinus petrosus superior

V. diploica

V. diploica

Emissarium
occipitalis

V. frontalis

V. supraorbitalis

V. ophthalmica
superior

Sinus
rectus

V. angularis

Aquaeductus
cerebri

V. ophthalm
ica inferior

Sinus
transversus

cornu inferius

Sinus
occipitalis

Foramen
mastoideum

V. occipitalis

Plexus
pterygoideus

Plexus
pharyngeus

Ventriculus quartus

V. facialis anterior

V. cervicalis profunda

V. facialis posterior

V. facialis communis

V. jugularis externa

V. vertebralis

V. jugularis interna

V. subclavia

V. anonyma

Fig. 619.—Venous drainage of the head and neck. The cerebral ventricles are projected in red. The veins in their extra-cranial portions are shown in deep blue; the intra-cranial portions in light blue. The numbers indicate the foramina through which these veins enter the cranium. These are: *1.* Fissura orbitalis superior. *2.* Fissura orbitalis inferior. *3.* Foramen ovale. *4.* Foramen spinosum. *5.* Foramen lacerum. *6.* Canalis caroticus. *7.* Foramen jugulare. *8.* Canalis hypoglossi. *9.* Canalis condyloideus. The black inverted crescents indicate openings through which emissary veins pass. (Eycleshymer and Jones.)

vein and deep veins of the neck.   (4) An inconstant condyloid emissary vein passes through the condyloid canal and connects the transverse sinus with the deep veins of the neck.   (5) A net-work of veins (*rete foraminis ovalis*) unites the cavernous sinus with the pterygoid plexus through the foramen ovale.   (6) Two or three small veins run through the foramen lacerum and connect the cavernous sinus with the pterygoid plexus.   (7) The emissary vein of the foramen of Vesalius connects the same parts.   (8) An internal carotid plexus of veins traverses the carotid canal and unites the cavernous sinus with the internal jugular vein.   (9) A vein is transmitted through the foramen cæcum and connects the superior sagittal sinus with the veins of the nasal cavity.

THE VEINS OF THE UPPER EXTREMITY AND THORAX.

The veins of the upper extremity are divided into two sets, **superficial** and **deep**; the two sets anastomose frequently with each other. The superficial veins are placed immediately beneath the integument between the two layers of superficial fascia.   The deep veins accompany the arteries, and constitute the venæ comitantes of those vessels.   Both sets are provided with valves, which are more numerous in the deep than in the superficial veins.

The Superficial Veins of the Upper Extremity.

The **superficial veins** of the upper extremity are the **digital, metacarpal, cephalic, basilic, median**.

Digital Veins.—The **dorsal digital veins** pass along the sides of the fingers and are joined to one another by oblique communicating branches. Those from the adjacent sides of the fingers unite to form three **dorsal metacarpal veins** (Fig. 620), which end in a dorsal venous net-work on the back of the hand. The radial part of the net-work is joined by the dorsal digital vein from the radial side of the index finger and by the dorsal digital veins of the thumb, and is prolonged upward as the cephalic vein. The ulnar part of the net-work receives the dorsal digital vein of the ulnar side of the little finger and is continued upward as the basilic vein.   A communicating branch frequently connects the dorsal venous network with the cephalic vein about the middle of the forearm.

The **volar digital veins** on each finger are connected to the dorsal digital veins by oblique **intercapitular veins**. They drain into a venous plexus which is situated over the thenar and hypothenar eminences and across the front of the wrist.

The **cephalic vein** (Fig. 621) *begins* in the radial part of the dorsal venous net-work and winds upward around the radial border of the forearm, receiving tributaries from both surfaces. Below the front of the elbow it gives off the **vena mediana cubiti** (*median cubital vein*), which receives a communicating branch from the deep veins of the forearm and passes across to join the basilic vein.   The cephalic vein then ascends in front of the elbow in the groove between the Brachioradialis and the Biceps brachii.   It crosses superficial to the musculocutaneous nerve and ascends in the groove along the lateral border of the Biceps brachii.   In the upper third of the arm it passes between the Pectoralis major and Deltoideus, where it is accompanied by the deltoid branch of the thoracoacromial artery.   It pierces the clavipectoral fascia and, crossing the axillary artery, ends in the axillary vein just below the clavicle.   Sometimes it communicates with the external jugular vein by a branch which ascends in front of the clavicle.

The **accessory cephalic vein** (*v. cephalica accessoria*) *arises* either from a small tributary plexus on the back of the forearm or from the ulnar side of the dorsal venous net-work; it joins the cephalic below the elbow.   In some cases the accessory cephalic springs from the cephalic above the wrist and joins it again higher up. A large oblique branch frequently connects the basilic and cephalic veins on the back of the forearm.

The **basilic vein** (*v. basilica*) (Fig. 621) *begins* in the ulnar part of the dorsal venous network. It runs up the posterior surface of the ulnar side of the forearm and inclines forward to the anterior surface below the elbow, where it is joined

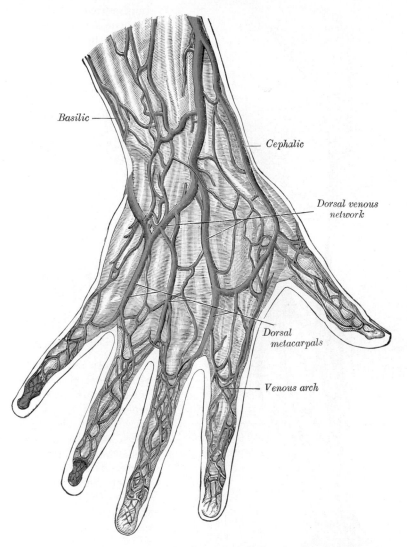

FIG. 620.—The veins on the dorsum of the hand. (Bourgery.)

by the vena mediana cubiti. It ascends obliquely in the groove between the Biceps brachii and Pronator teres and crosses the brachial artery, from which it is separated by the lacertus fibrosus; filaments of the medial antebrachial cutaneous nerve pass both in front of and behind this portion of the vein. It then runs upward along the medial border of the Biceps brachii, perforates the deep fascia a little below the middle of the arm, and, ascending on the medial side of the brachial artery to the lower border of the Teres major joins the brachial to form the axillary vein.

The **median antebrachial vein** (*v. mediana antebrachii*) drains the venous plexus on the volar surface of the hand. It ascends on the ulnar side of the front of the forearm and ends in the basilic vein or in the vena mediana cubiti; in a small proportion of cases it divides into two branches, one of which joins the basilic, the other the cephalic, below the elbow.

There is considerable variation in the superficial veins of the forearm. The basilic may be much larger than the cephalic and drain a correspondingly larger area, or the reverse may be true. The median antebrachial vein may be absent as a definite vessel. The median cubital vein may split into a distinct Y; one arm of the Y draining into the cephalic, the other into the basilic. In this case one branch is called the **median cephalic vein**, the other the **median basilic vein**.

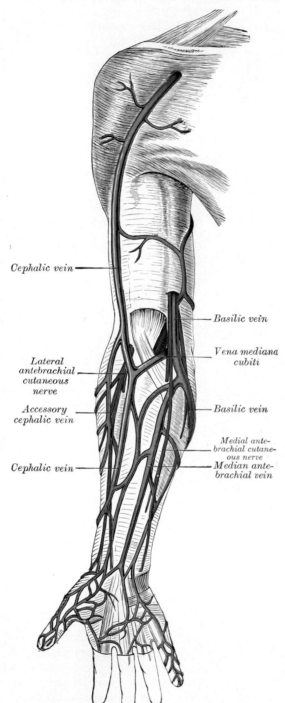

Cephalic vein

Lateral antebrachial cutaneous nerve

Accessory cephalic vein

Cephalic vein

Basilic vein

Vena mediana cubiti

Basilic vein

Medial antebrachial cutaneous nerve

Median antebrachial vein

FIG. 621.—The superficial veins of the upper extremity.

The Deep Veins of the Upper Extremity.

The **deep veins** follow the course of the arteries, forming their venæ comitantes. They are generally arranged in pairs, and are situated one on either side of the corresponding artery, and connected at intervals by short transverse branches.

Deep Veins of the Hand.— Each of the superficial and deep volar arterial arches is accompanied by a pair of venæ comitantes which constitute the **superficial** and **deep volar venous arches**, and receive the veins corresponding to the branches of the arterial arches; thus the **common volar digital veins**, formed by the union of the **proper volar digital veins**, open into the superficial, and the **volar metacarpal veins** into the deep volar venous arches. The **dorsal**

metacarpal veins receive perforating branches from the volar metacarpal veins and end in the radial veins and the superficial veins on the dorsum of the wrist.

The **deep veins of the forearm** are the venæ comitantes of the radial and ulnar arteries and constitute respectively the upward continuations of the deep and superficial volar venous arches; they unite in front of the elbow to form the brachial veins. The radial veins are smaller than the ulnar and receive the dorsal metacarpal veins. The ulnar veins receive tributaries from the deep volar venous arches and communicate with the superficial veins at the wrist; near the elbow they receive the volar and dorsal interosseous veins and send a large communicating branch (profunda vein) to the vena mediana cubiti.

The **brachial veins** (*vv. brachiales*) are placed one on either side of the brachial artery, receiving tributaries corresponding with the branches given off from that vessel; near the lower margin of the Subscapularis, they join the axillary vein; the medial one frequently joins the basilic vein.

These deep veins have numerous anastomoses, not only with each other, but also with the superficial veins.

The **axillary vein** (*v. axillaris*) begins at the junction of the basilic and brachial

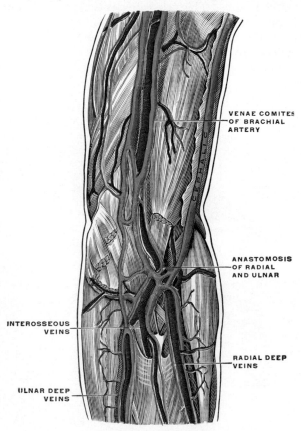

FIG. 622.—The deep veins of the upper extremity. (Bourgery.)

veins near the lower border of the Teres major, and ends at the outer border of the first rib, by becoming the subclavian vein. In addition to the tributaries which correspond to the branches of the axillary artery, it receives the cephalic vein near its termination and may receive an additional deeper brachial comitans near its beginning. It lies on the medial side of the artery, which it partly overlaps; between the two vessels are the medial cord of the brachial plexus, the median, the ulnar, and the medial anterior thoracic nerves. It is provided with a pair of valves opposite the lower border of the Subscapularis; valves are also found at the ends of the cephalic and subscapular veins.

The **subclavian vein** (*v. subclavia*), the continuation of the axillary, extends from the outer border of the first rib to the sternal end of the clavicle, where it unites with the internal jugular to form the innominate vein. It is in relation, in *front*, with the clavicle and Subclavius; *behind* and *above*, with the subclavian artery, from which it is separated medially by the Scalenus anterior and the phrenic nerve. *Below*, it rests in a depression on the first rib and upon the pleura. It is usually provided with a pair of valves, which are situated about 2.5 cm. from its termination.

The subclavian vein occasionally rises in the neck to a level with the third part of the subclavian artery, and occasionally passes with this vessel behind the Scalenus anterior.

Tributaries.—This vein receives the external jugular vein, sometimes the anterior jugular vein, and occasionally a small branch, which ascends in front of the clavicle, from the cephalic. At its angle of junction with the internal jugular, the left subclavian vein receives the thoracic duct, and the right subclavian vein the right lymphatic duct.

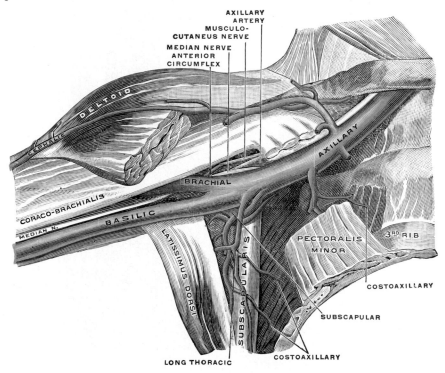

Fig. 623.—The veins of the right axilla, viewed from in front. (Spalteholz.)

The Veins of the Thorax (Fig. 624)

The **innominate veins** (*vv. anonymæ; brachiocephalic veins*) are two large trunks, one on either side of the root of the neck, and formed by the union of the internal jugular and subclavian veins of the corresponding side; they lack valves.

The **Right Innominate Vein** (*v. anonyma dextra*) is a short vessel, about 2.5 cm. in length, which begins behind the sternal end of the clavicle, and, passing almost vertically downward, joins with the left innominate vein just below the cartilage of the first rib, close to the right border of the sternum, to form the superior vena cava. It lies in front and to the right of the innominate artery; on its right side are the phrenic nerve and the pleura, which are interposed between it and the apex of the lung. This vein, at its commencement, receives the right vertebral vein; and, lower down, the right internal mammary and right inferior thyroid veins, and sometimes the vein from the first intercostal space.

The **Left Innominate Vein** (*v. anonyma sinistra*), about 6 cm. in length, *begins* behind the sternal end of the clavicle and runs obliquely downward and to the right behind the upper half of the manubrium sterni to the sternal end of the first right costal cartilage, where it unites with the right innominate vein to form the **superior vena cava**. It is separated from the manubrium sterni by the Sterno-hyoideus and Sternothyreoideus, the thymus or its remains, and some loose areolar tissue. Behind it are the three large arteries, innominate, left common carotid, and left subclavian, arising from the aortic arch, together with the vagus and phrenic nerves. The left innominate vein may occupy a higher level, crossing the jugular notch and lying directly in front of the trachea.

Tributaries.—Its tributaries are the left vertebral, left internal mammary, left inferior thyroid, and the left highest intercostal veins, and occasionally some thymic and pericardiac veins.

Variations.—Sometimes the innominate veins open separately into the right atrium; in such cases the right vein takes the ordinary course of the superior vena cava; the left vein—*left superior vena cava*, as it is then termed—which may communicate by a small branch with the right one, passes in front of the root of the left lung, and, turning to the back of the heart, ends in the right atrium. This occasional condition in the adult is due to the persistence of the early fetal condition, and is the normal state of things in birds and some mammalia.

The **internal mammary veins** (*vv. mammariæ internæ*) are venæ comitantes to the lower half of the internal mammary artery, and receive tributaries corresponding to the branches of the artery. They then unite to form a single trunk, which runs up on the medial side of the artery and ends in the corresponding innominate vein. The **superior phrenic vein**, *i. e.*, the vein accompanying the peri-cardiacophrenic artery, usually opens into the internal mammary vein.

The **inferior thyroid veins** (*vv. thyreoideæ inferiores*) two, frequently three or four, in number, *arise* in the venous plexus on the thyroid gland, communicating with the middle and superior thyroid veins. They form a plexus in front of the trachea, behind the Sternothyreoidei. From this plexus, a left vein descends and joins the left innominate trunk, and a right vein passes obliquely downward and to the right across the innominate artery to open into the right innominate vein, just at its junction with the superior vena cava; sometimes the right and left veins open by a common trunk in the latter situation. These veins receive esophageal tracheal, and inferior laryngeal veins, and are provided with valves at their terminations in the innominate veins. (Fig. 609)

The **highest intercostal veins** (*v. intercostalis suprema; superior intercostal veins*) (right and left) drain the blood from the upper three or four intercostal spaces. The **right vein** (*v. intercostalis suprema dextra*) passes downward and opens into the vena azygos; the **left vein** (*v. intercostalis suprema sinistra*) runs across the arch of the aorta and the origins of the left subclavian and left common carotid arteries and opens into the left innominate vein. It usually receives the left bronchial vein, and sometimes the left superior phrenic vein, and communicates below with the accessory hemiazygos vein.

The **superior vena cava** (*v. cava superior*) drains the blood from the upper half of the body. It measures about 7 cm. in length, and is formed by the junction of the two innominate veins. It *begins* immediately below the cartilage of the right first rib close to the sternum, and, descending vertically behind the first and second intercostal spaces, ends in the upper part of the right atrium opposite the upper border of the third right costal cartilage: the lower half of the vessel is within the pericardium. It describes a slight curve, the convexity of which is to the right (Fig. 519).

Relations.—*In front* are the anterior margins of the right lung and pleura with the pericardium intervening below; these separate it from the first and second intercostal spaces and from the second and third right costal cartilages; *behind* it are the root of the right lung and the right

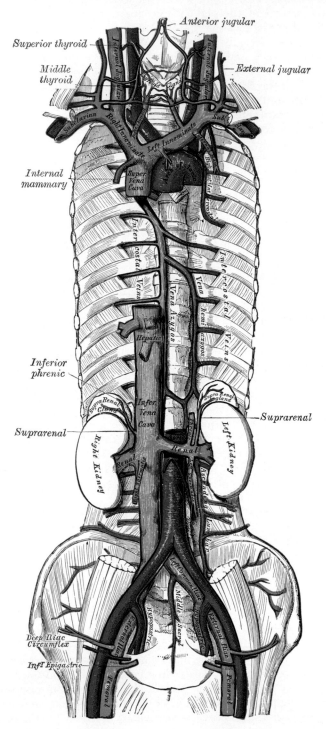

FIG. 624.—The venæ cavæ and azygos veins, with their tributaries.

vagus nerve. On its *right side* are the phrenic nerve and right pleura; on its *left side*, the commencement of the innominate artery and the ascending aorta, the latter overlapping it. Just before it pierces the pericardium, it receives the azygos vein and several small veins from the pericardium and other contents of the mediastinal cavity. The portion contained within the pericardium is covered, in front and laterally, by the serous layer of the membrane. The superior vena cava has no valves.

The **azygos vein** (*v. azygos; vena azygos major*) *begins* opposite the first or second lumbar vertebra, by a branch, the **ascending lumbar vein** (page 759); sometimes by a branch from the right renal vein, or from the inferior vena cava. It enters the thorax through the aortic hiatus in the diaphragm, and passes along the right side of the vertebral column to the fourth thoracic vertebra, where it arches forward over the root of the right lung, and ends in the superior vena cava, just before that vessel pierces the pericardium. In the aortic hiatus, it lies with the thoracic duct on the right side of the aorta; in the thorax it lies upon the intercostal arteries, on the right side of the aorta and thoracic duct, and is partly covered by pleura.

Tributaries.—It receives the right subcostal and intercostal veins, the upper three or four of these latter opening by a common stem, the highest superior intercostal vein. It receives the hemiazygos veins, several esophageal, mediastinal, and pericardial veins, and, near its termination, the right bronchial vein. A few imperfect valves are found in the azygos vein; but the valves of its tributaries are complete.

The intercostal veins on the left side, below the upper three intercostal spaces, usually form two trunks, named the **hemiazygos** and **accessory hemiazygos veins**.

The **Hemiazygos Vein** (*v. hemiazygos; vena azygos minor inferior*) *begins* in the left ascending lumbar or renal vein. It enters the thorax, through the left crus of the diaphragm, and, ascending on the left side of the vertebral column, as high as the ninth thoracic vertebra, passes across the column, behind the aorta, esophagus, and thoracic duct, to end in the azygos vein. It receives the lower four or five intercostal veins and the subcostal vein of the left side, and some esophageal and mediastinal veins.

The **Accessory Hemiazygos Vein** (*v. hemiazygos accessoria; vena azygos minor superior*) descends on the left side of the vertebral column, and varies inversely in size with the highest left intercostal vein. It receives veins from the three or four intercostal spaces between the highest left intercostal vein and highest tributary of the hemiazygos; the left bronchial vein sometimes opens into it. It either crosses the body of the eighth thoracic vertebra to join the azygos vein or ends in the hemiazygos. When this vein is small, or altogether wanting, the left highest intercostal vein may extend as low as the fifth or sixth intercostal space.

In obstruction of the inferior vena cava, the azygos and hemiazygos veins are the principal means by which the venous circulation is carried on, connecting as they do the superior and inferior venæ cavæ, and communicating with the common iliac veins by the ascending lumbar veins and with many of the tributaries of the inferior vena cava.

The **Bronchial Veins** (*vv. bronchiales*) return the blood from the larger bronchi, and from the structures at the roots of the lungs; that of the right side opens into the azygos vein, near its termination; that of the left side, into the highest left intercostal or the accessory hemiazygos vein. A considerable quantity of the blood which is carried to the lungs through the bronchial arteries is returned to the left side of the heart through the pulmonary veins.

The Veins of the Vertebral Column (Figs. 625, 626).

The veins which drain the blood from the vertebral column, the neighboring muscles, and the meninges of the medulla spinalis form intricate plexuses extending along the entire length of the column; these plexuses may be divided into two groups, external and internal, according to their positions inside or outside the vertebral canal. The plexuses of the two groups anastomose freely with each other and end in the intervertebral veins.

The **external vertebral venous plexuses** (*plexus venosi vertebrales externi; extra-spinal veins*) best marked in the cervical region, consist of anterior and posterior plexuses which anastomose freely with each other. The **anterior external plexuses** lie in front of the bodies of the vertebræ, communicate with the basivertebral and intervertebral veins, and receive tributaries from the vertebral bodies. The **posterior external plexuses** are placed partly on the posterior surfaces of the vertebral arches and their processes, and partly between the deep dorsal muscles. They are best developed in the cervical region, and there anastomose with the vertebral, occipital, and deep cervical veins.

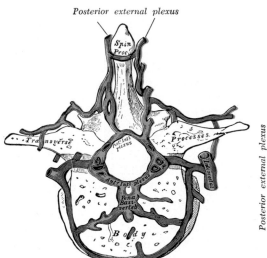

FIG. 625.—Transverse section of a thoracic vertebra, showing the vertebral venous plexuses.

FIG. 626.—Median sagittal section of two thoracic vertebræ, showing the vertebral venous plexuses.

The **internal vertebral venous plexuses** (*plexus venosi vertebrales interni; intra-spinal veins*) lie within the vertebral canal between the dura mater and the verte-bræ, and receive tributaries from the bones and from the medulla spinalis. They form a closer net-work than the external plexuses, and, running mainly in a vertical direction, form four longitudinal veins, two in front and two behind; they therefore may be divided into anterior and posterior groups. The **anterior internal plexuses** consist of large veins which lie on the posterior surfaces of the vertebral bodies and intervertebral fibrocartilages on either side of the posterior longitudinal ligament; under cover of this ligament they are connected by transverse branches into which the basivertebral veins open. The **posterior internal plexuses** are placed, one on either side of the middle line in front of the vertebral arches and ligamenta flava, and anastomose by veins passing through those ligaments with the posterior exter-nal plexuses. The anterior and posterior plexuses communicate freely with one another by a series of **venous rings** (*retia venosa vertebrarum*), one opposite each vertebra. Around the foramen magnum they form an intricate net-work which opens into the vertebral veins and is connected above with the occipital sinus, the basilar plexus, the condyloid emissary vein, and the rete canalis hypoglossi.

The **basivertebral veins** (*vv. basivertebrales*) emerge from the foramina on the posterior surfaces of the vertebral bodies. They are contained in large, tortuous channels in the substance of the bones, similar in every respect to those found in the diploë of the cranial bones. They communicate through small openings on the front and sides of the bodies of the vertebræ with the anterior external vertebral plexuses, and converge behind to the principal canal, which is sometimes double toward its posterior part, and open by valved orifices into the transverse branches which unite the anterior internal vertebral plexuses. They become greatly enlarged in advanced age.

The **intervertebral veins** (*vv. intervertebrales*) accompany the spinal nerves through the intervertebral foramina; they receive the veins from the medulla spinalis, drain the internal and external vertebral plexuses and end in the vertebral, intercostal, lumbar, and lateral sacral veins, their orifices being provided with valves.

The **veins of the medulla spinalis** (*vv. spinales; veins of the spinal cord*) are situated in the pia mater and form a minute, tortuous, venous plexus. They emerge chiefly from the median fissures of the medulla spinalis and are largest in the lumbar region. In this plexus there are (1) two median longitudinal veins, one in front of the anterior fissure, and the other behind the posterior sulcus of the cord, and (2) four lateral longitudinal veins which run behind the nerve roots. They end in the intervertebral veins. Near the base of the skull they unite, and form two or three small trunks, which communicate with the vertebral veins, and then end in the inferior cerebellar veins, or in the inferior petrosal sinuses.

According to Batson (1940) the veins of the vertebral column constitute a system paralleling the caval system. He reached this conclusion as a result of X-ray studies of human cadavers and living animals. A thin solution of radiopaque material which he injected into the dorsal vein of the penis in a cadaver found its way readily into the veins of the entire vertebral column, the skull, and the interior of the cranium. The material drained from the dorsal vein of the penis into the prostatic plexus and then followed communications with the veins of the sacrum, ilium, lumbar vertebræ, upper femur, and the venæ vasorum of the large femoral blood vessels, without traversing the main caval tributaries. Similarly, material injected into a small breast vein found its way into the veins of the clavicle, the intercostal veins, the head of the humerus, cervical vertebræ, and dural sinuses without following the caval paths. Thorium dioxide injected into the dorsal vein of the penis of an anæsthetized monkey drained into the caval system when the animal was undisturbed, but if its abdomen was put under pressure with a binder, simulating the increased intra-abdominal pressure of coughing or straining, the material drained into the veins of the vertebræ. Batson believes that the spread of metastases from tumors and abscesses, in many cases such as the metastases to the pelvic bones from the prostate, can be explained only through the channels of the vertebral venous system and its extensive communication with the caval system. When the pressure within the thorax and abdomen is increased by coughing or straining, the blood may flow along the vertebral system rather than the caval and it may even be forced into the vertebral veins from the viscera.

THE VEINS OF THE LOWER EXTREMITY, ABDOMEN, AND PELVIS.

The veins of the lower extremity are subdivided, like those of the upper, into two sets, **superficial** and **deep**; the superficial veins are placed beneath the integument between the two layers of superficial fascia; the deep veins accompany the arteries. Both sets of veins are provided with valves, which are more numerous in the deep than in the superficial set. Valves are also more numerous in the veins of the lower than in those of the upper limb.

The Superficial Veins of the Lower Extremity.

The **superficial veins** of the lower extremity are the **great** and **small saphenous veins** and their tributaries.

On the **dorsum of the foot** the **dorsal digital veins** receive, in the clefts between the toes, the **intercapitular veins** from the plantar cutaneous venous arch and join to form short **common digital veins** which unite across the distal ends of the metatarsal bones in a **dorsal venous arch.** Proximal to this arch is an irregular venous network which receives tributaries from the deep veins and is joined at the sides of the foot by a **medial** and a **lateral marginal vein,** formed mainly by the union of branches from the superficial parts of the sole of the foot.

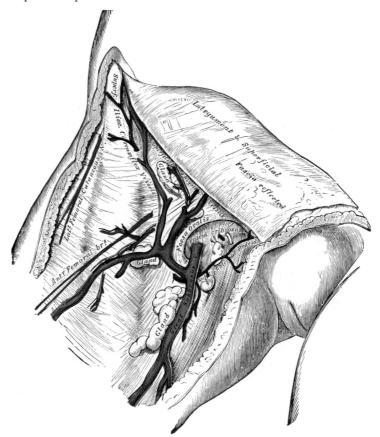

Fig. 627.—The great saphenous vein and its tributaries at the fossa ovalis.

On the **sole of the foot** the superficial veins form a **plantar cutaneous venous arch** which extends across the roots of the toes and opens at the sides of the foot into the medial and lateral marginal veins. Proximal to this arch is a **plantar cutaneous venous net-work** which is especially dense in the fat beneath the heel; this net-work communicates with the cutaneous venous arch and with the deep veins, but is chiefly drained into the medial and lateral marginal veins.

The **great saphenous vein** (*v. saphena magna; internal or long saphenous vein*) (Fig. 628), the longest vein in the body, *begins* in the medial marginal vein of the dorsum of the foot and ends in the femoral vein about 3 cm. below the inguinal ligament. It ascends in front of the tibial malleolus and along the medial side of the leg in relation with the saphenous nerve. It runs upward behind the medial condyles of the tibia and femur and along the medial side of the thigh and, passing through the fossa ovalis, ends in the femoral vein.

Tributaries.—At the ankle it receives branches from the sole of the foot through the medial marginal vein; in the leg it anastomoses freely with the small saphenous vein, communicates with the anterior and posterior tibial veins and receives many cutaneous veins; in the thigh it communicates with the femoral vein and receives numerous tributaries; those from the medial and posterior parts of the thigh frequently unite to form a large **accessory saphenous vein** which joins the main vein at a variable level. Near the fossa ovalis (Fig. 627) it is joined by the superficial epigastric, superficial iliac circumflex, and superficial external pudendal veins. A vein, named the **thoracoepigastric**, runs along the lateral aspect of the trunk between the superficial epigastric vein and the lateral thoracic vein and establishes an important communication between the femoral and axillary veins.

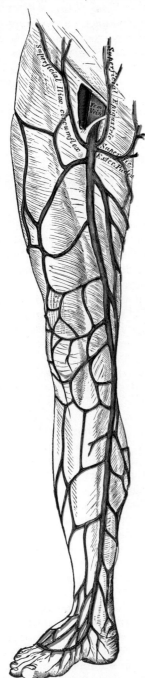

Fig. 628.—The great saphenous vein and its tributaries.

48

Fig. 629.—The small saphenous vein.

The valves in the great saphenous vein vary from ten to twenty in number; they are more numerous in the leg than in the thigh.

The **small saphenous vein** (*v. saphena parva; external or short saphenous vein*) (Fig. 629) *begins* behind the lateral malleolus as a continuation of the lateral marginal vein; it first ascends along the lateral margin of the tendo calcanei, and then crosses it to reach the middle of the back of the leg. Running directly upward, it perforates the deep fascia in the lower part of the popliteal fossa, and ends in the popliteal vein, between the heads of the Gastrocnemius. It communicates with the deep veins on the dorsum of the foot, and receives numerous large tributaries from the back of the leg. Before it pierces the deep fascia, it gives off a branch which runs upward and forward to join the great saphenous vein. The small saphenous vein possesses from nine to twelve valves, one of which is always found near its termination in the popliteal vein. In the lower third of the leg the small saphenous vein is in close relation with the sural nerve, in the upper two-thirds with the medial sural cutaneous nerve.

The Deep Veins of the Lower Extremity.

The **deep veins** of the lower extremity accompany the arteries and their branches; they possess numerous valves.

The **plantar digital veins** (*vv. digitales plantares*) *arise* from plexuses on the plantar surfaces of the digits, and, after sending **intercapitular veins** to join the dorsal digital veins, unite to form four **metatarsal veins**; these run backward in the metatarsal spaces, communicate, by means of perforating veins, with the veins on the dorsum of the foot, and unite to form the **deep plantar venous arch**

which lies alongside the plantar arterial arch. From the deep plantar venous arch the **medial** and **lateral plantar veins** run backward close to the corresponding arteries and, after communicating with the great and small saphenous veins, unite behind the medial malleolus to form the posterior tibial veins.

The **posterior tibial veins** (*vv. tibiales posteriores*) accompany the posterior tibial artery, and are joined by the **peroneal veins**.

The **anterior tibial veins** (*vv. tibiales anteriores*) are the upward continuation of the venæ comitantes of the dorsalis pedis artery. They leave the front of the leg by passing between the tibia and fibula, over the interosseous membrane, and unite with the posterior tibial, to form the **popliteal vein**.

The **Popliteal Vein** (*v. poplitea*) (Fig. 630) is formed by the junction of the anterior and posterior tibial veins at the lower border of the Popliteus; it ascends through the popliteal fossa to the aperture in the Adductor magnus, where it becomes the femoral vein. In the lower part of its course it is placed medial to the artery; between the heads of the Gastrocnemius it is superficial to that vessel; but above the knee-joint, it is close to its lateral side. It receives tributaries corresponding to the branches of the popliteal artery, and it also receives the small saphenous vein. The valves in the popliteal vein are usually four in number.

Fig. 630.—The popliteal vein.

The **femoral vein** (*v. femoralis*) accompanies the femoral artery through the upper two-thirds of the thigh.   In the lower part of its course it lies lateral to the artery; higher up, it is behind it; and at the inguinal laigment, it lies on its medial side, and on the same plane.   It receives numerous muscular tributaries, and about 4 cm. below the inguinal ligament is joined by the v. profunda femoris; near its termination it is joined by the great saphenous vein.   The valves in the femoral vein are three in number.

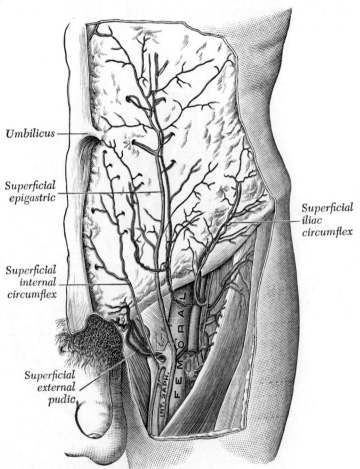

Fig. 631.—The femoral vein and its tributaries.   (Poirier and Charpy.)

The **Deep Femoral Vein** (*v. profunda femoris*) receives tributaries corresponding to the perforating branches of the profunda artery, and through these establishes communications with the popliteal vein below and the inferior gluteal vein above. It also receives the medial and lateral femoral circumflex veins.

The Veins of the Abdomen and Pelvis (Fig. 632).

The **external iliac vein** (*v. iliaca externa*), the upward continuation of the femoral vein, begins behind the inguinal ligament, and, passing upward along the brim of the lesser pelvis, ends opposite the sacroiliac articulation, by uniting with the hypogastric vein to form the common iliac vein.   On the right side, it lies at first medial to the artery: but, as it passes upward, gradually inclines behind it.   On the left side, it lies altogether on the medial side of the artery. It frequently contains one, sometimes two valves.

Tributaries.—The external iliac vein receives the inferior epigastric, deep iliac circumflex, and pubic veins.

The **Inferior Epigastric Vein** (*v. epigastrica inferior; deep epigastric vein*) is formed by the union of the venæ comitantes of the inferior epigastric artery, which communicate above with the superior epigastric vein; it joins the external iliac about 1.25 cm. above the inguinal ligament.

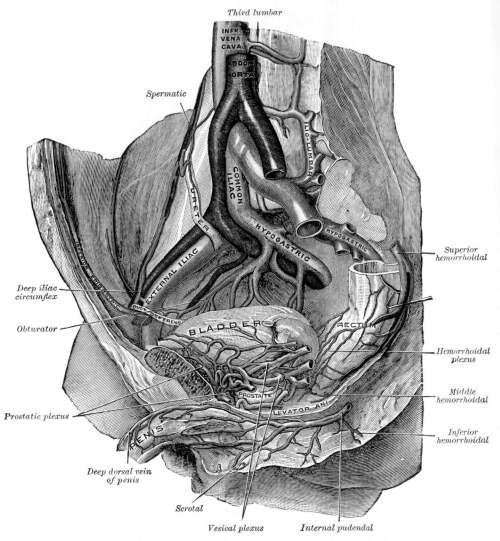

Fig. 632.—The veins of the right half of the male pelvis. (Spalteholz.)

The **Deep Iliac Circumflex Vein** (*v. circumflexa ilii profunda*) is formed by the union of the venæ comitantes of the deep iliac circumflex artery, and joins the external iliac vein about 2 cm. above the inguinal ligament.

The **Pubic Vein** communicates with the obturator vein in the obturator foramen, and ascends on the back of the pubis to the external iliac vein.

The **hypogastric vein** (*v. hypogastrica; internal iliac vein*) *begins* near the upper part of the greater sciatic foramen, passes upward behind and slightly medial to the hypogastric artery and, at the brim of the pelvis, joins with the external iliac to form the common iliac vein.

Tributaries.—With the exception of the fetal umbilical vein which passes upward and backward from the umbilicus to the liver, and the iliolumbar vein which usually joins the common iliac vein, the tributaries of the hypogastric vein correspond with the branches of the hypogastric artery. It receives (*a*) the **gluteal, internal pudendal,** and **obturator veins,** which have their origins outside the pelvis; (*b*) the **lateral sacral veins,** which lie in front of the sacrum; and (*c*) the **middle hemorrhoidal, vesical, uterine,** and **vaginal veins,** which originate in venous plexuses connected with the pelvic viscera.

1. The **Superior Gluteal Veins** (*vv. glutaeæ superiores; gluteal veins*) are venæ comitantes of the superior gluteal artery; they receive tributaries from the buttock corresponding with the branches of the artery, and enter the pelvis through the greater sciatic foramen, above the Piriformis, and frequently unite before ending in the hypogastric vein.

2. The **Inferior Gluteal Veins** (*vv. glutaeæ inferiores; sciatic veins*), or venæ comitantes of the inferior gluteal artery, *begin* on the upper part of the back of the thigh, where they anastomose with the medial femoral circumflex and first perforating veins. They enter the pelvis through the lower part of the greater sciatic foramen and join to form a single stem which opens into the lower part of the hypogastric vein.

3. The **Internal Pudendal Veins** (*internal pudic veins*) are the venæ comitantes of the internal pudendal artery. They *begin* in the deep veins of the penis which issue from the corpus cavernosum penis, accompany the internal pudendal artery, and unite to form a single vessel, which ends in the hypogastric vein. They receive the veins from the urethral bulb, and the perineal and inferior hemorrhoidal veins. The deep dorsal vein of the penis communicates with the internal pudendal veins, but ends mainly in the pudendal plexus.

4. The **Obturator Vein** (*v. obturatoria*) *begins* in the upper portion of the adductor region of the thigh and enters the pelvis through the upper part of the obturator foramen. It runs backward and upward on the lateral wall of the pelvis below the obturator artery, and then passes between the ureter and the hypogastric artery, to end in the hypogastric vein.

5. The **Lateral Sacral Veins** (*vv. sacrales laterales*) accompany the lateral sacral arteries on the anterior surface of the sacrum and end in the hypogastric vein.

6. The **Middle Hemorrhoidal Vein** (*v. hæmorrhoidalis media*) takes origin in the hemorrhoidal plexus and receives tributaries from the bladder, prostate, and seminal vesicle; it runs lateralward on the pelvic surface of the Levator ani to end in the hypogastric vein.

The **hemorrhoidal plexus** (*plexus hæmorrhoidalis*) surrounds the rectum, and communicates in front with the vesical plexus in the male, and the uterovaginal plexus in the female. It consists of two parts, an **internal** in the submucosa, and an **external** outside of the muscular coat. The internal plexus presents a series of dilated pouches which are arranged in a circle around the tube, immediately above the anal orifice, and are connected by transverse branches.

The lower part of the external plexus is drained by the **inferior hemorrhoidal** veins into the internal pudendal vein; the middle part by the **middle hemorrhoidal** vein which joins the hypogastric vein; and the upper part by the **superior hemorrhoidal** vein which forms the commencement of the inferior mesenteric vein, a tributary of the portal vein. A free communication between the portal and systemic venous systems is established through the hemorrhoidal plexus.

The veins of the hemorrhoidal plexus are contained in very loose, connective tissue, so that they get less support from surrounding structures than most other veins, and are less capable of resisting increased blood-pressure.

The **pudendal plexus** (*plexus pudendalis; vesicoprostatic plexus*) lies behind the arcuate pubic ligament and the lower part of the symphysis pubis, and in front of the bladder and prostate. Its chief tributary is the deep dorsal vein of the penis, but it also receives branches from the front of the bladder and prostate. It communicates with the vesical plexus and with the internal pudendal vein and drains into the vesical and hypogastric veins. The **prostatic veins** form a well-marked **prostatic plexus** which lies partly in the fascial sheath of the prostate and partly between the sheath and the prostatic capsule. It communicates with the pudendal and vesical plexuses and with tributaries of the vertebral veins.

The **vesical plexus** (*plexus vesicalis*) envelops the lower part of the bladder and the base of the prostate and communicates with the pudendal and prostatic plexuses. It is drained, by means of several vesical veins, into the hypogastric veins.

The **Dorsal Veins of the Penis** (*vv. dorsales penis*) are two in number, a superficial and a deep. The **superficial vein** drains the prepuce and skin of the penis, and, running backward in the subcutaneous tissue, inclines to the right or left, and opens into the corresponding superficial external pudendal vein, a tributary of the great saphenous vein. The **deep vein** lies beneath the deep fascia of the penis; it receives the blood from the glans penis and corpora cavernosa penis and courses backward in the mid-line between the dorsal arteries; near the root of the penis it passes between the two parts of the suspensory ligament and then through an aperture between the arcuate pubic ligament and the transverse ligament of the pelvis, and divides into two branches, which enter the pudendal plexus. The deep vein also communicates below the symphysis pubis with the internal pudendal vein.

The **uterine plexuses** lie along the sides and superior angles of the uterus between the two layers of the broad ligament, and communicate with the ovarian and vaginal plexuses. They are drained by a pair of uterine veins on either side: these *arise* from the lower part of the plexuses, opposite the external orifice of the uterus, and open into the corresponding hypogastric vein.

The **vaginal plexuses** are placed at the sides of the vagina; they communicate with the uterine, vesical, and hemorrhoidal plexuses, and are drained by the vaginal veins, one on either side, into the hypogastric veins.

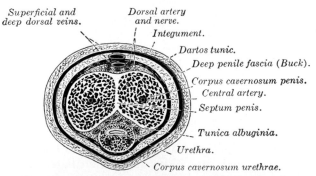

Superficial and deep dorsal veins.
Dorsal artery and nerve.
Integument.
Dartos tunic.
Deep penile fascia (Buck).
Corpus cavernosum penis.
Central artery.
Septum penis.
Tunica albuginia.
Urethra.
Corpus cavernosum urethrae.

FIG. 633.—The penis in transverse section showing the blood vessels.

The **common iliac veins** (*vv. iliacæ communes*) are formed by the union of the external iliac and hypogastric veins, in front of the sacroiliac articulation; passing obliquely upward toward the right side, they end upon the fifth lumbar vertebra, by uniting with each other at an acute angle to form the inferior vena cava. The **right common iliac** is shorter than the left, nearly vertical in its direction, and ascends behind and then lateral to its corresponding artery. The **left common iliac,** longer than the right and more oblique in its course, is at first situated on the medial side of the corresponding artery, and then behind the right common iliac. Each common iliac receives the iliolumbar, and sometimes the lateral sacral veins. The left receives, in addition, the middle sacral vein. No valves are found in these veins.

The **Middle Sacral Veins** (*vv. sacrales mediales*) accompany the corresponding artery along the front of the sacrum, and join to form a single vein, which ends in the left common iliac vein; sometimes in the angle of junction of the two iliac veins.

Variations.—The left common iliac vein, instead of joining with the right in its usual position, occasionally ascends on the left side of the aorta as high as the kidney, where, after receiving the left renal vein, it crosses over the aorta, and then joins with the right vein to form the vena cava. In these cases, the two common iliacs are connected by a small communicating branch at the spot where they are usually united. This variation represents a persisting left lumbar supra-cardinal.

The **inferior vena cava** (*v. cava inferior*) (Fig. 624), returns to the heart the blood from the parts below the diaphragm. It is formed by the junction of the two common iliac veins, on the right side of the fifth lumbar vertebra. It ascends along the front of the vertebral column, on the right side of the aorta, and, having reached the liver, is continued in a groove on its posterior surface. It then perforates the diaphragm between the median and right portions of its central tendon; it subsequently inclines forward and medialward for about 2.5 cm., and, piercing the fibrous pericardium, passes behind the serous pericardium to open into the lower and back part of the right atrium. In front of its atrial orifice is a semilunar valve, termed the **valve of the inferior vena cava**: this is rudimentary in the adult, but is of large size and exercises an important function in the fetus (see page 586).

Relations.—The *abdominal portion* of the inferior vena cava is in relation *in front*, from below upward, with the right common iliac artery, the mesentery, the right internal spermatic artery, the inferior part of the duodenum, the pancreas, the common bile duct, the portal vein, and the posterior surface of the liver; the last partly overlaps and occasionally completely surrounds it; *behind*, with the vertebral column, the right Psoas major, the right crus of the diaphragm, the right inferior phrenic, suprarenal, renal and lumbar arteries, right sympathetic trunk and right celiac ganglion, and the medial part of the right suprarenal gland; on the *right side*, with the right kidney and ureter; on the *left side*, with the aorta, right crus of the diaphragm, and the caudate lobe of the liver.

The *thoracic portion* is only about 2.5 cm. in length, and is situated partly inside and partly outside the pericardial sac. The *extrapericardial part* is separated from the right pleura and lung by a fibrous band, named the **right phrenicopericardiac ligament.** This ligament, often feebly marked, is attached below to the margin of the vena-caval opening in the diaphragm, and above to the pericardium in front of and behind the root of the right lung. The *intrapericardiac part* is very short, and is covered antero-laterally by the serous layer of the pericardium.

Variations.—This vessel is sometimes placed on the left side of the aorta, as high as the left renal vein, and, after receiving this vein, crosses over to its usual position on the right side; or it may be placed altogether on the left side of the aorta, and in such a case the abdominal and thoracic viscera, together with the great vessels, are all transposed. Most of the variations are due to the persistence of the left lumbar supracardinal vein of the embyo. Occasionally the inferior vena cava joins the azygos vein, which is then of large size. In such cases, the superior vena cava receives all the blood from the body before transmitting it to the right atrium, except the blood from the hepatic veins, which passes directly into the right atrium.

Collateral Circulation.—The inferior vena cava below the renal arteries is sometimes ligated for thrombosis with favorable results. The channels and anastomoses carrying the collateral circulation are as follows. (1) the vertebral veins, (2) anastomoses between the lumbar veins and the ascending lumbars of the azygos system, (3) anastomoses between the superior and inferior hemorrhoidal veins, (4) the thoracoepigastric vein, which connects the superficial inferior epigastric with the lateral thoracic vein, (5) several anastomoses with the portal system of veins.

Tributaries.—The inferior vena cava receives the following veins:

Lumbar.	Renal.	Inferior Phrenic.
Right Spermatic or Ovarian.	Suprarenal.	Hepatic.

The **Lumbar Veins** (*vv. lumbales*) *four* in number on each side, collect the blood by dorsal tributaries from the muscles and integument of the loins, and by abdominal tributaries from the walls of the abdomen, where they communicate with the epigastric veins. At the vertebral column, they receive veins from the vertebral plexuses, and then pass forward, around the sides of the bodies of the vertebræ, beneath the Psoas major, and end in the back part of the inferior cava. The left lumbar veins are longer than the right, and pass behind the aorta. The lumbar veins are connected together by a longitudinal vein which passes in front of the transverse processes of the lumbar vertebræ, and is called the **ascending lumbar**; it forms the most frequent origin of the corresponding azygos or hemiazygos vein,

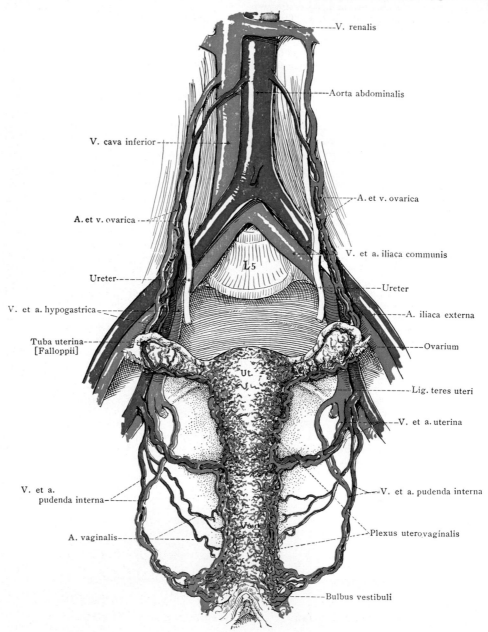

Fig. 634.—The blood vessels of the female pelvis, showing chief source of blood supply of the uterus and vagina. (Eycleshymer and Jones.)

and serves to connect the common iliac, iliolumbar, and azygos or hemiazygos veins of its own side of the body.

The **Spermatic Veins** (*vv. spermaticæ*) (Fig. 635) emerge from the back of the testis, and receive tributaries from the epididymis; they unite and form a convoluted plexus, called the **pampiniform plexus**, which constitutes the greater mass of the spermatic cord; the vessels composing this plexus are very numerous, and ascend along the cord, in front of the ductus deferens. Below the subcutaneous inguinal ring they unite to form three or four veins, which pass along the inguinal canal, and, entering the abdomen through the abdominal inguinal ring, coalesce

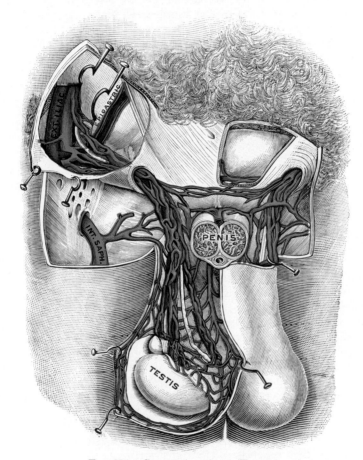

Fig. 635.—Spermatic veins. (Testut.)

to form two veins, which ascend on the Psoas major, behind the peritoneum, lying one on either side of the internal spermatic artery. These unite to form a single vein, which opens on the right side into the inferior vena cava, at an acute angle; on the left side into the left renal vein, at a right angle. The spermatic veins are provided with valves. The left spermatic vein passes behind the iliac colon, and is thus exposed to pressure from the contents of that part of the bowel.

The **Ovarian Veins** (*vv. ovaricæ*) correspond with the spermatic in the male; they form a plexus in the broad ligament near the ovary and uterine tube, and communicate with the uterine plexus. They end in the same way as the spermatic veins in the male. Valves are occasionally found in these veins. Like the uterine veins, they become much enlarged during pregnancy.

The **Renal Veins** (*vv. renales*) are of large size, and placed in front of the renal arteries. The left is longer than the right, and passes in front of the aorta, just below the origin of the superior mesenteric artery. It receives the left spermatic and left inferior phrenic veins, and, generally, the left suprarenal vein. It opens into the inferior vena cava at a slightly higher level than the right (Fig. 624).

The **Suprarenal Veins** (*vv. suprarenales*) are two in number: the right ends in the inferior vena cava; the left, in the left renal or left inferior phrenic vein.

The **Inferior Phrenic Veins** (*vv. phrenicæ inferiores*) follow the course of the inferior phrenic arteries; the right ends in the inferior vena cava; the left is often represented by two branches, one of which ends in the left renal or suprarenal vein, while the other passes in front of the esophageal hiatus in the diaphragm and opens into the inferior vena cava.

The **Hepatic Veins** (*vv. hepaticæ*) commence in the substance of the liver, in the terminations of the portal vein and hepatic artery, and are arranged in two groups, upper and lower. The **upper group** usually consists of three large veins, which converge toward the posterior surface of the liver, and open into the inferior vena cava, while that vessel is situated in the groove on the back part of the liver. The veins of the **lower group** vary in number, and are of small size; they come from the right and caudate lobes. The hepatic veins run singly, and are in direct contact with the hepatic tissue. They are destitute of valves.

THE PORTAL SYSTEM OF VEINS (Fig. 636).

The **portal system** includes all the veins which drain the blood from the abdominal part of the digestive tube (with the exception of the lower part of the rectum) and from the spleen, pancreas, and gall-bladder. From these viscera the blood is conveyed to the liver by the **portal vein.** In the liver this vein ramifies like an artery and ends in capillary-like vessels termed **sinusoids**, from which the blood is conveyed to the inferior vena cava by the hepatic veins. From this it will be seen that the blood of the portal system passes through two sets of minute vessels, viz., (*a*) the capillaries of the digestive tube, spleen, pancreas, and gall-bladder; and (*b*) the sinusoids of the liver. In the adult the portal vein and its tributaries are destitute of valves; in the fetus and for a short time after birth valves can be demonstrated in the tributaries of the portal vein; as a rule they soon atrophy and disappear, but in some subjects they persist in a degenerate form.

The **portal vein** (*vena portæ*) is about 8 cm. in length, and is formed at the level of the second lumbar vertebra by the junction of the superior mesenteric and lienal veins, the union of these veins taking place in front of the inferior vena cava and behind the neck of the pancreas. It passes upward behind the superior part of the duodenum and then ascends in the right border of the lesser omentum to the right extremity of the porta hepatis, where it divides into a right and a left branch, which accompany the corresponding branches of the hepatic artery into the substance of the liver. In the lesser omentum it is placed behind and between the common bile duct and the hepatic artery, the former lying to the right of the latter. It is surrounded by the hepatic plexus of nerves, and is accompanied by numerous lymphatic vessels and some lymph glands. The **right branch** of the portal vein enters the right lobe of the liver, but before doing so generally receives the cystic vein. The **left branch,** longer but of smaller caliber than the right, crosses the left sagittal fossa, gives branches to the caudate lobe, and then enters the left lobe of the liver. As it crosses the left sagittal fossa it is joined in front by a fibrous cord, the **ligamentum teres** (*obliterated umbilical vein*), and is united to the inferior vena cava by a second fibrous cord, the **ligamentum venosum** (*obliterated ductus venosus*).

Tributaries.—The tributaries of the portal vein are:

Lienal (Splenic).   Pyloric.
Superior Mesenteric.   Cystic.
Coronary.   Parumbilical.

The **Lienal Vein** (*v. lienalis; splenic vein*) *commences* by five or six large branches which return the blood from the spleen. These unite to form a single vessel, which passes from left to right, grooving the upper and back part of the pancreas, below

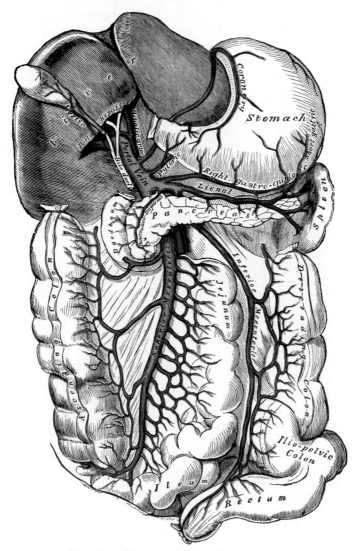

Fig. 636.—The portal vein and its tributaries.

the lienal artery, and ends behind the neck of the pancreas by uniting at a right angle with the superior mesenteric to form the portal vein. The lienal vein is of large size, but is not tortuous like the artery.

Tributaries.—The lienal vein receives the short gastric veins, the left gastro-epiploic vein, the pancreatic veins, and the inferior mesenteric veins.

The **short gastric veins** (*vv. gastricæ breves*), four or five in number, drain the fundus and left part of the greater curvature of the stomach, and pass between the two layers of the gastrolienal ligament to end in the lienal vein or in one of its large tributaries.

The **left gastroepiploic vein** (*v. gastroepiploica sinistra*) receives branches from the antero-superior and postero-inferior surfaces of the stomach and from the greater omentum; it runs from right to left along the greater curvature of the stomach and ends in the commencement of the lienal vein.

The **pancreatic veins** (*vv. pancreaticæ*) consist of several small vessels which drain the body and tail of the pancreas, and open into the trunk of the lienal vein.

The **inferior mesenteric vein** (*v. mesenterica inferior*) returns blood from the rectum and the sigmoid, and descending parts of the colon. It begins in the rectum as the **superior hemorrhoidal vein**, which has its origin in the hemorrhoidal plexus, and through this plexus communicates with the middle and inferior hemorrhoidal veins. The superior hemorrhoidal vein leaves the lesser pelvis and crosses the left common iliac vessels with the superior hemorrhoidal artery, and is continued upward as the inferior mesenteric vein. This vein lies to the left of its artery, and ascends behind the peritoneum and in front of the left Psoas major; it then passes behind the body of the pancreas and opens into the lienal vein; sometimes (10 per cent.) it ends in the angle of union of the lienal and superior mesenteric veins, or drains into the superior mesenteric vein.

Tributaries.—The inferior mesenteric vein receives the **sigmoid veins** from the sigmoid colon and iliac colon, and the **left colic vein** from the descending colon and left colic flexure.

The **Superior Mesenteric Vein** (*v. mesenterica superior*) returns the blood from the small intestine, from the cecum, and from the ascending and transverse portions of the colon. It begins in the right iliac fossa by the union of the veins which drain the terminal part of the ileum, the cecum, and vermiform process, and ascends between the two layers of the mesentery on the right side of the superior mesenteric artery. In its upward course it passes in front of the right ureter, the inferior vena cava, the inferior part of the duodenum, and the lower portion of the head of the pancreas. Behind the neck of the pancreas it unites with the lienal vein to form the portal vein.

Tributaries.—Besides the tributaries which correspond with the branches of the superior mesenteric artery, viz., the **intestinal, ileocolic, right colic**, and **middle colic veins**, the superior mesenteric vein is joined by the right gastroepiploic and pancreaticoduodenal veins.

The **right gastroepiploic vein** (*v. gastroepiploica dextra*) receives branches from the greater omentum and from the lower parts of the antero-superior and postero-inferior surfaces of the stomach; it runs from left to right along the greater curvature of the stomach between the two layers of the greater omentum.

The **pancreaticoduodenal veins** (*vv. pancreaticoduodenales*) accompany their corresponding arteries; the lower of the two frequently joins the right gastroepiploic vein.

The **Coronary Vein** (*v. coronaria ventriculi; gastric vein*) derives tributaries from both surfaces of the stomach; it runs from right to left along the lesser curvature of the stomach, between the two layers of the lesser omentum, to the esophageal opening of the stomach, where it receives some esophageal veins. It then turns backward and passes from left to right behind the omental bursa and ends in the portal vein.

The **Pyloric Vein** is of small size, and runs from left to right along the pyloric portion of the lesser curvature of the stomach, between the two layers of the lesser omentum, to end in the portal vein.

The **Cystic Vein** (*v. cystica*) drains the blood from the gall-bladder, and, accompanying the cystic duct, usually ends in the right branch of the portal vein.

Parumbilical Veins(*vv. parumbilicales*).—In the course of the ligamentum teres of the liver and of the middle umbilical ligament, small veins (*parumbilical*) are found which establish an anastomosis between the veins of the anterior abdominal wall and the portal, hypogastric, and iliac veins. The best marked of these small veins is one which commences at the umbilicus and runs backward and upward in, or on the surface of, the ligamentum teres between the layers of the falciform ligament to end in the left portal vein.

Collateral venous circulation to relieve portal obstruction in the liver is usually effected mainly: (*a*) by communications between the gastric veins and the esophageal veins which empty into the azygos system, and (*b*) by communications between the inferior mesenteric veins and the hemorrhoidal veins that empty into the hypogastric veins. Other possible collaterals which are not of much practical importance are (*c*) the accessory portal system of Sappey, branches of which pass in the round and falciform ligaments to unite with the superior and inferior epigastric, and internal mammary veins, and through the diaphragmatic veins with the azygos; a single large vein, shown to be a parumbilical vein, may pass from the hilus of the liver by the round ligament to the umbilicus, producing there a bunch of prominent varicose veins known as the caput medusæ; and (*d*) the veins of Retzius, which connect the intestinal veins with the inferior vena cava and its retroperitoneal branches.

HISTOLOGY OF THE BLOOD VESSELS

Arteries.—The arteries are composed of three coats: (1) an internal coat, the tunica intima; (2) a middle coat, the tunica media, and (3) an external coat, the tunica adventitia (Fig. 637). The composition and relative thickness of these coats is different in arteries of different size, a medium sized artery, 3-4 mm. in diameter, such as the distal portion of the radial artery has the characteristic features well represented.

(1) The **inner coat** (*tunica intima*) (Figs. 637, 638) is composed of: (a) a pavement membrane of **endothelium,** continuous with the endothelium of capillaries on the one hand and the endocardium of the heart on the other. The endothelium is a single layer of simple squamous or platelike cells, polygonal, oval, or fusiform in shape, with rounded oval or flattened nuclei. The outlines of the cells can be brought out by treatment with silver nitrate. (b) A **subendothelial layer** of delicate connective tissue intervenes between the endothelium, and (c) the **internal elastic membrane.** The latter consists of a network of elastic fibers arranged more or less longitudinally, leaving elongated apertures or perforations which give it a fenestrated appearance and account for its name, the *fenestrated membrane* (of Henle). This membrane forms the chief thickness of the intima. It is thrown into folds when the artery is empty and in a microscopic cross section appears as a wavy line, glassy and almost unstained with hematoxylin and eosin but stained heavily with special stains for elastic fibers (Fig. 637).

(2) The **middle coat** (*tunica media*) (Figs. 637, 638) makes up the bulk of the wall of an artery. It is composed of lamellæ of smooth muscle cells and elastic tissue which are disposed circularly around the vessel. The thickness of this coat as well as its composition varies with the size of the vessel.

(3) The **external coat** (*tunica adventitia*) (Figs. 637, 638) consists of areolar connective tissue with a fine feltwork of collagenous and elastic fibers. The elastic tissue is more abundant adjacent to the tunica media and is sometimes called the **tunica elastica externa.** The tunica adventitia contains the arteries and veins supplying the vessel walls, the vasa vasorum, in larger arteries and it also contains lymphatic vessels and the nerve fibers on their way to the cells of the smooth muscle coat.

Although the arteries of different sizes make gradual transitions into each other certain characteristic features should be mentioned. **Small arteries** have the different coats greatly reduced in thickness. The inner coat is composed primarily of the endothelium, the inner elastic membrane being scarcely identifiable. The middle coat contains only a single layer of smooth muscle cells (Fig. 639) in the smallest arterioles but it is relatively thick in small arteries (Fig. 638) and the elastic fibers are very sparse or non-existent. The outer coat is also very thin, being composed of fine collagenous and reticular fibrils.

Medium sized arteries have already been described as the typical arteries and include most of the named arteries which distribute the blood to the different organs and parts of the body. The muscular coat is especially well developed and by its innervation through the vasomotor nerves from the sympathetic system it controls the flow of blood into a particular area. In the somewhat smaller arteries the tunica media is almost entirely muscular, but in larger ones more and more of

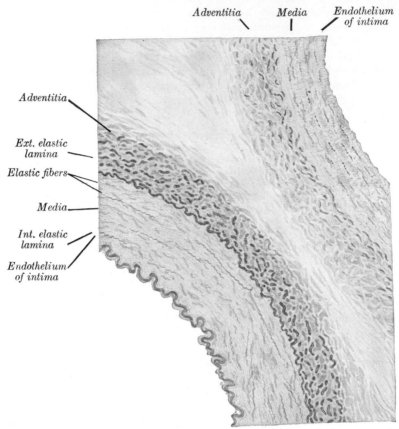

Adventitia   *Media*   *Endothelium of intima*

Adventitia

Ext. elastic lamina

Elastic fibers

Media

Int. elastic lamina

Endothelium of intima

Fig. 637.—Cross section of parts of the walls of adjacent medium-sized artery and vein. Artery, lower left; vein, upper right.

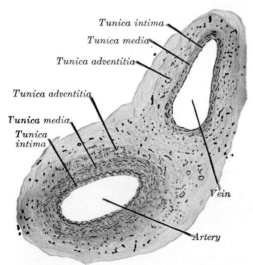

Tunica intima
Tunica media
Tunica adventitia

Tunica adventitia

Tunica media
Tunica intima

Vein

Artery

Fig. 638.—A transverse section through an artery and a vein of a child aged thirteen months. Stained with hematoxylin and eosin. × 20.

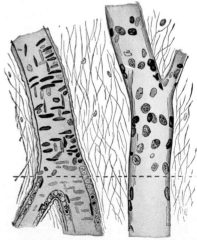

Fig. 639.—Small artery and vein, pia mater of sheep. × 250. Surface view above the interrupted line; longitudinal section below. Artery in red; vein in blue.

the muscle is replaced by elastic tissue. The thickness of the adventitia is variable; in arteries from protected areas such as those in the abdominal or cranial cavities it is relatively thin but it is much thickened in exposed areas such as the limbs. The bundles of nerve fibers are numerous in the adventia of many arteries and on the arteries supplying the abdominal organs frequently form an incomplete coat.

Large arteries have a thickened intima and in older people this layer is likely to contain plaques of cholesterol or calcium salts and other pathological changes. The internal elastic layer is made up of a number of strata rather than a single membrane. The middle coat contains relatively large amounts of elastic tissue interspersed between muscular lamellæ and held in place by areolar connective tissue. The adventitia is quite thick and contains well developed vasa vasorum, bundles of nerves and frequent lymphatic vessels. The **aorta** has these features most highly developed but they are also visible in the brachiocephalic, carotid, subclavian, axillary, vertebral, and iliac arteries. The pulmonary trunk and arteries resemble the aorta but all coats are thinner.

The Capillaries.—The smaller arterial branches (excepting those of the cavernouss tructure of the sexual organs, of the splenic pulp, and of the placenta) terminate in networks of vessels which pervade nearly every tissue of the body. These vessels, from their minute size, are termed capillaries. They are interpodes between the smallest branches of the arteries and the commencing veins, constituting a network, the branches of which maintain the same diameter throughout; the meshes of the network are more uniform in shape and size than those formed by the anastomoses of the small arteries and veins.

The *diameters* of the capillaries vary in the different tissues of the body, the usual size being about 8μ. The smallest are those of the brain and the mucous membrane of the intestines; and the largest those of the skin and the marrow of bone, where they are stated to be as large as 20μ in diameter. The *form* of the capillary net varies in the different tissues, the meshes being generally rounded or elongated.

The *rounded form of mesh* is most common, and prevails where there is a dense network, as in the lungs, in most glands and mucous membranes, and in the cutis; the meshes are not of an absolutely circular outline, but more or less angular, sometimes nearly quadrangular, or polygonal, or more often irregular.

Elongated meshes are observed in the muscles and nerves, the meshes resembling parallelograms in form, the long axis of the mesh running parallel with the long axis of the nerve or muscle. Sometimes the capillaries have a *looped arrangement;* a single vessel projecting from the common network and returning after forming one or more loops, as in the papillæ of the tongue and skin.

The number of the capillaries and the size of the meshes determine the degree of vascularity of a part. The closest network and the smallest interspaces are found in the lungs and in the choroid coat of the eye. In these situations the interspaces are smaller than the capillary vessels themselves. In the intertubular plexus of the kidney, in the conjunctiva, and in the cutis, the interspaces are from three to four times as large as the capillaries which form them; and in the brain from eight to ten times as large as the capillaries in the long diameters of the meshes, and

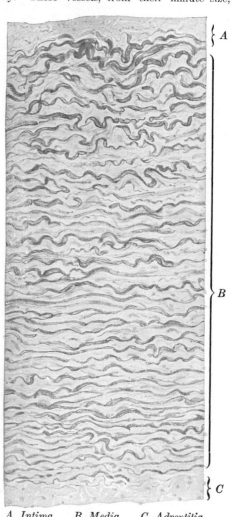

A. *Intima*   B. *Media*   C. *Adventitia*

Fig. 640.—A portion of a transverse section of the wall of the aorta. *A,* Intima; *B,* Media; *C,* Adventitia.

from four to six times as large in their transverse diameters. In the adventitia of arteries the width of the meshes is ten times that of the capillary vessels. As a general rule, the more active the function of the organ, the closer is its capillary net and the larger its supply of blood; the meshes of the network are very narrow in all growing parts, in the glands, and in the mucous membranes, wider in bones and ligaments which are comparatively inactive; bloodvessels are nearly absent in tendons, in which very little organic change occurs after their formation. In the liver the capillaries take a more or less radial course toward the intralobular vein, and their walls may be incomplete, so that the blood comes into direct contact with the liver cells. These vessels in the liver are not true capillaries but "sinusoids;" they are developed by the growth of columns of liver cells into the blood spaces of the embryonic organ, have an irregular lumen and have very little, if any, connective tissue covering.

Structure.—The wall of a capillary consists of a fine transparent endothelial layer, composed of cells joined edge to edge by an interstitial cement substance, and continuous with the endothelial cells which line the arteries and veins. When stained with nitrate of silver the edges which bound the endothelial cells are brought into view (Fig. 641). These cells are of large size and of an irregular polygonal or lanceolate shape, each containing an oval nucleus which may be displayed by carmine or hematoxylin.

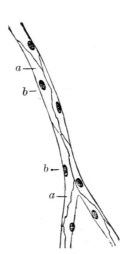

Fig. 641.—Capillaries from the mesentery of a guinea-pig, after treatment with solution of nitrate of silver. *a.* Cells. *b.* Their nuclei.

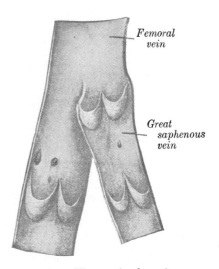

Fig. 642.—The proximal portions of the femoral and great saphenous veins laid open to show the valves. About two-thirds natural size.

In many situations a delicate sheath or envelope of branched nucleated connective tissue cells is found around the simple capillary tube, particularly in the larger ones; and in other places, especially in the glands, the capillaries are invested with retiform connective tissue.

Veins.—The veins have the same three coats as the arteries, **tunica intima, tunica media,** and **tunica adventitia.** The thickness and composition of the three coats is different, however, and at various points the veins contain valves (Figs. 637, 642).

In the **smallest veins,** three coats are scarcely distinguishable (Fig. 639). The endothelium is supported by delicate reticular and elastic fibers which merge with the connective tissue of the surrounding area. In slightly larger veins (0.4 mm diameter) there is a middle coat composed of connective tissue and circular smooth muscle cells and an adventia composed of areolar connective tissue.

In **medium sized veins** the tunica intima contains endothelial cells with nuclei more oval than those in the arteries. It is supported by delicate connective tissue and a network of elastic fibers takes the place of the fenestrated membrane of the arteries. The valves are part of the intima. The tunica media is composed of a thick layer of collagenous and elastic fibers intermingled with a variable number of circular smooth muscle cells. The elastic and muscular elements are much less numerous in veins than in arteries. The tunica adventitia consists of areolar connective tissue with longitudinal elastic fibers. In the **largest veins** the outer coat is from two to five times thicker than the middle coat, and contains a large number of longitudinal muscular fibers. These are most distinct in the inferior vena cava, especially at the termination of this vein in the heart, in the trunks of the hepatic veins, in all the large trunks of the portal vein, and in the external iliac, renal, and azygos veins. In the renal and portal veins they extend through the whole thickness of the outer coat, but in the other veins mentioned a layer of connective and elastic tissue is found external to the muscular fibers. All the large veins which open into the heart are covered for a short distance with a layer of striped muscular tissue continued on to them from the heart. Muscular tissue is wanting: (1) in the veins of the maternal part of the placenta; (2) in the venous sinuses of the dura mater and the veins of the pia mater of the brain and medulla spinalis; (3) in the veins of the retina; (4) in the veins of the cancellous tissue of bones; (5) in the venous spaces of the corpora cavernosa. The veins of the above-mentioned parts consist of an internal endothelial lining supported on one or more layers of areolar tissue.

Valves.—Most veins are provided with valves which serve to prevent the reflux of the blood. Each valve is formed by a reduplication of the inner coat, strengthened by connective tissue and elastic fibers, and is covered on both surfaces with endothelium, the arrangement of which differs on the two surfaces. On the surface of the valve next the wall of the vein the cells are arranged transversely; while on the other surface, over which the current of blood flows, the cells are arranged longitudinally in the direction of the current. Most commonly two such valves are found placed opposite one another, more especially in the smaller veins or in the larger trunks at the point where they are joined by smaller branches; occasionally there are three and sometimes only one. The valves are semilunar. They are attached by their convex edges to the wall of the vein; the concave margins are free, directed in the course of the venous current, and lie in close apposition with the wall of the vein as long as the current of blood takes its natural course; if, however, any regurgitation takes place, the valves become distended, their opposed edges are brought into contact, and the current is interrupted. The wall of the vein on the cardiac side of the point of attachment of each valve is expanded into a pouch or sinus, which gives to the vessel, when injected or distended with blood, a knotted appearance. The valves are very numerous in the veins of the extremities, especially of the lower extremities, these vessels having to conduct the blood against the force of gravity. They are absent in the very small veins, *i. e.*, those less than 2 mm. in diameter, also in the venæ cavæ, hepatic, renal, uterine, and ovarian veins. A few valves are found in each spermatic vein, and one also at its point of junction with the renal vein or inferior vena cava respectively. The cerebral and spinal veins, the veins of the cancellated tissue of bone, the pulmonary veins, and the umbilical vein and its branches, are also destitute of valves. A few valves are occasionally found in the azygos and intercostal veins. Rudimentary valves are found in the tributaries of the portal venous system.

The veins, like the arteries, are supplied with nutrient vessels, **vasa vasorum.** Nerves also are distributed to them in the same manner as to the arteries, but in much less abundance.

BLOOD

Blood consists of a fluid medium called the **plasma** in which are suspended minute structures called the **formed elements** of the blood. The formed elements include (1) the red blood corpuscles (RBC), (2) the white blood cells (WBC), and (3) the platelets. Very minute droplets of fat called chylomicra are also present, especially after the ingestion of fatty foods.

The **blood plasma** after the formed elements are removed by centrifugation is a clear, somewhat viscous, slightly yellowish fluid rich in dissolved proteins. One of these, fibrinogen, is precipitated out as very minute threads called fibrin when the blood clots. After the blood has clotted and the fibrin as well as the formed elements have been removed, the remaining fluid resembles plasma but is called serum.

The **red blood corpuscles,** or **erythrocytes,** (Fig. 643) are biconcave discs with an average diameter of 7.7 micra (μ) and a thickness of 1.9 μ. Variations in size of more than 1 or 2 μ are rare in normal blood, but in anemia they may be enlarged into macrocytes (megalocytes), or reduced into microcytes. Individual erythrocytes have a pale yellowish color when viewed in a thin film of fresh blood under the high power of a microscope, but when superimposed into several layers they take on their characteristic reddish hue. They have no nucleus and appear homogeneous when viewed with either the light or the electron microscopes. They are composed principally of an iron containing protein responsible for the color called hemoglobin and a lipoid constituent which appears to be in higher concentration in the surface membrane. The semipermeable properties of this membrane allow the erythrocyte to imbibe fluid by osmosis from a hypotonic medium, with the result that it enlarges and becomes spherical in shape. In a hypertonic medium it shrivels into a spine-covered sphere, a process called **crenation** (Fig. 643). The membrane can be torn with a microneedle and the hemoglobin released into the surrounding medium. The membrane also ruptures when erythrocytes are suspended in distilled water, leaving a faintly visible remnant called a *ghost cell.*

In a thin dried film of blood or **blood smear,** the erythrocytes are colored an orange pink by the eosin of Wright's stain (eosin and methylene blue). In a thin film of fresh blood stained

49

supravitally with neutral red or brilliant cresyl blue, a few erythrocytes contain dark staining inclusions. Such cells are called **reticulocytes**. There may be 0.1% in normal blood but their number is increased in conditions in which new erythrocytes are being formed rapidly in the bone marrow.

The number of erythrocytes per cubic millimeter of blood is 5,500,000 to 5,000,000 in men and 5,000,000 to 4,500,000 in women. A range of 4 to 6 million is considered normal and 8 million may be found in individuals living at high altitudes. There may be less than one million in severe anemia.

White Blood Cells, White Corpuscles, or **Leucocytes** are of different sizes, the majority being about 10 μ in diameter. They are much less numerous than erythrocytes, in a healthy individual from 7,000 to 12,000 per cubic millimeter of blood. The leucocytes are true cells, having a nucleus and cytoplasm. Several different types are recognized and are named according to (1) the condition of the nucleus as polymorphonuclear or mononuclear, (2) the presence or absence of granules in the cytoplasm as granulocytic and agranulocytic and (3) whether the granules stain with acid or basic dyes as neutrophilic, acidophilic, or basophilic. The **polymorphonuclear leucocytes** are also **granulocytes** and are given the specific names (a) **polymorphonuclear neutrophils,** (b) **eosinophils** (*acidophils*), and (c) **basophils.** The **mononuclear cells** are **agranular** and of two types based on the size, the shape of the nucleus, and the quality of the cytoplasm. The **lymphocytes** are smaller, have round nuclei, and clear cytoplasm. The **large mononuclears** or **monocytes** have crescentic nuclei and a very finely granular cytoplasm.

The leucocytes are actively amœboid cells. Living cells can be examined in a thin film of blood under high magnification with the microscope and may be recognized by their appearance and

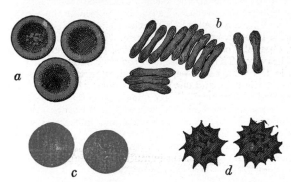

activity. If the stage of the microscope is warmed to body temperature, the polymorphonuclear cells immediately become motile. They send out pseudopods of clear protoplasm and the granular cytoplasm and the nuclei stream after them. The neutrophiles are **phagocytic,** especially for bacteria, both in the body and *in vitro.* In a dilute solution of neutral red, the granules segregate the dye and become red or brown in color. The lymphocytes in a fresh preparation are at first rounded and immobile, but after a few hours take up active locomotion. The nucleus is carried along in the front of the cell rather than behind as in the granulocytes. In a thin film of blood **supravitally stained** with a dilute solution of neutral red and janus green, shadowy, bluish green, rod-shaped

FIG. 643.—Human red blood corpuscles. Highly magnified. *a.* Seen from the surface. *b.* Seen in profile and forming rouleaux. *c.* Rendered spherical by water. *d.* Rendered crenate by salt solution.

mitochondria may be seen in the hollow of the bean-shaped nucleus, and one or two tiny round neutral red vacuoles. The monocytes send out filamentous or wavy pseudopods, but undergo very little locomotion. They are actively **phagocytic** and in a supravital stain of neutral red and janus green they develop a number of relatively large red vacuoles. A few small round mitochondria occupy a deep hollow in one side of the nucleus.

Blood is usually examined in a thin dry film or **blood smear,** stained with eosin and methylene blue (a Romanovsky stain such as Wright's stain). The polymorphonuclear **neutrophils** are about 10 μ in diameter, have a dark nucleus with one to five lobes and a cytoplasm filled with small lavender or purplish granules. They are the most numerous leucocytes (60%) and in an infection large numbers massed together are called pus. The polymorphonuclear **eosinophils** usually have a nucleus with two lobes and the cytoplasm is filled with large granules stained bright red with the eosin. They are not numerous (2%) in normal blood but are increased in parasitic and allergic diseases. The polymorphonuclear **basophils** are the least numerous of leucocytes (0.5% or less) and have a three or four lobed nucleus and large dark purple granules in the cytoplasm. The **lymphocytes** range from 6 to 9 μ in diameter and are in moderate numbers (20%). The nucleus is round and stains deeply. The cytoplasm is a transparent light blue and varies in amount according to the size of the cell. A few dark granules may be present. The **monocytes** are the largest leucocytes, 10 to 15 μ in diameter, but are not very numerous (4%). The nucleus is bean- or sausage-shaped and the abundant cytoplasm has an appearance like bluish ground glass.

Blood platelets (*thromboplastids, thrombocytes*) are small (2 to 4 μ) masses of protoplasm with central granular cytoplasm but no nucleus. They may be colorless, round or stellate, and in a fresh film form the centers of radiating threads of fibrin. In eosin and methylene blue they stain much like the cytoplasm of neutrophils. Their number varies greatly from 200,000 to 800,000.

The average number of formed elements in one cubic millimeter of blood:

Erthrocytes	4,500,000 to 5,500,000
Leucocytes	6,000 to 10,000
Platelets	200,000 to 800,000

A **differential count** of white blood cells gives the following averages:

Polymorphonuclear neutrophils	50 to 75%
Polymorphonuclear eosinophils	2 to 4%
Polymorphonuclear basophils	0.5%
Lymphocytes	20 to 40%
Monocytes	3 to 8%

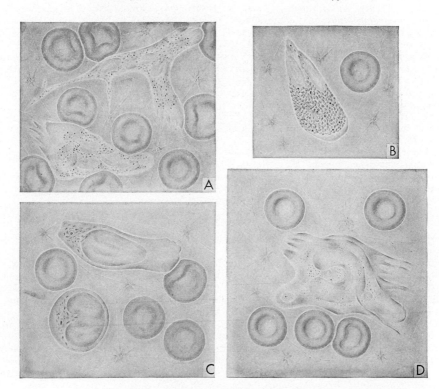

Fig. 644.—Human leucocytes in a thin film of fresh blood. Drawings of living cells warmed to body temperature, actively motile. Dark round objects are red blood corpuscles. Fibrin threads radiate out from platelets after clotting. *A*, Polymorphonuclear neutrophils pushing red corpuscles aside with their pseudopods. *B*, Polymorphonuclear eosinophil. *C*, Lymphocytes, one rounded, the other in locomotion. *D*, Monocyte with delicate undulating membranous pseudopodia. Approximately 1500 × magnification. (From Goss in Bailey, *Histology*, courtesy of Williams and Wilkins Company.)

REFERENCES

Embryology

Aüer, J. 1948. The development of the human pulmonary vein and its major variations. Anat. Rec., *101*, 581–594.

Bremer, J. L. 1937. Two reconstructions explaining the development of the veins of the liver. Anat. Rec., *68*, 165–168.

McClure, C. F. W. and G. S. Huntington. 1929. The mammalian vena cava posterior. Amer. anat. Mem., (Wistar Inst., Philadelphia), *15*, 5–149.

PADGET, D. H. 1956. The cranial venous system in man in reference to development, adult configuration, and relation to the arteries. Amer. J. Anat., *98*, 307–356.
SCHNEIDER, L. A. 1938. The development of the superior caval system in the rat. Anat. Rec., *71*, 265–276.

VEINS

BALÓ, J. 1950. The dural venous sinuses. Anat. Rec., *106*, 319–326.
BATSON, O. V. 1940. The function of the vertebral veins and their rôle in the spread of metastases. Ann. Surg., *112*, 138–149.
BATSON, O. V. 1942. The rôle of the vertebral veins in metastatic processes. Ann. intern. Med., *16*, 38–45.
BROWNING, H. C. 1953. The confluence of dural venous sinuses. Amer. J. Anat., *93*, 307–330.
DASELER, E. H., B. J. ANSON, A. F. REIMANN and L. E. BEATON. 1946. The saphenous venous tributaries and related structures in relation to the technique of high ligation. Based chiefly upon a study of 550 anatomical dissections. Surg. Gynec. Obstet., *82*, 53–63.
DOUGLASS, B. E., A. H. BAGGENSTOSS, and W. H. HOLLINSHEAD. 1950. The anatomy of the portal vein and its tributaries. Surg. Gynec. Obstet., *91*, 562–576.
EDWARDS, E. A. and J. D. ROBUCK, JR. 1947. Applied anatomy of the femoral vein and its tributaries. Surg. Gynec. Obstet., *85*, 547–557.
FRANKLIN, K. J. 1937. A Monograph on Veins. Charles C Thomas, Springfield, xxii + 410 pp.
HOLLINSHEAD, W. H. and J. A. McFARLANE. 1953. The collateral venous drainage from the kidney following occlusion of the renal vein in the dog. Surg. Gynec. Obstet., *97*, 213–219.
KEEN, J. A. 1941. The collateral venous circulation in a case of thrombosis of the inferior vena cava, and its embryological interpretation. Brit. J. Surg., *29*, 105–114.
KNISELY, W. H., M. S. MAHALEY, JR., and H. H. JETT. 1958. Approximation of "total vascular space" and its distribution in three sizes of blood vessels in rats by plastic casts. Circulat. Res. *6*, 20–25.
MASSOPUST, L. C. and W. D. GARDNER. 1950. Infrared photographic studies of the superficial thoracic veins in the female. Surg. Gynec. Obstet., *91*, 717–727.
TRUEX, R. C. and A. W. ANGULO. 1952. Comparative study of the arterial and venous systems of the ventricular myocardium with special reference to the coronary sinus. Anat. Rec., *113*, 467–492.

ANOMALIES

BRANTIGAN, O. C. 1947. Anomalies of the pulmonary veins; their surgical significance. Surg. Gynec. Obstet., *84*, 653–658.
CHOUKE, K. S. 1939. A case of bilateral superior vena cava in an adult. Anat. Rec., *74*, 151–157.
CONN, L. C., J. CALDER, J. W. MACGREGOR, and R. F. SHANER. 1942. Report of a case in which all pulmonary veins from both lungs drain into the superior vena cava. Anat. Rec., *83*, 335–340.
FRIEDMAN, S. M. 1945. Report of two unusual venous abnormalities (left postrenal inferior vena cava; postaortic left innominate vein). Anat. Rec., *92*, 71–76.
HOLLINSHEAD, W. H. 1955. Some variations and anomalies of the vascular system in the abdomen. Surg. Clin. N. Amer., *35*, 1123–1132.
VAKAET, L., G. POPPELIER, and P. VERMEIRE. 1958. Sur un cas d'anomalie combinée de la veine cave supérieure et du système azygos. Acta anat. (Basel), *32*, 235–239.
VAN CLEAVE, C. D. 1931. A multiple anomaly of the great veins and interatrial septum in a human heart. Anat. Rec., *50*, 45–51.

COMPARATIVE ANATOMY AND PHYSICAL ANTHROPOLOGY

BROWN, S. 1941. The external jugular vein in American whites and negroes. Am. J. phys. Anthrop., *28*, 213–226.
CHASE, R. E. and C. F. DeGARIS. 1938. Anomalies of venæ cavæ superiores in an Orang. Am. J. phys. Anthrop., *24*, 61–65.
McNUTT, C. W. and P. B. SAWIN 1943. Hereditary variations in the vena cava inferior of the rabbit. Amer. J. Anat., *72*, 259–289.
SCHNEIDER, L. A. 1938. The development of the superior caval system in the rat. Anat. Rec., *71*, 265–276.

VALVES

EDWARDS, E. A. 1936. The orientation of venous valves in relation to body surfaces. Anat. Rec. *64*, 369–385.
EDWARDS, E. A. and EDWARDS, J. E. 1943. The venous valves in thromboangiitis obliterans. Arch. Path., *35*, 242–252.

KAMPMEIER, O. F. and C. BIRCH. 1927. The origin and development of the venous valves, with particular reference to the saphenous district. Amer. J. Anat., *38*, 451–499.

CAPILLARIES

BENNETT, H. S. 1956. The concepts of membrane flow and membrane vesiculation as mechanisms for active transport and ion pumping. J. biophys. biochem. Cytol., *2*, Suppl., 99–104.

CHAMBERS, R. and B. W. ZWEIFACH. 1944. Topography and function of the mesenteric capillary circulation. Amer. J. Anat., *75*, 173–205.

CHAMBERS, R. and B. W. ZWEIFACH. 1947. Intercellular cement and capillary permeability Physiol. Rev., *27*, 436–463.

CLARK, E. R. and E. L. CLARK. 1939. Microscopic observations on the growth of blood capillaries in the living mammal. Amer. J. Anat., *64*, 251–302.

CLARK, E. R. and E. L. CLARK. 1943. Caliber changers in minute blood-vessels observed in the living mammal. Amer. J. Anat., *73*, 215–250.

LANDIS, E. M. 1934. Capillary pressure and capillary permeability. Physiol. Rev., *14*, 404–481,

PALADE, G. E. 1953. Fine structure of blood capillaries. J. appl. Phys., *24*, 1424.

ZWEIFACH, B. W. 1939. The character and distribution of the blood capillaries. Anat. Rec. *73*, 475–495.

ZWEIFACH, B. 1940. The structural basis of permeability and other functions of blood capillaries. Cold Sp. Harb. Symp. quant. Biol., *8*, 216–223.

ZWEIFACH, B. W. 1959. The microcirculation of the blood. Sci. Amer., *200*, 54–60.

HISTOLOGY OF THE BLOOD VESSELS

ALTSCHUL, R. 1954. Endothelium. The Macmillan Co., New York., viii + 157 pages.

HIBBS, R. G., G. E. BURCH and J. H. PHILLIPS. 1958. The fine structure of the small blood vessels of normal human dermis and subcutis. Amer. Heart J., *56*, 662–670.

BLOOD AND HEMATOPOIESIS

BLOOM, W. and G. W. BARTELMEZ. 1940. Hematopoiesis in young human embryos. Amer. J. Anat., *67*, 21–54.

CRAFTS, R. C. 1946. Effects of hypophysectomy, castration, and testosterone propionate on hemapoiesis in the adult male rat. Endocrinology, *39*, 401–413.

DOWNEY, H., editor. 1938. Handbook of Hematology. P. B. Hoeber, Inc., New York. 4. volumes.

HAYES, M. A. and B. L. BAKER. 1952. The effect of prolonged administration of adrenocortical extract on bone marrow cytology. Univ. of Mich. med. Bull., *18*, 109–114.

JONES, O. P. and A. SMITH. 1950. Transmission of antianemic principle across the placenta and its influence on embryonic erthropoiesis. II. Comparison of the effect of liver extract and pteroylglutamic acid (P G A). Blood, *5*, 499–521.

LOW, F. N. and J. A. FREEMAN. 1958. Electron Microscopic Atlas of Normal and Leukemic Human Blood. The Blakiston Division, McGraw-Hill Book Co., Inc., New York, ix + 347 pages.

OSOGOE, B. and K. OMURA. 1950. Transplantation of hematopoietic tissue into the circulating blood. II. Injection of bone marrow into normal rabbits, with special reference to the histogenesis of extramedullary foci of hematopoiesis. Anat. Rec., *108*, 663–686.

POLLAK, O. J. 1951. Grouping, Typing, and Banking of Blood. Charels C Thomas, Springfield, xiv + 163 pages.

WINTROBE, M. M. 1956. Clinical Hematology. Lea & Febiger, Philadelphia. 1184 pages. 4th Edition.

THE LYMPHATIC SYSTEM.

THE **lymphatic system** consists of: (1) an extensive capillary network which collects lymph in the various organs and tissues; (2) an elaborate system of collecting vessels which carry the lymph from the lymphatic capillaries to the blood stream, opening into the great veins at the root of the neck; (3) a number of firm rounded bodies called lymph nodes (B. N. A. lymphoglandulæ) which are placed like filters in the paths of the collecting vessels; (4) certain lymphatic organs which resemble the lymph nodes, that is, tonsils and solitary or aggregated lymphatic nodules; (5) the spleen, and (6) the thymus. Another element which might be added is the lymphoid, or, as it is often called, adenoid tissue. It is recognizable only with the aid of a microscope and consists of reticular or areolar connective tissue which contains an accumulation of lymphocytes but lacks the organized

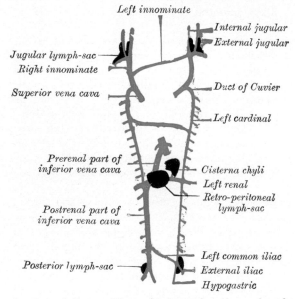

FIG. 645.—Scheme showing relative positions of primary lymph sacs based on the description given by Florence Sabin.

lymphatic nodules. The spleen is generally recognized as a lymphatic organ because it contains lymphatic nodules. The thymus, on the other hand, has been described previously with the ductless glands, but since no evidence of glandular function has been found, and since it is made up principally of lymphoid tissue, it is here classed as a lymphatic organ. The lymphatic capillaries and collecting vessels are lined throughout by a continuous layer of endothelial cells, forming thus a closed system. The lymphatic vessels of the small intestine receive the special designation of **lacteals** or **chyliferous vessels**; they differ in no respect from the lymphatic vessels generally excepting that during the process of digestion they contain a milk-white fluid, the **chyle**.

Development.—The earliest lymphatic endothelium probably arises from venous endothelium as sprouts from several regions of the primitive veins. The first sprouts came from the primitive right and left internal jugular veins at their junctions with the subclavians. They grow, branch, and anastomose to form the **jugular lymph sacs.** From these sacs lymphatic capillary plexuses spread to the neck, head, arms, and thorax. The more direct channels of the plexuses enlarge and form the lymphatic vessels. The larger vessels acquire smooth muscular coats with nerve connections, and exhibit contractility. Each jugular sac retains at least one connection with its jugular vein. From the left one the upper part of the thoracic duct develops. At a slightly older stage (8th week) lymphatic sprouts from the primitive vena cava and mesonephric veins form the unpaired **retro–peritoneal lymph sac.** From it, lymphatics spread to the abdominal viscera and diaphragm. The sac establishes connections with the cisterna chyli and loses its connections with the veins.

At about the same time another series of sprouts from the primitive veins of the Wolffian bodies forms the **cisterna chyli.** It gives rise to the cisterna chyli and to part of the thoracic duct. It joins that part of the duct which develops from the left jugular sac, and loses all its connections with the veins. At a slightly later stage (8th week) endothelial sprouts are given off from the primitive iliac veins at their junctions with the posterior cardinal veins. They form the paired **posterior lymph sacs.** From these sacs lymphatics spread to the abdominal wall, pelvic region, and legs. They join the cisterna chyli and lose all connections with the veins.

According to this view, all lymphatic endothelium is derived from venous endothelium which it resembles in many respects. An improbable opposing view derives lymphatic endothelium from mesenchymal cells which are supposed to flatten out into endothelium about small isolated accumulations of fluid in the neighborhood of the large primitive veins. These little sacs are supposed to join to form the first lymphatic capillaries and lymph sacs and to acquire secondary connections with the veins. It might be pointed out that this supposed origin of lymphatic endothelium is analogous to the formation of the mesothelium of joint cavities and that true lymphatic endothelium resembles venous endothelium, not mesothelium. Endothelium forms tubes which acquire muscle walls. Mesothelial sacs do neither.

The **primary lymph nodes** begin to develop during the third month in capillary lymphatic plexuses formed out of the large lymph sacs. Secondary lymph nodes develop later, and even after birth, in peripherally located capillary lymphatic plexuses. Lymphocytes are already present in the blood stream and tissues long before lymph nodes begin to appear. The earliest stages are obscure. It seems probable that lymphocytes lodge in special regions of the capillary plexuses and multiply to form larger and larger masses of lymphocytes which become the cortical lymphoid nodules and medullary cords. Parallel with this multiplication of lymphocytes, the surrounding mesenchyme forms a connective tissue capsule from which trabeculæ carrying bloodvessels grow into the lymphoid tissue. In the larger trabeculæ, collagenous fibers are laid down and continued as reticular fibrils into the smaller trabeculæ. The mesenchymal cells of the larger trabeculæ become fibroblasts, those accompanying the reticular fibrils are known as reticular cells. Just what happens to the lymphatic endothelium of the capillary plexus within the developing node is obscure. Some authors believe it forms the cortical and medullary sinuses. Others believe that the endothelial lining becomes incomplete and that the reticular cells are washed by the lymph. With this idea goes the theory that some of the reticular cells round up and become the first lymphocytes of the developing node and that they retain this potency throughout life.

Lymphatic Capillary Plexuses.—The networks which collect lymph from the intercellular fluid may be said to constitute the beginning of the lymphatic system, since from these plexuses arise the lymphatic vessels which conduct the lymph centrally through one or more lymph glands or nodes to the thoracic duct or to the right lymphatic duct. The number, the size, and the richness of the capillary plexuses differ in different regions and organs. Where abundant, they are usually arranged in two or more anastomosing layers. Most capillaries are without valves.

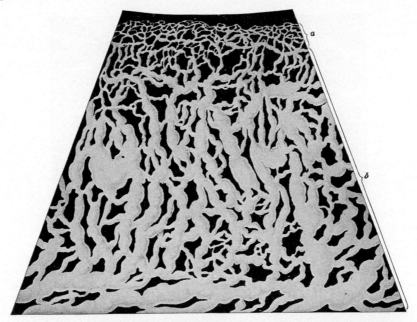

FIG. 646.—Lymph capillaries of the human conjunctiva: *a*, conjunctiva corneæ; *b*, conjunctiva scleroticæ. × 40 dia. (Teichmann.)

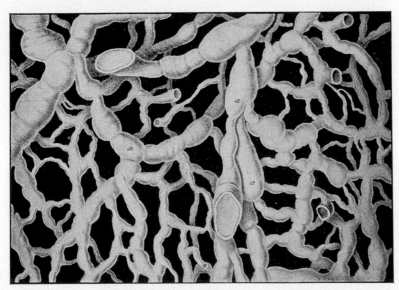

FIG. 647.—Lymph capillaries from the human scrotum, showing also transition from capillaries to the collecting vessels *a, a*. × 20 dia. (Teichmann.)

Lymphatic capillaries are especially abundant in the **dermis** of the skin. They form a continuous network over the entire surface of the body with the exception of the cornea. The dermis has a superficial plexus, without valves, connected by many anastomoses with a somewhat wider coarser deep plexus with a few valves.

The former sends blind ends into the papillæ. The plexuses are especially rich over the palmar surface of the hands and fingers, the plantar surface of the feet and toes, the conjunctiva, the scrotum, the vulva, and around the orifices where the skin becomes continuous with the mucous membranes.

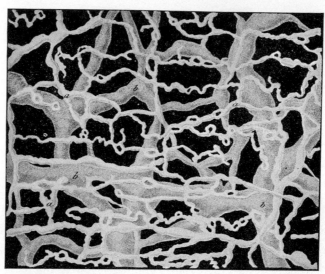

FIG. 648.—Lymph capillaries of the cutis from the inner border of the sole of the human foot. *a, a,* outer layer; *b, b,* inner layer. × 30 dia. (Teichmann.)

Lymphatic capillary plexuses are abundant in the **mucous membranes** of the respiratory and digestive systems. They form a continuous network from the nares and lips to the anus. In most places, there is a subepithelial plexus in the mucosa which anastomoses freely with a coarser plexus in the submucosa. Blind ends extend between the tubular glands of the stomach and into the villi of the intestine. The latter are the lacteals. They have a smooth muscle coat and are contractile.

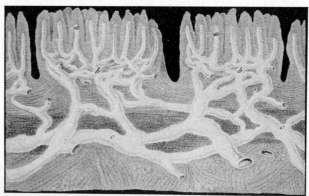

FIG. 649.—Vertical section through human tongue; *a, a,* blind lymph capillaries in the filiform papillæ with the underlying lymphatic plexus. × 45. (Teichmann.)

Those portions of the alimentary canal covered by peritoneum have a subserous capillary plexus beneath the mesothelium which anastomoses with the submucosal set.

The **lungs** have a rich subserous plexus which connects with the deep plexuses within the lungs. The latter accompanies the bronchi and bronchioles. Its capillaries do not extend to the alveoli.

The **salivary glands, pancreas** and **liver** possess deep lymphatic plexuses. They are perilobular and do not extend between the epithelial cells. The gall-bladder, cystic, hepatic, and common bile ducts have rich plexuses in the mucosa. The deep lymphatics of the liver deliver a copious supply of lymph. The liver and gall-bladder have rich subserous plexuses.

The **kidney** has a rich network in the capsule and a deep plexus between the tubules of the parenchyma. The renal pelvis and the ureters have rich networks in the mucosa and muscular layer which are continuous with similar plexuses of the urinary bladder. The male urethra has a dense plexus in the mucosa. The capillaries are especially abundant around the navicular fossa.

The **testis**, epididymis, ductus deferens, seminal vesicles and prostate have superficial capillary plexuses. Both the testis and prostate have deep interstitial plexuses.

The **ovary** has a rich capillary plexus in the parenchyma. Capillaries are absent in the tunica albuginea. The uterine tubes and uterus have mucous and muscular plexuses as well as serous and subserous ones. The vagina has a rich fine-meshed plexus in the mucosa and a coarser one in the muscular layer.

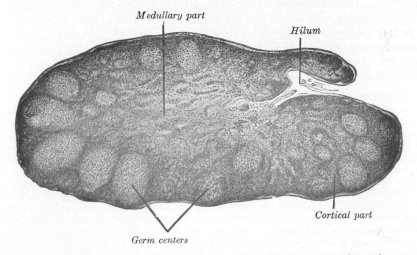

Medullary part

Hilum

Cortical part

Germ centers

Fig. 650.—A section through a lymph node of a dog. Stained with hematoxylin and eosin. × 34.

Lymphatic capillary plexuses are abundant beneath the mesothelial lining of the pleural, peritoneal, and pericardial cavities and the joint capsules. The dense connective tissues of tendons, ligaments, and periosteum are richly supplied with plexuses. The **heart** has a rich subepicardial plexus and a subendocardial one. The myocardium has a uniform capillary plexus which anastomoses with both the subendocardial and subepicardial ones. There are no collecting trunks in the myocardium.

Very fine capillary plexuses have been described about the fibers of **skeletal muscle**. Their occurrence in bone and bone marrow is not settled.

No lymphatic capillaries have been found in the central nervous system, the meninges, the eyeball and orbital fat, the cornea, the internal ear, cartilage, subcutaneous tissue, epidermis, and the spleen.

Lymphatic Vessels.—Lymphatic vessels of the first order arise in lymphatic capillary plexuses which they drain. They all enter lymph nodes as afferent vessels. From these nodes, efferent vessels usually pass to one or to a series of lymph nodes before they join the thoracic duct or the right lymphatic duct. Lymphatic vessels frequently anastomose and usually accompany bloodvessels. The larger collecting vessels often extend long distances without change of caliber. The lymphatic vessels are exceedingly delicate, and their coats are so transparent that the fluid they contain is readily seen through them. They are interrupted at intervals by constrictions, which give them a knotted or beaded appearance; these constrictions correspond to the situations of valves in their interior.

The lymphatic vessels are arranged into a **superficial** and a **deep set.** On the surface of the body the **superficial** lymphatic vessels are placed immediately beneath the integument, accompanying the superficial veins; they join the deep lymphatic vessels in certain situations by perforating the deep fascia. In the interior of the body they lie in the submucous areolar tissue, throughout the whole length of the digestive, respiratory, and genito-urinary tracts; and in the subserous tissue of the thoracic and abdominal walls. Plexiform networks of minute lymphatic vessels are found interspersed among the proper elements and bloodvessels of the several tissues; the vessels composing the net-work, as well as the meshes between them, are much larger than those of the capillary plexus. From these net-works small vessels emerge, which pass, either to a neighboring node, or to join some larger lymphatic trunk. The **deep** lymphatic vessels, fewer in number, but larger than the superficial, accompany the deep bloodvessels. Their mode of origin is probably similar to that of the superficial vessels. The lymphatic vessels of any part or organ exceed the veins in number, but in size they are much smaller. Their anastomoses also, especially those of the large trunks, are more frequent, and are effected by vessels equal in diameter to those which they connect, the continuous trunks retaining the same diameter.

Structure of Lymphatic Vessels.—The larger lymphatic vessels are each composed of three coats. The *internal* coat is thin, transparent, slightly elastic, and consists of a layer of elongated endothelial cells with wavy margins by which the contiguous cells are dovetailed into one another; the cells are supported on an elastic membrane. The *middle* coat is composed of smooth muscular and fine elastic fibers, disposed in a transverse direction. The *external* coat consists of connective tissue, intermixed with smooth muscular fibers longitudinally or obliquely disposed; it forms a protective covering to the other coats, and serves to connect the vessel with the neighboring structures. In the smaller vessels there are no muscular or elastic fibers, and the wall consists only of a connective-tissue coat, lined by endothelium. The thoracic duct has a more complex structure than the other lymphatic vessels; it presents a distinct subendothelial layer of branched corpuscles, similar to that found in the arteries; in the middle coat there is, in addition to the muscular and elastic fibers, a layer of connective tissue with its fibers arranged longitudinally. The lymphatic vessels are supplied by nutrient vessels, which are distributed to their outer and middle coats; and here also have been traced many non-medullated nerves in the form of a fine plexus of fibrils.

The valves of the lymphatic vessels are formed of thin layers of fibrous tissue covered on both surfaces by endothelium which presents the same arrangement as on the valves of veins (p. 592). In form the valves are semilunar; they are attached by their convex edges to the wall of the vessel, the concave edges being free and directed along the course of the contained current. Usually two such valves, of equal size, are found opposite one another; but occasionally exceptions occur, especially at or near the anastomoses of lymphatic vessels. Thus, one valve may be of small size and the other increased in proportion.

In the lymphatic vessels the valves are placed at much shorter intervals than in the veins. They are most numerous near the lymph nodes, and are found more frequently in the lymphatic vessels of the neck and upper extremity than in those of the lower extremity. The wall of the lymphatic vessel immediately above the point of attachment of each segment of a valve is expanded into a pouch or sinus which gives to these vessels, when distended, the knotted or beaded appearance already referred to. Valves are wanting in the vessels composing the plexiform net-work in which the lymphatic vessels originate.

The lymph is propelled by contractions of the vessel walls. The valves prevent the backward flow. The segments between the valves contract twelve to eighteen times per minute in the mesenteric lymphatic vessels of the rat.

Lymph Nodes (*nodi lymphatici*).—The lymph nodes are small oval or bean-shaped bodies, situated in the course of lymphatic and lacteal vessels so that the lymph and chyle pass through them on their way to the blood. Each generally presents on one side a slight depression—the hilum—through which the bloodvessels enter and leave and efferent lymphatic vessels emerge. Afferent lymphatic vessels enter the organ at various places on the periphery. On section (Fig. 650) a lymph node displays a lighter **cortical** part and a darker **medullary** part. The cortical part is deficient at the hilum. Here the medullary part reaches the surface.

Structure of Lymph Nodes.—A lymph node consists of enormous numbers of **lymphocytes** densely packed into masses that are partially subdivided into a series of cortical nodules and medullary cords by anastomosing connective tissue trabeculæ bordered by lymph sinuses. The **trabeculæ** extend into the node from the connective tissue **capsule** and the hilum. An extensive network of **reticular fibers** extends from the trabeculæ to all parts of the node. Narrow connecting zones just beneath the capsule and bordering the trabeculæ where the lymphocytes are less densely packed are known as the subcapsular, cortical, and medullary **sinuses** (Fig. 645). The afferent vessels open into the subcapsular, and the efferent vessels arise from the medullary sinuses. The lymph flow is retarded by the relatively enormous extent of the sinuses and the great numbers of reticular fibers which cross them in all directions. Numerous reticular cells and macrophages cling to the reticular fibers. Most authors believe that the sinuses are lined by reticular cells and not by lymphatic endothelium.

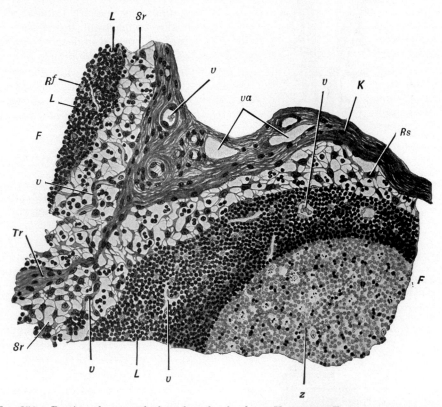

Fig. 651.—Portion of cortex of a lymph node of a dog. *K*, capsule; *Tr*, trabecula; *F*, periphery of follicle with a germinal center, *Z*; *Sr*, subcapsular sinuses; *v*, blood vessels; *va*, afferent lymphatic vessels; *L*, small lymphocytes; *Rf*, reticular cells in the follicles and *Rs* in the sinus. Hematoxylineosin-azure stain. × 187. (Maximow and Bloom, Textbook of Histology, courtesy of W. B. Saunders Company.)

The capsule consists of dense bundles of collagenous fibers, networks of elastic fibers, and a few smooth muscle cells. It is thickened at the hilum. The collagenous fibers are continued into the trabeculæ and seem to be continuous with the reticular fibers of the sinuses and nodules.

Lymphocytes increase by division and enter the lymph. The nodules or follicles in the cortical portion of the gland frequently show, in their centers, areas where karyokinetic figures indicate a division of the lymph corpuscles. These areas are termed **germ centers**. The cells composing them have more abundant protoplasm than the peripheral cells and consist of large and medium-sized lymphocytes.

Bloodvessels enter the hilum; branches traverse the trabeculæ and medullary cords to the cortex. A rich capillary plexus extends throughout the pulp.

Nerves, probably vasomotors, enter the hilum and accompany the blood vessels.

Hemolymph nodes or **glands** and **hemal nodes** occur in the prevertebral retroperitoneal and cervical regions, in the neighborhood of the adrenal and renal vessels, along the brim of the pelvis and in the root of the mesentery. They are deep red in color, very small in size, deeply imbedded in fat and few in number. They contain in addition varying amounts of lymphoid tissue blood sinuses.

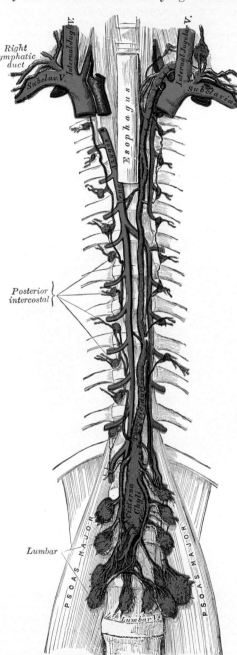

FIG. 652.—The thoracic and right lymphatic ducts.

Lymph.—Lymph, found only in the closed lymphatic vessels, is a transparent, colorless, or slightly yellow, watery fluid of specific gravity about 1.015; it closely resembles the blood plasma, but is more dilute. When it is examined under the microscope, leucocytes of the lymphocyte class are found floating in the transparent fluid; they are always increased in number after the passage of the lymph through lymphoid tissue, as in lymph glands. Lymph should be distinguished from "tissue fluid" which is found outside the lymphatic vessels in the tissue spaces.

THE THORACIC DUCT.

The **thoracic duct** (*ductus thoracicus*) (Fig. 652) conveys the greater part of the lymph and chyle into the blood. It is the common trunk of all the lymphatic vessels of the body, excepting those on the right side of the head, neck, and thorax, and right upper extremity, the right lung, right side of the heart, and the convex surface of the liver. In the adult it varies in length from 38 to 45 cm. and extends from the second lumbar vertebra to the root of the neck. It begins in the abdomen by a triangular dilatation, the **cisterna chyli**, which is situated on the front of the body of the second lumbar vertebra, to the right side of and behind the aorta, by the side of the right crus of the diaphragm. It enters the thorax through the aortic hiatus of the diaphragm, and ascends through the posterior mediastinal cavity between the aorta and azygos vein. Behind it in this region are the vertebral column, the right intercostal arteries, and the hemiazygos veins as they cross to open into the azygos vein; in front of it are the diaphragm, esophagus, and pericardium, the last being separated from it by a recess of the right pleural cavity. Opposite the fifth thoracic vertebra, it inclines toward the left side, enters the superior mediastinal cavity, and ascends behind the aortic arch and the thoracic part of the left subclavian artery and between the left side of the esophagus and the left pleura, to the upper orifice of the thorax. Passing into the neck it forms an arch which rises about 3 or 4 cm. above the clavicle and crosses anterior to the subclavian artery, the vertebral artery and vein, and the thyrocervical trunk or its branches. It also passes in front of the phrenic nerve and the medial border of the Scalenus anterior, but is separated from these two structures by the prevertebral fascia. In front of it are the left common carotid artery, vagus nerve, and internal jugular vein; it ends by opening into the angle of junction of the left subclavian vein with the left internal jugular vein.

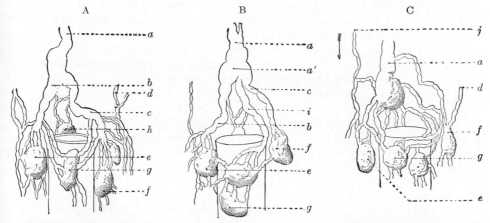

Fig. 653.—Modes of origin of thoracic duct. (Poirier and Charpy.) *a*, Thoracic duct. *a′*, Cisterna chyli. *b*, *c*, Efferent trunks from lateral aortic node. *d*, An efferent vessel which pierces the left crus of the diaphragm. *e*, *f*, Lateral aortic node. *h*, Retroaortic nodes. *i*, Intestinal trunk. *j*, Descending branch from intercostal lymphatics.

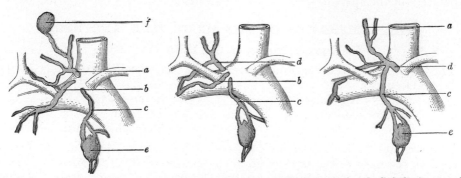

Fig. 654.—Terminal collecting trunks of right side. *a*, Jugular trunk. *b*, Subclavian trunk. *c*, Bronchomediastinal trunk. *d*, Right lymphatic trunk. *e*, Node of internal mammary chain. *f*, Node of deep cervical chain. (Poirier and Charpy.)

The thoracic duct, at its commencement, is about equal in diameter to a goose-quill, but it diminishes considerably in caliber in the middle of the thorax, and is again dilated just before its termination. It is generally flexuous, and constricted at intervals so as to present a varicose appearance. Not infrequently it divides in the middle of its course into two vessels of unequal size which soon reunite, or into several branches which form a plexiform interlacement. It occasionally divides at its upper part into two branches, right and left; the left ending in the usual manner, while the right opens into the right subclavian vein, in connection with the right lymphatic duct. The thoracic duct has several valves; at its termination it is provided with a pair, the free borders of which are turned toward the vein, so as to prevent the passage of venous blood into the duct.

The **cisterna chyli** (*receptaculum chyli*) (Fig. 653) receives the two lumbar lymphatic trunks, right and left, and the intestinal lymphatic trunk. The **lumbar trunks** are formed by the union of the efferent vessels from the lateral aortic lymph glands. They receive the lymph from the lower limbs, from the walls and viscera of the pelvis, from the kidneys and suprarenal nodes and the deep lymphatics of the greater part of the abdominal wall. The **intestinal trunk** receives the lymph from the stomach and intestine, from the pancreas and spleen, and from the lower and front part of the liver.

Tributaries.—Opening into the commencement of the thoracic duct, on either side, is a descending trunk from the posterior intercostal lymph nodes of the lower six or seven intercostal spaces. In the thorax the duct is joined, on either side, by a trunk which drains the upper lumbar lymph nodes and pierces the crus of the diaphragm. It also receives the efferents from the posterior mediastinal lymph glands and from the posterior intercostal lymph nodes of the upper six left spaces. In the neck it is joined by the **left jugular** and **left subclavian trunks,** and sometimes by the **left bronchomediastinal trunk**; the last-named, however, usually opens independently into the junction of the left subclavian and internal jugular veins.

The **right lymphatic duct** (*ductus lymphaticus dexter*) (Fig. 654), about 1.25 cm. in length, courses along the medial border of the Scalenus anterior at the root of the neck and ends in the right subclavian vein, at its angle of junction with the right internal jugular vein. Its orifice is guarded by two semilunar valves, which prevent the passage of venous blood into the duct.

Tributaries.—The right lymphatic duct receives the lymph from the right side of the head and neck through the **right jugular trunk**; from the right upper extremity through the **right subclavian trunk**; from the right side of the thorax, right lung, right side of the heart, and part of the convex surface of the liver, through the **right bronchomediastinal trunk.** These three collecting trunks frequently open separately in the angle of union of the two veins.

THE LYMPHATICS OF THE HEAD, FACE, AND NECK.

The Lymph Nodes of the Head (Fig. 655).

The lymph nodes of the head are arranged in the following groups:

Occipital.	Facial.
Posterior Auricular.	Deep Facial.
Anterior Auricular.	Lingual.
Parotid.	Retropharyngeal.

The **occipital nodes** (*nodi lymphatici occipitales*), one to three in number, are placed on the back of the head close to the margin of the Trapezius and resting on the insertion of the Semispinalis capitis. Their afferent vessels drain the occipital region of the scalp, while their efferents pass to the superior deep cervical nodes.

The **posterior auricular nodes** (*nodi lymphatici retro-auriculares*; *mastoid nodes*), usually two in number, are situated on the mastoid insertion of the Sternocleidomastoideus, beneath the Auricularis posterior. Their afferent vessels drain the posterior part of the temporoparietal region, the upper part of the cranial surface of the auricula or pinna, and the back of the external acoustic meatus; their efferents pass to the superior deep cervical nodes.

The **anterior auricular nodes** (*nodi lymphatici parotidei superficiales*; *superficial parotid or preauricular nodes*), from one to three in number, lie immediately in front of the tragus. Their afferents drain the lateral surface of the auricula and the skin of the adjacent part of the temporal region; their efferents pass to the superior deep cervical nodes.

The **parotid nodes** (*nodi lymphatici parotidei*), form two groups in relation with the parotid salivary gland, *viz.*, a group imbedded in the substance of the gland, and a group of subparotid nodes lying on the lateral wall of the pharynx. Occasionally small nodes are found in the subcutaneous tissue over the parotid gland. Their afferent vessels drain the root of the nose, the eyelids, the frontotemporal region, the external acoustic meatus and the tympanic cavity, possibly also the posterior parts of the palate and the floor of the nasal cavity. The efferents of these nodes pass to the superior deep cervical nodes. The afferents of the subparotid nodes drain the nasal part of the pharynx and the posterior parts of the nasal cavities; their efferents pass to the superior deep cervical nodes.

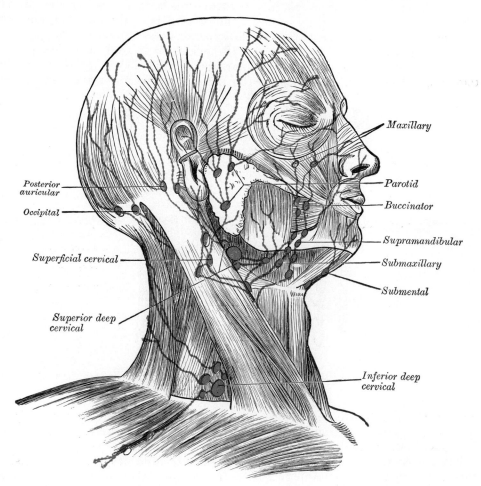

Fig. 655.—Superficial lymph nodes and lymphatic vessels of head and neck.

The **facial nodes** comprise three groups: (*a*) **infraorbital** or **maxillary**, scattered over the infraorbital region from the groove between the nose and cheek to the zygomatic arch; (*b*) **buccinator,** one or more placed on the Buccinator opposite the angle of the mouth; (*c*) **supramandibular,** on the outer surface of the mandible, in front of the Masseter and in contact with the external maxillary artery and anterior facial vein. Their afferent vessels drain the eyelids, the conjunctiva, and the skin and mucous membrane of the nose and cheek; their efferents pass to the submaxillary nodes.

50

The **deep facial nodes** (*nodi lymphatici buccales*; *internal maxillary glands*) are placed beneath the ramus of the mandible, on the outer surface of the Pterygoideus externus, in relation to the internal maxillary artery. Their afferent vessels drain the temporal and infratemporal fossæ and the nasal part of the pharynx their efferents pass to the superior deep cervical nodes.

The **lingual nodes** (*nodi lymphatici lunguales*) are two or three small nodules lying on the Hyoglossus and under the Genioglossus. They form merely glandular substations in the course of the lymphatic vessels of the tongue.

The **retropharyngeal nodes** (Fig. 656), from one to three in number, lie in the buccopharyngeal fascia, behind the upper part of the pharynx and in front of the arch of the atlas, being separated, however, from the latter by the Longus capitis. Their afferents drain the nasal cavities, the nasal part of the pharynx, and the auditory tubes; their efferents pass to the superior deep cervical nodes.

The **lymphatic vessels of the scalp** are divisible into (*a*) those of the frontal region, which terminate in the anterior auricular and parotid nodes; (*b*) those of the temporoparietal region, which end in the parotid and posterior auricular nodes;

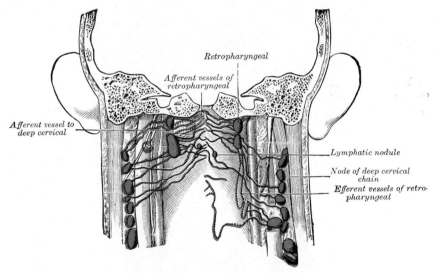

Fig. 656.—Lymphatics and lymph nodes of the pharynx. (Poirier and Charpy.)

and (*c*) those of the occipital region, which terminate partly in the occipital glands and partly in a trunk which runs down along the posterior border of the Sternocleidomastoideus to end in the inferior deep cervical nodes.

The **lymphatic vessels of the auricula and external acoustic meatus** are also divisible into three groups: (*a*) an anterior, from the lateral surface of the auricula and anterior wall of the meatus to the anterior auricular nodes; (*b*) a posterior, from the margin of the auricula, the upper part of its cranial surface, the internal surface and posterior wall of the meatus to the posterior auricular and superior deep cervical nodes; (*c*) an inferior, from the floor of the meatus and from the lobule of the auricula to the superficial and superior deep cervical nodes.

The **lymphatic vessels of the face** (Fig. 659) are more numerous than those of the scalp. Those from the eyelids and conjunctiva terminate partly in the submaxillary but mainly in the parotid nodes. The vessels from the posterior part of the cheek also pass to the parotid nodes, while those from the anterior portion of the cheek, the side of the nose, the upper lip, and the lateral portions of the lower lip end in the submaxillary nodes. The deeper vessels from the temporal and infratemporal fossæ pass to the deep facial and superior deep cervical nodes. The deeper vessels of the cheek and lips end, like the superficial, in the submaxillary nodes. Both superficial and deep vessels of the central part of the lower lip run to the submental nodes.

Lymphatic Vessels of the Nasal Cavities.—Those from the anterior parts of the nasal cavities communicate with the vessels of the integument of the nose and end in the submaxillary nodes; those from the posterior two-thirds of the nasal cavities and from the accessory air sinuses pass partly to the retropharyngeal and partly to the superior deep cervical nodes.

Lymphatic Vessels of the Mouth.—The vessels of the gums pass to the submaxillary nodes; those of the hard palate are continuous in front with those of the upper gum, but pass backward to pierce the Constrictor pharyngis superior and end in the superior deep cervical and subparotid nodes; those of the soft palate pass backward and lateralward and end partly in the retropharyngeal and subparotid, and partly in the superior deep cervical nodes. The vessels of the anterior part of the floor of the mouth pass either directly to the inferior nodes of the superior

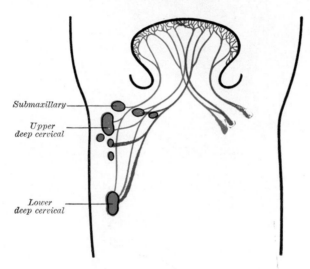

FIG. 657.—A diagram to show the course of the central lymphatic vessels of the tongue to the lymph nodes on both sides of the neck. (Jamieson and Dobson.)

deep cervical group, or indirectly through the submental nodes; from the rest of the floor of the mouth the vessels pass to the submaxillary and superior deep cervical nodes.

The **lymphatic vessels of the palatine tonsil,** usually three to five in number, pierce the buccopharyngeal fascia and constrictor pharyngis superior and pass between the Stylohyoideus and internal jugular vein to the uppermost of the superior deep cervical nodes. They end in a node which lies at the side of the posterior belly of the Digastricus, on the internal jugular vein; occasionally one or two additional vessels run to small glands on the lateral side of the vein under cover of the Sternocleidomastoideus.

The **lymphatic vessels of the tongue** (Fig. 657) are drained chiefly into the deep cervical nodes lying between the posterior belly of the Digastricus and the superior belly of the Omohyoideus; one node situated at the bifurcation of the common carotid artery is so intimately associated with these vessels that it is known as the **principal node of the tongue.** The lymphatic vessels of the tongue may be divided

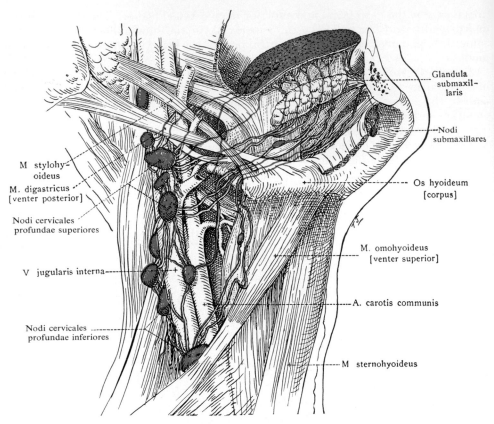

FIG. 658.—The deep cervical lymphatic nodes and vessels of the right upper cervical triangle. The lymphatic drainage of the tongue is shown. (Eycleshymer and Jones.)

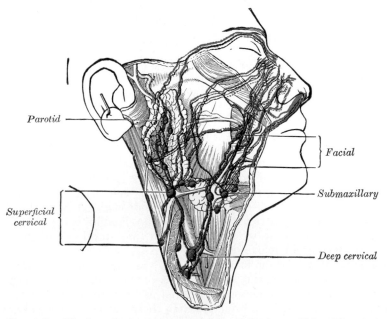

FIG. 659.—The lymphatics and lymph nodes of the face. (After Küttner.)

into four groups: (1) apical, from the tip of the tongue to the suprahyoid nodes and principal node of the tongue; (2) lateral, from the margin of the tongue— some of these pierce the Mylohyoideus to end in the submaxillary nodes, others pass down on the Hyoglossus to the superior deep cervical nodes; (3) basal, from the region of the vallate papillæ to the superior deep cervical nodes; and (4) median, a few of which perforate the Mylohyoideus to reach the submaxillary nodes, while the majority turn around the posterior border of the muscle to enter the superior deep cervical nodes.

The Lymph Nodes of the Neck.

The lymph nodes of the neck include the following groups:

Submaxillary.	Superficial Cervical.
Submental.	Anterior Cervical.

Deep Cervical.

The **submaxillary nodes** (*nodi lymphatici submandibulares*) (Fig. 658), three to six in number, are placed beneath the body of the mandible in the submaxillary triangle, and rest on the superficial surface of the submaxillary salivary gland. One node, the **middle node of Stahr,** which lies on the external maxillary artery as it turns over the mandible, is the most constant of the series; small lymph nodes are sometimes found on the deep surface of the submaxillary salivary gland. The afferents of the submaxillary nodes drain the medial palpebral commissure, the cheek, the side of the nose, the upper lip, the lateral part of the lower lip, the gums, and the anterior part of the margin of the tongue; efferent vessels from the facial and submental nodes also enter the submaxillary nodes. Their efferent vessels pass to the superior deep cervical nodes.

The **submental** or **suprahyoid nodes** are situated between the anterior bellies of the Digastrici. Their afferents drain the central portions of the lower lip and floor of the mouth and the apex of the tongue; their efferents pass partly to the submaxillary nodes and partly to a node of the deep cervical group situated on the internal jugular vein at the level of the cricoid cartilage.

The **superficial cervical nodes** (*nodi lymphatici cervicales superficiales*) lie in close relationship with the external jugular vein as it emerges from the parotid gland, and, therefore, superficial to the Sternocleidomastoideus. Their afferents drain the lower parts of the auricula and parotid region, while their efferents pass around the anterior margin of the Sternocleidomastoideus to join the superior deep cervical nodes.

The **anterior cervical nodes** form an irregular and inconstant group on the front of the larynx and trachea. They may be divided into (*a*) a **superficial set,** placed on the anterior jugular vein; (*b*) a **deeper set,** which is further subdivided into prelaryngeal, on the middle cricothyroid ligament, and pretracheal, on the front of the trachea. This deeper set drains the lower part of the larynx, the thyroid gland, and the upper part of the trachea; its efferents pass to the lowest of the superior deep cervical nodes.

The **deep cervical nodes** (*nodi lymphatici cervicales profundi*) (Figs. 658, 655) are numerous and of large size: they form a chain along the carotid sheath, lying by the side of the pharynx, esophagus, and trachea, and extending from the base of the skull to the root of the neck. They are usually described in two groups: (1) the **superior deep cervical nodes** lying under the Sternocleidomastoideus in close relation with the accessory nerve and the internal jugular vein, some of the nodes lying in front of and others behind the vessel; (2) the **inferior deep cervical nodes** extending beyond the posterior margin of the Sternocleidomastoideus into the supraclavicular triangle, where they are closely related to the brachial plexus and subclavian vein. A few minute **paratracheal nodes** are situated along-side the recurrent nerves on the lateral aspects of the trachea and esophagus. The superior deep cervical nodes drain the occipital portion of the scalp, the auricula, the back of the neck, a considerable part of the tongue, the larynx, thyroid gland, trachea, nasal part of the pharynx, nasal cavities, palate, and esophagus. They receive also the efferent vessels from all the other nodes of the head and neck, except those from the inferior deep cervical nodes.   The inferior deep cervical

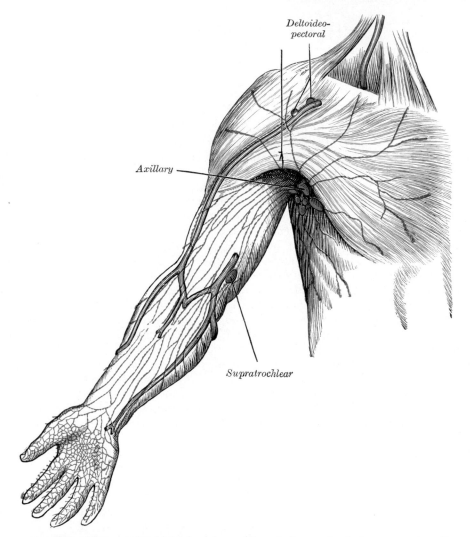

Deltoideo-
pectoral

Axillary

Supratrochlear

FIG. 660.—The superficial lymph nodes and lymphatic vessels of the upper extremity.

nodes drain the back of the scalp and neck, the superficial pectoral region, part of the arm (see page 793), and, occasionally, part of the superior surface of the liver, In addition, they receive vessels from the superior deep cervical nodes. The efferents of the superior deep cervical nodes pass partly to the inferior deep cervical nodes and partly to a trunk which unites with the efferent vessel of the inferior deep cervical nodes and forms the **jugular trunk**. On the right side, this trunk ends in the junction of the internal jugular and subclavian veins; on the left side it joins the thoracic duct.

The **lymphatic vessels of the skin and muscles of the neck** pass to the deep cervical nodes. From the upper part of the *pharynx* the lymphatic vessels pass to the retropharyngeal, from the lower part to the deep cervical nodes. From the *larynx*

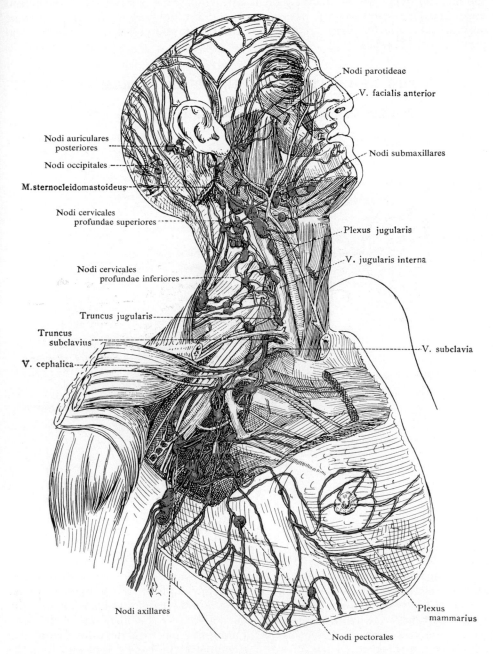

Nodi parotideae

V. facialis anterior

Nodi auriculares posteriores

Nodi occipitales

Nodi submaxillares

M. sternocleidomastoideus

Nodi cervicales profundae superiores

Plexus jugularis

V. jugularis interna

Nodi cervicales profundae inferiores

Truncus jugularis

Truncus subclavius

V. subclavia

V. cephalica

Nodi axillares

Plexus mammarius

Nodi pectorales

FIG. 661.—The deep lymphatic nodes and vessels of the right side of the head and neck, and of the mammary and axillary regions. (Eycleshymer and Jones.)

two sets of vessels arise, an upper and a lower. The vessels of the upper set pierce the hyothyroid membrane and join the superior deep cervical nodes. Of the lower set, some pierce the conus elasticus and join the pretracheal and prelaryngeal nodes; others run between the cricoid and first tracheal ring and enter the inferior deep cervical nodes. The lymphatic vessels of the *thyroid node* consist of two sets, an upper, which accompanies the superior thyroid artery and enters the superior deep cervical nodes, and a lower, which runs partly to the pretracheal nodes and partly to the small paratracheal nodes which accompany the recurrent nerves. These latter glands receive also the lymphatic vessels from the cervical portion of the trachea.

THE LYMPHATICS OF THE UPPER EXTREMITY.

The Lymph Nodes of the Upper Extremity (Fig. 660).

The lymph nodes of the upper extremity are divided into two sets, **superficial** and **deep**.

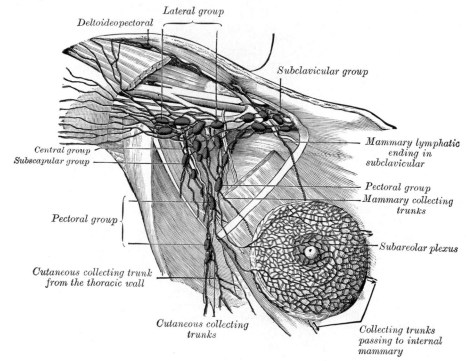

FIG. 662.—Lymphatics of the mamma, and the axillary nodes (semidiagrammatic). (Poirier and Charpy.)

The **superficial lymph nodes** are few and of small size. One or two **supratrochlear nodes** are placed above the medial epicondyle of the humerus, medial to the basilic vein. Their afferents drain the middle, ring, and little fingers, the medial portion of the hand, and the superficial area over the ulnar side of the forearm; these vessels are, however, in free communication with the other lymphatic vessels of the forearm. Their efferents accompany the basilic vein and join the deeper vessels. One or two **deltoideopectoral nodes** are found beside the cephalic vein, between the Pectoralis major and Deltoideus, immediately below the clavicle. They are situated in the course of the external collecting trunks of the arm.

The **deep lymph nodes** are chiefly grouped in the axilla, although a few may be found in the forearm, in the course of the radial, ulnar, and interosseous vessels, and in the arm along the medial side of the brachial artery.

The **Axillary Nodes** (*nodi lymphatici axillares*) (Fig. 662) are of large size, vary from twenty to thirty in number, and may be arranged in the following groups:

1. A **lateral group** of from four to six glands lies in relation to the medial and posterior aspects of the axillary vein; the afferents of these nodes drain the whole arm with the exception of that portion whose vessels accompany the cephalic vein. The efferent vessels pass partly to the central and subclavicular groups of axillary nodes and partly to the inferior deep cervical nodes.

2. An **anterior** or **pectoral group** consists of four or five nodes along the lower border of the Pectoralis minor, in relation with the lateral thoracic artery. Their afferents drain the skin and muscles of the anterior and lateral thoracic walls, and the central and lateral parts of the mamma; their efferents pass partly to the central and partly to the subclavicular groups of axillary nodes.

3. A **posterior** or **subscapular group** of six or seven nodes is placed along the lower margin of the posterior wall of the axilla in the course of the subscapular artery. The afferents of this group drain the skin and muscles of the lower part of the back of the neck and of the posterior thoracic wall; their efferents pass to the central group of axillary nodes.

4. A **central** or **intermediate group** of three or four large nodes is imbedded in the adipose tissue near the base of the axilla. Its afferents are the efferent vessels of all the preceding groups of axillary nodes; its efferents pass to the subclavicular group.

5. A **medial** or **subclavicular group** of six to twelve nodes is situated partly posterior to the upper portion of the Pectoralis minor and partly above the upper border of this muscle. Its only direct territorial afferents are those which accompany the cephalic vein and one which drains the upper peripheral part of the mamma, but it receives the efferents of all the other axillary nodes. The efferent vessels of the subclavicular group unite to form the **subclavian trunk,** which opens either directly into the junction of the internal jugular and subclavian veins or into the jugular lymphatic trunk; on the left side it may end in the thoracic duct. A few efferents from the subclavicular nodes usually pass to the inferior deep cervical nodes.

The Lymphatic Vessels of the Upper Extremity.

The lymphatic vessels of the upper extremity are divided into two sets, superficial and deep.

The **superficial lymphatic vessels** commence (Fig. 663) in the lymphatic plexus which everywhere pervades the skin; the meshes of the plexus are much finer in the palm and on the flexor aspect of the digits than elsewhere. The digital plexuses are drained by a pair of vessels which run on the sides of each digit, and incline backward to reach the dorsum of the hand. From the dense plexus of the palm, vessels pass in different directions, *viz.,* upward toward the wrist, downward to join the digital vessels, medialward to join the vessels on the ulnar border of the hand, and lateralward to those on the thumb. Several vessels from the central part of the plexus unite to form a trunk, which passes around the metacarpal bone of the index finger to join the vessels on the back of that digit and on the back of the thumb. Running upward in front of and behind the wrist, the lymphatic vessels are collected into radial, median, and ulnar groups, which accompany respectively the cephalic, median, and basilic veins in the forearm. A few of the ulnar lymphatics end in the supratrochlear nodes, but the majority pass directly to the lateral group of axillary nodes. Some of the radial vessels are collected into a trunk which ascends with the cephalic vein to the deltoideopectoral glands; the efferents from this group pass either to the subclavicular axillary glands or to the inferior cervical nodes.

The **deep lymphatic vessels** accompany the deep blood vessels. In the forearm, they consist of four sets, corresponding with the radial, ulnar, volar, and dorsal interosseous arteries; they communicate at intervals with the superficial lymphatics, and some of them end in the nodes which are occasionally found beside the arteries. In their course upward, a few end in the nodes which lie upon the brachial artery; but most of them pass to the lateral group of axillary nodes.

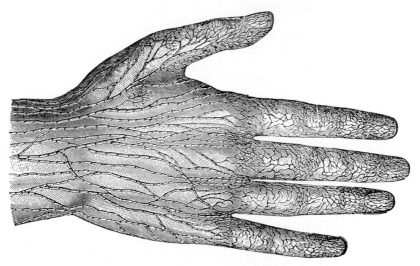

Fig. 663.—Lymphatic vessels of the dorsal surface of the hand. (Sappey.)

THE LYMPHATICS OF THE LOWER EXTREMITY.

The Lymph Nodes of the Lower Extremity.

The lymph glands of the lower extremity consist of the **anterior tibial node** and the **popliteal** and **inguinal nodes**.

The **anterior tibial node** (*nodus lymphaticus tibialis anterior*) is small and inconstant. It lies on the interosseous membrane in relation to the upper part of the anterior tibial vessels, and constitutes a substation in the course of the anterior tibial lymphatic trunks.

The **popliteal nodes** (*nodi lymphatici poplitei*) (Fig. 664), small in size and some six or seven in number, are imbedded in the fat contained in the popliteal fossa. One lies immediately beneath the popliteal fascia, near the terminal part of the small saphenous vein, and drains the region from which this vein derives its tributaries. Another is placed between the popliteal artery and the posterior surface of the knee-joint; it receives the lymphatic vessels from the knee-joint together with those which accompany the genicular arteries. The others lie at the sides of the popliteal vessels, and receive as afferents the trunks which accompany the anterior and posterior tibial vessels. The efferents of the popliteal nodes pass almost entirely alongside the femoral vessels to the deep inguinal nodes, but a few may accompany the great saphenous vein, and end in the nodes of the superficial subinguinal group.

The **inguinal nodes** (*nodi lymphatici inguinales*) (Fig. 665), from twelve to twenty in number, are situated at the upper part of the femoral triangle. They may be divided into two groups by a horizontal line at the level of the termination of the great saphenous vein; those lying above this line are termed the

superficial inguinal nodes, and those below it the **subinguinal nodes,** the latter group consisting of a *superficial* and a *deep* set.

The **Superficial Inguinal Nodes** form a chain immediately below the inguinal ligament. They receive as afferents lymphatic vessels from the integument of the penis, scrotum, perineum, buttock, and abdomnal wall below the level of the umbilicus.

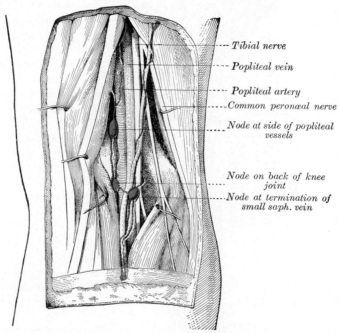

FIG. 664.—Lymph nodes of popliteal fossa. (Poirier and Charpy.)

The **Superficial Subinguinal Nodes** (*nodi lymphatici subinguinales superficiales*) are placed on either side of the upper part of the great saphenous vein; their afferents consist chiefly of the superficial lymphatic vessels of the lower extremity; but they also receive some of the vessels which drain the integument of the penis, scrotum, perineum, and buttock.

The **Deep Subinguinal Nodes** (*nodi lymphatici subinguinales profundæ*) vary from one to three in number, and are placed under the fascia lata, on the medial side of the femoral vein. When three are present, the lowest is situated just below the junction of the great saphenous and femoral veins, the middle in the femoral canal, and the highest in the lateral part of the femoral ring. The middle one is the most inconstant of the three, but the highest, the **node of Cloquet or Rosenmüller,** is also frequently absent. They receive as afferents the deep lymphatic trunks which accompany the femoral vessels, the lymphatics from the glans penis vel clitoridis, and also some of the efferents from the superficial subinguinal nodes.

The Lymphatic Vessels of the Lower Extremity.

The lymphatic vessels of the lower extremity consist of two sets, superficial and deep, and in their distribution correspond closely with the veins.

The **superficial lymphatic vessels** lie in the superficial fascia, and are divisible into two groups: a medial, which follows the course of the great saphe-

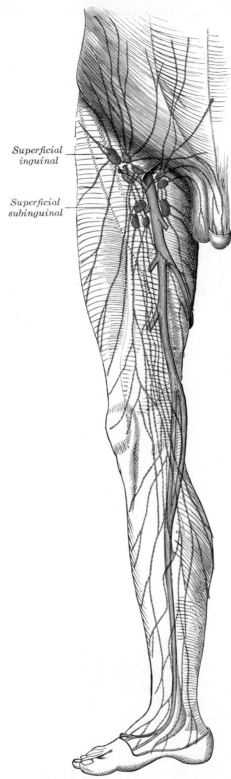

Superficial inguinal

Superficial subinguinal

FIG. 665.—The superficial lymph nodes and lymphatic vessels of the lower extremity.

nous vein, and a lateral, which accompanies the small saphenous vein. The vessels of the **medial group** (Fig. 665) are larger and more numerous than those of the lateral group, and commence on the tibial side and dorsum of the foot; they ascend both in front of and behind the medial malleolus, run up the leg with the great saphenous vein, pass with it behind the medial condyle of the femur, and accompany it to the groin, where they end in the subinguinal group of superficial nodes. The vessels of the **lateral group** *arise* from the fibular side of the foot; some ascend in front of the leg, and, just below the knee, cross the tibia to join the lymphatics on the medial side of the thigh; others pass behind the lateral malleolus, and, accompanying the small saphenous vein, enter the popliteal nodes.

The **deep lymphatic vessels** are few in number, and accompany the deep bloodvessels. In the leg, they consist of three sets, the anterior tibial, posterior tibial, and peroneal, which accompany the corresponding bloodvessels, two or three with each artery; they enter the popliteal lymph nodes.

The deep lymphatic vessels of the gluteal and ischial regions follow the course of the corresponding bloodvessels. Those accompanying the superior gluteal vessels end in a node which lies on the intrapelvic portion of the superior gluteal artery near the upper border of the greater sciatic foramen. Those following the inferior gluteal vessels traverse one or two small nodes which lie below the Piriformis muscle, and end in the hypogastric nodes.

THE LYMPHATICS OF THE ABDOMEN AND PELVIS.

The Lymph Nodes of the Abdomen and Pelvis.

The lymph nodes of the abdomen and pelvis may be divided, from their situations, into (*a*) **parietal**, lying behind the peritoneum and in close association with the larger bloodvessels; and (*b*) **visceral**, which are found in relation to the visceral arteries.

The **parietal nodes** (Figs. 666, 667) include the following groups:

External Iliac.	Iliac Circumflex.		Lateral Aortic.
Common Iliac.	Hypogastric.	Lumbar	Preaortic.
Epigastric.	Sacral.		Retroaortic.

The **External Iliac Nodes**, from eight to ten in number, lie along the external iliac vessels. They are arranged in three groups, one on the lateral, another on the medial, and a third on the anterior aspect of the vessels; the third group is, however, sometimes absent. Their principal afferents are derived from the inguinal

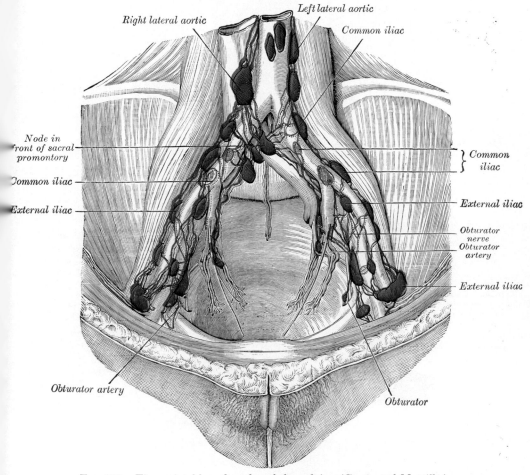

FIG. 666.—The parietal lymph nodes of the pelvis. (Cunéo and Marcille.)

and subinguinal nodes, the deep lymphatics of the abdominal wall below the umbilicus and of the adductor region of the thigh, and the lymphatics from the glans penis vel clitoridis, the membranous urethra, the prostate, the fundus of the bladder, the cervix uteri, and upper part of the vagina.

The **Common Iliac Nodes**, four to six in number, are grouped behind and on the sides of the common iliac artery, one or two being placed below the bifurcation of the aorta, in front of the fifth lumbar vertebra. They drain chiefly the hypogastric and external iliac nodes, and their efferents pass to the lateral aortic nodes.

The **Epigastric Nodes** (*nodi lymphatici epigastrici*), three or four in number, are placed alongside the lower portion of the inferior epigastric vessels.

The **Iliac Circumflex Nodes**, two to four in number, are situated along the course of the deep iliac circumflex vessels; they are sometimes absent.

The **Internal Iliac Nodes** (*nodi lymphatici iliaci interni*; *hypogastric nodes*) (Fig. 667) surround the hypogastric vessels, and receive the lymphatics corresponding to the distribution of the branches of the hypogastric artery, *i.e.*, they receive lymphatics from all the pelvic viscera, from the deeper parts of the perineum, including the membranous and cavernous portions of the urethra, and from the buttock and back of the thigh. An **obturator node** is sometimes seen in the upper part of the obturator foramen.

The **Sacral Nodes** are placed in the concavity of the sacrum, in relation to the middle and lateral sacral arteries; they receive lymphatics from the rectum and posterior wall of the pelvis.

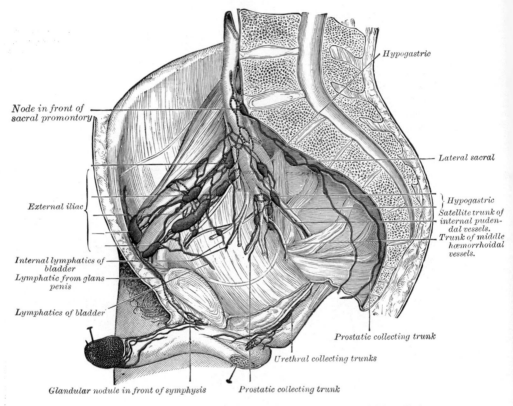

Fig. 667.—Iliopelvic nodes (lateral view). (Cunéo and Marcille.)

The efferents of the hypogastric group end in the common iliac nodes.

The **Lumbar Nodes** (*nodi lymphatici lumbales*) are very numerous, and consist of right and left lateral aortic, preaortic, and retroaortic groups.

The **right lateral aortic nodes** are situated partly in front of the inferior vena cava, near the termination of the renal vein, and partly behind it on the origin of the Psoas major, and on the right crus of the diaphragm. The **left lateral aortic nodes** form a chain on the left side of the abdominal aorta in front of the origin of the Psoas major and left crus of the diaphragm. The nodes on either side receive (*a*) the efferents of the common iliac glands, (*b*) the lymphatics from the testis in the male and from the ovary, uterine tube, and body of the uterus in the female; (*c*) the lymphatics from the kidney and suprarenal node; and (*d*) the lymphatics draining the lateral abdominal muscles and accompanying the lumbar veins. Most of the efferent vessels of the lateral aortic glands converge to form the **right and left lumbar trunks** which join the cisterna chyli, but some enter the pre- and retroaortic nodes, and others pierce the crura of the diaphragm to join the lower end of the thoracic duct. The **preaortic nodes** lie in front of the aorta, and may be divided into **celiac, superior mesenteric,** and **inferior mesenteric** groups, arranged around the origins of the corresponding arteries. They receive a few vessels from the lateral aortic nodes, but their principal afferents are derived from the viscera supplied by the three arteries with which they are associated. Some of their efferents pass to the retroaortic nodes, but the majority unite to form the **intestinal trunk,** which enters the cisterna chyli. The **retroaortic nodes** are placed below the cisterna chyli, on the bodies of the third and fourth lumbar vertebræ. They receive lymphatic trunks from the lateral and preaortic node, while their efferents end in the cisterna chyli.

The Lymphatic Vessels of the Abdomen and Pelvis.

The lymphatic vessels of the walls of the abdomen and pelvis may be divided into two sets, superficial and deep.

The **superficial vessels** follow the course of the superficial bloodvessels and converge to the superficial inguinal nodes; those derived from the integument of the front of the abdomen below the umbilicus follow the course of the superficial epigastric vessels, and those from the sides of the lumbar part of the abdominal wall pass along the crest of the ilium, with the superficial iliac circumflex vessels. The superficial lymphatic vessels of the gluteal region turn horizontally around the buttock, and join the superficial inguinal and subinguinal nodes.

The **deep vessels** run alongside the principal bloodvessels. Those of the parietes of the pelvis, which accompany the superior and inferior gluteal, and obturator vessels, follow the course of the hypogastric artery, and ultimately join the lateral aortic nodes.

Lymphatic Vessels of the Perineum and External Genitals.—The lymphatic vessels of the perineum, of the integument of the penis, and of the scrotum (or vulva), follow the course of the external pudendal vessels, and end in the superficial inguinal and subinguinal nodes. Those of the glans penis vel clitoridis terminate partly in the deep subinguinal nodes and partly in the external iliac nodes.

The Lymphatic Nodes of the Abdominal and Pelvic Viscera.

The **visceral nodes** are associated with the branches of the celiac, superior and inferior mesenteric arteries. Those related to the branches of the celiac artery form three sets, gastric, hepatic, and pancreaticolienal.

The **Gastric Nodes** (Figs. 668, 669) consist of two sets, **superior** and **inferior**.

The **Superior Gastric Nodes** (*nodi lymphatici gastrici sinistri*) accompany the left gastric artery and are divisible into three groups, viz.: (*a*) **upper,** on the stem of the artery; (*b*) **lower,** accompanying the descending branches of the artery along the cardiac half of the lesser curvature of the stomach, between the two layers of the lesser omentum; and (*c*) **paracardial** outlying members of the gastric nodes, disposed in a manner comparable to a chain of beads around the neck of the stomach. They receive their afferents from the stomach; their efferents pass to the celiac group of preaortic nodes.

The **Inferior Gastric Nodes** (*nodi lymphatici gastrici dextri*; *right gastro-epiploic glands*), four to seven in number, lie between the two layers of the greater omentum along the pyloric half of the greater curvature of the stomach.

The **Hepatic Nodes** (*nodi lymphatici hepaticæ*) (Fig. 668), consist of the following groups: (*a*) **hepatic,** on the stem of the hepatic artery, and extending upward along the common bile duct, between the two layers of the lesser omentum, as far as the porta hepatis; the **cystic node,** a member of this group, is placed near

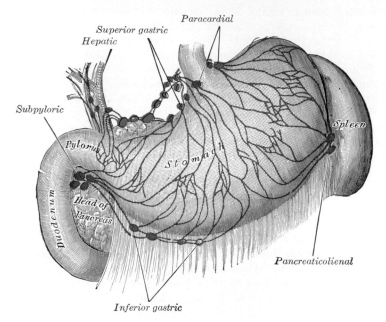

FIG. 668.—Lymphatics of stomach, etc.   (Jamieson and Dobson.)

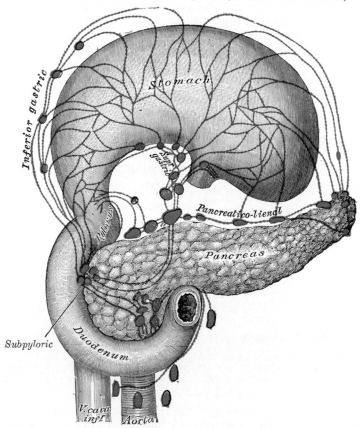

FIG. 669.—Lymphatics of stomach, etc.   The stomach has been turned upward.
(Jamieson and Dobson.)

the neck of the gall-bladder; (*b*) **subpyloric,** four or five in number, in close relation to the bifurcation of the gastroduodenal artery, in the angle between the superior and descending parts of the duodenum; an outlying member of this group is sometimes found above the duodenum on the right gastric (pyloric) artery. The nodes of the hepatic chain receive afferents from the stomach, duodenum, liver, gall-bladder, and pancreas; their efferents join the celiac group of preaortic nodes.

The **Pancreaticolienal Nodes** (*nodi lymphatici pancreaticolienales*; *splenic glands*) (Fig. 669) accompany the lienal (splenic) artery, and are situated in relation to the posterior surface and upper border of the pancreas; one or two members of this group are found in the gastrolienal ligament. Their afferents are derived from the stomach, spleen, and pancreas, their efferents join the celiac group of preaortic nodes.

The **superior mesenteric nodes** may be divided into three principal groups: mesenteric, ileocolic, and mesocolic.

The **Mesenteric Nodes** (*nodi lymphatici mesenterici*) lie between the layers of the mesentery. They vary from one hundred to one hundred and fifty in number, and may be grouped into three sets, *viz.*: one lying close to the wall of the small intestine, among the terminal twigs of the superior mesenteric artery; a second, in relation to the loops and primary branches of the vessels; and a third along the trunk of the artery.

The **Ileocolic nodes** (Figs. 670, 671), from ten to twenty in number, form a chain around the ileocolic artery, but show a tendency to subdivision into two groups, one near the duodenum and another on the lower part of the trunk of the artery. Where the vessel divides into its terminal branches the chain is broken up into several groups, viz.: (*a*) **ileal,** in relation to the ileal branch of the artery; (*b*) **anterior ileocolic,** usually of three nodes, in the ileocolic fold, near the wall of the cecum; (*c*) **posterior ileocolic,** mostly placed in the angle between the ileum and the colon, but partly lying behind the cecum at its junction with the ascending colon; (*d*) a single node, between the layers of the mesenteriole of the vermiform process; (*e*) **right colic,** along the medial side of the ascending colon.

The **Mesocolic Nodes** (*nodi lymphatici mesocolici*) are numerous, and lie between the layers of the transverse mesocolon, in close relation to the transverse colon; they are best developed in the neighborhood of the right and left colic flexures. One or two small nodes are occasionally seen along the trunk of the right colic artery and others are found in relation to the trunk and branches of the middle colic artery.

The superior mesenteric nodes receive afferents from the jejunum, ileum, cecum, vermiform process, and the ascending and transverse parts of the colon; their efferents pass to the preaortic nodes.

The **inferior mesenteric nodes** (Fig. 672) consist of: (*a*) small nodes on the branches of the left colic and sigmoid arteries; (*b*) a group in the sigmoid mesocolon, around the superior hemorrhoidal artery; and (*c*) a **pararectal** group in contact with the muscular coat of the rectum. They drain the descending, iliac and sigmoid parts of the colon and the upper part of the rectum; their efferents pass to the preaortic nodes.

The Lymphatic Vessels of the Abdominal and Pelvic Viscera.

The lymphatic vessels of the abdominal and pelvic viscera consist of (1) those of the subdiaphragmatic portion of the digestive tube and its associated glands, the liver and pancreas; (2) those of the spleen and suprarenal glands; (3) those of the urinary organs; (4) those of the reproductive organs.

1. The **lymphatic vessels of the subdiaphragmatic portion of the digestive tube** are situated partly in the mucous membrane and partly in the seromuscular

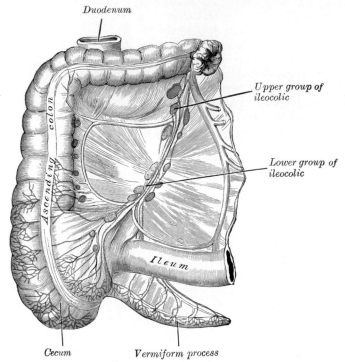

FIG. 670.—The lymphatics of cecum and vermiform process from the front.
(Jamieson and Dobson.)

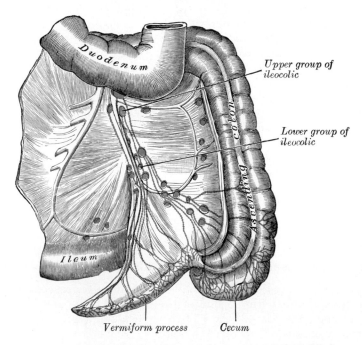

FIG. 671.—The lymphatics of cecum and vermiform process from behind.
(Jamieson and Dobson.)

coats, but as the former system drains into the latter, the two may be considered as one.

The **Lymphatic Vessels of the Stomach** (Figs. 668, 669) are continuous at the cardiac orifice with those of the esophagus, and at the pylorus with those of the duodenum. They mainly follow the bloodvessels, and may be arranged in four sets. Those of the first set accompany the branches of the left gastric artery, receiving tributaries from a large area on either surface of the stomach, and terminate in the superior gastric nodes. Those of the second set drain the fundus and body of the stomach on the left of a line drawn vertically from the esophagus; they accompany, more or less closely, the short gastric and left gastroepiploic

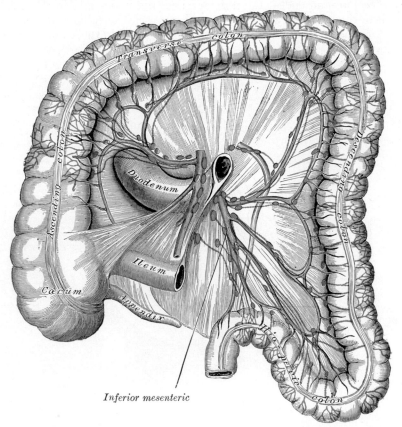

Fig. 672.—Lymphatics of colon. (Jamieson and Dobson.)

arteries, and end in the pancreaticolienal nodes. The vessels of the third set drain the right portion of the greater curvature as far as the pyloric portion, and end in the inferior gastric nodes, the efferents of which pass to the subpyloric group. Those of the fourth set drain the pyloric portion and pass to the hepatic and subpyloric nodes, and to the superior gastric nodes.

The **Lymphatic Vessels of the Duodenum** consist of an anterior and a posterior set, which open into a series of small **pancreaticoduodenal nodes** on the anterior and posterior aspects of the groove between the head of the pancreas and the duodenum. The efferents of these nodes run in two directions, upward to the hepatic glands and downward to the preaortic nodes around the origin of the superior mesenteric artery.

The **Lymphatic Vessels of the Jejunum and Ileum** are termed **lacteals**, from the milk-white fluid they contain during intestinal digestion. They run between the layers of the mesentery and enter the mesenteric nodes, the efferents of which end in the preaortic nodes.

The **Lymphatic Vessels of the Vermiform Process and Cecum** (Figs. 670, 671) are numerous, since in the wall of this process there is a large amount of adenoid tissue. From the body and tail of the vermiform process eight to fifteen vessels ascend between the layers of the mesenteriole, one or two being interrupted in the node which lies between the layers of this peritoneal fold. They unite to form three or four vessels, which end partly in the lower and partly in the upper nodes of the ileocolic chain. The vessels from the root of the vermiform process and from the cecum consist of an anterior and a posterior group. The anterior vessels pass in front of the cecum, and end in the anterior ileocolic nodes and in the upper and lower glands of the ileocolic chain; the posterior vessels ascend over the back of the cecum and terminate in the posterior ileocolic nodes and in the lower glands of the ileocolic chain.

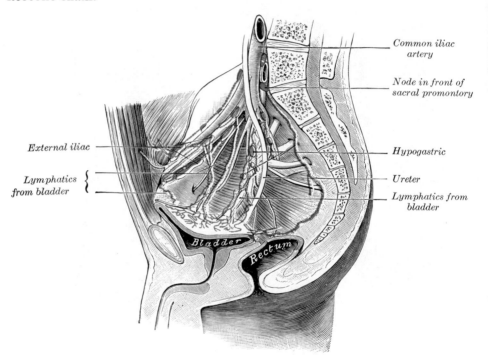

FIG. 673.—Lymphatics of the bladder. (Cunéo and Marcille.)

Lymphatic Vessels of the Colon (Fig. 672).—The lymphatic vessels of the ascending and transverse parts of the colon finally end in the mesenteric nodes, after traversing the right colic and mesocolic nodes. Those of the descending and iliac sigmoid parts of the colon are interrupted by the small nodes on the branches of the left colic and sigmoid arteries, and ultimately end in the preaortic nodes around the origin of the inferior mesenteric artery.

Lymphatic Vessels of the Anus, Anal Canal, and Rectum.—The lymphatics from the **anus** pass forward and end with those of the integument of the perineum and scrotum in the superficial inguinal nodes; those from the **anal canal** accompany the middle and inferior hemorrhoidal arteries, and end in the hypogastric nodes; while the vessels from the **rectum** traverse the pararectal glands and pass to those in the sigmoid mesocolon; the efferents of the latter terminate in the preaortic nodes around the origin of the inferior mesenteric artery.

The **Lymphatic Vessels of the Liver** are divisible into two sets, superficial and deep. The former arise in the subperitoneal areolar tissue over the entire surface of the organ, and may be grouped into (a) those on the convex surface, (b) those on the inferior surface.

(a) On the **convex surface:** The vessels from the back part of this surface reach their terminal nodes by three different routes; the vessels of the middle set, five or six in number, pass through the vena-caval foramen in the diaphragm and end in one or two nodes which are situated around the terminal part of the inferior vena cava; a few vessels from the left side pass backward toward the esophageal hiatus, and terminate in the paracardial group of superior gastric nodes; the vessels from the right side, one or two in number, run on the abdominal surface of the diaphragm, and, after crossing its right crus, end in the preaortic nodes which surround the origin of the celiac artery. From the portions of the right and left lobes adjacent to the falciform ligament, the lymphatic vessels converge to form two trunks, one of which accompanies the inferior vena cava through the diaphragm, and ends in the nodes around the terminal part of this vessel; the other runs downward and forward, and, turning around the anterior sharp margin of the liver, accompanies the upper part of the ligamentum teres, and ends in the upper hepatic nodes. From the anterior surface a few additional vessels turn around the anterior sharp margin to reach the upper hepatic nodes.

(b) On the **inferior surface:** The vessels from this surface mostly converge to the porta hepatis, and accompany the deep lymphatics, emerging from the porta to the hepatic nodes one or two from the posterior parts of the right and caudate lobes accompany the inferior vena cava through the diaphragm, and end in the nodes around the terminal part of this vein.

The deep lymphatics converge to ascending and descending trunks. The ascending trunks accompany the hepatic veins and pass through the diaphragm to end in the nodes around the terminal part of the inferior vena cava. The descending trunks emerge from the porta hepatis, and end in the hepatic nodes.

The **Lymphatic Vessels of the Gall-bladder** pass to the hepatic nodes in the porta hepatis; those of the **common bile duct** to the hepatic nodes alongside the duct and to the upper pancreaticoduodenal nodes.

The **Lymphatic Vessels of the Pancreas** follow the course of its bloodvessels. Most of them enter the pancreaticolienal nodes, but some end in the pancreatico-duodenal nodes, and others in the preaortic nodes near the origin of the superior mesenteric artery. (Fig. 669)

2. The **lymphatic vessels of the spleen** and **suprarenal glands.**

The **Lymphatic Vessels of the Spleen,** both superficial and deep, pass to the pancreaticolienal nodes. (Fig. 668)

The **Lymphatic Vessels of the Suprarenal Glands** usually accompany the suprarenal veins, and end in the lateral aortic nodes; occasionally some of them pierce the crura of the diaphragm and end in the nodes of the posterior mediastinum.

3. The **lymphatic vessels of the urinary organs.**

The **Lymphatic Vessels of the Kidney** form three plexuses: one in the substance of the kidney, a second beneath its fibrous capsule, and a third in the perinephric fat; the second and third communicate freely with each other. The vessels from the plexus in the kidney substance converge to form four or five trunks which issue at the hilum. Here they are joined by vessels from the plexus under the capsule, and, following the course of the renal vein, end in the lateral aortic nodes. The perinephric plexus is drained directly into the upper lateral aortic nodes.

The **Lymphatic Vessels of the Ureter** run in different directions. Those from its upper portion end partly in the efferent vessels of the kidney and partly in the lateral aortic nodes; those from the portion immediately above the brim of the lesser pelvis are drained into the common iliac nodes; while the vessels from the intrapelvic portion of the tube either join the efferents from the bladder, or end in the hypogastric nodes.

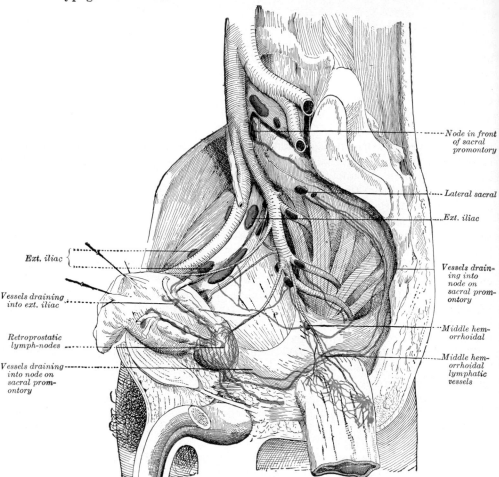

FIG. 674.—Lymphatics of the prostate. (Cunéo and Marcille.)

The **Lymphatic Vessels of the Bladder** (Fig. 673) originate in two plexuses, an intra- and an extramuscular, it being generally admitted that the mucous membrane is devoid of lymphatics. The efferent vessels are arranged in two groups, one from the anterior and another from the posterior surface of the bladder. The vessels from the *anterior* surface pass to the external iliac nodes, but in their course minute nodes are situated. These minute nodes are arranged in two groups, an **anterior vesical**, in front of the bladder, and a **lateral vesical**, in relation to the lateral umbilical ligament. The vessels from the *posterior* surface pass to the hypogastric, external, and common iliac nodes; those draining the upper part of this surface traverse the lateral vesical nodes.

The **Lymphatic Vessels of the Prostate** (Fig. 674) terminate chiefly in the hypogastric and sacral nodes, but one trunk from the posterior surface ends in the external iliac nodes, and another from the anterior surface joins the vessels which drain the membranous part of the urethra.

Lymphatic Vessels of the Urethra.—The lymphatics of the cavernous portion of the urethra accompany those of the glans penis, and terminate with them in the deep subinguinal and external iliac nodes. Those of the *membranous and prostatic* portions, and those of the whole urethra in the female, pass to the hypogastric nodes.

(4) The **lymphatic vessels of the reproductive organs.**

The **Lymphatic Vessels of the Testes** consist of two sets, superficial and deep, the former commencing on the surface of the tunica vaginalis, the latter in the epididymis and body of the testis. They form from four to eight collecting trunks

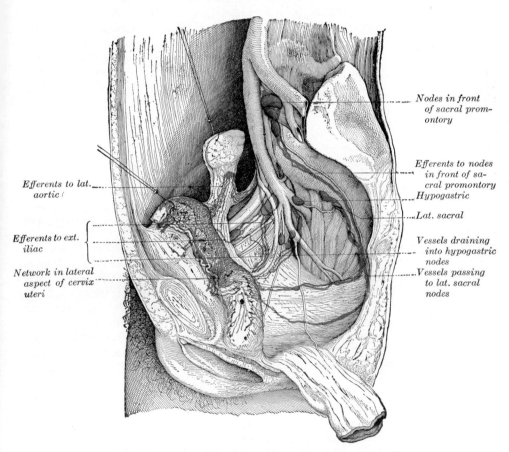

Efferents to lat. aortic

Efferents to ext. iliac

Network in lateral aspect of cervix uteri

Nodes in front of sacral promontory

Efferents to nodes in front of sacral promontory
Hypogastric

Lat. sacral

Vessels draining into hypogastric nodes

Vessels passing to lat. sacral nodes

FIG. 675.—Lymphatics of the uterus. (Cunéo and Marcille.)

which ascend with the spermatic veins in the spermatic cord and along the front of the Psoas major to the level where the spermatic vessels cross the ureter and end in the lateral and preaortic groups of lumbar nodes.

The **Lymphatic Vessels of the Ductus Deferens** pass to the external iliac nodes; those of the **vesiculæ seminales** partly to the hypogastric and partly to the external iliac nodes.

The **Lymphatic Vessels of the Ovary** are similar to those of the testis, and ascend with the ovarian artery to the lateral and preaortic nodes.

The **Lymphatic Vessels of the Uterine Tube** pass partly with those of the ovary and partly with those of the uterus.

The **Lymphatic Vessels of the Uterus** (Fig. 675) consist of two sets, superficial and deep, the former being placed beneath the peritoneum, the latter in the substance of the organ. The lymphatics of the cervix uteri run in three directions: transversely to the external iliac nodes, postero-laterally to the hypogastric nodes, and posteriorly to the common iliac nodes. The majority of the vessels of the body and fundus of the uterus pass lateralward in the broad ligaments, and are continued up with the ovarian vessels to the lateral and preaortic nodes: a few, however, run to the external iliac nodes, and one or two to the superficial inguinal nodes. In the unimpregnated uterus the lymphatic vessels are very small, but during gestation they are greatly enlarged.

The **Lymphatic Vessels of the Vagina** are carried in three directions: those of the upper part of the vagina to the external iliac nodes, those of the middle part to the hypogastric nodes, and those of the lower part to the common iliac glands. On the course of the vessels from the middle and lower parts small nodes are situated. Some lymphatic vessels from the lower part of the vagina join those of the vulva and pass to the superficial inguinal nodes. The lymphatics of the vagina anastomose with those of the cervix uteri, vulva, and rectum, but not with those of the bladder.

The **Lymphatic Vessels of the Omentum** accompany the arteries and veins and are richly supplied with valves.

THE LYMPHATICS OF THE THORAX.

The **lymph nodes of the thorax** may be divided into parietal and visceral—the former being situated in the thoracic wall, the latter in relation to the viscera.

The **parietal lymph nodes** include the **sternal, intercostal,** and **diaphragmatic glands.**

1. The **Sternal Nodes** (*nodi lymphatici sternales*; *internal mammary glands*) are placed at the anterior ends of the intercostal spaces, by the side of the internal mammary artery. They derive afferents from the mamma, from the deeper structures of the anterior abdominal wall above the level of the umbilicus, from the upper surface of the liver through a small group of nodes which lie behind the xiphoid process, and from the deeper parts of the anterior portion of the thoracic wall. Their efferents usually unite to form a single trunk on either side; this may open directly into the junction of the internal jugular and subclavian veins, or that of the right side may join the right subclavian trunk, and that of the left the thoracic duct.

2. The **Intercostal Nodes** (*nodi lymphatici intercostales*) occupy the posterior parts of the intercostal spaces, in relation to the intercostal vessels. They receive the deep lymphatics from the postero-lateral aspect of the chest; some of these vessels are interrupted by small lateral intercostal nodes. The efferents of the nodes in the lower four or five spaces unite to form a trunk, which descends and opens either into the cisterna chyli or into the commencement of the thoracic duct. The efferents of the nodes in the upper spaces of the left side end in the thoracic duct; those of the corresponding right spaces, in the right lymphatic duct.

3. The **Diaphragmatic Nodes** lie on the thoracic aspect of the diaphragm, and consist of three sets, anterior, middle, and posterior.

The **anterior set** comprises (*a*) two or three small nodes behind the base of the xiphoid process, which receive afferents from the convex surface of the liver, and (*b*) one or two nodes on either side near the junction of the seventh rib with its cartilage, which receive lymphatic vessels from the front part of the diaphragm. The efferent vessels of the anterior set pass to the sternal nodes.

The **middle set** consists of two or three nodes on either side close to where the phrenic nerves enter the diaphragm. On the right side some of the nodes of this group lie within the fibrous sac of the pericardium, on the front of the termination of the inferior vena cava. The afferents of this set are derived from the middle part of the diaphragm, those on the right side also receiving afferents from the convex surface of the liver. Their efferents pass to the posterior mediastinal nodes.

The **posterior set** consists of a few glands situated on the back of the crura of the diaphragm, and connected on the one hand with the lumbar nodes and on the other with the posterior mediastinal nodes.

The **superficial lymphatic vessels of the thoracic wall** ramify beneath the skin and converge to the axillary nodes. Those over the Trapezius and Latissimus dorsi run forward and unite to form about ten or twelve trunks which end in the subscapular group. Those over the pectoral region, including the vessels from the skin covering the peripheral part of the mamma, run backward, and those over the Serratus anterior upward, to the pectoral group. Others near the lateral margin of the sternum pass inward between the rib cartilages and end in the sternal nodes, while the vessels of opposite sides anastomose across the front of the sternum. A few vessels from the upper part of the pectoral region ascend over the clavicle to the supraclavicular group of cervical nodes.

The **Lymphatic Vessels of the Mamma** originate in a plexus in the interlobular spaces and on the walls of the galactophorous ducts. Those from the central part of the gland pass to an intricate plexus situated beneath the areola, a plexus which receives also the lymphatics from the skin over the central part of the gland and those from the areola and nipple. Its efferents are collected into two trunks which pass to the pectoral group of axillary nodes. The vessels which drain the medial part of the mamma pierce the thoracic wall and end in the sternal nodes, while a vessel has occasionally been seen to emerge from the upper part of the mamma and, piercing the Pectoralis major, terminate in the subclavicular nodes (Fig. 662).

The **deep lymphatic vessels of the thoracic wall** (Fig. 676) consist of:

1. The lymphatics of the muscles which lie on the ribs: most of these end in the axillary nodes, but some from the Pectoralis major pass to the sternal nodes.
2. The intercostal vessels which drain the Intercostales and parietal pleura. Those draining the Intercostales externi run backward and, after receiving the vessels which accompany the posterior branches of the intercostal arteries, end in the intercostal nodes. Those of the Intercostales interni and parietal pleura consist of a single trunk in each space. These trunks run forward in the subpleural tissue and the upper six open separately into the sternal nodes or into the vessels which unite them; those of the lower spaces unite to form a single trunk which terminates in the lowest of the sternal nodes. 3. The **lymphatic vessels of the diaphragm,** which form two plexuses, one on its thoracic and another on its abdominal surface. These plexuses anastomose freely with each other, and are best marked on the parts covered respectively by the pleuræ and peritoneum. That on the thoracic surface communicates with the lymphatics of the costal and mediastinal parts of the pleura, and its efferents consist of three groups: (*a*) anterior, passing to the nodes which lie near the junction of the seventh rib with its cartilage; (*b*) middle, to the nodes on the esophagus and to those around the termination of the inferior vena cava; and (*c*) posterior, to the nodes which surround the aorta at the point where this vessel leaves the thoracic cavity.

The plexus on the abdominal surface is composed of fine vessels, and anastomoses with the lymphatics of the liver and, at the periphery of the diaphragm, with those of the subperitoneal tissue. The efferents from the right half of this plexus terminate partly in a group of nodes on the trunk of the corresponding inferior phrenic artery, while others end in the right lateral aortic nodes. Those from the left half of the plexus pass to the pre- and lateral aortic nodes and to the glands on the terminal portion of the esophagus.

The **visceral lymph nodes** consist of three groups, *viz.:* **anterior mediastinal, posterior mediastinal,** and **tracheobronchial.**

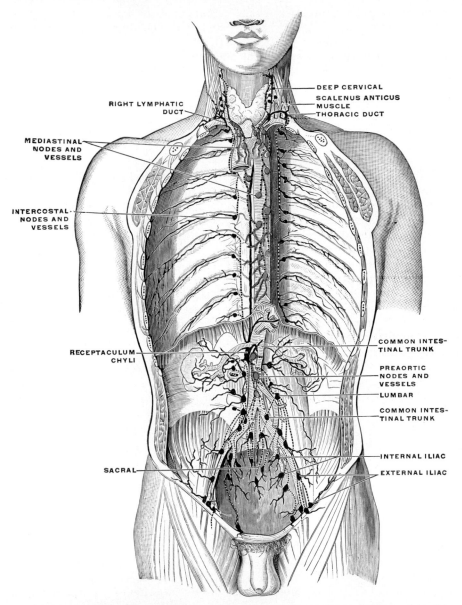

FIG. 676.—Deep lymph nodes and vessels of the thorax and abdomen (diagrammatic). Afferent vessels are represented by continuous lines, and efferent and internodular vessels by dotted lines. (Cunningham.)

The **Anterior Mediastinal Nodes** (*nodi lymphatici mediastinales anteriores*) are placed in the anterior part of the superior mediastinal cavity, in front of the aortic arch and in relation to the innominate veins and the large arterial trunks which arise from the aortic arch. They receive afferents from the thymus and pericardium, and from the sternal nodes; their efferents unite with those of the tracheo-bronchial nodes, to form the right and left bronchomediastinal trunks.

The **Posterior Mediastinal Nodes** (*nodi lymphatici mediastinales posteriores*) lie behind the pericardium in relation to the esophagus and descending thoracic aorta. Their afferents are derived from the esophagus, the posterior part of the pericardium, the diaphragm, and the convex surface of the liver. Their efferents mostly end in the thoracic duct, but some join the tracheobronchial nodes.

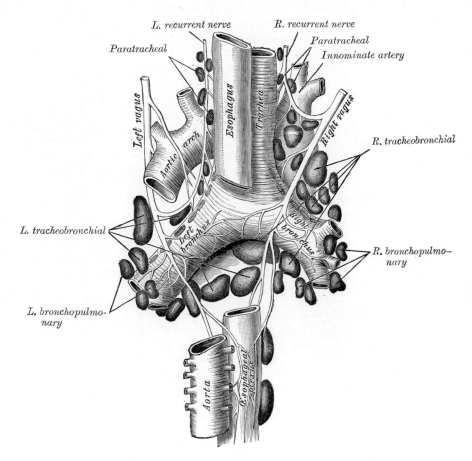

FIG. 677.—The tracheobronchial lymph nodes. (From a figure designed by M. Hallé.)

The **Tracheobronchial Nodes** (Fig. 677) form four main groups: (*a*) **tracheal,** on either side of the trachea; (*b*) **bronchial,** in the angles between the lower part of the trachea and bronchi and in the angle between the two bronchi; (*c*) **broncho-pulmonary,** in the hilum of each lung; and (*d*) **pulmonary,** in the lung substance, on the larger branches of the bronchi. The afferents of the tracheobronchial nodes drain the lungs and bronchi, the thoracic part of the trachea and the heart; some of the efferents of the posterior mediastinal nodes also end in this group. Their efferent vessels ascend upon the trachea and unite with efferents of the internal mammary and anterior mediastinal nodes to form the **right** and **left broncho-mediastinal trunks.** The right bronchomediastinal trunk may join the right lymphatic duct, and the left the thoracic duct, but more frequently they open independently of these ducts into the junction of the internal jugular and subclavian veins of their own side.

In all town dwellers there are continually being swept into these nodes from the bronchi and alveoli large quantities of the dust and black carbonaceous pigment that are so freely inhaled in cities. At first the nodes are moderately enlarged, firm, inky black, and gritty on section; later they enlarge still further, often becoming fibrous from the irritation set up by the minute foreign bodies with which they are crammed, and may break down into a soft slimy mass or may calcify.

The **lymphatic vessels of the thoracic viscera** comprise those of the **heart** and **pericardium**, **lungs** and **pleura**, **thymus**, and **esophagus**.

The **Lymphatic Vessels of the Heart** consist of two plexuses: (*a*) deep, immediately under the endocardium; and (*b*) superficial, subjacent to the visceral pericardium. The deep plexus opens into the superficial, the efferents of which form right and left collecting trunks. The **left trunks,** two or three in number, ascend in the anterior longitudinal sulcus, receiving, in their course, vessels from both ventricles. On reaching the coronary sulcus they are joined by a large trunk from the diaphragmatic surface of the heart, and then unite to form a single vessel which ascends between the pulmonary artery and the left atrium and ends in one of the tracheobronchial nodes. The **right trunk** receives its afferents from the right atrium and from the right border and diaphragmatic surface of the right ventricle. It ascends in the posterior longitudinal sulcus and then runs forward in the coronary sulcus, and passes up behind the pulmonary artery, to end in one of the tracheobronchial nodes.

The **Lymphatic Vessels of the Lungs** originate in two plexuses, a superficial and a deep. The superficial plexus is placed beneath the pulmonary pleura. The deep accompanies the branches of the pulmonary vessels and the ramifications of the bronchi. In the case of the larger bronchi the deep plexus consists of two net-works —one, submucous, beneath the mucous membrane, and another, peribronchial, outside the walls of the bronchi. In the smaller bronchi there is but a single plexus, which extends as far as the bronchioles, but fails to reach the alveoli, in the walls of which there are no traces of lymphatic vessels. The superficial efferents turn around the borders of the lungs and the margins of their fissures, and converge to end in some nodes situated at the hilum; the deep efferents are conducted to the hilum along the pulmonary vessels and bronchi, and end in the tracheobronchial nodes. Little or no anastomosis occurs between the superficial and deep lymphatics of the lungs, except in the region of the hilum.

The **Lymphatic Vessels of the Pleura** consist of two sets—one in the visceral and another in the parietal part of the membrane. Those of the visceral pleura drain into the superficial efferents of the lung, while the lymphatics of the parietal pleura have three modes of ending, viz.: (*a*) those of the costal portion join the lymphatics of the Intercostales interni and so reach the sternal glands; (*b*) those of the diaphragmatic part are drained by the efferents of the diaphragm; while (*c*) those of the mediastinal portion terminate in the posterior mediastinal nodes.

The **Lymphatic Vessels of the Thymus** end in the anterior mediastinal, tracheobronchial, and sternal nodes.

The **Lymphatic Vessels of the Esophagus** form a plexus around that tube, and the collecting vessels from the plexus drain into the posterior mediastinal nodes.

THE SPLEEN (LIEN) (Fig. 678).

The **spleen** is situated principally in the left hypochondriac region, but its superior extremity extends into the epigastric region; it lies between the fundus of the stomach and the diaphragm. It is oblong and flattened, soft, of very friable consistence, highly vascular, and of a dark purplish color. The distinctive function or functions of the spleen are not known. During fetal life and shortly after birth it gives rise to new red blood corpuscles but the evidence that this function is retained in adult life is not satisfactory. It is supposed to be an organ for the destruction of red blood corpuscles and the preparation of new hemoglobin from the iron thus set free.

Development.—The spleen appears about the fifth week as a localized thickening of the mesoderm in the dorsal mesogastrium above the tail of the pancreas. With the change in position of the stomach the spleen is carried to the left, and comes to lie behind the stomach and in contact with the left kidney. The part of the dorsal mesogastrium which intervened between the spleen and the greater curvature of the stomach forms the gastrosplenic ligament.

Relations.—The **diaphragmatic surface** (*facies diaphragmatica; external or phrenic surface*) is convex, smooth, and is directed upward, backward, and to the left, except at its upper end, where it is directed slightly medialward. It is in relation with the under surface of the diaphragm, which separates it from the ninth, tenth, and eleventh ribs of the left side, and the intervening lower border of the left lung and pleura.

The **visceral surface** (Fig. 678) is divided by a ridge into an **anterior or gastric** and a **posterior** or **renal portion.**

The **gastric surface** (*facies gastrica*), which is directed forward, upward, and medialward, is broad and concave, and is in contact with the posterior wall of the stomach; and below this with the tail of the pancreas. It presents near its medial border a long fissure, or more frequently a series of depressions termed the **hilum.** This is pierced by several irregular apertures, for the entrance and exit of vessels and nerves.

The **renal surface** (*facies renalis*) is directed medialward and downward. It is somewhat flattened, is considerably narrower than the gastric surface, and is in relation with the upper part of the anterior surface of the left kidney and occasionally with the left suprarenal gland.

The **superior extremity** (*extremitas posterior*) is directed toward the vertebral column, where it lies on a level with the eleventh thoracic vertebra. The **lower extremity** or **colic surface** (*extremitas anterior*) is flat, triangular in shape, and rests upon the left flexure of the colon and the phrenicocolic ligament, and is generally in contact with the tail of the pancreas. The **anterior border** (*margo anterior*) is free, sharp, and thin, and is often notched, especially below; it separates the diaphragmatic from the gastric surface. The **posterior border** (*margo posterior*), more rounded and blunter than the anterior, separates the renal from the diaphragmatic surface; it corresponds to the lower border of the eleventh rib and lies between the diaphragm and left kidney. The intermediate margin is the ridge which separates the renal and gastric surfaces. The **inferior border** (*internal border*) separates the diaphragmatic from the colic surface.

The spleen is almost entirely surrounded by peritoneum, which is firmly adherent to its capsule. It is held in position by two folds of this membrane. One, the **phrenicolienal ligament,** is derived from the peritoneum, where the wall of the general peritoneal cavity comes into contact with the omental bursa between the left kidney and the spleen; the lienal vessels pass between its two layers. The other fold, the **gastrolienal ligament,** is also formed of two layers, derived from the general cavity and the omental respectively, where they meet between the spleen and stomach; the short gastric and left gastroepiploic branches of the lienal artery run between its two layers. The lower end of the spleen is supported by the phrenicocolic ligament.

The size and weight of the spleen are liable to very extreme variations at different periods of life, in different individuals, and in the same individual under different conditions. *In the adult* it is usually about 12 cm. in length, 7 cm. in breadth, and 3 or 4 cm. in thickness. The spleen increases in weight from 17 grams or less during the first year to 170 grams at twenty years, and then slowly decreases to 122 grams at seventy-six to eighty years. Male spleens weigh more than female ones and spleens from whites weigh more than those from negroes. Variations of weight of adult spleens are 100 to 250 grams, and in extreme cases, 50 to 400 grams. The size of the spleen is increased during and after digestion, and varies according to the state of nutrition of the body, being large in highly fed, and small in starved animals. In malarial fever it becomes much enlarged, weighing occasionally as much as 9 kilos.

Frequently in the neighborhood of the spleen, and especially in the gastrolienal ligament and greater omentum, small nodules of splenic tissue may be found, either isolated or connected to the spleen by thin bands of splenic tissue. They are known as **accessory spleens** (*lien accessorius; supernumerary spleen*). They vary in size from that of a pea to that of a plum.

Structure.—The spleen is invested by two coats: an **external serous** and an **internal fibroelastic coat**.

The **external** or **serous coat** (*tunica serosa*) is derived from the peritoneum; it is thin, smooth, and in the human subject intimately adherent to the fibroelastic coat. It invests the entire organ, except at the hilum and along the lines of reflection of the phrenicolienal and gastrolienal ligaments.

The **fibroelastic coat** (*tunica albuginea*) invests the organ, and at the hilum is reflected inward upon the vessels in the form of sheaths. From these sheaths, as well as from the inner surface of the fibroelastic coat, numerous small fibrous bands, **trabeculæ** (Fig. 679), are given off in all directions; these uniting, constitute the frame-work of the spleen. The spleen therefore consists

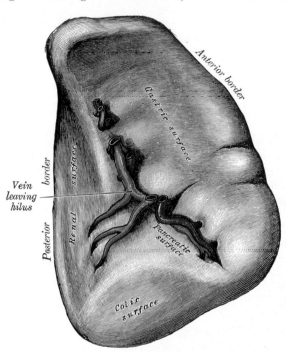

Fig. 678.—The visceral surface of the spleen.

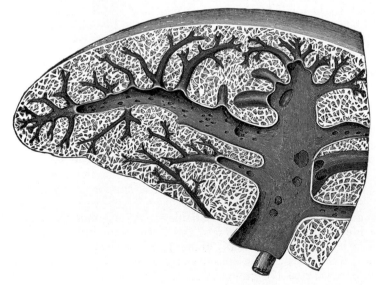

Fig. 679.—Transverse section of the spleen, showing the trabecular tissue and the splenic vein and its tributaries.

of a number of small spaces or **areolæ**, formed by the trabeculæ; in these areolæ is contained the **splenic pulp.**

The fibroelastic coat, the sheaths of the vessels, and the trabeculæ, are composed of white and yellow elastic fibrous tissues, the latter predominating. It is owing to the presence of the elastic tissue that the spleen possesses a considerable amount of elasticity, which allows of the very great variations in size that it presents under certain circumstances. In addition to these constituents of this tunic, there is found in man a small amount of non-striped muscular fiber; and in some mammalia, e. g., dog, pig, and cat, a large amount, so that the trabeculæ appear to consist chiefly of muscular tissue.

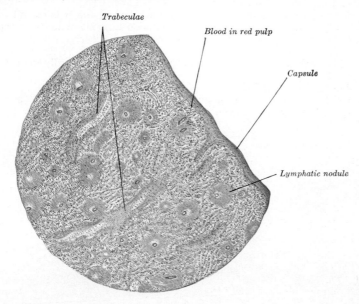

Trabeculae

Blood in red pulp

Capsule

Lymphatic nodule

Fig. 680.—A section through a portion of the human spleen, stained with hematoxylin and eosin. × 15. (After Sobotta).

The **splenic pulp** (*pulpa lienis*) is a soft mass of a dark reddish-brown color, resembling grumous blood; it consists of a fine reticulum of fibers, continuous with those of the trabeculæ, to which are applied flat, branching cells. The meshes of the reticulum are filled with blood, and many lymphocytes, polymorphonuclear neutrophiles, and monocytes or macrophages. The latter are often large and contain ingested and partly digested red blood cells and pigment. In the young spleen, giant cells may also be found, each containing numerous nuclei or one compound nucleus. Nucleated red-blood corpuscles have also been found in the spleen of young animals.

Blood vessels of the Spleen.—The **splenic artery** is remarkable for its large size in proportion to the size of the organ, and also for its tortuous course. It divides into six or more branches, which enter the hilum of the spleen and ramify throughout its substance (Fig. 680), receiving sheaths from an involution of the external fibrous tissue. Similar sheaths also invest the nerves and veins. Each of the larger branches of the artery supplies chiefly that region of the organ in which the branch ramifies, having no anastomosis with the majority of the other branches.

Each branch runs in the transverse axis of the organ, from within outward, diminishing in size during its transit, and giving off in its passage smaller branches, some of which pass to the anterior, others to the posterior part. These ultimately leave the trabecular sheaths, and terminate in the proper substance of the spleen in small tufts or pencils of minute arterioles.

Some authors claim that the arterioles are connected with venules by capillaries and that they have a complete endothelial lining. Most authors, however, maintain that the endothelial connections are incomplete. In this open type of circulation the blood moves slowly through the spleen pulp and bathes the reticular network of the sinuses. The flow through the pulp is controlled by rhythmic contractions and relaxations of smooth muscles in the trabeculæ and capsule and by intermittent constriction and relaxation of individual arterioles and groups of them.

The altered coat of the arterioles, consisting of lymphoid tissue, presents here and there thickenings of a spheroidal shape, the **lymphatic nodules** (*Malpighian bodies of the spleen*). These bodies vary in size from about 0.25 mm. to 1 mm. in diameter. They are merely local expansions or hyperplasiæ of the lymphoid tissue, of which the external coat of the smaller arteries of the spleen is formed. They are most frequently found surrounding the arteriole, which thus seems to tunnel them, but occasionally they grow from one side of the vessel only, and present the appearance of a sessile bud growing from the arterial wall. In transverse sections, the artery, in the majority of cases, is found in an eccentric position. These bodies are visible to the naked eye on the surface of a fresh section of the organ, appearing as minute dots of a semiopaque whitish color in the dark substance of the pulp. In minute structure they resemble the lymphoid tissue of lymph nodes, consisting of a delicate reticulum, in the meshes of which lie ordinary lymphocytes (Fig. 680). The reticulum is made up of extremely fine fibrils, and is comparatively open in the center of the corpuscle, becoming closer at its periphery. The cells which it encloses are possessed of ameboid movement. When treated with carmine they become deeply stained, and can be easily distinguished from those of the pulp.

The smaller veins unite to form larger ones; these do not accompany the arteries, but soon enter the trabecular sheaths of the capsule, and by their junction form six or more branches, which emerge from the hilum, and, uniting, constitute the lienal vein, the largest radicle of the portal vein.

The **veins** are remarkable for their numerous anastomoses, while the arteries hardly anastomose at all.

The **lymphatics** are described on page 805.

The **nerves** are derived from the celiac plexus and are chiefly non-medullated. They are distributed to the bloodvessels and to the smooth muscle of the capsule and trabeculæ.

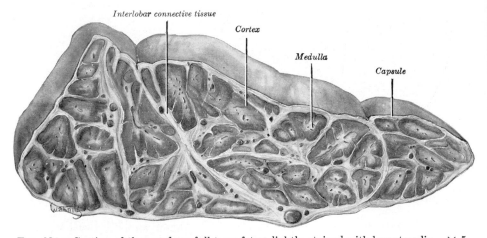

Interlobar connective tissue   *Cortex*   *Medulla*   *Capsule*

FIG. 681.—Section of thymus from full term fetus, lightly stained with hematoxylin. × 5.

THE THYMUS (Fig. 683).

The thymus of an infant is a prominent organ occupying the upper anterior part of the thorax, but the thymus in an adult of advanced years may be scarcely recognizable because of atrophic changes. During its growth period, it has much of the appearance and texture of a gland, and previously it has been classified as one of the ductless glands, but no glandular function has been established. It is included here among the lymphatic organs because it resembles them structurally in being composed largely of lymphocytes and because its only known function is that of producing lymphocytes.

Development.—The thymus appears in the form of two flask-shaped entodermal diverticula, which arise, one on either side, from the third branchial pouch (Fig. 1163), and extend lateralward and backward into the surrounding mesoderm in front of the ventral aortæ. Here they meet and become joined to one another by connective tissue, but there is never any fusion of the thymus tissue proper. The pharyngeal opening of each diverticulum is soon obliterated, but the neck of the flask persists for some time as a cellular cord. By further proliferation of the cells, buds are formed which become elongated and greatly branched, lose their epithelial character, and become the cellular reticulum which forms the core of the lobules. The lobules remain separated from each other by loose connective tissue and the

umerous small lymphocytes which make their appearance probably wander in
rom the surrounding mesenchyme.   As the lobules increase in size, there is a
differentiation into a peripheral zone or cortex in which the small lymphocytes
re concentrated, and a central medulla in which the cellular reticulum predom-
nates.   The thymus attains a weight of 12 to 14 grams before birth, but it does
ot reach its greatest relative size until the age of two years.   It continues to grow
until puberty, at which time it reaches its greatest absolute size, weighing about
5 grams.

Anatomy.—The thymus consists of two lateral lobes held in close contact by
connective tissue which also encloses the whole organ in a distinct capsule.   It is
situated partly in the thorax and partly in the neck, extending from the fourth
costal cartilage to the lower border of the thyroid gland.   In the neck it lies on the
front and sides of the trachea, deep to the origins of the Sternohyoidei and Sterno-
thyroidei.   In the thorax it occupies the anterior portion of the superior mediastinum

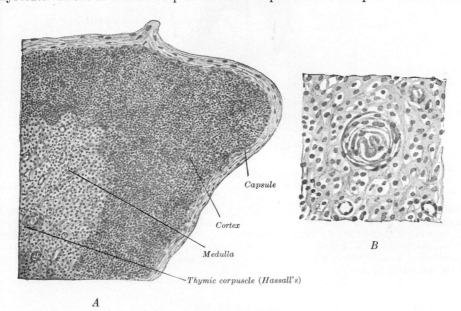

Capsule

Cortex

B

Medulla

Thymic corpuscle (Hassall's)

A

FIG. 682.—*A.* A section through a portion of the thymus of a kitten. $\times$ 120. *B.* A concentric
corpuscle of Hassall. $\times$ 350. Stained with hematoxylin and eosin.

(Fig. 984, page 1194); superficial to it is the sternum, and deep to it are the great
vessels and the upper part of the fibrous pericardium.   The two lobes generally
differ in size and shape, the right frequently overlapping the left. It is of a pinkish
gray color, soft and lobulated, measuring approximately 5 cm. in length, 4 cm. in
width, and 6 mm. in thickness.

Structure.—The two lobes are composed of numerous lobules, varying from 0.5 to 2 mm. in
diameter, separated from each other by delicate connective tissue, and visible with the unaided
eye.   With low magnification, two zones of tissue can be seen within each lobule, an outer cortex
and an inner medulla.   The cortical part is made up almost entirely of s. all lymphocytes, held in
place by reticular tissue composed of reticular (argyrophilic) fibers with relatively few reticular
cells.   The medullary portion contains much fewer lymphocytes, its reticulum is more cellular,
and it contains the characteristic thymic or Hassall's corpuscles.   These corpuscles are from
0.03 to 0.1 mm. in diameter; they have a central core of granular cells surrounded by concentric
lamellæ of epithelioid cells.   Although the lobules appear to be distinct from one another when
viewed in a cross section, it has been found by careful study that the medullary tissue forms a
continuous system of central stalks and branching cords.

Involution.—After puberty the thymus undergoes involution.   Usually this is a gradual process
called age involution, but it may be superseded by a rapid accidental involution due to starva-

tion or acute disease. The small lymphocytes of the cortex disappear and the reticular tissue becomes compressed. The disappearing thymic tissue is likely to be replaced by adipose tissue but the connective tissue capsule may persist, retaining its original shape and approximate size so that, in an older individual, what appears to be a yellowish colored thymus, when sectioned will reveal only small islands of thymic tissue surrounded by fat.

Function.—No function of the thymus is known except that of producing small lymphocytes and possibly plasma cells. The association of the growth of the organ with the growth of the individual and its involution after sexual maturity have made many investigators attempt to discover some endocrine function, but definite confirmation of claims along these lines is lacking except that its involution and regeneration may be influenced by known endocrine factors.

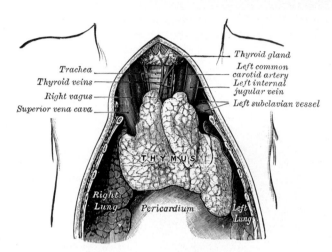

Thyroid gland
Left common carotid artery
Left internal jugular vein
Left subclavian vessel

Trachea
Thyroid veins
Right vagus
Superior vena cava

THYMUS

Right Lung   Pericardium   Left Lung

Fig. 683.—The thymus of a full-term fetus; exposed *in situ*.

Vessels and Nerves.—The **arteries** supplying the thymus are derived from the internal mammary, and from the superior and inferior thyroids. The **veins** end in the left innominate vein, and in the thyroid veins. The **lymphatics** end in the anterior mediastinal, tracheobronchial and sternal nodes. The **nerves** are exceedingly minute; they are derived from the vagi and sympathetic. Branches from the descendens hypoglossi and phrenic reach the investing capsule, but do not penetrate into the substance of the gland.

REFERENCES

EMBRYOLOGY

HAMMOND, S. 1954. Origin of thymus in the chicken embryo. J. Morph., 95, 501–522.
HOLYOKE, E. A. 1936. The role of the primitive mesothelium in the development of the mammalian spleen. Anat. Rec., 65, 333–350.
HUNTINGTON, G. S. 1911. The anatomy and development of the systemic lymphatic vessels in the domestic cat. American Anatomical Memoir No. 1, Wistar Institute of Anatomy and Biology, Philadelphia, 175 pages.
KAMPMEIER, O. F. 1928. The genetic history of the valves in the lymphatic system of man. Amer. J. Anat., 40, 413–458.
LEWIS, F. T. 1909. On the cervical veins and lymphatics in four human embryos, with interpretation of anomalies of the subclavian and jugular veins in the adult. Amer. J. Anat., 9, 33-42.
SABIN, F. R. 1916. The origin and development of the lymphatic system. Johns Hopk. Hosp. Rep., 17, 347–440.

LYMPH AND LYMPHOCYTES

BIERMAN, H. R., R. L. BYRON, JR., K. H. KELLY, R. S. GILFILLAN, L. P. WHITE, N. E. FREEMAN, and N. K. PETRAKIS. 1953. The characteristics of thoracic duct lymph in man. J. clin. Invest., 32, 637–649.
FICHTELIUS, K. E. 1953. On the fate of the lymphocyte. Acta anat. Suppl., 19, 1–78.
FICHTELIUS, K. E. 1958. A difference between lymph nodal and thymic lymphocytes shown by transfusion of labelled cells. Acta anat., 32, 114–125.

GAMBLE, J. L. 1954. Chemical Anatomy, Physiology and Pathology of Extracellular Fluid. Harvard University Press, Cambridge, Mass., 164 pages.

HALPERN, B. N. 1957. Physiopathology of the Reticulo-Endothelial System. A Symposium. Charles C Thomas, Publisher, Springfield. xii + 317 pages.

ROBINSON, D. S. 1955. The chemical composition of chylomicra in the rat. Quart. J. exp. Physiol., *40*, 112–126.

SHREWSBURY, M. M., JR., and W. O. REINHARDT. 1955. Relationships of adrenals, gonads, and thyroid to thymus and lymph nodes, and to blood and thoracic duct leucocytes. Blood, *10*, 633–645.

SIMMONDS, W. J. 1955. The intestinal absorption of fat, fatty acid and fat soluble dye into thoracic duct lymph in unanaesthetized rats. Aust. J. exp. Biol. med. Sci., *33*, 25–32.

LYMPHATIC VESSELS AND DRAINAGE

ALLEN, L. 1943. The lymphatics of the parietal tunica vaginalis propria of man. Anat. Rec., *85*, 427–433.

ALLEN, L. 1956. On the penetrability of the lymphatics of the diaphragm. Anat. Rec., *124*, 639–658.

BLAIR, J. B., E. A. HOLYOKE and R. R. BEST. 1950. A note on the lymphatics of the middle and lower rectum and anus. Anat. Rec., *108*, 635-644.

BUTLER, H. and K. BALANKURA. 1952. Preaortic thoracic duct and azygos vein. Anat. Rec., *113*, 409–420.

CLARK, E. R. and E. L. CLARK. 1937. Observations on isolated lymphatic capillaries in the living mammal. Amer. J. Anat., *62*, 59–92.

COURTICE, F. C. and W. J. SIMMONDS. 1954. Physiological significance of lymph drainage of the serous cavities and lungs. Physiol. Rev., *34*, 419–448.

DIXON, F. W. and N. L. HOERR. 1944. Lymphatic drainage of paranasal sinuses. Laryngoscope, *54*, 165–175.

PATEK, P. R. 1939. The morphology of the lymphatics of the mammalian heart. Amer. J. Anat., *64*, 203–249.

PIERCE, E. C. 1944. Renal lymphatics. Anat. Rec., *90*, 315–335.

RÉNYI-VÁMOS, F. and GY. SZINAY. 1958. Das Lymphgefässystem des Coecums. Acta anat., *34*, 124–130.

RODRIGUEZ, A. L. and J. M. GENIS-GALVEZ. 1957. Variété du "ductus thoracicus" non décrite chez l'homme: canal thoracique traversant l'anse de Vieussens. Acta anat., *31*, 61–65.

ROUVIÈRE, H. Anatomy of the Lymphatic System. Trans. by M. J. Tobias. Edwards Bros., Ann. Arbor, ix + 318 pages.

YOFFEY, J. M. and F. C. COURTICE. 1956. Lymphatics, Lymph and Lymphoid Tissue. For the Commonwealth Fund by Harvard University Press, Cambridge, Mass. vii + 510 pages.

LYMPH NODES

BAILLIF, R. N. 1951. Lymph node changes following repeated injections of acid coloidal substance in the albino rat. Amer. J. Anat., *88*, 109–162.

BAKER, B. L., D. J. INGLE and C. R. LI. 1951. The histology of the lymphoid organs of rats treated with adrenocorticotropin. Amer. J. Anat., *88*, 313–350.

FURUTA, W. J. 1948. The histologic structure of the lymph node capsule at the hilum. Anat. Rec., *102*, 213–224.

OSOGOE, B. and K. AWAYA. 1956. Formation of lymphoid aggregations in the bone marrow of saponin poisoned rabbits following lymphocyte transfusion. Anat. Rec., *125*, 121–132.

REINHARDT, W. O. 1946. Growth of lymph nodes, thymus, and spleen, and output of thoracic duct lymphocytes in the normal rat. Anat. Rec., *94*, 197–211.

SPLEEN

BAILLIF, R. N. 1953. Splenic reactions to colloidal thorium dioxide in the albino rat. Amer. J. Anat., *92*, 55–116.

KNISELY, M. H. 1936. Microscopic observations of the circulatory system of living traumatized spleens, and of dying spleens. Anat. Rec., *65*, 131–148.

KRUMBHAAR, E. B. and S. W. LIPPINCOTT. 1939. Postmortem weight of "normal" human spleen at different ages. Amer. J. med. Sci., *197*, 344–358.

MACKENZIE, D. W., JR., A. A. WHIPPLE and M. P. WINTERSTEINER. 1942. Studies on the microscopic anatomy and physiology of living transilluminated mammalian spleens. Amer. J. Anat., *68*, 397–456.

MICHELS, N. A. 1942. The variational anatomy of the spleen and splenic artery. Amer. J. Anat., *70*, 21–72.

PECK, H. M. and N. L. HOERR. 1951. The intermediary circulation in the red pulp of the mouse spleen. Anat. Rec., *109*, 447–478.

PECK, H. M. and N. L. HOERR. 1951. The effect of environmental temperature changes on the circulation of the mouse spleen. Anat. Rec., *109*, 479–494.

SNOOK, T. 1950. A comparative study of the vascular arrangements in mammalian spleens. Amer. J. Anat., *87*, 31–78.

THYMUS

BELL, R. H., B. I. KNAPP, B. J. ANSON and S. J. LARSON. 1954. Form, size, blood-supply and relations of the adult thymus. Quarterly Bulletin, Northw. Univ. med. Sch., Chicago, *28*, 156–164.

GRÈGOIRE, C. 1943. Regeneration of the involuted thymus after adrenalectomy. J. Morph., *72*, 239–261.

KARASAWA, K. 1954. Changes in the amount of myelocytes in the thymus during its accidental involution in young rabbits. Folia anat. jap., *26*, 377–385.

KINGSBURY, B. F. 1928. On the nature and significance of the thymic corpuscles (of Hassall). Anat. Rec., *38*, 141–160.

NORRIS, E. H. 1938. The morphogenesis and histogenesis of the thymus gland in man. Contr. Embryol. Carneg. Instn., *27*, 191–207.

SMITH, C. and H. T. PARKHURST. 1949. Studies on the thymus of the mammal. II. A comparison of the staining properties of Hassall's corpuscles and of thick skin of the guinea pig. Anat. Rec., *103*, 649–674.

THE NERVOUS SYSTEM.

THE nervous system is an extensive and complicated organization of structures by which the internal reactions of the individual are correlated and integrated and by which his adjustments with his environment are controlled. It is separated arbitrarily, for convenience in description, into two large divisions, the central nervous system and the peripheral nervous system.

The central nervous system, the subject of this chapter, is composed of the brain and spinal cord.

The peripheral nervous system is composed of the nerves, ganglia, and end organs which connect the central nervous system with all the other parts of the body. It is the subject of the next two chapters; the first deals with the peripheral nervous system proper and the second with the specialized sense organs.

DEVELOPMENT OF THE NERVOUS SYSTEM

The earliest stages of development of the nervous system are included in Chapter One and that account may be used as a background for the following description.

The entire nervous system is of ectodermal origin. Its first rudiment is the **neural plate** with its folds and **neural groove** which extend along the axis of the embryo (Fig. 12). The rostral part of the plate is broad and forms the brain. The narrow caudal part forms the spinal cord. The **neural folds** curl dorsally until their prominent edges meet and fuse in the midline to form the **neural tube** (Fig. 14). The cavity of the tube is retained in the ventricles of the brain and the central canal of the spinal cord. Certain of the malformations of the nervous system can be traced to this very early stage of development. If the neural groove fails to close, or having closed, fails to be separated completely from the overlying ectoderm, the development of the supporting bones is also abnormal and the condition known as spina bifida results. (Duncan '57).

After formation of the neural tube further development occurs by mitotic division in and near the layer of cells lining the central cavity, the medullary epithelium. All of the elements in the central nervous system except the microglia, meninges, and blood vessels are derived from this source. The primitive neural tube has three layers (Fig. 685): 1) The **ependymal layer** lines the lumen and becomes the ependyma of the adult nervous system. The processes of its cells extend out toward the periphery, acting as supporting elements. 2) **The mantle layer** is the middle bulky cellular portion of the tube and contains (*a*) the **germinal cells** whose proliferation provides the neuroblasts which develop into the nerve cells of the central gray substance and (*b*) **spongioblasts** which develop into the supporting elements or neuroglia (Fig. 684). 3) The **marginal layer** is not cellular and becomes the outer white substance when the fibers grow out from the mantle layer and accumulate at the periphery.

Development of the Spinal Cord.—As the lateral walls of the neural tube increase in thickness, the germinal cells remain near the ependyma. They are round or oval cells and many of the nuclei can be seen in stages of mitotic division in slide preparations. The daughter cells, **neuroblasts**, migrate out into the mantle layer and begin their differentiation into young nerve cells. The lumen of the tube becomes altered by the formation of a longitudinal groove, the **sulcus limitans** (Fig. 686,*A*), along the middle portion of each side. The sulcus marks the subdivision of the wall of the tube into a dorsal or alar lamina and a ventral or basal lamina. These laminæ represent an early functional differentiation, the **alar lamina** or **alar plate** becoming the sensory portion of the gray substance and the **basal lamina** or **basal plate** becoming the motor portion in later development (Figs. 685 688).

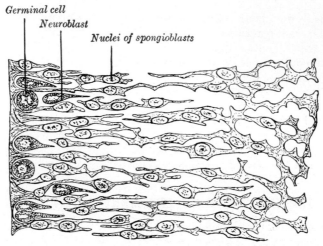

Germinal cell
Neuroblast
Nuclei of spongioblasts

Fig. 684.—Transverse section of the spinal cord of a human embryo at the beginning of the fourth week. The left edge of the figure corresponds to the lining of the central canal. (His.)

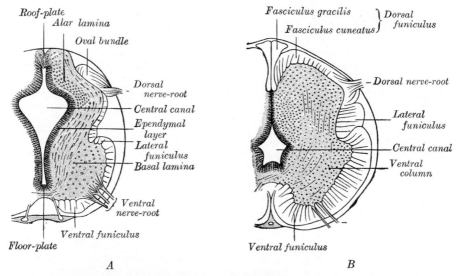

Roof-plate
Alar lamina
Oval bundle
Dorsal nerve-root
Central canal
Ependymal layer
Lateral funiculus
Basal lamina
Ventral nerve-root
Ventral funiculus
Floor-plate

A

Fasciculus gracilis ⎱ *Dorsal*
Fasciculus cuneatus ⎰ *funiculus*
Dorsal nerve-root
Lateral funiculus
Central canal
Ventral column
Ventral funiculus

B

Fig. 685.—Transverse sections through the spinal cords of human embryos. (His.) *A*, aged about four and half weeks, *B*, aged about three months.

The basal lamina becomes thickened, and in a cross section the mantle layer appears as an expanded zone between the marginal and ependymal layers. This thickening is the rudiment of the ventral gray column or **ventral horn**. Its neuroblasts send their axons out through the marginal layer, forming the ventral roots of the spinal nerves. The alar lamina also thickens gradually, becoming the **dorsal**

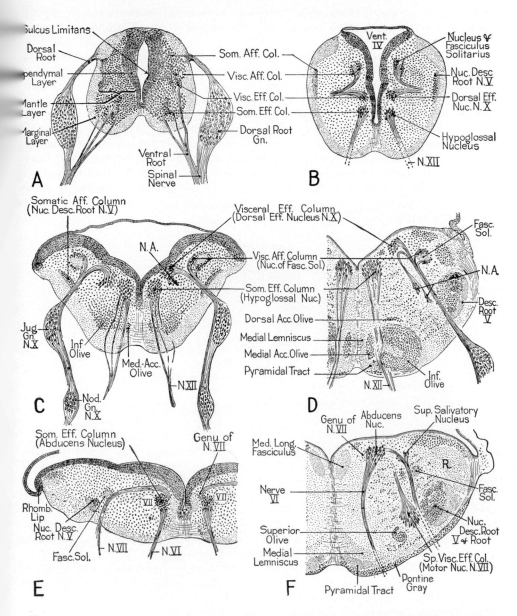

FIG. 686.—Cross-sections of cord and medulla comparing manner of origin of spinal and cranial nerves. *A*, Thoracic cord of 14.8-mm. embryo to show origin of typical spinal nerve. *B*, Lower part of medulla for comparison with cord structure. *C*, Medulla of 15-mm. embryo at level of upper rootlets of nerves X and XII. *D*, Medulla of 73-mm. embryo at level of upper rootlets of nerves X and XII. Compare with C. *E*, Medulla of 15-mm. embryo at level of pons showing the roots of nerves VI and VII. *F*, Medulla of 73-mm. embryo at level of pons showing the roots of nerves VI and VII. Compare with E.

Abbreviations: Acc., accessory; Aff., afferent; Col., column; Desc., descending; Eff., efferent; Fasc. Sol., fasciculus solitarius; Gn., ganglion; Inf., inferior; Jug., jugular; N.A., nucleus ambiguus, note that in the younger stage (*C*) it is not separated from the general afferent column as happens later (*D*). The nucleus ambiguus, since it supplies skeletal muscle of branchiomeric origin rather than smooth muscle, is classified as a *special* visceral efferent nucleus; Nuc., nucleus; R., restiform body; Rhomb., rhombic; Sp., special; Visc., visceral. (Courtesy of B. M. Patten, *Human Embryology*, 2nd. Copyright, 1953. Blakiston Div., McGraw-Hill Book Co.)

horn. Later, the axons of many of its cells grow cephalad to assist in forming the dorsal and lateral funiculi; a few cross to the opposite side, forming the ventral white commissure.

At about the end of the fourth week nerve fibers begin to appear in the marginal layer. The first to develop are the short intersegmental fibers from neuroblasts in the mantle layer. Fibers from the cells in the spinal ganglia grow into the marginal layer and by the sixth week have formed a well-defined oval bundle in the peripheral part of the alar lamina. This bundle gradually increases in size and spreads toward the midline forming the rudiment of the dorsal funiculus. Long intersegmental fibers appear about the third month and corticospinal fibers about the fifth month. The nerve fibers acquire their myelin sheaths at different times somewhat later, the dorsal and ventral roots about the fifth month, the corticospinal after the ninth month. The expanding growth of the ventral horn and ventral funiculus of the two sides cause these parts to bulge out beyond the floor plate, leaving a deep groove, the ventral median fissure.

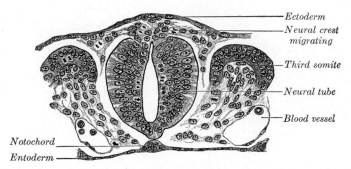

Fig. 687.—Neural crest formation. Transverse section through third somite of 9 somite rat embryo.

Segmentation.—The thickening of the wall of the neural tube is not uniform. At the level of the spinal nerves it is greater than in between, producing a beaded appearance and establishing the **neuromeres** or **segments**. The relative thickness of the segments varies according to the size of the nerves and the bulk of the peripheral field its nerve supplies. Experimental evidence indicates that segmentation in the nervous system is determined to a large extent by that of the mesodermal somites (Ditwiler '36, Chapter 12). In later development the long projection tracts growing into the marginal layer obliterate the segmental appearance.

Up to the third month of fetal life the spinal cord occupies the entire length of the vertebral canal. After this, the canal lengthens more rapidly than the cord. By the sixth month the caudal end of the cord reaches only as far as the upper part of the sacrum, at birth it is on a level with the third lumbar vertebra, and in the adult it lies at the disc between the first and second lumbar vertebra.

The Spinal Nerves.—The outgrowth of axons from neuroblasts in the basal lamina to form the ventral roots has been mentioned. The dorsal roots are formed by the ingrowth of fibers from the spinal ganglion cells.

The Spinal Ganglia.—Before the neural groove is closed into the neural tube of the early embryo, the prominent margin of the neural fold contains a ridge of special cells known as the **ganglionic ridge** or **neural crest** (see Chapter One). When the neural folds meet in the midline, the two ridges fuse along the line of closure (Fig. 687). The cells of the crest proliferate, separate from the neural tube, and migrate out from the narrow space between the ectoderm and neural tube. They gather into groups of cells corresponding to each somite, and become the primitive spinal ganglia. The sensory components of cranial nerves V, VII, IX, and X are developed from the neural crest in the head region (Yntema '44).

The cells of the ganglia are of two kinds, like those of the mantle layer of the cord, neuroblasts and spongioblasts. The **neuroblasts** send out processes both centrally and peripherally. The central ones form the dorsal roots, the peripheral ones join the ventral roots in forming the spinal nerves. Eventually the two processes come from a single stem of the cell which in consequence is called a unipolar cell.

The **spongioblasts** of the ganglion develop into **sheath cells** which not only form capsules around the nerve cell bodies in the ganglion but also migrate out along the nerves to form the **neurilemma** of peripheral nerves. In the peripheral growth of the spinal nerves the axons grow out first as naked protoplasmic processes. The spongioblasts of the ganglion migrate out on these nerve fibers, proliferate by mitosis, and provide *neurilemma* or *Schwann sheath cells* for the peripheral nerves. Later **myelin** develops by the spiral infolding of the surface membrane of the sheath cells of the larger fibers (Geren '54, Harrison '24).

Development of the Brain.—The cephalic portion of the neural tube, even before it is completely closed, enlarges and begins to change its shape (Fig. 15). The unequal growth of the different parts in size and thickness, together with the formation of certain flexures, very early establishes three recognizable regions within the primitive brain: the forebrain, midbrain, and hindbrain (Figs. 20, 689). The first of the flexures to appear is the **ventral cephalic flexure** in the region of the midbrain (Fig. 690). In it, the forebrain makes a U-shaped bend ventrally over the cephalic end of the notochord and foregut causing the midbrain to protrude dorsally as the most prominent

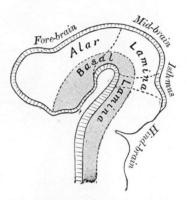

Fig. 688.—Diagram to illustrate the alar and basal laminæ of brain. The dotted line represents the sulcus limitans. (His.)

part of the brain. The second bend, the **cervical flexure**, appears at the junction of the hindbrain and spinal cord, where these two parts form a right angle with each other (Fig. 690). This flexure gradually diminishes as the body posture changes and the head becomes erect and it disappears some time after the fifth week. The third bend is named the **pontine flexure** because it occurs in the region of the future pons (Fig. 692).

The sulcus limitans which has been described as dividing the lateral wall of the spinal cord into alar and basal laminæ is clearly distinguishable extending through the hindbrain (Fig. 688) and midbrain but its termination in the forebrain is not established.

The **Hindbrain** or **Rhombencephalon.**—At the time of appearance of the cephalic flexure, the hindbrain is as long as the other two parts combined. Just caudal to the midbrain, its cavity is constricted into the *isthmus rhombencephali* (Fig. 688). The rest of the hindbrain is divided into a cephalic portion, the **metencephalon**, and a caudal portion, the **myelencephalon**. The metencephalon develops into the cerebellum and pons, the myelencephalon into the medulla oblongata (Fig. 691).

The **medulla oblongata** is at first similar to the spinal cord, with roof plate, floor plate, and side walls of alar and basal laminæ. The roof plate becomes greatly stretched out at an early stage (Fig. 686) but the floor plate holds the side walls together so that they flatten out into a plate-like structure. The sulcus limitans persists but now separates a laterally placed alar lamina from a more medially placed basal lamina. The functional pattern remains similar to the spinal cord with a sensory alar plate, a motor basal plate and with automonic nuclei along the sulcus limitans.

Sensory fibers from the neural crest ganglia of the glossopharyngeal and vagus nerves form a bundle opposite the sulcus limitans. This is the **tractus solitarius** and corresponds to the oval bundle of the primitive spinal cord (Fig. 685). At first it is applied to the outer surface of the alar lamina, but it becomes buried by the overgrowth of neighboring parts. At about five weeks, the part of the alar lamina next to the floor plate bends over laterally, forming the **rhombic lip** (Fig. 686E;

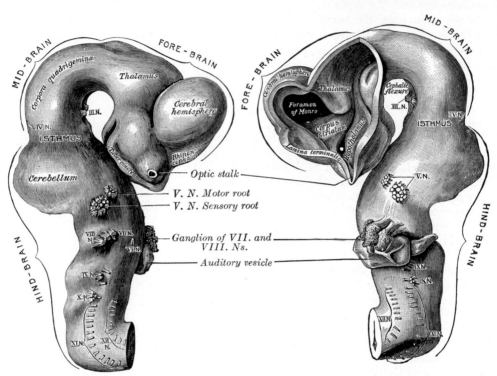

FIG. 689.—Exterior of brain of human embryo of four and a half weeks. (From model by His.)

FIG. 690.—Brain of human embryo of four and a half weeks showing interior of fore-brain. (From model by His.)

691). The rhombic lip folds down over the main part of the alar lamina, fuses with it, and buries the tractus solitarius and spinal root of the trigeminal nerve. Later, the nodulus and flocculus of the cerebellum are developed from the rhombic lip (Fig. 694).

Although the basal plate corresponds to the ventral horn of the spinal cord in giving rise to motor fibers, the cells become arranged in groups or nuclei instead of continuous columns. In addition, neuroblasts migrate from the alar plate and rhombic lip into the basal lamina and become aggregated into the **olivary nuclei** (Fig. 686D). Many of the fibers from these cells cross the midline of the floor plate, constituting the rudiment of the *raphe of the medulla*. The accumulation of these cells and fibers in the ventral part of the basal plate pushes the motor nuclei deeply into the interior and in the adult they are found close to the interior lumen. The change is still further accentuated by the development of the pyramids at about the fourth month and by the fiber connections of the cerebellum. On the floor of the fourth ventricle, the rhomboid fossa, a series of six temporary transverse grooves appear. The most cephalic or first and second lie over the trigeminal nucleus, the third over the facial, the fourth over the abducent, the fifth over the glossopharyngeal, and the sixth over the nucleus of the vagus nerve.

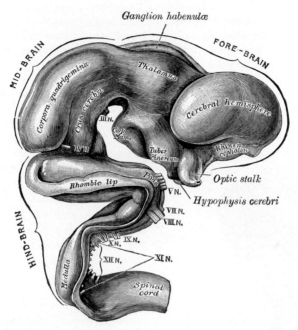

FIG. 691.—Exterior of brain of human embryo of five weeks. (From model by His.)

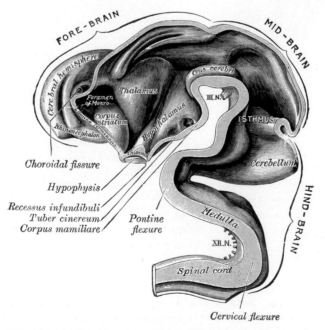

FIG. 692.—Interior of brain of human embryo of five weeks. (From model by His.)

The **Cerebellum.**—The alar laminæ of the cephalic portion of the hindbrain become thickened into plates which fuse in the midline (Fig. 693). The resulting thick lamina roofs over the cephalic part of the hindbrain vesicle as the rudiment of the cerebellum, the outer surface of which is at first smooth. **Fissures** appear first in the vermis and flocular regions during the third month. The fissures on the hemisphere appear during the fifth month. The order of appearance of the primitive fissures does not correspond to their relative importance in the adult. The best marked of the early fissures are as follows: (*a*) the *fissura posterolateralis*, first to develop, is formed by the folding of the rhombic lip and separates the flocculondular lobe from the corpus cerebelli; (*b*) the *fissura prima* is between the culmen and declive; (*c*) the *fissura secunda* is between the future pyramid and uvula. A transverse furrow, the *incisura fastigii*, crosses the ventricular surface, producing a recess like a tent in the roof of the fourth ventricle (Fig. 697).

The **Midbrain or Mesencephalon.**—The midbrain exists for a time as a thin-walled vesicle of some size (Figs. 688, 692). Its cavity, relatively reduced in size, becomes the adult cerebral aqueduct. The basal laminæ thicken into the **cerebral peduncles** which enlarge rapidly after the fourth month. Neuroblasts near the aqueduct very early establish the oculomotor and trochlear nuclei. The alar laminæ invade the roof plate which then becomes thickened into the **corpora quadrigemina.** Some of the cells form the mesencephalic root of the trigeminal nerve.

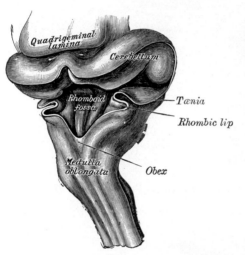

FIG. 693.—Hind-brain of a human embryo of three months—viewed from behind and partly from left side. (From model by His.)

The **Forebrain or Prosencephalon.**—The early forebrain has the same parts as similar stages of the spinal cord and medulla, namely, thick lateral walls connected by thin roof and floor plates (Fig. 688). The division of the rostral end into alar and basal laminæ, however, is not clear. Some authors consider the hypothalamus a derivative of the basal lamina, others maintain that the entire forebrain is derived from the alar lamina.

At a very early period, before the closure of the cranial part of the neural tube, the **optic vesicles** appear as diverticula on each side of the forebrain (Fig. 16). They communicate with the forebrain vesicle by wide openings at first. Later the proximal part of the vesicle is narrowed into the **optic stalk** (Figs. 698, 891) and the peripheral part is expanded into the **optic cup.** The cavity of the vesicle later disappears; the stalk is invaded by nerve fibers and becomes the optic nerve and tract; the cup becomes the retina (Fig. 893).

After closure of the neural tube, the lateral walls of the foerbrain grow much faster than the median portion resulting in a large pouch on each side, the **cerebral hemisphere** (Fig. 689). The cavity of the pouch is the rudiment of the lateral ventricle and its communication with the forebrain vesicle is the future interventricular foramen (of Monro) (Fig. 690). The rostral part of the forebrain, including the hemispheres, is the **telencephalon** or **endbrain.** The more caudal part is called the **diencephalon** or **between brain.** The cavity of the median part of the forebrain vesicle is the third ventricle and the median portion of the rostral wall of the vesicle is a thin plate, the lamina terminalis.

The **Diencephalon.**—The diencephalon gives rise to the thalamus, metathalamus, epithalamus, and hypothalamus. A groove in the lateral wall of this part of the forebrain vesicle, the **sulcus hypothalamicus,** (*cf.*-Fig. 692) is considered by many authorities to be the cephalic continuation of the sulcus limitans. Since the cephalic end of this groove bifurcates, the exact termination of the sulcus limitans is a matter of controversy. The **thalamus** arises as a thickening of the cephalic two-thirds of the alar plate. For some time it is visible as a prominence on the external surface of the brain (Figs. 689, 691), but it later becomes buried by the overgrowth of the hemispheres. The thalami of the two sides protrude medially into the ventricular cavity and in many brains eventually join across the midline in a small commissure-like junction of gray substance, the **massa intermedia.** The

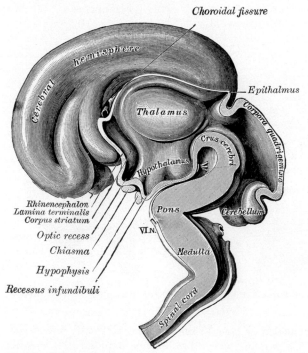

Fig. 694.—Median sagittal section of brain of human embryo of three months. (From model by His.)

metathalamus comprises the medial and lateral geniculate bodies which appear as slight prominences on the outer surface of the alar lamina. The **epithalamus** includes the epiphysis or pineal body, the posterior commissure, and the trigonum habenulæ. The pineal body arises as an evagination of the roof plate between the thalamus and the corpora quadrigemina (Fig. 694). The trigonum habenulæ develops in the roof plate just rostral to the pineal and the posterior commissure develops just caudal to it.

The **hypothalamus** (Fig. 690) is developed from the ventral part of the basal plate and the floor plate of the diencephalon. It comprises the tuber cinereum (Fig. 692) with the attached neurohypophysis, the optic vesicles and chiasma, and the mammillary bodies.

The roof plate of the diencephalon rostral to the pineal body remains thin and epithelial in character. It later combines with the pia mater over it to form the **choroid plexus** of the third ventricle.

Telencephalon.—The **Cerebral Hemispheres** increase rapidly in size and ultimately overlap the structures of the mid- and hindbrains. Each hemisphere has three fundamental parts, the rhinencephalon, the corpus striatum, and the neopallium.

Histogenesis.—The wall of the hemisphere remains typical of the primitive neural tube for some time, with three layers, a thick ependymal and mantle zone and a thin marginal zone. During the third month neuroblasts migrate peripherally from the ependymal and mantle zones. They collect in the deeper part of the marginal zone thus forming the outer layer of gray substance of the **cortex** or **pallium.** The white substance of the hemisphere is formed by the growth of fibers from the central nuclei of the corpus striatum into the outer part of the mantle zone. Later fibers from the newly formed outer cortex grow into the area also. The fibers in the white substance of the hemisphere begin to acquire myelin sheaths at the time of birth and the process continues until puberty. (Flexner, *et al.* '56, Ward, '54.)

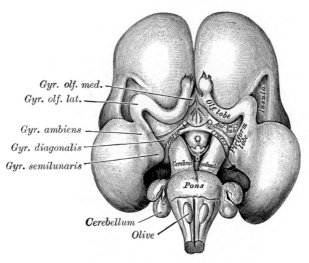

Fig. 695.—Inferior surface of brain of embryo at beginning of fourth month. (From Kollmann.)

The **rhinencephalon** or nose brain is phylogenetically the oldest part of the telencephalon and the part of the cerebral cortex included in it is called the **archipallium.** It forms almost the entire hemisphere in fishes, amphibians, and reptiles, but is poorly developed in man. In the embryo it first appears as a longitudinal ridge with a corresponding internal furrow at the rostral extremity of the hemisphere close to the lamina terminalis (Figs. 689, 692). It is separated from the lateral surface of the hemisphere by the external rhinal fissure but is continuous caudally with the future temporal lobe. The rostral part of the ridge is the **primitive olfactory lobe,** the caudal part the **piriform lobe** (Fig. 695). From the rostral end, a hollow stalk grows forward, retaining for a time its connection with the ventricle. During the third month the lumen is obliterated and the remaining stalk becomes the primitive olfactory bulb and tract. The proximal part of the olfactory lobe is connected with the parolfactory area adjacent to the lamina terminalis on the medial surface of the hemisphere by the gyrus olfactorius medialis.

The caudal part of the primitive olfactory ridge develops into the anterior perforated substance and piriform lobe (Fig. 695). At the beginning of the fourth month the piriform lobe appears as a curved elevation which continues caudally into the temporal lobe. The connection between the olfactory lobe and piriform lobe is the **lateral olfactory gyrus.** It makes a sharp bend in the position of the threshold of the future insula (*limen insulæ*) with which it later forms a connection. The caudal part of the piriform lobe is composed of the gyrus ambiens and gyrus semi-lunaris which are absorbed into the uncus of the adult gyrus hippocampus. The development of the fornix is described with that of the commissures.

The **corpus striatum** appears as a thickening in the ventral wall of the hemisphere between the optic stalk and the interventricular foramen, close against the thalamus (Figs. 690, 692). By the second month it is seen as a swelling in the floor of the lateral ventricle extending back to the occipital pole of the primitive hemisphere. When this portion of the hemisphere is expanded into the temporal lobe, a part of the corpus striatum is carried into the roof of the inferior horn where it becomes the tail of the caudate nucleus. During the fourth and fifth months, an invasion by fibers of the internal capsule incompletely divides the corpus striatum into the **caudate** and **lentiform nuclei.**

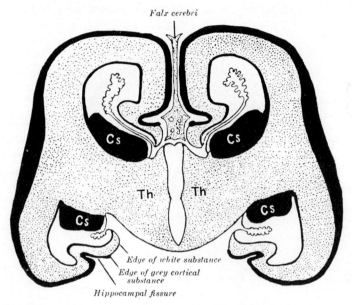

Falx cerebri

Edge of white substance
Edge of grey cortical substance
Hippocampal fissure

FIG. 696.—Diagrammatic coronal section of brain to show relations of neopallium. (After His.)
Cs, Corpus striatum. *Th*, Thalamus.

The **neopallium** or non-olfactory part of the cerebral cortex takes up the greater part of the hemisphere. Its cavity, the **primitive lateral ventricle,** expands in all directions, but more especially dorsally and caudally. By the third month the hemispheres cover the diencephalon, by the sixth month they overlap the midbrain and by the eighth they reach the hindbrain. The median lamina uniting the two hemispheres does not share in their expansion and remains as the thin roof of the third ventricle. Thus the hemispheres become separated by a deep cleft, the fore-runner of the longitudinal fissure. The cavity of the ventricle is gradually drawn out into three prolongations which represent the future anterior, inferior, and posterior horns.

The part of the wall along the medial border of the primitive lateral ventricle which is immediately continuous with the roof plate of the diencephalon lies over the primitive interventricular foramen and extends caudally. This border remains thin and of an ependymal or epithelial character. It is invaginated into the medial wall of the lateral ventricle to form the **choroid fissure** (Figs. 692, 697). Mesodermal tissue from the outer surface of the hemisphere, the rudiment of the pia mater,

spreads into the fissure between the two layers of the ependyma to form the rudiment of the **tela chorioidea**. The blood vessels accompanying the mesoderm form
the choroid plexus which almost completely fills the cavity of the ventricle for
several months. The tela chorioidea lying over the roof of the diencephalon also
invaginates the thin epithelial covering to form the choroid plexus of the third
ventricle.

The medial wall of the hemisphere along a line parallel with the choroid fissure
becomes pushed or folded into the cavity of the lateral ventricle. The prominence
inside the ventricle is the rudiment of the **hippocampus** and the groove outside is
the **hippocampal fissure** (Fig. 696). The outer gray substance of the cortex ends
along the prominence between the hippocampal fissure and the choroid fissure leaving the white substance exposed along a thin edge which is continuous with the
epithelium of the choroid plexus (Fig. 696). With the growth of the temporal lobe
rostrally the hippocampal fissure and parts associated with it extend from the

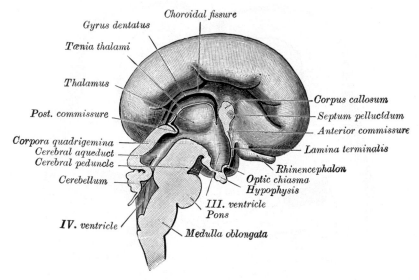

FIG. 697.—Median sagittal section of brain of human embryo of four months. (Marchand.)

interventricular foramen to the end of the inferior horn of the ventricle. The
thickened edge of gray substance becomes the **gyrus dentatus**, the **fasciola cinerea**,
and the **supra-** and **subcallosal gyri**. The free edge of the white substance forms the
fimbria hippocampi and the body and crus of the **fornix**.

The **Commissures.**—The development of the posterior commissure has already
been described (page 829). The corpus callosum, the fornix, and the anterior
commissure, arise from the lamina terminalis (Fig. 697). At about the fourth month
a small thickening appears in this lamina, immediately in front of the interventricular foramen. The lower part of this thickening is soon constricted off, and
fibers grow into it to form the **anterior commissure**. The upper part continues to
grow caudally with the hemispheres, and is invaded by two sets of fibers. Transverse fibers, extending between the hemispheres, pass into its dorsal part, which is
now differentiated as the **corpus callosum**. Longitudinal fibers from the hippocampus
pass into the ventral part of the lamina terminalis, and arching over the thalamus
to the corpora mamillaria, develop into the **fornix**. The anterior portion between
the corpus callosum and fornix is not invaded by commissural fibers, and becomes
the **septum pellucidum**.

Fissures and Sulci.—The outer surface of the cerebral hemisphere is at first smooth. Later it exhibits a number of elevations or convolutions, separated from each other by fissures and sulci, most of which make their appearance during the sixth or seventh months of fetal life. The term fissure is applied to such grooves as involve the entire thickness of the cerebral wall, and thus produce corresponding eminences in the ventricular cavity. The sulci affect only the superficial part of the wall, and therefore leave no impressions in the ventricle. The fissures are the choroidal and hippocampal already described, the calcarine, which produces the swelling in the ventricle known as the calcar avis, and the collateral fissure with its corresponding eminence in the ventricular cavity. The central sulcus (fissure of Rolando) is developed in two parts, the intraparietal sulcus in four parts, and the cingulate sulcus in two or three parts. The **lateral cerebral** or **Sylvian fissure** differs from all the other fissures in its mode of development. It appears about the third month as a depression, the **Sylvian fossa**, on the lateral surface of the hemisphere (Fig. 698). The floor of this fossa becomes the **insula** and its adherence to the subjacent corpus striatum, prevents this part of the cortex from expanding at the same rate as the portions which surround it. The neighboring parts of the hemisphere therefore gradually grow over and cover in the insula, and constitute the temporal, parietal, frontal, and orbital **opercula** of the adult brain. The frontal and orbital opercula are the last to form, but by the end of the first year after birth the insula is completely submerged. The fissures separating the opposed margins of the opercula constitute the adult lateral cerebral fissure.

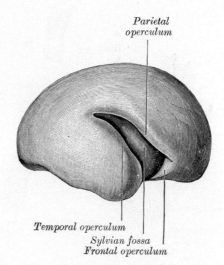

Parietal operculum

Temporal operculum

Sylvian fossa

Frontal operculum

FIG. 698.—Outer surface of cerebral hemisphere of human embryo of about five months.

The Autonomic Nervous System.—The cells in the central gray of the spinal cord occupying a lateral position between the afferent groups of the dorsal horn and the somatic efferent groups of the ventral horn send their axons out through the ventral roots (Fig. 986, *A*). These axons leave the spinal nerves in the thoracic and first two lumbar segments to enter the sympathetic ganglia. They are the preganglionic fibers and together with a few afferent fibers from the spinal ganglia become the white rami communicantes. In the medulla and pons, the nerve cells in the lateral part of the basal plate send axons out with the facial, glossopharyngeal, and vagus nerves. These fibers meet the various peripheral ganglia associated with them and become the parasympathic preganglionic fibers for smooth muscle, heart, and glands. In the sacral region, the lateral horn cells grow out into the pelvic nerves and become the preganglionics of the sacral portion of the parasympathic system.

Autonomic Ganglia.—When the cells of the *neural crest* (Fig. 687) gather into the primordia of the spinal ganglia along the primitive neural tube, a certain number of cells continue to migrate ventrally (Yntema and Hammond '45). In the region of the spinal cord these migrating cells collect into groups along the lateral aspect of the aorta and become the ganglia of the sympathetic trunk. Others migrate farther toward the alimentary tube and become the celiac and associated ganglia. The cells from the cranial neural crest migrate in a similar fashion and become the

53

parasympathetic ganglia. As mentioned above, axons from the central nervous system reach these sympathetic and parasympathetic ganglia to become the preganglionic fibers. The cells in the ganglia grow out to their various specific organs and become the postganglionic fibers.

The **Cranial Nerves.**—With the exception of the olfactory, optic, and acoustic nerves, which are considered elsewhere (see page 1096), the cranial nerves are developed in a manner similar to the spinal nerves. The sensory or afferent nerves are derived from the cells of the ganglion rudiments of the neural crest. The

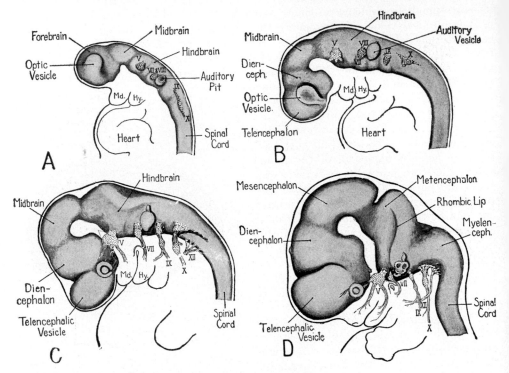

Fig. 699.—Four stages in early development of brain and cranial nerves of young human embryos. (Adapted from various sources, primarily figures by Streeter and reconstructions in the Carnegie Collection.)

A, At 20 somites—based on the Davis embryo—probable fertilization age of three and a half weeks.

B, At 4 mm., fertilization age of about four weeks.

C, At 8 mm., fertilization age a little over five weeks.

D, At 17 mm., fertilization age about seven weeks.

The cranial nerves are indicated by the appropriate Roman numerals:

V, Trigeminal; VII, facial; VIII, acoustic; IX, glossopharyngeal; X, vagus; XI, accessory; XII, hypoglossal. Abbreviations: Hy., hyoid arch; Md., mandibular arch. (Courtesy of B. M. Patten, Human Embryology 2nd Ed. Copyright, 1953. Blakiston Div., McGraw-Hill Book Co.)

central processes of these cells grow into the brain and form the roots of the nerves, while the peripheral processes extend outward and constitute their fibers of distribution (Fig. 685). It has been seen, in considering the development of the medulla oblongata (page 825), that the tractus solitarius (Fig. 686), derived from the fibers which grow inward from the ganglion rudiments of the glossopharyngeal and vagus nerves, is the homologue of the oval bundle in the cord, which had its origin in the posterior nerve roots. The motor or efferent nerves arise as outgrowths of the neuroblasts situated in the basal laminæ of the mid- and hindbrain. They are

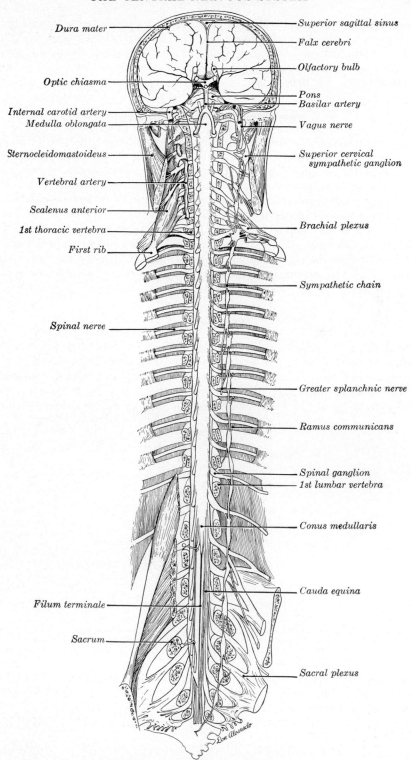

Dura mater

Optic chiasma

Internal carotid artery

Medulla oblongata

Sternocleidomastoideus

Vertebral artery

Scalenus anterior

1st thoracic vertebra

First rib

Spinal nerve

Filum terminale

Sacrum

Superior sagittal sinus

Falx cerebri

Olfactory bulb

Pons

Basilar artery

Vagus nerve

Superior cervical sympathetic ganglion

Brachial plexus

Sympathetic chain

Greater splanchnic nerve

Ramus communicans

Spinal ganglion

1st lumbar vertebra

Conus medullaris

Cauda equina

Sacral plexus

FIG. 700.—Dissection to show the ventral or anterior aspect of the brain and spinal cord in situ. (Redrawn from Hirschfeld and Leveille.)

grouped into two sets, according to whether they spring from the medial or the lateral parts of the basal laminal. To the former set belong the oculomotor, trochlear, abducent, and hypoglossal nerves; to the latter, the accessory and the motor fibers of the trigeminal, facial, glossopharyngeal, and vagus nerves (Figs. 686, 699) (Humphrey '52, Brown '56).

THE CENTRAL NERVOUS SYSTEM

The central nervous system is a single continuous structure which is divided for convenience in description into two parts: the brain or encephalon and the spinal cord or medulla spinalis. Both parts are composed of two substances or types of tissue: the gray substance or gray matter containing primarily nerve cells and their closely related processes, and the white substance or white matter composed of bundles or masses of nerve fibers, predominantly myelinated. The nerve cells or neurones are the control centers. By means of various processes, they form connections with each other called synapses. Their processes reach more remote nerve cells within the central nervous system as the fibers of the white substance and they reach the structures of the body with which they are associated functionally by means of the peripheral nervous system.

The Spinal Cord

The **spinal cord** (*medulla spinalis*) (Fig. 700) is an elongated, nearly cylindrical structure approximately 1 cm. in diameter, with an average length of 42 to 45 cm. and weight of 30 gm. It lies within the vertebral canal, its cephalic end continuous with the medulla oblongata of the brain at the upper border of the atlas. Its caudal extremity, at the lower border of the first or upper border of the second

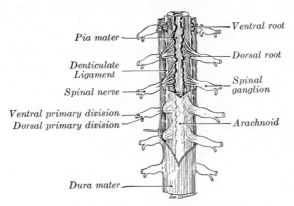

Fig. 701.—Several segments of the thoracic spinal cord showing the meninges and spinal roots. Dorsal aspect.

lumbar vertebra, tapers to a point, forming the **conus medullaris.** The position of the cord varies somewhat with the movements of the vertebral column, being drawn upward slightly when the column is flexed. At birth the lower end lies at the third lumbar vertebra but it gradually recedes during childhood until it reaches the adult position.

The spinal cord is enclosed by the three protective membranes called **meninges,** the dura mater, the arachnoid, and the pia mater, structures which are described at the end of this chapter (Fig. 701).

The **filum terminale** is a delicate filament which continues down the vertebral canal from the apex of the conus medullaris to the first segment of the coccyx (Fig. 700). It is approximately 20 cm. in length. Its first 15 cm., contained within the tubular sheath of the dura mater and surrounded by the nerves of the cauda equina, is called the **filum terminale internum**. The lower part, the **filum terminale externum**, is closely invested by the dura, is adherent to it, and extends beyond the apex of the sheath to the dorsal part of the first coccygeal vertebra to which it is attached. The filum consists mainly of fibrous tissue continuous with the pia mater. A few nerve fibers adherent to the outer surface probably represent rudimentary second and third coccygeal nerves. The central canal of the spinal cord continues down into the filum for 5 or 6 cm.

External Configuration of the Cord

Enlargements.—The spinal cord is slightly flattened dorsoventrally and its diameter is increased by enlargements in two areas, cervical and lumbar (Fig. 702). The **cervical enlargement** (*intumescentia cervicalis*) extends from the third cervical to the second thoracic vertebra, its maximum circumference (about 38 mm.) being on a level with the sixth pair of cervical nerves. It corresponds to the origin of the large nerves which supply the upper limbs. The **lumbar enlargement** (*intumescentia lumbalis*) begins at the level of the ninth thoracic vertebra and reaches its maximum circumference (about 33 mm.) opposite the last thoracic vertebra, after which it tapers rapidly into the conus medullaris. It corresponds to the origin of nerves which supply the lower limbs.

Fissures and Sulci (Fig. 702).—A ventral or anterior median fissure and a dorsal or posterior median sulcus divide the spinal cord longitudinally into symmetrical right and left halves (Fig. 703).

The **Ventral Median Fissure** (*fissura mediana anterior*) (Fig. 702) has an

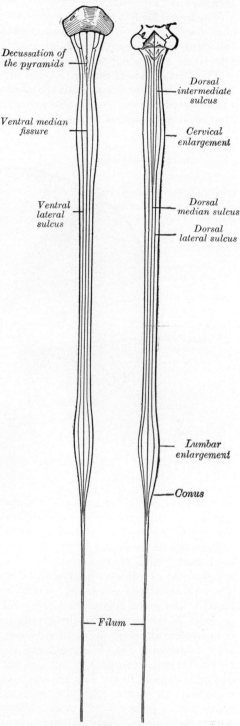

FIG. 702.—Diagrams of the spinal cord.

average depth of about 3 mm., increasing caudally. It contains a double fold of pia mater and its floor is formed by transverse white substance, the ventral white commissure (Fig. 703).

The **Dorsal Median Sulcus** (*sulcus medianus posterior*) (Fig. 702) is a shallow groove marking the position of the **dorsal median septum** (Fig. 703), a thin sheet of neuroglial tissue which penetrates more than half way into the substance of the cord, effectively separating the dorsal portion into right and left halves.

The **Dorsal Lateral Sulcus** (*sulcus lateralis posterior*) (Fig. 702, 703) is a longitudinal furrow corresponding to the position of the attachments of the dorsal roots of the spinal nerves. In the upper thoracic and cervical regions of the cord a groove, the **dorsal intermediate sulcus** (*sulcus intermedius posterior*), lies between the dorsa

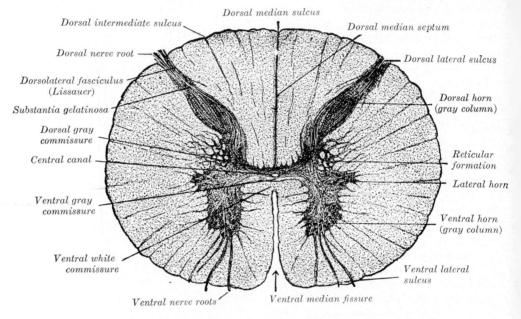

FIG. 703.—Transverse section of the spinal cord in the mid-thoracic region.

median and dorsal lateral sulci. It marks the separation between the fasciculus gracilis and cuneatus. The **ventral lateral sulcus** is an indistinct shallow groove where the ventral roots of the spinal nerves are attached.

Segments of the Cord.—Thirty-one pairs of spinal nerves originate from the spinal cord, each with a ventral or anterior root and a dorsal or posterior root. The pairs are grouped as follows: 8 cervical, 12 thoracic, 5 lumbar, 5 sacral, and 1 coccygeal. The cord itself also is divided for convenience of description into cervical, thoracic, lumbar, and sacral regions to correspond with the nerve roots. It is customary also to speak of the part of the cord giving rise to each pair of nerves as a **spinal segment** or **neuromere** although the distinguishing marks, except for the roots, are not retained after embryonic life. The segments vary in their extent along the cord, in the cervical region averaging 13 mm., in the mid-thoracic region 26 mm., whereas they diminish rapidly in the lumbar and sacral region from 15 to 4 mm. Because the cord is much shorter than the vertebral column, the more caudally placed nerve roots take a progressively more oblique direction, so that the lumbar and sacral nerves pass almost vertically downward within the dura for some distance before reaching their foramina of exit. The resulting collection of rootlets and nerves beyond the termination of the cord is called the **cauda equina** (Fig. 700).

Spinal Nerve Roots.—Each spinal nerve has two roots: (*a*) a dorsal or posterior root, also called the sensory root because its fibers bring impulses to the cord and (*b*) a ventral or anterior root, also called the motor root because its fibers carry impulses from the cord out to muscles and other structures (page 997).

The **Dorsal Roots** (*radix dorsalis; sensory root*) (Fig. 704) are attached in linear series along the dorsal lateral sulcus of the cord by six or eight **rootlets** (*fila radicularia*). They contain the central processes of spinal ganglion cells whose peripheral processes extend out to the sensory endings in the skin, muscles, tendons, viscera, *etc.* The rootlets are divided into two groups as they enter the cord, (*a*) a *medial bundle* containing mainly large myelinated fibers and (*b*) a *lateral bundle* containing fine myelinated and unmyelinated fibers.

The **Ventral Roots** (*radix ventralis; anterior root*) (Fig. 704) are attached to the spinal cord along the ventral lateral sulcus, in two or three irregular rows of rootlets spread over a strip about 2 or 3 mm. in width. They contain the axon sof the cells in the ventral and lateral cell columns of the central gray matter of the cord.

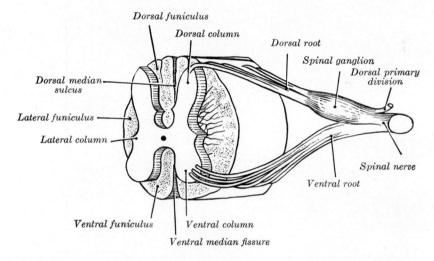

FIG. 704.—Diagram of an upper thoracic segment of the spinal cord with spinal roots and ganglion.

Internal Structure of the Spinal Cord

The spinal cord is composed of two principal parts extending the length of the cord, an inner core of gray substance where nerve cells predominate and an outer layer of white substance where myelinated nerve fibers predominate.

Gray Substance (*substantia grisea centralis; gray matter*) (Fig. 703).—The central gray core is arranged in two large lateral masses connected across the midline by a narrow but continuous strip, the **gray commissure.** In cross section this gives a configuration similar to the letter H. Each lateral portion splays outward like a crescent, or better, like an inverted comma (Fig. 703). The commissure or crossbar of the H is closer to the ventral than the dorsal surface of the cord and contains the central canal. The part of the lateral mass extending dorsalward from the commissure is called the **dorsal** or **posterior column** (*columna posterior*) (Fig. 704) that extending ventralward, the **ventral** or **anterior column** (*columna anterior*). Since they are usually studied in cross sections of the cord, they are commonly referred to as **dorsal** and **ventral horns** (see below).

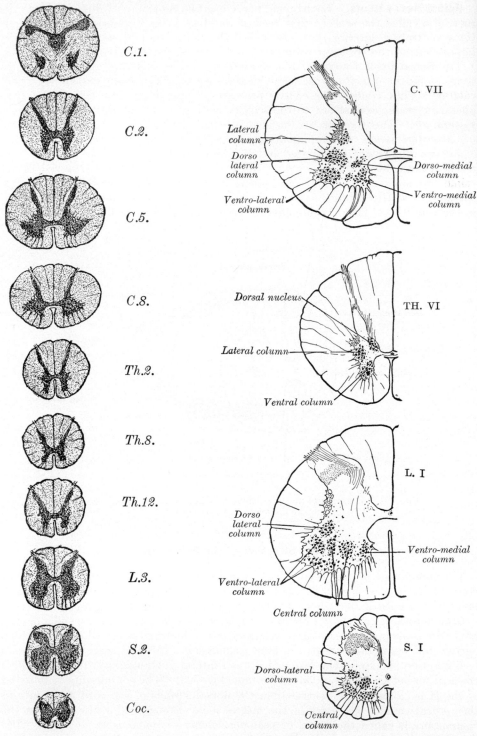

FIG. 705.—Transverse sections of the spinal cord at different levels.

FIG. 706.—Transverse sections of the spinal cord at different levels to show the arrangement of the principal cell columns.

The quantity of gray matter varies markedly at different levels of the cord and its configuration is more or less characteristic at each level (Fig. 705). In the thoracic region it is small, surrounded by a relatively large amount of white matter. It is increased in the cervical and lumbar enlargements, and its proportion to the white substance is greatest in the conus medullaris. In the cervical region the dorsal column is narrow, the ventral broad; in the thoracic region both columns are attenuated and the lateral column becomes evident; in the lumbar enlargement both ventral and dorsal columns are expanded, and in the conus medullaris they are merged into an oval outline with a broad commissure.

The centrally placed gray substance of the spinal cord consists of nerve cells with their dendrites and a dense feltwork of nerve fibers, the **neuropil** (Fig. 787), supported and held together by neuroglia (Fig. 788). The nerve fibers are the axons not only of the local nerve cells, but also of cells in other parts of the nervous system which synapse with these cells. Relatively few of the fibers are myelinated because they lose their sheaths at some distance before they terminate. In cross sections of the cord prepared with the Nissl stain (LaVelle '56), which colors the cell bodies, it can be seen that cells of recognizable types tend to be arranged in groups or nuclei which have a functional significance (Fig. 706). The individual groups or columns may extend through all or part of the length of the cord.

The **Dorsal Horn** (*cornu posterius*; *posterior horn*; *posterior column*) in a cross section (Fig. 703) projects farther and is more slender than the ventral horn. It reaches almost to the surface in the dorsal lateral sulcus, from which it is separated by a thin layer of white substance, the dorsolateral fasciculus. The dorsal extremity is also capped by a crescentic mass of translucent gelatinous tissue containing many small nerve cells, named the substantia gelatinosa (of Rolando). The cells of the dorsal horn belong to the sensory side of a neuronal or reflex arc and are concerned with receiving and relaying impulses from the dorsal root fibers of spinal nerves.

Nuclei or **Columns of Cells of the Dorsal Horn** (Fig. 706).—(1) The **substantia gelatinosa** (*of Rolando*) extends the entire length of the cord and into the medulla oblongata where it becomes the spinal nucleus of the trigeminal nerve. It contains numerous small cells whose axons end in adjacent columns, both gray and white. The fibers entering it are from the lateral bundle of the dorsal rootlets by way of the dorsolateral tract or tract of Lissauer (Fig. 708). (2) The **dorsal nucleus** or **Clarke's column** (Fig. 706) extends from the last cervical or first thoracic to the second or third lumbar segments, gradually decreasing in size both above and below a maximum at the twelfth thoracic. It is represented, however, in other regions by aggregates of cells, a cervical nucleus at the third cervical and a sacral at the middle or lower sacral region of the cord. It is a well-defined oval area in the medial part of the base of the dorsal horn, containing medium and large, oval or piriform cells. It receives fibers from the dorsal funiculus and the axons of its cells course laterally and turn cephalad in the dorsal spinocerebellar tract. (3) The **nucleus proprius** extends throughout the length of the cord in the body and basal regions of the dorsal horn. The cells are of medium and small size with occasional large solitary cells.

The **Ventral Horn** (*cornu anterius*; *anterior horn*; *anterior column*) (Figs. 703, 704) is broader and does not reach as near the surface as the dorsal horn. It is expanded in the cervical and lumbar enlargements to correspond with the innervation of the limbs (Fig. 705).

Columns of Cells of the Ventral Horn.—The nerve cells of the ventral horn are large polygonal cells with long branching dendrites. The axons of these cells leave the cord through the ventral roots and traverse the peripheral nerves to the various muscles, giving off collaterals near their termination to a large number of motor nerve end plates (125 to 400). The cells are arranged in columnar groups which extend longitudinally through varying numbers of segments (Fig. 706). In general the trunk musculature is represented medially and the limb musculature laterally. This is emphasized by the number of large columns placed laterally at the levels of the cervical and lumbosacral enlargements of the cord (Fig. 706). The nuclear groups have been mapped out with greater refinement (Elliott '42) but functional correlation with the muscles and muscle groups has been established in only a few instances.

The **phrenic nucleus** appears to be a well-defined group of cells at an intermediate position in the most ventral part of the ventral horn. The cells are arranged in globular clusters, like a string of beads, extending from the lowest part of the third cervical through the upper part of the sixth cervical segment of the cord. There is no central decussation but fibers do cross from the left to the right nerve at the level of the pericardium (Warwick and Mitchell '56).

Lateral Horn (*cornu laterale*; *lateral* or *intermediolateral gray column*) (Fig. 706).— In the thoracic and upper lumbar segments, the portion of the gray mass lateral to the commissure protrudes into the white substance to form the intermediate lateral gray column or lateral horn.

Its cells are fusiform or stellate and of medium size. Their axons pass out through the ventral roots and thence through the white rami communicantes into the sympathetic trunk (page 1065). They are the preganglionic fibers of the **sympathetic** or **thoracolumbar outflow** of the autonomic nervous system.

The column is again differentiated in the third and fourth sacral segments where the axons of its cells enter the pelvic nerves as the sacral portion of the **parasym-pathetic** or **craniosacral outflow** of the autonomic system. In the upper cervical region of the cord the column is also differentiated and in the medulla it is repre-sented by the dorsal nucleus of the vagus and other autonomic nuclei extending rostrally parallel with the sulcus limitans. The axons of certain other cells of the lateral column pass into the ventral and lateral funiculi.

Reticular Formation (*formatio reticularis*) (Fig. 703).—Between the lateral and dorsal horns the gray substance sends irregular slender projections into the white substance giving an appearance of a network in cross section and hence it is called the reticular formation. It is best developed in the cervical region and is continuous with the reticular formation of the medulla. It consists of medium and small cells scattered between strands of unmyelinated fibers which insinuate themselves into the white matter at the base of the dorsal horn.

The **Central Canal** (*canalis centralis*) (Fig. 703) runs throughout the entire length of the spinal cord, marking a division of the narrow strip of gray matter (*substantia intermedia centralis*) into a **ventral** and a **dorsal gray commissure**. The former is thin and in contact with the ventral white commissure. The dorsal gray commissure reaches to the dorsal median septum. The central canal continues cephalad into the medulla oblongata where it opens out into the fourth ventricle. Caudally, it reaches for a short distance into the filum terminale and in the conus medullaris there is a fusiform dilatation 8 to 10 mm. in length and triangular in cross section, the **terminal ventricle** (*ventriculus terminalis*). The canal is filled with spinal fluid, and is lined by the ependyma composed of ciliated, columnar epithelium. Just outside of the ependyma is the **substantia gelatinosa centralis**, consisting mainly of neuroglia and the processes of the ependymal cells, but also containing a few nerve cells and fibers.

White Substance.—The white substance of the spinal cord consists of myelinated and unmyelinated fibers in great numbers embedded in a spongework of neuroglia. The majority of fibers pursue a longitudinal course, but many cross from one side to the other in the ventral white commissure. Many of the longitudinal fibers are grouped into bundles with a common function, origin, and destination. These are called **fiber tracts**. The fibers of neighboring tracts tend to intermingle, so that they can seldom be identified without special methods.

Lamination.—During the development of the brain and spinal cord, fibers are usually added to the various tracts in an orderly manner. The new ingrowing fibers are placed beside the older ones, building up the tract toward the side from which they have approached it, by a process known as lamination. A clear example is found in the nucleus gracilis and cuneatus. The longest fibers beginning at the caudal end of the cord are placed against the dorsal median sulcus. Fibers are added laterally until the most cephalic part of the body is represented in the most lateral part of the posterior funiculus (Fig. 707).

The cord is also subdivided into groups of tracts more or less closely associated functionally. These are the **fasciculi**. The entire white matter is divided into the three **funiculi**, dorsal, ventral, and lateral (Fig. 704).

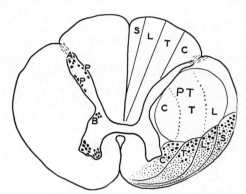

Fig. 707.—Semischematic drawing to show on the left side the cell groups of the posterior horn, and on the right side the arrangement of the spinothalamic and other tracts in the lower cervical region. The heavy dots represent fibers concerned with temperature; the medium-sized dots, fibers mediating pain, and the fine dots, fibers carrying touch and pressure impulses. Note the overlapping and topical arrangement of the fibers. *A*, apical group of large ganglion cells of the posterior horn; *B*, basal group of large ganglion cells of the posterior horn; *C*, fibers from the cervical segment of the spinal cord; *L*, fibers from the lumbar segment of the spinal cord; *P*, pericornual groups of large ganglion cells of the posterior horn; *PT*, tractus pyramidalis; *S*, fibers from the sacral segment of the spinal cord, and *T*, fibers from the thoracic segment of the spinal cord. (Walker, courtesy of Arch. Neur. and Psych.)

Dorsal Funiculus (*funiculus posterior*) (Fig. 704).—The dorsal funiculus contains two large ascending fasciculi, (1) the fasciculus gracilis, (2) the fasciculus cuneatus; a small descending fasciculus, (3) the comma fasciculus, and an intersegmental fasciculus, (4) the dorsal proper fasciculus.

(1) The **fasciculus gracilis** (*tract of Goll*) (Fig. 708) lies next to the dorsal median septum and extends throughout the cord. It increases in size as the myelinated fibers from the medial strand of the dorsal roots from the lumbar and lower thoracic segments are added to the sacral. The fibers from the lowest segments retain their medial position and by a process of lamination, the fibers from successively higher segments are placed more laterally (Fig. 707). Some fibers may give collaterals to the nucleus dorsalis, nucleus proprius, and ventral horn and finally end in the nucleus gracilis of the medulla. Others may terminate in these nuclei.

(2) The **fasciculus cuneatus** (*tract of Burdach*) (Fig. 708) is similar to the fasciculus gracilis in position, function, and origin and together they might, therefore, be considered as one fasciculus. They are, however, separated by the dorsal intermediate septum (Fig. 703) cephalic to the sixth thoracic segment. Fibers from the upper thoracic and cervical dorsal roots enter the fasciculus cuneatus and by the same process of lamination as in the gracilis, the fibers of the higher segments are placed more laterally. Those that reach the medulla end in the nucleus cuneatus.

Both gracile and cuneate fasciculi mediate discriminatory sensation; proprioception from muscles, tendons, and joints; tactile from the skin, and the vibratory sense.

(3) The **fasciculus interfascicularis** or **comma fasciculus** (*of Schultze*) (Fig. 708) is found in the cervical and upper thoracic region squeezed in between the fasciculus gracilis and cuneatus. In the lower thoracic region the fibers occupy a peripherally median position in the **septomarginal tract**; in the lumbar region, a deeper median position in the **oval area of Flechsig**; and in the sacral region in the **triangle of Phillipe-Gombault**. These tracts carry descending fibers; some are from the dorsal roots and some are intersegmental from cells in the dorsal horn.

(4) The **dorsal proper fasciculus** (*fasciculus proprius dorsalis; posterior ground bundle*) (Fig. 708) lies close to the central gray substance. It receives fibers from cells in the dorsal horn which bifurcate into ascending and descending branches.

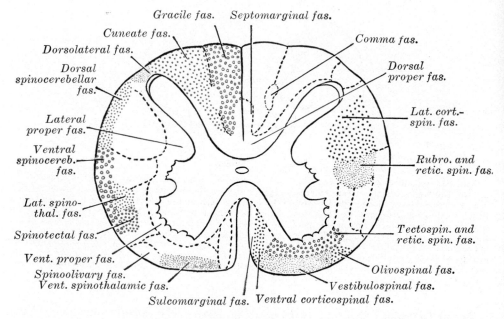

FIG. 708.—Diagram of the principal fasciculi of the spinal cord. Ascending fibers in blue, descending in red.

They are intersegmental, running for varying distances and sending off collaterals and terminals to the gray matter.

Lateral Funiculus.—The lateral funiculus contains the following: **A.** ascending tracts or fasciculi: (1) the dorsal spinocerebellar tract, (2) ventral spinocerebellar tract, (3) lateral spinothalamic tract, (4) spinotectal tract, (5) dorsolateral tract (of Lissauer), and (6) lateral proper fasciculus; **B.** descending fasciculi: (7) the lateral corticospinal tract (pyramidal tract), (8) rubrospinal tract, and (9) the olivospinal tract.

(1) **The dorsal spinocerebellar tract** (*tract of Flechsig; tractus spinocerebellaris posterior*) is a flattened peripheral band extending from the tip of the dorsal horn about half way ventrally (Fig. 708). It begins at about the second or third lumbar nerve, increasing in size as it ascends to the inferior cerebellar peduncle and vermis of the cerebellum. Its fibers are of large size, derived from the dorsal nucleus (Clarke's column) mainly of the same side.

(2) The **ventral spinocerebellar tract** (*tract of Gowers; tractus spinocerebellaris anterior*) forms a band which skirts the periphery from the dorsal spinocerebellar almost to the ventral lateral sulcus (Fig. 708). It begins at about the level of the third lumbar nerves, and can be followed through the medulla and pons to the superior cerebellar peduncle and vermis. Its fibers come from cells in the dorsal horn and intermediate gray matter of the same or opposite sides. They are proprioceptive fibers whose impulses do not reach the level of consciousness.

(3) The **lateral spinothalamic tract** (Fig. 708) lies deep to the ventral spinocerebellar tract. It conveys impulses for pain and temperature. Fibers entering the cord through the lateral strand of the dorsal root cross the dorsolateral tract (of

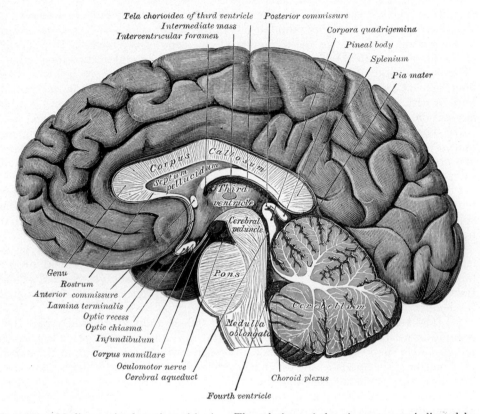

Tela chorioidea of third ventricle Posterior commissure
Intermediate mass
Interventricular foramen

Corpora quadrigemina
Pineal body
Splenium
Pia mater

Corpus Callosum
Septum pellucidum
Third ventricle
Cerebral peduncle
Pons
Cerebellum
Medulla oblongata

Genu
Rostrum
Anterior commissure
Lamina terminalis
Optic recess
Optic chiasma
Infundibulum
Corpus mamillare
Oculomotor nerve
Cerebral aqueduct
Choroid plexus
Fourth ventricle

FIG. 709.—Median sagittal section of brain. The relations of the pia mater are indicated by the red color.

Lissauer) and end about cells in the substantia gelatinosa within one or two segments. Axons from these cells cross in the ventral white commissure to this tract and ascend to the thalamus. Within the tract, the fibers for temperature are placed more dorsally than those for pain. The tract increases as it ascends, fibers being added by lamination to the deeper part from higher segments (Fig. 707).

(4) The **spinotectal tract** (Fig. 708) is ventral to the lateral spinothalamic tract and contains axons from cells in the dorsal horn of the opposite side. They come to lie in the medial portion of the lateral lemniscus and end in the superior colliculus of the midbrain.

(5) The **dorsolateral tract** (*tract of Lissauer*) (Fig. 708) lies at the tip of the dorsal horn, ventral and lateral to the incoming dorsal roots. It contains fine myelinated

and unmyelinated fibers, some from the lateral strand of the dorsal roots and some from the cells in the dorsal horn. They divide into short ascending and descending branches which end mostly in the substantia gelatinosa (Earle '52).

(6) The **lateral proper fasciculus** (*fasciculus proprius lateralis; lateral ground bundle*) (Fig. 708) consists chiefly of intersegmental fibers which arise from cells in the gray substance, and, after a longer or shorter course, reenter the gray substance and ramify in it. These fibers make up a moderately thick layer next to the gray substance. In addition, certain pathways, either long tracts or neuron chains, from autonomic centers in the brainstem to autonomic centers in the cord run in this area, near to the lateral horn.

(7) The **lateral corticospinal tract** (*crossed pyramidal tract*) (Figs. 708, 713) extends throughout the cord and is the principal pathway for voluntary movement. The fibers are axons of the pyramidal cells in the cortex which traverse the brain in the pyramidal tract. In the pyramidal decussation of the medulla 70 per cent of the fibers cross to the opposite side and become the lateral corticospinal tract. (The 30 per cent uncrossed are the ventral corticospinal tract, see below). The fibers give off many collaterals and synapse either with the motor cells in the ventral horn or with other cells in the base of the dorsal horn. The fibers are arranged by lamination, the cervical being the more medially placed (Fig. 707) (Lassek '54).

(8) The **rubrospinal tract** (Fig. 708) is less conspicuous in man than in most mammals. Its fibers arise in the red nucleus of the midbrain, cross to the opposite side, and probably terminate in relation to the motor horn cells either directly or through intercalated neurons.

(9) The **olivospinal tract** (Fig. 708) arises in the vicinity of the inferior olivary nucleus in the medulla oblongata, and is seen only in the cervical region of the spinal cord. It lies at the periphery close to the most lateral of the ventral spinal nerve rootlets.

Ventral Funiculus.—The ventral funiculus contains the following tracts or fasciculi: **A.** ascending tracts; (1) ventral spinothalamic tract, (2) ventral proper fasciculus; **B.** descending tracts: (3) ventral corticospinal tract, (4) vestibulospinal tract, (5) ventral reticulospinal tracts, (6) tectospinal tract and (7) sulcomarginal fasciculus.

(1) The **ventral spinothalamic tract** (*tractus spinothalamicus anterior*) (Fig. 708) occupies a peripheral position near the ventral median fissure more or less intermingled with the vestibulospinal tract. It receives fibers originating in the dorsal gray matter of the oppostie side which have crossed in the ventral white commissure. The fibers turn cephalad, reaching the thalamus directly or by relays of other cells. They convey tactile impulses of touch and pressure with considerable overlapping of segments and bilateral representation.

(2) The **ventral proper fasciculus** (*fasciculus proprius ventralis; anterior ground bundle*) (Fig. 708) includes a rather wide band of white substance next the gray substance of the ventral horn. It consists of (*a*) longitudinal intersegmental fibers which arise from cells in the gray substance, especially the medial group of the ventral horn (Fig. 706) and after a longer or shorter course reënter the gray substance; (*b*) commissural fibers which cross in the ventral white commissure to the gray of the opposite side; (*c*) fibers of autonomic neuron chains from the brainstem.

(3) The **ventral corticospinal tract** (*direct pyramidal tract*) (Fig. 708) lies close to the ventral median fissure and is present only in the cephalic part of the spinal cord, gradually increasing from a midthoracic level. It consists of fibers arising from pyramidal cells of the cortex of the same side.

(4) The **vestibulospinal tract** (Fig. 708) is placed peripherally in much the same area as the ventral spinothalamic tract. Its fibers arise from cells in the lateral vestibular nucleus (Deiters) and some of them can be traced as far as the sacral

region. Their terminals and collaterals end among the motor cells of the ventral horn and are concerned with the maintenance of tonus and equilibrium.

(5) The **ventral reticulospinal tract** (Fig. 708) arises from cells in various nuclei of the reticular substance of the medulla, pons, and mesencephalon and terminate among the anterior horn cells, mostly by the midthoracic level.

(6) The **tectospinal tract** (Fig. 708) is situated partly in the ventral and partly in the lateral funiculus. It is mainly derived from cells in the superior and inferior colliculi of the opposite side which cross the median raphè in the fountain decussation of Meynert and form the ventral longitudinal bundle of the reticular formation in the brainstem. Its terminals and collaterals end directly or indirectly among the anterior motor horn cells. It is primarily concerned with visual reflexes.

(7) The **sulcomarginal fasciculus** (Fig. 708) occupies a narrow marginal band along the border of the ventral median fissure. It is the caudal continuation as far as the upper thoracic cord of the medial longitudinal fasciculus of the medulla. It takes part in the vestibular and visual reflexes, coordinating movements of the head and eyes.

The Medulla Oblongata

The **medulla oblongata** or **bulb**, as it is commonly called in combined names such as the corticobulbar fibers, is continuous caudally with the spinal cord and rostrally with the pons (Fig. 709). Its dorsal surface fits into the fossa between the hemispheres of the cerebellum. Its approximate measurements are 3 cm. long, 2 cm. wide, and 1.25 cm. thick. The central canal continues upward from the spinal cord through its caudal half, but in the cephalic half the medulla is split open at the dorsal median sulcus, expanding the canal into the fourth ventricle (Fig. 718).

The **ventral median fissure** (*fissura mediana anterior*) (Fig. 717) continues along the medulla to a small pocket at the caudal border of the pons called the **foramen cecum**. It is crossed just rostral to the junction with the spinal cord by a series of oblique bundles which form the pyramidal decussation. Above the decussation delicate **ventral external arcuate fibers** emerge from the fissure and run on the surface to the inferior cerebellar peduncle.

The **dorsal median sulcus** (*sulcus medianus posterior*) (Fig. 718) in the caudal half of the medulla gradually becomes shallower and finally ends where the central canal opens out into the fourth ventricle. The floor of the ventricle, known as the rhomboid fossa, also is marked by a longitudinal groove, the median sulcus.

The **ventral lateral sulcus** (*sulcus lateralis anterior*) and the **dorsal lateral sulcus** (*sulcus lateralis posterior*) correspond to the same sulci in the spinal cord. The fibers of the hypoglossal nerve represent the upward continuation of the ventral spinal nerve roots and emerge in linear series with them from the ventral lateral sulcus. The accessory, vagus, and glossopharyngeal nerves correspond to the dorsal roots and attach to the dorsal lateral sulcus. Although the three districts on each lateral half of the medulla appear to be continuous with the funiculi of the spinal cord, they do not correspond exactly because of changes which take place within the medulla.

The **pyramid** (*pyramis medullæ oblongatæ*) (Fig. 717) is a rounded prominence which lies between the ventral median fissure and the ventral lateral sulcus and appears to be continuous with the ventral funiculus of the spinal cord. It contains mainly motor fibers from the cerebral cortex, corticobulbar and corticospinal fibers. About two-thirds of these fibers cross the midline in bundles, forming the **pyramidal decussation** (*decussatio pyramidum*) (Fig. 717) and become the lateral corticospinal tract of the spinal cord. They obliterate the ventral median fissure thus marking the point of transition from the spinal cord to medulla. The uncrossed one-third of the fibers enter the ventral corticospinal tract.

The **olive** (*oliva*) (Figs. 713, 720) is a prominent oval mass about 1.25 cm. long in what corresponds to an upward continuation of the lateral funiculus of the

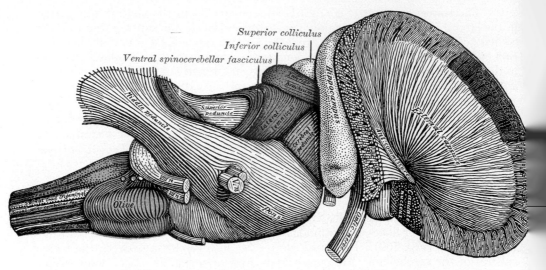

Fig. 710.—Superficial dissection of brain-stem. Lateral view.

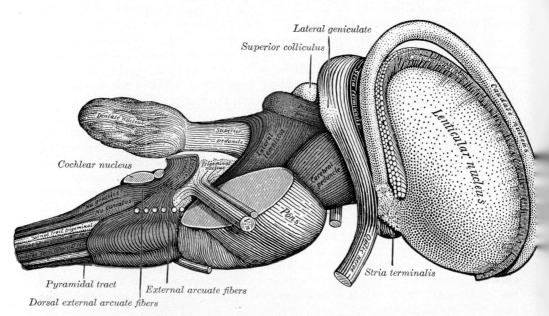

Fig. 711.—Dissection of brain-stem. Lateral view.

spinal cord. It lies between the rootlets of the spinal accessory, vagus, and glossopharyngeal nerves, in the dorsal lateral sulcus on the one hand, and those of the hypoglossal nerve in the ventral lateral sulcus on the other. In the depression between the upper end of the olive and the pons are the roots of the statoacoustic and facial nerves (Fig. 717).

The dorsal district of the medulla differs in its cephalic and caudal halves. The lower half appears to be an upward continuation of the dorsal funiculus of the spinal cord, and lies between the dorsal median sulcus and the dorsal lateral sulcus. The upper end of the fasciculus gracilis forms an elongated swelling, named the

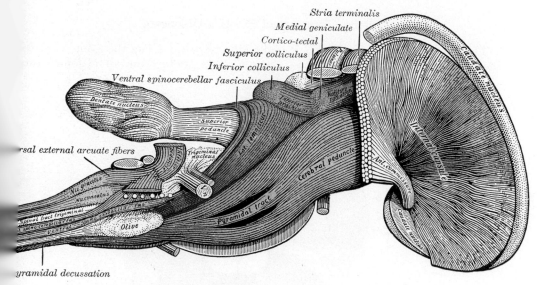

FIG. 712.—Deep dissection of brain-stem. Lateral view.

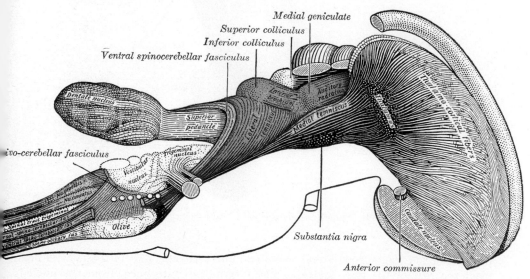

FIG. 713.—Deep dissection of brain-stem. Lateral view.

clava (*tuberculum nuclei gracilis*) (Fig. 718) containing the nucleus gracilis. That of the fasciculus cuneatus forms the **cuneate tubercle** (*tuberculum nuclei cuneati*), containing the nucleus cuneatus. Just lateral to the fasciculus cuneatus is an elevation produced by the substantia gelatinosa (of Rolando) which ends about 1.25 cm. below the pons in the **tuber cinereum** (*tubercle of Rolando*).

54

The cephalic half of the dorsal district of the medulla is composed of two prominent ridges which diverge to help form the lateral boundaries of the **rhomboid fossa** (Fig. 718). They contain the **inferior cerebellar peduncles** or **restiform bodies** (Figs. 710, 711) which connect the spinal cord and medulla with the cerebellum.

Internal Structure of Medulla Oblongata

The medulla changes rapidly as it makes the transition from the spinal cord to the brain stem. The decussation of the pyramids produces an alteration in the

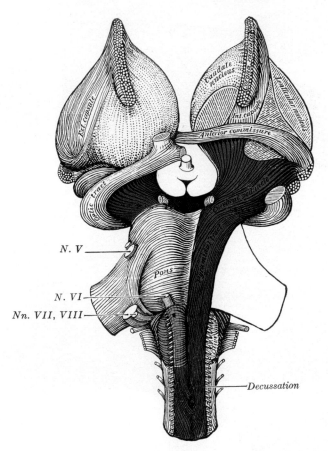

Fig. 714.—Superficial dissection of brain-stem. Ventral view.

position of the tracts from lateral to ventral and separates part of the ventral horn from the rest of the gray matter. The internal arcuate fibers from the nucleus gracilis and cuneatus sweep ventrally around the central gray matter. They separate it from the dorsal gray horn, and decussate between the central gray and the pyramidal tracts. New structures are added, the large inferior olives and the nuclei of certain cranial nerves. The central canal opens out into the fourth ventricle and the central gray becomes spread out in the floor of the rhomboid fossa. As the internal arcuate and other fibers traverse the gray matter, they disperse it into smaller masses, forming the reticular substance.

The **gray substance of the medulla oblongata.**—(1) The **nucleus gracilis** and **nucleus cuneatus** are buried deep to the fibers of the corresponding fasciculi in the clava and cuneate tubercles (Figs. 718, 719). They extend from the caudal end of the medulla to the level of the hypoglossal nerve. They are composed of small and medium sized cells about which the fibers of the fasiculi terminate. Most of the axons of these cells pass ventrally into the **internal arcuate fibers** (Figs. 715, 719).

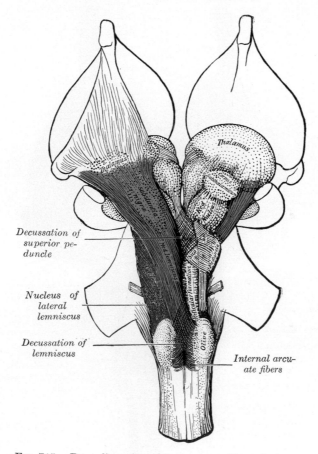

Fig. 715.—Deep dissection of brain-stem. Ventral view.

Others continue as the **dorsal external arcuate fibers** (Figs. 716, 711) into the inferior cerebullar peduncle.

The **lateral** or **accessory cuneate nucleus** occupies a position cephalic and superficial to the nucleus cuneatus. It begins at the caudal end of the olive, enlarging as the nucleus cuneatus decreases and extends into the medial margin of the restiform body. It contains large round or polygonal cells whose axons pass through the inferior cerebellar peduncle into the cerebellum.

(2) The **inferior olivary nucleus** (*nucleus olivaris*) is a characteristically folded gray lamina with an open part or **hilum** facing medially (Fig. 720). The axons of its cells pass out in the medullary white substance of the hilum in a fascicle called the **peduncle of the olive.** These are the olivocerebellar fibers. They cross the raphé in the midline, become part of the system of internal arcuate fibers, pass

partly through and partly around the olivary nucleus of the other side and enter the inferior cerebellar peduncle. The fibers are smaller than the internal arcuate fibers of the medial lemniscus and probably are accompanied by uncrossed olivo-cerebellar fibers. They are distributed to the cerebellar cortex in orderly sequence and there is a close functional association between the olive and the cerebellum.

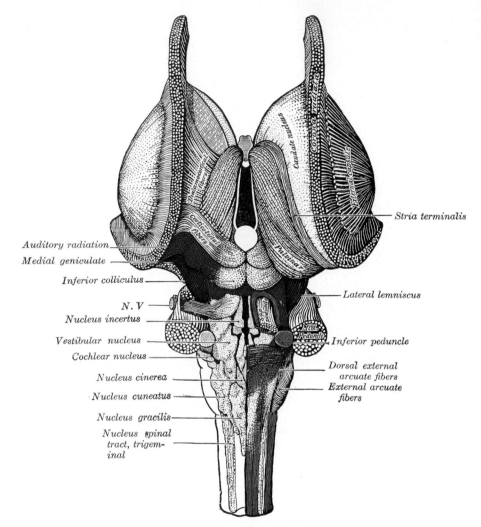

Stria terminalis

Auditory radiation
Medial geniculate

Inferior colliculus

N. V
Nucleus incertus

Vestibular nucleus
Cochlear nucleus

Nucleus cinerea

Nucleus cuneatus

Nucleus gracilis

Nucleus spinal
tract, trigem-
inal

Lateral lemniscus

Inferior peduncle

Dorsal external
arcuate fibers
External arcuate
fibers

Fig. 716.—Dissection of brain-stem. Dorsal view. The nuclear masses of the medulla are taken from model by Weed, Carnegie Publication, No. 19.

Fibers passing from cerebellum to olive have been described. The fibers of the **thalmo-olivary tract** (*central tract of the tegmentum*) which may or may not originate in the thalamus surround the olive in a dense capsule and terminate in relation to the cells of its gray nucleus. Many collaterals from the reticular formation and pyramid enter the olive, and fibers from the spinal cord enter by uncertain paths. The **medial** and **dorsal accessory olivary nuclei** are flattened plates of gray substance placed near the main inferior olivary nucleus (Fig. 720).

As the gray substance of the rostral part of the medulla becomes spread out by the expansion of the central canal into the fourth ventricle, the motor nuclei take up their positions medially and the sensory nuclei laterally in the floor of the rhomboid fossa.

(3) The **hypoglossal nucleus** (*nucleus n. hypoglossi*) (Fig. 719) occupies the central gray column ventral to the central canal in the closed part of the medulla and extends up into the open part in the floor of the rhomboid fossa. Here it produces an elevation, the **trigonum hypoglossi**, in the medial eminence of the **calamus scriptorius** (Fig. 731).

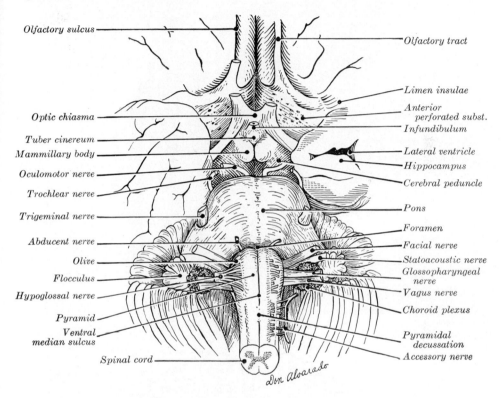

Olfactory sulcus — Olfactory tract — Limen insulae — Anterior perforated subst. — Optic chiasma — Infundibulum — Tuber cinereum — Lateral ventricle — Mammillary body — Hippocampus — Oculomotor nerve — Cerebral peduncle — Trochlear nerve — Trigeminal nerve — Pons — Abducent nerve — Foramen — Olive — Facial nerve — Flocculus — Statoacoustic nerve — Glossopharyngeal nerve — Hypoglossal nerve — Vagus nerve — Pyramid — Choroid plexus — Ventral median sulcus — Pyramidal decussation — Spinal cord — Accessory nerve

Don Alvarado

Fig. 717.—Ventral aspect of the brain stem, showing position of cranial nerves.

(4) The **nucleus ambiguous** (Fig. 719) is the cephalic continuation of the dorsal lateral group of cells in the ventral horn of the spinal cord. It is the motor nucleus of the special visceral motor fibers of the glossopharyngeal, vagus, and accessory nerves which supply the striated muscles of the pharynx and larynx.

(5) The **dorsal motor nucleus of the vagus** (*nucleus dorsalis n. vagi; nucleus alæ cinereæ*) (Fig. 719) occupies the **ala cinerea** of the rhomboid fossa (Fig. 731). It is a long column of cells lying lateral to the hypoglossal nucleus and extending from the decussation of the medial lemniscus through the medulla as far cephalically as the upper limit of the olive (Figs. 720, 724). It is the general visceral efferent nucleus of the vagus nerve supplying parasympathetic fibers to the smooth muscle and glands of the thorax and abdomen and inhibitory fibers to the heart.

(6) The **nucleus of the spinal tract of the trigeminal nerve** (*nucleus tractus spinalis n. trigemini*) is a direct continuation of the substantia gelatinosa (of Rolando) in the spinal cord. It lies between the nucleus cuneatus and the reticular substance (Fig.

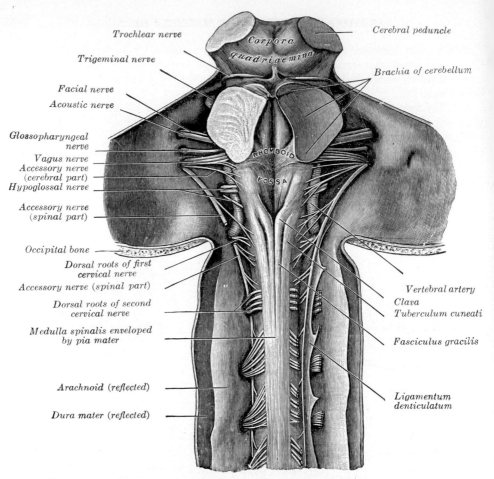

FIG. 718.—The upper part of the medulla spinalis, and the hind- and mid-brains. Dorsal aspect.

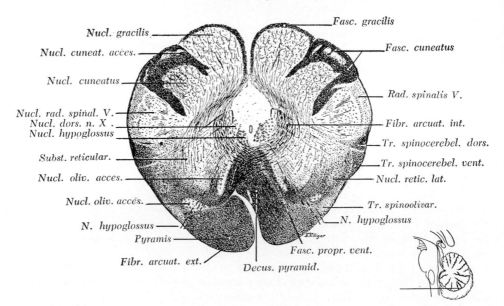

FIG. 719.—Transverse section of medulla oblongata at the decussation of the pyramids. Nuclear groups represented diagrammatically in color. (From Villiger-Addison, courtesy of J. B. Lippincott Co.)

719) and is surrounded by the fibers of its tract, the spinal tract of the trigeminal nerve.

(7) **Nucleus of the tractus solitarius** is a slender nucleus extending the entire length of the medulla, lying lateral to the dorsal nucleus of the vagus (Fig. 719). The caudal ends of the nuclei of the two sides are united dorsal to the central canal in the closed part of the medulla. Its cells are scattered around and among the fibers of its tract. It is especially concerned with taste in the facial, glossopharyngeal and vagus nerves and includes the sensory nucleus of these two nerves.

(8) The **reticular formation** (*substantia reticularis*) (Figs. 715, 719) of the medulla oblongata is a continuation of that of the spinal cord. It is composed of small groups of cells scattered among bundles of fibers. In the portion medial to the

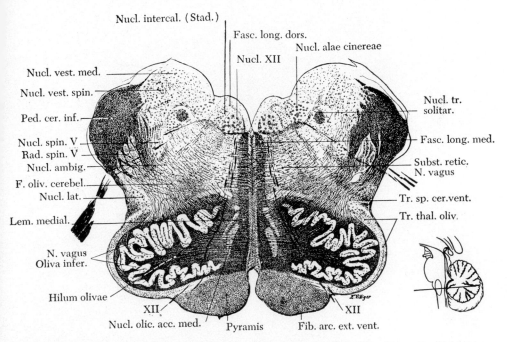

FIG. 720.—Transverse section of medulla oblongata at the middle of the olive. Nuclear groups represented diagrammatically in color. (From Villiger-Addison, courtesy of J. B. Lippincott Co.)

emerging fibers of the hypoglossal nerve, fibers predominate, and it is called the *white reticular substance*. This contains the medial lemniscus, tectospinal tract, and medial longitudinal fasciculus. The part lateral to the hypoglossal fibers and dorsal to the olive in which nuclei predominate is called the *gray reticular substance*. Its nuclei include the **lateral reticular nucleus** and the **nucleus magnocellularis** as well as nuclei of cranial nerves. It contains the internal arcuate fibers, the rubrospinal, thalamo-olivary, ventral and dorsal spinocerebellar, spinothalamic, and spinotectal tracts.

(9) The **nuclei arcuati** are groups of cells serially continuous with the nuclei pontis which lie superficial to the pyramid among the ventral external arcuate fibers.

(10) The **nucleus intercalatus** (*of Staderini*) (Fig. 720) occupies a position near the midline at the caudal end of the rhomboid fossa. It lies between the dorsal motor nucleus of the vagus and the hypoglossal nucleus. Some of its limits are not clearly

defined, making it appear to be continuous with the medial vestibular nucleus and
nucleus prepositus cephalically. It receives fibers from the vestibular nucleus, the
glossopharyngeal and vagus nerves, and from the dorsal longitudinal bundle (of
Schutz), close to which it lies. Its axons enter the reticular formation, and the
hypoglossal and vagus nuclei. Connections with the dorsal bundle and the nucleus
salivatorius probably give it a visceral function.

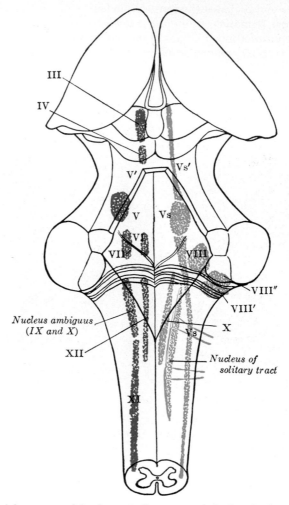

Fig. 721.—The cranial nerve nuclei schematically represented; dorsal view. Motor nuclei in
sensory in blue. (The olfactory and optic centers are not represented.)

(11) The **nucleus prepositus** occupies about the same position as the nucleus
intercalatus and may have the same function. It extends between the hypoglossal
and abducens nuclei.

The **white substance of the medulla oblongata.**—(1) The **internal arcuate fibers**
(*fibræ arcuatæ internæ*) (Fig. 719) are mainly from two sources, (*a*) the nucleus
gracilis and cuneatus, and (*b*) the inferior olive. The gracile and cuneate fibers
are larger than the olivary fibers. They curve around the central gray toward the
raphé and, as they cross the midline, form the **decussation of the medial lemniscus**
(*decussatio lemniscorum*).

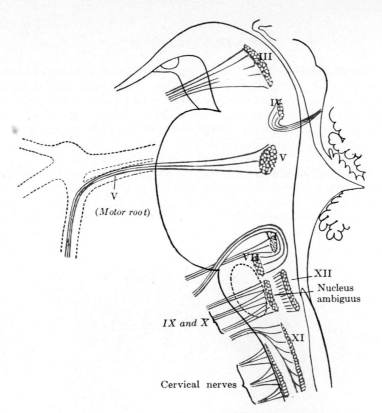

FIG. 722.—Nuclei of origin of cranial motor nerves schematically represented; lateral view.

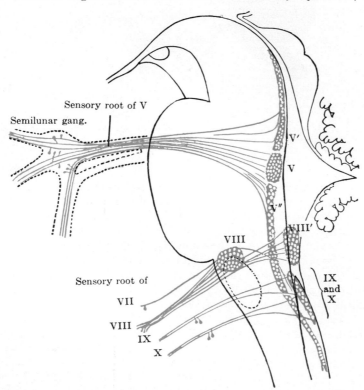

FIG. 723.—Primary terminal nuclei of the afferent (sensory) cranial nerves schematically represented—lateral view. The olfactory and optic centers are not represented.

(2) The **medial lemniscus** (Figs. 715, 720) occupies the angle between the pyramid and the inferior olive, beside the median raphé. The fibers running parallel are arranged so that those from the nucleus cuneatus (leg and lower trunk) are in the ventral part of the bundle; those from the nucleus gracilis (upper limb and trunk) in the dorsal part. As the band reaches the upper end of the olive in its cephalic course, it swings laterally and spreads out into a thin ribbon dorsal to the pontine nuceli.

(3) The **ventral spinothalamic tract** (Fig. 708) is deflected dorsally by the pyramidal decussation and continues rostrad just dorsal to the medial lemniscus. Where the latter swings laterally in front of the olive, the ventral spinothalamic tract also turns laterally and accompanies the lateral spinothalamic tract to the thalamus.

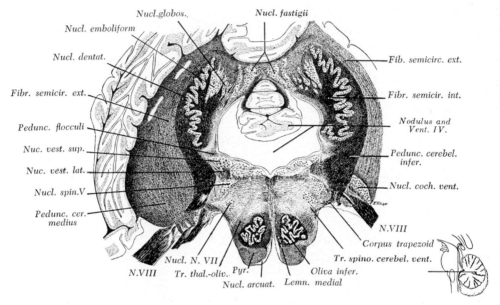

FIG. 724.—Transverse section through medulla oblongata and cerebellar peduncles at the level of the eighth cranial nerve. Nuclear groups represented diagrammatically in color. (From Villiger-Addison, courtesy of J. B. Lippincott Co.)

(4) The **dorsal spinocerebellar tract** (Fig. 713) leaves the lateral district of the medulla to enter the inferior cerebellar peduncle of the same side on its way to the vermis. The ventral spinocerebellar tract (Fig. 712) retains its lateral position in the medulla until it passes deep to the external arcuate fibers (Fig. 711). It lies between the olive and the roots of the vagus and glossopharyngeal nerves.

(5) The two **pyramids** (Fig. 720) contain the motor fibers from the precentral motor cortex, the corticobulbar fibers to the nuclei of cranial nerves, and the corticospinal to the ventral horns of the cord. At the caudal limit of the medulla, about two-thirds cross in the pyramidal decussation (Fig. 714) and continue in the cord as the lateral corticospinal tract. The fibers remaining on the same side, those more laterally placed, continue as the ventral corticospinal tract.

(6) The **tectospinal tract** lies close to the midline in the upper part of the medulla just dorsal to the medial lemniscus. It becomes more laterally placed as it courses caudad through the region of the decussations and finally reaches its ventral position in the spinal cord.

(7) The **medial longitudinal fasciculus** (*fasciculus longitudiinalis medalis*) (Fig. 720) occupies a postion close to the midline between the tectospinal tract and dorsal gray substance. It is a continuation upward of the sulcomarginal fasciculus of the spinal cord.

(8) The **inferior cerebellar peduncle** or **restiform body** (*pedunculus cerebellaris inferior*) (Figs. 710, 720) contains the following fibers: (1) the dorsal spinocerebellar tract, (2) the olivocerebellar fibers, (3) fibers from the ventral arcuate nuclei, (4) fibers from the lateral reticular nucleus, (5) dorsal external arcuate fibers, (6) fibers from the vestibular nuclei, and (7) probable cerebellobulbar, cerebello-olivary, and cerebelloreticular fibers.

The Pons

The **pons** (*pons Varolii*) produces a prominent swelling with well-defined borders on the ventral surface of the brain stem, between the medulla oblongata and the cerebral peduncles of the midbrain (Fig. 709). The dorsal surface, where it forms the cephalic part of the rhomboid fossa (Fig. 731), is hidden by the cerebellum. The ventral prominence consists of transverse strands arched across the midline like a bridge and gathered at each side into a compact bundle or arm, the middle cerebellar peduncle. The midline of the pons has a shallow depression, the sulcus basilaris, in which the basilar artery lies, and the entire structure rests upon the clivus of the sphenoid bone. At its caudal border are the origins of the abducent, facial, and statoacoustic nerves. At its cephalic border, the origin of the trigeminal nerve marks the boundary between the pons and the middle cerebellar peduncle (Fig. 710).

Structure of the pons.—The pons is composed of two parts which differ in appearance and structure (Fig. 725). The ventral or basilar portion consists of masses of transverse fibers, separated here and there by longitudinal bundles and small nuclei. The dorsal portion, called the tegmentum, is an upward continuation of the reticular formation of the medulla, with similar tracts and nuclei.

Nuclei of the tegmentum of the pons.—(1) The **nucleus of the abducens nerve** (*nucleus n. abducentis*; *N. VI*) forms part of the dorsal gray substance in the medial eminence of the floor of the fourth ventricle, deep to the colliculus facialis (Fig. 731). The axons of its cells penetrate the pons close to the median raphé and emerge on the ventral surface at the caudal border of the pons (Fig. 717).

(2) The **nucleus of the facial nerve** (*nucleus n. facialis*; *N. VII*) is situated deep in the reticular formation lateral to the abducens nucleus (Fig. 725). Its fibers take a tortuous course, first toward the floor of the fourth ventricle. Next, they loop around the abducens nucleus forming the internal genu and causing the elevation of the facial colliculus (Fig. 731). Finally they pass laterally and ventrally, penetrating the substance of the pons, and emerge at its caudal border between the olive and inferior cerebellar peduncle (Fig. 717).

(3) The **motor nucleus of the trigeminal nerve** (*nucleus motorius n. trigemini*; *N. V*) is situated in the rostral part of the pons, close to its dorsal surface along the lateral margin of the fourth ventricle (Fig. 725).

(4) The **sensory nuclei of the trigeminal nerve** represent a cephalic continuation of the sensory column of the spinal cord known as the substantia gelatinosa (of Rolando). The fibers entering the pons from the trigeminal (semilunar, Gasserian) ganglion divide into ascending and descending branches. The descending branches go to the caudal nucleus, the **nucleus of the spinal tract of the trigeminal nerve** (Fig. 720) described as part of the medulla (page 853). Its axons cross the midline and run upward to the thalamus just medial to the lateral spinothalamic tract. The ascending branches enter the **main sensory nucleus of the trigeminal nerve** (*nucleus*

sensorius superior n. trigemini; *N. V*) which lies lateral to the motor nucleus close to the superior cerebellar peduncle (Fig. 725). Its axons cross to the opposite side to join the medial margin of the medial lemniscus on their way to the thalamus. These two nuclei correspond to the posterior gray columns of the cord. The **mesencephalic root** (*tractus mesencephalicus*) of the trigeminal nerve consists of axons from cells in the central gray around the aqueduct and is included in the description of the midbrain.

(5) The **nucleus of the cochlear division** of the eighth nerve (*nucleus n. stato-acustici*) in the caudal part of the pons, is divided into two parts, a **dorsal** and a **ventral nucleus** (*nuclei cochleares, ventralis et dorsalis*) (Fig. 724). They are continuous with each other and lie on the dorsal and lateral aspect of the restiform body, producing an eminence, the acoustic tubercle (Fig. 731).

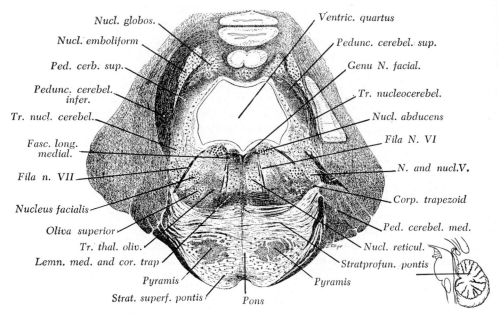

FIG. 725.—Transverse section through pons and cerebellum at the level of the facial nerve Nuclear groups represented diagrammatically in color. (From Villiger-Addison, courtesy of J. B. Lippincott Co.)

(6) The **superior olive** consists of two or three small masses of gray substance in the tegmentum of the pons rostral to the inferior olive and just dorsolateral to the trapezoid body (Fig. 725). It receives terminals and collaterals from the cochlear nuclei of the same and opposite sides by way of the trapezoid body. From its fusiform cells axons pass dorsally as the peduncle of the superior olive, and cross in the midline ventral to the abducens nucleus. The termination of these fibers is not well established; some enter the medial longitudinal fasciculus and others join the lateral lemniscus on both sides (Stotler '53).

(7) The **nuclei of the vestibular division** (*nuclei vestibulares*) of the eighth nerve (*nuclei n. stato-acustici*) occupy a large area in the lateral part of the floor of the fourth ventricle (Fig. 724). (*a*) The **medial nucleus** (*nucleus medialis; chief, dorsal, or triangular nucleus of Schwalbe*) is the largest and occupies most of the **area acoustica** (*area vestibularis*) of the rhomboid fossa (Fig. 731). (*b*) The **lateral vestibular nucleus** (*nucleus lateralis; nucleus of Deiters*) lies close to the restiform body at the entrance of the vestibular nerve. (*c*) The **superior vestibular nucleus**

(*nucleus superior; nucleus of Bechterew*) is just caudal to the motor nucleus of the trigeminal nerve. It occupies the wall of the ventricle and is almost continuous with the central nuclei of the cerebellum. (*d*) The **inferior nucleus** (*nucleus inferior; nucleus of the descending tract*) is medial to the restiform body and dorsal to the trigeminal spinal tract extending caudally almost to the nucleus cuneatus.

The **ventral or basilar part of the pons** (*pars basilaris pontis*).—The transverse fibers are divided into two groups, superficial and deep, by the scattered bundles of longitudinal fasciculi (Fig. 726). The **superficial transverse fibers** (*fibræ pontis superficialis*) form a thick layer on the ventral surface of the pons (Figs. 725, 726).

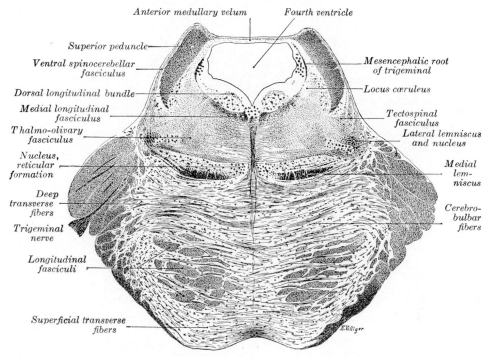

Anterior medullary velum

Fourth ventricle

Superior peduncle

Ventral spinocerebellar fasciculus

Dorsal longitudinal bundle

Medial longitudinal fasciculus

Thalmo-olivary fasciculus

Nucleus, reticular formation

Deep transverse fibers

Trigeminal nerve

Longitudinal fasciculi

Superficial transverse fibers

Mesencephalic root of trigeminal

Locus cœruleus

Tectospinal fasciculus

Lateral lemniscus and nucleus

Medial lemniscus

Cerebrobulbar fibers

Fig. 726.—Transverse section through cephalic part of pons. Nuclear groups represented diagrammatically in color. (From Villiger-Addison, courtesy of J. B. Lippincott Co.)

They are gathered into a massive bundle at each side, the brachium pontis or middle cerebellar peduncle. The **deep transverse fibers** (*fibræ pontis profundæ*) partly interweave with the longitudinal fasciculi and partly lie dorsal to them. They also enter the brachium pontis at each side.

The **longitudinal fasciculi** enter the pons from the cerebral peduncles of the midbrain and split up into smaller bundles, separated by transverse fibers and small pontine nuclei (Fig. 712). They are composed of two types of fibers. (*a*) The corticospinal fibers pass through the pons in bundles which are gathered together again at its caudal limit to form the pyramid of the medulla. They give collaterals to the pontine nuclei. (*b*) The corticopontine fibers end in the pontine nuclei of the same side and are relayed by the transverse fibers through the brachium pontis to the cerebellum of the opposite side.

The **pontine nuclei** (*nuclei pontis*) (Fig. 725) are small groups of cells scattered between the transverse fibers. They are relay stations in the corticopontocerebellar path.

The **tracts traversing the tegmental part of the pons** are chiefly the upward continuation of those of the reticular formation of the medulla: (1) the medial lemniscus, (2) the spinothalamic tracts, (3) the ventral spinocerebellar tract, (4) the thalamo-olivary fasciculus, (5) the medial longitudinal fasciculus (Fig. 726). In addition there are the aberrant pyramidal fibers and the trapezoid body.

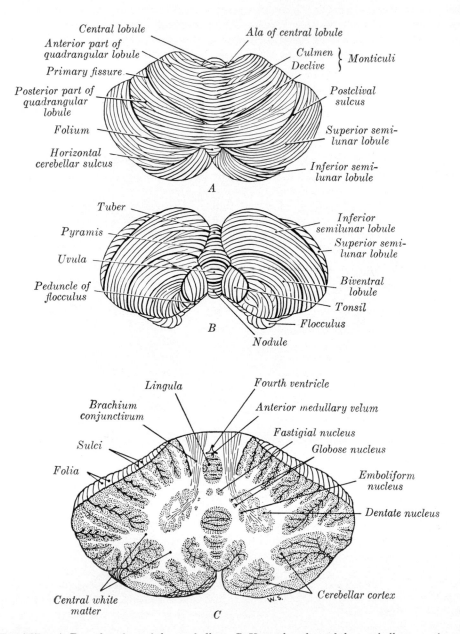

Fig. 727.—*A*, Dorsal surface of the cerebellum; *B*, Ventral surface of the cerebellum so oriented with relation to *A* as to indicate the continuity of folium and tuber; *C*, Horizontal section of the cerebellum showing the arrangement of the cortical gray matter and the locations of the central nuclei within the white matter (after Sobotta-McMurrich).

Aberrant pyramidal fibers leave the medial margins of the cerebral peduncles in the midbrain, turn dorsally, leaving the main bundles of fibers from the cortex, and run caudalward just medial to the medial lemniscus. Most of them cross, but some remain ipsilateral, and terminate in the motor nuclei of the cranial nerves.

The **trapezoid body** (*corpus trapezoideum*) is formed by a concentration of transverse fibers which show prominently in sections of the caudal part of the pons (Fig. 725). They occupy the ventral portion of the tegmentum where they mingle with the fibers of the medial lemniscus, crossing them at right angles. They arise primarily in the ventral and dorsal cochlear nuclei, cross the midline and turn cephalad at the superior olive of the opposite side to form the bulk of the lateral lemniscus. This is part of the central acoustic pathway.

The Cerebellum

The cerebellum rests on the floor of the posterior cranial fossa (Fig. 190) and occupies the interval between the brain stem and the occipital lobes of the cerebrum (Fig. 709). The tentorium cerebelli separates it from the occipital lobes, and the fourth ventricle intervenes between it and the brain stem. It is attached to the latter, however, by three peduncles (Fig. 728): (1) the superior peduncle or brachium conjunctivum connecting it with the midbrain, (2) the middle peduncle or brachium pontis connecting with the pons, and (3) the inferior peduncle or restiform body connecting with the medulla. Its average weight is between 140 and 150 gms.; the ratio of its size compared with the cerebrum is about 1 to 8 in the adult and 1 to 20 in the infant.

The cerebellum is composed of a narrow median portion, the **vermis** (Fig. 727), and two **hemispheres** which protrude laterally and posteriorly. On the superior surface, which is rather flat, the vermis forms a slight ridge, the **monticulus**. Posteriorly, a deep cleft between the hemispheres, called the posterior cerebellar notch, is occupied by the falx cerebelli. More anteriorly, over the medulla, the space between the hemispheres is called the **vallecula cerebelli** (Buchanan '37).

The surface of the cerebellum, the **cortex**, is thrown up into numerous parallel ridges called **folia cerebelli** which are separated by **fissures** (*fissuræ cerebelli*). The latter cut deeply into the substance and ramify like the leaves of a plant into what is called the **arbor vitæ** (Fig. 731). The fissures divide the cerebellum into lobes and lobules.

The superior part of the **vermis** beginning at the anterior medullary velum is composed of the lingula, the central lobule (*lobus centralis*), the culmen and declive of the *monticulus*, and the folium. The inferior vermis comprises the tuber, pyramis, uvula, and nodulus (Figs. 727).

Correspondingly, the **hemispheres** contain the vinculum as a lateral continuation of the lingula, separated by the precentral fissure from the ala of the central lobule. The anterior and posterior semilunar lobules, continuous with the culmen and declive, are separated from the ala and central lobule by the preculminate fissure and from each other by the anterior superior fissure or fissura prima. The superior and inferior semilunar lobules, continuous with the folium and tuber, are separated from the declive and posterior semilunar lobule by the posterior superior fissure and from each other by the horizontal sulcus.

Based upon comparative anatomy and embryology a more useful and functionally correlated division of the cerebellum (Larsell '47) is as follows (Fig. 729): The small floculonodular lobe is separated from the corpus cerebelli or the remainder of the cerebellum by the posterolateral and uvulonodular fissures. The corpus cerebelli is divided by the fissura prima into anterior and posterior lobes. The lobules of the anterior lobe are the lingula, central lobule, and culmen with their lateral connections. The posterior lobe contains the lobulus simplex or declive and posterior semilunar lobule; the ansiform lobule comprises the superior and inferior semilunar lobules, called crus I and crus II, and the folium and tuber of the vermis.

Internal structure of the cerebellum.—The cerebellum consists of an outer layer of gray substance, the cortex, and an inner core of white substance, in which certain nuclear groups are imbedded (Fig. 731).

White substance of the cerebellum.—The **central white substance** (*corpus medullare*) extends out into the **lobules** and **laminæ**, forming plate-like cores (*laminæ albæ*) for the **folia.** It consists of the fibræ propriæ and the projection fibers which pass through the superior, middle, and inferior peduncles.

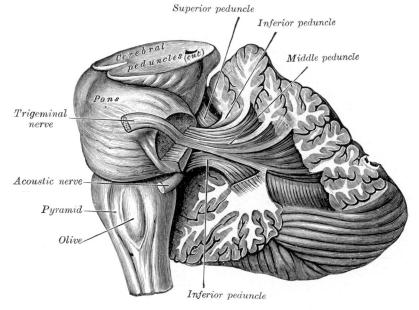

FIG. 728.—Dissection showing the projection fibers of the cerebellum. (After E. B. Jamieson.)

The **inferior cerebellar peduncle** or **restiform body** (*pedunculus cerebellaris inferior*) (Fig. 728) on each side forms the lateral wall of the fourth ventricle in its caudal half. It connects the cerebellum with the medulla oblongata and contains largely afferent fibers. (1) The dorsal spinocerebellar tract is a proprioceptive path from the nucleus dorsalis of the same side of the spinal cord which ends mainly in the superior vermis. (2) The dorsal external arcuate fibers are also proprioceptive from the nucleus gracilis and cuneatus of the same side. (3) The olivocerebellar tract from the inferior olivary nucleus crosses for the most part and goes to the cortex of the hemisphere, the vermis, and the central nuclei. (4) The ventral external arcuate fibers, crossed and uncrossed, come from the arcuate and reticular nuclei of the medulla. (5) The vestibulocerebellar tract, a proprioceptive path, is derived partly from direct fibers from the vestibular nuclei. They occupy the medial segment of the peduncle, along with fibers from the sensory nuclei of the cranial nerves, and end in the cortex of the vermis and in the central nuclei. (6) Also there are fibers from the central nuclei of the cerebellum to the vestibular nuclei and nuclei of the reticular formation.

The **middle cerebellar peduncle** or **brachium pontis** (*pedunculus cerebellaris medius*) (Fig. 728) of each side contains the transverse fibers of the pons which originate in the pontine nuclei of the opposite and the same side. They are distributed to all parts of the cerebellar cortex, completing the extensive cortico-ponto-cerebellar pathway which is particularly important in muscular synergy.

The **superior cerebellar peduncle** or **brachium conjunctivum** (*pedunculus cerebellaris superior*) (Fig. 728) forms the lateral wall on each side of the cephalic portion of the fourth ventricle. The bulk of its fibers are efferent, mainly from the nucleus dentatus (Fig. 724), which penetrate deeply into the tegmentum of the mesencephalon and cross in the decussation of the brachium conjunctivum. They are part of the cerebello-rubro-spinal pathway. The fibers of the ventral spinocerebellar tract (Gower) enter the cerebellum by arching over the main part of the brachium conjunctivum. They end in the medial portion of the anterior lobe. The uncinate bundle (of Russell) of the fastigiobulbar tract also hooks around the brachium conjunctivum just ventral to the spinocerebellar tract. Its fibers arise in the nucleus fastigii, cross, and reach the vestibular and reticular nuclei.

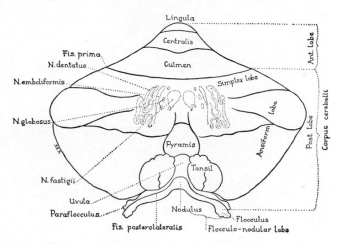

Fig. 729.—Diagrammatic representation of the lobes of the cerebellum redrawn after Larsell with the cerebellar nuclei as illustrated by Jakob projected in dotted lines.

The **fibræ propriæ.**—(1) Commissural fibers cross the midline at the cephalic and caudal parts of the vermis, connecting the two sides. (2) Association and arcuate fibers connect parts of the same side of the cerebellum.

Cerebellar cortex (*cortex cerebelli*).—The gray substance of the cortex forms a characteristic covering for the white substance or medullary core of the primary and secondary laminæ of the folia.

Microscopic appearance of cortex.—The cortex consists of two layers, an external molecular layer and an internal granule cell layer, separated by an incomplete stratum of Purkinje cells (Fig. 730).

The cells of the external gray or **molecular layer** (*stratum moleculare*) are arranged in two strata. An outer layer of small cells with branched axons and an inner layer containing the basket cells. The axons of the basket cells run for some distance parallel with the surface of the folium, giving off collaterals which pass vertically toward the Purkinje cells. They ramify about the bodies of the latter in basket-like networks.

The **Purkinje cells** have large flask-shaped cell bodies which lie in a single stratum at the separation of the molecular and nuclear layers. From the neck of the flask one or more large dendrites extend out into the molecular layer forming extensive and characteristic arborizations (Fig. 730). Both cell and arborization are flattened, narrow in the direction of the long axis of the folium but spread out widely in a plane perpendicular to this. The axon of the Purkinje cell leaves the bottom of the flask and runs toward the center of the folium. It passes through the nuclear layer, becomes myelinated, and traverses the white substance to the central nuclei of the cerebellum. It gives off fine collaterals as it passes through the granular layer, some of which run back into the molecular layer.

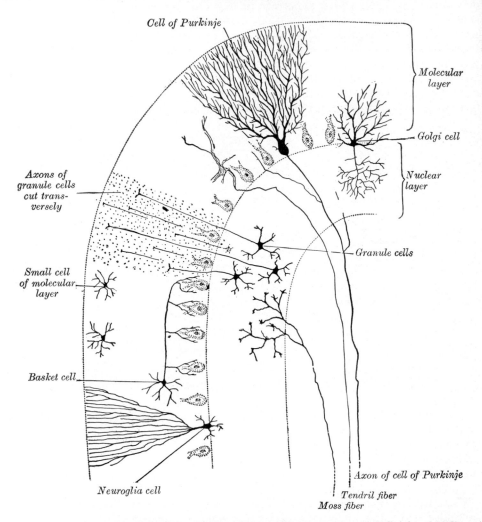

Cell of Purkinje

Molecular layer

Golgi cell

Axons of granule cells cut transversely

Nuclear layer

Granule cells

Small cell of molecular layer

Basket cell

Axon of cell of Purkinje

Neuroglia cell

Tendril fiber

Moss fiber

Fig. 730.—Transverse section of a cerebellar folium. (Diagrammatic, after Cajal and Kölliker.)

The **granular layer** (*statum granulosum; nuclear layer*) (Fig. 730) contains numerous small nerve cells of a reddish-brown color called granule cells. Most of the cells are spherical and are provided with short spider-like dendrites. Their axons pass peripherally into the molecular layer, bifurcate, and run at right angles to the axis of the folium. In the outer part of the granular layer there are larger Golgi type II cells, whose dendrites ramify in the molecular layer and axons in the nuclear layer.

The great majority of afferent fibers to the cerebellum terminate in one of two ways. (1) Fibers end in the nuclear layer by dividing into numerous branches or moss-like appendages around the cells. They were called **moss fibers** by Ramon y Cajal, and appear to come from the inferior peduncle. (2) The clinging or **tendril fibers** can be traced into the molecular layer where they cling to the branches of the Purkinje cells. They were said to come mainly from the middle peduncle.

The **central gray substance** of the cerebellum is divided into four nuclei on each side, a large nucleus dentatus and three small nuclei, emboliformis, globosus, and fastigii (Fig. 724) (Chambers and Sprague '55).

The **nucleus dentatus** (Fig. 731) is situated near the center of the central mass of white substance in each hemisphere. It consists of a folded gray lamina, very similar to the inferior olive, with a hilum facing medially through which most of the fibers emerge on their way to the superior peduncle.

The **nucleus emboliformis** lies just medial to the dentatus, partly covering its hilum. The **nucleus globosus** consist of several small, irregular groups of cells between the emboliformis and fastigii. Some authors regard the emboliformis and globosus as parts of one nucleus, the **nucleus interpositus**. The **nucleus fastigii** is situated close to the midline at the cephalic end of the superior vermis and immediately over the roof of the fourth ventricle, from which it is separated by a thin layer of white substance.

The Fourth Ventricle

The **fourth ventricle** (*ventriculus quartus*) (Fig. 731) is a flattened diamond-shaped cavity containing spinal fluid. It is the remains of the cavity of the embryonic neural tube in the hindbrain, that is, the region of the cerebellum, pons, and upper medula. The narrow cephalic angle opens into the cerebral aqueduct, and the narrow caudal angle into the central canal of the closed portion of the medulla. Its roof is composed of structures associated with the attachment of the cerebellum; its floor is the rhomboid fossa of the brain stem; its lateral walls are narrowed to mere boundaries.

The cephalic portion of the **roof** or **dorsal wall** (*tremen ventriculi quarti*) is formed by the superior cerebellar peduncles and the anterior medullary velum (Figs. 731, 732). Caudally it is formed by the posterior medullary velum, tela choroidea and choroid plexus, the taenia of the fourth ventricle, the ligula, and the obex. The superior peduncles are separated as they emerge from the central white substance of the cerebellum but converge as they approach the inferior colliculi. Between them is the **anterior medullary velum**, a thin white lamina which is continuous with the vermis and over which the lingula is prolonged. The frenulum veli, from between the inferior colliculi, joins the anterior velum where the trochlear nerves emerge.

The **posterior medullary velum** (*velum medullare posterius*) (Fig. 732) is a thin sheet composed of ependyma on the inside and pia mater on the outside. It stretches from the cerebellar attachment of the anterior medullary velum at the middle of the ventricle down to the clava, where it is called the **taenia ventriculi quarti**, becoming gradually narrower and ending caudally in the **obex**. Each lateral angle of the diamond-shaped cavity of the fourth ventricle is prolonged into the **lateral recess** which lies over the striæ medullares and under the choroid plexus.

The **choroid plexus** (*plexus chorioideus ventriculi quarti*) (Fig. 732) is an elongated tuft of tortuous blood vessels chiefly of capillary size, protruding into the fourth ventricle from its roof. The vessels belong to the layer of pia mater, the vascular coat of the brain, but are covered everywhere with the epithelial ependyma lining the ventricle. The plexus on each side is shaped like an inverted letter L with a median part close to the midline and a lateral part extending out into and somewhat beyond the lateral recess (Fig. 717).

Foramina or **openings in the roof of the fourth ventricle.**—There are three openings in the roof of the fourth ventricle through which the spinal fluid produced by the choroid plexuses can escape into the subarachnoid space. A **median aperture** (*apertura mediana ventriculi quarti; foramen of Magendie*) is just in front of the obex. Two **lateral apertures** (*aperturæ laterales ventriculi quarti; foramina of Luschka*) are located at the extremities of the lateral recesses.

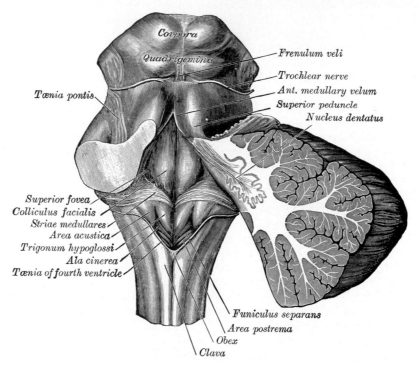

Fig. 731.—The floor of the fourth ventricle or rhomboid fossa after the structures of the roof have been cut or pulled aside.

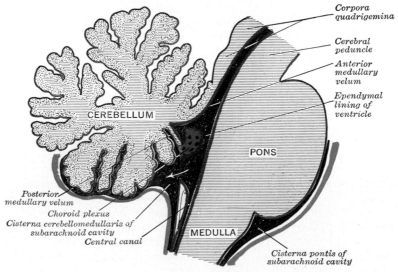

Fig. 732.—Scheme of roof of fourth ventricle. The arrow is in the foramen of Magendie.

The **rhomboid fossa** (*fossa rhomboidea*) (Fig. 731) occupies the floor or ventral wall of the fourth ventricle. It is formed by the dorsal surface of the pons and of the cephalic or open half of the medulla (Fig. 718). It is divided into a triangular cephalic portion with its apex at the cerebral aqueduct, a triangular caudal portion with its apex at the central canal of the medulla, and an intermediate portion prolonged outward into the lateral recesses. The apical part of the caudal portion is called the **calamus scriptorius** from its resemblance to the point of a quill pen.

The fossa is divided into symmetrical halves by a **median sulcus**. On each side of this sulvus is the **medial eminence** (*eminentia medialis*) which is bounded laterally by the **sulcus limitans** (Fig. 731). In the cephalic portion, the medial eminence occupies most of the fossa and contains an oval swelling, the **colliculus facialis** (Fig. 731), which overlies the root of the facial nerve as it encircles the nucleus of the abducens nerve. In the caudal portion, the medial eminence contains the **trigonum hypoglossi** (Fig. 731), overlying the nucleus of the hypoglossal nerve and the nucleus intercalatus.

Between the colliculus facialis and the brachium pontis the sulcus limitans widens into a flattened depression, the **superior fovea** (Fig. 731). Similarly, at the level of the trigonum hypoglossi is a depression, the **inferior fovea**. The cephalic portion of the sulcus is called the **locus coeruleus** because of a bluish color imparted to it by an underlying patch of deeply pigmented nerve cells termed the *substantia ferruginea*. Lateral to the sulcus and foveæ, in the intermediate portion of the pons, is a rounded elevation named the **area acustica** (*area vestibularis*) (Fig. 731) which extends out into the lateral recess as the **tuberculum acusticum**. The **striæ medullares** (Fig. 731) are raised bundles which cross the area acustica and medial eminence to disappear in the median sulcus. Between the trigonum hypoglossi and the caudal part of the area acustica is a dark triangular area, the **ala cinerea**, or **triangle of the vagus nerve** (*trigonum n. vagi*). The caudal part of the ala cinerea is crossed by a narrow translucent ridge, the *funiculus separans*, and between the latter and the clava is a small tongue-shaped region, the **area postrema** (Fig. 731) (Brizzee '54).

THE MIDBRAIN OR MESENCEPHALON

The mesencephalon or midbrain is a short constricted segment of the brain stem connecting the pons and cerebellum with the forebrain. Its ventral portion contains the cerebral peduncles; its dorsal portion, called the **tectum**, contains the corpora quadrigemina (Fig. 718). The cerebral aqueduct, connecting the fourth and third ventricles, is surrounded by the central gray stratum of the midbrain.

The two prominent ridges formed by the **cerebral peduncles** (Fig. 717) diverge as they approach the cerebral hemispheres, leaving a triangular depressed area, the **interpeduncular fossa**. The floor of this fossa is called the **posterior perforated substance** due to the numerous apertures for small blood vessels which penetrate it. At the angle between the medial surface of the peduncle and the perforated substance is a longitudinal furrow, the oculomotor sulcus, from which the oculomotor nerve emerges.

The **corpora quadrigemina** (*tectum of midbrain*) are four rounded prominences, the right and left **superior**, and right and left **inferior colliculi** (Figs. 731, 739), separated by a cruciate sulcus. At the upper end of the longitudinal part of this sulcus is a slight depression for the pineal body. At the lower end a white band, the **frenulum veli**, continues down into the anterior medullary velum. On each side of this band the trochlear nerve emerges and swings around the outside of the peduncles. The superior colliculi are larger than the inferior and oval in shape; the inferior are more prominent and hemispherical.

The **superior brachium** (*brachium colliculi superius*) (Fig. 739) extends lateralward from the superior colliculus. It passes under the pulvinar of the thalamus and above the medial geniculate body to reach the lateral geniculate body and the optic tract. Its fibers connect the occipital lobe or visual cortex with the superior colliculus. The **inferior brachium** (*brachium colliculi inferius*) passes in a cephalic and ventral direction to the medial geniculate body (Fig. 739). Its fibers connect the lateral lemniscus, medial geniculate body, and temporal lobe or auditory area of the cerebral cortex.

Internal Structure of the Mesencephalon.—The **cerebral peduncle** (*crus cerebri*) is separated by the substantia nigra into a ventral part, the **crusta** or **basis pedunculi**, and a more dorsal part, the **tegmentum** (Fig. 735). The crusta is made up principally of longitudinal bundles of efferent fibers from the cells of the cerebral cortex, the corticospinal and corticobulbar tracts. The fibers from the motor cortex occupy the middle three-fifths and continue mainly as the pyramids in the medulla oblongata. The frontopontine fibers occupy the medial fifth, and the parieto-temporopontine fibers the lateral fifth. In addition the fibers of the aberrant pyramidal tracts run in the most medial, lateral, and deepest layers of the crusta.

The **substantia nigra** (Fig. 735) is a layer of gray substance containing numerous deeply pigmented nerve cells. It extends from the cephalic part of the pons to the subthalamus. The *zona compacta* is the layer of gray substance next to the tegmentum. The *zona reticulata* is adjacent to the crusta and sends scattered prolongations between the bundles of its fibers.

The **tegmentum of the midbrain** is continuous with that of the pons and contains most of the same gray columns and fiber tracts as well as additional ones. It is also continued without sharp demarcation into the subthalamus of the diencephalon.

Nuclei of the Midbrain.—(1) The **nucleus of the mesencephalic root of the trigeminal nerve** (*nucleus tr. mesencephalicus n. trigemini*) (Fig. 735) forms a scattered strand in the lateral part of the central gray which surrounds the aqueduct. It also extends down along the lateral angle of the fourth ventricle to the main trigeminal nucleus. The axons of its cells gather at the lateral border of the nucleus and reach the motor root of the nerve, probably serving as its proprioceptive fibers.

(2) The **nucleus of the trochlear nerve** (*nucleus n. trochlearis*) (Fig. 734) is at the level of the inferior colliculus. It is a compact group of cells in the ventral part of the central gray close to the midline and to the medial longitudinal fasciculus. The trochlear fibers arch dorsally around the central gray, decussate in the anterior medullary velum, and emerge at the dorsal surface of the brain stem just caudal to the inferior colliculus (Fig. 717).

(3) The **nucleus of the oculomotor nerve** (*nucleus n. oculomotorius*) (Fig. 735) appears in a cross section in the interval between the V-shaped section of the medial longitudinal fasciculi of the two sides, immediately rostral to the trochlear nucleus. It extends as far as the rostral limit of the superior colliculus. Its cells are somewhat separated by fibers of the medial longitudinal fasciculus and one group of cells bridges the midline in what is called the *nucleus of Perlia* (see page 914). Its fibers run ventrally through the region of the red nucleus and emerge medial to the basis pedunculi (Fig. 743).

(4) The **central gray** (*substantia grisea centralis*) surrounding the aqueduct is continuous with the periventricular system of the hypothalamus. The nerve cells are small and arranged in a number of groups. The *nucleus of Darkschewitsch* in the ventrolateral margin at the transition between the midbrain and hypothalamus is better defined and contains larger cells. It is closely associated with the medial longitudinal fasciculus topographically and probably functionally.

(5) The **reticular formation** is continuous with the reticular nucleus of the thalamus, the zona incerta, and the lateral region of the hypothalamus. Central, lateral, and

dorsolateral nuclei have been defined. The *interstitial nucleus* (of Cajal) is located at the dorsomedial border of the capsule of the red nucleus, somewhat encroaching on the lateral border of the medial longitudinal fasciculus. It was early described as part of the nucleus of Darkschewitsch, but it is separated from the latter by a thin lamina of fibers. It is frequently known as the **nucleus of the medial longitudinal fasciculus** (Ingram and Ranson '35).

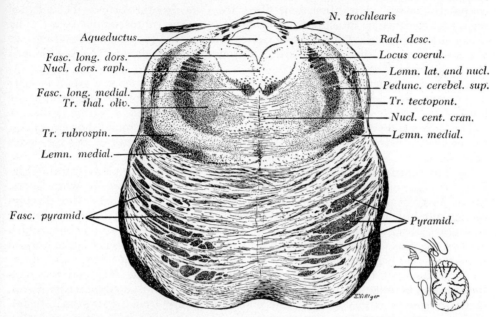

FIG. 733.—Transverse section through transition between pons and mesencephalon. Nuclear groups represented diagrammatically in color. (From Villiger-Addison, courtesy of J. B. Lippincott Co.)

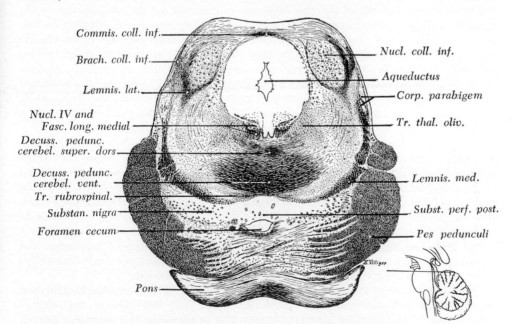

FIG. 734.—Transverse section through mesencephalon at inferior colliculus. Nuclear groups represented diagrammatically in color. (From Villiger-Addison, courtesy of J. B. Lippincott Co.)

(6) The **red nucleus** (*nucleus ruber*) (Fig. 735) is a prominent feature of the midbrain, occupying a large part of the tegmentum. It is an eggshaped mass extending from the caudal limit of the superior colliculus into the subthalamic region. It is circular in cross section and contains mainly small and medium sized cells which contain the reddish pigment responsible for the name given to the nucleus. It also contains less numerous large cells. It receives most of the fibers of the brachium conjunctivum and in addition some fibers from the frontal cortex. The smaller cells send their axons into the tegmentum to form the rubroreticular tract. The axons of the large cells take a caudal course and become the rubrospinal tract. It also sends fibers to the lateral ventral nucleus of the thalamus. (Carpenter and Pines '57, Stern '38).

(7) The **interpeduncular ganglion** (*nucleus interpeduncularis*) is a group of cells of uncertain function in the posterior perforated substance of the interpeduncular fossa.

The **tectum of the midbrain** (*lamina tecti*) is composed of four rounded prominences, the corpora quadrigemina or the superior and inferior colliculi of the two sides (Fig. 731).

(8) The **superior colliculus** (*colliculus superior*) contains four or five strata (Fig. 735). (*a*) The outermost layer, the **stratum zonale** is composed of fine white fibers, the majority of which are received from the optic tract and visual cortex through the superior brachium. (*b*) The second layer, the **stratum griseum** (*stratum cinereum*), is of gray substance consisting mostly of small multipolar nerve cells about which most of the fibers of the two adjacent strata terminate. (*c*) Deeper is the **stratum opticum** containing many fibers and scattered large multipolar cells. The fibers are from the optic tract, lateral geniculate body, and cortex. The majority send their axones peripherally into the stratum griseum. (*d*) The **stratum lemnisci** contains interspersed large multipolar cells and fibers mainly from the stratum opticum. (*e*) The **stratum profundum**, sometimes included in the stratum lemnisci, is a thin layer adjacent to the central gray and is composed of fibers from the spinotectal tract.

The superior colliculi of the two sides are connected by the commissure of the superior colliculus and the posterior commissure. They give rise to the tectobulbar and tectospinal tracts and are connected with the reticular formation, substantia nigra, zona incerta, and possibly the pontine nuclei. They are primary visual centers especially for coordination of eye movements (page 915).

(9) The **inferior colliculus** (*colliculus inferior*) (Fig. 734) consists of a compact nucleus of medium and small multipolar cells surrounded by a capsule of white fibers derived from the lateral lemniscus. Most of these fibers end in the nucleus of the same side but some cross in the commissure of the inferior colliculus. The axones of the cells in the nucleus pass through the inferior brachium to the lateral geniculate body. Fibers also cross in the commissure to the opposite side. Scattered large cells medial to the main nucleus send axones through the stratum profundum to the tectobulbar and tectospinal tracts. There are also connections between the inferior colliculus and the substantia nigra, the nuclei of the reticular formation, and the pontine nuclei. It is a center for correlation and control of reflexes in response to sound.

The **Pretectal Region** is a transition zone between the superior colliculus and thalamus. It contains nuclei which receive fibers from the optic tract and sends axons to the Edinger-Westphal nucleus of the oculomotor nerve.

The **Fiber Tracts of the Tegmentum of the Midbrain.**—(1) The **medial longitudinal fasciculus** (*fasciculus longitudinalis medialis*) (Fig. 735) lies close to the midline just ventral to and in close association with the oculomotor and trochlear nuclei. It occupies the same relative position in the pons and medulla oblongata and continues into the spinal cord as the sulcomarginal fasciculus. The cephalic origin of this tract is in the interstitial nucleus of Cajal in the reticular formation at the junction of the midbrain and hypothalamus. It receives a large number of its fibers from the vestibular nuclei and contributes fibers to the oculomotor, trochlear, abducens, and accessory nerve nuclei, and to the motor horn cells in the cervical spinal cord. It is the tract for correlation of eye, head, and neck movements, especially in response to sensations from the semicircular canals of the ear.

(2) The **medial lemniscus** (*lemniscus medialis*) together with the **trigeminothalamic lemniscus** forms a large bundle in the ventral and lateral part of the tegmentum in the more caudal part of the mesencephalon. In the cephalic position it is displaced dorsally and laterally close to the medial geniculate body and its inferior brachium.

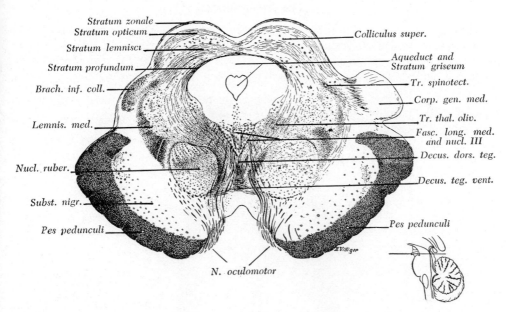

FIG. 735.—Transverse section through mesencephalon at superior colliculus. Nuclear groups represented diagrammatically in color. (From Villiger-Addison, courtesy of J. B. Lippincott Co.)

(3) The **lateral lemniscus** (*lemniscus lateralis*) in the caudal part of the midbrain lies close to the surface in the tegmentum, dorsal to the medial lemniscus. Its fibers run dorsally as well as rostrally and surround the nucleus of the inferior colliculus. Most of them end there but some continue in the inferior quadrigeminal brachium into the medial geniculate body.

(4) The **thalamoölivary tract** is in the reticular substance ventral and lateral to the central gray.

(5) The **rubrospinal tract** arises in the caudal part of the red nucleus and promptly decussates in the **ventral tegmental decussation** (Fig. 735). It passes laterally to a position just medial to the medial lemniscus where it turns caudally and continues into the lateral funiculus of the spinal cord.

(6) The **tectospinal** and **tectobulbar tracts** arise in the superior colliculus. The fibers sweep around the central gray in the stratum profundum of the colliculus and cross in the **dorsal tegmental decussation** (*fountain decussation of Meynert*) (Fig. 735). Turning caudally they lie ventral to the medial longitudinal fasciculus and enter the ventral funiculus of the spinal cord.

(7) The **decussation of the brachium conjunctivum** (*decussatio pedunculorum cerebellarium superiorum*) occupies the tegmentum ventral to the central gray at the level of the inferior colliculus. After crossing, most of the fibers ascend to the red nucleus and neighboring reticular substance. A few in the medial capsule of the red nucleus continue on to the nucleus ventralis lateralis of the thalamus.

THE FOREBRAIN OR PROSENCEPHALON

The forebrain or prosencephalon consists of: (1) the diencephalon or between brain and (2) the telencephalon or endbrain.

The Diencephalon

The Diencephalon connects the midbrain with the cerebral hemispheres, and corresponds to the structures which bound the third ventricle. It comprises (1) the thalamus, (2) the metathalamus, (3) the epithalamus, (4) the subthalamus, and (5) the hypothalamus (Hess '57, Kuhlenbeck '54, Sawyer *et al.* '54).

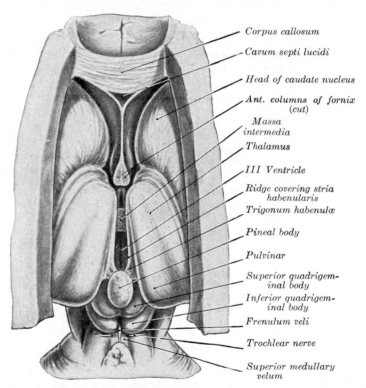

Corpus callosum

Cavum septi lucidi

Head of caudate nucleus

Ant. columns of fornix (cut)

Massa intermedia

Thalamus

III Ventricle

Ridge covering stria habenularis

Trigonum habenulæ

Pineal body

Pulvinar

Superior quadrigeminal body

Inferior quadrigeminal body

Frenulum veli

Trochlear nerve

Superior medullary velum

FIG. 736.—The thalami, exposed from above. The trunk and splenium of the corpus callosum, most of the septum lucidum, the body of the fornix, the tela chorioidea with its contained plexuses and the epithelial roof of the third ventricle have all been removed.

The **Thalamus** (*dorsal thalamus*) (Figs. 736, 737) is a large ovoid mass about 4 cm. long forming most of the side wall of the third ventricle and extending caudally for some distance beyond it. Its medial and superior surfaces are exposed in the ventricles and its inferior and lateral surfaces buried against other structures. The anterior or rostral extremities of the parts on the two sides lie close to the midline where they are narrow and form the posterior boundary of the interventricular foramina. The posterior extremities are thicker and diverge from each other extending out over the superior colliculi and having the pineal body between them. The medially prominent rounded posterior portion is the **pulvinar** (Fig. 736). The superior surface is free, covered only by the pia mater of the transverse cerebral fissure forming the tela chorioidea (Fig. 709). In a groove between the thalamus and caudate nucleus, the sulcus terminalis, are the stria and vena terminalis (Fig. 767). A shallow furrow in the position of the overlying fornix, divides the dorsal surface into a medial portion, covered by the tela and a lateral portion which forms part of the floor of the lateral ventricle (Fig. 766). The superior surface is separated from the medial surface by the taeniæ thalami (Fig. 737), the torn edges

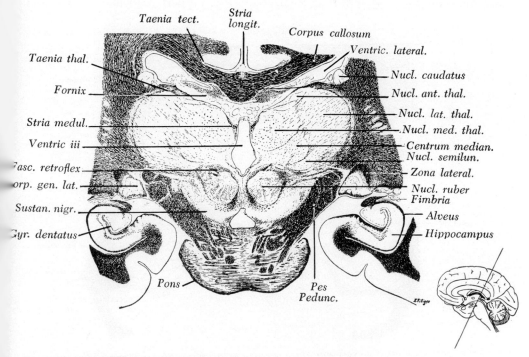

Fig. 737.—Frontal section through basal part of cerebral hemisphere and midbrain. Weigert myelin stain. (From Villiger-Addison, courtesy of J. B. Lippincott Co.)

of the ependymal roof of the third ventricle, which meet in the stalk of the pineal body. The protruding medial surfaces of the thalmus are usually joined across the narrow intervening third ventricle by a bridge known as the **massa intermedia** (*adhaesio interthalamicus; middle commissure*) (Figs. 736, 738). The inferior surface of the thalamus rests upon and is continuous with the upward prolongation of the tegmentum of the midbrain. The lateral surface is separated from the corpus striatum by the occipital part of the internal capsule (Fig. 738).

Structure.—The thalamus consists chiefly of gray substance, but its upper surface is covered by a layer of white substance, named the **stratum zonale**, and just under its lateral surface by a similar layer termed the **external medullary lamina**. Its gray substance is subdivided into three parts—anterior, medial, and lateral—by a white layer, the **internal medullary lamina**. The nuclei of which the thalamus is composed may be divided into the following groups: (1) Midline; (2) Anterior; (3) Medial; (4) Lateral; and (5) Posterior (Dekaban '53, Toncray and Krieg '46, Walker '38).

1. **Midline nuclei.**—The thin periventricular gray substance under the ependyma of the third ventricle is continuous with the central gray around the aqueduct and in a number of brains bridges the cavity in the massa intermedia. It contains groups of cells and is connected with the hypothalamus and cortex serving a visceral function.

2. **Anterior nuclei.**—There are three anterior nuclei, dorsal, ventral, and medial. All three receive connections with the mammillary body through the mammillo-thalamic tract (bundle of Vicq d'Azyr) and its fibers are projected to the gyrus cinguli. It is an olfactory center.

3. **Medial nuclei.**—There are several nuclei in the medial group, but the function of all is not known. The medial dorsal nucleus has two main parts, ventromedial and dorsolateral. The former is connected with the periventricular system and

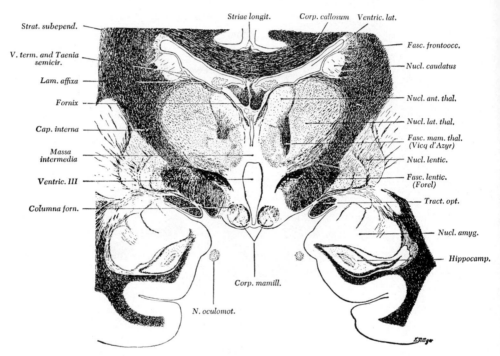

Fig. 738.—Frontal section through thalamus and corpus striatum. Weigert myelin stain. (From Villiger-Addison, courtesy of J. B. Lippincott Co.)

the hypothalamus, the latter has projections to area 9 (Brodmann) of the frontal cortex. The centrum medianum is a well-defined structure near the caudal end of the thalamus. Its connections are obscure and probably represent associations between other parts of the thalamus.

4. **Lateral nuclei** form a large mass rostral to the pulvinar between the external and internal medullary laminæ. The anterior ventral nucleus receives fibers from the globus pallidus through the ansa lenticualris and fasciculus thalamicus and sends others to the corpus striatum. The lateral ventral nucleus receives the dentato-rubro-thalamic tract and reticulothalamic fibers. Its efferent fibers go to the motor cortex, areas 4 and 6 (Brodmann).

The posterior ventral nucleus has two important subdivisions. (*a*) The **nucleus ventralis posteromedialis** (*nucleus semilunaris, n. arcuatus*) is a crescentic mass ventral to the centrum medianum. It receives the secondary trigeminal tract and its axons go to the somesthetic area of the postcentral gyrus for the face, areas 3, 1, 2. (*b*) The **nucleus ventralis posterolateralis** is a large area, the terminus of the spinothalamic tract and medial lemniscus, and projects to the sensory cortex, areas 3, 1 2 of Brodmann.

The nucleus lateralis dorsalis and nucleus lateralis posterior are connected with other parts of the thalamus and the parietal lobe.

The **nucleus reticularis** is a thin plate between the external medullary lamina and the internal capsule. It is continuous with the reticular formation of the mesencephalon through the zona incerta. Its connections are similar to neighboring nuclei.

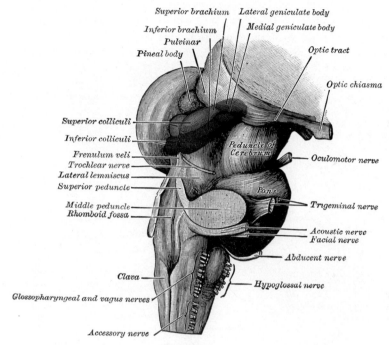

FIG. 739.—Hind- and mid-brains; postero-lateral view.

5. **Posterior nuclei.**—The major nucleus in this group is the **pulvinar**. It may be divided into lateral, medial, and inferior parts. It is projected to the parietal lobe, particularly to regions near the somatic sensory, auditory, and visual projection areas. It receives fibers from the same cortical areas and from the neighboring thalamic nuclei. It is an association area.

The **Metathalamus** is made up of the geniculate bodies, a medial and a lateral (Fig. 739) on each side. The **medial geniculate body** (*corpus geniculatum mediale*) is a small oval tubercle between the pulvinar, colliculi, and cerebral peduncle. It is connected with the inferior colliculus by the inferior brachium (Fig. 739) and is a relay station between the latter and the auditory cortex.

The **lateral geniculate body** (*corpus geniculatum laterale*) is an oval elevation of the lateral aspect of the posterior end of the thalamus. It is connected with the superior colliculus by the superior brachium. Most of the fibers of the optic tract end here (Fig. 739) and are relayed to the visual cortex surrounding the calcarine fissure.

The **Epithalamus** comprises the trigonum habenulæ, the pineal body, and the posterior commissure (Fig. 741).

The **trigonum habenulæ** is a triangular area at the posterior end of the taenia thalami close to the pineal body (Fig. 739). It contains the habenular nucleus and receives fibers from the stria medullaris which runs with the taenia thalami over the surface of the thalamus. The **habenular commissure** (Fig. 741), connecting the habenulæ of the two sides, lies just in front on the pineal body.

The **pineal body** (*corpus pineale*) (Figs. 736, 739) is a gland-like structure about 8 mm. long, shaped like a pine cone, lying in a pocket between the superior colliculi, the pulvinar, and the splenium of the corpus callosum. It is attached by a stalk which is composed of two laminæ, a superior and inferior which are separated by the pineal recess of the third ventricle. The inferior lamina is continuous with the posterior commissure, the superior with the habenular commissure (Gardner '53).

The **posterior commissure** (Fig. 741) is a rounded band of white fibers crossing the midline at the junction of the aqueduct with the third ventricle just anterior and superior to the superior colliculi. Some of its fibers connect these colliculi but the function of the rest is uncertain.

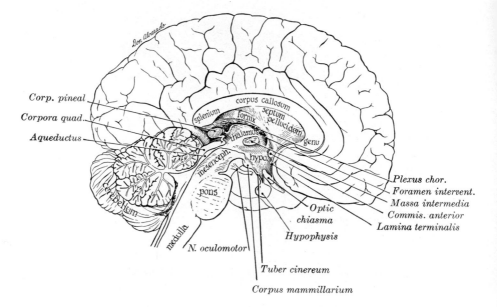

Fig. 740.—Median sagittal section of brain.

The **Subthalamus** (*tegmentum diencephali*; *ventral thalamus*) (Figs. 738, 741) is the transition zone between the thalamus (dorsal thalamus) and the tegmentum mesencephali. It is squeezed in between the cerebral peduncle and the mammillary area with the hypothalamus medial and rostral to it. The red nucleus and the substantia nigra are prolonged upward into it. It contains the nucleus subthalamicus and masses of fibers known as the fields H, H_1, and H_2 of Forel.

The **nucleus subthalamicus** (*corpus luysii*) is an oval, cylindrical mass lying on the dorsal surface of the transition from the internal capsule to cerebral peduncle. It receives fibers from the globus pallidus and peduncle as a part of the descending pathway from the corpus striatum.

The **zona incerta** is continuous with and similar to the reticular formation of the midbrain and the reticular nucleus of the thalamus. It has numerous connections, especially with the tectum, red nucleus, and tegmentum of the midbrain. It is a correlation center for optic and vestibular impulses relayed to the globus pallidus (Papez '42, '51).

Rostral to the red nucleus is a dense mass of longitudinally running fibers known as the **tegmental field** (*field H*) **of Forel.** The medial fibers are composed of dentato-, rubro-, and reticulothalamic connections. They continue rostrad as the **thalamic fasciculus,** field H_1 of Forel, which enters the medial part of the external medullary lamina and ends in the nucleus ventralis lateralis of the thalamus. The lateral fibers of the tegmental field come from field H_2 which is rostral and lateral. It is composed of fibers from the globus pallidus in the **ansa lenticularis** and **fasciculus lenticularis** which bend around the medial edge of the internal capsule on the way to the red nucleus and reticular substance.

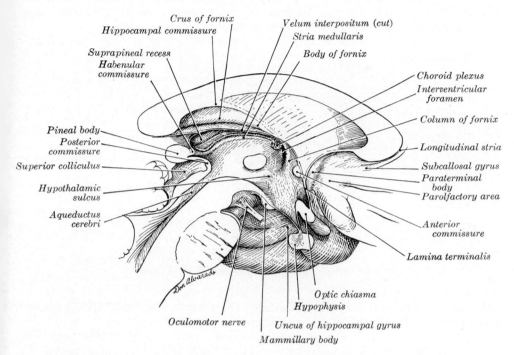

Fig. 741.—Median sagittal section of brain stem and region of third ventricle, part of Figure 740 enlarged.

The **Hypothalamus** (Figs. 740, 742) forms the ventral and rostral part of the wall of the third ventricle where it is marked off from the thalamus by the hypothalamic sulcus. It also includes the externally visible parts, (1) the corpora mammillaria, (2) tuber cinereum, (3) infundibulum, (4) hypophysis, and (5) optic chiasma.

The **mammillary bodies** (*corpora mammillaria*) are two round masses about 5 mm. in diameter placed close to the midline near the cerebral peduncles. The **tuber cinereum** is the lamina of gray substance situated between the mammillary bodies and the optic chiasma (Figs. 717, 743). Laterally it is bounded by the optic tracts and cerebral peduncles. From its under surface a hollow conical process, the **infundibulum** (Figs. 709, 717), projects downward and forward and ends in the posterior lobe of the hypophysis cerebri or pituitary body (Figs. 741, 743). At the floor of the ventricle the infundibulum produces a raised area, the *median eminence,* and it narrows into the stem of attachment to the **hypophysis.** The median eminence, the stem, and the infundibular process or neural lobe make up an entity of similar tissue known as the **neurohypophysis.** (see Hypophysis in last chapter). The **optic chiasma,** named from its resemblance to the Greek letter X, is situated at the junction of the floor and anterior wall of the third ventricle (Fig. 743). From the chiasma the optic nerves extend rostrally beside the hypophysis to enter the orbit. The optic tracts pass backward from the chiasma across the cerebral peduncles, between the anterior perforated substance and the tuber cinereum (Fig. 743), to the lateral geniculate body (Fig. 739).

Structure of the Hypothalamus.—The **periventricular area** (*nucleus paraventricularis*) connects that of the thalamus with the central gray around the aqueduct. It contains a few groups of small cells and fine fibers which pass to the nuclei of the pons and medulla through the dorsal longitudinal fasciculus (of Schütz) (Ingram '49).

The **supraoptic nucleus** consists of deeply staining moderately large cells and a rich capillary bed of particular pattern. Afferents come from the paraventricular nucleus and efferents constitute the supraopticohypophyseal tract.

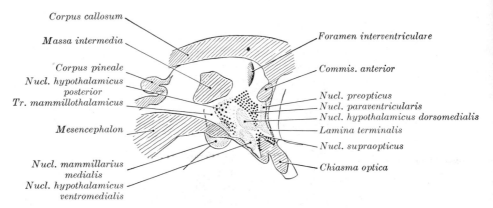

FIG. 742.—The nuclei of the hypothalamus in relation to the lateral wall of the third ventricle. (From Le Gros Clark '36, courtesy of Journal of Anatomy.)

Of the nuclei in the infundibular region, the **ventromedial hypothalamic nucleus** receives connections from the medial forebrain bundle, from the stria terminalis, from the periventricular system, from the fornix and from the globus pallidus. Its efferents enter the periventricular system. Closely related to this nucleus is the **dorsomedial nucleus** and the dorsal hypothalamic area.

The **posterior hypothalamic area** is a moderately extensive zone receiving fibers from the medial forebrain bundle, the fornix, the periventricular system and probably the tegmentum. It is thought to be the main origin of descending efferent hypothalamic systems which run rather diffusely scattered through the lateral parts of the tegmentum of the pons and medulla. They are largely short neuron chains and connect with the lateral and anterolateral columns of the cord.

The **mammillary region** contains the mammillary complex and scattered cells in the premammillary and supramammillary areas. The **medial mammillary nucleus** is an ovoid mass of cells producing the protuberance of the mammillary body. The **lateral mammillary nucleus** is smaller and fits into the angle between the medial nucleus and the base of the brain. The **nucleus intercalatus** is a separate group of slightly different cells in the dorsal part of the nucleus. Both medial and lateral nuclei receive fibers from the fornices of both sides, the fibers decussating just above the mammillary bodies. They also receive fibers from the medial forebrain bundle, from the thalamus and from the inferior mammillary peduncle from the tegmentum of the midbrain. The chief efferents from the mammillary nuclei form the principal mammillary peduncle which runs dorsorostrally to the thalamus as the **mammillo-thalamic tract** (bundle of Vicq d'Azyr). A short distance above the mammillary body descending collaterals are given off to form the **mammilotegmental tract**.

The **lateral hypothalamic area** extends from the lateral preoptic area to the tegmentum of the midbrain. It contains the **medial forebrain bundle,** scattered groups of cells, and two or three lateral tuberal nuclei (*nuclei tuberales*) (Crosby and Woodburne '51).

The **Preoptic Area** is derived from the telencephalon rostral to the hypothalamus, but it is closely associated with the latter functionally. The medial preoptic area is related to the middle region of the hypothalamus and rostrally to the nuclei associated with the stria terminalis, anterior commissure, and parolfactory areas.

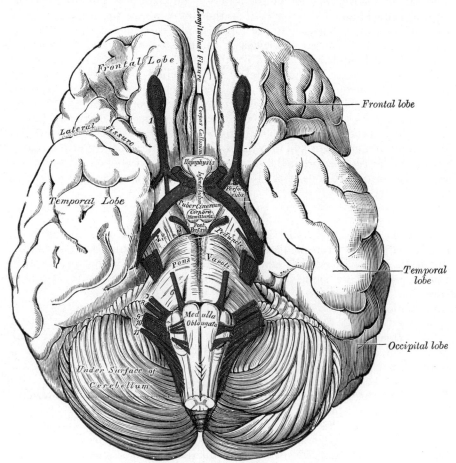

Fig. 743.—Base of brain.

The lateral preoptic area contains the medial forebrain bundle and is distinguishable from the lateral hypothalamic area only by its position. The connections of both areas are with olfactory areas, the hypothalamus, and the anterior and medial thalamic nuclei.

The Third Ventricle

The **third ventricle** (*ventriculus tertius*) (Fig. 736) is a narrow median cleft between the thalami of the two hemispheres. It is lined by ependyma and filled with spinal fluid. The rostral end has an opening on each side into the lateral ventricles, the **interventricular foramen** (of Monro), and at the posterior end it is continuous with the fourth ventricle through the cerebral aqueduct (of Sylvius).

The lateral wall, its most extensive surface, is divided into an upper and a lower part by the **hypothalamic sulcus** (Fig. 741). The upper part contains the columns of the fornix and the thalamus, the lower the subthalamus and hypothalamus. In most brains the thalami of the two sides come into contact at their most prominent medial eminence. The resulting continuity of thalamic substance bridges the third ventricle as the massa intermedia which appears like a commissure in a medial sagittal section (Fig. 742) but does not function as one.

The rostral boundary is formed by the lamina terminalis and anterior commissure. The part of the roof just above the anterior commissure is the inferior edge of the septum pellucidum. Posterior to this, the roof is above the interventricular foramen and continues back along the fornix to the splenium of the corpus callosum. It is composed of the **tela chorioidea** or **velum interpositum** and the **choroid plexus**. The posterior boundary is formed by the habenular commissure, the pineal stalk, and the posterior commissure. Below the posterior commissure is the opening of the cerebral aqueduct. The floor of the ventricle is composed of the tegmentum of the cerebral peduncles and the structures of the hypothalamus.

Certain recesses make the outline of the ventricle irregular. Between the lamina terminalis and the optic chiasma is the optic recess. Into the stalk of the hypophysis is the infundibular recess and into the stalk of the pineal is the pineal recess. Above the habenular commissure is the suprapineal recess and above the anterior commissure between the columns of the fornix is a slight recess called the vulva cerebri or triangular recess.

The Telencephalon

Cerebrum.—The cerebrum is the large rounded structure occupying most of the cranial cavity. A deep median sagittal groove, the longitudinal cerebral fissure, divides it into right and left cerebral hemispheres. At the bottom of this fissure, the hemispheres are connected with each other by the great central white commissure, the corpus callosum (Figs. 740, 743). The internal structures of the hemispheres merge with those of the diencephalon and further continuity with the brain stem is established through the cerebral peduncles (Fig. 741).

The **Cerebral Hemispheres** are composed of (1) the extensive outer gray substance or cerebral cortex, (2) the underlying white substance, the centrum semiovale, (3) internally located masses of central gray substance separated by intervening white laminæ, collectively known as the basal ganglia and corpus striatum, and (4) certain centrally and medially placed structures which are collectively known as the rhinencephalon.

Cerebral Cortex.—Each hemisphere presents a **convex** superior and lateral **surface** (*facies convexa cerebri*), a flat **medial surface** (*facies medialis cerebri*), and an irregular **inferior** or **basal surface** (*basis cerebri*). A distinct medial or **superior margin** separates the lateral and medial surfaces; a more rounded **lateral margin** separates the lateral and inferior surfaces. The anterior end is the **frontal pole**, the posterior end the **occipital pole**, and the anterior end of the laterally protruding temporal lobe is the **temporal pole**. The surface of the hemisphere is marked by numerous irregular grooves, the fissures and sulci, with intervening rounded eminences, the convolutions or gyri. At first glance they appear quite irregular, but they can, with study, be fitted into a basic plan. The two hemispheres of the same brain differ from each other and they in turn from every other brain.

The **Lateral Cerebral Fissure** (*fissure of Sylvius; sulcus lateralis*) (Fig. 745) is the well-marked groove on the lateral surface separating the larger superior masses of the frontal and parietal regions from the temporal region of the hemisphere. It is a complete fissure, isolating much of the temporal lobe and in the depths of its posterior portion is hidden the insula. At the tip of the temporal pole, it is widened into the lateral fossa. A short anterior part of the fissure is called its **stem**, the long backward extension (about 7 cm.) is called the **posterior ramus**. At the junction of the stem and posterior ramus two short branches (about 2 cm.) form a V-shaped extension into the frontal lobe, the **anterior horizontal** (*ramus anterior*) and **anterior ascending** (*ramus ascendens*) **rami** (Fig. 744).

The **Central Sulcus** (*fissure of Rolando; sulcus centralis*) (Fig. 744, 746) begins on the medial surface of the hemisphere at about the middle of the superior margin and runs downward and forward on the lateral surface until it almost meets the lateral cerebral fissure about 2.5 cm. posterior to the anterior ascending ramus. It has two sinuous curves, a superior genu with convexity posterior, and an inferior genu with convexity anterior (Fig. 744).

The **Calcarine Fissure** (*sulcus calcarinus*) (Fig. 745) is on the medial surface at the posterior part of the hemisphere. It begins anteriorly just below the splenium of the corpus callosum and runs with an upward arch toward the occipital pole. It is divided into an anterior and a posterior part by its junction with the parieto-occipital fissure. The anterior part is called a complete fissure, its depth causing an elevation in the wall of the posterior horn of the lateral ventricle, the calcar avis (Figs. 766, 770).

The **Parietooccipital Fissure** (*sulous parieto-occipitalis*) (Fig. 745), on the medial surface of the occipital region, appears to be an upward continuation of the anterior part of the calcarine fissure. It crosses the superior margin of the hemisphere about 5 cm. from the occipital pole and has a short (1.25 cm.) lateral segment. It usually covers a submerged gyrus.

The **Cingulate Sulcus** (*sulcus cinguli*) (Fig. 745), on the medial surface of the hemisphere, follows the curve of the superior margin from the rostrum of the corpus callosum to a point just posterior to the central fissure. Here it turns upward and just crosses the superior margin.

The **Collateral Fissure** (*sulcus collateralis*) (Fig. 745) is seen on the inferior or tentorial surface of the hemisphere. Its course is parallel with the inferior lateral margin, from near the occipital pole almost to the temporal pole.
with the inferior lateral margin, from near the occipital pole almost to the temporal pole.

The **Sulcus Circularis** (Fig. 748) is buried in the depths of the lateral cerebral fissure and surrounds the insula under the frontal, parietal, and temporal opercula.

Lobes of the Hemispheres (Fig. 744).—The cerebral cortex is divided into the following lobes: frontal, occipital, temporal, parietal, and central (insular) lobes.

The **Frontal Lobe** (*lobus frontalis*) is the largest, occupying part of the lateral, medial, and inferior surfaces. It extends posteriorly to the central sulcus and inferiorly to the lateral fissure.

On the lateral surface are three sulci (Fig. 744); the precentral sulcus and the superior and inferior frontal sulci running from the precentral toward the frontal pole. There are four gyri: anterior central and superior, middle, and inferior frontal gyri.

The **anterior central gyrus** lies between the central and precentral sulci, extending from the lateral fissure to the superior margin of the hemisphere. The **superior frontal gyrus** lies superior to the superior frontal sulcus and spreads over the superior margin of the hemisphere to its medial surface. It is usually subdivided by a longitudinal interrupted sulcus, the paramedian sulcus. The **middle frontal gyrus** lies between the superior and middle frontal sulci. It also is subdivided by a longitudinal sulcus, the middle frontal sulcus, which bifurcates widely at its anterior extremity.

The **inferior frontal gyrus** lies below the inferior frontal sulcus and spreads around the lateral margin onto the orbital part of the inferior surface of the hemisphere. It is subdivided by the rami of the lateral fissure (Fig. 744) into an anterior, a triangular, and a basal or opercular part. The left inferior frontal gyrus is usually more highly convoluted than the right and is referred to as **Broca's speech area.**

The inferior or orbital surface is divided by an H-shaped orbital sulcus into four gyri: medial, anterior, lateral, and posterior **orbital gyri** (Fig. 747). The olfactory sulcus, a groove which lodges the olfactory tract, separates the gyrus rectus from the medial orbital gyrus.

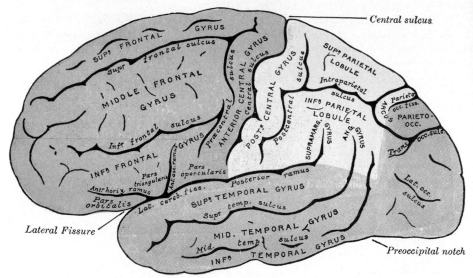

Fig. 744.—Lateral surface of left cerebral hemisphere, viewed from the side.

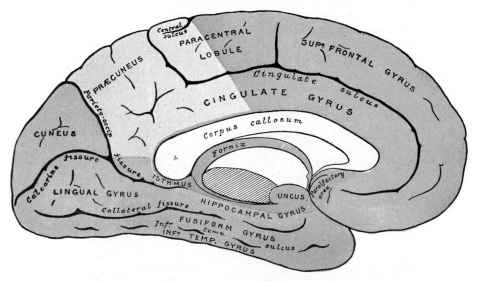

Fig. 745.—Medial surface of left cerebral hemisphere. Lobes in color.

The medial surface of the frontal lobe is limited posteriorly by a line drawn downward and anteriorly to the corpus callosum from the point where the central sulcus cuts the superior margin. It includes the superior frontal (marginal) gyrus and part of the **cingulate gyrus**. The posterior part of the superior frontal gyrus continuing somewhat into the parietal lobe may be marked off as the paracentral lobule.

The **Occipital Lobe** (*lobus occipitalis*) (Fig. 744) occupies a comparatively small pyramidal portion at the occipital pole, with medial, lateral, and inferior surfaces

The medial surface (Fig. 745) is bounded anteriorly by the parieto-occipital fissure and a line extending it to a shallow indentation of the lateral marbin named the **preoccipital notch**. The posterior calcarine fissure divides the medial surface of the lobe into a wedge-shaped area, the **cuneus**, and the **lingual gyrus**.

The anterior boundary of the lateral surface is a line from the lateral part of the parieto-occipital fissure to the preoccipital notch (Fig. 744). A lateral occipital sulcus divides the lateral surface into a **superior** and **inferior occipital gyrus**. Part of the arcus parieto-occipitalis lies between the parieto-occipital fissure and the transverse occipital sulcus.

The inferior or tentorial surface of the occipital lobe (Fig. 745) is limited by an imaginary transverse line across the preoccipital notch. The posterior segment of the collateral fissure separates the adjacent parts of the lingual and **fusiform gyri**.

The **Temporal Lobe** (*lobus temporalis*) (Fig. 744) is separated from the frontal lobe by the lateral fissure, from the occipital lobe by the line from the

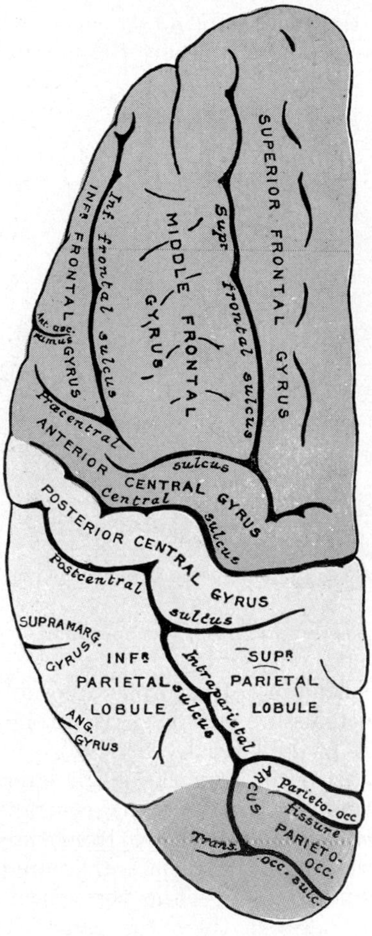

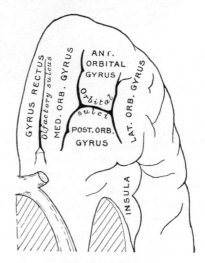

Fig. 746.—The lateral surface of left cerebral hemisphere, viewed from above.

Fig. 747.—Orbital surface of left frontal lobe.

preoccipital notch to the parieto-occipital fissure and from the parietal lobe by a line from the posterior extremity of the lateral fissure toward the occipital pole.

The lateral surface of the lobe (Fig. 744) is subdivided into three parallel gyri, superior, middle, and inferior temporal gyri by two sulci, superior (parallel sulcus) and middle temporal sulci.

The superior surface is hidden and extends deeply into the hemisphere as the inferior limit of the lateral fissure. It overlaps the insula as the **temporal operculum** (Fig. 748). Three or four gyri run from the posterior end of the lateral fissure obliquely outward and forward, they are the **transverse temporal gyri**, one of which is the cortical center for hearing.

The inferior surface of the temporal lobe (Fig. 745) is continuous with the tentorial surface of the occipital lobe, the separation being marked by the preoccipital notch. It is transversed by the inferior temporal sulcus and gyrus, the **fusiform gyrus,** and the collateral fissure. On the medial side of the collateral fissure are the lingual gyrus posteriorly and the hippocampal gyrus anteriorly.

The **hippocampal gryus** (*gyrus parahippocampalis*) lies between the collateral fissure and the hippocampal fissure. Posteriorly it is continuous above with the cingulate gyrus through the isthmus (Fig. 745) and below with the lingual gyrus. Its anterior extremity is curved into a hook, the **uncus** (Fig. 745), which is part of the rhinencephalon and is separated from the temporal pole by the incisura temporalis.

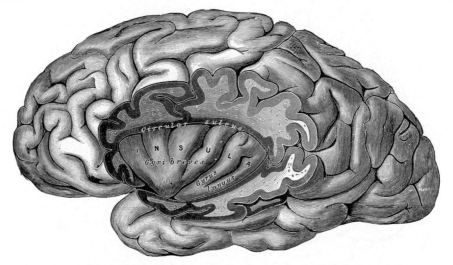

FIG. 748.—The insula of the left side, exposed by removing the opercula.

The **Hippocampal Fissure** extends from the splenium of the corpus callosum to the inside of the hook of the uncus. It is a complete fissure and gives rise to the prominence of the hippocampus in the inferior horn of the lateral ventricle.

The **Parietal Lobe** (*lobus parietalis*) (Fig. 744) occupies parts of the lateral and medial surfaces of the hemisphere. On the lateral surface the central sulcus separates it from the frontal lobe, the parieto-occipital fissure from the occipital lobe and an imaginary line from the posterior ramus of the lateral fissure toward the occipital pole separates it from the temporal lobe. The **postcentral sulcus** runs parallel with the central sulcus, leaving between them the **posterior central gyrus** (*gyrus centralis posterior*). The sulcus may be in two parts, an upper and a lower. From about the middle of the postcentral sulcus the intraparietal sulcus extends posteriorly toward the occipital pole and joins the transverse occipital sulcus. The part of the lobe posterior to the postcentral sulcus is divided by the horizontal intraparietal sulcus into a **superior** and an **inferior parietal lobule.** In the superior lobule, the arcus parieto-occipitalis encircles the end of the parieto-occipital fissure. In the inferior parietal lobule, the **supramarginal gyrus** arches over the upturned end of the lateral fissure (Fig. 744). The **angular gyrus** arches over the upturned end of the superior temporal sulcus.

On the medial surface, the parieto-occipital fissure separates the parietal from the occipital lobe. The anterior boundary is an imaginary line from the end of the central sulcus toward the middle of the corpus callosum. The upturned end of the sulcus cinguli divides the arc into a **precuneus** or **quadrate lobule** and a **paracentral lobule.**

The **Insula** (*central lobe*) lies hidden in the depths of the lateral fissure and can only be seen if the lips of the fissure are bent back or cut away (Fig. 748). These lips are parts of three lobes, frontal, parietal, and temporal. They are separated by the rami of the lateral fissure, and are named the frontal, parietal, and temporal opercula. The frontal operculum may also be described in two parts, an orbital and a frontal operculum, separated by the anterior horizontal ramus of the lateral fissure. The insula is encircled and separated from the opercula by a deep circular sulcus. When the opercula are cut away, the insula appears as a triangular area with an apex, the **limen insulæ**, directed toward the anterior perforated substance. It is crossed by the gyrus longus and gyri breves (Frontera '56).

STRUCTURE OF THE CEREBRAL CORTEX

It is customary to separate the cortex or pallium into the olfactory cortex, called the archipallium because it is phylogenetically old, and the non-olfactory younger cortex called the neopallium. The archipallium is described as part of the rhinencephalon. In addition to the distinction based upon olfaction and topographic position, it is possible to make a distinction on the basis of structure. The neopallium is called the isocortex because it all has a similar basic pattern in the distribution of its cellular and fibrous layers. The olfactory cortex is called the allocortex because its parts have quite different patterns.

Layers of the Isocortex (Fig. 749).—The isocortex is divided into six zones or layers:

Layer I. The outermost layer is the **plexiform layer** of Cajal (*lamina zonalis; molecular layer*). It is a narrow zone of white substance composed largely of myelinated fibers running tangentially. It contains the terminations of the apical dentrites of the pyramidal cells of deeper layers, horizontal cells, and granule cells with short axons.

Layer II. The **external granular layer** (*lamina granularis externa*) contains the shafts of pyramidal cells, and large numbers of granule cells (Golgi type II cells) with short axons and small pyramidal cells.

Layer III. The **layer of pyramidal cells** (*lamina pyramidalis*) has two zones, an outer with medium sized cells and an inner with larger pyramidal cells.

Layer IV. The **internal granular layer** (*lamina granularis interna*) contains a large number of small stellate cells with short axons and scattered small pyramidal cells. It is the site of the fibers of the outer band of Baillarger and contains the synapses with pyramidal cells of layer III.

Layer V. The **ganglionic layer** (*lamina ganglionaris*) includes the inner layer of large pyramidal cells and the horizontal fibers of the inner band of Baillarger. This layer contains the giant cells of Betz in the precentral cortex.

Layer VI. The **polymorphic layer** (*lamina multiformis*) contains cells of irregular shape whose axons enter the subjacent white substance of the hemisphere.

Localization

Special Types of Cerebral Cortex.—There is much evidence that individual areas of the human cerebral cortex do not function independently without the influence of other areas or of even the entire hemisphere. Nevertheless, study of the cellular components (cytoarchitectonics), or the arrangement of fibers (myeloarchitectonics) of different areas, partial extirpation at operation, disease, electrical stimulation under local anaesthesia, and animal experimentation have made it possible to give a functional identification to certain areas. Brodmann ('09) mapped forty-seven

I. *Plexiform*
   layer

II. *External*
    granular layer

III. *Pyramidal*
     cell layer

IV. *Internal*
    granular layer

V. *Ganglionic*
   layer

VI. *Polymorphic*
    layer

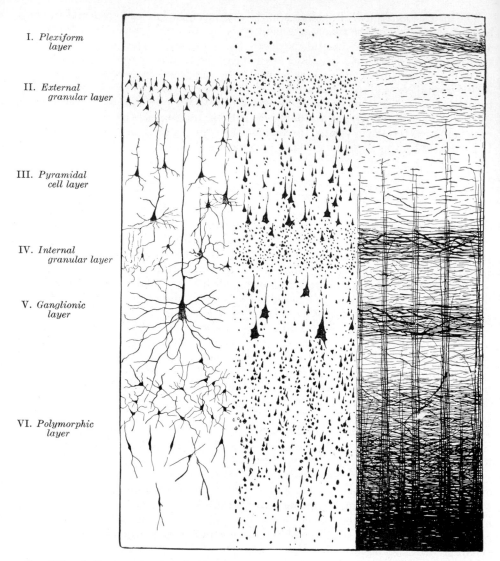

FIG. 749.—A diagram showing the layers of cells and fibers in the gray substance of the cortex of the human cerebral hemisphere, according to the histological methods of Golgi, Nissl and Weigert. *A*, Stained by the method of Golgi; *B*, by that of Nissl; *C*, by that of Weigert. (After Brodmann: from Luciani's Physiology, Macmillan & Co., Ltd.)

different areas as the result of a cytoarchitectonic survey with the Nissl stain for cells (Fig. 750). The Vogts ('09) described over two hundred areas on the basis of differences in the pattern made by the myelinated fibers. Von Economo ('29) has mapped out the cortex into areas containing five fundamental types of architecture. These maps are useful for topographical purposes but are only partly of value for functional identification (Von Bonin '50, Brody '55).

The **precentral cortex** or **motor area** includes the precentral gyrus and the caudal of the frontal gyri. It has received particular attention because its stimulation with electrodes causes contraction of the voluntary muscles. It corresponds to areas 4 and 6 of Brodmann (Fig. 750) and is characterized histologically by the absence of the granular layer, and the presence of large pyramidal cells in layer V.

The motor area (area 4, Fig. 750) contains the **giant pyramidal cells of Betz** in the ganglionic layer. It was thought formerly that these cells were responsible for the fibers of the pyramidal tract and that they controlled voluntary motion, but other pyramidal cells contribute extensively to the tract and normal voluntary

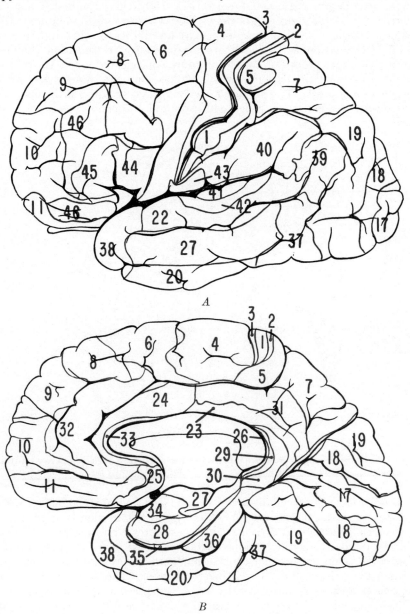

FIG. 750.—Diagram of cerebral cortex to show areas of localization according to Brodmann' 09. *A*, Lateral aspect of hemisphere; *B*, Medial.

activity requires associations with other parts of the cortex. It is an important motor area, nevertheless, because its removal causes paralysis of voluntary muscles, especially of the opposite side of the body. The different parts of the body are represented in sequence along the central sulcus. The lower limb area is at the superior margin of the hemisphere, the hand is half way around on the convex surface, and the face and mouth are at the lateral fissure. The size of the areas varies, those parts of the body with delicate complicated movements such as the hand being greater (Fig. 751).

The **premotor or precentral area** (area 6, Fig. 750) is like the motor area (area 4) except that it lacks the giant cells of Betz. The two areas stand in intimate relationship to each other functionally. The evidence indicates that motor responses elicited by stimulation of this area are produced by transmission through area 4 and involve larger groups of muscles in more complicated acts. In front of area 6 is area 8, electrical stimulation of which evokes conjugate movements of the eyes or of the eyes and head. The premotor area gives rise to some of the fibers making up the group heterogeneously called extrapyramidal fibers.

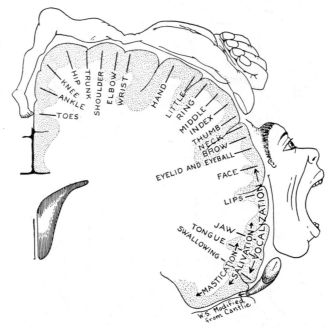

Fig. 751.—Motor homunculus illustrating motor representation in Area 4 (anterior central gyrus). (After Penfield and Rasmussen, *Cerebral Cortex of Man*, The Macmillan Co.)

Suppressor zones have been described in monkeys and other animals (McCulloch '44) in areas 6, 8, 2, 19, and 24. When electrical stimulation is applied to one of them, electrical evidence of cortical activity is suppressed in that area and gradually spreads throughout the cortex, taking as long as a half hour. Stimulation of area 8 may cause cessation of muscular contractions and suppress further motor response while the stimulus is applied. The connections involved are imperfectly understood.

The **frontal area** extending rostrally from the precentral area differs from the latter histologically in having the granular layer restored. The layer of large pyramidal cells and the polymorphous layer are reduced. This area contains extensive associations with other parts of the cortex and with the thalamus. The surgical operation of lobotomy, which isolates the area from the rest of the brain, especially the thalamus, has been used in the treatment of severe psychoses with generally favorable results (Freeman and Watts '48). Experimental evidence has also shown that stimulation of this area causes autonomic effects on the circulation, respiration, pupillary reaction, and other visceral activity (Beach *et al.* '55, Krieg '54).

A **speech area** (*Broca's area*) is located in the frontal operculum (area 44, Fig. 750). It is better developed in the left hemisphere of right handed persons and its destruction results in the inability to make articulate speech although the vocal organs are intact. This is called motor aphasia and the area is considered in consequence to be the motor speech area.

The **postcentral area** (areas 3, 1, 2. Fig. 750) is the sensory or conscious somesthetic area. It occupies all but the lowest part of the postcentral gyrus on the convex surface of the hemisphere and extends into the adjoining paracentral lobule of the medial surface. The rostral part, area 3, is characterized by the density of the granular layer, the breadth of the outer line of Baillarger and the large pyramidal cells. In the caudal part the large pyramidal cells are reduced in size and number and the granular layer is wider but not as dense.

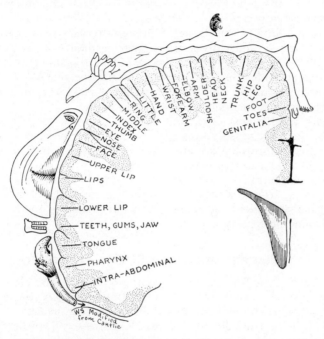

Fig. 752.—Sensory homunculus showing representation in the sensory cortex (after Penfield and Rasmussen, *Cerebral Cortex of Man*, Macmillan Co.).

The postcentral area receives exteroceptive and proprioceptive afferent fibers from the spinal cord and brain stem relayed through the thalamus. The different parts of the body are represented in a sequence similar to that of the precentral area. The area for the lower part of the body is at the superior margin of the hemisphere and the face and mouth at the lateral fissure. The more sensitive parts of the body, such as the face and mouth, have a larger area (Fig. 752).

The **visual sensory** or **striate area** (area 17, Fig. 750) occupies the walls of the posterior part of the calcarine fissure, extending into the cuneus above, the lingual gyrus below, and around the occipital pole to the lateral surface of the hemisphere. It has three distinguishing histological features: (1) The outer band of Baillarger is broad, prominent, and visible to the naked eye. It is named the stria of Gennari and gives the name striate area to this part of the cortex. (2) The outer layer of large pyramidal cells has large stellate cells instead of pyramidal cells. (3) The inner layer of large pyramidal cells contains the solitary cells of Meynert. It is the cortical center for vision, receiving fibers from the lateral geniculate body. Color, size, form, motion, illumination, and transparency are all recognized and determined in this area.

Owing to the decussation of part of the fibers of the optic nerves, the visual cortex of one hemisphere receives impressions from the temporal part of the retina of the same side and the nasal part of the opposite side. The upper lip of the calcarine fissure is associated with the upper quadrants of the retina, the lower lip with the lower quadrants. The macula is represented in the occipital pole and clinical evidence indicates that it is bilateral (Fulton '49).

The **visual psychic** or **parastriate area** (areas 18 and 19) surrounds the visual sensory area and is histologically similar to it. This area is responsible for elaboration of visual impressions and association of them with past experience for recognition and identification. It also relates eye movements to visual impressions.

The **auditory sensory area** (areas 41 and 42, Fig. 750) occupies the transverse temporal gyri and part of the superior temporal gyrus. It is characterized histologically by having an unusually large number of giant cells in the outer layer of large pyramidal cells, and by having great numbers of fibers. It receives fibers from the medial geniculate body through the auditory radiation of the sublentiform limb of the internal capsule. Auditory impressions reach this area as sounds which can be differentiated for loudness, quality, and pitch.

The **auditory psychic area** (area 22) occupies the superior temporal gyrus and surrounds the auditory sensory area and has a smaller number of giant cells. In this area auditory impressions are interpreted with respect to their probable source and associated with past experience.

The **parietal area** (areas 5, 7, 39 and 40) is situated between the visual, auditory, and somatic areas. It is characterized by the absence of large pyramidal cells and by the breadth of the inner band of Baillarger. It correlates and blends impressions from the surrounding sensory areas.

White Substance of the Cerebral Hemisphere

The outer layer of the hemisphere, the gray matter or cortex, has been described. The internal portion, except for the central gray nuclei of the basal ganglia, is composed of white matter and is called the **centrum semi-ovale.**

The fibers of the centrum are divided into three classes: (1) projection fibers which connect the cortex with the more caudal parts of the brain and the spinal cord; (2) commissural fibers which connect the two hemispheres, and (3) association fibers which connect the different parts of the cortex.

(1) **Projection fibers** are both afferent and efferent fibers which pass through the corona radiata and internal capsule (Fig. 753).

(2) The **Commissural fibers** pass through (a) the corpus callosum, (b) the anterior commissure and the hippocampal commissure, described as part of the rhinencephalon, and (c) the posterior commissure, described with the diencephalon.

(a) The **Corpus Callosum** (Fig. 736, 737, 743) is the great central white commissure connecting the two hemispheres. Its size and shape can be seen on a median sagittal section (Fig. 740). At the anterior end is the **genu** where it is bent back on itself around the anterior end of the septum pellucidum. The inferior limb of the genu tapers rather rapidly as the **rostrum** which is continuous with the lamina terminalis at the anterior commissure. The greater part of the corpus callosum extending posteriorly from the genu is called the **body** or **trunk** (*truncus corporis callosi*). The posterior end is enlarged into the thick, convex, free edge, the **splenium,** which overlaps the tela choroidea of the third ventricle and overhangs the epiphysis and midbrain.

The superior surface of the corpus callosum, at the bottom of the longitudinal cerebral fissure, is about 2.5 cm. wide (Fig. 755). It is overlapped on both sides by the gyrus cinguli from which it is separated by the slit-like callosal fissure (Fig. 746). It is covered by a thin layer of gray matter, the supracallosal gyrus and the white strands of the medial and lateral longitudinal striæ (page 906). The inferior surface in the midline is attached to the septum pellucidum anteriorly and to the body of the fornix posteriorly. The lateral portions of the inferior surface form the roof of the lateral ventricles.

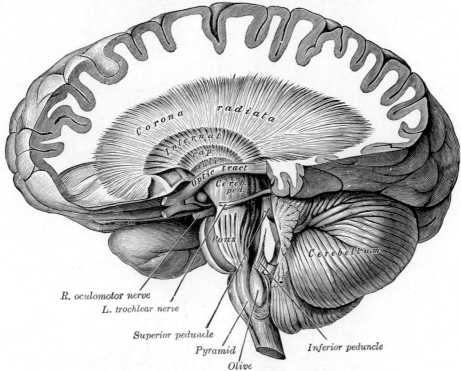

Fig. 753.—Dissection showing the course of the cerebrospinal fibers. (E. B. Jamieson.)

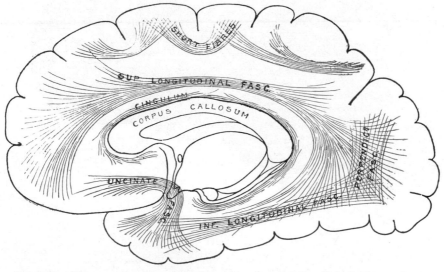

Fig. 754.—Diagram showing principal systems of association fibers in the cerebrum.

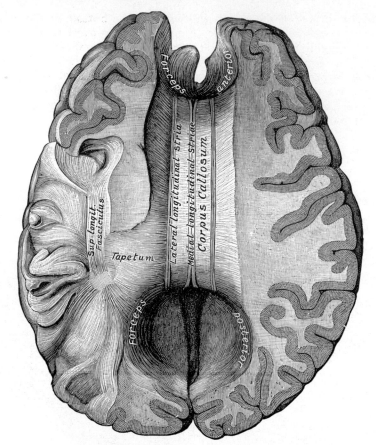

Fig. 755.—Corpus callosum from above.

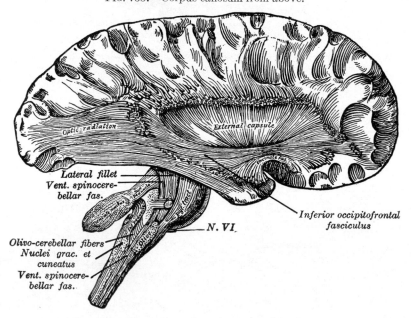

Fig. 756.—Deep dissection of cortex and brain-stem.

The fibers of the corpus callosum mingle with the projection fibers of the corona radiata as they radiate out to the cortex. The fibers to the frontal lobe from the genu of the corpus callosum constitute the **forceps anterior** (*forceps minor*) (Fig. 754) and those from the splenium to the occipital lobe the **forceps posterior** (*forceps major*). The fibers from the remaining body of the corpus callosum are called the **tapetum.**

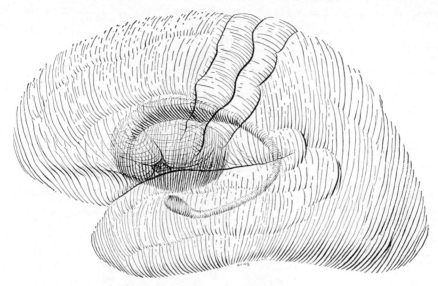

FIG. 757.—Phantom of the corpus striatum within the cerebral hemisphere. (Courtesy of W. J. S. Krieg's *Functional Neuro-anatomy*, 2 Ed. 1953. Blakiston Div., McGraw-Hill Book Co.)

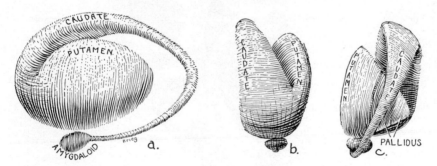

FIG. 758.—The corpus striatum of the left side with the internal capsule omitted; (*a*) latera aspect; (*b*) rostral aspect; (*c*) caudal aspect. (Courtesy of W. T. S. Krieg's *Functional Neuro-Anatomy*, 2nd Ed. 1953; Blakiston Div., McGraw-Hill Book Co.)

(3) The **Association fibers** are of two kinds, short association fibers connecting adjacent gyri and long association fibers connecting more distant parts of the hemisphere.

The short association fibers lie immediately beneath the gray matter of the cortex (Fig. 755).

The long association fibers form more or less distinct bundles and are given the following descriptive names:

(*a*) The **uncinate fasciculus** curves around the lateral cerebral fissure (of Sylvius) and unites the frontal lobe with the anterior end of the temporal lobe.

(*b*) The **cingulum** is a fasciculus contained within the cingulate gyrus (Fig. 746).

From the anterior perforated substance rostrally it follows the curve around the corpus callosum and ends in the hippocampal gyrus.

(c) The **superior longitudinal fasciculus** lies above the lentiform nucleus and the insula and extends from the frontal lobe anteriorly to the occipital lobe posteriorly and the temporal lobe inferiorly.

(d) The **inferior longitudinal fasciculus** connects the temporal and occipital lobes, running along the lateral walls of the inferior and posterior horns of the lateral ventricle.

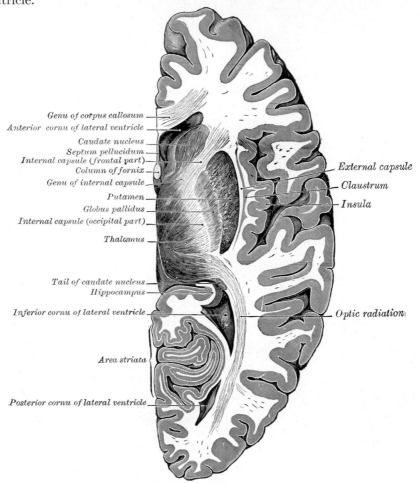

Genu of corpus callosum
Anterior cornu of lateral ventricle
Caudate nucleus
Septum pellucidum
Internal capsule (frontal part)
Column of fornix
Genu of internal capsule
Putamen
Globus pallidus
Internal capsule (occipital part)
Thalamus
Tail of caudate nucleus
Hippocampus
Inferior cornu of lateral ventricle
Area striata
Posterior cornu of lateral ventricle

External capsule
Claustrum
Insula
Optic radiation

Fig. 759.—Horizontal section of right cerebral hemisphere.

(e) The **superior occipitofrontal fasciculus** passes between the lateral aspect of the caudate nucleus and the corona radiata connecting the frontal with the occipital and temporal lobes.

(f) The **inferior occipitofrontal fasciculus** connecting the frontal lobe with the occipital lobe passes between the lentiform nucleus and the uncinate fasciculus at the base of the external capsule (Fig. 756).

(g) The **perpendicular fasciculus** runs vertically through the rostral part of the occipital lobe, connecting the inferior parietal lobule with the fusiform gyrus (Fig. 755, 746).

(h) The **fornix** and other parts of the rhinencephalon contain association fibers (page 907).

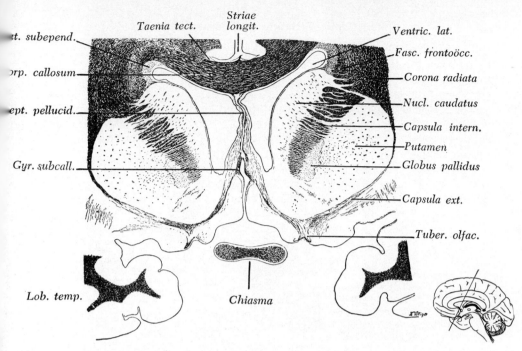

FIG. 760.—Frontal section through rostral part of corpus striatum. Weigert myelin stain. (From Villiger-Addison, courtesy of J. B. Lippincott Co.)

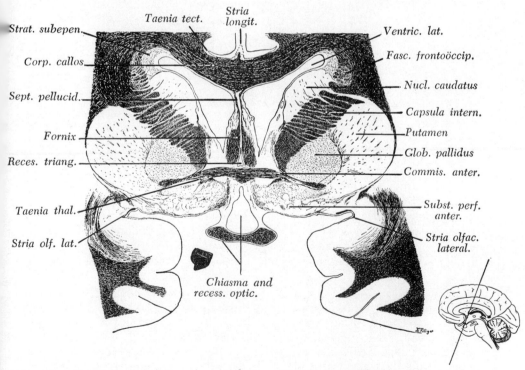

FIG. 761.—Frontal section through basal part of cerebral hemisphere at the anterior commissure. Weigert myelin stain. (From Villiger-Addison, courtesy of J. B. Lippincott Co.)

Corpus Striatum and Basal Ganglia

The **basal ganglia** represent the central gray matter of the telencephalon. They lie between the thalamus of the diencephalon, and the centrum semiovale or white matter of the hemisphere. They include the caudate nucleus, the lentiform nucleus, the claustrum, and the amygdaloid body.

The **corpus striatum** includes the caudate and lentiform nuclei, and a broad band of white fibers separating them, the internal capsule. Its name is derived from the striped appearance produced by narrow strands of gray matter crossing the white matter between the two nuclear masses (Fig. 760).

The **Caudate Nucleus** (*nucleus caudatus; caudatum*) (Fig. 758) is a prominent feature of the lateral ventricle (Figs. 760, 766) and forms an arch following its curvature. The anterior portion or head is enlarged and occupies most of the lateral wall of

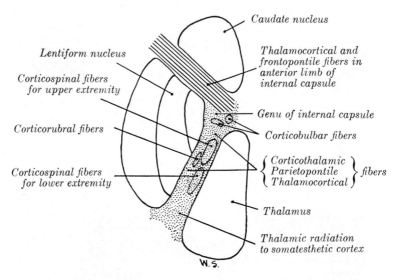

Fig. 762.—Diagram showing the locations of the various functional groups of fibers in the internal capsule as seen in a horizonal section. (Buchanan's Functional Neuro- Anatomy.)

the anterior horn of the ventricle. Its narrow posterior portion, the tail, is separated from the thalamus by the stria terminalis and terminal vein (Fig. 766). Its rostral extremity is continuous with the putamen (Figs. 758, 760) and its caudal extremity ends in the amygdaloid complex (Fig. 758).

The **Lentiform Nucleus** (*nucleus lentiformis; lenticular nucleus*) (Fig. 762) is a wedge-shaped mass of gray substance lying lateral to the thalamus and caudate nucleus (Fig. 759). It is divided by a layer of white matter, the lateral medullary lamina, into two parts the putamen which is larger and more lateral, and the globus pallidus.

The **Putamen** (Figs. 758, 761) is separated from the caudate nucleus by the anterior limb of the internal capsule except at its rostral extremity where the two nuclei are joined. Its lateral surface conforms roughly to the insula but it is separated from the latter by the external capsule and claustrum (Fig. 759).

The **Globus Pallidus** (Fig. 761) is separated from the putamen by the medial lamina and from the thalamus by the posterior limb of the internal capsule. It is divided into two parts, a medial and a lateral, by the medullary lamina.

The **Claustrum** (Fig. 759) is a thin layer of gray matter between the putamen and the insula. It is separated from the putamen by a lamina of white matter, the **external capsule** (*capusla externa*). It is regarded as a detached portion of the insula. Its lateral surface is somewhat irregular, following the gyri and sulci of the insula (Fig. 759), and is separated from the outer gray cortex of the insula by a layer of white fibers, the **capsula extrema,** which corresponds to the cortical band of Baillarger.

The **Amygdaloid Body** (*corpus amygdaloideum; amygdaloid nucleus; amygdala*) (Fig. 738) is an ovoid mass of gray matter about the size and shape of an almond in the roof of the rostral end of the lateral ventricle. It is closely associated with the cortex covering it, the uncus of the gyrus hippocampi. The tail of the caudate nucleus ends in it and it is in contact with a part of the putamen and the claustrum. It is divided by delicate white laminæ into several groups of nuclei.

The **Internal Capsule** (*capsula interna*) (Figs. 753, 762) is a thick lamina of white matter situated between the thalamus, caudate, and lentiform nuclei. Between the caudate nucleus and thalamus it is bent almost into a right angle. The angle is called the **genu** (*genu capsulæ internæ*). The portion rostral to the genu, the **anterior limb** (*crus anterior*) is between the caudate nucleus and the lentiform nucleus. The portion caudal to the genu, the **posterior limb** (*crus posterius*), is between the thalamus and the lentiform nucleus. The part of the posterior limb which curves around the caudal end of the lentiform nucleus is called the **retrolenticular part** (*pars retrolentiformis*); and the part which lies ventral to the lentiform nucleus is the *pars sublentiformis.*

The **anterior limb** of the internal capsule contains: thalamocortical fibers from the lateral nucleus of the thalamus to the frontal lobe; corticothalamic fibers from the frontal lobe to the thalamus; fronto-pontine fibers from the frontal lobe to the nuclei of the pons; probably collaterals from the above tracts to the caudate and putamen; and fibers from the caudate to the putamen. The **genu** contains in addition to corticothalamic and thalamocortical fibers, corticobulbar fibers to the motor nuclei of the cranial nerves. The adjoining region of the **posterior limb** contains in addition to corticothalamic and thalamocortical fibers, corticospinal and corticorubral fibers. The corticospinal fibers to the motor nuclei of the muscles of the arm are nearer to the genu than those to the leg. The **retrolenticular part** contains thalamocortical fibers, sensory fibers from the lateral nucleus of the thalamus to the postcentral gyrus. The **sublenticular part** contains: the temporopontine fibers from the cortex of the temporal lobe to the pontine nuclei; the auditory radiation from the medial geniculate body to the audiosensory area of the transverse temporal gyrus; the optic radiation (geniculocalcarine tract) from the lateral geniculate body to the visuosensory area of the occipital lobe; fibers from the cortex to the superior colliculus; corticothalamic fibers from the temporal and occipital lobes to the lateral nucleus of the thalamus.

The fibers of the internal capsule radiate widely as they pass to and from the various parts of the cerebral cortex, forming the corona radiata (Fig. 753) and intermingling with the fibers of the corpus callosum.

The **External Capsule** (*capsula externa*) (Fig. 759) is a lamina of white fibers between the putamen and the claustrum. It contains association and projection fibers associated with neighboring and adjacent tracts and nuclei similar to the parts of the internal capsule.

The Lateral Ventricle

The right and left lateral ventricles (*ventriculus lateralis*) (Fig. 763) are the cavities inside the cerebral hemispheres. Although they are the most cephalic representatives of the ventricular system, they are not called first and second ventricles, as would be expected to account for the numerical designation of the third ventricle. The lateral ventricle is medially placed within the hemisphere, separated from its fellow of the opposite side by a thin vertical partition, the septum pellucidum (Fig. 740). It is lined by ependyma, contains spinal fluid, and communicates with the third ventricle through the interventricular foramen of Monro. It is quite irregular in shape, consisting of a central part or body, and three prolongations, the anterior, posterior, and inferior horns (Fig. 764, 765).

The **central part** or **body** (*pars centralis*) extends from the interventricular foramen to the splenium of the corpus callosum. Its roof is formed by the under surface of the corpus callosum, its medial wall by the septum pellucidum, and its floor by the caudate nucleus, thalamus, stria and vena terminalis, the choroid plexus, and the lateral part of the fornix (Fig. 766).

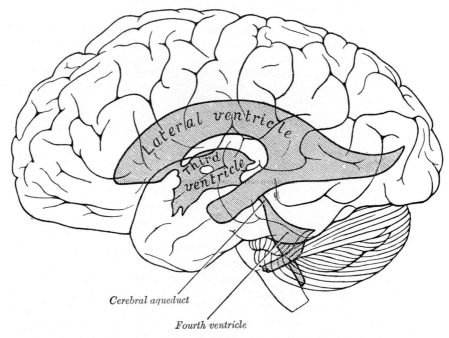

FIG. 763.—Scheme showing relations of the ventricles to the surface of the brain.

The **anterior horn** (*cornu anterius*) (Fig. 766) is the part of the ventricle which extends into the frontal lobe beyond the interventricular foramen. It curves around the rostral end of the caudate nucleus and is confined by the genu and rostrum of the corpus callosum.

The **posterior horn** (*cornu posterius*) (Fig. 766) is the somewhat narrowed extension of the lateral ventricle into the occipital lobe. Its roof is formed by the fibers of the corpus callosum passing to the temporal and occipital cortex. On its medial wall a longitudinal eminence, the calcar avis, is the result of the deep infolding of the calcarine fissure. The forceps posterior of the corpus callosum causes another projection, the bulb of the posterior horn, above the calcar avis, and the collateral fissure produces a prominence lateral to the calcar avis, the collateral trigone.

The **inferior horn** (*cornu inferius*) (Fig. 770) is the extension of the lateral ventricle into the temporal lobe, reaching rostrally to within 2.5 cm. of the temporal pole. It curves around the caudal end of the thalamus and follows the arch of the tail of the caudate nucleus. Its roof is formed chiefly by the inferior surface of the tapetum, but the tail of the caudate nucleus and the stria terminalis also extend forward in the roof to the rostral extremity of the horn. The floor is formed by the hippocampus, the fimbria hippocampi, the collateral eminence, and the choroid plexus. When the choroid plexus is torn away, a cleft-like opening is left along the medial wall of the horn. This is the inferior part of the choroid fissure.

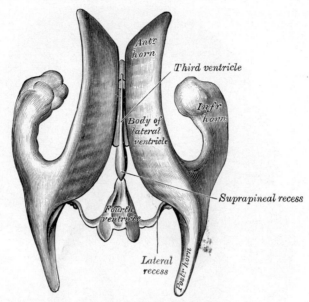

Fig. 764.—Drawing of a cast of the ventricular cavities, viewed from above. (Retzius.)

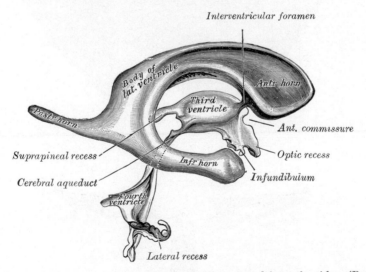

Fig. 765.—Drawing of a cast of the ventricular cavities, viewed from the side. (Retzius.)

The **interventricular foramen** (*foramen interventriculare; foramen of Monro*) (Fig. 741) is the opening between the lateral and third ventricle. It is situated between the columns of the fornix and the anterior end of the thalamus.

The **septum pellucidum** (Fig. 740) is a narrow partition between the two lateral ventricles. It is attached to the under surface of the body of the corpus callosum, to the concave surface of the genu and rostrum of the corpus callosum, and to the body of the fornix. It is composed of two thin sheets, the laminæ septi pellucidi, with a narrow cleft between, the cavum septi pellucidi. The cleft is not connected with the ventricles, but the lateral surfaces of the septum form part of the wall of the lateral ventricles and are therefore covered with ependyma.

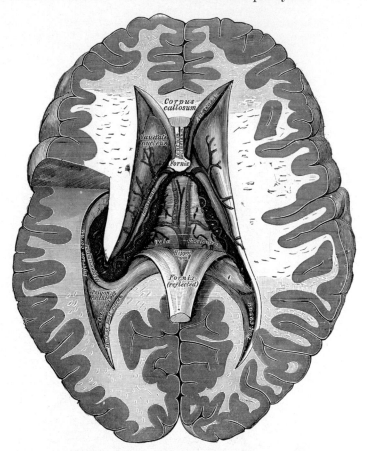

FIG. 766.—Tela chorioidea of the third ventricle, and the choroid plexus of the left lateral ventricle, exposed from above.

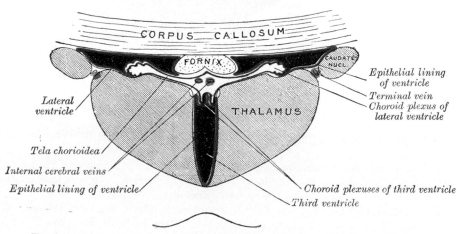

FIG. 767.—Coronal section of lateral and third ventricles. (Diagrammatic.)

The **choroid plexus** (*plexus chorioideus ventriculi lateralis*) (Fig. 766) extends from the interventricular foramen, where it is continuous with the plexus of the third ventricle, through the body and to the rostral end of the inferior horn. It does not extend into the anterior and posterior horns. The part in the body of the ventricle projects into the lateral wall from under the lateral edge of the fornix as an extension of the tela chorioidea of the third ventricle through a cleft called the choroid fissure (Fig. 768). The part in the inferior horn lies in the concavity of the hippocampus and overlaps the fibria hippocampi from which it is reflected over to the roof of the

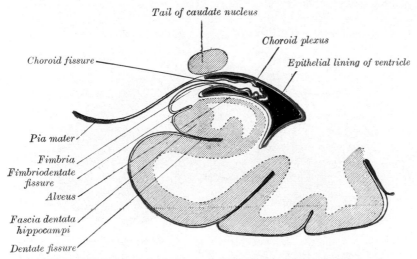

FIG. 768.—Coronal section of inferior horn of lateral ventricle. (Diagrammatic.)

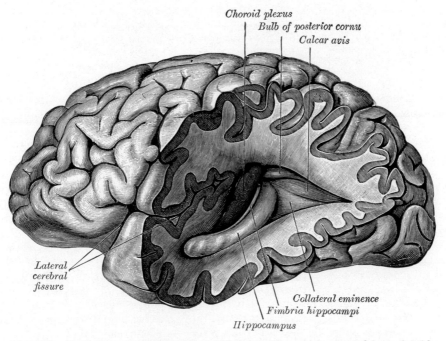

FIG. 769.—Posterior and inferior cornua of left lateral ventricle exposed from the side.

horn (Fig. 766). The plexus consists of minute villous processes or tufts of blood vessels brought into the tela choroidea by the pia mater (Fig. 768). The tufts are covered everywhere by a layer of epithelial cells derived from the ependyma. The arteries of the plexus are: (*a*) the anterior choroidal, a branch of the internal carotid which enters the plexus at the end of the inferior horn, and (*b*) the posterior choroidal, one or two small branches of the posterior cerebral which pass under the splenium. The veins of the choroid plexus unite into a tortuous vein which drains rostrally to the interventricular foramen where it joins the vena terminalis to form the internal cerebral vein (of Galen).

The **choroid fissure** is the cleft-like space which remains when the choroid plexus is torn away and the epithelial lining of the ventricle is severed. Its extent is the same as the plexus, from the interventricular foramen to the tip of the inferior horn.

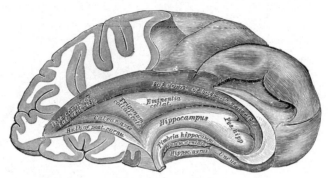

FIG. 770.—Temporal lobe with inferior and posterior horns of lateral ventricle viewed from above.

Near the foramen, the fissure is between the lateral edge of the fornix and the upper surface of the thalamus. At the beginning of the inferior horn it is between the commencement of the fimbria hippocampi and the caudal end of the thalamus. In the rest of the inferior horn it is between the fimbria in the floor and the stria terminalis in the roof.

The Rhinencephalon

The **Rhinencephalon** or smell brain is composed of a rather heterogeneous complex of structures concerned with the reception and conduction of olfactory impulses. In lower vertebrates, most of the pallium or cortex is taken up by the rhinencephalon and because of its great phylogenetic age is called the archipallium. In man, the exuberant growth of the cortex not involved in olfaction, called the neopallium, has submerged the archipallium and relegated it to more or less hidden areas of the medial and inferior surfaces of the hemispheres. The rhinencephalon includes: (1) the olfactory bulb, (2) the olfactory tract and striæ, (3) the anterior perforated substance, (4) the piriform area, (5) the hippocampal formation, (6) the paraterminal and parolfactory areas, and (7) the fornix.

(1) The **Olfactory Bulb** (*bulbus olfactorius*) (Figs. 743, 885) rests on the cribriform plate of the ethmoid bone through the foramina of which it receives the fila olfactoria of the olfactory nerve (page 1093). The bulb is connected with the hemisphere by the olfactory tract. The olfactory tract and bulb are really outgrowths of the brain, similar to the optic nerve, rather than peripheral nerves. In some lower animals and in the human embryo they contain a cavity linked with the ventricle but in the human adult the cavity is obliterated, its place being taken by neuroglia.

(2) The **Olfactory Tract** (*tractus olfactorius*) (Fig. 717) joins the inferior surface

of the frontal lobe just rostral to the anterior perforated substance, forming a triangular expansion, the **olfactory trigone**. Its fibers then diverge into three strands, the medial, intermediate, and lateral olfactory striæ. The **medial olfactory stria** is augmented by a small amount of gray matter and becomes the **medial olfactory gyrus**. It reaches the medial surface of the hemisphere, turns upward, and merges with the paraterminal and parolfactory area just rostral to the lamina terminalis (Fig. 717). The **lateral olfactory stria** with its accompanying gray matter, the **lateral olfactory gyrus**, bends laterally toward the exposed approach to the insula, the **limen insulæ**. Here it bends back sharply and continues medially into the piriform area and uncus. An **intermediate olfactory stria** between the medial and lateral striæ is occasionally present, blending directly with the anterior perforated substance.

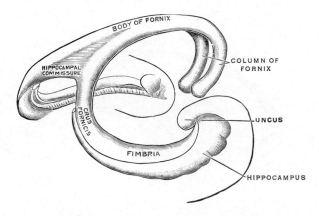

Fig. 771.—Diagram of the fornix. (Spitzka.)

(3) The **Anterior Perforated Substance** (Fig. 717) is a flattened, depressed area on the basal surface of the hemisphere just rostral to the optic tract. It is named from the numerous minute holes left in its surface by the withdrawal of the many small penetrating blood vessels when the pia mater is removed. Its rostral boundary is the olfactory trigone and striæ. The posterior boundary is the optic tract, parallel with which is a ridge on its surface, the **diagonal band of Broca**. In certain animals but rarely in man it contains a small oval elevation the **olfactory tubercle** (*tuberculum olfactorium*). In this area parts of the basal ganglia come close to the surface.

(4) The **Piriform Area** (*pyriform lobe*) includes the lateral olfactory gyrus, the limen insulæ, the uncus, and the adjacent part of the hippocampal gyrus (Fig. 717). In the brain of a four month fetus, the piriform lobe and its association with other parts of the rhinencephalon show more clearly before the neopallium overshadows them (Fig. 695).

(5) The **Hippocampal Formation** comprises (*a*) the subcallosal gyrus, (*b*) the supracallosal gyrus, the longitudinal striæ of the corpus callosum and the diagonal band of Broca, (*c*) the dentate fascia, and (*d*) the hippocampus.

(*a*) The **subcallosal gyrus** (Fig. 741) is the thin sheet of gray matter which covers the under surface of the rostrum of the corpus callosum. It is continuous inferiorly with the medial olfactory gyrus. Superiorly it follows around the genu of the corpus callosum and becomes the supracallosal gyrus.

(*b*) The **supracallosal gyrus** (*induseum griseum*) is a thin sheet of gray matter which covers the superior surface of the corpus callosum. It is continuous laterally under the callosal sulcus with the gyrus cinguli. Posteriorly it continues into the **fasciola cinerea** at the splenium of the corpus callosum (Fig. 772). The medial and lateral longitudinal striæ represent the white matter of the vestigial supracallosal gyrus. They are two ridges on the superior surface of the corpus callosum (Fig. 754). Anteriorly they sweep around the genu, enter the subcallosal gyrus, and emerge as a single band which courses laterally at the posterior part of the anterior perforated substance as the **diagonal band** (*of Broca*).

(*c*) The **hippocampus** (*Ammon's horn; cornu ammonis*), as its picturesque names imply, is a peculiarly shaped protuberance in the floor of the inferior horn of the lateral ventricle (Figs. 766, 770, 771). Its rostral extremity, the **pes hippocampi**, is enlarged and exhibits three or four rounded projections, the digitations of the hippocampus. Its substance is continuous with the hippocampal gyrus, the hippocampus having pushed inward at the hippocampal fissure and curled over on itself (Fig. 775).

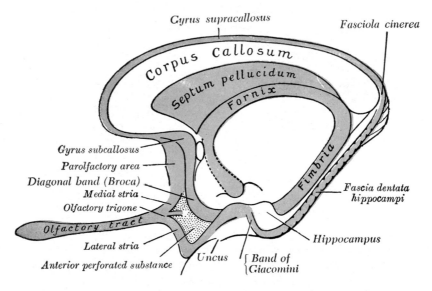

FIG. 772.—Scheme of rhinencephalon.

Its internal structure resembles a very specialized cerebral cortex, but its ventricular surface is covered by a layer of white fibers, the **alveus**. The fibers of the alveus converge toward the medial border of the hippocampus at the choroid fissure to form the **fimbria of the hippocampus** (*fimbria hippocampi*).

(*d*) The **dentate fascia** (*gyrus dentatus*) (Fig. 772) is a narrow crenated strip of cortex between the fimbria hippocampi and the hippocampal gyrus. It lies in the depths of the hippocampal fissure which separates it from the hippocampal gyrus. The fimbriodentate sulcus separates it from the fimbria. It is continued posteriorly, under the splenium of the corpus callosum, as the delicate fasciola cinerea which in turn is continuous with the supracallosal gyrus. Anteriorly it enters the notch of the uncus and bends medially as the **band of Giacomini.**

(6) The **Paraterminal Body** (*gyrus paraterminalis; precommissural area; septal area*) (Fig. 741) is immediately anterior to the lamina terminalis. It includes the parolfactory area and is continuous with the subcallosal gyrus and the medial olfactory gyrus. From the parolfactory area, the diagonal band (*of Broca*) swings ventrally and laterally across the anterior perforated substance just rostral to the optic tract and ends in the amygdaloid complex.

(7) The **Fornix** occupies a position close to the median plane and follows part of the under surface of the arch of the corpus callosum over the thalamus (Figs. 771, 772). It is composed of two stout bands, separated at both ends but joined together at the middle. Its parts are the crura, the hippocampal commissure, the body, and the columns. The **crus fornicis** begins posteriorly as a continuation of the fimbria of the hippocampus. It arches upward over the thalamus, closely applied to the inferior surface of the corpus callosum and inclines toward the midline. The two crura are connected by a lamina of transverse fibers variously called the **hippocampal commissure** (*commissura fornicis*), the **psalterium**, or the **lyra**. At the highest part of their arch the crura are fused into the **body of the fornix**. The body of the fornix lies above the tela chorioidea and ependymal roof of the third ventricle (Fig. 766) and is attached to the lower borders of the septum pellucidum (Fig. 772) and the under surface of the corpus callosum. Anteriorly, above the interventricular foramina, the body divides again into the **columns** or **anterior pillars of the fornix**. They bend downward, forming the anterior boundary of the interventricular foramina, become buried behind the wall of the third ventricle and end in the mammillary bodies.

The **anterior commissure** (Fig. 741) is a bundle of white fibers which crosses the midline just rostral to the columns in the anterior wall of the third ventricle at the junction of the lamina terminalis and rostrum of the corpus callosum. Its constituent fiber bundles are twisted like a rope and extend laterally ventral to the anterior limb of the internal capsule and between the anterior perforated substance and the ventral part of the lentiform nucleus (Fig. 761). Most of the fibers belong to the rhinencephalon, connecting the piriform areas and amygdalæ. Fibers have been traced to the external capsule and temporal neopallium (Fox *et al.*, '48). A second part of the commissure connecting the olfactory lobes of the two sides is prominent in some animals (Brodal '48) but is much reduced in man.

Structure of the Rhinencephalon

The **Olfactory Bulb.**—A section through the olfactory bulb shows it to be quite definitely stratified (Fig. 773). (1) The *outer layer*, concentrated on the inferior surface adjacent to the cribriform plate, contains unmyelinated fibers, the central processes from the olfactory neuroepithelial cells of the nasal mucosa (page 1093). (2) The *glomerular layer* contains numerous spheroidal structures called glomeruli which are formed by the interlacement of the ends of the unmyelinated olfactory fibers with the dendrites of the mitral and tufted cells. (3) The *molecular layer* contains a dense stratum of large **mitral cells** whose dendrites enter the glomeruli and whose axons penetrate to a deeper layer and enter the olfactory tract. Mingled with the granule cells of the molecular layer are **tufted cells** whose dendrites synapse with the unmyelinated olfactory fibers in tufts and glomeruli. Their axons are smaller than mitral cell axons. They cross to the olfactory bulb of the opposite side in the anterior commissure and form synapses with the mitral cells. (4) An *inner granule cell layer* or medullary layer contains mitral and tufted cell axons and granule cells. (5) The **layer of white substance** contains the myelinated axons of the mitral cells on their way to the olfactory tract. (6) An inner core of *neuroglia* is a remnant of the lining of the cavity which was present in the embryo.

The **anterior perforated substance** and **olfactory tubercle** shows three moderately well defined layers (Fig. 774): (1) an external molecular layer, (2) a layer of pyramidal cells, and (3) an irregular layer of polymorphic cells. In the third layer two specialized groups of cells are found. Several densely packed groups of small well stained cells are named the islands of Calleja. A band of large cells just under the ventral surface of the globus pallidus is the substantia innominata of Reichert. The

nucleus accumbens forms the floor of the caudal part of the anterior horn of the lateral ventricle, between the head of the caudate nucleus and the anterior perforated substance.

The **piriform area** shows a definitely stratified arrangement, which differs in certain respects from the cortex of the neopallium. The molecular layer is unusually broad and contains a large number of tangential fibers. The adjoining layer contains two varieties of cells, each arranged in clumps or cell nests. The larger

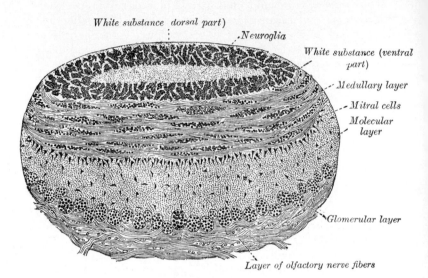

White substance dorsal part)

Neuroglia

White substance (ventral part)

Medullary layer

Mitral cells

Molecular layer

Glomerular layer

Layer of olfactory nerve fibers

Fig. 773.—Coronal section of olfactory bulb. (Schwalbe.)

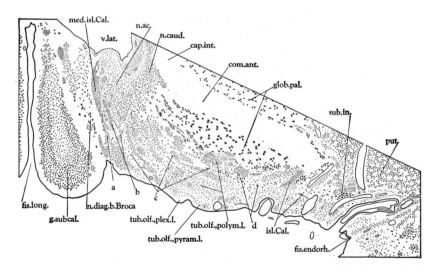

med.isl.Cal.

n.ac.

v.lat.

n.caud.

cap.int.

com.ant.

glob.pal.

sub.in.

put.

fis.long.

g.subcal.

n.diag.b.Broca

a   b   c

tub.olf.,plex.l.

tub.olf.,polym.l.   d   isl.Cal.

tub.olf.,pyram.l.

fis.endorh.

Fig. 774.—Drawing showing the mid-portion of the human tuberculum olfactorium. *Cap. int.*, capsula interna; *com. ant.*, commissura anterior; *d.*, large neurons of polymorph layer; *fis. endorh.*, fissura endorhinalis; *fis. long.*, fissura longitudinalis; *g. subcal.*, gyrus subcallosus; *isl. Cal.*, island of Calleja; *glob. pal.*, globus pallidus; *med. isl. Cal.*, medial island of Calleja; *n. ac.*, nucleus accumbens; *n. caud.*, nucleus caudatus; *n. diag. b. Broca*, nucleus of the diagonal band of Broca; *put.*, putamen; *sub. in.*, substantia innominata; *tub. olf.*, *plex. l.*, tuberculum olfactorium plexiform layer; *tub. olf.*, *plylm. l.*, tuberculum olfactorium polymorph layer; *tub. olf.*, *pryam. l.*, tuberculum olfactorium pyramidal layer; *v. lat.*, ventriculus lateralis. (Crosby and Humphrey, courtesy of Jour. Comp. Neur.)

cells average 28μ in diameter, are stellate in form, and poor in Nissl bodies. The smaller cells, although pyramidal in form, are smaller than the cells of the layer of small pyramidal cells in the neopallium. The third layer is deep, and the cells which it contains are chiefly pyramidal in shape, and their apices point obliquely to the surface. These cells are especially rich in basal dendrites. The fourth layer is much narrower and contains remarkably few cells, some resembling those of the

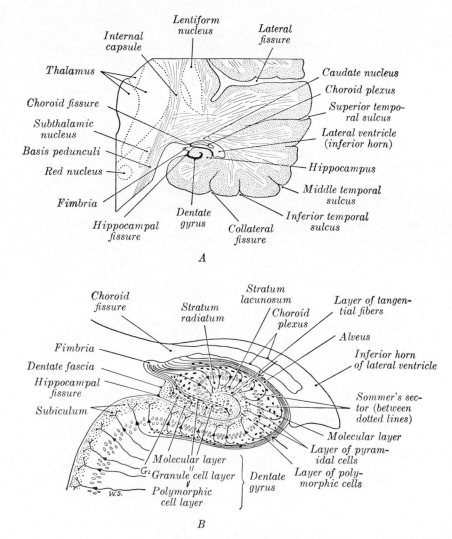

Fig. 775.—*A*, Frontal section through the temporal lobe and adjacent areas of the right half of the brain to show the structure and relations of the hppocampus. *B*, Diagrammatic representation of the histologic structure of the hippocampus. (Buchanan's, *Functional Neuroanatomy*.)

third layer, while others are small and stellate in shape. The fifth layer is broader and contains cells which resemble the pyramidal elements of the third layer. A sixth, deeper, layer of fusiform cells is also present. This area receives the olfactory neurones of the second order and gives rise to those of the third order, which proceed to the hippocampal formation.

The **hippocampus** is more primitive in its structure than the piriform area and consists essentially of three layers (Fig. 775). It represents a portion of the cortex which has been rolled into the inferior horn of the lateral ventricle and its superficial cortical layer lies in relation to the hippocampal fissure and the dentate fascia. (1) The superficial or *molecular layer* is unusually broad and is densely packed with tangential fibers. It is usually described as consisting of a superficial part, the *stratum moleculare* and a deep part, the *stratum lacunosum*. (2) This is succeeded by a broad layer of large pyramidal cells, which give off long apical dendrites into the molecular layer. Their basal axons run centrally through the succeeding polymorphous layer and pass into the subjacent white substance, which here constitutes the alveus. The numerous apical dendrites which are crowded together in the superficial part of this pyramidal layer have given rise to its subdivision into a *stratum radiatum* (or dendritic part) and a *stratum lucidum* (or cellular part). (3) The third layer contains *polymorphous cells* some of which are cells of Martinotti. Here, as elsewhere, they send their axons into the molecular layer. Others are aberrant pyramidal cells, and still others send their axons into the pyramidal layer where they end by arborizing around the pyramidal cells. The white fibers of the alveus cover the polymorphous layer and separate it from the ependyma on the free ventricular surface of the hippocampus (Buchanan '57, Kaada *et al.* '53).

The **dentate fascia** also consists of three layers, a molecular layer, a granular layer, and a polymorphous layer. (1) The molecular stratum is well developed, and receives the dendrites of the cells of the second layer. (2) These are, for the most part, small granule cells but a number of large pyramidal cells are found among them. The axones of these cells traverse the third, or polymorphous layer, and then enter the adjoining molecular layer of the hippocampus, through which they pass to reach the pyramidal layer where they terminate by arborizing around the large pyramidal cells. These axons are characterized by small varicosities as they run in the pyramidal layer. (3) The third, or polymorphous layer, contains many Golgi Type II cells and many cells which send their axons through the adjoining layers of the hippocampus to reach the alveus.

The neurones of the hippocampus appear to be particularly vulnerable in infections, and in degenerative and toxic processes. This may be associated with its peculiar blood supply (Nilges '44) particularly in the area marked Sommer's sector in Figure 775.

CRANIAL NERVE NUCLEI AND THEIR CONNECTIONS

I. The **Olfactory Nerves** (*first cranial nerve*; *N. I.*) or sensory nerves of smell are short bundles of fibers from the nasal mucous membrane which pass through the cribriform plate of the ethmoid bone to reach the olfactory bulb. The structure resembling a nerve on the basal aspect of the frontal lobe (Fig. 743) is the olfactory tract. The long processes of the neuroepithelial cells in the olfactory nerves described in the chapter on Sense Organs (page 1093) form synapses (1) with the mitral cells in the glomeruli of the olfactory bulb (Fig. 885) and (2) with the tufted cells of the bulb. The axons of the tufted cells cross to the bulb of the opposite side in the anterior commissure, reinforcing the sensory impulses.

The axons of the mitral cells traverse the olfactory tract and are distributed to different parts of the rhinencephalon through three strands, the lateral, intermediate, and medial olfactory striæ (Fig. 741). The final destinations of the impulses are mainly the hippocampal cortex, the fornix, and the mammillary bodies and thence either association paths through the thalamus to the cortex or motor and reflex paths to the brain stem. A great many of the collaterals and terminal fibers which interconnect all parts of the rhinencephalon are not understood, but the following basic pathways are quite well established (see Rhinencephalon for figure references).

Lateral Olfactory Stria.—The greater number of olfactory bulb mitral cell axons in the lateral olfactory stria traverse the piriform area and enter the uncus and rostral part of the hippocampal gyrus. Fibers arising here pass to the hippocampus and dentate gyrus. Axons of the pyramidal cells if the hippocampus, either by way of the alveus or more directly as perforant fibers, reach the fimbria of the hippocampus of the opposite side through the psalterium (*hippocampal commissure; commissura fornicis*). Most of the fibers continue through the columns of the fornix to the mammillary bodies (see below). Others of the mitral cell axons in the lateral stria end in the olfactory trigone and anterior perforated substance and are relayed to the amygdaloid mucleus.

The **mammillary bodies** contain the terminations of the fibers of the columns of the fornix. The two principal tracts from these bodies are (*a*) the mammilloteg-mental tract (of Gudden) to the nuclei of the tegmentum of the pons and medulla oblongata; and (*b*) the mammillothalamic tract (bundle of Vicq d'Azyr) which goes to the anterior nucleus of the thalamus. From the thalamus associations are made through the cingulum with the cingulate gyrus and thence with many parts of the hemisphere.

Amygdaloid Nuclei.—The amygdaloid nuclei are interconnected with the anterior perforated substance, the piriform area, the parolfcatory area, the corpus striatum, and the cortex of the temporal lobe. The amygdalæ of the two sides are connected with each other through the anterior commissure (Jiminez-Castellanos '49).

The **diagonal band of Broca** (*diagonal gyrus of the rhinencephalon*) forms a slight ridge across the caudal part of the anterior perforated substance, just rostral to and parallel with the optic tract. It extends from the parolfactory area on the medial surface of the hemisphere to the amygdaloid nuclei and serves to connect these two centers.

The **stria terminalis** arises in the amygdaloid nucleus and is visible in the wall of the lateral ventricle as a strand in the groove between the thalamus and the tail of the caudate nucleus. Separate components pass to the parolfactory area, to the habenular nuclei, and to the hypothalamus of the same and opposite sides.

Intermediate Olfactory Stria.—The axons of olfactory bulb mitral cells in the intermediate olfactory stria are relayed in the anterior perforated substance to the nuclei of the parolfactory area and subcallosal gyrus. Fibers from here course through the stria medullaris thalami to the habenular nuclei. Some fibers cross to the opposite side in the habenular commissure. Most fibers pass through the habenulopeduncular tract (*fasciculus retroflexus of Meynert*) and through the midbrain to the posterior perforated substance and end in the interpeduncular nucleus and dorsal tegmental nucleus.

Medial Olfactory Stria.—The axons of olfactory bulb mitral cells in the medial olfactory stria enter the parolfactory area and subcallosal gyrus. Fibers from the nuclei in this area pass through the indusium griseum and longitudinal striæ to the hippocampus and make other connections with olfactory centers through paths similar to those followed by fibers from the other olfactory striæ.

The **parolfactory area**, in addition to the above connections, is the source of a prominent tract called the medial forebrain bundle. Fibers from this bundle pass to the tuber cinereum, the brain stem and the mammillary bodies.

The **subcallosal gyrus** receives fibers from most of the same sources as the parolfactory area and by its continuity with the indusium griseum sends fibers through the medial and lateral longitudinal striæ caudalward around the corpus callosum. At the splenium the two striæ come together as the fasciola cinerea. The fibers enter the dentate gyrus and thence follow the paths within the hippocampal complex.

II. The **Optic Nerve** (*nervus opticus; second cranial nerve; N. II*) (page 956) consists chiefly of coarse myelinated fibers which arise in the ganglionic layer of the retina (page 1108). The majority are third neurons in the visual pathway. In the optic disc, the fibers from the macula lutea make up the temporal half, but in the nerve they soon take a central position having the fibers from the peripheral retinal quadrants placed around them. At the optic chiasma the fibers from the medial half of the retina cross to the optic tract of the opposite side, the fibers from the temporal half of the retina stay on the same side. Thus the fibers from the right half of both retinas pass to the right hemisphere and those from the left half to the left hemisphere. Approximately 60 per cent of the fibers cross.

Primary Visual Centers.—Most of the fibers of the optic tract terminate in (1) the lateral geniculate body, other fibers continue through the superior brachium to (2) the superior colliculus and to (3) the pretectal region.

(1) The **lateral geniculate body** receives the visual sensory fibers in an orderly manner (Fig. 776). The axons of the medium sized pigmented nerve cells leave its dorsal rostral surface, run rostrally and then laterally through the retrolenticular portion of the internal capsule as the geniculocalcarine fasciculus. They pass caudally and medially to terminate in the visual cortex or area striata (area 17, Fig. 750) in the immediate neighborhood of the calcarine fissure. Some of the fibers make a detour over the inferior horn of the ventricle before turning back to the occipital lobe. The representation of visual fields is illustrated in Figure 776. The cortex of the two sides is connected by commissural fibers in the optic radiation and splenium of the corpus callosum. Association fibers connect this area with other regions of the cortex and some fibers go back to the geniculate body. Clinical evidence indicates that the foveæ are represented bilaterally in the cortex.

(2) The **superior colliculus** receives fibers from the optic tract through the superior brachium as the visual afferent arm for reflex control of the ocular muscles. There is a point to point relationship between the retina and the colliculus similar to that with the geniculate body. It is the origin of the tectobulbar and tectospinal tracts and its other connections are described with the oculomotor nerve.

(3) In the **pretectal region** the fibers form synapses with cells whose axons pass ventrally around the cephalic end of the central gray of the midbrain to the oculomotor nucleus. They terminate in the nucleus of Edinger-Westphal as the afferent arm of reflex pupillary constriction in response to light.

III. The **Oculomotor Nerve** (*n. oculomotorius*; *N. III*; *third cranial nerve*) (page 957) contains somatic motor fibers for innervation of the Levator palpebræ and all the extraocular muscles except the Obliquus superior and the Rectus lateralis. It also contains autonomic fibers for the Ciliaris muscle and the Sphincter pupillæ and proprioceptive fibers from the above-mentioned extrinsic muscles.

The **oculomotor nucleus** (*nucleus n. oculomotorius*) (Fig. 735) lies in the gray substance ventral to the aqueduct. It is from 6 to 10 mm. in length, the cephalic portion extending under the floor of the third ventricle for a short distance and the caudal end reaching to the level of the trochlear nucleus. It is intimately related to the medial longitudinal fasciculus which lies against its ventrolateral aspect and many of its cells lie among the fibers of the posterior longitudinal fasciculus (of Schütz) as well. The fibers from the nucleus are collected into bundles which pass across the medial longitudinal fasciculus, the tegmentum, the red nucleus, and the medial margin of the substantia nigra in a series of curves, and finally emerge from the oculomotor sulcus medial to the cerebral peduncle (Fig. 741).

The oculomotor nucleus is in two parts, a large-celled somatic nucleus and a smaller-celled autonomic nucleus. The **somatic nucleus** in turn is composed of more or less definite groups of neurones for the individual muscles which can be mapped topographically (Fig. 777). The nucleus representing the Rectus medialis is the most ventral, the Rectus inferior most dorsal, and the Obliquus inferior intermediate between them. The Rectus superior is medial to the others in the caudal two-thirds

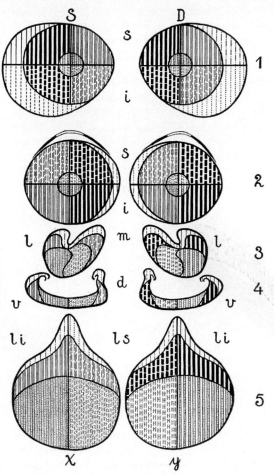

FIG. 776.—Diagrammatic illustrations of the projection of the various quadrants of the visual fields. Left (S) and right (D) sides of the visual fields and of the afferent visual apparatus. Number 1 represents both fields of vision with their upper (s) and lower (i), nasal and temporal halves; the smaller inner circles represent the "central" or macular portions (their relative size in comparison with the perimacular portion is somewhat exaggerated); the large circles represent the peri- or extramacular portions of the binocular visual fields; the outermost lightly shaded sickle-shaped zones represent the monocular portions of the visual fields. Number 2 represents left and right retinæ with their upper (s) and lower (i), nasal and temporal halves; smaller and larger circles and the monocular portions as above. Number 3 represents a schematic cross section through the left and right geniculate bodies; their internal margins (m) close to the thalamus; their external margins (l); their concave contours in the figure facing upward represent their ventral margins. Number 4 represents cross sections through the left and right visual radiation (external sagittal strata of the parieto-occipital lobes); their dorsal horizontal branches (d), their ventral horizontal branches (v), with perpendicular or vertical branches (in the figure horizontal) connecting both horizontal branches. Number 5 represents the left and right visual projection cortex, the area striata of Elliot Smith, field 17 of Brodmann, each subdivided into an upper (ls) and a lower half (li) corresponding with the upper and lower lips of the calcarine fissures. The dividing lines, vertical in the figure, and terminating at the letters x and y, correspond in their upper parts to the bottom of the calcarine fissures and to the horizontal meridians of both visual fields dividing the upper from the lower extramacular quadrants; in their lower parts (lower in the figure) these lines correspond to horizontal meridians dividing the upper from lower macular quadrants. The points where these lines reach the posterior limits of both striate areas, marked by the letters x and y in the figure, correspond to both points of fixation in the visual fields. The vertical lines or meridians dividing the left from the right homonymous halves of the macular portion of the visual fields, correspond to the posterior (lower in the figure) circumference of the striate areas close to the letters x and y. (Polyak, University of California Press, 1932.)

only of the somatic nucleus. The Levator palpebræ is represented by the caudal central nucleus. The fibers from the nuclei for the Rectus inferior, Obliquus inferior, and Rectus medialis are uncrossed, going to the ipsilateral eye. Those from the Rectus superior nucleus are crossed and those from the Levator nucleus are bilateral.

The **autonomic nucleus of the oculomotor nerve** (Fig. 777) is rostral and dorsal to the somatic nucleus. It is composed not only of the lateral portion known as the *nucleus of Edinger-Westphal* but also of a median portion containing a similar small motor type of cell. The fibers from the nucleus are uncrossed, transverse the inferior division of the oculomotor nerve and enter the ciliary ganglion as its preganglionic fibers. Experiments with monkeys indicate that 96 per cent of these preganglionic fibers are for the innervation of the Ciliaris muscle and only 3 or 4 per cent for the Sphincter pupillæ (Warwick '56).

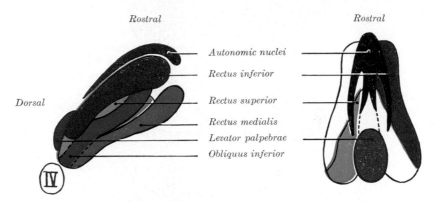

Rostral   *Rostral*

Autonomic nuclei

Rectus inferior

Dorsal   Rectus superior

Rectus medialis

Levator palpebrae

Obliquus inferior

Fig. 777.—Diagrams showing the representation of the right extra-ocular muscles in the oculomoton nucleus of a monkey. *A*, Right lateral aspect; *B*, Dorsal aspect. (Redrawn from Warwick, R., 1953, J. comp. Neurol.)

Experiments with monkeys indicate that a central *nucleus of Perlia* is inconstant in occurrence and when present is composed of neurones supplying the Rectus superior. It cannot, therefore, be a **center for** control of **convergence**, as is usually stated (Warwick '56). It is probable that this delicate adaptive mechanism is controlled by a correlating center, perhaps in the reticular formation like that for conjugate movements.

The **proprioceptive fibers in the oculomotor nerve** are probably from the mesencephalic nucleus of the trigeminal nerve which occupies a postion adjacent to the motor nuclei of all the extra-ocular muscles.

The fibers from the cerebral cortex controlling eye movements arise chiefly from area 8 of Brodmann (Fig. 750) for voluntary movement, and from the upper part of area 19, for fixation of gaze in response to a visual stimulus. Other fibers appear to come from parts of the parietal and temporal lobes. They leave the peduncles in the rostral part of the mesencephalon. It is doubtful whether many of them pass directly to the oculomotor nuclei. The majority apparently terminate in nuclei of the reticular substance where **conjugate movements** of the eyes are integrated. A center for conjugate lateral deviation of gaze lies close to the abducens nucleus, and one for conjugate upward deviation of gaze apparently lies dorsolateral to the oculomotor nucleus. From such centers connections pass to the eye muscle nuclei both directly and through the medial longitudinal fasciculus. The last mentioned fasciculus also carries the following types of connections: (1) from the vestibular nuclei, crossed and uncrossed; (2) from various nuclei of the reticular formation; (3) interconnections between the nuclei of the eye muscles and head and neck turning nuclei; (4) from proprioceptive systems in the cervical cord. Connections from the tectum of the mesencephalon are described under the heading of the superior colliculus.

The **superior colliculus** is a center for coordination of eye movements. It receives (1) fibers from the optic tract, (2) sensory fibers from the spinal cord in the spinotectal tract, (3) fibers from the central sensory path of the trigeminal nerve, (4) central auditory fibers from the lateral lemniscus for reflex movements of the eyes in response to sound, (5) fibers from the visual cortex through the corticotectal part of the optic radiations, (6) fibers from the stria medullaris thalami of the opposite side which pass through the habenular commissure for primary and cortical olfactory associations.

The descending **efferent fibers of the superior colliculus** arise from large cells in the stratum opticum and stratum lemnisci. They pass around the ventral aspect of the central gray substance where most of them cross in the dorsal tegmental decussation (fountain decussation of Meynert) and then turn caudad to form the tectobulbar and tectospinal tracts. From the tectobulbar tract terminals and collaterals are given off to the oculomotor, trochlear, and abducens nuclei and to the motor nucleus of the facial nerve. The tectospinal fibers end by terminals and collaterals either directly or indirectly among the ventral motor horn cells of the spinal cord, especially in the cervical segments, to coordinate head and neck movements with eye movements. Many collaterals from both tracts go to the red nucleus. Probably no fibers pass from the superior colliculus to the visual sensory cortex.

The **pupillary reflexes** are of two kinds, (1) in response to light and (2) associated with accomodation. The response to light is through the pretectal nuclei of the hypothalamus and the autonomic nucleus of the oculomotor. The contraction of the ciliary muscle and pupillary sphincter which accompanies the convergence for accomodation is probably inititated by proprioceptive impulses from the ocular muscles, and correlated in nuclei of the reticular formation.

IV. The **Trochlear Nerve** (*n. trochlearis; fourth cranial nerve; N. IV*) (page 960) contains somatic motor fibers for the Obliquius superior muscle of the eye. The trochlear nucleus (Fig. 734) is a small oval mass in the central gray of the cerebral aqueduct at the level of the inferior colliculus. The axons from the nucleus start caudad in the tegmentum but turn abruptly dorsalward before reaching the pons. They pass into the anterior medullary velum, cross to the opposite side, and emerge from the velum immediately caudal to the inferior colliculus.

The nucleus receives terminals from the medial longitudinal fasciculus and other sources similar to the oculomotor nucleus and it also contains similar proprioceptive connections.

V. The **Trigeminal Nerve** (*n. trigeminus; fifth cranial nerve; N. V.*) (page 960) contains somatic sensory, special visceral efferent, and proprioceptive fibers. They pass from their nuclei through the lateral part of the tegmentum of the pons (Fig. 711) then between the fibers of the brachium pontis (Fig. 726) and emerge at the middle of the line of transition from the pons to the brachium (Fig. 743).

The terminal sensory nucleus has an enlarged cephalic end, the main sensory nucleus, and a long slender caudal portion, the nucleus of the spinal tract of the trigeminal nerve which becomes continuous with the substantia gelatinosa (of Rolando) of the spinal cord.

The **main sensory nucleus** is lateral to the motor nucleus and ventral to the brachium conjuctivum (Fig. 721, 723). It is primarily for discriminative sense. It receives the short ascending branches of the fibers from the cells of the trigeminal (semilunar) ganglion. The axons of its large and medium sized cells cross to the opposite side and form two tracts, a ventral and a dorsal . The fibers of the ventral tract, sometimes called the **trigeminal lemniscus**, are myelinated and collect in a band along the dorsal medial margin of the medial lemniscus. The dorsal tract passes through the reticular substances near the central gray around the aqueduct. Both tracts terminate in the nucleus ventralis posteromedialis of the thalamus and are relayed to the postcentral cerebral cortex.

The descending branches of the sensory root fibers course through the pons and medulla in the **spinal tract of the trigeminal nerve** (Fig. 720, 724). They end by collaterals and terminals in the nucleus of the spinal tract (Fig. 721, 723) as far down as the second cervical segment. It is primarily the sensory nucleus for pain and temperature. The second neurons from the nucleus cross to the opposite side in the reticular substance, join the medial margin of the lateral spinothalamic tract, and terminate in the nucleus ventralis posteromedialis of the thalamus. In addition to these projection tracts there are numerous connections from the sensory trigeminal nuclei to the motor nuclei of the medulla and pons. The lateral third of the reticular formation is particularly related to the trigeminal system and contains many secondary and tertiary centers. There are numerous commissural fibers of this system in the rostral part of the pons. The somatic sensory fibers of the vagus, the glossopharyngeal, and the facial nerves probably end in the nucleus of the descending tract of the trigeminal and their cortical impulses are probably carried up in the central sensory path of the trigeminal.

The **mesencephalic root** (*descending root of the trigeminal*) arises from unipolar cells arranged in scattered groups in a strand at the lateral edge of the central gray matter surrounding the upper end of the fourth ventricle and the cerebral aqueduct (*nucleus mesencephalicus n. trigemini*). The cells develop from the alar lamina and are large, round, unipolar, and without dentrites like cells of the sensory type. The axons give off collaterals to the motor nucleus and pass between the motor and main sensory nuclei to enter the motor root and pass into the mandibular branch of the nerve. They are probably proprioceptive for the muscles of mastication. It is thought that the proprioceptive fibers for the extrinsic ocular muscles also arise in this nucleus.

The **motor nucleus** (Fig. 725) is situated in the cephalic part of the pons near the lateral angle of the fourth ventricle. It is serially homologous with the facial nucleus, and the nucleus ambiguous. The axons arise from large pigmented multipolar cells. The voluntary motor control for the muscles of mastication is mediated through aberrant pyramidal tract fibers, more from the opposite than the same side. The reflex control is provided by collaterals and terminals (1) from the sensory nucleus of the trigeminal of the same and a few from the opposie side by way of the trigeminothalamic tract; (2) from the mesencephalic root of the trigeminal; and (3) from nuclei in the reticular formation. Many of these connections have interposed association neurones.

VI. The **Abducens Nerve** (*n. abducentis; sixth cranial nerve; N. VI*) (page 973) contains somatic motor fibers for the Rectus lateralis muscle of the eye. The nucleus of this nerve is serially homologous with those of the oculomotor, and hypoglossal nerves, and the ventral column of the spinal cord. It is situated close to the floor of the fourth ventricle deep to the facial colliculus (Fig. 721, 722, 725).

It receives voluntary impulses from the aberrant pyramidal tract and has reflex connections with the medial longitudinal fasciculus as well as other connections similar to those of the oculomotor and trochlear nerves. The nerve probably contains proprioceptive fibers from the mesencephalic nucleus of the trigeminal.

VII. The **Facial Nerve** (*n. facialis; seventh cranial nerve; N. VII*) (page 973) contains somatic and visceral afferent, special visceral afferent (taste) and general and special visceral efferent fibers. It is in two parts, the motor root and the **nervous intermedius**. The intermedius is more lateral and lies between the motor root and the eighth nerve. It includes the sensory and parasympathetic components and is sometimes called the glossopalatine nerve (page 975).

The **somatic sensory** fibers are few in number and join the auricular branch of the vagus to supply the external acoustic meatus. They arise from cells in the geniculate ganglion and their central termination is probably with the spinal tract of the trigeminal nerve.

The **visceral afferent** fibers are probably the fibers which reach the mucous membrane of the pharynx, nose, and palate through the greater superficial petrosal nerve (Foley *et al.* '46). They arise from cells in the geniculate ganglion and in the medulla join the tractus solitarius.

The **taste fibers**, arising from cells in the geniculate ganglion join the tractus solitarius and terminate in the rostral portion of the nucleus of the tractus solitarius. There is some evidence that fibers from the nucleus join the medial lemniscus and reach the thalamus (Allen '23). There are connections with the salivatory nucleus, the nucleus ambiguous, the hypoglossal nucleus, the dorsal nucleus of the vagus, and with the spinal cord through the reticulospinal tract (Allen '27).

The **special visceral efferent** fibers supply the striated muscles of facial expression. The **motor nucleus of the facial nerve**, deep in the reticular formation of the pons, is serially homologous with the nucleus ambiguous and the lateral part of the ventral horn of the spinal cord. Axons from its cells leave the dorsal surface of the nucleus and in the first part of their course continue dorsally and medially until they reach the rhomboid fossa. They turn sharply and run rostrally, dorsal to the medial longitudinal fasciculus, along the medial side of the abducens nucleus. They are gathered into a compact bundle and turning abruptly to the side arch over the abducens nucleus dorsally, producing the elevation in the rhomboid fossa called the facial colliculus. The twist around the abducens nucleus is called the internal genu or genu of the root of the facial nerve. The second part of its course takes the root ventrad, laterad, and caudad to the superficial emergence of the nerve from a recess between the olive and restiform body at the caudal border of the pons.

Within the nucleus, the large multipolar motor type cells are arranged in small groups representing the various facial muscles (Szentágothai '48). The cells which innervate the lower part of the face receive connections from the aberrant pyramidal system which are entirely crossed. Those to the upper part of the face are both crossed and uncrossed. Reflex connections are formed with the nucleus of the spinal tract of the trigeminal, with the cochlear nuclei, and with numerous other nuclei and mechanisms in the reticular formation of the medulla and pons, some of them concerned with emotional expression.

General visceral efferent or **autonomic fibers** arise from the superior salivatory nucleus, usually described as a group of small cells dorsomedial to the facial nucleus. These preganglionic parasympathetic fibers join the nervus intermedius. They are distributed to the submaxillary ganglion by way of the chorda tympani for innervation of the submaxillary and sublingual glands, and to the sphenopalatine ganglion by way of the greater superficial petrosal nerve for innervation of the lacrimal gland and glands in the nasal and palatine mucosa.

VIII. The **Stato-acoustic Nerve** (n. stato-acustici; *acoustic nerve; eight cranial nerve; N. VIII*) (page 981) consists of two nerves, the cochlear nerve or the nerve of hearing, and the vestibular nerve or the sensory nerve of equilibration.

The **cochlear nerve** (Fig. 723) is composed of fibers from the spiral ganglion which bifurcate as they enter the cochlear nuclei. The short ascending branches end in the ventral cochlear nucleus; the longer descending branches end in the dorsal cochlear nucleus. The terminations of the fibers is very orderly, different parts of the cochlea being represented in different parts of the cochlear nuclei. Each branch of the entering fibers gives off many collaterals, usually about 50. In most cases one, and not more than three, of these collaterals ends in a giant synapse which makes contact with as much as two-thirds of the area of the cell body of the second neuron.

The **dorsal cochlear nucleus** forms a projection on the dorsal and lateral aspect of the inferior cerebellar peduncle, the acoustic tubercle. Axons of the second order from its large fusiform cells pass over the peduncle and cross the floor of the fourth ventricle as the striæ medullares acousticæ. These fibers run under the gray substance in the floor of the ventricle, through the upper margin of the reticular substance. Many of them cross in the median raphé, sink into the reticular formation

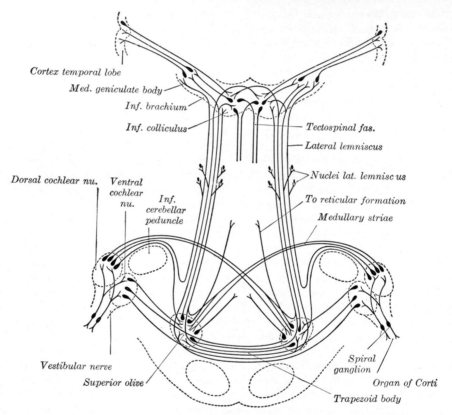

Cortex temporal lobe
Med. geniculate body
Inf. brachium
Inf. colliculus
Tectospinal fas.
Lateral lemniscus
Dorsal cochlear nu.
Ventral cochlear nu.
Inf. cerebellar peduncle
Nuclei lat. lemniscus
To reticular formation
Medullary striae
Vestibular nerve
Superior olive
Spiral ganglion
Organ of Corti
Trapezoid body

Fig. 778.—Connections of cochlear nerve.

and join the trapezoid body or the lateral lemniscus or terminate in the superior olivary nucleus on the side opposite their origin. They pass upward in the lateral lemniscus and end by terminals and collaterals either in the nuclei of the lateral lemniscus, in the inferior colliculus, or in the medial geniculate body. Some of the fibers in the striæ medullares do not cross the mid-line but dip into the reticular formation and end in the superior olivary nucleus of the same side or join the lateral lemniscus and pass upward in it to end by terminals and collaterals in the nuclei of the lateral lemniscus, in the inferior colliculus, and in the medial geniculate body of the same side. The **ventral cochlear nucleus** is continuous with the dorsal cochlear nucleus. Axons of the second order from its cells pass horizontally in the trapezoid body; here some of them end in the superior olivary nucleus of the same side; others cross the midline and end in the superior olivary nucleus of the opposite side or pass by these nuclei, giving off collaterals to them, and join the lateral lemniscus. They are distributed with fibers from the dorsal cochlear nucleus to the nuclei of the lateral lemniscus and to the inferior colliculus by collaterals and terminals. Other fibers from the ventral cochlear nucleus pass dorsal to the inferior peduncle and then dip into the substance of the pons to join the trapezoid body or the superior olivary nucleus of the same side.

Fibers from the **trapezoid body** and **superior olive** ascend in the lateral lemniscus. Many fibers are relayed in the nuclei of the lateral lemniscus on their way to the inferior colliculus and medial geniculate body. Others are relayed in the inferior colliculus and pass through the inferior brachium to the medial geniculate body. Fibers from large cells in the inferior colliculus pass through the deep white layer into the tegmentum of the same and opposite sides and descend to lower motor centers, perhaps with the tectospinal fasciculus. A large proportion of the axons from the medial geniculate body pass rostrally beneath the optic tract to join the corona radiata and auditory radiation to the cortex of the superior temporal gyrus.

The **vestibular nerve** (page 981) arises from the bipolar cells of the vestibular ganglion. The central fibers enter the medulla between the restiform body and the spinal tract of the trigeminal nerve (Fig. 741) and bifurcate into ascending and descending branches. The ascending branches go to the medial, lateral, and superior nuclei and a few through the inferior peduncle of the cerebellum to the nucleus fastigii and the vermis. The fibers from the semicircular canals go to the superior and rostral part of the medial nucleus. Those from the maculæ of the saccule and utricle go to the lateral and caudal part of the medial nucleus. The descending branches constitute the descending or spinal root of the vestibular nerve and terminate in the nucleus of the same name.

The connections of the **medial nucleus** are widespread through the medulla and pons to various nuclei of the reticular formation, to the motor nuclei of the cranial nerves, and to autonomic centers and nuclei. It contributes many fibers, both ascending and descending, to the medial longitudinal fasciculus of both sides (Buchanan '37).

The **superior nucleus** is particularly associated with the vermis, the flocculonodular lobe, and the central nuclei of the cerebellum. It contributes ascending fibers to the medial longitudinal fasciculus of the same side, and descending fibers to the vestibulospinal tract of the same side.

The **lateral nucleus** contains large polygonal cells whose axons at first run medially into the reticular formation and then turn caudalward. They shift to a more ventral position as they descend and in the spinal cord become the direct vestibulospinal tract. This is apparently the chief antigravity mechanism of the central nervous system. Collaterals from the axons ascend through the restiform body to terminate in the vermis. It also sends ascending and descending fibers to the medial longitudinal fasciculus of both sides.

The **nucleus of the spinal root of the vestibular** nerve contains large, medium, and small cells. It has widespread connections through the medulla and pons, particularly with nuclei of the reticular formation. It contributes descending fibers to the medial longitudinal fasciculus of both sides. Certain of the descending fibers form the crossed vestibulospinal tract which runs in the sulcomarginal fasciculus of the spinal cord.

IX. The **Glossopharyngeal Nerve** (*nervus glossopharyngeus, ninth cranial nerve*; *N. IX*) (page 981) contains general and special visceral afferent, and general and special visceral efferent fibers. It is similar to the vagus and is connected with the medulla by rootlets arranged in series with those of the vagus. There may be some somatic afferents similar to the auricular branch of the vagus.

The special visceral afferent fibers for taste arise from cells in the superior and inferior ganglia and after entering the medulla pass through the tractus solitarius to the nucleus solitarius. The nucleus has connections described with the facial nerve.

The general visceral afferent fibers also join the tractus solitarius.

The special visceral efferent fibers innervate the Stylopharyngeus muscle. They arise in the cephalic end of the nucleus ambiguous and have connections similar to those described with the vagus nerve.

The general visceral efferent or parasympathic preganglionic fibers arise in the nucleus salivatorius inferior and have connections similar to those described with the facial nerve. They supply secretomotor fibers to the parotid gland by relay in the otic ganglion.

X. The **Vagus Nerve** (*nervus vagus, tenth cranial nerve*; *N. X*) (page 986) contains somatic and visceral afferent, general and special visceral efferent, and special visceral afferent (taste) fibers. The afferent fibers have their cells of origin in the jugular and nodose ganglia. They enter the medulla accompanied by the motor fibers through eight or ten rootlets in the groove between the olive and the restiform body (Fig. 717) (Anderson and Berry '56).

The **somatic sensory fibers** supply part of the external acoustic meatus and a small area on the back of the ear. They probably join the spinal tract of the trigeminal nerve and have connections with the thalamus and sensory area of the cortex. Their descending fibers probably establish relations with motor nuclei of the spinal cord and medulla.

The **visceral afferent fibers** join the tractus solitarius and end in its nucleus. Their terminals make associations with centers in the reticular formation, especially those concerned with respiration, vasomotor control, cardiac activity, etc., and are relayed to motor nuclei in the medulla and spinal cord. They probably have connections with the dorsal motor nucleus of the vagus.

Taste fibers in the vagus nerve from a few taste buds on the epiglottis and larynx follow the pathways described for taste in the facial and glossopharyngeal nerves.

The **special visceral efferent** fibers of the vagus innervate the striated muscles of the pharynx and larynx. They arise in the nucleus ambiguous and after a short dorsal course turn back ventrally and laterally to emerge with the sensory fibers by several rootlets. The nucleus receives fibers either directly or indirectly through collaterals or terminals from the aberrant pyramidal tract of the opposite side. Reflex collaterals are also derived from the central tracts of the trigeminal, glossopharyngeal, vagus, and spinal nerves.

The autonomic fibers arise from cells in the **dorsal nucleus** (*Nucleus of the ala cinerea*). They are preganglionic parasympathetics for the smooth muscle and glands of the esophagus, stomach, small intestine, upper colon, gall bladder, pancreas, and lungs and inhibitory fibers to the heart. The nucleus receives terminals of visceral afferent fibers and from many other sources not exactly known. There are connections with the hypothalamus, probably through the dorsal longitudinal fasciculus of Schütz, as well with other nuclei and tracts in the reticular formation.

XI. The **Accessory Nerve** (*nervus accessorius*; *eleventh cranial nerve*; *N. XI*) (page 994) has two parts, the spinal part and the cranial or bulbar part. The cranial part is accessory to the vagus nerve, has an origin like the vagus, joins the vagus immediately after leaving the cranium and its fibers are distributed as branches of the vagus.

The **cranial part** contains special and general visceral efferent fibers which arise in the nucleus ambiguous. This nucleus appears to be an upward continuation of the lateral cell groups of the ventral horn of the spinal cord. The fibers leaving the nucleus pass ventral to the spinal tract of the trigeminal and emerge in a series of rootlets from the posterior lateral sulcus, in series with the roots of the vagus.

Through the nucleus ambiguous the cranial part makes connections with opposite aberrant pyramidal tract and with the terminal sensory nuclei of the cranial nerves.

The **visceral efferent** fibers are few in number and arise in the dorsal nucleus of the vagus. They join the vagus at the jugular foramen and are distributed as part of the vagus nerve.

The **spinal part** arises from lateral cell groups in the ventral horn of the first five or six cervical segments of the spinal cord. It is somatic motor and is described on page 994.

The nucleus of origin of the spinal part receives either directly or indirectly terminals and collaterals from the pyramidal and aberrant pyramidal tracts. It also receives fibers from the medial longitudinal fasciculus for coordination of head and eye movements and probably from the rubrospinal and vestibulospinal tracts. It is connected indirectly with spinal somatic sensory nerves by association fibers of the fasciculi proprii.

XII. The **Hypoglossal Nerve** (*nervus hypoglossus*; *twelfth cranial nerve*; *N. XII*) (page 995) contains somatic efferent fibers for innervation of the muscles of the tongue. Although Langworthy ('24) places the proprioceptive fibers to the tongue in the hypoglossal nerve, Pearson ('45) does not confirm this opinion.

The **hypoglossal nucleus** lies near the central canal in the caudal closed part of the medulla and under the trigonum hypoglossi of the floor of the rhomboid fossa. The cells of both nuclei send long dendritic processes across the midline to the opposite nucleus. The axons of the large multipolar cells pass ventrally through the reticular formation medial to the inferior olive and emerge as a number of rootlets from the ventral lateral sulcus in series with the motor rootlets of the spinal cord.

The hypoglossal nucleus receives, either directly or indirectly, numerous collaterals and terminals from the contralateral aberrant pyramidal tract and a few from the ipsilateral tract for voluntary control from the cerebral cortex. Many reflex collaterals are received from the secondary sensory paths of the trigeminal, facial, glossopharyngeal, and vagus nerves. Collaterals from the medial longitudinal fasciculus and the tectobulbar tract are said to enter the nucleus.

SPINAL NERVES—COMPOSITION AND CONNECTIONS

The spinal nerves consist of fibers conveying somatic and visceral afferent, and somatic and visceral efferent impulses.

The afferent fibers, both somatic and visceral, are processes of the spinal ganglion cells (see page 997) which enter the spinal cord through the dorsal root. The somatic afferents include those commonly called sensory for pain, temperature, and touch and deep sensation from muscles and joints. The visceral afferent fibers probably mediate reflex mechanisms which do not reach consciousness.

The somatic efferent fibers are motor for the voluntary or skeletal muscles of the body and are processes of anterior horn cells which leave the spinal cord through the ventral roots. Visceral efferent fibers, processes of lateral horn cells, also leave by the ventral roots and make up the preganglionic fibers of the sympathetic system and the sacral part of the parasympathetic system. They carry motor impulses to involuntary muscles of blood vessels and other viscera and secretory impulses to glands.

The **dorsal root fibers** entering the spinal cord promptly divide into ascending and descending branches. They make up the bulk of the posterior funiculus and give off a number of collaterals within the cord. Many of the ascending branches reach the brain, forming the tracts described below. The remainder of the ascending branches, together with the descending branches and the collaterals, form synapses with cells in the various parts of the gray matter of the cord itself. The axons of these cells may pass out into the lateral and ventral funiculi and turn upward to reach the brain. A large number complete their connections with the motor fibers within the cord, however, establishing a large number and variety of spinal cord reflexes (Fig. 779).

Somatic afferent paths.—The fibers in the dorsal roots are not segregated according to functional types until they enter the spinal cord. A partial separation is provided, however, by the formation of the two strands within the rootlets, a medial and a lateral strand. The medial strand contains mainly large myelinated fibers which carry touch, proprioception and vibratory sense. The lateral strand contains small fibers mostly not myelinated, which carry pain and temperature sensibility. Within the cord there is a further separation of fibers into functional pathways.

The sense of touch is carried by two different paths: (1) tactile discrimination, that is, (a) the ability to distinguish two points close together, (b) the exact location of a stimulus, and (c) stereognosis or recognition of the shape of an object; (2) touch and pressure of a diffuse nature.

Tactile descrimination is carried by large myelinated fibers through the medial strand of the dorsal rootlet into the dorsal funiculus. They ascend in the cuneate and gracile fasiculi to the corresponding nuclei. The secondary axons cross the midline in the internal arcuate fibers and pass through the medial lemniscus to the posterolateral ventral nucleus of the thalamus. They are relayed from here through the internal capsule and corona radiata to the somatic sensory area of the cortex in the postcentral gyrus (area 3, 1, 2 Fig. 750).

Diffuse touch and pressure fibers traverse the medial strand of the dorsal rootlets and enter the dorsal funiculus. As they run in the dorsal funiculus they give off collaterals to the gray substance of the successive levels through which they pass. In this way they reach the gray substance in a number of segments above their entrance. The collaterals synapse with neurons in the dorsal gray horn whose axons cross the midline in the ventral white commissure and form the ventral spinothalamic tract of the opposite side. These fibers join the medial lemniscus in the medulla and accompany the tactile fibers to the thalamus and cortex.

Pain and Temperature fibers in the dorsal root are small unmyelinated and myelinated fibers which enter the cord through the lateral strand of the rootlet and end in the substantia gelatinosa of Rolando within one or two segments. The axons of the second neurons cross in the ventral white commissure and ascend in the lateral spinothalamic tract to the postero-lateral ventral nucleus of the thalamus. An accessory interrupted pathway of intercalated neurons probably runs parallel with this tract. From the thalamus fibers pass through the caudal limb of the internal capsule to the somesthetic area of the postcentral gyrus of the cortex. Unmyelinated fibers of the posterior roots which turn into the dorsolateral tract (of Lissauer) ascend or descend for short distances and end in the substantia gelatinosa. They are part of the mechanism for reflexes associated with pian within the cord.

Proprioceptive fibers have two important destinations, the cerebrum and the cerebellum. The proprioceptive fibers are large myelinated fibers entering the cord through the medial strand of the dorsal rootlets. Those to the cerebrum ascend in the fasciculus gracilis and cuneatus to the nuclei of these names in the medulla oblongata. Axons from these nuclei cross to the opposite side in the internal arcuate fibers and their decussation. They then turn cephalad in the medial lemniscus and end in the posterolateral ventral nucleus of the thalamus. The third order neurons pass through the internal capsule and corona radiata to the somatic sensory area of the postcentral gyrus of the cortex.

The proprioceptive fibers to the cerebellum travel by three different pathways.

(1) Fibers traverse the gracile and cuneate fasciculi of the posterior funiculus along with the cerebral fibers and end in the lateral cuneate nucleus. Axons from cells in this nucleus pass along the dorsal external arcuate fibers through the restiform body of the same side to the cerebellar cortex. (2) Other proprioceptive fibers in the fasciculus cuneatus give off terminals or collaterals to the nucleus dorsalis of the spinal cord. Axons from the nucleus dorsalis pass to the dorsal spinocerebellar tract (of Flechsig) of the same side. At the level of the olive the fibers curve under the external arcuate fibers to the restiform body. They give off collaterals to the dentate nucleus and finally terminate in the cortex of the dorsal and rostral portion of the vermis on the same side. (3) Still other terminals and collaterals from fibers in the fasciculus cuneatus synapse with cells in the dorsal horn gray substance in or near the dorsal nucleus of the other side. They cross in the white and gray commissure and pass with fibers from the same side through the lateral funiculus to the ventral spinocerebellar tract (of Gowers). This tract ascends until it passes under the external arcuate fibers dorsal to the olive, and then joins the lateral edge of the lateral lemniscus. At the level of the motor nucleus of the trigeminal nerve it crosses over the brachium conjunctivum and turns abruptly caudad. It follows along the medial border of the brachium, enters the cerebellum, and ends in the vermis of the same and opposite sides.

The **visceral afferent fibers** have their cell bodies in the spinal ganglia. The peripheral branches probably traverse the rami communicantes from the sympathetic nerves of the viscera. The central fibers divide into ascending and descending branches in the spinal cord. Their terminations and connections are not known. Some fibers accompanying the peripheral sympathetics are pain fibers which enter the lateral spinothalamic tract with the other pain fibers.

Somatic Efferent Fibers to the Spinal Cord.—The large multipolar cells in the ventral horn of the spinal cord receive impulses from a number of higher centers. They are the cells whose axons terminate in the motor end plates of the skeletal muscle fibers and are called the lower motor neurons or the final common pathway for motor response. These same neurons receive fibers from other parts of the gray substance of the cord to complete the various spinal cord reflexes.

The **Pyramidal Tract.**—Voluntary control of muscles is conveyed by axons of the pyramidal cells in the precentral (area 4, Fig. 750) and adjacent cortex. As they pass through the corona radiata they are gathered together and occupy the rostral two-thirds of the occipital part of the internal capsule. They continue through the cerebral peduncle as the corticospinal fibers, occupying the middle three-fifths of the crusta. They split up into several bundles as they pass through the pons but come together again as the pyramids of the medulla oblongata. In the caudal part of the medulla, two-thirds to three-fourths of the fibers, those nearest the median fissure, cross to the other side in bundles as the decussation of the pyramids. They continue down the spinal cord as the lateral corticospinal or crossed pyramidal tract. The remaining fibers, more laterally placed, do not decussate but continue down the cord as the ventral corticospinal or direct (uncrossed) pyramidal tract. The lateral corticospinal fibers terminate either directly or through intercalated neurones in synapses with the ventral horn cells. The fibers of the ventral corticospinal tract cross to the opposite side in the ventral white commissure before they form connections with the ventral horn cells. A few fibers of both tracts remain uncrossed and terminate on the same side of the cord. The axons of the ventral horn cells pass out through the ventral roots to their specific muscles.

The **Rubrospinal Tract.**—The coordination and reflex control of motion from the cerebellum are conveyed by the cerebellorubral fibers in the superior cerebellar peduncle. From the red nucleus, fibers cross in the ventral tegmental decussation of Forel and as the rubrospinal tract pass through the pons, medulla, and lateral funiculus of the spinal cord. The rubrospinal fibers end either directly or indirectly through terminals and collaterals about the motor cells of the ventral horn of the side opposite the red nucleus of origin. A few are said to remain on the same side. The afferent arms of the cerebellar connections are described on page 867.

The **Tectospinal Tract.**—Reflexes of coordination with vision and probably with hearing are conveyed by the tectospinal tract. The axons of large cells in the stratum opticum and stratum lemnisci of the superior colliculus cross the median raphé of the midbrain in the fountain decussation of Meynert and descend in the tegmentum. Some of the fibers are said not to cross. The tectospinal tract continues through the reticular formation of the pons and medulla becoming more or less intermingled

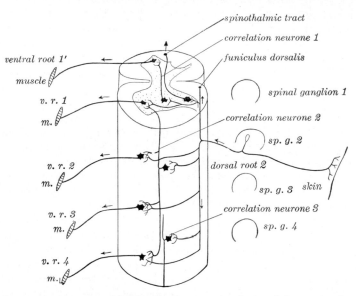

Fig. 779.—Diagram of the spinal cord reflex apparatus. Some of the connections of a single afferent neuron from the skin (*d.r.*2) are indicated; *d.r.*2, dorsal root from second spinal ganglion; *m*, muscles; *sp.g.* 1 to *sp. g.* 4, spinal ganglia; *v.r.* 1' to *v.r.*4, ventral roots. (After Herrick.)

with the medial longitudinal fasciculus, and in the spinal cord splits into a larger medial tectospinal tract and a smaller lateral tectospinal tract which runs with the rubrospinal tract. The fibers end either directly or indirectly by terminals and collaterals in relation with the motor cells of the ventral horn.

The **Direct Vestibulospinal Tract.**—The coordination and reflex control of equilibrium are conveyed through the vestibulospinal tract. Axons of cells in the lateral vestibular nucleus (magnocellular of Deiters) descend in the ventral funiculus of the cord and terminate directly or indirectly in relation to the ventral horn cells. These fibers are uncrossed and extend as far as the sacral region of the cord. They tend to mingle with the fibers of the spinothalamic, tectospinal tracts and the fasciculi proprii.

Meninges of the Brain and Spinal Cord

The brain and spinal cord are enclosed by three membranes, (1) an outer tough protective membrane, the dura mater, (2) an inner, more delicate, fibrous membrane, the pia mater, which carries the blood vessels to the brain and cord, and (3) an intermediate spiderweb-like structure, which, together with the spinal fluid, fills in the space between the other two (Sensenig '51).

The Dura Mater

The dura mater is composed of dense, fibrous connective tissue with collogenous bundles arranged in interlacing layers. It is a dual structure with an inner meningeal layer and an outer periosteal layer. Although these layers are continuous at the foramen magnum their disposition over the brain and spinal cord is different and will be described separately.

Cranial Dura Mater (*dura mater encephali*) (Fig. 614, *ff.*). The two layers of the dura over the brain are tightly fused together except in certain places where they are separated to provide space for the venous sinuses (page 735) and where the inner layer forms fibrous septa between parts of the brain. The outer surface is closely applied to the inner surface of the cranial bones. It sends many fine fibrous and vascular projections into the bony substance which give it a hairy appearance when the bones are stripped away. The attachment is more secure over the sutures and at the base of the skull. The internal surface of the dura is smooth, unattached, and covered with a layer of mesothelium lining the subdural space. The inner layer, leaving the outer layer at the position of certain venous sinuses, sends partitions inward between larger divisions of the brain named (*a*) the falx cerebri, (*b*) the tentorium cerebelli, and (*c*) the falx cerebelli. In addition, it forms smaller projections and partitions, the diaphragma sellæ and the pocket for the trigeminal ganglion (cavum Meckelii).

The **falx cerebri** (Fig. 615) is a strong membrane extending down into the longitudinal fissure between the two cerebral hemispheres. It is attached to the skull bones along the midline of the inner surface of the cranial vault from the christa galli to the internal occipital protuberance where it becomes continuous with the tentorium cerebelli (Fig. 204). At this attachment it is separated from the outer layer of dura, leaving space for the superior sagittal sinus (Figs. 614, 782). The inner free margin of the falx contains the inferior sagittal sinus (Fig. 615).

The **tentorium cerebelli** (Figs. 615, 801) is a transverse shelf of dura mater separating the cerebellum from the occipital part of the cerebral hemispheres. It is attached laterally and posteriorly to the transverse sinuses. Anteriorly it is attached along the superior border of the petrous portion of the temporal bone and to the posterior clinoid process of the sphenoid bone, leaving a narrow space for the superior petrosal sinus (Figs. 190, 212). It slopes upward toward the midline where it is continuous with the falx cerebri and there forms the straight sinus (Fig. 616). Its free border extends from the junction with the free border of the falx cerebri to the anterior clinoid process, curving laterally to leave a large oval opening, the incisura tentorii, for passage of the cerebral peduncles.

The **falx cerebelli** is a small triangular process of dura which is attached to the lower division of the vertical crest on the inner surface of the occipital bone with its free border projecting into the posterior cerebellar notch between the two cerebellar hemispheres.

The **diaphragma sellæ** (Fig. 615) connects the clinoid attachments of the two sides of the tentorium cerebelli. It forms a roof over the hypophysis lying in the sella turcica. A circular opening in the center which allows passage of the infundibulum, is surrounded by the circular or intercavernous sinus (Fig. 616).

The **Spinal Dura Mater** (*dura mater spinalis*) (Fig. 780) forms a loose sheath around the spinal cord and corresponds to the inner or meningeal layer of the cranial dura. The outer or periosteal layer is interrupted at the foramen magnum and is represented below this point by the periosteum of the vertebræ which lines the vertebral canal. A considerable interval, the epidural space, intervenes between the spinal dura and the vertebral canal. It contains a quantity of loose areolar tissue and a plexus of veins; the veins correspond in position with the cranial dural sinuses. The spinal dura is attached to the circumference of the foramen magnum, to the second and third cervical vertebræ, and by fibrous slips to the posterior longitudinal ligament, especially near the caudal end of the vertebral canal. The tubular sheath of the dura is much larger than is necessary for its contents, most of the interval between it and the cord being occupied by subarachnoid space (Fig. 782). The cavity of the tube ends at the level of the second sacral vertebra at which point the dura closely invests the filum terminale and is attached with the latter to the back of the coccyx, blending with the periosteum. The caudal part of the sheath, from the conus medullaris at the second lumbar to the second sacral vertebra, is occupied by the cauda equina. As the spinal nerves on each side pass through the intervertebral foramina they are covered by prolongations of the dura. These sheaths are short in the cephalic part of the vertebral column, but gradually become longer more caudally.

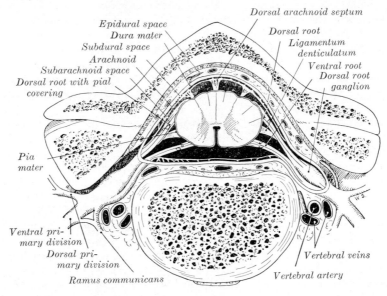

FIG. 780.—Cross-section of spinal cord in the spinal canal showing its meningeal coverings and the manner of exit of the spinal nerves (after Rauber in Buchanan's *Functional Neuro-anatomy.*)

The Pia Mater

The pia mater is a delicate connective tissue membrane, closely applied to the brain and spinal cord, and carrying the rich network of blood vessels which supply the nervous tissue. It is attached to the nervous tissue especially where the minute vessels penetrate the piaglial membrane. The outer surface is covered by ramifications of the arachnoid villi. The perineurium of the nerves leaving the brain and cord is reinforced by fibers from the pia mater which blend with the dura at the exit of the nerves.

The **Cranial Pia Mater** (*pia mater encephali*) (Fig. 709) invests the entire surface of the brain, dipping into the fissures and sulci of the cerebral and cerebellar hemispheres. It extends into the transverse cerebral fissure where it forms the tela choroidea of the third ventricle and combines with the ependyma to form the choroid plexuses of the third and lateral ventricles. It also passes over the roof of the fourth ventricle and forms its tela choroidea and choroid plexus.

The **Spinal Pia Mater** (*pia mater spinalis*) (Figs. 701, 780) is thicker, firmer, and less vascular than the cranial pia mater. It consists of two layers, the outer or additional one being composed of longitudinally arranged collagenous fibers. The inner layer is intimately adherent to the entire surface of the spinal cord and sends a septum into the anterior median fissure. The fibers of the outer layer are concentrated along this fissure into a stout glistening band, the **linea splendens.** Another concentration of fibers along each side forms the denticulate ligament. At the caudal end of the spinal cord, the pia mater is prolonged into the filum terminale which blends with the dura mater at the second sacral vertebra and continues caudally to the coccyx where it fuses with the periosteum. It secures the caudal end of the spinal cord, is called the central ligament of the spinal cord and assists in maintaining the cord in position during movements of the body.

The **denticulate ligament** (*ligamentum denticulatum*) (Fig. 701) is a fibrous band of pia mater extending the entire length of the spinal cord on each side between the dorsal and ventral spinal nerve roots. Its lateral border has a festooned appearance due to its attachment to the dura at regular intervals. There are twenty-one of these points of attachment, the most cephalic one at the foramen magnum between the vertebral artery and the hypoglossal rootlets and the most caudal at the conus medullaris.

The Arachnoid

The arachnoid (Fig. 701) is a delicate, avascular membrane lying between the dura mater and pia mater. It is separated from the dura by the subdural space and the pia by the subarachnoid space containing the cerebrospinal fluid.

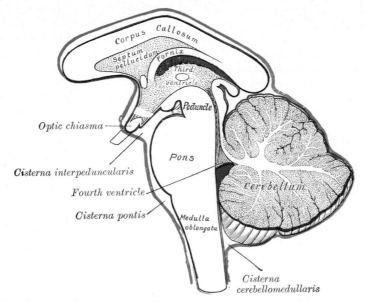

Fig. 781.—Diagram showing the positions of the three principal subarachnoid cisternæ.

The **Cranial Arachnoid** (*arachnoidea encephali*) (Fig. 781) is closely applied to the inner surface of the dura over the brain but is separated from it by a thin film of fluid in the subdural space. Its surface adjacent to the dura is covered with a layer of mesothelium. It does not dip into the sulci or fissures except to follow the falx and tentorium. The inner surface of the arachnoid membrane is connected with pia by delicate fibrous threads, the arachnoid trabeculæ, which traverse the subarachnoid space intervening between these two membranes.

The **Spinal Arachnoid** (*arachnoidea spinalis*) (Fig. 780) is a tubular membrane, loosely investing the spinal cord. It is continuous with the cranial arachnoid and caudally encloses the cauda equina.

The **Subarachnoid Space** (*cavum subarachnoidea*) (Fig. 781) is narrow on the surface of the hemispheres. Over the summit of the gyri the pia and arachnoid are in close contact, and together are called the piaärachnoid membrane. The arachnoid bridges over the sulci, leaving a wider space. At the base of the brain the arachnoid is somewhat thicker and in places leaves wide intervals of space, the subarachnoid cisternæ which are named from their positions.

The **cisterna cerebellomedularis** (*cisterna magna*) (Fig. 781) results from the arachnoid bridging over the interval between the projecting caudal part of the cerebellar hemispheres and the medulla oblongata, and is continuous with the spinal subarachnoid space. The **cisterna pontis** over the ventral aspect of the pons contains the basilar artery. The **cisterna interpeduncularis** (*cisterna basalis*) is a wide cavity between the two temporal lobes including the interpeduncular fossa. It contains the circle of Willis. It extends rostrally over the optic chiasma, forming the *cisterna chiasmatis*. The **cisterna fossæ cerebri lateralis** occupies the area over the stem of the lateral fissure and contains the lateral cerebral artery. The **cisterna venæ magnæ cerebri** occupies the interval between the splenium of the corpus callosum and the superior surface of the cerebellum. It reaches in between the layers of the tela choroidea of the third ventricle and contains the great cerebral vein of Galen.

The **ventricular system** of the brain (page 899) opens out into the subarachnoid space through the fourth ventricle by three holes. The foramen of Majendie (Fig. 732) is the caudal part of the roof of the fourth ventricle in the midline. The two foramina of Luschka are at the ends of the lateral recesses of the fourth ventricle (Fig. 717), between the flocculus of the cerebellum and the glossopharyngeal nerve.

The **spinal part of the subarachnoid space** is a wide interval, occupying much of the space within the dural sheath. It is incompletely divided by the longitudinal subarachnoid septum which connects the arachnoid and pia along the posterior median sulcus of the cord. It is further subdivided by the denticulate ligament of the pia mater.

The **arachnoid villi** (*Pacchionian bodies*; *granulationes arachnoidales*; *glandulæ Pacchioni*) (Fig. 782) are berry-like tufts of arachnoid which protrude into the superior sagittal sinus or venous lacunæ associated with it. They do not occur during infancy and are rare before the third year but usually are found after the seventh year. They increase in number and size as age advances. They push against the dura and eventually cause absorption of bone, leaving depressions in the inner table of the calvaria. The wall of a villus is composed only of arachnoid and endothelium of the venous sinus; the cerebrospinal fluid in the subarachnoid space passes through this thin membrane and is taken up by the blood stream.

The Cerebrospinal Fluid

The cerebrospinal fluid fills the ventricles of the brain and occupies the subarachnoid space (Fig. 782). It is a clear watery fluid, similar to tissue fluid and lymph in composition but exhibiting certain quantiative differences. Normally it is elaborated by the choroid plexus of the ventricles of the brain. There is some evidence that it may have other sources and the volume of its production can be altered by changes in blood pressure relationships.

The fluid drains from the lateral ventricles through the interventricular foramina of Monro into the third ventricle. This fluid, combined with that produced by the choroid plexus of the third ventricle, passes through the cerebral aqueduct of Sylvius into the fourth ventricle. Fluid escapes from the fourth ventricle through

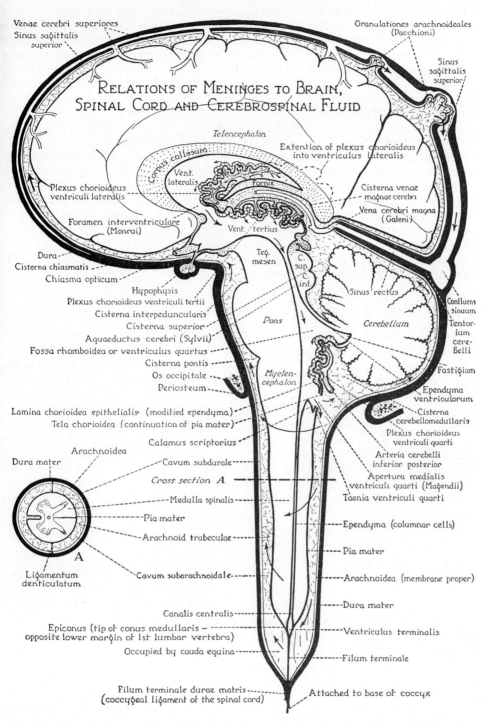

Venae cerebri superiores
Sinus sagittalis superior

Granulationes arachnoideales (Pacchioni)

Sinus sagittalis superior

RELATIONS OF MENINGES TO BRAIN, SPINAL CORD AND CEREBROSPINAL FLUID

Telencephalon

Corpus callosum

Vent. lateralis

Fornix

Extention of plexus chorioideus into ventriculus lateralis

Plexus chorioideus ventriculi lateralis

Cisterna venae magnae cerebri

Vena cerebri magna (Galeni)

Foramen interventriculare (Monroi)

Vent. tertius

Dura
Cisterna chiasmatis
Chiasma opticum

Teg. mesen

C. sup.
C. inf.

Sinus rectus

Hypophysis
Plexus chorioideus ventriculi tertii
Cisterna interpeduncularis
Cisterna superior
Aquaeductus cerebri (Sylvii)
Fossa rhomboidea or ventriculus quartus
Cisterna pontis
Os occipitale
Periosteum

Pons

Cerebellum

Confluens sinuum

Tentorium cerebelli

Myelencephalon

Fastigium

Ependyma ventriculorum

Lamina chorioidea epithelialis (modified ependyma)
Tela chorioidea (continuation of pia mater)

Cisterna cerebellomedullaris

Plexus chorioideus ventriculi quarti

Calamus scriptorius

Arteria cerebelli inferior posterior

Arachnoidea

Dura mater

Cavum subdurale

Cross section A

Medulla spinalis

Pia mater

Arachnoid trabeculae

A

Ligamentum denticulatum

Cavum subarachnoidale

Apertura medialis ventriculi quarti (Magendii)
Taenia ventriculi quarti

Ependyma (columnar cells)

Pia mater

Arachnoidea (membrane proper)

Dura mater

Canalis centralis

Epiconus (tip of conus medullaris — opposite lower margin of 1st lumbar vertebra)

Ventriculus terminalis

Occupied by cauda equina

Filum terminale

Filum terminale durae matris (coccygeal ligament of the spinal cord)

Attached to base of coccyx

FIG. 782.—The relations of the meninges to the brain, spinal cord, and cerebrospinal fluid. (From Rasmussen, *The Principal Nervous Pathways,* courtesy of the Macmillan Company.)

the openings in its roof, the median foramen of Magendie and the two lateral foramina of Luschka. The fluid in the central canal of the spinal cord apparently is produced by the ependymal lining and drains into the fourth ventricle. An obstruction of the foramina between the ventricles or of the exit from the fourth ventricle causes an accumulation of fluid in the ventricles with the resultant condition known as **hydrocephalus** (Sweet and Locksley '53).

From the foramina of the fourth ventricle the fluid enters the subarachnoid space and its various cysternæ. The fluid is absorbed by the blood stem through the arachnoid villi (pacchionian bodies) which protrude into the superior sagittal sinus (Fig. 614). Small amounts of fluid may escape through the perineural spaces of the cranial and spinal nerves and reach the lymphatic capillaries.

Lumbar puncture.—The spinal fluid is usually removed for diagnostic purposes from the subarachnoid space surrounding the cauda equina of the spinal cord. A needle inserted in the midline between the spines of the third and fourth lumbar vertebræ will enter the subarachnoid space, avoiding the spinal cord and insinuating itself among the nerves of the cauda equina (Fig. 700). **Cistern puncture** is performed by inserting a needle between the atlas and the occipital bone, entering the cisterna cerebellomedullaris or cisterna magna (Fig. 781).

Spinal anaesthesia is administered by introducing the anaesthetic into the subarachnoid space by lumbar puncture.

Histology of the Nervous System

The basic elements of the nervous system are the nerve cells or neurons with their processes and certain special supporting and protective structures.

The **Neuron** (Fig. 783).—The nerve cell has a nucleus and cell body or **perikaryon,** with the usual organelles and inclusion bodies. Characteristically the nucleus is large and vesicular with a prominent nucleolus in which the sex element may be clearly visible (Barr, Bertram and Lindsay '50). Adult nerve cells are never seen in mitosis. The cytoplasm contains clear cut mitochondria, and a golgi apparatus can be demonstrated with proper technique. The specialized structures of nerve cells include neurofibrillæ and Nissl granules. The delicate **neurofibrillæ** can be demonstrated with special stains and with the electron microscope but are not clearly visible in living mammalian cells. A chromophilic substance is usually visible in clumps known as Nissl granules or tigroid bodies when the tissue is stained with certain basic dyes (Fig. 783). Pigment granules of various shades of yellow, brown, black, and red are found in some nerve cells, especially in particular nuclear masses such as the substantia nigra and the red nucleus.

Nissl granules have become important structures in neurological research. Many nerve cells of a particular functional type have a characteristic size, shape, and distribution of the Nissl bodies, and this may be used as corroborative evidence in identifying the function of a nuclear group. When the axone of a nerve cell is cut, the number of Nissl bodies diminishes by a process known as chromatolysis. This is used extensively in following nerve tracts after injury or experimental interruption.

Processes of neurons are of two kinds, axons and **dendrites** (*dendrons*). There may be one or several dendrites. They are branched prolongations of the cytoplasm and contain all the structures found in the perikaryon, *i.e.*, Nissl bodies, mitochondria, fibrillæ, pigment, etc. They vary greatly in size, shape, and number with different types of neurons. They divide and subdivide into smaller and smaller branches. Many short processes called **gemmules** project from them and produce a ragged appearance. They are naked, without myelin or other sheath. Some are more or less characteristic such as the long apical dendrites of pyramidal cells in the cerebral cortex, or the Purkinje cells of the cerebellum (Figs. 730, 749).

Axons or **Axis Cylinders** (Fig. 704).—Typically, a nerve cell has only one axon, but his may give off a number of branches or collaterals during its course. Unlike the dendrite, the axon has a uniform small diameter and smooth surface except near its termination. It contains neurofibrillæ and mitochondria but not Nissl bodies nor granules. At its junction with the cell body there is commonly a low projection, also devoid of Nissl bodies, called the **axon hillock**. The unipolar neurons of the spinal ganglia are different from most others in having no dendrites and a single axon which divides into a central and a peripheral process. The cells in the cochlear and vestibular ganglia are bipolar, with two axons and no dendrites. (Hartmann '54).

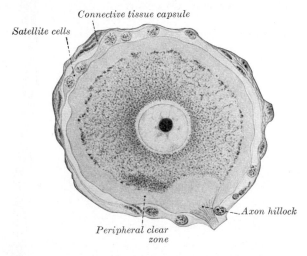

Connective tissue capsule

Satellite cells

Axon hillock

Peripheral clear zone

FIG. 783.—Large human spinal ganglion cell (100μ) with connective tissue capsule. (From Rauber-Kopsch, *Lehrbuch u. Altas d. Anatomie d. Menschen*, 19th Edition, Vol. II, courtesy of Georg Thieme Verlag, Stuttgart, 1955.)

Neuron doctrine and conduction of impulses.—The neuron theory was given its final corroboration by Harrison ('07) when he watched the axons grow out of tadpole neuroblasts in tissue cultures. A corollary of the doctrine is that the nervous impulse travels in a particular direction with respect to the processes of the nerve cell. The impulse is received by the dendrites and passed out to the next cell in the chain or to the end organ by the axon. The contact between two nerve cells is the **synapse**. The axon breaks up into a number of **telodendria** which terminate in special knobs or endings against the dendrites or perikaryon of the next nerve cell in the path of the impulse. Exceptions are found in the unipolar and bipolar sensory cells, in which both receiving and transmitting processes are called axons.

Nerve fibers (Fig. 786).—A nerve fiber is the axon of a nerve cell and may be short or very long, depending on its location and function. Nerve fibers usually have protective sheaths except at their origin from the perikaryon or near their termination. Longer naked fibers are found in the neuropil of the gray substance of the central nervous system (Fig. 787). Fibers with sheaths are of two types, myelinated (medullated) and unmyelinated (non-medullated). The myelinated fibers in the central nervous system make up the white substance and are embedded in a matrix of the neuroglia. The fibers of the peripheral nerves, both myelinated and unmyelinated, have cellular sheaths called neurilemma.

Myelin Sheath (Figs. 784, 785).—Myelin is a lipoidal substance which gives a whitish appearance to fresh nerves because of its high refractivity. Recent studies with the electron microscope have shown that the myelin occurs in multiple thin lamellæ (about 100 Å) wrapped around the axon (Robertson '54). In fresh or living nerve, the myelin sheath appears structureless except for certain irregular artifacts. The myelin sheaths in peripheral nerves have interruptions at more or less regular intervals 1 or 2 mm. apart known as **nodes of Ranvier.** In the central nervous system nodes occur rarely and only at a point of bifurcation of a fiber. The myelin sheaths generally vary in diameter from 2 to 10 micra, but larger and smaller ones do occur. (Bodian '51).

Myelin colors poorly in histological preparations of the commonly used cytoplasmic and nuclear stains. It blackens readily with osmic acid, however, and can be stained quite selectively by special methods such as the Weigert stain. This coloration of the myelin sheath

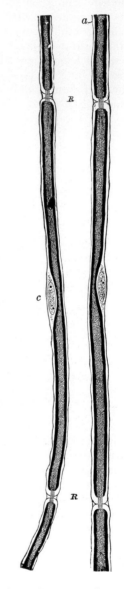

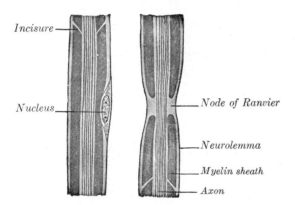

FIG. 784.—Diagram of longitudinal sections of myelinated nerve fibers. Osmic acid.

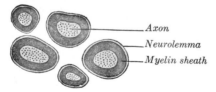

FIG. 785.—Transverse sections of myelinated nerve fibers. Osmic acid.

FIG. 786.—Diagram of myelinated nerve fibers stained with osmic acid. × 425. (Schafer.) *R*, Nodes of Ranvier. *a*, Neurilemma. *c*. Nucleus.

is used extensively in the study of the nervous system and pictures such as Figure 720 are the result of it.

Neurilemma.—The neurilemma or **sheath of Schwann** is composed of a series of very attenuated nucleated cells. On myelinated nerves, there is a neurilemma cell for each internodal segment between nodes of Ranvier. The nucleus is oval and flattened and lies in a slight depression in the myelin. The neurilemma cells of unmyelinated fibers are difficult to distinguish from the fibers except by the presence of their nuclei unless the nerve fibers themselves have been brought out by some special method such as a silver stain.

Since nerve fibers are protoplasmic threads of minute size, 1 or 2 micra in diameter, they are very difficult to distinguish from surrounding tissue in ordinary histological preparations. It is possible, however, to blacken them with silver and it is by this means that their morphological details have been studied. Another staining method is intravital methylene blue but both this and silver techniques are notoriously capricious.

Gray Substance of the Central Nervous System.—The gray substance of the brain and spinal cord is composed of nerve cells, naked nerve fibers, dendrites, and the supporting tissue neuroglia. In the usual histological preparations stained with hematoxylin and eosin, the tissue has a rather homogeneous appearance with a

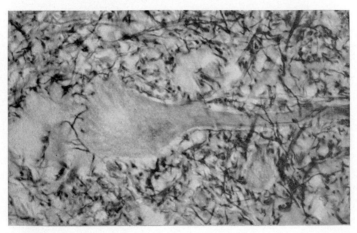

Fig. 787.—Neuropil from ventral horn of spinal cord. The large motor cell with nucleus is very faintly stained; the nerve fibers and terminal buttons are blackened with silver. Photograph by Charles O'Connor. Magnified 15000 ×.

preponderance of eosin-stained cytoplasm and scattered nuclei. The nuclei of the nerve cells can be distinguished by their greater size, vesicular appearance, and prominent nucleoli. The neuroglia are described below. Blood vessels appear as in other tissues except that their walls tend to be thinner and in sections including the surface of the brain, the pia mater and arachnoid can be seen. As mentioned above, the nerve cell bodies can be emphasized by the use of Nissl stain, the nerve fibers by silver methods, and the neuroglia by still other special methods.

White Substance.—The white substance is composed of fibers. The myelinated fibers predominate in bulk but may be outnumbered by unmyelinated fibers which are less prominent because of their small size. The fibers are supported by the neuroglia and blood vessels and at the surface the leptomeninges offer additional support. The myelin sheaths are easily distinguished by their circular shape, their size, and their refractivity although they stain but lightly in hematoxylin and eosin preparations. The only nuclei visible are those of the neuroglia and vascular tissue.

Neuroglia.—The supporting tissue of the central nervous system includes three cellular elements two of which, astrocytes and oligodendrocytes, are of ectodermal origin derived from the spongioblasts of the embryonic neural tube (page 821).

The third, microgliocyte, is of mesodermal origin, apparently being a specialized connective tissue histiocyte (Glees '55).

(1) **Astrocytes** or **macroglia** are moderately large cells with numerous processes which radiate out from the cell body. In most instances one or more processes have terminal expansions which attach to blood vessels or the pia mater. The marginal astrocytes together with the pia form the piaglial membrane, which invests the

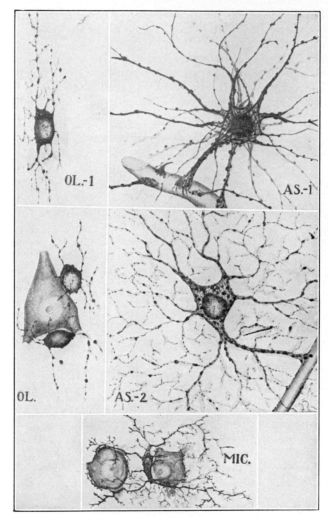

Fig. 788.—Interstitial cells of the central nervous system. *AS.–1*, Fibrous astrocyte with perivascular feet on vessel; *AS.–2*, protoplasmic astrocyte; *MIC.*, microglia; *OL.*, oligodendroglia. (Penfield and Cone, in Cowdry's *Special Cytology*, courtesy of Paul B. Hoeber, Inc.

brain and spinal cord and accompanies penetrating blood vessels as a cuff to considerable depths. There are two types of **astrocytes, fibrous** and protoplasmic (Fig. 788). The former are found chiefly in the white matter and, with appropriate fixation and staining, appear to contain fibers which run through the protoplasm of the cell body and processes. The **protoplasmic astrocytes** occur chiefly in the gray matter and their processes branch profusely . The nuclei of the astrocytes are moderately large, oval in shape, and contain scattered chromatin granules, but no nucleolus. The astrocytes provide the repair mechanism and replace lost tissue by forming glial scars.

(2) **Oligodendrocytes** or **oligodendroglia** are somewhat smaller than the astrocytes and have fewer processes. They are found either in close association with smaller blood vessels, or as satellite cells closely applied to large nerve cells, or in rows between bundles of fibers in the white matter (Fig. 788). In the latter situation, their processes clasp the nerve fibers. It is thought that the oligodendroglia play a metabolic role in the formation and preservation of the myelin sheaths of the nerve fibers in the central nervous system. The nuclei of these cells are round to oval, usually smaller in size but richer in chromatin than the nuclei of the astrocytes. They have no nucleoli.

(3) **Microgliocytes** or **microglia** are found diffusely through both the gray and white matter. Normally they are small cells, with two or more finely branching, feathery processes (Fig. 788). The nucleus is small and varies in shape from round

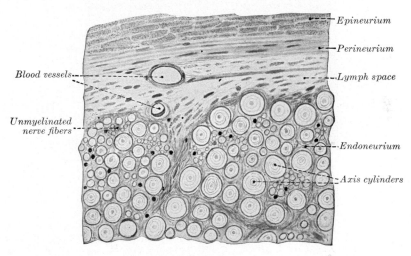

Fig. 789.—Cross section from human sciatic nerve. (From Rauber-Kopsch, *Lehrbuch u. Altas d. Anatomie d. Meschen,* 19th Edition, Vol. II, courtesy of Georg Thieme Verlag, Stuttgart, 1955.)

to oblong or angular. It stains deeply but contains no nucleolus. The microglia are the scavengers of the nervous system and become actively ameboid and phagocytic in case of injury and death of the other elements.

Peripheral Nerves.—The peripheral nerves are of two types depending on whether their fibers are predominately myelinated or whether they are almost exclusively unmyelinated. The former are the spinal nerves and their branches and, with certain exceptions, the cranial nerves. The latter are the nerves of the autonomic system.

Myelinated nerves (*medullated nerves*) are recognizable by the characteristic structure of the myelin sheaths. In cross sections they can be recognized by their large circular outline with the axon in the center (Fig. 785). In paraffin sections either the myelin sheath or the axon may be somewhat shrunken and displaced. In longitudinal sections the nodes of Ranvier are a distinguishing feature. Usually a nerve shortens or retracts during fixation with the result that the fibers have a wavy course and many of them are cut across or with varying degrees of obliquity.

Connective Tissue Sheath.—In addition to the special sheaths on individual fibers, peripheral nerves have well organized connective tissue sheaths (Fig. 789). Around and between the individual fibers is a sheath of reticular connective tissue fibrils called the **endoneurium**. The nerve fibers are collected into cylindrical bundles with an outer wrapping of the collagenous and elastic fibers of areolar tissue. This is called the **perineurium**. Large nerves have these secondary bundles bound together with an outside sheath called the **epineurium**. The connective tissue contains the usual cells, fibroblasts, macrophages, etc., and capillaries, arteries, veins, and lymphatic vessels appropriate to the size of the nerve.

Unmyelinated nerves (*non-medullated*) have the same basic connective tissue elements as myelinated nerves except that the nerves are usually much smaller. They make up the trunks and branches of the autonomic nervous system. In cross sections there is little of characteristic structure except the connective tissue sheath.

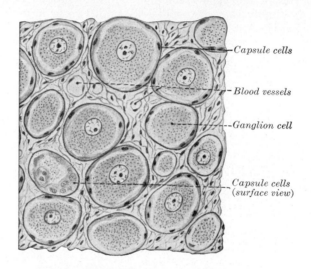

FIG. 790.—Section of the sixth cervical spinal ganglion of man. (From Rauber-Kopsch *Lehrbuch u. Atlas d. Anatomie d. Menschen*, 19th edition, Vol. II, courtesy of Georg Thieme Verlag, Stuttgart, 1955.)

In longitudinal section there is a considerable resemblance to non-striated muscle when a comparison is made in the usual histological slides. The unmyelinated fibers (Remak fibers) can be stained with silver and appear abundant in many so-called myelinated cranial and spinal nerves as well as in the unmyelinated nerves of the sympathetic and parasympathetic systems.

Ganglia.—The nerve cells occurring outside the central nervous system are chiefly collected into groups in ganglia although many individual cells and very small groups are found, especially in association with the alimentary organs. Ganglia are of two types, (1) sensory ganglia on the dorsal roots of spinal nerves and on the sensory roots of the trigeminal, facial, glossopharyngeal, and vagus nerves, and (2) the autonomic ganglia of the sympathetic and parasympathetic systems. The special sensory ganglia of the statoacoustic nerve are described in the chapter on the sense organs.

Sensory ganglia (Fig. 790).—In a sensory ganglion, the cluster of ganglion cells and traversing fibers is invested by a smooth, firm, closely adhering, membranous envelope of dense areolar tissue continuous with the perineurium of the nerves. Numerous septa penetrate the ganglia and carry blood vessels to supply it. Each nerve cell has a nucleated sheath which is continuous with the neurilemma of its axon. The nerve cells in the ganglia of the spinal nerves are piriform in shape, and have a single process, the axon, which divides a short distance from the cell, while still in the ganglion, in a T-shaped manner. One branch runs in the posterior root and enters the spinal cord: the larger peripheral branch joins the spinal nerve and runs uninterruptedly to its end organ in the skin or muscle. The larger unipolar neurons have coiled or split axons near the cell body, but the axon straightens into a single myelinated fiber before it divides. The smaller and more numerous unipolar cells, may or may not have the proximal part of the axon coiled. They have unmyelinated axons which divide in a T-like manner into a fine central and coarse peripheral branch. The central branches go to the spinal cord and the peripheral ones to the skin, a few to muscles (Hess '55, Adamstone *et al.* '53).

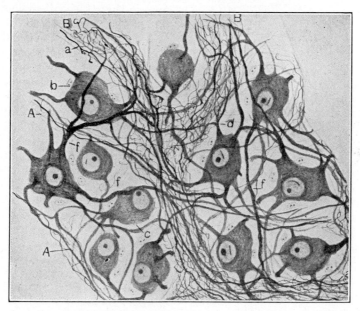

Fig. 791.—A portion of the stellate ganglion of a one and one-half-year-old child. *B*, Stout protoplasmic tract of articulation; *f*, very long primordial dendrite; *d*, very short dendrite; *c*, monopolar sympathetic cell; *a*, preganglionic fibers; *A*, tracts passing through the ganglion. Several of the neurons show intranuclear rods. (deCastro in Penfield's Cytology and Cellular Pathology of the Nervous System, courtesy of Paul B. Hoeber, Inc.)

Autonomic ganglia contain the cell bodies of multipolar postganglionic neurons with one axon and several dendrites (Fig. 791). Myelinated (preganglionic) and unmyelinated (postganglionic) fibers end, traverse, or arise in the ganglion. Sheath cells form capsules similar to those in the sensory ganglia around the bodies of the ganglion cells. In addition, the sheath cells extend along the dendrites forming what are known as protoplasmic bands or cords, in which little structure is visible. Inside these protoplasmic cords, the preganglionic fibers, having lost their myelin sheaths, end in an extraordinarily dense synaptic relationship with the dendrites of the neurons in the ganglion (Fig. 791).

Peripheral Termination of Nerves

Nerve fibers may terminate peripherally as simple naked fibers or, more frequently, they are enclosed in more or less elaborate end organs. For convenience they are divided into the two large functional groups of sensory or receptor and motor or effector endings.

Sensory Nerve Terminations or **Receptor Organs.**—It is customary to divide the sensory organs according to function also, into those of general and special sensibility. The special senses of vision, hearing, equilibration, taste, and smell are dealt with in the chapter on sense organs. The receptors of the general sensations of heat, cold, pain, touch, and proprioception are widely distributed throughout the body.

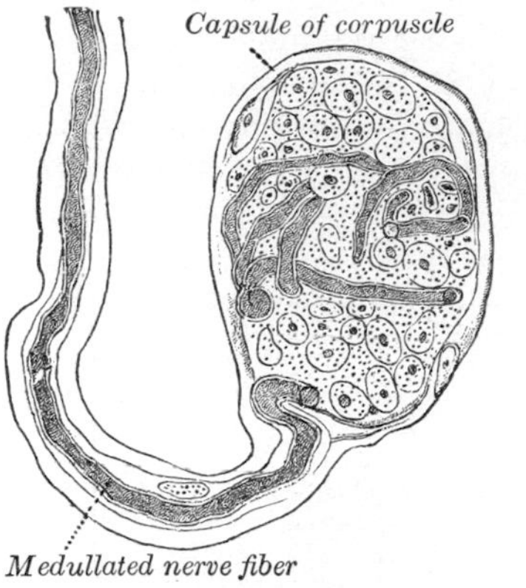

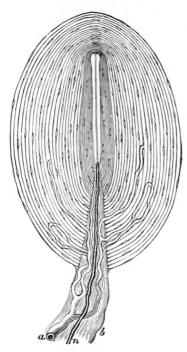

Capsule of corpuscle

Medullated nerve fiber

Fig. 792.—End-bulb of Krause. (Klein.)

Free nerve endings occur chiefly in the epidermis and in the epithelium covering certain mucous membranes; they are seen in the stratified squamous epithelium of the cornea, in the root sheaths and papillæ of the hairs, and around the bodies of the sudoriferous glands. As the nerve fiber approaches its termination, the myelin sheath disappears, leaving only the axon surrounded by the neurilemma. At its termination the fiber loses its neurilemma, and consists of an axon which breaks up into its constituent fine varicose fibrillæ. These often present regular varicosities, anastomose with each other, and end in small knobs or disks between the epithelial cells. They are probably the endings for sensations of pain and temperature.

The special sensory end organs exhibit great variety in size and shape, but have the common feature of a capsule enveloping the terminal nerve fibrillæ. Included in this group are the

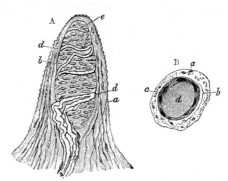

Fig. 793.—Pacinian corpuscle, with its system of capsules and central cavity. *a.* Arterial twig, ending in capillaries, which form loops in some of the intercapsular spaces, and one penetrates to the central capsule. *b.* The fibrous tissue of the stalk. *n.* Nerve tube advancing to the central capsule, there losing its white matter, and stretching along the axis to the opposite end, where it ends by a tuberculated enlargement.

Fig. 794.—Papilla of the hand, treated with acetic acid. Magnified 350 times. *A.* Side view of a papilla of the hand. *a.* Cortical layer. *b.* Tactile corpuscle of Meissner. *c.* Small nerve of the papilla, with neurilemma. *d.* Its two nervous fibers running with spiral coils around the tactile corpuscle. *e.* Apparent termination of one of these fibers. *B.* A tactile papilla seen from above so as to show its transverse section. *a.* Cortical layer. *b.* Nerve fiber. *c.* Outer layer of the tactile body, with nuclei. *d.* Clear interior substance.

endbulbs of Krause, the corpuscles of Pacini, of Golgi and Mazzoni, of Wagner and Meissner, and the neurotendinous and neuromuscular spindles.

The **end bulbs of Krause** (Fig. 792) are minute cylindrical or oval bodies, consisting of a capsule formed by the expansion of the connective tissue sheath of a medullated fiber. They contain a soft semifluid core in which the axon terminates either in a bulbous extremity or in a coiled plexiform mass. End bulbs are found in the conjunctiva of the eye (where they are spheroidal in shape in man, but cylindrical in most other animals), in the mucous membrane of the lips and tongue, and in the epineurium of nerve trunks. They are also found in the penis and the clitoris, and have received the name of genital corpuscles; in these situations they have a mulberry-like appearance, being constricted by connective tissue septa into from two to six knob-like masses. In the synovial membranes of certain joints, *e.g.*, those of the fingers, rounded or oval end bulbs occur, and are designated articular end bulbs.

The **Pacinian corpuscles** (Fig. 793) are found in the subcutaneous, submucous, and subserous connective tissue of many parts of the body. They are especially numerous in the palm of the hand, sole of the foot, the genital organs, about joints, and in the mesentary about the pancreas. Each corpuscle is attached to the end of a single nerve fiber and when dissected from fresh tissue is visible to the naked eye as a white bulb 2 to 4 mm. in diameter. Its structure is very characteristic, consisting of a number of concentric lamellæ, in cross section reminscent of an onion. In its elongated central core the nerve fiber loses, first its myelin sheath and then its neurolemma among specialized central layers.

The **corpuscles of Golgi** and **Mazzoni** are found in the subcutaneous tissue of the pulp of the fingers. They differ from Pacinian corpuscles in that their capsules are thinner, their contained cores thicker, and in the latter the axon ramify more extensively and end in flat expansions.

The **tactile corpuscles** of Meissner (Fig. 794) occur in the papillæ of the corium of the hand and foot, the front of the forearm, the skin of the lips, the mucous membrane of the tip of the tongue, the palpebral conjunctiva, and the skin of the mammary papilla. They are small oval bodies with a connective tissue capsule and tiny plates stacked one above the other. The nerve fiber penetrates the capsule, spirals through the interior, and ends in globular enlargements.

Corpuscles of Ruffini.—Ruffini described a special variety of nerve-ending in the subcutaneous tissue of the human finger (Fig. 795). They are principally situated at the junction of the corium with the subcutaneous tissue. They are oval in shape, and consist of strong connective tissue sheaths, inside which the nerve fibers divide into numerous branches, which show varicosities and end in small free knobs.

The **neurotendinous spindles** (*organs of Golgi*) are chiefly found near the junctions of tendons and muscles. Each is enclosed in a capsule which contains a number of enlarged tendon fasciculi (intrafusal fasciculi). One or more nerve fibers perforate the side of the capsule and lose their medullary sheaths; the axons subdivide and end between the tendon fibers in irregular disks or varicosities (Fig. 796).

The **neuromuscular spindles** are present in the majority of voluntary muscles. They consist of small bundles of rather delicate muscular fibers (intrafusal fibers), invested by a capsule within which the sensory nerve fibers terminate. These neuromuscular spindles vary in length from 0.8 mm. to 5 mm., and have a fusiform appearance. One to three or four large myelinated nerve fibers enter the fibrous capsule, divide several times, and, losing their myelin sheaths, ultimately end in naked axons encircling the intrafusal fibers by flattened expansions, or irregular ovoid or rounded disks (Fig. 797). Neuromuscular spindles have not yet been demonstrated in the tongue muscles, and only a few exist in the ocular muslces.

General Visceral Receptors.—Myelinated afferent fibers and probably unmyelinated afferent fibers traverse the sympathetic nerves and rami communicantes to

the spinal ganglia. They convey impulses from receptors in the abdominal and
thoracic viscera. Similar afferents traverse the vagus and glossopharyngeal nerves
to their sensory ganglia and branches of the pelvic nerves contain visceral afferents
from pelvic viscera. Afferent fibers from the lungs and heart especially are found
in the vagus.

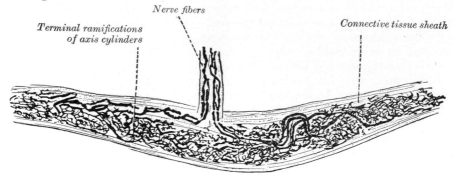

FIG. 795.—Nerve ending of Ruffini. (After A. Ruffini.)

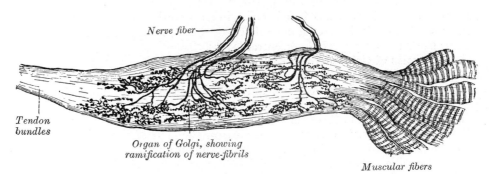

FIG. 796.—Organ of Golgi (neurotendinous spindle) from the human tendo calcaneus.
(After Ciaccio.)

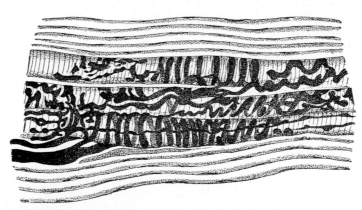

FIG. 797.—Middle third of a terminal plaque in the muscle spindle of an adult cat. (After Ruffini.)

Special visceral receptors for reflex control of respiration and the circulation are
supplied by branches of the vagus and glossopharyngeal nerves. The **carotid body**
(*glomus aorticum*) is an oval mass about 5 mm. in length situated at the bifurcation
of the common carotid artery. It has a fibrous capsule and contains cords and
clumps of epithelioid cells among which numerous nerve fibers branch into special

endings (Fig. 798, 799). The afferent fibers join the vagus through the intercarotid plexus and pharyngeal branches. They are chemoreceptors, sensitive to the concentration of carbon dioxide in the blood, and assist in reflex control of respiration. The **aortic bodies** (*glomera aortica*) are similar to the carotid bodies. They have been found in mammals and probably occur in man. The right aortic body is situated at the junction of the right subclavian and right common carotid arteries. The left body is situated in the angle between the left subclavian artery and the aorta. The afferent fibers join the cardiac branches of the vagus.

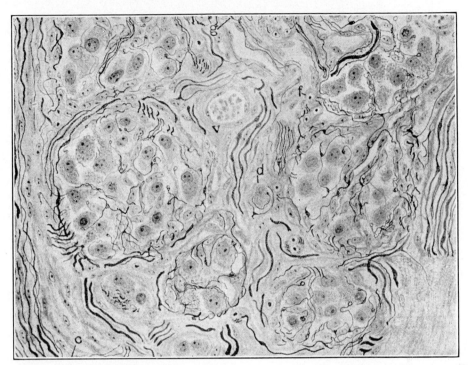

Fig. 798.—Human carotid body showing nerve endings and fibers among epithelioid cells. (De Castro, *Travaux du Laboratorie de Recherches Bibliogiques de Université de Madrid.*)

The **carotid sinus** is a slight enlargement of the beginning of the internal carotid or the immediately adjacent part of the common carotid artery. Its walls contain special sinuses and elaborate networks and terminations of nerves. The afferent fibers reach the glossopharyngeal nerve through the carotid sinus nerve (nerve of Hering). The receptors are sensitive to changes in blood pressure and enter into reflex control of the circulation.

Motor nerves are supplied to both striated and smooth muscular fibers. In the **smooth** or **involuntary muscles** the nerves are derived from the autonomic system and are composed mainly of unmyelinated fibers. Near their terminations they divide into numerous branches, which communicate and form intimate plexuses. There are, however, no fusions of axons or their branches. There is considerable variation in the relationship of these peripheral plexuses to the muscles and glands which the fibers innervate and also in the number and distribution of the ganglion cells which may be associated with them. From these plexuses minute branches are given off which divide and break up into the ultimate fibrillæ of which the nerves are composed. These fibrillæ course between the involuntary muscle cells and gland cells and terminate on the surfaces of the cells.

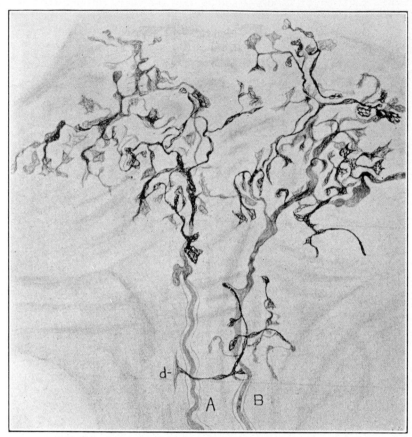

FIG. 799.—Receptor, Type II, of human carotid sinus. *A, B,* afferent medullated fibers to glossopharyngeal nerve. (De Castro, *Travaux du Laboratorie de Recherches Biologiques de Université de Madrid.*)

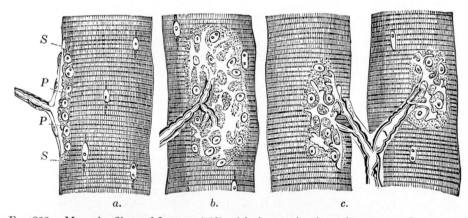

FIG. 800.—Muscular fibers of *Lacerta viridis* with the terminations of nerves. *a,* Seen in profile *P, P,* The nerve end-plates. *S, S,* The base of the plate, consisting of a granular mass with nuclei. *b,* The same as seen in looking at a perfectly fresh fiber, the nervous ends being probably still excitable. (The forms of the variously divided plate can hardly be represented in a woodcut by sufficiently delicate and pale contours to reproduce correctly what is seen in nature.) *c,* The same as seen two hours after death from poisoning by curare.

The **motor nerves** to the **striated** or **voluntary muscles** are derived from the cranial and spinal nerves, and are composed mainly of myelinated fibers. The nerve enters the sheath of the muscle and breaks up into fibers or bundles of fibers which gradually divide until, as a rule, a single nerve fiber reaches a single muscular fiber. As the nerve terminates in a special expansion, called a **motor end-plate** (Fig. 800), it loses its myelin sheath, ramifying like roots of a tree. The neurilemma merges with the sarcolemma of the muscle, and the axon makes an elaborate synaptic contact with the muscular fiber (Robertson '56, Cole '57).

Degenerative Changes.—Various types of degenerative change occur in neurons due to disease, trauma, senility, etc. Shrinkage and dissolution of cell bodies with consequent degeneration of the axons is a normal phenomenon which starts about the twentieth year and becomes increasingly pronounced with age. Symptoms resulting from such loss of neurons are rarely apparent until after the fifth decade.

Three types of degeneration of neurons have been of value for study of the anatomy of the nervous system. (1) If the cell body is destroyed the axon degenerates, or if an axon is cut that part severed from the cell body degenerates. This is known as **Wallerian degeneration.** Changes occur first at the cut end and progress peripherally. In fishes and amphibians this distal progression is slow and may take days to weeks, but in mammals it is rapid and requires only hours to days, so that at times it appears as though all parts of the severed axon were degenerating simultaneously. There is at first swelling with loss of internal structure. The axon becomes tortuous, then fragmented and soon disappears. The myelin breaks down into globules of fatty material which can be stained by the Marchi method. This change is at its maximum between two and three weeks. The degenerating myelin is gradually removed by the phagocytic cells. Fat globules, free and intracellular, can be found, for as long as three months, in the neighborhood of the degenerated fibers. In the central nervous system, no true regeneration occurs and the lost fibers are replaced by glia, chiefly astrocytes. The scar so formed does not stain by the Weigert method of staining normal myelin sheaths, and when the degenerated fibers form a compact bundle, such as the crossed corticospinal tract, their course can be followed by this method. Since these methods depend on changes in the myelin they have to be supplemented by silver stains on normal material in order to determine the exact termination of the axons.

Attempts to follow degenerating axons by silver and other stains, as well as attempts to identify degenerating synapses after lesions of the axons, have not proved satisfactory.

In peripheral nerves degeneration of the axon and myelin proceeds as described above. The sensory end organs, motor end plates, and striped muscles degenerate more slowly. Smooth muscles and glands undergo certain functional changes. The sheath of Schwann cells at first multiply markedly, and later become indistinguishable from connective tissue cells except by their arrangement in rows. Regeneration normally occurs in a manner closely resembling the original development of the peripheral nerves, though there are liable to be abnormalities in motor and in discriminatory distribution, which persist.

The second type of degeneration important in anatomical investigations is known as **retrograde degeneration.** This term is applied to the changes which occur in the cell body and in the proximal portion of an axon which has been transected. There are wide variations in the extent to which the degeneration may proceed. Many cells show no demonstrable change. In others a condition known as **chromatolysis** occurs, which consists in fragmentation and loss of the Nissl bodies and in nuclear changes. The nucleus becomes shrunken, irregular, and eccentrically placed, surrounded by a clear zone and the remaining Nissl substance appears in a finely divided, powdery form around the periphery of the cell. Chromatolysis is usually well developed in six to ten days after the lesion, although early changes may be noted in twenty-four hours. In certain cells the condition may remain unchanged for years; other cells rapidly recover; a few types of cells, usually belonging to highly specialized systems, proceed to complete degeneration and disappear. In the latter cases the proximal portions of the axons also degenerate. In peripheral nerves retrograde degeneration of the axons usually extends only one or two segments proximal to the injury.

The third type of degeneration is known as **transynaptic**. It occurs only in the cells of certain systems and is probably best illustrated in the case of the visual system. When the optic tract is cut the next neurons in the pathway to the cortex, namely the cells of the lateral geniculate body, undergo chromatolysis which proceeds to disintegration and disappearance.

Retrograde and transynaptic degeneration have been widely used for determining the origins of fibers, both of peripheral nerves and of tracts in the central nervous system, and for studies on the interrelations of various parts of the fore-brain. The methods obviously have their limitations, but with due care give reliable results where they are applicable.

REFERENCES

GENERAL

ARIËNS-KAPPERS, J. 1956. Progress in Neurobiology, Proceedings of the First International Meeting of Neurobiologists. Elsevier Publishing Company, Amsterdam and D. Van Nostrand Company, Inc., New York. xii + 384 pages.

BUCHANAN, A. R. 1957. Functional Neuro-Anatomy, including an Atlas of the Brain Stem. 3rd edition, Lea & Febiger, Publishers, Philadelphia. 362 pages.

BURR, H. S. 1958. Design in the nervous system. Anat. Rec., *131*, 405–415.

KOPSCH, F. 1955. Rauber-Kopsch Lehrbuch und Altas der Anatomie des Menschen. 19th edition. Georg Thieme Verlag, Stuttgart. 2 volumes.

KRIEG, W. J. S. 1953. Functional Neuroanatomy. The Blakiston Company, New York. xviii + 659 pages.

RASMUSSEN, A. T. 1954. The Principal Nervous Pathways. 4th edition. The Macmillan Company, New York. ix + 73 pages.

SINGER, M. and P. I. YAKOVLEV. 1954. The Human Brain in Sagittal Section. Charles C Thomas, Publisher, Springfield. v + 81 pages.

EMBRYOLOGY

BAKER, R. C., and G. O. GRAVES. 1939. The behavior of the neural crest in the forebrain region of Amblystoma. J. comp. Neurol., *71*, 389–415.

BROWN, J. W. 1956. The development of the nucleus of the spinal tract of V in human fetuses of 14 to 21 weeks of menstrual age. J. comp. Neurol., *106*, 393–424.

BUEKER, E. D. 1948. Implantation of tumors in the hind limb field of the embryonic chick and the developmental response of the lumbosacral nervous system. Anat. Rec., *102*, 369–390.

BURR, H. S. 1932. An electro-dynamic theory of development suggested by studies of proliferation rates in the brain of Amblystoma. J. comp. Neurol., *56*, 347–371.

CONEL, J. L. 1942. The origin of the neural crest. J. comp. Neurol., *76*, 191–215.

DETWILER, S. R. 1936. Neuroembryology. The Macmillan Company, New York, x + 218 pp.

DETWILER, S. R. 1937. Substitution of lateral for axial mesoderm in relation to the development and segmentation of spinal ganglia. J. exp. Zool., *76*, 35–46.

FLEXNER, L. B., J. B. FLEXNER, and L. HELLERMAN. 1956. Biochemical and physiological differentiation during morphogenesis. XX. In vitro observations on carbohydrate metabolism of the developing cerebral cortex of the fetal guinea pig. J. cell. comp. Physiol., *47*, 469–482.

HARRISON, R. G. 1924. Neuroblast versus sheath cell in the development of peripheral nerves. J. comp. Neurol., *37*, 123–206.

HOGG, I. D. 1944. The development of the nucleus dorsalis (Clarke's column). J. comp. Neurol. *81*, 69–95.

HÖRSTADIUS, S. 1950. The Neural Crest, its Properties and Derivatives in the Light of Experimental Research. Oxford University Press, London. ix + 111 pages.

HUMPHERY, T. 1944. Primitive neurons in the embryonic human central nervous system. J. comp. Neurol., *81*, 1–45.

HUMPHREY, T. 1952. The spinal tract of the trigeminal nerve in human embryos between $7\frac{1}{2}$ and $8\frac{1}{2}$ weeks of menstrual age and its relation to early fetal behavior. J. comp. Neurol., *97*, 143–210.

KIMMEL, D. L. 1941. Development of the afferent components of the facial, glossopharyngeal and vagus nerves in the rabbit embryo. J. comp. Neurol., *74*, 447–471.

PATTEN, B. M. 1953. Human Embryology. 2nd edition, The Blakiston Company, New York. xvii + 798 pages.

WAELSCH, H. 1955. Biochemistry of the Developing Nervous System; Proceedings International Neurochemical Symposium. Academic Press, Inc., Publishers, New York. xvii + 537 pages.

WARD, J. W. 1954. The development of the corticospinal tract in the pouch-young of the Virginia opossum, Didelphys virginiana. J. comp. Neurol., *101*, 483–494.

WILDE, C. E. 1955. The urodele neuroepithelium. I. The differentiation in vitro of the cranial neural crest. J. exp. Zool., *130*, 573–596.

YNTEMA, C. L. and W. S. HAMMOND. 1947. The development of the autonomic nervous system. Biol. Rev., *22*, 344–359.

YNTEMA, C. L. and W. S. HAMMOND. 1954. The origin of intrinsic ganglia of trunk viscera from vagal neural crest in the chick embryo. J. comp. Neurol., *101*, 515–542.

SPINAL CORD

EARLE, K. M. 1952. The tract of Lissauer and its possible relation to the pain pathway. J. comp. Neurol., *96*, 93–112.

ELLIOTT, H. C. 1942–3. Studies on the motor cells of the spinal cord. I. Distribution in the normal human cord. II. Distribution in the normal human fetal cord. Amer. J. Anat., *70*, 95–117 and *72*, 29–38.

GILLILAN, L. A. 1958. The arterial blood supply of the human spinal cord. J. comp. Neurol., *110*, 75–104

HUMPHREY, T. 1950. Intramedullary sensory ganglion cells in the roof plate area of the embryonic human spinal cord. J. comp. Neurol., *92*, 333–399.

LASSEK, A. M. 1954. The Pyramidal Tract: Its Status in Medicine. Charles C Thomas, Publisher, Springfield. v + 166 pages.

REED, A. F. 1940. The nuclear masses in the cervical spinal cord of Macaca mulatta. J. comp. Neurol., *72*, 187–206.

WARWICK, R. and G. A. G. MITCHELL. 1956. The phrenic nucleus of the macaque. J. comp. Neurol., *105*, 553–586.

BRAIN STEM AND CEREBELLUM

ALLEN, W. F. 1927. Experimental-anatomical studies on the visceral bulbo-spinal pathway in the cat and guinea-pig. J. comp. Neurol., *42*, 393–456.

ANDERSON, F. D. and C. M. BERRY. 1956. An oscillographic study of the central pathways of the central pathways of the vagus nerve in the cat. J. comp. Neurol., *106*, 163–182.

BRAITENBERG, V. and R. P. ATWOOD. 1958. Morphological observations on the cerebellar cortex. J. comp. Neurol., *109*, 1–34.

BROWN, J. O. 1943. The nuclear pattern of the non-tectal portions of the midbrain and isthmus in the dog and cat. J. comp. Neurol., *78*, 365–405.

BUCHANAN, A. R. 1937. The course of the secondary vestibular fibers in the cat. J. comp. Neurol., *67*, 183–204.

CARPENTER, M. B., G. M. BRITTIN, and J. PINES. 1958. Isolated lesions of the fastigial nuclei in the cat. J. comp. Neurol., *109*, 65–90.

CARPENTER M. B. and J. PINES. 1957. The rubro-bulbar tract: Anatomical relationships, course, and terminations in the rhesus monkey. Anat. Rec., *128*, 171–186.

CHAMBERS, W. W. and J. M. SPRAGUE. 1955. Functional localization in the cerebellum. I. Organization in longitudinal cortico-nuclear zones and their contribution to the control of posture, both extrapyramidal and pyramidal. J. comp. Neurol., *103*, 105–130.

HYDE, J. E. and S. G. ELIASSON. 1957. Brainstem induced eye movements in cats. J. comp. Neurol., *108*, 139–172.

INGRAM, W. R. and S. W. RANSON. 1935. The nucleus of Darkschewitsch and nucleus interslitialis in the brain of man. J. nerv. ment. Dis., *81*, 125–137.

LANGWORTHY, O. R. 1924. A study of the innervation of the tongue musculature with particular reference to the proprioceptive mechanism. J. comp. Neurol., *36*, 273–298.

LARSELL, O. 1947. The development of the cerebellum in man in relation to its comparative anatomy. J. comp. Neurol., *87*, 85–130.

PEARSON, A. A. 1939. The hypoglossal nerve in human embryos. J. comp. Neurol., *71*, 21–40.

60

RASMUSSEN, A. T. and W. T. PEYTON. 1948. The course and termination of the medial lemniscus in man. J. comp. Neurol., *88*, 411–424.

RASMUSSEN, G. L. 1946. The olivary peduncle and other fiber projections of the superior olivary complex. J. comp. Neurol., *84*, 141–219.

RUSSELL, G. V. 1957. The brainstem reticular formation. Tex. Rep. Biol. Med., *15*, 332–337.

SCHÜTZ, H. 1891. Anatomische Untersuchungen über den Faserverlauf in zentralen Höhlengrau und de Nervenfaserschund in denselben bei der progressiven Paralyse der Irren. Arch. Psychiat. Nervenkr., *22*, 527–587.

STERN, K. 1938. Note on the nucleus ruber magnocellularis and its efferent pathway in man. Brain., *61*, 284–289.

STOTLER, W. A. 1953. An experimental study of the cells and connections of the superior olivary complex of the cat. J. comp. Neurol., *98*, 401–431.

SZENTÁGOTHAI, J. 1948. The representation of facial and scalp muscles in the facial nucleus. J. comp. Neurol., *88*, 207–220.

VILLIGER, E. 1925. Brain and Spinal Cord. 3rd American Edition by W. H. F. Addison, J. B. Lippincott Company, Philadelphia. x + 335 pages.

WARWICK, R. 1953. Representation of the extra-ocular muscles in the oculomotor nuclei of the monkey. J. comp. Neurol., *98*, 449–503.

DIENCEPHALON

BISHOP, G. H. and M. H. CLARE. 1955. Organization and distribution of fibers in the optic tract of the cat. J. comp. Neurol., *103*, 269–304.

BRIZZEE, K. R. 1954. A comparison of cell structure in the area postrema, supraoptic crest, and intercolumnar tubercle with notes on the neurohypophysis and pineal body in the cat. J. comp. Neurol., *100*, 699–716.

CLARK, W. E. L. 1936. The topography and homologies of the hypothalamic nuclei in man. J. Anat. (Lond.), *70*, 203–214.

CROSBY, E. C. and R. T. WOODBURNE. 1951. The mammalian midbrain and isthums regions. Part II. The fiber connections. C. The hypothalamotegmental pathways. J. comp. Neurol., *94*, 1–32.

DEKABAN, A. 1953. Human thalamus, an anatomical, developmental and pathological study. I. Division of the adult human thalamus into nuclei by use of the cyto-myelo-architectonic method. J. comp. Neurol., *99*, 639–684.

FOX, C. A. 1943. The stria terminalis, longitudinal association bundle and precommissural fornix fibers in the cat. J. comp. Neurol., *79*, 277–295.

GARDNER, J. H. 1953. Innervation of the pineal gland in hooded rat. J. comp. Neurol., *99*, 319–330.

HESS, W. R. 1957. The Functional Organization of the Diencephalon. John R. Hughes, Editor. Grune and Stratton, New York. xii + 180 pages.

HUNT, W. E. and J. L. O'LEARY. 1952. Form of thalamic response evoked by peripheral nerve stimulation. J. comp. Neurol., *97*, 491–514.

INGRAM, W. R. 1940. Nuclear organization and chief connections of the primate hypothalamus. Ass. Res. nerv. Dis. Proc., *20*, 195–244.

KUHLENBECK, H. 1954. The Human Diencephalon—A Summary of Development, Structure, Function and Pathology. S. Karger, Basel. 230 pages.

KUHLENBECK, H., and R. N. MILLER. 1949. The pretectal region of the human brain. J. comp. Neurol., *91*, 369–407.

MAGOUN, H. W., and M. RANSON. 1942. The supraoptic decussations in the cat and monkey. J. comp. Neurol., *76*, 435–459.

SAWYER, C. H., J. W. EVERETT, and J. D. GREEN. 1954. The rabbit diencephalon in stereotaxic coordinates. J. comp. Neurol., *101*, 801–824.

TONCRAY, J. E. and W. J. S. KRIEG. 1946. The nuclei of the human thalamus: a comparative approach. J. comp. Neurol., *85*, 421–460.

WALKER, A. E. 1938. The primate thalamus. University of Chicago Press, Chicago. xxiii + 321 pages.

TELENCEPHALON

BARNARD, J. W. and C. N. WOOLSEY. 1956. A study of localization in the corticospinal tracts of monkey and rat. J. comp. Neurol., *105*, 25–50.

BEACH, F. A., A. ZITRIN, and J. JAYNES. 1955. Neural mediation of mating in male cats. II. Contributions of the frontal cortex. J. exp. Zool., *130*, 381–402.

BILLENSTIEN, D. C. 1953. The vascularity of the motor cortex of the dog. Anat. Rec., *117*, 129–144.

von Bonin, G. 1950. Essay on the Cerebral Cortex. Charles C Thomas, Publisher, Springfield. xiii + 150 pages.

Brodman, K. 1909. Vergleichende Lokalisationslehre der Grosshirnrinde in ihren Prinzipien dargestellt auf Grund des Zellenbaues. Reprinted 1925 by J. A. Barth, Leipzig. x + 324 pages.

Brody, H. 1955. Organization of the cerebral cortex. III. A study of aging in the human cerebral cortex. J. comp. Neurol., *102*, 511–556.

Bucy, P. C. and H. Klüver. 1955. An anatomical investigation of the temporal lobe in the monkey (Macaca mulatta). J. comp. Neurol., *103*, 151–252.

Carey, J. H. 1957. Certain anatomical and functional interrelations between the tegmentum of the midbrain and the basal ganglia. J. comp. Neurol., *108*, 57–90.

Freeman, W. and J. W. Watts. 1947. Retrograde degeneration of the thalamus following prefrontal lobotomy. J. comp. Neurol., *86*, 65–93.

Frontera, J. G. 1956. Some results obtained by electrical stimulation of the cortex of the island of Reil in the brain of the monkey (Macaca mulatta). J. comp. Neurol., *105*, 365–394.

Harman, P. J. and C. M. Berry. 1956. Neuroanatomical distribution of action potentials evoked by photic stimuli in cat fore- and midbrain. J. comp. Neurol., *105*, 395–416.

Krieg, W. J. S. 1954. Connections of the Frontal Cortex of the Monkey. Charles C Thomas, Publisher, Springfield. xi + 299 pages.

Lauer, E. W. 1945. The nuclear pattern and fiber connections of certain basal telencephalic centers in the Macaque. J. comp. Neurol., *82*, 215–254.

McCulloch, W. S. 1949. Cortico-cortical connections. In Bucy's The Precentral Motor Cortex, 2nd edition, University of Illinois Press, Urbana. xiv + 615 pages.

Peele, T. L. 1942. Cytoarchitecture of individual parietal areas in the monkey (Macaca mulatta) and the distribution of the efferent fibers. J. comp. Neurol., *77*, 693–737.

Penfield, W. and T. Rasmussen. 1950. The Cerebral Cortex of Man; a Clinical Study of Localization of Function. The Macmillan Company, New York. xv + 248 pages.

Rasmussen, A. T. 1943. The extent of recurrent geniculo-calcarine fibers (loop of Archambault and Meyer) as demonstrated by gross brain dissection. Anat. Rec., *85*, 277–284.

Tomasch, J. 1954. Size, distribution, and number of fibers in the human corpus callosum. Anat. Rec., *119*, 119–136.

Rhinencephalon

Allen, W. F. 1948. Fiber degeneration in Ammon's horn resulting from extirpations of the piriform and other cortical areas and from transection of the horn at various levels. J. comp. Neurol., *88*, 425–438.

Allison, A. C. 1953. The structure of the olfactory bulb and its relationship to the olfactory pathways in the rabbit and the rat. J. comp. Neurol., *98*, 309–354.

Harrison, J. M. and M. Lyon. 1957. The role of the septal nuclei and components of the fornix in the behavior of the rat. J. comp. Neurol., *108*, 121–137.

Jiminez-Castellanos, J. 1949. The amygdaloid complex in monkey studied by reconstructional methods. J. comp. Neurol., *91*, 507–526.

Kaada, B. R., J. Jansen, Jr., and P. Andersen. 1953. Stimulation of the hippocampus and medial cortical areas in unanaesthetized cats. Neurology, (Minneap.), *3*, 844–857.

Macchi, G. 1951. The ontogenetic development of the olfactory telencephalon in man. J. comp. Neurol., *95*, 245–306.

Nilges, R. G. 1944. The arteries of the mammalian cornu ammonis. J. comp. Neurol., *80*, 177–190.

Ramon y Cajal, S. 1955. Studies on the Cerebral Cortex (Limbic Structure). Translated from Spanish by Lisbeth M. Kraft. The Year Book Publishers, New York. xi + 179 pages.

Rioch, D. McK., and C. Brenner. 1938. Experiments on the corpus striatum and rhinencephalon. J. comp. Neurol., *68*, 491–507.

Neuroglia, Meninges and Spinal Fluid

Flyger, G. and U. B. E. Hjelmquist. 1957. Normal variations in the caliber of the human cerebral aqueduct. Anat. Rec., *127*, 151–162.

Glees, P. 1955. Neuroglia: Morphology and Function. Charles C Thomas, Publisher, Springfield. xii + 111 pages.

Harvey, S. C. and H. S. Burr. 1926. The development of the meninges. Arch. Neurol. Psychiat. (Chicago), *15*, 545–565.

Pease, D. C. and R. L. Schultz. 1958. Electron microscopy of rat cranial meninges. Amer. J. Anat., *102*, 301–322.

Schultz, R. L., E. A. Maynard, and D. C. Pease. 1957. Electron microscopy of neurons and neuroglia of cerebral cortex and corpus callosum. Amer. J. Anat., *100*, 369–408.

SENSENIG, E. C. 1951. The early development of the meninges of the spinal cord in human embryos. Contr. Embryol. Carneg. Instn., *34*, 147–157.

STRONG, L. H. 1956. Early development of the ependyma and vascular pattern of the fourth ventricular choroid plexus in the rabbit . Amer. J. Anat., *99*, 249–290.

SWEET, W. H. and H. B. LOCKSLEY. Formation, flow and reabsorption of cerebrospinal fluid in man. Proc. Soc. exp. Biol. (N.Y.), *84*, 397–402.

HISTOLOGY

ADAMSTONE, F. B. and A. B. TAYLOR. 1953. Structure and physical nature of the cytoplasm of living spinal ganglion cells of the adult rat. J. Morph., *92*, 513–530.

BARR, M. L., L. F. BERTRAM, and H. A. LINDSAY. 1950. The morphology of the nerve cell nucleus, according to sex. Anat. Rec., *107*, 283–297.

BODIAN, D. 1951. As note on nodes of Ranvier in the central nervous system. J. comp. Neurol., *94*, 475–484.

BUEKER, E. D. 1943. Intracentral and peripheral factors in the differentiation of motor neurons in transplanted lumbosacral spinal cords of chick embryos. J. exp. Zool., *93*, 99–129.

D'ANGELO, C., M. ISSIDORIDES, and W. M. SHANKLIN. 1956. A comparative study of the staining reactions of granules in the human neuron. J. comp. Neurol., *106*, 487–506.

DUNCAN, D. 1957. Electron microscope study of the embryonic neural tube and notochord. Tex. Rep. Biol. Med., *15*, 367–377.

FORD, D. H. and S. KANTOUNIS. 1957 The localization of neurosecretory structures and pathways in the male albino rabbit. J. comp. Neurol., *108*, 91–108.

GEREN, B. B. 1954. The formation from the Schwann cell surface of myelin in the peripheral nerves of chick embryos. Exp. Cell Res., *7*, 558–562.

HARTMANN, J. F. 1954. Electron microscopy of motor nerve cells following section of axones. Anat. Rec., *118*, 19–34.

HESS, A. 1955. The fine structure of young and old spinal ganglia. Anat. Rec., *123*, 399–424.

HOERR, N. L. 1936. Cytological studies by the Altmann-Gersh freezing-drying method. III. The preëxistence of neurofibrillæ and their disposition in the nerve fiber. IV. The structure of the myelin sheath of nerve fibers. Anat. Rec., *66*, 81–90 and 91–95.

LA VELLE, A. 1956. Nucleolar and Nissl substance development in nerve cells. J. comp. Neurol., *104*, 175–206.

PENFIELD, W. 1932. Cytology and Cellular Pathology of the Nervous System. P. B. Hoeber, Inc., New York. 3 volumes.

ROBERTSON, J. D. 1956. The ultrastructure of a reptilian myoneural junction. J. biophys. biochem. Cytol., *2*, 381–394.

SCHMITT, F. O. 1957. The fibrous protein of the nerve axon. J. cell. comp. Physiol., *49*, 165–174.

PERIPHERAL NERVE ENDINGS

CAUNA, N. 1958. Structure of digital touch corpuscles. Acta Anat., *32*, 1–23.

COLE, W. V. 1957. Structural variations of nerve endings in the striated muscles of the rat. J. comp. Neurol., *108*, 445–464.

GARNER, C. M. and D. DUNCAN. 1958. Observations on the fine structure of the carotid body. Anat. Rec., *130*, 691–709.

HERING, H. E. 1927. Die Karotissinusreflexe auf Herz und Gefässe vom normalphysiologischen, pathologisch-physiologischen und klinischen Standpunkt. Th. Steinkopff, Dresden.

HOFFMAN, H. and J. H. W. BIRRELL. 1958. The carotid body in normal and anoxic states; an electron microscopic study. Acta Anat., *32*, 297–311.

HOLLINSHEAD, W. H. 1941. Chemoreceptors in the abdomen. J. comp. Neurol., *74*, 269–285.

KOUSDA, T. 1951. Study on the pressoreceptor area of the aortic arch. Nippon J. Angio-Cardiol., *15*, 4–10.

MERRILLEES, N. C. R., S. SUNDERLAND, and W. HAYHOW. 1950. Neuromuscular spindles in the extraocular muscles in man. Anat. Rec., *108*, 23–30.

REGER, J. F. 1958. The fine structure of neuromuscular synapses of gastrocnemii from mouse and frog Anat. Rec., *130*, 7–23.

ROSS, L. L. 1957. A cytological and histochemical study of the carotid body of the cat. Anat. Rec., *129*, 433–455.

SHEEHAN, D. 1933. The clinical significance of the nerve-endings in the mesentery. Lancet, *1*, 409–413.

SCHWARZACHER, H. G. 1957. Zur Lage der motorischen Endplatten in den Skelet muskeln. Acta Anat., *30*, 758–744.

TAKASHI, M. 1957. On the development of the complex pattern of Pacinian corpuscle distributed in the human retroperitoneum. Anat. Rec., *128*, 665–678.

REGENERATION

BUEKER E. D. and C. E. MEYERS. 1951. The maturity of peripheral nerves at the time of injury as a factor in nerve regeneration. Anat. Rec., *109*, 723–744.

CHAN-NAO, L. and D. SCOTT, JR. 1958. Regeneration in the dorsal spinocerebellar tract of the cat. J. comp. Neurol., *109*, 153–168.

CLARK, E. R., and E. L. CLARK. 1947. Microscopic studies on the regeneration of medullated nerves in the living mammal. Amer. J. Anat., *81*, 233–268.

MOYER, E. K., D. L. KIMMEL, and L. W. WINBORNE. 1953. Regeneration of sensory spinal nerve roots in young and in senile rats. J. comp. Neurol., *98*, 283–308.

TURNER, R. S. 1943. Chromatolysis and recovery of efferent neurons. J. comp. Neurol., *79*, 73–78.

THE PERIPHERAL NERVOUS SYSTEM.

THE Peripheral Nervous System carries the nervous impulses to and from the Central Nervous System. It is composed of nerve fibers, ganglia, and end organs. Afferent or sensory fibers carry toward the Central Nervous System the impulses arising from stimulation of sensory end organs. Efferent or motor fibers carry impulses from the Central Nervous System to the muscles and other responsive organs. The somatic fibers, both afferent and efferent, are associated with the general body, typified by the bones, skeletal muscles, and skin. The visceral fibers are also both afferent and efferent, and are associated with the internal organs, vessels, and mucous membranes.

The Peripheral Nervous System consists of (a) the cranial nerves, (b) the spinal nerves, and (c) the sympathetic nervous system. These three morphological subdivisions are not independent functionally, but combine and communicate with each other to supply both the somatic and visceral parts with both afferent and efferent fibers. For example, the efferent impulses for control of the viscera are carried partly by the sympathetic system and partly by portions of certain cranial and sacral nerves. The latter are grouped under the name parasympathetic or craniosacral system, and both sympathetic and parasympathetic systems together make up the visceral motor or autonomic nervous system, described in later pages.

THE CRANIAL NERVES.

The **cranial nerves** (*nervi cerebrales; cerebral nerves*) are attached to the base of the brain (Fig. 743) and make their passage from the cranial cavity through various openings or foramina in the skull (Fig. 801). There are twelve pairs, and beginning with the most anterior, they are designated by Roman numerals and named as follows:

I. Olfactory	V. Trigeminal	IX. Glossopharyngeal
II. Optic	VI. Abducent	X. Vagus
III. Oculomotor	VII. Facial	XI. Accessory
IV. Trochlear	VIII. Acoustic	XII. Hypoglossal

Since certain of these nerves, particularly V, VII, and VIII, contain two or more distinct functional components, their parts have been given the status of independent nerves by some authorities. In this classification, the **Masticatory nerve** would be separated from the trigeminal, the **Glossopalatine** from the facial, and the **Equilibratory** from the acoustic, making fifteen pairs in all (Hardesty '33).

In addition to the commonly accepted cranial nerves, there is a small nerve named the Nervus Terminalis, classified morphologically by some comparative anatomists as the first cranial nerve.

The **Nervus Terminalis** (*terminal nerve*) originates from the cerebral hemisphere in the region of the olfactory trigone, courses anteriorly along the medial surface of the olfactory tract and bulb to the lateral surface of the crista galli, and passes through the anterior part of the cribriform plate of the ethmoid bone. It is a compact bundle beside the olfactory tract, a close plexus beside the bulb, and a loose plexus on the crista galli, where it is imbedded in the dura mater some distance

(951)

OUTLINE OF THE CRANIAL NERVES

Nerves	Components		Function	Central Connection	Cell Bodies	Peripheral Distribution
I. Olfactory	Afferent	Special visceral	Smell	Olfactory bulb and tract	Olfactory epithelial cells	Olfactory nerves
II. Optic	Afferent	Special somatic	Vision	Optic nerve and tract	Ganglion cells of retina	Rods and cones of retina
III. Oculomotor	Efferent	Somatic	Ocular movement	Nucleus III	Nucleus III	Branches to Levator palpebræ, Rectus superior, medius, inferior, Obliquus inferior
	Efferent	General visceral	Contraction of pupil and accommodation	Nucleus of Edinger-Westphal	Nucleus of Edinger-Westphal	Ciliary ganglion; Ciliaris and Sphincter pupillæ
	Afferent	Proprioceptive	Muscular sensibility	Nucleus mesencephalicus V	Nucleus mesencephalicus V	Sensory endings in ocular muscles
IV. Trochlear	Efferent	Somatic	Ocular movement	Nucleus IV	Nucleus IV	Branches to Obliquus superior
	Afferent	Proprioceptive	Muscular sensibility	Nucleus mesencephalicus V	Nucleus mesencephalicus V	Sensory endings in Obliquus superior
V. Trigeminal	Afferent	General somatic	General sensibility	Trigeminal sensory nucleus	Trigeminal ganglion (Gasserian)	Sensory branches of ophthalmic maxillary and mandibular nerves to skin and mucous membranes of face and head
	Efferent	Special visceral	Mastication	Motor V nucleus	Motor V nucleus	Branches to Temporalis, Masseter, Pterygoidei, Mylohyoideus, Digastricus, Tensores tympani and palatini
	Afferent	Proprioceptive	Muscular sensibility	Nucleus mesencephalicus V	Nucleus mesencephalicus V	Sensory endings in muscles of mastication
VI. Abducent	Efferent	Somatic	Ocular movement	Nucleus VI	Nucleus VI	Branches to Rectus lateralis
	Afferent	Proprioceptive	Muscular sensibility	Nucleus mesencephalicus V	Nucleus mesencephalicus V	Sensory endings in Rectus lateralis
VII. Facial	Efferent	Special visceral	Facial expression	Motor VII nucleus	Motor VII nucleus	Branches to facial muscles, Stapedius, Stylohyoideus, Digastricus
	Efferent	General visceral	Glandular secretion	Nucleus salivatorius	Nucleus salivatorius	Greater superficial petrosal nerve, sphenopalatine ganglion, with branches of maxillary V to glands of nasal mucosa. Chorda tympani, lingual nerve, submaxillary ganglion, submaxillary and sublingual glands
	Afferent	Special visceral	Taste	Nucleus tractus solitarius	Geniculate ganglion	Chorda tympani, lingual nerve, taste buds, anterior tongue
	Afferent	General visceral	Visceral sensibility	Nucleus tractus solitarius	Geniculate ganglion	

Nerve	Component	Function	Nucleus	Nucleus	Ganglion	Distribution
VIII. Acoustic	Afferent General somatic	Cutaneous sensibility	Nucleus spinal tract of V	Nucleus spinal tract of V	Geniculate ganglion	With auricular branch of vagus to external ear and mastoid region
	Afferent Special somatic	Hearing	Cochlear nuclei	Cochlear nuclei	Spiral ganglion	Organ of Corti in cochlea
	Afferent Proprioceptive	Sense of equilibrium	Vestibular nuclei	Vestibular nuclei	Vestibular ganglion	Semicircular canals, saccule, and utricle
IX. Glossopharyngeal	Afferent Special visceral	Taste	Nucleus tractus solitarius	Nucleus tractus solitarius	Inferior ganglion IX	Lingual branches, taste buds, posterior tongue
	Afferent General visceral	Visceral sensibility	Nucleus tractus solitarius	Nucleus tractus solitarius	Inferior ganglion IX	Tympanic nerve to middle ear, branches to pharynx and tongue, carotid sinus nerve
	Efferent General visceral	Glandular secretion	Nucleus salivatorius	Nucleus salivatorius	Nucleus salivatorius	Tympanic, lesser superficial petrosal nerves, otic ganglion, with auriculotemporal V to parotid gland
	Efferent Special visceral	Swallowing	Nucleus ambiguus	Nucleus ambiguus	Nucleus ambiguus	Branch to Stylopharyngeus
X. Vagus	Efferent General visceral	Involuntary muscle and gland control	Dorsal motor nucleus X	Dorsal motor nucleus X	Dorsal motor nucleus X	Cardiac nerves and plexus; ganglia on heart. Pulmonary plexus; ganglia, respiratory tract. Esophageal, gastric, celiac plexuses; myenteric and submucous plexuses, muscle and glands of digestive tract down to transverse colon
	Efferent Special visceral	Swallowing and phonation	Nucleus ambiguus	Nucleus ambiguus	Nucleus ambiguus	Pharyngeal branches, superior and inferior laryngeal nerves
	Afferent General visceral	Visceral sensibility	Nucleus tractus solitarius		Ganglion nodosum	Fibers in all cervical, thoracic, and abdominal branches; carotid and aortic bodies
	Afferent Special visceral	Taste	Nucleus tractus solitarius		Ganglion nodosum	Branches to region of epiglottis and taste buds
	Afferent General somatic	Cutaneous sensibility	Nucleus spinal tract V		Jugular ganglion	Auricular branch to external ear and meatus
XI. Accessory	Efferent Special visceral	Swallowing and phonation	Nucleus ambiguus	Nucleus ambiguus	Nucleus ambiguus	Bulbar portion, communication with vagus, in vagus branches to muscles of pharynx and larynx
	Efferent Special somatic	Movements of shoulder and head	Lateral column of upper cervical spinal cord	Lateral column of upper cervical spinal cord	Lateral column of upper cervical spinal cord	Spinal portion, branches to Sternocleidomastoideus and Trapezius
XII. Hypoglossal	Efferent General somatic	Movements of tongue	Nucleus XII	Nucleus XII	Nucleus XII	Branches to extrinsic and intrinsic muscles of tongue

above the cribriform bone. Within the cranium, filaments join the olfactory bundles and *vomeronasal nerves*, and apparently pass to the mucous membrane of the septum along with them. The majority of filaments form a single strand which passes through the cribriform plate anterior to the vomeronasal nerves, and is distributed to the membrane near the anterior superior border of the nasal septum. In the nasal cavity, the nerve communicates with the medial nasal branch of the an-

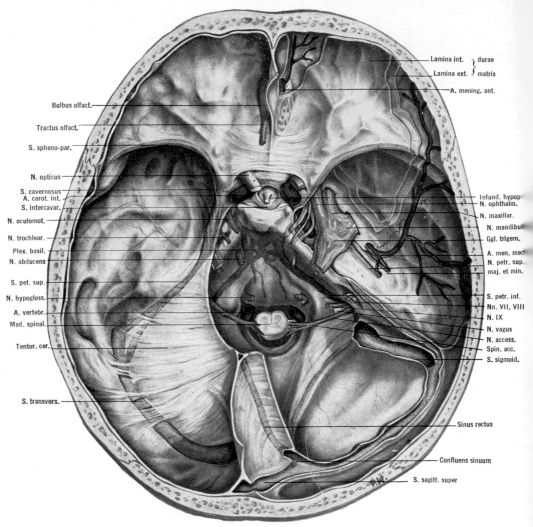

FIG. 801.—Interior of base of skull, showing dura mater, dural sinuses, and exit of cranial nerves
(Töndury, Angewandte und topographische Anatomie, courtesy of Georg Thieme Verlag.)

terior ethmoidal branch of the ophthalmic division of the trigeminal nerve (McCotter '15).

In the embryo, a loose mass of fibers and cells in the portion of the nerve medial to the rostral end of the olfactory bulb is called the **ganglion terminale**. The nerve fibers are unmyelinated and ganglion cells are scattered in groups along the peripheral course of the nerve. The cells in the ganglion and along the nerve have been described by different authors as unipolar, bipolar, and multipolar (Pearson '41).

The central connections of the nervus terminalis end in the septal nuclei, the olfactory lobe, the posterior precommissural region, and the anterior portion of the supraoptic region of the brain. Those in the first three are sensory, those in the supraoptic region may be preganglionic autonomic fibers associated with the serous glands (of Bowman) or with blood vessels in the olfactory membrane (Larsell '50).

I. THE OLFACTORY NERVE.

The **olfactory nerve** (*nervus olfactorius; first nerve*) (Fig. 802), or nerve of smell, in its properly restricted sense is represented on both sides of the nasal cavity by a number of bundles of nerve fibers which are the central processes of the neuro-

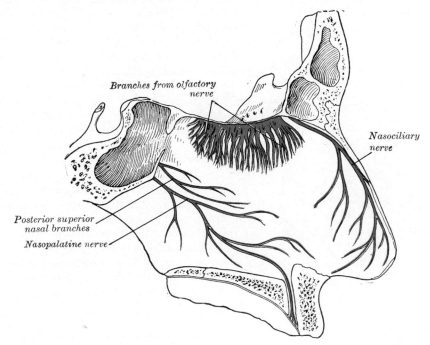

Branches from olfactory nerve

Nasociliary nerve

Posterior superior nasal branches

Nasopalatine nerve

FIG. 802.—The nerves of the right side of the septum of the nose.

epithelial cells in the olfactory mucous membrane of the nose. These cells are described in more detail as part of the organ of smell in the Chapter on Sense Organs. The nerve fibers make a plexiform network in the mucous membrane of the superior nasal concha and the part of the septum opposite, and then are gathered into approximately twenty bundles which pass through the foramina of the cribriform plate of the ethmoid bone in two groups. A lateral group comes from the concha, a medial group from the septum. The fibers are unmyelinated, and the bundles have connective tissue sheaths derived from the tissues of the dura, arachnoid, and pia mater. After passing through the foramina, the fibers end in the glomeruli of the olfactory bulb, an oval mass measuring approximately 3 × 15 mm., which rests against the intracranial surface of the cribriform plate of the ethmoid. (Fig. 773.)

Although the olfactory bulb and its connection with the brain, the olfactory tract, have a gross appearance like that of a nerve, they are more accurately classed as parts of the brain. They are components of the rhinencephalon, the portion of the brain associated with the sense of smell, which is described in the Chapter on the Central Nervous System, pages 904–911.

The **vomeronasal nerve,** which is an important part of the olfactory system in macrosmatic animals, is present in the human fetus but disappears before birth. The nerve fibers originate in the olfactory epithelial cells of the vomeronasal organ (organ of Jacobson), a rudiment of which may persist in man; they pass upward in the submucous tissue of the nasal septum and through the cribiform plate of the ethmoid bone to end in the accessory olfactory bulb.

II. **THE OPTIC NERVE.**

The **optic nerve** (*n. opticus; second nerve*) (Fig. 803), or nerve of sight, consists mainly of the axones or central processes of the cells in the ganglionic layer of the retina.

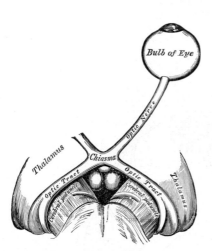

FIG. 803.—The left optic nerve and the optic tracts.

Within the bulb of the eye, these axones lie in the stratum opticum or layer of nerve fibers of the retina (see page 1109). They converge toward the optic papilla, or disc, which is 3 mm. medial to the posterior pole of the bulb, and are gathered there into small bundles which pierce the choroid and sclerotic coats by means of the many small foramina of the lamina cribrosa scleræ, to become the optic nerve. The nerve, as it courses posteriorly toward the brain, traverses the central region of the orbit, passes through the optic foramen, and then, approaching the nerve of the other side, joins it to form the optic chiasma. From the chiasma, the fibers are continued in the optic tracts, which diverge from each other to reach the base of the brain near the cerebral peduncle. The central connections of the fibers are described in the Chapter on the Central Nervous System, page 912.

The optic nerve has four portions, contained in: (*a*) the bulb, (*b*) the orbit, (*c*) the optic foramen, and (*d*) the cranial cavity. The **intraocular portion** is very short, about 1 mm., and the nerve fibers within it are unmyelinated until they pass through the lamina cribrosa, when they become myelinated and supported by neuroglia.

The **orbital portion,** 3 to 4 mm. in diameter, is from 20 to 30 mm. long, and has a slightly sinuous course which allows greater length for unrestricted movement of the eyeball. It is invested by sheaths derived from the dura, arachnoid, and pia mater, all three of which fuse and become continuous with the sclera at the lamina cribrosa; the dura extends as far back as the cranial cavity, the arachnoid somewhat farther, and the pia all the way to the chiasma. The pia closely ensheaths the nerve, and sends numerous septa into its substance, carrying the blood supply. Between the sheaths are subarachnoid and subdural spaces similar to and continuous with those of the cranial cavity, the subarachnoid ending in a cul-de-sac at the lamina cribrosa. As it traverses the orbit, the optic nerve is surrounded by the posterior part of the fascia bulbi (Tenon's capsule), the orbital fat, and, in its anterior two-thirds, by the ciliary nerves and arteries. Toward the posterior part of the orbit, it is crossed obliquely by the nasociliary nerve, the ophthalmic artery, the superior ophthalmic vein, and the superior division of the oculomotor nerve. Farther toward the roof of the orbit are the Rectus superior and Levator palpebræ superioris muscles, and the trochlear and frontal nerves. Inferior to it are the inferior division of the oculomotor nerve and the Rectus inferior; medial to it the Rectus medialis; and lateral to it the abducent nerve and Rectus lateralis, and, in the posterior part of the orbit, the ciliary ganglion and the ophthalmic artery (Figs. 555, 806). As it passes into the optic foramen, accompanied by the ophthalmic artery, it is surrounded by the annulus tendineus communis (of Zinn), which serves as the origin of the ocular muscles. A short distance behind the bulb, the optic nerve is pierced by the central artery of the retina and its accompanying vein. These vessels enter the bulb through an opening in the lamina cribrosa and supply the retina.

Within the optic foramen, the ophthalmic artery lies inferior to the nerve, just after it has branched off of the internal carotid. Medially, separated by a thin plate of bone, is the sphenoidal air sinus. If the pneumatization of the bone is extensive, the nerve may be almost completely surrounded by the sphenoidal sinus or the posterior ethmoidal cells. Superior to the nerve, the three sheaths, dura, arachnoid, and pia, are fused to each other, to the nerve, and to the periosteum of the bone, fixing the nerve and preventing it from being forced back and forth in the foramen. The subarachnoid and subdural spaces are present only below the nerve.

The **intracranial portion** of the nerve (Fig. 801) rests on the anterior part of the cavernous sinus, and on the diaphragma sellæ which overlies the hypophysis. The part of the brain above the nerve is the anterior perforated substance. The internal carotid artery approaches it laterally, and then is directly inferior to it at the origin of the ophthalmic artery. The anterior cerebral artery crosses superior to it.

The **Optic Chiasma** (*chiasma opticum*) (Fig. 803), as the name indicates, resembles the Greek letter "X," from the convergence of the optic nerves in front and the divergence of the optic tracts behind. It rests upon the tuberculum sellæ of the sphenoid bone and on the diaphragma sellæ of the dura. It is continuous superiorly with the lamina terminalis, and posteriorly with the tuber cinereum and the infundibulum of the hypophysis. Lateral to it, on each side, are the anterior perforated substance and the internal carotid artery.

The **Optic Tract** (*tractus opticus*) (Fig. 803), leaving the chiasma, diverges from its fellow of the opposite side until it reaches the cerebral peduncle, across whose under surface it winds obliquely. It is adjacent to the tuber cinereum and peduncle, thus having contact with the third ventricle. As it terminates, a shallow groove divides it into a medial and lateral root. The lateral root contains fibers of visual function and ends in the lateral geniculate body. The medial root probably is auditory rather than visual, carrying commissural fibers connecting the two medial geniculate bodies (commissure of Gudden and probably other non-visual commissures, those of Meynert and Darkschewitsch).

The fibers lying medially in the optic nerve cross in the chiasma and continue in the optic tract of the other side. The lateral fibers are uncrossed, and continue to the brain in the optic tract of the same side. The fibers from the two sides become intermingled in the tract (Mayer '40).

The optic nerve corresponds to a tract of fibers within the brain rather than to the other cranial nerves because of its embryological development and its structure. It is developed from a diverticulum of the lateral aspect of the forebrain; its fibers probably are third in the chain of neurons from the receptors to the brain; they are supported by neuroglia instead of having neurilemmal sheaths, and the nerve has three sheaths prolonged from the corresponding meninges of the brain (see Sense Organ Chapter).

III. THE OCULOMOTOR NERVE.

The **oculomotor nerve** (*n. oculomotorius; third nerve*) (Figs. 806, 807) supplies the Levator palpebræ superioris, the extrinsic muscles of the eye except the Obliquus superior and Rectus lateralis, and the intrinsic muscles with the exception of the Dilatator pupillæ. Its superficial origin (Fig. 743) is from the midbrain at the oculomotor sulcus on the medial side of the cerebral peduncle. Its deep origin and central connections within the brain are described with the Central Nervous System, page 912. The oculomotor nerve is traditionally considered to be a motor nerve, containing special somatic efferent fibers for the ocular muscles and parasympathetic fibers for the ciliary ganglion, but experimental evidence indicates that it contains proprioceptive fibers from cells in the brain stem near the motor cells (Corbin and Oliver '42).

As it emerges from the brain into the posterior cranial fossa, the nerve is invested with pia mater, and is bathed in the cerebrospinal fluid of the cysterna interpeduncularis (basalis). It passes between the superior cerebellar and posterior cerebral arteries near the termination of the basilar artery. Lateral to the posterior clinoid process, it is covered with arachnoid, and between the anterior and posterior clinoid processes it pierces the dura (Fig. 801) by passing between the free and attached borders of the tentorium cerebelli. It runs anteriorly, embedded in the lateral wall of the cavernous sinus (Fig. 814), superior to the other orbital nerves (see page 973), and enters the superior orbital fissure between the two heads of the Rectus lateralis (Fig. 804) in two divisions, a superior and an inferior. Within the fissure, the trochlear, lacrimal, and frontal nerves lie superior to it, the abducent nerve inferior and lateral to it, and the nasociliary nerve passes between its two divisions.

Two **communications** join the oculomotor as it runs along the wall of the cavernous sinus, (*a*) one from the **cavernous plexus** of the sympathetic, carrying postganglionic fibers from the superior cervical ganglion, and (*b*) one from the **ophthalmic** division of the trigeminal nerve.

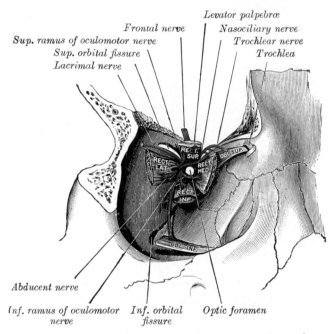

FIG. 804.—Dissection showing origins of right ocular muscles, and nerves entering by the superior orbital fissure.

The **superior division** (Fig. 806), smaller than the inferior, passes medialward across the optic nerve, and sends branches to: (*a*) the **Rectus superior**, and (*b*) the **Levator palpebræ superioris.** The branch to the Levator contains sympathetic postganglionic fibers from the cavernous plexus, which continue anteriorly to reach the non-striated muscle attached to the superior tarsus.

The **inferior division** has four branches: (*a*) to the **Rectus medialis**, passing inferior to the optic nerve, (*b*) to the **Rectus inferior**, and (*c*) to the **Obliquus inferior.** The latter runs forward between the inferior and lateral Recti, and gives off a short, rather thick branch, (*d*) the root of the ciliary ganglion.

The **Ciliary Ganglion** (*g. ciliare; ophthalmic or lenticular ganglion*) (Figs. 805, 806) is a very small (1 or 2 mm. in diameter) parasympathetic ganglion whose preganglionic fibers come from the oculomotor nerve and whose postganglionic fibers carry motor impulses to the Ciliaris and Sphincter pupillæ muscles. It is situated about 1 cm. from the posterior boundary of the orbit, close to the lateral surface of the optic nerve and between it and the Rectus lateralis and the ophthalmic artery.

The **parasympathetic motor root** (*radix oculomotorii; short root*) of the ganglion is a rather short, thick nerve, which may be double. It comes from the branch of the inferior division of the oculomotor nerve which supplies the Obliquus inferior and is connected with the posterior inferior angle of the ganglion. It contains preganglionic parasympathetic fibers from the Edinger-Westphal group of cells of the third nerve nucleus, which form synapses in the ganglion with cells whose postganglionic fibers pass through the short ciliary nerves into the bulb.

Two communications were formerly called roots of the ganglion: (*a*) a **communication with the nasociliary nerve** (*radix longa or long root; sensory root*) joins the posterior superior angle of the ganglion, and contains sensory fibers which traverse the short ciliary nerves on their way from the cornea, iris, and ciliary body, without

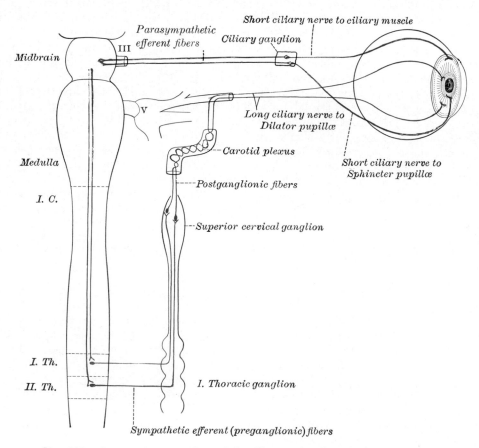

Fɪɢ. 805.—Autonomic connections of the ciliary and superior cervical ganglia.

forming synapses in the ganglion; (*b*) a **communication with the sympathetic** (*sympathetic root*) is a slender filament from the cavernous plexus, and frequently it is blended with the communication with the nasociliary. It contains postganglionic fibers from the superior cervical ganglion which pass through the ciliary ganglion without forming synapses and reach the Dilatator pupillæ muscle and the blood vessels of the bulb through the short ciliary nerves.

The branches of the ganglion are the **short ciliary nerves,** from six to ten delicate filaments, which leave the anterior part of the ganglion in two bundles, superior and inferior. They run anteriorly with the ciliary arteries in a wavy course, one set above and the other below the optic nerve, and are accompanied by the long ciliary nerves from the nasociliary. They pierce the sclera at the posterior part of the bulb, pass anteriorly in delicate grooves on the inner surface of the sclera, and are distributed to the ciliary body, iris, and cornea. The parasympathetic postganglionic fibers supply the Ciliaris and Sphincter pupillæ muscles. The short ciliary nerves also carry sympathetic postganglionic fibers to the Dilatator pupillæ muscle, and sensory fibers from the cornea, iris, and ciliary body.

IV. **THE TROCHLEAR NERVE.**

The **trochlear nerve** (*n. trochlearis; fourth nerve*) (Fig. 807) is the smallest of the cranial nerves and supplies the Obliquus superior oculi. Its superficial origin (Fig. 739) is from the surface of the anterior medullary velum at the side of the frenulum veli, immediately posterior to the inferior colliculus. Its deep origin and central connections are described with the Central Nervous System on page 915.

The nerve is directed laterally across the superior cerebellar peduncle, and winds around the cerebral peduncle (Fig. 743) near the pons. It runs forward along the free border of the tentorium cerebelli for 1 or 2 cm. (Fig. 801), pierces the dura just posterior to the posterior clinoid process, and without changing the direction of its course, takes its place in the lateral wall of the cavernous sinus between the oculomotor nerve and the ophthalmic division of the trigeminal (Fig. 814), It crosses the oculomotor nerve in a slightly upward course, enters the orbit through the superior orbital fissure, and becomes superior to the other nerves. In the orbit it passes medialward, above the origin of the Levator palpebræ superioris (Fig. 804), and finally enters the orbital surface of the Obliquus superior.

In the lateral wall of the cavernous sinus the trochlear nerve forms **communications** with the cavernous plexus of the sympathetic and with the ophthalmic division of the trigeminal.

Variations.—Occasionally sensory branches appear to come from the trochlear nerve, but they are probably aberrant fibers which have come from the ophthalmic nerve.

V. **THE TRIGEMINAL NERVE.**

The **trigeminal nerve** (*n. trigeminus; fifth or trifacial nerve*) is the largest of the cranial nerves, and is the great cutaneous sensory nerve of the face, the sensory nerve to the mucous membranes and other internal structures of the head, and the motor nerve of the muscles of mastication. It has two roots, the sensory being much larger (*portio major*) than the motor (*portio minor*) (Fig. 806). At the superficial origin of the nerve, the fibers of the sensory root enter the pons through the lateral part of its ventral surface (Fig. 743); the motor root emerges beside the sensory but anterior (rostral) and medial to it. The fibers of the **sensory root** are the central processes of ganglion cells in the trigeminal (semilunar) ganglion. The **motor root** includes, in addition to the motor fibers, proprioceptive sensory fibers from the mesencephalic root of the nerve (Corbin and Harrison '40). The two roots pass anteriorly in the posterior cranial fossa, under the shadow of the tentorium where the latter is attached to the petrous portion of the temporal bone, to reach the trigeminal ganglion. The deep origin and central connections of these roots are described with the Central Nervous System on page 915.

The **Trigeminal Ganglion** (*ganglion semilunare; Gasserian ganglion*) (Fig. 808) lies in a pocket of dura mater (*cavum Meckelii*) which occupies the trigeminal impression near the apex of the petrous portion of the temporal bone (Burr and Robinson '25). The ganglionic mass is flat and semilunar in shape, measuring approximately 1×2 cm. (Fig. 808), with the central processes of the cells leaving the concavity and the peripheral fibers the convexity of the crescent. The ganglion is lateral to the posterior part of the cavernous sinus and the internal carotid artery at the foramen lacerum, and the central fibers pass under the superior petrosal sinus. The motor root, being medial to the sensory, passes beneath the ganglion, that is, between it and the petrous bone, and leaves the skull through the foramen ovale with the mandibular nerve. The greater superficial petrosal nerve also passes between the ganglion and the bone. The ganglion receives filaments from the carotid plexus of the sympathetic, and it gives off minute branches to the tentorium cerebelli, and to the dura mater of the middle cranial fossa.

The peripheral fibers from the ganglion are collected into three large divisions: 1. the Ophthalmic, 2. the Maxillary, and 3. the Mandibular Nerves. The ophthalmic and maxillary remain sensory, but the mandibular becomes mixed, being joined by the motor root just outside the skull.

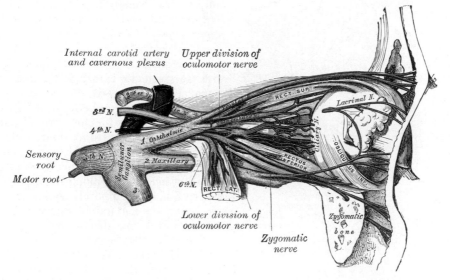

Fig. 806.—Nerves of the orbit. Side view. The ciliary ganglion is shown but not labelled.

Four small ganglia are associated with these nerves and have previously been described with them: the ciliary ganglion with the ophthalmic, the sphenopalatine with the maxillary, and the otic and submaxillary with the mandibular. These ganglia are not a part of the trigeminal complex functionally, however, and the trigeminal fibers which communicate with them pass through without synapses. The ganglia are parasympathetic and are therefore described with the nerves which supply their motor roots with preganglionic fibers, viz., the ciliary ganglion with the oculomotor nerve (page 958), the pterygopalatine and submandibular ganglia with the facial nerve (page 976), and the otic ganglion with the glossopharyngeal nerve (page 894).

1. The Ophthalmic Nerve.

The **Ophthalmic Nerve** (n. ophthalmicus) (Figs. 806, 807), or first division of the trigeminal, leaves the anterior superior part of the trigeminal ganglion, and enters the orbit through the superior orbital fissure. It is a flattened band about 2.5 cm. long and lies in the lateral wall of the cavernous sinus, inferior to the oculomotor and trochlear nerves (Fig. 814). It is a sensory nerve supplying the bulb of the eye, conjunctiva, lacrimal gland, part of the mucous membrane of the nose and paranasal sinuses, and the skin of the forehead, eyelids, and nose.

The ophthalmic nerve is joined by **communicating filaments** from the cavernous plexus of the **sympathetic**, and communicates with the **oculomotor, trochlear,** and **abducent** nerves. It gives off a recurrent filament to the dura mater and just before

61

it passes through the superior orbital fissure it divides into three branches: frontal, lacrimal, and nasociliary.

1. The **tentorial branch** (*n. tentorii*) (Fig. 807) arises near the ganglion, passes across and is adherent to the trochlear nerve, and runs between the layers of the tentorium to which it is distributed.

2. The **Lacrimal Nerve** (*n. lacrimalis*) (Fig. 807) is the smallest of the three branches of the ophthalmic. It passes forward in a separate tube of dura mater, and enters the orbit through the narrowest part of the superior orbital fissure. In the orbit it runs along the superior border of the Rectus lateralis close to the periorbita, and enters the lacrimal gland with the lacrimal artery, giving off filaments to supply the gland and adjacent conjunctiva. Finally it pierces the orbital septum, and ends in the skin of the upper eyelid, joining with filaments of the facial nerve.

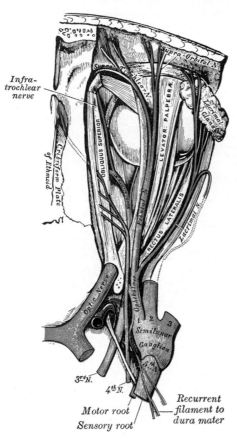

In the orbit, through a **communication with the zygomatic branch of the maxillary nerve** (Figs. 806, 808), it receives postganglionic parasympathetics which are the secretomotor fibers for the lacrimal gland. These fibers pass from their cells of origin in the sphenopalatine ganglion, through the sphenopalatine nerves to the maxillary nerve, then along the zygomatic and zygomaticotemporal nerves, finally traversing the communication mentioned above, and being distributed with the branches of the lacrimal nerve to the gland. The preganglionic fibers reach the ganglion from the facial nerve by way of the greater superficial petrosal and Vidian nerves.

Variations.—The lacrimal nerve is occasionally absent, and its place is then taken by the zygomaticotemporal branch of the maxillary. Sometimes the latter is absent and a communication of the lacrimal is substituted for it.

FIG. 807.—Nerves of the orbit. Seen from above.

3. The **Frontal Nerve** (*n. frontalis*) (Fig. 807) is the largest branch of the ophthalmic, and may be regarded, both from its size and direction, as the continuation of the nerve. It enters the orbit through the superior orbital fissure, continues rostrally between the Levator palpebræ superioris and the periorbita, and at a variable distance approximately half way to the supraorbital margin, it divides into a large supraorbital and a small supratrochlear branch.

a. The **supratrochlear nerve** (*n. supratrochlearis*) (Fig. 807) bends medially to pass above the pulley of the Obliquus superior and gives off a filament which communicates with the infratrochlear branch of the nasociliary. It pierces the orbital fascia, sends filaments to the conjunctiva and skin of the medial part of the upper lid, passes beneath the Corrugator and Frontalis, and divides into branches which pierce the muscles to supply the skin of the lower and mesial part of the forehead.

b. The **supraorbital nerve** (*n. supraorbitalis*) (Fig. 807), the continuation of the frontal nerve, leaves the orbit through the supraorbital notch or foramen. It gives filaments to the upper lid and continues upon the forehead, dividing into medial and lateral branches beneath the Frontalis. The **medial branch**, sometimes called the **frontal branch** (*ramus frontalis*), is smaller; it pierces the muscle and supplies the scalp as far as the parietal bone. The larger **lateral branch** pierces the galea aponeurotica and supplies the scalp nearly as far back as the lambdoidal suture (Fig. 818). The supraorbital nerve may divide before leaving the orbit, in which case the lateral branch occupies the suprarobital notch or foramen and the medial or frontal branch may have a notch of its own.

The Branch to the Frontal Sinus.—In the supraorbital notch, a small filament pierces the bone to supply the mucous membrane of the frontal sinus.

4. The **Nasociliary Nerve** (*n. nasociliaris; nasal nerve*) (Fig. 807) is intermediate in size between the frontal and lacrimal, and is more deeply placed in the orbit. It enters the orbit between the two heads of the Rectus lateralis, and between the superior and inferior divisions of the oculomotor nerve. It passes across the optic nerve and runs obliquely beneath the Rectus superior and Obliquus superior, to the medial wall of the orbital cavity. Here it passes through the anterior ethmoidal foramen as the **anterior ethmoidal nerve** (*n. ethmoideus anterior*), and enters the cranial cavity just above the cribriform plate of the ethmoid bone. It runs along a shallow groove on the lateral margin of the plate, and, penetrating the bone through a slit at the side of the crista galli, it enters the nasal cavity. It supplies branches to the mucous membrane of nasal cavity (Figs. 802, 809) and finally it emerges between the inferior border of the nasal bone and the lateral nasal cartilage as the external nasal branch.

The branches of the nasociliary nerve are as follows:

a. The **communication with the ciliary ganglion** (*long or sensory root of the ganglion; radix longa ganglii ciliaris*) (Fig. 806) usually arises from the nasociliary between the two heads of the Rectus lateralis. It runs anteriorly on the lateral side of the optic nerve, and enters the posterior superior angle of the ciliary ganglion. It contains sensory fibers which pass through the ganglion without synapses and continue on into the bulb by way of the short ciliary nerves. It is sometimes joined by a filament from the cavernous plexus of the sympathetic, or from the superior ramus of the oculomotor nerve. The ciliary ganglion is described with the oculomotor nerve.

b. The **long ciliary nerves** (*nn. ciliares longi*), two or three in number, are given off from the nasociliary, as it crosses the optic nerve. They accompany the short ciliary nerves from the ciliary ganglion, pierce the posterior part of the sclera, and running anteriorly between it and the choroid, are distributed to the iris and cornea. In addition to afferent fibers, the long ciliary nerves probably contain sympathetic fibers from the superior cervical ganglion to the Dilatator pupillæ muscle, which pass through the communication between the cavernous plexus and the ophthalmic nerve.

c. The **infratrochlear nerve** (*n. infratrochlearis*) (Fig. 807) is given off from the nasociliary just before it enters the anterior ethmoidal foramen. It runs anteriorly along the superior border of the Rectus medialis, and is joined, near the pulley of the Obliquus superior, by a filament from the supratrochlear nerve. It then passes to the medial angle of the eye, and supplies the skin of the eyelids and side of the nose, the conjunctiva, lacrimal sac, and caruncula lacrimalis.

d. The **ethmoidal branches** supply the mucous membrane of the sinuses. The **posterior ethmoidal nerve** (*n. ethmoidalis posterior*) leaves the orbit through the posterior ethmoidal foramen and supplies the posterior ethmoidal and the sphenoidal sinuses. The **anterior ethmoidal branches** (*n. ethmoidalis anterior*) are filaments which are given off as the nerve passes through the anterior ethmoidal foramen, and supply the anterior ethmoidal and frontal sinuses.

e. The **internal nasal branches** supply the mucous membrane of the anterior part of the septum and lateral wall of the nasal cavity (Figs. 802, 809).

f. The **external nasal branch** emerges between the nasal bone and the lateral nasal cartilage, passes deep to the Nasalis muscle, and supplies the skin of the ala and apex of the nose (Fig. 808).

2. The Maxillary Nerve.

The **Maxillary Nerve** (*n. maxillaris; superior maxillary nerve*) (Fig. 808) or second division of the trigeminal, arises from the middle of the trigeminal ganglion, is intermediate between the other two divisions in size and position, and, like the

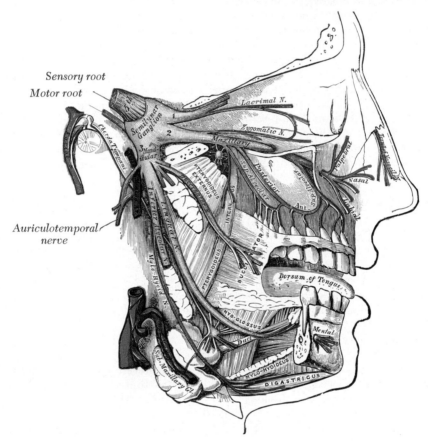

Fig. 808.—Distribution of the maxillary and mandibular nerves, and the submaxillary ganglion.

ophthalmic, is entirely sensory. It supplies the skin of the middle portion of the face, lower eyelid, side of the nose, and upper lip (Fig. 810); the mucous membrane of the nasopharynx, maxillary sinus, soft palate, tonsil and roof of the mouth, the upper gums and teeth. It passes horizontally forward, at first in the lower part of the lateral wall of the cavernous sinus and then beneath the dura, to the foramen rotundum, through which it leaves the cranial cavity. From the foramen rotundum, it crosses the pterygopalatine fossa, inclines lateralward in a groove on the posterior surface of the maxilla, and enters the orbit through the inferior orbital fissure. In the posterior part of the orbit it becomes the **infraorbital nerve,** lies in the infra-orbital groove, and, continuing anteriorly, dips into the infraorbital canal. It emerges into the face through the infraorbital foramen, where it is deep to the Quadratus labii superioris, and divides into branches for the skin of the face, nose, lower eyelid, and upper lip.

The branches of the maxillary nerve may be divided into four groups, those given off: (A) in the cranium, (B) in the pterygopalatine fossa, (C) in the infraorbital canal, and (D) on the face.

Branches in the Cranium.—

1. The **Middle Meningeal Nerve** (*n. meningeus medius; meningeal or dural branch*) is given off from the maxillary nerve directly after its origin from the trigeminal (semilunar) ganglion; it accompanies the middle meningeal artery and supplies the dura mater.

Branches in the Pterygopalatine Fossa.—

2. The **Zygomatic Nerve** (*n. zygomaticus; temporomalar nerve; orbital nerve*) (Fig. 806) arises in the pterygopalatine fossa, enters the orbit by the inferior orbital fissure, and divides into two branches, zygomaticotemporal and zygomaticofacial.

a. The **zygomaticotemporal branch** (*r. zygomaticotemporalis; temporal branch*) runs along the lateral wall of the orbit in a groove in the zygomatic bone, and, passing through a small foramen or through the sphenozygomatic suture, enters the temporal fossa. It runs upward between the bone and substance of the Temporalis muscle, pierces the temporal fascia about 2.5 cm. above the zygomatic arch, is distributed to the skin of the side of the forehead, and communicates with the facial nerve and with the auriculotemporal branch of the mandibular nerve. As it pierces the temporal fascia, it gives off a slender twig, which runs between the two layers of the fascia to the lateral side of the orbit (Fig. 818).

Before it leaves the orbit, it sends a **communication to the lacrimal nerve** through which the postganglionic parasympathetic fibers from the sphenopalatine ganglion reach the lacrimal gland.

b. The **zygomaticofacial branch** (*r. zygomaticofacialis; malar branch*) passes along the inferior lateral angle of the orbit, through the zygomatic bone by way of the zygomaticoörbital and zygomaticofacial foramina, emerges upon the face, and, perforating the Orbicularis oculi, supplies the skin on the prominence of the cheek. It joins with the facial nerve and with the inferior palpebral branches of the infraorbital (Fig. 819).

Variations.—The two branches are variable in size, a deficiency in one being made up by the other or by the lacrimal or infraorbital nerves.

3. The **Pterygopalatine Nerves** (*nn. pterygopalatini*) (Figs. 808, 809) are two short trunks which unite at the pterygopalatine ganglion, and then are redistributed into a number of branches. Formerly these trunks were called the sensory roots of the ganglion, and their peripheral branches were listed as the branches of distribution of the ganglion. Since the great majority of the fibers in the trunks are trigeminal somatic afferents which merely pass beside or through the ganglion without synapses, the branches are listed here as belonging to the maxillary nerve rather than the ganglion.

The pterygopalatine nerves serve also as important functional communications between the ganglion and the maxillary nerve. Postganglionic parasympathetic secretomotor fibers from the ganglion pass through them and back along the main maxillary nerve to the zygomatic nerve, through which they are routed to the lacrimal nerve and lacrimal gland. Other fibers from the ganglion accompany the branches of distribution of the maxillary nerve to the glands of the nasal cavity and palate.

The **branches of distribution** from the pterygopalatine nerves are divisible into four groups, *viz.*, (*a*) orbital, (*b*) palatine, (*c*) posterior superior nasal, and (*d*) pharyngeal.

a. The **orbital branches** (*rr. orbitales; ascending branches*) are two or three delicate filaments which enter the orbit by the inferior orbital fissure, and supply the periosteum. Filaments pass through foramina in the frontoëthmoidal suture to supply the mucous membrane of the posterior ethmoidal and sphenoidal sinuses.

b. The **greater palatine nerve** (*n. palatinus anterior; anterior palatine nerve; descending branch*) (Figs. 809, 813) passes through the pterygopalatine canal, emerges upon the hard palate through the greater palatine foramen, and divides into several branches, the longest of which passes anteriorly in a groove in the hard palate nearly as far as the incisor teeth. It supplies the gums and mucous membrane of the hard palate and adjacent parts of the soft palate, and communicates with the terminal filaments of the nasopalatine nerve. Posterior inferior nasal branches leave the nerve while it is in the canal, enter the nasal cavity through openings in the palatine bone, and ramify over the inferior nasal concha and middle and inferior meatuses.

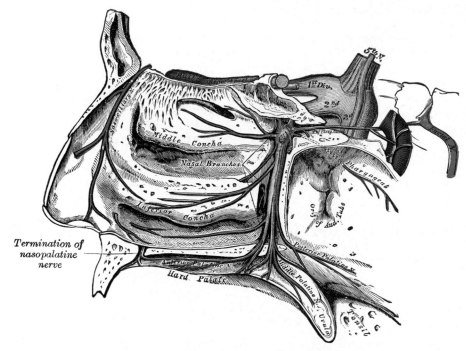

Fig. 809.—The pterygopalatine ganglion and its branches.

The **lesser palatine nerves** (*nn. palatini medius et posterior*) (Fig. 809) emerge through the lesser palatine foramina and distribute branches to the soft palate, uvula, and tonsil. They join with the tonsillar branches of the glossopharyngeal nerve to form a plexus around the tonsil (*circulus tonsillaris*). Many of the somatic afferent fibers contained in the lesser palatine nerves belong to the facial nerve, have their cells in the geniculate ganglion, and traverse the greater superficial petrosal and Vidian nerves (page 976).

c. The **posterior superior nasal branches** (*rr. nasales posteriores superiores*) enter the posterior part of the nasal cavity by the sphenopalatine foramen and supply the mucous membrane covering the superior and middle conchæ, the lining of the posterior ethmoid sinuses, and the posterior part of the septum. One branch, longer and larger than the others, and named the nasopalatine nerve, passes across the roof of the nasal cavity below the ostium of the sphenoidal sinus to reach the septum. It runs obliquely forward and downward, lying between the mucous membrane and periosteum of the septum, to the incisive canal (Fig. 809). It passes through the canal and communicates with the corresponding nerve of the opposite side and with the greater palatine nerve.

d. The **pharyngeal nerve** (*pterygopalatine nerve*) (Fig. 809) leaves the posterior part of the sphenopalatine ganglion. It passes through the pharyngeal canal with the pharyngeal branch of the internal maxillary artery, and is distributed to the mucous membrane of the nasal part of the pharynx posterior to the auditory tube.

4. The **Posterior Superior Alveolar Branches** (*rr. alveolares superiores posteriores; posterior superior dental branches*) (Fig. 808) arise from the trunk of the nerve just before it enters the infraorbital groove; there are generally two, but sometimes they arise by a single trunk. They cross the tuberosity of the maxilla and give off several twigs to the gums and neighboring parts of the mucous membrane of the cheek. They then enter the posterior alveolar canals on the infratemporal surface of the maxilla, and, passing anteriorly in the substance of the bone, communicate with the middle superior alveolar nerve, and give off branches to the lining membrane of the maxillary sinus and three twigs to each molar tooth; these twigs enter the foramina at the apices of the roots of the teeth

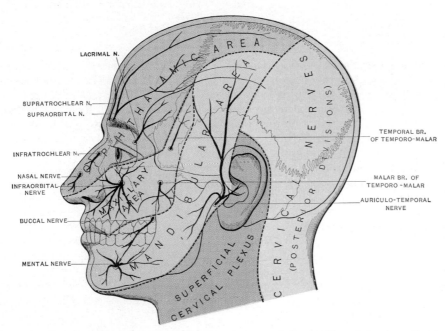

Fig. 810.—Sensory areas of the head, showing the general distribution of the three divisions of the fifth nerve. (Modified from Testut.)

Branches in the Infraorbital Canal.—

5. The **Middle Superior Alveolar Branch** (*r. alveolaris superior medius; middle superior dental branch*) is given off from the nerve in the posterior part of the infraorbital canal, and runs downward and forward in a canal in the lateral wall of the maxillary sinus to supply the two premolar teeth. It forms a superior dental plexus with the anterior and posterior superior alveolar branches.

6. The **Anterior Superior Alveolar Branch** (*r. alveolaris superior anterior; anterior superior dental branch*) (Fig. 808), of considerable size, is given off from the nerve just before its exit from the infraorbital foramen; it courses in a canal in the anterior wall of the maxillary sinus, and divides into branches which supply the incisor and canine teeth. It communicates with the middle superior alveolar branch, and give off a nasal branch, which passes through a minute canal in the lateral wall of the

inferior meatus, and supplies the mucous membrane of the anterior part of the inferior meatus and the floor of the nasal cavity, communicating with the nasal branches from the sphenopalatine nerves.

Branches in the Face.—The infraorbital nerve emerges through the infraorbital foramen and supplies the following branches:

7. The **Inferior Palpebral Branches** (*rr. palpebrales inferiores; palpebral branches*) (Fig. 808) pass upward underneath the Orbicularis oculi, and supply the skin and conjunctiva of the lower eyelid, joining at the lateral angle of the orbit with the facial and zygomaticofacial nerves.

8. The **External Nasal Branches** (*rr. nasales externi*) (Fig. 808) supply the skin of the side of the nose and of the septum mobile nasi, and join with the terminal twigs of the nasociliary nerve.

9. The **Superior Labial Branches** (*rr. labiales superiores; labial branches*) (Fig. 808), the largest and most numerous, pass deep to the Quadratus labii superioris, and are distributed to the skin of the upper lip, to the mucous membrane of the mouth, and to the labial glands. They communicate immediately beneath the orbit, with filaments from the facial nerve, forming with them the **infraorbital plexus**.

3. **The Mandibular Nerve.**

The **Mandibular Nerve** (*n. mandibularis; inferior maxillary nerve*) (Figs. 808, 812, 813) or third and largest division of the trigeminal is a mixed nerve and has two roots: a *large sensory root* arising from the inferior angle of the trigeminal ganglion, and a *small motor root* (the entire motor root of the trigeminal). The sensory fibers supply the skin of the temporal region, auricula, external meatus, cheek, lower lip, and lower part of the face; the mucous membrane of the cheek, tongue, and mastoid air cells; the lower teeth and gums; the mandible and temporomandibular joint; and part of the dura mater and skull. The motor fibers supply the muscles of mastication (Masseter, Temporalis, Pterygoidei), the Mylohyoideus and anterior belly of the Digastricus, and the Tensores tympani and veli palatini. The two roots leave the middle cranial fossa through the foramen ovale, the motor part medial to the sensory, and unite just outside the skull. The main trunk thus formed is very short, 2 or 3 mm., and divides into a smaller anterior and a larger posterior division. The otic ganglion lies close against the medial surface of the nerve, just outside of the foramen ovale where the two roots fuse, and it surrounds the origin of the internal pterygoid nerve (Fig. 811). A **communication to the otic ganglion** from the internal pterygoid nerve was formerly called a root of the ganglion, but the fibers pass through without synapses.

Variations.—The two divisions are separated by a fibrous band, the pterygospinous ligament, which may become ossified and the anterior division then passes through a separate opening in the bone, the pterygospinous foramen.

A. The branches of the *main trunk* of the nerve are as follows:

1. The **Ramus Meningeus** (*nervus spinosus, recurrent branch*) enters the skull through the foramen spinosum with the middle meningeal artery. It divides into two branches which accompany the anterior and posterior divisions of the artery and supply the dura mater. The anterior branch communicates with the meningeal branch of the maxillary nerve; the posterior sends filaments to the mucous membrane of the mastoid air cells.

2. The **Medial Pterygoid Nerve** (*n. pterygoideus medialis*) (Fig. 811) is a slender branch which penetrates the otic ganglion, and after a short course, enters the deep surface of the muscle. It has two small branches which have a close association with the otic ganglion, and have been described as branches of the ganglion, but their fibers pass through the ganglion without interruption.

a. The **nerve to the Tensor veli palatini** (Fig. 811) enters the muscle near its origin.

b. The **nerve to the Tensor tympani** lies close to and nearly parallel with the lesser superficial petrosal nerve, and penetrates the cartilage of the auditory tube to supply the muscle.

B. The *anterior division* of the mandibular nerve (Fig. 808) receives a small contribution of sensory fibers and all of the motor fibers from the motor root except those in the internal pterygoid and mylohyoid nerves. Its branches supply the muscles of mastication and the skin and mucous membrane of the cheek as follows:

3. The **Masseteric Nerve** (*n. massetericus*) (Fig. 812) passes lateralward, above the Pterygoideus externus, to the mandibular notch, where it crosses with the masseteric artery to enter the Masseter near its origin from the zygomatic arch. It gives a filament to the temporomandibular joint.

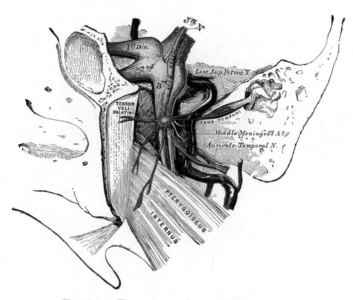

Fig. 811.—The otic ganglion and its branches.

4. The **Deep Temporal Nerves** (*nn. temporales profundi*) (Fig. 812) are usually two, anterior and posterior, but a third or intermediate may be present. The anterior deep temporal frequently is given off from the buccal nerve; it emerges with the latter between the two heads of the Pterygoideus externus and turns upward into the anterior portion of the Temporalis. The posterior deep temporal, and the intermediate if present, pass over the superior border of the Pterygoideus externus close to the bone of the temporal fossa, and enter the deep surface of the muscle. The posterior sometimes arises in common with the masseteric nerve.

5. The **Lateral Pterygoid Nerve** (*n. pterygoideus lateral*) enters the deep surface of the muscle. It frequently arises in conjunction with the buccal nerve.

6. The **Buccal Nerve** (BNA *n. buccinatorius;* BR *and* INA *n. buccalis; buccinator nerve; long buccal nerve*) (Fig. 812) passes between the two heads of the Pterygoideus externus to reach its superficial surface, follows or penetrates the inferior part of the Temporalis, and emerges from under the anterior border of the Masseter. It ramifies on the surface of the Buccinator, forming a plexus of communications with the buccal branches of the facial nerve, supplies the skin of the cheek over this muscle, and sends penetrating branches to supply the mucous membrane of the mouth and part of the gums in the same area.

Variations.—The buccal nerve may supply a branch to the Pterygoideus externus as it passes through that muscle, and frequently it gives off the anterior deep temporal nerve. It may arise from the trigeminal ganglion, passing through its own foramen; it may be a branch of the inferior alveolar nerve; or it may be replaced by a branch of the maxillary nerve.

C. The *posterior division* of the mandibular nerve is mainly sensory, but it has a small motor component. Its branches are as follows:

7. The **Auriculotemporal Nerve** (*n. auriculotemporalis*) (Fig. 808) generally arises by two roots which join after encircling the middle meningeal artery close to the foramen spinosum. It runs posteriorly, deep to the Pterygoideus externus, along the medial side of the neck of the mandible, and turns upward with the superficial temporal artery, between the auricula and the condyle of the mandible, under cover of the parotid gland. Escaping from beneath the gland, it passes over the root of

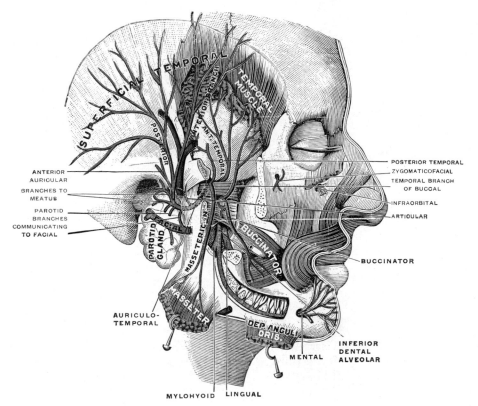

Fig. 812.—Mandibular division of the trigeminal nerve. (Testut.)

the zygomatic arch, and divides into superficial temporal branches (Fig. 818). The branches and communications of the auriculotemporal nerve are as follows:

a. The **communications with the facial nerve** (Fig. 812), usually two of considerable size, pass anteriorly from behind the neck of the mandible, and join the facial nerve in the substance of the parotid gland at the posterior border of the Masseter. They carry sensory fibers which accompany the zygomatic, buccal, and mandibular branches of the facial nerve and supply the skin of these areas.

b. **Communications with the otic ganglion** (Fig. 811) join the roots of the auriculotemporal nerve close to their origin. They carry postganglionic parasympathetic fibers whose preganglionics come from the glossopharyngeal nerve and supply the parotid gland with secretomotor fibers.

c. The **anterior auricular branches** (*nn. auriculares anteriores*) (Fig. 812), usually two, supply the skin of the anterior superior part of the auricula, principally the helix and tragus.

d. The **branches to the external acoustic meatus** (*nn. meatus auditorii externii*) (Fig. 812), two in number, enter the meatus between its bony and cartilaginous portions and supply the skin lining it; the upper one sends a filament to the tympanic membrane.

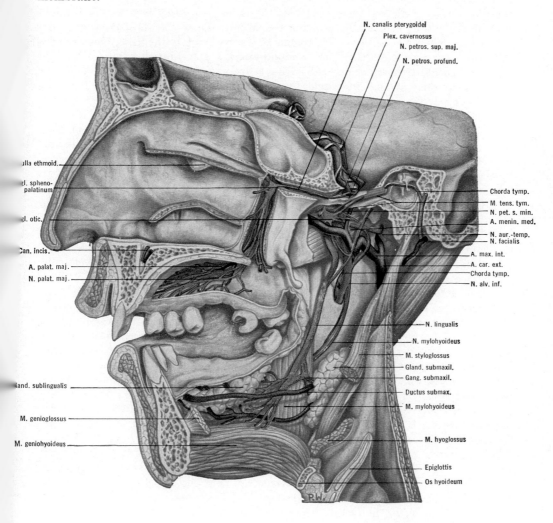

N. canalis pterygoidei
Plex. cavernosus
N. petros. sup. maj.
N. petros. profund.

ulla ethmoid.
gl. spheno-palatinum
gl. otic.
Can. incis.
A. palat. maj.
N. palat. maj.
Hand. sublingualis
M. genioglossus
M. geniohyoideus

Chorda tymp.
M. tens. tym.
N. pet. s. min.
A. menin. med.
N. aur.-temp.
N. facialis
A. max. int.
A. car. ext.
Chorda tymp.
N. alv. inf.
N. lingualis
N. mylohyoideus
M. styloglossus
Gland. submaxil.
Gang. submaxil.
Ductus submax.
M. mylohyoideus
M. hyoglossus
Epiglottis
Os hyoideum

FIG. 813.—Deep dissection of the region of the face viewed from its medial aspect, showing the pterygopalatine, otic, and submaxillary ganglia and associated structures. (Töndury, Angewandte und topographische Anatomie, courtesy of Georg Thieme Verlag.)

e. The **articular branches** consist of one or two twigs which enter the posterior part of the temporomandibular joint.

f. **Parotid branches** (*rami parotidei*) supply the parotid gland, carrying the parasympathetic postganglionic fibers transmitted by the communication between the auriculotemporal nerve and the otic ganglion.

g. The **superficial temporal branches** (*rr. temporales superficiales*) accompany the superficial temporal artery to the vertex of the skull; they supply the skin of the temporal region and communicate with the facial and zygomaticotemporal nerves.

8. The **Lingual Nerve** (*n. lingualis*) (Figs. 808, 813, 836) is at first deep to the Pterygoideus externus, running parallel with the inferior alveolar nerve, lying medial and anterior to it, and frequently joined to it by a branch which may cross the internal maxillary artery. The chorda tympani nerve joins it here also. The lingual nerve runs between the Pterygoideus internus and the mandible, and then crosses obliquely over the Constrictor pharyngis superior and the Styloglossus to reach the side of the tongue. It passes between the Hyoglossus and deep part of the submandibular gland, and finally, crossing the lateral side of the submandibular duct runs along the under surface of the tongue to its tip, lying immediately beneath the mucous membrane (Fig. 813). Its communications and branches are as follows:

a. The **chorda tympani** (Figs. 808, 813), a branch of the facial nerve, joins the lingual posteriorly at an acute angle, 1 or 2 cm. from the foramen ovale. It carries special sensory fibers for taste and parasympathetic preganglionic fibers for the submaxillary ganglion.

b. The **communications with the submandibular ganglion** are usually two or more short nerves by which the ganglion seems to be suspended (Fig. 813). The proximal nerves carry the preganglionic parasympathetic fibers communicated to the lingual by the chorda tympani. The distal communication contains postganglionic fibers for distribution to the sublingual gland.

c. **Communications with the hypoglossal nerve** (Fig. 836) form a plexus at the anterior margin of the Hyoglossus.

d. The **branches of distribution** supply the mucous membrane of the anterior two-thirds of the tongue, the adjacent mouth and gums, and the sublingual gland. The taste buds of the anterior two-thirds of the tongue are supplied by the fibers communicated through the chorda tympani.

9. The **Inferior Alveolar Nerve** (*n. alveolaris inferior; inferior dental nerve*) (Fig. 812) accompanies the inferior alveolar artery, at first deep to the Pterygoideus externus, and then between the sphenomandibular ligament and the ramus of the mandible, to the mandibular foramen. It enters the mandibular canal through the foramen, and passes forward within the bone as far as the mental foramen, where it divides into two terminal branches. The branches of the nerve are as follows:

a. The **mylohyoid nerve** (*n. mylohyoideus*) (Fig. 808) leaves the inferior alveolar nerve just before it enters the mandibular foramen, and continues downward and forward in a groove on the deep surface of the ramus of the mandible to reach the Mylohyoideus. It supplies this muscle and crosses its superficial surface to reach the anterior belly of the Digastricus (Fig. 808), which it supplies also.

b. The **dental branches** form a plexus within the bone, and supply the molar and premolar teeth, filaments entering the pulp canal of each root through the apical foramen and supplying the pulp of the tooth.

c. The **incisive branch** is one of the terminal branches. It continues forward within the bone, after the mental nerve separates from it, and forms a plexus which supplies the canine and incisor teeth.

d. The **mental nerve** (*n. mentalis*) (Fig. 812), the other terminal branch, emerges from the bone at the mental foramen, and divides beneath the Triangularis muscle into three branches; one is distributed to the skin of the chin, the other two to the skin and mucous membrane of the lower lip. These branches communicate freely with branches of the facial nerve.

The otic and submandibular ganglia, although closely associated with the mandibular nerve, are not connected functionally, and are described, therefore, with the nerves which supply them with preganglionic fibers; the otic ganglion with the glossopharyngeal nerve and the submandibular with the facial nerve.

Variations.—The inferior alveolar and lingual nerves may form a single trunk, or they may have communications of variable size; the chorda tympani may appear to join the inferior alveolar and a later communication carry the fibers to the lingual. The inferior alveolar nerve is occasionally perforated by the internal maxillary artery. It may have accessory roots from other branches of the mandibular, or have a separate root from the trigeminal ganglion. The mylohyoid nerve may communicate with the lingual and it has been described as sending filaments to the Triangularis, Platysma, submandibular gland, or integument below the chin.

Trigeminal Nerve Pain.—The trigeminal nerve is more frequently the seat of severe neuritic or neuralgic pain than any other nerve in the body. The pain of a localized infection or irritation may be confined to that area, but quite commonly this is not the case. Involvement of an internal branch is likely to set up severe distress in a related cutaneous area by referred pain. As a general rule the diffusion of pain over the branches of the nerve is confined to one of the main divisions, although in severe cases it may radiate over the other main divisions.

The commonest example of this condition is the neuralgia which is often associated with dental caries—here, although the tooth itself may not appear to be painful, the most distressing referred pains may be experienced, and those be at once relieved by treatment of the affected tooth. With the ophthalmic nerve, severe supraorbital pain is commonly associated with acute glaucoma or with frontal or ethmoidal sinusitis. Malignant growths or empyema of the maxillary sinus, and diseased conditions in the nasal cavity, as well as dental caries, may cause neuralgia of the second division. Pain in the mandibular division is likely to be in the ear or other distribution of the auriculotemporal nerve although the actual disease may involve one of the lower teeth or the tongue.

When a focus of infection or irritation cannot be found, as is all too frequently the case, various measures may be taken to interrupt the pain fibers. Local injection of alcohol into the painful nerve may give temporary relief, and injection of a main division close to the ganglion has been performed with a certain measure of success. The main divisions have been incised surgically, and the entire ganglion removed in intractable cases. In the latter operation bleeding is likely to be dangerous and the nerves to the muscles of mastication may be paralyzed. In more recent operations the motor root is spared by cutting the sensory root inside the cranium before it reaches the ganglion.

VI. **THE ABDUCENT NERVE.**

The **abducent nerve** (*n. abducens; sixth nerve*) (Fig. 806) supplies the Rectus lateralis oculi. Its superficial origin (Fig. 743) is in the furrow between the inferior border of the pons and the superior end of the pyramid of the medulla oblongata. The deep origin and central connections are described on page 916. It pierces the dura mater on the dorsum sellæ of the sphenoid bone, runs through a notch below the posterior clinoid process, and traverses the cavernous sinus lateral to the internal carotid artery (see below). It enters the orbit through the superior orbital fissure, above the ophthalmic vein, from which it is separated by a lamina of dura mater. After passing between the two heads, it enters the ocular surface of the Rectus lateralis.

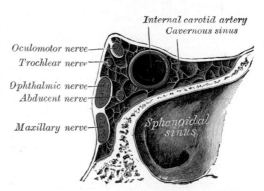

FIG. 814.—Oblique section through the right cavernous sinus.

Communication with the **sympathetic** system is by several filaments from the carotid and cavernous plexuses, and with the **trigeminal** by a filament from the ophthalmic nerve.

Relation of Orbital Nerves to the Cavernous Sinus.

Imbedded in the lateral wall of the cavernous sinus, in order beginning with the most superior, are the oculomotor, trochlear, ophthalmic, and maxillary nerves (Fig. 814). The abducent nerve is suspended by connective tissue trabeculæ within the sinus, lateral to the internal carotid artery and medial to the ophthalmic nerve. The maxillary nerve is related to the posterior portion of the sinus, and soon diverges from the other nerves. As the nerves approach the superior orbital fissure, the oculomotor and ophthalmic divide into branches, and the abducent nerve approaches the others, so that their relative positions are considerably changed.

VII. **THE FACIAL NERVE.**

The **facial nerve** (*n. facialis; seventh nerve*) has two roots of unequal size (Fig. 815). The larger is the **motor root**; the smaller, lying between the motor root and the acoustic nerve, is called the **nervus intermedius** (*pars intermedia; nerve of Wrisberg*), and contains special sensory fibers for taste and parasympathetic fibers. The superficial origin of both roots is at the inferior border of the pons (Fig. 743) in the

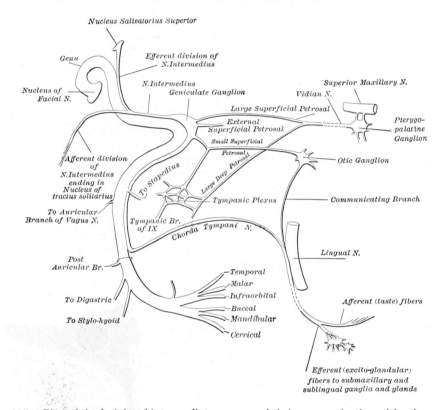

FIG. 815.—Plan of the facial and intermediate nerves and their communication with other nerves.

recess between the olive and the inferior cerebellar peduncle, the motor root being medial, the acoustic nerve lateral, and the intermedius between. The deep origin and central connections within the medulla are described on page 916.

The facial is the motor nerve to the muscles of facial expression, to those in the scalp, and external ear, to the Buccinator, Platysma, Stapedius, Stylohyoideus, and posterior belly of the Digastricus. The sensory part supplies the anterior two-thirds of the tongue with taste, and parts of the external acoustic meatus, soft palate, and adjacent pharynx with general sensation. The parasympathetic part supplies secretomotor fibers for the submaxillary, sublingual, lacrimal, nasal, and palatine glands.

From their superficial attachment, the two roots pass lateralward with the acoustic nerve into the internal acoustic meatus (Fig. 801). At the fundus of the meatus (Fig. 214), the facial nerve separates from the acoustic and enters the substance of the petrous portion of the temporal bone, through which it runs a serpentine course in its own canal, the **facial canal** (*aqueductus Fallopii*). At first it continues lateralward in the region between the cochlea and semicircular canals (Fig. 939); near the tympanic cavity it makes an abrupt bend posteriorly, runs in the medial wall of the cavity just above the oval window (Fig. 929), covered by a thin plate of bone which causes a slight prominence in the wall (Fig. 932), and then dips down beside the mastoid air cells to reach the stylomastoid foramen. At the point mentioned, where it changes its course abruptly, there is an exaggeration of the bend into a U-shaped structure named the **geniculum**; at this point also, the two roots become fused and the nerve is swollen by the presence of the geniculate ganglion (Fig. 816). As it emerges from the stylomastoid foramen, the nerve runs anteriorly in the substance of the parotid gland, crosses the external carotid artery, and divides at the posterior border of the ramus of the mandible into two primary branches, a superior, the temporofacial, and an inferior, the cervicofacial, from which numerous offsets, in a plexiform arrangement (*parotid plexus*), are distributed over the head, face, and upper part of the neck, supplying the superficial muscles in these regions.

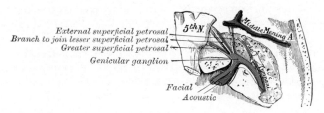

FIG. 816.—The course and connections of the facial nerve in the temporal bone.

The **Geniculate Ganglion** (*g. geniculi*) (Fig. 816) is a small fusiform swelling of the geniculum, where the facial nerve bends abruptly backward at the hiatus of the facial canal. It is the sensory ganglion of the facial nerve. The central processes of its unipolar ganglion cells reach the brain stem through the nervus intermedius; the majority of the peripheral processes pass to the taste buds of the anterior two-thirds of the tongue through the chorda tympani and lingual nerves; a considerable number of peripheral processes pass through the greater superficial petrosal and lesser palatine nerves to the soft palate; and a smaller number join the auricular branch of the vagus to supply the skin of the external acoustic meatus and mastoid process (Foley *et al.* '46).

The **glossopalatine nerve** is the name given by some authorities (Hardesty '33) to that portion of the facial nerve contributed by the nervus intermedius. It comprises, therefore, the sensory part, including the geniculate ganglion, the chorda tympani, and greater superficial petrosal nerve; and the parasympathetic part, including the submaxillary and sphenopalatine ganglia and their branches. Although this separation is suggested by the similarity between this complex and the glossopharyngeal nerve, it has not been generally adopted.

Communications of the Facial Nerve.—

A. In the internal acoustic meatus, communications with the **acoustic nerve** probably contain fibers which leave the facial, run with the acoustic for a short distance, and return to the facial nerve.

B. At the geniculate ganglion, it communicates (1) with the **otic ganglion** by filaments which join the lesser superficial petrosal nerve; (2) with the **sympathetic** fibers on the middle meningeal artery (*external superficial petrosal nerve*).

C. In the facial canal, just before it leaves the stylomastoid foramen, it communicates with the **auricular branch of the vagus** as the latter runs across it in the substance of the bone.

D. After its exit from the Stylomastoid foramen, it communicates with (1) the **glossopharyngeal** nerve, (2) the **vagus** nerve, and (3) the **great auricular** nerve from the cervical plexus. (4) The **auriculotemporal** nerve from the mandibular division of the trigeminal usually sends two **communications** of considerable size which pass forward from behind the neck of the mandible to join the facial nerve in the substance of the parotid gland (Fig. 812). They carry sensory fibers which accompany the terminal zygomatic, buccal, and mandibular branches (see below) to the skin of these areas.

E. Peripheral branches communicate: behind the ear, with the **lesser occipital** nerve; on the face, with the **trigeminal branches**; and in the neck, with the **cervical cutaneous** nerve.

The **branches of the facial nerve** are as follows:

A. From the geniculate ganglion.—

1. The **Greater Superficial Petrosal Nerve** (*n. petrosus major*) (Fig. 819) arises from the geniculate ganglion, and, after a short course in the bone, emerges through the hiatus of the facial canal (Fig. 201) into the middle cranial fossa. It runs forward beneath the dura mater and the trigeminal ganglion in a sulcus on the anterior surface of the petrous portion of the temporal bone, passes over the cartilage of the auditory tube which fills the foramen lacerum, crosses the lateral side of the internal carotid artery, and unites with the deep petrosal nerve to form the nerve of the pterygoid canal (Vidian nerve). The greater superficial petrosal nerve is a mixed nerve, containing sensory and parasympathetic fibers. The parasympathetic fibers, from the nervus intermedius, become the motor root of the pterygopalatine ganglion. The bulk of the nerve consists of sensory fibers which are the peripheral processes of cells in the geniculate ganglion and are distributed to the soft palate through the lesser palatine nerves, with a few filaments to the auditory tube.

The **nerve of the pterygoid canal** (*n. canalis pterygoidei [Vidii]; Vidian nerve*) (Fig. 813), formed by the union of the greater superficial petrosal and deep petrosal nerves of the foramen lacerum, enters the posterior opening of the pterygoid canal with the corresponding artery, and is joined by a small *ascending sphenoidal branch* from the otic ganglion. The bony wall of the canal commonly causes a ridge in the floor of the sphenoidal sinus, and while the nerve is in the canal it gives off one or two filaments for the mucous membrane of the sinus. From the anterior opening of the canal, the nerve crosses the pterygopalatine fossa, and enters the pterygopalatine ganglion.

The **Pterygopalatine Ganglion** (*g. pterygopalatinum; sphenopalatine ganglion; Meckel's ganglion*) (Figs. 809, 813) is deeply placed in the pterygopalatine fossa, just inferior to the maxillary nerve as the latter crosses the fossa close to the pterygopalatine foramen. It is triangular or heart-shaped, about 5 mm. in length, is imbedded in the fibrous tissue between the neighboring bones, and is closely attached to the pterygopalatine branches of the maxillary division of the trigeminal nerve. It is a parasympathetic ganglion relaying chiefly secretomotor impulses from the facial (Fig. 817A).

The **parasympathetic root** (*visceral efferent*) of the pterygopalatine ganglion is the greater superficial petrosal nerve, and its continuation, the nerve of the pterygoid canal. The fibers are preganglionic parasympathetic fibers which leave the brain stem in the nervus intermedius.

Communications of the Pterygopalatine Ganglion.—(*a*) Two short trunks from the **maxillary nerve**, the pterygopalatine nerves, are commonly called the sensory root of the ganglion although they have no such functional connection with it. They contain mainly sensory fibers from the trigeminal ganglion which pass through or beside the pterygopalatine ganglion without synapses, and continue on their way to the mucous membrane of the nasal cavity and palate. These trunks are important communications for the ganglion, however, since they are traversed by the postganglionic fibers of distribution on their way to the maxillary nerve, whence they reach the lacrimal gland and the small glands of the nasal cavity and palate.

(*b*) The **deep petrosal nerve** is commonly called the sympathetic root of the sphenopalatine ganglion, although it is merely a communication between the ganglion and the sympathetic system. It contains postganglionic fibers from the superior cervical sympathetic ganglion, by way of the carotid plexus, which pass through the pterygopalatine ganglion without synapses and accompany the branches of the pterygopalatine nerves (trigeminal branches) to their destination in the mucous membrane of the nasal cavity and palate.

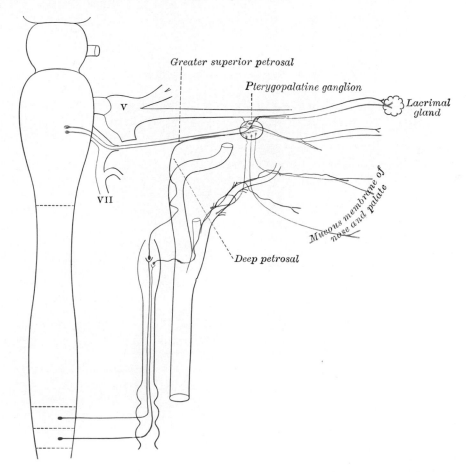

Fig. 817A.—Autonomic connections of the pterygopalatine and superior cervical ganglia.

The **branches of distribution from the pterygopalatine ganglion,** containing the postganglionic fibers of the cells within the ganglion, are not independent nerves for the most part, but find their way to their destinations by accompanying other nerves, mainly the branches of the maxillary nerve.

(*a*) The **fibers for the lacrimal gland** pass back to the main trunk of the maxillary nerve through the pterygopalatine nerves. They leave the maxillary through the zygomatic and zygomaticotemporal nerves, pass through a communication between the latter and the lacrimal nerve in the orbit, and are then distributed to the gland (Fig. 806).

62

(b) Fibers for the **small glands** of the mucous membrane **of the nasal cavity, pharynx**, and **palate** join the greater and lesser palatine nerves, the posterior superior nasal branches, and the pharyngeal nerve, and are distributed with them.

B. Branches of the Facial Nerve Within the Facial Canal.—

2. The **nerve to the Stapedius muscle** (*n. stapedius*) arises from the facial nerve as it passes downward in the posterior wall of the tympanum, and reaches the muscle through a minute opening in the base of the pyramid (see Middle Ear).

3. The **Chorda Tympani Nerve** (*n. chorda tympani*) (Figs. 808, 813) arises from the part of the facial nerve which runs vertically downward in the posterior wall of the tympanum just above the stylomastoid foramen. Entering its own canal in the bone

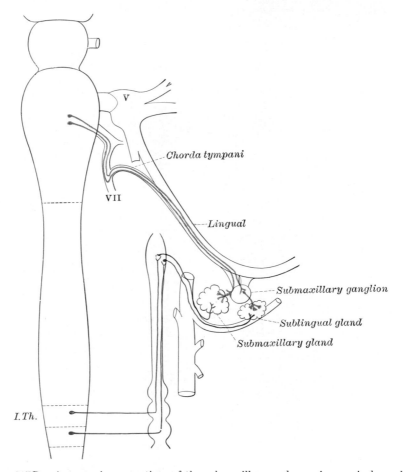

Fig. 817*B*.—Autonomic connections of the submaxillary and superior cervical ganglia.

about 6 mm. above the stylomastoid foramen, the chorda passes back upward almost parallel with the facial nerve but diverges toward the lateral wall of the tympanum. It emerges through an aperture in the posterior wall of the tympanum (iter chordæ posterius) between the base of the pyramid and the attachment of the tympanic membrane. It runs horizontally along the lateral wall of the tympanum covered by the thin mucous membrane, and, lying against the tympanic membrane, crosses the attached manubrium of the malleus (Fig. 930). It leaves the tympanic cavity near the anterior border of the membrane through the iter chordæ anterius, traverses a canal in the petrotympanic fissure (canal of Huguier), and emerges from he skull on the medial surface of the spina angularis of the sphenoid bone. After crossing the spine, usually in a groove, and being joined by a small communication from the otic ganglion, it unites with the lingual nerve at an acute angle between the Pterygoideus externus and internus.

The bulk of the fibers of the chorda tympani are special visceral afferents for taste which are distributed with the branches of the lingual nerve to the anterior two-thirds of the tongue. It also contains preganglionic parasympathetic fibers (secretomotor) from the nervus intermedius, which terminate in synapses with cells in the submaxillary ganglion (Foley '45).

The **Submandibular Ganglion** (*g. submandibular*) (Figs. 808, 813) is a small mass, 2 to 5 mm. in diameter, situated above the deep portion of the submandibular gland, on the Hyoglossus, near the posterior border of the Mylohyoideus, and suspended from the lower border of the lingual nerve by two filaments approximately 5 mm. in length. The proximal filament is the **parasympathetic root** which conveys fibers originating in the nervus intermedius and communicated to the lingual by the chorda tympani. These are preganglionic visceral efferent fibers (secretomotor) whose postganglionic fibers innervate the submandibular, sublingual, lingual, and neighboring small salivary glands (Fig. 817B).

The **branches of distribution** are (*a*) five or six filaments distributed to the **submandibular gland** and its duct, (*b*) to the **small glands** about the floor of the mouth, and (*c*) the distal filament attaching the ganglion to the lingual nerve which communicates the fibers distributed to the **sublingual** and small lingual **glands** with the terminal branches of the lingual nerve. Small groups of ganglion cells are constantly found in the stroma of the submandibular gland, usually near the larger branches of the duct, and are considered to be functionally a part of the submandibular ganglion.

A **communication** with the **sympathetic** bundles on the external maxillary artery have been called the *sympathetic root of the ganglion*, but the fibers are postganglionic and have no synapses in the ganglion.

Visceral afferent fibers passing through the root to the lingual and thence to the chorda tympani have been called the *sensory root*, but they have no synapses in the ganglion and their cell bodies are in the geniculate ganglion.

C. Branches of the Facial Nerve in the Face and Neck.—

4. The **Posterior Auricular Nerve** (*n. auricularis posterior*) (Fig. 818) arises close to the stylomastoid foramen, and runs upward in front of the mastoid process; here it is joined by a filament from the auricular branch of the vagus, and communicates with the posterior branch of the great auricular, and with the lesser occipital. Between the external acoustic meatus and mastoid process it divides into auricular and occipital branches. The auricular branch supplies the Auricularis posterior and the intrinsic muscles on the cranial surface of the auricula. The occipital branch, the larger, passes backward along the superior nuchal line of the occipital bone, and supplies the Occipitalis.

5. The **Digastric Branch** (*r. digastricus*) arises close to the stylomastoid foramen, and divides into several filaments which supply the posterior belly of the Digastricus.

6. The **Stylohyoid Branch** (*r. stylohyoideus*) frequently arises in conjunction with the digrastric branch; it is long and slender, and enters the Stylohyoideus about its middle.

7. The **Temporal Branches** (*rr. temporales*) (Fig. 818) cross the zygomatic arch to the temporal region, supplying the Auriculares anterior and superior. They communicate with the zygomaticotemporal branch of the maxillary, and with the auriculotemporal branch of the mandibular division of the trigeminal nerve. The more anterior branches supply the Frontalis, the Orbicularis oculi, and the Corrugator, and join the supraorbital and lacrimal branches of the ophthalmic nerve.

8. The **Zygomatic Branches** (*rr. zygomatici; malar branches*) run across the face in the region of the zygomatic arch to the lateral angle of the orbit, where they supply the Orbicularis oculi, and communicate with filaments from the lacrimal nerve of the ophthalmic division and the zygomaticofacial branch of the maxillary division of the trigeminal nerve. The lower zygomatic branches commonly join the deep buccal branches and assist in forming the infraorbital plexus (Anson '50).

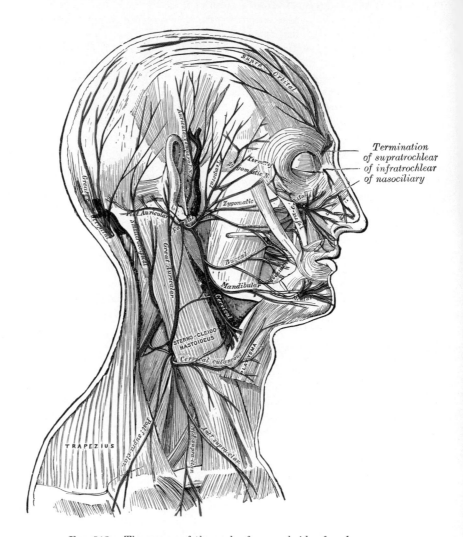

Termination of supratrochlear of infratrochlear of nasociliary

Fig. 818.—The nerves of the scalp, face, and side of neck.

9. The **Buccal Branches** (*rr. buccales; infraorbital branches*) of larger size than the, rest, pass horizontally forward to be distributed below the orbit and around the mouth. The superficial branches run beneath the skin and above the superficial muscles of the face, which they supply: some are distributed to the Procerus, communicating at the medial angle of the orbit with the infratrochlear and naso-ciliary branches of the ophthalmic nerve. The deep branches, commonly rein-forced by zygomatic branches, pass beneath the Zygomaticus and the Quadratus labii superioris, supplying them and forming an infraorbital plexus with the infra-orbital branch of the maxillary division of the trigeminal nerve (Fig. 818). These branches also supply the small muscles of the nose. The lower deep branches supply

the Buccinator and Orbicularis oris, and communicate with filaments of the buccal branch of the mandibular division of the trigeminal nerve.

10. The **Mandibular Branch** (*r. marginalis mandibulæ*) passes forward beneath the Platysma and Triangularis, supplying the muscles of the lower lip and chin, and communicating with the mental branch of the inferior alveolar nerve.

11. The **Cervical Branch** (*r. colli*) runs forward beneath the Platysma which it supplies, and forms a series of arches across the side of the neck over the suprahyoid region. One branch joins the cervical cutaneous nerve from the cervical plexus.

VIII. THE ACOUSTIC NERVE.

The **acoustic nerve** (*n. acousticus; eighth nerve*) (Fig. 743) consists of two distinct sets of fibers, the **Cochlear and Vestibular Nerves**, which differ in their peripheral endings, central connections, functions, and time of myelination. These two portions of the acoustic nerve are joined into a common trunk which enters the internal acoustic meatus with the facial nerve (Fig. 816). Centrally, the acoustic nerve divides into a lateral (cochlear) root and a medial (vestibular) root. As it passes distally in the internal auditory meatus, it divides into the various branches which are distributed to the receptor areas in the membranous labyrinth (see Sense Organ Chapter). Both divisions of this nerve are sensory and the fibers arise from bipolar ganglion cells.

Cochlear Nerve.—The cochlear nerve or root, the nerve of hearing, arises from bipolar cells in the *spiral ganglion of the cochlea*, situated near the inner edge of the osseous spiral lamina. The peripheral fibers pass to the organ of Corti. The central ones pass through the modiolus and then through the foramina of the tractus spiralis foraminosus or through the foramen centrale into the lateral or outer end of the internal acoustic meatus. The nerve passes along the internal acoustic meatus with the vestibular nerve and across the subarachnoid space, just above the flocculus, almost directly medialward toward the inferior peduncle to terminate in the cochlear nuclei.

The cochlear nerve is placed lateral to the vestibular root. Its fibers end in two nuclei: one, the ventral cochlear nucleus, lies immediately in front of the inferior cerebellar peduncle; the other, the dorsal cochlear nucleus, tuberculum acusticum, somewhat lateral to it (see Central Nervous System).

Vestibular Nerve.—The vestibular nerve or root, the nerve of equilibration, arises from bipolar cells in the *vestibular ganglion (ganglion of Scarpa)*, which is situated in the upper part of the outer end of the internal auditory meatus. The peripheral fibers divide into three branches: the superior branch passes through the foramina in the area vestibularis superior and ends in the utricle and in the ampullæ of the superior and lateral semicircular ducts; the fibers of the inferior branch traverse the foramina in the area vestibularis inferior and end in the saccule; the posterior branch runs through the foramen singulare and supplies the ampulla of the posterior semicircular duct.

The fibers of the vestibular nerve enter the medulla oblongata, pass between the inferior cerebellar peduncle and the spinal tract of the trigeminal, and bifurcate into ascending and descending branches. The descending branches form the spinal root of the vestibular nerve and terminate in the associated nucleus. The ascending branches pass to the medial, lateral, and superior vestibular nuclei, and to the nucleus fastigii and the vermis (see Central Nervous System.)

IX. THE GLOSSOPHARYNGEAL NERVE.

The **glossopharyngeal nerve** (*n. glossopharyngeus; ninth nerve*) (Figs. 822, 836) as its name implies, is distributed to the tongue and pharynx. It is a mixed nerve, its sensory fibers being both visceral and somatic, and its motor fibers both general and special visceral efferents. The somatic afferent fibers supply the mucous membrane of the pharynx, fauces, palatine tonsil, and posterior part of the tongue; special visceral afferents supply the taste buds of the posterior part of the tongue; general visceral afferents supply the blood pressure receptor of the carotid sinus. The special visceral efferent fibers supply the Stylopharyngeus; the general visceral efferents are mainly secretomotor for the parotid and small glands in the mucous membrane of the posterior part of the tongue and neighboring pharynx. The superficial origin is by three or four rootlets in series with those of the vagus nerve, attached to the superior part of the medulla oblongata in the groove between the olive and the inferior peduncle (Figs. 717, 743). The deep origin and central connections are described on page 919.

From its superficial origin the nerve passes lateralward across the flocculus to the jugular foramen, through which it passes, lateral and anterior to the vagus and

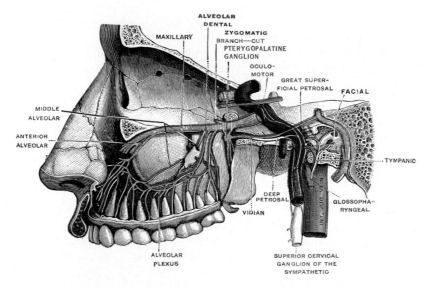

Fig. 819.—Alveolar branches of superior maxillary nerve and sphenopalatine ganglion. (Testut.)

accessory nerves (Fig. 822), in a separate sheath of dura mater, and lying in a groove on the lower border of the petrous portion of the temporal bone. After its exit from the skull, it runs anteriorly between the internal jugular vein and internal carotid artery, superficial to the latter vessel and posterior to the styloid process and its muscles. It follows the posterior border of the Stylopharyngeus for 2 or 3 cm., then curves across its superficial surface to the posterior border of the Hyoglossus, and penetrates more deeply to be distributed to the palatine tonsil, the mucous membrane of the fauces and base of the tongue, and the glands of that region. The portion of the nerve which lies in the jugular foramen has two enlargements, the superior and inferior ganglia.

The **Superior Ganglion** (*g. superius; jugular ganglion*) is situated in the upper part of the groove in which the nerve is lodged during its passage through the jugular foramen. It is very small, may be absent, and is usually regarded as a detached portion of the inferior ganglion.

The **Inferior Ganglion** (*g. petrosum; petrous ganglion*) is situated in a depression in the lower border of the petrous portion of the temporal bone. These ganglia contain the cell bodies for the sensory fibers of the nerve.

Communications.—(1) The communications with the **vagus nerve** are two filaments, one joining the auricular branch, the other the jugular ganglion. (2) The superior cervical **sympathetic** ganglion communicates with the inferior ganglion. (3) The communication with the **facial nerve** is between the trunk of the glossopharyngeal below the inferior ganglion and the facial nerve after its exit from the stylomastoid foramen; it perforates the posterior belly of the Digastricus.

The **branches of the glossopharyngeal nerve** are as follows:

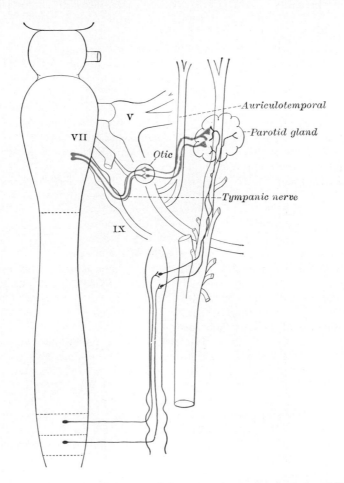

FIG. 820.—Autonomic connections of the otic and superior cervical ganglia.

1. The **Tympanic Nerve** (*n. tympanicus; nerve of Jacobson*) (Fig. 820) supplies parasympathetic fibers to the parotid gland, through the otic ganglion, and sensory fibers to the mucous membrane of the middle ear. It arises from the inferior ganglion, enters a small canal through an opening in the bony ridge which separates the carotid canal from the jugular fossa on the inferior surface of the petrous portion of the temporal bone. After a short upward course in the bone, it enters the tympanic cavity by an aperture in its floor near the medial wall. It continues upward in a groove on the surface of the promontory (Fig. 932), helps to form the tympanic plexus, reenters a canaliculus at the level of the processus cochleariformis, passes internal to the semicanal for the Tensor tympani, and continues as the lesser superficial petrosal nerve (Rosen '50).

The **Tympanic Plexus** lies in grooves on the surface of the promontory (Fig. 929), and is formed by the junction of the tympanic and caroticotympanic nerves. The caroticotympanic nerves, superior and inferior, are communications from the carotid plexus of the sympathetic which enter the tympanic cavity by perforating the wall of the carotid canal. The plexus communicates with the greater superficial petrosal nerve by a filament which passes through an opening on the labyrinthic wall, in front of the fenestra vestibuli.

a. **Sensory branches** are distributed through the plexus to the mucous membrane of the fenestra ovalis, fenestra rotunda, tympanic membrane, auditory tube, and mastoid air cells.

b. The **lesser superficial petrosal nerve** (*n. petrosus superficialis minor*) (Figs. 811, 813) is the terminal branch or continuation of the tympanic nerve beyond the plexus. After penetrating the bone medial to the Tensor tympani, it emerges into the cranial cavity on the superior surface of the petrous portion of the temporal bone, immediately lateral to the hiatus of the facial canal. It leaves the cranial cavity again through the fissure between the petrous portion and the great wing of the sphenoid, or through a small opening in the latter bone, and terminates in the otic ganglion as its visceral motor or parasympathetic root. In the canal it is joined by a filament from the geniculate ganglion of the facial nerve.

The **Otic Ganglion** (*g. oticum*) (Figs. 811, 813) is a flattened, oval, or stellate ganglion, 2 to 4 mm. in diameter, closely approximated to the medial surface of the mandibular division of the trigeminal, immediately outside of the foramen ovale, and it has the origin of the internal pterygoid nerve imbedded in it. It is lateral to the cartilaginous portion of the auditory tube, anterior to the middle meningeal artery, and posterior to the origin of the Tensor veli palatini.

The **root of the otic ganglion**, which is **parasympathetic**, is the lesser superficial petrosal nerve. It contains preganglionic fibers from the nucleus salivatorius inferior in the medulla oblongata, principally through the glossopharyngeal but probably partly through the facial nerve.

Communications of the Otic Ganglion.—(1) A communication with the **sympathetic** network on the middle meningeal artery has been called the sympathetic root of the ganglion, but these fibers are already postganglionic and pass through the ganglion without synapses. (2) A communication with the **internal pterygoid nerve** has been described as a motor root, and the continuation of the fibers to the Tensor veli palatini and Tensor tympani as branches of the ganglion, but they are trigeminal fibers which pass through the ganglion. (3) A communication with the **mandibular nerve** has been called a sensory root, but the fibers have no functional connection with the ganglion. (4) A slender filament, the **sphenoidal branch**, connects with the nerve of the pterygoid canal, and a small branch communicates with the chorda tympani.

Branches of Distribution of the Otic Ganglion.—The postganglionic fibers arising in the otic ganglion pass mainly through a communication with the auriculotemporal nerve and are distributed with its **branches to the parotid gland**. Other filaments probably accompany other nerves to reach small glands in the mouth and pharynx.

2. The **Carotid Sinus Nerve** (*carotid nerve; nerve of Hering*) (Fig. 821) arises from the main trunk of the glossopharyngeal nerve just beyond its emergence from the jugular foramen, and communicates with the nodose ganglion or the pharyngeal branch of the vagus near its origin. Its continuation or principal branch runs down the anterior surface of the internal carotid artery to the carotid bifurcation and terminates in the wall of the dilated portion of the artery at this point, called the carotid sinus, supplying it with afferent fibers for its blood pressure receptors. It has a rather constant branch which joins the intercarotid plexus, formed principally by vagus and sympathetic branches, or communicates with these nerves independently, and reaches the carotid body. Glossopharyngeal fibers may traverse the

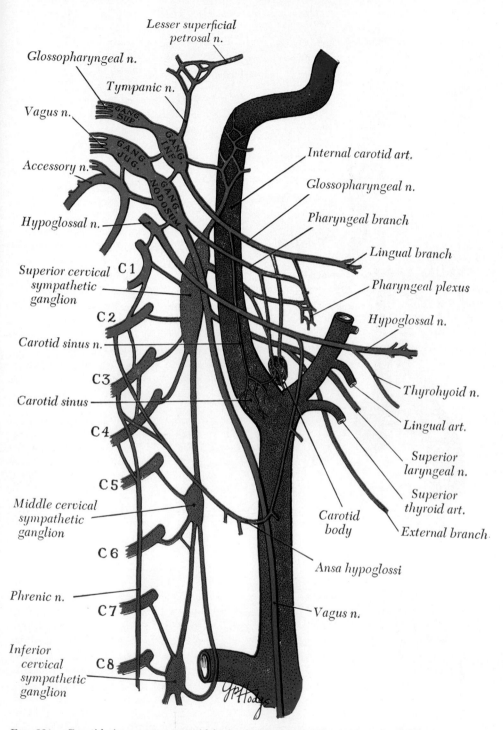

FIG. 821.—Carotid sinus nerve, carotid body, internal carotid artery, and neighboring cranial spinal, and sympathetic nerve connections. Semidiagrammatic.

plexus and its branches to the carotid body on their way to the carotid sinus (Sheehan *et al.* '41). Its functional association with the carotid body is questionable.

3. **Pharyngeal Branches** (*rr. pharyngei*) are three or four filaments which join pharyngeal branches of the vagus and sympathetic opposite the Constrictor pharyngis medius, to form the pharyngeal plexus. Branches from the plexus penetrate the muscular coat of the pharynx and supply its muscles and mucous membrane; the exact contribution of the glossopharyngeal is uncertain.

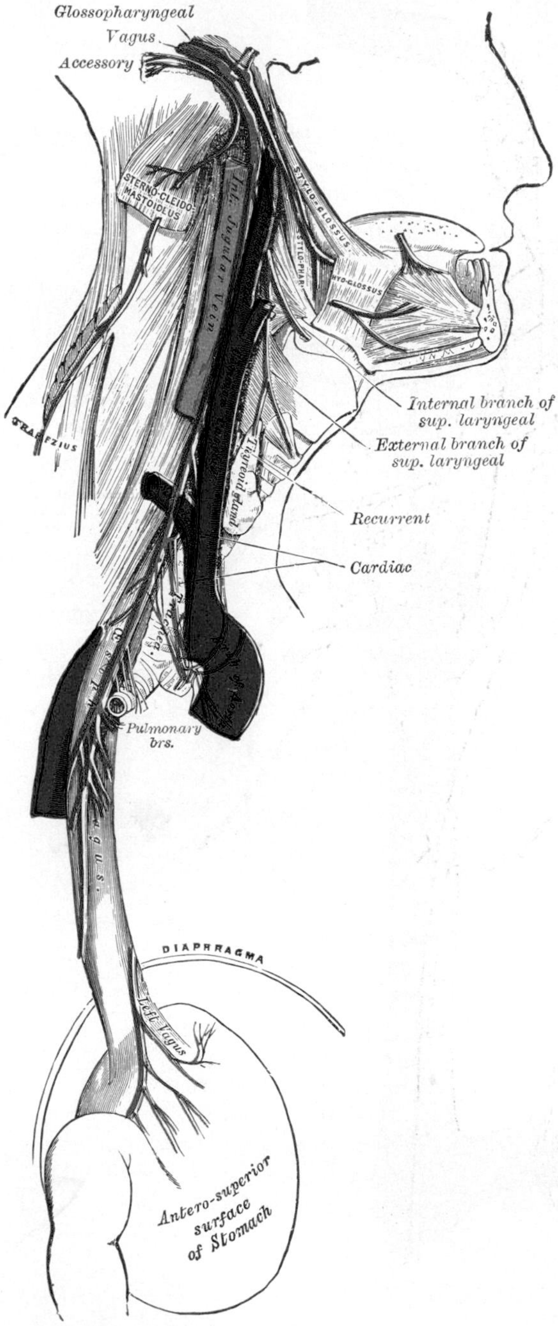

4. The **Branch to the Stylopharyngeus** (*r. stylopharyngeus*) is its only muscular branch.

5. The **Tonsillar Branches** (*rr. tonsillares*) supply the palatine tonsil, forming around it a network from which filaments are distributed to the soft palate and fauces, where they communicate with the lesser palatine nerves.

6. The **Lingual Branches** (*rr. linguales*) are two in number; one supplies the vallate papillæ with afferent fibers for taste, and general afferents to the mucous membrane at the base of the tongue; the other supplies the mucous membrane and glands of the posterior part of the tongue, and communicates with the lingual nerve.

Neuralgic pain or "tic douloureux" of the glossopharyngeal nerve occurs in the ear, throat, base of the tongue, rim of the palate, and the lower lateral and posterior part of the pharynx. The most common trigger zone is the tonsillar fossa (Pastore and Meredith '49).

Fig. 822.—Course and distribution of the glossopharyngeal, vagus, and accessory nerves.

X. THE VAGUS NERVE.

The **vagus nerve** (*n. vagus; tenth nerve; pneumogastric nerve*) (Figs. 822, 837) named from its wandering course, is the longest of the cranial nerves, and has the most extensive distribution, passing through the neck and thorax into the abdomen. It has both somatic and visceral afferent fibers, and general and special visceral efferent fibers. The somatic sensory fibers supply the skin of the posterior surface of the external ear and the external acoustic meatus; the visceral afferent fibers supply the mucous membrane of the pharynx, larynx, bronchi, lungs, heart, esophagus, stomach, intestines, and kidney. General visceral efferent fibers (parasympathetic) are distributed to the heart and supply the non-striated muscle and glands of the esophagus, stomach, trachea, bronchi, biliary tract, and most of the intestine; special visceral efferent fibers supply the voluntary muscles of the larynx, pharynx, and palate (except the Tensor), but most of the latter fibers originate in the cranial part of the accessory nerve.

The superficial origin of the vagus is composed of eight or ten rootlets attached to the medulla oblongata in the groove between the olive and the inferior peduncle, inferior to those of the glossopharyngeal and superior to those of the accessory nerve (Fig. 743). The deep origin and central connections are described on page 920. The rootlets unite into a flat cord which passes beneath the flocculus of the cerebellum to the jugular foramen. The nerve leaves the cranial cavity through this opening, accompanied by the accessory nerve and contained in the same dural sheath, but separated by a septum from the glossopharyngeal nerve, which lies anteriorly. This portion of the vagus presents two enlargements, the jugular and nodose ganglia which are the **Sensory Ganglia** of the nerve.

The **Jugular Ganglion** (*g. superius; g. of the root; g. jugulare;*) (Fig. 821) is a spherical swelling, about 4 mm. in diameter, of the vagus nerve as it lies in the jugular foramen. The central processes of its unipolar (sensory) ganglion cells enter the medulla, usually in three or four large independent rootlets, slightly dorsal to the motor rootlets. Most of the peripheral processes of the ganglion cells enter the auricular branch of the vagus, but a few probably are distributed with the pharyngeal branches.

The **Nodose Ganglion** (*g. inferius; g. of the trunk; g. nodosum;*) (Fig. 821) forms a fusiform swelling about 2.5 cm. long on the vagus nerve after its exit from the jugular foramen and about 1 cm. distal to the jugular ganglion. The central processes of its unipolar (sensory) cells pass through the jugular ganglion without traversing the region occupied by cells, and frequently accompany motor fibers in the rootlets for a short distance but enter the medulla slightly dorsal to them, in line with the jugular rootlets. Some of the peripheral processes of the ganglion cells make up the internal ramus of the superior laryngeal nerve and the rest are distributed with other branches of the vagus to the larynx, trachea, bronchi, esophagus, and other thoracic and abdominal viscera (Foley and DuBois '34).

Communications.—A. At the jugular ganglion, several delicate filaments communicate with (1) the cranial portion of the **accessory** nerve; (2) with the inferior ganglion of the **glossopharyngeal**; (3) with the **facial** by means of the auricular branch; and (4) with the superior cervical ganglion of the **sympathetic** (*jugular nerve*).

B. The cranial part of the **accessory** nerve joins the vagus just proximal to the nodose ganglion, and is the source of the greater part of the fibers in the motor branches of the vagus to the pharynx and larynx.

C. At the nodose ganglion, communication is with (1) the **hypoglossal** nerve, (2) the superior cervical **sympathetic** ganglion, and (3) the loop between the **first** and **second cervical** spinal nerves.

The resulting **vagus nerve trunk**, after it has been joined by the cranial part of the accessory nerve just distal to the nodose ganglion, passes vertically down the neck within the carotid sheath, deep to and between the internal jugular vein and the internal and common carotid arteries. Beyond the root of the neck the course of the nerve differs on the two sides of the body.

The **right vagus** crosses the first part of the subclavian artery, lying superficial to it and between it and the innominate vein (Fig. 824), and continues along the side of the trachea to the dorsal aspect of the root of the lung, where it spreads out in the posterior pulmonary plexus (Fig. 825). Below this plexus, it splits into cords

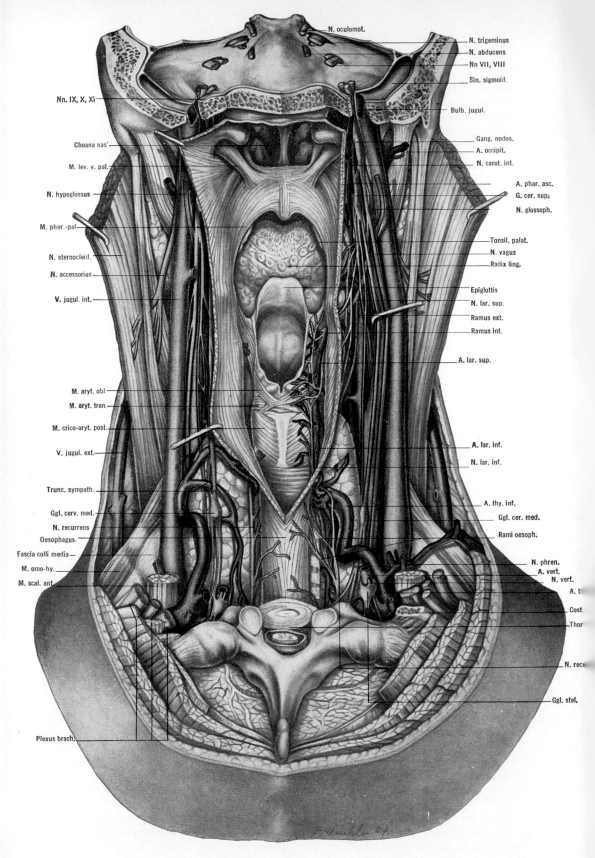

N. oculomot.

N. trigeminus
N. abducens
Nn VII, VIII
Sin. sigmoid.

Nn. IX, X, Xi

Bulb. jugul.

Gang. nodos.
Choana nas'
A. occipit.
M. lev. v. pal.
N. carot. int.

N. hypoglossus
A. phar. asc.
G. cer. sup.
N. glossoph.

M. phar.-pal.

Tonsil. palat.
N. sternocleid.
N. vagus
Radix ling.
N. accessorius

Epiglottis
V. jugul. int.
N. lar. sup.
Ramus ext.
Ramus int.

A. lar. sup.

M. aryt. obl.
M. aryt. tran.

M. crico-aryt. post.

V. jugul. ext.
A. lar. inf.
N. lar. inf.

Trunc. sympath.

A. thy. inf.
Ggl. cerv. med.
Ggl. cer. med.
N. recurrens
Rami oesoph.
Oesophagus.
Fascia colli media
M. omo-hy.
N. phren.
M. scal. ant.
A. vert.
N. vert.
A. t

Cost
Thor

N. rec

Ggl. stel.

Plexus brach.

Fig. 823.—Dorsal view of the pharynx and associated nerves and blood vessels after removal of the cervical vertebræ and part of the occipital bone. (Töndury, Angewandte und topographische Anatomie, courtesy of Georg Thieme Verlag.)

which enter into the formation of the plexus on the dorsal aspect of the esophagus. After sending communications to the left vagus, these cords unite with each other and with communications from the left vagus to form a single trunk, the posterior vagus nerve, before passing through the esophageal hiatus in the diaphragm (Fig.

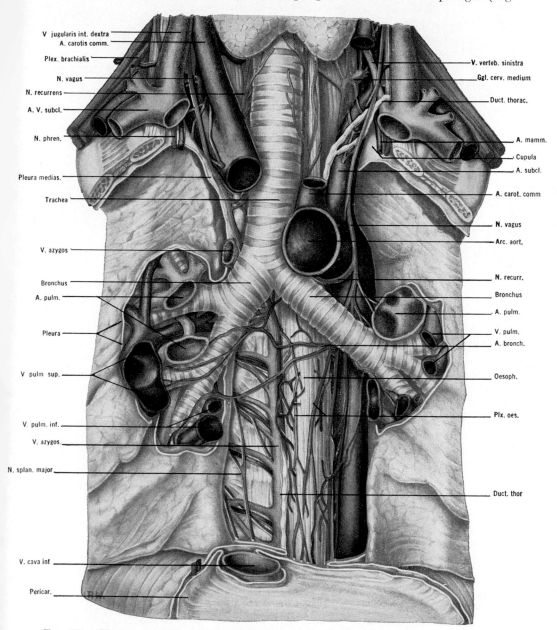

V jugularis int. dextra
A. carotis comm.
Plex. brachialis
N. vagus
N. recurrens
A. V. subcl.
N. phren.
Pleura medias.
Trachea
V. azygos
Bronchus
A. pulm.
Pleura
V pulm sup.
V. pulm. inf.
V. azygos
N. splan. major
V. cava inf
Pericar.

V. verteb. sinistra
Ggl. cerv. medium
Duct. thorac.
A. mamm.
Cupula
A. subcl.
A. carot. comm
N. vagus
Arc. aort.
N. recurr.
Bronchus
A. pulm.
V. pulm.
A. bronch.
Oesoph.
Plx. oes.
Duct. thor

FIG. 824.—The mediastinal organs and the roots of the lungs after removal of the heart and pericardium. (Töndury, Angewandte und topographische Anatomie, courtesy of Georg Thieme Verlag.)

825). Below the diaphragm, the posterior vagus continues along the lesser curvature of the stomach on its posterior surface for a short distance, and divides into a celiac and several gastric branches.

The **left vagus** enters the thorax between the left carotid and subclavian arteries, deep to the left innominate vein (Fig. 837). It crosses the left side of the arch of the aorta (Fig. 824), angling dorsally in its downward course, passes between the aorta and the left pulmonary artery just distal to the ligamentum arteriosum, and reaches the dorsal aspect of the root of the lung where it flattens out into the posterior pulmonary plexus (Fig. 825). It reaches the esophagus as a variable number of strands which follow down the ventral aspect of the esophagus, send communications to the right vagus, and usually unite with each other and with substantial communications from the right vagus to form a single trunk, the anterior vagus nerve, before passing through the diaphragm. Below the diaphragm, the anterior vagus, on the anterior aspect of the stomach, divides into an hepatic and several gastric branches (Jackson '49).

A. Branches in the jugular fossa:

1. The **Meningeal Branch** (*r. meningeus; dural branch*) is a recurrent filament which arises at the jugular ganglion, and is distributed to the dura mater in the posterior cranial fossa.

2. The **Auricular Branch** (*r. auricularis; nerve of Arnold*) arises from the jugular ganglion and soon communicates by a filament with the inferior ganglion of the glossopharyngeal. It passes behind the internal jugular vein, and when it reaches the lateral wall of the jugular fossa, enters the mastoid canaliculus, which crosses the facial canal in the bone about 4 mm. above the stylomastoid foramen, and communicates with the facial nerve. It is a somatic afferent nerve and reaches the surface by passing through the tympanomastoid fissure. It divides into two branches: (*a*) one joins the posterior auricular nerve, and (*b*) the other is distributed to the skin of the back of the auricula and to the posterior part of the external acoustic meatus.

B. Branches of the vagus nerve in the neck:

3. The **Pharyngeal Branches** (*rr. pharyngei*), usually two, arise at the upper part of the ganglion nodosum, and contain sensory fibers from the ganglion and motor fibers from the communication with the accessory nerve. They pass across the internal carotid artery to the upper border of the Constrictor pharyngis medius where they divide into several bundles which join branches of the glossopharyngeal, sympathetic, and external branch of the superior laryngeal to form the **pharyngeal plexus** (Braeucker '23).

a. Through the plexus, **branches** are distributed to the muscles and mucous membrane of the **pharynx**, and the muscles of the **soft palate**, except the Tensor veli palatini.

b. The **nerves to the carotid body** are filaments from the pharyngeal and possibly from the superior laryngeal branches which join with similar filaments from the glossopharyngeal nerve and the superior cervical sympathetic ganglion to form the intercarotid plexus between the internal and external carotid arteries at the bifurcation. The vagus fibers are visceral afferents which terminate in the carotid body, a chemoreceptor sensitive to changes in oxygen tension of the blood, located at the carotid bifurcation (Sheehan *et al.* '41).

4. The **Superior Laryngeal Nerve** (*n. laryngeus superior*) (Fig. 822) arises near the caudal end of the nodose ganglion, passes downward and medialward deep to the internal carotid artery and along the pharynx toward the superior cornu of the thyroid cartilage. It has a communication with the superior cervical sympathetic ganglion and may contribute to the intercarotid plexus. It terminates by dividing into a smaller external and a larger internal branch.

a. The **external branch** (*r. externus*) (Fig. 822) continues downward beside the larynx, deep to the Sternothyroideus, and supplies motor fibers to the Cricothyroideus muscle and part of the Constrictor pharyngis inferior. It contributes fibers to the pharyngeal plexus and communicates with the superior sympathetic cardiac nerve.

b. The **internal branch** (*r. internus*) swings anteriorly to reach the thyrohyoid membrane which it pierces with the superior laryngeal artery. It supplies sensory fibers to the mucous membrane and parasympathetic secretomotor fibers to the associated glands through branches to the epiglottis, base of the tongue, aryepiglottic fold, and the larynx as low down as the vocal folds. A filament passes down beneath the mucous membrane on the inner surface of the thyroid cartilage and joins the recurrent nerve (Fig. 823).

5. The **Superior Cardiac Branches** (*rr. cardiaci superiores; cervical cardiac branches*), two or three in number, arise from the vagus at the upper and lower parts of the neck. The upper branches are small, and communicate with the cardiac branches of the sympathetic. They can be traced to the deep part of the cardiac plexus. The lower branch arises at the root of the neck just above the first rib. On the right side it passes ventral or lateral to the innominate artery and joins the deep part of the cardiac plexus. On the left side it passes across the left side of the arch of the aorta, and joins the superficial part of the cardiac plexus.

6. The **Recurrent Nerve** (*n. recurrens; inferior or recurrent laryngeal nerve*) (Fig. 825), as its name implies, arises low down and runs back upward in the neck to its destination, the muscles of the larynx. The origin and early part of its course are different on the two sides. On the right side, it arises in the root of the neck, as the vagus crosses superficial to the first part of the subclavian artery. It loops under the arch of this vessel and passes behind it to the side of the trachea and esophagus. On the left side, the recurrent nerve arises in the upper part of the thorax, as the vagus crosses the left side of the arch of the aorta. Just distal to the ligamentum arteriosum, it loops under the arch and passes behind it to the side of the trachea. The further course on the two sides is similar; it passes deep to the common carotid artery, and along the groove between the trachea and esophagus, medial to the overhanging deep surface of the thyroid lobe. Here it comes into close relationship with the terminal portion of the inferior thyroid artery. It runs under the lower border of the Constrictor pharyngis inferior, enters the larynx through the cricothyroid membrane behind the articulation of the inferior cornu of the thyroid with the cricoid cartilage, and is distributed to all the muscles of the larynx except the Cricothyroideus. Its branches are as follows:

a. **Cardiac branches** are given off as the nerve loops around the subclavian artery or the aorta, and are described below as the inferior cardiac branches of the vagus.

b. **Tracheal** and **esophageal branches**, more numerous on the left than on the right, are distributed to the mucous membranes and muscular coats (Fig. 823).

c. **Pharyngeal branches** are filaments to the Constrictor pharyngis inferior.

d. Sensory and secretomotor filaments, which reach the recurrent through the communication with the internal branch of the superior laryngeal, supply the mucous membrane of the larynx below the vocal folds.

e. The **inferior laryngeal nerves** are the terminal branches which supply motor fibers to all the intrinsic muscles of the larynx except the Cricothyroideus.

Variations.—When the right subclavian artery arises from the descending aorta, the recurrent nerve arises in the neck and passes directly to the larynx.

C. Branches of the Vagus Nerve in the Thorax.—

7. The **Inferior Cardiac Branches** (*rr. cardiaci inferiores; thoracic cardiac branches*) arise on the right side from the trunk of the vagus as it lies by the side of the trachea and from the recurrent nerve, and on the left side from the recurrent only. They end in the deep part of the cardiac plexus.

a. The *visceral efferent fibers to the heart* in all the cardiac branches are preganglionic. After passage through the cardiac and coronary plexuses (see page 1083)

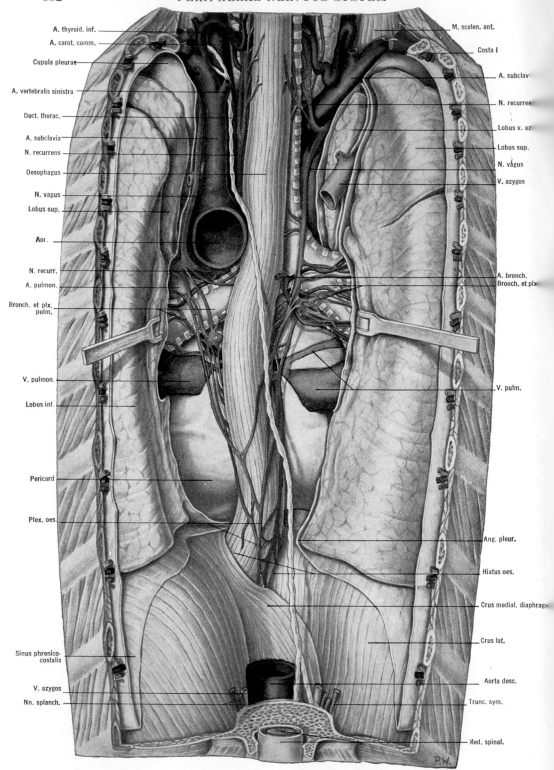

FIG. 825.—Dorsal view of the mediastinal structures, the heart, and roots of the lungs, after removal of the vertebral column, ribs, and thoracic aorta. (Töndury, Angewandte und topographische Anatomie, courtesy of Georg Thieme Verlag.)

these fibers form synapses with groups of ganglion cells in the heart wall, and the postganglionic fibers terminate about the conduction system and musculature of the heart.

b. *Visceral afferent fibers* from cells in the nodose ganglion traverse the cardiac plexus and cardiac nerves, supplying the **heart** and **great vessels.**

c. The *visceral afferent fibers* supplying the **aortic bodies** (*glomera aortica*) are carried mainly by the cardiac branches of the right vagus, and those supplying the **supracardial bodies** (*aortic paraganglia*) mainly by those of the left vagus. These bodies are chemoreceptors similar to the carotid body; the cell bodies of the afferent fibers are in the nodose ganglion (Hollinshead '39, '40).

The Depressor Nerve or Nerve of Cyon.—In some animals, the afferent fibers of the vagus from the heart and great vessels are largely contained in a separate nerve whose stimulation causes depression of the activity of the heart. In man, these fibers are probably contained in the inferior cardiac branches (Mitchell '53).

8. The **Anterior Bronchial Branches** (*rr. bronchiales anteriores; anterior or ventral pulmonary branches*) are two or three small nerves on the anterior surface of the root of the lung which join with filaments from the sympathetic to form the anterior pulmonary plexus. From this plexus filaments follow the ramifications of the bronchi and pulmonary vessels, or communicate with the cardiac or posterior pulmonary plexuses.

9. The **Posterior Bronchial Branches** (*rr. bronchiales posteriores; posterior or dorsal pulmonary branches*) (Fig. 825) are numerous offshoots from the main trunk of the vagus as it passes posterior to the root of the lung. The vagus itself in this region is flattened and spread out so that it combines with the bronchial branches and with the sympathetic communications to form what is called the **posterior pulmonary plexus.** The plexus has communications with the cardiac, aortic, and esophageal plexuses and its branches follow the ramifications of the bronchi and pulmonary vessels.

a. The *visceral efferent fibers* form synapses with small groups of ganglion cells in the walls of the bronchi, and the postganglionic fibers terminate in the non-striated muscle and glands of the bronchi (Larsell '51).

b. *Afferent fibers* supply the lungs and bronchi.

10. The **Esophageal Branches** (*rr. œsophagei*) (Fig. 825) consist of upper filaments from the recurrent nerve and lower branches from the trunk of the vagus and the esophageal plexus. They contain both visceral efferent (parasympathetic preganglionic) and visceral afferent fibers.

The **Esophageal Plexus** (*pl. œsophageus anterior et posterior*).—The fibers of the vagus below the root of the lung split into several bundles (Fig. 825), usually two to four larger bundles and a variable number of smaller parallel and communicating strands on each side, which spread out on the esophagus and become partly imbedded in its adventitial coat. Filaments are given off for the innervation of the esophagus and there are communications with the splanchnic nerves and sympathetic trunk, forming as a whole the esophageal plexus. The bundles from the left vagus (Fig. 824) gradually swing around to the anterior surface of the esophagus, those from the right (Fig. 825) to the posterior surface. Just above the diaphragm, the larger bundles from the left vagus usually combine with one or two strands from the right on the anterior surface of the esophagus to form a single trunk, and this newly constituted vagus, which is not strictly the equivalent of the left vagus, passes through the esophageal hiatus of the diaphragm as the **anterior vagus.** A similar combination on the posterior surface of the esophagus, mostly right vagus but with a communication from the left, passes through the esophageal hiatus as the **posterior vagus** (Jackson '49; Doubilet *et al.* '48).

D. Branches of the Anterior and Posterior Vagi in the Abdomen.—These branches contain both *visceral efferent* (parasympathetic preganglionic) and *visceral afferent* fibers. The cells of the *postganglionic* fibers of the stomach and intestines are in the myenteric plexus (of Auerbach) and the submucous plexus (of Meissner); those of the glands are either in small local groups of ganglion cells or possibly in the celiac plexus.

11. **Gastric Branches** (*rr. gastrici*).—Usually four to six branches are given off by both anterior and posterior vagi, at the cardiac end of the stomach. They fan out over their respective surfaces of the fundus and body, and penetrate the wall to be distributed to the myenteric and submucous plexuses. On both anterior and posterior surfaces, one branch, longer than the others, follows along the lesser curvature and has been called the *principal nerve of the lesser curvature;* it is distributed to the pyloric vestibule rather than the pylorus itself.

12. The **Hepatic Branches** (*rr. hepatici*) from the anterior are larger than those from the posterior vagus. They cross from the stomach to the liver in the lesser omentum, and continue along the fissure for the ductus venosus to the porta hepatis where they give off right and left branches to the liver. The large hepatic branch of the anterior vagus contributes to the plexus on the hepatic artery and has the following branches:

a. **Branches to the gall bladder** and bile ducts come from the hepatic branches or the plexus on the artery.

b. A **pancreatic branch** runs posteriorly to its destination.

c. A **branch** along the right gastric artery is distributed to the **pylorus** and the first part of the **duodenum.**

d. A **branch** accompanies the gastroduodenal artery and right gastroepiploic artery and is distributed to the **duodenum** and **stomach.**

13. **Celiac Branches.**—A large terminal division of the posterior vagus follows the left gastric artery or runs along the crus of the diaphragm to the celiac plexus. The terminal branches cannot be followed once the nerve has entered the plexus, but the vagus fibers, through the secondary plexuses, reach the duodenum, pancreas, kidney, spleen, small intestine, and large intestine as far as the splenic flexure. Before the nerve enters the plexus it may give a branch to the superior mesenteric artery or to the aortic plexus (see Celiac Plexus).

XI. THE ACCESSORY NERVE.

The **accessory nerve** (*n. accessorius; eleventh nerve; spinal accessory nerve*) (Figs. 819, 822, 823, 824) is a motor nerve consisting of two parts, a cranial and a spinal part.

A. The **Cranial part** (*r. internus; accessory portion*) arises by four or five delicate rootlets from the side of the medulla oblongata, below and in series with those of the vagus. From its deep origin, described on page 920, and from its destination, it might well be considered a part of the vagus. It runs lateralward to the jugular foramen, where it interchanges fibers with the spinal part or becomes united with it for a short distance, and has one or two filaments of communication with the jugular ganglion of the vagus. It then passes through the jugular foramen, separates from the spinal part and joins the vagus just proximal to the ganglion nodosum. Its fibers are distributed through the pharyngeal branch of the vagus to the Musculus uvulæ, Levator veli palatini, and the Constrictores pharyngis and through the superior and inferior laryngeal branches of the vagus to the muscles of the larynx and the esophagus.

B. The **Spinal part** (*r. externus; spinal portion*) originates from motor cells in the lateral part of the anterior column of gray substance of the upper five cervical segments of the spinal cord. The fibers pass through the lateral funiculus, emerge on the surface, and join each other seriatim as they follow up the cord between the ligamentum denticulatum and the dorsal rootlets of the spinal nerves. The nerve passes through the foramen magnum into the cranial cavity, crosses the occipital bone to the jugular notch, and penetrates the dura mater over the jugular bulb. It passes through the jugular foramen lying in the same sheath of dura as the vagus, but separated from it by a fold of the arachnoid. In the jugular foramen, it interchanges fibers with the cranial part or joins it for a short distance and separates from it again. At its exit from the foramen, it turns backward, lying in front of the internal jugular vein in two-thirds and behind in one-third of the bodies. It passes posterior to the Stylohyoideus and Digastricus to the upper part of the Sternocleidomastoideus, which it pierces, and then courses obliquely downward across the posterior triangle of the neck to the anterior border of the Trapezius. In the posterior triangle it is covered only by the outer investing layer of deep fascia, the superficial fascia and the skin. It **communicates** with the **second, third,** and **fourth cervical nerves,** and with a plexiform arrangement continues on the deep surface of the Trapezius almost to its lower border. Experimental observations with monkeys (Corbin and Harrison '38) indicate that the communications with the cervical nerves carry proprioceptive sensory fibers from cells in the dorsal root ganglia of the spinal nerves. The branches of the accessory nerve are as follows:

1. **Sternocleidomastoideus branches** are given off as the nerve penetrates this muscle.

2. **Trapezius branches** are supplied from the part of the nerve lying deep to the muscle.

Variations.—The lower limit of the origin of the spinal part may vary from C 3 to C 7. It may pass beneath the Sternocleidomastoideus without piercing it, and in one instance it ended in that muscle, the Trapezius being supplied by the third and fourth cervical nerves.

XII. **THE HYPOGLOSSAL NERVE.**

The **hypoglossal nerve** (*n. hypoglossus; twelfth nerve*) (Fig. 836) is the motor nerve of the tongue. Its superficial origin from the medulla oblongata is by a series of rootlets in the anterolateral sulcus between the pyramid and the olive (Fig. 743). The deep origin is described on page 921.

The rootlets are collected into two bundles which perforate the dura mater separately, opposite the hypoglossal canal in the occipital bone, and unite after their passage through it; in some instances the canal is divided by a small bony spicule. As the nerve emerges from the skull, it is deeply placed beneath the internal carotid artery and internal jugular vein, and is closely bound to the vagus nerve. It runs downward and forward between the vein and artery, becomes superficial to them near the angle of the mandible, loops around the occipital artery, and passes forward across the external carotid and lingual arteries below the tendon of the Digastricus (Fig. 836). It curves slightly upward above the hyoid bone, and passes deep to the tendon of the Digastricus and the Stylohyoideus, between the Mylohyoideus and the Hyoglossus, and continues forward among the fibers of the Genioglossus as far as the tip of the tongue, distributing branches to the intrinsic muscles.

Communications.—(1) The communications with the **vagus** take place close to the skull, numerous filaments passing between the hypoglossal and the ganglion nodosum of the vagus through the mass of connective tissue which binds the two nerves together. (2) As the nerve winds around the occipital artery, it communicates by a filament with the **pharyngeal plexus.** (3) The communication with the **sympathetic** takes place opposite the atlas by branches of the superior cervical ganglion. (4) The communications with the **lingual** take place near the anterior border of the Hyoglossus by numerous filaments which lie upon the muscle. (5) The communication which takes place opposite the atlas, between the hypoglossal and the loop connecting the anterior primary divisions of the **first** and **second cervical nerves,** is especially significant because it contains the motor fibers for the nerves to the supra- and infrahyoid muscles. This communication probably also contains sensory fibers from the uppermost cervical dorsal root ganglia (Pearson '39).

Branches.—1. **Meningeal branches** are minute filaments which are given off in the hypoglossal canal and pass back to the dura mater of the posterior cranial fossa. They probably contain sensory fibers communicated to the hypoglossal from the loop between the first and second cervical nerves.

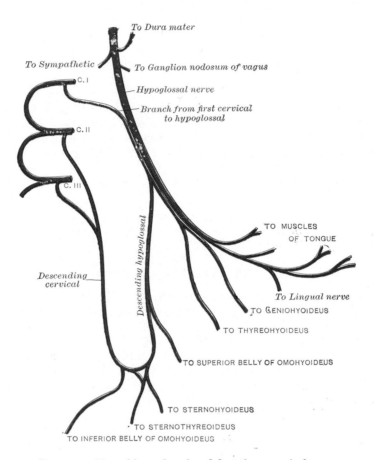

To Dura mater

To Sympathetic

To Ganglion nodosum of vagus

C. I

Hypoglossal nerve

Branch from first cervical to hypoglossal

C. II

C. III

TO MUSCLES OF TONGUE

Descending hypoglossal

Descending cervical

To Lingual nerve

TO GENIOHYOIDEUS

TO THYREOHYOIDEUS

TO SUPERIOR BELLY OF OMOHYOIDEUS

TO STERNOHYOIDEUS

TO STERNOTHYREOIDEUS

TO INFERIOR BELLY OF OMOHYOIDEUS

Fig. 826.—Plan of hypoglossal and first three cervical nerves.

2. The **Descending Hypoglossal** (*r. descendens; descendens hypoglossi*) (Fig. 836) is a long slender branch which leaves the hypoglossal as it loops around the occipital artery. It runs along the superficial surface of the carotid sheath to the middle of the neck, gives a branch to the superior belly of the Omohyoideus, and becomes the medial arm of a loop, the ansa hypoglossi (see page 1009). The lateral arm of the loop is the descending cervical nerve (communicantes cervicales) from the second and third cervicals. The branches from the loop supply (1) the inferior belly of the Omohyoideus, (2) the Sternohyoideus, and (3) the Sternothyroideus. The fibers in the descending hypoglossal originate in the first cervical nerve, not in the hypoglossal nucleus, and pass through the communication between the first cervical and the hypoglossal described above.

3. The **Thyrohyoid Branch** and the **Geniohyoid Branch** are also made up of fibers from the first cervical nerve. They leave the hypoglossal near the posterior border of the Hyoglossus. The thyrohyoid branch runs obliquely across the greater cornu of the hyoid bone to reach the muscle which it supplies.

4. The **Muscular Branches** containing true hypoglossal fibers are distributed to the Styloglossus, Hyoglossus, Genioglossus, and intrinsic muscles. At the under surface of the tongue, numerous slender branches pass upward into the substance of the organ to supply its intrinsic muscles. The branches of the hypoglossal to the tongue probably contain proprioceptive sensory fibers with cells of origin in the first (if present) and second cervical dorsal root ganglia.

THE SPINAL NERVES.

The **spinal nerves** (*nervi spinales*) arise from the spinal cord within the spinal canal and pass out through the intervertebral foramina. The thirty-one pairs are grouped as follows: 8 Cervical; 12 Thoracic; 5 Lumbar; 5 Sacral; 1 Coccygeal. The first cervical leaves the vertebral canal between the occipital bone and the atlas and is therefore called the suboccipital nerve; the eighth leaves between the seventh cervical and first thoracic vertebræ.

Roots of the Spinal Nerves.—(Fig. 704) Each spinal nerve is attached to the spinal cord by two roots, a ventral or motor root, and a dorsal or sensory root; a third root, the sympathetic root, is commonly called the gray ramus communicans.

The **Ventral Root** (*radix anterior; anterior root; motor root*) emerges from the ventral surface of the spinal cord as a number of **rootlets** or filaments (*fila radicularia*) which usually combine to form two bundles near the intervertebral foramen.

The **Dorsal Root** (*radix posterior; posterior root; sensory root*) is larger than the ventral root because of the greater size and number of its rootlets; these are attached along the posterior lateral furrow of the spinal cord and unite to form two bundles which enter the spinal ganglion.

The dorsal and ventral roots unite immediately beyond the spinal ganglion to form the spinal nerve which then emerges through the intervertebral foramen. Both nerve roots receive a covering from the pia mater, and are loosely invested by the arachnoid, the latter being prolonged as far as the points where the roots pierce the dura mater. The two roots pierce the dura separately, each receiving from this membrane a sheath which becomes continuous with the connective tissue of the epineurium after the roots join to form the spinal nerve.

The **Spinal Ganglion** (*ganglion spinale; dorsal root ganglion*) (Fig. 704) is a collection of nerve cells on the dorsal root of the spinal nerve. It is oval in shape and proportional in size to the dorsal root on which it is situated; it is bifid medially where it is joined by the two bundles of rootlets. The ganglion is usually placed in the intervertebral foramen, immediately outside the dura mater, but there are exceptions to this rule; the ganglia of the first and second cervical nerves lie on the vertebral arches of the axis and atlas respectively, those of the sacral nerves are inside the vertebral canal, and that of the coccygeal nerve is within the sheath of the dura mater.

Size and Direction.—In the cervical region, the roots of the upper four nerves are small, the lower four large and the dorsal roots are three times as large as the ventral, a larger proportion than in any other region; their individual filaments are also larger than in the ventral roots. The first cervical is an exception, its dorsal root being smaller than its ventral. The roots of the first and second cervical nerves are short and run nearly horizontally to their exits from the vertebral canal. The roots of the third to the eighth nerves run obliquely downward, the obliquity and length successively increasing, but the distance between the attachment to the spinal cord and the exit from the canal never exceeds the height of one vertebra.

In the thoracic region the roots, with the exception of the first, are small and the dorsal is only slightly larger than the ventral. They increase successively in length, and in the lower thoracic region descend in contact with the spinal cord for a distance equal to the height of at least two vertebræ before they emerge from the vertebral canal.

In the lumbar and upper sacral regions are found the largest roots, with the most numerous individual filaments. The roots of the coccygeal nerve are the smallest. The roots of the lumbar, sacral, and coccygeal nerves run vertically downward, and since the spinal cord ends near the

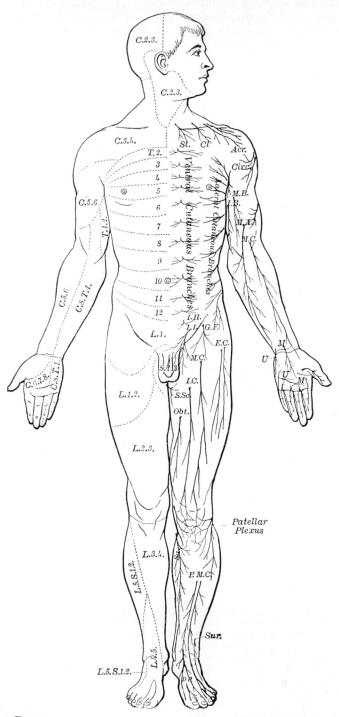

Fig. 827.—Distribution of cutaneous nerves. Ventral aspect.

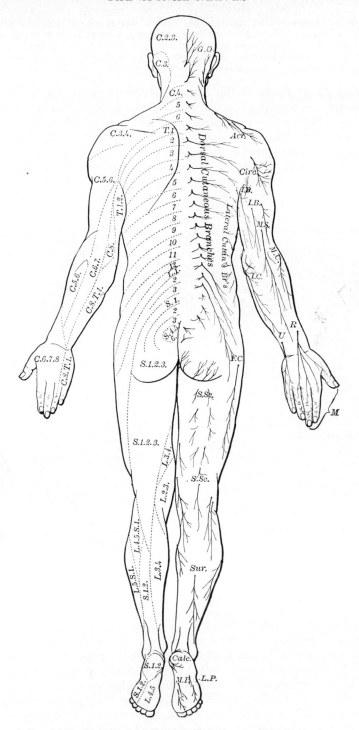

FIG. 828.—Distribution of cutaneous nerves. Dorsal aspect.

FIGS. 827 and 828 (and others like them) which show areas of skin supplied by each of the dorsal root ganglia are diagrammatic. The work of Sherrington has demonstrated that the "sensory root field" of a particular dorsal root ganglion overlaps that of the zones or "dermatomes" supplied by the ganglion above and below (Fig. 832). In fact fibers carrying different modalities, *i.e.*, pain and touch, vary in the amount of this overlap. This interesting subject is discussed by Fulton, J. F. (Physiology of the Nervous System, Oxford University Press, New York, 1938, see pages 34–38).

lower border of the first lumbar vertebra, the roots of the successive segments are increasingly long. The name cauda equina is given to the resulting collection of nerve roots below the termination of the spinal cord. The largest nerve roots, and consequently the largest spinal nerves, are attached to the cervical and lumbar swellings of the spinal cord and are the nerves largely distributed to the upper and lower limbs.

The **Sympathetic Roots of the spinal nerves** are provided by the **gray rami communicantes** (postganglionic rami) which contain the postganglionic fibers from the adjacent sympathetic chain ganglia (Duncan '43). These fibers are visceral efferents running in the nerves and their branches toward the periphery where they supply the smooth muscle in the blood vessel walls, the Arrectores pilorum muscles, and the sweat glands. Since there are not as many sympathetic ganglia as there are spinal nerves, some ganglia supply roots to more than one nerve. Although variations are common, a simple plan may be given as follows. The first

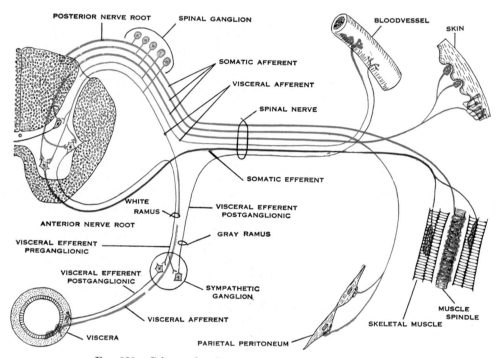

Fig. 829.—Scheme showing structure of a typical spinal nerve.

four cervical nerves receive their roots from the superior cervical ganglion, the fifth and sixth from the middle, and the seventh and eighth cervical nerves from the inferior cervical ganglion. The first ten thoracic nerves receive roots from corresponding ganglia, but the eleventh and twelfth receive roots from a single coalesced ganglion. The lumbar and sacral nerves receive their roots from a variable number of ganglia which correspond only approximately with the nerves.

Each spinal nerve usually receives two or three sympathetic roots (gray rami communicantes). They join the nerve just distal to the union between the dorsal and ventral roots, and in the thoracic and upper lumbar region are regularly medial to the white rami communicantes which are the branches of the spinal nerves carrying preganglionic fibers to the sympathetic chain. The ventral and dorsal primary divisions (described below) may each receive a root, but if the roots join the ventral division only, some of the fibers course back centrally until they can reach the dorsal division (Dass '52).

A small **Meningeal Branch** is given off from each spinal nerve immediately after it emerges from the intervertebral foramen. This branch re-enters the vertebral canal through the foramen, supplies afferent fibers to the vertebræ and their ligaments, and carries sympathetic postganglionic fibers to the blood vessels of the spinal cord and its membranes.

The **White Ramus Communicans** (*ramus communicans alba; preganglionic ramus*) is the branch of the spinal nerve through which the preganglionic fibers from the spinal cord reach the sympathetic chain and are thus the roots of the sympathetic ganglia. They arise from the twelve thoracic and first two lumbar nerves only and usually join the sympathetic chain at or near a ganglion. They leave the ventral primary division of the spinal nerve soon after it has emerged from the intervertebral foramen.

The spinal nerve splits into its two **primary divisions**, ventral and dorsal, almost as soon as the two roots join and both divisions receive fibers from all three roots.

DORSAL PRIMARY DIVISIONS OF THE SPINAL NERVES.

The **dorsal primary divisions** (*rami dorsales*) are smaller, as a rule, than the ventral divisions. As they arise from the spinal nerve, they are directed dorsalward, and, with the exceptions of those of the first cervical, the fourth and fifth sacral, and the coccygeal, divide into **medial** and **lateral branches** for the supply of the muscles and skin of the dorsal part of the neck and trunk (Fig. 854).

The Cervical Nerves.

The dorsal primary division of the **suboccipital** or **first cervical nerve** is larger than the ventral. It emerges from the spinal canal above the posterior arch of the atlas and below the vertebral artery to enter the suboccipital triangle (Fig. 438). It supplies the muscles which bound this triangle, *viz.*, the Rectus capitis posterior major, and the Obliquus superior and inferior, and it gives branches to the Rectus capitis posterior minor and the Semispinalis capitis. A filament from the branch to the Obliquus inferior joins the dorsal division of the second cervical nerve.

Variations.—The first nerve occasionally has a cutaneous branch which accompanies the occipital artery to the scalp and communicates with the greater and lesser occipital nerves.

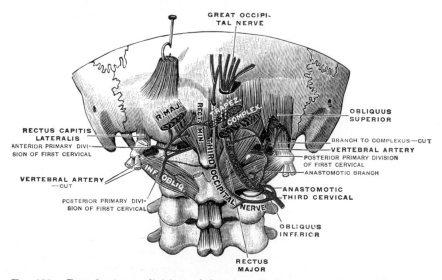

FIG. 830.—Dorsal primary divisions of the upper three cervical nerves. (Testut.)

The dorsal division of the **second cervical nerve** is much larger than the anterior and is the greatest of the cervical dorsal divisions. It emerges between the posterior arch of the atlas and the lamina of the axis, below the Obliquus inferior, which it supplies. It communicates with the first cervical and then divides into a large medial branch and a small lateral branch.

a. The **greater occipital nerve** (*n. occipitalis major*) (Figs. 438, 835) is the name given to the medial branch because of its size and distribution. It crosses obliquely between the Obliquus inferior and the Semispinalis capitis, pierces the latter and the Trapezius near their attachments to the occipital bone, and becomes subcutaneous (Fig. 830). It communicates with the third cervical, runs upward on the back of the head with the occipital artery, and divides into branches which supply the scalp over the vertex and top of the head, communicating with the lesser occipital nerve. It gives muscular branches to the Semispinalis capitis.

b. The **lateral branch** (*r. lateralis; external branch*) supplies branches to the Splenius and Semispinalis capitis, and often communicates with the lateral branch of the third nerve.

The dorsal division of the **third cervical nerve** is intermediate in size between the second and fourth. Its medial branch runs between the Semispinalis capitis and cervicis, pierces the Splenius and Trapezius, and gives branches to the skin. One branch, called the **third occipital nerve**, pierces the Trapezius medial to the greater occipital nerve, with which it communicates, and is distributed to the skin of the lower part of the back of the head (Fig. 830). The lateral branch communicates with that of the second cervical, supplies the same muscles, and gives a branch to the Longissimus capitis.

The dorsal primary divisions of the **fourth to eighth cervical nerves** divide into medial and lateral branches. The medial branches of the fourth and fifth run between the Semispinalis capitis and cervicis which they supply, and near the spinous processes of the vertebræ pierce the Splenius and Trapezius to end in the skin (Fig. 831). Those of the lower three nerves are small and end in the Semispinalis cervicis and capitis, Multifidus, and Interspinales. The lateral branches of the lower five nerves supply the Splenius, Iliocostalis cervicis, and Longissimus capitis and cervicis.

The dorsal divisions of the first, and the medial branches of the dorsal divisions of the second and third cervical nerves are sometimes joined by communicating loops to form a **posterior cervical plexus** (Cruveilhier). The greater and lesser occipital nerves vary reciprocally with each other; the greater may communicate with the great auricular or posterior auricular nerves, and a branch to the auricula has been observed. The cutaneous branch of the fifth nerve may be lacking and the lower cervical nerves occasionally have cutaneous twigs.

The Thoracic Nerves.

The dorsal primary divisions of all the thoracic nerves have medial and lateral branches, but the cutaneous branches are different in the upper and lower thorax.

a. The **medial branch** (*r. medialis; internal branch*) (Fig. 854) from the dorsal divisions of the **upper six thoracic nerves** passes between the Semispinalis and Multifidus, supplying them, pierces the Rhomboidei and Trapezius, and approaching the skin close to the spinous process of the vertebra (Fig. 831), extends out laterally over the back. The medial branches of the lower six nerves end in the Transversospinales and Longissimus muscles, usually without cutaneous branches.

b. The **lateral branches** (*r. lateralis; external branch*) run through or under the Longissimus to the interval between it and the Iliocostalis and supply these muscles. They gradually increase in size from the first to the twelfth; the upper six end in the muscles, but the **lower six** have **cutaneous branches** which pierce the Serratus posterior inferior and the Latissimus dorsi along the line of junction between the fleshy and aponeurotic portions of the latter muscle (Fig. 831).

The cutaneous portions of both medial and lateral branches have a downward course which becomes more pronounced from above downward, that of the twelfth nerve reaching down to the skin of the buttocks. The cutaneous part of the first thoracic may be lacking. Both medial and lateral branches of some nerves may have cutaneous fibers, especially those of the sixth, seventh, and eighth (Fig. 832).

The Lumbar Nerves.

a. The **medial branches** of the dorsal primary divisions of the lumbar nerves run close to the articular processes of the vertebræ and end in the Multifidus.

b. The **lateral branches** supply the Sacrospinalis. The upper three give off cutaneous nerves which pierce the aponeurosis of the Latissimus dorsi at the lateral border of the Sacrospinalis and cross the posterior part of

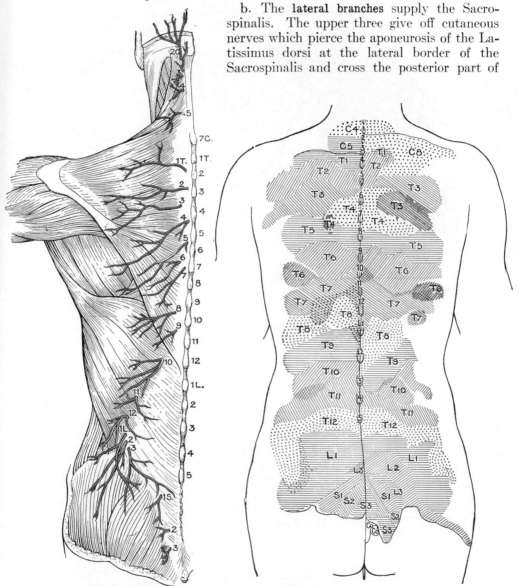

FIG. 831.—Diagram of the distribution of the cutaneous branches of the dorsal divisions of the spinal nerves.

FIG. 832.—Areas of distribution of the cutaneous branches of the dorsal divisions of the spinal nerves. The areas of the medial branches are in black, those of the lateral in red. (H. M. Johnston.)

the iliac crest to be distributed, as the **superior clunial nerves** (*nn. clunium superiores*), to the skin of the buttocks as far as the greater trochanter (Fig. 831).

The Sacral and Coccygeal Nerves.

The dorsal divisions of the sacral nerves are small, and diminish in size from above downward; they emerge, except the last, through the posterior sacral foramina under cover of the Multifidus.

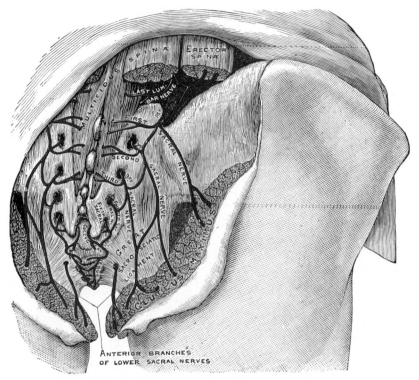

Fig. 833.—The dorsal divisions of the sacral nerves.

a. The **medial branches** of the first three are small, and end in the Multifidus.

b. The **lateral branches** of the first three join with one another and with the last lumbar and fourth sacral to form loops on the dorsal surface of the Sacrum (Fig. 833). From these loops branches run to the dorsal surface of the sacrotuberous ligament and form a second series of loops under the Gluteus maximus. From this second series two or three cutaneous branches pierce the Gluteus maximus along a line from the posterior superior iliac spine to the tip of the coccyx, and supply the the skin over the medial part of the buttocks.

The dorsal divisions of the last two sacral and the coccygeal nerves do not divide into medial and lateral branches, but unite with each other on the back of the sacrum, to form loops which then supply the skin over the coccyx.

VENTRAL PRIMARY DIVISIONS OF THE SPINAL NERVES.

The **ventral primary divisions** (*rr. ventrales*) of the spinal nerves supply the ventral and lateral parts of the trunk and all parts of the limbs. They are for the most part larger than the dorsal divisions. In the thoracic region they remain independent of one another, but in the cervical, lumbar, and sacral regions they unite near their origins to form plexuses.

The Cervical Nerves (Nn. Cervicales).

The ventral division of the **first cervical** or **suboccipital nerve** issues from the vertebral canal above the posterior arch of the atlas and runs forward around the lateral aspect of the superior articular process, medial to the vertebral artery. In most instances it is medial and anterior to the Rectus capitis lateralis, but occasionally it pierces the muscle.

The ventral divisions of the other cervical nerves pass outward between the anterior and posterior Intertransversarii, lying on the grooved upper surfaces of the transverse processes of the vertebræ. The upper four cervical nerves form the cervical plexus; the lower four, together with the first thoracic, form the brachial plexus. They all receive sympathetic roots (gray rami communicantes) from the sympathetic chain.

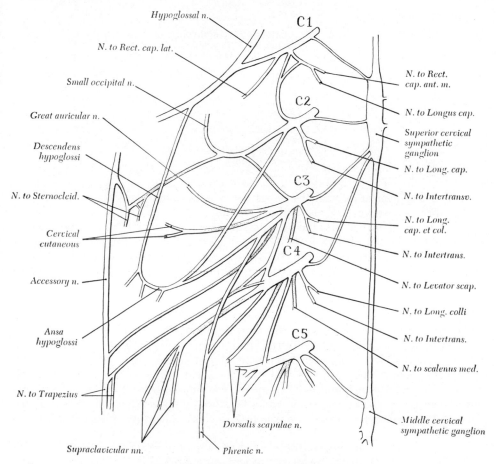

FIG. 834.—Plan of the cervical plexus.

The Cervical Plexus.

The **cervical plexus** (*plexus cervicalis*) (Fig. 834) is formed by the ventral primary divisions of the upper four cervical nerves; each nerve, except the first, divides into an upper and a lower branch, and the branches unite to form three loops. The sympathetic roots may join the nerves or the loops. The plexus is situated opposite the upper four cervical vertebræ, ventrolateral to the Levator scapulæ and Scalenus medius and deep to the Sternocleidomastoideus.

The cervical plexus has communications with certain cranial nerves, and muscular and cutaneous branches which may be arranged in tabular form as follows, the numbers indicating the segmental components:

Communications	1. with Vagus nerve	C 1, 2
	2. with Hypoglossal nerve	C 1, 2
	3. with Accessory nerve	C 2, 3, 4
Superficial or Cutaneous Branches	1. Smaller occipital	C 2
	2. Great auricular	C 2, 3
	3. Cervical cutaneous	C 2, 3
	4. Supraclavicular	C 3, 4
Deep or Muscular Branches	5. Rectus capitis anterior and lateralis	C 1, 2 / C 1
	6. Longus capitis and cervicis	C 1, 2, 3 / C 2, 3, 4
	7. Hypoglossal branches Geniohyoideus	C 1, 2
	Thyrohyoideus	C 1, 2
	Omohyoideus (superior)	C 1, 2
	8. Ansa Hypoglossi Sternohyoideus	C 2, 3
	Sternothyroideus	C 2, 3
	Omohyoideus (inferior)	C 2, 3
	9. Phrenic	C 3, 4, 5
	10. Sternocleidomastoideus	C 2, 3
	11. Trapezius	C 3, 4
	12. Levator scapulæ	C 3, 4
	13. Scalenus medius	C 3, 4

1. The **communication with the vagus nerve** is between the loop connecting the first and second nerves and the nodose ganglion.

2. The **communication with the hypoglossal nerve** (Figs. 826, 834) is a short bundle which leaves the loop between the first and second nerves. The great bulk of its fibers are from the first nerve and run distally with the hypoglossal for two or three centimeters and leave it again as the descending hypoglossal. It contains motor and proprioceptive fibers for certain of the hyoid muscles and will be described below as part of the ansa hypoglossi.

3. The **communications with the accessory nerve** (Fig. 834) leave the cervical plexus at several points; (a) one leaves the loop between the second and third nerves, frequently appearing to come from the small occipital nerve, and joins the fibers of the accessory which supply the Sternocleidomastoideus; (b) a bundle leaves the third nerve, sometimes in association with the great auricular nerve, and joins the accessory fibers to the Trapezius; (c) one or two bundles leave the fourth nerve and join the accessory directly or enter into a network on the deep surface of the Trapezius. These communications contain proprioceptive sensory fibers (Corbin and Harrison '39).

A. Superficial or Cutaneous Branches of the Cervical Plexus.—

1. The **Smaller Occipital Nerve** (*n. occipitalis minor*) (Fig. 835) arises from the second cervical nerve or the loop between the second and third, and ascends along the Sternocleidomastoideus, curving around its posterior border. Near the insertion of the muscle on the cranium, it perforates the deep fascia, and is continued upward along the side of the head behind the ear, supplying the skin and communicating with the greater occipital and the great auricular nerves, and the posterior auricular

branch of the facial. It has an auricular branch which supplies the upper and back part of the auricula, communicating with the mastoid branch of the great auricular.

Variations.—The smaller occipital nerve varies reciprocally with the greater occipital; it is frequently duplicated or may be wanting.

2. The **Great Auricular Nerve** (*n. auricularis magnus*) (Fig. 835), larger than the preceding, arises from the second and third nerves, winds around the posterior border of the Sternocleidomastoideus, and, after perforating the deep fascia, ascends

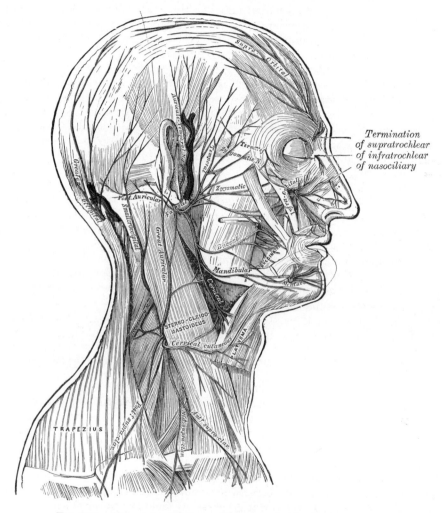

Termination
of supratrochlear
of infratrochlear
of nasociliary

FIG. 835.—The nerves of the scalp, face, and side of neck.

on the surface of that muscle but deep to the Platysma, where it divides into an anterior and a posterior branch.

a. The **anterior branch** (*r. anterior; facial branch*) is distributed to the skin of the face over the parotid gland. It communicates in the substance of the gland with the facial nerve.

b. The **posterior branch** (*r. posterior; mastoid branch*) supplies the skin over the mastoid process and back of the auricula except its upper part; a filament pierces the auricula to reach its lateral surface, where it is distributed to the lobule and lower part of the concha. It communicates with the smaller occipital, the auricular branch of the vagus, and the posterior auricular branch of the facial nerve.

3. The **Cervical Cutaneous** (*n. transversus colli; superficial or transverse cervical nerve*) (Fig. 835) arises from the second and third cervical nerves and bends around the posterior border of the Sternocleidomastoideus about at its middle. Crossing the surface of the muscle obliquely as it runs horizontally forward, passing deep to the external jugular vein, and the Platysma, it perforates the deep fascia, and divides into ascending and descending branches.

a. The **ascending branches** (*rr. superiores*) pass upward to the submaxillary region, pierce the Platysma, and are distributed to the upper, ventral, and lateral parts of the neck. One filament accompanies the external jugular vein toward the angle of the mandible and communicates with the cervical branch of the facial nerve under cover of the Platysma.

b. The **descending branches** (*rr. inferiores*) pierce the Platysma and are distributed to the skin of the ventral and lateral parts of the neck as far down as the sternum.

4. The **Supraclavicular Nerves** (*nn. supraclaviculares; descending branches*) (Fig. 835) arise from the third and fourth, mainly the fourth, cervical nerves. They emerge from under the posterior border of the Sternocleidomastoideus and cross the posterior triangle of the neck under cover of the investing layer of deep fascia. Near the clavicle they perforate the fascia and Platysma in three bundles or groups —anterior, middle, and posterior.

a. The **anterior supraclavicular nerves** (*nn. supraclaviculares anteriores; suprasternal nerves*) cross the external jugular vein, the clavicular head of the Sternocleidomastoideus, and the clavicle to supply the skin of the medial infraclavicular region as far as the midline. They furnish one or two filaments to the sternoclavicular joint.

b. The **middle supraclavicular nerves** (*nn. s. medii; supraclavicular nerves*) cross the clavicle and supply the skin over the Pectoralis major and Deltoideus, communicating with the cutaneous branches of the upper intercostal nerves.

c. The **posterior supraclavicular nerves** (*nn. s. posteriores; supra-acromial nerves*) pass obliquely across the outer surface of the Trapezius and the acromion, and supply the skin of the upper and posterior parts of the shoulder.

Variations.—One of the middle supraclavicular nerves may perforate the clavicle.

B. Deep or Muscular Branches of the Cervical Plexus.—

5. **Branches** to the **Rectus capitis anterior** and **Rectus capitis lateralis** come from the loop between the first and second nerves.

6. **Branches** to the **Longus capitis** and **Longus cervicis** are given off separately; for the capitis from the first, second, and third; for the cervicis from the second, third, and fourth nerves.

The **branches to the hyoid musculature** are usually described as branches of the hypoglossal nerve, but the fibers do not come from the hypoglossal nucleus in the brain; they originate in the cervical nerves. Fibers are communicated to the hypoglossal from the first cervical or the loop between the first and second cervical and either (*a*) leave as individual branches to the Geniohyoideus and Thyrohyoideus, or (*b*) leave the hypoglossal as the descending hypoglossal and join the descending cervical nerve from the second and third cervical nerves to form the ansa hypoglossi.

7. Branches from the hypoglossal nerve or the **descending hypoglossal** are as follows:

a. The fibers to the **Thyrohyoideus** are communicated to the hypoglossal nerve from the first cervical, leave the hypoglossal nerve after the latter has given off the descending hypoglossal, and enter the muscle as a slender filament.

b. The fibers to the **Geniohyoideus** leave the nerve more distally and have a course similar to those for the Thyrohyoideus.

c. The fibers for the **superior belly** of the **Omohyoideus** leave the descending hypoglossal nerve before it forms the ansa and reach the muscle as a slender filament.

8. **Ansa Hypoglossi.**—The ansa hypoglossi is a loop of slender nerves which may be somewhat plexiform, lying on the superficial surface of the carotid sheath (Fig. 836), usually near the middle of the neck. It is formed by the union of the descending hypoglossal nerve and the descending cervical nerve and sends branches to the infrahyoid muscles.

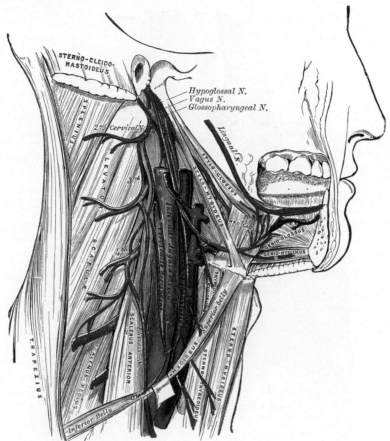

Fig. 836.—Hypoglossal nerve, cervical plexus, and their branches.

The **descending hypoglossal nerve** (*r. descendens hypoglossi* BNA) (Fig. 836) leaves the hypoglossal nerve as the latter loops around the occipital artery, high in the neck, and runs along the lateral surface of the common carotid artery to its junction with the descending cervical nerve just above the tendon of the Omohyoideus. In its course it gives a branch to the superior belly of the Omohyoideus.

The **descending cervical nerve** (*descendens cervicalis; communicantes cervicales; communicantes hypoglossi*) (Fig. 826) is formed by two filaments, one from the second and one from the third cervical, which unite at the lateral side of the internal jugular vein. The slender nerve crosses the vein and becomes the lateral strand of the ansa hypoglossi.

a. The nerve to the **inferior belly** of the **Omohyoideus** quits the loop and crosses the neck below the tendon of the muscle to reach the inferior belly.

64

b. The nerves to the **Sternohyoideus** and **Sternothyroideus** leave the convexity of the loop and run down the superficial surface of the carotid artery to enter their muscles at the root of the neck. They may be separate filaments or be combined into a single nerve for a variable distance.

Variations.—The ansa is quite variable in position; it may occur at any level, frequently high, near the bifurcation of the carotid; it may be within the carotid sheath. The descendens hypoglossi may appear to arise wholly or in part from the vagus. A branch to the Sternocleidomastoideus and filaments entering the thorax to join the vagus or sympathetic have been described.

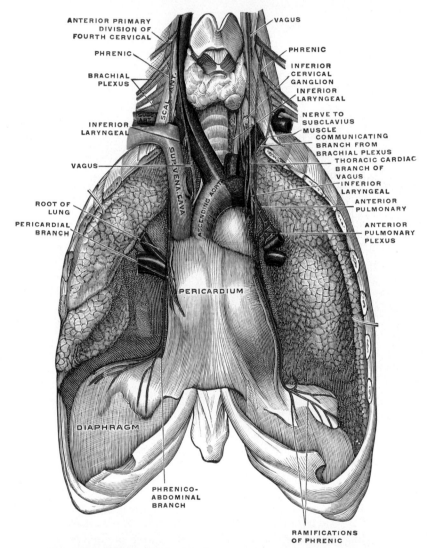

Fig. 837.—The phrenic nerve and its relations with the vagus nerve.

9. The **Phrenic Nerve** (*n. phrenicus; internal respiratory nerve of Bell*) (Fig. 837) is generally known as the motor nerve to the Diaphragm, but it contains about half as many sensory as motor fibers, and it should not be forgotten that the lower thoracic nerves also contribute to the innervation of the Diaphragm. The phrenic nerve originates chiefly from the fourth cervical nerve but is augmented by fibers

from the third and fifth nerves. It lies on the ventral surface of the Scalenus anterior, gradually crossing from its lateral to its medial border (Fig. 836). Under cover of the Sternocleidomastoideus, it is crossed by the inferior belly of the Omohyoideus and the transverse cervical and transverse scapular vessels. It continues with the Scalenus anterior between the subclavian vein and artery, and as it enters the thorax, it crosses the origin of the internal mammary artery and is joined by the pericardiophrenic branch of this artery. It passes downward over the cupula of the pleura and in front of the root of the lung, then along the lateral aspect of the pericardium, between it and the mediastinal pleura, until it reaches the diaphragm, where it divides into its terminal branches. At the root of the neck it is joined by a communication from the sympathetic trunk.

The right nerve is more deeply placed, is shorter, and runs more vertically downward than the left. In the upper part of the thorax it is lateral to the right innominate vein and the superior vena cava (Fig. 837).

The left nerve is longer than the right because of the inclination of the heart toward the left and because of the lower position of the diaphragm on this side. At the root of the neck it is crossed by the thoracic duct, and in the superior mediastinum it lies between the left common carotid and subclavian arteries, and is lateral to the vagus as it crosses the left side of the arch of the aorta (Fig. 837).

a. The **pleural branches** of the phrenic are very fine filaments supplied to the costal and mediastinal pleura over the apex of the lung.

b. The **pericardial branches** are delicate filaments to the upper part of the pericardium.

c. The **terminal branches** pass through the diaphragm separately, and diverging from each other, are distributed on the under surface, supplying the Diaphragma muscle and sensory fibers to the peritoneum. On the right side, a branch near the inferior vena cava communicates with the phrenic plexus which accompanies the inferior phrenic artery from the celiac plexus, and where they join there is usually a small ganglion, the phrenic ganglion. On the left, there is a communication with the phrenic plexus also, but without a ganglion.

Variations.—The phrenic nerve may receive fibers from the descendens cervicalis, or from the second or sixth nerves. At the root of the neck or in the thorax it may be joined by an accessory phrenic from the fifth nerve or from the nerve to the Subclavius. It may arise from the nerve to the Subclavius or give a branch to that muscle. It may pass ventral to the subclavian vein or perforate it.

10. The branches to the **Sternocleidomastoideus** may be independent or partly be communications with the accessory nerve (described above). They are proprioceptive sensory rather than motor nerves and are derived from the second and third nerves (Corbin and Harrison '39).

11. The branches to the **Trapezius** are like those to the Sternocleidomastoideus and are derived from the third and fourth nerves.

12. Muscular branches to the **Levator Scapulæ** are supplied by the third and fourth nerves.

13. Branches to the **Scalenus medius** are from the third and fourth nerves.

The Brachial Plexus.

The **brachial plexus** (*plexus brachialis*) (Figs. 838, 840), as its name implies, supplies the nerves to the upper extremity. It is formed by the ventral primary divisions of the fifth to eighth cervical and the first thoracic nerves. A communicating loop from the fourth to the fifth cervical, and one from the second to the first thoracic also usually contribute to the plexus. It lies in the lower lateral part of the neck and in the clavicular region, extending from the Scalenus anterior to the axilla.

Components.—The brachial plexus is composed of roots, trunks, divisions, cords, and terminal nerves. The **roots** of the brachial plexus are provided by the anterior primary divisions of the lower four cervical and the first thoracic nerves. The trunks are formed from these roots and are named according to their position relative to each other. The **superior trunk** is formed by the union of the fifth and sixth cervical nerves as they emerge between the Scalenus medius and anterior. The **middle trunk** is formed by the seventh cervical alone. The **inferior trunk** is formed by the union of the eighth cervical and first thoracic nerves. The trunks, after a short course, split into **anterior** and **posterior divisions**. The anterior and posterior divisions of the superior and middle trunks are about equal in size, but the posterior division

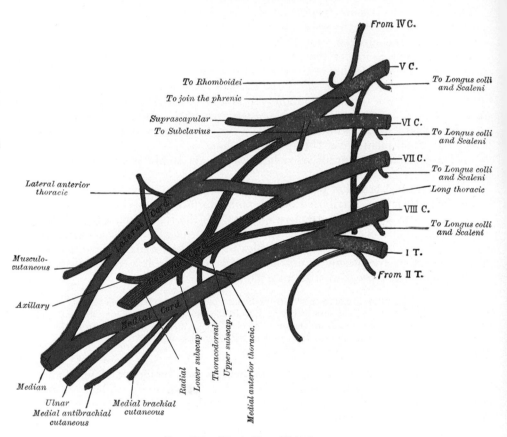

Fig. 838.—Plan of brachial plexus.

of the inferior trunk is much smaller than the anterior because it receives a very small or no contribution from the first thoracic nerve. The **cords,** formed from these divisions, are named according to their relation to the axillary artery: **lateral, medial,** and **posterior.** The anterior divisions of the superior and middle trunks are united into the lateral cord. The anterior division of the inferior trunk becomes the medial cord. The posterior divisions of all three trunks are united into the posterior cord. The cords in turn break up into the nerves which are the terminal branches.

Sympathetic Contributions to the Brachial Plexus.—The ventral primary divisions of the spinal nerves which enter into the brachial plexus obtain their sympathetic roots in the form of the gray rami communicantes from the sympathetic chain. The fifth and sixth nerves receive fibers from the middle cervical ganglion;

the sixth, seventh, and eighth nerves from the inferior cervical or stellate ganglion; the first and second thoracic nerves from the stellate or the first and second thoracic ganglia.

Relations.—In the neck, the brachial plexus lies in the posterior triangle, being covered by the skin, Platysma, and deep fascia; it is crossed by the supraclavicular nerves, the inferior belly of the Omohyoideus, the external jugular vein, and the transverse cervical artery. The roots emerge between the Scaleni anterior and medius, above the third part of the subclavian artery, while the

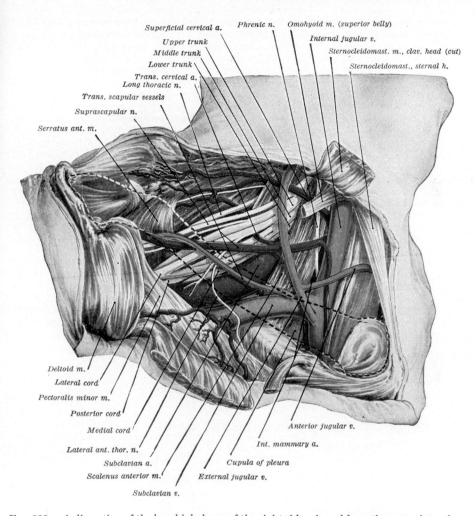

Superficial cervical a.
Phrenic n.
Omohyoid m. (superior belly)
Upper trunk
Internal jugular v.
Middle trunk
Lower trunk
Sternocleidomast. m., clav. head (cut)
Trans. cervical a.
Sternocleidomast., sternal h.
Long thoracic n.
Trans. scapular vessels
Suprascapular n.
Serratus ant. m.

Deltoid m.
Lateral cord
Pectoralis minor m.
Posterior cord
Medial cord
Anterior jugular v.
Lateral ant. thor. n.
Int. mammary a.
Subclavian a.
Cupula of pleura
Scalenus anterior m.
External jugular v.
Subclavian v.

Fig. 839.—A dissection of the brachial plexus of the right side, viewed from the anterolateral aspect.

trunk formed by the union of the eighth cervical and first thoracic is placed behind the artery; the plexus next passes behind the clavicle, the Subclavius, and the transverse scapular vessels, and lies upon the first digitation of the Serratus anterior, and the Subscapularis. In the axilla it is placed lateral to the first portion of the axillary artery; it surrounds the second part of the artery, one cord lying medial to it, one lateral to it, and one behind it; in the lower part of the axilla it gives off its terminal branches to the upper limb.

Variations of the brachial plexus are of several types: (*a*) variations in the contributions of the spinal nerves to the roots of the plexus, (*b*) variations in the formation of the trunks, divisions, or cords, (*c*) variations in the origin or combination of the branches, (*d*) variations in the relation to the artery.

(*a*) The fourth cervical nerve contributes to two-thirds of the plexuses, and T 2 contributes to more than one-third. When the contribution from C 4 is large and that from T 2 lacking, the plexus appears to have a cephalic position and has been termed prefixed. Similarly, when the contribution from T 2 is large and from C 4 lacking, the plexus appears to have a caudad position and has been termed postfixed. It is doubtful whether this shifting of position is more common than one in which the plexus is spread out to include both C 4 and T 2, or contracted to exclude both (Kerr '18). Variations in the contribution to the plexus may be correlated with the position of the limb bud at the time the nerves first grow into it in the embryo (Miller and Detwiler '36), and many variations are similar to the usual conditions found in the different primates (Miller '34).

(*b*) The trunks vary little in their formation from the cervical roots, but the upper and lower trunks especially may appear to be absent because the nerves split into dorsal and ventral divisions before they combine into trunks. The cords in these instances are formed from the divisions of the nerves but the sources of the fibers can be readily traced and made to correspond with the usual pattern. Many of these instances may be the result of too vigorous a removal of the connective tissue sheaths of the nerves in dissection. The medial cord may receive a contribution from the middle trunk and the lateral cord may receive fibers from C 8 or the lower trunk.

(*c*) The median nerve may have small heads either medial or lateral, in addition to the usual two. It appears to receive fibers from all segments entering the plexus in most instances. Many peculiarities involve combined origins of the median and musculocutaneous with separation into definitive nerves or branches farther down the arm; thus the musculocutaneous gives a branch to the median in the arm in a fourth of the cases, but a branch from the median to the ulnar is much less frequent. The musculocutaneous frequently receives fibers from C 4 in addition to the usual C 5 and C 6, and appears to receive fibers from C 7 in only two-thirds. The nerve to the Coracobrachialis is a branch of the lateral cord or some part of the plexus (exclusive of C 8 and T 1) other than the musculocutaneous in almost half of the cases. The ulnar nerve may have a lateral head from the lateral cord, the lateral head of the median, or from C 7; in two-thirds of the plexuses the ulnar may receive fibers from C 7 or possibly more cephalic segments. The radial and axillary nerves may be formed from the trunks and divisions without the presence of a true posterior cord. The radial nerve appears to receive fibers from all segments contributing to the plexus in most instances, but participation of C 4 and T 1 is probably incidental because C 4 may not enter the plexus and in a few instances T 1 can be definitely excluded. The axillary nerve probably receives no fibers from C 8 and T 1 and the contribution from C 7 is undetermined (Kerr '18).

(*d*) Among the variations in the relationship between the axillary artery and the brachial plexus, the most common is an artery superficial to the median nerve; also, the median nerve may be split by a branch of the artery. An aberrant axillary artery, *i.e.*, one not derived from the seventh segmental, has a different relation to the roots of the plexus depending on whether it was derived from a segmental artery above or below the seventh. The cords of the plexus may be split by arterial branches, and communicating loops of nerves may be formed around the artery or its branches (Miller '39).

BRANCHES FROM THE CERVICAL NERVES

To the phrenic nerve	C 5.
To Longus colli and the Scaleni	C 5, 6, 7, 8.
Accessory phrenic	C 5.

BRANCHES FROM THE ROOTS

Dorsal scapular	C 5.
Long thoracic	C 5, 6, 7.

BRANCHES FROM THE TRUNKS

Nerve to the Subclavius	C 5, 6.
Suprascapular	C 5, 6.

BRANCHES FROM THE CORDS

Anterior thoracic	C 5, 6, 7, 8, T 1.
Subscapular	C 5, 6.
Thoracodorsal	C 5, 6, 7.
Axillary	C 5, 6.
Medial brachial cutaneous	C 8, T 1.
Medial antebrachial cutaneous	C 8, T 1.

TERMINAL NERVES

Musculocutaneous	C 5, 6, 7.
Median	C 6, 7, 8, T 1.
Ulnar	C 8, T 1.
Radial	C 5, 6, 7, 8, T 1.

The ventral primary divisions of the lower cervical nerves give branches before they enter into the plexus, and the brachial plexus may be divided into the branches which arise from the roots, from the trunks, or from the cords, and into the terminal nerves. From their topographical relation to the clavicle, the branches may be divided into supra- and infraclavicular branches.

A. Branches of the anterior primary divisions of the lower four cervical and first thoracic nerves before they enter the brachial plexus.—

1. The fifth cervical may contribute to the **phrenic nerve** at its origin.

2. **Muscular branches** from each of the four lower cervical nerves are supplied to the Longus colli and the Scalenus anterior, medius, and posterior.

3. The **Accessory Phrenic Nerve** is an inconstant branch which may come from the nerve to the Subclavius or from the fifth nerve. It passes ventral to the subclavian vein and joins the phrenic nerve at the root of the neck or in the thorax, forming a loop around the vein.

Surgical Considerations.—The operation of resection of the phrenic nerve for immobilization of the diaphragm may be only partially successful if the accessory is not resected also. In avulsion of the phrenic nerve, the subclavian vein is in danger of being torn by the loop between the accessory and the phrenic nerves.

Supraclavicular Branches.

B. Branches from the roots (spinal nerves).—

4. The **Dorsal Scapular Nerve** (*n. dorsalis scapulæ; nerve to the Rhomboidei; posterior scapular nerve*) (Fig. 838) arises from the fifth cervical nerve near the intervertebral foramen, frequently in common with a root of the long thoracic nerve. It pierces the Scalenus medius and runs dorsally as well as downward on the deep surface of the Levator scapulæ to the vertebral border of the scapula. It supplies the Rhomboideus major and minor and, along with the third and fourth nerves, gives a branch to the Levator.

5. The **Long Thoracic Nerve** (*n. thoracalis longus; external respiratory nerve of Bell; posterior thoracic nerve*) (Fig. 840) is the nerve to the Serratus anterior. It arises by three roots: from the fifth, sixth, and seventh cervical nerves; those from the fifth and sixth join just after they pierce the Scalenus medius; the seventh joins them at the level of the first rib. It runs dorsal to the brachial plexus and axillary vessels and continues along the lateral surface of the Serratus anterior, under cover of the Subscapularis. It sends branches to all the digitations of the Serratus, the fibers from the fifth nerve supply the upper part, the sixth the middle, and the seventh the lower part of the muscle.

Variations.—The root from the fifth nerve may remain independent; the root from the seventh may be lacking.

C. Branches from the Trunks.—

6. The **Nerve to the Subclavius** (*n. subclavius*) is a small branch which arises from the superior trunk, although its fibers are mainly from the fifth nerve, and passes ventral to the lower part of the plexus, the subclavian artery, and the subclavian vein to reach the Subclavius muscle.

Variations.—The accessory phrenic may arise from the subclavius nerve or the phrenic nerve may supply the branch to the Subclavius.

7. The **Suprascapular Nerve** (*n. suprascapularis*) (Figs. 839, 841) arises from the superior trunk and takes a more or less direct course across the posterior triangle to the scapular notch, passing under the inferior belly of the Omohyoideus and the anterior border of the Trapezius. It passes through the notch, under the superior transverse ligament, runs deep to the Supraspinatus, and around the lateral border

of the spine of the scapula into the infraspinatous fossa. In the supraspinatous fossa it gives two branches, one to the Supraspinatus and the other an articular filament to the shoulder joint. In the infraspinatous fossa it gives two branches to the Infraspinatus, and filaments to the shoulder joint and scapula.

Infraclavicular Branches.

The infraclavicular branches arise from the three cords of the brachial plexus, but it should be emphasized that a particular branch of any cord need not contain fibers from all the cervical nerves contributing to that cord. For example, the axillary nerve, from the posterior cord, contains fibers from C 5 and 6 only, not from C 5, 6,

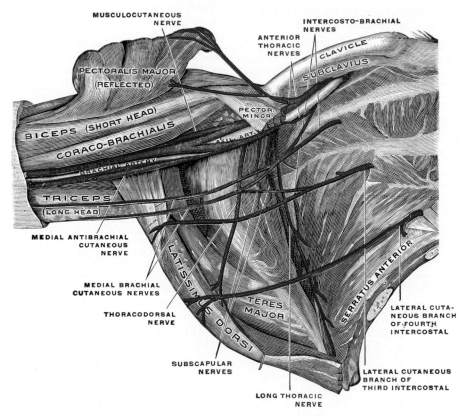

FIG. 840.—The right brachial plexus (infraclavicular portion) in the axillary fossa; viewed from below and in front. The Pectoralis major and minor muscles have been in large part removed; their attachments have been reflected. (Spalteholz.)

7, 8, and T 1. Likewise, a branch from one of the larger terminal nerves may not contain fibers from all the cervical segments contributing to that nerve; the branch of the radial nerve to the Supinator, for example, contains only fibers from C 6.

D. Branches from the cords.—

8. The **Anterior Thoracic Nerves** (*nn. thoracales anteriores; pectoral nerves*) (Fig. 840) are two nerves, one lateral and one medial to the axillary artery, which arise at the level of the clavicle and supply the pectoral muscles.

a. The **lateral anterior thoracic nerve** (*fasciculus lateralis*) is so named because it is lateral to the artery and arises from the lateral cord of the brachial plexus or from the anterior divisions of the fifth, sixth, and seventh nerves just before they unite into the cord. It passes superficial to the first part of the axillary artery and vein, sends a communicating branch to the medial anterior thoracic, and then pierces the clavipectoral fascia to reach the deep surface of the clavicular and upper sternocostal portions of the Pectoralis major.

b. The **medial anterior thoracic nerve** (*fasciculus medialis*) is so named because its origin from the medial cord of the brachial plexus is medial to the artery although it is more lateral in position with respect to the midline of the body than that of the lateral nerve. It passes between the axillary artery and vein, gives a branch which joins the communication from the lateral nerve to form a plexiform loop around the artery, and enters the deep surface of the Pectoralis minor. It supplies this muscle and two or three of its branches continue through the muscle to supply the lower part of the Pectoralis major. The lowest branch may pass around the lower border of the minor. The loop gives off branches which supply both muscles.

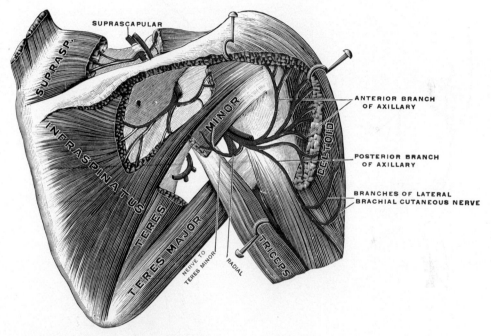

Fig. 841.—Suprascapular and axillary nerves of right side, seen from behind. (Testut.)

9. The **Subscapular Nerves** (*nn. subscapulares*) (Fig. 840), usually two in number, arise from the posterior cord of the brachial plexus, deep in the axilla.

a. The **upper subscapular** (*short subscapular*), the smaller of the two, enters the upper part of the Subscapularis and is frequently double.

b. The **lower subscapular** supplies the lower part of the Subscapularis and ends in the Teres major.

Variations.—The nerve to the Teres major may be a separate branch of the posterior cord, or, more rarely, of the axillary nerve.

10. The **Thoracodorsal Nerve** (*n. thoracodorsalis; middle or long subscapular nerve*) (Fig. 840) is a branch of the posterior cord of the brachial plexus, usually arising between the two subscapular nerves. It follows the course of the subscapular and thoracodorsal arteries along the posterior wall of the axilla, under cover of the anterior border of the Latissimus dorsi, and terminates in branches which supply this muscle.

11. The **Axillary Nerve** (*n. axillaris; circumflex nerve*) (Fig. 841) is the last branch of the posterior cord of the brachial plexus before the latter becomes the radial nerve. It passes over the insertion of the Subscapularis, dorsal to the axillary artery, crosses the Teres minor, and leaves the axilla, accompanied by the posterior humeral circumflex artery, by passing through the quadrilateral space bounded by the surgical neck of the humerus, the Teres major and minor, and the long head of the Triceps. It divides into two branches.

a. The **posterior branch** (*lower branch*) supplies the Teres minor and the posterior part of the Deltoideus, and then pierces the deep fascia at the posterior border of

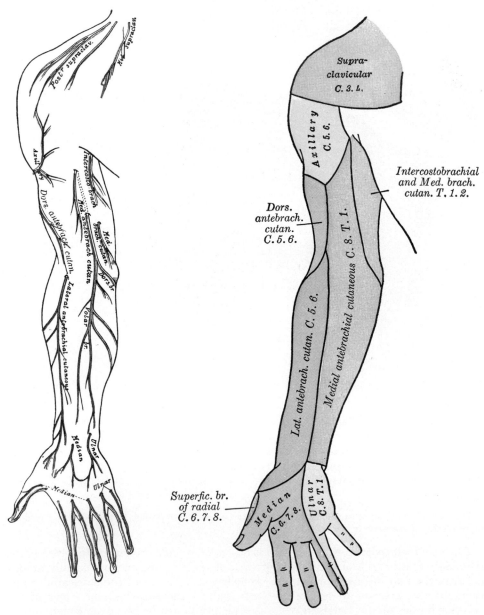

FIG. 842.—Cutaneous nerves of right upper extremity. Anterior view.

FIG. 843.—Diagram of segmental distribution of the cutaneous nerves of the right upper extremity Anterior view.

the Deltoideus as the **lateral brachial cutaneous nerve,** to supply the skin over the lower two-thirds of the posterior part of this muscle and the adjacent long head of the Triceps brachii.

b. The **anterior branch** (*upper branch*) winds around the surgical neck of the humerus with the posterior humeral circumflex vessels, under cover of the Deltoideus as far as its anterior border. It supplies this muscle and sends a few small cutaneous filaments to the skin covering its lower part.

c. **Articular filaments** leave the nerve near its origin and in the quadrilateral space, and supply the anterior inferior part of the capsule of the shoulder joint.

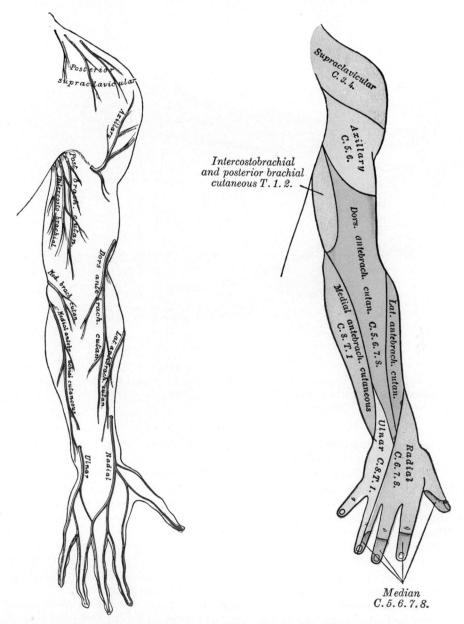

Intercostobrachial
and posterior brachial
cutaneous T. 1. 2.

FIG. 844.—Cutaneous nerves of right upper extremity. Posterior view.

FIG. 845.—Diagram of segmental distribution of the cutaneous nerves of the right upper extremity. Posterior view.

12. The **Medial Brachial Cutaneous Nerve** (*n. cutaneus brachii medialis; nerve of Wrisberg*), a small nerve, arises from the medial cord of the brachial plexus and is distributed to the medial side of the arm. It passes through the axilla, at first lying behind, then medial to the axillary vein and brachial artery. It pierces the deep fascia in the middle of the arm and is distributed to the skin of the arm as far as the medial epicondyle and olecranon. A part of it forms a loop with the intercostobrachial nerve in the axilla, and there is a reciprocal relationship in size between these two nerves. It also communicates with the ulnar branch of the medial antebrachial cutaneous nerve or it may be a branch of the latter nerve.

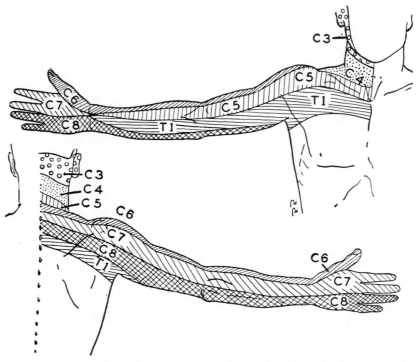

Fig. 846.—Dermatome chart of the upper extremity of man outlined by the pattern of hyposensitivity from loss of function of a single nerve root. (From the original of Fig. 7, Keegan and Garrett, courtesy of Anatomical Record, *102*, 415.)

13. The **Medial Antebrachial Cutaneous Nerve** (*n. cutaneous antebrachii medialis*) (Fig. 847) arises from the medial cord of the brachial plexus, medial to the axillary artery. Near the axilla, it gives off a filament which pierces the fascia and supplies the skin over the Biceps nearly as far as the elbow. The nerve runs down the ulnar side of the arm medial to the brachial artery, pierces the deep fascia with the basilic vein about the middle of the arm, and divides into a volar and an ulnar branch.

a. The **ulnar branch** (*r. ulnaris; posterior branch*) passes obliquely downward on the medial side of the basilic vein, in front of the medial epicondyle of the humerus to the back of the forearm, and continues on its ulnar side as far as the wrist, supplying the skin. It communicates with the medial brachial cutaneous, the dorsal antebrachial cutaneous, and the dorsal branch of the ulnar nerve.

b. The **anterior branch** (*r. anterior*) is larger and passes, usually in front of but occasionally behind, the median basilic vein. It continues on the front of the ulnar side of the forearm, distributing filaments to the skin as far as the wrist, and communicating with the palmar cutaneous branch of the ulnar nerve.

E. The terminal branches of the brachial plexus are the musculocutaneous, median, ulnar, and radial nerves.

14. The Musculocutaneous Nerve.

The **musculocutaneous nerve** (*n. musculocutaneous*) (Fig. 847) is formed by the splitting of the lateral cord of the brachial plexus at the inferior border of the Pectoralis minor into two branches, the other branch being the lateral root of the median nerve. It pierces the Coracobrachialis, and lying between the Brachialis and the Biceps brachii, crosses to the lateral side of the arm. A short distance above the elbow it pierces the deep fascia lateral to the tendon of the Biceps and continues into the forearm as the lateral antebrachial cutaneous nerve.

1. The **branch to the Coracobrachialis** leaves the nerve close to its origin.

2. **Muscular branches** are supplied to the **Biceps** and the greater part of the **Brachialis**.

3. An **articular filament** given off from the nerve to the Brachialis supplies the elbow joint.

4. A **filament to the humerus** enters the nutrient foramen with the artery.

5. The **lateral antebrachial cutaneous nerve** (*n. cutaneous antebrachii lateralis*) passes deep to the cephalic vein and divides opposite the elbow joint into a volar and a dorsal branch.

a. The **volar branch** (*r. volaris; anterior branch*) follows along the radial border of the forearm to the wrist, and supplies the skin over the radial half of its volar surface. At the wrist it is superficial to the radial artery, and some of its filaments pierce the deep fascia to follow the vessel to the dorsal surface of the carpus. It terminates in cutaneous filaments at the thenar eminence after communicating with the superficial branch of the radial and the palmar cutaneous branch of the median nerve.

b. The **dorsal branch** (*r. dorsalis; posterior branch*) passes distally along the dorsal part of the radial surface of the forearm, supplying the skin almost to the wrist, and communicating with the dorsal antebrachial cutaneous nerve and the superficial branch of the radial.

Variations.—The musculocutaneous and median nerves present frequent irregularities in their origins from the lateral cord of the plexus. The branch to the Coracobrachialis may be a separate nerve. In this condition the musculocutaneous may continue with the median for a variable distance before it passes under the Biceps. Some of the fibers of the median may run for some distance in the musculocutaneous before they join their proper trunk; less frequently the reverse is the case and fibers of the musculocutaneous run with the median. It may give a branch to the Pronator teres or it may supply the dorsum of the thumb in the absence of the superficial branch of the radial.

15. The Median Nerve.

The **median nerve** (*n. medianus*) (Fig. 847) is the nerve to the radial side of the flexor portion of the forearm and hand. It takes its origin from the brachial plexus by two large roots, one from the lateral and one from the medial cord. The roots at first lie on each side of the third part of the axillary artery, then embracing it, they unite on its ventral surface to form the trunk of the nerve. In its course down the arm it accompanies the brachial artery, to which it is at first lateral, but it gradually crosses the ventral surface of the artery in the middle or lower part of the arm and lies medial to it at the bend of the elbow, where it is deep to the lacertus fibrosus and superficial to the Brachialis. In the forearm it passes between the two heads of the Pronator teres, being separated from the ulnar artery by the deep head. It continues distally between the Flexores digitorum sublimis and profundus almost to the transverse carpal ligament where it becomes more superficial (Fig.

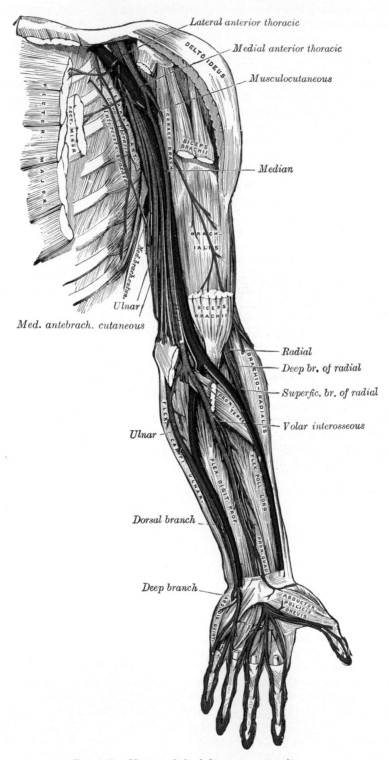

FIG. 847.—Nerves of the left upper extremity.

848) and lies between the tendons of the Flexor digitorum sublimis and the Flexor carpi radialis. It is deep to the tendon of the Palmaris longus and slightly medial to it, and it is the most superficial of the structures which pass through the tunnel under the transverse carpal ligament. In the palm of the hand it is covered only by the skin and the palmar aponeurosis and rests on the tendons of the flexor muscles. Immediately after emerging from under the transverse carpal ligament it becomes enlarged and flattened and splits into muscular and digital branches.

Branches.—The median nerve has no branches above the elbow joint unless, as occasionally happens, the nerve to the Pronator teres arises there.

1. **Articular branches** to the elbow joint are one or two twigs given off as the nerve passes in front of the joint.

2. **Muscular branches** (*r. musculares*) leave the nerve near the elbow and supply all the superficial muscles of the volar part of the forearm except the Flexor carpi ulnaris, *i. e.*, the **Pronator teres, Flexor carpi radialis, Palmaris longus** and **Flexor digitorum sublimis.**

3. The **volar interosseous nerve** (*n. interosseus anterior*) (Fig. 847) accompanies the volar interosseous artery along the volar surface of the interosseous membrane in the interval between the Flexor pollicis longus and the Flexor digitorum profundus, ending in the Pronator quadratus and the wrist joint. It supplies all the deep volar muscles of the forearm except the ulnar half of the profundus, *i. e.*, the radial half of the **Flexor digitorum profundus,** the **Flexor pollicis longus,** and the **Pronator quadratus.**

4. The **palmar branch of the median** (*r. cutaneous palmaris n. mediani*) (Fig. 848) pierces the antebrachial fascia or the volar carpal ligament above the wrist and divides into a medial and lateral branch. The medial branch supplies the skin of the palm and communicates with the palmar cutaneous branch of the ulnar nerve. The lateral branch supplies the skin over the thenar eminence and communicates with the lateral antebrachial cutaneous nerve.

5. The **muscular branch** in the hand (Fig. 850) is a short stout nerve which leaves the radial side of the median nerve, sometimes in company with the first common volar digital nerve, just after the former passes under the transverse carpal ligament. It supplies the muscles of the thenar eminence with the exception of the deep head of the short flexor, *i. e.*, the **Abductor pollicis brevis,** the **Opponens pollicis** and the superficial head of the **Flexor pollicis brevis.**

6. The **first common volar digital nerve** (Figs. 849, 850, 852) divides into three proper volar digital nerves (*digital collaterals*), two of which supply the sides of the thumb, the third gives a **twig to the first Lumbricalis** and continues as the proper volar digital for the radial side of the index finger.

7. The **second common volar digital nerve** gives a twig to the **second Lumbricalis** and continuing to the web between the index and middle fingers, splits into proper digital nerves for the adjacent sides of these fingers.

8. The **third common volar digital nerve** occasionally gives a twig to the third Lumbricalis, in which case it has a double innervation, it communicates with a branch of the ulnar nerve, and continues to the web between the middle and ring fingers where it splits into proper digital nerves for the adjacent sides of these digits.

The **proper digital nerves** (*digital collaterals*) (Figs. 849, 850, 852) supply the skin of the palmar surface and the dorsal surface over the terminal phalanx of their digits. At the end of the digit each nerve terminates in two branches, one of which ramifies in the skin of the ball, the other in the pulp under the nail. They communicate with the dorsal digital branches of the superficial radial, and in the fingers they are superficial to the corresponding arteries.

Variations.—The relation of the median nerve to the two heads of the Pronator teres varies from that described in 16 per cent; it may pass deep to the humeral head in the absence of an ulnar head, or deep to the ulnar head, or split the humeral head (Jamieson and Anson '52). There is overlapping of territory in the innervation of the Flexor digitorum profundus by the median and ulnar nerves in 50 per cent; it is twice as common for the median to encroach on the ulnar. The portion of the Profundus attached to the index finger is the only one constantly supplied by one nerve, the median. In the majority of cases the Profundus and Lumbricalis of a particular digit are innervated by the same nerve. Encroachment of the median on the ulnar is less common for the Lumbricales than the Profundus. The median nerve may supply the first dorsal Interosseus (Sunderland '45, '46).

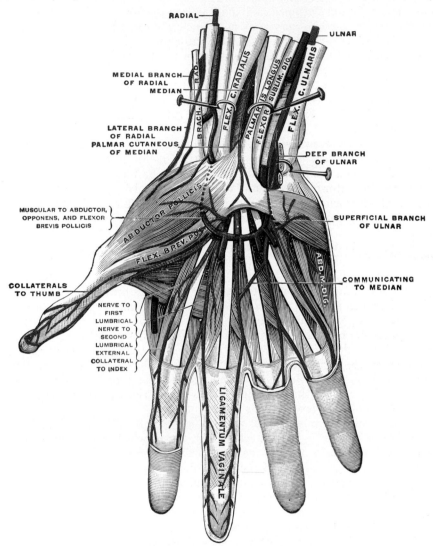

FIG. 848.—Superficial palmar nerves. (Testut.)

16. The Ulnar Nerve.

The **ulnar nerve** (*n. ulnaris*) (Fig. 847) occupies a superficial position along the medial side of the arm and is the nerve to the muscles and skin of the ulnar side of the forearm and hand. It is the terminal continuation of the medial cord of the brachial plexus, after the medial head of the median has separated from it. It is medial, at first to the axillary, and then to the brachial artery as far as the middle of the arm, and is parallel with and not far distant from the medial antebrachial cutaneous median and nerves. In the middle of the arm it angles dorsally, pierces the medial intermuscular septum, and follows along the medial head of the Triceps to the groove between the olecranon and the medial epicondyle of the humerus. In this position it is covered only by the skin and fascia and can readily be palpated as the "funny bone" of the elbow. It is accompanied in its course through the lower half of the arm by the superior ulnar collateral artery and the ulnar collateral branch of the radial nerve. It enters the forearm between the two heads of the Flexor carpi ulnaris and continues between this muscle and the Flexor digitorum

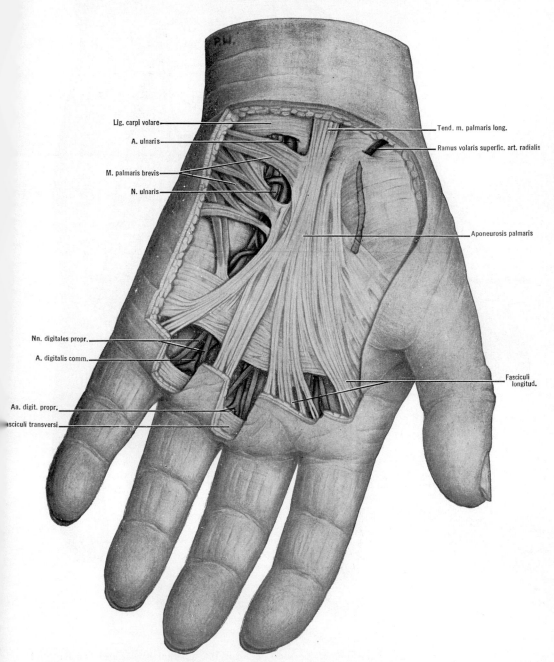

Fig. 849.—Superficial dissection of the palm of the hand. (Töndury, Angewandte und topographische Anatomie, courtesy of Georg Thieme Verlag.)

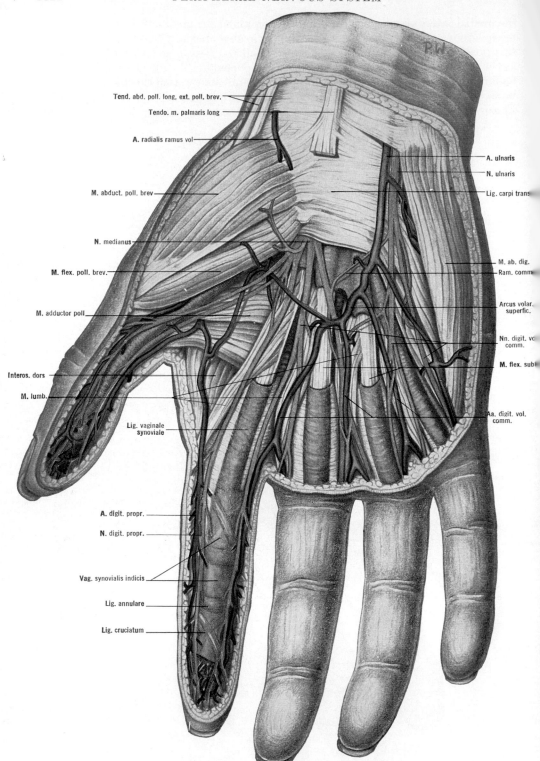

Tend. abd. poll. long, ext. poll. brev.

Tendo. m. palmaris long

A. radialis ramus vol

M. abduct. poll. brev

N. medianus

M. flex. poll. brev.

M. adductor poll

Interos. dors

M. lumb.

Lig. vaginale
synoviale

A. digit. propr.

N. digit. propr.

Vag. synovialis indicis

Lig. annulare

Lig. cruciatum

A. ulnaris

N. ulnaris

Lig. carpi trans

M. ab. dig.

Ram. comm

Arcus volar.
superfic.

Nn. digit. vo
comm.

M. flex. subl

Aa. digit. vol.
comm.

FIG. 850.—Dissection of the palm of the hand, showing the superficial volar arch, median and ulnar nerves, and synovial sheaths.   (Töndury, Angewandte und topographische Anatomie, courtesy of Georg Thieme Verlag.)

profundus half way down the forearm. In the upper part of the forearm it is separated from the ulnar artery by a considerable distance, but in the lower half it lies close to its medial side, lateral to the Flexor carpi ulnaris, and covered only by the skin and fascia. Above the wrist it gives off a large dorsal branch and continues into the hand where it has muscular and digital branches.

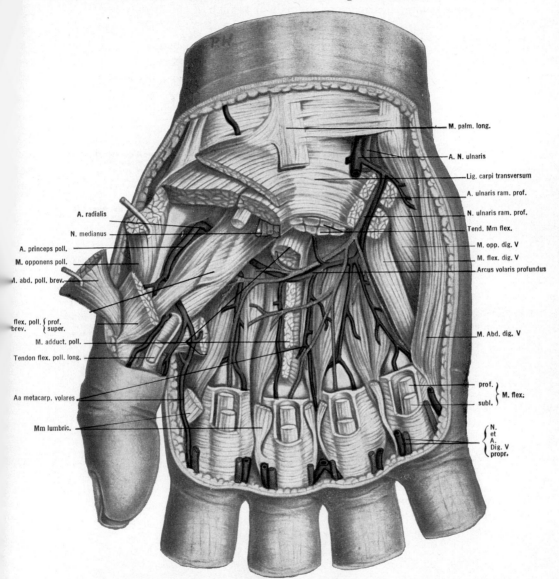

FIG. 851.—Deep dissection of the palm of the hand, showing the deep volar arch and the deep volar branch of the ulnar nerve. (Töndury, Angewandte und topographische Anatomie, courtesy of Georg Thieme Verlag.)

Branches.—The ulnar nerve usually has no branches above the elbow. Below the elbow its branches are as follows:

1. The **articular branches** to the elbow joint are several small filaments which leave the nerve as it lies in the groove between the olecranon and the medial epicondyle of the humerus.

2. **Muscular branches** (*rr. musculares*), two in number, arise near the elbow, and supply the **Flexor carpi ulnaris** and the ulnar half of the **Flexor digitorum profundus**.

3. The **palmar cutaneous branch of the ulnar** (*r. cutaneous palmaris*) arises near the middle of the forearm and accompanies the ulnar artery into the hand. It gives filaments to the artery, perforates the volar carpal ligament, and ends in the skin of the palm, communicating with the palmar branch of the median nerve.

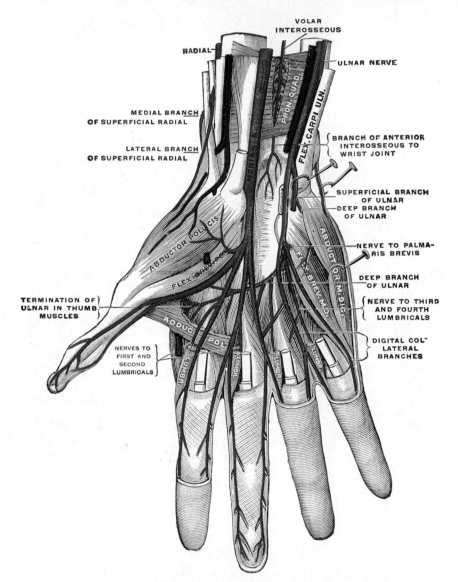

FIG. 852.—Deep palmar nerves. (Testut.)

4. The **dorsal branch** (*r. dorsalis manus*) (Figs. 844, 847) arises in the lower half of the forearm, and reaches the dorsum of the wrist by passing between the Flexor carpi ulnaris and the ulna. It pierces the deep fascia and divides into two **dorsal digital nerves** and a metacarpal communicating branch. The more medial digital nerve supplies the ulnar side of the little finger; the other digital branch, the adjacent sides of the little and ring fingers. The metacarpal branch supplies the skin

of that area and continues toward the web between the ring and middle fingers where it joins a similar branch of the superficial radial to supply the adjacent sides of these two fingers. On the little finger the dorsal digital branches extend only as far as the base of the terminal phalanx, and on the ring finger as far as the base of the second phalanx; the more distal parts of these digits are supplied by the dorsal branches of the proper volar digital nerves from the ulnar.

5. The **palmar branch** (*r. palmaris*) or terminal portion of the ulnar nerve crosses the medial border of the wrist in company with the ulnar artery, superficial to the transverse carpal ligament and under cover of the Palmaris brevis, and divides into a superficial and deep branch.

a. The **superficial branch** (*r. superficialis*) (Figs. 848, 850, 852) supplies the **Palmaris brevis** and the skin of the hypothenar eminence, and divides into **digital branches**. A proper palmar digital branch goes to the ulnar side of the little finger; a common palmar digital divides into proper digital branches for the adjacent sides of the **little and ring fingers** and communicates with the branches of the median nerve. The proper digital branches are distributed to the fingers in the same manner as those of the median.

b. The **deep branch** (*r. profundus*) (Figs. 851, 852) passes between the Abductor digiti quinti and Flexor digiti quinti brevis accompanied by the deep branch of the ulnar artery, it then pierces the Opponens digiti quinti and follows the course of the deep palmar arch across the Interossei, deep to the midpalmar and thenar fascial clefts. Near its origin it gives branches to the **three small muscles of the little finger**, and as it crosses the hand it supplies the **third** and **fourth Lumbricales** and **all the Interossei**, both palmar and dorsal. It ends by supplying the **Adductores pollicis** and the deep head of the **Flexor pollicis brevis**. It also sends articular filaments to the wrist joint.

Variations.—The ulnar nerve may pass in front of the medial epicondyle. It frequently has a communication with the median nerve in the forearm, rarely with the medial antebrachial cutaneous, median, or musculocutaneous in the arm. It may send muscular branches to the medial head of the Triceps, the Flexor digitorum sublimis, the first and second Lumbricales and the superficial head of the Flexor pollicis brevis. It may have deficiencies on the dorsum of the hand which are supplied by the radial or it may encroach upon the area usually supplied by that nerve (Sunderland and Hughes '46). See variations of the median nerve and brachial plexus.

17. The Radial Nerve.

The **radial nerve** (*n. radialis; musculospiral nerve*) (Fig. 853), the largest branch of the brachial plexus, is the continuation of the posterior cord, and supplies the extensor muscles of the arm and forearm, as well as the skin covering them. It crosses the tendon of the Latissimus dorsi, deep to the axillary artery, and after passing the inferior border of the Teres major, it winds around the medial side of the humerus and enters the substance of Triceps between the medial and long heads. It takes a spiral course down the arm close to the humerus in the groove which separates the origins of the medial and lateral heads of the Triceps, accompanied by the arteria profunda brachii. Having reached the lateral side of the arm, it pierces the lateral intermuscular septum and runs between the Brachialis and Brachioradialis to the front of the lateral epicondyle, where it divides into superficial and deep branches (Fig. 847).

A. Branches of the radial nerve in the arm are both muscular and cutaneous:

1. The **medial muscular branches** arise in the axilla and supply the **medial** and **long heads** of the **Triceps**. That to the medial head is a long filament which accompanies the ulnar nerve and superior ulnar collateral artery as far as the lower third of the arm and is therefore named the **ulnar collateral nerve**.

2. The **posterior brachial cutaneous nerve** (*n. cutaneus brachii posterior; internal cutaneous branch of the musculospiral*) arises in the axilla, usually with the medial muscular branches. This small nerve passes through the axilla to the medial side of the arm, supplying the skin on the dorsal surface nearly as far as the olecranon. In its course it crosses behind, and communicates with, the intercostobrachial nerve.

3. The **posterior muscular branches** arise from the nerve as it lies in the spiral groove of the humerus, and supply the **medial** and **lateral heads** of the **Triceps** and the **Anconaeus**. The nerve to the latter muscle is a long, slender filament which lies buried in the substance of the medial head of the Triceps.

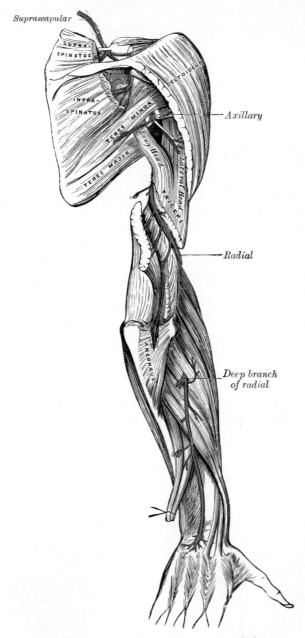

4. The **dorsal antebrachial cutaneous nerve** (*n. cutaneus antebrachii dorsalis; external cutaneous branch of the musculo- spiral*) perforates the lateral head of the Triceps at its at- tachment to the humerus and divides into upper and lower branches.

a. The **upper** and smaller **branch** lies close to the cephalic vein and supplies the skin of the dorsal part of the lower half of the arm.

b. The **lower branch** pierces the deep fascia below the in- sertion of the Deltoideus and continues along the lateral side of the arm and elbow, and dorsal side of the forearm to the wrist. It supplies the skin in its course and near its termination communicates with the dorsal branch of the lateral antebrachial cutaneous nerve.

5. The **lateral muscular branches** supply the **Brachio- radialis**, **Extensor carpi radialis longus**, and the lateral part of the **Brachialis**.

6. **Articular branches** to the elbow come from the radial, between the Brachialis and Brachioradialis, from the ulnar collateral nerve, and from the nerve to the Anconaeus.

B. The branches of the radial nerve in the forearm are:

7. The **Superficial Branch of the Radial Nerve** (*r. superf. n. radialis; radial nerve; superficial radial*) runs along the lateral border of the **forearm** under

Fig. 853.—The suprascapular, axillary, and radial nerves.

cover of the Brachioradialis. In the upper third of the forearm it gradually approaches the radial artery, in the middle third it lies just lateral to the artery, and in the lower third it quits the artery and angles dorsally under the tendon of the Brachioradialis toward the dorsum of the wrist where it pierces the deep fascia and divides into two branches.

a. The **lateral branch** is smaller, supplies the skin of the radial side and ball of the thumb, and communicates with the volar branch of the lateral antebrachial cutaneous nerve.

b. The **medial branch** communicates, above the wrist, with the dorsal branch of the lateral antebrachial cutaneous nerve, and, on the back of the hand, with the dorsal branch of the ulnar nerve. It then divides into four **dorsal digital nerves** which are distributed as follows: (*1*) supplies the ulnar side of the thumb, (*2*) the radial side of the index finger, (*3*) the adjacent sides of the index and middle fingers, and (*4*) communicates with the dorsal branch of the ulnar nerve, and supplies the adjacent sides of the middle and ring fingers (Fig. 844).

8. The **Deep Branch of the Radial Nerve** (*r. profundus; deep radial; posterior interosseous nerve*) (Fig. 853) winds to the back of the forearm around the lateral side of the radius between the planes of fibers of the Supinator (Fig. 467, page 509), and continues between the superficial and deep layers of muscles to the middle of the forearm. Considerably diminished in size and named the **dorsal interosseous nerve**, it lies on the dorsal surface of the interosseous membrane, and under cover of the Extensor pollicis longus continues to the dorsum of the carpus where it ends in a gangliform enlargement.

a. **Muscular Branches.**—Those to the Extensor carpi radialis brevis and the Supinator are given off before the nerve turns dorsally. After passing through the Supinator, branches are given to the Extensor digitorum communis, Extensor digiti quinti proprius, Extensor carpi ulnaris, the two Extensores and Abductor longus pollicis, and the Extensor indicis proprius.

b. **Articular filaments** from the terminal enlargement are distributed to the ligaments and articulations of the carpus and metacarpus.

Variations.—The radial nerve may pass through the quadrilateral space with the axillary nerve, and when the profunda brachii supplies the nutrient artery of the humerus it may be accompanied by a filament from the radial. The nerve to the Brachialis is inconstant. The deep branch may pass superficial to the entire Supinator. There is great variation in the distribution and overlapping of the radial and ulnar nerves on the back of the hand; the primitive arrangement appears to be that the radial supplies three and a half, the ulnar one and a half digits (Sunderland '45, '46).

Thoracic Nerves (nn. Thoracales.)

The **ventral primary divisions** (*rami anteriores; anterior divisions*) (Fig. 854) of the thoracic nerves number twelve on each side. The first eleven, situated between the ribs, are termed **intercostals**; the twelfth lies below the last rib and is called the **subcostal** (*n. subcostalis* BR). The intercostal nerves are distributed chiefly to the parieties of the thorax and abdomen, and differ from the other spinal nerves, in that each pursues an independent course, *i. e.*, they do not enter into a plexus. The first two contribute to the upper limb as well as to the thorax; the next four are limited in their distribution to the thorax; the lower five supply the parietes of the thorax and the abdomen. The twelfth thoracic is distributed to the abdominal wall and the skin of the buttock.

Rami Communicantes.—Each thoracic nerve contributes preganglionic sympathetic fibers to the sympathetic chain through a **white ramus communicans**, and receives postganglionic fibers from the chain ganglia through **gray rami communicantes**. Both rami are attached to the spinal nerves near their exit from the intervertebral

foramina, the gray rami being more medial than the white. For more details see
the section on the Sympathetic System.

The First Thoracic Nerve.—The anterior primary division of the first thoracic
nerve divides immediately into two parts: (*a*) the larger part leaves the thorax in
front of the neck of the first rib, and becomes one of the roots of the brachial plexus
(described above); (*b*) the smaller part becomes the first intercostal nerve. The
first intercostal runs along the first intercostal space to the sternum, perforates the

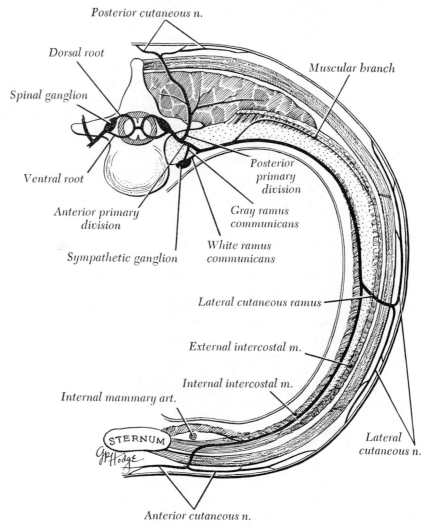

Fig. 854.—Plan of a typical intercostal nerve.

muscles and deep fascia, and ends as the first anterior cutaneous nerve of the thorax.
It has no lateral cutaneous branch, as a rule, but it may have a communication with
the intercostobrachial branch of the second nerve. A communication between the
first and second nerves inside the thorax is of frequent occurrence, and contains
postganglionic sympathetic fibers from the second or even the third thoracic sympathetic ganglion (Kirgis and Kuntz '42).

The Upper Thoracic Nerves (Figs. 854, 855, 856, 879).—The anterior primary
divisions of the second to the sixth thoracic nerves and the intercostal portion of the

first thoracic are known as the **thoracic intercostal nerves** (*nn. intercostales*). They pass ventrally in the intercostal spaces with the intercostal vessels; from the vertebral column to the angles of the ribs, they lie between the pleura and the posterior intercostal membrane; from the angle to the middle of the ribs, they pass between the Intercostales interni and externi. They then enter the substance of the Intercostales interni where they remain concealed until they reach the costal cartilages, where they again emerge on the inner surface of the muscle and lie between it and

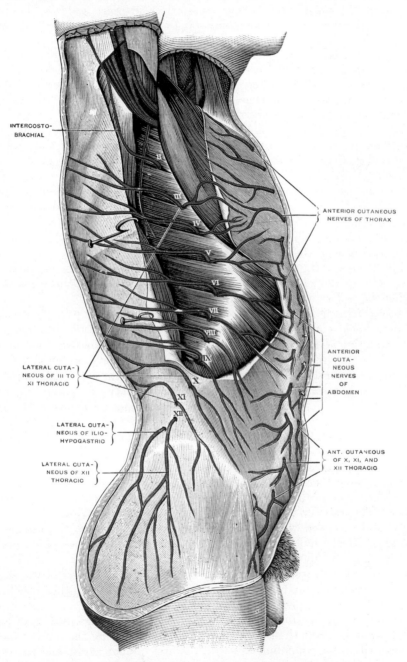

INTERCOSTO-
BRACHIAL

ANTERIOR CUTANEOUS
NERVES OF THORAX

LATERAL CUTA-
NEOUS OF III TO
XI THORACIC

ANTERIOR
CUTA-
NEOUS
NERVES
OF
ABDOMEN

LATERAL CUTA-
NEOUS OF ILIO-
HYPOGASTRIC

LATERAL CUTA-
NEOUS OF XII
THORACIC

ANT. CUTANEOUS
OF X, XI, AND
XII THORACIC

FIG. 855.—Cutaneous distribution of thoracic nerves. (Testut.)

the pleura. The nerves are inferior to the vessels and with them are at first close to the rib above, but as they proceed ventrally may approach the middle of the intercostal space. Near the sternum they pass ventral to the Transversus thoracis and the internal mammary vessels, and near the sternum pierce the Intercostalis internus, the anterior intercostal membrane, the Pectoralis major and pectoral fascia, terminating as the anterior cutaneous nerves of the thorax. They have short medial and longer lateral branches which supply the skin and mamma.

Muscular branches supply the Intercostales interni and externi, the Subcostales, the Levatores costarum, the Serratus posterior superior, and the Transversus thoracis. At the front of the thorax some of these branches cross the costal cartilages from one intercostal space to another.

Cutaneous Branches.—The **lateral cutaneous nerves** (*rr. cutanei laterales*) (Figs. 855, 856) arise from the intercostal nerves about midway between the vertebral column and the sternum, pierce the Intercostales externi and Serratus anterior, and divide into anterior and posterior branches. The anterior branches supply the skin of the lateral and ventral part of the chest and mammæ; those of the fifth and sixth nerves also supply the upper digitations of the Obliquus externus abdominis. The posterior branches supply the skin over the Latissimus dorsi and scapular region.

The **intercostobrachial nerve** (Figs. 840, 847, 855, 856) arises from the second intercostal nerve as if it were a lateral cutaneous nerve, but it fails to divide into an anterior and a posterior branch. After piercing the Intercostales and the Serratus anterior, it crosses the axilla, imbedded in the adipose tissue, to reach the medial side of the arm. It forms a loop of communication with the medial brachial cutaneous nerve of the brachial plexus and assists it in supplying the skin of the medial and posterior part of the arm. It also communicates with the posterior brachial cutaneous branch of the radial nerve.

An intercostobrachial branch frequently arises from the third intercostal nerve, supplying the axilla and medial side of the arm.

The Lower Thoracic Nerves (Figs. 855, 856).—The anterior primary divisions of the seventh to eleventh thoracic nerves are continued beyond the intercostal spaces into the anterior abdominal wall and are named the **thoracoabdominal intercostal nerves**. They have the same arrangement as the upper nerves as far as the anterior ends of the intercostal spaces, where they pass dorsal to the costal cartilages. They run forward between the Obliquus internus and Transversus abdominis, pierce the sheath of the Rectus abdominis, supply this muscle, and terminate as the anterior cutaneous branches.

1. **Muscular branches** supply the Intercostales, the Obliqui and Transversus abdominis, and the last three the Serratus posterior inferior.

2. The **lateral cutaneous branches** (Figs. 855, 856) arise midway along the nerves, pierce the Intercostales externi and the Obliquus externus in line with the lateral cutaneous branches of the upper intercostals, and divide into anterior and posterior branches. The anterior branches give branches to the digitations of the Obliquus externus, and extend downward and forward nearly as far as the margin of the Rectus abdominis, supplying the skin. The posterior branches pass dorsally to supply the skin over the Latissimus dorsi.

3. The **anterior cutaneous branches** penetrate the anterior layer of the sheath of the Rectus abdominis, and divide into medial and lateral branches which supply the skin of the anterior part of the abdominal wall.

The anterior primary division of the **twelfth thoracic** (Figs. 855, 856, 859), or **subcostal nerve**, is larger than those above it. It runs along the inferior border of the twelfth rib, often communicates with the first lumbar nerve, and passes under the lateral lumbocostal arch. It crosses the ventral surface of the Quadratus lumborum, penetrates the Transversus abdominis, and continues anteriorly to be distributed in the same manner as the lower intercostal nerves. It communicates with the iliohypogastric nerve of the lumbar plexus and gives a branch to the Pyramidalis. The lateral cutaneous branch is large and does not divide into an-

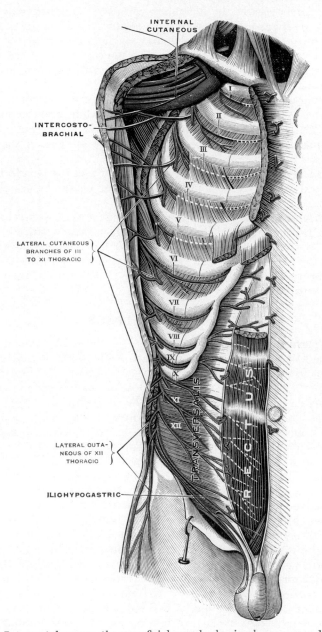

Fig. 856.—Intercostal nerves, the superficial muscles having been removed. (Testut.)

terior and posterior branches. It perforates the Obliqui, passes downward over the crest of the ilium anterior to a similar branch of the iliohypogastric nerve, and is distributed to the skin of the anterior part of the gluteal region, some filaments extending as far down as the greater trochanter.

The Lumbar Nerves (nn. lumbales).

The **ventral primary divisions** (*rr. anteriores*) are increasingly large as they are placed more caudally in the lumbar region. Their course is lateralward and downward, either under cover of the Psoas major or between its fasciculi. The first three nerves and the larger part of the fourth are connected together by communicating loops, and they are frequently joined by a communication from the twelfth thoracic, forming the lumbar plexus. The smaller part of the fourth joins the fifth nerve to form the lumbosacral trunk which enters into the formation of the sacral plexus. The fourth nerve, because it is divided between the two plexuses, has been named the **nervus furcalis**.

Rami Communicantes.—Only the first two lumbar nerves contribute preganglionic sympathetic fibers to the sympathetic chain through **white rami communicantes**. All the lumbar nerves receive postganglionic fibers from the sympathetic chain through **gray rami communicantes**. For more details see the section on the Sympathetic Nervous System.

Muscular branches are supplied to the Psoas major and the Quadratus lumborum from the ventral primary divisions of the lumbar nerves before they enter the lumbar plexus.

The Lumbosacral Plexus (*p. lumbosacralis*) is the name given to the combination of all the ventral primary divisions of the lumbar, sacral, and coccygeal nerves. The lumbar and sacral plexuses supply the lower limb, but in addition the sacral nerves supply the perineum through the pudendal plexus, and the coccygeal region through the coccygeal plexus. For convenience in description, these plexuses will be considered separately.

THE LUMBAR PLEXUS.

The **lumbar plexus** (*plexus lumbalis*) (Fig. 857) is formed by the ventral primary divisions of the first three and the greater part of the fourth lumbar nerves, with a communication from the twelfth thoracic usually joining the first lumbar nerve. It is situated on the inside of the posterior abdominal wall, either dorsal to the Psoas major or among its fasciculi, and ventral to the transverse processes of the lumbar vertebræ. The lumbar plexus is not an intricate interlacement like the brachial plexus, but its branches usually arise from two or three nerves, so that the resulting junctions between adjacent nerves have the appearance of loops.

The manner in which the plexus is formed is the following (Figs. 857, 858): the first lumbar nerve, usually supplemented by a communication from the twelfth thoracic, splits into an upper and a lower branch; the upper forms the iliohypogastric and ilioinguinal; the lower and smaller branch unites with a branch from the second lumbar to form the genitofemoral nerve. The remainder of the second, and the third and fourth nerves each split into a small ventral and a large dorsal portion; the ventral portions unite into one nerve, the obturator. The dorsal portions of the second and third nerves each divide again into unequal branches; the two smaller branches unite to form the lateral femoral cutaneous nerve; the two larger branches join the dorsal portion of the fourth nerve to form the femoral nerve. The accessory obturator, present in about one out of five individuals, comes from the third and fourth. A considerable part of the fourth nerve joins the fifth lumbar in the lumbosacral trunk.

The branches of the lumbar plexus are as follows:

1) Iliohypogastric	L 1, (T 12)	4) Lateral femoral cutaneous	L 2, 3
2) Ilioinguinal	L 1	5) Obturator	L 2, 3, 4
3) Genitofemoral	L 1, 2	6) Accessory obturator	L 3, 4
	7) Femoral	L 2, 3, 4	

These branches may be divided into two groups according to their distribution. The first three supply the lower part of the parietes of the abdominal wall; the last four supply the anterior thigh and medial part of the leg.

1. **The Iliohypogastric Nerve** (*n. iliohypogastricus*) (Figs. 856, 859) arises from the first lumbar and from the communication with the twelfth thoracic when this is present. It emerges from the upper part of the lateral border of the Psoas major, crosses the Quadratus lumborum to the crest of the ilium, and penetrates the posterior part of the Transversus abdominis near the crest of the ilium. Between the Transversus and the Obliquus internus it divides into a lateral and an anterior cutaneous branch.

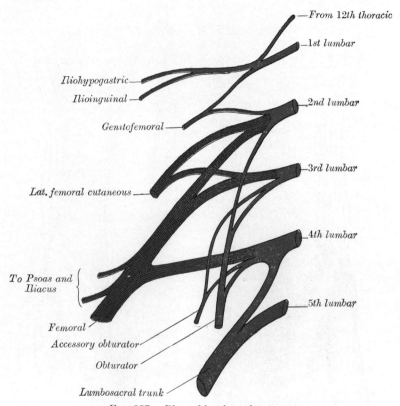

FIG. 857.—Plan of lumbar plexus.

a. The **lateral cutaneous branch** (*r. cutaneus lateralis; iliac branch*) pierces the Obliqui internus and externus immediately above the iliac crest, and is distributed to the skin of the gluteal region posterior to the lateral cutaneous branch of the twelfth thoracic (Figs. 855, 866), these two nerves being inversely proportional in size.

b. The **anterior cutaneous branch** (*r. cutaneus anterior; hypogastric branch*) (Figs. 856, 860) continues its course between the Obliquus internus and Transversus, pierces the former, and becomes subcutaneous by passing through a perforation in the aponeurosis of the Obliquus externus about 2.5 cm. above the subcutaneous inguinal ring. It is distributed to the skin of the hypogastric region (Fig. 827).

2. **The Ilioinguinal Nerve** (*n. ilioinguinalis*) (Figs. 858, 859) arises from the lateral border of the Psoas major just below the iliohypogastric and follows a similar course obliquely across the fibers of the Quadratus lumborum to the crest of the ilium. It penetrates the Transversus near the anterior part of the crest, communicates with

the iliohypogastric nerve, and pierces the Obliquus internus, distributing filaments to it. It then accompanies the spermatic cord through the subcutaneous inguinal ring, and is distributed to the skin over the upper and medial part of the thigh, the root of the penis and the scrotum in the male (Fig. 861), and the mons pubis and labium majus in the female.

The optimum point for blocking the iliohypogastric and ilioinguinal nerves with local anesthetic is 4 to 6 cm. posterior to the anterior superior spine of the ilium, along the lateral aspect of the external lip of the crest, where the nerves perforate the Transversus abdominis (Jamieson et al. '52).

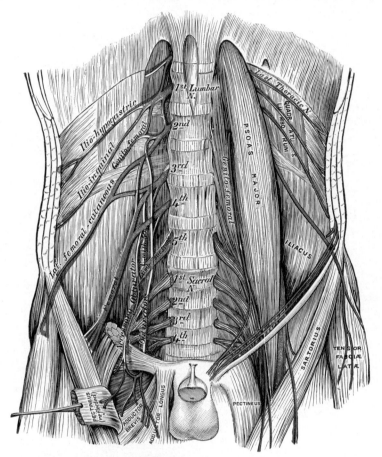

Fig. 858.—The lumbar plexus and its branches.

3. **The Genitofemoral Nerve** (*n. genitofemoralis; genitocrural nerve*) (Figs. 858, 859, 861) arises from the first and second lumbar nerves, passes downward through the substance of the Psoas major until it emerges on its ventral surface opposite the third or fourth lumbar vertebra, where it is covered by transversalis fascia and peritoneum. On the surface of the muscle, or occasionally within its substance, it divides into the external spermatic and lumboinguinal nerves.

a. The **genital branch** (*r. genitalis; external spermatic nerve*) continues along the Psoas major to the inguinal ligament, where it either pierces the transversalis and internal spermatic fascia or passes through the internal inguinal ring to reach the spermatic cord. It lies against the posterior aspect of the cord, supplies the Cremaster, and is distributed to the skin of the scrotum and adjacent thigh. In the female it accompanies the round ligament of the uterus.

b. The **femoral branch** (*r. femoralis*; *lumboinguinal nerve*) lies on the Psoas major, lateral to the external spermatic nerve, and passes under the inguinal ligament with the external iliac artery. It enters the femoral sheath, superficial and lateral to the artery, then pierces the sheath and fascia lata to supply the skin of the upper part of the anterior surface of the thigh. It gives a filament to the femoral artery and communicates with the anterior cutaneous branches of the femoral nerve (Figs. 860, 861).

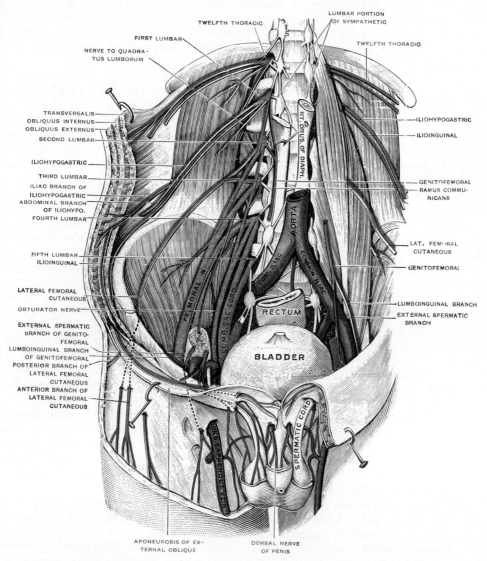

Fig. 859.—Deep and superficial dissection of the lumbar plexus. (Testut.)

Variations.—The iliohypogastric or ilioinguinal nerves may arise from a common trunk or the ilioinguinal may join the iliohypogastric at the iliac crest, the latter nerve then supplying the missing branches. The ilioinguinal may be lacking and the external spermatic supply its branches, or the external spermatic may be absent and the ilioinguinal substitute for it. The lumboinguinal and lateral femoral cutaneous nerves, or the anterior cutaneous branches of the femoral may substitute for each other to a greater or lesser extent.

4. **The Lateral Femoral Cutaneous Nerve** (*n. cutaneus femoralis lateralis; external cutaneous nerve*) (Figs. 857 to 862) arises from the dorsal portions of the second and third lumbar nerves. It emerges from the lateral border of the Psoas major about its middle, and runs across the Iliacus obliquely toward the anterior superior iliac spine. It then passes under the inguinal ligament and over the Sartorius into the subcutaneous tissues of the thigh, dividing into an anterior and a posterior branch (Fig. 859).

a. The **anterior branch** becomes superficial about 10 cm. below the inguinal ligament, and is distributed to the skin of the lateral and anterior parts of the thigh as far as the knee (Fig. 860). The terminal filaments communicate with the anterior cutaneous branches of the femoral nerve and the infrapatellar branches of the saphenous nerve, forming the **patellar plexus**.

b. The **posterior branch** pierces the fascia lata and subdivides into filaments which pass backward across the lateral and posterior surfaces of the thigh, supplying the skin from the level of the greater trochanter to the middle of the thigh (Fig. 867).

5. **The Obturator Nerve** (*n. obturatorius*) (Figs. 857, 858, 862, 863, 873), the motor nerve to the Adductores, arises by three roots from the ventral portions of the second, third, and fourth lumbar nerves; that from the third is the largest, and that from the second is often very small. It emerges from the medial border of Psoas major near the brim of the pelvis, under cover of the common iliac vessels, passes lateral to the hypogastric vessels and the ureter, and runs along the lateral wall of the lesser pelvis, to enter the upper part of the obturator foramen with the obturator vessels. As it enters the thigh it divides into anterior and posterior branches which are separated by some of the fibers of the Obturator externus and the Adductor brevis.

a. The **anterior or superficial branch** (*r. anterior*) (Fig. 862) communicates with the accessory obturator nerve, when this is present, and passes over the superior border of the Obturator externus, deep to the Pectineus and Adductor longus and superficial to the Adductor brevis. At the lower border of the Adductor longus it communicates with the anterior cutaneous and saphenous branches of the femoral nerve, forming the **subsartorial plexus**, and terminates in filaments accompanying the femoral artery. Its branches are as follows:

1. An **articular branch** to the hip joint is given off near the obturator foramen.

2. **Muscular branches** are supplied to the Adductor longus, Gracilis, and usually to the Adductor brevis; in rare instances it gives a branch to the Pectineus.

3. A **cutaneous branch** is occasionally found as a continuation of the communication with the anterior cutaneous and saphenous branches. It emerges from beneath the inferior border of the Adductor longus, continues along the posterior margin of the Sartorius to the medial side of the knee, where it pierces the deep fascia, communicates with the saphenous nerve, and is distributed to the skin of the medial side of the proximal half of the leg.

b. The **posterior branch** (*r. posterior*) pierces the anterior part of the Obturator externus, passes posterior to the Adductor brevis and anterior to the Adductor magnus, and divides into muscular and articular branches.

1. **Muscular branches** are given (*a*) to the Obturator externus as it passes between its fibers, (*b*) to the Adductor magnus, and (*c*) to the Adductor brevis when it is not supplied by the anterior branch.

2. The **articular branch** for the knee joint either perforates the Adductor magnus or passes under the arch through which the femoral artery passes and enters the popliteal fossa. It accompanies the popliteal artery, supplying it with filaments, and reaches the back of the knee joint where it perforates the oblique popliteal ligament and is distributed to the synovial membrane.

6. **The Accessory Obturator Nerve** (*n. obturatorius accessorius*) (Fig. 858), present in about 29 per cent, is of small size. It arises from the ventral part of the third

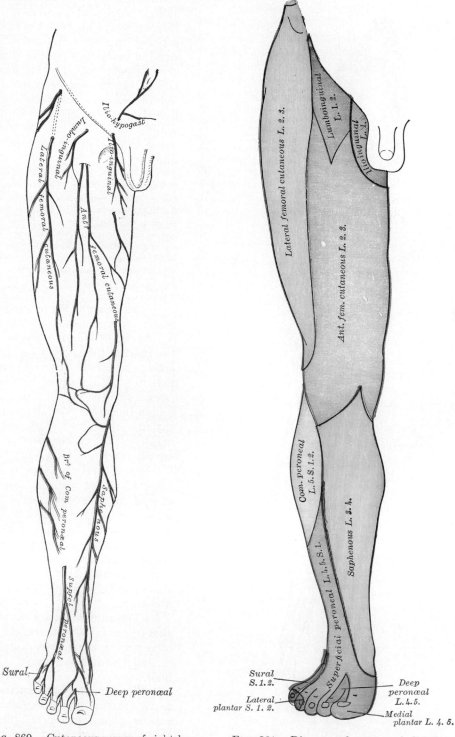

FIG. 860.—Cutaneous nerves of right lower extremity. Front view.

FIG. 861.—Diagram of segmental distribution of the cutaneous nerves of the right lower extremity. Front view.

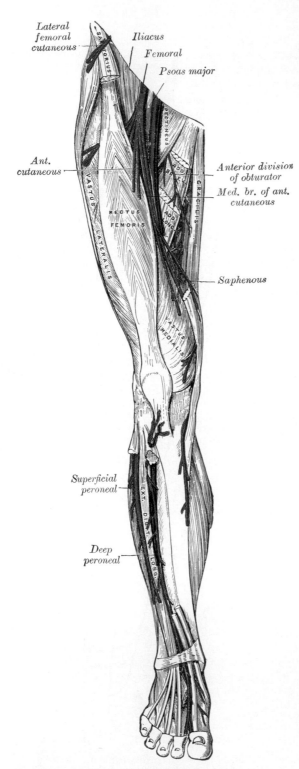

FIG. 862.—Nerves of the right lower extremity.
Front view.

and fourth lumbar nerves, follows along the medial border of the Psoas major, and crosses over the superior ramus of the pubis instead of going through the obturator foramen with the obturator nerve. It passes deep to the Pectineus, supplying it with branches, communicates with the anterior branch of the obturator nerve, and sends a branch to the hip joint.

Variations.—When the obturator nerve has a cutaneous branch, the medial cutaneous branch of the femoral is correspondingly small. When the accessory obturator is lacking, the obturator supplies two nerves to the hip joint; the accessory may be very small and be lost in the capsule of the hip joint.

7. **The Femoral Nerve** (*n. femoralis; anterior crural nerve*) (Figs. 857 to 862), the largest branch of the lumbar plexus and the principal nerve of the anterior part of the thigh, arises from the dorsal portions of the second, third, and fourth lumbar nerves. It emerges through the fibers of the Psoas major at the lower part of its lateral border, and passes down between it and the Iliacus, being covered by the iliac portion of the transversalis fascia. It passes under the inguinal ligament, lateral to the femoral artery, and breaks up into branches soon after it enters the thigh.

a. **Muscular branches** to the Iliacus are given off within the abdomen.

b. The **anterior cutaneous branches** (*rr. cutanei anteriores*) are two large nerves, the intermediate and medial cutaneous nerves (Fig. 860).

1. The **intermediate cutaneous nerve** (*ramus cutaneus anterior; middle cutaneous nerve*) pierces the fascia lata (and generally the Sartorius) about 7.5 cm. below the inguinal ligament, and divides into two branches which descend in immediate proximity along the forepart of the thigh, to supply the skin as low as the front of the knee. Here they communicate with the medial cutaneous nerve and the infra patellar branch of the saphenous, to form the **patellar plexus**. In the upper part of the thigh the lateral branch of the intermediate cutaneous communicates with the lumboinguinal branch of the genitofemoral nerve.

2. The **medial cutaneous nerve** (*ramus cutaneus anterior; internal cutaneous nerve*) passes obliquely across the upper part of the sheath of the femoral artery, and divides in front, or at the medial side of that vessel, into two branches, an anterior and a posterior. Before dividing, it gives off a few filaments, which pierce the fascia lata, to supply the integument of the medial side of the thigh, accompanying the great saphenous vein. One of these filaments passes through the saphenous opening; a second becomes subcutaneous about the middle of the thigh; a third pierces the fascia at its lower third. The anterior branch runs downward on the Sartorius, perforates the fascia lata at the lower third of the thigh, and divides into two branches: one supplies the integument as low down as the medial side of the knee; the other crosses to the lateral side of the patella, communicating in its course with the infrapatellar branch of the saphenous nerve. The posterior branch descends along the medial border of the Sartorius muscle to the knee, where it pierces the fascia lata, communicates with the saphenous nerve, and gives off several cutaneous branches. It then passes down to supply the integument of the medial side of the leg. Beneath the fascia lata, at the lower border of the Adductor longus, it joins to form a plexiform network (*subsartorial plexus*) with branches of the saphenous and obturator nerves.

Variations.—When the communicating branch from the obturator nerve is large and continued to the integument of the leg, the posterior branch of the medial cutaneous is small, and terminates in the plexus, occasionally giving off a few cutaneous filaments.

c. The **nerve to the Pectineus** arises immediately below the inguinal ligament, and passes deep to the femoral sheath to enter the anterior surface of the muscle; it is often double.

d. The **nerve to the Sartorius** arises in common with the intermediate cutaneous nerve and enters the deep surface of the proximal part of the muscle.

e. The **saphenous nerve** (*n. saphenus*) (Figs. 860 to 862, 866) is the largest and longest branch of the femoral nerve, and supplies the skin of the medial side of the leg. It passes deep to the Sartorius in company with the femoral artery, and lies anterior to the artery, crossing from its lateral to its medial side, within the fascial covering of the adductor canal (Fig. 592). At the tendinous arch in the Adductor magnus, it quits the artery, penetrates the fascial covering of the adductor canal, continues along the medial side of the knee deep to the Sartorius, and pierces the fascia lata between the tendons of the Sartorius and Gracilis to become subcutaneous. It then accompanies the great saphenous vein along the tibial side of the leg, and at the medial border of the tibia in the lower third of the leg, it divides into two terminal branches.

The branches of the saphenous nerve are:

1. A branch joins the medial cutaneous and obturator nerves in the middle of the thigh to form the **subsartorial plexus.**

2. A large **infrapatellar branch**, given off at the medial side of the knee, pierces the Sartorius and fascia lata, and is distributed to the skin in front of the patella. Above the knee it communicates with the anterior cutaneous branches of the femoral nerve; below the knee with other branches of the saphenous; and, on the lateral side of the joint, with branches of the lateral femoral cutaneous nerve to form the **patellar plexus** (*plexus patellæ*).

3. **Branches below the knee** are distributed to the skin of the front and medial side of the leg, communicating with the medial cutaneous nerve and the cutaneous branch of the obturator if present. One branch continues along the margin of the tibia, and ends at the ankle. The other terminal branch passes in front of the ankle, and is distributed to the medial side of the foot, as far as the ball of the great toe, communicating with the medial branch of the superficial peroneal nerve.

f. **Branches to the Quadriceps Femoris** (Fig. 862).—The branch to the Rectus femoris enters the upper part of the deep surface of the muscle. The branch to the Vastus lateralis, of large size, accompanies the descending branch of the lateral

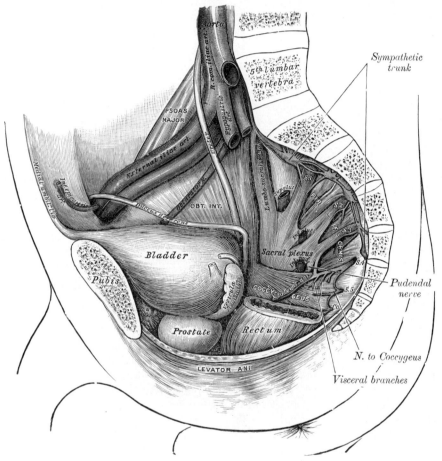

Fig. 863.—Dissection of side wall of pelvis showing sacral and pudendal plexuses. (Testut.)

femoral circumflex artery to the lower part of the muscle. The branch to the Vastus medialis runs parallel with the saphenous nerve, lateral to the femoral vessels and outside of the adductor canal, and enters the muscle about at its middle. The branches to the Vastus intermedius, two or three in number, enter the anterior surface of the muscle about the middle of the thigh; a filament from one of these descends through the muscle to the Articularis genu and the knee joint.

g. The **articular branch to the hip joint** is derived from the nerve to the Rectus femoris.

h. **Articular branches to the knee joint** are three in number. (1) A long slender filament derived from the nerve to the Vastus lateralis penetrates the capsule of the joint on its anterior aspect. (2) A filament derived from the nerve to the Vastus medialis can usually be traced downward on the surface of this muscle; it pierces the muscle and accompanies the articular branch of the highest genicular artery to the medial side of the articular capsule, which it penetrates, to supply the synovial membrane. (3) The branch to the Vastus intermedius which supplies the Articularis genu also is distributed to the knee joint.

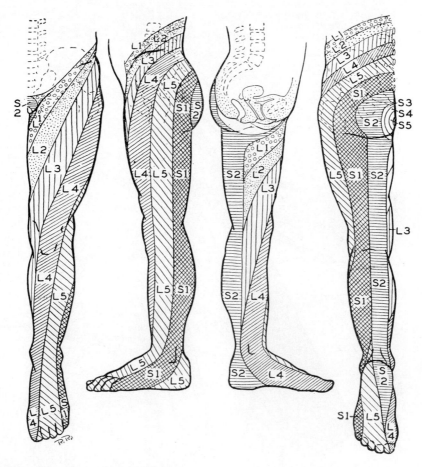

FIG. 864.—Dermatome chart of the lower extremity of man outlined by the pattern of hyposensitivity from loss of funcion of a single nerve root. (From the original of Fig. 9; Keegan and Garrett, courtesy of Anatomical Record, *102*, 417)

The Sacral and Coccygeal Nerves (Nn. Sacrales et Coccygeus).

The **ventral primary divisions** (*rr. anteriores*) of the sacral and coccygeal nerves enter into the formation of the sacral and pudendal plexuses. Those from the upper four sacral nerves enter the pelvis through the anterior sacral foramina, the fifth between the sacrum and coccyx, and the coccygeals below the first piece of the coccyx. The first and second sacrals are large; the third, fourth, and fifth diminish progressively in size.

THE SACRAL PLEXUS.

The **sacral plexus** (*plexus sacralis*) (Figs. 863, 865, 873) is formed by the lumbosacral trunk from the fourth and fifth lumbar, and by the first, second, and third sacral nerves. They converge toward the lower part of the greater sciatic foramen, and unite into a large flattened band, most of which is continued into the thigh as the sciatic nerve. The plexus lies against the posterior and lateral wall of the pelvis,

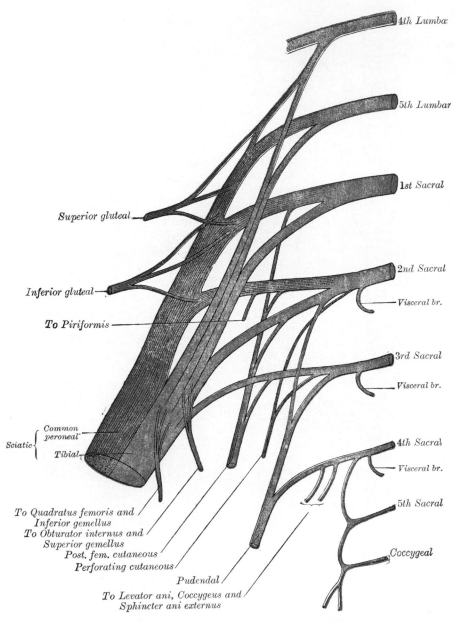

Fig. 865.—Plan of sacral and coccygeal plexuses.

between the Piriformis and the hypogastric vessels which are embedded in the pelvic subserous fascia. The nerves entering the plexus, with the exception of the third sacral, split into ventral and dorsal divisions, and the branches arising from them are as follows:

	Ventral Divisions	Dorsal Divisions
1. Nerve to Quadratus femoris and Gemellus inferior	L 4, 5, S 1	
2. Nerve to Obturator internus and Gemellus superior	L 5, S 1, 2	
3. Nerve to Piriformis		S (1), 2
4. Superior gluteal		L 4, 5, S 1
5. Inferior gluteal		L 5, S 1, 2
6. Posterior femoral cutaneous	S 2, 3	S 1, 2
7. Perforating cutaneous		S 2, 3
8. Sciatic { Tibial	L 4, 5, S 1, 2, 3	
{ Common peroneal		L 4, 5, S 1, 2
9. Pudendal	S 2, 3, 4	

1. **The Nerve to the Quadratus femoris and Gemellus inferior**, from the ventral divisions of L 4, 5, and S 1, leaves the pelvis through the greater sciatic foramen, below the Piriformis, and ventral to the sciatic nerve. It runs ventral or deep to the tendon of the Obturator internus and Gemelli, and enters the deep surface of the Quadratus and Gemellus inferior.

An articular branch is given to the hip joint.

2. **The Nerve to the Obturator internus and Gemellus superior** (Fig. 868), from the ventral divisions of L 5, and S 1, 2, leaves the pelvis through the greater sciatic foramen below the Piriformis. It gives off the branch to the Gemellus superior, then crosses the spine of the ischium, reënters the pelvis through the lesser sciatic foramen, and enters the pelvic surface of the Obturator internus.

3. **The Nerve to the Piriformis**, from the dorsal division of S 2, or S 1 and S 2, enters the ventral surface of the muscle; it may be double.

4. **The Superior Gluteal Nerve** (*n. glutaeus superior*) (Figs. 868, 873), from the dorsal divisions of L 4, 5, and S 1, leaves the pelvis through the greater sciatic foramen above the Piriformis, and accompanying the superior gluteal vessels and their branches, divides into a superior and an inferior branch.

a. The **superior branch** is distributed to the Gluteus minimus.

b. The **inferior branch** crosses the Gluteus minimus, gives filaments to the Gluteus medius and minimus, and ends in a branch to the Tensor fasciæ latæ.

5. **The Inferior Gluteal Nerve** (*n. glutaeus inferior*), from the dorsal divisions of L 5, and S 1, 2, leaves the pelvis through the greater sciatic foramen below the Piriformis, and enters the deep surface of the Gluteus maximus.

6. **The Posterior Femoral Cutaneous Nerve** (*n. cutaneus femoralis posterior; small sciatic nerve*) (Figs. 866 to 868) is distributed to the skin of the perineum and posterior surface of the thigh and leg. It arises from the dorsal divisions of S 1 and 2, and from the ventral divisions of S 2 and 3, and leaves the pelvis through the greater sciatic foramen below the Piriformis. It accompanies the inferior gluteal artery to the inferior border of the Gluteus maximus, and runs down the back of the thigh, superficial to the long head of the Biceps femoris and deep to the fascia lata to the back of the knee. It pierces the deep fascia and accompanies the small saphenous vein to the middle of the back of the leg, its terminal twigs communicating with the sural nerve.

a. The **gluteal branches** (*nn. clunium inferiores*), three or four in number, turn upward around the lower border of the Gluteus maximus, and supply the skin covering the lower and lateral part of that muscle.

b. The **perineal branches** (*rr. perineales*) (Fig. 868) arise at the lower border of the Gluteus maximus, run medially over the origin of the hamstrings toward the groove between the thigh and perineum, and pierce the deep fascia to supply the skin of the external genitalia and adjacent upper medial surface of the thigh. One long branch, the inferior pudendal (long scrotal nerve) (Fig. 873), runs forward in the

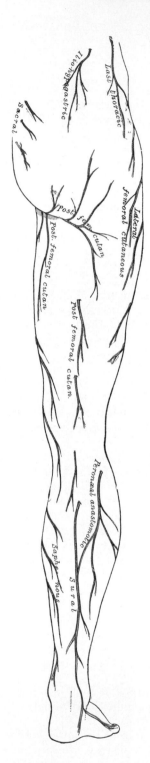

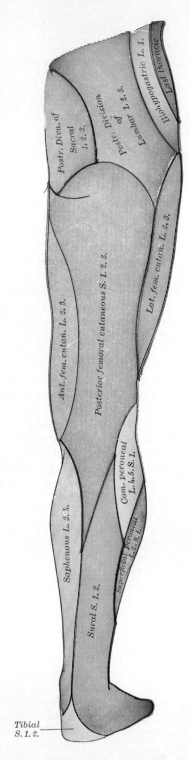

Fig. 866.—Cutaneous nerves of right
lower extremity. Posterior view.

Fig. 867.—Diagram of the segmental distribution of the cutaneous nerves of the right lower
extremity. Posterior view.

superficial fascia of the perineum to the skin of the scrotum and base of the penis in the male, and of the labium majus in the female, communicating with the posterior scrotal and inferior hemorrhoidal branches of the pudendal nerve.

c. The **femoral branches** consist of numerous filaments from both sides of the nerve which are distributed to the skin of the back and medial sides of the thigh and the popliteal fossa (Fig. 866).

d. The **sural branches** are usually two terminal twigs which supply the skin of the back of the leg to a varying extent, and communicate with the sural nerve.

Variations.—When the tibial and peroneal nerves arise separately, the posterior femoral cutaneous also arises from the sacral plexus in two parts. The ventral portion accompanies the tibial nerve and gives off the perineal and medial femoral branches; the dorsal portion passes through the Piriformis with the peroneal and supplies the gluteal and lateral femoral branches. The inferior pudendal branch may pierce the sacrotuberous ligament. The sural branches may be lacking or may extend down as far as the ankle.

7. The Perforating Cutaneous Nerve (*n. clunium inferior medialis*) arises from the posterior surface of the second and third sacral nerves. It pierces the lower part of the sacrotuberous ligament, winds around the inferior border of the Gluteus maximus, and is distributed to the skin over the medial and lower parts of that muscle.

Variations.—The perforating cutaneous nerve is lacking in one third of the bodies; its place may be taken by a branch of the posterior femoral cutaneous nerve, or by a branch from S 3 and 4, or S 4 and 5. It may pierce the Gluteus maximus as well as the ligament, or instead of piercing the ligament it may accompany the pudendal nerve or go between the muscle and the ligament. It may arise in common with the pudendal nerve.

8. The Sciatic Nerve (*n. ischiadicus; great sciatic nerve*) (Fig. 868) is the largest nerve in the body. It supplies the skin of the foot and most of the leg, the muscles of the back of

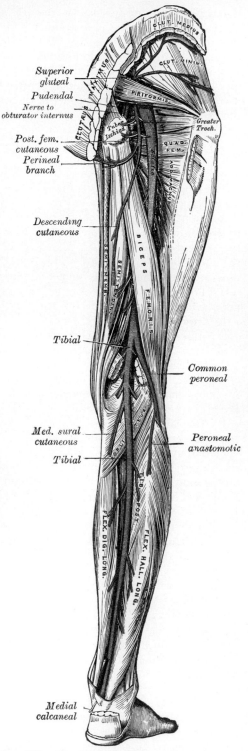

FIG. 868.—Nerves of the right lower extremity.[1] Posterior view.

[1] N. B.—In this diagram the medial sural cutaneous and peroneal anastomotic are not in their normal position. They have been displaced by the removal of the superficial muscles.

the thigh, all the muscles of the leg and foot, and contributes filaments to all the joints of the lower extremity. It is the continuation of the main part of the sacral plexus, arising from L 4, 5, and S 1, 2, 3. It passes out of the pelvis through the greater sciatic foramen, and extends from the inferior border of the Piriformis to the lower third of the thigh, where it splits into two large terminal divisions, the tibial and common peroneal nerves. In the upper part of its course it rests upon the posterior surface of the ischium, between the ischial tuberosity and the greater trochanter of the femur, and crosses the Obturator internus, Gemelli, and Quadratus femoris. It is accompanied by the posterior femoral cutaneous nerve and the inferior gluteal artery, and is covered by the Gluteus maximus. More distally it lies upon the Adductor magnus, and is crossed obliquely by the long head of the Biceps femoris.

The tibial and common peroneal nerves represent two divisions within the sciatic nerve which are manifest at the origin of the nerve and preserve their identity throughout its length although combined into one large nerve by a common connective tissue sheath. The tibial division takes its origin in the sacral plexus from the ventral divisions of L 4, 5 and S 1, 2, 3; the peroneal division originates from the dorsal divisions of L 4, 5 and S 1, 2. In some bodies these two divisions remain separate throughout their course, no true sciatic nerve being formed.

A. The branches of the sciatic nerve before it splits into the tibial and common peroneal nerves are as follows:

1. **Articular branches** (*rr. articulares*) arise from the proximal part of the nerve and supply the hip joint, perforating the posterior part of the capsule. They may arise from the sacral plexus.

2. The **muscular branches** (*rr. musculares*) to the hamstrings, *viz.*, the long head of the Biceps femoris, the Semitendinosus, and the Semimembranosus, and to the Adductor magnus come from the tibial division; the branch to the short head of the Biceps comes from the common peroneal.

B. **The Tibial Nerve** (*n. tibialis; internal popliteal nerve*) (Fig. 868), the larger of the two terminal divisions of the sciatic nerve, is composed of fibers from the ventral divisions of L 4, 5, and S 1, 2, 3. It continues in the same direction as the sciatic nerve, at first deep to the long head of the Biceps, then through the middle of the popliteal fossa covered by adipose tissue and fascia. After crossing the Popliteus, it passes between the heads of the Gastrocnemius and under the Soleus. It remains deep to these muscles down to the medial margin of the tendo calcaneus, along which it runs to the laciniate ligament, and there divides into the medial and lateral plantar nerves. At its origin it is some distance lateral to the popliteal artery and vein, but as it continues in a straight course it crosses superficial to the vessels in the popliteal fossa, and lying medial to them, passes with them under the tendinous arch formed by the Soleus. It accompanies the posterior tibial artery, at first being medial but soon crossing the artery and lying lateral to it down to the ankle (Fig. 593). The branches of the tibial nerve are as follows:

1. **Articular branches** (*rr. articulares*) supply the knee and ankle joints.

a. Three branches, accompanying the superior and inferior medial genicular, and the middle genicular arteries, pierce the ligaments and supply the **knee joint**. The superior branch is inconstant.

b. Just above the bifurcation at the laciniate ligament, an articular branch is given off to the **ankle joint**.

2. **Muscular branches** (*rr. musculares*) are supplied to the muscles of the back of the leg. Branches arising as the nerve lies between the two heads of the Gastrocnemius are distributed to (*a*) both heads of the Gastrocnemius, (*b*) Plantaris, (*c*) Soleus, and (*d*) Popliteus; the latter turns around the inferior border and is distributed to the deep surface of the muscle. Arising more distally, either separately or by a

common trunk, are branches to (*e*) the Soleus, (*f*) Tibialis posterior, (*g*) Flexor digitorum longus, and (*h*) Flexor hallucis longus; the branch to the last muscle accompanies the peroneal artery; that to the Soleus enters the deep surface of the muscle.

3. The **medial sural cutaneous nerve** (*n. cutaneus suræ medialis; n. communicans tibialis*) remains superficial in the groove between the two heads of the Gastrocnemius, accompanied by the small saphenous vein, and about the middle of the back of the leg, pierces the deep fascia and is joined by the communicating ramus of the lateral sural cutaneous branch of the peroneal nerve, to form the sural nerve.

a. The **sural nerve** (*n. suralis; short saphenous nerve*) (Fig. 866) is formed by the union of the medial sural cutaneous nerve and the communicating ramus of the lateral sural cutaneous nerve (peroneal anastomotic) (Fig. 866). Lying with the small saphenous vein near the lateral margin of the tendo calcaneus, it continues distally to the interval between the lateral malleolus and the calcaneus, supplying branches to the skin of the back of the leg, and communicating with the posterior

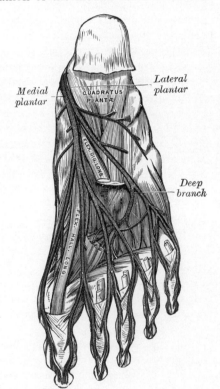

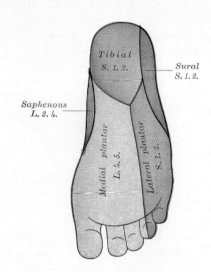

FIG. 869.—The plantar nerves.

FIG. 870.—Diagram of the segmental distribution of the cutaneous nerves of the sole of the foot.

femoral cutaneous nerve. The nerve turns anteriorly below the lateral malleolus, and is continued as the lateral dorsal cutaneous nerve along the lateral side of the foot and little toe (Fig. 860), communicating on the dorsum of the foot with the intermediate dorsal cutaneous nerve, a branch of the superficial peroneal.

4. The **medial calcaneal branches** (*rr. calcanei mediales; internal calcaneal branches*) (Fig. 868) perforate the laciniate ligament, and are distributed to the skin of the heel and medial side of the sole of the foot.

5. The **medial plantar nerve** (*n. plantaris medialis; internal plantar nerve*) (Fig. 869), the larger of the two terminal branches of the tibial nerve, accompanies the medial plantar artery. From its origin under the laciniate ligament it passes deep to the Abductor hallucis, and, appearing between this muscle and the Flexor digitorum brevis, gives off the proper plantar digital nerve to the great toe, and finally

divides opposite the bases of the metatarsal bones into three common digital nerves. The branches of the medial plantar nerve are as follows:

a. The **plantar cutaneous branches** pierce the plantar aponeurosis between the Abductor hallucis and the Flexor digitorum brevis and are distributed to the skin of the sole of the foot (Fig. 870).

b. **Muscular branches** for the Abductor hallucis and Flexor digitorum brevis arise from the trunk of the nerve and enter the deep surfaces of the muscles. A branch for the Flexor hallucis brevis springs from the proper digital nerve to the medial side of the great toe. A branch for the first Lumbricalis comes from the first common digital nerve.

c. The **articular branches** supply the joints of the tarsus and metatarsus.

d. The **proper digital nerve** of the great toe pierces the plantar aponeurosis posterior to the tarso-metatarsal joint, sends a branch to the Flexor hallucis brevis, and is distributed to the skin of the medial side of the great toe (Fig. 869).

e. The **three common digital nerves** (*nn. digitales plantares communes*) pass between the divisions of the plantar aponeurosis, and each splits into two **proper digital nerves** (*nn. plantares digitales propriæ*). Those of the first common digital supply the adjacent sides of the great and second toes; those of the second, the adjacent sides of the second and third toes; those of the third, the adjacent sides of the third and fourth toes. The first common digital gives a twig to the first Lumbricalis. The third communicates with the lateral plantar nerve. Each proper digital nerve gives off cutaneous and articular filaments along the digit, finally terminating in the ball of the toe, and opposite the distal phalanx sends a dorsal branch which is distributed to the structures around the nail.

6. The **lateral plantar nerve** (*n. plantaris lateralis; external plantar nerve*) (Figs. 869, 870) supplies the skin of the fifth and lateral half of the fourth toes, as well as most of the deep muscles of the foot, its distribution being similar to that of the ulnar nerve in the hand. It passes distally with the lateral plantar artery to the lateral side of the foot, lying between the Flexor digitorum brevis and Quadratus plantæ, and in the interval between the former muscle and the Abductor digiti quinti, divides into a superficial and a deep branch. The branches of the lateral plantar nerve are as follows:

a. **Muscular branches** to the Quadratus plantæ and the Abductor digiti quinti are given off before the division into superficial and deep branches.

b. The **superficial branch** (*r. superficialis*) splits into a common digital nerve and a nerve which supplies the proper digital for the lateral side of the little toe, and muscular branches to the Flexor digiti quinti brevis and the two Interossei of the fourth intermetatarsal space. The common digital nerve has a communication with the third common digital branch of the medial plantar nerve and divides into two proper digital nerves which are distributed to the adjacent sides of the fourth and fifth toes.

c. The **deep branch** (*r. profundus; muscular branch*) accompanies the lateral plantar artery on the deep surface of the tendons of the Flexores longi and the Adductor hallucis, and supplies all the Interossei except those in the fourth intermetatarsal space, the second, third, and fourth Lumbricales, and the Adductor hallucis.

C. The **common peroneal nerve** (*n. peronaeus communis; external popliteal nerve; peroneal nerve*) (Fig. 868), the smaller of the two terminal divisions of the sciatic nerve, is composed of fibers from the dorsal divisions of the fourth and fifth lumbar, and first and second sacral nerves. It runs obliquely along the lateral side of the popliteal fossa, close to the medial border of the Biceps femoris and between that muscle and the lateral head of the Gastrocnemius, to the head of the fibula. It winds around the neck of the fibula and passes deep to the Peronaeus longus, where it divides into the superficial and deep peroneal nerves. The branches of the common peroneal nerve are as follows:

1. The **articular branches** (*rr. articulares*) to the knee are three in number: (*a*) one accompanies the superior lateral genicular artery to the knee, occasionally arising from the trunk of the sciatic; (*b*) one accompanies the inferior lateral genicular artery to the joint; and (*c*) the third (recurrent) articular nerve is given off at the point of division of the common peroneal nerve and accompanies the anterior tibial recurrent artery (Fig. 595) through the substance of the Tibialis anterior to the anterior part of the knee (Fig. 862, not labelled).

2. The **lateral sural cutaneous nerve** (*n. cutaneus suræ lateralis; lateral cutaneous branch*) is distributed to the skin of the posterior and lateral surfaces of the leg (Fig. 867) and has an important communicating ramus:

The **communicating ramus** (*n. communicans fibularis; peroneal anastomotic nerve*) (Figs. 866, 868) arises near the head of the fibula, crosses superficial to the lateral head of the Gastrocnemius, and in the middle of the leg joins the medial sural cutaneous nerve to form the sural nerve.

3. The **deep peroneal nerve** (*n. peronaeus profundus; anterior tibial nerve*) (Figs. 862, 871), arising from the bifurcation of the common peroneal nerve between the fibula and the Peronaeus longus, continues deep to the Extensor digitorum longus to the anterior surface of the interosseous membrane. It meets the anterior tibial artery in the upper third of the leg (Fig. 595) and continues with it distally, passes under the cruciate crural ligament, and terminates at the ankle in a medial and a lateral branch.

a. **Muscular branches** are supplied in the leg to (*1*) the Tibialis anterior, (*2*) Extensor digitorum longus, (*3*) Peronaeus tertius, and (*4*) Extensor hallucis longus.

b. An **articular branch** is supplied to the ankle joint.

c. The **lateral terminal branch** (*external or tarsal branch*) passes across the tarsus deep to the Extensor digitorum brevis, and having become enlarged like the dorsal interosseous nerve at the wrist, supplies the Extensor digitorum brevis. (*1*) Three minute interosseous branches are given off from the enlargement; they supply the tarsal joints and the metatarsophalangeal joints of the second, third, and fourth toes. (*2*) A muscular filament is sent to the second Interosseus dorsalis from the first of these interosseous branches.

d. The **medial terminal branch** (*internal branch*) accompanies the dorsalis pedis artery along the dorsum of the foot, and, at the first interosseous space, divides into two dorsal digital nerves (Fig. 872) which supply adjacent sides of the great and second toes, communicating with the medial dorsal cutaneous branch of the superficial peroneal nerve. An interosseous branch, given off before it divides, enters the first space, supplying the metatarsophalangeal joint of the great toe and sending a filament to the first Interosseus dorsalis.

4. The **superficial peroneal nerve** (*n. peronaeus superficialis; musculocutaneous nerve*) (Figs. 871, 872) passes distally between the Peronaei and the Extensor digitorum longus, pierces the deep fascia in the lower third of the leg, and divides into a medial and intermediate dorsal cutaneous nerve.

a. **Muscular branches** are given off in its course between the muscles to the Peronaeus longus and brevis.

b. **Cutaneous filaments** are supplied to the skin of the lower part of the leg.

c. The **medial dorsal cutaneous nerve** (*n. cutaneus dorsalis medialis; internal dorsal cutaneous branch*) (Fig. 872) passes in front of the ankle joint and divides into two dorsal digital branches. The medial one supplies the medial side of the great toe and communicates with the deep peroneal nerve. The lateral one supplies the adjacent sides of the second and third toes. It also supplies the skin of the medial side of the foot and ankle, and communicates with the saphenous nerve.

d. The **intermediate dorsal cutaneous nerve** (*n. cutaneus dorsalis intermedius; external dorsal cutaneous branch*) (Fig. 872) passes along the lateral part of the dorsum of the foot, supplying the skin of the lateral side of the foot and ankle and communicating with the sural nerve. It terminates by dividing into two dorsal digital branches, one of which supplies the adjacent sides of the third and fourth toes, the other the adjacent sides of the fourth and little toes. Frequently some of the lateral branches of the superficial peroneal nerve are absent, and their places are then taken by branches of the sural nerve.

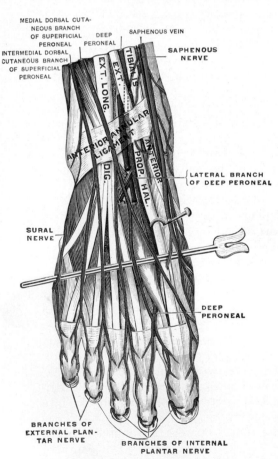

FIG. 871.—Nerves of the dorsum of the foot. (Testut.)

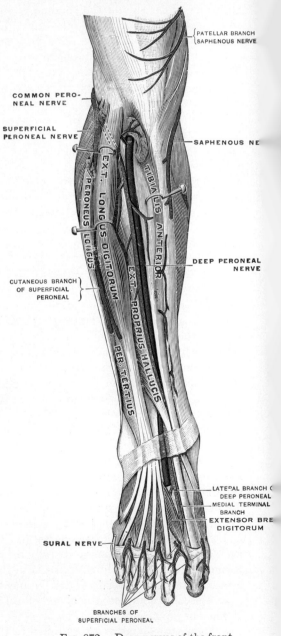

FIG. 872.—Deep nerves of the front of the leg. (Testut.)

THE PUDENDAL PLEXUS.

The **pudendal plexus** (*plexus pudendus*) (Figs. 865, 873) is formed from the anterior branches of the second and third, and all of the fourth sacral nerves. It is sometimes considered to be a part of the sacral plexus. It lies in the posterior hollow of the

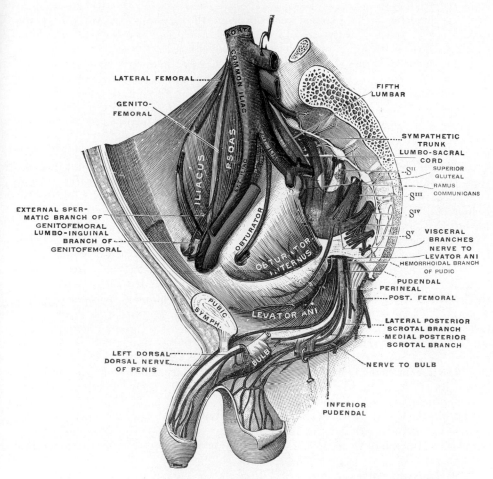

Fig. 873.—Pudendal nerve, and sacral and pudendal plexus of the right side. (Testut.)

pelvis, on the anterior surface of the Piriformis. The branches of the pudendal plexus are as follows:

1. The **Visceral Branches** (*rr. viscerales*) arise from the second, third, and fourth sacral nerves, and contain parasympathetic visceral efferent preganglionic fibers which form synapses with the cells in the small scattered ganglia located in or near the walls of the pelvic viscera, and visceral afferent fibers from the pelvic organs. These nerves join branches of the hypogastric plexus of the sympathetic and the sympathetic chain to form the pelvic plexus, which lies in the deeper portion of the pelvic subserous fascia (Ashley and Anson '46).

The various elements of the pelvic plexus can not be followed by dissection, but the destination of the sacral parasympathetic fibers has been traced by clinical observation and animal experimentation as follows:

a. The **branches to the bladder, prostate, and seminal vesicles** approach these organs from their posterior and lateral sides, and terminate in groups of ganglion cells in the pelvic plexus or in the walls of the organs. The postganglionic fibers are efferents to the muscles and glands except the sphincters, to which they are inhibitory.

b. The **branches to the uterus** reach the ganglia in the uterine plexus. The postganglionic fibers are inhibitory except during pregnancy when their function is said to be reversed.

c. The **branches to the external genitalia** leave the pelvic plexus to join the pudendal nerve, and are distributed through its branches to the corpora cavernosa, causing active dilatation of the cavernous blood sinuses.

d. The **branches to the alimentary tract** consist of (*1*) filaments which go directly to the rectum from the pelvic plexus, and (*2*) fibers which pass through the hypogastric plexus, the hypogastric nerves, and the inferior mesenteric plexus to reach the descending and sigmoid colon. These are preganglionic fibers which have synapses with the cells in the myenteric and submucous plexuses and are efferent to this part of the intestine except for the sphincter ani internus, to which they are inhibitory.

2. The **Muscular Branches** (Fig. 863), derived mainly from the fourth (sometimes from the third and fifth) sacral, enter the pelvic surfaces of the Levator ani and Coccygeus; the nerve to the Sphincter ani externus (perineal branch) reaches the ischiorectal fossa by piercing the Coccygeus or by passing between it and the Levator.

3. The **Pudendal Nerve** (*n. pudendus; internal pudic nerve*) (Figs. 584, 873) arises from the second, third, and fourth sacral nerves, and passing between the Piriformis and Coccygeus, leaves the pelvis through the lower part of the greater sciatic foramen. It then crosses the spine of the ischium, and reënters the pelvis through the lesser sciatic foramen. It accompanies the internal pudendal vessels along the lateral wall of the ischiorectal fossa in a tunnel formed by a splitting of the obturator fascia known as Alcock's canal, and as it approaches the urogenital diaphragm, splits into two terminal branches. The branches of the pudendal nerve are as follows:

a. The **inferior hemorrhoidal nerve** (*n. rectalis inferior*) arises from the pudendal before its terminal division or occasionally directly from the sacral plexus, and coursing medially across the ischiorectal fossa with the inferior hemorrhoidal vessels, breaks up into branches which are distributed to the Sphincter ani externus, and the integument around the anus. Branches of this nerve communicate with the perineal branch of the posterior femoral cutaneous and with the posterior scrotal nerves.

b. The **perineal nerve** (*n. perinei*) (Fig. 873), the larger and more superficial of the two terminal branches of the pudendal, accompanies the perineal artery and at the urogenital diaphragm divides into superficial and deep branches.

1. The **superficial branches** of the perineal nerve are two in number, the medial and lateral posterior scrotal (or labial) nerves (*nn. scrotales [labiales] posteriores*). They pierce the fascia of the urogenital diaphragm, and run anteriorly along the lateral part of the urogenital triangle in company with the posterior scrotal branches of the perineal artery (Fig. 584). They are distributed to the skin of the scrotum in the male, or of the labium majus in the female, and the lateral branch communicates with the perineal branch of the posterior femoral cutaneous nerve.

2. The **deep branch** is mainly muscular, supplying branches to the Transversus perinaei superficialis, Bulbocavernosus, Ischiocavernosus, Transversus perinaei profundus and Sphincter urethræ membranaceæ. The nerve to the bulb is given off from the nerve to the Bulbocavernosus, pierces this muscle, and supplies the corpus cavernosum urethræ and the mucous membrane of the urethra.

c. **The dorsal nerve of the penis** (*n. dorsalis penis*) (Fig. 873), the deeper terminal branch of the pudendal nerve, accompanies the internal pudendal artery along the ramus of the ischium, and then runs forward along the margin of the inferior ramus of the pubis, lying between the superficial and deep layers of fascia of the urogenital diaphragm. Piercing the superficial layer, it gives a branch to the corpus caverno-sum penis, and continuing forward in company with the dorsal artery of the penis between the layers of the suspensory ligament, it runs along the dorsum of the penis, and is distributed to the skin of that organ, ending on the glans penis.

The **dorsal nerve of the clitoris** (*n. dorsalis clitoridis*) is smaller and has a distribu-tion corresponding to that of the penis in the male.

The Coccygeal Plexus (*plexus coccygeus*) (Fig. 865) is formed by the coccygeal nerve with communications from the fourth and fifth sacral nerves. From this delicate plexus, a few fine filaments, the Anococcygeal Nerves, pierce the sacro-tuberous ligament and supply the skin in the region of the coccyx.

THE VISCERAL NERVOUS SYSTEM.

The **Visceral Nervous System** or visceral portion of the peripheral nervous system (*vegetative nervous system; involuntary nervous system; major sympathetic system; plexiform nervous system*) comprises the whole complex of fibers, nerves, ganglia, and plexuses by means of which impulses are conveyed from the central nervous system to the viscera and from the viscera to the central nervous system. It has the usual two groups of fibers necessary for reflex connections: (*a*) afferent fibers, receiving stimuli and carrying impulses toward the central nervous system, and (*b*) efferent fibers, carrying impulses from the appropriate centers to the active effector organs, which, in this instance, are the non-striated muscle, cardiac muscle, and glands of the body.

Attention is called to a new use of the term sympathetic system in this edition. In former editions it was used for the visceral nervous system and included both afferent and efferent, auto-nomic and parasympathetic components. Although the central nervous system is involved in all nervous or reflex control of the viscera, with the possible exception of the enteric plexus, it is more convenient for the purposes of description to separate the peripheral from the central portions. It must be emphasized, however, that the separation is artificial and should not be carried over into physiological considerations. In the present edition it is used in the restricted meaning of the thoracolumbar division of the visceral efferent system. The terms sympathetic afferent and autonomic afferent will be replaced by visceral afferent.

THE VISCERAL AFFERENT FIBERS.

The **visceral afferent fibers** can not be separated into a morphologically independent system because, like the somatic sensory fibers, they have their cell bodies situated in the sensory ganglia of the cerebrospinal nerves. The distinction between somatic and visceral afferent fibers is one of peripheral distribution rather than one of funda-mental anatomical and physiological significance. The visceral afferents, however, commonly have modalities of sensation which are different from those of somatic afferents, and most of them are either vaguely localized or have no representation in consciousness. The visceral efferent fibers make reflex connections with both somatic and visceral afferents, and somatic efferents may have reflex connections with visceral afferents. The number and extent of the visceral afferents are not clearly established, and the peripheral processes reach the ganglia by various routes. Many traverse the branches and plexuses of the autonomic system, most of them accompany blood vessels for at least a part of their course, and a certain number run in the cerebrospinal nerves.

Referred Pain.—Although many, perhaps most, of the physiological impulses carried by visceral afferent fibers fail to reach consciousness, pathological conditions or excessive stimulation may bring into action those which carry pain. The central nervous system has a poorly developed power of localizing the source of such pain, and by some mechanism not clearly understood, the pain may be referred to the region supplied by the somatic afferent fibers whose central connections are the same as those of the visceral afferents. For example, the visceral afferents from the heart enter the upper thoracic nerves, and impulses traversing them may cause painful sensations in the axilla, down the ulnar surface of the arm, and in the precordial region. The study of clinical cases of referred pain has been very useful in tracing the path of afferent fibers from the various viscera, and a knowledge of these paths may be of great assistance to the diagnostician in locating a pathological process.

The visceral afferent fibers are summarized below; for more complete descriptions of the individual nerves mentioned, consult the accounts given elsewhere.

The Head.—Visceral afferents from endings on the peripheral blood vessels of the face and scalp probably accompany the branches of the external carotid artery to the superior cervical ganglion, and through communicating rami to the spinal nerves. Afferents on the blood vessels of the brain and meninges may accompany the branches of the internal carotid and vertebral arteries, passing through the upper cervical spinal nerves or possibly the ninth and tenth cranial nerves (Christensen *et al.* '52).

The Nose and Nasal Cavity.—There is some evidence that a few visceral afferent fibers from the nose are brought to the brain by the nervus terminalis (Larsell '50). Others traverse the branches of the sphenopalatine and palatine nerves, to reach the facial nerve through the Vidian and greater superficial petrosal nerves.

The Mouth and Pharynx.—The visceral afferents from the mouth, pharynx, and salivary glands pass through the pharyngeal plexus to the glossopharyngeal, vagus, and facial nerves.

The Neck.—Visceral afferents from the larynx, trachea, esophagus, and thyroid gland are carried by the vagus or reach the sympathetic trunk through the pharyngeal plexus and pass through rami communicantes to the cervical or upper thoracic nerves.

The **carotid sinus nerve** carries the visceral afferents from the pressoreceptor endings in the carotid sinus through the glossopharyngeal nerve. The chemoreceptor afferents from the carotid body reach the vagus nerve through branches of the pharyngeal or superior laryngeal nerves.

The Thorax.—The visceral afferents from the thoracic wall and parietal pleura join the intercostal nerves, after following the arteries for variable distances, and thus enter the spinal ganglia. Those from the parietal pericardium join either the phrenic nerve or the intercostal nerves.

Visceral afferents from the heart and the origins of the great vessels enter the cardiac plexus and either join the branches of the vagus or reach the upper thoracic spinal nerves and their ganglia by way of sympathetic branches, the sympathetic trunk, and rami communicantes.

The **aortic bodies** (*glomera aortica*) are chemoreceptors similar to the carotid bodies; their afferent fibers run in the right vagus and have cell bodies in the nodose ganglion (Hollinshead '39). The supracardial bodies (aortic paraganglia) are also chemoreceptors with their afferent fibers in the left vagus and cell bodies in the nodose ganglion (Hollinshead '40).

The Depressor Nerve.—In some animals, the afferent fibers of the vagus from the heart and great vessels are contained in a separate nerve whose stimulation depresses the activity of the heart. In man, these fibers are probably contained in the cardiac branches of the recurrent nerves (Mitchell '53).

Visceral afferents from the lungs, bronchi, and pulmonary pleura, through the pulmonary plexuses, reach either the vagus nerve, or, through the sympathetic branches and rami communicantes, the spinal nerves and their ganglia.

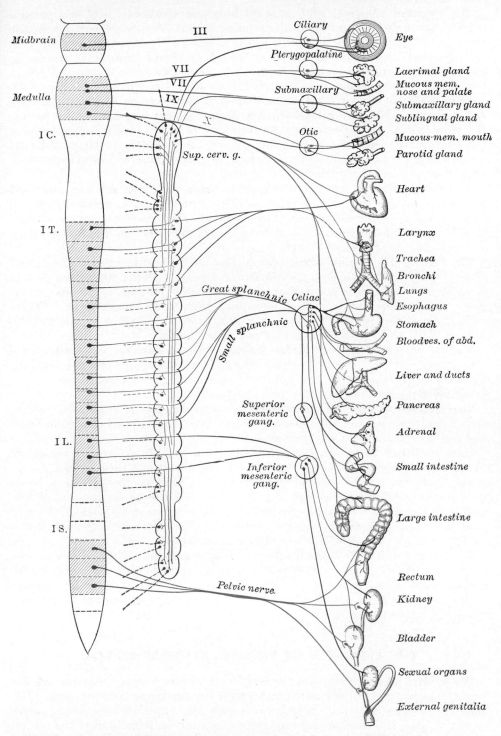

Fig. 874.—Diagram of efferent autonomic nervous system. Blue, cranial and sacral outflow, parasympathetic. Red, thoracolumbar outflow, sympathetic. ...., postganglionic fibers to spinal and cranial nerves to supply vasomotors to head, trunk and limbs, motor fibers to smooth muscles of skin and fibers to sweat glands. (Modified after Meyer and Gottlieb.) This is only a diagram and does not accurately portray all of the details of distribution.

The Abdomen.—Visceral afferent fibers from the abdominal wall and parietal peritoneum probably accompany the arteries in part of their course and finally, through the spinal nerves, reach the spinal ganglia. The myelinated fibers from the Paccinian corpuscles in the mesentery and about the pancreas at its base run in the thoracic splanchnic nerves, then through the sympathetic trunk, and finally over the white rami communicantes to the spinal nerves and ganglia (Sheehan '33).

Visceral afferent fibers from the stomach, small intestine, cecum, appendix, ascending and transverse colon, liver, gall bladder, bile ducts, pancreas, and suprarenals traverse the celiac plexus and its secondary plexuses and branches, mainly accompanying the arteries, pass through the splanchnic nerves, the sympathetic trunk, and rami communicantes to reach the spinal nerves and ganglia. Some of these afferents may enter the vagus nerve (Mitchell '53).

The **visceral afferents from the kidney, ureter, testis and ductus deferens, ovary and uterine tube** traverse the renal and celiac plexuses or parts of their secondary plexuses, pass through the lower thoracic and upper lumbar splanchnic nerves to the sympathetic trunk, and thence through white rami communicantes to the spinal nerves and ganglia (Christensen *et al.* '51).

The Pelvis.—The **visceral afferent fibers from the descending colon, sigmoid**, and **rectum** traverse the pelvic plexus, hypogastric nerves and plexus, the inferior mesenteric plexus, celiac plexus, and lumbar splanchnic nerves on their way to the sympathetic trunk, white rami communicantes, and spinal nerves and ganglia. Others from the rectum pass through the pelvic plexus into the visceral branches of the second, third, and fourth sacral nerves and their ganglia.

Visceral afferents from the bladder, prostate, seminal vesicles, and **urethra** pass through the pelvic plexus and through the hypogastric nerves and plexuses, splanchnic nerves, and sympathetic rami, into the lumbar ganglia or through the visceral branches of the sacral nerves into the sacral ganglia.

Visceral afferents from the uterus traverse the pelvic plexus, hypogastric nerves and plexus, lumbar splanchnic nerves, sympathetic trunk, rami communicantes, and lumbar spinal nerves and their ganglia.

Visceral afferent fibers from the external genitalia pass through either the pelvic plexus or the pudendal nerve and reach the sacral nerves and their ganglia.

The Upper Extremity.—Visceral afferent fibers accompany the peripheral blood vessels for some distance, but may join the larger branches of the brachial plexus, and reach the dorsal root ganglia through the spinal nerves, or they may follow the paths of the sympathetic fibers and reach the dorsal ganglia, especially the first two or three thoracic, through the white rami communicantes.

The Lower Extremity.—Visceral afferents accompany the peripheral vessels and the femoral artery to the aortic plexus, then through the lumbar splanchnic nerves to the rami communicantes, spinal nerves and ganglia. Others may join the tibial or peroneal nerves and traverse the sacral and lumbar sympathetic trunk and rami communicantes to reach the lumbar nerves and their ganglia (Kuntz '51).

THE AUTONOMIC OR VISCERAL EFFERENT SYSTEM.

The **Visceral Efferent** portions of the peripheral nervous system are combined into a morphological and physiological entity called the **autonomic nervous system**. The fundamental morphological difference between the visceral and somatic motor systems is that two neurones are required to transmit an impulse from the central nervous system to the active effector organ in the viscera, while only a single neuron is required to carry an impulse from the central nervous system to a skeletal muscle fiber. As the name autonomic implies, this system has a certain amount of independence because, in most individuals, it is not under direct voluntary command.

It is controlled by neurons within the central nervous system, nevertheless, and is connected with the latter at various levels. The enteric plexus is the only portion of the visceral system which seems to carry out reflex responses without involving the central nervous system (Kuntz '53).

The Autonomic Nervous System is composed of two divisions or systems which differ from each other morphologically and which are for the most part antagonistic to each other physiologically. The morphological differences have to do (*a*) with the manner in which the two systems are connected with the central nervous system and (*b*) with the location of their ganglia. The sympathetic or thoracolumbar system is connected with the central nervous system through the thoracic and upper lumbar segments of the spinal cord, and its ganglia tend to be placed near the spinal column rather than near the viscera innervated. The parasympathetic or craniosacral system is connected with the central nervous system through certain of the cranial nerves and through the middle three sacral segments of the spinal cord, and its ganglia tend to be placed peripherally near the organs innervated.

The sympathetic and parasympathetic systems both innervate many of the same organs, and in this double innervation the two systems are usually antagonistic to each other physiologically. No consistent rule can be given for the effect of each, but in general the sympathetic system mobilizes the energy for sudden activity such as that in rage or flight; for example, the pupils dilate, the heart beats faster, the peripheral blood vessels constrict and the blood pressure rises. The parasympathetic system aims more toward restoring the reserves; for example, the pupils contract, the heart beats more slowly, and the alimentary tract and its glands become active.

The two systems frequently travel together, especially in the thorax, abdomen, and pelvis, with the result that extensive plexuses are formed which contain the fibers of both. The arrangement of the bundles within these plexuses is very complicated and the identity of individual fibers cannot be determined with certainty. For the purposes of description, therefore, a third subdivision of the autonomic system is recognized, the great autonomic plexuses.

Parasympathetic System.

The parasympathetic system is the **craniosacral portion of the autonomic nervous system** and contains visceral efferent fibers which originate in certain cranial nerves and in the sacral portion of the spinal cord.

A. The Cranial Portion of the Parasympathetic System.

The **cranial outflow** includes fibers in the oculomotor, facial, glossopharyngeal, and vagus nerves. These nerves have been described in previous pages and the details will be repeated here only as far as they apply to the visceral efferent fibers.

The Oculomotor Nerve contains efferent fibers for the non-striated muscle making up the Ciliaris and Sphincter pupillæ muscles of the eyeball (for diagram, see Fig. 805). The preganglionic fibers arise from cells in the Edinger-Westphal nucleus located in the anterior part of the oculomotor nucleus in the tegmentum of the mid-brain. They run in the inferior division of the oculomotor nerve to the ciliary ganglion (Fig. 806) and there form synapses with the ganglion cells. The postganglionic fibers proceed in the short ciliary nerves to the eyeball, penetrate the sclera, and reach the muscles named above.

The Facial Nerve contains efferent fibers for the lacrimal gland, the submaxillary and sublingual glands, and many small glands in the mucous membrane of the nasal cavity, palate, and tongue (for diagrams, see Figs. 817, 818). The preganglionic fibers arise from cells in the superior salivatory nucleus in the reticular formation, dorsomedial to the facial nucleus in the pons, and leave the brain in the nervus intermedius.

1. **Pterygopalatine Ganglion.**—(Fig. 813) Certain of the preganglionic fibers branch from the facial nerve at the geniculum via the greater superficial petrosal, course through the pterygoid canal, and terminate by forming synapses with the cells in the pterygopalatine ganglion. Some of the postganglionic fibers reach the **lacrimal gland** via the maxillary, zygomatic, and lacrimal nerve route; others accompany the branches of the maxillary nerve to the **glands in the mucous membrane of the nasal cavity and nasopharynx**; and still others accompany the palatine nerves to the **glands of the soft palate, tonsils, uvula, roof of the mouth, and upper lip.**

2. **Submaxillary Ganglion.**—(Fig. 813) Other preganglionic fibers leave the facial nerve in the chorda tympani and with it join the lingual nerve to reach the submaxillary ganglion. They form synapses in the ganglion or with groups of ganglion cells in the substance of the gland. The postganglionic fibers form the secretomotor supply to the **submaxillary** and the **sublingual glands**.

3. Filaments communicating with the otic ganglion may contribute preganglionic fibers which join those from the glossopharyngeal nerve to supply the parotid gland.

The Glossopharyngeal Nerve contains efferent fibers for the parotid gland and small glands in the mucous membrane of the tongue and floor of the mouth (for diagram see Fig. 821). The preganglionic fibers arise in the inferior salivatory nucleus in the medulla oblongata, traverse the tympanic and lesser superficial petrosal nerves, and form synapses in the otic ganglion (Fig. 813). Most of the postganglionic fibers join the auriculotemporal nerve, and are distributed with its branches to the **parotid gland**, providing its secretomotor fibers. Other postganglionic fibers are said to supply the glands of the mucous membrane of the tongue and floor of the mouth.

The Vagus Nerve contains efferent fibers for the non-striated muscle and glands of the bronchial tree, of the alimentary tract as far as the transverse colon, of the gall bladder and bile ducts, the pancreas, and inhibitory fibers for the heart. The preganglionic fibers arise from cells in the dorsal motor nucleus of the vagus in the medulla oblongata, and run in the vagus nerve and its branches to ganglia situated in or near the organs innervated.

1. **The Heart.**—(Figs. 519, 880) The preganglionic fibers for the heart reach the cardiac plexus by way of the superior and inferior cardiac nerves of the vagus, and are distributed by branches of the plexus to the ganglion cells in the heart wall. The ganglion cells form numerous clusters in the connective tissue of the epicardium on the surface of the atrium, on the auricular appendages, and in the interatrial septum. The postganglionic fibers terminate in relation to the specialized muscular elements in the sino-atrial and atrio-ventricular nodes, and atrio-ventricular bundle and its branches as far as the Purkinje fibers (Stotler and McMahon '47).

2. **The Lungs.**—The preganglionic fibers for the bronchi leave the main trunk of the vagus nerve in the thorax as the anterior and posterior bronchial branches. They traverse the anterior and posterior pulmonary plexuses (Figs. 824, 825), and terminate in the clusters of ganglion cells scattered along the ramifications of the bronchial tree. The postganglionic fibers are distributed to the bronchial musculature and bronchial glands (Larsell '51).

3. **The alimentary tract** receives, through various branches, preganglionic fibers which end in the myenteric plexus of Auerbach and the submucous plexus of Meissner, forming synapses with the ganglion cells scattered in groups throughout these plexuses. The postganglionic fibers are the efferents for the muscular walls and the secreting cells of the tunica mucosa.

(a) The preganglionic fibers reach the upper part of the **esophagus** through the recurrent nerve, and the lower part, below the hilum of the lung, through branches from the esophageal plexus (Fig. 879).

(*b*) The **stomach** receives an average of four branches from the anterior vagus and six from the posterior vagus. The pylorus and duodenum receive fibers from the hepatic branch of the anterior vagus.

(*c*) The **small intestine,** cecum, appendix vermiformis, ascending and transverse colon receive fibers from the posterior vagus which join the celiac plexus (Fig. 883) and accompany the branches of the superior mesenteric artery (Jackson '49).

(*d*) The **gall bladder** and bile ducts receive preganglionic fibers through the vagus branches in the celiac plexus which traverse the gastrohepatic ligament and terminate in the small clusters of ganglion cells in the wall of the gall bladder and in the region adjacent to the bile ducts. The postganglionic fibers are the efferents for the muscular walls and mucous membrane.

(*e*) The **pancreas** receives fibers through the hepatic branches of the anterior and posterior vagi, and through the branches of the celiac plexus which accompany the arteries supplying this organ.

B. The Sacral Portion of the Parasympathetic System.

The cells which give rise to the sacral outflow are in the second, third, and fourth sacral segments of the spinal cord, and pass out with the corresponding sacral nerves. They leave the sacral nerves in the visceral branches and join the pelvic plexus (Fig. 884) in the deeper portions of the pelvic subserous fascia. Branches from this plexus contain preganglionic fibers for the scattered ganglia in or near the walls of the various pelvic viscera (Ashley and Anson '46).

(*a*) The **branches to the bladder, prostate** and **seminal vesicles** supply efferent fibers to these organs except for the fibers to the sphincter which are inhibitory.

(*b*) The **branches to the uterus** and **vagina** reach ganglia in the uterovaginal plexus; the postganglionic fibers being inhibitory except during pregnancy when their function is said to be reversed.

(*c*) The **branches** of the **pelvic plexus** which join the pudendal nerve and are distributed to the **external genitalia** cause active dilatation of the cavernous blood sinuses of the erectile corpora.

The visceral branches of the sacral nerves in laboratory animals are concentrated in a single trunk called the "**nervus erigens**" because of this function, but the term is not directly applicable to the conditions in man because there is no single nerve such as that used for experimentation in the animals.

(*d*) **Branches** from the **pelvic plexus** containing preganglionic fibers, join the **hypogastric nerve,** and through it and the inferior mesenteric plexus are distributed to the **descending** and **sigmoid colon** and **rectum.** They are efferent to this part of the intestine except for the sphincter ani internus, for which they are inhibitory. Small branches from the pelvic plexus go directly to the rectum.

The Sympathetic System.

The **sympathetic system** (*systema nervorum sympathicum*) (Fig. 875) receives its fibers of connection with the central nervous system through the **thoracolumbar outflow** of visceral efferent fibers. These fibers are the axons of cells in the lateral column of gray matter in the thoracic and upper lumbar segments of the spinal cord. They leave the cord through the ventral roots of the spinal nerves and traverse short communications to reach the sympathetic trunk, where they may terminate in the chain ganglia of the trunk itself, or they may continue into the collateral ganglia of the prevertebral plexuses. They are the preganglionic fibers, and are mostly of the small myelinated variety (3μ or less in diameter). The postganglionic fibers are the axons of the cells in these chain and collateral ganglia and are generally unmyelinated. They are distributed to the heart, non-striated muscle, and glands all over the body, which they reach by way of communications with the cerebrospinal nerves, by way of various plexuses, and by their own visceral branches of distribution.

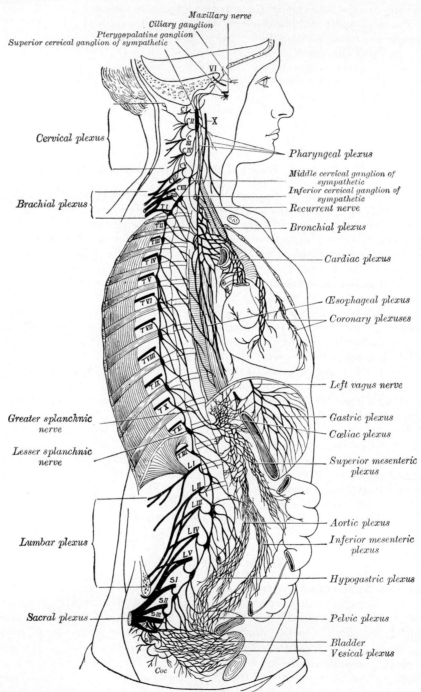

Fig. 875.—The right sympathetic chain and its connections with the thoracic, abdominal, and pelvic plexuses. (After Schwalbe.)

Variability is a prominent characteristic of the sympathetic system, and although a description which will correspond with even the majority of individuals is impossible, certain general principles of organization can be recognized. These are incorporated in the account which follows and the general description is supplemented and made specific by giving a few of the common variations. Many of the details concerning the paths taken by the fibers are still unknown, and we must rely heavily upon information obtained from animal experimentation although it may not have been confirmed by clinical observations with human patients.

The **Sympathetic Trunk** consists of a series of ganglia called the central or chain ganglia (Fig. 879), connected by intervening cords and extending along the lateral aspect of the vertebral column from the base of the skull to the coccyx. The cephalic end of the trunk proper is formed by the superior cervical ganglion (Fig. 875), but there is a direct continuation into the head, the internal carotid nerve. The caudal ends of the two trunks converge at the coccyx and may merge into a single ganglion, the ganglion impar. Cross connections between the two cords in the sacral region are frequent, but rarely occur above the fifth lumbar.

The trunk contains, in addition to the ganglia, the preganglionic fibers which are small (1 to 3μ in diameter) and myelinated, the postganglionic fibers which are mostly unmyelinated, and a smaller number of afferent fibers which are both myelinated (medium, 5μ, and large, 10μ) and unmyelinated. All types of fibers may run up or down in the trunk for the distance between two or many segments. The cords intervening between the ganglia are usually single except in the lower cervical region, but doubling is frequent in any part of the trunk although it very rarely extends farther than between two adjacent ganglia. Small collections of ganglion cells occur outside of the major ganglia, and may be microscopic in size, or grossly visible. They are called intermediary ganglia, and are found in the roots or branches of the trunk and even in the spinal nerves close to these communicating rami (Kuntz and Alexander '50).

Ganglia.—The **central** or **chain ganglia** of the sympathetic trunk are rounded, fusiform or irregular in shape, with diameters usually ranging from 1 to 10 mm., but neighboring ganglia may fuse into larger masses and the superior cervical is always larger. They contain multipolar neurons whose processes are the postganglionic fibers.

The **roots of the ganglia** of the sympathetic trunk are commonly called the **white rami communicantes** (*rami communicantes albi*) because of the whitish color imparted to them by the preponderance of myelinated fibers which they contain. These myelinated fibers are mainly the small (1–3μ in diameter) preganglionic axons of the thoracolumbar outflow whose cell bodies are in the lateral column of gray matter in the spinal cord. They emerge from the spinal cord with the somatic motor fibers in the ventral roots of the spinal nerves of the thoracic, and the first and second lumbar segments. Many of the preganglionic fibers in each root fail to make synaptic connections in the ganglia at the level of entrance; some travel upward to the cervical ganglia, some downward to the lumbar and sacral ganglia, and many in the lower thoracic and upper lumbar levels pass out of the trunk and reach the celiac and related collateral ganglia through the splanchnic nerves. One preganglionic fiber may give collaterals to several of the chain ganglia and may terminate about as many as 15 to 20 ganglionic neurons.

The roots of the ganglia or white rami communicantes are to be distinguished from the branches to the spinal nerves or gray rami communicantes with which they are closely related. The white rami leave the anterior primary divisions of the spinal nerves close outside of the intervertebral foramina but are regularly more distal than the gray rami. They contain a number of medium and large myelinated fibers, probably afferents, and some unmyelinated fibers in addition to the small myelinated preganglionic fibers. In the lower thoracic and upper lumbar regions the white rami take an oblique course from the nerve of one segment to the ganglion of the segment below and have been called, therefore, the oblique rami, as opposed to the transverse gray rami (Botar '32). They are more likely to be attached to the intervening cords than the gray rami. The white rami, varying from 0.5 to 2 cm., are longer in the lower thoracic and lumbar region where they are also usually double or triple.

The sympathetic trunk has branches of distribution, containing the postganglionic fibers originating in the ganglia, and branches of communication, containing preganglionic fibers which pass through the trunk, without synapses, on their way to the collateral ganglia in the abdomen.

A. The **branches of distribution** are of several types: (1) branches to the spinal nerves, (2) branches to the cranial nerves, (3) branches accompanying blood vessels, (4) separate branches to individual organs, and (5) branches to the great autonomic plexuses.

1. The **branches to the spinal nerves** are commonly called the **gray rami communicantes** (Fig. 876) because the preponderance of unmyelinated fibers gives them a more grayish cast than the roots or white rami, which are adjacent to them in the

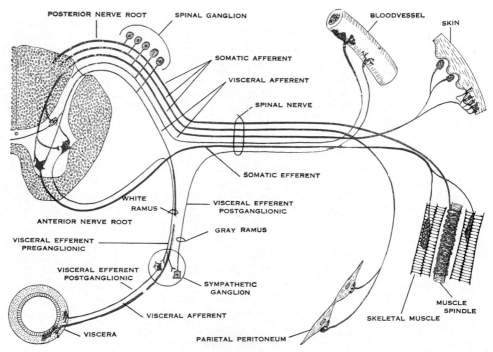

Fig. 876.—Scheme showing structure of a typical spinal nerve.

thoracic area. These branches are the sympathetic roots of the spinal nerves (Duncan '43), and contribute postganglionic fibers, most of which accompany the cutaneous branches of the spinal nerves to supply the Arrectores pilorum muscles, the sweat glands, and the vasoconstrictor fibers of the peripheral blood vessels.

Gray rami join all of the spinal nerves, while the white rami arise only from the thoracic and upper lumbar segments. The gray ramus usually leaves the trunk at a ganglion near the same level as the spinal nerve, and in the thoracic and lumbar regions, where there are both gray and white rami, it is regularly proximal to the white.

2. **Branches to the cranial nerves** may go directly to the nerves or they may pass through plexuses on blood vessels. Direct communications are encountered to the ganglion nodosum and jugular ganglion of the vagus, the inferior ganglion of the glossopharyngeal, and the hypoglossal nerves.

3. **Branches accompanying the arteries** are too numerous to list here, but will be given with the detailed description of the different parts of the system in later pages.

Prominent examples are the nerves on the internal and external carotid arteries and their branches.

4. **Branches to individual organs** may take an independent course but they commonly pass through plexuses, for example, the cardiac branches, or accompany blood vessels for some distance, for example, those to the bulb of the eye.

5. **Branches to the cardiac, pulmonary**, and **pelvic plexuses** probably contain postganglionic fibers, but most of the branches from the trunk to the abdominal plexuses probably contain preganglionic fibers.

B. The principal **branches of communication** containing preganglionic fibers are the **splanchnic nerves.** They branch from the ganglia or the trunk of the thoracic and lumbar regions and supply the fibers which are the roots to the celiac, aortico-renal, and mesenteric ganglia. The postganglionic fibers from these ganglia supply the various abdominal and pelvic organs.

Divisions of the Sympathetic System.—The sympathetic nervous system is divided into portions according to topographical position as follows: (1) cephalic, (2) cervical, (3) thoracic, (4) abdominal or lumbar, and (5) pelvic. These parts are not independent and are chosen merely for convenience in description. In addition to these portions, concerned primarily with the sympathetic trunk and ganglia, there are the autonomic plexuses which are described separately.

The Cephalic Portion of the Sympathetic System.

The **cephalic portion** of the sympathetic system (*pars cephalica s. sympathici*) contains no part of the ganglionated cord, but is formed largely by a direct cephalic prolongation from the superior cervical ganglion, named the internal carotid nerve. In addition, there are nerves accompanying the vertebral artery and the various branches of the external carotid artery which supply fibers to many structures in the head, such as the pilomotor muscles, sweat glands, and peripheral arteries of the face, and the salivary and other glands.

The **Internal Carotid Nerve** (Fig. 823), arising from the cephalic end of the superior cervical ganglion, accompanies the internal carotid artery, and, entering the carotid canal in the petrous portion of the temporal bone, divides into two branches which lie against the medial and lateral aspects of the artery. The lateral branch, the larger of the two, distributes filaments to the carotid artery and forms the internal carotid plexus. The medial branch also distributes filaments to the artery and, following the artery to the cavernous sinus, forms the cavernous plexus.

A. The **Internal Carotid Plexus** (*pl. caroticus internus; carotid plexus*) (Fig. 819) is the continuation of the lateral branch of the internal carotid nerve and surrounds the lateral aspect of the artery, occasionally containing a small carotid ganglion. In addition to filaments to the artery, it has the following branches:

(1) A **communication with the trigeminal** nerve joins the latter at the trigeminal ganglion.

(2) A **communication** joins the **abducent nerve** as it lies near the lateral aspect of the internal carotid artery.

(3) The **deep petrosal nerve** (*n. petrosus profundus*) (Fig. 819) leaves the plexus at the lateral side of the artery, passes through the cartilage of the auditory tube which fills the foramen lacerum, and joins the greater superficial petrosal nerve to form the nerve of the pterygoid canal (Vidian nerve). In the pterygopalatine fossa, the Vidian nerve joins the sphenopalatine ganglion and its contribution through the deep petrosal nerve has been called the sympathetic root of the ganglion, but the sympathetic fibers, already postganglionic, pass through or beside the ganglion without synapses, and are distributed to the glands and blood vessels of the pharynx, nasal cavity, and palate by accompanying the branches of the maxillary nerve (for diagram, see Fig. 817A).

(4) The **caroticotympanic nerves** (*nn. caroticotympanici superior et inferior*) are two or three filaments which pass through foramina in the bony wall of the carotid canal and join the tympanic plexus on the promontory of the middle ear (Fig. 929).

B. **The cavernous plexus** (*pl. cavernosus*) (Fig. 813) is the continuation of the medial branch of the internal carotid nerve, and lies inferior and medial to the part of the internal carotid artery enclosed by the cavernous sinus. It communicates

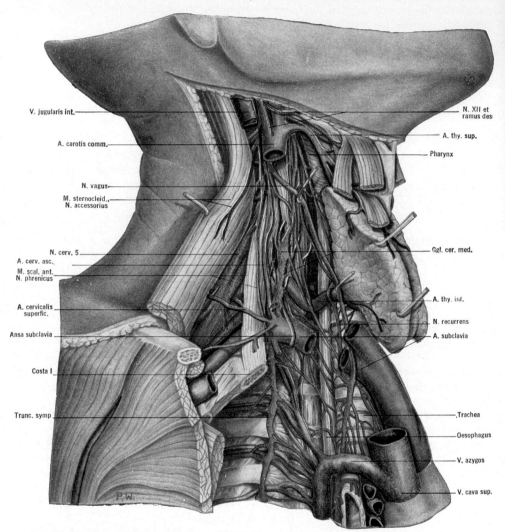

Fig. 877.—Cervical portion of the sympathetic nervous system on the right side, with the common carotid artery and internal jugular vein removed and with the vagus nerve and thyroid gland drawn aside. (Töndury, Angewandte und topographische Anatomie, courtesy of Georg Thieme Verlag.)

with the adjacent cranial nerves and continues along the artery to its terminal branches.

(1) The **communication** with the **oculomotor nerve** enters the orbit and joins the nerve at its point of division.

(2) A **communication** joins the **trochlear nerve** as it lies in the lateral wall of the cavernous sinus.

(3) The **communication** with the **ophthalmic** division of the **trigeminal** joins the latter nerve at its inferior surface.

(4) Fibers to the **Dilatator pupillæ muscle** of the iris traverse the communication with the ophthalmic nerve, accompany the nasociliary nerve, and the long ciliary nerves to the posterior part of the bulb where they penetrate the sclera and run forward to the iris (for diagram, see Fig. 805).

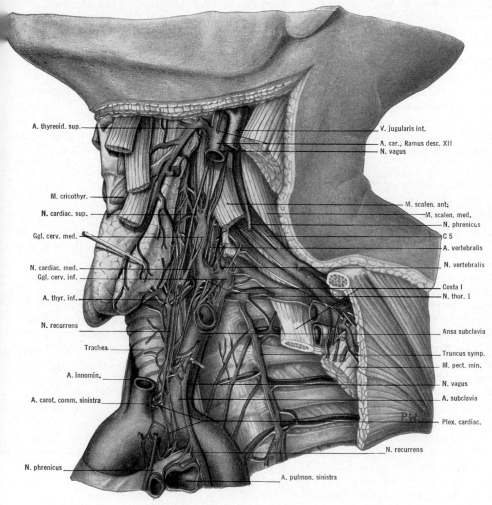

FIG. 878.—Cervical portion of the sympathetic system on the left side, with the common carotid artery, internal jugular vein, vagus nerve, and subclavian artery partly removed, and the thyroid gland drawn forward. (Töndury, Angewandte und topographische Anatomie, courtesy of Georg Thieme Verlag.)

(5) The **communication** with the **ciliary ganglion** leaves the anterior part of the cavernous plexus and enters the orbit through the superior orbital fissure. It may join the nasociliary nerve and reach the ganglion through the latter's branch to the ganglion, or it may take an independent course to the ganglion.

(6) **Filaments to the hypophysis** accompany its blood vessels.

(7) The **terminal filaments** from the internal carotid and cavernous plexuses continue along the anterior and middle cerebral arteries, and the ophthalmic artery. Fibers on the cerebral arteries may be traced to the pia mater; those on the ophthal-

mic artery accompany all its branches in the orbit. The filaments on the anterior communicating artery may connect the sympathetic nerves of the right and left sides.

C. **The External Carotid Nerves** (*nn. carotici externi*), which are branches of the superior cervical ganglion, send filaments out along all the branches of the external carotid artery. The filaments on the external maxillary artery join the **submaxillary ganglion**; they have formerly been called the sympathetic root of the ganglion, but they pass through it without forming synapses and supply the submaxillary and probably the sublingual glands (for diagram, see Fig. 817B). The network of filaments on the middle meningeal artery gives off the **small deep petrosal nerve**, which has been called the sympathetic root of the **otic ganglion**, but its fibers pass through the ganglion without synapses, some accompanying the auriculotemporal nerve to the parotid gland (for diagram, see Fig. 820), others forming the **external superficial petrosal nerve** which is a communication with the geniculate ganglion. Filaments on the external maxillary, superficial temporal, and other arteries which are distributed to the skin supply the Arrectores pilorum muscles, and sweat glands, as well as the muscles constricting the arteries themselves.

The Cervical Portion of the Sympathetic System.

The **cervical portion** (*pars cervicalis s. sympathici*) of the sympathetic trunk consists of three ganglia, superior, middle, and inferior, connected by intervening cords (Fig. 877). It is ventral to the transverse processes of the vertebræ, close to the carotid artery, being imbedded in the fascia of the carotid sheath itself, or in the connective tissue between the sheath and the Longus colli and capitis. It receives no roots or white rami communicantes from the cervical spinal nerves; its preganglionic fibers enter the trunk through the white rami from the upper five thoracic spinal nerves, mainly the second and third, and travel upward in the trunk to the three ganglia. The trunk also contains postganglionic fibers from various sources, and visceral afferent fibers with their cell bodies in the dorsal root ganglia.

The **Superior Cervical Ganglion** (*g. cervicale superius*) (Fig. 823), much larger than the other cervical ganglia and usually the largest of all the trunk ganglia, is approximately 28 mm. long and 8 mm. wide, fusiform in shape, frequently broad and flat, and occasionally constricted into two or more parts. It is imbedded in the connective tissue between the carotid sheath and the prevertebral fascia over the Longus capitis, at the level of the second cervical vertebra. It is the cephalic end of the sympathetic chain, and is connected with the middle ganglion caudally by a rather long interganglionic cord. It is believed to be formed by the coalescence of sympathetic primordia from the upper four cervical segments of the body. Its branches are as follows:

1. **The internal carotid nerve** (described above, p. 1067) leaves the cephalic pole of the ganglion, and serves as a direct continuation of the sympathetic trunk into the head.

2. **Communications with the cranial** nerves are delicate filaments which join (*a*) the inferior ganglion of the glossopharyngeal nerve, (*b*) the jugular and nodose ganglia of the vagus, and (*c*) the hypoglossal nerve. The jugular nerve is a filament which passes upward to the base of the skull and divides to join the inferior ganglion of the glossopharyngeal and the jugular ganglion of the vagus nerve.

3. **Branches to the upper two to four cervical** spinal nerves are the **sympathetic roots** of these nerves **(gray rami communicantes)**. They course laterally, dorsally, and backward, and have been called the lateral or external branches of the ganglion. The branches to any one nerve are variable and may be multiple or absent.

a. **The branches to the first** and **second nerves** are constantly present. Since the spinal nerves in the neck are connected by loops, as parts of the cervical plexus, the branch to the first nerve may join the loop between the first and second nerves, and the branch to the second may join the loop between the second and third nerves. There may be two to four branches to each of these nerves.

b. The **third cervical nerve** receives a branch from the ganglion in the majority of individuals, but in many instances it comes from the trunk below the superior ganglion. A branch for the third nerve often forms a loop with a lower branch which then supplies roots to both the third and fourth nerves. Branches may join the third nerve itself or the loop between it and the fourth nerve.

c. The **fourth nerve** receives a branch from the ganglion only occasionally. Its roots frequently arise in common with those of either the third, fifth, or even the sixth nerves, and may come from the trunk or from nerves accompanying the vertebral artery.

4. **Pharyngeal branches** (*rr. laryngopharyngei*), commonly four to six, leave the medial aspect of the ganglion, and, in their course toward the pharynx, communicate with pharyngeal branches of the glossopharyngeal and vagus nerves opposite the Constrictor pharyngis medius to form the **pharyngeal plexus**. Some of the filaments form a plexus on the lateral wall of the pharynx, others travel in the substance of the prevertebral fascia to the back of the pharynx and form a posterior pharyngeal plexus. Filaments communicate with the superior laryngeal nerve (Braeucker '22).

5. The **nerves to the external carotid artery** usually are two relatively large bundles which form a network about the artery and continue as secondary branches to the common carotid artery and to the branches of the external carotid. The latter are described as part of the cephalic sympathetic system (page 1068).

6. The **intercarotid plexus** receives one or two branches, either from the ganglion or from the external carotid nerves. They communicate with filaments from the pharyngeal branch of the vagus and the carotid branch of the glossopharyngeal in the region of the carotid bifurcation, and are distributed in the plexus to the carotid sinus and the carotid body, probably serving a vasomotor function.

7. The **superior cardiac nerve** (*n. cardicus superior*) (Figs. 877, 878) arises by two or three filaments from the ganglion, and occasionally also by a filament from the trunk between the superior and middle ganglia. It runs down the neck in the connective tissue of the posterior layers of the carotid sheath superficial to the Longus colli, and crosses ventral or dorsal to the inferior thyroid artery and recurrent nerve. The course of the nerves on the two sides then differs. The right nerve, at the root of the neck, passes either ventral or dorsal to the subclavian artery, and along the innominate artery to the deep part of the cardiac plexus. The left nerve passes ventral to the common carotid and across the left side of the arch of the aorta, to reach the superficial part of the cardiac plexus. The superior cardiac nerves may communicate with the middle and inferior cardiac sympathetic nerves, with the cardiac branches of the vagus, the external branch of the superior laryngeal nerve, the recurrent nerve, the thyroid branch of the middle ganglion, the nerves on the inferior thyroid artery, and the tracheal and anterior pulmonary plexuses.

The **Middle Cervical Ganglion** (*g. cervicale medium*) (Fig. 878), the smallest of the three cervical ganglia, is quite variable in size, form, and position, and may be either absent or double. It probably represents a fusion of the two sympathetic primordia corresponding to the fifth and sixth cervical nerves. When single, the ganglion may have a high position, at the level of the transverse process of the sixth cervical vertebra (the carotid or Chassaignac's tubercle), or a low position nearer the level of the seventh cervical vertebra (Axford '28; Jamieson et al. '52). In the high position it lies on the Longus colli above the cephalic bend of the inferior thyroid artery. In the low position it lies in close association with the ventral or ventromedial aspect of the vertebral artery, 1 to 3 cm. from the latter's origin. The middle cervical ganglion has no root (white ramus communicans); its preganglionic fibers probably leave the spinal cord through the white rami of the second and third thoracic nerves and reach the ganglion through the intervening sympathetic trunk.

Variations.—The middle cervical ganglion was absent in 5, single in 10 and double in 10 of 25 dissections (Pick and Sheehan '46). It was present in 53 and double in two of 100 body halves

(Jamieson *et al.* '52), with 64 per cent in the high position. A small ganglion in the low position may have no branches. Several small thickenings may occur along the trunk between the superior and inferior ganglia. The ganglion may be split, surrounding the inferior thyroid artery (Axford '28).

The **intermediate cervical sympathetic ganglion** (of Jonnesco '23) corresponds to a middle ganglion in the low position described above. According to Saccomanno ('43) it is of more constant appearance than a middle ganglion in the high position. A ganglion in the low position has been called the **thyroid ganglion** because of its close relationship to the inferior thyroid artery (Jamieson *et al.* '52). The **vertebral ganglion** is a name given to a ganglion in the low position, on the deep part of the loop of the ansa subclavia, included as part of the stellate ganglionic configuration (Pick and Sheehan '46; Woollard and Norrish '33).

The branches of the middle cervical ganglion are as follows:

1. The **branches** which form the **sympathetic roots** of the spinal nerves (*gray rami communicantes*) are constantly supplied **to the fifth and sixth nerves.** A ganglion in the high position may send branches to the fourth or even the third nerve, and a ganglion in the low position may send branches to the seventh nerve.

a. The **roots of the fifth cervical** nerve number from one to three. (1) The most constant arises from the middle ganglion or the trunk just above it, runs upward and laterally across the Scalenus anterior, winds around the carotid tubercle and along a groove in the transverse process of the fifth cervical vertebra to the fifth nerve. It may pierce the Scalenus anterior, it may divide, one branch going to the sixth nerve, or it may be prolonged to give a branch to the fourth or even the third nerve (Axford '28). (2) A root present in the majority of individuals leaves the trunk just above the carotid tubercle, pierces the Longus colli either medial or lateral to the vertebral artery and receives a communication from the nerve of the vertebral artery. (3) An inconstant root is a branch of the root of the sixth nerve which accompanies the vertebral artery.

b. The **roots of the sixth cervical** nerve may be from two to four in number, one from the middle and one from the inferior ganglion being constant. (1) A short root from the middle ganglion runs upward through the Longus colli just above the carotid tubercle to join the sixth nerve as it lies in its groove, medial to the vertebral artery. (2) A long fine branch from the middle ganglion or the trunk just above it crosses the vertebral artery and Scalenus anterior, and joins the nerve lateral to the carotid tubercle, sometimes continuing on to the fifth nerve.

2. **The middle cardiac nerve** (*n. cardiacus medius; great cardiac nerve*) (Fig. 878), the largest of the three cardiac nerves in the neck, arises from the middle cervical ganglion, from the trunk between the middle and inferior ganglia, or both. As it runs down behind the common carotid artery, it communicates with the superior cardiac nerve and the inferior laryngeal nerve. On the right side, at the root of the neck, it goes either deep or superficial to the subclavian artery, continues along the trachea, communicates with the recurrent nerve, and joins the right side of the deep part of the cardiac plexus. The left nerve enters the thorax between the common carotid and subclavian arteries, and joins the left side of the deep part of the cardiac plexus.

3. **Thyroid Nerves.**—Branches from the middle cervical ganglion form a plexus on the inferior thyroid artery, supply the thyroid gland, join the plexus on the common carotid artery, and may communicate with the inferior laryngeal and external branch of the superior laryngeal nerves (Braeucker '22).

The trunk between the middle and inferior cervical ganglia is constantly double, the two strands enclosing the subclavian artery. The superficial strand is usually much longer than the deep, forms a loop about the artery supplying it with branches, and is called the **ansa subclavia** (of Vieussens) (Fig. 878). Since it is a rather constant feature, it may be used to identify and distinguish the middle and inferior ganglia or the components representing them. Occasionally the loop is formed about the vertebral artery instead of the subclavian, or there may be individual loops about both.

The **Inferior Cervical Ganglion** (*g. cervicale inferius*) (Fig. 878) is situated between the base of the transverse process of the seventh cervical vertebra and the neck of the first rib, on the medial side of the costocervical artery. In most instances it is incompletely separated from or fused with the first thoracic ganglion, but it will be described as it appears when discrete, and the fused ganglion, called the stellate, also will be described below. It is larger than the middle ganglion, is irregular in shape, and probably represents the fusion of sympathetic primordia corresponding to the seventh and eighth cervical nerves. It has no root or white ramus, but receives its preganglionic fibers from the thoracic part of the trunk through its connection with the first thoracic ganglion.

Variations.—The inferior cervical ganglion was independent in 5 out of 25 (Pick and Sheehan '46) and in 18 out of 100 cases (Jamieson *et al.* '52). A white ramus has been described joining the eighth cervical nerve and the sympathetic (Pearson '52).

The branches of the inferior cervical ganglion are as follows:

1. **Branches** which are the **sympathetic roots** (*gray rami communicantes*) of the spinal nerves are constantly supplied **to the sixth, seventh,** and **eighth cervical nerves.**

a. The **sixth cervical** nerve commonly receives branches from the inferior cervical ganglion as well as from the middle cervical ganglion. (1) A constant rather thick root from the deep part of the inferior cervical ganglion runs upward along the medial aspect of the vertebral artery, anterior to the vertebral veins and lateral to the Longus colli, and enters the foramen in the transverse process of the sixth cervical vertebra with the vertebral artery. It communicates with the plexus on the vertebral artery and supplies roots for the sixth and seventh, sometimes the fifth or even more cephalic nerves. (2) An inconstant root from the inferior ganglion is similar to the last, but pierces the Scalenus anterior instead of passing through the foramen (Axford '28).

b. The **seventh cervical** nerve receives from two to five branches (gray rami) from the inferior cervical ganglion. (1) A constant, well-defined branch 15 to 25 mm. long crosses ventral to the eighth cervical nerve, either deep to, superficial to, or piercing the Scalenus anterior. It may be composed of two or three parallel filaments. (2) A constant branch accompanies the vertebral artery and is shared by the sixth nerve. (3) A frequent branch lies close to the vertebral vein, crosses the eighth cervical nerve, to which it may give filaments, and enters the foramen in the seventh cervical vertebra with the vein (Axford '28).

c. The **eighth cervical** nerve receives from two to five rather short branches (averaging 10 mm. in length), from the inferior cervical ganglion. (1) A constant, well-defined, thick branch runs upward and lateralward, often across the neck of the first rib, and joins the eighth cervical nerve deep to the Scalenus anterior. It is dorsal to the first part of the subclavian artery and is intimately related to the superior intercostal artery. It may be represented by two to four parallel filaments. (2) A constant short thick branch from the upper pole of the inferior ganglion runs vertically upward, medial and dorsal to the vertebral artery, a few millimeters lateral to the Longus colli. It passes ventral to the transverse process of the first thoracic vertebra and medial to the first costocentral articulation, and joins the eighth cervical nerve as it emerges from its foramen. (3) A frequent ramus accompanies the vertebral vein with a similar root to the seventh nerve.

2. **The inferior cardiac nerve** (*n. cardiacus inferior*) (Fig. 878) arises from either the inferior cervical ganglion, the first thoracic ganglion, the stellate ganglion, or the ansa subclavia. It passes deep to the subclavian artery and along the anterior surface of the trachea to the deep cardiac plexus. It communicates with the middle cardiac nerve and the recurrent laryngeal nerve, and supplies twigs to various cervical structures (Saccomanno '43).

3. **Vertebral Nerve.**—The branches which accompany the vertebral artery through the vertebral foramina are of considerable size. They join similar branches from the first thoracic ganglion to form the vertebral nerve which continues into the cranial cavity on the basilar, posterior cerebral, and cerebellar arteries. Communications between the vertebral nerve and the cervical spinal nerves frequently serve as roots of these nerves (Christensen *et al.* '52).

The junction of the cervical with the thoracic portion of the sympathetic trunk requires special consideration, first, because the lowest cervical and highest thoracic ganglia are usually fused, and second, because the trunk makes an abrupt change of direction at this point. The cervical portion of the trunk lies upon the ventral aspect of the transverse processes, but is also in a plane ventral to the vertebral bodies on account of the latter's small size and the presence of the Longus colli muscle. The trunk drops back dorsalward as it enters the thorax, winding around the transverse process of the seventh cervical vertebra to reach the neck of the first rib.

The **Stellate Ganglion** (*cervicothoracic ganglion*) (Fig. 878) is the name given to the ganglionic mass which results when, as is usually the case, the inferior cervical and first thoracic ganglia are fused. It is quite variable in size and form, occasionally including the middle cervical or the second thoracic ganglia, and is located between the eighth cervical and first thoracic nerves. Its roots, branches, and communications are modifications of those which would be found if the component ganglia remained separate. The root of the ganglion or white ramus communicans, therefore, comes from the first thoracic nerve, or from the second also if the mass includes the second ganglion.

The **branches of the stellate ganglion** which supply the roots or gray rami to the spinal nerves include: (*a*) a frequent branch to the sixth nerve, (*b*) a constant branch to the seventh, and (*c*) constant double or multiple branches to the eighth cervical, (*d*) first thoracic, and (*e*) second thoracic nerves. The branch to the vertebral artery is a large one leaving the superior border of the ganglion, and forming the major portion of the vertebral nerve. Other branches are similar to those described for the independent ganglia (Kirgis and Kuntz '42).

Variations.—In 25 bodies, the inferior cervical ganglion was independent in 5, used with the first thoracic in 17, and with both the first and second thoracic in 3 (Pick and Sheehan '46). A stellate ganglion was present in 82 of 100 (Jamieson *et al.* '52) and in 40 of 48 (Perlow and Vehe '35). When the second thoracic is fused with the first, the inferior cervical is more likely to be independent.

Surgical Considerations.—The branches (gray rami) from the stellate ganglion to the eighth cervical and first thoracic nerve carry the bulk of the sympathetic fibers to the upper extremity (Kirgis and Kuntz '42). Other branches also carry fibers, however, and Woollard and Norrish ('33) recommend that the middle cervical and second thoracic ganglia be included in the "stellate complex," and that the description of the independent ganglia be abandoned. The sympathetic roots of the brachial plexus are described in more detail on page 1012.

Comparative Anatomical Considerations.—The stellate ganglion in cats includes the inferior cervical and first three thoracic ganglia (Saccomanno '43) and in rhesus monkeys the inferior cervical and first two thoracic ganglia (Sheehan and Pick '43). The function of the stellate ganglion in control of the heart, as it is revealed by animal experimentation with dogs, cats, and monkeys, does not agree entirely with that revealed by clinical observations. A partial explanation of this is provided by the fact that more thoracic ganglia are included in the stellate complex and a much greater bulk of the accelerator nerves arises from the ganglion in these animals than in man.

The Thoracic Portion of the Sympathetic System.

The **thoracic portion of the sympathetic trunk** (*pars thoracalis s. sympathici*) (Figs. 879, 880) contains a series of ganglia which correspond approximately to the thoracic spinal nerves, but the coalescence of adjacent ganglia commonly reduces the number to fewer than twelve. The ganglia are oval, fusiform, triangular, or irregular in shape; they lie against the necks of the ribs in the upper thorax, gradually they become more ventrally placed in the lower thorax, and finally they lie at the sides of the bodies of the lowest thoracic vertebræ. The trunk is covered by the costal portion of the parietal pleura, and the interganglionic cords are between the pleura and the intercostal vessels which they cross.

The roots of the ganglia are the white rami communicantes which are supplied by each spinal nerve to the corresponding ganglion or the trunk nearby. They contain predominantly small myelinated fibers (1 to 3μ in diameter) which leave the spinal cord through the ventral roots of the spinal nerves, and whose cell bodies are in the lateral column of gray matter in the spinal cord. A large number of the preganglionic fibers fail to make synapses in their ganglia of entrance. From the upper five roots, these fibers take a cephalic direction in the trunk and, for the most part, terminate in the cervical ganglia. Many of the fibers in the lower six or seven roots traverse the trunk for a variable distance and then emerge into the splanchnic nerves which are the roots of the celiac and related ganglia.

The **first thoracic ganglion**, when independent, is larger than the rest, is elongated or crescentic in shape, and because of the change in direction of the trunk as it passes from the neck into the thorax, the ganglion is elongated dorsoventrally. It lies at the medial end of the first intercostal space, or in front of the neck of the first rib, medial to the costocervical arterial trunk. It is usually combined with the inferior cervical ganglion into a stellate ganglion (see above) or it may coalesce with the second thoracic ganglion. The second to the tenth ganglia lie opposite the intervertebral disc or the upper border of the next lower vertebra, slightly lower than the corresponding spinal nerve. In the majority of individuals, the last thoracic ganglion, lying on the body of the twelfth vertebra, is larger and by its connection to both the eleventh and twelfth nerves takes the place of these two ganglia.

Variations.—The first thoracic ganglion was independent of the stellate in 5, the second thoracic in 22 out of 25 instances. Fusion occurred between the 3rd and 4th three times, 4th and 5th five times, 5th and 6th once, 6th and 7th once, 7th and 8th four times, 8th and 9th twice, 9th and 10th twice (Pick and Sheehan '46). Small accessory ganglia occur at or near the junction of the communicating rami with the thoracic nerves, especially the upper four. Those at the white rami may provide sympathetic pathways to spinal nerves without traversing the sympathetic trunk (Ehrlich and Alexander '51).

The branches of the thoracic trunk are of three varieties: sympathetic roots of the spinal nerves or gray rami communicantes, visceral branches, and the splanchnic nerves.

1. The **branches** which form the **sympathetic roots** of the spinal nerves **(gray rami communicantes)** are supplied to each spinal nerve. Usually two or three short branches are sent to each corresponding spinal nerve, and occasionally a slender branch reaches the next lower ganglion. When there are two or more branches to a single nerve, one branch may go to the anterior and one to the posterior primary division of the nerve. When the branches go only to the anterior primary division, the fibers turn back within the nerve to reach the posterior division (Dass '52). The gray rami are regularly proximal and transverse, the white rami distal and oblique.

2. **Visceral branches** are supplied to the cardiac, pulmonary, esophageal and aortic plexuses.

a. **Branches** from the upper five thoracic ganglia join the **cardiac plexus**; they are variable in number both in different individuals and between the two sides in the same individual, and may be fifteen or twenty in some cases. The larger ones usually come from ganglia, smaller ones from intervening cords. They course medially close to the intercostal artery and vein, usually between them and in the same connective tissue sheath, supplying filaments to them and communicating with the esophageal and pulmonary plexuses. From the right side they approach the deep part of the plexus, between the esophagus and the lateral aspect of the aorta. From the left side, they pass dorsal to the aorta and approach the deep part of the plexus from the right side (Kuntz and Morehouse '30). Branches from the third, fourth, and fifth ganglia are more abundant than the first two and branches may come from the sixth and seventh, but the latter usually enter the aortic network. The cross sectional area of the thoracic cardiac nerves, as they enter the plexus, is twice as large as that of the cervical cardiac nerves (Saccomanno '43).

b. Delicate **esophageal branches** from several of the thoracic ganglia, both upper and lower, may follow the intercostal vessels to the esophagus and join the plexus formed by the vagus, or filaments may be supplied by the cardiac and aortic plexuses, or by the splanchnic nerves.

c. The **posterior pulmonary plexus** receives from the second, third, and fourth ganglia, twigs which follow the intercostal arteries to the hilum of the lung.

d. **Branches to the aortic network** come from the lower five or six thoracic ganglia, from the cardiac plexus, and from the splanchnic nerves. Branches from these bundles accompany the branches of the artery, and probably supplement the splanchnic nerves.

3. **The Splanchnic Nerves** arise from the lower six or seven thoracic and upper lumbar ganglia. They are not, strictly speaking, true branches of the ganglia, since they contain but a small number of postganglionic fibers. They are composed

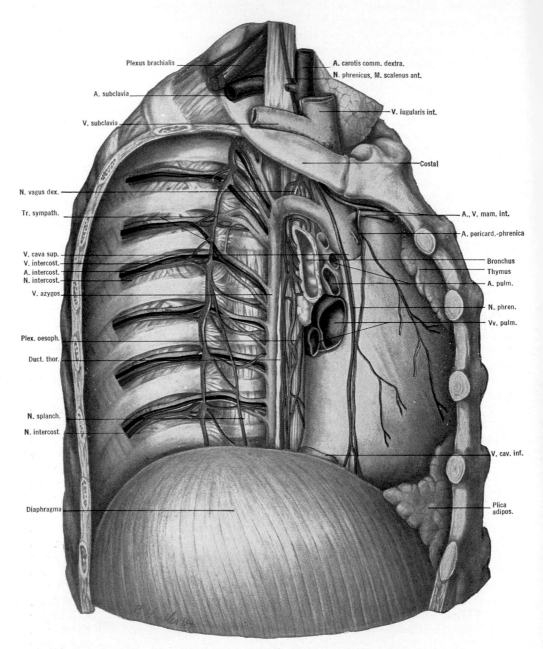

Fig. 879.—The mediastinum from the right side. (Töndury, Angewandte und topographische Anatomie, courtesy of Georg Thieme Verlag.)

principally of myelinated fibers, and accordingly have a whitish color and firm consistency similar to those of the somatic nerves. The small myelinated fibers, 1 to 3μ in diameter, which predominate are the preganglionic fibers which pass through the chain ganglia without synapses, to become the roots of the celiac and related ganglia. There are appreciable numbers of large myelinated fibers also which are probably visceral afferents with their cell bodies in the dorsal root ganglia of the spinal nerves. Many of the fibers of all types probably come from spinal cord segments higher than the ganglia from which the branches arise.

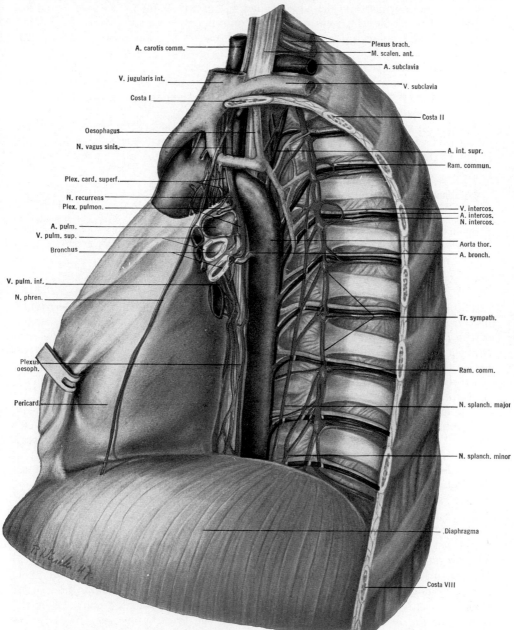

Fig. 880.—The mediastinum from the left side. (Töndury, Angewandte und topographische Anatomie, courtesy of Georg Thieme Verlag.)

a. **The Greater Splanchnic Nerve** (*n. splanchnicus major*) (Figs. 879, 880) is formed by contributions from the fifth (or sixth) to the ninth (or tenth) thoracic ganglia, which leave the ganglia in a medial direction and angle across the vertebral bodies obliquely in their downward course. They are combined into a single nerve which pierces the crus of the diaphragm and, after making an abrupt bend or loop ventralward, ends in the celiac ganglion by entering the lateral border of its principal mass (Fig. 881). A small splanchnic ganglion occurs commonly in the nerve at the level of the eleventh or twelfth thoracic vertebra; it is considered to be part of the celiac ganglion formed by cells which failed to migrate as far as the large ganglion during embryonic development. Preganglionic fibers to the suprarenal glands are conveyed by the splanchnic nerves and pass through the celiac plexus without synapses in the ganglion.

The Lesser Splanchnic Nerve (*n. splanchnicus minor*) (Fig. 880) is formed by branches of the ninth and tenth thoracic ganglia, or from the cord between them. It pierces the crus of the diaphragm with the greater splanchnic nerve and ends in the aorticorenal ganglion.

The **lowest splanchnic nerve** (*n. splanchnicus imus; least splanchnic nerve*), when present, is a branch of the last thoracic ganglion or of the lesser splanchnic nerve. It passes through the diaphragm with the sympathetic trunk and ends in the renal plexus.

Variations.—The uppermost branch to the splanchnics in 25 dissections were the 4th, once; 5th, twice; 6th, eleven times; 7th, seven times; 8th, four times (Pick and Sheehan '46). Filaments from the upper thoracic and stellate ganglia, from the cardiac nerves, or from the branches to the pulmonary and aortic plexuses sometimes continue down to join the celiac plexus and have been considered to be a fourth splanchnic nerve. Lumbar splanchnic nerves are described below.

The Abdominal Portion of the Sympathetic System.

The **abdominal portion of the sympathetic trunk** (*pars abdominalis s. sympathici; lumbar portion of the ganglionated cord*) (Fig. 882) is situated ventral to the bodies of the lumbar vertebræ, along the medial margin of the Psoas major. The cord connecting the last thoracic and first lumbar ganglia bends ventrally as it passes under the medial lumbocostal arch of the diaphragm, bringing the trunk rather abruptly into its ventral relationship with the lumbar vertebræ. The left trunk is partly concealed by the aorta, the right by the inferior vena cava.

The **lumbar ganglia** have no fixed pattern. The number varies from two to six, with four or five occurring in three-fourths of the trunks, but massive fusions are frequent and two examples with four ganglia may bear no resemblance to each other. Although the five individual lumbar ganglia should not be expected in any particular instance, each one occurs with sufficient frequency to make an anatomical description possible. The numbering of the ganglia is based upon the spinal nerves with which they are connected as well as upon the relationship to the vertebræ (Pick and Sheehan '46).

The **roots of the lumbar ganglia** (*white rami communicantes*) are found only as far as the second lumbar spinal nerve, the caudal limit of the thoracolumbar outflow. The preganglionic fibers for the rest of the lumbar, and the sacral and coccygeal ganglia run caudally in the trunk, mainly from these first two lumbar roots. One or two roots (white rami) are supplied to each of the first three lumbar ganglia (or their representatives in fused ganglia) by the spinal nerve one segment above; the roots take an oblique course downward while the branches to the spinal nerves (gray rami) take a transverse course (Botar '32). Thus the twelfth thoracic nerve sends roots to the first lumbar ganglion, the first lumbar nerve to the second ganglion, and the second nerve to the third ganglion.

The ganglia of the lumbar trunk, when independently represented, lie on the bodies of the corresponding vertebræ or the intervertebral discs below. The first ganglion is close to or partly concealed by the medial lumbocostal arch. The ganglion on the second lumbar vertebra is the most constant, largest, and most easily palpated and identified by the surgeon. The fifth ganglion is relatively inaccessible to the surgeon because of the common iliac vessels (Cowley and Yeager '49).

Variations.—In 25 bodies, the first lumbar ganglion (identified by its rami) was independent in 13, fused with other ganglia in 10, and separated into two parts in 2; the second ganglion was missing in 2, independent in 12, fused in 7 and split in 4; the third ganglion was independent in 2, fused in 17, split in 4, and connected only with L 3 nerve in 3; the fourth ganglion was independent in one, fused in 12, split in 12, and of these, 11 connected with L 4 only; the fifth ganglion was independent in 4, fused in 3, split in 18, and of these 15 connected with L 5 only (Pick and Sheehan '46).

The branches of the lumbar trunk may be divided into three groups: (1) the branches which are the sympathetic roots of the spinal nerves (gray rami communicantes), (2) the lumbar splanchnic nerves, and (3) the visceral branches.

The **branches** which are the **sympathetic roots** of the spinal nerves (**gray rami communicantes**) are supplied to each of the lumbar nerves. They take a transverse path, in contrast to the oblique path of the white rami, and they are more proximal than the white rami in the segments where both are present. They are longer than those in the thoracic region because the lumbar trunk is more ventrally placed, at some distance from the spinal nerves, and they commonly accompany the lumbar arteries under the fibrous arches of the Psoas, frequently splitting, doubling, and rejoining (Kuntz and Alexander '50).

The **lumbar splanchnic nerves** are two to four relatively short branches of the lumbar trunk at the level of the first, second, and third lumbar vertebræ, and are, therefore, caudal to the last root of the lesser splanchnic nerve. They pass either medially, downward, and forward to join the aortic network, or, in the case of the most caudal lumbar splanchnic, downward and forward around the aorta to the inferior mesenteric ganglion or the hypogastric nerve; on the right side they pass between the aorta and the inferior vena cava (Trumble '34). Frequently they contain small groups of ganglion cells which are believed to be displaced from the sympathetic trunk (Harris '43).

The Celiac Ganglion (*g. celiaca; semilunar ganglion*) (Fig. 883) comprises two masses of ganglionic tissue approximately 2 cm. in diameter, superficially resembling lymph nodes, lying ventral and lateral to the abdominal aorta, one on each side, at the level of the first lumbar vertebra. The ganglia are irregular in shape, are usually partly dispersed into several small ganglionic masses, and are connected with each other across the midline by a dense network of bundles, especially caudal to the celiac artery. The ganglia lie on the ventral surface of the crura of the diaphragm, close to the medial border of the suprarenal glands. The right ganglion is covered by the inferior vena cava; the left is covered by the peritoneum of the lesser sac in close relation to the pancreas.

The **aorticorenal** and **superior mesenteric ganglia** are masses which are more or less completely detached from the caudal portion of the celiac ganglion but represent portions of the larger celiac ganglionic complex. The aorticorenal ganglion lies at the origin of the renal artery, the superior mesenteric ganglion at the origin of the corresponding artery.

The **roots** of these ganglia are the **splanchnic nerves** (see above). The greater splanchnic nerve enters the dorsal and lateral border of the main celiac ganglion (Fig. 883); the lesser splanchnic nerve enters the aorticorenal ganglion (Fig. 881) and the lowest splanchnic joins the renal plexus. They contain preganglionic fibers from the lower six or seven thoracic spinal cord segments which pass through the sympathetic trunk without synapses.

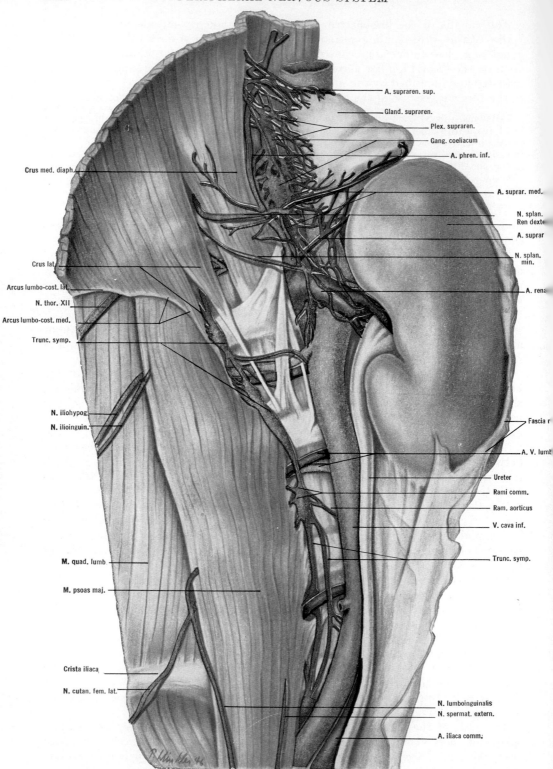

A. supraren. sup.

Gland. supraren.

Plex. supraren.

Gang. coeliacum

A. phren. inf.

A. suprar. med.

N. splan.
Ren dexte

A. suprar

N. splan.
min.

A. rena

Fascia r

A. V. lumb

Ureter

Rami comm.

Ram. aorticus

V. cava inf.

Trunc. symp.

N. lumboinguinalis

N. spermat. extern.

A. iliaca comm.

Crus med. diaph.

Crus lat.

Arcus lumbo-cost. lat.

N. thor. XII

Arcus lumbo-cost. med.

Trunc. symp.

N. iliohypog.

N. ilioinguin.

M. quad. lumb.

M. psoas maj.

Crista iliaca

N. cutan. fem. lat.

FIG. 881.—The lumbar portion of the right sympathetic trunk, the celiac ganglion, splanchnic nerves, suprarenal gland, and kidney. (Töndury, Angewandte und topographische Anatomie, courtesy of Georg Thieme Verlag.)

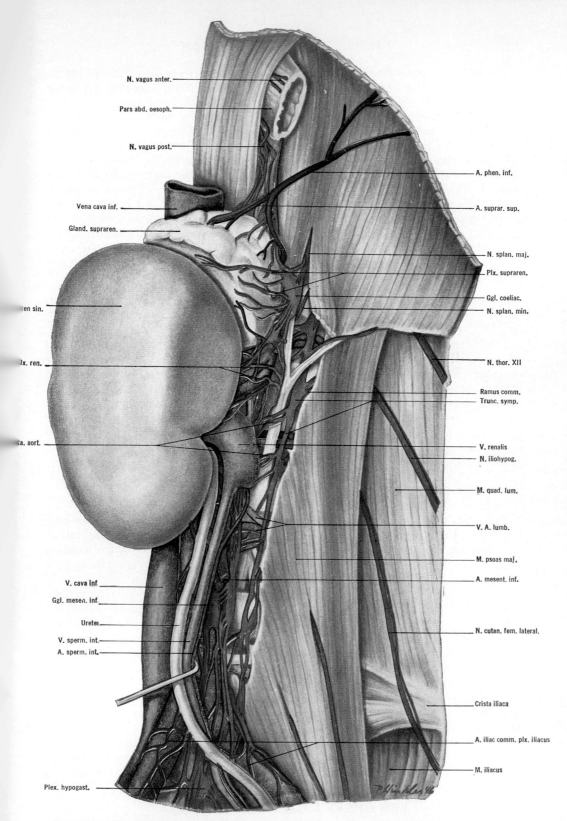

N. vagus anter.

Pars abd. oesoph.

N. vagus post.

A. phen. inf.

Vena cava inf.

A. suprar. sup.

Gland. supraren.

N. splan. maj.

Plx. supraren.

Ggl. coeliac.

ren sin.

N. splan. min.

lx. ren.

N. thor. XII

Ramus comm.

Trunc. symp.

a. aort.

V. renalis

N. iliohypog.

M. quad. lum.

V. A. lumb.

M. psoas maj.

V. cava inf.

A. mesent. inf.

Ggl. mesen. inf.

Ureter

N. cutan. fem. lateral.

V. sperm. int.

A. sperm. int.

Crista iliaca

A. iliac comm. plx. iliacus

M. iliacus

Plex. hypogast.

FIG. 882.—The lumbar portion of the left sympathetic trunk, celiac and mesenteric ganglia, splanchnic nerves, hypogastric plexus, suprarenal gland, and kidney. (Töndury, Angewandte und topographische Anatomie, courtesy of Georg Thieme Verlag.)

(1081)

The postganglionic fibers arising in the celiac ganglia form an extensive plexus (the celiac plexus) of nerve bundles and filaments which branch off into a number of subsidiary plexuses, in general following the branches of the abdominal aorta.

The Inferior Mesenteric Ganglion is more difficult to define in man than in many animals, but a considerable amount of ganglionic tissue is almost invariably present at the origin of the inferior mesenteric artery. The roots of the ganglion are provided by nerves from the celiac plexus, the celiac roots, and by the lumbar splanchnic nerves. The nerves from the celiac plexus pass down the aorta in the form of a network which is penetrated by the inferior mesenteric artery. The more cranial lumbar splanchnic nerves make a stout contribution to this net and join the caudal lumbar splanchnic nerves to form thick ganglionated nerve bundles on each side of the midline. These bundles converge and meet at the bifurcation of the aorta, with a free decussation of fibers, and then continue as the right and left hypogastric nerves. Small ganglionic nodes are present, especially if the network is compressed (Trumble '34).

The inferior mesenteric ganglion in cats (Harris '43) is composed of three distinct masses arranged in a triangle about the origin of the inferior mesenteric artery. Ganglia are found in dogs, guinea pigs, rabbits, and monkeys also (Trumble '34).

The branches of the inferior mesenteric ganglion are (*a*) the **hypogastric nerves** and (*b*) nerves which accompany the inferior mesenteric artery and its **branches to supply the colon.** Each hypogastric nerve continues from the bifurcation to join the pelvic plexus. It crosses the medial side of the ureter and contributes to the ureteric network of nerves. It contains mainly fine unmyelinated fibers but has many medium myelinated fibers (4 to 6μ) and a few large ones, probably afferent. The hypogastric nerves fan out into an extensive network just under the parietal peritoneum in the subserous fascia. They supply the hemorrhoidal, rectal, vesical, prostatic, ureteric, and ductus deferens nerves (Ashley and Anson '46).

The Pelvic Portion of the Sympathetic System.

The **pelvic portion of the sympathetic trunk** (*pars pelvina s. symphathici*) (Fig. 884) lies against the ventral surface of the sacrum, medial to the anterior sacral foramina. It is the direct continuation of the lumbar trunk and contains four or five ganglia, smaller than those in other parts of the chain. Fusion of adjacent ganglia is quite common and cords connecting the trunks of the two sides across the midline are of regular occurrence. There are no roots of the ganglia (white rami communicantes) in the sacral region; small myelinated preganglionic fibers from the second, third, and fourth sacral nerves enter the pelvic plexus but they belong to the parasympathetic or craniosacral outflow rather than the sympathetic. The coccygeal ganglion is the most caudal ganglion of the sympathetic trunk; it is commonly a single ganglion, the ganglion impar, representing a fusion of the ganglia of the two sides, and usually lies in the midline but may be at one side.

The branches of the sacral and coccygeal ganglia which are the **sympathetic roots of the sacral spinal nerves** are supplied to each of the sacral and the coccygeal nerves. In the majority of instances, each ganglion, or its representative in a fused ganglion, supplies roots to two adjacent spinal nerves (Pick and Sheehan '46).

Visceral branches in variable numbers join the hypogastric and pelvic plexuses, and are supplied through them to the pelvic viscera and blood vessels (Trumble '34).

THE GREAT AUTONOMIC PLEXUSES.

The two subdivisions of the autonomic nervous system, the sympathetic and parasympathetic, are combined into extensive plexuses in the thorax, abdomen, and pelvis, named respectively, the cardiac plexus, the celiac plexus, and the pelvic plexus. Experimental and clinical observations have made it possible to trace the sympathetic and parasympathetic components to some extent, but on the morphological evidence of dissections, it is almost impossible to distinguish the ultimate paths of the fibers belonging to the two systems. These plexuses also contain visceral afferent fibers, described in earlier pages.

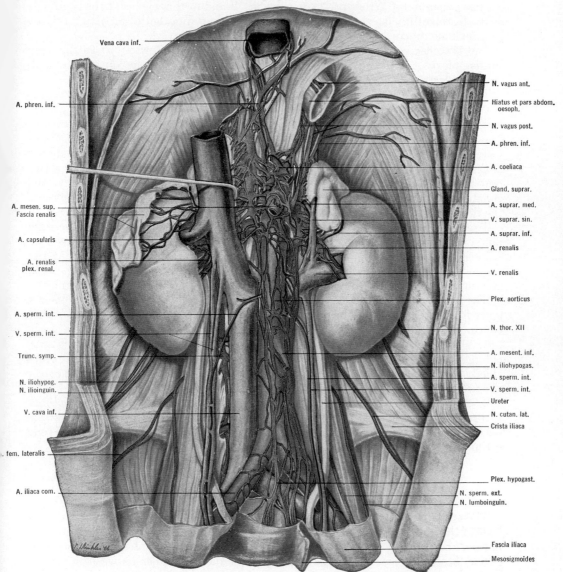

Fig. 883.—View of the posterior abdominal wall, showing the celiac, aortic, and hypogastric plexuses of autonomic nerves. (Töndury, Angewandte und topographische Anatomie, courtesy of Georg Thieme Verlag.)

THE CARDIAC PLEXUS.

The **cardiac plexus** (*plexus cardiacus*) (Fig. 519) is situated at the base of the heart, close to the arch of the aorta, and is traditionally subdivided into a superficial and a deep part for topographical reasons although the functional associations do not follow this division. The sympathetic contribution is largely postganglionic, the parasympathetic largely preganglionic with scattered groups of ganglion cells.

The **superficial part of the cardiac plexus** (Fig. 880) lies in the arch of the aorta somewhat on the left side between it and the bifurcation of the pulmonary artery. It is formed by the superior cervical cardiac branch of the left sympathetic and the lower of the two superior cardiac branches of the left vagus. A small ganglion, the cardiac ganglion (of Wrisberg), is occasionally found in this plexus at the right side of the ligamentum arteriosum; it is probably a parsaympathetic ganglion receiving preganglionic fibers from the vagus.

The **branches** of the superficial cardiac plexus are as follows: (*a*) to the deep cardiac plexus, (*b*) to the anterior coronary plexus, and (*c*) to the left anterior pulmonary plexus.

The **deep part of the cardiac plexus** is situated deep to the arch of the aorta, between it and the bifurcation of the trachea and superior to the pulmonary artery. It is much more extensive than the superficial part and receives all the cardiac branches of both vagi and sympathetic trunks except the two mentioned above which enter the superficial part (left superior sympathetic and left lower superior of the vagus); it also receives the lower cardiac branches of the vagus and the recurrent nerve, visceral rami from the upper four thoracic sympathetic ganglia, and communications from the superficial part of the cardiac plexus. The branches of the deep part of the cardiac plexus may be divided into right and left halves.

The right half of the deep cardiac plexus gives branches which follow the right pulmonary artery; those anterior to the artery are more numerous and, after contributing a few filaments to the anterior pulmonary plexus, continue into the anterior coronary plexus; those posterior to the artery distribute a few filaments to the right atrium, and are then continued onward to form part of the posterior coronary plexus.

The left half of the deep cardiac plexus communicates with the superficial plexus, gives filaments to the left atrium and to the anterior pulmonary plexus, and is then continued into the greater part of the posterior coronary plexus.

1. **The Posterior Coronary Plexus** (*pl. coronarius posterior; left coronary plexus*) is larger than the anterior, and accompanies the left coronary artery. It is formed chiefly by filaments from the left half, and by a few from the right half of the deep plexus. It is distributed to the left atrium and ventricle.

2. **The Anterior Coronary Plexus** (*pl. coronarius anterior; right coronary plexus*) is formed partly from the superficial and partly from the deep parts of the cardiac plexus. It accompanies the right coronary artery, and is distributed to the right atrium and ventricle (Stotler and McMahon '47).

THE CELIAC PLEXUS.

The **celiac plexus** (*plexus coeliacus; solar plexus*) (Figs. 881, 883) is situated at the level of the upper part of the first lumbar vertebra, and contains two large ganglionic masses and a dense network of fibers surrounding the roots of the celiac and superior mesenteric arteries. The denser part of the plexus lies between the suprarenal glands, on the ventral surface of the crura of the diaphragm and abdominal aorta, and dorsal to the stomach and the omental bursa, but it has extensive prolongations downward on the aorta and out along its branches. The celiac ganglia are described with the abdominal portion of the sympathetic system (page 1079). The preganglionic parasympathetic fibers reach the plexus through the anterior (left) and posterior (right) vagi on the stomach. The preganglionic sympathetic fibers reach the celiac, aorticorenal, and superior mesenteric ganglia through the greater and lesser splanchnic nerves. These nerves also supply preganglionic fibers to the cells in the medulla of the suprarenal glands, which correspond developmentally to postganglionic neurons. The secondary plexuses and prolongations from the celiac plexus are as follows:

1. The **phrenic plexus** (*pl. phrenicus*) (Fig. 883) accompanies the inferior phrenic artery to the diaphragm. It arises from the superior part of the celiac plexus, and is larger on the right side than on the left. It communicates with the phrenic nerve; at the point of junction with the right phrenic, near the vena caval foramen in the diaphragm, there may be a small ganglion, the phrenic ganglion. The phrenic plexus gives filaments to the inferior vena cava, inferior phrenic arteries, and to the suprarenal and hepatic plexuses.

2. The **hepatic plexus** (*pl. hepaticus*) accompanies the hepatic artery, ramifying upon its branches, and upon those of the portal vein in the substance of the liver. A considerable network accompanies the gastroduodenal artery and is continued as the inferior gastric plexus on the right gastroepiploic artery along the greater curvature of the stomach, communicating with the lienal plexus. Extensions from the hepatic plexus supply the pancreas and gall bladder, and there is a communication with the phrenic plexus.

3. The **splenic plexus** (*pl. lienalis*), containing mainly fibers from the left celiac ganglion and the anterior (left) vagus, accompanies the splenic artery to the spleen and in its course sends filaments along its branches, especially to the pancreas.

4. The **superior gastric plexus** (*pl. gastricus superior; gastric or coronary plexus*) accompanies the left gastric artery along the lesser curvature of the stomach and communicates with the anterior (left) vagus.

5. The **suprarenal plexus** (*pl. suprarenalis*) (Fig. 881) is composed principally of short, rather stout, branches from the celiac ganglion, with some contributions from the greater splanchnic nerve and the phrenic plexus. The fibers it contains are predominantly preganglionic sympathetics which pass through the celiac ganglion without synapses and are distributed to the medulla whose cells are homologous with postganglionic neurones. Postganglionic fibers to the blood vessels are present, also (Swinyard '37).

6. The **renal plexus** (*pl. renalis*) (Fig. 881) is formed by filaments from the celiac plexus, the aorticorenal ganglion, the aortic plexus, and the smallest splanchnic nerve. It accompanies the renal artery into the kidney, giving some filaments to the spermatic plexus and to the inferior vena cava on the right side (Christensen *et al.* '51).

7. The **spermatic plexus** (*pl. spermaticus*) receives filaments from the renal and aortic plexuses, and accompanies the internal spermatic artery to the testis. In the female the ovarian plexus (*pl. arteriæ ovaricæ*) arises from the renal plexus, accompanies the ovarian artery, and is distributed to the ovary, uterine tubes, and the fundus of the uterus.

8. The **superior mesenteric plexus** (*pl. mesentericus superior*) is essentially the lower part of the celiac plexus; it may appear more or less detached from the rest of the plexus and frequently it contains a separate ganglionic mass, the superior mesenteric ganglion (g. mesentericum superius). Its vagus fibers come principally from the posterior vagus. It surrounds and accompanies the superior mesenteric artery being distributed with the latter's pancreatic, intestinal, ileocolic, right colic, and middle colic branches, which supply the corresponding organs.

9. The **abdominal aortic plexus** (*pl. aorticus abdominalis; aortic plexus*) (Fig. 883) is formed from both right and left celiac plexuses and ganglia, and from the lumbar splanchnic nerves. It lies upon the ventral and lateral surfaces of the aorta between the origins of the superior and inferior mesenteric arteries. From this plexus arise the spermatic, inferior mesenteric, external iliac, and hypogastric plexuses, and filaments to the inferior vena cava.

10. The **inferior mesenteric plexus** (*pl. mesentericus inferior*) surrounds the origin of the inferior mesenteric artery and contains a ganglion (Fig. 883), the inferior

mesenteric ganglion, or thickened bundles which contain ganglion cells. It is derived from the aortic plexus, through whose celiac and lumbar splanchnic contributions it receives preganglionic as well as postganglionic fibers. It surrounds the inferior mesenteric artery, and divides into a number of subsidiary plexuses

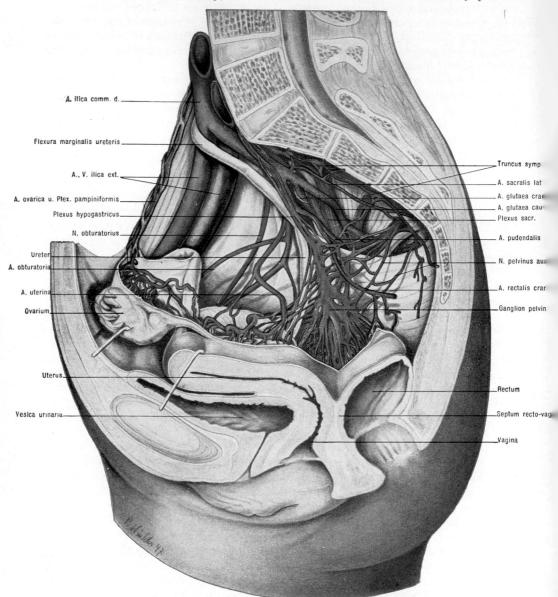

FIG. 884.—Sagittal section of an adult female pelvis, with the peritoneum and subserous fascia partially dissected away to show the pelvic plexus of autonomic nerves. (Töndury, Angewandte und topographische Anatomie, courtesy of Georg Thieme Verlag.)

which accompany its branches, the left colic, sigmoid, and superior hemorrhoidal, to the corresponding organs (Harris '43).

11. The **superior hypogastric plexus** (*pl. hypogastricus; hypogastric plexus; presacral nerve*) (Fig. 883) is the downward continuation of the aortic and inferior

mesenteric plexuses. It extends from the level of the fourth lumbar to the first sacral vertebræ and lies in the subserous fascia just under the peritoneum. It is at first ventral to the aorta, then between the common iliac arteries, crosses the left common iliac vein and enters the pelvis to lie against the middle sacral vessels and the vertebræ. At the first sacral vertebra it divides into two parts, the hypogastric nerves.

The **hypogastric nerve** may be a single rather large nerve or several bundles forming a parallel network. It lies medial and dorsal to the common iliac and hypogastric arteries, crosses the branches of the latter, and enters the inferior hypogastric plexus.

The **inferior hypogastric plexus** is a fan like expansion from the hypogastric nerves at the upper part of the rectum and bladder in the subserous fascia just above the sacrogenital fold It receives filaments from the sacral portion of the sympathetic chain and from the deeper parts of the pelvic plexus.

THE PELVIC PLEXUS.

The pelvic plexus (Fig. 884) of the autonomic system is formed by the hypogastric plexus, by rami from the sacral portion of the sympathetic chain, and by the visceral branches of the second, third, and fourth sacral nerves. Through its secondary plexuses it is distributed to all the pelvic viscera.

1. The **hemorrhoidal plexus** (*pl. hemorrhoidalis medius*) is contained in the tissue of the sacrogenital fold and is therefore the most superficial part of the pelvic plexus, with relation to the peritoneum. It is usually independent of the middle hemorrhoidal artery and, except for its terminal filaments to the lower sigmoid colon and rectum, is several centimeters from the bowel itself. From its superficial position, it appears to be the continuation of the inferior hypogastric plexus, but the latter has a number of other continuations and the hemorrhoidal plexus supplies the lower bowel with parasympathetic fibers through contributions from the visceral branches of the sacral nerves. It communicates with the superior hemorrhoidal branches from the inferior mesenteric plexus (Ashley and Anson '46).

2. The **vesical plexus** (*pl. vesicalis*) arises from the anterior part of the pelvic plexus, its fibers derived from the superficial or hypogastric network and the deeper bundles from the sacral nerves. The filaments are divisible into periureteric, prostatic, seminal vesicle, and lateral vesical groups.

3. The **prostatic plexus** (*pl. prostaticus*), from the deeper anterior part of the pelvic plexus, is composed of larger nerves which are distributed to the prostate, seminal vesicles, and corpora cavernosa. The nerves supplying the corpora consist of two sets, the greater and lesser cavernous nerves, which arise from the anterior part of the prostatic plexus, join with branches of the pudendal nerve, and pass beneath the pubic arch. Filaments at the base of the gland supply the prostatic and membranous urethra, the ejaculatory ducts, and the bulbourethral glands.

a. The **greater cavernous nerve** (*n. cavernousus penis major*) passes forward along the dorsum of the penis, joins the dorsal nerve of the penis, and is distributed to the corpus cavernosum penis.

b. The **lesser cavernous nerves** (*nn. cavernosi penis minores*) perforate the fibrous covering of the penis near its root, and are distributed to the corpus cavernosum urethræ and the penile urethra.

4. The **vaginal plexus** arises from the lower part of the pelvic plexus, and is distributed to the walls of the vagina, and to the erectile tissue of the vestibule and clitoris.

5. The **uterine plexus** arises from the inferior portion of the pelvic plexus, and approaches the uterus from its inferior and lateral aspect in the base of the broad ligament, in the same region as the uterine artery. It is distributed to its muscula-

ture, supplies filaments to the uterine tube, and communicates with the ovarian plexus (Curtis *et al.* '42).

REFERENCES

PERIPHERAL NERVOUS SYSTEM

CRANIAL NERVES

ANSON, B. J. 1950. An Atlas of Human Anatomy. W. B. Saunders Company, Philadelphia xxi + 518 pp.

ARMSTRONG, W. G., and J. W. HINTON. 1951. Multiple divisions of the recurrent laryngeal nerve: an anatomic study. Arch. Surg., *62*, 532–539.

BRUESCH, S. R. 1944. The distribution of myelinated afferent fibers in the branches of the cat's facial nerve. J. comp. Neurol., *81*, 169–191.

BURR, H. S., and G. B. ROBINSON. 1925. An anatomical study of the Gasserian ganglion, with particular reference to the nature and extent of Meckel's cave. Anat. Rec., *29*, 269–282.

CORBIN, K. B., and F. HARRISON. 1938. Proprioceptive components of cranial nerves. The spinal accessory nerve. J. comp. Neurol., *69*, 315–328.

CORBIN, K. B., and F. HARRISON. 1940. Function of mesencephalic root of fifth cranial nerve. J. Neurophysiol., *3*, 423–435.

CORBIN, K. B., and R. K. OLIVER. 1942. The origin of fibers to the grape-like endings in the insertion third of the extra-ocular muscles. J. comp. Neurol., *77*, 171–186.

DOUBILET, H., B. G. P. SHAFIROFF, and J. H. MULHOLLAND. 1948. The anatomy of the peri-esophageal vagi. Ann. Surg., *127*, 128–135.

FOLEY, J. O. 1945. The sensory and motor axons of the chorda tympani. Proc. Soc. Exp. Biol. and Med., *60*, 262, 267.

FOLEY, J. O., and F. S. DuBois. 1934. An experimental study of the rootlets of the vagus nerve in the cat. J. comp. Neurol., *60*, 137–159.

FOLEY, J. O., H. R. PEPPER, and W. H. KESSLER. 1946. The ratio of nerve fibers to nerve cells in the geniculate ganglion. J. comp. Neurol., *85*, 141–148.

GUTH, L. 1957. The effects of glossopharyngeal nerve transection on the circumvallate papilla of the rat. Anat. Rec., *128*, 715–732.

HARDESTY, I. 1933. The Nervous System. In Morris' Human Anatomy, 9th edition, P. Blakiston's Sons and Company, Philadelphia, pp. 1000–1038.

HEYMANS, C. 1938. Role of the cardioaortic and carotid-sinus nerves in the reflex control of the respiratory center. New Engl. J. Med., *219*, 157–159.

HOFFMAN, H. H., and A. KUNTZ. 1957. Vagus nerve components. Anat. Rec., *127*, 551–568.

HOLLINSHEAD, W. H. 1939. The origin of the nerve fibers to the glomus aorticum of the cat. J. comp. Neurol., *71*, 417–426.

HOLLINSHEAD, W. H. 1940. The innervation of the supracardial bodies in the cat. J. comp. Neurol., *73*, 37–48.

JACKSON, R. G. 1949. Anatomy of the vagus nerves in the region of the lower esophagus and the stomach. Anat. Rec., *103*, 1–18.

JAMES, T. W., and W. H. HOLLINSHEAD. 1950. Distribution of the inferior alveolar nerve in fetuses. Oral Surg., *3*, 1151–1158.

LARSELL, O. 1950. The nervus terminalis. Ann. Otol., (St. Louis), *59*, 414–438.

MAYER, L. L. 1940. The optic pathway. Arch. Ophthol., *23*, 382–394.

McCORMACK, L. J., E. W. CAULDWELL, and B. J. ANSON. 1945. The surgical anatomy of the facial nerve with special reference to the parotid gland. Surg. Gynec., Obstet., *80*, 620–630.

McCOTTER, R. E. 1915. A note on the course and distribution of the nervus terminalis in man. Anat. Rec., *9*, 243–246.

PASTORE, P. N., and J. M. MEREDITH. 1949. Glossopharyngeal neuralgia. Arch. Otolaryng., *50*, 789–794.

PEARSON, A. A. 1939. The hypoglossal nerve in human embryos. J. comp. Neurol., *71*, 21–39.

PEARSON, A. A. 1941. The development of the nervus terminalis in man. J. comp. Neurol., *75*, 39–66.

ROSEN, S. 1950. The tympanic plexus. Arch. Otolaryng., *52*, 15–18.

SCHNITZLEIN, H. N., L. C. ROWE, and H. H. HOFFMAN. 1958. The myelinated component of the vagus nerves in man. Anat. Rec., *131*, 649–668.

SCHWADRON, L., and B. C. MOFFETT. 1950. Relationships of cranial nerves to Meckel's cave and the cavernous sinus. Anat. Rec., *106*, 131–139.

SHEEHAN, D., J. H. MULHOLLAND, and B. SHAFIROFF. 1941. Surgical anatomy of the carotid sinus nerve. Anat. Rec., *80*, 431–442.

SPRAGUE, J. M. 1944. The innervation of the pharynx in the rhesus monkey, and the formation of the pharyngeal plexus in primates. Anat. Rec., *90*, 197–208.

SUNDERLAND, S., and D. F. COSSAR. 1953. The structure of the facial nerve. Anat. Rec., *116*, 147–165.

SUNDERLAND, S., and W. E. SWANEY. 1952. The intraneural topography of the recurrent laryngeal nerve in man. Anat. Rec., *114*, 411–426.

TRUEX, R. C., and C. E. KELLNER. 1948. Detailed Atlas of the Head and Neck. Oxford University Press, New York. xiii + 162 pp.

SPINAL NERVES

BARRY, A. 1956. A quantitative study of the prenatal changes in angulation of the spinal nerves. Anat. Rec., *126*, 97–110.

BEATON, L. E., and B. J. ANSON. 1938. The sciatic nerve and the piriformis muscle: their interrelation a possible cause of coccygodynia. J. Bone Jt. Surg., *20*, 686–688.

CORBIN, K. B., and F. HARRISON. 1939. The sensory innervation of the spinal accessory and tongue musculature in the rhesus monkey. Brain, *62*, 191–197.

DEMPSHER, J., and J. M. SPRAGUE. 1948. A study of the distribution of sensory and motor fibers in the lumbosacral plexus and in the thoracic nerves of the cat. Anat. Rec., *102*, 195–204.

FENART, R. 1958. La morphogénèse du plexus brachial, ses rapports avec la formation du cou et du membre supérieure. Acta anat., *32*, 322–360.

GITLIN, G. 1957. Concerning the gangliform enlargement ('Pseudo-ganglion') on the nerve to the teres minor muscle. J. Anat. (Lond.), *91*, 466–470.

FOERSTER, O. 1933. The dermatomes in man. Brain, *56*, 1–39.

HARRIS, W. 1939. The Morphology of the Brachial Plexus. Oxford University Press, London. xviii + 117 pp.

HINSEY, J. C. 1933. The functional components of the dorsal roots of spinal nerves. Quart. Rev. Biol., *8*, 457–464.

HOGG, I. D. 1941. Sensory nerves and associated structures in the skin of human fetuses of 8 to 14 weeks of menstrual age correlated with functional capability. J. comp. Neurol., *75*, 371–410.

HUELKE, D. F. 1957. A study of the formation of the sural nerve in adult man. Amer. J. phys. Anthrop., *15*, 137–148.

JAMIESON, R. W., and B. J. ANSON. 1952. The relation of the median nerve to the heads of origin of the pronator teres muscle. Quart. Bull. Northw. Univ. Med. Sch., *26*, 34–35.

JAMIESON, R. W., L. L. SWIGART, and B. J. ANSON. 1952. Points of parietal perforation of the ilioinguinal and iliohypogastric nerves in relation to optimal sites for local anaesthesia. Quart. Bull. Northw. Univ. Med. Sch., *26*, 22–26.

KEEGAN, J. J., and F. D. GARRETT. 1948. The segmental distribution of the cutaneous nerves in the limbs of man. Anat. Rec., *102*, 409–437.

KERR, A. T. 1918. The brachial plexus of nerves in man, the variations in its formation and branches. Amer. J. Anat., *23*, 285–395.

METZ, G. E., R. C. JUDICE, and J. C. FINERTY. 1958. Occurrence of neurons in the sciatic nerves of albino rats. Anat. Rec., *130*, 197–206.

MILLER, M. R., H. J. RALSTON, III, and M. KASAHARA. 1958. The pattern of cutaneous innervation of the human hand. Amer. J. Anat., *102*, 183–218.

MILLER, R. A. 1934. Comparative studies upon the morphology and distribution of the brachial plexus. Amer. J. Anat., *54*, 143–175.

MILLER, R. A. 1939. Observations upon the arrangement of the axillary artery and brachial plexus. Amer. J. Anat., *64*, 143–163.

MILLER, R. A., and S. R. DETWILER. 1936. Comparative studies upon the origin and development of the brachial plexus. Anat. Rec., *65*, 273–292.

MOYER, E. K., and D. L. KIMMEL. 1948. The repair of severed motor and sensory spinal nerve roots by the arterial sleeve method of anastomosis. J. comp. Neurol., *88*, 285–317.

MOYER, E. K., and B. F. KALISZEWSKI. 1958. The number of nerve fibers in motor spinal nerve roots of young, mature and aged cats. Anat. Rec., *131*, 681–700.

CARVALHO PINTO, V. A. DE. 1957. On the anatomy of the nerves in the ventrolateral wall of the abdomen in the new-born. Acta anat., *31*, 261–272.

ROOFE, P. G. 1940. Innervation of the annulus fibrosus and posterior longitudinal ligament. Arch. Neurol. Psychiat., (Chicago), *44*, 100–103.

SEYMOUR, R. J. and J. B. CAMPBELL. 1957. The sacral levels contributing afferent fibers to the feline pelvic and pudendal nerves: Verification by silver impregnation of degenerating axons after dorsal root ganglionectomy. Anat. Rec., *128*, 401–410.

STILWELL, D. L., JR. 1957. Regional variations in the innervation of deep fasciæ and aponeuroses. Anat. Rec., *127*, 635–654.

STILWELL, D. L., JR. 1957. The innervation of deep structures of the hand. Amer. J. Anat., *101*, 75–100.

STILWELL, D. L., JR. 1957. The innervation of deep structures of the foot. Amer. J. Anat., *101*, 59–74.

STILWELL, D. L., JR. 1957. The innervation of tendons and aponeuroses. Amer. J. Anat., *100*, 289–318.

SUNDERLAND, S. 1945. The innervation of the flexor digitorum profundus and lumbrical muscles. Anat. Rec., *93*, 317–321.

SUNDERLAND, S. 1946. The innervation of the first dorsal interosseous muscle of the hand. Anat. Rec., *95*, 7–10.

SUNDERLAND, S., and G. M. BEDBROOK. 1949. The relative sympathetic contribution to individual roots of the brachial plexus in man. Brain, *72*, 297–301.

SUNDERLAND, S., and G. M. BEDBROOK. 1949. The cross-sectional area of peripheral nerve trunks occupied by the fibers representing individual muscular and cutaneous branches. Brain, *72*, 613–624.

SUNDERLAND, S., and K. C. BRADLEY. 1949. The cross-sectional area of peripheral nerve trunks devoted to nerve fibers. Brain, *72*, 428–449.

SUNDERLAND, S., and E. S. R. HUGHES. 1946. Metrical and non-metrical features of the muscular branches of the ulnar nerve. J. comp. Neurol., *85*, 113–125.

VISCERAL AFFERENT FIBERS

BROWN, F. R. 1949. Testicular pain: its significance and localization. Lancet, *1*, 994–999.

COSTEN, J. B., M. H. CLARE, and G. H. BISHOP. 1951. The transmission of pain impulses via the chorda tympani nerve. Ann. Otol. (St. Louis), *60*, 591–609.

DeTAKATS, G., L. E. WALTER, and J. LASNER. 1950. Splanchnic nerve section for pancreatic pain. Ann. Surg., *131*, 44–57.

FREEMAN, L. W., H. B. SHUMACKER, JR., and L. R. RADIGAN. 1950. A functional study of afferent fibers in peripheral sympathetic nerves. Surgery, *28*, 274–281.

KELLGREN, J. H., and E. P. SAMUEL. 1950. The sensitivity and innervation of the articular capsule. J. Bone Jt. Surg., *32-B*, 84–92.

KUNTZ, ALBERT. 1936. Pathways involved in pains of nasal and paranasal origin referred to the lower cervical and upper thoracic segments and the upper extremity. Ann. Otol. (St. Louis), *45*, 394–399.

KUNTZ, A. 1951. Afferent innervation of peripheral blood vessels through sympathetic trunks. South. Med. J., *44*, 673–678.

POLLOCK, L. J., and L. DAVIS. 1935. Visceral and referred pain. Arch. Neurol. and Psychiat., *34*, 1041–1054.

WHITTERIDGE, D. 1948. Afferent nerve fibers from the heart and lungs in the cervical vagus. J. Physiol. (Lond.), *107*, 496–512.

AUTONOMIC NERVOUS SYSTEM

ASHLEY, F. L., and B. J. ANSON. 1946. The pelvic autonomic nerves in the male. Surg., Gynec. Obstet., *82*, 598–608.

AXFORD, M. 1928. Some observations on the cervical sympathetic in man. J. Anat. (Lond.), *62*, 301–318.

BECKER, R. F., and J. A. GRUNT. 1957. The cervical sympathetic ganglia. Anat. Rec., *127*, 1–14.

BOTÁR, J. 1932. La chaîne sympathique latéro-vertébrale lombaire, ses ganglions et ses rameaux communicants chez le nouveau-né. Ann. anat. path., *9*, 449–455.

BRAEUCKER, W. 1923. Die Nerven der Schilddrüse und der Epithelkörperchen. Anat. Anz., *56*, 225–249.

CHRISTENSEN, K., E. LEWIS, and A. KUNTZ. 1951. Innervation of the renal blood vessels in the cat. J. comp. Neurol., *95*, 373–385.

CHRISTENSEN, K., E. H. POLLEY, and E. LEWIS. 1952. The nerves along the vertebral artery and innervation of the blood vessels of the hindbrain of the cat. J. comp. Neurol., *96*, 71–91.

COWLEY, R. A., and G. H. YEAGER. 1949. Anatomic observations on the lumbar sympathetic nervous system. Surgery, *25*, 880–890.

CURTIS, A. H., B. J. ANSON, F. L. ASHLEY, and T. JONES. 1942. The anatomy of the pelvic autonomic nerves in relation to gynecology. Surg. Gynec. Obstet., *75*, 743–750.

DASS, R. 1952. Sympathetic components of the dorsal primary divisions of human spinal nerves. Anat. Rec., *113*, 493–501.

DUNCAN, D. 1943. The roots of spinal nerves. Science, *98*, 515.

EDWARDS, E. A. 1951. Operative anatomy of the lumbar sympathetic chain. Angiology, *2*, 184–198.

EDWARDS, L. F., and R. C. BAKER. 1940. Variations in the formation of the splanchnic nerves in man. Anat. Rec., *77*, 335–342.

EHRLICH, E., JR. and W. F. ALEXANDER. 1951. Surgical implications of upper thoracic independent sympathetic pathways. Arch. Surg., *62*, 609–614.

EULER, U. S. VON. 1951. The nature of adrenergic nerve mediators. Pharmacol. Rev., *3*, 247–277.

FOLEY, J. O., and H. N. SCHNITZLEIN. 1957. The contribution of individual thoracic spinal nerves to the upper cervical sympathetic trunk. J. comp. Neurol., *108*, 109–120.

FREEMAN, N. E., S. A. SHAFFER, A. E. SCHECHTER and H. E. HOLLING. 1938. The effect of total sympathectomy on the occurrence of shock from hemorrhage. J. clin. Invest., *17*, 359–368.

GREENBERG, S. R. 1956. A fiber analysis of the vagus cardiac rami and the cervical sympathetic nerves in the dog. J. comp. Neuro.., *104*, 33–48.

HARRIS, A. J. 1943. An experimental analysis of the inferior mesenteric plexus. J. comp. Neurol., *79*, 1–17.

JAMIESON, R. W., D. B. SMITH, and B. J. ANSON. 1952. The cervical sympathetic ganglia. Quart. Bull. Northw. Univ. Med. Sch., *26*, 219–227.

JONNESCO, T. 1923. Le Sympathique Cervicothoracique. Masson, Paris. 91 pages.

KIRGIS, H. D., and A. KUNTZ. 1942. Inconstant sympathetic neural pathways. Their relation to sympathetic denervation of the upper extremity. Arch. Surg., *44*, 95–102.

KISNER, W. H., and H. MAHORNER. 1952. An evaluation of lumbar sympathectomy. Amer. Surg., *18*, 30–35.

KUNTZ, A. 1952. Visceral functions of the nervous system. Ann. Rev. Physiol., *14*, 409–432.

KUNTZ, A. 1953. The Autonomic Nervous System. 4th edition, Lea & Febiger, Philadelphia, 605 pp.

KUNTZ, A., and W. F. ALEXANDER. 1950. Surgical implications of lower thoracic and lumbar independent sympathetic pathways. Arch. Surg., *61*, 1007–1018.

KUNTZ, A., H. H. HOFFMAN and E. M. SCHAEFFER. 1957. Fiber components of the splanchnic nerves. Anat. Rec., *128*, 139–146.

KUNTZ, A., and A. MOREHOUSE. 1930. Thoracic sympathetic cardiac nerves in man. Their relation to cervical sympathetic ganglionectomy. Arch. Surg., *20*, 607–613.

LARSELL, O. 1951. Anatomy of the Nervous System. Appleton-Century-Crofts, Inc., New York. xiv + 520 pp.

MITCHELL, G. A. G. 1951. The intrinsic renal nerves. Acta anat., *13*, 1–15.

MITCHELL, G. A. G. 1953. Anatomy of the Autonomic Nervous System. E. and S. Livingston Ltd., Edinburgh, and Williams & Wilkins Co., Baltimore. xvi + 356 pp.

NONIDEZ, J. N. 1939. Studies on the innervation of the heart. I. Distribution of the cardiac nerves, with special reference to the identification of the sympathetic and parasympathetic postganglionics. Amer. J. Anat., *65*, 361–413.

PEARSON, A. A. 1952. The connections of the sympathetic trunk in the cervical and upper thoracic levels in the human fetus. Anat. Rec., *106*, 231.

PEDERSEN, H. E., C. F. J. BLUNCK, and E. GARDNER. 1956. The anatomy of lumbosacral posterior rami and meningeal branches of spinal nerves (sinu-vertebral nerves). J. Bone J. Surg., *38-A*, 377–391.

PICK, J. 1958. The innervation of the arteries in the upper limb of man. Anat. Rec., *130*, 103–124.

PICK, J., and D. SHEEHAN. 1946. Sympathetic rami in man. J. Anat. (Lond.), *80*, 12–20.

POTTS, T. K. 1925. The main peripheral connections of the human sympathetic nervous system. J. Anat. (Lond.), *59*, 129–135.

RANDALL, W. C., R. H. MCDONALD, JR., and R. C. STALZER. 1958. A functional study of sympathetic neuroeffector terminations. Anat. Rec., *130*, 39–52.

RICHARDSON, K. C. 1958. Electronmicroscopic observations on Auerbach's plexus in the rabbit, with special reference to the problem of smooth muscle innervation. Amer. J. Anat., *103*, 99–136.

SACCOMANNO, G. 1943. The components of the upper thoracic sympathetic nerves. J. comp. Neurol., *79*, 355–378.

SHEEHAN, D. 1933. The afferent nerve supply of the mesentery and its significance in the causation of abdominal pain. J. Anat. (Lond.), *67*, 233–249.

SHEEHAN, D., and A. S. MARRAZZI. 1940. The sympathetic component of the sciatic nerve. Proc. Soc. exp. Biol. (N.Y.), *44*, 297–299.

STÖHR, P., JR. 1957. Mikroskopische Anatomie des vegetativen Nervensystems. In Handbuch der mikroskopischen Anatomie des Menschen (von Möllendorff). *4*, part 5, xii + 678 pp.

STOTLER, W. A., and R. A. MCMAHON. 1947. The innervation and structure of the conductive system of the human heart. J. comp. Neurol., *87*, 57–72.

SULKIN, N. M., and A. KUNTZ. 1950. A histochemical study of the autonomic ganglia of the cat following prolonged preganglionic stimulation. Anat. Rec., *108*, 255–277.

SWINYARD, C. A. 1937. The innervation of the suprarenal glands. Anat. Rec., *68*, 417–429.

TAKASE, B. and S. NOMURA. 1957. Studies on the innervation of the bone marrow. J. comp. Neurol., *108*, 421–444.

TRUMBLE, H. C.   1934.   The plan of the visceral nerves in the lumbar and sacral outflows of the autonomic nervous system.   Brit. J. Surg., *21*, 664–676.

WEBBER, R. H.   1958.   A contribution on the sympathetic nerves in the lumbar region.   Anat. Rec., *130*, 581–604.

WOLF, G. A., JR.   1941.   The ratio of preganglionic neurons to postganglionic neurons in the visceral nervous system.   J. comp. Neurol., *75*, 235–243.

WOOLLARD, H. H., and R. E. NORRISH.   1933.   The anatomy of the peripheral sympathetic nervous system.   Brit. J. Surg., *21*, 83–103.

WRETE, M.   1951.   Ganglia of rami communicantes in man and mammals particularly monkey.   Acta anat., *13*, 329–336.

YNTEMA, C. L., and W. S. HAMMOND.   1945.   Depletions and abnormalities in the cervical sympathetic system of the chick following extirpation of neural crest.   J. exp. Zool , *100*, 237–263.

THE ORGANS OF THE SENSES.

THE sensory endings and end organs of the peripheral nervous system may be divided into two large groups: (1) the organs of the special senses of smell, taste, sight, and hearing, and (2) the sensory endings of general sensation of heat, cold, touch, pain, pressure, etc.

THE SPECIAL SENSES.

THE ORGAN OF SMELL (ORGANON OLFACTUS).

The sensory endings for the sense of smell are located in the nose, and for this reason the entire nose has, by long tradition, been described in this chapter. In the present edition, however, all but the olfactory area will be described in the Chapter on the Respiratory System because the nose and nasal cavity are of more importance as air passages than for the sense of smell and they are customarily referred to by clinicians as the upper respiratory tract.

The **olfactory region** is located in the uppermost part of both nasal fossæ, and occupies the mucous membrane covering the superior nasal concha and the septum opposite (Fig. 887), and is confined, therefore, to an area of the fossa of which the walls are formed by the ethmoid bone.

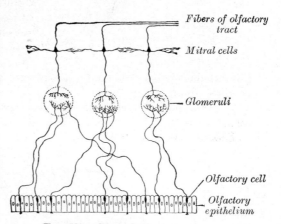

FIG. 885.—Plan of olfactory neurons.

The olfactory sensory endings are the least specialized of the special senses. They are modified epithelial cells liberally scattered among the columnar epithelium of

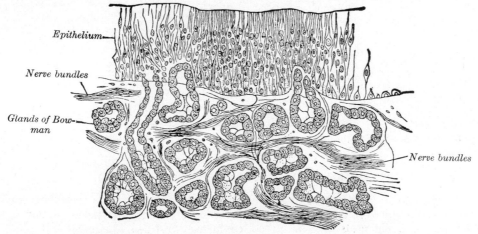

FIG. 886.—Section of the olfactory mucous membrane. (Cadiat.)

(1093)

the mucous membrane. The sensory cells are known as **olfactory cells,** the other epithelial cells as **supporting cells,** and although the epithelium appears pseudo-stratified, the supporting cells are not ciliated and goblet cells are lacking (Fig. 888).

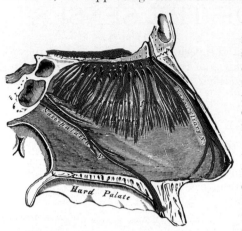

FIG. 887.—Nerves of septum of nose. Right side.

The **olfactory cells** are bipolar in form, with a small amount of cytoplasm surrounding a large spherical nucleus. The slender peripheral or superficial process extends to the surface of the epithelial membrane and sends out beyond the surface a tuft of very fine processes known as **olfactory hairs.** The central or deep process finds its way through the basement membrane and in the underlying connective tissue joins neighboring processes to form the bundles of unmyelinated fibers of the **olfactory nerves.** Mingled with the nerve bundles in the subepithelial tissue are numerous branched tubular glands of a serous secreting type (glands of Bowman), which keep the membrane protected with moisture.

The bundles of nerve fibers form a plexus in the submucosa and are finally collected into about twenty nerves which pass through the openings in the cribriform plate of the ethmoid bone as the **fila olfactoria.** The nerve fibers end by forming synapses with processes of the mitral cells in the glomeruli of the olfactory bulb (Fig. 885, also see page 908).

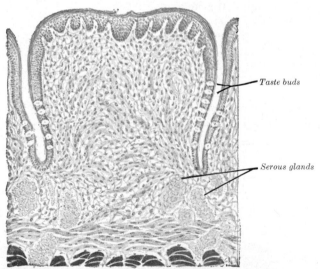

FIG. 888.—Section through a vallate papilla. Stained with hematoxylin and eosin. × 25. (After Sobotta.)

THE ORGAN OF TASTE (ORGANON GUSTUS).

The peripheral taste organs (*gustatory organs*) are the **taste buds** (*gustatory calyculi*) distributed over the tongue and occasionally on adjacent parts. They are spherical or ovoid nests of cells imbedded in the stratified squamous epithelium (Fig. 889), and are present in large numbers on the sides of the vallate papillæ

(*papillæ vallatæ*) and to a lesser extent on the opposed walls of the fossæ around them (Fig. 888). They are also found over the sides and back of the tongue, especially on the fungiform papillæ (Fig. 1030). They are plentiful over the fimbriæ linguæ, and are occasionally present on the under surface of the soft palate and on the posterior surface of the epiglottis.

Each **taste bud** occupies an ovoid pocket which extends through the thickness of the epithelium. It has two openings, one at the surface and the other at the basement membrane. The cells within the bud are of two kinds, **gustatory cells** and **supporting cells** (Fig. 889). The supporting cells are elongated, extending between the basement membrane and the surface; they form an outer shell for the taste bud,

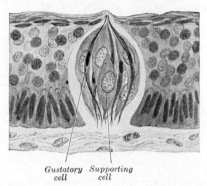

Gustatory   Supporting
cell   cell

FIG. 889.—Section through a taste bud. Semidiagrammatic. × 450.

arranged like the staves of a wooden cask, and are also scattered through the bud between the gustatory cells. The latter occupy the interior portion of the bud; they are spindle-shaped with a large round central nucleus. The peripheral end of each gustatory cell protrudes through the opening at the surface, the gustatory pore, as a delicate hair like process, the **gustatory hair**. The central end of the gustatory cell does not end in an axone, as in the case of the olfactory cell, but remains within the taste bud where it has intimate contact with many fine terminations of nerves which pass into the taste bud through an opening in the basement membrane. The nerves are myelinated until they reach the taste buds but lose their sheaths as they enter the bud.

Nerves of Taste.—The posterior third of the tongue, including the taste buds on the vallate papillæ, is supplied by the glossopharyngeal nerve. The fibers for taste to the anterior two-thirds leave the brain in the nervus intermedius, are continued in the chorda tympani, and reach the tongue in the branches of the lingual nerve. It is believed that taste buds on the epiglottis are supplied by the vagus nerve.

THE ORGAN OF SIGHT (ORGANON VISUS; THE EYE).

The **bulb of the eye** (*bulbus oculi; eyeball*), or **organ of sight**, is contained in the cavity of the orbit, where it is protected from injury and moved by the ocular muscles. Associated with it are certain accessory structures, *viz.*, the muscles, fasciæ, eyebrows, eyelids, conjunctiva, and lacrimal apparatus.

The bulb of the eye is imbedded in the fat of the orbit, but is separated from it by a thin membranous sac, the fascia bulbi (page 1117). It is composed of segments of two spheres of different sizes. The anterior segment is one of a small sphere; it is transparent, and forms about one-sixth of the bulb. It is more prominent than the posterior segment, which is one of a larger sphere, and is opaque, and forms about five-sixths of the bulb. The term **anterior pole** is applied to the central point of the anterior curvature of the bulb, and that of **posterior pole** to the central point of its posterior curvature; a line joining the two poles forms the **optic axis**. The axes of the two bulbs are nearly parallel, and therefore do not correspond to the axes of the orbits, which are directed forward and lateralward. The optic nerves follow the direction of the axes of the orbits, and are therefore not parallel; each enters its eyeball 3 mm. to the nasal side and a little below the level of the posterior pole. The bulb measures rather more in its transverse and antero-posterior diameters than in its vertical diameter, the former amounting to about 24 mm., the latter

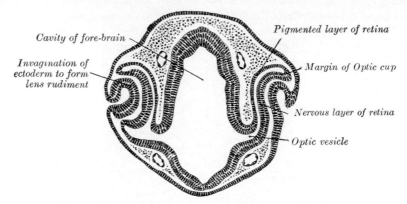

FIG. 890.—Transverse section of head of chick embryo of forty-eight hours' incubation. (Duval.)

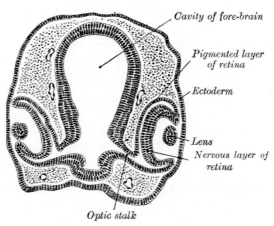

FIG. 891.—Transverse section of head of chick embryo of fifty-two hours' incubation. (Duval.)

to about 23.5 mm.; in the female all three diameters are rather less than in the male; its antero-posterior diameter at birth is about 17.5 mm., and at puberty from 20 to 21 mm.

Development.—The retina and optic nerve come from the forebrain; the lens from the overlying ectoderm; and the accessory structures from the mesenchyme. The eyes begin to develop as a pair of diverticula from the lateral aspects of the fore brain. These diverticula make their appearance before the closure of the anterior end of the neural tube; after the closure of the tube they are known as the **optic vesicles**. They project toward the sides of the head, and the peripheral part of each expands to form a hollow bulb, while the proximal part remains narrow and constitutes the **optic stalk**. The optic vesicle comes in contact with and adheres to the ectoderm; here the latter thickens, invaginates, becomes severed from the ectoderm, and forms the **lens vesicle**. At the same time the optic vesicle invaginates to form the **optic cup**. Its two layers are continuous with each other at the cup margin, which ultimately overlaps the front of the lens and reaches as far forward as the future aperture of the pupil (Fig. 890). The invagination also involves the postero-inferior surface of the vesicle and the optic stalk. It produces the **choroidal fissure** of the optic cup and optic stalk (Fig. 892). Mesenchyme and the retinal blood vessels (hyaloid artery) grow into the fissure. The fissure closes during the seventh week and the two-layered optic cup and optic stalk become complete. Sometimes the choroidal fissure persists, and when this occurs the choroid and iris in the region of the fissure remain undeveloped, giving rise to the condition known as *coloboma* of the choroid or iris.

The **retina** is developed from the optic cup. The outer stratum of the cup persists as a single layer of cells which assume a columnar shape, acquire pigment, and form the pigmented layer of the retina; the pigment first appears in the cells near the edge of the cup. The cells of the inner stratum proliferate and form a layer of considerable thickness from which the nervous elements and the sustentacular fibers of the retina are developed. In that portion of the cup which overlaps the lens the inner stratum is not differentiated into nervous elements, but forms a layer of columnar cells which is applied to the pigmented layer, and these two strata form the **pars ciliaris** and **pars iridica retinæ**.

The cells of the inner or retinal layer of the optic cup become differentiated into spongioblasts and germinal cells, and the latter by their subdivisions give rise to neuroblasts. From the spongioblasts the sustentacular fibers of Müller, the outer and inner limiting membranes, together with the groundwork of the molecular layers of the retina are formed. The neuroblasts become arranged to form the ganglionic and nuclear layers. The layer of rods and cones is first developed in the central part of the optic cup, and from there gradually extends toward the cup margin. All the layers of the retina are completed by the eighth month of fetal life.

The optic stalk is converted into the **optic nerve** by the obliteration of its cavity and the growth of nerve fibers into it. Most of these fibers are centripetal, and grow backward into the optic stalk from the nerve cells of the retina, but a few extend in the opposite direction and are derived from nerve cells in the brain. The fibers of the optic nerve receive their medullary sheaths about the tenth week after birth. The **optic chiasma** is formed by the meeting and partial decussation of the fibers of the two optic nerves. Behind the chiasma the fibers grow backward as the optic tracts to the thalami and mid-brain.

The **crystalline lens** is developed from the lens vesicle, which recedes within the margin of the cup, and becomes separated from the overlying ectoderm by mesoderm. The cells forming the posterior wall of the vesicle lengthen and are converted into the lens fibers, which grow forward and fill up the cavity of the vesicle (Fig. 893). The cells forming the anterior wall retain their cellular character, and form the epithelium on the anterior surface of the adult lens.

The Hyaloid Artery.—A capillary net continuous with the primitive choroid net enters the choroid fissure. As the fissure closes, connections with the choroid net are all cut off except at the edge of the cup. The vessel enclosed in the optic stalk is the hyaloid artery. Its branches surround the deep surface of the lens and drain into the choroid net at the margin of the cup. As the vitreous body increases, the hyaloid supplies branches to it. By the second month the lens is invested by a vascular mesodermal capsule, the **capsula vasculosa lentis**; the bloodvessels supplying the posterior part of this capsule are derived from the hyaloid artery; those for the anterior part from the anterior ciliary arteries; the portion of the capsule which covers the front of the lens is named the **pupillary membrane**. By the sixth month all the vessels of the capsule are atrophied except the hyaloid artery, which disappears during the ninth month; the position of this artery is indicated in the adult by the hyaloid canal, which reaches from the optic disk to the posterior surface of the lens. With the loss of its bloodvessels the capsula vasculosa lentis disappears, but sometimes the pupillary membrane persists at birth, giving rise to the condition termed *congenital atresia of the pupil.*

The Central Artery of the Retina.—By the fourth month branches of the hyaloid artery and veins which have developed during the third month begin to spread out in the retina and reach the ora serrata by the eighth month. After atrophy of the vitreous part of the hyaloid vessels, the proximal part in the optic nerve and retina becomes the central artery of the retina.

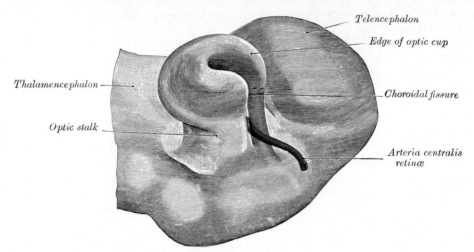

Telencephalon

Edge of optic cup

Thalamencephalon

Choroidal fissure

Optic stalk

Arteria centralis retinæ

FIG. 892.—Optic cup and choroidal fissure seen from below, from a human embryo of about four weeks. (Kollmann.)

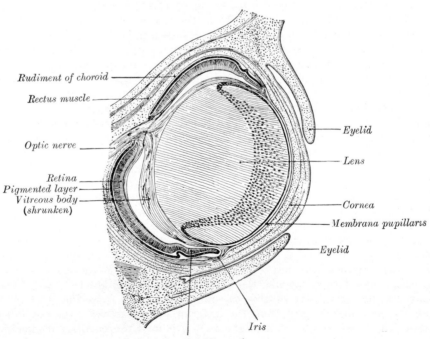

Rudiment of choroid

Rectus muscle

Optic nerve

Retina
Pigmented layer
Vitreous body
(shrunken)

Eyelid

Lens

Cornea

Membrana pupillaris

Eyelid

Iris

Pars ciliaris and pars iridica retinæ

FIG. 893.—Horizontal section through the eye of an eighteen days' embryo rabbit. × 30. (Kölliker.)

The **choroid** is analogous to the pia-arachnoid of the brain and spinal cord. It develops from mesenchyme between the sclera (dura) and the optic cup (an extension of the brain wall). The mesenchyme is invaded by capillaries, from the ciliary vessels. They form a rich plexus over the outer surface of the optic cup and connect in the pupillary region with the hyaloid capillary plexus. The mesenchyme forms a loose network of multipolar and pigmented cells and white fibrils, partially separated by mesothelial-lined, fluid-containing spaces.

Canal of Schlemm (*sinus venosus scleræ*) and the circular vessels of the iris develop from the anterior extension of the choroid plexus. The former is analogous to a venous sinus of the dura mater; the anterior chamber to the subarachnoid spaces. The drainage of aqueous humor via the pectinate villi into the canal of Schlemm is analogous to the drainage of the subarachnoid fluid via the arachnoid villi into the dural sinuses.

The **vitreous body** develops between the lens and the optic cup as the two structures become separated. Some authors believe that at the beginning, the retina, and perhaps the lens also, play rôles in the formation of the vitreous body; others believe that the retina plays the sole rôle; and still others, that both retina and invading mesenchyme are involved. Fixed and stained preparations show throughout the vitreous body a delicate network of fibrils continuous with the long processes of stellate mesenchyme cells and with the retina. Later the fibrils are limited to the ciliary region where they are supposed to form the **zonula ciliaris.**

The **sclera** is derived from the mesenchyme surrounding the optic cup. A dense layer of white or collagenous fibers, continuous with the sheath of the optic nerve, is formed by the fibroblasts. The sclera is analogous to the dura mater.

Most of the **cornea** is derived from mesenchyme which invades the region between the lens and ectoderm. The overlying ectoderm becomes the corneal epithelium. The endothelial (mesothelial) layer comes from mesenchyme cells which line the corneal side of the cleft (anterior chamber) which develops between the cornea and pupillary membrane. The factors responsible for the transparency of the cornea are unknown.

The **anterior chamber** of the eye appears as a cleft in the mesoderm separating the lens from the overlying ectoderm. The layer of mesoderm in front of the cleft forms the substantia propria of the cornea, that behind the cleft the stroma of the iris and the pupillary membrane.

The fibers of the **ciliary muscle** are derived from the mesoderm, but those of the Sphincter and Dilatator pupillæ are of ectodermal origin, being developed from the cells of the pupillary part of the optic cup.

The **eyelids** are formed as small cutaneous folds (Figs. 893, 894), which about the middle of the third month come together and unite in front of the cornea. They remain united until about the end of the sixth month.

The **lacrimal sac** and **nasolacrimal duct** result from a thickening of the ectoderm in the groove, **nasoöptic furrow,** between the lateral nasal and maxillary processes. This thickening forms a solid cord of cells which sinks into the mesoderm; during the third month the central cells of the cord break down, and a lumen, the nasolacrimal duct, is established. The lacrimal ducts arise as buds from the upper part of the cord of cells and secondarily establish openings (*puncta lacrimalia*) on the margins of the lids. The **epithelium** of the cornea and conjunctiva, and that which lines the ducts and alveoli of the lacrimal gland, are of ectodermal origin, as are also the **eyelashes** and the lining cells of the glands which open on the lid-margins.

The Tunics of the Eye (Fig. 895).

From without inward the three tunics are: (1) A fibrous tunic, consisting of the **sclera** behind and the **cornea** in front; (2) a vascular pigmented tunic, comprising, from behind forward, the **choroid**, **ciliary body**, and **iris**; and (3) a nervous tunic, the **retina**.

The Fibrous Tunic (*tunica fibrosa bulbi*).—The sclera and cornea (Fig. 895) form the fibrous tunic of the bulb of the eye; the sclera is opaque, and constitutes the posterior five-sixths of the tunic; the cornea is transparent, and forms the anterior sixth.

The Sclera.—The sclera has received its name from its extreme density and hardness; it is a firm, unyielding membrane, serving to maintain the form of the bulb. It is much thicker behind than in front; the thickness of its posterior part is 1 mm. Its **external surface** is of white color, and is in contact with the inner surface of the

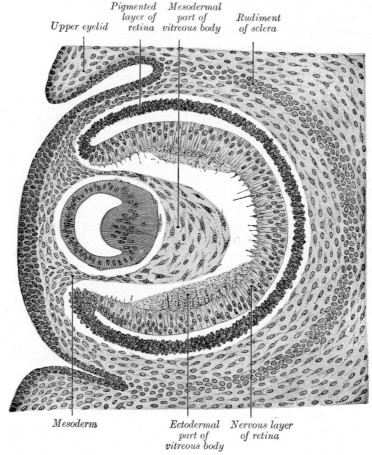

Fig. 894.—Sagittal section of eye of human embryo of six weeks. (Kollmann.)

fascia of the bulb; it is quite smooth, except at the points where the Recti and Obliqui are inserted into it; its anterior part is covered by the conjunctival membrane; the rest of the surface is separated from the fascia bulbi (capsule of Tenon) by very loose connective tissue containing mesothelial-lined, fluid-containing spaces (spaces of Tenon) of capillary dimensions. This permits rotation of the eyeball within the fascia bulbi. Its **inner surface** is brown in color and marked by grooves, in which the ciliary nerves and vessels are lodged; it is loosely attached to the pigmented lamina suprachoroidea of the choroid. Behind it is pierced by the optic nerve, and is continuous through the fibrous sheath of this nerve with the dura mater. Where the optic nerve passes through the sclera, the latter forms a thin cribriform lamina, the **lamina cribrosa scleræ**; the minute orifices in this lamina serve for the transmission of the nervous filaments, and the fibrous septa dividing them from one another are continuous with the membranous processes which separate the bundles of nerve fibers. One of these openings, larger than the rest, occupies the center of the lamina; it transmits the central artery and vein of the retina. Around the entrance of the optic nerve are numerous small apertures for the transmission of the ciliary vessels and nerves, and about mid-way between this entrance and the sclero-corneal junction are four or five large apertures for the transmission of veins (**venæ vorticosæ**). In front, the sclera is directly continuous with the cornea, the oblique line of union being termed the **sclero-corneal junction**.

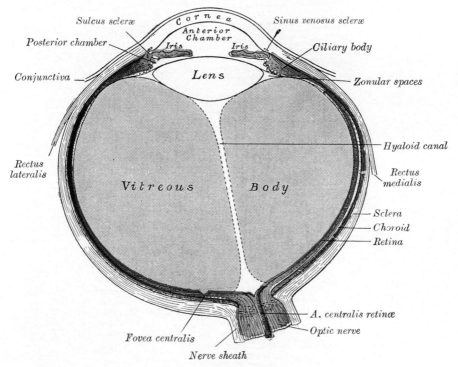

FIG. 895.—Horizontal section of the eyeball.

Near the sclero-corneal junction the inner surface of the sclera projects to form a circular ridge, the **scleral spur**. To it is attached the ciliary muscle and the iris. In front of this ridge there is a circular depression, the scleral sulcus, crossed by trabecular tissue which separates the angle of the anterior chamber from the sinus venosus scleræ (canal of Schlemm). The spaces of the trabecular tissue (spaces of Fontana) connect on one side with the anterior chamber of the eye and on the other with the pectinate villi. The aqueous humor filters through the walls of the villi into the sinus venosus scleræ.

Structure.—The sclera is formed of white fibrous tissue intermixed with fine elastic fibers; flattened connective-tissue corpuscles, some of which are pigmented, are contained in cell spaces between the fibers. The fibers are aggregated into bundles, which are arranged chiefly in a longitudinal direction. Its *vessels* are not numerous, the capillaries being of small size, uniting at long and wide intervals. Its *nerves* are derived from the ciliary nerves, but their exact mode of ending is not known.

The Cornea.—The cornea is the projecting transparent part of the external tunic, and forms the anterior sixth of the surface of the bulb. It is almost circular in outline, occasionally a little broader in the transverse than in the vertical direction. It is convex anteriorly and projects like a dome in front of the sclera. Its degree of curvature varies in different individuals, and in the same individual at different periods of life, being more pronounced in youth than in advanced life. The cornea is dense and of uniform thickness throughout; its posterior surface is perfectly

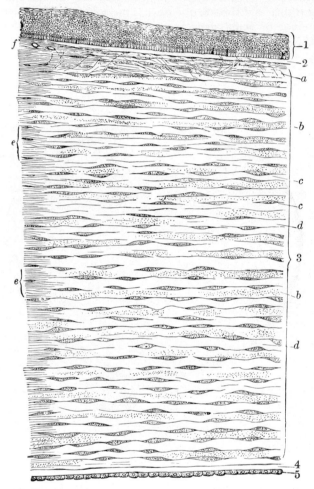

FIG. 896.—Vertical section of human cornea from near the margin. (Waldeyer.) Magnified. 1. Epithelium. 2. Anterior lamina. 3. Substantia propria. 4. Posterior elastic lamina. 5. Endothelium of the anterior chamber. *a.* Oblique fibers in the anterior layer of the substantia propria. *b.* Lamellæ the fibers of which are cut across, producing a dotted appearance. *c.* Corneal corpuscles appearing fusiform in section. *d.* Lamellæ the fibers of which are cut longitudinally. *e.* Transition to the sclera, with more distinct fibrillation, and surmounted by a thicker epithelium. *f.* Small bloodvessels cut across near the margin of the cornea.

circular in outline, and exceeds the anterior surface slightly in diameter. Immediately in front of the sclero-corneal junction the cornea bulges inward as a thickened rim.

Structure (Fig. 896).—The cornea consists of five layers, *viz.:* (1) the **corneal epithelium**, continuous with that of the conjunctiva; (2) the **anterior lamina**; (3) the **substantia propria**; (4) the **posterior lamina**; and (5) the **endothelium** (mesothelium) of the anterior chamber.

The **corneal epithelium** (*epithelium anterius corneæ; anterior layer*) covers the front of the cornea and consists of several layers of cells. The cells of the deepest layer are columnar; then follow two or three layers of polyhedral cells, the majority of which are prickle cells similar to those found in the stratum mucosum of the cuticle. Lastly, there are three or four layers of squamous cells, with flattened nuclei.

The **substantia propria** is fibrous, tough, unyielding, and perfectly transparent. It is composed of about sixty flattened lamellæ, superimposed one on another. These lamellæ are made up of bundles of modified connective tissue, the fibers of which are directly continuous with those of the sclera. The fibers of each lamella are for the most part parallel with one another, but at right angles to those of adjacent lamellæ. Fibers, however, frequently pass from one lamella to the next. The lamellæ are connected with each other by an interstitial cement substance, in which are spaces, the **corneal spaces.** These are stellate in shape and communicate with one another by numerous offsets. Each contains a cell, the **corneal corpuscle,** a modified fibroblast, resembling in form the space in which it is lodged, but not entirely filling it.

The **anterior lamina** (*lamina limitans anterior; anterior limiting layer; Bowman's membrane*) consists of extremely closely interwoven fibrils, similar to those found in the substantia propria, but contains no corneal corpuscles. It may be regarded as a condensed part of the substantia propria.

The **posterior elastic lamina** (*lamina limitans posterior; membrane of Descemet; membrane of Demours*) covers the posterior surface of the substantia propria, and is an elastic, transparent homogeneous membrane, of extreme thinness, which is not rendered opaque by either water, alcohol, or acids. When stripped from the substantia propria it curls up, or rolls upon itself with the attached surface innermost.

At the margin of the cornea the posterior elastic lamina breaks up into fibers which form the trabecular tissue already described. Some of the fibers of this trabecular tissue are continued into the substance of the iris, forming the **pectinate ligament of the iris;** while others are connected with the forepart of the sclera and choroid.

The endothelium of the anterior chamber (*endothelium cameræ anterioris; posterior layer; corneal endothelium*).—This is a mesothelial, not an endothelial layer. It covers the posterior surface of the elastic lamina, is reflected on to the front of the iris, and also lines the spaces of the angle of the iris; it consists of a single stratum of polygonal, flattened, nucleated cells.

Vessels and Nerves.—The cornea is a non-vascular structure: the capillary vessels ending in loops at its circumference are derived from the anterior ciliary arteries. Lymphatic vessels have not yet been demonstrated in it, but are represented by the channels in which the bundles of nerves run; these channels are lined by an endothelium. The **nerves** are numerous and are derived from the ciliary nerves. Around the periphery of the cornea they form an *annular plexus,* from which fibers enter the substantia propria. They lose their medullary sheaths and ramify throughout its substance in a delicate net-work, and their terminal filaments form a firm and closer plexus on the surface of the cornea proper, beneath the epithelium. This is termed the *subepithelial plexus,* and from it fibrils are given off which ramify between the epithelial cells, forming an *intraepithelial plexus.*

The Vascular Tunic (*tunica vasculosa bulbi; uvea*) (Figs. 898, 899, 900).—The vascular tunic of the eye is formed from behind forward by the choroid, the ciliary body, and the iris.

The choroid invests the posterior five-sixths of the bulb, and extends as far forward as the ora serrata of the retina. The ciliary body connects the choroid to the circumference of the iris. The iris is a circular diaphragm behind the cornea, and presents near its center a rounded aperture, the **pupil.**

The Choroid (*chorioidea*).—The choroid is a thin, highly vascular membrane, of a dark brown or chocolate color, investing the posterior five-sixths of the globe; it is pierced behind by the optic nerve, and in this situation is firmly adherent to the sclera. It is thicker behind than in front. Its outer surface is loosely connected by the lamina suprachorioidea with the sclera; its inner surface is attached to the pigmented layer of the retina.

Structure.—The choroid consists mainly of a dense capillary plexus, and of small arteries and veins carrying blood to and returning it from this plexus. On its external surface is a thin membrane, the **lamina suprachorioidea,** composed of delicate non-vascular lamellæ—each lamella consisting of a net-work of fine elastic fibers among which are branched pigment cells. The potential spaces between the lamellæ are lined by mesothelium, and open freely into the perichoroidal space.

Internal to this lamina is the **choroid proper,** consisting of two layers: an outer, composed of small arteries and veins, with pigment cells interspersed between them; and an inner, consisting of a capillary plexus. The **outer layer** (*lamina vasculosa*) consists, in part, of the larger branches of the short ciliary arteries which run forward between the veins, before they bend inward to end in the capillaries, but is formed principally of veins, named, from their arrangement, the **venæ vorticosæ**. They converge to four or five equidistant trunks, which pierce the sclera about midway between the sclero-corneal junction and the entrance of the optic nerve. Interspersed between the vessels are dark star-shaped pigment cells, the processes of which, communicating with those of neighboring cells, form a delicate network or stroma, which toward the inner surface of the choroid loses its pigmentary character. The **inner layer** (*lamina choriocapillaris*) consists of an exceedingly fine capillary plexus, formed by the short ciliary vessels; the network is closer and finer in the posterior than in the anterior part of the choroid. About 1.25 cm. behind the cornea its meshes become larger, and are continuous with those of the ciliary processes. These two laminæ are connected by a **stratum intermedium** consisting of fine elastic fibers. On the inner surface of the lamina choriocapillaris is a very thin, structureless, or faintly fibrous membrane, called the **lamina basalis**; it is closely connected with the stroma of the choroid, and separates it from the pigmentary layer of the retina.

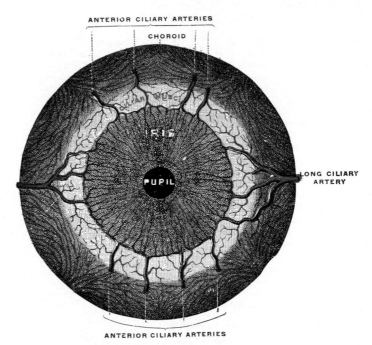

FIG. 897.—Iris, front view.

One of the functions of the choroid is to provide nutrition for the retina, and to convey vessels and nerves to the ciliary body and iris.

Tapetum.—This name is applied to the outer and posterior part of the choroid, which in many animals presents an iridescent appearance.

The Ciliary Body (*corpus ciliare*).—The ciliary body extends from the ora serrata of the retina to the outer edge of the iris and the sclero-corneal junction. It consists of the thickened vascular tunic of the eye and the ciliary muscle. Its inner surface is covered by the thin, pigmented ciliary part of the retina. The suspensory ligament of the lens is attached to the ciliary body. The ciliary body comprises two zones, the orbiculus ciliaris and the ciliary processes (Fig. 901).

The **orbiculus ciliaris** is 4 mm. wide and extends from the ora serrata to the ciliary processes. Its thickness increases as it approaches the ciliary processes owing to the increase in thickness of the ciliary muscle. The choroid layer is thicker here than over the optical part of the retina. Its inner surface presents numerous small radial ridges.

The **ciliary processes** (*processus ciliares*) are formed by the inward folding of the various layers of the choroid, *i. e.*, the choroid proper and the lamina basalis, and are received between corresponding foldings of the suspensory ligament of the lens. They are arranged in a circle, and form a sort of frill behind the iris, around the margin of the lens (Fig. 901). They vary from sixty to eighty in number, lie side by side, and may be divided into large and small; the former are about 2.5 mm. in length, and the latter, consisting of about one-third of the entire number, are situated in spaces between them, but without regular arrangement. They are

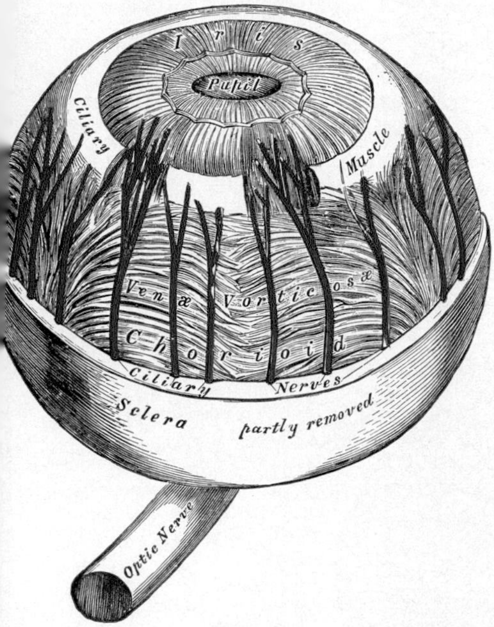

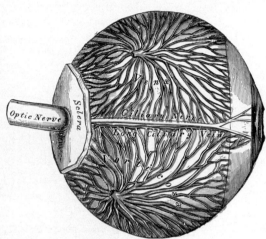

FIG. 898.—The choroid and iris. (Enlarged.)

FIG. 899.—The veins of the choroid. (Enlarged.)

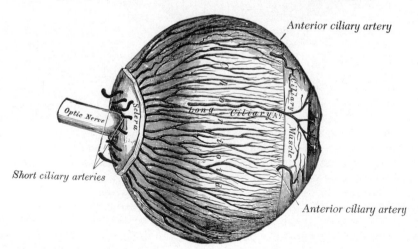

FIG. 900.—The arteries of the choroid and iris. The greater part of the sclera has been removed. (Enlarged.)

attached by their periphery to three or four of the ridges of the orbiculus ciliaris, and are continuous with the layers of the choroid: their opposite extremities are free and rounded, and are directed toward the posterior chamber of the eyeball and circumference of the lens. In front, they are continuous with the periphery of the iris. Their posterior surfaces are connected with the suspensory ligament of the lens.

Structure.—The ciliary processes (Fig. 901) are similar in structure to the choroid, but the vessels are larger, and have chiefly a longitudinal direction. Their posterior surfaces are covered by a bilaminar layer of black pigment cells, which is continued forward from the retina, and is named the **pars ciliaris retinæ.** In the stroma of the ciliary processes there are also stellate pigment cells, but these are not so numerous as in the choroid itself.

The **Ciliaris muscle** (*m. ciliaris; ciliary muscle*) consists of unstriped fibers; it forms a grayish, semitransparent, circular band, about 3 mm. broad, on the outer surface of the forepart of the choroid. It is thickest in front, and consists of two sets of fibers, **meridional** and **circular.** The meridional fibers, much the more numerous, arise from the posterior margin of the scleral spur; they run backward, and are attached to the ciliary processes and orbiculus ciliaris. The circular fibers are internal to the meridional ones, and in a meridional section appear as a triangular zone behind the filtration angle and close to the circumference of the

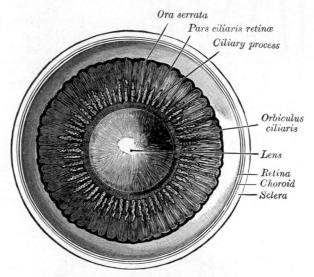

FIG. 901.—Interior of anterior half of bulb of eye.

iris. They are well-developed in hypermetropic, but are rudimentary or absent in myopic eyes. The Ciliaris muscle is the chief agent in accommodation, *i. e.*, in adjusting the eye to the vision of near objects. When it contracts it draws forward the ciliary processes, relaxes the suspensory ligament of the lens, and thus allows the lens to become more convex.

The Iris.—The iris has received its name from its various colors in different individuals. It is a thin, circular, contractile disk, suspended in the aqueous humor between the cornea and lens, and perforated a little to the nasal side of its center by a circular aperture, the **pupil.** By its periphery it is continuous with the ciliary body, and is also connected with the posterior elastic lamina of the cornea by means of the pectinate ligament; its surfaces are flattened, and look forward and backward, the anterior toward the cornea, the posterior toward the ciliary processes and lens. The iris divides the space between the lens and the cornea into an anterior and a posterior chamber. The **anterior chamber** of the eye is bounded in front by the posterior surface of the cornea; behind by the front of the iris and the central part of the lens. The **posterior chamber** is a narrow chink behind the peripheral part of the iris, and in front of the suspensory ligament of the lens and the ciliary processes. In the adult the two chambers communicate through the pupil, but in the fetus up to the seventh month they are separated by the *membrana pupillaris.*

Structure.—The iris is composed of the following structures:

1. In front is a layer of flattened mesothelial cells placed on a delicate hyaline basement membrane. This layer is continuous with the mesothelium covering the posterior elastic lamina of the cornea, and in individuals with dark-colored irides the cells contain pigment granules.

2. The **stroma** (*stroma iridis*) of the iris consists of fibers and cells. The former are made up of delicate bundles of fibrous tissue; a few fibers at the circumference of the iris have a circular direction; but the majority radiate toward the pupil, forming by their interlacement, delicate meshes, in which the vessels and nerves are contained. Interspersed between the bundles of connective tissue are numerous branched cells with fine processes. In dark eyes many of them contain pigment granules, but in blue eyes and the eyes of albinos they are unpigmented.

3. The **muscular fibers** are involuntary, and consist of circular and radiating fibers. The **circular fibers** form the Sphincter pupillæ; they are arranged in a narrow band about 1 mm. in width which surrounds the margin of the pupil toward the posterior surface of the iris; those near the free margin are closely aggregated; those near the periphery of the band are somewhat separated and form incomplete circles. The **radiating fibers** form the Dilatator pupillæ; they converge from the circumference toward the center, and blend with the circular fibers near the margin of the pupil.

4. The posterior surface of the iris is of a deep purple tint, being covered by two layers of pigmented columnar epithelium, continuous at the periphery of the iris with the pars ciliaris retinæ. This pigmented epithelium is named the **pars iridica retinæ.**

The color of the iris is produced by the reflection of light from dark pigment cells underlying a translucent tissue, and is therefore determined by the amount of the pigment and its distribution throughout the texture of the iris. The number and the situation of the pigment cells differ in different irides. In the albino pigment is absent; in the various shades of blue eyes the pigment cells are confined to the posterior surface of the iris, whereas in gray, brown, and black eyes pigment is found also in the cells of the stroma and in those of the endothelium on the front of the iris.

The iris may be absent, either in part or altogether as a congenital condition, and in some instances the pupillary membrane may remain persistent, though it is rarely complete. Again, the iris may be the seat of a malformation, termed *coloboma*, which consists in a deficiency or cleft, clearly due in a great number of cases to an arrest in development. In these cases the cleft is found at the lower aspect, extending directly downward from the pupil, and the gap frequently extends through the choroid to the porus opticus. In some rarer cases the gap is found in other parts of the iris, and is not then associated with any deficiency of the choroid.

Vessels and Nerves.—The **arteries of the iris** are derived from the long and anterior ciliary arteries, and from the vessels of the ciliary processes (see p. 637). Each of the two long ciliary arteries, having reached the attached margin of the iris, divides into an upper and lower branch; these anastomose with corresponding branches from the opposite side and thus encircle the iris; into this vascular circle (*circulus arteriosus major*) the anterior ciliary arteries pour their blood, and from it vessels converge to the free margin of the iris, and there communicate and form a second circle (*circulus arteriosus minor*) (Fig. 897).

The **nerves of the choroid and iris** are the long and short ciliary; the former being branches of the nasociliary nerve, the latter of the ciliary ganglion. They pierce the sclera around the entrance of the optic nerve, run forward in the perichoroidal space, and supply the bloodvessels of the choroid. After reaching the iris they form a plexus around its attached margin; from this are derived non-medullated fibers which end in the Sphincter and Dilatator pupillæ; their exact mode of termination has not been ascertained. Other fibers from the plexus end in a net-work on the anterior surface of the iris. The fibers derived through the motor root of the ciliary ganglion from the oculomotor nerve, supply the Sphincter, while those derived from the sympathetic supply the Dilatator.

Membrana Pupillaris.—In the fetus, the pupil is closed by a delicate vascular membrane, the **membrana pupillaris**, which divides the space in which the iris is suspended into two distinct chambers. The vessels of this membrane are partly derived from those of the margin of the iris and partly from those of the capsule of the lens; they have a looped arrangement, and converge toward each other without anastomosing. About the sixth month the membrane begins to disappear by absorption from the center toward the circumference, and at birth only a few fragments are present; in exceptional cases it persists.

The Retina (*tunica interna*).—The retina is a delicate nervous membrane, upon which the images of external objects are received. Its outer surface is in contact with the choroid; its inner with the vitreous body. Behind, it is continuous with the optic nerve; it gradually diminishes in thickness from behind forward, and

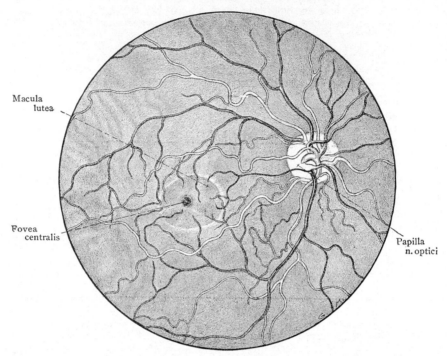

Fig. 902.—Interior of posterior half of right eye as viewed from in front. The distribution of blood vessels is shown (veins darker than arteries) and their relation to the optic disc. The area of most acute vision, the macula lutea, is shown. (Eycleshymer and Jones.)

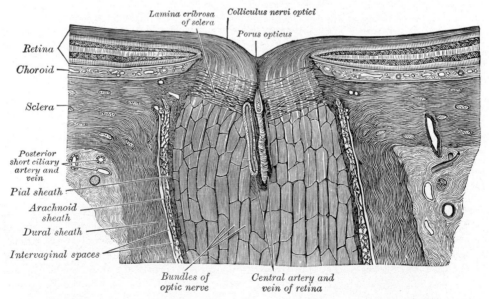

Fig. 903.—The terminal portion of the optic nerve and its entrance into the eyeball, in horizontal section. (Toldt.)

extends nearly as far as the ciliary body, where it appears to end in a jagged margin, the **ora serrata**. Here the nervous tissues of the retina end, but a thin prolongation of the membrane extends forward over the back of the ciliary processes and iris, forming the **pars ciliaris retinæ** and **pars iridica retinæ** already referred to. This forward prolongation consists of the pigmentary layer of the retina together with a stratum of columnar epithelium. The retina is soft, semitransparent, and of a purple tint in the fresh state, owing to the presence of a coloring material named **rhodopsin** or **visual purple**; but it soon becomes clouded, opaque, and bleached when exposed to sunlight. Exactly in the center of the posterior part of the retina, corresponding to the axis of the eye, and at a point in which the sense of vision is most perfect, is an oval yellowish area, the **macula lutea**; in the macula is a central depression, the **fovea centralis** (Fig. 902). At the fovea centralis the retina is exceedingly thin, and the dark color of the choroid is distinctly seen through it. About 3 mm. to the nasal side of the macula lutea is the exit of the optic nerve (*optic disk*), the circumference of which is slightly raised to form an eminence (*papilla nervi optici*) (Fig. 903); the arteria centralis retinæ pierces the center of the disk. This is the only part of the surface of the retina which is insensitive to light, and it is termed the **blind spot**.

Structure (Figs. 904, 905).—The retina consists of an outer pigmented layer and an inner nervous stratum or retina proper.

The **pigmented layer** consists of a single stratum of cells. When viewed from the outer surface these cells are smooth and hexagonal in shape; when seen in section each cell consists of an outer non-pigmented part containing a large oval nucleus and an inner pigmented portion which extends as a series of straight thread-like processes between the rods, this being especially the case when the eye is exposed to light. In the eyes of albinos the cells of this layer are destitute of pigment.

Retina Proper.—The nervous structures of the retina proper are supported by a series of non-nervous or sustentacular fibers, and, when examined microscopically by means of sections made perpendicularly to the surface of the retina, are found to consist of seven layers, named from within outward as follows:

1. Stratum opticum.
2. Ganglionic layer.
3. Inner plexiform layer.
4. Inner nuclear layer, or layer of inner granules.
5. Outer plexiform layer.
6. Outer nuclear layer, or layer of outer granules.
7. Layer of rods and cones.

1. The **stratum opticum** or **layer of nerve fibers** is formed by the expansion of the fibers of the optic nerve; it is thickest near the porus opticus, gradually diminishing toward the ora serrata. As the nerve fibers pass through the lamina cribrosa scleræ they lose their medullary sheaths and are continued onward through the choroid and retina as simple axis-cylinders. When they reach the internal surface of the retina they radiate from their point of entrance over this surface grouped in bundles, and in many places arranged in plexuses. Most of the fibers are centripetal, and are the direct continuations of the axis-cylinder processes of the cells of the ganglionic layer, but a few of them are centrifugal and ramify in the inner plexiform and inner nuclear layers, where they end in enlarged extremities.

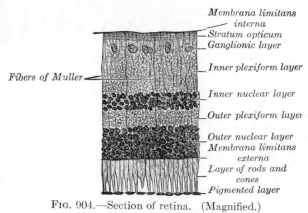

FIG. 904.—Section of retina. (Magnified.)

Membrana limitans interna
Stratum opticum
Ganglionic layer
Inner plexiform layer
Inner nuclear layer
Outer plexiform layer
Outer nuclear layer
Membrana limitans externa
Layer of rods and cones
Pigmented layer

Fibers of Muller

2. The **ganglionic layer** consists of a single layer of large ganglion cells, except in the macula lutea, where there are several strata. The cells are somewhat flask-shaped; the rounded internal surface of each resting on the stratum opticum, and sending off an axon which is prolonged into it. From the opposite end numerous dendrites extend into the inner plexiform layer, where

they **branch** and form flattened arborizations at different levels. The ganglion cells vary much in size, and the dendrites of the smaller ones as a rule arborize in the inner plexiform layer as soon as they enter it; while those of the larger cells ramify close to the inner nuclear layer.

3. The **inner plexiform layer** is made up of a dense reticulum of minute fibrils formed by the interlacement of the dendrites of the ganglion cells with those of the cells of the inner nuclear layer; within this reticulum a few branched spongioblasts are sometimes imbedded.

4. The **inner nuclear layer** or **layer of inner granules** is made up of a number of closely packed cells, of which there are three varieties, *viz.:* bipolar cells, horizontal cells, and amacrine cells.

The **bipolar cells,** by far the most numerous, are round or oval in shape, and each is prolonged into an inner and an outer process. They are divisible into rod bipolars and cone bipolars. The inner processes of the **rod bipolars** run through the inner plexiform layer and arborize around the bodies of the cells of the ganglionic layer; their outer processes end in the outer plexiform layer in tufts of fibrils around the button-like ends of the inner processes of the rod granules. The inner processes of the **cone bipolars** ramify in the inner plexiform layer in contact with the dendrites of the ganglionic cells.

The **horizontal cells** lie in the outer part of the inner nuclear layer and possess somewhat flattened cell bodies. Their dendrites divide into numerous branches in the outer plexiform layer, while their axons run horizontally for some distance and finally ramify in the same layer.

The **amacrine cells** are placed in the inner part of the inner nuclear layer, and are so named because they have not yet been shown to possess axis-cylinder processes. Their dendrites undergo extensive ramification in the inner plexiform layer.

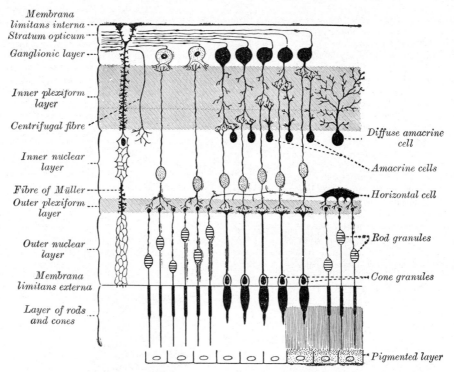

F_IG. 905.—Plan of retinal neurons. (After Cajal.)

5. The **outer plexiform layer** is much thinner than the inner; but, like it, consists of a dense net-work of minute fibrils derived from the processes of the horizontal cells of the preceding layer, and the outer processes of the rod and cone bipolar granules, which ramify in it, forming arborizations around the enlarged ends of the rod fibers and with the branched foot plates of the cone fibers.

6. The **outer nuclear layer** or **layer of outer granules,** like the inner nuclear layer, contains several strata of oval nuclear bodies; they are of two kinds, *viz.:* rod and cone granules, so named on account of their being respectively connected with the rods and cones of the next layer. The **rod granules** are much the more numerous, and are placed at different levels throughout the layer. Their nuclei present a peculiar cross-striped appearance, and prolonged from either

extremity of each cell is a fine process; the outer process is continuous with a single rod of the layer of rods and cones; the inner ends in the outer plexiform layer in an enlarged extremity, and is imbedded in the tuft into which the outer processes of the rod bipolar cells break up. In its course it presents numerous varicosities. The **cone granules,** fewer in number than the rod granules, are placed close to the membrana limitans externa, through which they are continuous with the cones of the layer of rods and cones. They do not present any cross-striation, but contain a pyriform nucleus, which almost completely fills the cell. From the inner extremity of the granule a thick process passes into the outer plexiform layer, and there expands into a pyramidal enlargement or foot plate, from which are given off numerous fine fibrils, that come in contact with the outer processes of the cone bipolars.

7. **The Layer of Rods and Cones** (*Jacob's membrane*).—The elements composing this layer are of two kinds, **rods** and **cones,** the former being much more numerous than the latter except in the macula lutea. The **rods** are cylindrical, of nearly uniform thickness, and are arranged perpendicularly to the surface. Each rod consists of two segments, an outer and inner, of about equal lengths. The segments differ from each other as regards refraction and in their behavior toward coloring reagents; the inner segment is stained by carmine, iodine, etc.; the outer segment is not stained by these reagents, but is colored yellowish brown by osmic acid. The outer segment is marked by transverse striæ, and tends to break up into a number of thin disks superimposed on one another; it also exhibits faint longitudinal markings. The deeper part of the inner segment is indistinctly granular; its more superficial part presents a longitudinal striation, being composed of fine, bright, highly refracting fibrils. The visual purple or rhodopsin is found only in the outer segments.

The **cones** are conical or flask-shaped, their broad ends resting upon the membrana limitans externa, the narrow-pointed extremity being turned to the choroid. Like the rods, each is made up of two segments, outer and inner; the outer segment is a short conical process, which, like the outer segment of the rod, exhibits transverse striæ. The inner segment resembles the inner segment of the rods in structure, presenting a superficial striated and deep granular part, but differs from it in size and shape, being bulged out laterally and flask-shaped. The chemical and optical characters of the two portions are identical with those of the rods.

Supporting Frame-work of the Retina.—The nervous layers of the retina are connected together by a supporting frame-work, formed by the **sustentacular fibers of Müller;** these fibers pass through all the nervous layers, except that of the rods and cones. Each begins on the inner surface of the retina by an expanded, often forked base, which sometimes contains a spheroidal body staining deeply with hematoxylin, the edges of the bases of adjoining fibers being united to form the **membrana limitans interna.** As the fibers pass through the nerve fiber and ganglionic layers they give off a few lateral branches; in the inner nuclear layer they give off numerous lateral processes for the support of the bipolar cells, while in the outer nuclear layer they form a network around the rod- and cone-fibrils, and unite to form the **membrana limitans externa** at the bases of the rods and cones. At the level of the inner nuclear layer each sustentacular fiber contains a clear oval nucleus.

Macula Lutea and Fovea Centralis.—In the macula lutea the nerve fibers are wanting as a continuous layer, the ganglionic layer consists of several strata of cells, there are no rods, but only cones, which are longer and narrower than in other parts, and in the outer nuclear layer there are only cone-granules, the processes of which are very long and arranged in curved lines. In the fovea centralis the only parts present are (1) the cones; (2) the outer nuclear layer, the cone-fibers of which are almost horizontal in direction; (3) an exceedingly thin inner plexiform layer. The pigmented layer is thicker and its pigment more pronounced than elsewhere. The color of the macula seems to imbue all the layers except that of the rods and cones; it is of a rich yellow, deepest toward the center of the macula, and does not appear to be due to pigment cells, but simply to a staining of the constituent parts.

At the **ora serrata** the nervous layers of the retina end abruptly, and the retina is continued onward as a single layer of columnar cells covered by the pigmented layer. This double layer is known as the **pars ciliaris retinæ,** and can be traced forward from the ciliary processes on to the back of the iris, where it is termed the **pars iridica retinæ.**

The **arteria centralis retinæ** (Fig. 902) and its accompanying vein pierce the optic nerve, and enter the bulb of the eye through the porus opticus. The artery immediately bifurcates into an upper and a lower branch, and each of these again divides into a medial or nasal and a lateral or temporal branch, which at first run between the hyaloid membrane and the nervous layer; but they soon enter the latter, and pass forward, dividing dichotomously. From these branches a minute capillary plexus is given off, which does not extend beyond the inner nuclear layer. The macula receives two small branches (superior and inferior macular arteries) from the temporal branches and small twigs directly from the central artery; these do not, however, reach as far as the fovea centralis, which has no bloodvessels. The branches of the arteria centralis retinæ do not anastomose with each other—in other words they are terminal arteries. In the fetus, a small vessel, the arteria hyaloidea, passes forward as a continuation of the arteria centralis retinæ through the vitreous humor to the posterior surface of the capsule of the lens.

The Refracting Media.

The refracting media are four, *viz.:*
The Cornea (see page 1102).   Aqueous humor.   Vitreous body.   Crystalline lens.

The Aqueous Humor (*humor aqueus*).—The aqueous humor fills the anterior and posterior chambers of the eyeball. It is small in quantity, has an alkaline reaction, and consists mainly of water, less than one-fiftieth of its weight being solid matter, chiefly chloride of sodium. The aqueous humor is secreted by the ciliary processes. The fluid passes through the posterior chamber and the pupil into the anterior chamber. From the angle of the anterior chamber it passes into the spaces of Fontana to the pectinate villi through which it is filtered into the venous canal of Schlemm.

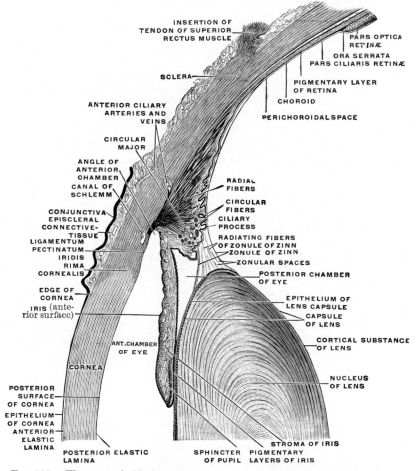

Fig. 906.—The upper half of a sagittal section through the front of the eyeball.

The **Vitreous Body** (*corpus vitreum*) fills the concavity of the pars optica retinæ to which it is firmly adherent especially at the ora serrata. It is hollowed in front for the lens. It is transparent, semigelatinous, and consists of water (99 per cent.), salts, and albumen. Some indications of the hyaloid canal, between the optic nerve and lens may persist.

No bloodvessels penetrate the vitreous body, so that its nutrition must be carried on by vessels of the retina and ciliary processes, situated upon its exterior.

The **Zonula Ciliaris** (*zonule of Zinn, suspensory ligament of the lens*) consists of a series of straight fibrils which radiate from the ciliary body to the lens. It is attached to the capsule of the lens a short distance in front of its equator. Scattered and delicate fibers are also attached to the region of the equator itself. This ligament retains the lens in position, and is relaxed by the contraction of the meridional fibers of the Ciliaris muscle, so that the lens is allowed to become more convex. Behind the suspensory ligament there is a sacculated canal, the **spatia zonularia** (*canal of Petit*), which encircles the equator of the lens; it can be easily inflated through a fine blowpipe inserted under the suspensory ligament.

The **Crystalline Lens** (*lens crystallina*). — The crystalline lens, enclosed in its capsule, is situated immediately behind the iris, in front of the vitreous body, and encircled by the ciliary processes, which slightly overlap its margin.

FIG. 907—The crystalline lens, hardened and divided. (Enlarged.)

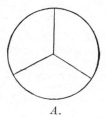

A.

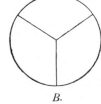

B.

FIG. 908—Diagram to show the direction and arrangement of the radiating lines on the front and back of the fetal lens. *A.* From the front. *B.* From the back.

1   2   3

FIG. 909.—Profile views of the lens at different periods of life. 1. In the fetus. 2. In adult life. 3. In old age.

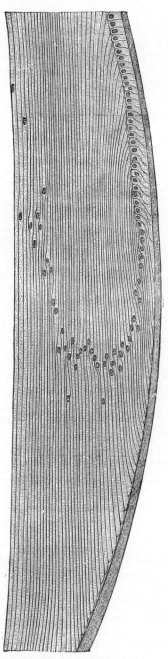

FIG. 910.—Section through the margin of the lens, showing the transition of the epithelium into the lens fibers. (Babuchin.)

The **capsule of the lens** (*capsula lentis*) is a transparent, structureless membrane which closely surrounds the lens, and is thicker in front than behind. It is brittle but highly elastic, and when ruptured the edges roll up with the outer surface innermost. It rests, behind, in the hyaloid fossa in the forepart of the vitreous body; in front, it is in contact with the free border of the iris, but recedes from it at the circumference, thus forming the posterior chamber of the eye; it is retained in its position chiefly by the suspensory ligament of the lens, already described.

The **lens** is a transparent, biconvex body, the convexity of its anterior being less than that of its posterior surface. The central points of these surfaces are termed respectively the **anterior** and **posterior poles**; a line connecting the poles constitutes the **axis** of the lens, while the marginal circumference is termed the **equator**.

Structure.—The lens is made up of soft cortical substance and a firm, central part, the **nucleus** (Fig. 907). Faint lines (*radii lentis*) radiate from the poles to the equator. In the adult there may be six or more of these lines, but in the fetus they are only three in number and diverge from each other at angles of 120° (Fig. 908); on the anterior surface one line ascends vertically and the other two diverge downward; on the posterior surface one ray descends vertically and the other two diverge upward. They correspond with the free edges of an equal number of septa composed of an amorphous substance, which dip into the substance of the lens. When the lens has been hardened it is seen to consist of a series of concentrically arranged laminæ, each of which is interrupted at the septa referred to. Each lamina is built up of a number of hexagonal, ribbon-like lens fibers, the edges of which are more or less serrated—the serrations fitting between those of neighboring fibers, while the ends of the fibers come into apposition at the septa. The fibers run in a curved manner from the septa on the anterior surface to those on the posterior surface. No fibers pass from pole to pole; they are arranged in such a way that those which begin near the pole on one surface of the lens end near the peripheral extremity of the plane on the other, and *vice versa*. The fibers of the outer layers of the lens are nucleated, and together form a nuclear layer, most distinct toward the equator. The anterior surface of the lens is covered by a layer of transparent, columnar, nucleated epithelium. At the equator the cells become elongated, and their gradual transition into lens fibers can be traced (Fig. 910).

In the fetus, the lens is nearly spherical, and has a slightly reddish tint; it is soft and breaks down readily on the slightest pressure. A small branch from the arteria centralis retinæ runs forward, as already mentioned, through the vitreous body to the posterior part of the capsule of the lens, where its branches radiate and form a plexiform network, which covers the posterior surface of the capsule, and they are continuous around the margin of the capsule with the vessels of the pupillary membrane, and with those of the iris. **In the adult,** the lens is colorless, transparent, firm in texture, and devoid of vessels. **In old age** it becomes flattened on both surfaces, slightly opaque, of an amber tint, and increased in density (Fig. 909).

Vessels and Nerves.—The **arteries** of the bulb of the eye are the long, short, and anterior ciliary arteries, and the arteria centralis retinæ. They have already been described (see p. 636).

The **ciliary veins** are seen on the outer surface of the choroid, and are named, from their arrangement, the *venæ vorticosæ;* they converge to four or five equidistant trunks which pierce the sclera midway between the sclero-corneal junction and the porus opticus. Another set of veins accompanies the anterior ciliary arteries. All of these veins open into the ophthalmic veins.

The **ciliary nerves** are derived from the nasociliary nerve and from the ciliary ganglion.

The Accessory Organs of the Eye (Organa Oculi Accessoria).

The accessory organs of the eye include the **ocular muscles**, the **fasciæ**, the **eyebrows**, the **eyelids**, the **conjunctiva**, and the **lacrimal apparatus**.

The Ocular Muscles (*musculi oculi*).—The ocular muscles are the:

Levator palpebræ superioris.	Rectus medialis.
Rectus superior.	Rectus lateralis.
Rectus inferior.	Obliquus superior.

Obliquus inferior.

The **Levator palpebræ superioris** (Fig. 911) is thin, flat, and triangular in shape. It *arises* from the under surface of the small wing of the sphenoid, above and in front of the optic foramen, from which it is separated by the origin of the Rectus superior. At its origin, it is narrow and tendinous, but soon becomes broad and fleshy, and ends anteriorly in a wide aponeurosis which splits into three lamellæ. The superficial lamella blends with the upper part of the orbital septum, and is prolonged forward above the superior tarsus to the palpebral part of the Orbicularis oculi, and to the deep surface of the skin of the upper eyelid. The middle lamella, largely made up of non-striped muscular fibers, is inserted into the upper margin of the superior tarsus, while the deepest lamella blends with an expansion from the sheath of the Rectus superior and with it is attached to the superior fornix of the conjunctiva.

Whitnall has pointed out that the upper part of the sheath of the Levator palpebræ becomes thickened in front and forms, above the anterior part of the muscle, a transverse ligamentous band which is attached to the sides of the orbital cavity. On the medial side it is mainly fixed to the pulley of the Obliquus superior, but some fibers are attached to the bone behind the pulley and a slip passes forward and bridges over the supraorbital notch; on the lateral side it is fixed to the capsule of the lacrimal gland and to the frontal bone. In front of the transverse ligamentous band the sheath is continued over the aponeurosis of the Levator palpebræ, as a thin connective-tissue layer which is fixed to the upper orbital margin immediately behind the attachment of the orbital septum. When the Levator palpebræ contracts, the lateral and medial parts of the ligamentous band are stretched and check the action of the muscle; the retraction of the upper eyelid is checked also by the orbital septum coming into contact with the transverse part of the ligamentous band.

The four **Recti** (Fig. 912) *arise* from a fibrous ring (*anulus tendineus communis*) which surrounds the upper, medial, and lower margins of the optic foramen and encircles the optic nerve (Fig. 913). The ring is completed by a tendinous bridge prolonged over the lower and medial part of the superior orbital fissure and attached to a tubercle on the margin of the great wing of the sphenoid, bounding the fissure. Two specialized parts of this fibrous ring may be made out: a lower, the **ligament** or **tendon of Zinn**, which gives origin to the Rectus inferior, part of the Rectus medialis, and the lower head of origin of the Rectus lateralis; and an upper, which gives origin to the Rectus superior, the rest of the Rectus medialis, and the upper head of the Rectus lateralis. This upper band is sometimes termed the **superior tendon of Lockwood.** Each muscle passes forward in the position implied by its name, to be inserted by a tendinous expansion into the sclera, about 6 mm. from the margin of the cornea. Between the two heads of the Rectus lateralis is a narrow interval, through which pass the two divisions of the oculomotor nerve, the naso-ciliary nerve, the abducent nerve, and the ophthalmic vein. Although these muscles present a common origin and are inserted in a similar manner into the sclera, there are certain differences to be observed in them as regards their length and breadth. The Rectus medialis is the broadest, the Rectus lateralis the longest, and the Rectus superior the thinnest and narrowest.

The **Obliquus oculi superior** (*superior oblique*) is a fusiform muscle, placed at the upper and medial side of the orbit. It *arises* immediately above the margin of the optic foramen, above and medial to the origin of the Rectus superior, and, passing forward, ends in a rounded tendon, which plays in a fibrocartilaginous ring or pulley attached to the trochlear fovea of the frontal bone. The contiguous surfaces of the tendon and ring are lined by a delicate mucous sheath, and enclosed in a thin fibrous investment. The tendon is reflected backward, lateralward, and downward beneath the Rectus superior to the lateral part of the bulb of the eye, and is inserted into the sclera, behind the equator of the eyeball, the insertion of the muscle lying between the Rectus superior and Rectus lateralis.

The **Obliquus oculi inferior** (*inferior oblique*) is a thin, narrow muscle, placed near the anterior margin of the floor of the orbit. It *arises* from the orbital surface of the maxilla, lateral to the lacrimal groove. Passing lateralward, backward, and upward, at first between the Rectus inferior and the floor of the orbit, and then between the bulb of the eye and the Rectus lateralis, it is inserted into the lateral part of the sclera between the Rectus superior and Rectus lateralis, near to, but somewhat behind the insertion of the Obliquus superior.

Nerves.—The Levator palpebræ superioris, Obliquus inferior, and the Recti superior, inferior, and medialis are supplied by the oculomotor nerve; the Obliquus superior, by the trochlear nerve; the Rectus lateralis, by the abducent nerve.

Actions.—The Levator palpebræ *raises* the upper eyelid, and is the direct antagonist of the Orbicularis oculi. The four Recti are attached to the bulb of the eye in such a manner that, acting singly, they will turn its corneal surface either upward, downward medialward, or lateralward, as expressed by their names. The movement produced by the Rectus superior or Rectus inferior is not quite a simple one, for inasmuch as each passes obliquely lateralward and forward

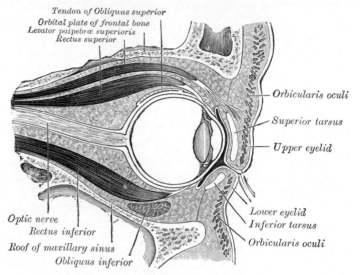

Fig. 911.—Sagittal section of right orbital cavity.

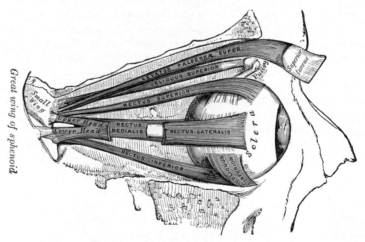

Fig. 912.—Muscles of the right orbit.

to the bulb of the eye, the elevation or depression of the cornea is accompanied by a certain deviation medialward, with a slight amount of rotation. These latter movements are corrected by the Obliqui, the Obliquus inferior correcting the medial deviation caused by the Rectus superior and the Obliquus superior that caused by the Rectus inferior. The contraction of the Rectus lateralis or Rectus medialis, on the other hand, produces a purely horizontal movement. If any two neighboring Recti of one eye act together they carry the globe of the eye in the diagonal of these directions, *viz.*, upward and medialward, upward and lateralward, downward and medialward, or downward and lateralward. Sometimes the corresponding Recti of the two eyes act in unison, and at other times the opposite Recti act together. Thus, in turning the eyes to the right, the Rectus lateralis of the right eye will act in unison with the Rectus medialis of the left eye; but if both eyes are directed to an object in the middle line at a short distance, the two Recti mediales will act in unison. The movement of circumduction, as in looking around a room, is performed by the successive actions of the four Recti. The Obliqui rotate the eyeball on its antero-posterior axis, the superior directing the cornea downward and lateralward, and the inferior directing it upward and lateralward; these movements are required for the correct viewing of an object when the head is moved laterally, as from shoulder to shoulder, in order that the picture may fall in all respects on the same part of the retina of either eye.

A layer of non-striped muscle, the **Orbitalis muscle** of H. Müller, may be seen bridging across the inferior orbital fissure.

The **Fascia Bulbi** (*capsule of Tenon*) is a thin membrane which envelops the eyeball from the optic nerve to the ciliary region, separating it from the orbital fat and forming a socket in which it plays. Its inner surface is smooth, and is separated from the outer surface of the sclera by the **periscleral space**. This space is continuous with the subdural and subarachnoid cavities, and is traversed by delicate bands of connective tissue which extend between the fascia and the sclera. The fascia is perforated behind by the ciliary vessels and nerves, and fuses with the sheath of the optic nerve and with the sclera around the entrance of the optic

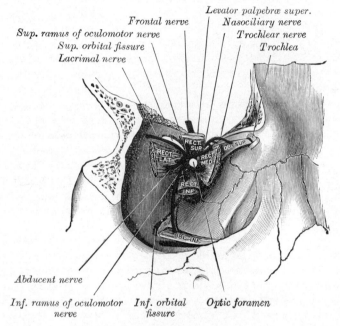

Fig. 913.—Dissection showing origins of right ocular muscles, and nerves entering by the superior orbital fissure.

nerve. In front it blends with the ocular conjunctiva, and with it is attached to the ciliary region of the eyeball. It is perforated by the tendons of the ocular muscles, and is reflected backward on each as a tubular sheath. The sheath of the Obliquus superior is carried as far as the fibrous pulley of that muscle; that on the Obliquus inferior reaches as far as the floor of the orbit, to which it gives off a slip. The sheaths on the Recti are gradually lost in the perimysium, but they give off important expansions. The expansion from the Rectus superior blends with the tendon of the Levator palpebræ; that of the Rectus inferior is attached to the inferior tarsus. The expansions from the sheaths of the Recti medialis and lateralis are strong, especially that from the latter muscle, and are attached to the lacrimal and zygomatic bones respectively. As they probably check the actions of these two Recti they have been named the **medial** and **lateral check ligaments**. Lockwood has described a thickening of the lower part of the fascia bulbi, which he has named the **suspensory ligament of the eye**. It is slung like a hammock below the eyeball, being expanded in the center, and narrow at its extremities which are attached to the zygomatic and lacrimal bones respectively.

The Periorbita forms the periosteum of the orbit. It is loosely connected to the bones and can be readily separated from them. Behind, it is united with the dura mater by processes which pass through the optic foramen and superior orbital fissure, and with the sheath of the optic nerve. In front, it is connected with the periosteum at the margin of the orbit, and sends off a process which assists in forming the **orbital septum**. From it two processes are given off; one to enclose the lacrimal gland, the other to hold the pulley of the Obliquus superior in position.

The **Eyebrows** (*supercilia*) are two arched eminences of integument, which surmount the upper circumference of the orbits, and support numerous short, thick hairs, directed obliquely on the surface. The eyebrows consist of thickened integument, connected beneath with the Orbicularis oculi, Corrugator, and Frontalis muscles.

The **Eyelids** (*palpebræ*) are two thin, movable folds, placed in front of the eye, protecting it from injury by their closure. The upper eyelid is the larger, and the more movable of the two, and is furnished with an elevator muscle, the Levator palpebræ superioris. When the eyelids are open, an elliptical space, the palpebral **fissure** (*rima palpebrarum*), is left between their margins, the angles of which correspond to the junctions of the upper and lower eyelids, and are called the **palpebral commissures** or **canthi**.

The **lateral palpebral commissure** (*commissura palpebrarum lateralis; external canthus*) is more acute than the medial, and the eyelids here lie in close contact with the bulb of the eye: but the **medial palpebral commissure** (*commissura palpebrarum medialis; internal canthus*) is prolonged for a short distance toward the nose, and the two eyelids are separated by a triangular space, the **lacus lacrimalis** (Fig. 914). At the basal angles of the lacus lacrimalis, on the margin of each eyelid, is a small conical elevation, the **lacrimal papilla**, the apex of which is pierced by a small orifice, the **punctum lacrimale**, the commencement of the lacrimal duct.

The **eyelashes** (*cilia*) are attached to the free edges of the eyelids; they are short, thick, curved hairs, arranged in a double or triple row: those of the upper eyelid, more numerous and longer than those of the lower, curve upward; those of the lower eyelid curve downward, so that they do not interlace in closing the lids. Near the attachment of the eyelashes are the openings of a number of glands, the **ciliary glands**, arranged in several rows close to the free margin of the lid; they are regarded as enlarged and modified sudoriferous glands.

Structure of the Eyelids.—The eyelids are composed of the following structures taken in their order from without inward: integument, areolar tissue, fibers of the Orbicularis oculi, tarsus orbital septum, tarsal glands and conjunctiva. The upper eyelid has, in addition, the aponeurosis of the Levator palpebræ superioris (Fig. 916).

The **integument** is extremely thin, and continuous at the margins of the eyelids with the conjunctiva.

The **subcutaneous areolar tissue** is very lax and delicate, and seldom contains any fat.

The **palpebral fibers of the Orbicularis oculi** are thin, pale in color, and possess an involuntary as well as a voluntary action.

The **tarsi** (*tarsal plates*) (Fig. 916) are two thin, elongated plates of dense connective tissue, about 2.5 cm. in length; one is placed in each eyelid, and contributes to its form and support, The **superior tarsus** (*tarsus superior; superior tarsal plate*), the larger, is of a semilunar form, about 10 mm. in breadth at the center, and gradually narrowing toward its extremities. To the anterior surface of this plate the aponeurosis of the Levator palpebræ superioris is attached The **inferior tarsus** (*tarsus inferior; inferior tarsal plate*), the smaller, is thin, elliptical in form, and has a vertical diameter of about 5 mm. The free or ciliary margins of these plates are thick and straight. The attached or orbital margins are connected to the circumference of the orbit by the orbital septum. The lateral angles are attached to the zygomatic bone by the lateral palpebral raphé. The medial angles of the two plates end at the lacus lacrimalis, and are attached to the frontal process of the maxilla by the medial palpebral ligament (page 416).

The **orbital septum** (*septum orbitale; palpebral ligament*) is a membranous sheet, attached to the edge of the orbit, where it is continuous with the periorbita. In the upper eyelid it blends

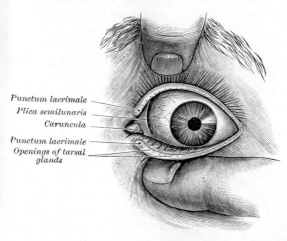

Punctum lacrimale
Plica semilunaris
Caruncula
Punctum lacrimale
Openings of tarsal glands

Fig. 914.—Front of left eye with eyelids separated to show medial canthus

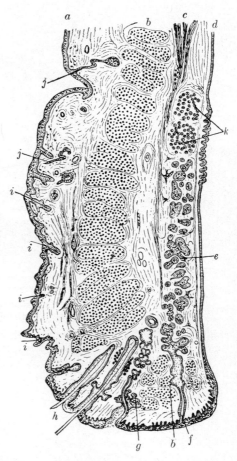

by its peripheral circumference with the tendon of the Levator palpebræ superioris and the superior tarsus, in the lower eyelid with the inferior tarsus. Medially it is thin, and, becoming separated from the medial palpebral ligament, is fixed to the lacrimal bone immediately behind the lacrimal sac. The septum is perforated by the vessels and nerves which pass from the orbital cavity to the face and scalp. The eyelids are richly supplied with blood.

The **Tarsal Glands** (*glandulæ tarsales* [*Meibomi*]; *Meibomian glands*) (Fig. 915). —The tarsal glands are situated upon the inner surfaces of the eyelids, between the tarsi and conjunctiva, and may be distinctly seen through the latter on everting the eyelids, presenting an appearance like parallel strings of pearls. There are about thirty in the upper eyelid, and somewhat fewer in the lower. They are imbedded in grooves in the inner surfaces of the tarsi, and correspond in length with the breadth

Fig. 915.—Sagittal section through the upper eyelid. (After Waldeyer.) *a.* Skin. *b.* Orbicularis oculi. *b'.* Marginal fasciculus of Orbicularis (ciliary bundle). *c.* Levator palpebræ. *d.* Conjunctiva. *e.* Tarsus. *f.* Tarsal gland. *g.* Sebaceous gland. *h.* Eyelashes. *i.* Small hairs of skin. *j.* Sweat glands. *k.* Posterior tarsal glands.

of these plates; they are, consequently, longer in the upper than in the lower eyelid. Their ducts open on the free magins of the lids by minute foramina.

Structure.—The tarsal glands are modified sebaceous glands, each consisting of a single straight tube or follicle, with numerous small lateral diverticula. The tubes are supported by a basement membrane, and are lined at their mouths by stratified epithelium; the deeper parts of the tubes and the lateral offshoots are lined by a layer of polyhedral cells.

The **conjunctiva** is the mucous membrane of the eye. It lines the inner surfaces of the eyelids or palpebræ, and is reflected over the forepart of the sclera and cornea.

The **Palpebral Portion** (*tunica conjunctiva palpebrarum*) is thick, opaque, highly vascular, and covered with numerous papillæ, its deeper part presenting a considerable amount of lymphoid tissue. At the margins of the lids it becomes continuous with the lining membrane of the ducts of the tarsal glands, and, through the lacrimal ducts, with the lining membrane of the lacrimal sac and nasolacrimal duct. At the lateral angle of the upper eyelid the ducts of the lacrimal gland open on its free surface; and at the medial angle it forms a semilunar fold, the **plica**

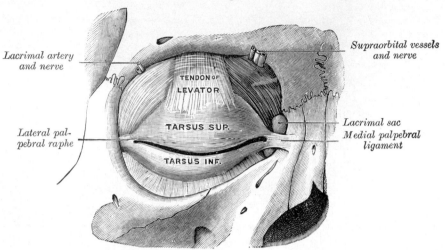

Fig. 916.—The tarsi and their ligaments. Right eye; front view.

semilunaris. The line of reflection of the conjunctiva from the upper eyelid on to the bulb of the eye is named the **superior fornix,** and that from the lower lid the **inferior fornix.**

The **Bulbar Portion** (*tunica conjunctiva bulbi*).—Upon the *sclera* the conjunctiva is loosely connected to the bulb of the eye; it is thin, transparent, destitute of papillæ, and only slightly vascular. Upon the *cornea,* the conjunctiva consists

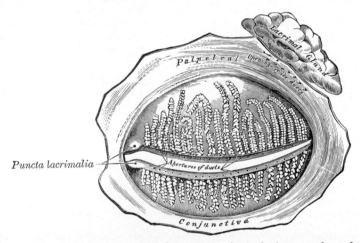

Fig. 917.—The tarsal glands, etc., seen from the inner surface of the eyelids.

only of epithelium, constituting the epithelium of the cornea, already described (see page 1103). *Lymphatics* arise in the conjunctiva in a delicate zone around the cornea, and run to the ocular conjunctiva.

In and near the fornices, but more plentiful in the upper than in the lower eyelid, a number of convoluted tubular glands open on the surface of the conjunctiva.

Other glands, analogous to lymphoid follicles, and called by Henle **trachoma glands,** are found in the conjunctiva, and, according to Strohmeyer, are chiefly situated near the medial palpebral commissure. They were first described by Brush, in his description of Peyer's patches of the small intestine, as "identical structures existing in the under eyelid of the ox."

The **caruncula lacrimalis** is a small, reddish, conical-shaped body, situated at the medial palpebral commissure, and filling up the **lacus lacrimalis.** It consists of a small island of skin containing sebaceous and sudoriferous glands, and is the source of the whitish secretion which constantly collects in this region. A few slender hairs are attached to its surface. Lateral to the caruncula is a slight semi-

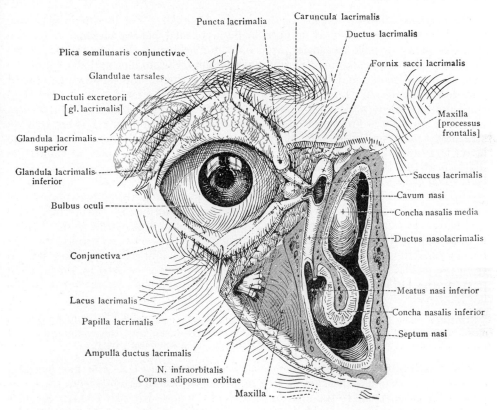

Fig. 918.—Topography of the lacrimal apparatus. The lacrimal and tarsal glands are shown in blue. The nose and a portion of the face have been cut away. (Eycleshymer and Jones).

lunar fold of conjunctiva, the concavity of which is directed toward the cornea; it is called the **plica semilunaris.** Müller found smooth muscular fibers in this fold; in some of the domesticated animals it contains a thin plate of cartilage.

The nerves in the conjunctiva are numerous and form rich plexuses. According to Krause they terminate in a peculiar form of tactile corpuscle, which he terms "terminal bulbs."

The **Lacrimal Apparatus** (*apparatus lacrimalis*) (Fig. 918) consists of (*a*) the **lacrimal gland,** which secretes the tears, and its excretory ducts, which convey the fluid to the surface of the eye; (*b*) the **lacrimal ducts, the lacrimal sac,** and the **nasolacrimal duct,** by which the fluid is conveyed into the cavity of the nose.

The Lacrimal Gland (*glandula lacrimalis*).—The lacrimal gland is lodged in the lacrimal fossa, on the medial side of the zygomatic process of the frontal bone.

It is of an oval form, about the size and shape of an almond, and consists of two portions, described as the superior and inferior lacrimal glands. The **superior lacrimal gland** is connected to the periosteum of the orbit by a few fibrous bands, and rests upon the tendons of the Recti superioris and lateralis, which separate it from the bulb of the eye. The **inferior lacrimal gland** is separated from the superior by a fibrous septum, and projects into the back part of the upper eyelid, where its deep surface is related to the conjunctiva. The ducts of the glands, from six to twelve in number, run obliquely beneath the conjunctiva for a short distance, and open along the upper and lateral half of the superior conjunctival fornix.

Structures of the Lacrimal Gland.—In structure and general appearance the lacrimal resembles the serous salivary glands.

The Lacrimal Ducts (*ductus lacrimalis; lacrimal canals*).—The lacrimal ducts, one in each eyelid, commence at minute orifices, termed **puncta lacrimalia,** on the summits of the **papillæ lacrimales,** seen on the margins of the lids at the lateral extremity of the lacus lacrimalis. The **superior duct,** the smaller and shorter of the two, at first ascends, and then bends at an acute angle, and passes medialward and downward to the lacrimal sac. The **inferior duct** at first descends, and then runs almost horizontally to the lacrimal sac. At the angles they are dilated into **ampullæ;** their walls are dense in structure and their mucous lining is covered by stratified squamous epithelium, placed on a basement membrane. Outside the latter is a layer of striped muscle, continuous with the lacrimal part of the Orbicularis oculi; at the base of each lacrimal papilla the muscular fibers are circularly arranged and form a kind of sphincter.

The Lacrimal Sac (*saccus lacrimalis*).—The lacrimal sac is the upper dilated end of the nasolacrimal duct, and is lodged in a deep groove formed by the lacrimal bone and frontal process of the maxilla. It is oval in form and measures from 12 to 15 mm. in length; its upper end is closed and rounded; its lower is continued into the nasolacrimal duct. Its superficial surface is covered by a fibrous expansion derived from the medial palpebral ligament, and its deep surface is crossed by the lacrimal part of the Orbicularis oculi (page 415), which is attached to the crest on the lacrimal bone.

Structure.—The lacrimal sac consists of a fibrous elastic coat, lined internally by mucous membrane: the latter is continuous, through the lacrimal ducts, with the conjunctiva, and through the nasolacrimal duct with the mucous membrane of the nasal cavity.

The **Nasolacrimal Duct** (*ductus nasolacrimalis; nasal duct*).—The nasolacrimal duct is a membranous canal, about 18 mm. in length, which extends from the lower part of the lacrimal sac to the inferior meatus of the nose, where it ends by a somewhat expanded orifice, provided with an imperfect valve, the **plica lacrimalis** (*Hasneri*), formed by a fold of the mucous membrane. It is contained in an osseous canal, formed by the maxilla, the lacrimal bone, and the inferior nasal concha; it is narrower in the middle than at either end, and is directed downward, backward, and a little lateralward. The mucous lining of the lacrimal sac and nasolacrimal duct is covered with columnar epithelium, which in places is ciliated.

THE EAR (ORGANON STATO-ACUSTICUM).

The **ear,** or **organ of hearing,** is divisible into three parts: the **external ear,** the **middle ear** or **tympanic cavity,** and the **internal ear** or **labyrinth.**

The Development of the Ear.—The first rudiment of the internal ear appears shortly after that of the eye, in the form of a patch of thickened ectoderm, the **auditory plate,** over the region of the hind-brain. The auditory plate becomes depressed and converted into the **auditory pit** (Fig. 919). The mouth of the pit is then closed, and thus a shut sac, the **auditory vesicle,** is formed (Fig. 920); from it the epithelial lining of the membranous labyrinth is derived. The vesicle becomes pear-shaped, and the neck of the flask is obliterated (Fig. 921). From the vesicle certain diverticula are given off which form the various parts of the membranous labyrinth. One from the middle part forms the ductus and saccus endolymphaticus, another from the anterior end gradually elongates, and, forming a tube coiled on itself, becomes the cochlear duct, the vestibular extremity of which is subsequently constricted to form the canalis reuniens. Three others appear as disk-like evaginations on the surface of the vesicle; the central parts of the walls of the disks coalesce and disappear, while the peripheral portions persist to form the semicircular ducts; of these the superior is the first and the lateral the last to be com-

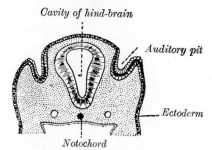

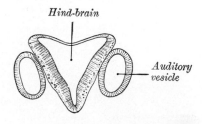

FIG. 919.—Section through the head of a human embryo, about twelve days old, in the region of the hind-brain. (Kollmann.)

FIG. 920.—Section through hind-brain and auditory vesicles of an embryo more advanced than that of Fig. 943. (After His.)

pleted. The central part of the vesicle represents the membranous vestibule, and is subdivided by a constriction into a smaller ventral part, the saccule, and a larger dorsal and posterior part, the utricle. This subdivision is effected by a fold which extends deeply into the proximal part of the ductus endolymphaticus, with the result that the utricle and saccule ultimately communicate with each other by means of a Y-shaped canal. The saccule opens into the cochlear duct, through the canalis reuniens, and the semicircular ducts communicate with the utricle.

The mesodermal tissue surrounding the various parts of the epithelial labyrinth is converted into a cartilaginous ear-capsule, and this is finally ossified to form the bony labyrinth. Between the cartilaginous capsule and the epithelial structures is a stratum of mesodermal tissue which is differentiated into three layers, *viz.,* an outer, forming the periosteal lining of the bony labyrinth; an inner, in direct contact with the epithelial structures; and an intermediate, consisting of gelatinous tissue: by the absorption of this latter tissue the perilymphatic spaces are developed. The modiolus and osseous spiral lamina of the cochlea are not preformed in cartilage but are ossified directly from connective tissue.

The **middle ear** and **auditory tube** are developed from the first pharyngeal pouch. The entodermal lining of the dorsal end of this pouch is in contact with the ectoderm of the corresponding pharyngeal groove; by the extension of the mesoderm between these two layers the tympanic membrane is formed. During the sixth or seventh month the tympanic antrum appears as an upward and backward expansion of the tympanic cavity. With regard to the exact mode of development of the ossicles of the middle ear there is some difference of opinion. The view generally held is that the **malleus** is developed from the proximal end of the mandibular (Meckel's) cartilage (Fig. 23), the **incus** in the proximal end of the mandibular arch, and that the **stapes** is formed from the proximal end of the hyoid arch. The malleus, with the exception of its anterior process is ossified from a single center which appears near the neck of the bone; the anterior process is ossified separately in membrane and joins the main part of the bone about the sixth month

of fetal life.   The incus is ossified from one center which appears in the upper
part of its long crus and ultimately extends into its lenticular process.   The
stapes first appears as a ring (*annulus stapedius*) encircling a small vessel, the stapedial artery, which subsequently undergoes atrophy; it is ossified from a single
center which appears in its base.

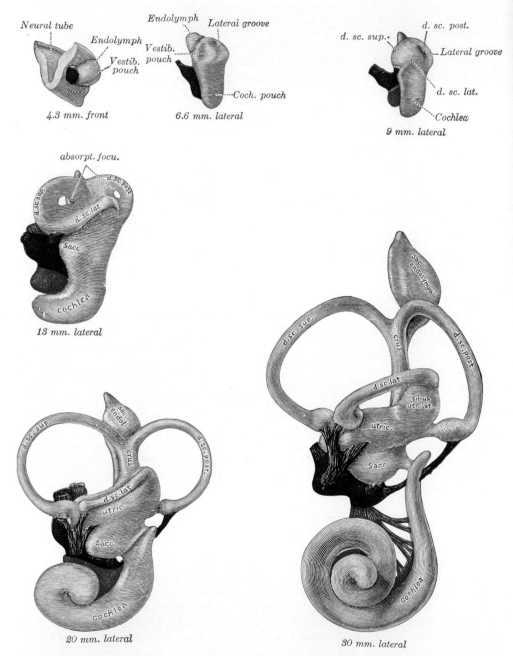

Fig. 921.—Lateral views of membranous labyrinth and acoustic complex.   × 25 dia.   (Streeter.)
absorpt. focu, area of wall where absorption is complete; *amp.,* ampulla membranacea; *crus,* crus
commune; *d. sc. lat.,* ductus semicircularis lateralis; *d. sc. post.,* ductus semicircularis posterior;
d. sc. sup., ductus semicircular superior; *coch. or cochlea,* ductus cochltaris; *duct. endolymph,*
ductus endolymphaticus; *d. reuniens,* ductus reuniens Henseni; *endol. or endolymphs* appendix
endolymphaticus; *rec. utr.,* recessus utriculi; *sacc.,* sacculus; *sac. endol.,* saccus endolymphaticus;
sinus utr. lat., sinus utriculi lateralis; *utric.,* utriculus; *vestib. p.,* vestibular pouch.

The **external acoustic meatus** is developed from the first branchial groove. The lower part of this groove extends inward as a funnel-shaped tube (primary meatus) from which the cartilaginous portion and a small part of the roof of the osseous portion of the meatus are developed. From the lower part of the funnel-shaped tube an epithelial lamina extends downward and inward along the inferior wall of the primitive tympanic cavity; by the splitting of this lamina the inner part of

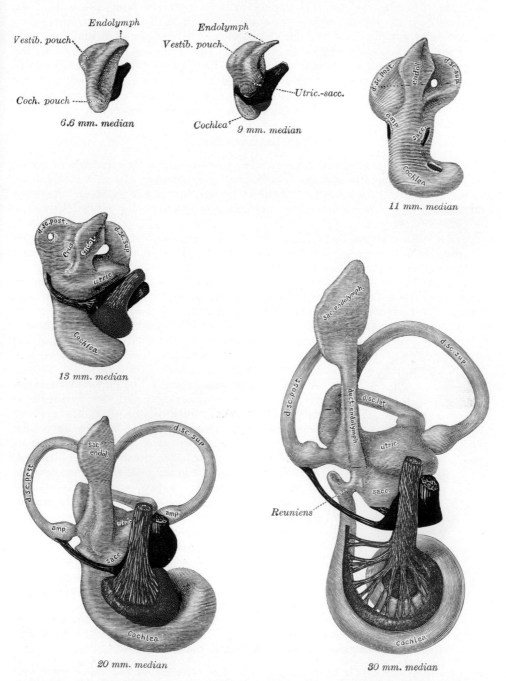

FIG. 922.—Median views of membranous labyrinth and acoustic complex in human embryos. × 25 dia. (Streeter.)

the meatus (secondary meatus) is produced, while the inner portion of the lamina forms the cutaneous stratum of the tympanic membrane. The **auricula** or **pinna** is developed by the gradual differentiation of tubercles which appear around the margin of the first branchial groove. The rudiment of the **acoustic nerve** appears about the end of the third week as a group of ganglion cells closely applied to the cephalic edge of the auditory vesicle. Whether these cells are derived from the ectoderm adjoining the auditory vesicle, or have migrated from the wall of the neural tube, is as yet uncertain. The ganglion gradually splits into two parts, the **vestibular ganglion** and the **spiral ganglion.** The peripheral branches of the vestibular ganglion pass in two divisions, the pars superior giving rami to the superior ampulla of the superior semicircular duct, to the lateral ampulla and to the utricle; and the pars inferior giving rami to the saccule and the posterior ampulla. The proximal fibers of the vestibular ganglion form the vestibular nerve; the proximal fibers of the spiral ganglion form the cochlear nerve.

The External Ear.

The **external ear** consists of the expanded portion named the **auricula** or **pinna,** and the **external acoustic meatus.** The former projects from the side of the head and serves to collect the vibrations of the air by which sound is produced; the latter leads inward from the bottom of the auricula and conducts the vibrations to the tympanic cavity.

The **Auricula** or **Pinna** (Fig. 923) is of an ovoid form, with its larger end directed upward. Its lateral surface is irregularly concave, directed slightly forward, and presents numerous eminences and depressions to which names have been assigned. The prominent rim of the auricula is called the **helix;** where the helix turns downward behind, a small tubercle, the **auricular tubercle of Darwin,** is frequently seen; this tubercle is very evident about the sixth month of fetal life when the whole auricula has a close resemblance to that of some of the adult monkeys. Another

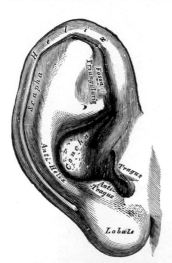

curved prominence, parallel with and in front of the helix, is called the **antihelix;** this divides above into two crura, between which is a triangular depression, the **fossa triangularis.** The narrow curved depression between the helix and the antihelix is called the **scapha;** the antihelix describes a curve around a deep, capacious cavity, the **concha,** which is partially divided into two parts by the **crus** or commencement of the helix; the upper part is termed the **cymba conchæ,** the lower part the **cavum conchæ.** In front of the concha, and projecting backward over the meatus, is a small pointed eminence, the **tragus,** so called from its being generally covered on its under surface with a tuft of hair, resembling a goat's beard. Opposite the tragus, and separated from it by the **intertragic notch,** is a small tubercle, the **antitragus.** Below this is the **lobule,** composed of tough areolar and adipose tissues, and wanting the firmness and elasticity of the rest of the auricula.

Fig. 923.—The auricula. Lateral surface.

The cranial surface of the auricula presents elevations which correspond to the depressions on its lateral surface and after which they are named, *e. g.,* **eminentia conchæ, eminentia triangularis,** etc.

Structure.—The auricula is composed of a thin plate of yellow fibrocartilage, covered with integument, and connected to the surrounding parts by ligaments and muscles; and to the commencement of the external acoustic meatus by fibrous tissue.

The **skin** is thin, closely adherent to the cartilage, and covered with fine hairs furnished with sebaceous glands, which are most numerous in the concha and scaphoid fossa. On the tragus and antitragus the hairs are strong and numerous. The skin of the auricula is continuous with that lining the external acoustic meatus.

The **cartilage of the auricula** (*cartilago auriculæ; cartilage of the pinna*) (Figs. 923, 924) consists of a single piece; it gives form to this part of the ear, and upon its surface are found the eminences and depressions above described. It is absent from the lobule; it is deficient, also, between the tragus and beginning of the helix, the gap being filled up by dense fibrous tissue. At the front part of the auricula, where the helix bends upward, is a small projection of cartilage, called the *spina helicis*, while in the lower part of the helix the cartilage is prolonged downward as a tail-like process, the **cauda helicis;** this is separated from the antihelix by a fissure, the **fissura antitragohelicina.** The cranial aspect of the cartilage exhibits a transverse furrow, the **sulcus antihelicis transversus,** which corresponds with the inferior crus of the antihelix and separates the eminentia conchæ from the eminentia triangularis. The eminentia conchæ is crossed by a vertical ridge (*ponticulus*), which gives attachment to the Auricularis posterior muscle. In the cartilage of the auricula are two fissures, one behind the crus helicis and another in the tragus.

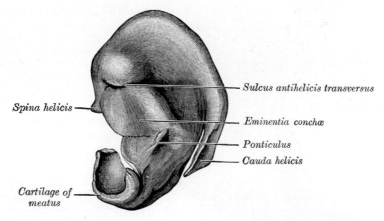

Spina helicis — — *Sulcus antihelicis transversus*

Eminentia conchæ

Ponticulus

Cauda helicis

Cartilage of meatus —

Fig. 924.—Cranial surface of cartilage of right auricula.

The **ligaments of the auricula** (*ligamenta auricularia* [*Valsalva*]; *ligaments of the pinna*) consist of two sets: (1) **extrinsic,** connecting it to the side of the head; (2) **intrinsic,** connecting various parts of its cartilage together.

The **extrinsic ligaments** are two in number, anterior and posterior. The *anterior ligament* extends from the tragus and spina helicis to the root of the zygomatic process of the temporal bone. The *posterior ligament* passes from the posterior surface of the concha to the outer surface of the mastoid process.

The chief **intrinsic ligaments** are: (*a*) a strong fibrous band, stretching from the tragus to the commencement of the helix, completing the meatus in front, and partly encircling the boundary of the concha; and (*b*) a band between the antihelix and the cauda helicis. Other less important bands are found on the cranial surface of the pinna.

The **muscles of the auricula** (Fig. 925) consist of two sets: (1) the **extrinsic,** which connect it with the skull and scalp and move the auricula as a whole; and (2) the **intrinsic,** which extend from one part of the auricle to another.

The **extrinsic muscles** are the Auriculares anterior, superior, and posterior.

The *Auricularis anterior* (*Attrahens aurem*), the smallest of the three, is thin, fan-shaped, and its fibers are pale and indistinct. It *arises* from the lateral edge of the galea aponeurotica, and its fibers converge to be inserted into a projection on the front of the helix.

The *Auricularis superior* (*Attolens aurem*), the largest of the three, is thin and fan-shaped. Its fibers *arise* from the galea aponeurotica, and converge to be inserted by a thin, flattened tendon into the upper part of the cranial surface of the auricula.

The *Auricularis posterior* (*Retrahens aurem*) consists of two or three fleshy fasciculi, which *arise* from the mastoid portion of the temporal bone by short aponeurotic fibers. They are inserted into the lower part of the cranial surface of the concha.

Actions.—In man, these muscles possess very little action: the Auricularis anterior draws the auricula forward and upward; the Auricularis superior slightly raises it; and the Auricularis posterior draws it backward.

The *intrinsic* muscles are the:

| Helicis major. | Tragicus. | Transversus auriculæ. |
| Helicis minor. | Antitragicus. | Obliquus auriculæ. |

The *Helicis major* is a narrow vertical band situated upon the anterior margin of the helix. It *arises* below, from the spina helicis, and is inserted into the anterior border of the helix, just where it is about to curve backward.

The *Helicis minor* is an oblique fasciculus, covering the crus helicis.

The *Tragicus* is a short, flattened vertical band on the lateral surface of the tragus.

The *Antitragicus arises* from the outer part of the antitragus, and is inserted into the cauda helicis and antihelix.

The *Transversus auriculæ* is placed on the cranial surface of the pinna. It consists of scattered fibers, partly tendinous and partly muscular, extending from the eminentia conchæ to the prominence corresponding with the scapha.

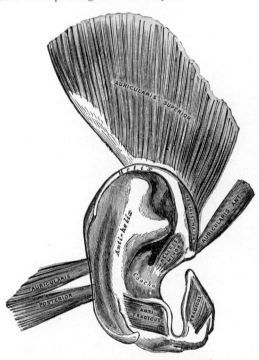

FIG. 925.—The muscles of the auricula.

The *Obliquus auriculæ*, also on the cranial surface, consists of a few fibers extending from the upper and back part of the concha to the convexity immediately above it.

Nerves.—The Auriculares anterior and superior and the intrinsic muscles on the lateral surface are supplied by the temporal branch of the facial nerve, the Auricularis posterior and the intrinsic muscles on the cranial surface by the posterior auricular branch of the same nerve.

The **arteries of the auricula** are the posterior auricular from the external carotid, the anterior auricular from the superficial temporal, and a branch from the occipital artery.

The **veins** accompany the corresponding arteries.

The **sensory nerves** are: the great auricular, from the cervical plexus; the auricular branch of the vagus; the auriculotemporal branch of the mandibular nerve; and the lesser occipital from the cervical plexus.

The **External Acoustic Meatus** (*meatus acusticus externus; external auditory canal or meatus*) extends from the bottom of the concha to the tympanic membrane (Figs. 926, 927). It is about 4 cm. in length if measured from the tragus; from the bottom of the concha its length is about 2.5 cm. It forms an S-shaped curve, and is directed at first inward, forward, and slightly upward (*pars externa*); it then passes inward and backward (*pars media*), and lastly is carried inward, forward, and slightly downward (*pars interna*). It is an oval cylindrical canal, the greatest diameter being directed downward and backward at the external orifice, but nearly horizontally at the inner end. It presents two constrictions, one near the inner end of the cartilaginous portion, and another, the **isthmus**, in the osseous portion, about 2 cm. from the bottom of the concha. The tympanic membrane, which closes the inner end of the meatus, is obliquely directed; in consequence of this the floor and anterior wall of the meatus are longer than the roof and posterior wall.

The external acoustic meatus is formed partly by cartilage and membrane, and partly by bone, and is lined by skin.

The **cartilaginous portion** (*meatus acusticus externus cartilagineus*) is about 8 mm. in length; it is continuous with the cartilage of the auricula, and firmly attached to the circumference of the auditory process of the temporal bone. The cartilage is deficient at the upper and back part of the meatus, its place being supplied by fibrous membrane; two or three deep fissures are present in the anterior part of the cartilage.

The **osseous portion** (*meatus acusticus externus osseus*) is about 16 mm. in length, and is narrower than the cartilaginous portion. It is directed inward and a little forward, forming in its course a slight curve the convexity of which is upward and backward. Its inner end is smaller than the outer, and sloped, the anterior wall

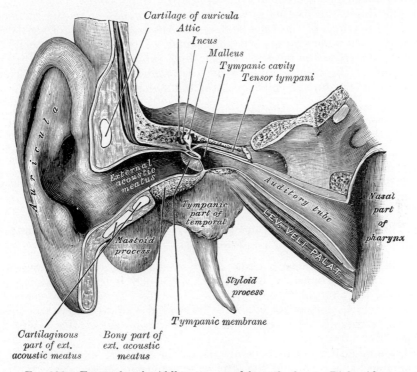

FIG. 926.—External and middle ear, opened from the front. Right side.

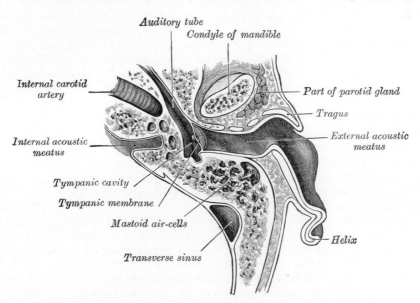

FIG. 927.—Horizontal section through left ear; upper half of section.

projecting beyond the posterior for about 4 mm.; it is marked, except at its upper part, by a narrow groove, the **tympanic sulcus,** in which the circumference of the tympanic membrane is attached. Its outer end is dilated and rough in the greater part of its circumference, for the attachment of the cartilage of the auricula. The front and lower parts of the osseous portion are formed by a curved plate of bone, the tympanic part of the temporal, which, in the fetus, exists as a separate ring **(annulus tympanicus,)** incomplete at its upper part (page 203).

The **skin** lining the meatus is very thin; adheres closely to the cartilaginous and osseous portions of the tube, and covers the outer surface of the tympanic membrane. After maceration, the thin pouch of epidermis, when withdrawn, preserves the form of the meatus. In the thick subcutaneous tissue of the cartilaginous part of the meatus are numerous ceruminous glands, which secrete the ear-wax; their structure resembles that of the sudoriferous glands.

Relations of the Meatus.—In front of the osseous part is the condyle of the mandible, which however, is frequently separated from the cartilaginous part by a portion of the parotid gland. The movements of the jaw influence to some extent the lumen of this latter portion. Behind the osseous part are the mastoid air cells, separated from the meatus by a thin layer of bone.

The **arteries** supplying the meatus are branches from the posterior auricular, internal maxillary, and temporal.

The **nerves** are chiefly derived from the auriculotemporal branch of the mandibular nerve and the auricular branch of the vagus.

The Middle Ear or Tympanic Cavity (Cavum Tympani; Drum; Tympanum).

The **middle ear** or **tympanic cavity** is an irregular, laterally compressed space within the temporal bone. It is filled with air, which is conveyed to it from the nasal part of the pharynx through the auditory tube. It contains a chain of movable bones, which connect its lateral to its medial wall, and serve to convey the vibrations communicated to the tympanic membrane across the cavity to the internal ear.

The tympanic cavity consists of two parts: the **tympanic cavity proper,** opposite the tympanic membrane, and the **attic** or **epitympanic recess,** above the level of the membrane; the latter contains the upper half of the malleus and the greater part of the incus. Including the attic, the vertical and antero-posterior diameters of the cavity are each about 15 mm. The transverse diameter measures about 6 mm. above and 4 mm. below; opposite the center of the tympanic membrane it is only about 2 mm. The tympanic cavity is bounded laterally by the tympanic membrane; medially, by the lateral wall of the internal ear; it communicates, behind, with the tympanic antrum and through it with the mastoid air cells, and in front with the auditory tube (Fig. 926).

The **Tegmental Wall** or **Roof** (*paries tegmentalis*) is formed by a thin plate of bone, the **tegmen tympani,** which separates the cranial and tympanic cavities. It is situated on the anterior surface of the petrous portion of the temporal bone close to its angle of junction with the squama temporalis; it is prolonged backward so as to roof in the tympanic antrum, and forward to cover in the semicanal for the Tensor tympani muscle. Its lateral edge corresponds with the remains of the petrosquamous suture.

The **Jugular Wall** or **Floor** (*paries jugularis*) is narrow, and consists of a thin plate of bone (**fundus tympani**) which separates the tympanic cavity from the jugular fossa. It presents, near the labyrinthic wall, a small aperture for the passage of the tympanic branch of the glossopharyngeal nerve.

The **Membranous** or **Lateral Wall** (*paries membranaceus; outer wall*) is formed mainly by the tympanic membrane, partly by the ring of bone into which this membrane is inserted. This ring of bone is incomplete at its upper part, forming a notch **(notch of Rivinus)**, close to which are three small apertures: the **iter chordæ posterius**, the **petrotympanic fissure**, and the **iter chordæ anterius**.

The **iter chordæ posterius** (*apertura tympanica canaliculi chordæ*) is situated in the angle of junction between the mastoid and membranous wall of the tympanic cavity immediately behind the tympanic membrane and on a level with the upper

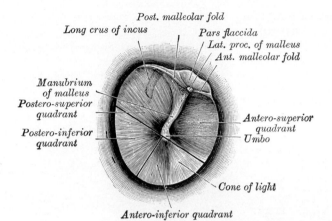

Fig. 928.—Right tympanic membrane as seen through a speculum.

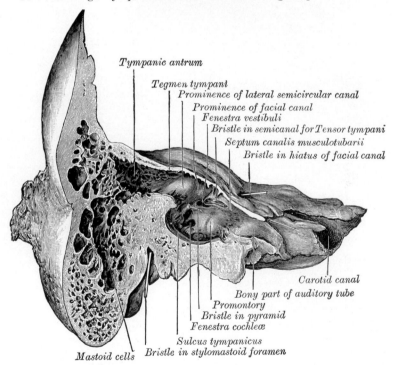

Fig. 929.—Coronal section of right temporal bone.

end of the manubrium of the malleus; it leads into a minute canal, which descends in front of the canal for the facial nerve, and ends in that canal near the stylomastoid foramen. Through it the chorda tympani nerve enters the tympanic cavity.

The **petrotympanic fissure** (*fissura petrotympanica; Glaserian fissure*) opens just above and in front of the ring of bone into which the tympanic membrane is inserted; in this situation it is a mere slit about 2 mm. in length. It lodges the anterior process and anterior ligament of the malleus, and gives passage to the anterior tympanic branch of the internal maxillary artery.

The **iter chordæ anterius** (*canal of Huguier*) is placed at the medial end of the petrotympanic fissure; through it the chorda tympani nerve leaves the tympanic cavity.

The **Tympanic Membrane** (*membrana tympani*) (Figs. 928, 930) separates the tympanic cavity from the bottom of the external acoustic meatus. It is a thin, semitransparent membrane, nearly oval in form, somewhat broader above than

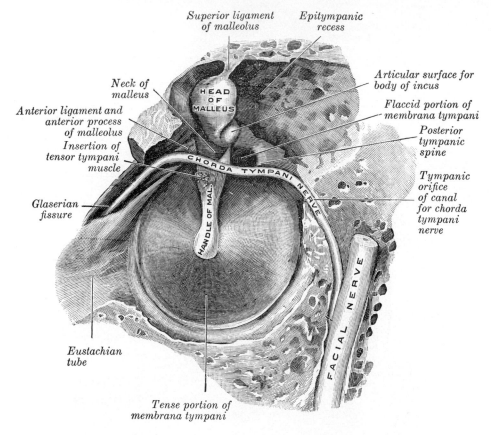

Fig. 930.—The right membrana tympani with the hammer and the chorda tympani, viewed from within, from behind and from above. (Spalteholz.)

below, and directed very obliquely downward and inward so as to form an angle of about fifty-five degrees with the floor of the meatus. Its longest diameter is downward and forward, and measures from 9 to 10 mm.; its shortest diameter measures from 8 to 9 mm. The greater part of its circumference is thickened, and forms a **fibrocartilaginous ring** which is fixed in the **tympanic sulcus** at the inner end of the meatus. This sulcus is deficient superiorly at the notch of Rivinus, and from the ends of this notch two bands, the **anterior** and **posterior malleolar folds**, are prolonged to the lateral process of the malleus. The small, somewhat triangular part of the membrane situated above these folds is lax and thin, and is named the **pars flaccida**; in it a small orifice is sometimes seen. The manubrium of the malleus is firmly attached to the medial surface of the membrane as far as its center, which it draws toward the tympanic cavity; the lateral surface of the membrane is thus concave, and the most depressed part of this concavity is named the **umbo**.

Structure.—The tympanic membrane is composed of three strata: a **lateral** (*cutaneous*), an **intermediate** (*fibrous*), and a **medial** (*mucous*). The **cutaneous stratum** is derived from the integument lining the meatus. The **fibrous stratum** consists of two layers: a radiate stratum, the fibers of which diverge from the manubrium of the malleus, and a circular stratum, the fibers of which are plentiful around the circumference but sparse and scattered near the center of the membrane. Branched or dendritic fibers, as pointed out by Grüber, are also present, especially in the posterior half of the membrane.

Vessels and Nerves.—The **arteries** of the tympanic membrane are derived from the deep auricular branch of the internal maxillary, which ramifies beneath the cutaneous stratum; and from the stylomastoid branch of the posterior auricular, and tympanic branch of the internal maxillary, which are distributed on the mucous surface. The superficial **veins** open into the external jugular; those on the deep surface drain partly into the transverse sinus and veins of the dura mater, and partly into a plexus on the auditory tube. The membrane receives its chief **nerve supply** from the auriculotemporal branch of the mandibular; the auricular branch of the vagus, and the tympanic branch of the glossopharyngeal also supply it.

The **Labyrinthic** or **Medial Wall** (*paries labyrinthicus*; *inner wall*) (Fig. 929) is vertical in direction, and presents for examination the **fenestræ vestibuli** and **cochleæ**, the **promontory**, and the **prominence of the facial canal.**

The **fenestra vestibuli** (*fenestra ovalis*) is a reniform opening leading from the tympanic cavity into the vestibule of the internal ear; its long diameter is horizontal, and its convex border is upward. In the recent state it is occupied by the base of the stapes, the circumference of which is fixed by the annular ligament to the margin of the foramen (Fig. 932).

The **fenestra cochleæ** (*fenestra rotunda*) is situated below and a little behind the fenestra vestibuli, from which it is separated by a rounded elevation, the **promontory.** It is placed at the bottom of a funnel-shaped depression and, in the macerated bone, leads into the cochlea of the internal ear; in the fresh state it is closed by a membrane, the **secondary tympanic membrane**, which is concave toward the tympanic cavity, convex toward the cochlea. This membrane consists of three layers: an external, or mucous, derived from the mucous lining of the tympanic cavity; an internal, from the lining membrane of the cochlea; and an intermediate, or fibrous layer.

The **promontory** (*promontorium*) is a rounded hollow prominence, formed by the projection outward of the first turn of the cochlea; it is placed between the fenestræ, and is furrowed on its surface by small grooves, for the lodgment of branches of the tympanic plexus. A minute spicule of bone frequently connects the promontory to the pyramidal eminence.

The **prominence of the facial canal** (*prominentia canalis facialis; prominence of aqueduct of Fallopius*) indicates the position of the bony canal in which the facial nerve is contained; this canal traverses the labyrinthic wall of the tympanic cavity above the fenestra vestibuli, and behind that opening curves nearly vertically downward along the mastoid wall.

The **Mastoid** or **Posterior Wall** (*paries mastoidus*) is wider above than below, and presents for examination the **entrance to the tympanic antrum**, the **pyramidal eminence**, and the **fossa incudis.**

The **entrance to the antrum** is a large irregular aperture, which leads backward from the epitympanic recess into a considerable air space, named the **tympanic** or **mastoid antrum** (see page 199). The antrum communicates behind and below with the **mastoid air cells**, which vary considerably in number, size, and form; the antrum and mastoid air cells are lined by mucous membrane, continuous with that lining the tympanic cavity. On the medial wall of the entrance to the antrum is a rounded eminence, situated above and behind the prominence of the facial canal; it corresponds with the position of the ampullated ends of the superior and lateral semicircular canals.

The **pyramidal eminence** (*eminentia pyramidalis; pyramid*) is situated immediately behind the fenestra vestibuli, and in front of the vertical portion of the facial canal; it is hollow, and contains the Stapedius muscle; its summit projects forward toward the fenestra vestibuli, and is pierced by a small aperture which transmits the tendon of the muscle. The cavity in the pyramidal eminence is prolonged downward and backward in front of the facial canal, and communicates with it by a minute aperture which transmits a twig from the facial nerve to the Stapedius muscle.

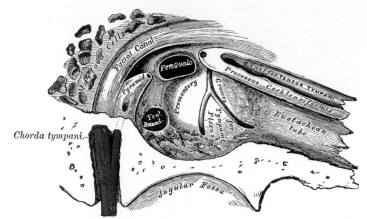

FIG. 931.—View of the inner wall of the tympanum (enlarged).

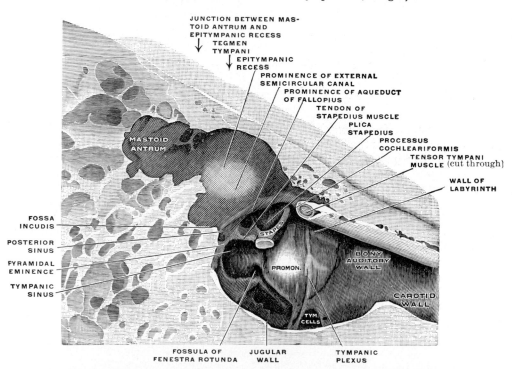

FIG. 932.—The medial wall and part of the posterior and anterior walls of the right tympanic cavity, lateral view. (Spalteholz.)

The **fossa incudis** is a small depression in the lower and back part of the epitympanic recess; it lodges the short crus of the incus.

The **Carotid** or **Anterior Wall** (*paries caroticus*) is wider above than below; it corresponds with the carotid canal, from which it is separated by a thin plate of bone perforated by the tympanic branch of the internal carotid artery, and by the carotico-tympanic nerve which connects the sympathetic plexus on the internal carotid artery with the tympanic plexus on the promontory. At the upper part of the anterior wall are the orifice of the semicanal for the Tensor tympani muscle and the tympanic orifice of the auditory tube, separated from each other by a thin horizontal plate of bone, the **septum canalis musculotubarii**. These canals run from the tympanic cavity forward and downward to the retiring angle between the squama and the petrous portion of the temporal bone.

The **semicanal for the Tensor tympani** (*semicanalis m. tensoris tympani*) is the superior and the smaller of the two; it is cylindrical and lies beneath the tegmen tympani. It extends on to the labyrinthic wall of the tympanic cavity and ends immediately above the fenestra vestibuli.

The **septum canalis musculotubarii** (*processus cochleariformis*) passes backward below this semicanal, forming its lateral wall and floor; it expands above the anterior end of the fenestra vestibuli and terminates there by curving laterally so as to form a pulley over which the tendon of the muscle passes.

The **Auditory Tube** (*tuba auditiva; Eustachian tube*) is the channel through which the tympanic cavity communicates with the nasal part of the pharynx. Its length is about 36 mm., and its direction is downward, forward, and medialward, forming an angle of about 45 degrees with the sagittal plane and one of from 30 to 40 degrees with the horizontal plane. It is formed partly of bone, partly of cartilage and fibrous tissue (Fig. 926).

The **osseous portion** (*pars ossea tubæ auditivæ*) is about 12 mm. in length. It begins in the carotid wall of the tympanic cavity, below the septum canalis musculotubarii, and, gradually narrowing, ends at the angle of junction of the squama and the petrous portion of the temporal bone, its extremity presenting a jagged margin which serves for the attachment of the cartilaginous portion.

The **cartilaginous portion** (*pars cartilaginea tubæ auditivæ*), about 24 mm. in length, is formed of a triangular plate of elastic fibrocartilage, the apex of which is attached to the margin of the medial end of the osseous portion of the tube, while its base lies directly under the mucous membrane of the nasal part of the pharynx, where it forms an elevation, the **torus tubarius** or **cushion**, behind the pharyngeal orifice of the tube. The upper edge of the cartilage is curled upon itself, being bent laterally so as to present on transverse section the appearance of a hook; a groove or furrow is thus produced, which is open below and laterally, and this part of the canal is completed by fibrous membrane. The cartilage lies in a groove between the petrous part of the temporal and the great wing of the sphenoid; this groove ends opposite the middle of the medial pterygoid plate. The cartilaginous and bony portions of the tube are not in the same plane, the former inclining downward a little more than the latter. The diameter of the tube is not uniform throughout, being greatest at the pharyngeal orifice, least at the junction of the bony and cartilaginous portions, and again increased toward the tympanic cavity; the narrowest part of the tube is termed the **isthmus**. The position and relations of the pharyngeal orifice are described with the nasal part of the pharynx. The mucous membrane of the tube is continuous in front with that of the nasal part of the pharynx, and behind with that of the tympanic cavity; it is covered with ciliated epithelium and is thin in the osseous portion, while in the cartilaginous portion it contains many mucous glands and near the pharyngeal orifice a considerable amount of adenoid tissue, which has been named by Gerlach the **tubal tonsil**. The tube is opened during deglutition by the Salpingopharyngeus and Dilatator tubæ. The latter arises from the hook of the cartilage and from the membranous part of the tube, and blends below with the Tensor veli palatini.

The Auditory Ossicles (Ossicula Auditus).

The tympanic cavity contains a chain of three movable ossicles, the **malleus, incus,** and **stapes.** The first is attached to the tympanic membrane, the last to the circumference of the fenestra vestibuli, the incus being placed between and connected to both by delicate articulations (Fig. 936).

The **Malleus** (Fig. 933), so named from its fancied resemblance to a hammer, consists of a **head, neck,** and three processes, *viz.,* the **manubrium,** the **anterior** and **lateral processes.**

The **head** (*caput mallei*) is the large upper extremity of the bone; it is oval in shape, and articulates posteriorly with the incus, being free in the rest of its extent. The facet for articulation with the incus is constricted near the middle, and consists of an upper larger and lower smaller part, which form nearly a right angle with each other. Opposite the constriction the lower margin of the facet projects in the form of a process, the **cog-tooth** or **spur of the malleus.**

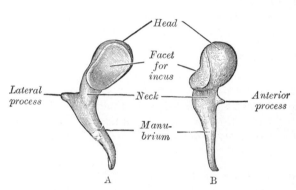

FIG. 933.—Left malleus. *A.* From behind. *B.* From within.

The **neck** (*collum mallei*) is the narrow contracted part just beneath the head; below it, is a a prominence, to which the various processes are attached.

The **manubrium mallei** (*handle*) is connected by its lateral margin with the tympanic membrane. It is directed downward, medialward, and backward; it decreases in size toward its free end, which is curved slightly forward, and flattened transversely. On its medial side, near its upper end, is a slight projection, into which the tendon of the Tensor tympani is inserted.

The **anterior process** (*processus anterior* [*Folii*]; *processus gracilis*) is a delicate spicule, which springs from the eminence below the neck and is directed forward to the petrotympanic fissure, to which it is connected by ligamentous fibers. In the fetus this is the longest process of the malleus, and is in direct continuity with the cartilage of Meckel.

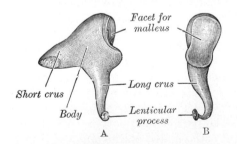

FIG. 934.—Left incus. *A.* From within. *B.* From the front.

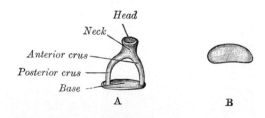

FIG. 935.—*A.* Left stapes. *B.* Base of stapes, medial surface.

The **lateral process** (*processus lateralis; processus brevis*) is a slight conical projection, which springs from the root of the manubrium; it is directed laterally, and is attached to the upper part of the tympanic membrane and, by means of the anterior and posterior malleolar folds, to the extremities of the notch of Rivinus.

The **Incus** (Fig. 934) has received its name from its supposed resemblance to an anvil, but it is more like a premolar tooth, with two roots, which differ in length, and are widely separated from each other. It consists of a **body** and **two crura.**

The **body** (*corpus incudis*) is somewhat cubical but compressed transversely. On its anterior surface is a deeply concavo-convex facet, which articulates with the head of the malleus.

The two crura diverge from one another nearly at right angles.

The **short crus** (*crus breve; short process*), somewhat conical in shape, projects almost horizontally backward, and is attached to the **fossa incudis,** in the lower and back part of the epitympanic recess.

The **long crus** (*crus longum; long process*) descends nearly vertically behind and parallel to the manubrium of the malleus, and, bending medialward, ends in a rounded projection, the **lenticular process,** which is tipped with cartilage, and articulates with the head of the stapes.

The **Stapes** (Fig. 935), so called from its resemblance to a stirrup, consists of a **head, neck, two crura, and a base.**

The **head** (*caput stapedis*) presents a depression, which is covered by cartilage, and articulates with the lenticular process of the incus.

The **neck,** the constricted part of the bone succeeding the head, gives insertion to the tendon of the Stapedius muscle.

The **two crura** (*crus anterius and crus posterius*) diverge from the neck and are connected at their ends by a flattened oval plate, the **base** (*basis stapedis*), which forms the foot-plate of the stirrup and is fixed to the margin of the fenestra vestibuli by a ring of ligamentous fibers. Of the two crura the anterior is shorter and less curved than the posterior.

Articulations of the Auditory Ossicles (*articulationes ossiculorum auditus*).— The incudomalleolar joint is a saddle-shaped diarthrosis; it is surrounded by an articular capsule, and the joint cavity is incompletely divided into two by a wedge-shaped articular disk or meniscus. The incudostapedial joint is an enarthrosis, surrounded by an articular capsule; some observers have described an articular disk or meniscus in this joint; others regard the joint as a syndesmosis.

Ligaments of the Ossicles (*ligamenta ossiculorum auditus*).—The ossicles are connected with the walls of the tympanic cavity by ligaments: three for the malleus, and one each for the incus and stapes.

The **anterior ligament of the malleus** (*lig. mallei anterius*) is attached by one end to the neck of the malleus, just above the anterior process, and by the other to the anterior wall of the tympanic cavity, close to the petrotympanic fissure, some of its fibers being prolonged through the fissure to reach the spina angularis of the sphenoid.

The **superior ligament of the malleus** (*lig. mallei superius*) is a delicate, round bundle which descends from the roof of the epitympanic recess to the head of the malleus.

The **lateral ligament of the malleus** (*lig. mallei laterale: external ligament of the malleus*) is a

72

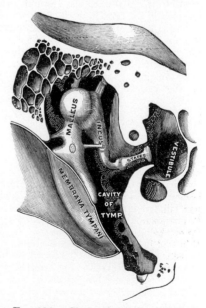

Fig. 936.—Chain of ossicles and their ligaments, seen from the front in a vertical, transverse section of the tympanum. (Testut.)

triangular band passing from the posterior part of the notch of Rivinus to the head of the malleus. Helmholtz described the anterior ligament and the posterior part of the lateral ligament as forming together the **axis ligament** around which the malleus rotates.

The **posterior ligament of the incus** (*lig. incudis posterius*) is a short, thick band connecting the end of the short crus of the incus to the fossa incudis.

A **superior ligament of the incus** (*lig. incudis superius*) has been described, but it is little more than a fold of mucous membrane.

The vestibular surface and the circumference of the base of the stapes are covered with hyaline cartilage; that encircling the base is attached to the margin of the fenestra vestibuli by a fibrous ring, the **annular ligament of the base of the stapes** (*lig. annulare baseos stapedis*).

The **Muscles of the Tympanic Cavity** (*musculi ossiculorum auditus*) are the Tensor tympani and Stapedius (Figs. 926, 932).

The **Tensor tympani**, the larger, is contained in the bony canal above the osseous portion of the auditory tube, from which it is separated by the septum canalis musculotubarii. It *arises* from the cartilaginous portion of the auditory tube and the adjoining part of the great wing of the sphenoid, as well as from the osseous canal in which it is contained. Passing backward through the canal, it ends in a slender tendon which enters the tympanic cavity, makes a sharp bend around the extremity of the septum, the processus cochleariformis, and is inserted into the manubrium of the malleus, near its root. It is supplied by a branch of the mandibular nerve which passes through the otic ganglion.

The **Stapedius** *arises* from the wall of a conical cavity, hollowed out of the interior of the pyramidal eminence; its tendon emerges from the orifice at the apex of the eminence, and, passing forward, is inserted into the posterior surface of the neck of the stapes. It is supplied by a branch of the facial nerve.

Actions.—The Tensor tympani draws the tympanic membrane medialward, and thus increases its tension. The Stapedius pulls the head of the stapes backward and thus causes the base of the bone to rotate on a vertical axis drawn through its own center; the back part of the base is pressed inward toward the vestibule, while the forepart is withdrawn from it. By the action of the muscle the tension of the fluid within the internal ear is probably increased.

The **Mucous Membrane of the Tympanic Cavity** is continuous with that of the pharynx, through the auditory tube. It invests the auditory ossicles, and the muscles and nerves contained in the tympanic cavity; forms the medial layer of the tympanic membrane, and the lateral layer of the secondary tympanic membrane, and is reflected into the tympanic antrum and mastoid cells, which it lines throughout. It forms several vascular folds, which extend from the walls of the tympanic cavity to the ossicles; of these, one descends from the roof of the cavity to the head of the malleus and upper margin of the body of the incus, a second invests the Stapedius muscle: other folds invest the chorda tympani nerve and the Tensor tympani muscle. These folds separate off pouch-like cavities, and give the interior of the tympanum a somewhat honey-combed appearance. One of these pouches, the **pouch of Prussak**, is well-marked and lies between the neck of the malleus and the membrana flaccida. Two other recesses may be mentioned: they are formed by the mucous membrane which envelops the chorda tympani nerve and are situated, one in front of, and the other behind the manubrium of the malleus; they are named the **anterior** and **posterior recesses of Troltsch**. In the tympanic cavity this membrane is pale, thin, slightly vascular, and covered for the most part with columnar ciliated epithelium, but over the pyramidal eminence, ossicles, and tympanic membrane it possesses a flattened non-ciliated epithelium. In the tympanic antrum and mastoid cells its epithelium is also non-ciliated. In the osseous portion of the auditory tube the membrane is thin; but in the cartilaginous portion it is very thick, highly vascular, and provided with numerous mucous glands; the epithelium which lines the tube is columnar and ciliated.

Vessels and Nerves.—The **arteries** are six in number. Two of them are larger than the others, *viz.*, the tympanic branch of the internal maxillary, which supplies the tympanic membrane; and the stylomastoid branch of the posterior auricular, which supplies the back part of the tympanic cavity and mastoid cells. The smaller arteries are—the petrosal branch of the middle meningeal, which enters through the hiatus of the facial canal; a branch from the ascending pharyngeal, and another from the artery of the pterygoid canal, which accompany the auditory tube; and the tympanic branch from the internal carotid, given off in the carotid canal and perforating the thin anterior wall of the tympanic cavity. The **veins** terminate in the pterygoid plexus and the superior petrosal sinus. The **nerves** constitute the tympanic plexus, which ramifies upon the surface of the promontory. The plexus is formed by (1) the tympanic branch of the glossopharyngeal; (2) the caroticotympanic nerves; (3) the smaller superficial petrosal nerve; and (4) a branch which joins the greater superficial petrosal.

The **tympanic branch of the glossopharyngeal** (*Jacobson's nerve*) enters the tympanic cavity by an aperture in its floor close to the labyrinthic wall, and divides into branches which ramify on the promontory and enter into the formation of the tympanic plexus. The **superior and inferior caroticotympanic nerves** from the carotid plexus of the sympathetic pass through the wall of the carotid canal, and join the branches of the tympanic branch of the glossopharyngeal. The branch to the greater superficial petrosal passes through an opening on the labyrinthic wall, in front of the fenestra vestibuli. The **smaller superficial petrosal nerve** is a continuation of the tympanic branch of the glossopharyngeal nerve beyond the tympanic plexus. It penetrates the bone near the geniculate ganglion of the facial nerve with which it communicates by a filament, continues upward through the bone, and enters the middle cranial fossa through a small aperture situated lateral to the hiatus of the facial canal on the anterior surface of the petrous portion of the temporal bone. It leaves the middle fossa through a fissure or foramen of its own or through the foramen ovale, and ends in the otic ganglion, constituting its root and supplying it with preganglionic parasympathetic fibers.

The **branches of distribution** of the tympanic plexus are supplied to the mucous membrane of the tympanic cavity; a branch passes to the fenestra vestibuli, another to the fenestra cochleæ, and a third to the auditory tube. The smaller superficial petrosal may be looked upon as the continuation of the tympanic branch of the glossopharyngeal through the plexus to the otic ganglion.

In addition to the tympanic plexus there are the nerves supplying the muscles. The Tensor tympani is supplied by a branch from the mandibular which passes through the otic ganglion, and the Stapedius by a branch from the facial.

The **chorda tympani nerve** crosses the tympanic cavity. It is given off from the sensory part of the facial, about 6 mm. before the nerve emerges from the stylomastoid foramen. It runs from below upward and forward in a canal, and enters the tympanic cavity through the iter chordæ posterius, and becomes invested with mucous membrane. It traverses the tympanic cavity, crossing medial to the tympanic membrane and over the upper part of the manubrium of the malleus to the carotid wall, where it emerges through the iter chordæ anterius (*canal of Huguier*).

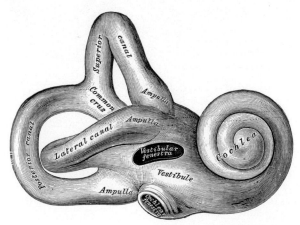

Fig. 937.—Right osseous labyrinth with spongy bone removed. Lateral view.

The Internal Ear or Labyrinth (Auris Interna).

The **internal ear** is the essential part of the organ of hearing, receiving the ultimate distribution of the auditory nerve. It is called the **labyrinth**, from the complexity of its shape, and consists of two parts: the **osseous labyrinth**, a series of cavities within the petrous part of the temporal bone, and the **membranous labyrinth**, a series of communicating membranous sacs and ducts, contained within the bony cavities.

The Osseous Labyrinth (*labyrinthus osseus*) (Figs. 937, 938).—The osseous labyrinth consists of three parts: the **vestibule, semicircular canals,** and **cochlea.** These are cavities hollowed out of the substance of the bone, and lined by periosteum; they contain a clear fluid, the **perilymph,** in which the membranous labyrinth is situated.

The Vestibule (*vestibulum*).—The vestibule is the central part of the osseous labyrinth, and is situated medial to the tympanic cavity, behind the cochlea, and in front of the semicircular canals. It is somewhat ovoid in shape, but flattened transversely; it measures about 5 mm. from before backward, the same from above downward, and about 3 mm. across. In its *lateral* or *tympanic wall* is the **fenestra vestibuli,** closed, in the fresh state, by the base of the stapes and annular ligament. On its *medial wall*, at the forepart, is a small circular depression, the **recessus sphæricus,** which is perforated, at its anterior and inferior part, by several minute holes (**macula cribrosa media**) for the passage of filaments of the acoustic nerve to the saccule; and behind this depression is an oblique ridge, the **crista vestibuli,** the anterior end of which is named the **pyramid of the vestibule.** This ridge bifurcates below to enclose a small depression, the **fossa cochlearis,** which is perforated

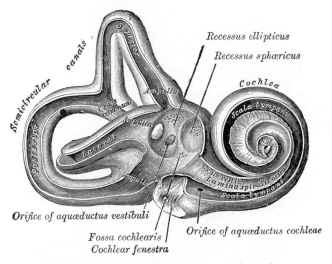

FIG. 938.—Interior of right osseous labyrinth.

by a number of holes for the passage of filaments of the acoustic nerve which supply the vestibular end of the ductus cochlearis. At the hinder part of the medial wall is the orifice of the **aquæductus vestibuli,** which extends to the posterior surface of the petrous portion of the temporal bone. It transmits a small vein, and contains a tubular prolongation of the membranous labyrinth, the **ductus endolymphaticus,** which ends in a cul-de-sac between the layers of the dura mater within the cranial cavity. On the *upper wall* or *roof* is a transversely oval depression, the **recessus ellipticus,** separated from the recessus sphæricus by the crista vestibuli already mentioned. The pyramid and adjoining part of the recessus ellipticus are perforated by a number of holes (**macula cribrosa superior**). The apertures in the pyramid transmit the nerves to the utricle; those in the recessus ellipticus the nerves to the ampullæ of the superior and lateral semicircular ducts. *Behind* are the five orifices of the semicircular canals. In *front* is an elliptical opening, which communicates with the scala vestibuli of the cochlea.

The Bony Semicircular Canals (*canales semicirculares ossei*).—The bony semicircular canals are three in number, **superior, posterior,** and **lateral,** and are situated above and behind the vestibule. They are unequal in length, compressed from side to side, and each describes the greater part of a circle. Each measures about 0.8 mm. in diameter, and presents a dilatation at one end, called the **ampulla,** which measures more than twice the diameter of the tube. They open into the vestibule by five orifices, one of the apertures being common to two of the canals.

The **superior semicircular canal** (*canalis semicircularis anterior*), 15 to 20 mm. in length, is vertical in direction, and is placed transversely to the long axis of the petrous portion of the temporal bone, on the anterior surface of which its arch forms a round projection. It describes about two-thirds of a circle. Its lateral extremity is ampullated, and opens into the upper part of the vestibule; the opposite end joins with the upper part of the posterior canal to form the **crus commune,** which opens into the upper and medial part of the vestibule.

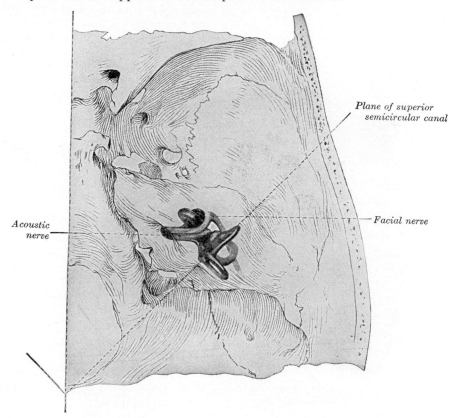

Plane of superior semicircular canal

Facial nerve

Acoustic nerve

FIG. 939.—Position of the right bony labyrinth of the ear in the skull, viewed from above. The temporal bone is considered transparent and the labyrinth drawn in from a corrosion preparation. (Spalteholz.)

The **posterior semicircular canal** (*canalis semicircularis posterior*), also vertical, is directed backward, nearly parallel to the posterior surface of the petrous bone; it is the longest of the three, measuring from 18 to 22 mm.; its lower or ampullated end opens into the lower and back part of the vestibule, its upper into the crus commune already mentioned.

The **lateral** or **horizontal canal** (*canalis semicircularis lateralis; external semicircular canal*) is the shortest of the three. It measures from 12 to 15 mm., and its arch is directed horizontally backward and lateralward; thus each semicircular canal stands at right angles to the other two. Its ampullated end corresponds to the upper and lateral angle of the vestibule, just above the fenestra vestibuli, where it opens close to the ampullated end of the superior canal; its opposite end opens at the upper and back part of the vestibule. The lateral canal of one ear is very nearly in the same plane as that of the other; while the superior canal of one ear is nearly parallel to the posterior canal of the other.

The **Cochlea** (Figs. 937, 938).—The cochlea bears some resemblance to a common snail-shell; it forms the anterior part of the labyrinth, is conical in form, and placed almost horizontally in front of the vestibule; its **apex** (*cupula*) is directed forward and lateralward, with a slight inclination downward, toward the upper and front part of the labyrinthic wall of the tympanic cavity; its **base** corresponds with the bottom of the internal acoustic meatus, and is perforated by numerous apertures for the passage of the cochlear division of the acoustic nerve. It measures about 5 mm. from base to apex, and its breadth across the base is about 9 mm. It consists of a conical shaped central axis, the **modiolus**; of a canal, the inner wall of which is formed by the central axis, wound spirally around it for two turns and three quarters, from the base to the apex; and of a delicate lamina, the **osseous spiral**

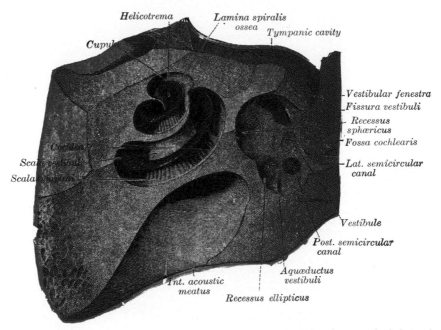

FIG. 940.—The cochlea and vestibule, viewed from above. All the hard parts which form the roof of the internal ear have been removed with the saw.

lamina, which projects from the modiolus, and, following the windings of the canal, partially subdivides it into two. In the recent state a membrane, the **basilar membrane**, stretches from the free border of this lamina to the outer wall of the bony cochlea and completely separates the canal into two passages, which, however, communicate with each other at the apex of the modiolus by a small opening, named the **helicotrema**.

The **modiolus** is the conical central axis or pillar of the cochlea. Its base is broad, and appears at the bottom of the internal acoustic meatus, where it corresponds with the area cochleæ; it is perforated by numerous orifices, which transmit filaments of the cochlear division of the acoustic nerve; the nerves for the first turn and a half pass through the foramina of the tractus spiralis foraminosus; those for the apical turn, through the foramen centrale. The canals of the tractus spiralis foraminosus pass up through the modiolus and successively bend outward to reach the attached margin of the lamina spiralis ossea. Here they become enlarged, and by their apposition form the **spiral canal of the modiolus,** which follows the course of the attached margin of the osseous spiral lamina and lodges the **spiral ganglion** (*ganglion of Corti*). The foramen centrale is continued into a canal which runs up the middle of the modiolus to its apex. The modiolus diminishes rapidly in size in the second and succeeding coil.

The bony canal of the cochlea takes two turns and three-quarters around the modiolus. It is about 30 mm. in length, and diminishes gradually in diameter from the base to the summit, where it terminates in the **cupula,** which forms the apex of the cochlea. The beginning of this canal is about 3 mm. in diameter; it diverges from the modiolus toward the tympanic cavity and vestibule, and presents three openings. One, the **fenestra cochleæ,** communicates with the tympanic cavity—in the fresh state this aperture is closed by the **secondary tympanic membrane;** another, of an elliptical form, opens into the vestibule. The third is the aperture of the aquæductus cochleæ, leading to a minute funnel-shaped canal, which opens on the inferior surface of the petrous part of the temporal bone and transmits a small vein, and also forms a communication between the subarachnoid cavity and the scala tympani.

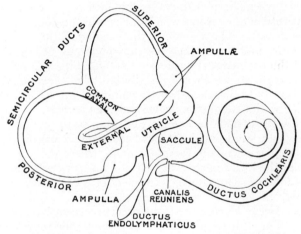

Fig. 941.—The membranous labyrinth. (Enlarged.)

The **osseous spiral lamina** (*lamina spiralis ossea*) is a bony shelf or ledge which projects from the modiolus into the interior of the canal, and, like the canal, takes two- and three-quarter turns around the modiolus. It reaches about half-way toward the outer wall of the tube, and partially divides its cavity into two passages or scalæ, of which the upper is named the **scala vestibuli,** while the lower is termed the **scala tympani.** Near the summit of the cochlea the lamina ends in a hook-shaped process, the **hamulus laminæ spiralis;** this assists in forming the boundary of a small opening, the **helicotrema,** through which the two scalæ communicate with each other. From the spiral canal of the modiolus numerous canals pass outward through the osseous spiral lamina as far as its free edge. In the lower part of the first turn a second bony lamina, the **secondary spiral lamina,** projects inward from the outer wall of the bony tube; it does not, however, reach the primary osseous spiral lamina, so that if viewed from the vestibule a narrow fissure, the **vestibule fissure,** is seen between them.

The *osseous labyrinth* is lined by an exceedingly thin fibro-serous membrane; its attached surface is rough and fibrous, and closely adherent to the bone; its free surface is smooth and pale, covered with a layer of epithelium, and secretes a thin, limpid fluid, the **perilymph**. A delicate tubular process of this membrane is prolonged along the aqueduct of the cochlea to the inner surface of the dura mater.

The Membranous Labyrinth (*labyrinthus membranaceus*) (Figs. 941, 942, 943).— The membranous labyrinth is lodged within the bony cavities just described, and has the same general form as these; it is, however, considerably smaller, and is partly separated from the bony walls by a quantity of fluid, the **perilymph**. In certain places it is fixed to the walls of the cavity. The membranous labyrinth contains fluid, the **endolymph**, and on its walls the ramifications of the acoustic nerve are distributed.

Within the osseous vestibule the membranous labyrinth does not quite preserve the form of the bony cavity, but consists of two membranous sacs, the **utricle**, and the **saccule**.

The Utricle (*utriculus*).—The utricle, the larger of the two, is of an oblong form, compressed transversely, and occupies the upper and back part of the vestibule, lying in contact with the recessus ellipticus and the part below it. That portion which is lodged in the recess forms a sort of pouch or cul-de-sac, the floor and anterior wall of which are thickened, and form the **macula acustica utriculi**, which receives the utricular filaments of the acoustic nerve. The cavity of the utricle communicates behind with the semicircular ducts by five orifices. From its anterior wall is given off the **ductus utriculosaccularis**, which opens into the ductus endolymphaticus.

The Saccule (*sacculus*).—The saccule is the smaller of the two vestibular sacs; it is globular in form, and lies in the recessus sphæricus near the opening of the scala vestibuli of the cochlea. Its anterior part exhibits an oval thickening, the **macula acustica sacculi**, to which are distributed the saccular filaments of the acoustic nerve. Its cavity does not directly communicate with that of the utricle. From the posterior wall a canal, the **ductus endolymphaticus**, is given off; this duct is joined by the ductus utriculosaccularis, and then passes along the aquæductus vestibuli and ends in a blind pouch **(saccus endolymphaticus)** on the posterior surface of the petrous portion of the temporal bone, where it is in contact with the dura mater. From the lower part of the saccule a short tube, the **canalis reuniens of Hensen**, passes downward and opens into the ductus cochlearis near its vestibular extremity (Fig. 941).

The Semicircular Ducts (*ductus semicirculares; membranous semicircular canals*), (Figs. 942, 943).—The semicircular ducts are about one-fourth of the diameter of the osseous canals, but in number, shape, and general form they are precisely similar, and each presents at one end an ampulla. They open by five orifices into the utricle, one opening being common to the medial end of the superior and the upper end of the posterior duct. In the ampullæ the wall is thickened, and projects into the cavity as a fiddle-shaped, transversely placed elevation, the **septum transversum**, in which the nerves end.

The utricle, saccule, and semicircular ducts are held in position by numerous fibrous bands which stretch across the space between them and the bony walls.

Structure (Fig. 944).—The walls of the utricle, saccule, and semicircular ducts consist of three layers. The *outer layer* is a loose and flocculent structure, apparently composed of ordinary fibrous tissue containing bloodvessels and some pigment-cells. The *middle layer*, thicker and more transparent, forms a homogeneous membrana propria, and presents on its internal surface, especially in the semicircular ducts, numerous papilliform projections, which, on the addition of acetic acid, exhibit an appearance of longitudinal fibrillation. The *inner layer* is formed of polygonal nucleated epithelial cells. In the maculæ of the utricle and saccule, and in the transverse septa of the ampullæ of the semicircular ducts, the middle coat is thickened and the epithelium is columnar, and consists of **supporting cells** and **hair cells**. The former are fusiform, and their deep ends are attached to the membrana propria, while their free extremities are united to form a thin cuticle. The hair cells are flask-shaped, and their deep, rounded ends do not reach the membrana propria, but lie between the supporting cells. The deep part of each contains a large nucleus, while its more superficial part is granular and pigmented. The free end

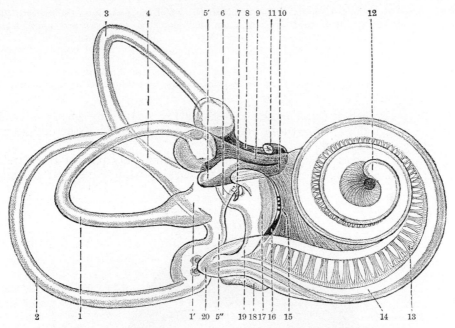

FIG. 942.—Right human membranous labyrinth, removed from its bony enclosure and viewed from the antero-lateral aspect. (G. Retzius.)

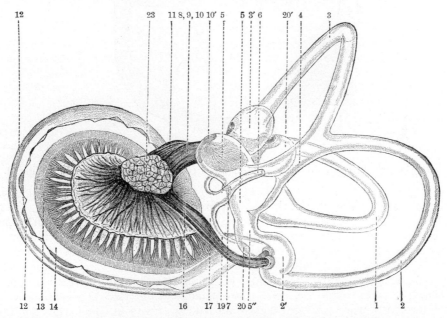

FIG. 943.—The same from the postero-medial aspect. 1. Lateral semicircular canal; 1′, its ampulla; 2. Posterior canal; 2′, its ampulla. 3. Superior canal; 3′, its ampulla. 4. Conjoined limb of superior and posterior canals (*sinus utriculi superior*). 5. Utricle. 5′. Recessus utriculi. 5″. Sinus utriculi posterior. 6. Ductus endolymphaticus. 7. Canalis utriculosaccularis. 8. Nerve to ampulla of superior canal. 9. Nerve to ampulla of lateral canal. 10. Nerve to recessus utriculi (in Fig. 942, the three branches appear conjoined). 10′. Ending of nerve in recessus utriculi. 11. Facial nerve. 12. Lagena cochleæ. 13. Nerve of cochlea within spiral lamina. 14. Basilar membrane. 15. Nerve fibers to macula of saccule. 16. Nerve to ampulla of posterior canal. 17. Saccule. 18. Secondary membrane of tympanum. 19. Canalis reuniens. 20. Vestibular end of ductus cochlearis. 23. Section of the facial and acoustic nerves within internal acoustic meatus. The separation between them is not apparent in the section. (G. Retzius.)

is surmounted by a long, tapering, hair-like filament, which projects into the cavity. The filaments of the acoustic nerve enter these parts, and having pierced the outer and middle layers, they lose their medullary sheaths, and their axis-cylinders ramify between the hair cells.

Two small rounded bodies termed **otoconia**, each consisting of a mass of minute crystalline grains of carbonate of lime, held together in a mesh of gelatinous tissue, are suspended in the endolymph in contact with the free ends of the hairs projecting from the maculæ. According to Bowman, a calcareous material is also sparingly scattered in the cells lining the ampullæ of the semicircular ducts.

The Ductus Cochlearis (*membranous cochlea; scala media*).—The ductus cochlearis consists of a spirally arranged tube enclosed in the bony canal of the cochlea and lying along its outer wall.

As already stated, the osseous spiral lamina extends only part of the distance between the modiolus and the outer wall of the cochlea, while the **basilar membrane**

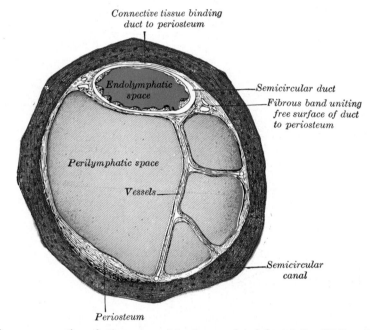

Fig. 944.—Transverse section of a human semicircular canal and duct (after Rüdinger).

stretches from its free edge to the outer wall of the cochlea, and completes the roof of the scala tympani. A second and more delicate membrane, the **vestibular membrane** (*Reissneri*) extends from the thickened periosteum covering the osseous spiral lamina to the outer wall of the cochlea, where it is attached at some little distance above the outer edge of the basilar membrane. A canal is thus shut off between the scala tympani below and the scala vestibuli above; this is the **ductus cochlearis** or **scala media** (Fig. 945). It is triangular on transverse section, its roof being formed by the vestibular membrane, its outer wall by the periosteum lining the bony canal, and its floor by the membrana basilaris and the outer part of the lamina spiralis ossea. Its extremities are closed; the upper is termed the **lagena** and is attached to the cupula at the upper part of the helicotrema; the lower is lodged in the recessus cochlearis of the vestibule. Near the lower end the ductus cochlearis is brought into continuity with the saccule by a narrow, short canal, the **canalis reuniens of Hensen** (Fig. 941). On the membrana basilaris is situated the spiral organ of Corti. The vestibular membrane is thin and homogeneous, and is covered on its upper and under surfaces by a layer of epithelium. The periosteum, forming the outer wall of the ductus cochlearis, is greatly thickened and altered in character, and is called the **spiral ligament**. It projects inward below as a triangular prominence, the **basilar crest,** which gives attachment to the outer edge of the basilar membrane; immediately above the crest is a concavity, the **sulcus spiralis externus.** The upper portion of the spiral ligament contains numerous capillary loops and small bloodvessels, and is termed the **stria vascularis.**

The osseous spiral lamina consists of two plates of bone, and between these are the canals for the transmission of the filaments of the acoustic nerve. On the upper plate of that part of the lamina which is outside the vestibular membrane, the perios-

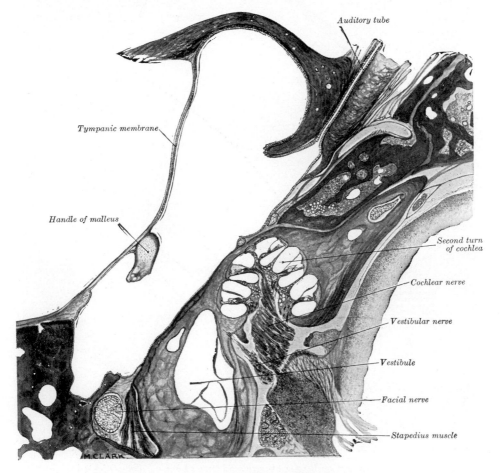

FIG. 945.—A section through the left temporal bone. (Drawn from a section prepared at the Ferens Institute, kindly lent by Prof. J. Kirk.)

teum is thickened to form the **limbus laminæ spiralis** (Fig. 946), this ends externally in a concavity, the **sulcus spiralis internus,** which represents, on section, the form of the letter C; the upper part, formed by the overhanging extremity of the limbus, is named the **vestibular lip;** the lower part, prolonged and tapering, is called the **tympanic lip,** and is perforated by numerous foramina for the passage of the cochlear nerves. The upper surface of the vestibular lip is intersected at right angles by a number of furrows, between which are numerous elevations; these present the appearance of teeth along the free surface and margin of the lip, and have been named by Huschke the **auditory teeth.** The limbus is covered by a layer of what appears to be squamous epithelium, but the deeper parts of the cells with their contained nuclei occupy the intervals between the elevations and between the auditory teeth. This layer of epithelium is continuous on the one hand with that lining the sulcus spiralis internus, and on the other with that covering the under surface of the vestibular membrane.

Basilar Membrane.—The basilar membrane stretches from the tympanic lip of the osseous spiral lamina to the basilar crest and consists of two parts, an inner and an outer. The inner is thin, and is named the **zona arcuata**: it supports the spiral

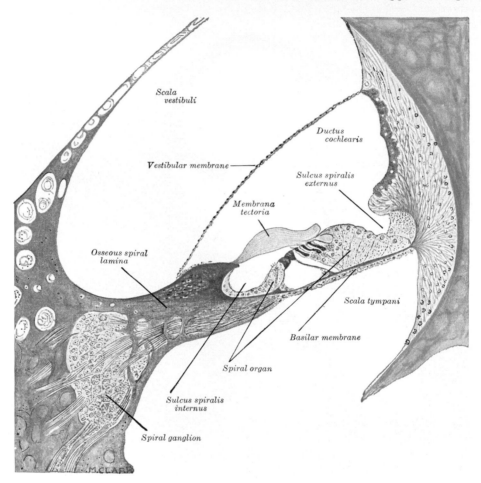

Fig. 946.—A section through the second turn of the cochlea indicated in the previous figure. (Mallory's stain.)

organ of Corti. The outer is thicker and striated, and is termed the **zona pectinata**. The under surface of the membrane is covered by a layer of vascular connective tissue; one of the vessels in this tissue is somewhat larger than the rest, and is named the **vas spirale**; it lies below Corti's tunnel.

The **spiral organ of Corti** (*organon spirale* [*Corti*]; *organ of Corti*) (Fig. 947) is composed of a series of epithelial structures placed upon the inner part of the basilar membrane. The average length is 31.5 mm. The more central of these structures are two rows of rod-like bodies, the **inner and outer rods** or **pillars of Corti**. The bases of the rods are supported on the basilar membrane, those of the inner row at some distance from those of the outer; the two rows incline toward each other and, coming into contact above, enclose between them and the basilar membrane a triangular tunnel, the **tunnel of Corti**. On the inner side of the inner rods is a single row of hair cells, and on the outer side of the outer rods three or four rows of similar cells, together with certain supporting cells termed the cells of Deiters and Hensen. The free ends of the outer hair cells occupy a series of apertures in a net-like membrane, the **reticular membrane**, and the entire organ is covered by the tectorial membrane.

RODS OF CORTI.—Each of these consists of a base or foot-plate, and elongated part or body, and an upper end or head; the body of each rod is finely striated, but in the head there is an oval non-striated portion which stains deeply with carmine. Occupying the angles between the rods and the basilar membrane are nucleated cells which partly envelop the rods and extend on to the floor of Corti's tunnel; these may be looked upon as the undifferentiated parts of the cells from which the rods have been formed.

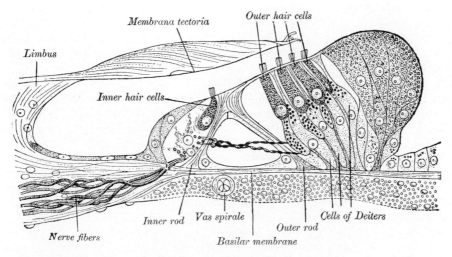

FIG. 947.—Section through the spiral organ of Corti. Magnified. (G. Retzius.)

The **inner rods** number nearly 6000, and their bases rest on the basilar membrane close to the tympanic lip of the sulcus spiralis internus. The shaft or body of each is sinuously curved and forms an angle of about 60 degrees with the basilar membrane. The head resembles the proximal end of the ulna and presents a deep concavity which accommodates a convexity on the head of the outer rod. The head-plate, or portion overhanging the concavity, overlaps the head-plate of the outer rod.

The **outer rods**, nearly 4000 in number, are longer and more obliquely set than the inner, forming with the basilar membrane an angle of about 40 degrees. Their heads are convex internally; they fit into the concavities on the heads of the inner rods and are continued outward as thin flattened plates, termed **phalangeal processes**, which unite with the phalangeal processes of Deiters' cells to form the reticular membrane.

Hair Cells.—The hair cells are short columnar cells; their free ends are on a level with the heads of Corti's rods, and each is surmounted by about twenty hair-like processes arranged in the form of a crescent with its concavity directed inward. The deep ends of the cells reach about half-way along Corti's rods, and each contains a large nucleus; in contact with the deep ends of the hair cells are the terminal filaments of the cochlear division of the acoustic nerve. The *inner* hair cells, about 3500 in number, are arranged in a single row on the medial side of the inner rods, and their diameters being greater than those of the rods it follows that each hair cell is supported by more than one rod. The free ends of the inner hair cells are encircled by a cuticular membrane which is fixed to the heads of the inner rods. Adjoining the inner hair cells are one or two rows of columnar supporting cells, which, in turn, are continuous with the cubical cells lining the sulcus spiralis internus. The *outer* hair cells number about 12,000, and are nearly twice as long as the inner. In the basal coil of the cochlea they are arranged in three regular rows; in the apical coil, in four, somewhat irregular, rows. The studies of Crowe, Guild and Polvogt show that the receptors for high tones are located in the basal turn of the cochlea.

Between the rows of the outer hair cells are rows of supporting cells, called the **cells of Deiters;** their expanded bases are planted on the basilar membrane, while the opposite end of each presents a clubbed extremity or **phalangeal process.** Immediately to the outer side of Deiters' cells are five or six rows of columnar cells, the **supporting cells of Hensen.** Their bases are narrow, while their upper parts are expanded and form a rounded elevation on the floor of the ductus cochlearis. The columnar cells lying outside Hensen's cells are termed the **cells of Claudius.** A space exists between the outer rods of Corti and the adjacent hair cells; this is called the **space of Nuel.**

The **reticular lamina** (Fig. 947) is a delicate frame-work perforated by rounded holes which are occupied by the free ends of the outer hair cells. It extends from the heads of the outer rods of Corti to the external row of the outer hair cells, and is formed by several rows of "minute fiddle-shaped cuticular structures," called **phalanges,** between which are circular apertures containing the free ends of the hair cells. The inner most row of phalanges consists of the phalangeal processes of the outer rods of Corti; the outer rows are formed by the modified free ends of Deiters' cells.

Covering the sulcus spiralis internus and the spiral organ of Corti is the **tectorial membrane,** which is attached to the limbus laminæ spiralis close to the inner edge of the vestibular membrane. Its inner part is thin and overlies the auditory teeth of Huschke; its outer part is thick, and along its lower surface, opposite the inner hair cells, is a clear band, named **Hensen's stripe,** due to the intercrossing of its fibers. The lateral margin of the membrane is much thinner. Hardesty considers the tectorial membrane as the vibrating mechanism in the cochlea. It is inconceivably delicate and flexible; far more sensitively flexible in the transverse than in the longitudinal direction and the readiness with which it bends when touched is beyond description. It is ectodermal in origin. It consists of fine colorless fibers embedded in a transparent matrix (the matrix may be a variety of soft keratin), of a soft collagenous, semisolid character with marked adhesiveness. The general transverse direction of the fibers inclines from the radius of the cochlea toward the apex.

The **acoustic nerve** (*n. acusticus; auditory nerve or nerve of hearing*) divides near the bottom of the internal acoustic meatus into an anterior or cochlear and a posterior or vestibular branch.

The **vestibular nerve** (*n. vestibularis*) supplies the utricle, the saccule, and the ampullæ of the semicircular ducts. On the trunk of the nerve, within the internal acoustic meatus, is a ganglion, the **vestibular ganglion** (*ganglion of Scarpa*); the fibers of the nerve arise from the cells of this ganglion. On the distal side of the ganglion the nerve splits into a superior, an inferior, and a posterior branch. The filaments of the *superior branch* are transmitted through the foramina in the area vestibularis superior, and end in the macula of the utricle and in the ampullæ of the superior and lateral semicircular ducts; those of the *inferior branch* traverse the foramina in the area vestibularis inferior, and end in the macula of the saccule.

The *posterior branch* runs through the foramen singulare at the postero-inferior part of the bottom of the meatus and divides into filaments for the supply of the ampulla of the posterior semicircular duct.

The **cochlear nerve** (*n. cochlearis*) divides into numerous filaments at the base of the modiolus; those for the basal and middle coils pass through the foramina in the tractus spiralis foraminosis, those for the apical coil through the canalis centralis, and the nerves bend outward to pass between the lamellæ of the osseous spiral lamina. Occupying the spiral canal of the modiolus is the **spiral ganglion of the cochlea** (*ganglion of Corti*) (Fig. 946), consisting of bipolar nerve cells, which constitute the cells of origin of this nerve. Reaching the outer edge of the osseous spiral lamina, the fibers of the nerve pass through the foramina in the tympanic lip; some end by arborizing around the bases of the inner hair cells, while others pass

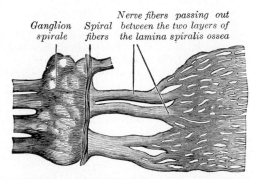

Ganglion spirale   *Spiral fibers*   *Nerve fibers passing out between the two layers of the lamina spiralis ossea*

FIG. 948.—Part of the cochlear division of the acoustic nerve, highly magnified. (Henle.)

between Corti's rods and across the tunnel, to end in a similar manner in relation to the outer hair cells. The cochlear nerve gives off a vestibular branch to supply the vestibular end of the ductus cochlearis; the filaments of this branch pass through the foramina in the fossa cochlearis.

Vessels.—The **arteries of the labyrinth** are the internal auditory, from the basilar, and the stylomastoid, from the posterior auricular. The internal auditory artery divides at the bottom of the internal acoustic meatus into two branches: cochlear and vestibular. The cochlear branch subdivides into twelve or fourteen twigs, which traverse the canals in the modiolus, and are distributed, in the form of a capillary net-work, in the lamina spiralis and basilar membrane. The vestibular branches are distributed to the utricle, saccule, and semicircular ducts.

The **veins** of the vestibule and semicircular canals accompany the arteries, and, receiving those of the cochlea at the base of the modiolus, unite to form the internal auditory veins which end in the posterior part of the superior petrosal sinus or in the transverse sinus.

REFERENCES

TASTE AND SMELL

BECKER, R. F. and J. E. KING. 1957. Delineation of the nasal air streams in the living dog. Arch. Otolaryng. (Chicago), *65*, 428–436.

BECKER, F., J. E. MARKEE and J. E. KING. 1957. Studies on olfactory acuity in dogs. (1) Discriminatory behaviour in problem box situations. Brit. J. Anim. Behav., *3*, 94–103.

FISHMAN, I. Y. 1957. Single fiber gustatory impulses in rat and hamster. J. cell. comp. Physiol., *49*, 319–334.

GUTH, L. 1958. Taste buds on the cat's circumvallate papilla after reinnervation by glossopharyngeal, vagus, and hypoglossal nerves. Anat. Rec., *130*, 25–38.

EYE

ADELMANN, H. B. 1936. The problem of cyclopia. Quart. Rev. Biol., *11*, 284–304.

BODEMER, C. W. 1958. The origin and development of the extrinsic ocular muscles in the trout (Salmo trutta). J. Morph., *102*, 119–156.

BURCH, G. E. 1939. Superficial lymphatics of human eyelids observed by injection *in vivo*. Anat. Rec., *73*, 443–446.

CHOW, K. L., A. H. Riesen, and F. W. Newell. 1957. Degeneration of retinal ganglion cells in infant chimpanzees reared in darkness. J. comp. Neurol., *107*, 27–42.

COOPER, S., and P. M. DANIEL. 1949. Muscle spindles in human extrinsic eye muscles. Brain, *72*, 1–24.

COULOMBRE, A. J., and E. S. CRELIN. 1958. The role of the developing eye in the morphogenesis of the avian skull. Amer. J. phys. Anthrop., *16*, 25–38.

DE ROBERTIS, E., and C. M. FRANCHI. 1956. Electron microscope observations on synaptic vesicles in synapses of the retinal rods and cones. J. biophys. biochem. Cytol., *2*, 307–318.

DETWILER, S. R. 1938. Vertebrate photoreceptors. Yale J. Biol. Med., *10*, 485–512.

DETWILER, S. R. 1945. On the role of chemical factors in retinal photomechanical responses. Amer. J. Anat., *77*, 117–157.

DETWILER, S. R. 1955. The eye and its structural adaptations. Proc. Amer. Philos. Soc., *99*, 224–238.

GÉNIS-GÁLVEZ, J. M. 1957. Innervation of the ciliary muscle. Anat. Rec., *127*, 219–230.

GILBERT, P. W. 1957. The origin and development of the human extrinsic ocular muscles. Contr. Embryol. Carneg. Instn., *36*, 59–78.

JOY, E. A. 1939. Intra-coelomic grafts of the eye primordium of the chick. Anat. Rec., *74*, 461–485.

KUNTZ, A., C. A. RICHENS, and E. J. CASEY. 1946. Reflex control of the ciliary muscle. J. Neurophysiol., *9*, 445–451.

LANCASTER, W. B. 1952. Refraction Correlated with Optics and Physiological Optics, and Motility Limited to Heterophoria. Charles C Thomas, Publisher, Springfield, xiv + 310 pages.

LOW, F. N. 1951. Peripheral visual acuity. Arch. Ophthal. (Chicago), *45*, 80–99.

LOW, F. N. 1947. Peripheral visual acuity of 55 subjects under conditions of flash presentation. Amer. J. Physiol., *151*, 319–324.

MANN, I. C. 1957. Developmental Abnormalities of the Eye. J. B. Lippincott Co., Philadelphia, xi + 419 pages.

MICHAELSON, I. C. 1954. Retinal Circulation in Man and Animals. Charles C Thomas, Publisher, Springfield, xvii + 146 pages.

PRINCE, J. H. 1956. Comparative Anatomy of the Eye. Charles C Thomas, Publisher, Springfield, ix + 418 pages.

REYER, R. W. 1954. Regeneration of the lens in the amphibian eye. Quart. Rev. Biol., *29*, 1–46.

SMELSER, G. K., V. OZANICS, and F. T. ZUGIBE. 1958. The production of exophthalmos in the absence of adrenal and ovarian hormones. Anat. Rec., *131*, 701–716.

STONE, L. S. 1954. Lens regeneration in secondary pupils experimentally produced in eyes of the adult newt, Triturus v. viridescens. J. exp. Zool., *127*, 463–492.

WOOLF, D. 1956. A comparative cytological study of the ciliary muscle. Anat. Rec., *124*, 145–164.

EAR

ALTMANN, F. 1950. Normal development of the ear and its mechanics. Arch. Otolaryng., (Chicago), *52*, 725–766.

ALTMANN, F. 1951. Malformations of the Eustachian tube, the middle ear, and its appendages. Arch. Otolaryng. (Chicago), *54*, 241–266.

ANSON, B. J. and T. H. BAST. 1955. The ear and the temporal bone. Development and adult structure. Otolaryngology, *1*, 1–111.

ANSON, B. J. and T. H. BAST. 1956. Development and adult anatomy of the auditory ossicles in relation to the operation for mobilization of the stapes in otosclerotic deafness. Laryngoscope, *66*, 785–795.

GRAVES, G. O., and L. F. EDWARDS. 1944. The eustachian tube. A review of its descriptive, microscopic, topographic and clinical anatomy. Arch. Otolaryng. (Chicago), *39*, 359–397.

LAWRENCE, M. 1950. Recent investigations of sound conduction. I. The normal ear. Ann. Otol. (St. Louis), *59*, 1020–1036.

SCHUKNECHT, H. F. 1950. A clinical study of auditory damage following blows to the head. Ann. Otol. (St. Louis), *59*, 331–358.

SMITH, C. A. and E. W. DEMPSEY. 1957. Electron microscopy of the organ of Corti. Amer. J. Anat., *100*, 337–368.

SPECTOR, B. 1944. Storage of trypan blue in the internal ear of the rat. Anat. Rec., *88*, 83–89.

SUNDERLAND, S. 1945. The arterial relations of the internal auditory meatus. Brain, *68*, 23–27.

WEVER, E. G. 1950. Recent investigations of sound conduction. II. The ear with conductive impairment. Ann. Otol. (St. Louis), *59*, 1037–1061.

WITTMAACK, K. 1956. Die Ortho- und Pathobiologie des Labyrinthes. Georg Thieme Verlag, Stuttgart, xii + 294 pages.

YNTEMA, C. L. 1933. Experiments on the determination of the ear ectoderm in the embryo of Amblystoma punctatum. J. exp. Zool., *65*, 317–357.

THE INTEGUMENT (SKIN).

THE integument (Fig. 949) covers the body and protects the deeper tissues from injury, from drying and from invasion by foreign organisms; it contains the peripheral endings of many of the sensory nerves; it plays an important part in the regulation of the body temperature, and has also limited excretory and absorbing powers. It consists principally of a layer of dense connective tissue, named the **corium** or **cutis vera,** and an external covering of epithelium, termed the **epidermis** or **cuticle.** On the surface of the former layer are sensitive and **vascular papillæ;** within, or beneath it, are certain organs with special functions: namely, the **sudoriferous** and **sebaceous glands,** and the **hair follicles.**

Development.—The epidermis and its appendages, consisting of the hairs, nails, sebaceous and sweat glands, are developed from the ectoderm, while the corium or true skin is of mesodermal origin. About the fifth week the epidermis consists of two layers of cells, the deeper one corresponding to the rete mucosum. The subcutaneous fat appears about the fourth month, and the papillæ of the true skin about the sixth. A considerable desquamation of epidermis takes place during fetal life, and this desquamated epidermis, mixed with sebaceous secretion, constitutes the **vernix caseosa,** with which the skin is smeared during the last three months of fetal life. The nails are formed at the third month, and begin to project from the epidermis about the sixth. The hairs appear between the third and fourth months in the form of solid downgrowths of the deeper layer of the epidermis, the growing extremities of which become inverted by papillary projections from the corium. The central cells of the solid downgrowths undergo alteration to form the hair, while the peripheral cells are retained to form the lining cells of the hair-follicle. About the fifth month the fetal hairs **(lanugo)** appear, first on the head and then on the other parts; they drop off after birth, and give place to the permanent hairs. The cellular structures of the sudoriferous and sebaceous glands are formed from the ectoderm, while the connective tissue and bloodvessels are derived from the mesoderm. All the sweat-glands are fully formed at birth; they begin to develop as early as the fourth month.

Structure.—The **epidermis, cuticle, or scarf skin** is non-vascular, and consists of stratified epithelium, and is accurately moulded on the papillary layer of the corium. It varies in thickness in different parts. In some situations, as in the palms of the hands and soles of the feet, it is thick, hard, and horny in texture. This may be in a measure due to the fact that these parts are exposed to intermittent pressure, but that this is not the only cause is proved by the fact that the condition exists to a very considerable extent at birth. The more superficial layers of cells, called the **horny layer** (*stratum corneum*), may be separated by maceration from a deeper stratum, which is called the **stratum mucosum,** and which consists of several layers of differently shaped cells. The free surface of the epidermis is marked by a net-work of linear furrows of variable size, dividing the surface into a number of polygonal or lozenge-shaped areas. Some of these furrows are large, as opposite the flexures of the joints, and correspond to the folds in the corium produced by movements. In other situations, as upon the back of the hand, they are exceedingly fine, and intersect one another at various angles. Upon the palmar surfaces of the hands and fingers, and upon the soles of the feet, the epidermal ridges are very distinct, and are disposed in curves; they depend upon the large size and peculiar arrangements of the papillæ upon which the epidermis is placed. The function

73

of these ridges is primarily to increase resistance between contact surfaces for the purpose of preventing slipping whether in walking or prehension. The direction of the ridges is at right angles with the force that tends to produce slipping or to the resultant of such forces when these forces vary in direction. In each individual the lines on the tips of the fingers and thumbs form distinct patterns unlike those of any other person. A method of determining the identity of a criminal is based on this fact, impressions ("finger-prints") of these lines being made on paper covered with soot, or on white paper after first covering the fingers with ink. The deep surface of the epidermis is accurately moulded upon the papillary layer of the corium, the papillæ being covered by a basement membrane; so that when the epidermis is removed by maceration, it presents on its under surface a number of pits or depressions corresponding to the papillæ, and ridges corresponding to the intervals between them. Fine tubular prolongations are continued from this layer into the ducts of the sudoriferous and sebaceous glands.

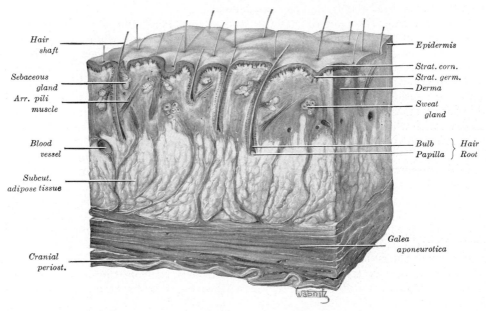

FIG. 949.—Section through scalp of adult cadaver. × 5.

The epidermis consists of stratified squamous epithelium which is arranged in four layers from within outward as follows: (a) **stratum mucosum**, (b) **stratum granulosum**, (c) **stratum lucidum**, and (d) **stratum corneum**.

The **stratum mucosum** (*mucous layer*) is composed of several layers of cells; those of the deepest layer are columnar in shape and placed perpendicularly on the surface of the basement membrane, to which they are attached by toothed extremities; this deepest layer is sometimes termed the **stratum germinativum**; the succeeding strata consist of cells of a more rounded or polyhedral form, the contents of which are soft, opaque, granular, and soluble in acetic acid. These are known as prickle cells because of the bridges by which they are connected to one another. They contain fine fibrils which are continuous across the connecting processes with corresponding fibrils in adjacent cells. Between the bridges are fine intercellular clefts serving for the passage of lymph, and in these lymph corpuscles or pigment granules may be found.

The **stratum granulosum** comprises two or three layers of flattened cells which contain granules of *eleidin*, a substance readily stained by hematoxylin or carmine, and probably an intermediate substance in the formation of keratin. They are supposed to be cells in a transitional stage between the protoplasmic cells of the stratum mucosum and the horny cells of the superficial layers.

The **stratum lucidum** appears in section as a homogeneous or dimly striated membrane, composed of closely packed cells in which traces of flattened nuclei may be found, and in which minute granules of a substance named *keratohyalin* are present.

The **stratum corneum** (*horny layer*) consists of several layers of horny epithelial scales in which no nuclei are discernible, and which are unaffected by acetic acid, the protoplasm having become changed into horny material or **keratin**. According to Ranvier they contain granules of a material which has the characteristics of beeswax.

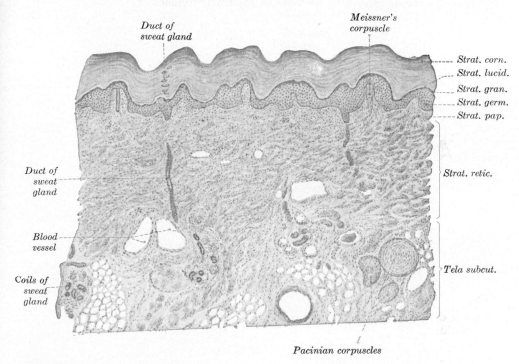

FIG. 950.—Section through the skin of the human foot cut perpendicularly to the surface. (From Rauber-Kopsch, *Lehrbuch u. Altas d. Anatomie d. Menschen*, 19th Edition, Vol. II, courtesy Georg Thieme Verlag, Stuttgart, 1955).

The black color of the skin in the negro, and the tawny color among some of the white races, is due to the presence of pigment in the cells of the epidermis. This pigment is more especially distinct in the cells of the stratum mucosum, and is similar to that found in the cells of the pigmentary layer of the retina. As the cells approach the surface and desiccate, the color becomes partially lost; the disappearance of the pigment from the superficial layers of the epidermis is, however, difficult to explain.

The pigment **(melanin)** consists of dark brown or black granules of very small size, closely packed together within the cells, but not involving the nucleus.

The main purpose served by the epidermis is that of protection, as the surface is worn away new cells are supplied and thus the true skin, the vessels and nerves which it contains are defended from damage.

The **Corium, Cutis Vera, Dermis,** or **True Skin** is tough, flexible, and elastic. It varies in thickness in different parts of the body. Thus it is very thick in the palms of the hands and soles of the feet; thicker on the dorsal aspect of the body than on the ventral, and on the lateral than on the medial sides of the limbs. In the eyelids, scrotum, and penis it is exceedingly thin and delicate.

It consists of felted connective tissue, with a varying amount of elastic fibers and numerous bloodvessels, lymphatics, and nerves. The connective tissue is arranged in two layers: a **deeper** or **reticular**, and a **superficial** or **papillary** (Fig. 950).

Smooth muscle cells are found in the corium and the subcutaneous layers of the scrotum, penis, labia majora, and nipples. In the mammary papilla, the smooth muscle cells are disposed in circular bands and radiating bundles, arranged in superimposed laminæ. In parts of the skin where there are hairs, discrete bundles of smooth muscle called the Arrectores pilorum are attached in the superficial layers of the corium and near the base of each hair follicle.

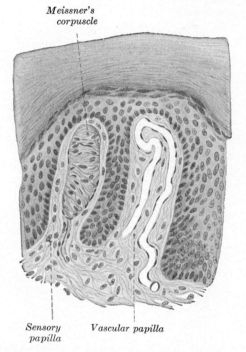

Meissner's corpuscle

Sensory papilla   *Vascular papilla*

Fig. 951.—Vascular and sensory papillæ in the skin of the human foot. (From Rauber-Kopsch, *Lehrbuch u. Altas d. Anatomie d. Menschen*, 19th Edition, Vol. II, courtesy Georg Thieme Verlag, Stuttgart, 1955.)

The **papillary layer** (*stratum papillare*; *superficial layer*; *corpus papillare of the corium*) consists of numerous small, highly sensitive, and vascular eminences, the **papillæ**, which rise perpendicularly from its surface. The papillæ are minute conical eminences, having rounded or blunted extremities, occasionally divided into two or more parts, and are received into corresponding pits on the under surface of the cuticle. On the general surface of the body, more especially in parts endowed with slight sensibility, they are few in number, and exceedingly minute; but in some situations, as upon the palmar surfaces of the hands and fingers, and upon the plantar surfaces of the feet and toes, they are long, of large size, closely aggregated together, and arranged in parallel curved lines, forming the elevated ridges seen on the free surface of the epidermis. Each ridge contains two rows of papillæ, between which the ducts of the sudoriferous glands pass outward to open on the summit of the ridge. Each papilla consists of very small and closely interlacing bundles of finely fibrillated tissue, with a few elastic fibers; within this tissue is a capillary loop, and in some papillæ, especially in the palms of the hand and the fingers, there are tactile corpuscles (Fig. 951).

The **reticular layer** (*stratum reticulare*; *deep layer*) consists of fibro-elastic connective tissue, composed chiefly of collagenous bundles, but containing yellow elastic fibers in varying number in different parts of the body. The cells it contains are principally fibroblasts and histiocytes, but other types may be found. Near the papillary layer the collagenous bundles are small and compactly arranged; in the deeper layers they are larger and coarser and between their meshes are sweat glands, sebaceous glands, hair shafts or follicles, and small collections of fat cells. The deep surface of the reticular layer merges with the adipose tissue of the subcutaneous superficial fascia (tela subcutanea).

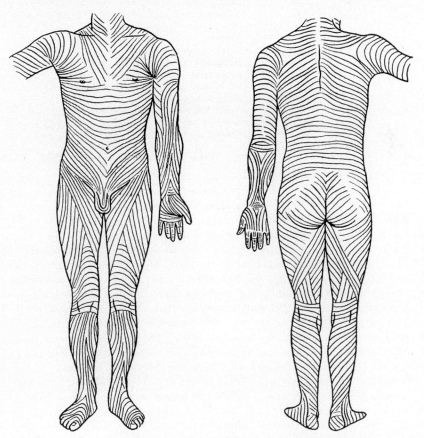

Fig. 952.—Cleavage lines (Langer's lines) of the skin. Trunk and extremities. (Eller.)

Cleavage Lines of the Skin (*Langer's lines*).—When a penetrating wound is made with a sharp conical instrument it does not leave a round hole in the skin, as might be expected, but a slit such as would be expected from a flat blade. Maps of the directions of these slits from puncture wounds over all parts of the body have been made from dissecting room material (Fig. 952). These maps indicate that there are definite lines of **tension** or **cleavage lines** within the skin which are characteristic for each part of the body. In microscopic sections cut parallel with these lines, most of the collagenous bundles of the reticular layer are cut longitudinally, while in sections cut across the lines, the bundles are in cross section. The cleavage lines correspond closely with the crease lines on the surface of the skin in most parts of the body. The pattern of the cleavage lines, according to Cox (1941) varies with body configuration, but is constant for individuals of similar build, regardless of age. There are limited areas of the body in which the orientation of the bundles is irregular and confused. The cleavage lines are of particular interest to the surgeon because an incision parallel to the lines heals with a fine linear scar while an incision across the lines may set up irregular tensions which result in an unsightly scar.

The **arteries** supplying the skin form a net-work in the subcutaneous tissue, and from this net-work branches are given off to supply the sudoriferous glands, the hair follicles, and the fat. Other branches unite in a plexus immediately beneath the corium; from this plexus, fine capillary vessels pass into the papillæ, forming, in the smaller ones, a single capillary loop, but in the larger, a more or less convoluted vessel. The **lymphatic vessels** of the skin form two net-works, superficial and deep, which communicate with each other and with those of the subcutaneous tissue by oblique branches.

The **nerves** of the skin terminate partly in the epidermis and partly in the corium; their different modes of ending are described on pages 937 to 940.

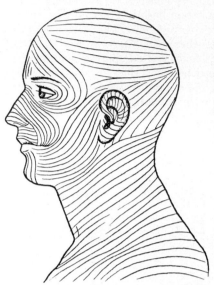

FIG. 953.—Cleavage lines (Langer's lines) of the skin. Head and neck. (Eller.)

THE APPENDAGES OF THE SKIN.

The appendages of the skin are the **nails**, the **hairs**, and the **sudoriferous** and **sebaceous glands** with their ducts.

The **Nails** (*ungues*) (Fig. 954) are flattened, elastic structures of a horny texture, placed upon the dorsal surfaces of the terminal phalanges of the fingers and toes. Each nail is convex on its outer surface, concave within, and is implanted by a portion, called the **root**, into a groove in the skin; the exposed portion is called the **body**, and the distal extremity the **free edge**. The nail is firmly adherent to the corium, being accurately moulded upon its surface; the part beneath the body and root of the nail is called the **nail matrix**, because from it the nail is produced. Under the greater part of the body of the nail, the matrix is thick, and raised into a series of longitudinal ridges which are very vascular, and the color is seen through the transparent tissue. Near the root of the nail, the papillæ are smaller, less vascular, and have no regular arrangement, and here the tissue of the nail is not firmly adherent to the connective-tissue stratum but only in contact with it; hence this portion is of a whiter color, and is called the **lunula** on account of its shape.

The cuticle as it passes forward on the dorsal surface of the finger or toe is attached to the surface of the nail a little in advance of its root; at the extremity of the finger it is connected with the under surface of the nail a little behind its free edge. The cuticle and the horny substance of the nail (both epidermic structures) are thus directly continuous with each other. The superficial, horny part of the nail consists of a greatly thickened stratum lucidum, the stratum corneum forming merely the thin cuticular fold **(eponychium)** which overlaps the lunula; the deeper part consists of the stratum mucosum. The cells in contact with the papillæ of the matrix are columnar in form and arranged perpendicularly to the surface; those which succeed them are of a rounded or polygonal form, the more superficial ones becoming broad, thin, and flattened, and so closely packed as to make the limits of the cells very indistinct. The nails grow in length by the proliferation of the cells of the stratum mucosum at the root of the nail, and in thickness from that part of the stratum mucosum which underlies the lunula.

Hairs (*pili*) are found on nearly every part of the surface of the body, but are absent from the palms of the hands, the soles of the feet, the dorsal surfaces of the terminal phalanges, the glans penis, the inner surface of the prepuce, and the inner surfaces of the labia. They vary much in length, thickness, and color in different parts of the body and in different races of mankind. In some parts, as in the skin of the eyelids, they are so short as not to project beyond the follicles containing them; in others, as upon the scalp, they are of considerable lengths again, in other parts, as the eyelashes, the hairs of the pubic region, and the whiskers and beard, they are remarkable for their thickness. Straight hairs are stronger than curly hairs, and present on transverse section a cylindrical or oval outline; curly hairs, on the other hand, are flattened. A hair consists of a **root**, the part implanted in the skin; and a **shaft** or **scapus**, the portion projecting from the surface.

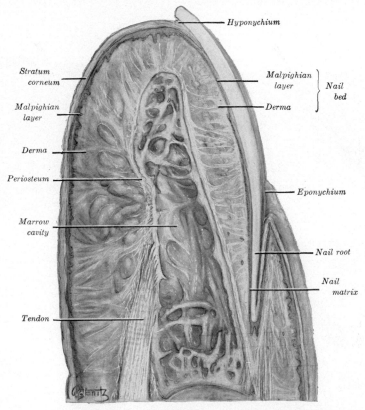

Fig. 954.—Median longitudinal section through finger of adult cadaver. The marrow has been removed to show bony trabeculæ. × 5.

The **root of the hair** (*radix pili*) ends in an enlargement, the **hair bulb**, which is whiter in color and softer in texture than the shaft, and is lodged in a follicular involution of the epidermis called the **hair follicle** (Fig. 955). When the hair is of considerable length the follicle extends into the subcutaneous cellular tissue. The hair follicle commences on the surface of the skin with a funnel-shaped opening, and passes inward in an oblique or curved direction—the latter in curly hairs—to become dilated at its deep extremity, where it corresponds with the hair bulb. Opening into the follicle, near its free extremity, are the ducts of one or more sebaceous glands. At the bottom of each hair follicle is a small conical, vascular eminence or papilla, similar in every respect to those found upon the surface of the skin; it is continuous with the dermic layer of the follicle, and is supplied with nerve fibrils. The hair follicle consists of two coats—an **outer** or **dermic**, and an **inner** or **epidermic**.

The **outer** or **dermic coat** is formed mainly of fibrous tissue; it is continuous with the corium, is highly vascular, and supplied by numerous minute nervous filaments. It consists of three layers (Fig. 957). The most internal is a hyaline basement membrane, which is well-marked in the larger hair follicles, but is not very distinct in the follicles of minute hairs; it is limited to the deeper part of the follicle. Outside this is a compact layer of fibers and spindle-shaped cells arranged circularly around the follicle; this layer extends from the bottom of the follicle as high as the entrance of the ducts of the sebaceous glands. Externally is a thick layer of connective tissue, arranged in longitudinal bundles, forming a more open texture and corresponding to the reticular part of the corium; in this are contained the bloodvessels and nerves.

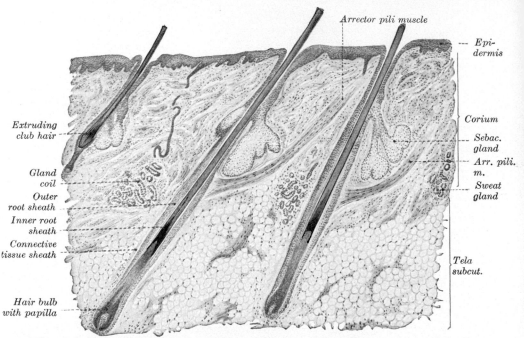

FIG. 955.—Section of human scalp with hairs cut lungitudinally. (From Rauber-Kopsch, *Lehrbuch u. Altas d. Anatomie d. Menschen*, 19th Edition, Vol. II, courtesy Georg Thieme Verlag, Stuttgart, 1955.)

The **inner** or **epidermic coat** is closely adherent to the root of the hair, and consists of two strata named respectively the **outer** and **inner root sheaths**; the former of these corresponds with the stratum mucosum of the epidermis, and resembles it in the rounded form and soft character of its cells; at the bottom of the hair follicle these cells become continuous with those of the root of the hair. The inner root sheath consists of (1) a delicate cuticle next the hair, composed of a single layer of imbricated scales with atrophied nuclei; (2) one or two layers of horny, flattened, nucleated cells, known as **Huxley's layer**; and (3) a single layer of cubical cells with clear flattened nuclei, called **Henle's layer**.

The hair bulb is moulded over the papilla and composed of polyhedral epithelial cells, which as they pass upward into the root of the hair become elongated and spindle-shaped, except some in the center which remain polyhedral. Some of these latter cells contain pigment granules which give rise to the color of the hair. It occasionally happens that these pigment granules completely fill the cells in the center of the bulb; this gives rise to the dark tract of pigment often found, of greater or less length, in the axis of the hair.

The **shaft of the hair** (*scapus pili*) consists, from within outward, of three parts, the medulla, the cortex, and the cuticle. The **medulla** is usually wanting in the fine hairs covering the surface of the body, and commonly in those of the head. It is more opaque and deeper colored than the cortex when viewed by transmitted light; but when viewed by reflected light it is white. It is composed of rows of polyhedral cells, containing granules of eleidin and frequently air spaces. The **cortex** constitutes the chief part of the shaft; its cells are elongated and united to form flattened fusiform fibers which contain pigment granules in dark hair, and air in white hair. The **cuticle** consists of a single layer of flat scales which overlap one another from below upward.

Connected with the hair follicles are minute bundles of involuntary muscular fibers, termed the **Arrectores pilorum.** They *arise* from the superficial layer of the corium, and are inserted into the hair follicle, below the entrance of the duct of the sebaceous gland. They are placed on the side toward which the hair slopes, and

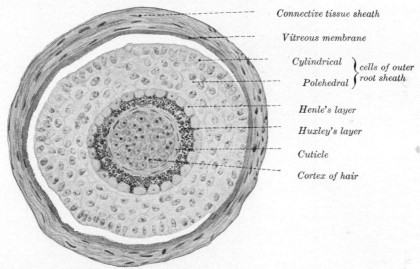

Connective tissue sheath

Vitreous membrane

Cylindrical } *cells of outer*
Polehedral } *root sheath*

Henle's layer

Huxley's layer

Cuticle

Cortex of hair

Fig. 956.—Cross section through hair root and root sheath. The red granules in Huxley's layer are keratohyalin. The space between hair and sheath is an artifact. (From Rauber-Kopsch, *Lehrbuch u. Altas d. Anatomie d. Menschen*, 19th Edition, Vol. II, courtesy Georg Thieme Verlag, Stuttgart, 1955.)

by their action diminish the obliquity of the follicle and elevate the hair (Fig. 955). The sebaceous gland is situated in the angle which the Arrector muscle forms with the superficial portion of the hair follicle, and contraction of the muscle thus tends to squeeze the sebaceous secretion out from the duct of the gland.

The **Sebaceous Glands** (*glandulæ sebaceæ*) are small, sacculated, glandular organs, lodged in the substance of the corium. They are found in most parts of the skin, but are especially abundant in the scalp and face; they are also very numerous around the apertures of the anus, nose, mouth, and external ear, but are wanting in the palms of the hands and soles of the feet. Each gland consists of a single duct, more or less capacious, which emerges from a cluster of oval or flask-shaped alveoli which vary from two to five in number, but in some instances there may be as many as twenty. Each alveolus is composed of a transparent basement membrane, enclosing a number of epithelial cells. The outer or marginal cells are small and polyhedral, and are continuous with the cells lining the duct. The remainder of the alveolus is filled with larger cells, containing fat, except in the center, where the cells have become broken up, leaving a cavity filled with their

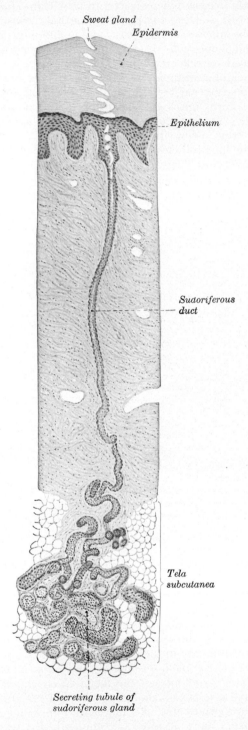

FIG. 957.—Sweat gland from the sole of the human foot. (From Rauber-Kopsch, *Lehrbuch u. Altas d. Anatomie d. Menschen*, 19th Edition, Vol. II, courtesy Georg Thieme Verlag, Stuttgart, 1955.)

débris and a mass of fatty matter, which constitutes the **sebum cutaneum**. The ducts open most frequently into the hair follicles, but occasionally upon the general surface, as in the labia minora and the free margin of the lips. On the nose and face the glands are of large size, distinctly lobulated, and often become much enlarged from the accumulation of pent-up secretion. The tarsal glands of the eyelids are elongated sebaceous glands with numerous lateral diverticula.

The **Sudoriferous** or **Sweat Glands** (*glandulæ sudoriferæ*) (Fig. 957) are found in almost every part of the skin, and are situated in small pits on the under surface of the orium, or, more frequently, in the subcutaneous areolar tissue, surrounded by a quantity of adipose tissue. Each consists of a single tube, the deep part of which is rolled into an oval or spherical ball, named the **body** of the gland, while the superficial part, or **duct,** traverses the corium and cuticle and opens on the surface of the skin by a funnel-shaped aperture. In the superficial layers of the corium the duct is straight, but in the deeper layers it is convoluted or even twisted; where the epidermis is thick, as in the palms of the hands and soles of the feet, the part of the duct which passes through it is spirally coiled. The size of the glands varies. They are especially large in those regions where the amount of perspiration is great, as in the axillæ, where they form a thin, mammilated layer of a reddish color, which corresponds exactly to the situation of the hair in this region; they are large also in the groin. Their number varies. They are very plentiful on the palms of the hands, and on the soles of the feet, where the orifices of the ducts are exceedingly regular, and open on the curved ridges; they are least numerous in the neck and back. On the palm there are about 370 per square centimeter; on the back of the hand about 200; forehead 175, breast, abdomen and forearm 155, and on the leg and back from 60 to 80 per square centimeter. Krause estimates the total number at about 2,000,000. The average number of sweat glands per square centimeter of skin area in various races as shown by the fingers is as follows:[1]

American (white)	558.2
American (negro)	597.2
Filipino	653.6
Moro	684.4
Negrito (adult)	709.2
Hindu	738.2
Negrito (youth).	950.0

They are absent in the deeper portion of the external auditory meatus, the prepuce and the glans penis. The tube, both in the body of the gland and in the duct consists of two layers—an outer, of fine **areolar tissue,** and an inner of **epithelium** The outer layer is thin and is continuous with the superficial stratum of the corium. In the body of the gland the epithelium consists of a single layer of cubical cells, between the deep ends of which the basement membrane is a layer of longitudinally or obliquely arranged non-striped muscular fibers. The ducts are destitute of muscular fibers and are composed of a basement membrane lined by two or three layers of polyhedral cells; the lumen of the duct is coated by a thin cuticle. When the epidermis is carefully removed from the surface of the corium, the ducts may be pulled out from the corium in the form of short, thread-like processes. The ceruminous glands of the external acoustic meatus, the ciliary glands at the margins of the eyelids, the circumanal glands and probably the mammary glands are modified sudoriferous glands. The average quantity of sweat secreted in twenty-four hours varies from 700 to 900 grams.

[1]Clark and Lhamon, Anatomical Record, 1917, vol. **12.**

REFERENCES

Skin

Andrew, W., and N. V. Andrew. 1949. Lymphocytes in the normal epidermis of the rat and of man. Anat. Rec., *104*, 217–241.

Clark, E. R., and E. L. Clark. 1953. Growth and behavior of epidermis as observed microscopically in observation chambers inserted in the ears of rabbits. Am. J. Anat., *93*, 171–219.

Edwards, E. A., and S. Q. Duntley. 1939. The pigments and color of living human skin. Am. J. Anat., *65*, 1–33.

Katzberg, A. A. 1958. The area of the dermo-epidermal junction in human skin. Anat. Rec., *131*, 717–726.

Lee, M. M. C. 1957. Physical and structural age changes in human skin. Anat. Rec., *129*, 473–494.

Lee, M. M. C., and G. W. Lasker. 1958. The thickness of subcutaneous fat in elderly men. Amer. J. phys. Anthrop., *16*, 125–134.

Matoltsy, A. G., and S. J. Sinesi. 1957. A study of the mechanism of keratinization of human epidermal cells. Anat. Rec., *128*, 55–68.

Montagna, W. 1956. The Structure and Function of Skin. Academic Press Inc., Publishers, New York. xvii + 356 pages.

Odland, G. F. 1950. The morphology of the attachment between the dermis and the epidermis. Anat. Rec., *108*, 399–413.

Rothman, S. 1954. Physiology and Biochemistry of the Skin. University of Chicago Press, Chicago. 741 pages.

Selby, C. C. 1955. An electron microscope study of the epidermis of mammalian skin in thin sections. I. Dermo-epidermal junction and basal cell layer. J. biophys. biochem. Cytol., *1*, 429–444.

Taussig, J., and G. D. Williams. 1940. Skin color and skin cancer. Arch. Path., *30*, 721–730.

Dermatoglyphics

Cummins, H. and C. Midlo. 1927. Dermatoglyphics in Jews. Amer. J. physiol. Anthrop., *10*, 91–113.

Cummins, H. 1940. Finger prints correlated with handedness. Amer. J. phys. Anthrop., *26*, 151–166.

Cummins, H. 1955. Dermatoglyphics of Bushmen (South Africa). Amer. J. physiol. Anthrop., *13*, 699–710.

Cummins, H., W. J. Waits, and J. T. McQuitty. 1941. The breadths of the epidermal ridges on the finger tips and palms: A study of variation. Amer. J. Anat., *68*, 127–150.

Hale, A. R. 1949. Breadth of epidermal ridges in the human fetus and its relation to the growth of the hand and foot. Anat. Rec., *105*, 763–776.

Midlo, C. and H. Cummins. 1942. Palmar and plantar dermatoglyphics in primates. Amer. anat. Mem. No. 20, Wistar Press, Philadelphia. iii + 198 pages.

Cleavage Lines

Cox, H. T. 1941. The cleavage lines of the skin. Brit. J. Surg., *29*, 234–240.

Gardner, J. H., and H. E. Raybuck. 1954. Development of cleavage line patterns in the human fetus. Anat. Rec., *118*, 745–754.

Hutchinson, C., and C. E. Koop. 1956. Lines of cleavage in the skin of the newborn infant. Anat. Rec., *126*, 299–310.

Hair

Argyris, T. S. 1956. The distribution of succinic dehydrogenase and non-specific esterase in mouse skin throughout the hair growth cycle. Anat. Rec., *125*, 105–120.

Baker, B. L. 1951. The relationship of the adrenal, thyroid, and pituitary glands to the growth of hair. Ann. N. Y. Acad. Sci., *53*, 690–707.

Birbeck, M. S. C., E. H. Mercer, and N. A. Barnicot. 1956. The structure and formation of pigment granules in human hair. Exp. Cell Res., *10*, 505–514.

Birbeck, M. S. C., and E. H. Mercer. 1957. The electron microscopy of the human hair follicle. I. Introduction and the hair cortex. II. The hair cuticle. III. The inner root sheath and trichohyaline. J. biophys. biochem. Cytol., *3*, 203–230.

Butcher, E. O. 1946. Hair growth and sebaceous glands in skin transplanted under the skin and into the peritoneal cavity in the rat. Anat. Rec., *96*, 101–109.

Butcher, E. O. 1951. Development of the pilary system and the replacement of hair in mammals. Ann. N. Y. Acad. Sci., *53*, 508–516.

CHASE, H. B. 1954. Growth of the hair. Physiol. Rev., *34*, 113–126.

DUGGINS, O. H. 1954. Age changes in head hair from birth to maturity. IV. Refractive indices and birefringence of the cuticle of hair of children. Amer. J. phys. Anthrop., *12*, 89–114.

HAMILTON, J. B. 1942. Male hormone stimulation is prerequisite and an incitant in common baldness. Amer. J. Anat., *71*, 451–480.

HAMILTON, J. B. 1951. Patterned loss of hair in man: types and incidence. Ann. N. Y. Acad. Sci., *53*, 708–728.

JOHNSON, P. L., and G. BEVELANDER. 1946. Glycogen and phosphatase in the developing hair. Anat. Rec., *95*, 193–199.

THOMAS, P. K., and D. G. FERRIMAN. 1957. Variation in facial and pubic hair growth in white women. Amer. J. phys. Anthrop., *15*, 171–180.

TROTTER, M. 1938. A review of the classifications of hairs. Am. J. Phys. Anthrop., *24*, 105–126.

TROTTER, M. 1939. Classifications of hair color. Amer. J. phys. Anthrop., *25*, 237–260.

TROTTER, M., and O. H. DUGGINS. 1950. Age changes in head hair from birth to maturity. III. Cuticular scale counts of hair of children. Amer. J. phys. Anthrop., n.s., *8*, 467–484.

TROTTER, M., and O. H. DUGGINS. 1948. Age changes in head hair from birth to maturity. I. Index and size of hair of children. Amer. J. phys. Anthrop., *6*, 489–506.

VAN SCOTT, E. J., and REINERTSON, R. P. 1957. Detection of radiation effects on hair roots of the human scalp. J. invest. Derm., *29*, 205–212.

GLANDS AND NAILS

BABCOCK, M. J. 1955. Methods for measuring fingernail growth rates in nutritional studies. J. Nutr., *55*, 323–336.

McGREGOR, I. A. 1952. The sweating reactions of the forehead. J. Physiol. (Lond.), *116*, 26–34.

MONTAGNA, W., and P. KENYON. 1949. Growth potentials and mitotic division in the sebaceous glands of the rabbit. Anat. Rec., *103*, 365–380.

MONTAGNA, W., H. B. CHASE, and W. C. LOBITZ, JR. 1953. Histology and cytochemistry of human skin. V. Axillary apocrine sweat glands. Amer. J. Anat., *92*, 451–470.

SULZBERGER, M. B., F. HERRMANN, R. KELLER, and B. V. PISHA. 1950. Studies of sweating: III. Experimental factors influencing the function of the sweat ducts. J. invest. Derm., *14*, 91–112.

SUNDERLAND, S. and L. J. RAY. 1952. The effect of denervation on nail growth. J. Neurol. Neurosurg. Psychiat., *15*, 50–53.

THE RESPIRATORY SYSTEM.

THE respiratory system (*apparatus respiratorius; respiratory apparatus*) consists of the nose, nasal passages, nasopharynx, larynx, trachea, bronchi and lungs. The pleura, pleural cavities and the topography of other structures in the thorax are also described in this chapter. The muscular actions associated with respiration are discussed with the description of the diaphragm in the chapter on Muscles.

Development.—The development of the nose is described in the chapter on Embryology.

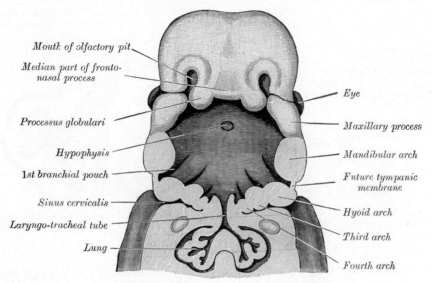

FIG. 958.—The head and neck of a human embryo thirty-two days old, seen from the ventral surface. The floor of the mouth and pharynx have been removed. (His.)

The primordium of the principal respiratory organs appears as a median longitudinal groove in the ventral wall of the pharynx. The groove deepens and its lips fuse to form a septum which grows from below upward and converts the groove into a tube, the **laryngo-tracheal tube** (Fig. 958), the cephalic end of which opens into the pharynx by a slit-like aperture formed by the persistent anterior part of the groove. The tube is lined by entoderm from which the epithelial lining of the respiratory tract is developed. The cephalic part of the tube becomes the larynx, and its next succeeding part the trachea, while from its caudal end two lateral outgrowths, the right and left **lung buds**, arise, and from them the bronchi and lungs are developed. The first rudiment of the larynx consists of two **arytenoid swellings,** which appear, one on either side of the cephalic end of the laryngotracheal groove, and are continuous in front of the groove with a transverse ridge **(furcula of His)** which lies between the ventral ends of the third branchial arches and from which the epiglottis is subsequently developed (Figs. 997, 998). After the separation of the trachea from the esophagus the arytenoid swellings come into contact with one another and with the back of the epiglottis, and the entrance to the larynx assumes the form of a T-shaped cleft, the margins of the cleft adhere

(1167)

to one another and the laryngeal entrance is for a time occluded. The mesodermal wall of the tube becomes condensed to form the cartilages of the larynx and trachea. The arytenoid swellings are differentiated into the arytenoid and corniculate cartilages, and the folds joining them to the epiglottis form the aryepiglottic folds in which the cuneiform cartilages are developed as derivatives of the epiglottis. The thyroid cartilage appears as two lateral plates, each chondrified from two centers and united in the mid-ventral line by membrane in which an additional center of chondrification develops. The cricoid cartilage arises from two cartilaginous centers, which soon unite ventrally and gradually extend and ultimately fuse on the dorsal aspect of the tube.

The opening of the pulmonary diverticulum lies between the two fifth arch masses and behind a "central mass" in the middle line—the proximal end of the diverticulum is compressed between the fifth arch masses. The fifth arch is joined by the fourth to form a "lateral mass" on each side of the opening, and these "lateral masses" grow forward and overlap the central mass and so form a secondary transverse cavity, which is really a part of the cavity of the pharynx. The two parts of the cavity of the larynx are separated in the adult by a line drawn back along the vocal fold and then upward along the border of the arytenoid eminence to the interarytenoid notch. The arytenoid and cricoid are developed in the fifth arch mass. The thyroid is primarily a fourth arch derivative, and if it has a fifth arch element this is a later addition. The epiglottis is derived from the "central mass," and has a third arch element in its oral and upper aspect; the arch value of the "central mass" is doubtful.

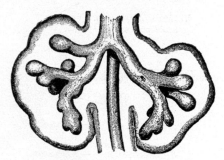

FIG. 959.—Lung buds from a human embryo of about four weeks, showing commencing lobulations. (His.)

FIG. 960.—Lungs of a human embryo more advanced in development. (His.)

The right and left lung buds grow out behind the ducts of Cuvier, and are at first symmetrical, but their ends soon become lobulated, three lobules appearing on the right, and two on the left; these subdivisions are the early indications of the corresponding lobes of the lungs (Figs. 959, 960). The buds undergo further subdivision and ramification, and ultimately end in minute expanded extremities— the infundibula of the lung. After the sixth month the air-sacs begin to make their appearance on the infundibula in the form of minute pouches. The pulmonary arteries are derived from the sixth aortic arches. During the course of their development the lungs migrate in a caudal direction, so that by the time of birth the bifurcation of the trachea is opposite the fourth thoracic vertebra. As the lungs grow they project into that part of the celom which will ultimately form the pleural cavities, and the superficial layer of the mesoderm enveloping the lung rudiment expands on the growing lung and is converted into the pulmonary pleura.

THE EXTERNAL NOSE (NASUS EXTERNUS; OUTER NOSE).

The **external nose** is pyramidal in form, and its upper angle or **root** is connected directly with the forehead; its free angle is termed the **apex**. The two elliptical orifices, the **nares,** are separated from each other by an antero-posterior septum, the **columna.** The margins of the nares are provided with a number of stiff hairs, or **vibrissæ,** which arrest the passage of foreign substances carried with the current of air intended for respiration. The lateral surfaces of the nose form by their union in the middle line, the **dorsum nasi,** the direction of which varies considerably in different individuals; the upper part of the dorsum is supported by the nasal bones, and is named the **bridge.** The lateral surface ends below in a rounded eminence, the **ala nasi.**

Structure.—The framework of the external nose is composed of bones and cartilages; it is covered by the integument, and lined by mucous membrane.

The **bony framework** occupies the upper part of the organ; it consists of the nasal bones, and the frontal processes of the maxillæ.

The **cartilaginous framework** (*cartilagines nasi*) consists of five large pieces, *viz.,* the **cartilage**

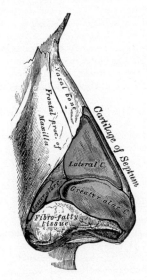

Fig. 961.—Cartilages of the nose. Side view.

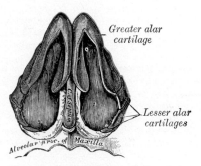

Fig. 962.—Cartilages of the nose, seen from below.

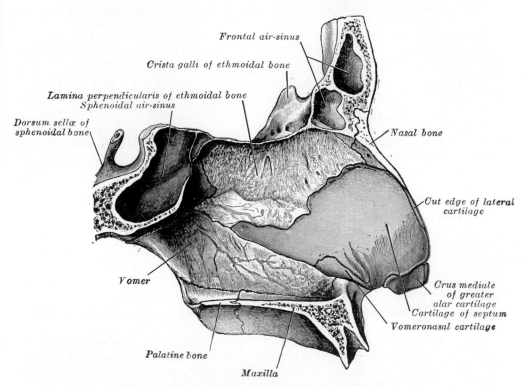

Fig. 963.—Bones and cartilages of septum of nose. Right side.

74

of the septum, the **two lateral** and the **two greater alar cartilages,** and several smaller pieces, the **lesser alar cartilages** (Figs. 961, 962, 963). The various cartilages are connected to each other and to the bones by a tough fibrous membrane.

The **cartilage of the septum** (*cartilago septi nasi*) is somewhat quadrilateral in form, thicker at its margins than at its center, and completes the separation between the nasal cavities in front. Its anterior margin, thickest above, is connected with the nasal bones, and is continuous with the anterior margins of the lateral cartilages; below, it is connected to the medial crura of the greater alar cartilages by fibrous tissue. Its posterior margin is connected with the perpendicular plate of the ethmoid; its inferior margin with the vomer and the palatine processes of the maxillæ.

It may be prolonged backward (especially in children) as a narrow process, the **sphenoidal process,** for some distance between the vomer and perpendicular plate of the ethmoid. The septal cartilage does not reach as far as the lowest part of the nasal septum. This is formed by the medial crura of the greater alar cartilages and by the skin; it is freely movable, and hence is termed the **septum mobile nasi.**

The **lateral cartilage** (*cartilago nasi lateralis; upper lateral cartilage*) is situated below the inferior margin of the nasal bone, and is flattened, and triangular in shape. Its anterior margin is thicker than the posterior, and is continuous above with the cartilage of the septum, but separated from it below by a narrow fissure; its superior margin is attached to the nasal bone and the frontal process of the maxilla; its inferior margin is connected by fibrous tissue with the greater alar cartilage.

The **greater alar cartilage** (*cartilago alaris major; lower lateral cartilage*) is a thin, flexible plate, situated immediately below the preceding, and bent upon itself in such a manner as to form the medial and lateral walls of the naris of its own side. The portion which forms the **medial wall** (*crus mediale*) is loosely connected with the corresponding portion of the opposite cartilage, the two forming, together with the thickened integument and subjacent tissue, the **septum mobile nasi.** The part which forms the **lateral wall** (*crus laterale*) is curved to correspond with the ala of the nose; it is oval and flattened, narrow behind, where it is connected with the frontal process of the maxilla by a tough fibrous membrane, in which are found three or four small cartilaginous plates, the **lesser alar cartilages** (*cartilagines alares minores; sesamoid cartilages*). Above, it is connected by fibrous tissue to the lateral cartilage and front part of the cartilage of the septum; below, it falls short of the margin of the naris, the ala being completed by fatty and fibrous tissue covered by skin. In front, the greater alar cartilages are separated by a notch which corresponds with the apex of the nose.

The **muscles** acting on the external nose have been described in the section on Myology.

The **integument** of the dorsum and sides of the nose is thin, and loosely connected with the subjacent parts; but over the tip and alæ it is thicker and more firmly adherent, and is furnished with a large number of sebaceous follicles, the orifices of which are usually very distinct.

The **arteries** of the external nose are the alar and septal branches of the external maxillary, which supply the alæ and septum; the dorsum and sides being supplied from the dorsal nasal branch of the ophthalmic and the infraorbital branch of the internal maxillary. The **veins** end in the anterior facial and ophthalmic veins.

The **nerves** for the muscles of the nose are derived from the facial, while the skin receives branches from the infratrochlear and nasociliary branches of the ophthalmic, and from the infraorbital of the maxillary.

THE NASAL CAVITY

The **nasal cavity** (*cavum nasi*) is divided by the median nasal septum into two symmetrical and approximately equal chambers, the **nasal fossæ.** They have their external openings through the nostrils or nares, and they open into the nasopharynx behind through the choanæ. The nares are oval apertures measuring about 1.5 cm. anteroposteriorly and 1 cm. transversely. The choanæ are two oval openings measuring approximately 2.5 cm. vertically and 1.5 cm. transversely.

The bony boundaries of the nasal cavity are described in the chapter on Osteology, page 175.

Inside the aperture of the nostril is a slight dilatation, the **vestibule,** bounded laterally by the ala and lateral crus of the greater alar cartilage, and medially by the medial crus of the same cartilage. It is lined by skin containing hairs and sebaceous glands, and extends as a small recess toward the apex of the nose. Each

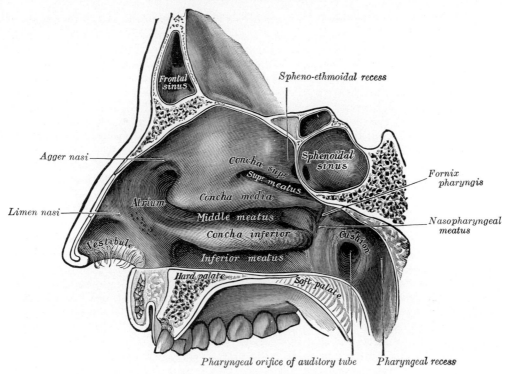

Fig. 964.—Lateral wall of nasal cavity.

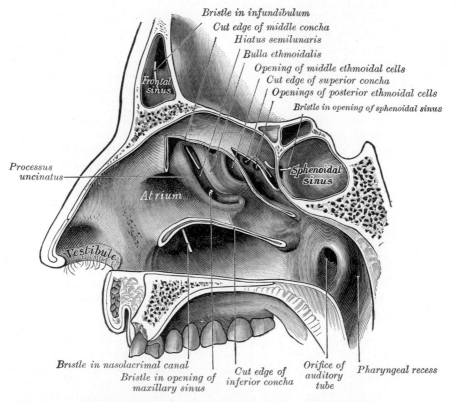

Fig. 965.—Lateral wall of nasal cavity; the three nasal conchæ have been removed.

nasal fossa, above and behind the vestibule, is divided into two parts: an **olfactory region**, consisting of the superior nasal concha and the opposed part of the septum, and a **respiratory region**, which comprises the rest of the cavity.

Lateral Wall (Figs. 964, 965).—On the lateral wall are the **superior, middle,** and **inferior nasal conchæ,** and below and lateral to each concha is the corresponding nasal passage or meatus. Above the superior concha is a narrow recess, the **sphenoethmoidal recess,** into which the sphenoidal sinus opens. The **superior meatus** is a short oblique passage extending about half-way along the upper border of the middle concha; the posterior ethmoidal cells open into the front part of this meatus. The **middle meatus** is below and lateral to the middle concha, and is continued anteriorly into a shallow depression, situated above the vestibule and named the **atrium** of the middle meatus. By raising or removing the middle concha the lateral wall of this meatus is fully displayed. On it is a rounded elevation, the **bulla ethmoidalis,** and below and in front of this is a curved cleft, the **hiatus semilunaris.**

The **bulla ethmoidalis** is caused by the bulging of the middle ethmoidal cells which open on or immediately above it, and the size of the bulla varies with that of its contained cells.

The **hiatus semilunaris** is bounded inferiorly by the sharp concave margin of the **uncinate process** of the ethmoid bone, and leads into a curved channel, the **infundibulum,** bounded above by the bulla ethmoidalis and below by the lateral surface of the uncinate process of the ethmoid. The anterior ethmoidal cells open into the front part of the infundibulum, and this in slightly over 50 per cent. of subjects is directly continuous with the frontonasal duct or passage leading from the frontal air sinus; but when the anterior end of the uncinate process fuses with the front part of the bulla, this continuity is interrupted and the frontonasal duct then opens directly into the anterior end of the middle meatus.

Below the bulla ethmoidalis, and partly hidden by the inferior end of the uncinate process, is the **ostium maxillare,** or opening from the maxillary sinus; in a frontal section this opening is seen to be placed near the roof of the sinus. An accessory opening from the sinus is frequently present below the posterior end of the middle nasal concha. The **inferior meatus** is below and lateral to the inferior nasal concha; the nasolacrimal duct opens into this meatus under cover of the anterior part of the inferior concha.

Medial Wall (Fig. 963).—The medial wall or septum is frequently more or less deflected from the median plane, thus lessening the size of one nasal fossa and increasing that of the other; ridges or spurs of bone growing into one or other fossa from the septum are also sometimes present. Immediately over the incisive canal at the lower edge of the cartilage of the septum a depression, the **nasopalatine recess,** is seen. In the septum close to this recess a minute orifice may be discerned; it leads backward into a blind pouch, the rudimentary **vomeronasal organ of Jacobson,** which is supported by a strip of cartilage, the **vomeronasal cartilage.** This organ is well-developed in many of the lower animals, where it apparently plays a part in the sense of smell, since it is supplied by twigs of the olfactory nerve and lined by epithelium similar to that in the olfactory region of the nose.

The **roof** of the nasal fossa is narrow from side to side, except at its posterior part, and may be divided, from behind forward, into sphenoidal, ethmoidal, and frontonasal parts, after the bones which form it.

The **floor** is concave from side to side and almost horizontal antero-posteriorly; its anterior three-fourths are formed by the palatine process of the maxilla, its posterior fourth by the horizontal process of the palatine bone. In its antero-medial part, directly over the incisive foramen, a small depression, the **nasopalatine recess,** is sometimes seen; it points downward and forward and occupies the position of a canal which connected the nasal with the buccal cavity in early fetal life.

The Mucous Membrane (*membrana mucosa nasi*).—The nasal mucous membrane lines the nasal fossæ, and is intimately adherent to the periosteum or perichondrium. It is continuous with the skin through the nares, and with the mucous membrane of the nasal part of the pharynx through the choanæ. From the nasal fossa its continuity with the conjunctiva may be traced, through the nasolacrimal and lacrimal ducts; and with the frontal, ethmoidal, sphenoidal, and maxillary sinuses, through the several openings in the meatuses. The mucous membrane is thickest, and most vascular, over the nasal conchæ. It is also thick over the septum; but it is very thin in the meatuses on the floor of the nasal cavity, and in the various sinuses.

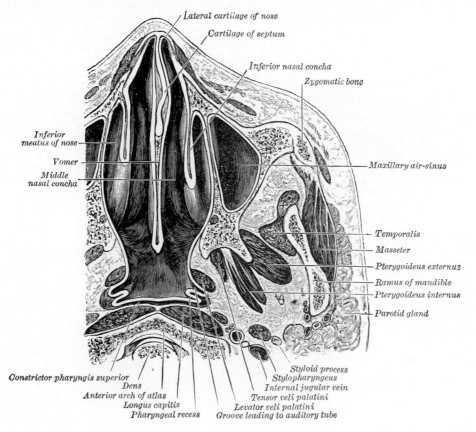

FIG. 966.—Transverse section through the anterior part of the head at a level just below the apex of the dens (odontoid process). Viewed from below.

Owing to the thickness of the greater part of this membrane, the nasal cavities are much narrower, and the middle and inferior nasal conchæ appear larger and more prominent than in the skeleton; also the various apertures communicating with the meatuses are considerably narrowed.

Structure of the Mucous Membrane.—The mucous membrane covering the respiratory portion of the nasal cavity has a pseudostratified, ciliated, columnar epithelium, liberally interspersed with goblet cells. Beneath the basement membrane of the epithelium, the areolar connective tissue is infiltrated with lymphocytes which may be so numerous that they form a diffuse lymphoid tissue. The lamina propria is composed of a layer of glands toward the surface and a layer of blood vessels next the periosteum. The glands may be large or small and contain either mucous or serous alveoli. They have individual openings on the surface, and their secretion forms a protective layer over the membrane which serves to warm and moisten the inspired air. In the deeper layers of the lamina propria, especially over the conchæ, the dilated veins and blood spaces form a rich plexus which bears a superficial resemblance to erectile tissue; they easily become engorged as the result of irritation or inflammation, causing the membrane to swell, encroaching upon the lumen of the meatuses and even occluding the ostia of the sinuses.

The mucous membrane of the paranasal sinuses is columnar ciliated, similar to that of the nasal fossæ, but is much thinner and for the most part is lacking in glands in the lamina propria.

Vessels and Nerves.—The **arteries** of the nasal cavities are the anterior and posterior ethmoidal branches of the ophthalmic, which supply the ethmoidal cells, frontal sinuses, and roof of the nose; the sphenopalatine branch of the internal maxillary, which supplies the mucous membrane covering the conchæ, the meatuses and septum; the septal branch of the superior labial of the external maxillary; the infraorbital and alveolar branches of the internal maxillary, which supply the lining membrane of the maxillary sinus; and the pharyngeal branch of the same artery, distributed to the sphenoidal sinus. The ramifications of these vessels form a close plexiform network, beneath and in the substance of the mucous membrane.

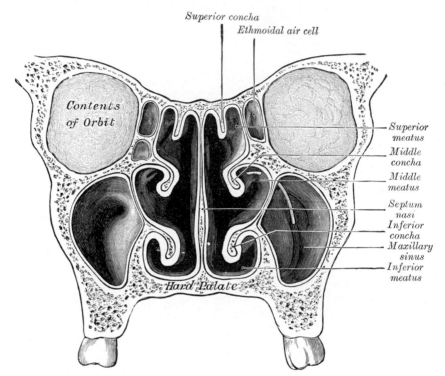

FIG. 967.—Coronal section of nasal cavities.

Some **veins** open into the sphenopalatine vein; others join the anterior facial vein; some accompany the ethmoidal arteries, and end in the ophthalmic veins; and, lastly, a few communicate with the veins on the orbital surface of the frontal lobe of the brain, through the foramina in the cribriform plate of the ethmoid bone; when the foramen cecum is patent it transmits a vein to the superior sagittal sinus.

The **lymphatics** have already been described (page 787).

The **nerves** of ordinary sensation are: the nasociliary branch of the ophthalmic, filaments from the anterior alveolar branch of the maxillary, the nerve of the pterygoid canal, the nasopalatine, the anterior palatine, and nasal branches of the sphenopalatine ganglion.

The nasociliary branch of the ophthalmic distributes filaments to the forepart of the septum and lateral wall of the nasal cavity. Filaments from the anterior alveolar nerve supply the inferior meatus and inferior concha. The nerve of the pterygoid canal supplies the upper and back part of the septum, and superior concha; and the upper nasal branches from the sphenopalatine ganglion have a similar distribution. The nasopalatine nerve supplies the middle of the septum. The anterior palatine nerve supplies the lower nasal branches to the middle and inferior conchæ.

The *olfactory*, the special nerve of the sense of smell, is distributed to the olfactory region Its fibers arise from the bipolar olfactory cells and are destitute of medullary sheaths. They unite in fasciculi which form a plexus beneath the mucous membrane and then ascend in grooves or canals in the ethmoid bone; they pass into the skull through the foramina in the cribriform plate of the ethmoid and enter the under surface of the olfactory bulb, in which they ramify and form synapses with the dendrites of the mitral cells (see Organs of the Senses, page 1093).

The Accessory Sinuses of the Nose (Sinus Paranasales) (Figs. 964, 965, 967.)

The **accessory sinuses** or **air cells of the nose** are the **frontal, ethmoidal, sphenoidal**, and **maxillary**; they vary in size and form in different individuals, and are lined by ciliated mucous membrane directly continuous with that of the nasal cavities.

The **Frontal Sinuses** (*sinus frontales*), situated behind the superciliary arches, are rarely symmetrical, and the septum between them frequently deviates to one or other side of the middle line. Their average measurements are as follows: height, 3 cm.; breadth, 2.5 cm.; depth from before backward, 2.5 cm. Each opens into the anterior part of the corresponding middle meatus of the nose through the frontonasal duct which traverses the anterior part of the labyrinth of the ethmoid. Absent at birth, they are generally fairly well developed between the seventh and eighth years, but only reach their full size after puberty.

The **Ethmoidal Air Cells** (*cellulæ ethmoidales*) consist of numerous thin-walled cavities situated in the ethmoidal labyrinth and completed by the frontal, maxilla, lacrimal, sphenoidal, and palatine. They lie between the upper parts of the nasal cavities and the orbits, and are separated from these cavities by thin bony laminæ. On either side they are arranged in three groups, **anterior, middle,** and **posterior.** The anterior and middle groups open into the middle meatus of the nose, the former by way of the infundibulum, the latter on or above the bulla ethmoidalis. The posterior cells open into the superior meatus under cover of the superior nasal concha; sometimes one or more opens into the sphenoidal sinus. The ethmoidal cells begin to develop during fetal life.

The **Sphenoidal Sinuses** (*sinus sphenoidales*) (Fig. 965) contained within the body of the sphenoid vary in size and shape; owing to the lateral displacement of the intervening septum they are rarely symmetrical. The following are their average measurements: vertical height, 2.2 cm.; transverse breadth, 2 cm.; antero-posterior depth, 2.2 cm. When exceptionally large they may extend into the roots of the pterygoid processes or great wings, and may invade the basilar part of the occipital bone. Each sinus communicates with the sphenoethmoidal recess by means of an aperture in the upper part of its anterior wall. They are present as minute cavities at birth, but their main development takes place after puberty.

The **Maxillary Sinus** (*sinus maxillaris; antrum of Highmore*), the largest of the accessory sinuses of the nose, is a pyramidal cavity in the body of the maxilla. Its base is formed by the lateral wall of the nasal cavity, and its apex extends into the zygomatic process. Its roof or orbital wall is frequently ridged by the infra-orbital canal, while its floor is formed by the alveolar process and is usually $\frac{1}{2}$ to 10 mm. below the level of the floor of the nose; projecting into the floor are several conical elevations corresponding with the roots of the first and second molar teeth, and in some cases the floor is perforated by one or more of these roots. The size of the sinus varies in different skulls, and even on the two sides of the same skull. The adult capacity varies from 9.5 c.c. to 20 c.c., average about 14.75 c.c. The following measurements are those of an average-sized sinus: vertical height opposite the first molar tooth, 3.75 cm.; transverse breadth, 2.5 cm.; antero-posterior depth, 3 cm. In the antero-superior part of its base is an opening through which it communicates with the lower part of the hiatus semilunaris; a second orifice is frequently seen in, or immediately behind, the hiatus. The maxillary sinus appears as a shallow groove on the medial surface of the bone about the fourth month of fetal life, but does not reach its full size until after the second dentition. At birth it measures about 7 mm. in the dorso-ventral direction and at twenty months about 20 mm.

THE LARYNX.

The **larynx** or **organ of voice** is placed at the upper part of the air passage. It is situated between the trachea and the root of the tongue, at the upper and forepart of the neck, where it presents a considerable projection in the middle line. It forms the lower part of the anterior wall of the pharynx, and is covered behind by the mucous lining of that cavity; on either side of it lie the great vessels of the neck. Its vertical extent corresponds to the fourth, fifth, and sixth cervical vertebræ, but it is placed somewhat higher in the female and also during childhood. Symington found that in infants between six and twelve months of age the tip of the epiglottis was a little above the level of the fibrocartilage between the odontoid process and body of the axis, and that between infancy and adult life the larynx descends for a distance equal to two vertebral bodies and two intervertebral fibrocartilages. According to Sappey the average measurements of the adult larynx are as follows:

	In males.	In females.
Length	44 mm.	36 mm.
Transverse diameter	43 "	41 "
Antero-posterior diameter	36 "	26 "
Circumference	136 "	112 "

Until puberty the larynx of the male differs little in size from that of the female. In the female its increase after puberty is only slight; in the male it undergoes considerable increase; all the cartilages are enlarged and the thyroid cartilage becomes prominent in the middle line of the neck, while the length of the rima glottidis is nearly doubled.

The larynx is broad above, where it presents the form of a triangular box flattened behind and at the sides, and bounded in front by a prominent vertical ridge. Below, it is narrow and cylindrical. It is composed of cartilages, which are connected together by ligaments and moved by numerous muscles. It is lined by mucous membrane continuous above with that of the pharynx and below with that of the trachea.

The **Cartilages of the Larynx** (*cartilagines laryngis*) (Fig. 968) are nine in number, three single and three paired, as follows:

Thyroid.	Two Corniculate.
Cricoid.	Two Cuneiform.
Two Arytenoid.	Epiglottis.

The **Thyroid Cartilage** (*cartilago thyreoidea*) is the largest cartilage of the larynx. It consists of two laminæ the anterior borders of which are fused with each other at an acute angle in the middle line of the neck, and form a subcutaneous projection named the **laryngeal prominence** (Adam's apple). This prominence is most distinct at its upper part, and is larger in the male than in the female. Immediately above it the laminæ are separated by a V-shaped notch, the **superior thyroid notch**. The laminæ are irregularly quadrilateral in shape, and their posterior angles are prolonged into processes termed the **superior** and **inferior cornua.**

On the *outer surface* of each lamina an **oblique line** runs downward and forward from the superior thyroid tubercle situated near the root of the superior cornu, to the inferior thyroid tubercle on the lower border. This line gives attachment to the Sternothyreoideus, Thyreohyoideus, and Constrictor pharyngis inferior. The *inner surface* is smooth; above and behind, it is slightly concave and covered by mucous membrane. In front, in the angle formed by the junction of the laminæ, are attached the stem of the epiglottis, the ventricular and vocal ligaments, the Thyreoarytænoidei, Thyreoepiglottici and Vocales muscles, and the thyroepiglottic ligament. The *upper border* is concave behind and convex in front; it gives attachment to the corresponding half of the hyothyroid membrane. The *lower border* is concave behind, and nearly straight in front, the two parts being separated by the inferior thyroid tubercle. A small part of it in and near the middle line is connected to the cricoid cartilage by the middle cricothyroid ligament. The *posterior border*, thick and rounded, receives the insertions of the Stylopharyngeus and Pharyngopalatinus. It ends above, in the superior cornu, and below, in the inferior cornu.

The **superior cornu** is long and narrow, directed upward, backward, and medialward, and ends in a conical extremity, which gives attachment to the lateral hyothyroid ligament. The **inferior cornu** is short and thick; it is directed downward, with a slight inclination forward and medialward, and presents, on the medial side of its tip, a small oval articular facet for articulation with the side of the cricoid cartilage.

During infancy the laminæ of the thyroid cartilage are joined to each other by a narrow, lozenge-shaped strip, named the **intrathyroid cartilage**. This strip extends from the upper to the lower border of the cartilage in the middle line, and is distinguished from the laminæ by being more transparent and more flexible.

The **Cricoid Cartilage** (*cartilago cricoidea*) is smaller, but thicker and stronger than the thyroid, and forms the lower and posterior parts of the wall of the larynx. It consists of two parts: a **posterior quadrate lamina**, and a narrow **anterior arch**, one-fourth or one-fifth of the depth of the lamina.

The **lamina** (*lamina cartilaginis cricoideæ; posterior portion*) is deep and broad, and measures from above downward about 2 or 3 cm.; on its posterior surface, in the middle line, is a vertical ridge to the lower part of which are attached the longitudinal fibers of the esophagus; and on either side of this a broad depression for the Cricoarytænoideus posterior.

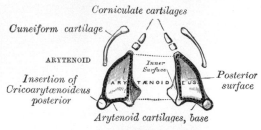

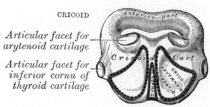

FIG. 968.—The cartilages of the larynx. Posterior view.

The **arch** (*arcus cartilaginis cricoideæ; anterior portion*) is narrow and convex, and measures vertically from 5 to 7 mm.; it affords attachment externally in front and at the sides to the Cricothyreiodei, and behind, to part of the Constrictor pharyngis inferior.

On either side, at the junction of the lamina with the arch, is a small round articular surface, for articulation with the inferior cornu of the thyroid cartilage.

The lower border of the cricoid cartilage is horizontal, and connected to the highest ring of the trachea by the cricotracheal ligament. The upper border runs obliquely upward and backward, owing to the great depth of the lamina. It gives attachment, in front, to the middle cricothyroid ligament; at the side, to the conus elasticus and the Cricoarytænoidei laterales; behind, it presents, in the middle, a shallow notch, and on either side of this is a smooth, oval, convex surface, directed upward and lateralward, for articulation with the base of an arytenoid cartilage. The inner surface of the cricoid cartilage is smooth, and lined by mucous membrane.

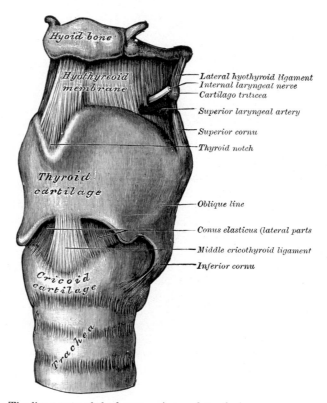

Fig. 969.—The ligaments of the larynx. Antero-lateral view.

The **Arytenoid Cartilages** (*cartilagines arytænoideæ*) are two in number, and situated at the upper border of the lamina of the cricoid cartilage, at the back of the larynx. Each is pyramidal in form, and has three surfaces, a base, and an apex.

The posterior surface is triangular, smooth, concave, and gives attachment to the Arytænoidei obliquus and transversus. The antero-lateral surface is somewhat convex and rough. On it, near the apex of the cartilage, is a rounded elevation **(colliculus)** from which a ridge **(crista arcuata)** curves at first backward and then downward and forward to the vocal process. The lower part of this crest intervenes between two depressions or **foveæ**, an upper, triangular, and a lower oblong in shape; the latter gives attachment to the Vocalis muscle. The medial surface is narrow, smooth, and flattened, covered by mucous membrane, and forms the lateral boundary of the intercartilaginous part of the rima glottidis. The base of each cartilage is broad, and on it is a concave smooth surface, for articulation with the cricoid cartilage. Its lateral angle is short, rounded, and prominent; it projects backward and lateralward, and is termed the **muscular process**; it gives insertion to the Crico-arytænoideus posterior behind, and to the Cricoarytænoideus lateralis in front. Its anterior angle, also prominent, but more pointed, projects horizontally forward; it gives attachment to the vocal ligament, and is called the **vocal process** (Fig. 971).

The **apex** of each cartilage is pointed, curved backward and medialward, and surmounted by a small conical, cartilaginous nodule, the **corniculate cartilage.**

The **Corniculate Cartilages** (*cartilagines corniculatæ; cartilages of Santorini*) are two small conical nodules consisting of yellow elastic cartilage, which articulate with the summits of the arytenoid cartilages and serve to prolong them backward and medialward. They are situated in the posterior parts of the aryepiglottic folds of mucous membrane, and are sometimes fused with the arytenoid cartilages.

The **Cuneiform Cartilages** (*cartilagines cuneiformes; cartilages of Wrisberg*) are two small, elongated pieces of yellow elastic cartilage, placed one on either side, in the aryepiglottic fold, where they give rise to small whitish elevations on the surface of the mucous membrane, just in front of the arytenoid cartilages.

The **Epiglottis** (*cartilago epiglottica*) is a thin lamella of yellow elastic cartilage, shaped like a leaf, and projecting obliquely upward behind the root of the tongue, in front of the entrance to the larynx. The free extremity is broad and rounded; the attached part or stem is long, marrow, and connected by the **thyroepiglottic ligament** to the angle formed by the two laminæ of the thyroid cartilage, a short distance below the superior thyroid notch. The lower part of its anterior surface is connected to the upper border of the body of the hyoid bone by an elastic ligamentous band, the **hyoepiglottic ligament.**

The **anterior** or **lingual surface** is curved forward, and covered on its upper, free part by mucous membrane which is reflected on to the sides and root of the tongue, forming a median and two lateral **glossoepiglottic folds;** the lateral folds are partly attached to the wall of the pharynx. The depressions between the epiglottis and the root of the tongue, on either side of the median fold, are named the **valleculæ** (Fig. 973). The lower part of the anterior surface lies behind the hyoid bone, the hyothyroid membrane, and upper part of the thyroid cartilage, but is separated from these structures by a mass of fatty tissue.

The **posterior** or **laryngeal surface** is smooth, concave from side to side, concavo-convex from above downward; its lower part projects backward as an elevation, the **tubercle** or **cushion.** When the mucous membrane is removed, the surface of the cartilage is seen to be indented by a number of small pits, in which mucous glands are lodged. To its sides the aryepiglottic folds are attached.

Structure.—The corniculate and cuneiform cartilages, the epiglottis, and the apices of the arytenoids at first consist of hyaline cartilage, but later elastic fibers are deposited in the matrix, converting them into yellow elastic cartilage, which shows little tendency to calcification. The thyroid, cricoid, and the greater part of the arytenoids consist of hyaline cartilage, and become more or less ossified as age advances. Ossification commences about the twenty-fifth year in the thyroid cartilage, and somewhat later in the cricoid and arytenoids; by the sixty-fifth year these cartilages may be completely converted into bone.

Ligaments.—The ligaments of the larynx (Figs. 969, 970) are **extrinsic,** *i. e.,* those connecting the thyroid cartilage and epiglottis with the hyoid bone, and the cricoid cartilage with the trachea; and **intrinsic,** those which connect the several cartilages of the larynx to each other.

Extrinsic Ligaments.—The ligaments connecting the thyroid cartilage with the hyoid bone are the thyrohyoid membrane, and a middle and two lateral thyrohyoid ligaments.

The **Thyrohyoid Membrane** (*membrana thyreohyoidea; hyothyroid membrane*) is a broad, fibro-elastic layer, attached below to the upper border of the thyroid cartilage and to the front of its superior cornu, and above to the upper margin of the posterior surface of the body and greater cornua of the hyoid bone, thus passing behind the posterior surface of the body of the hyoid, and being separated from it by a mucous bursa, which facilitates the upward movement of the larynx during deglutition. Its middle thicker part is termed the **middle thyrohyoid ligament** (*ligamentum thyreohyoideum medium; middle hyothyroid ligament*), its lateral thinner portions are pierced by the superior laryngeal vessels and the internal branch of the superior laryngeal nerve. Its anterior surface is in relation with the Thyreo-hyoideus, Sternohyoideus, and Omohyoideus, and with the body of the hyoid bone.

The **Thyrohyoid Ligament** (*ligamentum thyreohyoideum; lateral hyothyroid ligament*) is a round elastic cord, which forms the posterior border of the hyothyroid membrane and passes between the tip of the superior cornu of the thyroid cartilage and the extremity of the greater cornu of the hyoid bone. A small cartilaginous nodule (*cartilago triticea*), sometimes bony, is frequently found in it.

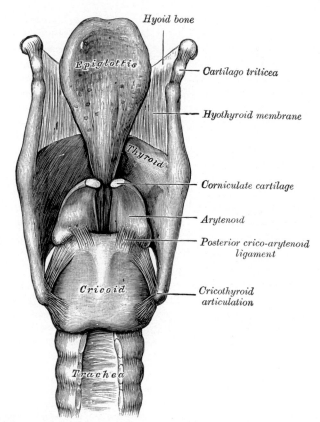

Fig. 970.—Ligaments of the larynx. Posterior view.

The **Epiglottis** is connected with the hyoid bone by an elastic band, the **hyo-epiglottic ligament** (*ligamentum hyoepiglotticum*), which extends from the anterior surface of the epiglottis to the upper border of the body of the hyoid bone. The glossoepiglottic folds of mucous membrane (page 1179) may also be considered as extrinsic ligaments of the epiglottis.

The **Cricotracheal Ligament** (*ligamentum cricotracheale*) connects the cricoid cartilage with the first ring of the trachea. It resembles the fibrous membrane which connects the cartilaginous rings of the trachea to each other.

Intrinsic Ligaments.—Beneath the mucous membrane of the larynx is a broad sheet of fibrous tissue containing many elastic fibers, and termed the **elastic membrane of the larynx.** It is subdivided on either side by the interval between the ventricular and vocal ligaments, the upper portion extends between the arytenoid cartilage and the epiglottis and is often poorly defined; the lower part is a well-marked membrane forming, with its fellow of the opposite side, the conus elasticus which connects the thyroid, cricoid, and arytenoid cartilages to one another. In addition the joints between the individual cartilages are provided with ligaments.

The **Conus Elasticus** (*cricothyroid membrane*) is composed mainly of yellow elastic tissue. It consists of an anterior and two lateral portions. The **anterior part** or **middle cricothyroid ligament** (*ligamentum cricothyreoideum medium; central part of cricothyroid membrane*) is thick and strong, narrow above and broad below. It connects together the front parts of the contiguous margins of the thyroid and cricoid cartilages. It is overlapped on either side by the Cricothyreoideus, but between these is subcutaneous; it is crossed horizontally by a small anastomotic arterial arch, formed by the junction of the two cricothyroid arteries, branches of which pierce it. The **lateral portions** are thinner and lie close under the mucous membrane of the larynx; they extend from the superior border of the cricoid cartilage to the inferior margin of the vocal ligaments, with which they are continuous. These ligaments may therefore be regarded as the free borders of the lateral portions of the conus elasticus, and extend from the vocal processes of the arytenoid cartilages to the angle of the thyroid cartilage about midway between its upper and lower borders.

An **articular capsule**, strengthened posteriorly by a well-marked fibrous band, encloses the articulation of the inferior cornu of the thyroid with the cricoid cartilage on either side.

Each arytenoid cartilage is connected to the cricoid by a capsule and a posterior cricoarytenoid ligament. The **capsule** (*capsula articularis cricoarytenoidea*) is thin and loose, and is attached to the margins of the articular surfaces. The **posterior cricoarytenoid ligament** (*ligamentum cricoarytenoideum posterius*) extends from the cricoid to the medial and back part of the base of the arytenoid.

The **thyroepiglottic ligament** (*ligamentum thyreoepiglotticum*) is a long, slender, elastic cord which connects the stem of the epiglottis with the angle of the thyroid cartilage, immediately beneath the superior thyroid notch, above the attachment of the ventricular ligaments.

Movements.—The articulation between the inferior cornu of the thyroid cartilage and the cricoid cartilage on either side is a diarthrodial one, and permits of rotatory and gliding movements. The rotatory movement is one in which the cricoid cartilage rotates upon the inferior cornua of the thyroid cartilage around an axis passing transversely through both joints. The gliding movement consists in a limited shifting of the cricoid on the thyroid in different directions.

The articulation between the arytenoid cartilages and the cricoid is also a diarthrodial one, and permits of two varieties of movement: one is a rotation of the arytenoid on a vertical axis, whereby the vocal process is moved lateralward or medialward, and the rima glottidis increased or diminished; the other is a gliding movement, and allows the arytenoid cartilages to approach or recede from each other; from the direction and slope of the articular surfaces lateral gliding is accompanied by a forward and downward movement. The two movements of gliding and rotation are associated, the medial gliding being connected with medialward rotation, and the lateral gliding with lateralward rotation. The posterior cricoarytenoid ligaments limit the forward movement of the arytenoid cartilages on the cricoid.

Interior of the Larynx (Figs. 971, 972).—The **cavity of the larynx** (*cavum laryngis*) extends from the laryngeal entrance to the lower border of the cricoid cartilage where it is continuous with that of the trachea. It is divided into two parts by the projection of the vocal folds, between which is a narrow triangular fissure or chink, the **rima glottidis**. The portion of the cavity of the larynx above the vocal folds is called the **vestibule**; it is wide and triangular in shape, its base or anterior wall presenting, however, about its center the backward projection of the tubercle of the epiglottis. It contains the ventricular folds, and between these and the vocal folds are the **ventricles of the larynx**. The portion below the vocal folds is at first of an elliptical form, but lower down it widens out, assumes a circular form, and is continuous with the tube of the trachea.

The **entrance of the larynx** (Fig. 973) is a triangular opening, wide in front, narrow behind, and sloping obliquely downward and backward. It is bounded, in front, by the epiglottis; behind, by the apices of the arytenoid cartilages, the corniculate cartilages, and the interarytenoid notch; and on either side, by a fold of mucous membrane, enclosing ligamentous and muscular fibers, stretched between the side of the epiglottis and the apex of the arytenoid cartilage; this is the **aryepiglottic fold,** on the posterior part of the margin of which the cuneiform cartilage forms a more or less distinct whitish prominence, the **cuneiform tubercle.**

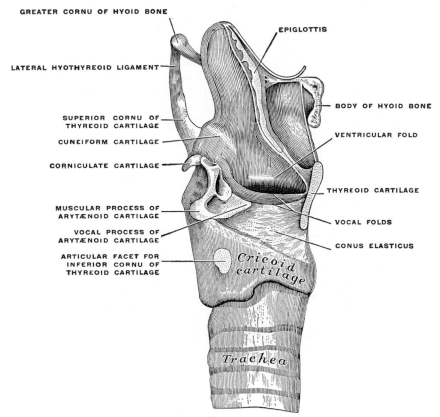

GREATER CORNU OF HYOID BONE

EPIGLOTTIS

LATERAL HYOTHYREOID LIGAMENT

BODY OF HYOID BONE

SUPERIOR CORNU OF THYREOID CARTILAGE

VENTRICULAR FOLD

CUNEIFORM CARTILAGE

CORNICULATE CARTILAGE

THYREOID CARTILAGE

MUSCULAR PROCESS OF ARYTÆNOID CARTILAGE

VOCAL FOLDS

VOCAL PROCESS OF ARYTÆNOID CARTILAGE

CONUS ELASTICUS

ARTICULAR FACET FOR INFERIOR CORNU OF THYREOID CARTILAGE

Cricoid cartilage

Trachea

Fig. 971.—A dissection to show the right half of the conus elasticus. The right lamina of the thyroid cartilage and the subjacent muscles have been removed.

The **Ventricular Folds** (*plicæ ventriculares; superior or false vocal cords*) are two thick folds of mucous membrane, each enclosing a narrow band of fibrous tissue, the **ventricular ligament** which is attached in front to the angle of the thyroid cartilage immediately below the attachment of the epiglottis, and behind to the antero-lateral surface of the arytenoid cartilage, a short distance above the vocal process. The lower border of this ligament, enclosed in mucous membrane, forms a free crescentic margin, which constitutes the upper boundary of the ventricle of the larynx.

The **Vocal Folds** (*plicæ vocales; inferior or true vocal cords*) are concerned in the production of sound, and enclose two strong bands, named the **vocal ligaments** (*ligamenta vocales; inferior thyroarytenoid*). Each ligament consists of a band of yellow elastic tissue, attached in front to the angle of the thyroid cartilage, and behind to the vocal process of the arytenoid. Its lower border is continuous with the thin lateral part of the conus elasticus. Its upper border forms the lower boundary of the ventricle of the larynx. Laterally, the Vocalis muscle lies parallel with it. It is covered medially by mucous membrane, which is extremely thin and closely adherent to its surface.

The **Ventricle of the Larynx** (*ventriculus laryngis* [*Morgagnii*]; *laryngeal sinus*) is a fusiform fossa, situated between the ventricular and vocal folds on either side, and extending nearly their entire length. The fossa is bounded, *above*, by the free crescentic edge of the ventricular fold; *below*, by the straight margin of the vocal fold; *laterally*, by the mucous membrane covering the corresponding Thyreoarytaenoideus. The anterior part of the ventricle leads up by a narrow opening into a cecal pouch of mucous membrane of variable size called the **appendix**.

The **appendix of the laryngeal ventricle** (*appendix ventriculi laryngis; laryngeal saccule*) is a membranous sac, placed between the ventricular fold and the inner

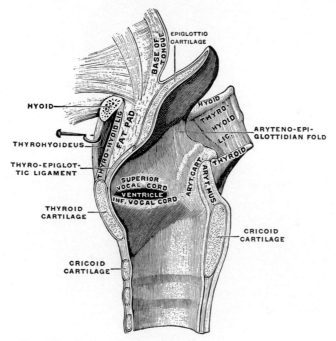

Fig. 972.—Sagittal section of larynx, right half. (Testut.)

surface of the thyroid cartilage, occasionally extending as far as its upper border or even higher; it is conical in form, and curved slightly backward. On the surface of its mucous membrane are the openings of sixty or seventy mucous glands, which are lodged in the submucous areolar tissue. This sac is enclosed in a fibrous capsule, continuous below with the ventricular ligament. Its medial surface is covered by a few delicate muscular fasciculi, which *arise* from the apex of the arytenoid cartilage and become lost in the aryepiglottic fold of mucous membrane; laterally it is separated from the thyroid cartilage by the Thyreoepiglotticus. These muscles compress the sac, and express the secretion it contains upon the vocal folds to lubricate their surfaces.

The **Rima Glottidis** (Fig. 974) is the elongated fissure or chink between the vocal folds in front, and the bases and vocal processes of the arytenoid cartilages behind. It is therefore subdivided into a larger anterior intramembranous part (*glottis vocalis*), which measures about three-fifths of the length of the entire aperture, and a posterior intercartilaginous part (*glottis respiratoria*). Posteriorly it is limited by the mucous membrane passing between the arytenoid cartilages. The rima glottidis is the narrowest part of the cavity of the larynx, and its level corresponds with the bases of the arytenoid cartilages. Its length, in the male, is about 23 mm.; in the female from 17 to 18 mm. The width and shape of the rima glottidis vary with the movements of the vocal folds and arytenoid cartilages during respiration and phonation. In the condition of rest, *i.e.*, when these structures are uninfluenced by muscular action, as in quiet respiration, the intermembranous part is triangular, with its apex in front and its base behind—the latter being represented by a line, about 8 mm. long, connecting the anterior ends of the vocal processes, while the medial surfaces of the arytenoids are parallel to each other, and hence the intercartilaginous part

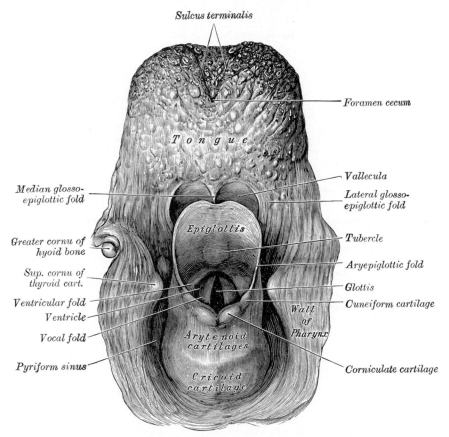

FIG. 973.—The entrance to the larynx, viewed from behind.

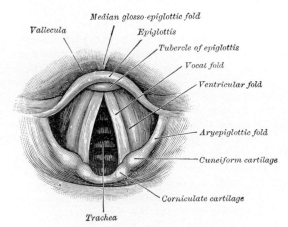

FIG. 974.—Laryngoscopic view of interior of larynx.

is rectangular. During extreme adduction of the vocal folds, as in the emission of a high note, the intermembranous part is reduced to a linear slit by the apposition of the vocal folds, while the intercartilaginous part is triangular, its apex corresponding to the anterior ends of the vocal processes of the arytenoids, which are approximated by the medial rotation of the cartilages. Conversely in extreme abduction of the vocal folds, as in forced inspiration, the arytenoids and their vocal processes are rotated lateralward, and the intercartilaginous part is triangular in shape but with its apex directed backward. In this condition the entire glottis is somewhat lozenge-shaped, the sides of the intramembranous part diverging from before backward, those of the intercartilaginous part diverging from behind forward—the widest part of the aperture corresponding with the attachments of the vocal folds to the vocal processes.

Muscles.—The muscles of the larynx are *extrinsic*, passing between the larynx and parts around—these have been described in the section on Myology; and *intrinsic*, confined entirely to the larynx.

The intrinsic muscles are:

Cricothyreoideus.   Cricoarytænoideus lateralis.
Cricoarytænoideus posterior.   Arytænoideus.
                  Thyroarytænoideus.

The **Cricothyreoideus** (*Cricothyroid*) (Fig. 975), triangular in form, *arises* from the front and lateral part of the cricoid cartilage; its fibers diverge, and are arranged in two groups. The lower fibers constitute a **pars obliqua** and slant backward and lateralward to the anterior border of the inferior cornu; the anterior fibers, forming a **pars recta**, run upward, backward, and lateralward to the posterior part of the lower border of the lamina of the thyroid cartilage.

The medial borders of the two muscles are separated by a triangular interval, occupied by the middle cricothyroid ligament.

The **Cricoarytænoideus posterior** (*posterior cricoarytenoid*) (Fig. 976) *arises* from the broad depression on the corresponding half of the posterior surface of the lamina of the cricoid cartilage; its fibers run upward and lateralward, and converge to be *inserted* into the back of the muscular process of the arytenoid cartilage. The uppermost fibers are nearly horizontal, the middle oblique, and the lowest almost vertical.

The **Cricoarytænoideus lateralis** (*lateral cricoarytenoid*) (Fig. 977) is smaller than the preceding, and of an oblong form. It *arises* from the upper border of the arch of the cricoid cartilage, and, passing obliquely upward and backward, is inserted into the front of the muscular process of the arytenoid cartilage.

The **Arytænoideus** (Fig. 976) is a single muscle, filling up the posterior concave surfaces of the arytenoid cartilages. It *arises* from the posterior surface and lateral border of one arytenoid cartilage, and is inserted into the corresponding parts of the opposite cartilage. It consists of oblique and transverse parts. The **Arytænoideus obliquus**, the more superficial, forms two fasciculi, which pass from the base of one cartilage to the apex of the opposite one, and therefore cross each other like the limbs of the letter X;

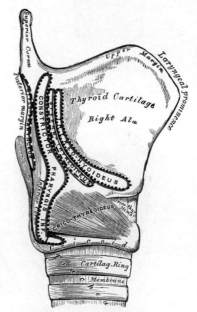

Fig. 975.—Side view of the larynx, showing muscular attachments.

a few fibers are continued around the lateral margin of the cartilage, and are prolonged into the aryepiglottic fold; they are sometimes described as a separate muscle, the **Aryepiglotticus**.   The **Arytænoideus transversus** crosses transversely between the two cartilages.

The **Thyreoarytænoideus** (*Thyroarytenoid*) (Figs. 977, 978) is a broad, thin, muscle which lies parallel with and lateral to the vocal fold, and supports the wall

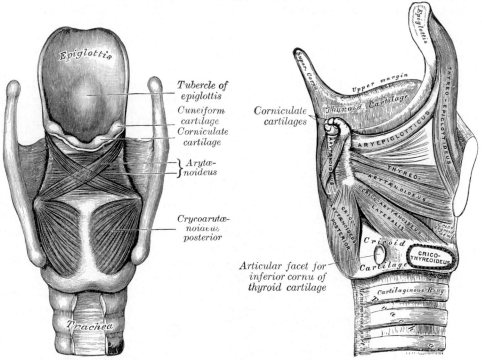

FIG. 976.—Muscles of larynx.
Posterior view.

FIG. 977.—Muscles of larynx. Side view. Right lamina of thyroid cartilage removed.

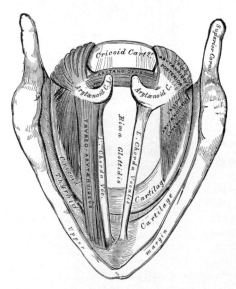

FIG. 978.—Muscles of the larynx, seen from above. (Enlarged.)

of the ventricle and its appendix. It *arises in front* from the lower half of the angle of the thyroid cartilage, and from the middle cricothyroid ligament. Its fibers pass backward and lateralward, to be *inserted* into the base and anterior surface of the arytenoid cartilage. The lower and deeper fibers of the muscle can be differentiated as a triangular band which is inserted into the vocal process of the arytenoid cartilage, and into the adjacent portion of its anterior surface; it is termed the **Vocalis**, and lies parallel with the vocal ligament, to which it is adherent.

A considerable number of the fibers of the Thyreoarytænoideus are prolonged into the aryepiglottic fold, where some of them become lost, while others are continued to the margin of the epiglottis. They have received a distinctive name,

Thyreoepiglotticus, and are sometimes described as a separate muscle. A few fibers extend along the wall of the ventricle from the lateral wall of the arytenoid cartilage to the side of the epiglottis and constitute the **Ventricularis** muscle.

Actions.—In considering the actions of the muscles of the larynx, they may be conveniently divided into two groups, *viz.*: 1. Those which open and close the glottis. 2. Those which regulate the degree of tension of the vocal folds.

The *Cricoarytænoidei posteriores* separate the vocal folds, and, consequently, open the glottis, by rotating the arytenoid cartilages outward around a vertical axis passing through the cricoarytenoid joints; so that their vocal processes and the vocal folds attached to them become widely separated.

The *Cricoarytænoidei laterales* close the glottis by rotating the arytenoid cartilages inward, so as to approximate their vocal processes.

The *Arytænoideus* approximates the arytenoid cartilages, and thus closes the opening of the glottis, especially at its back part.

The *Cricothyreoidei* produce tension and elongation of the vocal folds by drawing up the arch of the cricoid cartilage and tilting back the upper border of its lamina; the distance between the vocal processes and the angle of the thyroid is thus increased, and the folds are consequently elongated.

The *Thyreoarytænoidei,* consisting of two parts having different attachments and different directions, are rather complicated as regards their action. Their main use is to draw the arytenoid cartilages forward toward the thyroid, and thus shorten and relax the vocal folds. Their lateral portions rotate the arytenoid cartilage inward, and thus narrow the rima glottidis by bringing the two vocal folds together. Certain minute fibers of the vocalis division, inserting obliquely upon the vocal ligament and designated as the aryvocalis muscle, are considered by Strong to be chiefly responsible for the control of pitch, through their ability to regulate the length of the vibrating part of the vocal folds.

The manner in which the entrance of the larynx is closed during deglutition is referred to on page 1246.

Mucous Membrane.—The mucous membrane of the larynx is continuous above with that lining the mouth and pharynx, and is prolonged through the trachea and bronchi into the lungs. It lines the posterior surface and the upper part of the anterior surface of the epiglottis, to which it is closely adherent, and forms the aryepiglottic folds which bound the entrance of the larynx. It lines the whole of the cavity of the larynx; forms, by its reduplication, the chief part of the ventricular fold, and, from the ventricle, is continued into the ventricular appendix. It is then reflected over the vocal ligament, where it is thin, and very intimately adherent; covers the inner surface of the conus elasticus and cricoid cartilage; and is ultimately continuous with the lining membrane of the trachea. The anterior surface and the upper half of the posterior surface of the epiglottis, the upper part of the aryepiglottic folds and the vocal folds are covered by stratified squamous epithelium; all the rest of the laryngeal mucous membrane is covered by columnar ciliated cells, but patches of stratified squamous epithelium are found in the mucous membrane above the glottis.

Glands.—The mucous membrane of the larynx is furnished with numerous mucous secreting glands, the orifices of which are found in nearly every part; they are very plentiful upon the epiglottis, being lodged in little pits in its substance; they are also found in large numbers along the margin of the aryepiglottic fold, in front of the arytenoid cartilages, where they are termed the **arytenoid glands.** They exist also in large numbers in the ventricular appendages. None are found on the free edges of the vocal folds.

Vessels and Nerves.—The chief **arteries** of the larynx are the laryngeal branches derived from the superior and inferior thyroid. The **veins** accompany the arteries; those accompanying the superior laryngeal artery join the superior thyroid vein which opens into the internal jugular vein; while those accompanying the inferior laryngeal artery join the inferior thyroid vein which opens into the innominate vein. The **lymphatic vessels** consist of two sets, superior and inferior. The former accompany the superior laryngeal artery and pierce the hyothyroid membrane, to end in the nodes situated near the bifurcation of the common carotid artery. Of the latter, some pass through the middle cricothyroid ligament and open into nodes lying in front of that ligament or in front of the upper part of the trachea, while others pass to the deep cervical nodes and to the nodes accompanying the inferior thyroid artery. The **nerves** are derived from the internal and external branches of the superior laryngeal nerve, from the recurrent nerve, and from the sympathetic. The internal laryngeal branch is sensory. It enters the larynx by piercing the posterior part of the hyothyroid membrane above the superior laryngeal vessels, and divides into a branch which is distributed to both surfaces of the epiglottis, a second to the aryepiglottic fold, and a third, the largest, which supplies the mucous membrane over the back of the larynx and communicates with the recurrent nerve. The external laryngeal branch supplies the Cricothyreoideus. The recurrent nerve passes upward beneath the lower border of the Constrictor pharyngis inferior immediately behind the cricothyroid joint. It supplies all the muscles of the larynx except the Cricothyreoideus. The sensory branches of the laryngeal nerves form subepithelial plexuses, from which fibers pass to end between the cells covering the mucous membrane.

Over the posterior surface of the epiglottis, in the aryepiglottic folds, and less regularly in some other parts, taste-buds, similar to those in the tongue, are found.

THE TRACHEA AND BRONCHI (Figs. 979).

The **trachea** or **windpipe** is a cartilaginous and membranous tube, extending from the lower part of the larynx, on a level with the sixth cervical vertebra, to the

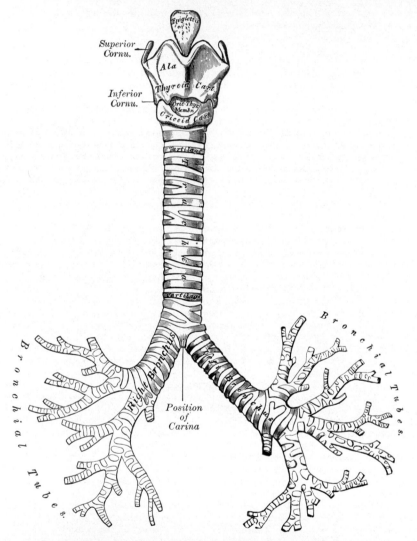

FIG. 979.—Front view of cartilages of larynx, trachea, and bronchi.

upper border of the fifth thoracic vertebra, where it divides into the two bronchi, one for each lung. The trachea is nearly but not quite cylindrical, being flattened posteriorly; it measures about 11 cm. in length; its diameter, from side to side, is from 2 to 2.5 cm., being always greater in the male than in the female. In the child the trachea is smaller, more deeply placed, and more movable than in the adult.

Relations.—The *anterior surface* of the trachea is convex, and covered, **in the neck,** from above downward, by the isthmus of the thyroid gland, the inferior thyroid veins, the arteria thyroidea ima (when that vessel exists), the Sternothyreoideus and Sternohyoideus muscles, the cervical fascia, and, more superficially, by the anastomosing branches between the anterior jugular veins; **in the thorax,** it is covered from before backward by the manubrium sterni, the remains of the thymus, the left innominate vein, the aortic arch, the innominate and left common carotid arteries, and the deep cardiac plexus. Posteriorly it is in contact with the esophagus. *Laterally,* **in the neck,** it is in relation with the common carotid arteries, the right and left lobes of the thyroid gland, the inferior thyroid arteries, and the recurrent nerves; **in the thorax,** it lies in the superior mediastinum, and is in relation on the right side with the pleura and right vagus, and near the root of the neck with the innominate artery; on its left side are the left recurrent nerve, the aortic arch, and the left common carotid and subclavian arteries.

The **Right Bronchus** (*bronchus dexter*) is wider, shorter, and less abrupt in its divergence from the trachea than the left. It is about 2.5 cm. long and enters the right lung nearly opposite the fifth thoracic vertebra. The azygos vein arches over it and the pulmonary artery lies at first inferior and then ventral to it. It gives rise to three subsidiary bronchi, one to each of the lobes. The superior lobe bronchus comes off above the pulmonary artery and was called by Aeby, therefore, the **eparterial bronchus.** The bronchi to the middle and inferior lobes separate below the pulmonary artery and are accordingly hyparterial in position.

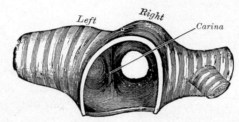

FIG. 980.—Bifurcation of the trachea, viewed from above, the interior showing the carina as it would be seen through a bronchoscope.

The **right superior lobe bronchus** divides into three branches named, according to the bronchopulmonary segments which they enter, the bronchus for the apical segment, for the posterior segment, and for the anterior segment. The **right middle lobe bronchus** divides into two branches, the bronchus for the lateral and for the medial segments. The **right inferior lobe bronchus** first gives off the bronchus to the superior segment, and then divides into four bronchi for the basal segments, the medial basal, anterior basal, lateral basal, and posterior basal segments.

The **Left Bronchus** (*bronchus sinister*) is smaller in caliber but about twice as long as the right (5 cm.). It passes under the aortic arch, and crosses ventral to the esophagus, thoracic duct, and descending aorta. It is superior to the pulmonary artery at first, then dorsal, and finally passes inferior to the artery before it divides into the bronchi for the superior and inferior lobes. Both lobar bronchi, therefore, are hyparterial in position.

The **left superior lobe bronchus** divides into two branches, one of which is distributed to a portion of the left lung corresponding to the right superior lobe, the other to a portion corresponding to the right middle lobe. These two branches are called the superior division and inferior division bronchi to differentiate them from segmental bronchi. The *superior division bronchus* of the left superior lobe divides into branches for the apical-posterior segment and the anterior segment. The *inferior division bronchus* divides into bronchi for the superior and inferior segments. The **left inferior lobe bronchus** gives off first the bronchus for the superior segment and then divides into three branches for basal segments, the anterior-medial basal, lateral basal, and posterior basal segments.

The picture seen through a bronchoscope may be reproduced if a section is made across the trachea and a bird's eye view taken of its interior (Fig. 980). At the bottom of the trachea, the septum which separates the two bronchi is visible as a spur (in bronchoscopic terminology) and is named in this case the carina. The **carina** is placed to the left of the middle line and the right bronchus appears as a more direct continuation of the trachea than the left. Because of this asymmetry and because the right bronchus is larger in diameter than the left, foreign bodies which enter the trachea have a tendency to drop into the right bronchus rather than the left.

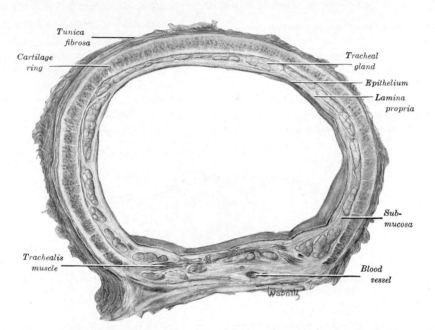

FIG. 981.—Cross section of trachea. Adult cadaver. × 5.

Structure (Fig. 981).—The trachea and extrapulmonary bronchi are composed of imperfect rings of hyaline cartilage, fibrous tissue, muscular fibers, mucous membrane, and glands.

The **cartilages** of the trachea vary from sixteen to twenty in number: each forms an imperfect ring, which occupies the anterior two-thirds or so of the circumference of the trachea, being deficient behind, where the tube is completed by fibrous tissue and unstriped muscular fibers. The cartilages are placed horizontally above each other, separated by narrow intervals. They measure about 4 mm. in depth and 1 mm. in thickness. Their outer surfaces are flattened in a vertical direction, but the internal are convex, the cartilages being thicker in the middle than at the margins. Two or more of the cartilages often unite, partially or completely, and they are sometimes bifurcated at their extremities. They are highly elastic, but may become calcified in advanced life. In the right bronchus the cartilages vary in number from six to eight; in the left, from nine to twelve. They are shorter and narrower than those of the trachea, but have the same shape and arrangement. The peculiar tracheal cartilages are the first and the last (Fig. 979).

The **first cartilage** is broader than the rest, and often divided at one end; it is connected by the cricotracheal ligament with the lower border of the cricoid cartilage, with which, or with the succeeding cartilage, it is sometimes blended.

The **last cartilage** is thick and broad in the middle, in consequence of its lower border being prolonged into a triangular hook-shaped process, which curves downward and backward between the two bronchi. It ends on each side in an imperfect ring, which encloses the commencement of the bronchus. The cartilage above the last is somewhat broader than the others at its center.

The Fibrous Membrane.—The cartilages are enclosed in an elastic fibrous membrane, which consists of two layers; one, the thicker, passing over the outer surface of the ring, the other over the inner surface: at the upper and lower margins of the cartilages the two layers blend together to form a single membrane, which connects the rings one with another. They are thus invested by the membrane. In the space behind, between the ends of the rings, the membrane forms a single layer.

The **muscular tissue** consists of two layers of non-striated muscle, longitudinal and transverse. The **longitudinal fibers** are external, and consist of a few scattered bundles. The **transverse fibers** (Trachealis muscle) are arranged internally in branching and anastomosing bands which extend more or less transversely between the ends of the cartilage.

Mucous Membrane.—The mucous membrane is continuous above with that of the larynx, and below with that of the bronchi. It consists of areolar and lymphoid tissue, and presents a well-marked basement membrane, supporting a stratified epithelium, the surface layer of which is columnar and ciliated, while the deeper layers are composed of oval or rounded cells. Beneath the basement membrane there is a distinct layer of longitudinal elastic fibers with a small amount of intervening areolar tissue. The submucous layer is composed of a loose mesh-work of connective tissue, containing large bloodvessels, nerves, and mucous glands; the ducts of the latter pierce the overlying layers and open on the surface (Fig. 981).

Vessels and Nerves.—The trachea is supplied with blood by the inferior thyroid **arteries.** The **veins** end in the thyroid venous plexus. The **nerves** are derived from the vagus and the recurrent nerves, and from the sympathetic; they are distributed to the Trachealis muscles and between the epithelial cells.

THE PLEURÆ.

Each lung is invested by an exceedingly delicate serous membrane, the **pleura** which is arranged in the form of a closed invaginated sac. A portion of the serous membrane covers the surface of the lung and dips into the fissures between its lobes; it is called the **pulmonary pleura.** The rest of the membrane lines the inner surface of the chest wall, covers the diaphragm, and is reflected over the structures occupying the middle of the thorax; this portion is termed the **parietal pleura.** The two layers are continuous with one another around and below the root of the lung; in health they are in actual contact with one another, but the potential space between them is known as the **pleural cavity.** When the lung collapses or when air or fluid collects between the two layers the cavity becomes apparent. The right and left pleural sacs are entirely separate from one another; between them are all the thoracic viscera except the lungs, and they only touch each other for a short distance in front, opposite the second and third pieces of the sternum; the interval between the two sacs is termed the mediastinum.

Different portions of the parietal pleura have received special names which indicate their position: thus, that portion which lines the inner surfaces of the ribs and Intercostales is the **costal pleura;** that clothing the convex surface of the diaphragm is the **diaphragmatic pleura;** that which rises into the neck, over the summit of the lung, is the **cupula of the pleura** (*cervical pleura*); and that which is applied to the other thoracic viscera is the **mediastinal pleura.**

Reflections of the Pleura (Figs. 982, 983).—Commencing at the sternum, the pleura passes lateralward, lines the inner surfaces of the costal cartilages, ribs, and Intercostales, and at the back part of the thorax passes over the sympathetic trunk and its branches, and is reflected upon the sides of the bodies of the vertebræ, where it is separated by a narrow interval, the **posterior mediastinum,** from the opposite pleura. From the vertebral column the pleura passes to the side of the pericardium, which it covers to a slight extent; it then covers the back part of the root of the lung, from the lower border of which a triangular sheet descends vertically toward the diaphragm. This sheet is the posterior layer of a wide fold, known as the **pulmonary ligament.** From the back of the lung root, the pleura may be traced over the costal surface of the lung, the apex and base, and also over the sides of the fissures between the lobes, on to its mediastinal surface and the front part of its root. It is continued from the lower margin of the root as the anterior layer of the pulmonary ligament, and from this it is reflected on to the pericardium **(pericardial pleura),** and from it to the back of the sternum. Above the level of the root of the lung, however, the mediastinal pleura passes uninterruptedly from the vertebral column to the sternum over the structures in the superior mediastinum. *Below*, it covers the upper surface of the diaphragm and extends, in front, as low as the costal cartilage of the seventh rib; at the side of the chest, to the lower border of the tenth rib on the left side and to the upper border of the same rib on the right side; and *behind*, it reaches as low as the twelfth rib, and sometime even to the transverse process of the first lumbar vertebra. *Above*, its cupula projects through the superior opening of the thorax into the neck, extending from 2.5 to 5 cm. above the sternal end of the first rib; this portion of the sac is strengthened by a dome-like expansion of fascia **(Sibson's fascia)**, attached in front to the inner border of the first rib, and behind to the anterior border of the transverse process of the seventh cervical vertebra. This is covered and strengthened by a few spreading muscular fibers derived from the Scaleni (see Figs. 984, 985).

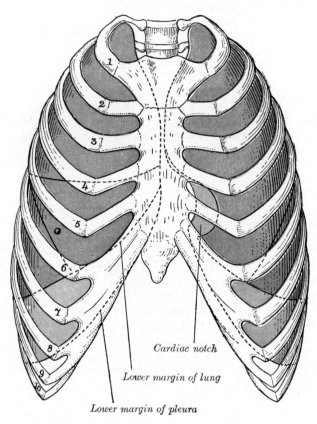

Cardiac notch

Lower margin of lung

Lower margin of pleura

Fig. 982.—Front view of thorax, showing the relations of the pleuræ and lungs to the chest wall. Phrenicocostal and costomediastinal sinus in blue; lungs in purple.

In the front of the chest, where the parietal pleura is reflected backward to the pericardium, the two pleural sacs are in contact for a short distance. At the upper part of the chest, behind the manubrium, they are separated by an angular interval; the line of reflection being represented by a line drawn from the sternoclavicular articulation to the mid-point of the junction of the manubrium with the body of the sternum. From this point the two pleuræ descend in close contact to the level of the fourth costal cartilages, and the line of reflection on the right side is continued downward in nearly a straight line to the xiphoid process, and then turns lateralward, while on the left side the line of reflection diverges lateralward and is continued downward, close to the left border of the sternum, as far as the sixth costal cartilage. The inferior limit of the pleura is on a considerably lower

level than the corresponding limit of the lung, but does not extend to the attachment of the diaphragm, so that below the line of reflection of the pleura from the
chest wall on to the diaphragm the latter is in direct contact with the rib cartilages
and the Intercostales interni. Moreover, in ordinary inspiration the thin inferior
margin of the lung does not extend as low as the line of the pleural reflection, with
the result that the costal and diaphragmatic pleuræ are here in contact, the intervening narrow slit being termed the **phrenicocostal sinus.** A similar condition
exists behind the sternum and rib cartilages, where the anterior thin margin of
the lung falls short of the line of pleural reflection, and where the slit-like cavity
between the two layers of pleura forms what is called the **costomediastinal sinus.**

The line along which the right pleura is reflected from the chest-wall to the
diaphragm starts in front, immediately below the seventh sternocostal joint, and
runs downward and backward be-
hind the seventh costal cartilage
so as to cross the tenth rib in the
mid-axillary line, from which it is
prolonged to the spinous process of
the twelfth thoracic vertebra. The
reflection of the left pleura follows
at first the ascending part of the
sixth costal cartilage, and in the
rest of its course is slightly lower
than that of the right side.

The free surface of the pleura
is smooth, polished, and moistened
by a serous fluid; its attached surface is intimately adherent to the
lung, and to the pulmonary vessels
as they emerge from the pericardium; it is also adherent to the
upper surface of the diaphragm:
throughout the rest of its extent it
is easily separable from the adjacent parts.

The right pleural sac is shorter,
wider, and reaches higher in the
neck than the left.

Pulmonary Ligament (*ligamentum
pulmonale; ligamentum latum pulmonis*).—From the above description it will be seen that the root
of the lung is covered in front above,
and behind by pleura, and that at its

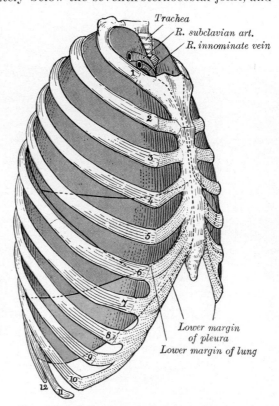

Trachea
R. subclavian art.
R. innominate vein

*Lower margin
of pleura*
Lower margin of lung

Fig. 983.—Lateral view of thorax; showing the
relations of the pleuræ and lungs to the chest wall.
Phrenicocostal and costomediastinal sinus in blue;
lungs in purple.

lower border the investing layers come into contact. Here they form a sort of
mesenteric fold, the pulmonary ligament, which extends between the lower part
of the mediastinal surface of the lung and the pericardium. Just above the diaphragm the ligament ends in a free falciform border. It serves to retain the
lower part of the lung in position.

Structure of Pleura.—Like other serous membranes, the pleura is covered by a single layer
of flattened mesothelial cells resting upon a delicate basement membrane, beneath which lies a
stroma of collagenous tissue containing several prominent net-works of yellow elastic fibers. Bloodvessels, lymphatics, and nerves are distributed in the substance of the pleura.

Vessels and Nerves.—The **arteries of the pleura** are derived from the intercostal, internal
mammary, musculophrenic, thymic, pericardiac, pulmonary, and bronchial vessels. The **veins**

correspond to the arteries. The **lymphatics** are described on page 812. The **nerves** of the parietal pleura are derived from the phrenic, intercostal, vagus and sympathetic nerves; those of the pulmonary pleura from the vagus and sympathetic through the pulmonary plexuses at the hilum of the lung. Kölliker states that nerves accompany the ramifications of the bronchial arteries in the pulmonary pleura.

THE MEDIASTINUM.

The **mediastinum** is interposed as a septum, the **mediastinal septum** (*septum mediastinale*), in the median portion of the thorax, separating the pleural sacs of the two lungs (Fig. 985). It extends from the sternum ventrally to the vertebral column dorsally and comprises all the thoracic viscera, except the lungs and pleuræ, imbedded in a thickening and expansion of the subserous fascia of the

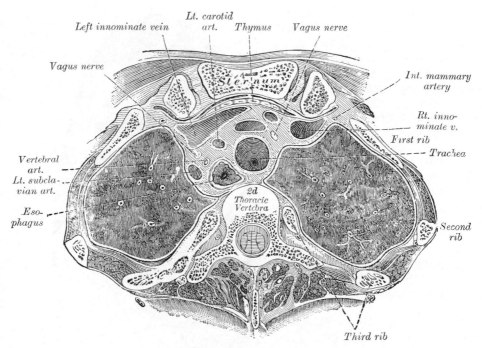

Fig. 984.—Transverse section through the upper margin of the second thoracic vertebra, showing the superior mediastinum. (Braune.)

thorax. It is divided arbitrarily, for the purposes of description, into upper and lower parts, at the upper level of the pericardium, by a plane which extends from the sternal angle to the lower border of the fourth thoracic vertebra. The upper part is named the **superior mediastinum**; the lower part is again subdivided into three parts: the **anterior mediastinum**, in front of the pericardium; the **middle mediastinum**, containing the pericardium; and the **posterior mediastinum**, behind the pericardium.

The **superior mediastinum** (Fig. 984) is bounded above, by the superior aperture of the thorax; below, by the plane of the superior limit of the pericardium; ventrally, by the manubrium; dorsally, by the upper four thoracic vertebræ; and laterally, by the mediastinal pleuræ of the two lungs. It contains the origins of the Sternohyoidei and Sternothyreoidei and the lower ends of the Longi colli; the aortic arch; the innominate artery and the thoracic portions of the left common carotid and the left subclavian arteries; the innominate veins and the upper half of the superior vena cava; the left highest intercostal vein; the vagus, cardiac, phrenic, and left recurrent nerves; the trachea, esophagus, and thoracic duct; the remains of the thymus, and some lymph nodes.

The **anterior mediastinum** (Fig. 985) is bounded ventrally by the body of the sternum and, because of the position of the heart, the left Transversus thoracis muscle and parts of the fourth, fifth, sixth, and seventh costal cartilages. It is bounded dorsally by the parietal pericardium and extends downward as far as the diaphragm. Besides a few lymph nodes and vessels, it contains only a thin layer of subserous fascia which is separated from the endothoracic or deep fascia superiorly by a fascial cleft, but there is a firm attachment in its lower part which forms the pericardio-sternal ligament.

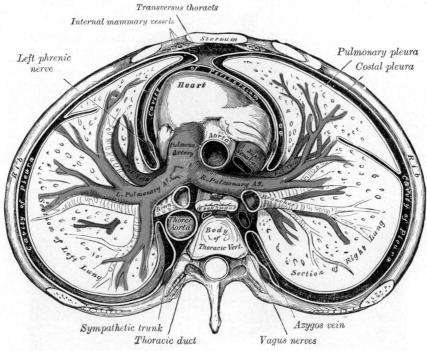

Fig. 985.—A transverse section of the thorax, showing the contents of the middle and the posterior mediastinum. The pleural and pericardial cavities are exaggerated since normally there is no space between parietal and viscera pleura and between pericardium and heart.

The **middle mediastinum** (Fig. 985) is the broadest part of the interpleural septum. It contains the heart enclosed in the pericardium, the ascending aorta, the lower half of the superior vena cava with the azygos vein opening into it, the pulmonary artery dividing into its two branches, the right and left pulmonary veins, and the phrenic nerves.

The **posterior mediastinum** (Fig. 985) is an irregularly shaped mass running parallel with the vertebral column, and because of the slope of the diaphragm, extends caudally beyond the pericardium. It is bounded ventrally, by the pericardium and, more caudally, by the diaphragm; dorsally, by the vertebral column from the lower border of the fourth to the twelfth thoracic vertebra; and on either side, by the mediastinal pleuræ. It contains the thoracic part of the descending aorta, the azygos and hemiazygos veins, the vagus and splanchnic nerves, the bifurcation of the trachea and the two bronchi, the esophagus, the thoracic duct, and many large lymph nodes.

The bifurcation of the trachea, the two bronchi, and the roots of the two lungs are included in the middle mediastinum by some authorities.

THE LUNGS (PULMONES).

The **lungs** are the essential organs of respiration; they are two in number, placed one on either side within the thorax, and separated from each other by the heart and other contents of the mediastinum (Fig. 879). The substance of the lung is of a light, porous, spongy texture; it floats in water, and crepitates when handled, owing to the presence of air in the alveoli; it is also highly elastic; hence the retracted state of these organs when they are removed from the closed cavity of the thorax. The surface is smooth, shining, and marked out into numerous polyhedral areas, indicating the lobules of the organ: each of these areas is crossed by numerous lighter lines.

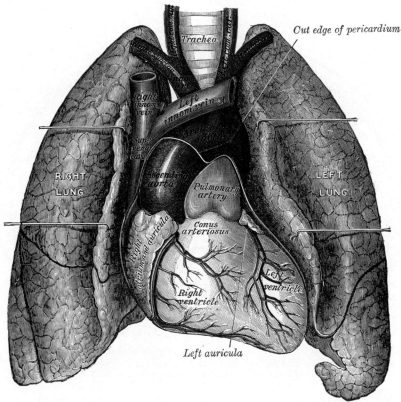

Fig. 986.—Front view of heart and lungs.

At birth the lungs are pinkish-white in color; in adult life the color is a dark slaty-gray, mottled in patches, and as age advances, this mottling assumes a black color. The coloring matter consists of granules of a carbonaceous substance deposited in the areolar tissue near the surface of the organ. It increases in quantity as age advances, and is more abundant in males than in females. As a rule, the posterior border of the lung is darker than the anterior.

The right lung usually weighs about 625 gm., the left 567 gm., but much variation is met with according to the amount of blood or serous fluid they may contain. The lungs are heavier in the male than in the female, their proportion to the body being, in the former, as 1 to 37, in the latter as 1 to 43. The vital capacity, the quantity of air that can be exhaled by the deepest expiration after making the deepest inspiration varies greatly with the individual; an average for an adult man is 3700 cc. The total volume of the fully expanded lungs is about 6500 cc., this includes both tissues and contained air. The tidal air, the amount of air breathed in or out during quiet respiration is about 500 cc. for the adult man. Various calculations indicate that the total epithelial area of the respiratory and non-respiratory surfaces during ordinary deep inspiration of the adult is not greater than 70 square meters.

Each lung is conical in shape, and presents for examination an **apex,** a **base,** three **borders,** and two **surfaces.**

The **apex** (*apex pulmonis*) is rounded, and extends into the root of the neck, reaching from 2.5 to 4 cm. above the level of the sternal end of the first rib. A sulcus produced by the subclavian artery as it curves in front of the pleura runs upward and lateralward immediately below the apex.

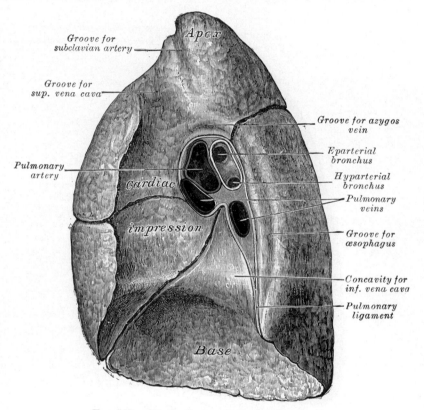

Fig. 987.—Mediastinal surface of right lung.

The **base** (*basis pulmonis*) is broad, concave, and rests upon the convex surface of the diaphragm, which separates the right lung from the right lobe of the liver, and the left lung from the left lobe of the liver, the stomach, and the spleen. Since the diaphragm extends higher on the right than on the left side, the concavity on the base of the right lung is deeper than that on the left. Laterally and behind, the base is bounded by a thin, sharp margin which projects for some distance into the phrenicocostal sinus of the pleura, between the lower ribs and the costal attachment of the diaphragm. The base of the lung descends during inspiration and ascends during expiration.

Surfaces.—The **costal surface** (*facies costalis; external or thoracic surface*) is smooth, convex, of considerable extent, and corresponds to the form of the cavity of the chest, being deeper behind than in front. It is in contact with the costal pleura, and presents, in specimens which have been hardened *in situ,* slight grooves corresponding with the overlying ribs.

The **mediastinal surface** (*facies mediastinalis; inner surface*) is in contact with the mediastinal pleura.   It presents a deep concavity, the **cardiac impression,** which accommodates the pericardium; this is larger and deeper on the left than on the right lung, on account of the heart projecting farther to the left than to the right side of the median plane. Above and behind this concavity is a triangular depression named the **hilum,** through which the structures which form the root of the lung enter and leave. These structures are invested by pleura, which, below the hilum and behind the pericardial impression, forms the pulmonary ligament. On the *right* lung (Fig. 987), immediately above the hilum, is an arched furrow which accommodates the azygos vein; while running upward, and then arching

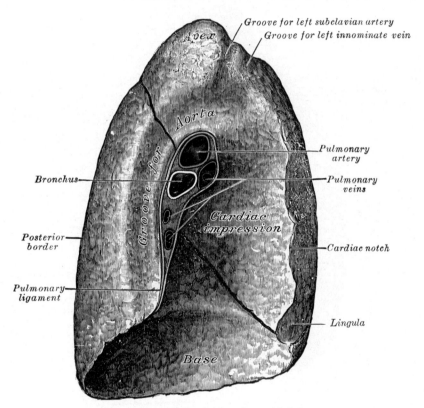

FIG. 988.—Mediastinal surface of left lung.

lateralward some little distance below the apex, is a wide groove for the superior vena cava and right innominate vein; behind this, and nearer the apex, is a furrow for the subclavian artery. Behind the hilum and the attachment of the pulmonary ligament is a vertical groove for the esophagus; this groove becomes less distinct below, owing to the inclination of the lower part of the esophagus to the left of the middle line. In front and to the right of the lower part of the esophageal groove is a deep concavity for the extrapericardiac portion of the thoracic part of the inferior vena cava. On the *left* lung (Fig. 988), immediately above the hilum, is a well-marked curved furrow produced by the aortic arch, and running upward from this toward the apex is a groove accommodating the left subclavian artery; a slight impression in front of the latter and close to the margin of the lung lodges the left innominate vein. Behind the hilum and pulmonary ligament is a vertical furrow produced by the descending aorta, and in front of this, near the base of the lung, the lower part of the esophagus causes a shallow impression.

Borders.—The **inferior border** (*margo inferior*) is thin and sharp where it separates the base from the costal surface and extends into the phrenicocostal sinus; medially where it divides the base from the mediastinal surface it is blunt and rounded.

The **posterior border** (*margo posterior*) is broad and rounded, and is received into the deep concavity on either side of the vertebral column. It is much longer than the anterior border, and projects, below, into the phrenicocostal sinus.

The **anterior border** (*margo anterior*) is thin and sharp, and overlaps the front of the pericardium. The anterior border of the *right* lung is almost vertical, and projects into the costomediastinal sinus; that of the *left* presents, below, an angular notch, the **cardiac notch**, in which the pericardium is exposed. Opposite this notch the anterior margin of the left lung is situated some little distance lateral to the line of reflection of the corresponding part of the pleura.

Fissures and Lobes of the Lungs.—The **left lung** is divided into two lobes, an upper and a lower, by an interlobar fissure, which extends from the costal to the mediastinal surface of the lung both above and below the hilum. As seen on the surface, this fissure begins on the mediastinal surface of the lung at the upper and posterior part of the hilum, and runs backward and upward to the posterior border, which it crosses at a point about 6 cm. below the apex. It then extends downward and forward over the costal surface, and reaches the lower border a little behind its anterior extremity, and its further course can be followed upward and backward across the mediastinal surface as far as the lower part of the hilum. The **superior lobe** lies above and in front of this fissure, and includes the apex, the anterior border, and a considerable part of the costal surface and the greater part of the mediastinal surface of the lung. The **inferior lobe**, the larger of the two, is situated below and behind the fissure, and comprises almost the whole of the base, a large portion of the costal surface, and the greater part of the posterior border.

The **right lung** is divided into three lobes, superior, middle, and inferior, by two interlobar fissures. One of these separates the inferior from the middle and superior lobes, and corresponds closely with the fissure in the left lung. Its direction is, however, more vertical, and it cuts the lower border about 7.5 cm. behind its anterior extremity. The other fissure separates the superior from the middle lobe. It begins in the previous fissure near the posterior border of the lung, and, running horizontally forward, cuts the anterior border on a level with the sternal end of the fourth costal cartilage; on the mediastinal surface it may be traced backward to the hilum. The **middle lobe**, the smallest lobe of the right lung, is wedge-shaped, and includes the lower part of the anterior border and the anterior part of the base of the lung.

The right lung, although shorter by 2.5 cm. than the left, in consequence of the diaphragm rising higher on the right side to accommodate the liver, is broader, owing to the inclination of the heart to the left side; its total capacity is greater and it weighs more than the left lung.

Further Subdivision of the Lung. — The importance of certain smaller units of structure of the lungs, called bronchopulmonary segments, has been emphasized by the thoracic surgeon, bronchoscopist, and radiologist. In order to interpret these units correctly, one should give particular attention to the concept that the lung is fundamentally the aggregate of all the branchings of the bronchus. According to this concept, a bronchopulmonary segment would be that portion of the lung to which any particular bronchus is distributed and the term might conceivably be applied to the lobule, supplied by its lobular bronchus. In actual practice, however, it is customary to restrict the term bronchopulmonary segment to the portion of the lung supplied by the direct branches of the lobar bronchi (and of the division bronchi in the case of the left superior lobe). These segments are as definite as the lobes and their relative extent and position can be demonstrated by introducing different colored gelatin into their bronchi. It is possible, in many cases, to follow the delicate connective tissue between them and dissect them apart. Another demonstration of their fundamental nature is given by the fact that the majority of extra fissures follow the planes of separation between the segments.

The Bronchopulmonary Segments (Fig. 989).—The bronchopulmonary segments are named according to their positions in the lobes and the bronchus to each is named after its segment. The right superior lobe has three segments, an apical, a posterior, and an anterior segment. The right middle lobe has a lateral and a

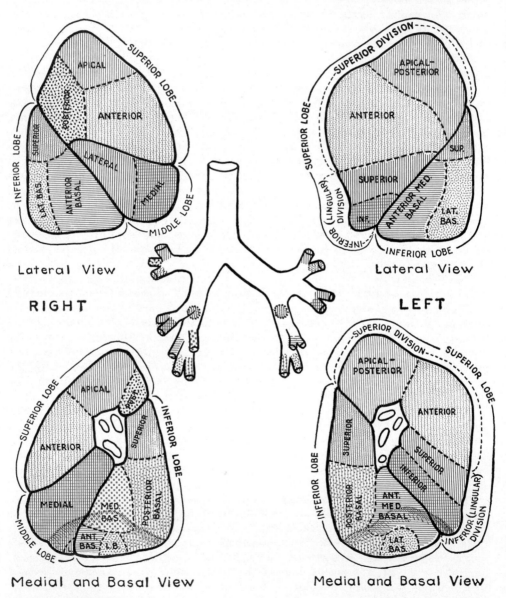

Fig. 989.—The Bronchopulmonary Segments. The segmental branches of the bronchi are shown in corresponding colors. (After J. F. Huber by W. B. Stewart.)

medial segment. The right inferior lobe has a superior and four basal segments, the medial basal, anterior basal, lateral basal, and posterior basal segments. The left superior lobe is first separated into two divisions, the superior division corresponding to the right superior lobe and an inferior division, corresponding to the right middle lobe. The superior division of the left superior lobe has an apical-posterior and an anterior segment. The inferior division of the left superior lobe has a superior and an inferior segment. The left inferior lobe has a superior and three basal segments, the anterior-medial basal, lateral basal, and posterior basal segments.

Right Lung		Left Lung		
LOBES	SEGMENTS	LOBES		SEGMENTS
Superior	Apical Posterior Anterior	Superior	Superior Division	Apical-posterior Anterior
Middle	Lateral Medial		Inferior (Lingular) Division	Superior Inferior
Inferior	Superior Medial Basal Anterior Basal Lateral Basal Posterior Basal	Inferior	Superior Anterior-medial Basal Lateral Basal Posterior Basal	

Variations.—The branching of the lobar bronchi to form segmental bronchi is reasonably constant, according to Huber (1947). The superior lobe bronchus is somewhat more constant than the inferior lobe bronchus. In approximately 95 per cent of the specimens, it is possible to identify three segmental bronchi coming from the right superior lobe bronchus, although in some of these cases, two segmental bronchi may seem to arise from a very short common stem. The size of the lung segment supplied by a particular bronchus may be larger or smaller than expected, even when the branching appears at first glance to follow the usual pattern, because it may have exchanged a smaller branch bronchus with an adjacent segmental bronchus. In the case of the lower lobe bronchus, the superior and the medial basal segmental bronchi are about as constant as the branches in the superior lobe, but there is more variation in the anterior basal, lateral basal, and posterior basal segments. In somewhat less than 50 per cent of the specimens, branches come from the posterior aspect of the inferior lobe bronchus between the superior segmental and the basal segmental bronchi, or from the stem below the anterior basal segmental bronchus.

The Root of the Lung (*radix pulmonis*) (Figs. 987, 988) is formed by the bronchus, pulmonary artery, pulmonary veins, bronchial arteries and veins, pulmonary plexuses of nerves, lymphatic vessels, and bronchial lymph nodes. These structures are all imbedded in mediastinal connective tissue and the entire mass is encircled by a reflection of the pleura. It corresponds to the hilum, which is near the center of the mediastinal surface of the lung, dorsal to the cardiac impression and closer to the posterior than the anterior border. The root of the right lung lies dorsal to the superior vena cava and the right atrium, and the azygos vein arches over it (Fig. 879). The root of the left lung is ventral to the descending aorta and inferior to the aortic arch (Fig. 880). The phrenic nerve, the pericardiophrenic artery and vein, and the anterior pulmonary plexus of nerves are ventral, while the vagus nerve and its posterior pulmonary plexus are dorsal to the root of the lung on both sides. Below the root of each lung, the reflection of the pleura from mediastinum to lung is prolonged downward toward the diaphragm as the pulmonary ligament (page 1193).

The chief structures of the roots of both lungs have a similar relation to each other in a dorso-ventral direction, but there is a difference in their superior and inferior relations on the two sides. Thus the pulmonary veins are ventral, the bronchi dorsal, and the pulmonary arteries between, on both sides. On the right side, the superior lobe bronchus is superior, the pulmonary artery is slightly lower, next are the bronchi to the middle and inferior lobes, and most inferior is the pulmonary vein (Fig. 987). On the left side, the pulmonary artery is superior, the pulmonary veins inferior, and the bronchus between (Fig. 988).

Structure.—The lungs are composed of an external serous coat, a subserous areolar tissue and the pulmonary substance or parenchyma.

The **serous coat** is the pulmonary pleura (page 1191); it is thin, transparent, and invests the entire organ as far as the root.

The **subserous areolar tissue** contains a large proportion of elastic fibers; it invests the entire surface of the lung, and extends inward between the lobules.

The **parenchyma** is composed of secondary lobules which, although closely connected together by an interlobular areolar tissue, are quite distinct from one another, and may be teased asunder without much difficulty in the fetus. The secondary lobules vary in size; those on the surface are large, of pyramidal form, the base turned toward the surface; those in the interior smaller, and of various forms. Each secondary lobule is composed of several primary lobules, the anatomical units of the lung. The primary lobule consists of an alveolar duct, the air spaces connected with it and their bloodvessels, lymphatics and nerves (Fig. 990).

The **intrapulmonary bronchi** divide and subdivide throughout the entire organ, the smallest subdivisions constituting the lobular bronchioles. The *larger divisions* consist of: (1) an outer coat of fibrous tissue in which are found at intervals irregular plates of hyaline cartilage, most developed at the points of division; (2) internal to the fibrous coat, an interlacing net-work of circularly disposed smooth muscle fibers, the bronchial muscle; and (3) most internally, the mucous membrane, lined by columnar ciliated epithelium resting on a basement membrane.

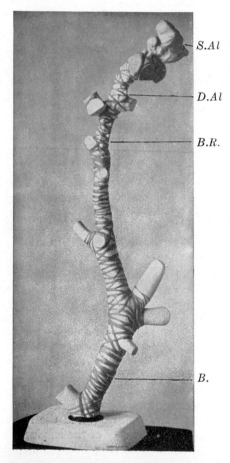

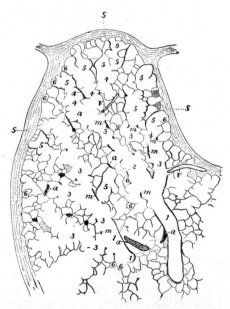

FIG. 990.—Part of a secondary lobule from the depth of a human lung, showing parts of several primary lobules. 1, bronchiole; 2, respiratory bronchiole; 3, alveolar duct; 4, atria; 5, alveolar sac; 6, alveolus or air cell; *m*, smooth muscle; *a*, branch pulmonary artery; *v*, branch pulmonary vein; *s*, septum between secondary lobules. Camera drawing of one 50 μ section. × 20 diameters. (Miller, Jour. Morph.)

FIG. 991.—View of a reconstruction, from a dog's lung, of the musculature of a non-cartilaginous bronchiolus (lobular bronchiole), 0.565 mm. in diameter, its branches, and its termination in a primary lobule of which only a single alveolar sac is shown completely reconstructed. *B*, bronchiolus; *B.R.*, bronchiolus respiratorius; *D.Al.*, ductulus alveolaris; *S.Al.*, sacculus alveolaris. × 125 and reduced to 8. (Miller, The Lung, courtesy of Charles C Thomas.)

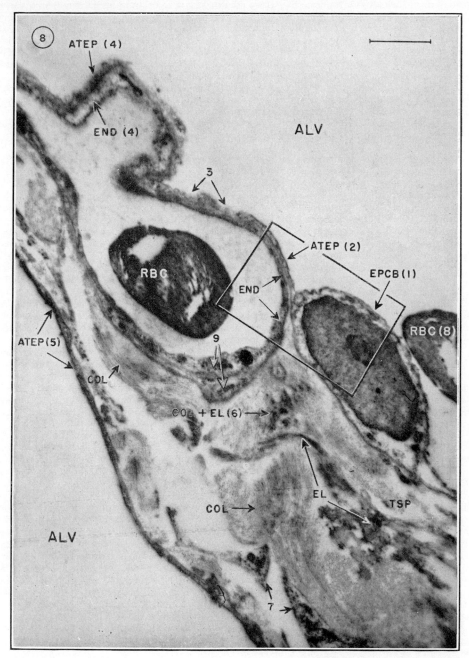

FIG. 992.—Electron micrograph of the alveolar wall in an adult human lung. × 11,000. ALV, alveolus. ATEP, attenuated epithelium. COL, unit fibers of collagen. EL, elastic tissue. END, endothelium. EPCB, epithelial cell body. RBC, red blood cell. TSP, tissue space. The epithelial cell body (1) attenuates (2) to cover the underlying capillary. The cellular duality of the blood-air barrier is obscured at (3) due to bias cut of endothelium and epithelium but these layers are again distinguishable at (4). A continuous cytoplasmic layer of epithelium lines the opposite surface of the wall (5). Both unit fibers of collagen and elastic fibers are visible. At (6) unit fibers of collagen pass through an elastic fiber cut in cross section. At (7) small portions of cells are visible. The erythrocyte at (8) is extravasated. Note the overlap of endothelial cells at (9), a common feature of capillaries. (Low, Anat. Rec., *117*, No. 2, 261, from original of figure 8, plate 4, F.N.)

The corium of the mucous membrane contains numerous elastic fibers running longitudinally, and a certain amount of lymphoid tissue; it also contains the ducts of mucous glands, the acini of which lie in the fibrous coat. In the **lobular bronchioles** (terminal bronchioles) the ciliated epithelial cells become cuboidal in shape, and cartilage plates cease to exist when the diameter of the bronchiole reaches about 1 mm. Branching and anastomosing bands of smooth muscle fibers, continuous with those of the intrapulmonary bronchi, invest the bronchiole and its subdivisions to the point of junction between alveolar duct and atrium (Fig. 991).

Each bronchiole, according to Miller, divides into two or more **respiratory bronchioles,** with scattered alveoli, and each of these again divides into several **alveolar ducts,** with a greater number of alveoli connected with them. Each alveolar duct is connected with a variable number of irregularly spherical spaces, which also possess alveoli, the **atria.** With each atrium a variable number (2–5) of **alveolar sacs** are connected which bear on all parts of their circumference **alveoli** or air spaces.

The alveoli are lined by a continuous layer of pulmonary alveolar epithelium (Fig. 992). The nuclei of the epithelial cells protrude into the air spaces, and the perinuclear cytoplasm attenuates quite abruptly into thin sheets of cytoplasm. The cytoplasmic sheets, averaging about 0.2μ in thickness, rest on a basement membrane and face on the alveolar air spaces. The alveolar walls contain blood capillaries, collagenous, reticular and elastic connective tissue fibers. The barrier between the capillary blood and alveolar air includes two thin layers of cytoplasm, alveolar epithelium and capillary endothelium with adherent basement membranes for each. Tissue space between these two membranes may be potential or real, but they are not adherent and variable amounts of interstitial elements may separate them (see marked area in Fig. 992) (Low '53).

The fetal lung resembles a gland in that the alveoli have a small lumen and are lined by cubical epithelium. After the first respiration the alveoli become distended, and the epithelium takes on the characters described above.

Blood vessels (Fig. 993).—The lung receives two sets of bloodvessels; one derived from the pulmonary artery and serving for respiratory or functional circulation, one derived from the bronchial arteries and furnishing nutritive supply to the lung tissue, including the walls of the pulmonary vessels.

A single **pulmonary artery** conveys the venous blood to each lung; it divides into branches which accompany the bronchi, coursing chiefly along their posterior surface. The bronchopulmonary segments are supplied by main intrasegmental branches of the pulmonary arteries, which are single, for the most part, but which may arise as common trunks for adjacent segments (Boyden, 1945). The artery for one segment is likely to supply small branches to the neighboring segments. Distal to the alveolar duct branches are distributed to each atrium, from which arise smaller radicles terminating in a dense capillary net-work in the walls of the alveoli.

These **pulmonary capillaries** form the richest capillary net-work in the body, the meshes of which are smaller than the vessels themselves. These plexuses lie immediately beneath the lining epithelium in the walls of the alveoli, of which they form a part; the network forming a single layer, which is usually common to two or more adjacent alveoli. The arteries of neighboring lobules are independent of each other, but the veins freely anastomose.

The **pulmonary veins,** of which there are usually two for each lung, have their chief origin in the pulmonary capillaries of the alveoli, twenty-five or more capillary loops intervening between the arterial and venous radicles. Other origins consist of capillary net-works within the pleura, and in the walls of the atria, alveolar ducts, and bronchioles. These venous radicles coalesce into larger branches which run through the substance of the lung, independently of the pulmonary arteries and bronchi. The veins are usually intersegmental in position and drain the blood from adjacent parts of two neighboring bronchopulmonary segments. After freely communicating with other branches they form large vessels, which ultimately come into relation with the arteries and bronchial tubes, and accompany them to the hilum of the organ. Finally they open into the left atrium of the heart, conveying oxygenated blood to be distributed to all parts of the body by the aorta.

The **bronchial arteries** supply blood for the nutrition of the lung; the right lung usually receives a single artery and the left lung two. They are derived from the ventral side of the upper part of the thoracic aorta or from the upper aortic intercostal arteries. Some are distributed to the bronchial glands and to the walls of the bronchi and pulmonary vessels; those supplying the bronchi extending as far as the respiratory bronchioles, where they form capillary plexuses which unite with similar plexuses formed by the pulmonary artery, both of which give rise to small venous trunks forming one of the sources of the pulmonary vein. Others are distributed in the interlobular areolar tissue, and end partly in the deep, partly in the superficial, bronchial veins. Lastly, some ramify upon the surface of the lung, beneath the pleura, where they form a capillary network.

The **bronchial vein** is formed at the root of the lung, receiving superficial and deep veins from a limited area about the hilum; the larger part of the blood supplied by the bronchial arteries being returned by the pulmonary veins. It ends on the right side in the azygos vein, and on the left side in the highest intercostal or in the accessory hemiazygos vein.

The **lymphatics** are described on page 812.

Nerves.—The lungs are supplied from the anterior and posterior pulmonary plexuses, formed chiefly by branches from the sympathetic and vagus. The filaments from these plexuses accompany the bronchial tubes, supplying efferent fibers to the bronchial muscle and afferent fibers to the bronchial mucous membrane and probably to the alveoli of the lung. Small ganglia are found upon these nerves.

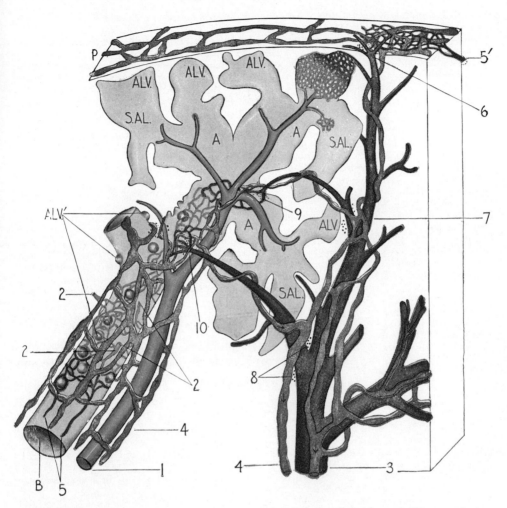

Fig. 993.—General scheme of a primary lobule, showing the subdivisions of (*B*) a respiratory bronchiole into two alveolar ducts; and the atria (*A*), alveolar sacs (*S.AL.*) of one of these ducts. *ALV,'* alveoli scattered along the bronchioles; *P*, pleura; *1*, pulmonary artery, dividing into smaller radicles for each atrium, one of which terminates in a capillary plexus on the wall of an alveolus; *2*, its branches to the respiratory bronchiole and alveolar duct; *3*, pulmonary vein with its tributaries from the pleura *6*, capillary plexus of alveolus, and wall of the atrium *9* and alveolar duct *10*; *4*, lymphatics; dotted areas at *7, 8, 9* and *10*, indicating areas of lymphoid tissue; *5*, bronchial artery terminating in a plexus on the wall of the bronchiole; *5'*, bronchial artery terminating in pleura. (Miller, The Lung, courtesy of Charles C Thomas.)

REFERENCES

Nose and Paranasal Sinuses

Jacobs, M. H. 1947. Anatomic study of the maxillary sinus from the standpoint of the oral surgeon. J. oral Surg., *5*, 282–291.

Rose, J. M., C. M. Pomerat, and B. Danes. 1949. Tissue culture studies of ciliated nasal mucosa in man. Anat. Rec., *104*, 409–420.

ROSEN, M. D. and B. G. SARNAT. 1954. A comparison of the volume of the left and right maxillary sinuses in dogs. Anat. Rec., *120*, 65–72.
SCHAEFFER, J. P. 1920. The Nose, Paranasal Sinuses, Nasolacrimal Passageways, and Olfactory Organ in Man. Blakiston, Philadelphia, xxii + 370 pp.

LARYNX, TRACHEA, AND BRONCHI

KING, B. T. and R. L. GREGG. 1948. An anatomical reason for the various behaviors of paralyzed vocal cords. Ann. Otol. (St. Louis), *57*, 925–944.
MILLER, R. A. 1941. The laryngeal sacs of an infant and an adult gorilla. Amer. J. Anat., *69*, 1–17.
SMITH, E. I. 1957. The early development of the trachea and esophagus in relation to atresia of the esophagus and tracheoesophageal fistula. Contr. Embryol. Carneg. Intn., *36*, 41–58.
STRONG, L. H. 1935. The mechanism of laryngeal pitch. Anat. Rec., *63*, 12–28.

LUNGS AND PLEURA

ANSON, B. J., R. G. SIEKERT, T. E. RICHMOND, and W. E. BISHOP. 1950. The accessory pulmonary lobe of the azygos vein. Quart. Bull. Northw. Univ. med. Sch., *24*, 285–290.
BOYDEN, E. A. 1952. The distribution of bronchi in gross anomalies of the right upper lobe, particularly lobes subdivided by the Azygos vein and those containing pre-eparterial bronchi. Radiology, *58*, 797–807.
DRINKER, C. K. 1954. The Clinical Physiology of the Lungs. Charles C Thomas, Publisher, Springfield. ix + 84 pages.
KRAHL, V. E. 1955. Current concept of the finer structure of the lung. Arch. intern. Med., *96*, 342–356.
LACHMAN, E. 1942. A comparison of the posterior boundaries of lungs and pleura as demonstrated on the cadaver and on the roentgenogram of the living. Anat. Rec., *83*, 521–542.
LACHMAN, E. 1946. The dynamic concept of thoracic topography: A critical review of present day teaching of visceral anatomy. Amer. J. Roentgenol., *56*, 419–440.
LOW, F. N. 1953. The pulmonary alveolar epithelium of laboratory mammals and man. Anat. Rec., *117*, 241–263.
MILLER, W. S. 1937. The Lung. Charles C Thomas, Springfield, xiv + 209 pp.
POLICARD, A. 1955. Le poumon: structures et méchanismes à l'état normal et pathologique. 2nd edition. Masson et Cie, Editeurs, Paris. 363 pages.
THOMAS, L. B. and E. A. BOYDEN. 1952. Agenesis of the right lung. Surgery, *31*, 429–435.
TOBIN, C. E. 1952. Methods of preparing and studying human lungs expanded and dried with compressed air. Anat. Rec., *114*, 453–465.
WELLS, L. J. 1954. Development of the human diaphragm and pleural sacs. Contr. Embryol. Carneg. Instn., *35*, 107–134.

BRONCHOPULMONARY SEGMENTS

ANGULO, A. W., V. P. KOWNACKI, and E. C. HESSERT. 1958. Additional evidence of collateral ventilation between adjacent bronchopulmonary segments. Anat. Rec., *139*, 207–212.
BIRNBAUM, G. L. 1954. Anatomy of the Bronchovascular System: Its Application to Surgery. Year Book Publishers, Inc., Chicago. xv + 300 pages.
BOYDEN, E. A. 1953. A critique of the international nomenclature on bronchopulmonary segments. Dis. Chest, *23*, 266–270.
JACKSON, C. L. and J. F. HUBER. 1943. Correlated applied anatomy of the bronchial tree and lungs with a system of nomenclature. Dis. Chest, *9*, 319–326.
TOBIN, C. E. and M. O. ZARIQUIEY. 1950. Bronchopulmonary segments and blood supply of the human lung. Med. Radiogr. Photogr., *26*, 38–45.

BLOOD VESSELS, NERVES, AND LYMPHATICS

ALEXANDER, H. L. 1933. The autonomic control of the heart, lungs, and bronchi. Ann. intern. Med., *6*, 1033–1043.
FINDLAY, C. W., JR. and H. C. MAIER. 1951. Anomalies of the pulmonary vessels and their surgical significance. Surgery, *29*, 604–641.
KOHN, K. and M. RICHTER. 1958. Die Lungenarterienbahn bei angeborenen Herzfehlern. Georg Thieme Verlag, Stuttgart. viii + 112 pages.
LARSELL, O. 1922. The ganglia, plexuses and nerve-terminations of the mammalian lung and pleura pulmonalis. J. comp. Neurol., *35*, 97–132.
SIMER, P. H. 1952. Drainage of pleural lymphatics. Anat. Rec., *113*, 269–283.
TOBIN, C. E. 1952. The bronchial arteries and their connections with other vessels in the human lung. Surg., Gynec., Obstet., *95*, 741–750.
TOBIN, C. E. 1954. Lymphatics of the pulmonary alveoli. Anat. Rec., *120*, 625–636.

THE DIGESTIVE SYSTEM.

(APPARATUS DIGESTORIUS; ORGANS OF DIGESTION.)

THE apparatus for the digestion of the food consists of the **digestive tube** and of certain **accessory organs.**

The **Digestive Tube** (*alimentary canal*) is a musculomembranous tube, about 9 meters long, extending from the mouth to the anus, and lined throughout its entire extent by mucous membrane. It has received different names in the various parts of its course: at its commencement is the **mouth,** where provision is made for the mechanical division of the food (*mastication*), and for its admixture with a fluid secreted by the salivary glands (*insalivation*); beyond this are the organs of deglutition, the **pharynx** and the **esophagus,** which convey the food into the **stomach,** in which it is stored for a time and in which also the first stages of the digestive process take place; the stomach is followed by the **small intestine,** which is divided for purposes of description into three parts, the **duodenum,** the **jejunum,** and **ileum.** In the small intestine the process of digestion is completed and the resulting products are absorbed into the blood and lacteal vessels. Finally the small intestine ends in the **large intestine,** which is made up of **cecum, colon, rectum,** and **anal canal,** the last terminating on the surface of the body at the **anus.**

The accessory organs are the **teeth,** for purposes of mastication; the three pairs of **salivary glands**—the **parotid, submaxillary,** and **sublingual**—the secretion from which mixes with the food in the mouth and converts it into a bolus and acts chemically on one of its constituents; the **liver** and **pancreas,** two large glands in the abdomen, the secretions of which, in addition to that of numerous minute glands in the walls of the alimentary canal, assist in the process of digestion.

The Development of the Digestive Tube.—The primitive digestive tube consists of two parts, *viz.*: (1) the **fore-gut,** within the cephalic flexure, and dorsal to the heart; and (2) the **hind-gut,** within the caudal flexure (Fig. 994). Between these is the wide opening of the yolk-sac, which is gradually narrowed and reduced to a small foramen leading into the vitelline duct. At first the fore-gut and hind-gut end blindly. The anterior end of the fore-gut is separated from the stomodeum by the buccopharyngeal membrane (Fig. 994); the hind-gut ends in the cloaca, which is closed by the cloacal membrane.

The Mouth.—The mouth is developed partly from the stomodeum, and partly from the floor of the anterior portion of the fore-gut. By the growth of the head end of the embryo, and the formation of the cephalic flexure, the pericardial area and the buccopharyngeal membrane come to lie on the ventral surface of the embryo. With the further expansion of the brain, and the forward bulging of the pericardium, the buccopharyngeal membrane is depressed between these two prominences. This depression constitutes the **stomodeum** (Fig. 994). It is lined by ectoderm, and is separated from the anterior end of the fore-gut by the buccopharyngeal membrane. This membrane is devoid of mesoderm, being formed by the apposition of the stomodeal ectoderm with the fore-gut entoderm; at the end of the third week it disappears, and thus a communication is established between the mouth and the future pharynx. No trace of the membrane is found in the adult; and the communication just mentioned must not be confused with the permanent isthmus faucium. The lips, teeth, and gums are formed from the walls of the stomodeum, but the tongue is developed in the floor of the pharynx.

The visceral arches extend in a ventral direction between the stomodeum and the pericardium; and with the completion of the mandibular arch and the formation of the maxillary processes, the mouth assumes the appearance of a pentagonal orifice. The orifice is bounded in front by the fronto-nasal process, behind by the

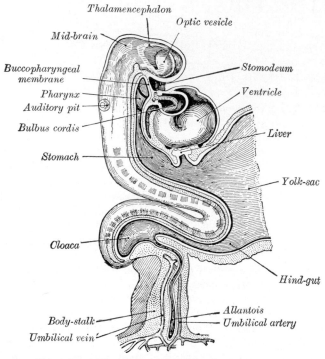

FIG. 994.—Human embryo about fifteen days old. Brain and heart represented from right side. Digestive tube and yolk sac in median section. (After His.)

mandibular arch, and laterally by the maxillary processes (Fig. 995). With the inward growth and fusion of the palatine processes (Figs. 30, 31), the stomodeum

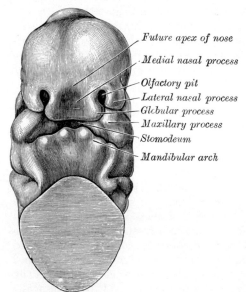

FIG. 995.—Head end of human embryo of about thirty to thirty-one days. (From model by Peters.)

is divided into an upper nasal, and a lower buccal part. Along the free margins of the processes bounding the mouth cavity a shallow groove appears; this is termed the **primary labial groove**, and from the bottom of it a downgrowth of ectoderm takes place into the underlying mesoderm. The central cells of the ectodermal downgrowth degenerate and a **secondary labial groove** is formed; by the deepening of this, the lips and cheeks are separated from the alveolar processes of the maxillæ and mandible.

The Salivary Glands. — The salivary glands arise as buds from the epithelial lining of the mouth; the parotid appears during the fourth week in the angle between the maxillary process and the mandibular arch; the submaxillary appears in the sixth week, and the sublingual during the ninth week in the hollow between the tongue and the mandibular arch.

The Tongue (Figs. 996 to 998).—The tongue is developed in the floor of the pharynx, and consists of an anterior or buccal and a posterior or pharyngeal part which are separated in the adult by the V-shaped sulcus terminalis. During the third week there appears, immediately behind the ventral ends of the two halves of the mandibular arch, a rounded swelling named the **tuberculum impar**, which was described by His as undergoing enlargement to form the buccal part of the tongue. More recent researches, however, show that this part of the tongue is

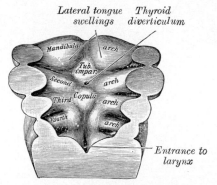

Fig. 996.—Floor of pharynx of human embryo about twenty-six days old. (From model by Peters.)

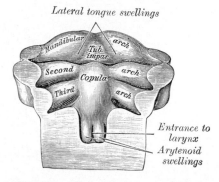

Fig. 997.—Floor of pharynx of human embryo of about the end of the fourth week. (From model by Peters.)

mainly, if not entirely, developed from a pair of lateral swellings which rise from the inner surface of the mandibular arch and meet in the middle line. The tuberculum impar is said to form the central part of the tongue immediately in front of the foramen cecum, but Hammar insists that it is purely a transitory structure and forms no part of the adult tongue. From the ventral ends of the fourth arch there arises a second and larger elevation, in the center of which is a median groove or furrow. This elevation was named by His the **furcula**, and is at first separated from the tuberculum impar by a depression, but later by a ridge, the **copula**, formed by the forward growth and fusion of the ventral ends of the second and third arches. The posterior or pharyngeal part of the tongue is developed from the copula, which extends forward in the form of a V, so as to embrace between its two limbs the buccal part of the tongue. At the apex of the V a pit-like invagination occurs, to form the thyroid gland, and this depression is represented in the adult by the **foramen cecum** of the tongue. In the adult the union of the anterior and posterior parts of the tongue is marked by the V-shaped sulcus terminalis, the apex of which is at the foramen cecum, while the two limbs run lateralward and forward, parallel to, but a little behind, the vallate papillæ.

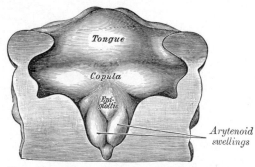

Fig. 998.—Floor of pharynx of human embryo about thirty days old. (From model by Peters.)

The Palatine Tonsils.—The palatine tonsils are developed from the dorsal angles of the second branchial pouches. The entoderm which lines these pouches grows in the form of a number of solid buds into the surrounding mesoderm. These buds become hollowed out by the degeneration and casting off of their central cells, and by this means the tonsillar crypts are formed. Lymphoid cells accumulate around the crypts, and become grouped to form the lymphoid follicles; the latter, however, are not well-defined until after birth.

The Further Development of the Digestive Tube.—The upper part of the fore-gut becomes dilated to form the pharynx (Fig. 994), in relation to which the branchial

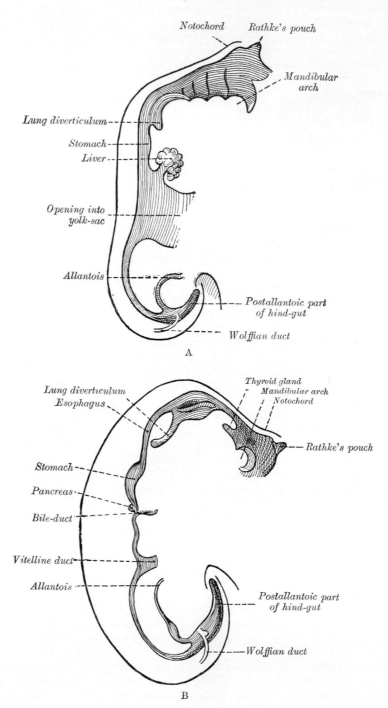

Fig. 999.—Sketches in profile of two stages in the development of the human digestive tube. (His.) $A \times 30$. $B \times 20$.

arches are developed (see page 37); the succeeding part remains tubular, and with the descent of the stomach is elongated to form the esophagus. About the fourth week a fusiform dilatation, the future stomach, makes its appearance, and beyond this the gut opens freely into the yolk-sac (Fig. 999, *A* and *B*). The opening is at

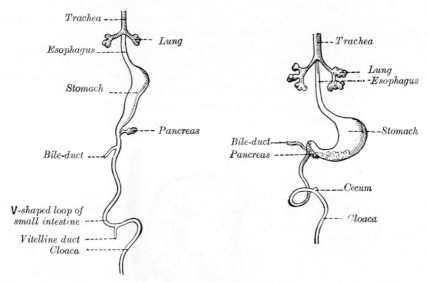

Fig. 1000.—Front view of two successive stages in the development of the digestive tube. (His.)

first wide, but is gradually narrowed into a tubular stalk, the **yolk-stalk** or **vitelline duct**. Between the stomach and the mouth of the yolk-sac the liver diverticulum appears. From the stomach to the rectum the alimentary canal is attached to the notochord by a band of mesoderm, from which the common mesentery of the gut is subsequently developed. The stomach has an additional attachment, *viz.*,

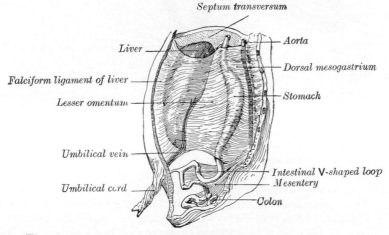

Fig. 1001.—The primitive mesentery of a six weeks' human embryo, half schematic. (Kollmann).

to the ventral abdominal wall as far as the umbilicus by the septum transversum. The cephalic portion of the septum takes part in the formation of the diaphragm, while the caudal portion into which the liver grows forms the **ventral mesogastrium** (Fig. 1001). The stomach undergoes a further dilatation, and its two curvatures can be recognized (Figs. 999, *B* and 1000), the greater directed toward the vertebral column and the lesser toward the anterior wall of the abdomen, while its two surfaces look to the right and left respectively. Behind the stomach the gut undergoes great elongation, and forms a V-shaped loop which projects downward and forward; from the bend or angle of the loop the vitelline duct passes to the umbilicus (Fig. 1001). For a time a considerable part of the loop extends beyond the abdominal cavity into the umbilical cord, but by the end of the third month it is withdrawn within the cavity. With the lengthening of the tube, the mesoderm, which attaches it to the future vertebral column and carries the bloodvessels for the supply of the gut, is thinned and drawn out to form the **posterior common mesentery.** The portion of this mesentery attached to the greater curvature of the stomach is named the **dorsal mesogastrium,** and the part which suspends the colon is termed the **mesocolon** (Fig. 1002). About the sixth week a diverticulum

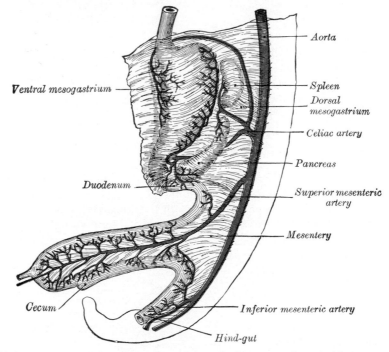

Fig. 1002.—Abdominal part of digestive tube and its attachment to the primitive or common mesentery. Human embryo of six weeks. (After Toldt.)

of the gut appears just behind the opening of the vitelline duct, and indicates the future cecum and vermiform process. The part of the loop on the distal side of the cecal diverticulum increases in diameter and forms the future ascending and transverse portions of the large intestine. Until the fifth month the cecal diverticulum has a uniform caliber, but from this time onward its distal part remains rudimentary and forms the vermiform process, while its proximal part expands to form the cecum. Changes also take place in the shape and position of the stomach. Its dorsal part or greater curvature, to which the dorsal meso-gastrium is attached, grows much more rapidly than its ventral part or lesser curvature to which the ventral mesogastrium is fixed. Further, the greater curva-ture is carried downward and to the left, so that the right surface of the stomach is now directed backward and the left surface forward (Fig. 1003), a change in position which explains why the left vagus nerve is found on the front, and the right vagus

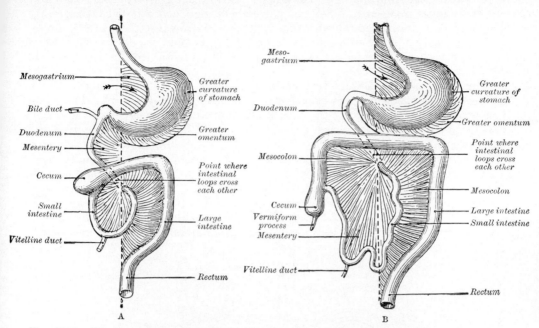

Fig. 1003.—Diagrams to illustrate two stages in the development of the digestive tube and its mesentery. The arrow indicates the entrance to the bursa omentalis.

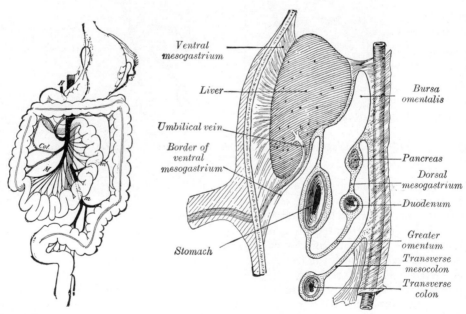

Fig. 1004.—Final disposition of the intestines and their vascular relations. (Jonnesco.) *A.* Aorta. *H.* Hepatic artery. *M, Col.* Branches of superior mesenteric artery. *m, m'.* Branches of inferior mesenteric artery. *S.* Splenic artery.

Fig. 1005.—Schematic figure of the bursa omentalis, etc. Human embryo of eight weeks. (Kollmann.)

on the back of the stomach. The dorsal mesogastrium being attached to the greater curvature must necessarily follow its movements, and hence it becomes greatly elongated and drawn lateralward and ventralward from the vertebral column, and, as in the case of the stomach, the right surfaces of both the dorsal and ventral mesogastria are now directed backward, and the left forward. In this way a pouch, the **bursa omentalis,** is formed behind the stomach, and this increases in size as the digestive tube undergoes further development; the entrance to the pouch constitutes the future **foramen epiploicum** or **foramen of Winslow.** The duodenum is developed from that part of the tube which immediately succeeds the stomach; it undergoes little elongation, being more or less fixed in position by the liver and pancreas, which arise as diverticula from it. The duodenum is at first suspended by a mesentery, and projects forward in the form of a loop. The loop and its mesentery are subsequently displaced by the transverse colon, so that the right surface of the duodenal mesentery is directed backward, and, adhering to the parietal peritoneum, is lost. The remainder of the digestive tube becomes greatly elongated, and as a consequence the tube is coiled on itself, and this elongation demands a corresponding increase in the width of the intestinal attachment of the mesentery, which becomes folded.

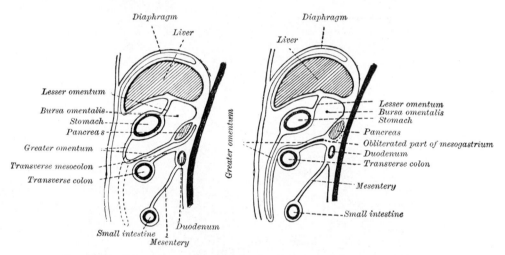

Fig. 1006.—Diagrams to illustrate the development of the greater omentum and transverse mesocolon.

At this stage the small and large intestines are attached to the vertebral column by a common mesentery, the coils of the small intestine falling to the right of the middle line, while the large intestine lies on the left side[1] (Fig. 1003).

The gut is now rotated upon itself, so that the large intestine is carried over in front of the small intestine, and the cecum is placed immediately below the liver; about the sixth month the cecum descends into the right iliac fossa, and the large intestine forms an arch consisting of the ascending, transverse, and descending portions of the colon—the transverse portion crossing in front of the duodenum and lying just below the greater curvature of the stomach; within this arch the coils of the small intestine are disposed (Fig. 1004). Sometimes the downward progress of the cecum is arrested, so that in the adult it may be found lying immediately below the liver instead of in the right iliac region.

[1] Sometimes this condition persists throughout life, and it is then found that the duodenum does not cross from the right to the left side of the vertebral column, but lies entirely on the right side of the median plane, where it is continued into the jejunum; the arteries to the small intestine (*aa. intestinales*) also arise from the right instead of the left side of the superior mesenteric artery.

Further changes take place in the bursa omentalis and in the common mesentery, and give rise to the peritoneal relations seen in the adult. The bursa omentalis, which at first reaches only as far as the greater curvature of the stomach, grows downward to form the greater omentum, and this downward extension lies in front of the transverse colon and the coils of the small intestine (Fig. 1005). Above, before the pleuro-peritoneal opening is closed, the bursa omentalis sends up a diverticulum on either side of the esophagus; the left diverticulum soon disappears, but the right is constricted off and persists in most adults as a small sac lying within the thorax on the right side of the lower end of the esophagus. The anterior layer of the transverse mesocolon is at first distinct from the posterior layer of the greater omentum, but ultimately the two blend, and hence the greater omentum appears as if attached to the transverse colon (Fig. 1006). The mesenteries of the ascending and descending parts of the colon disappear in the majority of cases, while that of the small intestine assumes the oblique attachment characteristic of its adult condition.

The lesser omentum is formed, as indicated above, by a thinning of the mesoderm or **ventral mesogastrium**, which attaches the stomach and duodenum to the anterior abdominal wall. By the subsequent growth of the liver this leaf of mesoderm is divided into two parts, *viz.*, the lesser omentum between the stomach and liver, and the falciform and coronary ligaments between the liver and the abdominal wall and diaphragm (Fig. 1005).

The Rectum and Anal Canal.—The hind-gut is at first prolonged backward into the body-stalk as the tube of the allantois; but, with the growth and flexure of the tail-end of the embryo, the body-stalk, with its contained allantoic tube, is carried forward to the ventral aspect of the body, and consequently a bend is formed at the junction of the hind-gut and allantois. This bend becomes dilated into a pouch, which constitutes the **entodermal cloaca**; into its dorsal part the hind-gut opens, and from its ventral part the allantois passes forward. At a later stage the Wolffian and Müllerian ducts open into its ventral portion. The cloaca is, for a time, shut off from the exterior by a membrane, the **cloacal membrane**, formed by the apposition of the ectoderm and entoderm, and reaching, at first, as far forward as the future umbilicus. Behind the umbilicus, however, the mesoderm subsequently extends to form the lower part of the abdominal wall and symphysis pubis. By the growth of the surrounding tissues the cloacal membrane comes to lie at the bottom of a depression, which is lined by ectoderm and named the **ectodermal cloaca** (Fig. 1005).

The entodermal cloaca is divided into a dorsal and a ventral part by means of a partition, the **urorectal septum** (Fig. 1008), which grows downward from the ridge separating the allantoic from the cloacal opening of the intestine and ultimately fuses with the cloacal membrane and divides it into an anal and a urogenital part. The dorsal part of the cloaca forms the rectum, and the anterior part forms the urogenital sinus and bladder. For a time a communication named the **cloacal duct** exists between the two parts of the cloaca below the urorectal septum; this duct occasionally persists as a passage between the rectum and urethra. The anal canal is formed by an invagination of the ectoderm behind the urorectal septum. This invagination is termed the **proctodeum**, and it meets with the entoderm of the hind-gut and forms with it the **anal membrane**. By the absorption of this membrane the anal canal becomes continuous with the rectum (Fig. 1009). A small part of the hind-gut projects backward beyond the anal membrane; it is named the **post-anal gut** (Fig. 1007), and usually becomes obliterated and disappears.

THE MOUTH (CAVUM ORIS; ORAL OR BUCCAL CAVITY).

The **cavity of the mouth** is placed at the commencement of the digestive tube (Fig. 1010); it is a nearly oval-shaped cavity which consists of two parts: an outer, smaller portion, the **vestibule**, and an inner, larger part, the **mouth cavity proper**.

The **Vestibule** (*vestibulum oris*) is a slit-like space, bounded externally by the lips and cheeks; internally by the gums and teeth. It communicates with the surface of the body by the **rima** or **orifice of the mouth**. Above and below, it is limited by the reflection of the mucous membrane from the lips and cheeks to the gum covering the upper and lower alveolar arch respectively. It receives the secretion from the parotid salivary glands, and communicates, when the jaws are closed, with the mouth cavity proper by an aperture on either side behind the wisdom teeth, and by narrow clefts between opposing teeth.

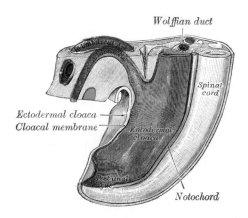

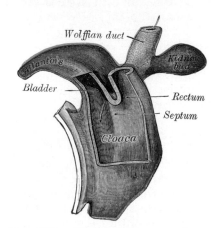

Fig. 1007.—Tail end of human embryo from fifteen to eighteen days old. (From model by Keibel.)

Fig. 1008.—Cloaca of human embryo from twenty-five to twenty-seven days old. (From model by Keibel.)

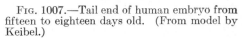

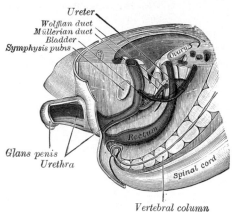

Fig. 1009.—Tail end of human embryo, from eight and a half to nine weeks old. (From model by Keibel.)

The **Mouth Cavity Proper** (*cavum oris proprium*) (Fig. 1010) is bounded laterally and in front by the alveolar arches with their contained teeth; behind, it communicates with the pharynx by a constricted aperture termed the **isthmus faucium**. It is roofed in by the hard and soft palates, while the greater part of the floor is formed by the tongue, the remainder by the reflection of the mucous membrane from the sides and under surface of the tongue to the gum lining the inner aspect of the mandible. It receives the secretion from the submaxillary and sublingual salivary glands.

The **Lips** (*labia oris*) (Fig. 1010), the two fleshy folds which surround the rima or orifice of the mouth, are formed externally of integument and internally of mucous membrane, between which are found the Orbicularis oris muscle, the labial vessels,

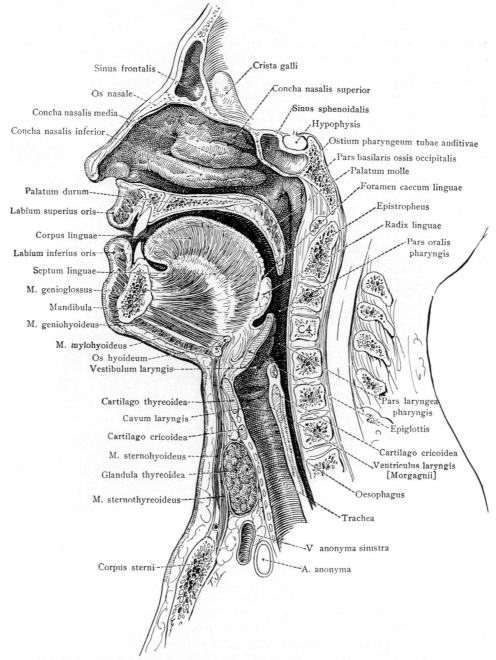

Fig. 1010.—Median sagittal section of head and neck showing nasal, pharyngeal, and laryngeal cavities. (Eycleshymer and Jones.)

some nerves, areolar tissue, and fat, and numerous small labial glands. The inner surface of each lip is connected in the middle line to the corresponding gum by a fold of mucous membrane, the **frenulum**—the upper being the larger.

77

The **Labial Glands** (*glandulæ labiales*) are situated between the mucous membrane and the Orbicularis oris, around the orifice of the mouth. They are circular in form and about the size of small peas; their ducts open by minute orifices upon the mucous membrane. In structure they resemble the salivary glands.

The **Cheeks** (*buccæ*) form the sides of the face, and are continuous in front with the lips. They are composed externally of integument; internally of mucous membrane; and between the two of a muscular stratum, besides a large quantity of fat, areolar tissue, vessels, nerves, and buccal glands.

Structure.—The **mucous membrane** lining the cheek is reflected above and below upon the gums, and is continuous behind with the lining membrane of the soft palate. Opposite the second molar tooth of the maxilla is a papilla, on the summit of which is the aperture of the parotid duct. The principal muscle of the cheek is the Buccinator; but other muscles enter into its formation, viz., the Zygomaticus, Risorius, and Platysma.

The *buccal glands* are placed between the mucous membrane and Buccinator muscle: they are similar in structure to the labial glands, but smaller. About five, of a larger size than the rest, are placed between the Masseter and Buccinator muscles around the distal extremity of the parotid duct; their ducts open in the mouth opposite the last molar tooth. They are called **molar glands.**

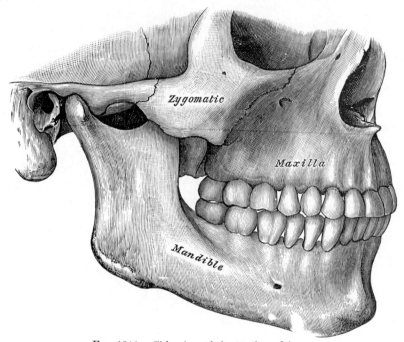

Fig. 1011.—Side view of the teeth and jaws.

The **Gums** (*gingivæ*) are composed of dense fibrous tissue, closely connected to the periosteum of the alveolar processes, and surrounding the necks of the teeth. They are covered by smooth and vascular mucous membrane, which is remarkable for its limited sensibility. Around the necks of the teeth this membrane presents numerous fine papillæ, and is reflected into the alveoli, where it is continuous with the periosteal membrane lining these cavities.

The **Palate** (*palatum*) forms the roof of the mouth; it consists of two portions, the **hard palate** in front, the **soft palate** behind.

The **Hard Palate** (*palatum durum*) (Fig. 1010) forms the roof of the mouth and separates the oral and nasal cavities. It is bounded in front and at the sides by the alveolar arches and gums; behind, it is continuous with the soft palate. Its bony support, formed by the palatine process of the maxilla and the horizontal part of the palatine bone (Fig. 1012), is covered by a dense structure, formed by the periosteum and mucous membrane of the mouth, which are intimately adherent. Along the middle line is a linear raphé, which ends anteriorly in a small papilla corresponding with the incisive canal. On either side and in front of the raphé the mucous membrane is thick, pale in color, and corrugated; behind, it is thin, smooth, and of a deeper color; it is covered with stratified squamous epithelium, and furnished with numerous palatal glands, which lie between the mucous membrane and the surface of the bone.

The **Soft Palate** (*palatum molle*) (Fig. 1010) is a movable fold, suspended from the posterior border of the hard palate. It consists of a fold of mucous membrane enclosing muscular fibers, an aponeurosis, vessels, nerves, lymphoid tissue, and mucous glands. These are described on page 1270. When elevated, as in swallowing and in sucking, it completely separates the nasal cavity and nasopharynx from the posterior part of the oral cavity and the oral portion of the pharynx (Fig. 1010).

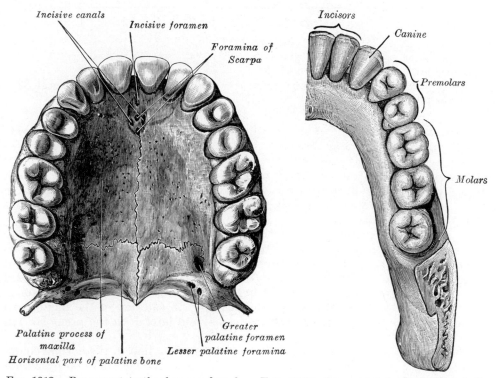

Incisive canals

Incisive foramen

Foramina of Scarpa

Incisors

Canine

Premolars

Molars

Palatine process of maxilla

Horizontal part of palatine bone

Greater palatine foramen

Lesser palatine foramina

FIG. 1012.—Permanent teeth of upper dental arch, seen from below.

FIG. 1013.—Permanent teeth of right half of lower dental arch, seen from above.

When occupying its usual position, *i. e.*, relaxed and pendent, its anterior surface is concave, continuous with the roof of the mouth, and marked by a median raphé. Its posterior surface is convex, and continuous with the mucous membrane covering the floor of the nasal cavities. Its upper border is attached to the posterior margin of the hard palate, and its sides are blended with the pharynx. Its lower border is free. Its lower portion, which hangs like a curtain between the mouth and pharynx is termed the **palatine velum.**

Hanging from the middle of its lower border is a small, conical, pendulous process, the **palatine uvula;** and arching lateralward and downward from the base of the uvula on either side are two curved folds of mucous membrane, containing muscular fibers, called the **arches** or **pillars of the fauces** (Fig. 1036).

The Teeth (*dentes*) (Figs. 1011 to 1017).—Man is provided with two sets of teeth, which make their appearance at different periods of life. Those of the first set appear in childhood, and are called the **deciduous** or **milk teeth**. Those of the second set, which also appear at an early period, may continue until old age, and are named **permanent**.

The **deciduous teeth** are twenty in number: four incisors, two canines, and four molars, in each jaw.

The **permanent teeth** are thirty-two in number: four incisors, two canines, four premolars, and six molars, in each jaw.

The dental formulæ may be represented as follows:

Deciduous Teeth.

	mol.	can.	in.	in.	can.	mol.	
Upper jaw	2	1	2	2	1	2	
							Total 20
Lower jaw	2	1	2	2	1	2	

Permanent Teeth.

	mol.	pr. mol.	can.	in.	in.	can.	pr. mol.	mol.	
Upper jaw	3	2	1	2	2	1	2	3	
									Total 32
Lower jaw	3	2	1	2	2	1	2	3	

General Characteristics. — Each tooth consists of three portions: the **crown**, projecting above the gum; the **root**, imbedded in the alveolus; and the **neck**, the constricted portion between the crown and root (Fig. 1017).

The roots of the teeth are firmly implanted in depressions within the alveoli; these depressions are lined with periosteum which invests the tooth as far as the neck. At the margins of the alveoli, the periosteum is continuous with the fibrous structure of the gums.

In consequence of the curve of the dental arch, terms such as anterior and posterior, as applied to the teeth, are misleading and confusing. Special terms are therefore used to indicate the different surfaces of a tooth: the surface directed toward the lips or cheek is known as the **labial** or **buccal surface**; that directed toward the tongue is described as the **lingual surface**; those surfaces which touch neighboring teeth are termed **surfaces of contact**. In the case of the incisor and canine teeth the surfaces of contact are medial and lateral; in the premolar and molar teeth they are anterior and posterior.

The superior dental arch is larger than the inferior, so that in the normal condition the teeth in the maxillæ slightly overlap those of the mandible both in front and at the sides. Since the upper central incisors are wider than the lower, the other teeth in the upper arch are thrown somewhat distally, and the two sets do not quite correspond to each other when the mouth is closed: thus the upper canine tooth rests partly on the lower canine and partly on the first premolar, and the cusps of the upper molar teeth lie behind the corresponding cusps of the lower molar teeth. The two series, however, end at nearly the same point behind; this is mainly because the molars in the upper arch are the smaller.

The Permanent Teeth (*dentes permanentes*) (Figs. 1014, 1015).—The **Incisors** (*dentes incisivi; incisive or cutting teeth*) are so named from their presenting a sharp cutting edge, adapted for biting the food. They are eight in number, and form the four front teeth in each dental arch.

The **crown** is directed vertically, and is chisel-shaped, being bevelled at the expense of its lingual surface, so as to present a sharp horizontal cutting edge, which, before being subjected to attrition, presents three small prominent points separated by two slight notches. It is convex, smooth, and highly polished on its labial surface; concave on its lingual surface, where, in the teeth of the upper arch, it is frequently marked by an inverted V-shaped eminence, situated near the gum. This is known as the **basal ridge** or **cingulum**. The **neck** is constricted. The **root** is long, single, conical, transversely flattened, thicker in front than behind, and slightly grooved on either side in the longitudinal direction.

The **upper incisors** are larger and stronger than the lower, and are directed obliquely downward and forward. The central ones are larger than the lateral, and their roots are more rounded.

The **lower incisors** are smaller than the upper, the central ones are smaller than the lateral, and are the smallest of all the incisors. They are placed vertically and are somewhat bevelled in front, where they have been worn down by contact with the overlapping edge of the upper teeth. The cingulum is absent.

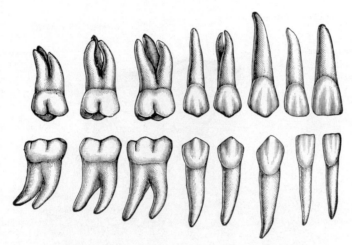

Fig. 1014.—Permanent teeth. Right side. (Burchard.)

The **Canine Teeth** (*dentes canini*) are four in number, two in the upper, and two in the lower arch, one being placed laterally to each lateral incisor. They are larger and stronger than the incisors, and their roots sink deeply into the bones, and cause well-marked prominences upon the surface.

The **crown** is large and conical, very convex on its labial surface, a little hollowed and uneven on its lingual surface, and tapering to a blunted point or cusp, which projects beyond the level of the other teeth. The **root** is single, but longer and thicker than that of the incisors, conical in form, compressed laterally, and marked by a slight groove on each side.

The **upper canine teeth** (popularly called *eye teeth*) are larger and longer than the lower, and usually present a distinct basal ridge.

The **lower canine teeth** (popularly called *stomach teeth*) are placed nearer the middle line than the upper, so that their summits correspond to the intervals between the upper canines and the lateral incisors.

The **Premolars** or **Bicuspid teeth** (*dentes præmolares*) are eight in number, four in each arch. They are situated lateral to and behind the canine teeth, and are smaller and shorter than they.

The **crown** is compressed antero-posteriorly, and surmounted by two pyramidal eminences or cusps, a labial and a lingual, separated by a groove; hence their name **bicuspid**. Of the two cusps the labial is the larger and more prominent. The **neck** is oval. The **root** is generally single, compressed, and presents in front and behind a deep groove, which indicates a tendency in the root to become double. The apex is generally bifid.

The **upper premolars** are larger, and present a greater tendency to the division of their roots than the lower; this is especially the case in the first upper premolar.

The **Molar Teeth** (*dentes molares*) are the largest of the permanent set, and their broad crowns are adapted for grinding and pounding the food. They are twelve in number; six in each arch, three being placed posterior to each of the second premolars.

The **crown** of each is nearly cubical in form, convex on its buccal and lingual surfaces, flattened on its surfaces of contact; it is surmounted by four or five tubercles, or cusps, separated from each other by a crucial depression; hence the molars are sometimes termed **multicuspids**. The **neck** is distinct, large, and rounded.

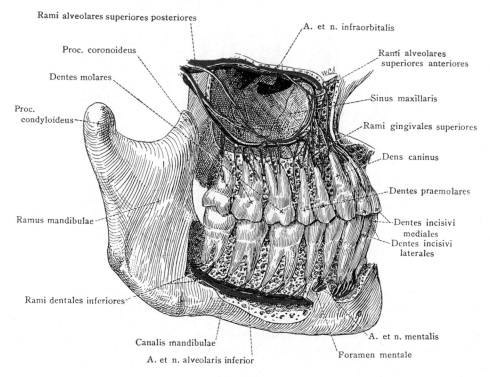

FIG. 1015.—The permanent teeth, viewed from the right. The external layer of bone has been partly removed and the maxillary sinus has been opened. (Eycleshymer and Jones.)

Upper Molars.—As a rule the first is the largest, and the third the smallest of the upper molars. The crown of the first has usually four tubercles; that of the second, three or four; that of the third, three. Each upper molar has three roots, and of these two are buccal and nearly parallel to one another; the third is lingual and diverges from the others as it runs upward. The roots of the third molar (*dens serotinus* or *wisdom-tooth*) are more or less fused together.

Lower Molars.—The lower molars are larger than the upper. On the crown of the first there are usually five tubercles; on those of the second and third, four or five. Each lower molar has two roots, an anterior, nearly vertical, and a posterior, directed obliquely backward; both roots are grooved longitudinally, indicating a tendency to division. The two roots of the third molar (*dens serotinus* or *wisdom tooth*) are more or less united.

The Deciduous Teeth (*dentes decidui; temporary or milk teeth*) (Fig. 1016).—The deciduous are smaller than, but, generally speaking, resemble in form, the teeth which bear the same names in the permanent set. The hinder of the two molars is the largest of all the deciduous teeth, and is succeeded by the first molar. The first upper molar has only three cusps—two labial, one lingual; the second upper molar has four cusps. The first lower molar has four cusps; the second lower molar has five. The roots of the deciduous molars are smaller and more divergent than those of the permanent molars, but in other respects bear a strong resemblance to them.

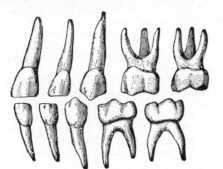

FIG. 1016.—Deciduous teeth. Left side.

Structure of the Teeth.—On making a vertical section of a tooth (Figs. 1017, 1018), a cavity will be found in the interior of the crown and the center of each root; it opens by a minute orifice at the extremity of the latter. This is called the **pulp cavity,** and contains the **dental pulp,** a loose connective tissue richly supplied with vessels and nerves, which enter the cavity through the

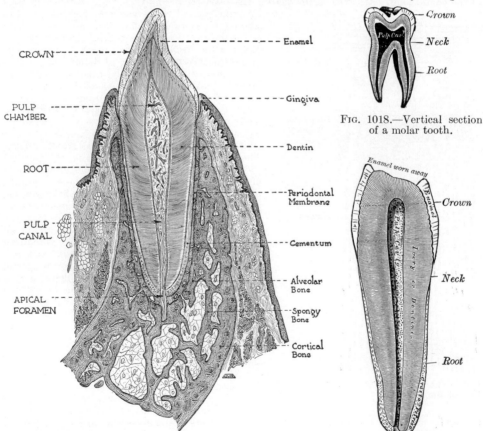

FIG. 1017.—Diagrammatic representation of the dental tissue. (Schour, Noyes: Oral Histology and Embryology.)

FIG. 1018.—Vertical section of a molar tooth.

FIG. 1019.—Vertical section of a premolar tooth. (Magnified.)

small aperture at the point of each root. Some of the cells of the pulp are arranged as a layer on the wall of the pulp cavity; they are named the **odontoblasts of Waldeyer,** and during the development of the tooth, are columnar in shape, but later on, after the dentin is fully formed, they become flattened and resemble osteoblasts. Each has two fine processes, the outer one passing into a dental canaliculus, the inner being continuous with the processes of the connective-tissue cells of the pulp matrix.

The solid portion of the tooth consists of (1) the **ivory** or **dentin,** which forms the bulk of the tooth; (2) the **enamel,** which covers the exposed part of the crown; and (3) a thin layer of bone, the **cement** or **crusta petrosa,** which is disposed on the surface of the root.

The **dentin** (*substantia eburnea; ivory*) (Fig. 1017) forms the principal mass of a tooth. It is a modification of osseous tissue, from which it differs, however, in structure. On microscopic examination it is seen to consist of a number of minute wavy and branching tubes, the **dental canaliculi,** imbedded in a dense homogeneous substance, the **matrix.**

The **dental canaliculi** (*dentinal tubules*) (Fig. 1020) are placed parallel with one another, and open at their inner ends into the pulp cavity. In their course to the periphery they present two or three curves, and are twisted on themselves in a spiral direction. These canaliculi vary in direction: thus in a tooth of the mandible they are vertical in the upper portion of the crown, becoming oblique and then horizontal in the neck and upper part of the root, while toward the lower part of the root they are inclined downward. In their course they divide and subdivide dichotomously, and, especially in the root, give off minute branches, which join together in loops in the matrix, or end blindly. Near the periphery of the dentin, the finer ramifications of the canaliculi terminate imperceptibly by free ends. The dental canaliculi have definite walls, consisting of an elastic homogeneous membrane, the **dentinal sheath of Neumann,** which resists the action of acids: they contain slender cylindrical prolongations of the odontoblasts, first described by Tomes, and named **Tomes' fibers** or **dentinal fibers.**

The **matrix** (*intertubular dentin*) is translucent, and contains the chief part of the earthy matter of the dentin. In it are a number of fine fibrils, which are continuous with the fibrils of the dental pulp. After the earthy matter has been removed by steeping a tooth in weak acid, the animal basis remaining may be torn into laminæ which run parallel with the pulp cavity, across the direction of the tubes. A section of dry dentin often displays a series of some-what parallel lines—the **incremental lines of Salter.** These lines are composed of imperfectly calcified dentin arranged in layers. In consequence of the imperfection in the calcifying process, little irregular cavities are left, termed **interglobular spaces** (Fig. 1020). Normally a series of these spaces is found toward the outer surface of the dentin, where they form a layer which is sometimes known as the **granular layer.** They have received their name from the fact that they are surrounded by minute nodules or globules of dentin. Other curved lines may be seen parallel to the surface. These are the **lines of Schreger,** and are due to the optical effect of simultaneous curvature of the dentinal fibers.

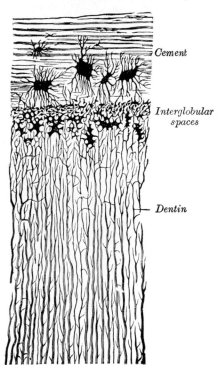

Cement

Interglobular spaces

Dentin

FIG. 1020.—Transverse section of a portion of the root of a canine tooth. × 300.

Chemical Composition.—According to Berzelius and von Bibra, dentin consists of 28 parts of animal and 72 parts of earthy matter. The organic matter is a sclero-protein containing an abundance of tyrosin. The earthy matter consists of phosphate of lime, carbonate of lime, a trace of fluoride of calcium, magnesium, phosphate of magnesium, and other salts.

The **enamel** (*substantia adamantina*) is the hardest and most compact part of the tooth, and forms a thin crust over the exposed part of the crown, as far as the commencement of the root. It is thickest on the grinding surface of the crown, until worn away by attrition, and becomes thinner toward the neck. It consists of minute hexagonal rods or columns termed **enamel fibers** or **enamel prisms** (*prismata adamantina*). They lie parallel with one another, resting by one extremity upon the dentin, which presents a number of minute depressions for their reception; and forming the free surface of the crown by the other extremity. The columns are directed vertically on the summit of the crown, horizontally at the sides; they are about 4μ in diameter, and pursue a more or less wavy course. Each column is a six-sided prism and presents numerous dark transverse shadings; these shadings are probably due to the manner in which the columns are developed in successive stages, producing shallow constrictions, as will be subsequently explained. Another series of lines, having a brown appearance, the **parallel striæ** or **colored lines of Retzius,** is seen on section. According to Ebner, they are produced by air in the interprismatic spaces; others believe that they are the result of true pigmentation.

Numerous minute interstices intervene between the enamel fibers near their dentinal ends, a provision calculated to allow of the permeation of fluids from the dental canaliculi into the substance of the enamel.

Chemical Composition.—According to von Bibra, enamel consists of 96.5 per cent. of earthy matter, and 3.5 per cent. of animal matter. The earthy matter consists of phosphate of lime, with traces of fluoride of calcium, carbonate of lime, phosphate of magnesium, and other salts. According to Tomes, the enamel contains the merest trace of organic matter.

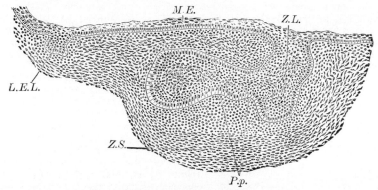

Fig. 1021.—Sagittal section through the first lower deciduous molar of a human embryo 30 mm. long. (Röse.) × 100. *L.E.L.* Labiodental lamina, here separated from the dental lamina. *Z.L.* Placed over the shallow dental furrow, points to the dental lamina, which is spread out below to form the enamel germ of the future tooth. *P.p.* Bicuspid papilla, capped by the enamel germ. *Z.S.* Condensed tissue forming dental sac. *M.E.* Mouth epithelium.

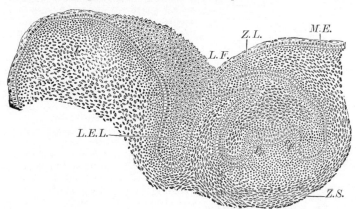

Fig. 1022.—Similar section through the canine tooth of an embryo 40 mm. long. (Röse.) × 100 *L.F.* Labiodental furrow. The other lettering as in Fig. 1021.

The **crusta petrosa** or **cement** (*substantia ossea*) is disposed as a thin layer on the roots of the teeth, from the termination of the enamel to the apex of each root, where it is usually very thick. In structure and chemical composition it resembles bone. It contains, sparingly, the lacunæ and canaliculi which characterize true bone; the lacunæ placed near the surface receive the canaliculi radiating from the side of the lacunæ toward the periodontal membrane; and those more deeply placed join with the adjacent dental canaliculi. In the thicker portions of the crusta petrosa, the lamellæ and Haversian canals peculiar to bone are also found.

As age advances, the cement increases in thickness, and gives rise to those bony growths or exostoses so common in the teeth of the aged; the pulp cavity also becomes partially filled up by a hard substance, intermediate in structure between dentin and bone (*osteodentin*, Owen; *secondary dentin*, Tomes). It appears to be formed by a slow conversion of the dental pulp, which shrinks, or even disappears.

Development of the Teeth (Figs. 1021 to 1024).—In describing the development of the teeth the mode of formation of the deciduous teeth must first be considered, and then that of the permanent series.

Development of the Deciduous Teeth.—The development of the deciduous teeth begins about the sixth week of fetal life as a thickening of the epithelium along the line of the future jaw, the thickening being due to a rapid multiplication of the more deeply situated epithelial cells. As the cells multiply they extend into the subjacent mesoderm, and thus form a ridge or strand of cells imbedded in mesoderm. About the seventh week a longitudinal splitting or cleavage of this strand of cells takes place, and it becomes divided into two strands; the separation begins in front and extends laterally, the process occupying four or five weeks. Of the two strands thus formed, the **labial** forms the **labiodental lamina;** while the other, the **lingual,** is the ridge of cells in connection with which the teeth, both deciduous and permanent, are developed. Hence it is known as the **dental lamina** or **common dental germ.** It forms a flat band of cells, which grows into the substance of the embryonic jaw, at first horizontally inward, and then, as the teeth develop, vertically, *i. e.*, upward in the upper jaw, and downward in the lower jaw. While still maintaining a horizontal direction it has two edges —an *attached edge*, continuous with the epithelium lining the mouth, and a *free edge*, projecting inward, and imbedded in the mesodermal tissue of the embryonic jaw. Along its line of attachment to the buccal epithelium is a shallow groove, the **dental furrow.**

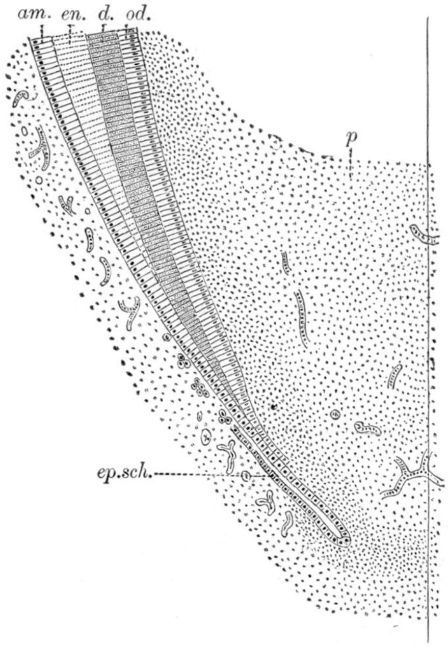

FIG. 1023.—Longitudinal section of the lower part of a growing tooth, showing the extension of the layer of ameloblasts beyond the crown to mark off the limit of formation of the dentin of the root. (Röse.) *am.* Ameloblasts, continuous below with *ep. sch.*, the epithelial sheath of Hertwig. *d.* Dentin. *en.* Enamel. *od.* Odontoblasts. *p.* Pulp.

About the ninth week the dental lamina begins to develop enlargements along its free border. These are ten in number in each jaw, and each corresponds to a future deciduous tooth. They consist of masses of epithelial cells; and the cells of the deeper part—that is, the part farthest from the margin of the jaw—increase rapidly and spread out in all directions. Each mass thus comes to assume a club shape, connected with the general epithelial lining of the mouth by a narrow neck, embraced by mesoderm. They are now known as **special dental germs.** After a time the lower expanded portion inclines outward, so as to form an angle with the superficial constricted portion, which is sometimes known as the neck of the special dental germ. About the tenth week the mesodermal tissue beneath these special dental germs becomes differentiated into papillæ; these grow upward, and come in contact with the epithelial cells of the special dental germs, which become folded over them like a hood or cap. There is, then, at this stage a papilla (or papillæ) which has already begun to assume somewhat the shape of the crown of the future tooth, and from which the dentin and pulp of the tooth are formed, surmounted by a dome or cap of epithelial cells from which the enamel is derived.

In the meantime, while these changes have been going on, the dental lamina has been extending backward behind the special dental germ corresponding to the second deciduous molar tooth, and at about the seventeenth week it presents an enlargement, the special dental germ, for the first permanent molar, soon followed by the formation of a papilla in the mesodermal tissue for the same tooth. This is followed, about the sixth month after birth, by a further extension backward of the dental lamina, with the formation of another enlargement and its corresponding papilla for the second molar. And finally the process is repeated for the third molar, its papilla appearing about the fifth year of life.

After the formation of the special dental germs, the dental lamina undergoes atrophic changes and becomes cribriform, except on the lingual and lateral aspects of each of the special germs of the temporary teeth, where it undergoes a local thickening forming the special dental germ of each of the successional permanent teeth—*i. e.*, the ten anterior ones in each jaw. Here the same process goes on as has been described in connection with those of the deciduous teeth: that is, they recede into the substance of the gum behind the germs of the deciduous teeth. As they recede they become club-shaped, form expansions at their distal extremities, and finally meet papillæ, which have been formed in the mesoderm, just in the same manner as was the case in the deciduous teeth. The apex of each papilla indents the dental germ, which encloses it, and, forming a cap for it, becomes converted into the enamel, while the papilla forms the dentin and pulp of the permanent tooth.

The special dental germs consist at first of rounded or polyhedral epithelial cells; after the formation of the papillæ, these cells undergo a differentiation into three layers. Those which are in immediate contact with the papilla become elongated, and form a layer of well-marked columnar epithelium coating the papilla. They are the cells which form the enamel fibers, and are therefore termed **enamel cells** or **ameloblasts**. The cells of the outer layer of the special dental germ, which are in contact with the inner surface of the dental sac, presently to be described, are much shorter, cubical in form, and are named the **external enamel epithelium**. All the intermediate round cells of the dental germ between these two layers undergo a peculiar change. They become stellate in shape and develop processes, which unite to form a net-work into which fluid is secreted; this has the appearance of a jelly, and to it the name of enamel pulp is given. This transformed special dental germ is now known under the name of **enamel organ** (Fig. 1024).

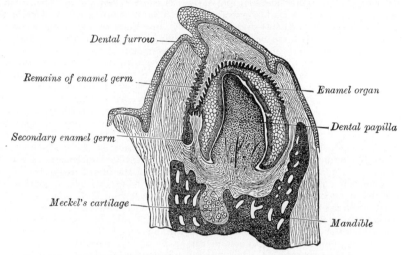

FIG. 1024.—Vertical section of the mandible of an early human fetus. × 25.

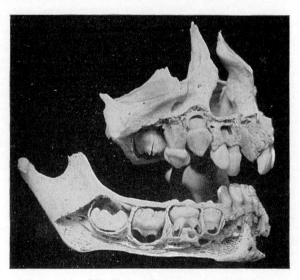

FIG. 1025.—Maxillæ at about one year. (Noyes.)

While these changes are going on, a sac is formed around each enamel organ from the surrounding mesodermal tissue. This is known as the **dental sac**, and is a vascular membrane of connective tissue. It grows up from below, and thus encloses the whole tooth germ; as it grows it causes the neck of the enamel organ to atrophy and disappear; so that all communication between the enamel organ and the superficial epithelium is cut off. At this stage there are vascular papillæ surmounted by caps of epithelial cells, the whole being surrounded by membranous sacs.

Formation of the Enamel.—The enamel is formed exclusively from the enamel cells or amelo-blasts of the special dental germ, either by direct calcification of the columnar cells, which become elongated into the hexagonal rods of the enamel; or, as is more generally believed, as a secretion from the ameloblasts, within which calcareous matter is subsequently deposited.

The process begins at the apex of each cusp, at the ends of the enamel cells in contact with the dental papilla. Here a fine globular deposit takes place, being apparently shed from the end of the ameloblasts. It is known by the name of the **enamel droplet,** and resembles keratin in its resistance to the action of mineral acids. This droplet then becomes fibrous and calcifies and forms the first layer of the enamel; a second droplet now appears and calcifies, and so on; successive droplets of keratin-like material are shed from the ameloblasts and form successive layers of enamel, the ameloblasts gradually receding as each layer is produced, until at the termination of the process they have almost disappeared. The intermediate cells of the enamel pulp atrophy and disappear, so that the newly formed calcified material and the external enamel epithelium come into apposition. This latter layer, however, soon disappears on the emergence of the tooth beyond the gum. After its disappearance the crown of the tooth is still covered by a distinct membrane, which persists for some time. This is known as the **cuticula dentis,** or **Nasmyth's membrane,** and is believed to be the last-formed layer of enamel derived from the ameloblasts, which has not become calcified. It forms a horny layer, which may be separated from the subjacent calcified mass by the action of strong acids. It is marked by the hexagonal impressions of the enamel prisms, and, when stained by nitrate of silver, shows the characteristic appearance of epithelium.

Formation of the Dentin.—While these changes are taking place in the epithelium to form the enamel, contemporaneous changes occurring in the differentiated mesoderm of the dental papillæ result in the formation of the dentin. As before stated, the first germs of the dentin are the papillæ, corresponding in number to the teeth, formed from the soft mesodermal tissue which bounds the depressions containing the special enamel germs. The papillæ grow upward into the enamel germs and become covered by them, both being enclosed in a vascular connective tissue, the **dental sac,** in the manner above described. Each papilla then constitutes the formative pulp from which the dentin and permanent pulp are developed; it consists of rounded cells and is very vascular, and soon begins to assume the shape of the future tooth. The next step is the appearance of the **odontoblasts,** which have a relation to the development of the teeth similar to that of the osteoblasts to the formation of bone. They are formed from the cells of the periphery of the papilla—that is to say, from the cells in immediate contact with the ameloblasts of the special dental germ. These cells become elongated, one end of the elongated cell resting against the epithelium of the special dental germs, the other being tapered and oftened branched. By the direct transformation of the peripheral ends of these cells, or by a secretion from them, a layer of uncalcified matrix (**prodentin**) is formed which caps the cusp or cusps, if there are more than one, of the papillæ. This matrix becomes fibrillated, and in it islets of calcification make their appearance, and coalescing give rise to a continuous layer of calcified material which covers each cusp and constitutes the first layer of dentin. The odontoblasts, having thus formed the first layer, retire toward the center of the papilla, and, as they do so, produce successive layers of dentin from their peripheral extremities—that is to say, they form the dentinal matrix in which calcification subsequently takes place. As they thus recede from the periphery of the papilla, they leave behind them filamentous processes of cell protoplasm, provided with finer side processes; these are surrounded by calcified material, and thus form the dental canaliculi, and, by their side branches, the anastomosing canaliculi: the processes of protoplasm contained within them constitute the **dentinal fibers** (*Tomes' fibers*). In this way the entire thickness of the dentin is developed, each canaliculus being completed throughout its whole length by a single odontoblast. The central part of the papilla does not undergo calcification, but persists as the pulp of the tooth. In this process of formation of dentin it has been shown that an uncalcified matrix is first developed, and that in this matrix islets of calcification appear which subsequently blend together to form a cap to each cusp: in like manner successive layers are produced, which ultimately become blended with each other. In certain places this blending is not complete, portions of the matrix remaining uncalcified between the successive layers; this gives rise to little spaces, which are the interglobular spaces alluded to above.

Formation of the Cement.—The root of the tooth begins to be formed shortly before the crown emerges through the gum, but is not completed until some time afterward. It is produced by a downgrowth of the epithelium of the dental germ, which extends almost as far as the situation of the apex of the future root, and determines the form of this portion of the tooth. This fold of epithelium is known as the **epithelial sheath,** and on its papillary surface odontoblasts appear, which in turn form dentin, so that the dentin formation is identical in the crown and root of the tooth. After the dentin of the root has been developed, the vascular tissues of the dental sac begin to break through the epithelial sheath, and spread over the surface of the root as a layer of bone-forming material. In this osteoblasts make their appearance, and the process of ossification goes on in identically the same manner as in the ordinary intramembranous ossification of bone. In this way the cement is formed, and consists of ordinary bone containing canaliculi and lacunæ.

Formation of the Alveoli.—About the fourteenth week of embryonic life the dental lamina becomes enclosed in a trough or groove of mesodermal tissue, which at first is common to all the dental germs, but subsequently becomes divided by bony septa into loculi, each loculus containing the special dental germ of a deciduous tooth and its corresponding permanent tooth. After birth each cavity becomes subdivided, so as to form separate loculi (the future alveoli) for the deciduous tooth and its corresponding permanent tooth. Although at one time the whole of the growing tooth is contained in the cavity of the alveolus, the latter never completely encloses it, since there is always an aperture over the top of the crown filled by soft tissue, by which the dental sac is connected with the surface of the gum, and which in the permanent teeth is called the **gubernaculum dentis.**

Development of the Permanent Teeth.—The permanent teeth as regards their development may be divided into two sets: (1) those which replace the deciduous teeth, and which, like them, are ten in number in each jaw: these are the **successional permanent teeth;** and (2) those which have no deciduous predecessors, but are superadded distal to the temporary dental series. These are three in number on either side in each jaw, and are termed **superadded permanent teeth.** They are the three molars of the permanent set, the molars of the deciduous set being replaced by the premolars of the permanent set. The development of the successional permanent teeth—the ten anterior ones in either jaw—has already been indicated. During their development the permanent teeth, enclosed in their sacs, come to be placed on the lingual side of the deciduous teeth and more distant from the margin of the future gum, and, as already stated, are separated from them by bony partitions. As the crown of the permanent tooth grows, absorption of these bony partitions and of the root of the deciduous tooth takes place, through the agency of **osteoclasts,** which appear at this time, and finally nothing but the crown of the deciduous tooth remains. This is shed or removed, and the permanent tooth takes its place.

The superadded permanent teeth are developed in the manner already described, by extensions backward of the posterior part of the dental lamina in each jaw.

Eruption of the Teeth.—When the calcification of the different tissues of the tooth is sufficiently advanced to enable it to bear the pressure to which it will be afterward subjected, eruption takes place, the tooth making its way through the gum. The gum is absorbed by the pressure of the crown of the tooth against it, which is itself pressed up by the increasing size of the root. At the same time the septa between the dental sacs ossify, and constitute the alveoli; these firmly embrace the necks of the teeth, and afford them a solid basis of support.

The eruption of the deciduous teeth commences about the seventh month after birth, and is completed about the end of the second year, the teeth of the lower jaw preceding those of the upper.

The following, according to C. S. Tomes, are the most usual times of eruption:

Lower central incisors	6 to 9 months.
Upper incisors	8 to 10 months.
Lower lateral incisors and first molars	15 to 21 months.
Canines	16 to 20 months.
Second molars	20 to 24 months.

There are, however, considerable variations in these times; thus, according to Holt:

At the age of 1 year a child should have 6 teeth.
" " 1½ years " " 12 "
" " 2 " " " 16 "
" " 2½ " " " 20 "

Calcification of the permanent teeth proceeds in the following order in the lower jaw (in the upper jaw it takes place a little later): the first molar, soon after birth; the central and lateral incisors, and the canine, about six months after birth; the premolars, at the second year, or a little later; the second molar, about the end of the second year; the third molar, about the twelfth year.

The eruption of the permanent teeth takes place at the following periods, the teeth of the lower jaw preceding those of the upper by short intervals:

First molars	6th year.
Two central incisors	7th year.
Two lateral incisors	8th year.
First premolars	9th year.
Second premolars	10th year.
Canines	11th to 12th year.
Second molars . . .	12th to 13th year.
Third molars	17th to 25th year.

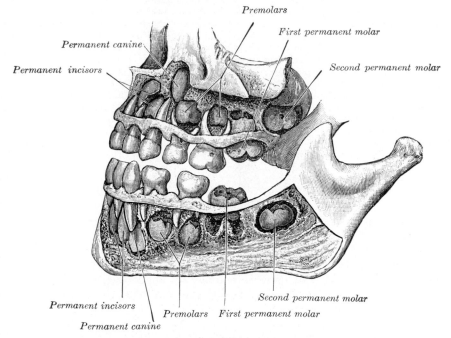

Fig. 1026.—The teeth of a child aged about seven years. The permanent teeth are colored *blue*.

Toward the sixth year, before the shedding of the deciduous teeth begins, there are twenty-four teeth in each jaw, *viz.*, the ten deciduous teeth and the crowns of all the permanent teeth except the third molars.

The Tongue (*lingua*).—The tongue is the principal organ of the sense of taste, and an important organ of speech; it also assists in the mastication and deglutition of the food. It is situated in the floor of the mouth, within the curve of the body of the mandible.

Its **Root** (*radix linguæ; base*) is directed backward, and connected with the hyoid bone by the Hyoglossi and Genioglossi muscles and the hyoglossal membrane; with the epiglottis by three folds (*glossoepiglottic*) of mucous membrane; with the soft palate by the glossopalatine arches; and with the pharynx by the Constrictores pharyngis superiores and the mucous membrane.

Its **Apex** (*apex linguæ; tip*), thin and narrow, is directed forward against the lingual surfaces of the lower incisor teeth.

Its **Inferior Surface** (*facies inferior linguæ; under surface*) (Fig. 1027) is connected with the mandible by the Genioglossi; the mucous membrane is reflected from it to the lingual surface of the gum and on to the floor of the mouth, where, in the middle line, it is elevated into a distinct vertical fold, the **frenulum linguæ**. On either side lateral to the frenulum is a slight fold of the mucous membrane, the **plica fimbriata,** the free edge of which occasionally exhibits a series of fringe-like processes.

The apex of the tongue, part of the inferior surface, the sides, and dorsum are free.

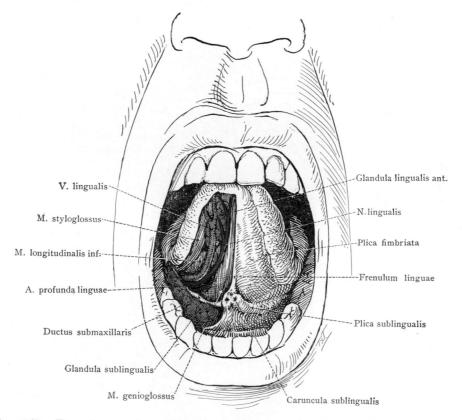

Fig. 1027.—The inferior surface of the tongue, with the right side dissected to show the blood vessels, nerve and salivary glands. (Eycleshymer and Jones.)

The **Dorsum of the Tongue** (*dorsum linguæ*) (Fig. 1028) is convex and marked by a **median sulcus**, which divides it into symmetrical halves; this sulcus ends behind, about 2.5 cm. from the root of the organ, in a depression, the **foramen cecum**, from which a shallow groove, the **sulcus terminalis**, runs lateralward and forward on either side to the margin of the tongue. The part of the dorsum of the tongue in front of this groove, forming about two-thirds of its surface, looks upward, and is rough and covered with papillæ; the posterior third looks backward, and is smoother, and contains numerous muciparous glands and lymph follicles **(lingual tonsil)**. The foramen cecum is the remains of the upper part of the **thyroglossal duct** or diverticulum from which the thyroid gland is developed; the pyramidal lobe of the thyroid gland indicates the position of the lower part of the duct.

The **Papillæ of the Tongue** (Fig. 1028) are projections of the corium. They are thickly distributed over the anterior two-thirds of its dorsum, giving to this surface its characteristic roughness. The varieties of papillæ met with are the **papillæ vallatæ, papillæ fungiformes, papillæ filiformes,** and **papillæ simplices.**

The **papillæ vallatæ** (*circumvallate papillæ*) (Fig. 1029) are of large size, and vary from eight to twelve in number. They are situated on the dorsum of the tongue immediately in front of the foramen cecum and sulcus terminalis, forming a row on either side; the two rows run backward and medialward, and meet in the middle line, like the limbs of the letter V inverted. Each papilla consists of a projection of mucous membrane from 1 to 2 mm. wide, attached to the bottom of a circular depression of the mucous membrane; the margin of the depression is elevated to

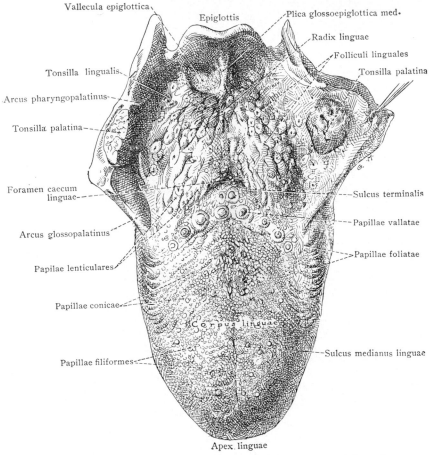

FIG. 1028.—The dorsum of the tongue. (Eycleshymer and Jones.)

form a wall (*vallum*), and between this and the papilla is a circular sulcus termed the fossa. The papilla is shaped like a truncated cone, the smaller end being directed downward and attached to the tongue, the broader part or base projecting a little above the surface of the tongue and being studded with numerous small secondary papillæ and covered by stratified squamous epithelium.

The **papillæ fungiformes** (*fungiform papillæ*) (Fig. 1030), more numerous than the preceding, are found chiefly at the sides and apex, but are scattered irregularly and sparingly over the dorsum. They are easily recognized, among the other papillæ, by their large size, rounded eminences, and deep red color. They are narrow at their attachment to the tongue, but broad and rounded at their free extremities, and covered with secondary papillæ.

The **papillæ filiformes** (*filiform or conical papillæ*) (Fig. 1030) cover the anterior two-thirds of the dorsum. They are very minute, filiform in shape, and arranged in lines parallel with the two rows of the papillæ vallatæ, excepting at the apex of the organ, where their direction is transverse. Projecting from their apices are numerous filamentous processes, or secondary papillæ; these are of a whitish

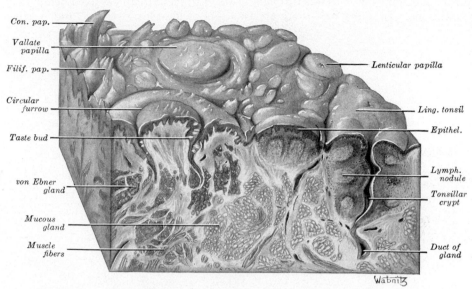

Fig. 1029.—Section of posterior part of dorsum of tongue showing circumvalate papillæ and lingual tonsil. (Redrawn from Braus.)

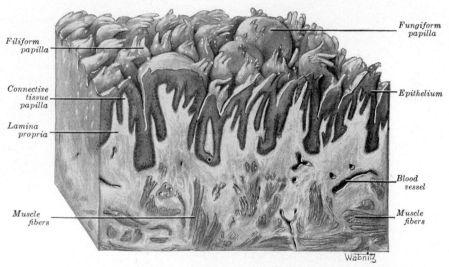

Fig. 1030.—Section of anterior part of dorsum of tongue showing fungiform and filiform papillæ. (Redrawn from Braus.)

tint owing to the thickness and density of the epithelium of which they are composed, which has here undergone a peculiar modification, the cells having become cornified and elongated into dense, imbricated, brush-like processes. They contain also a number of elastic fibers, which render them firmer and more elastic than the papillæ of mucous membrane generally. The larger and longer papillæ of this group are sometimes termed **papillæ conicæ.**

78

The **papillæ simplices** are similar to those of the skin, and cover the whole of the mucous membrane of the tongue, as well as the larger papillæ. They consist of closely set microscopic elevations of the corium, each containing a capillary loop, covered by a layer of epithelium.

Muscles of the Tongue.—The tongue is divided into lateral halves by a median fibrous septum which extends throughout its entire length and is fixed below to the hyoid bone. In either half there are two sets of muscles, extrinsic and intrinsic;

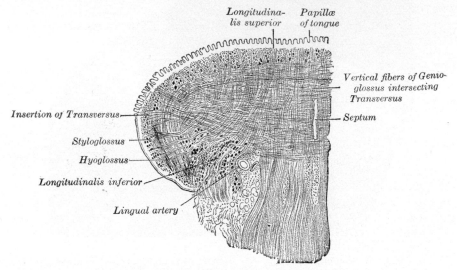

Fig. 1031.—Coronal section of tongue, showing intrinsic muscles. (Altered from Krause.)

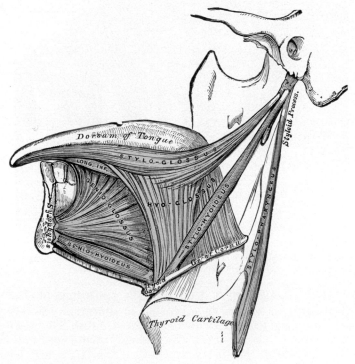

Fig. 1032.—Extrinsic muscles of the tongue. Left side.

the former have their origins outside the tongue, the latter are contained entirely within it.

The **extrinsic muscles** (Fig. 1032) are:

Genioglossus.   Chondroglossus.
Hyoglossus.   Styloglossus.
                    Glossopalatinus.[1]

The **Genioglossus** (*Geniohyoglossus*) is a flat triangular muscle close to and parallel with the median plane, its apex corresponding with its point of origin from the mandible, its base with its insertion into the tongue and hyoid bone. It *arises* by a short tendon from the superior mental spine on the inner surface of the symphysis menti, immediately above the Geniohyoideus, and from this point spreads out in a fan-like form. The inferior fibers extend downward, to be attached by a thin aponeurosis to the upper part of the body of of the hyoid bone, a few passing between the Hyoglossus and Chondroglossus to blend with the Constrictores pharyngis; the middle fibers pass backward, and the superior ones upward and forward, to enter the whole length of the under surface of the tongue, from the root to the apex. The muscles of opposite sides are separated at their insertions by the median fibrous septum of the tongue; in front, they are more or less blended owing to the decussation of fasciculi in the median plane.

The **Hyoglossus**, thin and quadrilateral, *arises* from the side of the body and from the whole length of the greater cornu of the hyoid bone, and passes almost vertically upward to enter the side of the tongue, between the Styloglossus and Longitudinalis inferior. The fibers arising from the body of the hyoid bone overlap those from the greater cornu.

The **Chondroglossus** is sometimes described as a part of the Hyoglossus, but is separated from it by fibers of the Genioglossus, which pass to the side of the pharynx. It is about 2 cm. long, and *arises* from the medial side and base of the lesser cornu and contiguous portion of the body of the hyoid bone, and passes directly upward to blend with the intrinsic muscular fibers of the tongue, between the Hyoglossus and Genioglossus.

A small slip of muscular fibers is occasionally found, arising from the cartilago triticea in the lateral hyothyroid ligament and entering the tongue with the hindermost fibers of the Hyoglossus.

The **Styloglossus**, the shortest and smallest of the three styloid muscles, *arises* from the anterior and lateral surfaces of the styloid process, near its apex, and from the stylomandibular ligament. Passing downward and forward between the internal and external carotid arteries, it divides upon the side of the tongue into two portions: one, longitudinal, enters the side of the tongue near its dorsal surface, blending with the fibers of the Longitudinalis inferior in front of the Hyoglossus; the other, oblique, overlaps the Hyoglossus and decussates with its fibers.

The **intrinsic muscles** (Fig. 1031) are:

Longitudinalis superior.   Transversus.
Longitudinalis inferior.   Verticalis.

The **Longitudinalis linguæ superior** (*Superior lingualis*) is a thin stratum of oblique and longitudinal fibers immediately underlying the mucous membrane on the dorsum of the tongue. It *arises* from the submucous fibrous layer close to the epiglottis and from the median fibrous septum, and runs forward to the edges of the tongue.

---

[1] The *Glossopalatinus* (*Palatoglossus*), although one of the muscles of the tongue, is more closely associated with the soft palate both in situation and function; it has consequently been described with the muscles of that structure (p. 1245).

The **Longitudinalis linguæ inferior** (*Inferior lingualis*) is a narrow band situated on the under surface of the tongue between the Genioglossus and Hyoglossus. It extends from the root to the apex of the tongue: behind, some of its fibers are connected with the body of the hyoid bone; in front it blends with the fibers of the Styloglossus.

The **Transversus linguæ** (*Transverse lingualis*) consists of fibers which *arise* from the median fibrous septum and pass lateralward to be inserted into the submucous fibrous tissue at the sides of the tongue.

The **Verticalis linguæ** (*Vertical lingualis*) is found only at the borders of the fore-part of the tongue. Its fibers extend from the upper to the under surface of the organ.

The median fibrous septum of the tongue is very complete, so that the anastomosis between the two lingual arteries is not very free.

Nerves.—The muscles of the tongue described above are supplied by the hypoglossal nerve.

Actions.—The movements of the tongue, although numerous and complicated, may be understood by carefully considering the direction of the fibers of its muscles. The Genioglossi, by means of their posterior fibers, draw the root of the tongue forward, and protrude the apex from the mouth. The anterior fibers draw the tongue back into the mouth. The two muscles acting in their entirety draw the tongue downward, so as to make its superior surface concave from side to side, forming a channel along which fluids may pass toward the pharynx, as in sucking. The Hyoglossi depress the tongue, and draw down its sides. The Styloglossi draw the tongue upward and backward. The Glossopalatini draw the root of the tongue upward. The intrinsic muscles are mainly concerned in altering the shape of the tongue, whereby it becomes shortened, narrowed, or curved in different directions; thus, the Longitudinalis superior and inferior tend to shorten the tongue, but the former, in addition, turn the tip and sides upward so as to render the dorsum concave, while the latter pull the tip downward and render the dorsum convex. The Transversus narrows and elongates the tongue, and the Verticalis flattens and broadens it. The complex arrangement of the muscular fibers of the tongue, and the various directions in which they run, give to this organ the power of assuming the forms necessary for the enunciation of the different consonantal sounds; and Macalister states "there is reason to believe that the musculature of the tongue varies in different races owing to the hereditary practice and habitual use of certain motions required for enunciating the several vernacular languages."

Structure of the Tongue.—The tongue is partly invested by mucous membrane and a submucous fibrous layer.

The **mucous membrane** (*tunica mucosa linguæ*) differs in different parts. That covering the under surface of the organ is thin, smooth, and identical in structure with that lining the rest of the oral cavity. The mucous membrane of the dorsum of the tongue behind the foramen cecum and sulcus terminalis is thick and freely movable over the subjacent parts. It contains a large number of lymphoid follicles, which together constitute what is sometimes termed the **lingual tonsil** (Fig. 1029). Each follicle forms a rounded eminence, the center of which is perforated by a minute orifice leading into a funnel-shaped cavity or recess; around this recess are grouped numerous oval or rounded nodules of lymphoid tissue, each enveloped by a capsule derived from the submucosa, while opening into the bottom of the recesses are also seen the ducts of mucous glands. The mucous membrane on the anterior part of the dorsum of the tongue is thin, intimately adherent to the muscular tissue, and presents numerous minute surface eminences, the **papillæ** of the tongue. It consists of a layer of connective tissue, the **corium or mucosa**, covered with epithelium. (Fig. 1029, 1030).

The epithelium is of the stratified squamous variety, similar to but much thinner than that of the skin: and each papilla has a separate investment from root to summit. The deepest cells may sometimes be detached as a separate layer, corresponding to the rete mucosum, but they never contain coloring matter.

The **corium** consists of a dense felt-work of fibrous connective tissue, with numerous elastic fibers, firmly connected with the fibrous tissue forming the septa between the muscular bundles of the tongue. It contains the ramifications of the numerous vessels and nerves from which the papillæ are supplied, large plexuses of lymphatic vessels, and the glands of the tongue.

Structure of the Papillæ.—The papillæ apparently resemble in structure those of the cutis, consisting of cone-shaped projections of connective tissue, covered with a thick layer of stratified squamous epithelium, and containing one or more capillary loops among which nerves are distributed in great abundance. If the epithelium be removed, it will be found that they are not simple elevations like the papillæ of the skin, for the surface of each is studded with minute conical processes which form secondary papillæ. In the papillæ vallatæ, the nerves are numerous and of large size; in the papillæ fungiformes they are also numerous, and end in a plexiform net-work, from which brush-like branches proceed; in the papillæ filiformes, their mode of termination is uncertain.

Glands of the Tongue.—The tongue is provided with mucous and serous glands.

The **mucous glands** are similar in structure to the labial and buccal glands. They are found especially at the back part behind the vallate papillæ, but are also present at the apex and marginal parts. In this connection the anterior lingual glands (Blandin or Nuhn) require special notice. They are situated on the under surface of the apex of the tongue (Fig. 1027), one on either side of the frenulum, where they are covered by a fasciculus of muscular fibers derived from the Styloglossus and Longitudinalis inferior. They are from 12 to 25 mm. long, and about 8 mm. broad, and each opens by three or four ducts on the under surface of the apex.

The **serous glands** occur only at the back of the tongue in the neighborhood of the taste-buds, their ducts opening for the most part into the fossæ of the vallate papillæ. These glands are racemose, the duct of each branching into several minute ducts, which end in alveoli, lined by a single layer of more or less columnar epithelium. Their secretion is of a watery nature, and probably assists in the distribution of the substance to be tasted over the taste area. (Ebner.)

The **septum** consists of a vertical layer of fibrous tissue, extending throughout the entire length of the median plane of the tongue, though not quite reaching the dorsum. It is thicker behind than in front, and occasionally contains a small fibrocartilage, about 6 mm. in length. It is well displayed by making a vertical section across the organ.

The **hyoglossal membrane** is a strong fibrous lamina, which connects the under surface of the root of the tongue to the body of the hyoid bone. This membrane receives, in front, some of the fibers of the Genioglossi.

Taste-buds, the end-organs of the gustatory sense, are scattered over the mucous membrane of the mouth and tongue at irregular intervals. They occur especially in the sides of the vallate papillæ. They are described under the Organs of the Senses (page 1095).

Vessels and Nerves.—The main **artery** of the tongue is the lingual branch of the external carotid, but the external maxillary and ascending pharyngeal also give branches to it. The **veins** open into the internal jugular.

The **lymphatics of the tongue** have been described on page 787.

The **sensory nerves of the tongue** are: (1) the lingual branch of the mandibular, which is distributed to the papillæ at the forepart and sides of the tongue, and forms the nerve of ordinary sensibility for its anterior two-thirds; (2) the chorda tympani branch of the facial, which runs in the sheath of the lingual, and is generally regarded as the nerve of taste for the anterior two-thirds; this nerve is a continuation of the sensory root of the facial (*nervus intermedius*); (3) the lingual branch of the glossopharyngeal, which is distributed to the mucous membrane at the base and sides of the tongue, and to the papillæ vallatæ, and which supplies both gustatory filaments and fibers of general sensation to this region; (4) the superior laryngeal, which sends some fine branches to the root near the epiglottis.

The Salivary Glands (Fig. 1033).—Three pairs of large salivary glands communicate with the mouth, and pour their secretion into its cavity; they are the **parotid, submandibular,** and **sublingual.**

Parotid Gland (*glandula parotis*).—The parotid gland, the largest of the three, varies in weight from 14 to 28 gm. It lies upon the side of the face, immediately below and in front of the external ear. The main portion of the gland is superficial, somewhat flattened and quadrilateral in form, and is placed between the ramus of the mandible in front and the mastoid process and Sternocleidomastoideus behind, overlapping, however, both boundaries. Above, it is broad and reaches nearly to the zygomatic arch; below, it tapers somewhat to about the level of a line joining the tip of the mastoid process to the angle of the mandible. The remainder of the gland is irregularly wedge-shaped, and extends deeply inward toward the pharyngeal wall.

The gland is enclosed within a capsule continuous with the deep cervical fascia; the layer covering the superficial surface is dense and closely adherent to the gland; a portion of the fascia, attached to the styloid process and the angle of the mandible, is thickened to form the stylomandibular ligament which intervenes between the parotid and submaxillary glands.

The **anterior surface** of the gland is moulded on the posterior border of the ramus of the mandible, clothed by the Pterygoideus internus and Masseter. The inner lip of the groove dips, for a short distance, between the two Pterygoid muscles, while the outer lip extends for some distance over the superficial surface of the Masseter; a small portion of this lip immediately below the zygomatic arch is usually detached, and is named the **accessory part** (*socia parotidis*) of the gland.

The **posterior surface** is grooved longitudinally and abuts against the external acoustic meatus, the mastoid process, and the anterior border of the Sterno-cleidomastoideus.

The **superficial surface**, slightly lobulated, is covered by the integument, the superficial fascia containing the facial branches of the great auricular nerve and some small lymph glands, and the fascia which forms the capsule of the gland.

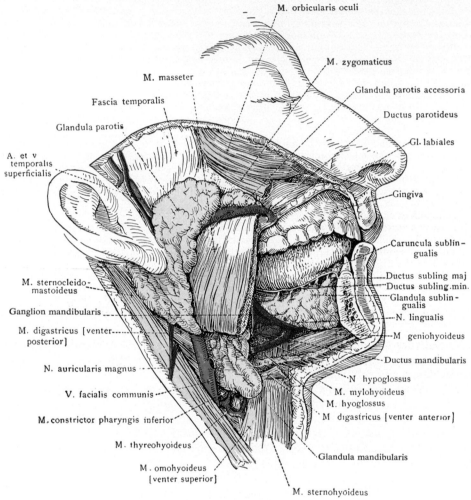

M. orbicularis oculi

M. zygomaticus

M. masseter

Fascia temporalis

Glandula parotis accessoria

Ductus parotideus

Glandula parotis

Gl. labiales

A. et v temporalis superficialis

Gingiva

Caruncula sublin-gualis

M. sternocleido-mastoideus

Ductus subling maj
Ductus subling.min.
Glandula sublin-gualis

Ganglion mandibularis

N. lingualis

M. digastricus [venter posterior]

M geniohyoideus

Ductus mandibularis

N. auricularis magnus

N hypoglossus
M. mylohyoideus
M. hyoglossus

V. facialis communis

M digastricus [venter anterior]

M. constrictor pharyngis inferior

M. thyreohyoideus

Glandula mandibularis

M. omohyoideus [venter superior]

M. sternohyoideus

Fig. 1033.—The salivary glands in a dissection of the right side of the face.
(Eycleshymer and Jones.)

The **deep surface** extends inward by means of two processes, one of which lies on the Digastricus, styloid process, and the styloid group of muscles, and projects under the mastoid process and Sternocleidomastoideus; the other is situated in front of the styloid process, and sometimes passes into the posterior part of the mandibular fossa behind the temporomandibular joint. The deep surface is in contact with the internal and external carotid arteries, the internal jugular vein, and the vagus and glossopharyngeal nerves.

The gland is separated from the pharyngeal wall by some loose connective tissue.

Structures within the Gland.—The *external carotid artery* lies at first on the deep surface, and then in the substance of the gland. The artery gives off its *posterior* *auricular* branch which emerges from the gland behind; it then divides into its terminal branches, the *internal maxillary* and *superficial temporal;* the former runs forward deep to the neck of the mandible; the latter runs upward across the zygomatic arch and gives off its *transverse facial* branch which emerges from the front of the gland. Superficial to the arteries are the *superficial temporal* and *internal maxillary veins,* uniting to form the *posterior facial* vein; in the lower part of the gland this vein splits into anterior and posterior divisions. The anterior division emerges from the gland and unites with the anterior facial to form the *common facial* vein; the posterior unites in the gland with the posterior auricular to form the *external jugular* vein. On a still more superficial plane is the facial nerve, the branches of which emerge from the borders of the gland. Branches of the *great auricular nerve* pierce the gland to join the facial, while the *auriculotemporal nerve* issues from the upper part of the gland.

The **parotid duct** (*ductus parotideus; Stensen's duct*) is about 7 cm. long. It begins by numerous branches from the anterior part of the gland, crosses the Masseter, and at the anterior border of this muscle turns inward nearly at a right angle, passes through the corpus adiposum of the cheek and pierces the Buccinator; it then runs for a short distance obliquely forward between the Buccinator and mucous membrane of the mouth, and opens upon the oral surface of the cheek by a small orifice, opposite the second upper molar tooth. While crossing the Masseter, it receives the duct of the accessory portion; in this position it lies between the branches of the facial nerve; the accessory part of the gland and the transverse facial artery are above it.

Structure.—The parotid duct is dense, its wall being of considerable thickness; its canal is about the size of a crow-quill, but at its orifice on the oral surface of the cheek its lumen is greatly reduced in size. It consists of a thick external fibrous coat which contains contractile fibers, and of an internal or mucous coat lined with short columnar epithelium.

Vessels and Nerves.—The **arteries** supplying the parotid gland are derived from the external carotid, and from the branches given off by that vessel in or near its substance. The **veins** empty themselves into the external jugular, through some of its tributaries. The **lymphatics** end in the superficial and deep cervical lymph nodes, passing in their course through two or three nodes, placed on the surface and in the substance of the parotid. The **nerves** are derived from the plexus of the sympathetic on the external carotid artery, and from the auriculotemporal nerve. The fibers from the latter nerve are cranial parasympathetics derived from the glosso-pharyngeal, and possibly from the facial, through the otic ganglion. The sympathetic fibers are regarded as chiefly vasoconstrictors, the parasympathetic fibers as secretory.

Submandibular Gland (*glandula mandibularis*).—The submandibular gland (Fig. 1033) is irregular in form and about the size of a walnut. A considerable part of it is situated in the submandibular triangle, reaching forward to the anterior belly of the Digastricus and backward to the stylomandibular ligament, which intervenes between it and the parotid gland. Above, it extends under cover of the body of the mandible; below, it usually overlaps the intermediate tendon of the Digastricus and the insertion of the Stylohyoideus, while from its deep surface a tongue-like *deep process* extends forward above the Mylohyoideus muscle.

Its **superficial surface** consists of an upper and a lower part. The **upper part** is directed outward, and lies partly against the submandibular depression on the inner surface of the body of the mandible, and partly on the Pterygoideus internus. The **lower part** is directed downward and outward, and is covered by the skin, superficial fascia, Platysma, and deep cervical fascia; it is crossed by the anterior facial vein and by filaments of the facial nerve; in contact with it, near the mandible, are the submandibular lymph nodes.

The **deep surface** is in relation with the Mylohyoideus, Hyoglossus, Styloglossus, Stylohyoideus, and posterior belly of the Digastricus; in contact with it are the mylohyoid nerve and the mylohyoid and submental vessels.

The external maxillary artery is imbedded in a groove in the posterior border of the gland.

The **deep process** of the gland extends forward between the Mylohyoideus below and externally, and the Hyoglossus and Styloglossus internally; above it are the lingual nerve and submandibular ganglion; below it the hypoglossal nerve and its accompanying vein.

The **submandibular duct** (*ductus submandibular*; *Wharton's duct*) is about 5 cm. long, and its wall is much thinner than that of the parotid duct. It begins by numerous branches from the deep surface of the gland, and runs forward between the Mylohyoideus and the Hyoglossus and Genioglossus, then between the sublingual gland and the Genioglossus, and opens by a narrow orifice on the summit of a small papilla, at the side of the frenulum linguæ. On the Hyoglossus it lies between the lingual and hypoglossal nerves, but at the anterior border of the muscle it is crossed laterally by the lingual nerve; the terminal branches of the lingual nerve ascend on its medial side.

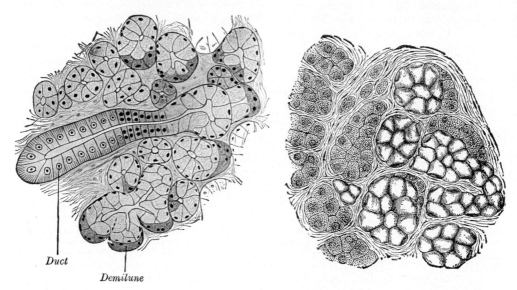

Duct

Demilune

Fig. 1034.—Section of submaxillary gland of kitten. Duct semidiagrammatic. × 200.

Fig. 1035.—Human submaxillary gland. (R. Heidenhain.) At the right is a group of mucous alveoli; at the left a group of serous alveoli.

Vessels and Nerves.—The **arteries** supplying the submandibular gland are branches of the external maxillary and lingual. Its **veins** follow the course of the arteries. The **nerves** are derived from the sympathetic, through a plexus of fibers extending along the external maxillary artery from the carotid plexus; and from cranial parasympathetic fibers of the facial, and perhaps the glossopharyngeal, which pass via the chorda tympani and submandibular ganglion.

Sublingual Gland (*glandula sublingualis*).—The sublingual gland (Fig. 1033) is the smallest of the three glands. It is situated beneath the mucous membrane of the floor of the mouth, at the side of the frenulum linguæ, in contact with the sublingual depression on the inner surface of the mandible, close to the symphysis. It is narrow, flattened, shaped somewhat like an almond, and weighs nearly 2 gm. It is in relation, *above*, with the mucous membrane; *below*, with the Mylohyoideus; *behind*, with the deep part of the submandibular gland; *laterally*, with the mandible; and *medially*, with the Genioglossus, from which it is separated by the lingual nerve and the submandibular duct. Its excretory ducts are from eight to twenty in number. Of the **small sublingual ducts** (*ducts of Rivinus*), some join the submandibular duct; others open separately into the mouth, on the elevated crest of mucous membrane (*plica sublingualis*), caused by the projection of the gland, on either side of the frenulum linguæ. One or more join to form the **larger sublingual duct** (*duct of Bartholin*), which opens into the submandibular duct.

Vessels and Nerves.—The sublingual gland is supplied with blood from the sublingual and submental arteries. Its nerves are derived in a manner similar to those of the submaxillary gland.

Structure of the Salivary Glands.—The salivary glands are compound racemose glands consisting of numerous lobes, which are made up of smaller lobules, connected together by dense areolar tissue, vessels, and ducts. Each lobule consists of the ramifications of a single duct, the branches ending in dilated ends or alveoli on which the capillaries are distributed. The alveoli are enclosed by a basement membrane, which is continuous with the membrana propria of the duct and consists of a net-work of branched and flattened nucleated cells.

The alveoli of the salivary glands are of two kinds, which differ in the appearance of their secreting cells, in their size, and in the nature of their secretion. (1) The mucous variety secretes a viscid fluid, which contains mucin; (2) the serous variety secretes a thinner and more watery fluid. The sublingual gland consists of mucous, the parotid of serous alveoli. The submaxillary contains both mucous and serous alveoli, the latter, however, preponderating.

The cells in the **mucous alveoli** are columnar in shape. In the fresh condition they contain large granules of mucinogen. In hardened preparations a delicate protoplasmic net-work is seen, and the cells are clear and transparent. The nucleus is usually situated near the basement membrane, and is flattened.

In some alveoli are seen peculiar crescentic bodies, lying between the cells and the membrana propria. They are termed the **crescents of Gianuzzi**, or the **demilunes of Heidenhain** (Fig. 1034), and are composed of polyhedral granular cells, which Heidenhain regards as young epithelial cells destined to supply the place of those salivary cells which have undergone disintegration. This view, however, is not accepted by Klein. Fine canaliculi pass between the mucus-secreting cells to reach the demilunes and even penetrate the cells forming these structures.

In the **serous alveoli** the cells almost completely fill the cavity, so that there is hardly any lumen perceptible; they contain secretory granules imbedded in a closely reticulated protoplasm (Fig. 1035). The cells are more cubical than those of the mucous type; the nucleus of each is spherical and placed near the center of the cell, and the granules are smaller.

Both mucous and serous cells vary in appearance according to whether the gland is in a resting condition or has been recently active. In the former case the cells are large and contain many secretory granules; in the latter case they are shrunken and contain few granules, chiefly collected at the inner ends of the cells. The granules are best seen in fresh preparations.

The ducts are lined at their origins by epithelium which differs little from the pavement form. As the ducts enlarge, the epithelial cells change to the columnar type, and the part of the cell next the basement membrane is finely striated.

The lobules of the salivary glands are richly supplied with bloodvessels which form a dense net-work in the interalveolar spaces. Fine plexuses of nerves are also found in the interlobular tissue. The nerve fibrils pierce the basement membrane of the alveoli, and end in branched varicose filaments between the secreting cells. In the hilum of the submaxillary gland there is a collection of nerve cells termed **Langley's ganglion**.

Accessory Glands.—Besides the salivary glands proper, numerous other glands are found in the mouth. Many of these glands are found at the posterior part of the dorsum of the tongue behind the vallate papillæ, and also along its margins as far forward as the apex. Others lie around and in the palatine tonsil between its crypts, and large numbers are present in the soft palate, the lips, and cheeks. These glands are of the same structure as the larger salivary glands, and are of the mucous or mixed type.

THE FAUCES.

The aperture by which the mouth communicates with the pharynx is called the **isthmus faucium**. (Fig. 1036). It is bounded, above, by the soft palate; below, by the dorsum of the tongue; and on either side, by the glossopalatine arch.

The **glossopalatine arch** (*arcus glossopalatinus; anterior pillar of fauces*) on either side runs downward, lateralward, and forward to the side of the base of the tongue, and is formed by the projection of the Glossopalatinus with its covering mucous membrane.

The **pharyngopalatine arch** (*arcus pharyngopalatinus; posterior pillar of fauces*) is larger and projects farther toward the middle line than the anterior; it runs downward, lateralward, and backward to the side of the pharynx, and is formed by the projection of the Pharyngopalatinus, covered by mucous membrane. On either side the two arches are separated below by a triangular interval, in which the palatine tonsil is lodged.

The **Palatine Tonsils** (*tonsillæ palatinæ*; *tonsil*,) (Figs. 1036, 1037) are two prominent masses situated one on either side between the glossopalatine and pharyngopalatine arches. Each tonsil consists fundamentally of an aggregation of lymphatic tissue underlying the mucous membrane between the palatine arches. The lymphatic mass, however, does not completely fill the interval between the two arches, so that a small depression, the **supratonsillar fossa**, exists at the upper part of the interval. Further, the tonsil extends for a variable distance under cover of the

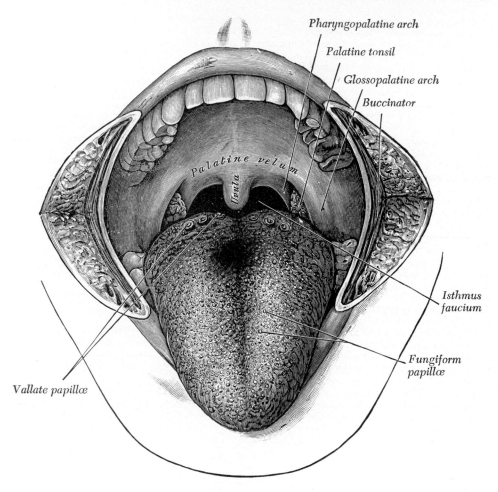

FIG. 1036.—The mouth cavity. The cheeks have been slit transversely and the tongue pulled forward.

glossopalatine arch, and is here covered by a reduplication of mucous membrane; the upper part of this fold reaches across the supratonsillar fossa, between the two arches, as a thin fold sometimes termed the **plica semilunaris**; the remainder of the fold is called the **plica triangularis**. Between the plica triangularis and the surface of the tonsil is a space known as the **tonsillar sinus**; in many cases, however, this sinus is obliterated by its walls becoming adherent. From this description it will be apparent that a portion of the tonsil is below the level of the surrounding mucous membrane, *i. e.*, is imbedded, while the remainder projects as the visible tonsil. In the child the tonsils are relatively (and frequently absolutely) larger than in the adult, and about one-third of the tonsil is imbedded. After puberty the imbedded portion diminishes considerably in size and the tonsil assumes a disk-like form, flattened from side to side; the shape and size of the tonsil, however, vary considerably in different individuals.

The **medial surface** of the tonsil is free except anteriorly, where it is covered by the plica triangularis; it presents from twelve to fifteen orifices leading into **crypts**

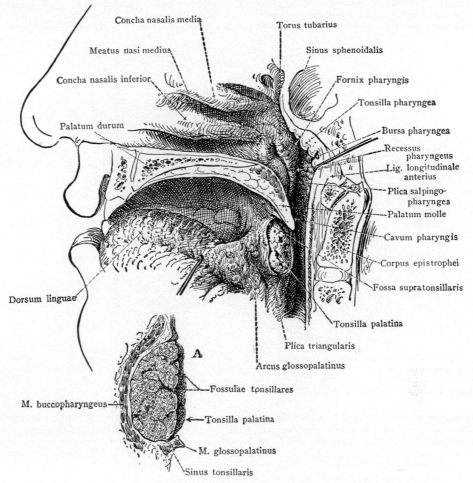

Concha nasalis media
Torus tubarius
Meatus nasi medius
Sinus sphenoidalis
Concha nasalis inferior
Fornix pharyngis
Palatum durum
Tonsilla pharyngea
Bursa pharyngea
Recessus pharyngeus
Lig. longitudinale anterius
Plica salpingo-pharyngea
Palatum molle
Cavum pharyngis
Corpus epistrophei
Dorsum linguae
Fossa supratonsillaris
Tonsilla palatina
A
Plica triangularis
Arcus glossopalatinus
Fossulae tonsillares
M. buccopharyngeus
Tonsilla palatina
M. glossopalatinus
Sinus tonsillaris

FIG. 1037.—The oral and nasal pharynx in median sagittal section, showing palatine and pharyngeal tonsils. A. Detail of palatine tonsil in frontal section. (Eycleshymer and Jones.)

or recesses (*fossulæ tonsillares*) which may branch and extend deeply into the tonsillar substance.

The **lateral** or **deep surface** is adherent to a fibrous capsule which is continued into the plica triangularis. It is separated from the inner surface of the Constrictor pharyngis superior usually by some loose connective tissue; this muscle intervenes between the tonsil and the external maxillary artery with its tonsillar and ascending palatine branches. The internal carotid artery lies behind and lateral to the tonsil at a distance of 20 to 25 mm. from it.

The tonsils form part of a circular band of lymphatic tissue which guards the opening into the digestive and respiratory tubes (Fig. 1037). The anterior part of the ring is formed by the submucous lymphatic collections (**lingual tonsil**) on the posterior part of the tongue; the lateral portions consist of the palatine tonsils and the lymphatic collections in the vicinity of the auditory tubes, while the ring is completed behind by the pharyngeal tonsil on the posterior wall of the pharynx. In the intervals between these main masses are smaller collections of lymphoid tissue.

Structure (Fig. 1038).—Stratified squamous epithelium, like that of the palate and oral pharynx, covers the free surface of the tonsil and extends down into its substance to form the lining of the crypts. Each **crypt** is surrounded by a layer of lymphatic tissue containing numerous scattered lymphatic nodules whose germinal centers are especially prominent in children and young adults. A thin connnective tissue capsule, derived from the submucosa of the pharynx, encloses the whole

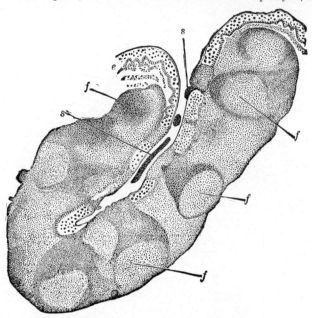

FIG. 1038.—Section through one of the crypts of the tonsil. (Stöhr.) Magnified. *e.* Stratified epithelium of general surface, continued into crypt. *f, f.* Nodules of lymphoid tissue—opposite each nodule numbers of lymph cells are passing into or through the epithelium. *s, s.* Cells which have thus escaped to mix with the saliva as salivary corpuscles.

tonsil and sends delicate septa in between the lymphatic tissue layers surrounding the crypts. The epithelium of the crypts is so invaded by leucocytes in many places that it is scarcely distinguishable from the lymphatic tissue. Polymorphonuclear leucocytes from the blood as well as lymphocytes penetrate the epithelium, and when they are found as free swimming cells in the saliva, they are known as *salivary corpuscles*. Small mucous glands occur in the submucosa about the tonsil but their ducts, as a rule, do not open into the crypts.

Vessels and Nerves.—The **arteries** supplying the tonsil are the dorsalis linguæ from the lingual, the ascending palatine and tonsillar from the external maxillary, the ascending pharyngeal from the external carotid, the descending palatine branch of the internal maxillary, and a twig from the small meningeal.

The **veins** end in the tonsillar plexus, on the lateral side of the tonsil.

The **lymphatic vessels,** beginning in the dense network of capillaries surrounding the lymphatic tissue, penetrate the pharyngeal wall (page 787) and pass to the deep cervical nodes. The largest of these nodes, lying beside the posterior belly of the Digastricus, is especially associated with the tonsil and is easily palpated when the latter is inflamed.

The **nerves** are derived from the middle and posterior palatine branches of the maxillary, and from the glossopharyngeal.

Palatine Aponeurosis.—Attached to the posterior border of the hard palate is a thin, firm fibrous lamella which supports the muscles and gives strength to the soft palate. It is thicker above than below, where it becomes very thin and difficult to define. Laterally it is continuous with the pharyngeal aponeurosis.

Muscles of the Palate.—The muscles of the palate (Fig. 1039) are:

Levator veli palatini.   Glossopalatinus.
Tensor veli palatini.   Pharyngopalatinus.
Musculus uvulæ.

The **Levator veli palatini** (*Levator palati*) is a thick, rounded muscle situated lateral to the choanæ. It *arises* from the under surface of the apex of the petrous part of the temporal bone and from the medial lamina of the cartilage of the auditory tube. After passing above the upper concave margin of the Constrictor pharyngis superior it spreads out in the palatine velum, its fibers extending obliquely downward and medialward to the middle line, where they blend with those of the opposite side.

The **Tensor veli palatini** (*Tensor palati*) is a broad, thin, ribbon-like muscle placed lateral to the Levator veli palatini. It *arises* by a flat lamella from the scaphoid fossa at the base of the medial pterygoid plate, from the spina angularis of the sphenoid and from the lateral wall of the cartilage of the auditory tube. Descending vertically between the medial pterygoid plate and the Pterygoideus internus it ends in a tendon which winds around the pterygoid hamulus, being retained in this situation by some of the fibers of origin of the Pterygoideus internus. Between the tendon and the hamulus is a small bursa. The tendon then passes medialward and is *inserted* into the palatine aponeurosis and into the surface behind the transverse ridge on the horizontal part of the palatine bone.

The **Musculus uvulæ** (*Azygos uvulæ*) *arises* from the posterior nasal spine of the palatine bones and from the palatine aponeurosis; it descends to be inserted into the uvula.

The **Glossopalatinus** (*Palatoglossus*) is a small fleshy fasciculus, narrower in the middle than at either end, forming, with the mucous membrane covering its surface, the glossopalatine arch. It *arises* from the anterior surface of the soft palate, where it is continuous with the muscle of the opposite side, and passing downward, forward, and lateralward in front of the palatine tonsil, is inserted into the side of the tongue, some of its fibers spreading over the dorsum, and others passing deeply into the substance of the organ to intermingle with the Transversus linguæ.

The **Pharyngopalatinus** (*Palatopharyngeus*) is a long, fleshy fasciculus narrower in the middle than at either end, forming, with the mucous membrane covering its surface, the pharyngopalatine arch. It is separated from the Glossopalatinus by an angular interval, in which the palatine tonsil is lodged. It *arises* from the soft palate, where it is divided into two fasciculi by the Levator veli palatini and Musculus uvulæ. The **posterior fasciculus** lies in contact with the mucous membrane, and joins with that of the opposite muscle in the middle line; the **anterior fasciculus**, the thicker, lies in the soft palate between the Levator and Tensor, and joins in the middle line the corresponding part of the opposite muscle. Passing lateralward and downward behind the palatine tonsil, the Pharyngopalatinus joins the Stylopharyngeus, and is inserted with that muscle into the posterior border of the thyroid cartilage, some of its fibers being lost on the side of the pharynx and others passing across the middle line posteriorly, to decussate with the muscle of the opposite side.

Nerves.—The Tensor veli palatini is supplied by a branch of the fifth cranial nerve; the remaining muscles of this group are in all probability supplied by the bulbar portion of the accessory nerve through the pharyngeal plexus.

Actions.—During the *first stage* of deglutition, the bolus of food is driven back into the fauces by the pressure of the tongue against the hard palate, the base of the tongue being, at the same time, retracted, and the larynx raised with the pharynx. During the second stage the entrance to the larynx is closed by the drawing forward of the arytenoid cartilages toward the cushion of the epiglottis—a movement produced by the contraction of the Thyreoarytænoidei, the Arytænoidei, and the Arytænoepiglottidei.

After leaving the tongue the bolus passes on to the posterior or laryngeal surface of the epiglottis, and glides along this for a certain distance; then the Glossopalatini, the constrictors of the fauces, contract behind it; the palatine velum is slightly raised by the Levator veli palatini, and made tense by the Tensor veli palatini; and the Pharyngopalatini, by their contraction, pull the pharynx upward over the bolus, and come nearly together, the uvula filling up the slight interval between them. By these means the food is prevented from passing into the nasal part of the pharynx; at the same time, the Pharyngopalatini form an inclined plane, directed obliquely downward and backward along the under surface of which the bolus descends into the lower part of the pharynx. The Salpingopharyngei raise the upper and lateral parts of the pharynx—*i. e.*, those parts which are above the points where the Stylopharyngei are attached to the pharynx.

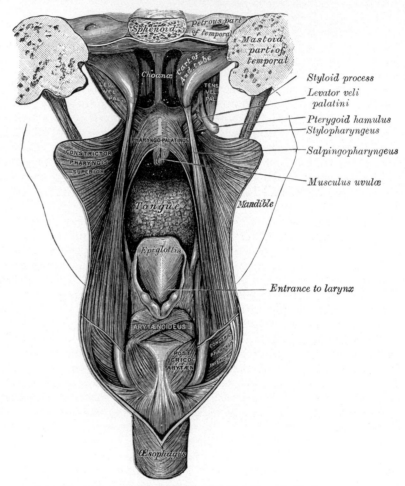

Fig. 1039.—Dissection of the muscles of the palate from behind.

Mucous Membrane.—The *mucous membrane of the soft palate* is thin, and covered with stratified squamous epithelium on both surfaces, excepting near the pharyngeal ostium of the auditory tube, where it is columnar and ciliated. According to Klein, the mucous membrane on the nasal surface of the soft palate in the fetus is covered throughout by columnar ciliated epithelium, which subsequently becomes squamous except at its free margin. Beneath the mucous membrane on the oral surface of the soft palate is a considerable amount of adenoid tissue. The palatine glands form a continuous layer on its posterior surface and around the uvula.

Vessels and Nerves.—The **arteries** supplying the palate are the descending palatine branch of the internal maxillary, the ascending palatine branch of the external maxillary, and the palatine branch of the ascending pharyngeal. The **veins** end chiefly in the pterygoid and tonsillar plexuses. The **lymphatic vessels** pass to the deep cervical nodes. The **sensory nerves** are derived from the palatine and nasopalatine nerves and from the glossopharyngeal.

THE PHARYNX.

The **pharynx** is that part of the digestive tube which is placed behind the nasal cavities, mouth, and larynx. It is a musculomembranous tube, somewhat conical in form, with the base upward, and the apex downward, extending from the under

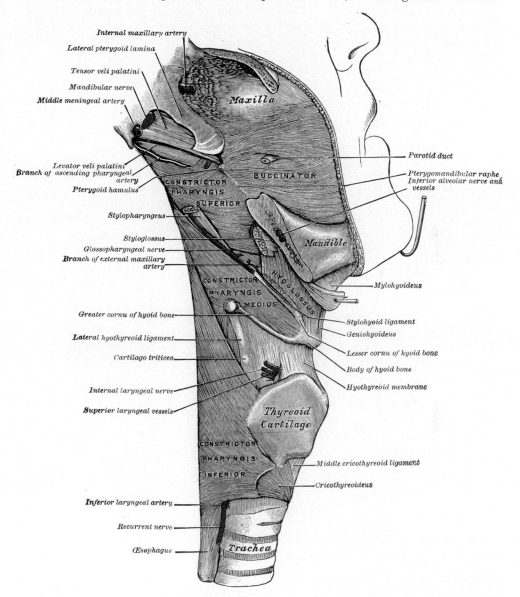

Internal maxillary artery

Lateral pterygoid lamina

Tensor veli palatini

Mandibular nerve

Middle meningeal artery

Levator veli palatini
Branch of ascending pharyngeal artery
Pterygoid hamulus

Stylopharyngeus

Styloglossus
Glossopharyngeal nerve
Branch of external maxillary artery

Greater cornu of hyoid bone

Lateral hyothyreoid ligament

Cartilago triticea

Internal laryngeal nerve

Superior laryngeal vessels

Inferior laryngeal artery

Recurrent nerve

Œsophagus

Maxilla

BUCCINATOR

CONSTRICTOR PHARYNGIS SUPERIOR

CONSTRICTOR PHARYNGIS MEDIUS

HYOGLOSSUS

Mandible

Thyreoid Cartilage

CONSTRICTOR PHARYNGIS INFERIOR

Trachea

Parotid duct

Pterygomandibular raphe
Inferior alveolar nerve and vessels

Mylohyoideus

Stylohyoid ligament
Geniohyoideus

Lesser cornu of hyoid bone

Body of hyoid bone

Hyothyreoid membrane

Middle cricothyreoid ligament

Cricothyreoideus

Fig. 1040.—The Buccinator and muscles of the pharynx.

surface of the skull to the level of the cricoid cartilage in front, and that of the sixth cervical vertebra behind.

The cavity of the pharynx is about 12.5 cm. long, and broader in the transverse than in the antero-posterior diameter. Its greatest breadth is immediately below the base of the skull, where it projects on either side, behind the pharyngeal ostium of the auditory tube, as the **pharyngeal recess** (*fossa of Rosenmüller*); its narrowest point is at its termination in the esophagus. It is limited, *above*, by the body of the sphenoid and basilar part of the occipital bone; *below*, it is continuous with the esophagus; *posteriorly*, it is connected by loose areolar tissue with the cervical portion of the vertebral column, and the prevertebral fascia covering the Longus colli and Longus capitis muscles; *anteriorly*, it is incomplete, and is attached in succession to the medial pterygoid plate, pterygomandibular raphé, mandible, tongue, hyoid bone, and thyroid and cricoid cartilages; *laterally*, it is connected to the styloid processes and their muscles, and is in contact with the common and

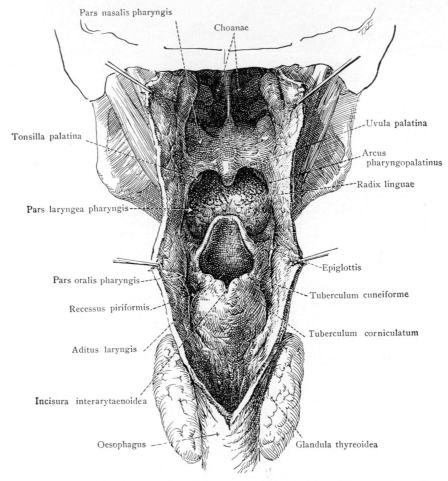

Fig. 1041.—The pharynx viewed through a median incision of its posterior wall. (Eycleshymer and Jones.)

internal carotid arteries, the internal jugular veins, the glossopharyngeal, vagus, and hypoglossal nerves, and the sympathetic trunks, and above with small parts of the Pterygoidei interni. Seven cavities communicate with it, *viz.*, the two nasal cavities, the two tympanic cavities, the mouth, the larynx, and the esophagus. The cavity of the pharynx may be subdivided from above downward into three parts: **nasal, oral,** and **laryngeal** (Fig. 1010).

The **Nasal Part of the Pharynx** (*pars nasalis pharyngis; nasopharynx*) lies behind the nose and above the level of the soft palate: it differs from the oral and laryngeal parts of the pharynx in that its cavity always remains patent. In front (Fig. 1041) it communicates through the choanæ with the nasal cavities. On its lateral wall is the **pharyngeal ostium of the auditory tube,** somewhat triangular in shape, and bounded behind by a firm prominence, the **torus** or **cushion**, caused by the medial end of the cartilage of the tube which elevates the mucous membrane. A vertical fold of mucous membrane, the **salpingopharyngeal fold**, stretches from the lower part of the torus; it contains the Salpingopharyngeus muscle. A second and smaller fold, the **salpingopalatine fold**, stretches from the upper part of the torus to the palate. Behind the ostium of the auditory tube is a deep recess, the **pharyngeal recess** (*fossa of Rosenmüller*) (Fig. 1037). On the posterior wall is a prominence produced by lymphatic tissue, which is known as the **pharyngeal tonsil**; during childhood it is likely to be hypertrophied into a considerable mass when it is called **adenoids** (Fig. 1037). Above the pharyngeal tonsil, in the middle line, an irregular flask-shaped depression of the mucous membrane sometimes extends up as far as the basilar process of the occipital bone; it is known as the **pharyngeal bursa**.

The **Oral Part of the Pharynx** (*pars oralis pharyngis*) reaches from the soft palate to the level of the hyoid bone. It opens anteriorly, through the isthmus faucium, into the mouth, while in its lateral wall, between the two palatine arches, is the **palatine tonsil**.

The **Laryngeal Part of the Pharynx** (*pars laryngea pharyngis*) reaches from the hyoid bone to the lower border of the cricoid cartilage, where it is continuous with the esophagus. In front it presents the triangular entrance of the larynx, the base of which is directed forward and is formed by the epiglottis, while its lateral boundaries are constituted by the aryepiglottic folds. On either side of the laryngeal orifice is a recess, termed the **sinus piriformis**, which is bounded medially by the aryepiglottic fold, laterally by the thyroid cartilage and hyothyroid membrane.

Muscles of the Pharynx.—The muscles of the pharynx (Fig. 1040) are:

Constrictor inferior.	Stylopharyngeus.
Constrictor medius.	Salpingopharyngeus.
Constrictor superior.	Pharyngopalatinus.[1]

The **Constrictor pharyngis inferior** (*Inferior constrictor*) (Figs. 1040, 1042), the thickest of the three constrictors, *arises* from the sides of the cricoid and thyroid cartilages. From the cricoid cartilage it arises in the interval between the Cricothyreoideus in front, and the articular facet for the inferior cornu of the thyroid cartilage behind. On the thyroid cartilage it arises from the oblique line on the side of the lamina, from the surface behind this nearly as far as the posterior border and from the inferior cornu. From these origins the fibers spread backward and medialward to be *inserted* with the muscle of the opposite side into the fibrous raphé in the posterior median line of the pharynx. The inferior fibers are horizontal and continuous with the circular fibers of the esophagus; the rest ascend, increasing in obliquity, and overlap the Constrictor medius.

The **Constrictor pharyngis medius** (*Middle constrictor*) (Figs. 1040, 1042) is a fan-shaped muscle, smaller than the preceding. It *arises* from the whole length of the upper border of the greater cornu of the hyoid bone, from the lesser cornu, and from the stylohyoid ligament. The fibers diverge from their origin: the lower ones descend beneath the Constrictor inferior, the middle fibers pass transversely, and the upper fibers ascend and overlap the Constrictor superior. It is *inserted* into the posterior median fibrous raphé, blending in the middle line with the muscle of the opposite side.

The **Constrictor pharyngis superior** (*Superior constrictor*) (Figs. 1040, 1042) is a quadrilateral muscle, thinner and paler than the other two. It *arises* from the lower third of the posterior margin of the medial pterygoid plate and its hamulus, from the pterygomandibular raphé, from the alveolar process of the mandible above the posterior end of the mylohyoid line, and by a few fibers from the side of the tongue. The fibers curve backward to be inserted into the median raphé, being

---

[1] The Pharyngopalatinus is described with the muscles of the palate (p. 1246).

also prolonged by means of an aponeurosis to the pharyngeal spine on the basilar part of the occipital bone. The superior fibers arch beneath the Levator veli palatini and the auditory tube. The interval between the upper border of the muscle and the base of the skull is closed by the pharyngeal aponeurosis, and is known as the **sinus of Morgagni.**

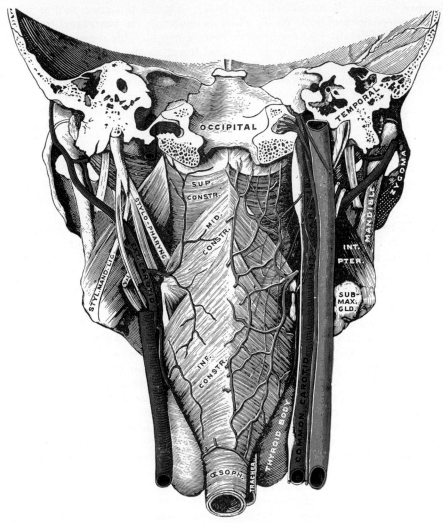

Fig. 1042.—Muscles of the pharynx, viewed from behind, together with the associated vessels and nerves. (Modified after Testut.)

The **Stylopharyngeus** (Fig. 1032) is a long, slender muscle, cylindrical above, flattened below. It *arises* from the medial side of the base of the styloid process, passes downward along the side of the pharynx between the Constrictores superior and medius, and spreads out beneath the mucous membrane. Some of its fibers are lost in the Constrictor muscles, while others, joining with the Pharyngopalatinus, are inserted into the posterior border of the thyroid cartilage. The glossopharyngeal nerve runs on the lateral side of this muscle, and crosses over it to reach the tongue.

The **Salpingopharyngeus** (Fig. 1039) *arises* from the inferior part of the auditory tube near its orifice; it passes downward and blends with the posterior fasciculus of the Pharyngopalatinus.

Nerves.—The Constrictores and Salpingopharyngeus are supplied by branches from the pharyngeal plexus, the Constrictor inferior by additional branches from the external laryngeal and recurrent nerves, and the Stylopharyngeus by the glossopharyngeal nerve.

Actions.—When deglutition is about to be performed, the pharynx is drawn upward and dilated in different directions, to receive the food propelled into it from the mouth. The Stylopharyngei, which are much farther removed from one another at their origin than at their insertion, draw the sides of the pharynx upward and lateralward, and so increase its transverse diameter; its breadth in the antero-posterior direction is increased by the larynx and tongue being carried forward in their ascent. As soon as the bolus of food is received in the pharynx, the elevator muscles relax, the pharynx descends, and the Constrictores contract upon the bolus, and convey it downward into the esophagus.

Structure.—The pharynx is composed of three coats: **mucous, fibrous,** and **muscular.**

The **pharyngeal aponeurosis,** or **fibrous coat,** is situated between the mucous and muscular layers. It is thick above where the muscular fibers are wanting, and is firmly connected to the basilar portion of the occipital and the petrous portions of the temporal bones. As it descends it diminishes in thickness, and is gradually lost. It is strengthened posteriorly by a strong fibrous band, which is attached above to the pharyngeal spine on the under surface of the basilar portion of the occipital bone, and passes downward, forming a median raphé, which gives attachment to the Constrictores pharyngis.

The **mucous coat** is continuous with that lining the nasal cavities, the mouth, the auditory tubes, and the larynx. In the nasal part of the pharynx it is covered by columnar ciliated epithelium; in the oral and laryngeal portions the epithelium is stratified squamous. Beneath the mucous membrane are found racemose mucous glands: they are especially numerous at the upper part of the pharynx around the orifices of the auditory tubes.

THE ESOPHAGUS (Fig. 825).

The **esophagus** or **gullet** is a muscular canal, about 23 to 25 cm. long, extending from the pharynx to the stomach. It begins in the neck at the lower border of the cricoid cartilage, opposite the sixth cervical vertebra, descends along the front of the vertebral column, through the superior and posterior mediastina, passes through the diaphragm, and, entering the abdomen, ends at the cardiac orifice of the stomach, opposite the eleventh thoracic vertebra. The general direction of the esophagus is vertical; but it presents two slight curves in its course. At its commencement it is placed in the middle line; but it inclines to the left side as far as the root of the neck, gradually passes to the middle line again at the level of the fifth thoracic vertebra, and finally deviates to the left as it passes forward to the esophageal hiatus in the diaphragm. The esophagus also presents antero-posterior flexures corresponding to the curvatures of the cervical and thoracic portions of the vertebral column. It is the narrowest part of the digestive tube, and is most contracted at its commencement, and at the point where it passes through the diaphragm.

Relations.—The **cervical portion** of the esophagus is in relation, *in front,* with the trachea; and at the lower part of the neck, where it projects to the left side, with the thyroid gland; *behind,* it rests upon the vertebral column and Longus colli muscles; *on either side* it is in relation with the common carotid artery (especially the left, as it inclines to that side), and parts of the lobes of the thyroid gland; the recurrent nerves ascend between it and the trachea; to its left side is the thoracic duct.

The **thoracic portion** of the esophagus is at first situated in the superior mediastinum between the trachea and the vertebral column, a little to the left of the median line. It then passes behind and to the right of the aortic arch, and descends in the posterior mediastinum along the right side of the descending aorta, then runs in front and a little to the left of the aorta, and enters the abdomen through the diaphragm at the level of the tenth thoracic vertebra. Just before it perforates the diaphragm it presents a distinct dilatation. It is in relation, *in front,* with the trachea, the left bronchus, the pericardium, and the diaphragm;

behind, it rests upon the vertebral column, the Longus colli muscles, the right aortic intercostal arteries, the thoracic duct, and the hemiazygos veins; and below, near the diaphragm, upon the front of the aorta. On its *left* side, in the superior mediastinum, are the terminal part of the aortic arch, the left subclavian artery, the thoracic duct, and left pleura, while running upward in the angle between it and the trachea is the left recurrent nerve; below, it is in relation with the descending thoracic aorta. On its *right* side are the right pleura, and the azygos vein which it overlaps. Below the roots of the lungs the vagi descend in close contact with it, the right nerve passing down behind, and the left nerve in front of it; the two nerves uniting to form a plexus around the tube.

In the lower part of the posterior mediastinum the thoracic duct lies to the right side of the esophagus; higher up, it is placed behind it, and, crossing about the level of the fourth thoracic vertebra, is continued upward on its left side.

The **abdominal portion** of the esophagus lies in the esophageal groove on the posterior surface of the left lobe of the liver. It measures about 1.25 cm. in length, and only its front and left aspects are covered by peritoneum. It is somewhat conical with its base applied to the upper orifice of the stomach, and is known as the **antrum cardiacum.**

Structure (Fig. 1043).—The esophagus has four coats: an **external or fibrous,** a **muscular,** a **submucous or areolar,** and an **internal or mucous coat.**

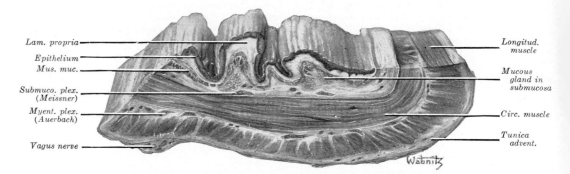

Lam. propria
Epithelium
Mus. muc.
Submuco. plex.
(Meissner)
Myent. plex.
(Auerbach)
Vagus nerve

Longitud. muscle
Mucous gland in submucosa
Circ. muscle
Tunica advent.

FIG. 1043.—Cross section through lower part of esophagus of adult cadaver. × 5.

The **muscular coat** (*tunica muscularis*) is composed of two planes of considerable thickness: an external of longitudinal and an internal of circular fibers.

The *longitudinal fibers* are arranged, at the commencement of the tube, in three fasciculi: one in front, which is attached to the vertical ridge on the posterior surface of the lamina of the cricoid cartilage; and one at either side, which is continuous with the muscular fibers of the pharynx: as they descend they blend together, and form a uniform layer, which covers the outer surface of the tube.

Accessory slips of muscular fibers pass between the esophagus and the left pleura, where the latter covers the thoracic aorta, or the root of the left bronchus, or the back of the pericardium.

The *circular fibers* are continuous above with the Constrictor pharyngis inferior; their direction is transverse at the upper and lower parts of the tube, but oblique in the intermediate part.

The muscular fibers in the upper part of the esophagus are of a red color, and consist chiefly of skeletal muscle; the intermediate part is mixed and the lower part with rare exceptions contains only smooth muscle.

The **areolar** or **submucous coat** (*tela submucosa*) connects loosely the mucous and muscular coats. It contains blood vessels, nerves, and mucous glands.

The **mucous coat** (*tunica mucosa*) is thick, of a reddish color above, and pale below. It is disposed in longitudinal folds, which disappear on distension of the tube. Its surface is studded with minute papillæ, and it is covered throughout with a thick layer of stratified squamous epithelium. Beneath the mucous membrane, between it and the areloar coat, is a layer of longitudinally arranged non-striped muscular fibers. This is the **muscularis mucosæ.** At the commencement of the esophagus it is absent, or only represented by a few scattered bundles; lower down it forms a considerable stratum. The **esophageal glands** (*glandulæ œsophageæ*) are small compound racemose glands of the mucous type: they are lodged in the submucous tissue, and each opens upon the surface by a long excretory duct.

Vessels and Nerves.—The **arteries** supplying the esophagus are derived from the inferior thyroid branch of the thyrocervical trunk, from the descending thoracic aorta, from the bronchial arteries, from the left gastric branch of the celiac artery, and from the left inferior phrenic of the abdominal aorta. They have for the most part a longitudinal direction.

The **veins** end in the inferior thyroid, azygos, hemiazygos, and gastric veins, thereby forming a connection between the portal and systemic venous systems (see p. 765).

The **nerves** are derived from the recurrent vagus, supplying the striated musculature of the organ, and from the vagus and sympathetic trunks which supply fibers to the smooth musculature; these cranial parasympathetic and sympathetic fibers form plexuses between the two layers of the muscular coat, and in the submucosa, as in the stomach and intestines.

THE ABDOMEN.

The **abdomen** is the largest cavity in the body. It is of an oval shape, the extremities of the oval being directed upward and downward. The upper boundary is formed by the diaphragm which extends as a dome over the abdomen, so that the cavity extends high into the bony thorax, reaching on the right side, in the mammary line, to the upper border of the fifth rib; on the left side it falls below this level by about 2.5 cm. The lower boundary is formed principally by the Levator ani and Coccygeus or the **diaphragm of the pelvis**. In order to facilitate description, it is artificially divided into two parts: an upper and larger part, the **abdomen proper**; and a lower and smaller part, the **pelvis**, the limit between them being marked by the superior aperture of the lesser pelvis.

The **abdomen proper** differs from the other great cavities of the body in being bounded for the most part by muscles and fasciæ, so that it can vary in capacity and shape according to the condition of the viscera which it contains; but, in addition to this, the abdomen varies in form and extent with age and sex. In the adult male, with moderate distension of the viscera, it is oval in shape, but at the same time flattened from before backward. In the adult female, with a fully developed pelvis, it is ovoid with the narrower pole upward, and in young children it is also ovoid but with the narrower pole downward.

Boundaries.—It is bounded *in front* and *at the sides* by the abdominal muscles and the Iliacus muscles; *behind* by the vertebral column and the Psoas and Quadratus lumborum muscles; *above* by the diaphragm; *below* by the plane of the superior aperture of the lesser pelvis. The muscles forming the boundaries of the cavity are lined upon their inner surfaces by transversalis fascia.

The abdomen contains the greater part of the digestive tube; some of the accessory organs of digestion, *viz.*, the liver and pancreas; the spleen, the kidneys, and the suprarenal glands. Most of these structures, as well as the wall of the cavity in which they are contained, are more or less covered by an extensive and complicated serous membrane, the **peritoneum**.

The Apertures in the Walls of the Abdomen.—The apertures in the walls of the abdomen, for the transmission of structures to or from it, are, *in front*, the **umbilical**, for the transmission of the umbilical vessels, the allantois, and vitelline duct in the fetus; *above*, the **vena caval opening**, for the transmission of the inferior vena cava, the **aortic hiatus**, for the passage of the aorta, azygos vein, and thoracic duct, and the **esophageal hiatus**, for the esophagus and vagi. *Below*, there are two apertures on either side: one for the passage of the femoral vessels and lumboinguinal nerve, and the other for the transmission of the spermatic cord in the male, and the round ligament of the uterus in the female.

Regions.—For convenience of description, the abdomen is artificially divided into nine regions by two horizontal and two sagittal planes, indicated by lines drawn on the surface of the body (Fig. 77). Of the horizontal planes the upper or **transpyloric** is indicated by a line midway between the jugular notch and the symphysis pubis, the lower by a line midway between the transpyloric and the symphysis pubis. The latter is the **intertubercular plane**; its level corresponds with the prominent tubercle on the iliac crest about 5 cm. behind the anterior superior iliac spine. By means of these planes the abdomen is divided into three zones, the **subcostal, umbilical,** and **hypogastric zones.** Each of these is further subdivided into three regions by the two sagittal planes, which pass vertically through points half-way between the anterior superior iliac spines and the symphysis pubis.

The middle region of the upper zone is called the **epigastric;** and the two lateral regions, the **right** and **left hypochondriac.** The central region of the middle zone

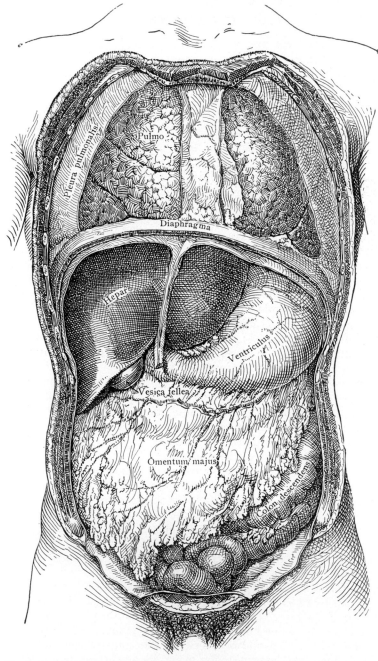

FIG. 1044.—Ventral view of the thoracic and abdominal viscera in position after removal of the anterior thoracic and abdominal walls. (Eycleshymer and Jones.)

is the **umbilical**; and the two lateral regions, the **right** and **left lumbar**. The middle region of the lower zone is the **hypogastric** or **pubic region**; and the lateral regions are the **right** and **left iliac** or **inguinal** (Fig. 77).

The **pelvis** is that portion of the abdominal cavity which lies below and behind a plane passing through the promontory of the sacrum, lineæ terminales of the hip bones, and the pubic crests. It is bounded behind by the sacrum, coccyx, Piriformes, and the sacrospinous and sacrotuberous ligaments; in front and

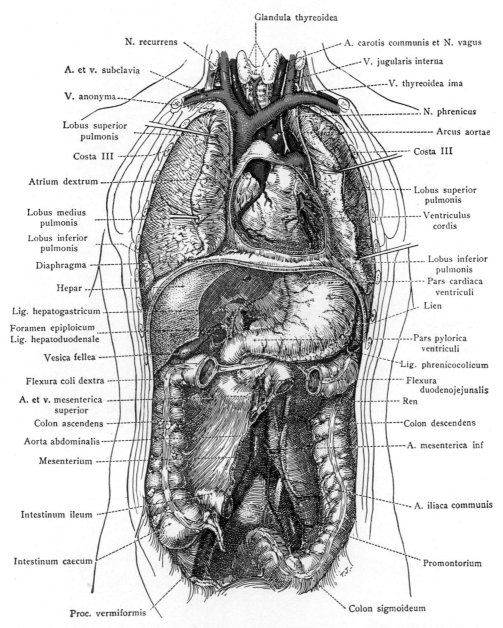

Glandula thyreoidea
N. recurrens
A. et v. subclavia
V. anonyma
Lobus superior pulmonis
Costa III
Atrium dextrum
Lobus medius pulmonis
Lobus inferior pulmonis
Diaphragma
Hepar
Lig. hepatogastricum
Foramen epiploicum
Lig. hepatoduodenale
Vesica fellea
Flexura coli dextra
A. et v. mesenterica superior
Colon ascendens
Aorta abdominalis
Mesenterium
Intestinum ileum
Intestinum caecum
Proc. vermiformis

A. carotis communis et N. vagus
V. jugularis interna
V. thyreoidea ima
N. phrenicus
Arcus aortae
Costa III
Lobus superior pulmonis
Ventriculus cordis
Lobus inferior pulmonis
Pars cardiaca ventriculi
Lien
Pars pylorica ventriculi
Lig. phrenicocolicum
Flexura duodenojejunalis
Ren
Colon descendens
A. mesenterica inf
A. iliaca communis
Promontorium
Colon sigmoideum

Fig. 1045.—Ventral view of the thoracic and abdominal viscera partially dissected. The anterior pleuræ and pericardium have been removed; the structures at the root of the neck dissected. The left lobe of the liver, the greater omentum, transverse colon, jejunum and ileum have been removed. (Eycleshymer and Jones.)

laterally by the pubes and ischia and Obturatores interni; above it is continuous with the abdomen proper; below it is closed by the Levatores ani and Coccygei and the urogenital diaphragm. The pelvis contains the urinary bladder, the sigmoid colon and rectum, a few coils of the small intestine, and some of the generative organs.

When the anterior abdominal wall is removed (Fig. 1044), the viscera are partly exposed as follows: above and to the right side is the liver, situated chiefly under the

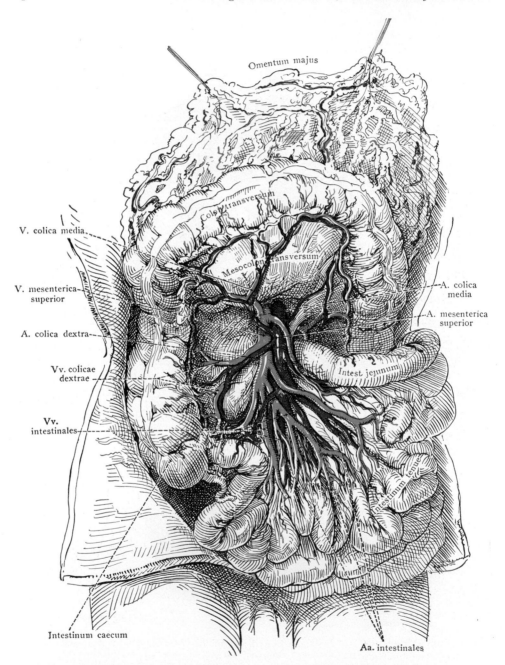

Fig. 1046.—Small and large intestines with their mesenteries and blood vessels viewed after the greater omentum has been drawn upward over the chest. (Eycleshymer and Jones.)

shelter of the right ribs and their cartilages, but extending across the middle line and reaching for some distance below the level of the xiphoid process. To the left of the liver is the stomach, from the lower border of which an apron-like fold of peritoneum, the **greater omentum**, descends for a varying distance, and obscures, to a greater or lesser extent, the other viscera. Below it, however, some of the coils of the small intestine can generally be seen, while in the right and left iliac regions respectively the cecum and the iliac colon are partly exposed. The bladder oc-

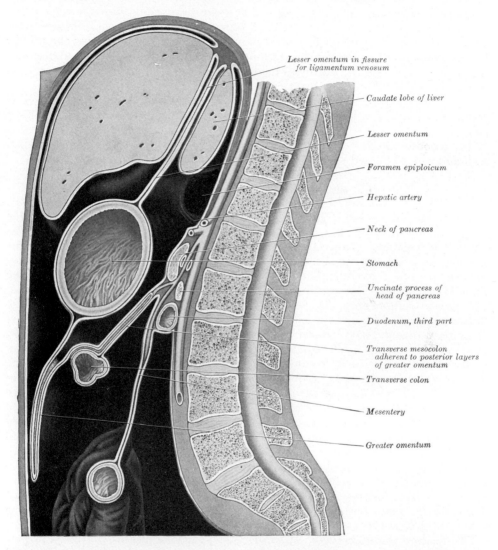

Lesser omentum in fissure for ligamentum venosum

Caudate lobe of liver

Lesser omentum

Foramen epiploicum

Hepatic artery

Neck of pancreas

Stomach

Uncinate process of head of pancreas

Duodenum, third part

Transverse mesocolon adherent to posterior layers of greater omentum

Transverse colon

Mesentery

Greater omentum

Fig. 1047.—A sagittal section through the abdomen, approximately in the median plane Diagrammatic. Compare with Fig. 1050. The section cuts the posterior abdomen along the line *YY* in Fig. 1050. The peritoneum is shown in *blue* except along the cut edges, which are left white.

cupies the anterior part of the pelvis, and, if distended, will project above the symphysis pubis; the rectum lies in the concavity of the sacrum, but is usually obscured by the coils of the small intestine. The sigmoid colon lies between the rectum and the bladder.

When the stomach is followed from left to right (Fig. 1045) it is seen to be continuous with the first part of the small intestine, or duodenum, the point being marked by a thickened ring, the pyloric valve. The duodenum passes toward the under surface of the liver, and then, curving downward, is lost to sight. If, however, the greater omentum be thrown upward over the chest (Fig. 1046), the inferior part of the duodenum will be observed passing across the vertebral column toward the left side, where it becomes continuous with the coils of the jejunum and ileum. These measure some 6 meters in length, and if followed downward the ileum will be seen to end in the right iliac fossa by opening into the cecum, the commencement of the large intestine. From the cecum the large intestine takes an arched course, passing at first upward on the right side, then across the middle line and downward on the left side, forming the ascending, transverse, and descending colon. In the pelvis it assumes the form of a loop, the sigmoid colon, and ends in the rectum.

The spleen (*lien*) lies behind the stomach in the left hypochondriac region (Fig. 1045), and may be in part exposed by pulling the stomach over toward the right side.

The smooth and glistening appearance of the internal surface of the abdominal wall and of the exposed viscera is due to the serous membrane, or **peritoneum**.

The Peritoneum (Tunica Serosa).

The peritoneum is the largest serous membrane in the body, and consists, in the male, of a closed sac, a part of which is applied against the abdominal parietes, while the remainder is reflected over the contained viscera. In the female the peritoneum is not a closed sac, since the free ends of the uterine tubes open directly into the peritoneal cavity. The part which lines the abdominal wall is named the **parietal peritoneum**; that which is reflected over the contained viscera constitutes the **visceral peritoneum**. The *free surface* of the membrane is a smooth layer of flattened mesothelium, lubricated by a small quantity of serous fluid, which allows the viscera to glide freely against the wall of the cavity or upon each other with the least possible friction. The *attached* surface is connected to the viscera and inner surface of the parietes by means of areolar tissue, termed the **subserous fascia**. The parietal portion is separated by a fascial cleft from the transversalis fascia lining of the abdomen and pelvis, but is more closely adherent to the under surface of the diaphragm, and also in the middle line of the abdomen.

The space between the parietal and visceral layers of the peritoneum is named the **peritoneal cavity**; but under normal conditions this cavity is merely a potential one, since the parietal and visceral layers are in contact. The peritoneal cavity gives off a large diverticulum, the **omental bursa**, which is situated behind the stomach and adjoining structures; the neck of communication between the cavity and the bursa is termed the **epiploic foramen** (*foramen of Winslow*). (Fig. 1053) Formerly the main portion of the cavity was described as the greater, and the omental bursa as the lesser sac.

The peritoneum differs from the other serous membranes of the body in presenting a much more complex arrangement, and one that can be clearly understood only by following the changes which take place in the digestive tube during its development (pages 1210 to 1215).

To trace the membrane from one viscus to another, and from the viscera to the parietes, it is necessary to follow its continuity in the vertical and horizontal directions, and it will be found simpler to describe the main portion of the cavity and the omental bursa separately.

Vertical Disposition of the main Peritoneal Cavity (*greater sac*) (Fig. 1047). It is convenient to trace this from the back of the abdominal wall at the level of the umbilicus. On following the peritoneum upward from this level it is seen to be reflected around a fibrous cord, the **ligamentum teres** (*obliterated umbilical vein*), which reaches from the umbilicus to the under surface of the liver. This reflection forms a somewhat triangular fold, the **falciform ligament of the liver,** attaching the upper and anterior surfaces of the liver to the diaphragm and abdominal wall (Figs. 1054, 1082.) With the exception of the line of attachment of this ligament the peritoneum covers the whole of the under surface of the anterior part of the

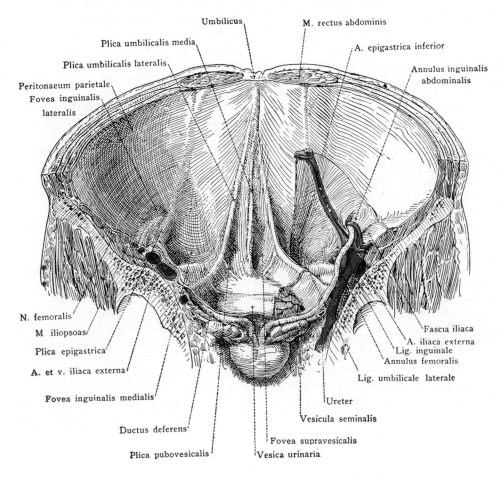

Fig. 1048.—The lower portion of the anterior abdominal wall, viewed from within. The peritoneum has been partially removed from the right side. (Eycleshymer and Jones.)

diaphragm, and is continued from it on to the upper surface of the right lobe of the liver as the **anterior layer of the coronary ligament** and on to the upper surface of the left lobe as the **anterior layer of the left triangular ligament** of the liver. Covering upper and anterior surfaces of the liver, it is continued around its sharp margin on to the under surface, where it presents the following relations: (*a*) It covers the under surface of the right lobe and is reflected from the back part of this on to the right suprarenal gland and upper extremity of the right kidney, forming in this situation the **posterior layer of the coronary ligament;** a special fold, the **hepatorenal ligament** is frequently present between the inferior surface of the liver and the front of the kidney. From the kidney it is carried downward to the duodenum and right colic flexure and medialward in front of the inferior vena cava, where it is continuous with the posterior wall of the omental bursa. Between the two layers of the coronary ligament there is a large triangular surface of the liver devoid of peritoneal covering; this is named the **bare area** of the liver, and is attached to the diaphragm by areolar tissue. Toward the right margin of the liver the two layers of the coronary ligament gradually approach each other, and ultimately fuse to form a small triangular fold connecting the right lobe of the liver to the diaphragm, and named the **right triangular ligament** of the liver. The apex of the triangular bare area corresponds with the point of meeting of the two layers of the coronary ligament, its base with the fossa for the inferior vena cava. (*b*) It covers the lower surface of the quadrate lobe, the under and lateral surfaces of the gall-bladder, and the under surface and posterior border of the left lobe; it is then reflected from the upper surface of the left lobe to the diaphragm as the **inferior layer of the left triangular ligament,** and from the porta of the liver and the fossa for the ductus venosus to the lesser curvature of the stomach and the first 2.5 cm. of the duodenum as the anterior layer of the **hepatogastric** and **hepatoduodenal ligaments,** which together constitute the **lesser omentum.** If this layer of the lesser omentum be followed to the right it will be found to turn around the hepatic artery, bile duct, and portal vein, and become continuous with the anterior wall of the omental bursa, forming a free folded edge of peritoneum. Traced downward, it covers the antero-superior surface of the stomach and the commencement of the duodenum, and is carried down into a large free fold, known as the **gastrocolic ligament** or **greater omentum.** Reaching the free margin of this fold, it is reflected upward to cover the under and posterior surfaces of the transverse colon, and thence to the posterior abdominal wall as the inferior layer of the **transverse mesocolon.** It reaches the abdominal wall at the head and anterior border of the pancreas, is then carried down over the lower part of the head and over the inferior surface of the pancreas on the superior mesenteric vessels, and thence to the small intestine as the anterior layer of the **mesentery.** It encircles the intestine, and subsequently may be traced, as the posterior layer of the mesentery, upward and backward to the abdominal wall. From this it sweeps down over the aorta into the pelvis, where it invests the sigmoid colon, its reduplication forming the **sigmoid mesocolon.** Leaving first the sides and then the front of the rectum, it is reflected on to the seminal vesicles and fundus of the urinary bladder and, after covering the upper surface of that viscus, is carried along the medial and lateral umbilical ligaments (Fig. 1048) on to the back of the abdominal wall to the level from which a start was made.

Between the rectum and the bladder it forms, in the male, a pouch, the **recto-vesical excavation,** the bottom of which is slightly below the level of the upper-ends of the vesiculæ seminales—*i. e.*, about 7.5 cm. from the orifice of the anus. When the bladder is distended, the peritoneum is carried up with the expanded viscus so that a considerable part of the anterior surface of the latter lies directly against the abdominal wall without the intervention of peritoneal membrane (*pre-vesical space of Retzius*). In the female the peritoneum is reflected from the rectum over the posterior vaginal fornix to the cervix and body of the uterus, forming the **rectouterine excavation** (*pouch of Douglas*). It is continued over the intestinal surface and fundus of the uterus on to its vesical surface, which it covers as far as the junction of the body and cervix uteri, and then to the bladder, forming here a second, but shallower, pouch, the **vesicouterine excavation.** It is also reflected from the sides of the uterus to the lateral walls of the pelvis as two expanded folds, the **broad ligaments of the uterus,** in the free margin of each of which is the uterine tube.

Vertical Disposition of the Omental Bursa (*lesser peritoneal sac*) (Fig. 1047).—A start may be made in this case on the posterior abdominal wall at the anterior border of the pancreas. From this region the peritoneum may be followed upward over the pancreas on to the inferior surface of the diaphragm, and thence on to the caudate lobe and caudate process of the liver to the fossa from the ductus venosus and the porta of the liver. Traced to the right, it is continuous over the inferior vena cava with the posterior wall of the main cavity. From the liver it is carried downward to the lesser curvature of the stomach and the commencement of the duodenum as the posterior layer of the lesser omentum, and is continuous on the right, around the hepatic artery, bile duct, and portal vein, with the anterior layer of this omentum. The posterior layer of the lesser omentum is carried down as a covering for the postero-inferior surfaces of the stomach and commencement of the duodenum, and is continued downward as the deep layer of the **gastrocolic ligament** or **greater omentum.** From the free margin of this fold it is reflected upward on

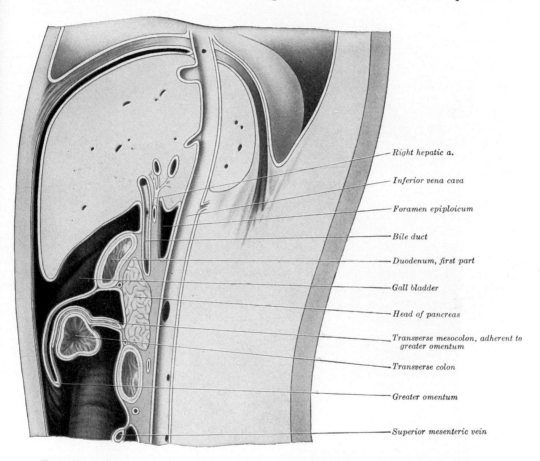

Right hepatic a.

Inferior vena cava

Foramen epiploicum

Bile duct

Duodenum, first part

Gall bladder

Head of pancreas

Transverse mesocolon, adherent to greater omentum

Transverse colon

Greater omentum

Superior mesenteric vein

Fig. 1049.—A section through the upper part of the abdominal cavity, along the lines *XX* in Figure 1050. The boundaries of the aditus to the lesser sac are shown, and a small recess of the lesser sac is displayed in front of the head of the pancreas. Note that the transverse colon and its mesocolon are adherent to the posterior two layers of the greater omentum.

itself to the anterior and superior surfaces of the transverse colon, and thence as the superior layer of the transverse mesocolon to the anterior border of the pancreas, the level from which a start was made. It will be seen that the loop formed by the wall of the omental bursa below the transverse colon follows, and is closely applied to, the deep surface of that formed by the peritoneum of the main cavity, and that the greater omentum or large fold of peritoneum which hangs in front of the small intestine therefore consists of four layers, two anterior and two posterior separated by the potential cavity of the omental bursa.

Horizontal Disposition of the Peritoneum.—Below the transverse colon the arrangement is simple, as it includes only the main cavity; above the level of the transverse colon it is more complicated on account of the existence of the omental bursa. Below the transverse colon it may be considered in the two regions, *viz.*, in the **pelvis** and in the **abdomen proper**.

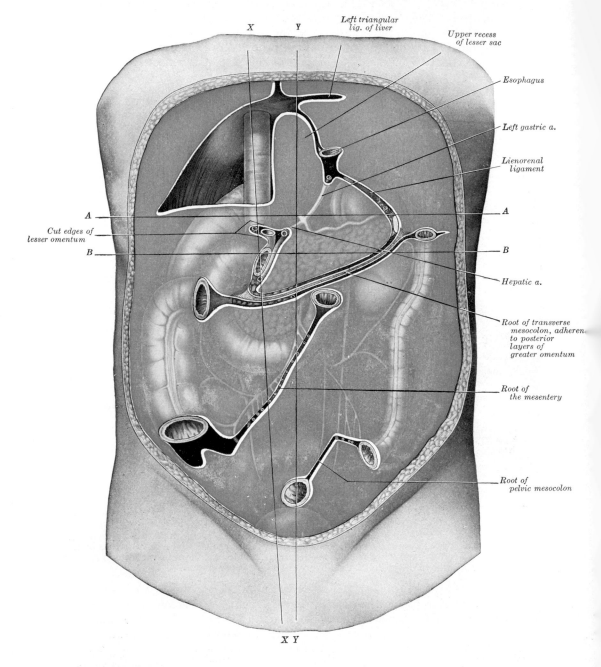

FIG. 1050.—The posterior abdominal wall, showing the lines of peritoneal reflection; after removal of the liver, spleen, stomach, jejunum, cecum, transverse colon and pelvic colon. Line *YY* represents the plane of Fig. 1047. Line *AA* represents the plane of Fig. 1051. Line *XX* represents the plane of Fig. 1049. Line *BB* represents the plane of Fig. 1052.

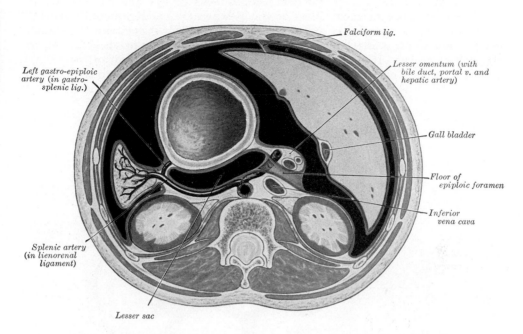

Falciform lig.

Left gastro-epiploic artery (in gastro-splenic lig.)

Lesser omentum (with bile duct, portal v. and hepatic artery)

Gall bladder

Floor of epiploic foramen

Inferior vena cava

Splenic artery (in lienorenal ligament)

Lesser sac

FIG. 1051.—A transverse section through the abdomen, at the level of *AA*; Fig. 1050, viewed from above. Diagrammatic. The peritoneal cavity is shown in *dark blue;* the peritoneum and its cut edges in *lighter blue*.

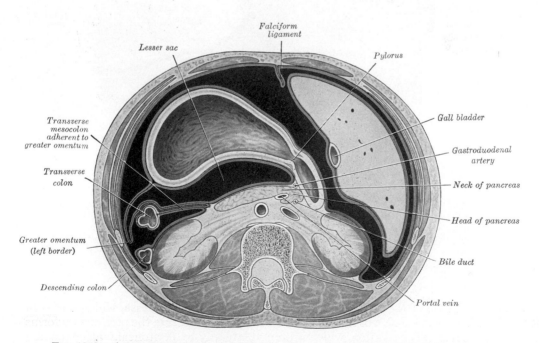

Falciform ligament

Lesser sac

Pylorus

Transverse mesocolon adherent to greater omentum

Gall bladder

Gastroduodenal artery

Transverse colon

Neck of pancreas

Head of pancreas

Greater omentum (left border)

Bile duct

Descending colon

Portal vein

FIG. 1052.—A transverse section through the abdomen, at the level of *BB* in Fig. 1050, viewed from above. Diagrammatic. Colors as in Fig. 1051.

(1) **In the Pelvis.**—The peritoneum here follows closely the surfaces of the pelvic viscera and the inequalities of the pelvic walls, and presents important differences in the two sexes. (*a*) **In the male** (Fig. 1055) it encircles the sigmoid colon, from which it is reflected to the posterior wall of the pelvis as a fold, the **sigmoid mesocolon.** It then leaves the sides and, finally, the front of the rectum, and is continued on to the upper ends of the seminal vesicles and the bladder;

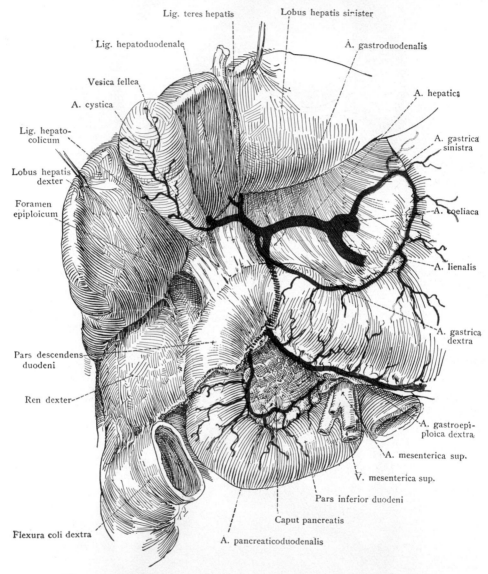

FIG. 1053.—The epiploic foramen (of Winslow) and neighboring structures. (Eycleshymer and Jones.)

on either side of the rectum it forms a fossa, the **pararectal fossa,** which varies in size with the distension of the rectum. In front of the rectum the peritoneum forms the rectovesical excavation, which is limited laterally by peritoneal folds extending from the sides of the bladder to the rectum and sacrum. These folds are known from their position as the **rectovesical** or **sacrogenital folds.** The peritoneum of the anterior pelvic wall covers the superior surface of the bladder, and on either

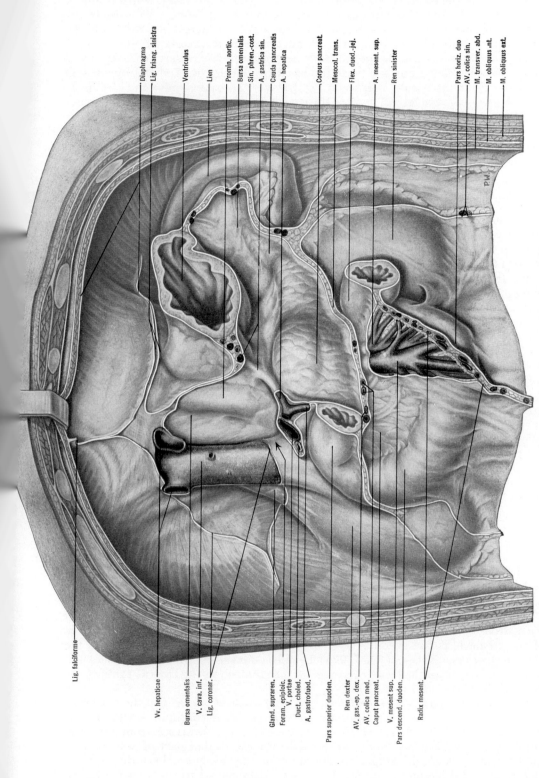

Lig. falciforme

Diaphragma
Lig. triang. sinistra
Ventriculus
Lien
Promin. aortic.
Bursa omentalis
Sin. phren.-cost.
A. gastrica sin.
Cauda pancreatis
A. hepatica
Corpus pancreat.
Mesocol. trans.
Flex. duod.-jej.
A. mesent. sup.
Ren sinister
Pars horiz. duo
AV. colica sin.
M. transver. abd.
M. obliquus .nt.
M. obliquus ext.

Vv. hepaticae
Bursa omentalis
V. cava. inf.
Lig. coronar.
Gland. supraren,
Foram. epiploic,
V. portae
Duct. choled.
A. gastroduod.
Pars superior duoden.
Ren dexter
AV. gas.-ep. dex.
AV. colica med.
Caput pancreat.
V. mesent sup.
Pars descend. duoden.
Radix mesent.

FIG. 1054.—View of the posterior wall of the lesser sac of the peritoneum (omental bursa), showing the attachment of the ligaments of the liver, the hepatoduodenal ligament, the root of the mesentery and transverse mesocolon, and reflection of peritoneum from the stomach. The aorta, pancreas, kidneys, spleen, and duodenum are covered by peritoneum. (Töndury, Angewandte und topographische Anatomie, courtesy of Georg Thieme Verlag.)

side of this viscus forms a depression, termed the **paravesical fossa,** which is limited laterally by the fold of peritoneum covering the ductus deferens. The size of this fossa is dependent on the state of distension of the bladder; when the bladder is empty, a variable fold of peritoneum, the **plica vesicalis transversa,** divides the fossa into two portions. On the peritoneum between the paravesical and pararectal fossæ the only elevations are those produced by the ureters and the hypogastric vessels. (*b*) **In the female,** pararectal and paravesical fossæ similar to those in the male are present: the lateral limit of the paravesical fossa is the peritoneum investing the round ligament of the uterus. The rectovesical excavation is, however, divided by the uterus and vagina into a small anterior vesicouterine and a large, deep, posterior rectouterine excavation. The sacrogenital folds form the margins of the latter, and are continued on to the back of the uterus to form a transverse fold, the **torus uterinus.** The broad ligaments extend from the sides of the uterus to the lateral walls of the pelvis; they contain in their free margins the uterine tubes, and in their posterior layers the ovaries. Below, the broad ligaments are continuous with the peritoneum on the lateral walls of the pelvis. On the lateral pelvic wall behind the attachment of the broad ligament, in the angle between the elevations produced by the diverging hypogastric and external iliac vessels is a slight fossa, the **ovarian fossa,** in which the ovary normally lies.

(2) **In the Lower Abdomen** (Fig. 1052).—Starting from the linea alba, below the level of the transverse colon, and tracing the continuity of the peritoneum in a horizontal direction to the right, the membrane covers the inner surface of the abdominal wall almost as far as the lateral border of the Quadratus lumborum; it encloses the cecum and vermiform process, and is reflected over the sides and front of the ascending colon: it may then be traced over the duodenum, Psoas major, and inferior vena cava toward the middle line, whence it passes along the mesenteric vessels to invest the small intestine, and back again to the large vessels in front of the vertebral column, forming the **mesentery,** between the layers of which are contained the mesenteric bloodvessels, nerves, lacteals, and lymph nodes. It is then continued over the left Psoas; it covers the sides and front of the descending colon, and, reaching the abdominal wall, is carried on it to the middle line.

(3) **In the Upper Abdomen** (Fig. 1051).—Above the transverse colon the omental bursa is superadded to the general sac, and the communication of the two cavities with one another through the epiploic foramen can be demonstrated.

(*a*) **Main Cavity.**—Commencing on the posterior abdominal wall at the inferior vena cava, the peritoneum may be followed to the right over the front of the suprarenal gland and upper part of the right kidney on to the antero-lateral abdominal wall. From the middle line of the anterior wall a backwardly directed fold encircles the obliterated umbilical vein and forms the falciform ligament of the liver. Continuing to the left, the peritoneum lines the antero-lateral abdominal wall and covers the lateral part of the front of the left kidney, and is reflected to the posterior border of the hilus of the spleen as the posterior layer of the **lienorenal ligament.** It can then be traced around the surface of the spleen to the front of the hilum, and thence to the cardiac end of the greater curvature of the stomach as the anterior layer of the **gastrolienal ligament.** It covers the antero-superior surfaces of the stomach and commencement of the duodenum, and extends up from the lesser curvature of the stomach to the liver as the anterior layer of the lesser omentum.

(*b*) **Omental Bursa** (*bursa omentalis; lesser peritoneal sac*).—On the posterior abdominal wall the peritoneum of the general cavity is continuous with that of the omental bursa in front of the inferior vena cava. Starting from here, the bursa may be traced across the aorta and over the medial part of the front of the left kidney and diaphragm to the hilum of the spleen as the anterior layer of the lienorenal ligament. From the spleen it is reflected to the stomach as the posterior layer of the gastrolienal ligament. It covers the postero-inferior surfaces of the stomach and commencement of the duodenum, and extends upward to the liver as the posterior layer of the lesser omentum; the right margin of this layer is continuous around the hepatic artery, bile duct, and portal vein, with the wall of the general cavity.

The **epiploic foramen** (*foramen epiploicum; foramen of Winslow*) is the passage of communication between the general cavity and the omental bursa. It is bounded *in front* by the free border of the lesser omentum, with the common bile duct, hepatic artery, and portal vein between its two layers; *behind* by the peritoneum covering the inferior vena cava; *above* by the peritoneum on the caudate process of the liver, and *below* by the peritoneum covering the commencement of the duodenum and the hepatic artery, the latter passing forward below the foramen before ascending between the two layers of the lesser omentum.

The boundaries of the *omental bursa* will now be evident. It is bounded *in front*, from above downward, by the caudate lobe of the liver, the lesser omentum, the stomach, and the greater omentum. *Behind*, it is limited, from below upward, by the greater omentum, the transverse colon, the transverse mesocolon, the upper surface of the pancreas, the left suprarenal gland, and the upper end of the left kidney. To the right of the esophageal opening of the stomach it is formed by that part of the diaphragm which supports the caudate lobe of the liver. *Laterally*, the bursa extends from the epiploic foramen to the hilum of the spleen, where it is limited by the phrenicolienal and gastrolienal ligaments.

The omental bursa, therefore, consists of a series of pouches or recesses to which the following terms are applied: (1) the **vestibule**, a narrow channel continued from the epiploic foramen, over the head of the pancreas to the **gastropancreatic fold**; this fold extends from the omental tuberosity of the pancreas to the right side of the fundus of the stomach, and contains the left gastric artery and coronary vein; (2) the **superior omental recess**, between the caudate lobe of the liver and the diaphragm; (3) the **lienal recess**, between the spleen and the stomach; (4) the **inferior omental recess**, which comprises the remainder of the bursa.

In the fetus the bursa reaches as low as the free margin of the greater omentum, but in the adult its vertical extent is usually more limited owing to adhesions between the layers of the omentum. During a considerable part of fetal life the transverse colon is suspended from the posterior abdominal wall by a mesentery of its own, the two posterior layers of the greater omentum passing at this stage in front of the colon. This condition occasionally persists throughout life, but as a rule adhesion occurs between the mesentery of the transverse colon and the posterior layer of the greater omentum, with the result that the colon appears to receive its peritoneal covering by the splitting of the two posterior layers of the latter fold. In the adult the omental bursa intervenes between the stomach and the structures on which that viscus lies, and performs therefore the functions of a serous bursa for the stomach.

Numerous peritoneal folds extend between the various organs or connect them to the parietes; they serve to hold the viscera in position, and, at the same time, enclose the vessels and nerves proceeding to them. They are grouped under the three headings of **ligaments**, **omenta**, and **mesenteries**.

The **ligaments** will be described with their respective organs.

There are two **omenta**, the lesser and the greater.

The **lesser omentum** (*omentum minus; small omentum; gastrohepatic omentum*) is the duplicature which extends to the liver from the lesser curvature of the stomach and the commencement of the duodenum. It is extremely thin, and is continuous with the two layers of peritoneum which cover respectively the antero-superior and postero-inferior surfaces of the stomach and first part of the duodenum. When these two layers reach the lesser curvature of the stomach and the upper border of the duodenum, they join together and ascend as a double fold to the porta of the liver; to the left of the porta the fold is attached to the bottom of the fossa for the ductus venosus, along which it is carried to the diaphragm, where the two layers separate to embrace the end of the esophagus. At the right border of the omentum the two layers are continuous, and form a free margin which constitutes the anterior boundary of the epiploic foramen. The portion of the lesser omentum extending between the liver and stomach is termed the **hepatogastric ligament**, while that between the liver and duodenum is the **hepatoduodenal ligament**. Between the two

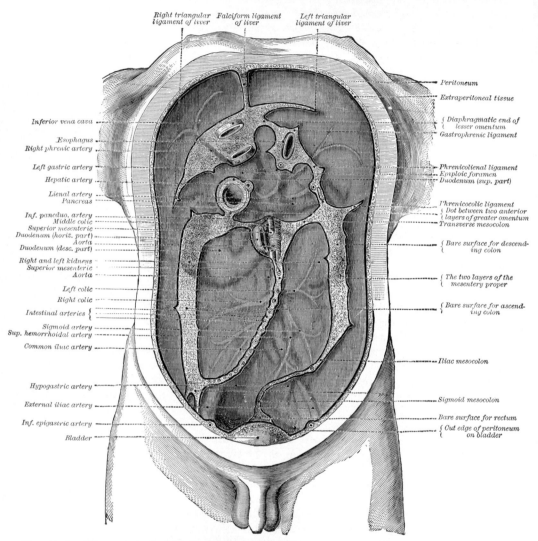

Fig. 1055.—Diagram devised by Delépine to show the lines along which the peritoneum leaves the wall of the abdomen to invest the viscera.

layers of the lesser omentum, close to the right free margin, are the hepatic artery, the common bile duct, the portal vein, lymphatics, and the hepatic plexus of nerves—all these structures being enclosed in a **fibrous capsule** (*Glisson's capsule*). Between the layers of the lesser omentum, where they are attached to the stomach, run the right and left gastric vessels.

The **greater omentum** (*omentum majus; great omentum; gastrocolic omentum*) is the largest peritoneal fold. It consists of a double sheet of peritoneum, folded on itself so that it is made up of four layers. The two layers which descend from the stomach and commencement of the duodenum pass in front of the small intestines, sometimes as low down as the pelvis; they then turn upon themselves, and ascend again as far as the transverse colon, where they separate and enclose that part of the intestine. These individual layers may be easily demonstrated in the young subject, but in the adult they are more or less inseparably blended. The left border of the greater omentum is continuous with the gastrolienal ligament; its right border extends as far as the commencement of the duodenum. The greater omentum is usually thin, presents a cribriform appearance, and always contains some adipose tissue, which in fat people accumulates in considerable quantity. Between its two anterior layers, a short distance from the greater curvature of the stomach, is the anastomosis between the right and left gastroepiploic vessels.

The **mesenteries** are: the **mesentery proper**, the **transverse mesocolon**, and the **sigmoid mesocolon.** In addition to these there are sometimes present an ascending and a descending mesocolon.

The **mesentery proper** (*mesenterium*) is the broad, fan-shaped fold of peritoneum which connects the convolutions of the jejunum and ileum with the posterior wall of the abdomen. Its **root**—the part connected with the structures in front of the vertebral column—is narrow, about 15 cm. long, and is directed obliquely from the duodenojejunal flexure at the left side of the second lumbar vertebra to the right sacroiliac articulation (Fig. 1055). Its **intestinal border** is about 6 metres long; and here the two layers separate to enclose the intestine, and form its peritoneal coat. It is narrow above, but widens rapidly to about 20 cm., and is thrown into numerous plaits or folds. It suspends the small intestine, and contains between its layers the intestinal branches of the superior mesenteric artery, with their accompanying veins and plexuses of nerves, the lacteal vessels, and mesenteric lymph nodes.

The **transverse mesocolon** (*mesocolon transversum*) is a broad fold, which connects the transverse colon to the posterior wall of the abdomen. It is continuous with the two posterior layers of the greater omentum, which, after separating to surround the transverse colon, join behind it, and are continued backward to the vertebral column, where they diverge in front of the anterior border of the pancreas. This fold contains between its layers the vessels which supply the transverse colon.

The **sigmoid mesocolon** (*mesocolon sigmoideum*) is the fold of peritoneum which retains the sigmoid colon in connection with the pelvic wall. Its line of attachment forms a V-shaped curve, the apex of the curve being placed about the point of division of the left common iliac artery. The curve begins on the medial side of the left Psoas major, and runs upward and backward to the apex, from which it bends sharply downward, and ends in the median plane at the level of the third sacral vertebra. The sigmoid and superior hemorrhoidal vessels run between the two layers of this fold.

In most cases the peritoneum covers only the front and sides of the ascending and descending parts of the colon. Sometimes, however, these are surrounded by the serous membrane and attached to the posterior abdominal wall by an ascending and a descending mesocolon respectively. A fold of peritoneum, the **phrenicocolic ligament,** is continued from the left colic flexure to the diaphragm opposite the tenth and eleventh ribs; it passes below and serves to support the spleen, and therefore has received the name of **sustentaculum lienis.**

The **appendices epiploicæ** are small pouches of the peritoneum filled with fat and situated along the colon and upper part of the rectum. They are chiefly appended to the transverse and sigmoid parts of the colon.

Peritoneal Recesses or Fossæ (*retroperitoneal fossæ*).—In certain parts of the abdominal cavity there are recesses of peritoneum forming culs-de-sac or pouches, which are of surgical interest in connection with the possibility of the occurrence of "retroperitoneal" herniæ. The largest of these is the omental bursa (already described), but several others, of smaller size, require mention, and may be divided into three groups, *viz.*: **duodenal, cecal,** and **intersigmoid.**

1. **Duodenal Fossæ** (Figs. 1056, 1057).—Three are fairly constant, *viz.*: (*a*) The **inferior duodenal fossa,** present in about 75 per cent of bodies, is situated opposite the third lumbar vertebra on the left side of the ascending portion of the duodenum.

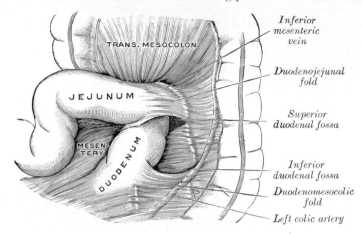

FIG. 1056.—Superior and inferior duodenal fossæ.   (Poirier and Charpy.)

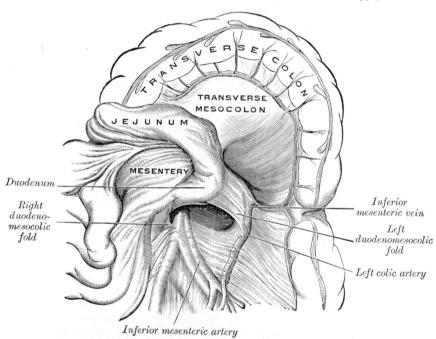

FIG. 1057.—Duodenojejunal fossa. (Poirier and Charpy.)

Its opening is directed upward, and is bounded by a thin sharp fold of peritoneum The tip of the index finger introduced into the fossa under the fold passes some little distance behind the ascending portion of the duodenum.   (*b*) The **superior duodenal fossa,** present in about 50 per cent of bodies, often coexists with the inferior one, and its orifice looks downward.   It lies on the left of the ascending portion of the duodenum, in front of the second lumbar vertebra, and behind a sickle-shaped fold of peritoneum, the **duodenojejunal fold,** and has a depth of about 2 cm.   (*c*) The **duodenojejunal fossa** exists in about 20 per cent of bodies.   It is bounded above by the pancreas, to the right by the aorta, and to the left by the kidney; beneath is the left renal vein. It has a depth of from 2 to 3 cm., and its orifice, directed downward and to the right, is nearly circular and will admit the tip of the little finger. (*d*) The **paraduodenal fossa**, rarely found, lies a short distance to the left of the ascending portion of the duodenum behind a peritoneal fold which contains the ascending branch of the left colic artery. (*e*) The **retroduodenal fossa**, only occasionally present, lies behind the horizontal and ascending parts of the duodenum and in front of the aorta.

2. **Cecal Fossæ** (*pericecal folds or fossæ*).—There are three principal pouches or recesses in the neighborhood of the cecum (Figs. 1058 to 1060): (*a*) The **superior ileocecal fossa** is formed by a fold of peritoneum, arching over the branch of the ileocolic artery which supplies the ileocolic junction. The fossa is a narrow chink situated between the mesentery of the small intestine, the ileum, and the small portion of the cecum behind. (*b*) The **inferior ileocecal fossa** is situated behind the angle of junction of the ileum and cecum. It is formed by the **ileocecal fold** of peritoneum (*bloodless fold of Treves*), the upper border of which is fixed to the ileum,

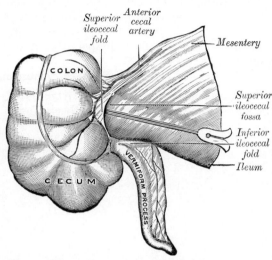

FIG. 1058.—Superior ileocecal fossa. (Poirier and Charpy.)

opposite its mesenteric attachment, while the lower border, passing over the ileocecal junction, joins the mesenteriole of the vermiform process, and sometimes the process itself. Between this fold and the mesenteriole of the vermiform process is the inferior ileocecal fossa. It is bounded above by the posterior surface of the

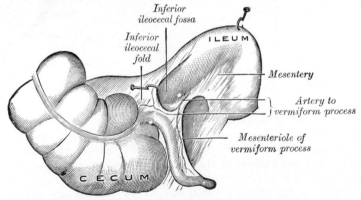

FIG. 1059.—Inferior ileocecal fossa. The cecum and ascending colon have been drawn lateralward and downward, the ileum upward and backward, and the vermiform process downward. (Poirier and Charpy.)

ileum and the mesentery; in front and below by the ileocecal fold, and behind by the upper part of the mesenteriole of the vermiform process. (*c*) The **cecal fossa** is situated immediately behind the cecum, which has to be raised to bring it into view. It varies much in size and extent. In some cases it is sufficiently large to admit the index finger, and extends upward behind the ascending colon in the direction of the kidney; in others it is merely a shallow depression. It is bounded on the right by the cecal fold, which is attached by one edge to the abdominal wall from the lower border of the kidney to-the iliac fossa and by the other to the postero-lateral aspect of the colon. In some instances additional fossæ, the retrocecal fossæ, are present.

3. The **intersigmoid fossa** (*recessus intersigmoideus*) is constant in the fetus and during infancy, but disappears in a certain percentage of cases as age advances. When the sigmoid colon is drawn upward, the left surface of the sigmoid mesocolon is exposed, and on it will be seen a funnel-shaped recess of the peritoneum, lying on the external iliac vessels, in the interspace between the Psoas and Iliacus muscles. This is the orifice leading to the intersigmoid fossa, which lies behind the sigmoid mesocolon, and in front of the parietal peritoneum. The fossa varies in size; in some instances it is a mere dimple, whereas in others it will admit the whole of the index finger.

The Stomach (Ventriculus; Gaster).

The **stomach** is the most dilated part of the digestive tube, and is situated between the end of the esophagus and the beginning of the small intestine. It lies in the

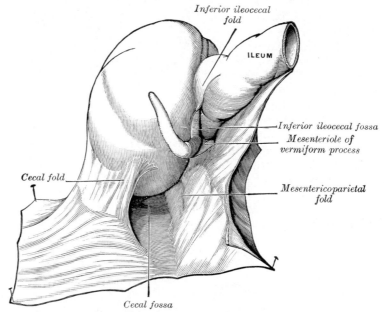

Fig. 1060.—The cecal fossa. The ileum and cecum are drawn backward and upward. (Souligoux.)

epigastric, umbilical, and left hypochondriac regions of the abdomen, and occupies a recess bounded by the upper abdominal viscera, and completed in front and on the left side by the anterior abdominal wall and the diaphragm.

The **shape and position** of the stomach are so greatly modified by changes within itself and in the surrounding viscera that no one form can be described as typical. The chief modifications are determined by (1) the amount of the stomach contents, (2) the stage which the digestive process has reached, (3) the degree of development of the gastric musculature, and (4) the condition of the adjacent intestines. It is, however, possible by comparing a series of stomachs to determine certain markings more or less common to all (Figs. 1061, 1062).

Openings. —The opening by which the esophagus communicates with the stomach is known as the **cardiac orifice**, and is situated on the left of the middle line at the level of the tenth thoracic vertebra. The short abdominal portion of the esophagus (*antrum cardiacum*) is conical in shape and curved sharply to the left the base of the cone being continuous with the cardiac orifice of the stomach.

The right margin of the esophagus is continuous with the lesser curvature of the stomach, while the left margin joins the greater curvature at an acute angle, termed the **incisura cardiaca.**

The **pyloric orifice** communicates with the duodenum, and its position is usually indicated on the surface of the stomach by a circular groove, the **duodenopyloric constriction.** This orifice lies to the right of the middle line at the level of the upper border of the first lumbar vertebra.

Curvatures.—The **lesser curvature** (*curvatura ventriculi minor*) (Fig. 1064), extending between the cardiac and pyloric orifices, forms the right or concave border of the stomach. It descends as a continuation of the right margin of the esophagus in front of the fibers of the right crus of the diaphragm, and then, turning to the right, it crosses the first lumbar vertebra and ends at the pylorus. Nearer its pyloric than its cardiac end is a well-marked notch, the **incisura angularis** (Fig. 1062), which varies somewhat in position with the state of distension; it serves to separate the stomach into a right and a left portion. The lesser curvature gives attachment to the hepatogastric ligament which contains the left gastric artery and the right gastric branch of the hepatic artery.

The **greater curvature** (*curvatura ventriculi major*) is directed mainly forward, and is four or five times as long as the lesser curvature. Starting from the cardiac orifice at the incisura cardiaca, it forms an arch backward, upward, and to the left; the highest point of the convexity is on a level with the sixth left costal cartilage. From this level it may be followed downward and forward, with a slight convexity to the left as low as the cartilage of the ninth rib; it then turns to the right, to the end of the pylorus. Directly opposite the incisura angularis of the lesser curvature the greater curvature presents a dilatation, which is the **pyloric vestibule;** this dilatation is limited on the right by a slight groove, the **sulcus intermedius,** which is about 2.5 cm. from the pyloric valve. The portion between the sulcus intermedius and the pyloric valve is termed the **pyloric antrum.** At its commencement the greater curvature is covered by peritoneum continuous with that covering the front of the organ. The left part of the curvature gives attachment to the gastrolienal ligament, the anterior portion to the greater omentum.

Surfaces.—When the stomach is in the contracted condition, its surfaces are directed upward and downward respectively, but when the viscus is distended they are directed forward, and backward. They may therefore be described as anterosuperior and postero-inferior.

Antero-superior Surface.—The left half of this surface is in contact with the diaphragm, which separates it from the base of the left lung, the heart, and the seventh, eighth, and ninth ribs, and intercostal spaces of the left side. The right half is in relation with the left and quadrate lobes of the liver and with the anterior abdominal wall. When the stomach is empty, the transverse colon may lie on the front part of this surface. The whole surface is covered by peritoneum.

The **Postero-inferior Surface** is in relation with the diaphragm, the spleen, the left suprarenal gland, the upper part of the front of the left kidney, the anterior surface of the pancreas, the left colic flexure, and the upper layer of the transverse mesocolon. These structures form a shallow bed, the **stomach bed,** on which the viscus rests. The transverse mesocolon separates the stomach from the duodenojejunal flexure and small intestine. The postero-inferior surface is covered by peritoneum, except over a small area close to the cardiac orifice; this area is limited by the lines of attachment of the **gastrophrenic ligament,** and lies in apposition with the diaphragm, and frequently with the upper portion of the left suprarenal gland.

Component Parts of the Stomach.—A plane passing through the incisura angularis on the lesser curvature and the left limit of the opposed dilatation on the greater curvature divides the stomach into a left portion or **body** and a right or **pyloric portion.** The superior portion of the body is known as the **fundus,** and is marked off from the remainder of the body by a plane passing horizontally through the cardiac orifice. The pyloric portion is divided by a plane through the sulcus inter-medius at right angles to the long axis of this portion; the part to the right of this plane is the **pyloric antrum** (Fig. 1062).

If the stomach be examined during the process of digestion it will be found divided by a muscular constriction into a large dilated left portion, and a narrow contracted tubular right portion. The constriction is in the body of the stomach, and does not follow any of the anatomical landmarks; indeed, it shifts gradually toward the left as digestion progresses, *i. e.*, more of the body is gradually absorbed into the tubular part.

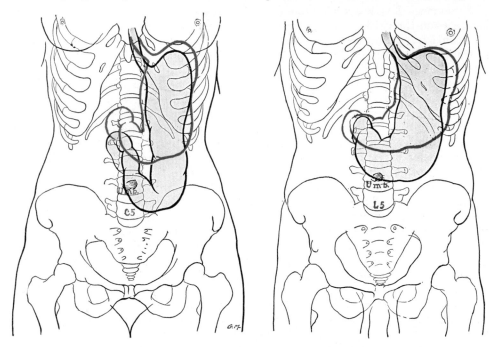

Female   Male

FIG. 1061.—Average position of the stomach based on X-ray studies. Standing position in black; reclining position in red. (Eycleshymer and Jones.)

Position of the Stomach.—The position of the stomach varies with the posture, with the amount of the stomach contents and with the condition of the intestines on which it rests. According to Moody, radiographs of the normal erect living body show the ordinary range of variation of the most caudal part of the greater curvature to be from 7.3 cm. above to 13.5 cm. below the interiliac line in males and from 6.5 cm. above to 13.7 cm. below the line in females. It is below the interiliac line in 74.4 per cent of males and in 87 per cent of females.

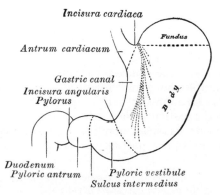

FIG. 1062.—Diagram showing the sub-divisions of the human stomach. (F. T. Lewis.)

With the body horizontal the most caudal part of the greater curvature is in males from 16.5 cm. above to 7.3 cm. below the interiliac line and in females 15.5 cm. above to 8.4 cm. below the line. The most common position in the erect male (26 per cent) is 2.6 cm. to 5 cm. below and in the horizontal male (22.4 per cent) 2.5 cm. to 5 cm. above the interiliac line. In the erect female the most common position (22.4 per cent) is 5 cm. to 7.5 cm. below and in the horizontal female (24 per cent) 2.5 cm. to 5 cm. above the interiliac line.

The position of the pylorus in the erect living body of the male varies from 14.5 cm. above to 8 cm. below and in the female from 15 cm. above to 2.5 cm. below the interiliac line. The range of position in regard to the sagittal axis of the erect body varies in males from 8.8 cm. to the right to 2 cm. to the left of the axis. In 84 per cent it is to the right of the axis. In females the position ranges from 6 cm. to the right to 2.6 cm. to the left of the sagittal axis, In 89.5 per cent it is to the right. The most common position in both males and females is from 2.5 cm. to 5 cm. to the right.

Interior of the Stomach.—When examined after death, the stomach is usually fixed at some temporary stage of the digestive process. A common form is that shown in Fig. 1064. If the viscus be laid open by a section through the plane of its two curvatures, it is seen to consist of two segments: (*a*) a large globular portion on the left and (*b*) a narrow tubular part on the right. These correspond to the clinical subdivisions of fundus and pyloric portions already described, and are separated by a constriction which indents the body and greater curvature, but does not involve the lesser curvature. To the left of the cardiac orifice is the incisura cardiaca: the projection of this notch into the cavity of the stomach increases as the organ distends, and has been supposed to act as a valve preventing regurgitation into the esophagus. In the pyloric portion are seen: (*a*) the elevation corresponding to the incisura angularis, and (*b*) the circular projection from the duodenopyloric constriction which forms the pyloric valve; the separation of the pyloric antrum from the rest of the pyloric part is scarcely indicated.

The **pyloric valve** (*valvula pylori*) is a muscular ring formed by a thickening of the circular layer of the muscular coat. Some of the deeper longitudinal fibers turn in and interlace with the circular fibers of the valve.

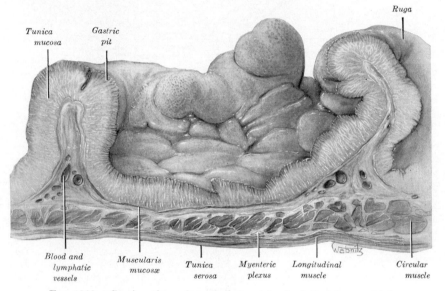

FIG. 1063.—Section through wall of stomach of adult cadaver. × 5.

Structure.—The wall of the stomach has four coats: **mucous, submucous, muscular,** and **serous.**

The **mucous membrane** (*tunica mucosa*) (Fig. 1063) lining the stomach has a soft, velvety appearance and pinkish color in the fresh state, and is thrown into thick folds, known as **rugæ,** which tend to have a longitudinal direction along the lesser curvature and at the pylorus but elsewhere somewhat resemble a honeycomb. The folds involve both the mucosa and submucosa but are transient and movable, and are gradually obliterated as the stomach is distended.

The surface of the membrane does not appear smooth when examined with a lens because closely scattered everywhere are the openings of the **gastric pits** or **foveolæ.** On the cut surface of the stomach wall, the mucous membrane appears quite thick (5 mm.) because tubular gastric glands extend down into it from the foveolæ.

The **lining epithelium** which covers the surface and extends down into the foveolæ is composed of tall columnar cells of characteristic and rather uniform appearance called **theca cells.** They secrete mucus, and within the part of the cell toward the surface the precursor of the mucus can be seen in a shallow pocket or theca, much smaller and more difficult to identify than the pocket of a goblet cell. They do not have a cuticular border like that seen in the cells of the intestine, and there are no goblet cells.

The **gastric glands** are simple tubular glands which open in groups of two or three into the bottoms of the gastric pits. Three kinds may be distinguished: (*a*) Fundic Glands, (*b*) Cardiac

Glands, and (c) Pyloric Glands, but the last two, being local modifications, will be described with the appropriate parts. The **fundic glands** are frequently called simply gastric glands because they are the most characteristic of the stomach and occur throughout the fundus and body of the stomach. The epithelial cells are of two types, chief cells and parietal cells. The **chief cells** are again subdivided into neck chief cells and body chief cells. The **neck chief cells** provide a transi-

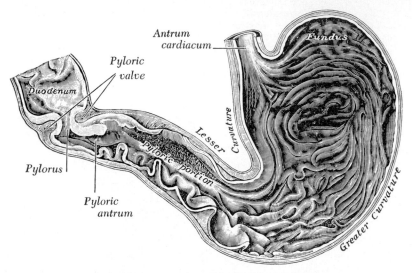

FIG. 1064.—Interior of the stomach.

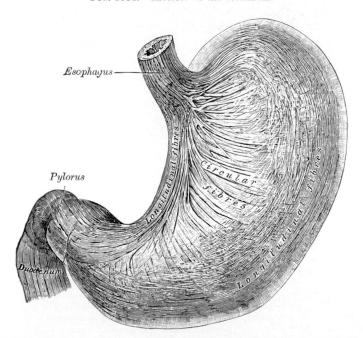

FIG. 1065.—The longitudinal and circular muscular fibers of the stomach, viewed from above and in front. (Spalteholz.)

tion between the lining epithelium of the foveolæ and the secreting part of the glands. They are cuboidal or columnar in shape, have a basophilic cytoplasm and, since they appear to be the source of new epithelial cells, they frequently contain mitotic nuclei. The **body chief cells** extend down to the bottom of the glands and resemble the neck chief cells but are slightly more basophilic and have a prominent basal striation. They contain many small secretion granules which can be made clearly visible with special stains (Bowie '40), and are the cells which secrete pepsin. The **parietal**

cells are the most characteristic cells in the gastric glands. Their name originated from the fact that they are pushed back against the basement membrane. They do not form a continuous layer but are scattered all along the walls of the glands, separated by several chief cells and usually parts of the neighboring body chief cells overlap them, intervening between them and the internal surface of the gland. They are four or five times as large as chief cells, have a granular, intensely acidophilic cytoplasm and are the source of the hydrochloric acid in the gastric juice. The tissue surrounding and intervening between the gastric pits and the glands is composed of areolar connective tissue, and blood and lymphatic capillaries with scattered lymphocytes or occasionally even lymphatic nodules. The boundary between the mucosa and submucosa is marked by a thin sheet of smooth muscle cells, the **muscularis mucosæ**, made up of an inner circular and outer longitudinal layer.

The **tela submucosa** is composed of areolar connective tissue, and blood and lymphatic vessels, and extends up into the rugæ.

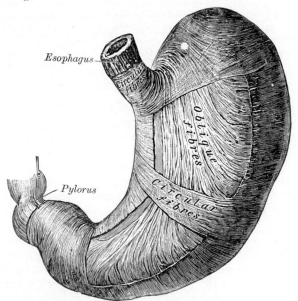

Fig. 1066.—The oblique muscular fibers of the stomach, viewed from above and in front. (Spalteholz.)

The **muscular coat** (tunica muscularis) of the stomach has the two layers of smooth muscle fibers characteristic of the digestive tube, inner circular and outer longitudinal, but in addition has a layer of oblique fibers. The inner circular layer is well represented over the entire organ (Fig. 1063). The outer longitudinal layer is not as uniform as the circular and is more concentrated along the lesser curvature and the greater curvature (Fig. 1064). The oblique fibers are internal to the circular fibers, chiefly at the cardiac end of the stomach, and spread over the anterior and posterior surfaces.

The **serous coat** (*tunica serosa*) is composed of a small amount of areolar tissue connecting the peritoneum to the muscular coat. It contains some of the larger blood vessels and lymphatics. A narrow strip along the lesser and greater curvatures, where the two omenta are attached, is not covered by peritoneum.

The **cardiac portion** of the stomach has certain peculiarities. The stratified squamous epithelium of the esophagus is abruptly replaced by the columnar epithelium of the stomach. The **cardiac glands** are longer, more twisted, and contain no parietal cells; they resemble somewhat the esophageal glands and secrete mucous. Aggregations of lymph nodes or lymphatic nodules are not uncommon. The muscular layers are continuous with those of the esophagus.

The **pylorus** is distinctively marked by the thickening of the circular layer into the pyloric sphincter which constricts the lumen. The lining epithelium makes an abrupt transition from the gastric type with its theca cells to the intestinal epithelium with striated cuticular border and interspaced goblet cells. The **pyloric glands** are devoid of parietal cells, are longer, more tortuous, and have the appearance of mucous secreting cells. At the transition from stomach to duodenum, the gastric glands can be distinguished from the Brunner glands of the duodenum because the former lie in the tunica mucosa, that is, inside the muscularis mucosæ, whereas the latter are in the submucosa.

Vessels and Nerves.—The arteries supplying the stomach are: the left gastric, the right gastric and right gastroepiploic branches of the hepatic, and the left gastroepiploic and short gastric branches of the lienal. They supply the muscular coat, ramify in the submucous coat, and are finally distributed to the mucous membrane. The arrangement of the vessels in the mucous membrane is somewhat peculiar. The arteries break up at the base of the gastric tubules into a plexus of fine capillaries which run upward between the tubules, anastomosing with each other, and ending in a plexus of larger capillaries, which surround the mouths of the tubes, and also form hexagonal meshes around the ducts. From these the **veins** arise, and pursue a straight course downward, between the tubules, to the submucous tissue; they end either in the lienal and superior mesenteric veins, or directly in the portal vein. The **lymphatics** are numerous: they consist of a superficial and a deep set, and pass to the lymph nodes found along the two curvatures of the organ (page 803). The **nerves** are the terminal branches of the right and left vagi, the former usually being distributed upon the back, and the latter upon the front part of the organ; and numerous sympathetic fibers arising chiefly from the various subdivisions of the celiac plexus and accompanying the different bloodvessels to the organ. According to Mitchell[1], small sympathetic filaments may also arise directly from the phrenic and splanchnic trunks. Nerve plexuses are found in the submucous coat and between the layers of the muscular coat as in the intestine. From these plexuses fibrils are distributed to the muscular tissue and the mucous membrane.

The Small Intestine (Intestinum Tenue).

The **small intestine** is a convoluted tube, extending from the pylorus to the colic valve, where it ends in the large intestine. It is about 7 meters long,[2] and gradually diminishes in size from its commencement to its termination. It is contained in the central and lower part of the abdominal cavity, and is surrounded above and at the sides by the large intestine; a portion of it extends below the superior aperture of the pelvis and lies in front of the rectum. It is in relation, in front, with the greater omentum and abdominal parietes, and is connected to the vertebral column by a fold of peritoneum, the **mesentery.** The small intestine is divisible into three portions: the **duodenum,** the **jejunum,** and the **ileum.**

The **Duodenum** (Fig. 1053) has received its name from being about equal in length to the breadth of twelve fingers (25 cm.). It is the shortest, the widest, and the most fixed part of the small intestine, and has no mesentery, being only partially covered by peritoneum. Its course presents a remarkable curve, somewhat of the shape of an imperfect circle, so that its termination is not far removed from its starting-point.

In the adult the course of the duodenum is as follows: commencing at the pylorus it passes backward, upward, and to the right, beneath the quadrate lobe of the liver to the neck of the gall-bladder, varying slightly in direction according to the degree of distension of the stomach: it then takes a sharp curve and descends along the right margin of the head of the pancreas, for a variable distance, generally to the level of the upper border of the body of the fourth lumbar vertebra. It now takes a second bend, and passes from right to left across the vertebral column, having a slight inclination upward; and on the left side of the vertebral column it ascends for about 2.5 cm., and then ends opposite the second lumbar vertebra in the jejunum. As it unites with the jejunum it turns abruptly forward, forming the **duodenojejunal flexure.** From the above description it will be seen that the duodenum may be divided into four portions: **superior, descending, horizontal,** and **ascending.**

Relations.—The **superior portion** (*pars superior; first portion*) is about 5 cm. long. Beginning at the pylorus, it ends at the neck of the gall-bladder. It is the most movable of the four portions. It is almost completely covered by peritoneum, but a small part of its posterior surface near the neck of the gall-bladder and the inferior vena cava is uncovered; the upper border of its first half has the hepatoduodenal

---

[1] Jour. Anat., 1940, vol. 75.
[2] Treves states that, in one hundred cases, the average length of the small intestine in the adult male was 22 feet 1 inches, and in the adult female 23 feet 4 inches: but that it varies very much, the extremes in the male being 31 feet 10 inches, and 15 feet 6 inches. He states that in the adult the length of the bowel is independent of age, height, and weight.

ligament attached to it, while to the lower border of the same segment the greater omentum is connected. It is in such close relation with the gall-bladder that it is usually found to be stained by bile after death, especially on its anterior surface. It is in relation above and in front with the quadrate lobe of the liver and the gall-bladder; behind with the gastroduodenal artery, the common bile duct, and the portal vein; and below and behind with the head and neck of the pancreas.

The **descending portion** (*pars descendens; second portion*) is from 7 to 10 cm. long, and extends from the neck of the gall-bladder, on a level with the first lumbar vertebra, along the right side of the vertebral column as low as the upper border of the body of the fourth lumbar vertebra. It is crossed in its middle third by the transverse colon, the posterior surface of which is uncovered by peritoneum and is connected to the duodenum by a small quantity of connective tissue. The supra- and infra-colic portions are covered in front by peritoneum, the infracolic part by the right leaf of the mesentery. Posteriorly the descending portion of the duodenum is not covered by peritoneum. The descending portion is in relation, in front, from above downward, with the duodenal impression on the right lobe of the liver, the transverse colon, and the small intestine; behind, it has a variable relation to the front of the right kidney in the neighborhood of the hilum, and is connected to it by loose areolar tissue; the renal vessels, the inferior vena cava, and the Psoas below, are also behind it. At its medial side is the head of the pancreas, and the common bile duct; to its lateral side is the right colic flexure. The common bile duct and the pancreatic duct together perforate the medial side of this portion of the intestine obliquely (Figs. 1094 and 1095), some 7 to 10 cm. below the pylorus; the accessory pancreatic duct sometimes pierces it about 2 cm. above and slightly in front of these.

The **horizontal portion** (*pars horizontalis; third or preaortic or transverse portion*) is from 5 to 7.5 cm. long. It begins at the right side of the upper border of the fourth lumbar vertebra and passes from right to left, with a slight inclination upward, in front of the great vessels and crura of the diaphragm, and ends in the ascending portion in front of the abdominal aorta. It is crossed by the superior mesenteric vessels and the mesentery. Its front surface is covered by peritoneum, except near the middle line, where it is crossed by the superior mesenteric vessels. Its posterior surface is uncovered by peritoneum, except toward its left extremity, where the posterior layer of the mesentery may sometimes be found covering it to a variable extent. This surface rests upon the right crus of the diaphragm, the inferior vena cava, and the aorta. The upper surface is in relation with the head of the pancreas.

The **ascending portion** (*pars ascendens; fourth portion*) of the duodenum is about 2.5 cm. long. It ascends on the left side of the aorta, as far as the level of the upper border of the second lumbar vertebra, where it turns abruptly forward to become the jejunum, forming the **duodenojejunal flexure**. It lies in front of the left Psoas major and left renal vessels, and is covered in front, and partly at the sides, by peritoneum continuous with the left portion of the mesentery.

The superior part of the duodenum, as stated above, is somewhat movable, but the rest is practically fixed, and is bound down to neighboring viscera and the posterior abdominal wall by the peritoneum. In addition to this, the duodenojejunal flexure is held in place by a fibrous and muscular band, the **ligament of Treitz** (*Musculus suspensorius duodeni*). This structure commences in the connective tissue around the celiac artery and right crus of the diaphragm, and passes downward to be inserted into the superior border of the duodenojejunal curve and a part of the ascending duodenum, and from this it is continued into the mesentery. It possesses, according to Treitz, smooth muscular fibers mixed with the fibrous tissue of which it is principally made up. It is of little importance as a muscle, but acts as a suspensory ligament.

Vessels and Nerves.—The **arteries** supplying the duodenum are the right gastric and superior pancreaticoduodenal branches of the hepatic, and the inferior pancreaticoduodenal branch of the superior mesenteric. The **veins** end in the lienal and superior mesenteric. The **nerves** are derived from the cœliac plexus.

Jejunum and Ileum.—The remainder of the small intestine from the end of the duodenum is named **jejunum** and **ileum**; the former term being given to the upper two-fifths and the latter to the lower three-fifths. There is no morphological line of distinction between the two, and the division is arbitrary; but at the same time the character of the intestine gradually undergoes a change from the commencement of the jejunum to the end of the ileum, so that a portion of the bowel taken from these two situations would present characteristic and marked differences. These are briefly as follows:

The **Jejunum** (*intestinum jejunum*) is wider, its diameter being about 4 cm., and is thicker, more vascular, and of a deeper color than the ileum, so that a given length weighs more. The circular folds (*valvulæ conniventes*) of its mucous membrane are large and thickly set, and its villi are larger than in the ileum. The aggregated lymph nodules are almost absent in the upper part of the jejunum, and in the lower part are less frequently found than in the ileum, and are smaller and tend to assume a circular form. By grasping the jejunum between the finger and thumb the circular folds can be felt through the walls of the gut; these being absent in the lower part of the ileum, it is possible in this way to distinguish the upper from the lower part of the small intestine.

The **Ileum** (*intestinum ileum*) is narrow, its diameter being 3.75 cm., and its coats thinner and less vascular than those of the jejunum. It possesses but few circular folds, and they are small and disappear entirely toward its lower end, but aggregated lymph nodules (Peyer's patches) are larger and more numerous. The jejunum for the most part occupies the umbilical and left iliac regions, while the ileum occupies chiefly the umbilical, hypogastric, right iliac, and pelvic regions. The terminal part of the ileum usually lies in the pelvis, from which it ascends over the right Psoas and right iliac vessels; it ends in the right iliac fossa by opening into the medial side of the commencement of the large intestine. The jejunum and ileum are attached to the posterior abdominal wall by an extensive fold of peritoneum, the **mesentery**, which allows the freest motion, so that each coil can accommodate itself to changes in form and position. The mesentery is fan-shaped: its posterior border or root, about 15 cm. long, is attached to the posterior abdominal wall from the left side of the body of the second lumbar vertebra to the right sacro-iliac articulation, crossing successively the horizontal part of the duodenum, the aorta, the inferior vena cava, the ureter, and right Psoas muscle (Fig. 1045). Its breadth between its vertebral and intestinal borders averages about 20 cm., and is greater in the middle than at its upper and lower ends. According to Lockwood it tends to increase in breadth as age advances. Between the two layers of which it is composed are contained bloodvessels, nerves, lacteals, and lymph glands, together with a variable amount of fat.

Meckel's Diverticulum (*diverticulum ilei*).—This consists of a pouch which projects from the lower part of the ileum in about 2 per cent. of subjects. Its average position is about 1 meter above the colic valve, and its average length about 5 cm. Its caliber is generally similar to that of the ileum, and its blind extremity may be free or may be connected with the abdominal wall or with some other portion of the intestine by a fibrous band. It represents the remains of the proximal part of the vitelline duct, the duct of communication between the yolk-sac and the primitive digestive tube in early fetal life.

Structure.—The wall of the small intestine is composed of four coats: mucous, submucous, muscular, and serous.

The internal surface has two types of irregularities or projections which are characteristic of the small intestine. They are the large circular folds and the minute villi (Fig. 1067).

The **circular folds** (*plicæ circulares* [Kerkringi]; *valvulæ conniventes; valves of Kerkring*) (Fig. 1067) are valvelike folds which project into the lumen from 3 to 10 mm. The majority extend transversely around the inside of the cylinder of the intestine for about one-half to two-thirds of its circumference, but others complete the circle or form a spiral extending more than once around, even making two or three turns. The folds are also of different height, the high ones tending to alternate with low ones. The size and frequency of the folds are different in the three parts of the small intestine. The folds are formed by both the tela submucosa and tunica mucosa. The core of submucosal connective tissue is quite firm, making these folds permanent structures which are not obliterated by distension as are the transient rugæ of the stomach.

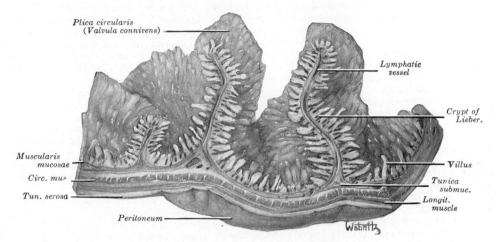

Fɪɢ. 1067.—Section through wall of small intestine (jejunum) of adult cadaver. × 5.

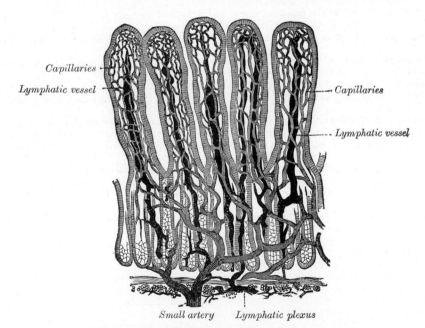

Fɪɢ. 1068.—Villi of small intestine, showing blood vessels and lymphatic vessels. (Cadiat.)

The **villi** (*villi intestinales*) (Fig. 1068) are tiny fingerlike projections, of a size just at the border-line of visibility with the naked eye, crowded together over the entire mucous surface and giving it a velvety appearance. They are quite irregular in size and shape, are larger in some parts of the intestine than in others and become considerably flattened out by distension of the intestine. The villi are entirely made up of tissue belonging to the tunica mucosa.

81

The **mucous membrane** (*tunica mucosa*) is composed of the villi, the intestinal glands, a connective tissue framework, and a muscularis mucosæ. The surface epithelium covering the villi is a simple columnar type in which the majority of cells have a characteristic striated free border. Recent observations with the electron microscope have demonstrated that the striated appearance is due to innumerable closely set projections of cytoplasm which are too small (diameter 0.08μ) to be distinguished with the best light microscopes (Granger and Baker '50). Scattered liberally among the striated epithelial cells are numerous mucus-secreting goblet cells.

Structure of the Villi.—Each villus has a core of delicate areolar and reticular connective tissue which provides a basement membrane for the epithelium and supports the rich network of capillary blood vessels and the usually single lymphatic vessel. The lymphatic capillary begins blindly near the tip of the villus, occupies a more or less central position, and opens into the lymphatic vessels in the submucosa. This central lymphatic capillary is called a **lacteal**, the name having been given because it is filled with a white milky fluid, known as chyle, during the digestion of a meal rich in fat. Scattered single strands of smooth muscle run parallel with the lacteal and appear to be extensions of the muscularis mucosæ into the villus.

The **intestinal glands** (*glandulæ intestinales* [Lieberkühni]; *crypts of Lieberkühn*) are simple tubular glands which open into the depressions between the villi and form a rather uniform layer of glandular tissue between the bases of the villi and the muscularis mucosæ. The striated surface epithelium and goblet cells extend quite far down into the crypts, but at the bottom or fundus is a group of glandular secreting cells known as the **cells of Paneth.** These cells contain large secretion granules which stain a bright red with eosin, and it is probable that they secrete the digestive enzymes of the small intestine. Mitotic divisions are frequently observed in the cells of the wall of the crypt and it is believed that proliferation of these cells makes up for the loss of surface cells from the natural attrition (Hunt '51).

The **muscularis mucosæ** is a thin sheet of non-striated muscle cells, composed of inner circular and outer longitudinal layers at the boundary between the mucosa and submucosa.

The **submucous coat** (*tela submucosa*) is composed of fibro-elastic and areolar connective tissue. It is a strong layer, forming the core of the circular folds. It contains the blood vessels and lymphatics which supply the mucous membrane and, near the muscularis, the **submucous nerve plexus of Meissner** (Fig. 1070). Small collections of lymphocytes and solitary lymphatic nodules may occur in any part of the small intestine, and groups of nodules, known as Peyer's patches, occur in the ileum. The lymphatic nodules usually occupy the submucosa, infiltrate the muscularis mucosæ, and extend out to the free surface, often appearing to obliterate some of the villi (Fig. 1071).

The **muscular coat** (*tunica muscularis*) is composed of the two layers, usual in the alimentary tube, outer longitudinal and inner circular. Between these two layers is a net of nervous tissue containing non-myelinated nerve fibers and ganglion cells (Fig. 1069 known as the **myenteric** or **Auerbach's plexus.** The muscularis is somewhat thicker in the proximal than in the distal part of the intestine.

The **serous coat** (*tunica serosa*) is composed of the peritoneum and the areolar connective tissue connecting it to the muscular coat. The small intestine is covered by peritoneum except along the narrow strip or border attached to the mesentery, and the parts of the duodenum which are retroperitoneal.

Special Features.—Duodenum.—The circular folds are not found in the first 2.5 to 5 cm. beyond the pylorus, but in the descending part, distal to the openings of the bile and pancreatic ducts, they are especially large and numerous. The villi are also especially large and numerous in the duodenum.

The **duodenal glands** (*glandulæ duodenales* [*Brunneri*], *Brunner's glands*) differ from the other intestinal glands in occupying the submucosa. The usual intestinal glands or crypts are found in the duodenum and the ducts from the duodenal glands, after penetrating the muscularis mucosæ, open into the bottoms of occasional crypts. The duodenal glands are compound tubulo-alveolar glands; they resemble the pyloric glands of the stomach in appearance but are larger, and, as mentioned, they lie in the submocosa. The cells stain lightly in histological preparations, but they give some of the reactions of mucus. The duodenal glands are largest and most numerous near the pylorus, forming there a rather thick complete layer, but they diminish in the horizontal portion and disappear near the duodenojejunal junction.

Jejunum.—The circular folds and villi are almost as large and numerous in the proximal part of the jejunum as in the duodenum but they gradually decrease in size and number toward the ileum.

Ileum.—The circular folds and villi are smaller and less numerous in the ileum than in the jejunum, and toward the terminal part the folds may be widely scattered or even lacking.

Aggregated lymphatic nodules or **Peyer's patches** (*noduli lymphatici aggregati; Peyer's glands; agminated follicles; tonsillæ intestinales*) are groups of lymphatic nodules spread out as a single layer in the mucous membrane of the wall of the ileum opposite the mesenteric attachment. The patches are circular or oval, approximately 1 cm. wide and may extend along the intestine for 3 to 5 cm. They are largest and most frequent in the distal ileum but are occasionally seen even in the jejunum. They can be recognized in gross specimens at autopsy as thickened whitish patches where the circular folds are absent and the villi are very sparse or lacking. In the dissecting room, where the subjects are usually of advanced age, the patches are difficult to identify because of the atrophy of the lymphatic tissue which takes place in older individuals.

Vessels and Nerves.—The jejunum and ileum are supplied by the **superior mesenteric artery,** the intestinal branches of which, having reached the attached border of the bowel, run between the serous and muscular coats, with frequent inosculations to the free border, where they also anastomose with other branches running around the opposite surface of the gut. From these vessels numerous branches are given off, which pierce the muscular coat, supplying it and forming an intricate plexus in the submucous tissue. From this plexus minute vessels pass to the glands and villi of the mucous membrane. The **veins** have a course and arrangement similar to that of

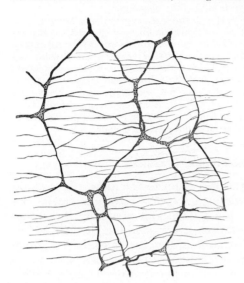

FIG. 1069.—The myenteric plexus from the rabbit. × 50.

FIG. 1070.—The plexus of the submucosa from the rabbit. × 50.

the arteries. The **lymphatics** of the small intestine (lacteals) are arranged in two sets, those of the mucous membrane and those of the muscular coat. The lymphatics of the villi commence in

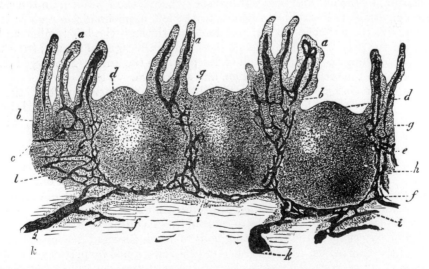

FIG. 1071.—Vertical section of a human aggregated lymphatic nodule, injected through its lymphatic canals. *a,* Villi with their chyle passages. *b.* Intestinal glands. *c.* Muscularis mucosæ. *d.* Cupola or apex of solitary nodule. *e.* Mesial zone of nodule. *f.* Base of nodule. *g.* Points of exit of the lacteals from the villi, and entrance into the true mucous membrane. *h.* Retiform arrangement of the lymphatics in the mesial zone. *i.* Course of the latter at the base of the nodule. *k.* Confluence of the lymphatics opening into the vessels of the submucous tissue. *l.* Follicular tissue of the latter.

these structures in the manner described above. They form an intricate plexus in the mucous and submucous tissue, being joined by the lymphatics from the lymph spaces at the bases of the solitary nodules, and from this pass to larger vessels at the mesenteric border of the gut. The lymphatics of the muscular coat are situated to a great extent between the two layers of muscular fibers, where they form a close plexus; throughout their course they communicate freely with the lymphatics from the mucous membrane, and empty themselves in the same manner as these into the origins of the lacteal vessels at the attached border of the gut.

The **nerves** of the small intestines are derived from the plexuses of sympathetic nerves around the superior mesenteric artery, representing cranial parasympathetic fibers of the vagus and post-ganglionic sympathetic fibers from the celiac plexus. From this source they run to the **myenteric plexus** (*Auerbach's plexus*) (Fig. 1069) of nerves and ganglia situated between the circular and longitudinal muscular fibers from which the nervous branches are distributed to the muscular coats of the intestine. From this a secondary plexus, the **plexus of the submucosa** (*Meissner's plexus*) (Fig. 1070) is derived, and is formed by branches which have perforated the circular muscular fibers. This plexus lies in the submucous coat of the intestine; it also contains ganglia from which nerve fibers pass to the muscularis mucosæ and to the mucous membrane. The nerve bundles of the submucous plexus are finer than those of the myenteric plexus.

The Large Intestine (Intestinum Crassum).

The **large intestine** extends from the end of the ileum to the anus. It is about 1.5 meters long, being one-fifth of the whole extent of the intestinal canal. Its caliber is largest at its commencement at the cecum, and gradually diminishes as far as the rectum, where there is a dilatation of considerable size just above the anal canal. It differs from the small intestine in its greater caliber, its more fixed position, its sacculated form, and in possessing certain appendages to its external coat, the **appendices epiploicæ**. Further, its longitudinal muscular fibers do not form a continuous layer around the gut, but are arranged in three **longitudinal bands** or **tæniæ**. The large intestine, in its course, describes an arch which surrounds the convolutions of the small intestine. It commences in the right iliac region, in a dilated part, the **cecum**. It ascends through the right lumbar and hypochondriac regions to the under surface of the liver; it here takes a bend, the **right colic flexure**, to the left and passes transversely across the abdomen on the confines of the epigastric and umbilical regions, to the left hypochondriac region; it then bends again, the **left colic flexure**, and descends through the left lumbar and iliac regions to the pelvis, where it forms a bend called the **sigmoid flexure**; from this it is continued along the posterior wall of the pelvis to the anus. The large intestine is divided into the **cecum, colon, rectum**, and **anal canal**.

The **Cecum** (*intestinum cæcum*) (Fig. 1072), the commencement of the large intestine, is the large blind pouch situated below the colic valve. Its blind end is directed downward, and its open end upward, communicating directly with the colon, of which this blind pouch appears to be the beginning or head, and hence the old name of **caput cæcum coli** was applied to it. Its size is variously estimated by different authors, but on an average it may be said to be 6.25 cm. in length and 7.5 in breadth. It is situated in the right iliac fossa, above the lateral half of the inguinal ligament: it rests on the Iliacus and Psoas major, and usually lies in contact with the anterior abdominal wall, but the greater omentum and, if the cecum be empty, some coils of small intestine may lie in front of it. According to Moody the common position of the cecum in the erect living body is not in the right iliac fossa but in the cavity of the true pelvis. As a rule, it is entirely enveloped by peritoneum, but in a certain number of cases (5 per cent., Berry) the peritoneal covering is not complete, so that the upper part of the posterior surface is uncovered and connected to the iliac fascia by connective tissue. The cecum lies quite free in the abdominal cavity and enjoys a considerable amount of movement, so that it may become herniated down the right inguinal canal, and has occasionally been found in an inguinal hernia on the left side. The cecum varies in shape, but, according to Treves, in man it may be classified under one of four types. In early fetal life it is short, conical, and broad at the base, with its apex turned upward and medialward toward the ileocolic junction. It then resembles the cecum of some monkeys, *e. g.*, mangabey monkey. As the fetus grows the cecum increases in length more than in breadth, so that it forms a longer tube than in the primitive form and without the broad base, but with the same inclination of the apex toward the ileocolic junction. This form is seen in other monkeys, *e. g.*, the spider monkey. As development goes on, the lower part of the tube ceases to grow and the upper part becomes greatly increased, so that at birth there is a narrow tube, the vermiform process, hanging from a conical projection, the cecum. This is the infantile form, and as it persists throughout life in about 2 per cent. of cases, it is regarded by Treves as the *first* of his four types of human ceca. The cecum is conical and the appendix rises from its apex. The three longitudinal bands start from the appendix and are equidistant from each other. In the second type, the conical cecum has become quadrate by the growing out of a saccule on either side of the anterior longitudinal band. These saccules are of equal size, and the appendix arises from between them, instead of from the apex of a cone. This type is found in about 3 per cent. of cases. The *third* type is the normal type of man. Here the two saccules, which in the second type were uniform, have grown at unequal rates: the right with greater rapidity than the left. In consequence of this an apparently new apex has been formed by the growing downward of the right saccule, and the original apex, with the appendix attached, is pushed over to the left toward the ileocolic junction. The three longitudinal bands still start from the base of the vermiform process, but they are now no longer equidistant from each other, because the right saccule has grown between the anterior and postero-lateral bands, pushing them over to the left. This type occurs in about 90 per cent. of cases. The *fourth* type is merely an exaggerated condition of the third; the right saccule is still larger, and at the same time the left saccule has become atrophied, so that the original apex of the cecum, with the vermiform process, is close to the ileocolic junction, and the anterior band courses medialward to the same situation. This type is present in about ½ per cent. of cases.

The **Appendix** or **Vermiform Process** (*processus vermiformis*) (Fig. 1073) is a long, narrow, worm-shaped tube, which starts from what was originally the apex of the cecum, and may pass in one of several directions: upward behind the cecum; to the left behind the ileum and mesentery; or downward into the lesser pelvis. It varies from 2 to 20 cm. in length, its average being about 8.3 cm. It is retained in position by a fold of peritoneum (mesenteriole), derived from the left leaf of the mesentery. This fold, in the majority of cases, is more or less triangular in shape, and as a rule extends along the entire length of the tube. Between its two layers and close to its free margin lies the appendicular artery (Fig. 1072). The canal of the vermiform process is small, extends throughout the whole length of the tube, and communicates with the cecum by an orifice which is placed below and behind the ileocecal opening. It is sometimes guarded by a semilunar valve formed by a fold of mucous membrane, but this is by no means constant.

The **Colic Valve** (*valvula coli; ileocecal valve*) (Fig. 1073).—The lower end of the ileum ends by opening into the medial and back part of the large intestine, at the point of junction of the cecum with the colon. The opening is guarded by a valve, consisting of two segments or lips, which project into the lumen of the large intestine. If the intestine has been inflated and dried, the lips are of a semilunar shape. The upper one, nearly horizontal in direction, is attached by its convex border to the line of junction of the ileum with the colon; the lower lip, which is longer and more concave, is attached to the line of junction of the ileum with the cecum. At the ends of the aperture the two segments of the valve coalesce, and are continued as narrow membranous ridges around the canal for a short distance, forming the **frenula of the valve.** The left or anterior end of the aperture is rounded; the right or posterior is narrow and pointed. In the fresh condition, or in specimens which

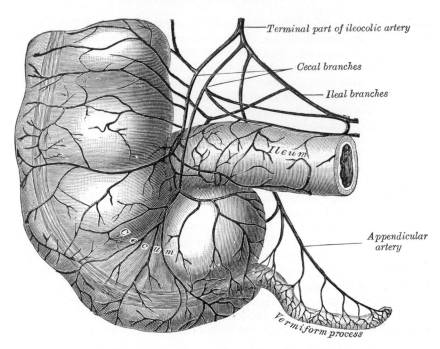

Fig. 1072.—The cecum and appendix, with their arteries.

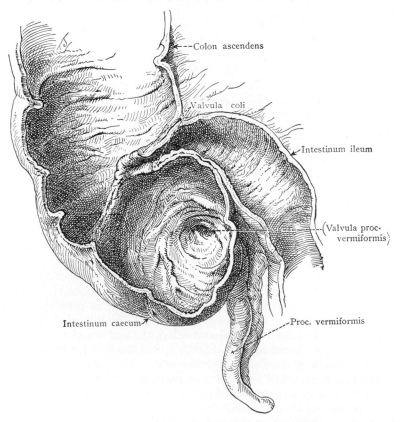

Fig. 1073.—The cecum, colic valve, and appendix vermiformis, with anterior wall of terminal ileum and cecum removed.   (Eycleshymer and Jones.)

have been hardened *in situ,* the lips project as thick cushion-like folds into the lumen of the large gut, while the opening between them may present the appearance of a slit or may be somewhat oval in shape.

Each lip of the valve is formed by a reduplication of the mucous membrane and of the circular muscular fibers of the intestine, the longitudinal fibers and peritoneum being continued uninterruptedly from the small to the large intestine.

The surfaces of the valve directed toward the ileum are covered with villi, and present the characteristic structure of the mucous membrane of the small intestine; while those turned toward the large intestine are destitute of villi, and marked with the orifices of the numerous tubular glands peculiar to the mucous membrane of the large intestine. These differences in structure continue as far as the free margins of the valve. It is generally maintained that this valve prevents reflux from the cecum into the ileum, but in all probability it acts as a sphincter around the end of the ileum and prevents the contents of the ileum from passing too quickly into the cecum.

The **Colon** is divided into four parts: the **ascending, transverse, descending iliac,** and **sigmoid.**

The **Ascending Colon** (*colon ascendens*) is smaller in caliber than the cecum, with which it is continuous. It passes upward, from its commencement at the cecum, opposite the colic valve, to the under surface of the right lobe of the liver, on the right of the gall-bladder, where it is lodged in a shallow depression, the **colic impression;** here it bends abruptly forward and to the left, forming the **right colic** (*hepatic*) **flexure** (Fig. 1045). It is retained in contact with the posterior wall of the abdomen by the peritoneum, which covers its anterior surface and sides, its posterior surface being connected by loose areolar tissue with the Iliacus, Quadratus lumborum, aponeurotic origin of Transversus abdominis, and with the front of the lower and lateral part of the right kidney. Sometimes the peritoneum completely invests it, and forms a distinct but narrow mesocolon. It is in relation, in front, with the convolutions of the ileum and the abdominal parietes.

The **Transverse Colon** (*colon transversum*) the longest and most movable part of the colon, passes with a downward convexity from the right hypochondriac region across the abdomen, opposite the confines of the epigastric and umbilical zones, into the left hypochondriac region, where it curves sharply on itself beneath the lower end of the spleen, forming the **left colic** (*splenic*) **flexure.** In the erect posture the most caudal part is in the majority of males from 7.5 cm. to 10 cm. below the interiliac line and in the majority of females from 10 cm. to 12.5 cm. below the line. (Moody.) It is almost completely invested by peritoneum, and is connected to the inferior border of the pancreas by a large and wide duplicature of that membrane, the **transverse mesocolon.** It is in relation, by its upper surface, with the liver and gall-bladder, the greater curvature of the stomach, and the lower end of the spleen; by its under surface, with the small intestine; by its anterior surface, with the anterior layers of the greater omentum and the abdominal parietes; its posterior surface is in relation from right to left with the descending portion of the duodenum, the head of the pancreas, and some of the convolutions of the jejunum and ileum.

The **left colic** or **splenic flexure** (Fig. 1045) is situated at the junction of the transverse and descending parts of the colon, and is in relation with the lower end of the spleen and the tail of the pancreas; the flexure is so acute that the end of the transverse colon usually lies in contact with the front of the descending colon. It lies at a higher level than, and on a plane posterior to, the right colic flexure, and is attached to the diaphragm, opposite the tenth and eleventh ribs, by a peritoneal fold, named the **phrenicocolic ligament,** which assists in supporting the lower end of the spleen (see page 1269). Its position varies greatly.

The **Descending Colon** (*colon descendens*) passes downward through the left hypochondriac and lumbar regions along the lateral border of the left kidney.

At the lower end of the kidney it turns medialward toward the lateral border of the Psoas, and then descends, in the angle between Psoas and Quadratus lumborum, to the crest of the ilium, where it ends in the iliac colon. The peritoneum covers its anterior surface and sides, while its posterior surface is connected by areolar tissue with the lower and lateral part of the left kidney, the aponeurotic origin of the Transversus abdominis, and the Quadratus lumborum (Fig. 1045). It is smaller in caliber and more deeply placed than the ascending colon, and is more frequently covered with peritoneum on its posterior surface than the ascending colon (Treves). In front of it are some coils of small intestine.

The **iliac colon** (Fig. 1074) is situated in the left iliac fossa, and is about 12 to 15 cm. long. It begins at the level of the iliac crest, where it is a continuation of the descending colon, and ends in the sigmoid colon at the superior aperture of the lesser pelvis. It curves downward and medialward in front of the Iliacus and Psoas, and, as a rule, is covered by peritoneum on its sides and anterior surface only.

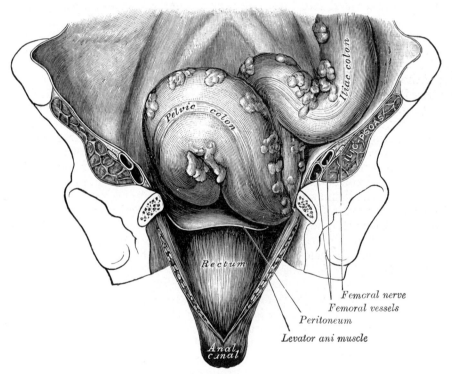

FIG. 1074.—Iliac colon, sigmoid or pelvic colon, and rectum seen from the front, after removal of pubic bones and bladder.

The **Sigmoid Colon** (*colon sigmoideum; pelvic colon; sigmoid flexure*) (Fig. 1074) forms a loop which averages about 40 cm. in length, and normally lies within the pelvis, but on account of its freedom of movement it is liable to be displaced into the abdominal cavity. It begins at the superior aperture of the lesser pelvis, where it is continuous with the iliac colon, and passes transversely across the front of the sacrum to the right side of the pelvis; it then curves on itself and turns toward the left to reach the middle line at the level of the third piece of the sacrum, where it bends downward and ends in the rectum. It is completely surrounded by peritoneum, which forms a mesentery (**sigmoid mesocolon**), which diminishes in length from the center toward the ends of the loop, where it disappears, so that the loop is fixed at its junctions with the iliac colon and rectum, but enjoys a considerable range of movement in its central portion. *Behind* the sigmoid colon are the external iliac vessels, the left Piriformis, and left sacral plexus of nerves; in *front*, it is separated from the bladder in the male, and the uterus in the female, by some coils of the small intestine.

The **Rectum** (*intestinum rectum*) (Fig. 1075) is continuous above with the sigmoid colon, while below it ends in the anal canal. From its origin at the level of the third sacral vertebra it passes downward, lying in the sacrococcygeal curve, and

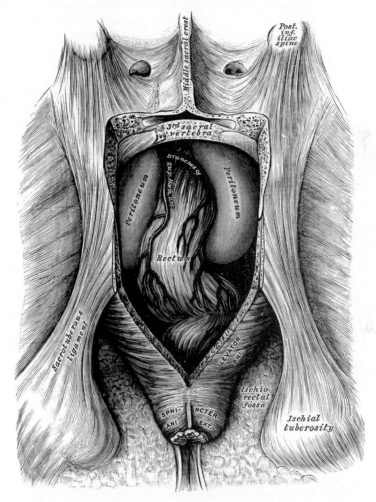

Fig. 1075.—The posterior aspect of the rectum exposed by removing the lower part of the sacrum and the coccyx.

extends for about 2.5 cm. in front of, and a little below, the tip of the coccyx, as far as the apex of the prostate. It then bends sharply backward into the anal canal. It therefore presents two antero-posterior curves: an upper, with its convexity backward, and a lower, with its convexity forward. Two lateral curves are also described, one to the right opposite the junction of the third and fourth sacral vertebræ, and the other to the left, opposite the left sacrococcygeal articulation; they are, however, of little importance. The rectum is about 12 cm. long, and at its commencement its caliber is similar to that of the sigmoid colon, but near its termination it is dilated to form the **rectal ampulla**. The rectum has no sacculations comparable to those of the colon, but when the lower part of the rectum is con-tracted, its mucous membrane is thrown into a number of folds, which are longitudi-nal in direction and are effaced by the distension of the gut. Besides these there are certain permanent transverse folds, of a semilunar shape, known as **Houston's valves** (Fig. 1076). They are usually three in number; sometimes a fourth is found, and occasionally only two are present. One is situated near the commencement of the rectum, on the right side; a second, about 3 cm. below the first; extends inward from the left side of the tube; a third, the largest and most constant, projects backward from the forepart of the rectum, opposite the fundus of the urinary blad-der. When a fourth is present, it is situated nearly 2.5 cm. above the anus on the left and posterior wall of the tube. These folds are about 12 mm. in width, and contain some of the circular fibers of the gut. In the empty state of the intestine they overlap each other, as Houston remarks, so effectually as to require consider-able maneuvering to conduct a bougie or the finger along the canal. Their use seems to be, "to support the weight of fecal matter, and prevent its urging toward the anus, where its presence always excites a sensation demanding its discharge."

The peritoneum is related to the upper two-thirds of the rectum, covering at first its front and sides, but lower down its front only; from the latter it is reflected on to the seminal vesicles in the male and the posterior vaginal wall in the female.

The level at which the peritoneum leaves the anterior wall of the rectum to be reflected on to the viscus in front of it is of considerable impor-tance from a surgical point of view, in connec-tion with the removal of the lower part of the rectum. It is higher in the male than in the female. In the former the height of the recto-vesical excavation is about 7.5 cm., *i. e.*, the height to which an ordinary index finger can reach from the anus. In the female the height of the rectouterine excavation is about 5.5 cm. from the anal orifice. The rectum is surrounded by a dense tube of fascia loosely attached to the rectal wall by areolar tissue in order to allow distension.

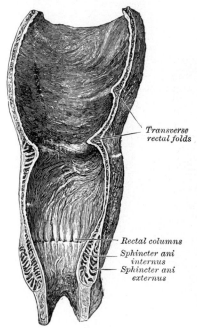

Transverse rectal folds

Rectal columns
Sphincter ani internus
Sphincter ani externus

Fig. 1076.—Coronal section of rectum and anal canal.

Relations of the Rectum.—The upper part of the rectum is in relation, *behind*, with the superior hemorrhoidal vessels, the left Piriformis, and left sacral plexus of nerves, which separate it from the pelvic surfaces of the sacral vertebræ; in its lower part it lies directly on the sacrum, coccyx, and Levatores ani, a dense fascia alone intervening; *in front*, it is separated above, in the male, from the fundus of the bladder; in the female, from the intestinal surface of the uterus and its appendages, by some convolutions of the small intestine, and frequently by the sigmoid colon; *below*, it is in relation in the male with the triangular portion of the fundus of the bladder, the vesiculæ seminales, and ductus deferentes, and more anteriorly with the pos-terior surface of the prostate; in the female, with the posterior wall of the vagina.

The **Anal Canal** (*pars analis recti*) (Figs. 1074, 1076, 1080), or terminal portion of the large intestine, begins at the level of the apex of the prostate, is directed downward and backward, and ends at the anus. It forms an angle with the lower part of the rectum, and measures from 2.5 to 4 cm. in length. It has no peritoneal cov-ering, but is invested by the Sphincter ani internus, supported by the Levatores ani, and surrounded at its termination by the Sphincter ani externus. In the empty condition it presents the appearance of an antero-posterior longitudinal slit. Behind it is a mass of muscular and fibrous tissue, the **anococcygeal body** (Symington); in front of it, in the male, but separated by the perineal center from it, are the membranous portion and bulb of the urethra, and the fascia of the urogenital diaphragm; and in the female it is separated from the lower end of the vagina by a mass of muscular and fibrous tissue, named the **perineal body.**

The lumen of the anal canal presents, in its upper half, a number of vertical folds, produced by an infolding of the mucous membrane and some of the muscular tissue. They are known as the **rectal columns** [*Morgagni*] (Fig. 1080), and are separated from one another by furrows **(rectal sinuses)**, which end below in small valve-like folds, termed **anal valves**, which join together the lower ends of the rectal columns.

Structure of the Large Intestine.—The large intestine has four coats: mucous, submucous, muscular and serous.

The wall of the cecum and colon has certain folds and irregularities which are characteristic and which show up most prominently on the internal surface, but, unlike those in the small intestine, these folds include all four layers and may be seen on the external surface. The longi-

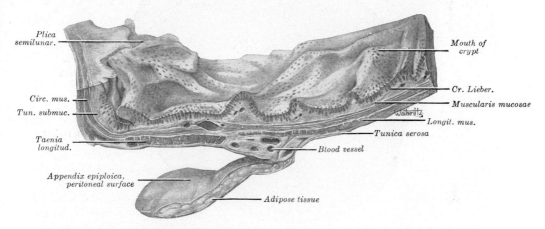

FIG. 1077.—Section through colon of adult cadaver. × 5.

tudinal bands of the muscular coat, which will be described below, cause a puckering of the wall, so that between them it is bulged out into sacculations called **haustræ.** The wall between the haustræ is thrown into folds which have a crescentic form on the interior of the colon and are called the **semilunar folds** (*plicæ semilunares*) in contrast with the plicæ circulares of the small intestine.

The **mucous coat** (*tunica mucosa*) is smooth, that is, devoid of villi, and covers the inner surface of haustræ and semilunar folds in a coat of uniform thickness. The surface is covered with simple columnar epithelium containing large numbers of goblet cells. The glands of the large intestine are simple, straight, tubular glands containing the same type of epithelium as the surface; they are packed quite closely together and they open on the surface in tiny round holes which can readily be seen with a hand lens (Fig. 1077). There is a delicate **muscularis mucosæ** composed of inner circular and outer longitudinal fibers. Collections of lymphocytes and solitary lymphatic nodules are of frequent occurrence, especially near the colic valve and in the rectum.

The **submucous coat** (*tela submucosa*) is a rather uniform layer of areolar tissue containing blood and lymphatic vessels and connecting the mucosa with the muscularis.

The **muscular coat** (*tunica muscularis*) is composed of the usual inner circular and outer longitudinal layers of non-striated muscle.

The circular fibers form a thin layer over the cecum and colon; it is somewhat thickened in the semilunar folds between the haustræ, uniformly thickened in the rectum, and, in the anal canal, constitutes the strong circular non-striated muscle, the Sphincter ani internus.

The longitudinal muscle fibers are concentrated into three flat longitudinal bands about equally spaced and about 12 mm. in width. They are easily seen in a gross specimen (Fig. 1046) and are called **tæniæ coli.** They have specific positions in relation to the position of the colon itself: (1)

the posterior tænia is placed along the attached border, (2) the anterior tænia is the one easily visible on the exposed surface of the ascending and descending colon but is covered by the attachment of the greater omentum on the transverse colon, and (3) the lateral tænia is found on the medial side of the ascending and descending colon and on the under aspect of the transverse colon. The anterior tænia is a useful guide for locating the position of the appendix vermiformis because the latter is a direct extension from it (Fig. 1072).

The tæniæ are shorter than the other coats of colon and cecum, causing the intervening wall to bulge into the sacculations known as haustra which are typical of this part of the intestine (Fig. 1045) and are responsible for the deep depressions in its outline in an *x*-ray (Fig. 84). Between adjacent haustra are the crescentic folds or plicæ semilunares which encroach on the lumen of the intestine.

The **serous coat** (*tunica serosa*), derived from the peritoneum, is complete over the cecum, appendix, transverse colon, and sigmoid colon except for their mesenteric attachments. It is incomplete on the ascending and descending colons, where they are attached to the posterior abdominal wall, and on the rectum.

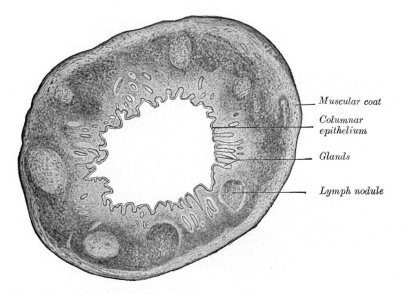

Muscular coat

Columnar epithelium

Glands

Lymph nodule

Fig. 1078.—Transverse section of human appendix. × 20.

The **appendices epiploicæ** are characteristic features of the large intestine and may be used for its identification. They are small, rounded, irregular masses of fat, averaging 0.5 to 1.0 cm. in diameter, almost completely covered by peritoneum and suspended from the surface of the colon and cecum by slender stalks. They are usually attached along the tæniæ, and are most numerous on the transverse colon.

Special Features.—Appendix or Vermiform Process.—The appendix has the same four coats as the colon. The epithelial lining and the glands are similar, but the glands are much fewer and the mucosa and submucosa are much thickened and almost entirely occupied by lymphatic nodules and lymphocytes (Fig. 1078). The longitudinal fibers of the tunica muscularis are evenly distributed, not arranged into tæniæ, as in the colon, and the circular muscle is more prominent than the longitudinal.

Rectum.—The mucous membrane in the rectum is thicker and more vascular than in the colon and is more loosely attached to the muscularis, as in the esophagus. The longitudinal fibers of the tunica muscularis are spread out into a layer which completely surrounds the rectum, but is thicker on the anterior and posterior walls.

Anal Canal.—The mucous membrane in the anal canal is thick and vascular. Beneath the longitudinal folds or **rectal columns** of Morgagni are dilated veins, often knotted and tortuous, where the tributaries of the superior and inferior hemorrhoidal veins anastomose. The epithelium changes abruptly at about 1.5 to 2 cm. above the anal opening, the transition is marked by a white line, below which the epithelium is stratified squamous continuous with the skin. In the region of this line there are the openings of the **anal glands,** very much enlarged modified skin glands (Fig. 1080).

The proper circular muscle layer, continuous with that of the rectum, is greatly thickened in the anal canal, forming the non-striated **internal anal sphincter** (*Sphincter ani internus*). In the tissue surrounding the anus is a circular ring of striated muscle, the external anal sphincter, and diverging from this to the walls of the pelvis is the Levator ani. Just beneath the integument at the anal orifice is a more delicate striated muscle, the Corrugator cutis ani; its fibers are closely associated with the tributaries of the inferior hemorrhoidal veins draining the plexuses in the rectal columns and spasm of its fibers may seriously retard the venous drainage.

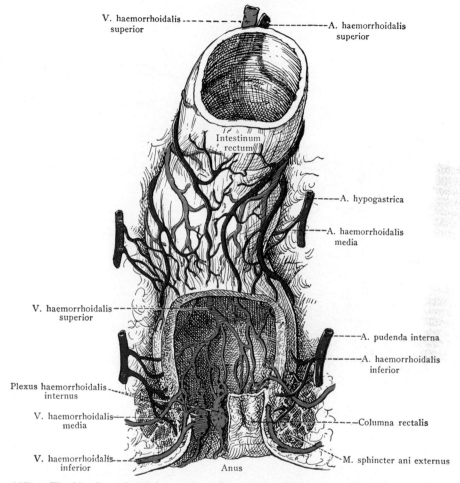

Fig. 1079.—The blood supply of the rectum. A portion of the anterior wall has been cut away to show the rectal columns and the internal hæmorrhoidal plexus. (Eycleshymer and Jones.)

Vessels and Nerves (Fig. 1079).—The **arteries** supplying the colon are derived from the colic and sigmoid branches of the mesenteric arteries. They give off large branches, which ramify between and supply the muscular coats, and after dividing into small vessels in the submucous tissue, pass to the mucous membrane. The rectum is supplied by the superior hemorrhoidal branch of the inferior mesenteric, and the anal canal by the middle hemorrhoidal from the hypogastric, and the inferior hemorrhoidal from the internal pudendal artery. The superior hemorrhoidal, the continuation of the inferior mesenteric, divides into two branches, which run down either side of the rectum to within about 12.5 cm. of the anus; they here split up into about six branches, which pierce the muscular coat and descend between it and the mucous membrane in a longitudinal direction, parallel with each other as far as the Sphincter ani internus, where they anastomose with the other hemorrhoidal arteries and form a series of loops around the anus. The **veins** of the rectum commence in a plexus of vessels which surrounds the anal canal. In the vessels forming this plexus are smaller saccular dilatations just within the margin of the anus; from the plexus about six vessels of considerable size are given off. These ascend between the muscular and mucous coats for about 12.5 cm., running parallel to each other; they then pierce the muscular coat (Fig. 1079), and unite to form a single trunk, the superior hemorrhoidal vein. This arrangement is termed the **hemorrhoidal plexus**; it communicates with the tributaries of the middle and inferior hemorrhoidal veins, at its commencement, and thus a communication is established between the systemic and portal circulations. The **lymphatics** of the large intestine are described on page 804. The **nerves** to that region of the colon supplied by the superior mesenteric artery are derived in the same manner as those for the small intestine; those to the

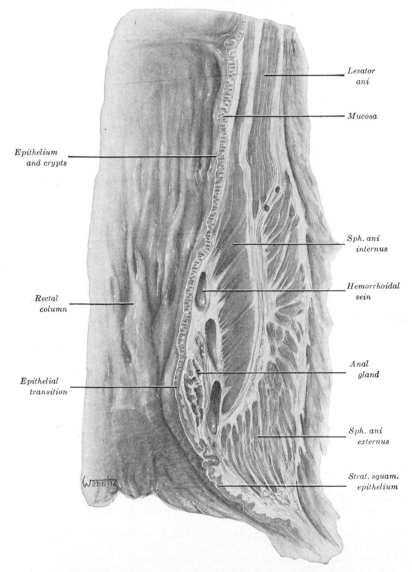

Levator ani

Mucosa

Epithelium and crypts

Sph. ani internus

Hemorrhoidal vein

Rectal column

Anal gland

Epithelial transition

Sph. ani externus

Strat. squam. epithelium

FIG. 1080.—Section of the rectum and anus of an adult cadaver. Lightly stained with hematoxylin. $\times$ 5.

more distal portions of the colon, and to the rectum, are derived from sympathetic and sacral parasympathetic fibers through the inferior mesenteric and hypogastric plexuses (see pages 1063, 1087). They are distributed in a similar way to those found in the small intestine.

The Liver (Hepar).

Development.—The liver arises in the form of a diverticulum or hollow outgrowth from the ventral surface of that portion of the gut which afterward becomes the descending part of the duodenum (Fig. 1081). This diverticulum is lined by entoderm, and grows upward and forward into the septum transversum, a mass of mesoderm between the vitelline duct and the pericardial cavity, and there gives off two solid buds of cells which represent the right and the left lobes of the liver. The solid buds of cells grow into columns or cylinders, termed the **hepatic cylinders,** which branch and anastomose to form a close meshwork. This network invades the vitelline and umbilical veins, and breaks up these vessels into a series of capillary-like vessels termed **sinusoids** (Minot), which ramify in the meshes of the cellular network and ultimately form the venous capillaries of the liver (see page 1303). By the continued growth and ramification of the hepatic cylinders the mass of the liver is gradually formed. The original diverticulum from the duodenum forms the common bile-duct, and from this the cystic duct and gall-bladder arise as a

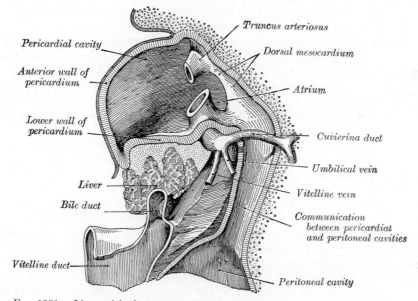

FIG. 1081.—Liver with the septum transversum. Human embryo 3 mm. long.
(After model and figure by His.)

solid outgrowth which later acquires a lumen. The opening of the common duct is at first in the ventral wall of the duodenum; later, owing to the rotation of the gut, the opening is carried to the left and then dorsalward to the position it occupies in the adult.

As the liver undergoes enlargement, both it and the ventral mesogastrium of the fore-gut are gradually differentiated from the septum transversum; and from the under surface of the latter the liver projects downward into the abdominal cavity. By the growth of the liver the ventral mesogastrium is divided into two parts, of which the anterior forms the falciform and coronary ligaments, and the posterior the lesser omentum. About the third month the liver almost fills the abdominal cavity, and its left lobe is nearly as large as its right. From this period the relative development of the liver is less active, more especially that of the left lobe, which actually undergoes some degeneration and becomes smaller than the right; but up to the end of fetal life the liver remains relatively larger than in the adult.

The **liver,** the largest gland in the body, is situated in the upper and right parts of the abdominal cavity, occupying almost the whole of the right hypochondrium, the greater part of the epigastrium, and not uncommonly extending into the left hypochondrium as far as the mammillary line. In the male it weighs from 1.4 to 1.6 kilogm., in the female from 1.2 to 1.4 kilogm. It is relatively much larger in the fetus than in the adult, constituting, in the former, about one-eighteenth, and in the latter about one thirty-sixth of the entire body weight. Its greatest transverse measurement is from 20 to 22.5 cm. Vertically, near its lateral or right surface, it measures about 15 to 17.5 cm., while its greatest antero-posterior diameter is on a level with the upper end of the right kidney, and is from 10 to 12.5 cm. Opposite the vertebral column its measurement from before backward is reduced to about 7.5 cm. Its consistence is that of a soft solid; it is friable, easily lacerated and highly vascular; its color is a dark reddish-brown, and its specific gravity is 1.05.

It is irregularly hemispherical in shape with an extensive, relatively smooth, convex diaphragmatic surface and a more irregular concave visceral surface. The diaphragmatic surface has four parts: ventral, superior, dorsal, and right portions. The human liver has four lobes: a large right lobe, a smaller left lobe, and much smaller caudate and quadrate lobes.

The **ventral** or **anterior portion** (*pars anterior*) of the **diaphragmatic surface** (*facies diaphragmatica*) (Fig. 1082) is separated by the diaphragm from the sixth to tenth ribs and their costal cartilages on the right side and from the seventh and eighth cartilages on the left. In the medial region it lies behind the xyphoid process and that part of the muscular anterior abdominal wall between the diverging costal margins. It is completely covered by peritoneum except along the line of attachment of the falciform ligament.

The **superior portion** (*pars superior*) (Fig. 1083) is separated by the dome of the diaphragm from the pleura and lungs on the right and the pericardium and heart on the left. The area near the heart is marked by a shallow concavity, the **cardiac fossa.** The surface is mostly covered by peritoneum but along its dorsal part it is attached to the diaphragm by the superior reflection of the coronary ligament which separates the part covered with peritoneum from the so-called bare area.

The **dorsal** or **posterior portion** (*pars posterior*) (Fig. 1083) is broad and rounded on the right but narrow on the left. The central part presents a deep concavity which is moulded to fit against the vertebral column and crura of the diaphragm. Close to the right of this concavity the **inferior vena cava** lies almost buried in its **fossa.** Two or three centimeters to the left of the vena cava is the narrow **fossa for the ductus venosus.** The caudate lobe lies between these two fossæ. To the right of the vena cava and partly on the visceral surface is a small triangular depressed area, the **suprarenal impression** for the right suprarenal gland. To the left of the fossa for the ductus venosus is the **esophageal groove** for the antrum cardiacum of the esophagus.

A large part of the dorsal portion of the diaphragmatic surface is not covered by peritoneum. It is attached to the diaphragm by loose connective tissue. The uncovered area, frequently called the **bare area,** is bounded by the superior and inferior reflections of the coronary ligament.

The **right portion** (*pars dextra*) merges with the other three parts of the diaphragmatic surface and continues down to the right margin which separates it from the visceral surface.

The **visceral surface** is concave, facing dorsalward, caudalward, and to the left. It contains several fossæ and impressions for neighboring viscera. A prominent marking of the left central part is the **porta hepatis,** a fissure for the passage of the blood vessels and bile duct. The visceral surface is covered by peritoneum except where the gall bladder is attached to it and at the porta. The right lobe, lying to the right of the gall bladder, has three impressions. Farthest to the right is the **colic impression** a flattened or shallow area for the right colic flexure, more dorsally a larger and deeper hollow is the **renal impression** for the right kidney, and the **duodenal impression** is a narrow and poorly marked area lying along the neck of

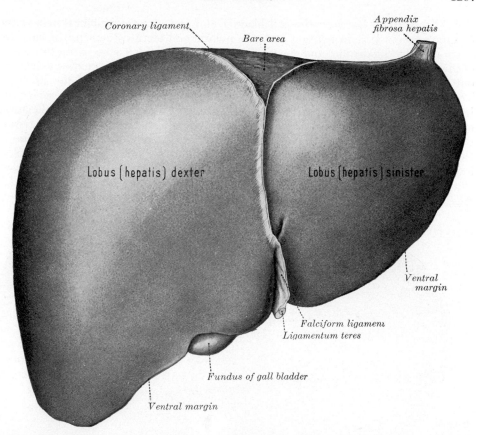

FIG. 1082.—Ventral or anterior portion of diaphragmatic surface of the liver. (From Rauber-Kopsch, *Lehrbuch u. Altas d. Anatomie d. Menschen*, 19th Edition, Vol. II, courtesy of Georg Thieme Verlag, Stuttgart, 1955.)

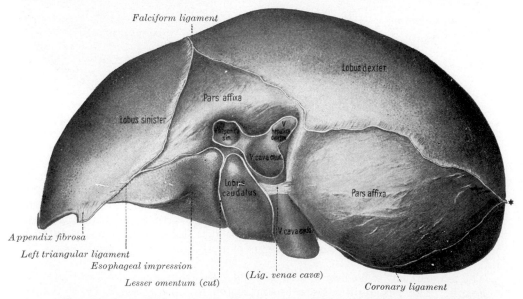

FIG. 1083.—Superior portion of diaphragmatic surface of liver. *Right triangular ligament. (From Rauber-Kopsch, *Lehrbuch u. Altas d. Anatomie d. Menschen*, 19th Edition, Vol. II, courtesy of Georg Thieme Verlag, Stuttgart, 1955.)

82

the gall bladder. Between the gall bladder and **fossa for the umbilical vein** is the quadrate lobe. It is in relation with the pyloric end of the stomach, the superior portion of the duodenum, and the transverse colon. The left lobe, lying to the left of the umbilical vein fossa, has two prominent markings. A large hollow extending out to the margin is the **gastric impression** for the ventral surface of the stomach. Toward the right it merges into a rounded eminence, the **tuber omentale**, which fits into the lesser curvature of the stomach and lies over the ventral surface of the lesser omentum. Just in front of the inferior vena cava is a narrow strip of liver tissue, the **caudate process**, which connects the right inferior angle of the caudate lobe to the right lobe. Its peritoneal covering forms the upper boundary of the epiploic foramen.

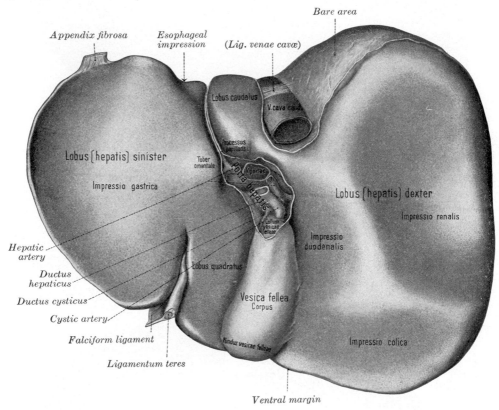

FIG. 1084.—Visceral surface of the liver. (From Rauber-Kopsch, *Lehrbuch u. Altas d. Anatomie d. Menschen*, 19th Edition, Vol. II, courtesy of Georg Thieme Verlag, Stuttgart, 1955.)

The **anterior border** (*margo anterior*) is thin and sharp, and marked opposite the attachment of the falciform ligament by a deep notch, the **umbilical notch**, and opposite the cartilage of the ninth rib by a second notch for the fundus of the gall-bladder. In adult males this border generally corresponds with the lower margin of the thorax in the right mammillary line; but in women and children it usually projects below the ribs. In the erect position it often extends below the interiliac line.

The **left extremity of the liver** is thin and flattened from above downward.

Fossæ.—The **left sagittal fossa** (*fossa sagittalis sinistra; longitudinal fissure*) is a deep groove, which extends from the notch on the anterior margin of the liver to the upper border of the posterior surface of the organ; it separates the right and left lobes. The porta joins it, at right angles, and divides it into two parts. The anterior part, or **fossa for the umbilical vein,** lodges the umbilical vein in the fetus, and its remains (the ligamentum teres) in the adult; it lies between the quadrate lobe and the left lobe of the liver, and is often partially bridged over by a prolongation of the hepatic substance, the **pons hepatis.** The posterior part, or **fossa**

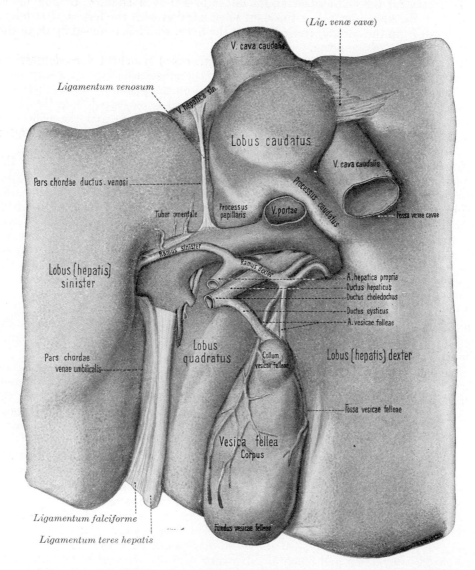

Fig. 1085.—The gall bladder and portal area of the visceral surface of the liver with blood vessels and ducts exposed. (From Rauber-Kopsch, *Lehrbuch u. Altas d. Anatomie d. Menschen,* 19th Edition, Vol. II, courtesy of Georg Thieme Verlag, Stuttgart, 1955.)

for the ductus venosus, lies between the left lobe and the caudate lobe; it lodges in the fetus, the ductus venosus, and in the adult a slender fibrous cord, the **ligamentum venosum,** the obliterated remains of that vessel.

The **porta** or **transverse fissure** (*porta hepatis*) is a short but deep fissure, about 5 cm. long, extending transversely across the under surface of the left portion of the right lobe, nearer its posterior surface than its anterior border. It joins nearly at right angles with the left sagittal fossa, and separates the quadrate lobe in front from the caudate lobe and process behind. It transmits the portal vein, the hepatic artery and nerves, and the hepatic duct and lymphatics. The hepatic duct lies in front and to the right, the hepatic artery to the left, and the portal vein behind and between the duct and artery.

The **fossa for the gall-bladder** (*fossa vesicæ felleæ*) is a shallow, oblong fossa, placed on the under surface of the right lobe, parallel with the left sagittal fossa. It extends from the anterior free margin of the liver, which is notched by it, to the right extremity of the porta.

The **fossa for the inferior vena cava** (*fossa venæ cavæ*) is a short deep depression, occasionally a complete canal in consequence of the substance of the liver surrounding the vena cava. It extends obliquely upward on the posterior surface between the caudate lobe and the bare area of the liver, and is separated from the porta by the caudate process. On slitting open the inferior vena cava the orifices of the hepatic veins will be seen opening into this vessel at its upper part, after perforating the floor of this fossa.

Lobes.—The **right lobe** (*lobus hepatis dexter*) is much larger than the left; the proportion between them being as six to one. It occupies the right hypochondrium, and is separated from the left lobe on its upper surface by the falciform ligament; on its under and posterior surfaces by the left sagittal fossa; and in front by the umbilical notch. It is of a somewhat quadrilateral form, its under and posterior surfaces being marked by three fossæ: the porta and the fossæ for the gall-bladder and inferior vena cava, which separate its left part into two smaller lobes; the **quadrate** and **caudate lobes.** The impressions on the right lobe have already been described.

The **quadrate lobe** (*lobus quadratus*) is situated on the under surface of the right lobe, bounded in front by the anterior margin of the liver; behind by the porta; on the right, by the fossa for the gall-bladder; and on the left, by the fossa for the umbilical vein. It is oblong in shape, its antero-posterior diameter being greater than its transverse.

The **caudate lobe** (*lobus caudatus; Spigelian lobe*) is situated upon the posterior surface of the right lobe of the liver, opposite the tenth and eleventh thoracic vertebræ. It is bounded, below, by the porta; on the right, by the fossa for the inferior vena cava; and, on the left, by the fossa for the ductus venosus. It looks backward, being nearly vertical in position; it is longer from above downward than from side to side, and is somewhat concave in the transverse direction. The **caudate process** is a small elevation of the hepatic substance extending obliquely lateralward, from the lower extremity of the caudate lobe to the under surface of the right lobe. It is situated behind the porta, and separates the fossa for the gall-bladder from the commencement of the fossa for the inferior vena cava.

The **left lobe** (*lobus hepatis sinister*) is smaller and more flattened than the right. It is situated in the epigastric and left hypochondriac regions. Its upper surface is slightly convex and is moulded on to the diaphragm; its under surface presents the gastric impression and omental tuberosity, already referred to on page 1298.

Ligaments.—The liver is connected to the under surface of the diaphragm and to the anterior wall of the abdomen by five ligaments; four of these—the **falciform**, the **coronary**, and the two **lateral**—are peritoneal folds; the fifth, the **round ligament**, is a fibrous cord, the obliterated umbilical vein. The liver is also attached to the lesser curvature of the stomach by the hepatogastric and to the duodenum by the hepatoduodenal ligament (see page 1260).

The **falciform ligament** (*ligamentum falciforme hepatis*) is a broad and thin antero-posterior peritoneal fold, falciform in shape, its base being directed downward and backward, its apex upward and backward. It is situated in an antero-posterior plane, but lies obliquely so that one surface faces forward and is in contact with the peritoneum behind the right Rectus and the diaphragm, while the other is directed backward and is in contact with the left lobe of the liver. It is attached by its left margin to the under surface of the diaphragm, and the posterior surface of the sheath of the right Rectus as low down as the umbilicus; by its right margin it extends from the notch on the anterior margin of the liver, as far back as the posterior surface. It is composed of two layers of peritoneum closely united together. Its base or free edge contains between its layers the round ligament and the parumbilical veins.

The **coronary ligament** (*ligamentum coronarium hepatis*) consists of an anterior and a posterior layer. The *anterior layer* is formed by the reflection of the peritoneum from the upper margin of the bare area of the liver to the under surface of the diaphragm, and is continuous with the right layer of the falciform ligament. The *posterior layer* is reflected from the lower margin of the bare area on to the right kidney and suprarenal gland, and is termed the **hepatorenal ligament**.

The **triangular ligaments** (*lateral ligaments*) are two in number, right and left. The **right triangular ligament** (*ligamentum triangulare dextrum*) is situated at the right extremity of the bare area, and is a small fold which passes to the diaphragm, being formed by the apposition of the anterior and posterior layers of the coronary ligament. The **left triangular ligament** (*ligamentum triangulare sinistrum*) is a fold of some considerable size, which connects the posterior part of the upper surface of the left lobe to the diaphragm; its anterior layer is continuous with the left layer of the falciform ligament.

The **round ligament** (*ligamentum teres hepatis*) is a fibrous cord resulting from the obliteration of the umbilical vein. It ascends from the umbilicus, in the free margin of the falciform ligament, to the umbilical notch of the liver, from which it may be traced in its proper fossa on the inferior surface of the liver to the porta, where it becomes continuous with the *ligamentum venosum*.

Fixation of the Liver.—Several factors contribute to maintain the liver in place. The attachments of the liver to the diaphragm by the coronary and triangular ligaments and the intervening connective tissue of the uncovered area, together with the intimate connection of the inferior vena cava by the connective tissue and hepatic veins would hold up the posterior part of the liver. The lax falciform ligament certainly gives no support though it probably limits lateral displacement.

Vessels and Nerves.—The vessels connected with the liver are: the **hepatic artery**, the **portal vein**, and the **hepatic veins**.

The **hepatic artery** and **portal vein**, accompanied by numerous nerves, ascend to the porta, between the layers of the lesser omentum. The *bile duct* and the lymphatic vessels descend from the porta between the layers of the same omentum. The relative positions of the three structures are as follows: the bile duct lies to the right, the hepatic artery to the left, and the portal vein behind and between the other two. They are enveloped in a loose areolar tissue, the **fibrous capsule of Glisson,** which accompanies the vessels in their course through the portal canals in the interior of the organ (Fig. 1089).

The **hepatic veins** (Fig. 1054) convey the blood from the liver, and are described on page 762. They have very little cellular investment, and what there is binds their parietes closely to the walls of the canals through which they run; so that, on section of the organ, they remain widely open and are solitary, and may be easily distinguished from the branches of the portal vein, which are more or less collapsed, and always accompanied by an artery and duct.

The **lymphatic vessels** of the liver are described under the lymphatic system.

The **nerves** of the liver, are derived from the right and left vagus and the celiac plexuses of the sympathetic. The fibers form plexuses along the hepatic artery and portal vein, enter the porta, and accompany the vessels and ducts to the interlobular spaces. The hepatic vessels are said to receive only sympathetic fibers; while both sympathetic and parasympathetic fibers are distributed to the walls of the bile ducts and gall bladder, where they form plexuses similar to the enteric plexuses of the intestinal wall.

Structure of the Liver.—The substance of the liver is composed of lobules, held together by an extremely fine areolar tissue, in which ramify the portal vein, hepatic ducts, hepatic artery, hepatic veins, lymphatics, and nerves; the whole being invested by a serous and a fibrous coat.

The **serous coat** (*tunica serosa*) is derived from the peritoneum, and invests the greater part of the surface of the organ. It is intimately adherent to the fibrous coat.

The **fibrous coat** (*areolar coat*) lies beneath the serous investment, and covers the entire surface of the organ. It is difficult of demonstration, excepting where the serous coat is deficient. At the porta it is continuous with the fibrous capsule of Glisson, and on the surface of the organ with the areolar tissue separating the lobules.

The **lobules** (*lobuli hepatis*) form the chief mass of the hepatic substance; they may be seen either on the surface of the organ, or by making a section through the gland, as small granular bodies, about the size of a millet-seed, measuring from 1 to 2.5 mm. in diameter. In the human subject their outlines are very irregular; but in some of the lower animals (for example, the pig) they are well-defined, and, when divided transversely, have polygonal outlines. The bases of the lobules are clustered around the smallest radicles (*sublobular*) of the hepatic veins, to which each is connected (Fig. 1086) by means of a small branch which issues from the center of the lobule (*intralobular*). The remaining part of the surface of each lobule is imperfectly isolated from the surrounding lobules by a thin stratum of areolar tissue, in which is contained a plexus of vessels, the **interlobular plexus** (Fig. 1086), and ducts. In some animals, as the pig, the lobules are completely isolated from one another by the interlobular areolar tissue.

If one of the sublobular veins be laid open, the bases of the lobules may be seen through the thin wall of the vein on which they rest, arranged in a form resembling a tesselated pavement, the center of each polygonal space presenting a minute aperture, the mouth of an intraobular vein.

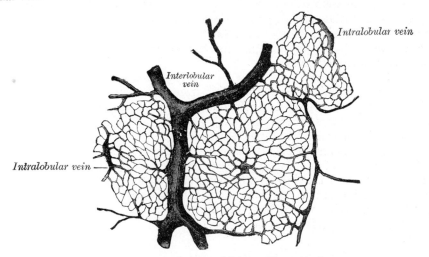

Intralobular vein

Interlobular vein

Intralobular vein

FIG. 1086.—Section of injected liver (dog).

Microscopic Appearance (Fig. 1087).—Each lobule consists of a mass of cells, **hepatic cells**, arranged in irregular radiating columns between which are the blood channels (*sinusoids*). Between the cells are also the minute bile capillaries. Therefore, in the lobule there are all the essentials of a secreting gland; that is to say: (1) **cells**, by which the secretion is formed; (2) **bloodvessels**, in close relation with the cells, containing the blood from which the secretion is derived; (3) **ducts**, by which the secretion, when formed, is carried away.

1. The *hepatic cells* are polyhedral in form. They vary in size from 12 to 25μ in diameter. They contain one or sometimes two distinct nuclei. The nucleus exhibits an intranuclear network and one or two refractile nucleoli. The cells usually contain granules; some of which are protoplasmic, while others consist of glycogen, fat, or an iron compound. In the lower vertebrates, *e. g.*, frog, the cells are arranged in tubes with the bile duct forming the lumen and bloodvessels externally. According to Delépine, evidences of this arrangement can be found in the human liver.

2. *The Bloodvessels.*—The blood in the capillary plexus around the liver cells is brought to the liver principally by the portal vein, but also to a certain extent by the hepatic artery.

The **hepatic artery**, entering the liver at the porta with the portal vein and hepatic duct, ramifies with these vessels through the portal canals. It gives off **vaginal branches**, which ramify in the fibrous capsule of Glisson, and appear to be destined chiefly for the nutrition of the coats of the vessels and ducts. It also gives off **capsular branches**, which reach the surface of the organ, ending in its fibrous coat in stellate plexuses. Finally, it gives off **interlobular branches**, which form a plexus outside each lobule, to supply the walls of the interlobular veins and the accompanying bile ducts. From these plexuses capillaries join directly with the sinusoids of the liver lobule at its periphery.

The **portal vein** also enters at the porta, and runs through the portal canals (Fig. 1089), enclosed in Glisson's capsule, dividing in its course into branches, which finally break up in the interlobular spaces, into the **interlobular plexus**, which give off portal venules, these divide into small branches and twigs as they pass to the surfaces of the lobules to join directly the hepatic sinusoids.

Hepatic sinusoids are large richly anastomosing modified capillary channels lying between the cords of liver cells. They traverse the liver lobule from its periphery to the intralobular or central vein. At the periphery of the lobule they connect with interlobular branches of the portal vein and hepatic artery. Thus all the blood which enters the liver passes through the sinusoids to the central veins. The sinusoids are lined by modified endothelium and contain many macrophages (v. Kupffer cells) attached to their walls.

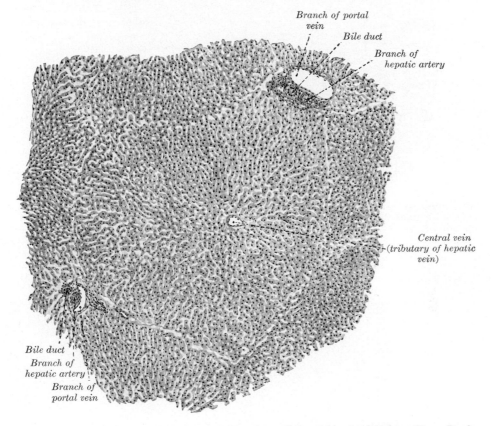

FIG. 1087.—Human liver lobule surrounded by parts of six neighboring lobules. (From Rauber-Kopsch, *Lehrbuch u. Altas d. Anatomie d. Menschen*, 19th Edition, Vol. II, courtesy Georg Thieme Verlag, Suttgart, 1955.)

Hepatic Veins.—At the center of the lobule, the sinusoids empty into one vein, of considerable size, which runs down the center of the lobule from apex to base, and is called the **intralobular** or **central vein**. At the base of the lobule this vein opens directly into the **sublobular vein,** with which the lobule is connected. The sublobular veins unite to form larger and larger trunks, and end at last in the hepatic veins, these converge to form three large trunks which open into the inferior vena cava while that vessel is situated in its fossa on the posterior surface of the liver.

The **bile ducts** commence by little passages in the liver cells which communicate with canaliculi termed **intercellular biliary passages** (*bile capillaries*). These passages are merely little channels or spaces left between the contiguous surfaces of two cells, or in the angle where three or more liver cells meet (Fig. 1088), and they are always separated from the blood capillaries by at least half the width of a liver cell. The channels thus formed radiate to the circumference of the lobule, and open into the interlobular bile ducts which run in Glisson's capsule, accompanying the portal vein and hepatic artery. (Fig. 1089). These join with other ducts to form two main trunks, which leave the liver at the transverse fissure, and by their union form the **hepatic duct.**

3. *Structure of the Ducts.*—The walls of the biliary ducts consist of a connective-tissue coat, in which are muscle cells, arranged both circularly and longitudinally, and an epithelial layer, consisting of short columnar cells resting on a distinct basement membrane.

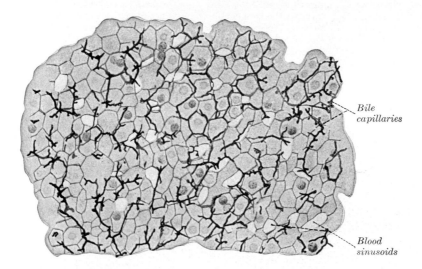

Bile capillaries

Blood sinusoids

FIG. 1088.—Bile capillaries in the liver of a rabbit demonstrated by silver chromate, counterstained with alum carmine. (From Rauber-Kopsch. *Lehrbuch u. Altas d. Anatomie d. Menschen,* 19th Edition, Vol. II, courtesy Georg Thieme Verlag, Stuttgart, 1955.)

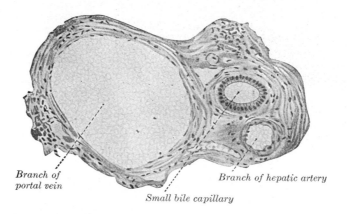

Branch of portal vein

Branch of hepatic artery

Small bile capillary

FIG. 1089.—Interlobular connective tissue surrounding branches of the portal vein, hepatic artery, and hepatic duct. (Glisson's capsule of a portal canal) (From Rauber-Kopsch, *Lehrbuch u. Altas d. Anatomie d. Menschen,* 19th Edition, Vol. II, courtesy Georg Thieme Verlag, Stuttgart, 1955.)

Excretory Apparatus of the Liver.—The excretory apparatus of the liver consists of (1) the **hepatic duct,** formed by the junction of the two main ducts, which pass out of the liver at the porta; (2) the **gall bladder,** which serves as a reservoir for the bile; (3) the **cystic duct,** or the duct of the gall-bladder; and (4) the **common bile duct,** formed by the junction of the hepatic and cystic ducts.

The Hepatic Duct (*ductus hepaticus*) (Fig. 1091).—Two main trunks of nearly equal size issue from the liver at the porta, one from the right, the other from the left lobe; these unite to form the hepatic duct, which passes downward and to the right for about 4 cm., between the layers of the lesser omentum, where it is joined at an acute angle by the cystic duct, and so forms the common bile duct. The hepatic duct is accompanied by the hepatic artery and portal vein.

The **Gall-bladder** (*vesica fellea*) (Fig. 1090).—The gall-bladder is a conical or pear-shaped musculomembranous sac, lodged in a fossa on the under surface of the right lobe of the liver, and extending from near the right extremity of the porta to the anterior border of the organ. It is from 7 to 10 cm. in length, 2.5 cm. in breadth at its widest part, and holds from 30 to 35 cc. It is divided into a fundus, body, and neck. The **fundus**, or broad extremity, is directed downward, forward, and to the right, and projects beyond the anterior border of the liver; the **body** and **neck** are directed upward and backward to the left. The upper surface of the gall-bladder is attached to the liver by connective tissue and vessels. The under surface is covered by peritoneum, which is reflected on to it from the surface of the liver. Occasionally the whole of the organ is invested by the serous membrane, and is then connected to the liver by a kind of mesentery.

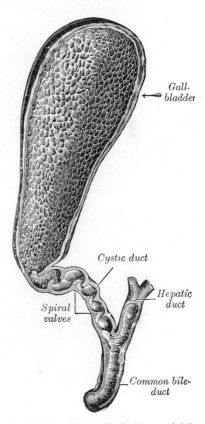

FIG. 1090.—The gall-bladder and bile ducts laid open. (Spalteholz.)

Relations.—The **body** is in relation, by its upper surface, with the liver; by its under surface, with the commencement of the transverse colon; and farther back usually with the upper end of the descending portion of the duodenum, but sometimes with the superior portion of the duodenum or pyloric end of the stomach. The **fundus** is completely invested by peritoneum; it is in relation, in front, with the abdominal parietes, immediately below the ninth costal cartilage; behind with the transverse colon. The **neck** is narrow, and curves upon itself like the letter S; at its point of connection with the cystic duct it presents a well-marked constriction.

Structure (Fig. 1090).—The gall-bladder consists of three coats: **serous**, **fibromuscular**, and **mucous**.

The **external** or **serous coat** (*tunica serosa vesicæ felleæ*) is derived from the peritoneum; it completely invests the fundus, but covers the body and neck only on their under surfaces.

The **fibromuscular coat** (*tunica muscularis vesicæ felleæ*), a thin but strong layer forming the framework of the sac, consists of dense fibrous tissue, which interlaces in all directions, and is mixed with plain muscular fibers, disposed chiefly in a longitudinal direction, a few running transversely.

The **internal** or **mucous coat** (*tunica mucosa vesicæ felleæ*) is loosely connected with the fibrous layer. It is generally of a yellowish-brown color, and is elevated into minute rugæ. Opposite the neck of the gallbladder the mucous membrane projects inward in the form of oblique ridges or folds, forming a sort of spiral valve.

The mucous membrane is continuous through the hepatic duct with the mucous membrane lining the ducts of the liver, and through the common bile duct with the mucous membrane of the duodenum. It is covered with columnar epithelium, and secretes mucin; in some animals it secretes a nucleoprotein instead of mucin.

Vessels and Nerves.—The **arteries** to the gall bladder are derived from the cystic artery; its **veins** drain into liver capillaries and into the portal vein. The **lymphatics** are described under the lymphatic system. The **nerves** are described on page 1063.

The **Cystic Duct** (*ductus cysticus*).—The cystic duct about 4 cm. long, runs backward, downward, and to the left from the neck of the gall-bladder, and joins the hepatic duct to form the common bile duct. The mucous membrane lining its interior is thrown into a series of crescentic folds, from five to twelve in number, similar to those found in the neck of the gall-bladder. They project into the duct in regular succession, and are directed obliquely around the tube, presenting much the appearance of a continuous spiral valve. They constitute the "spiral valve of Heister," which is found only in primates and represents a device to prevent distension or collapse of the cystic duct with changing pressures in the gall bladder or common duct, associated with the assumption of an erect posture. When the duct is distended, the spaces between the folds are dilated, so as to give to its exterior a twisted appearance.

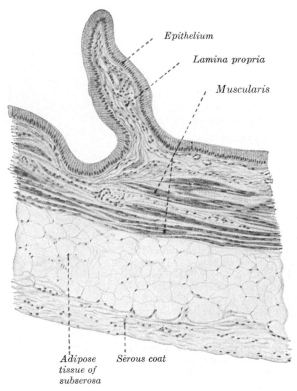

Epithelium

Lamina propria

Muscularis

Adipose tissue of subserosa *Serous coat*

FIG. 1091.—Cross section through the wall of the human gall bladder. (From Rauber-Kopsch, *Lehrbuch u. Altas d. Anatomie d. Menschen*, 19th Edition, Vol. II, courtesy Georg Thieme Verlag, Stuttgart, 1955.)

The **Common Bile Duct** (*ductus choledochus*) (Fig. 1090).—The common bile duct is formed by the junction of the cystic and hepatic ducts; it is about 7.5 cm. long, and of the diameter of a goose-quill, or soda fountain straw.

It descends along the right border of the lesser omentum behind the superior portion of the duodenum, in front of the portal vein, and to the right of the hepatic artery; it then runs in a groove near the right border of the posterior surface of the head of the pancreas; here it is situated in front of the inferior vena cava, and is occasionally completely imbedded in the pancreatic substance. At its termination it is closely associated with the terminal portion of the pancreatic duct as it passes obliquely through the muscular and mucous coats of the duodenum. The walls of the terminal portions of both ducts are thickened by the presence of a sphincter muscle, the sphincter of Oddi, which usually causes a protrusion into the lumen, the **duodenal papilla** or papilla of Vater. A common orifice for the two ducts is present in about 60 per cent and they have separate openings in about 40 per cent. The ducts are narrowed rather than widened as they traverse the papilla and the length of common channel shared by bile and pancreatic ducts is less than one half the papilla in 75 per cent. The term "ampula of Vater" should therefore be discarded in favor of the "papilla of Vater" (Sterling '55).

Structure.—The coats of the large biliary ducts are an **external** or **fibrous**, and an **internal** or **mucous**. The **fibrous coat** is composed of strong fibroareolar tissue, with a certain amount of muscular tissue, arranged, for the most part, in a circular manner around the duct. The **mucous coat** is continuous with the lining membrane of the hepatic ducts and gall-bladder, and also with that of the duodenum; and, like the mucous membrane of these structures, its epithelium is of the columnar variety. It is provided with numerous mucous glands, which are lobulated and open by minute orifices scattered irregularly in the larger ducts.

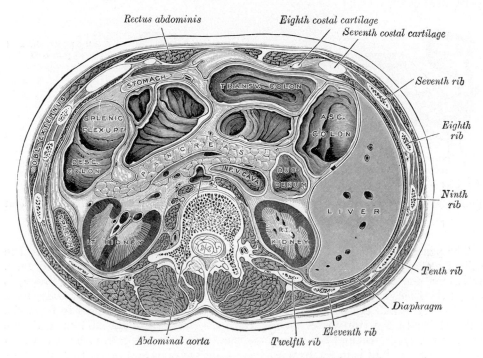

FIG. 1092.—Transverse section through the middle of the first lumbar vertebra, showing the relations of the pancreas. (Braune.)

The Pancreas (Fig. 1095).

Development (Figs. 1093, 1094).—The pancreas is developed in two parts, a dorsal and a ventral. The former arises as a diverticulum from the dorsal aspect of the duodenum a short distance above the hepatic diverticulum, and, growing upward and backward into the dorsal mesogastrium, forms a part of the head and uncinate process and the whole of the body and tail of the pancreas. The ventral part appears in the form of a diverticulum from the primitive bile duct and forms the remainder of the head and uncinate process of the pancreas. The duct of the dorsal part (**accessory pancreatic duct**) therefore opens independently into the duodenum, while that of the ventral part (**pancreatic duct**) opens with the common bile duct. About the sixth week the two parts of the pancreas meet and fuse and a communication is established between their ducts. After this has occurred the terminal part of the accessory duct, *i. e.*, the part between the duodenum and the point of meeting of the two ducts, undergoes little or no enlargement, while the pancreatic duct increases in size and forms the main duct of the gland. The opening of the accessory duct into the duodenum is sometimes obliterated, and even when it remains patent it is probable that the whole of the pancreatic secretion is conveyed through the pancreatic duct.

At first the pancreas is directed upward and backward between the two layers of the dorsal mesogastrium, which give to it a complete peritoneal investment, and its surfaces look to the right and left. With the change in the position of the stomach the dorsal mesogastrium is drawn downward and to the left, and the right side of the pancreas is directed backward and the left forward. The right surface becomes applied to the posterior abdominal wall, and the peritoneum which covered it undergoes absorption; and thus, in the adult, the gland appears to lie behind the peritoneal cavity.

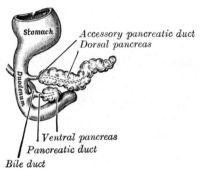

Fig. 1093.—Pancreas of a human embryo of five weeks. (Kollmann.)

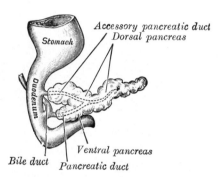

Fig. 1094.—Pancreas of a human embryo at end of sixth week. (Kollmann.)

The **pancreas** is a compound racemose gland, analogous in its structures to the salivary glands, though softer and less compactly arranged than those organs. It is long and irregularly prismatic in shape; its right extremity, being broad, is called the **head**, and is connected to the main portion of the organ, or **body**, by a slight constriction, the **neck**; while its left extremity gradually tapers to form the **tail**. It is situated transversely across the posterior wall of the abdomen, at the back of the epigastric and left hypochondriac regions. Its length varies from 12.5 to 15 cm.; its weight is in the female 84.88 ± 14.95 grams and in the male 90.41 ± 16.08 grams (Schaefer '26).

Relations.—The **Head** (*caput pancreatis*) is flattened from before backward, and is lodged within the curve of the duodenum. Its upper border is overlapped by the superior part of the duodenum and its lower overlaps the horizontal part; its right and left borders overlap in front of, and insinuate themselves behind, the descending and ascending parts of the duodenum respectively. The angle of junction of the lower and left lateral borders forms a prolongation, termed the **uncinate process**. In the groove between the duodenum and the right lateral and lower borders in front are the anastomosing superior and inferior pancreaticoduodenal arteries (Fig. 575); the common bile duct descends behind, close to the right border, to its termination in the descending part of the duodenum.

Anterior Surface.—The greater part of the right half of this surface is in contact with the transverse colon, only areolar tissue intervening. From its upper part the **neck** springs, its right limit being marked by a groove for the gastroduodenal artery. The lower part of the right half, below the transverse colon, is covered by peritoneum continuous with the inferior layer of the transverse mesocolon, and is in contact with the coils of the small intestine. The superior mesenteric artery passes down in front of the left half across the uncinate process; the superior mesenteric vein runs upward on the right side of the artery and, behind the neck, joins with the lienal vein to form the portal vein (Fig. 636).

Posterior Surface.—The posterior surface is in relation with the inferior vena cava, the common bile duct, the renal veins, the right crus of the diaphragm, and the aorta.

The **Neck** springs from the right upper portion of the front of the head. It is about 2.5 cm. long, and is directed at first upward and forward, and then upward and to the left to join the body; it is somewhat flattened from above downward and backward. Its antero-superior surface supports the pylorus; its postero-inferior surface is in relation with the commencement of the portal vein; on the right it is grooved by the gastroduodenal artery.

The **Body** (*corpus pancreatis*) is somewhat prismatic in shape, and has three surfaces: **anterior, posterior,** and **inferior.**

The **anterior surface** (*facies anterior*) is somewhat concave; and is directed forward and upward: it is covered by the postero-inferior surface of the stomach which rests upon it, the two organs being separated by the omental bursa. Where it joins the neck there is a well-marked prominence, the **tuber omentale,** which abuts against the posterior surface of the lesser omentum.

The **posterior surface** (*facies posterior*) is devoid of peritoneum, and is in contact with the aorta, the lienal vein, the left kidney and its vessels, the left suprarenal gland, the origin of the superior mesenteric artery, and the crura of the diaphragm.

The **inferior surface** (*facies inferior*) is narrow on the right but broader on the left, and is covered by peritoneum; it lies upon the duodenojejunal flexure and on some coils of the jejunum; its left extremity rests on the left colic flexure.

The **superior border** (*margo superior*) is blunt and flat to the right; narrow and sharp to the left, near the tail. It commences on the right in the omental tuberosity, and is in relation with the celiac artery, from which the hepatic artery courses to the right just above the gland, while the lienal artery runs toward the left in a groove along this border.

The **anterior border** (*margo anterior*) separates the anterior from the inferior surface, and along this border the two layers of the transverse mesocolon diverge from one another; one passing upward over the anterior surface, the other backward over the inferior surface.

The **inferior border** (*margo inferior*) separates the posterior from the inferior surface; the superior mesenteric vessels emerge under its right extremity.

The **Tail** (*cauda pancreatis*) is narrow; it extends to the left as far as the lower part of the gastric surface of the spleen, lying in the phrenicolienal ligament, and it is in contact with the left colic flexure.

Birmingham described the body of the pancreas as projecting forward as a prominent ridge into the abdominal cavity and forming part of a shelf on which the stomach lies. "The portion of the pancreas to the left of the middle line has a very considerable antero-posterior thickness; as a result the anterior surface is of considerable extent; it looks strongly upward, and forms a large and important part of the shelf. As the pancreas extends to the left toward the spleen it crosses the upper part of the kidney, and is so moulded on to it that the top of the kidney forms an extension inward and backward of the upper surface of the pancreas and extends the bed in this direction. On the other hand, the extremity of the pancreas comes in contact with the spleen in such a way that the plane of its upper surface runs with little interruption upward and backward into the concave gastric surface of the spleen, which completes the bed behind and to the left, and, running upward, forms a partial cap for the wide end of the stomach.

The **Pancreatic Duct** (*ductus pancreaticus* [*Wirsungi*]; *duct of Wirsung*) extends transversely from left to right through the substance of the pancreas (Fig. 1095). It commences by the junction of the small ducts of the lobules situated in the tail of the pancreas, and, running from left to right through the body, it receives the ducts of the various lobules composing the gland. Considerably augmented in size, it reaches the neck, and turning downward, backward, and to the right, it comes into relation with the common bile duct, which lies to its right side; leaving the head of the gland, it passes very obliquely through the muscular and mucous coats of the duodenum,

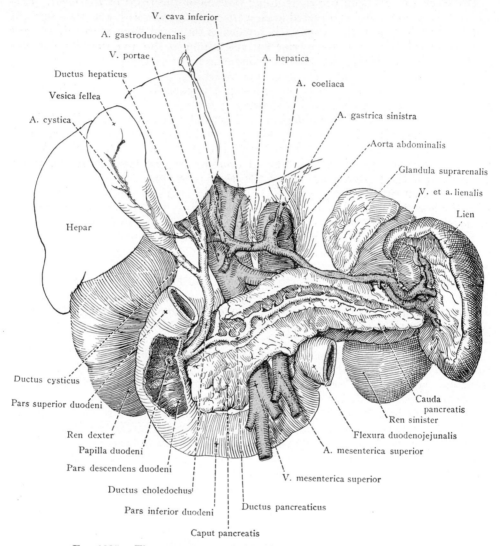

Fig. 1095.—The pancreas, pancreatic duct, and neighboring structures.
(Eycleshymer and Jones.)

and ends by an orifice common to it and the common bile duct upon the summit of the duodenal papilla, situated at the medial side of the descending portion of the duodenum, 7.5 to 10 cm. below the pylorus. Sometimes the pancreatic duct and the common bile duct open separately into the duodenum. Frequently there is an additional duct, which is given off from the pancreatic duct in the neck of the pancreas and opens into the duodenum about 2.5 cm. above the duodenal papilla. It receives the ducts from the lower part of the head, and is known as the **accessory pancreatic duct** (*duct of Santorini*) (see Development).

Function.—The pancreas is a gland of both external (exocrine) and internal (endocrine) secretion. The greater part of its bulk is formed by the exocrine gland. Its secretion, the **pancreatic juice**, is conveyed by the pancreatic duct to the duodenum where its several enzymes aid in the digestion of proteins, carbohydrates, and fats. The endocrine gland is formed by small clumps of cells known as islands of Langerhans scattered throughout the pancreas. The secretion of these cells, called **insulin**, is taken up by the blood stream and is an important factor in the control of sugar metabolism in the body.

Structure.—The **exocrine pancreas** is a compound tubulo-acinar or racemose gland, resembling the parotid gland in microscopic structure. It has a connective tissue covering but no distinct capsule. It is made up of lobes and lobules which are identifiable but indistinctly marked with connective tissue in the human pancreas. The main **pancreatic duct** extends throughout the length of the gland receiving smaller ducts from the lobes and lobules along its course (Fig. 1095). Although two ducts are formed in the embryo, they are usually combined into a single system in the adult (see page 1307). The main duct is lined with cylindrical epithelium containing occasional goblet cells; the smaller intermediate and intercalated ducts have lower cuboidal cells. The

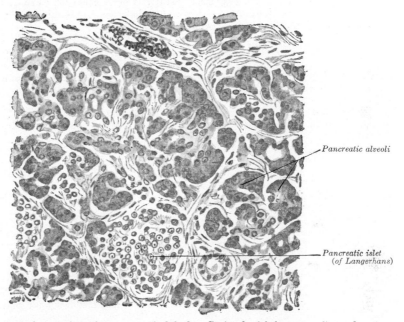

Pancreatic alveoli

Pancreatic islet (of Langerhans)

FIG. 1096.—Section of a portion of a pancreatic lobule. Stained with hematoxylin and eosin. × 300. (Drawn from a preparation lent by Dr. E. E. Hewer.)

secreting acini are almost filled by the protruding apices of the glandular cells which are of the serous or zymogenic type. The basal portion of these cells, resting on a basement membrane, contains the nucleus and a *basophilic substance* which has a striated appearance and is identified as the cytoplasmic reticulum by the electron microscope. The apical portion of these cells contains *zymogen granules*, easily seen in the usual eosin-stained preparations because of their red color. During digestion the granules become reduced in number. A characteristic feature of the pancreas is the presence of **centroacinar cells**. They represent a continuation of the terminal duct into the secreting acini. They are smaller than the secreting cells and have a clear cytoplasm (Munger '58, Oram '55).

The **Island of Langerhans** can be identified in the usual histological preparations as a cluster of less deeply stained cells. They are scattered throughout the gland but usually appear near the center of a lobule. The cells are arranged in cords or plates one or two cells thick between which there are abundant capillaries. By the use of special stains it has been shown that there are three types of cells: **alpha cells, beta cells** and **delta cells**. The beta cells are most abundant, and are the source of insulin (Ferner '52, Lacy '57).

Vessels.—The **arteries** of the pancreas are mainly branches of the splenic (page 675) which form several arcades with the pancreatic branches of the gastroduodenal (page 673) and superior mesenteric arteries (Michels '55). The **veins** are tributaries of the splenic and superior mesenteric portions of the portal vein. The **lymphatics** drain into the regional nodes associated with the major arteries to the gland.

Nerves.—The autonomic innervation is both parasympathetic and sympathetic through the splenic subdivision of the celiac plexus. The **sympathetic nerves** are post ganglionic; the **parasympathetic nerves** are preganglionics from the vagus which synapse with ganglion cells scattered throughout the gland. **Sensory nerves** to the pancreas are mainly conveyed by way of the splanchnic nerves (Alvarado '55).

REFERENCES

EMBRYOLOGY AND GENERAL

DE GARIS, C. F. 1950. Teaching the anatomy of the nerve supply of the abdominal digestive tract, a critical summary for the medical student. J. Ass. Amer. med. Coll., *25*, 417.

MICHELS, N. A. 1955. Blood Supply and Anatomy of the Upper Abdominal Organs, with a Descriptive Atlas J. B. Lippincott Co., Philadelphia. xiv + 581 pages.

SMITH, E. I. 1957. The early development of the trachea and esophagus in relation to atresia of the esophagus and tracheoesophageal fistula. Contr. Embryol. Carneg. Instn, *36*, 41–58.

SPECHT, N. W., and E. H. SHRYOCK. 1943. Omphalocele. Anatomical and clinical considerations. Surg. Gynec. Obstet., *77*, 319–325.

MOUTH, PHARYNX, AND ESOPHAGUS

BENNETT, G. A., and R. C. HUTCHINSON. 1946. Experimental studies on the movements of the mammalian tongue. II. The protrusion mechanism of the tongue (dog). Anat. Rec., *94*, 57–84.

BUTLER, H. 1951. The veins of the oesophagus. Thorax, *6*, 276–296.

COHN, S. A. 1957. Development of the molar teeth in the albino mouse. Amer. J. Anat., *101*, 295–320.

GARN, S. M., K. KOSKI, and A. B. LEWIS. 1957. Problems in determing the tooth eruption sequence in fossil and modern man. Amer. J. phys. Anthrop., *15*, 313–332.

GRAY, H. K., and F. B. WHITESELL, JR. 1950. Hemorrhage from esophageal varices, surgical management. Ann. Surg., *132*, 798–810.

JOHNSTONE, A. S. 1942. A radiological study of deglutition. J. Anat., *77*, 97–100.

HOUSE, E. L. 1953. A myology of the pharyngeal region of the albino rat. Anat. Rec., *116*, 363–382.

LERCHE, W. 1950. The Esophagus and Pharynx in Action: A Study of Structure in Relation to Function. Charles C Thomas, Springfield. xii + 222 pp.

NONIDEZ, J. F. 1946. Afferent nerve endings in the ganglia of the intermuscular plexus of the dog's oesophagus. J. comp. Neurol., *85*, 177–189.

RIVES, J. D., and L. H. STRUG. 1950. Surgical repair of esophageal hiatus hernias. Trans. sth. surg. Ass., *61*, 399–408.

SAUER, M. E. 1951. The cricoesophageal tendon. A recommendation for its inclusion in official anatomical nomenclature. Anat. Rec., *109*, 691–697.

SAUNDERS, R. L. DE C. H. 1957. Microradiographic studies of human adult and fetal dental pulp vessels. In X-Ray Microscopy and Microradiography, Symp. ed. by V. E. Cosslett, A. Engström, and H. H. Pattee, Jr. Academic Press Inc., New York. 561–571.

SHAPIRO, H. H. 1954. Maxillofacial Anatomy with Practical Applications. J. B. Lippincott Co., Philadelphia. xiv + 392 pages.

SPRAGUE, J. M. 1944. The innervation of the pharynx in the rhesus monkey, and the formation of the pharyngeal plexus in primates. Anat. Rec., *90*, 197–208.

STRONG, L. H. 1956. Muscle fibers of the tongue functional in consonant production. Anat. Rec., *126*, 61–80.

SWIGART, L. L., SIEKERT, R. G., HAMBLEY, W. C. and B. J. ANSON. 1950. The esophageal arteries—an anatomic study of 150 specimens. Surg., Gynec. Obstet., *90*, 234–243.

TELFORD, I. R. 1946. Pigment studies on the incisor teeth of vitamin E deficient rats of the Long-Evans strain. Proc. Soc. exp. Biol. Med., *63*, 89–91.

PERITONEUM AND HERNIA

BARON, M. A. 1941. Structure of the intestinal peritoneum in man. Amer. J. Anat., *69*, 439–496

GARDNER, J. H., E. A. HOLYOKE, and R. P. GIOVACCHINI. 1957. Cleavage lines of the visceral and parietal peritoneum. Anat. Rec., *127*, 247–256.

HUNTINGTON, G. S. 1903. The Anatomy of the Human Peritoneum and Abdominal Cavity. Lea Brothers and Co., Philadelphia, vii + 292 pp.

KINDRED, J. E. 1957. Eventration of the abdominal viscera associated with umbilical hernia, hemipenes and hydromyelomeningocele in a newborn infant. Anat. Rec., *128*, 379–400.

MADDEN, J. L. 1956. Anatomic and technical considerations in the treatment of esophageal hiatal hernias. Surg. Gynec. Obstet., *102*, 187–194.

MAYO, C. W., L. K. STALKER, and J. M. MILLER. 1941. Intra-abdominal hernia—Review of 39 cases in which treatment was surgical. Ann. Surg., *114*, 875–885.

STOMACH

BAKER, B. L. and G. D. ABRAMS. 1954. Effect of hypophysectomy on the cytology of the fundic glands of the stomach and on the secretion of pepsin. Amer. J. Physiol., *177*, 409–412.

BOWIE, D. J. 1940. The distribution of the chief or pepsin-forming cells in the gastric mucosa of the cat. Anat. Rec., *78*, 9–17.

CAREY, J. M. and W. H. HOLLINSHEAD. 1955. An anatomic study of the esophageal hiatus. Surg. Gynec. Obstet., *100*, 196–200.

HUNT, T. E. 1957. Mitotic activity in the gastric mucosa of the rat after fasting and refeeding. Anat. Rec., *127*, 539–550.

LACHMAN, E. 1957. Roentgenologic manifestations of emotional disturbances in the stomach. Amer. J. Roentgenol., *77*, 162–166.

MITCHELL, G. A. G. 1940. A macroscopic study of the nerve supply of the stomach. J. Anat., (Lond.), *75*, 50–63.

MULLER BOTHA, G. S. 1958. A note on the comparative anatomy of the cardio-oesophageal junction. Acta Anat., *34*, 52–84.

SCHNITZLEIN, H. N. 1957. Regulation of blood flow through the stomach of the rat. Anat. Rec. *127*, 735–754.

WEBER, J. 1958. The basophilic substance of the gastric chief cells and its relation to the process of secretion. Acta Anat., *33*, Suppl. 31, 1–79.

SMALL AND LARGE INTESTINE

BEATON, L. E., and B. J. ANSON. 1942. The arterial supply of the small intestine. Quart. Bull. Northw. Univ. Med. Sch., *16*, 114–122.

BLAIR, J. B., E. A. HOLYOKE, and R. R. BEST. 1950. A note on the lymphatics of the middle and lower rectum and anus. Anat. Rec., *108*, 635–644.

BUIRGE, R. E. 1943. Gross variations in the ileocecal valve. A study of the factors underlying incompetency. Anat. Rec., *86*, 373–385.

EVANS, T. H. 1955. Valve at middle of duodenum. Amer. J. dig. Dis., *22*, 295–296.

FRIEDMAN, S. M. 1946. The position and mobility of the duodenum in the living subject. Amer. J. Anat., *79*, 147–165.

GRANGER, B., and R. F. BAKER. 1950. Electron microscope investigation of the striated border of intestinal epithelium. Anat. Rec., *107*, 423–441.

HABER, J. J. 1947. Meckel's diverticulum. Amer. J. Surg., *73*, 468–485.

HALEY, J. C., and J. K. PEDEN. 1943. The suspensory muscle of the duodenum. Amer. J. Surg., *59*, 546–550.

JACOBSON, L. F., and R. J. NOER. 1952. The vascular pattern of the intestinal villi in various laboratory animals and man. Anat. Rec., *114*, 85–101.

JIT, INDAR. 1952. The development and the structure of the suspensory muscle of the duodenum. Anat. Rec., *113*, 395–407.

NOER, R. J. 1943. The blood vessels of the jejunum and ileum: A comparative study of man and certain laboratory animals. Amer. J. Anat., *73*, 293–334.

SAUER, M. E., and C. T. RUMBLE. 1946. The number of nerve cells in the myenteric and sub-mucous plexuses of the small intestine of the cat. Anat. Rec., *96*, 373–381.

SHAH, M. A., and M. SHAH. 1946. The arterial supply of the vermiform appendix. Anat. Rec., *95*, 457–460.

VON BONIN, G. 1944. Partial inversion of the duodenum. Anat. Rec., *89*, 71–73.

LIVER AND BILIARY APPARATUS

ALEXANDER, W. F. 1940. The innervation of the biliary system. J. comp. Neurol., *72*, 357–370.

ANSON, B. J. 1956. Anatomical considerations in surgery of the gallbladder. Quar. Bull. Northw. Univ. med. Sch., *30*, 250–260.

HAMMOND, W. S. 1939. On the origin of the cells lining the liver sinusoids in the cat and the rat. Amer. J. Anat., *65*, 199–227.

HARD, W. L., and R. K. HAWKINS. 1950. The role of the bile capillaries in the secretion of phosphatase by the rabbit liver. Anat. Rec., *106*, 395–411.

HEALY, J. E., JR. and P. C. SCHROY. 1953. Anatomy of the biliary ducts within the human liver; analysis of the prevailing pattern of branchings and the major variations of the biliary ducts. Arch. Surg., *66*, 599–616.

JIT, INDAR. 1957. The development of the sphincter of Oddi. Indian J. med. Res., *45*, 133–142.

JOHNSON, F. E., and E. A. BOYDEN. 1952. The effect of double vagotomy on the motor activity of the human gall bladder. Surgery, *32*, 591–601.

JOHNSTON, E. V., and B. J. ANSON. 1952. Variations in the formation and vascular relationships of the bile duct. Surg. Gynec. Obstet., *94*, 669–686.

KIRKMAN, H. 1946. A simian, deeply cleft, bilobed gall bladder with a "phrygian cap." Anat. Rec., *95*, 423–447.

MEADER, R. D., and W. L. WILLIAMS. 1957. Choline deficiency in the mouse. Amer. J. Anat., *100*, 167–204.

MICHELS, N. A. 1953. Variational anatomy of the hepatic, cystic, and retroduodenal arteries. Arch. Surg., *66*, 20–32.

PEREZ CASAS, A. 1958. Contribution à l'étude du sphincter d'Oddi chez canis familiaris. Acta Anat., *34*, 130–153.

POPPEL, M. H., H. G. JACOBSON, and R. W. SMITH. 1953. The Roentgen Aspects of the Papilla and Ampulla of Vater. Charles C Thomas, Springfield. xvi + 195 pp.

POPPER, H. P. and F. SCHAFFNER. 1957. Liver: Structure and Function. The Blakiston division, McGraw-Hill Book Co., New York. xv + 777 pages.

RAPPAPORT, A. M. 1958. The structural and functional unit in the human liver (liver acinus). Anat. Rec., *130*, 673–690.

SCHWEGLER, R. A., JR. and E. A. BOYDEN. 1937. The development of the pars intestinalis of the common bile duct in the human fetus, with special reference to the origin of the ampulla of Vater and the sphincter of Oddi. I. The involution of the ampulla. Anat. Rec., *67*, 441–468. II. The early development of the musculus proprius. Anat. Rec., *68*, 17–42. III. The composition of the musculus proprius. Anat. Rec., *68*, 193–220.

STERLING, J. A. 1955. The Biliary Tract with Special Reference to the Common Bile Duct. The Williams & Wilkins Co., Baltimore. ix + 424 pages.

WILLIAMS, W. L. 1948. Vital staining of damaged liver cells. I. Reactions to acid azo dyes following acute chemical injury. Anat. Rec., *101*, 133–147.

PANCREAS

ALVARADO, F. 1955. Distribution of nerves within the pancreas. J. int. Coll. Surg., *23*, 675–700

BECKER, V. 1957. Sekretionsstudien am Pankreas. George Thieme Verlag, Stuttgart. vii + 119 pages.

BENCOSME, S. A. 1955. The histogenesis and cytology of the pancreatic islets in the rabbit. Amer. J. Anat., *96*, 103–152.

FERNER, H. 1952. Das Inselsystem des Pankreas. Georg Thieme Verlag, Stuttgart. xi + 186. pages.

GRAFFLIN, A. L. 1940. Histological observations upon an adult human pancreas (autofluorescence, fat and pigment). Anat. Rec., *78*, 207–214.

HARD, W. L. 1944. The origin and differentiation of the alpha and beta cells in the pancreatic islets of the rat. Amer. J. Anat., *75*, 369–403.

KUNTZ, A., and C. A. RICHINS. 1949. Effects of direct and reflex nerve stimulation of the exocrine secretory activity of pancreas. J. Neurophysiol., *12*, 29–35.

LACY, P. E. 1957. Electron microscopic identification of different cell types in the islets of Langerhans of the guinea pig, rat, rabbit and dog. Anat. Rec., *128*, 255–268.

LATTA, J. S., and H. T. HARVEY. 1942. Changes in the islets of Langerhans of the albino rat induced by insulin administration. Anat. Rec., *82*, 281–295.

MUNGER, B. L. 1958. A phase and electron microscopic study of cellular differentiation in pancreatic acinar cells of the mouse. Amer. J. Anat., *103*, 1–34.

ORAM, V. 1955. The cytoplasmic basophilic substance of the exocrine pancreatic cells. Acta Anat., *25*, Suppl. 23-1, 1–114.

RICHINS, C. A. 1945. The innervation of the pancreas. J. Comp. Neurol., *83*, 223–236.

SCHAEFER, J. H. 1926. The normal weight of the pancreas in the adult human being: a biometric study. Anat. Rec., *32*, 119–132.

THE UROGENITAL SYSTEM.

(APPARATUS UROGENITALIS; UROGENITAL ORGANS).

THE urogenital apparatus consists of (a) the **urinary organs** for the formation and discharge of the urine, and (b) the **genital organs**, which are concerned with the process of reproduction.

DEVELOPMENT OF THE URINARY AND GENERATIVE ORGANS.

The urogenital glands and ducts are developed from the intermediate cell-mass which is situated between the primitive segments and the lateral plates of meso-derm. The permanent organs of the adult are preceded by structures which,

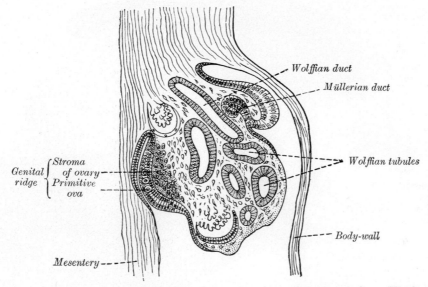

FIG. 1097.—Section of the urogenital fold of a chick embryo of the fourth day. (Waldeyer.)

with the exception of the ducts, disappear almost entirely before the end of fetal life. These paired structures are: the **pronephros**, the **mesonephros**, and the **Wolffian** and **Müllerian ducts**. The pronephros disappears very early. The structural elements of the mesonephros almost entirely degenerate, but in their place the genital gland develops. The Wolffian duct remains as the duct of the male genital gland, the Müllerian as that of the female. The final kidney is a new organ, the metanephros.

The Pronephros and Wolffian Duct.—In the outer part of the intermediate cell-mass, immediately under the ectoderm, in the region from the fifth cervical to the third thoracic segments, a series of short evaginations from each segment grows dorso-laterally and caudally, fusing successively from before backward to form the **pronephric duct**. This continues to grow caudally until it opens into the ventral part of the cloaca; beyond the pronephros it is termed the **Wolffian duct**.

The original evaginations form a series of transverse tubules each of which com-municates by means of a funnel-shaped ciliated opening with the celomic cavity, and in the course of each duct a glomerulus also is developed. A secondary glomerulus is formed ventral to each of these, and the complete group constitutes the **pronephros.** The pronephros undergoes rapid atrophy and disappears in 4 mm. embryos except for the pronephric ducts which persist as the excretory ducts of the succeeding kidneys, the mesonephroi.

The Mesonephros, Müllerian Duct, and Genital Gland.—On the medial side of the Wolffian duct, from the sixth cervical to the third lumbar segments, a series of tubules, the **Wolffian tubules** (Fig. 1097), is developed; at a later stage in development they increase in number by outgrowths from the original tubules. These tubules first appear as solid masses of cells, which later develop lumina; one end grows toward and finally opens into the Wolffian duct, the other dilates and is invaginated by a tuft of capillary bloodvessels to form a glomerulus. The tubules collectively constitute the **mesonephros** or **Wolffian body** (Figs. 1098, 1099 and 1101). By the fifth or sixth week this body forms an elongated spindle-shaped structure, termed

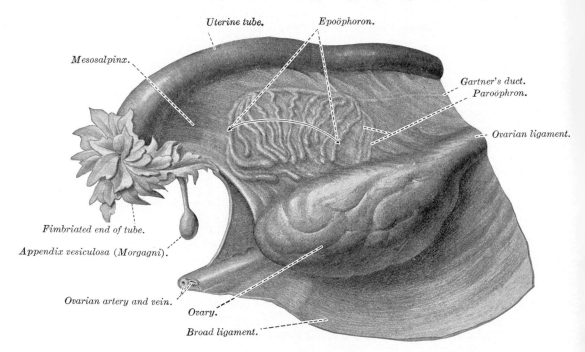

FIG. 1098.—Broad ligament of adult, showing remains of the Wolffian body and duct. (Modified from Farre.)

the **urogenital fold** (Fig. 1097), which projects into the celomic cavity at the side of the dorsal mesentery, reaching from the septum transversum in front to the fifth lumbar segment behind. The reproductive glands develop in the urogenital folds. The Wolffian bodies are the permanent kidneys in fishes and amphibians, but in reptiles, birds, and mammals, they atrophy and for the most part disappear coincidentally with the development of the permanent kidneys. The atrophy begins during the sixth or seventh week and rapidly proceeds, so that by the beginning of the fourth month only the ducts and a few of the tubules remain.

In the male the Wolffian duct persists, and forms the epididymis, the ductus deferens and the ejaculatory duct, while the seminal vesicle arises during the third month as a lateral diverticulum from its caudal end. A large part of the cephalic portion of the mesonephros atrophies and disappears, but a few tubules may persist as the appendix of the epididymis, vestigial structures which end blindly. From the remainder of the anterior tubules the efferent ducts of the testis form.

The posterior tubules are represented by the ductuli aberrantes, and by the para-didymis (Fig. 1099, *C*).

In the female the Wolffian bodies and ducts atrophy. The remains of the Wolffian tubules may be roughly divided into three groups. One group of tubules from the cranial portion of the mesonephros or Wolffian body persists and produces one or more **vesicular appendices** in the fringes of the uterine tube. The middle and largest group, together with a segment of the mesonephric (Wolffian) duct persist as the **epoöphoron** or **organ of Rosenmüller**. Persistent portions of the Wolffian duct are known as **Gartner's ducts**. These may exist as part of the epoöphoron or as isolated segments as far as the hymen. The third and most caudal group of remaining mesonephric ducts constitutes the paroöphoron, which usually disappears completely before the adult stage. Any one of these vestigial tubules which persists in the adult as a stalked vesicle is called an hydatid (Fig. 1099, *B*).

The Müllerian Ducts.—Shortly after the formation of the Wolffian ducts a second pair of ducts is developed; these are named the **Müllerian ducts**. Each arises on the lateral aspect of the corresponding Wolffian duct as a tubular invagination of the cells lining the celom (Fig. 1097). The orifice of the invagination remains patent, and undergoes enlargement and modification to form the abdominal ostium of the uterine tube. The ducts pass backward lateral to the Wolffian ducts, but toward the posterior end of the embryo they cross to the medial side of these ducts, and thus come to lie side by side between and behind the latter—the four ducts forming what is termed the **genital cord** (Fig. 1099*A*). The Müllerian ducts end in an epithelial elevation, the **Müllerian eminence,** on the ventral part of the cloaca between the orifices of the Wolffian ducts; at a later date they open into the cloaca in this situation.

In the male the Müllerian ducts atrophy, but traces of their cephalic ends are represented by the **appendices testis** (*hydatids of Morgagni*), while their caudal portions fuse to form the utriculus in the floor of the prostatic portion of the urethra (Fig. 1099, *C*).

In the female the Müllerian ducts persist and undergo further development. The portions which lie in the genital core fuse to form the uterus and vagina; the parts in front of this cord remain separate, and each forms the corresponding uterine tube—the abdominal ostium of which is developed from the anterior extremity of the original tubular invagination from the celom (Fig. 1099 *B*,). The fusion of the Müllerian ducts begins in the third month, and the septum formed by their fused medial walls disappears from below upward. Entodermal epithelium of the urogenital sinus invades the region where the vagina forms, replacing the Müllerian epithelium almost entirely, and for a time the vagina is represented by a solid rod of epithelial cells, but in fetuses of five months the lumen reappears. About the fifth month an annular constriction marks the position of the neck of the uterus, and after the sixth month the walls of the uterus begin to thicken. A ring-like outgrowth of epithelium occurs at the lower end of the uterus and marks the future vaginal fornices. The hymen arises at the site of the Müllerian eminence. It represents the separation between vagina and urogenital sinus.

Genital Glands.—The first appearance of the genital gland is essentially the same in the two sexes, and consists in a thickening of the epithelial layer which lines the peritoneal cavity on the medial side of the urogenital fold. The thick plate of epithelium pushes the mesoderm before it and forms a distinct projection. This is termed the **genital ridge** (Fig. 1099*A*), and from it the testis in the male and the ovary in the female are developed. At first the mesonephros and genital ridge are suspended by a common mesentery, but as the embryo grows the genital ridge gradually becomes pinched off from the mesonephros, with which it is at first continuous, though it still remains connected to the remnant of this body by a fold of peritoneum, the **mesorchium** or **mesovarium** (Fig.

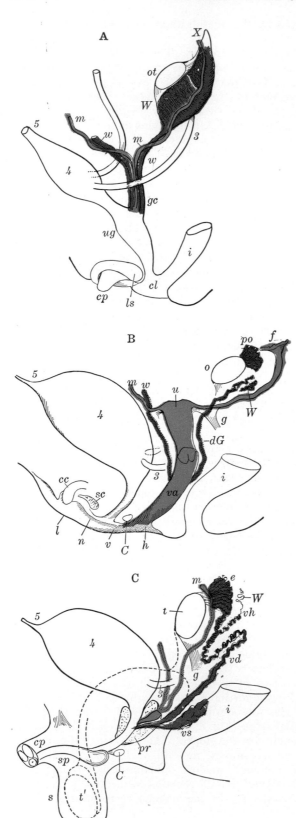

Fig. 1099.—Diagrams to show the development of male and female generative organs from the common type. (Allen Thomson.)

A.—Diagram of the primitive urogenital organs in the embryo previous to sexual distinction. *3.* Ureter. *4.* Urinary bladder. *5.* Urachus. *cl.* Cloaca. *cp.* Elevation which becomes clitoris or penis. *i.* Lower part of the intestine. *ls.* Fold of integument from which the labia majora or scrotum are formed. *m, m.* Right and left Müllerian ducts uniting together and running with the Wolffian ducts in *gc*, the genital cord. *ot.* The genital ridge from which either the ovary or testis is formed. *ug.* Sinus urogenitalis. *W.* Left Wolffian body. *w, w.* Right and left Wolffian ducts.

B.—Diagram of the female type of sexual organs. *C.* Greater vestibular gland, and immediately above it the urethra. *cc.* Corpus cavernosum clitoridis. *dG.* Remains of the left Wolffian duct, such as give rise to the duct of Gartner, represented by dotted lines; that of the right side is marked *w*. *f.* The abdominal opening of the left uterine tube. *g.* Round ligament, corresponding to gubernaculum. *h.* Situation of the hymen. *i.* Lower part of the intestine. *l.* Labium major. *n.* Labium minus. *o.* The left ovary. *po.* Epöophoron. *sc.* Corpus cavernosum urethræ. *u.* Uterus. The uterine tube of the right side is marked *m*. *v.* Vulva. *va.* Vagina. *W.* Scattered remains of Wolffian tubes near it (paroöphoron of Waldeyer).

C.—Diagram of the male type of sexual organs. *C.* Bulbo-urethral gland of one side. *cp.* Corpora cavernosa penis cut short. *e.* Caput epididymis. *g.* The gubernaculum. *i.* Lower part of the intestine. *m.* Müllerian duct, the upper part of which remains as the hydatid of Morgagni; the lower part, represented by a dotted line descending to the prostatic utricle, constitutes the occasionally existing cornu and tube of the uterus masculinus. *pr.* The prostate. *s.* Scrotum. *sp.* Corpus cavernosum urethræ. *t.* Testis in the place of its original formation. *t',* together with the dotted lines above, indicates the direction in which the testis and epididymis descend from the abdomen into the scrotum. *vd.* Ductus deferens. *vh.* Ductus aberrans. *vs.* The vesicula seminalis. *W.* Scattered remains of the Wolffian body, constituting the organ of Giraldès, or the paradidymis of Waldeyer.

1101). About the seventh week the distinction of sex in the genital ridge begins to be perceptible.

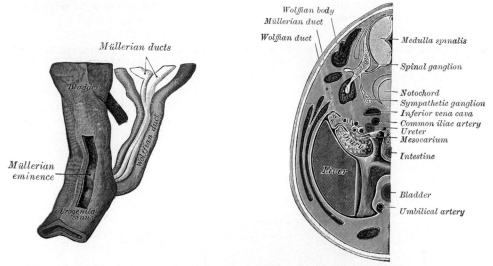

FIG. 1100.—Urogenital sinus of female human embryo eight and a half to nine weeks old. (From model by Keibel.)

FIG. 1101.—Transverse section of human embryo eight and a half to nine weeks old. (From model by Keibel.)

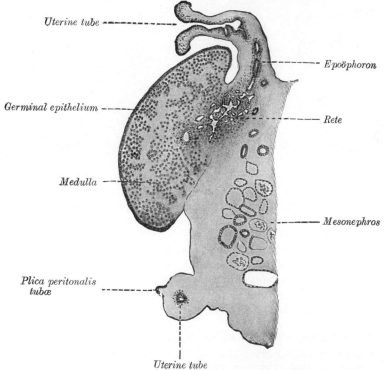

FIG. 1102.—Longitudinal section of ovary of cat embryo of 9.4 cm. long. Schematic. (After Coert.)

The Ovary.—The ovary, thus formed from the genital ridge, is at first a mass of cells derived from the celomic epithelium; later the mass is differentiated into a central part or medulla (Fig. 1102) covered by a surface layer, the **germinal epithelium.** Between the cells of the germinal epithelium a number of larger cells, the **primitive ova,** are found. These are carried into the subjacent stroma by bud-like ingrowths **(genital cords)** of the germinal epithelium (Fig. 1103). The surface epithelium ultimately forms the permanent epithelial covering of this organ; it soon loses its connection with the central mass, and a tunica albuginea develops between them. The ova are chiefly derived from the cells of the central mass; these are separated from one another by the growth of connective tissue in an irregular manner; each ovum acquires a covering of connective tissue (follicle) cells, and in this way the rudiments of the ovarian follicles are formed.

Primordial germ cells are according to some authors set aside at a very early age from the somatic cells. They are first recognized in the yolk sac. Later they migrate through the mesentery into the primitive germinal epithelium to be carried into the gonad with the sex cords and later develop either into ova or sperm cells. Some authors deny their existence while others claim they all degenerate and take no part in formation of the adult sex cells.

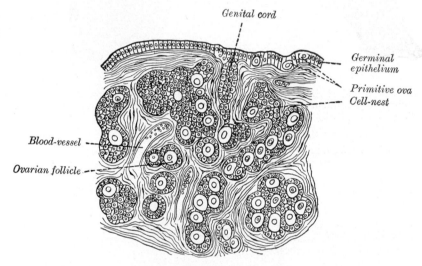

FIG. 1103.—Section of the ovary of a newly born child. (Waldeyer.)

The Testis.—The testis is developed in much the same way as the ovary. Like the ovary, in its earliest stages it consists of a central mass of epithelium covered by a surface epithelium. In the central mass a series of cords appear (Fig. 1104), and the periphery of the mass is converted into the tunica albuginea, thus excluding the surface epithelium from any part in the formation of the tissue of the testis. The cords of the central mass run together toward the future hilum and form a net-work which ultimately becomes the rete testis. From the cords the seminiferous tubules are developed, and between them connective tissue septa extend. The seminiferous tubules become connected with outgrowths from the Wolffian body, which, as before mentioned, form the efferent ducts of the testis.

Descent of the Testes.—The testes, at an early period of fetal life, are placed at the back part of the abdominal cavity, behind the peritoneum, and each is attached by a peritoneal fold, the **mesorchium,** to the mesonephros. From the front of the mesonephros a fold of peritoneum termed the **inguinal fold** grows forward to meet and fuse with a peritoneal fold, the **inguinal crest,** which grows backward from the anterolateral abdominal wall. The testis thus acquires an indirect connection with the anterior abdominal wall; and at the same time a portion of the peritoneal cavity lateral to these fused folds is marked off as the future saccus vaginalis. In the inguinal crest a peculiar structure, the **gubernaculum testis**, makes its appearance. This is at first a slender band, extending from that part of the skin of the groin which afterward forms the scrotum through the inguinal canal to the body and epididymis of the testis. As development advances, the peritoneum enclosing the gubernaculum forms two folds, one above the testis and the other below it. The one above the testis is the **plica vascularis**, and contains ultimately the internal spermatic vessels; the one below, the **plica gubernatrix**, contains the lower part of the gubernaculum, which has now grown into a thick cord; it ends below at the abdominal inguinal ring in a tube of peritoneum, the **saccus vaginalis**, which protrudes itself down the inguinal canal. By the fifth month the lower part of the gubernaculum has become a thick cord, while the upper part has disappeared. The lower part now consists of a central core of unstriped muscle fiber, and outside this of a firm layer of striped elements, connected, behind the peritoneum, with the abdominal wall. The main portion of the gubernaculum is attached to the skin at the point where the scrotum develops and as the pouch forms, most of the lower end of the gubernaculum is carried with it; other bands extend to the medial side of the thigh and to the perineum. The tube of peritoneum constituting the saccus vaginalis projects itself downward into the inguinal canal, and emerges at the subcutaneous inguinal ring, pushing

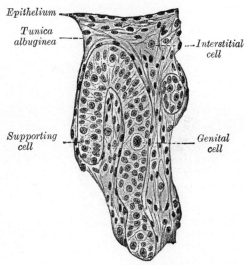

FIG. 1104.—Section of a genital cord of the testis of a human embryo 3.5 cm. long. (Felix and Bühler.)

before it a part of the Obliquus internus and the fascia of the Obliquus externus, which form respectively the Cremaster muscle and the intercrural fascia. It forms a gradually elongating pouch, which eventually reaches the bottom of the scrotum,

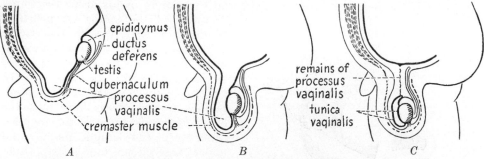

FIG. 1105.—Diagram illustrating descent of the testis: *A*, Before descent. The processus vaginalis is present before descent begins, the testis lying behind the peritoneum. *B*. Descent nearly complete but processus vaginalis not obliterated. *C*. Processus vaginalis obliterated except for the terminal portion, which persists as the tunica vaginalis of the adult.

and behind this pouch the testis descends. Since the growth of the gubernaculum is not commensurate with the growth of the body of the fetus, the latter increasing more rapidly in relative length, it has been assumed that this prevents cephalad displacement of the testis. In addition the gubernaculum may actually shorten, in which case it might exert traction on the testis and tend to displace it toward the scrotum. Occasionally the testis fails to descend or the descent is incomplete, a condition known as cryptorchidism. In such cases administration of an extract of the pituitary gland may cause the testis to occupy its normal position. This would seem to indicate that the descent may to some extent be under hormonal control. By the end of the eighth month the testis has reached the scrotum, preceded by the saccus vaginalis, which communicates by its upper extremity with the peritoneal cavity. Just before birth the upper part of the saccus vaginalis normally becomes closed, and this obliteration extends gradually downward to within a short distance of the testis. The process of peritoneum surrounding the testis is now entirely cut off from the general peritoneal cavity and constitutes the **tunica vaginalis**.

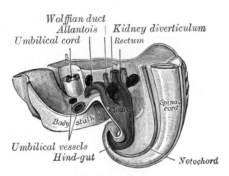

Fig. 1106.—Tail end of human embryo twenty-five to twenty-nine days old. (From model by Keibel.)

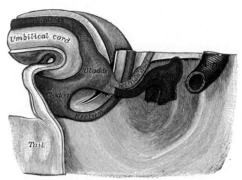

Fig. 1107.—Tail end of human embryo thirty-two to thirty-three days old. (From model by Keibel.)

Descent of the Ovaries.—In the female there is also a gubernaculum, which effects a considerable change in the position of the ovary, though not so extensive a change as in that of the testis. The gubernaculum in the female lies in contact with the fundus of the uterus and acquires adhesions to this organ, thus the ovary is prevented from descending below this level. The part of the gubernaculum between the ovary and the uterus becomes ultimately the proper ligament of the ovary, while the part between the uterus and the labium majus forms the round ligament of the uterus. A pouch of peritoneum analogous to the saccus vaginalis in the male accompanies it along the inguinal canal: it is called the **canal of Nuck**. In rare cases the gubernaculum may fail to develop adhesions to the uterus, and then the ovary descends through the inguinal canal into the labium majus, and under these circumstances its position resembles that of the testis.

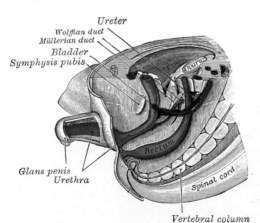

Fig. 1108.—Tail end of human embryo; from eight and a half to nine weeks old. (From model by Keibel.)

The Metanephros and the Permanent Kidney.—The rudiments of the permanent kidneys make their appearance about the end of the first or the beginning of the second month. Each kidney has a two-fold origin, part arising from the metanephros, and part as a diverticulum from the hind-end of the Wolffian duct, close to where the latter opens into the cloaca (Figs. 1106, 1107). The metanephros arises in the intermediate cell mass, caudal to the mesonephros, which it resembles in structure. The diverticulum from the Wolffian duct grows dorsally and cephalad along the posterior abdominal wall, where its blind extremity expands and subsequently divides into several buds, which form the rudiments of the pelvis and calyces of the kidney; by continued growth and subdivision it gives rise to the collecting tubules of the kidney. The proximal portion of the diverticulum becomes the ureter. The secretory tubules are developed from the metanephros, which is moulded over the growing end of the diverticulum from the Wolffian duct. The tubules of the metanephros, unlike those of the pronephros and mesonephros, do not open into the Wolffian duct. One end expands to form a glomerulus, while the rest of the tubule rapidly elongates to form the convoluted and straight tubules, the loops of Henle, and the connecting tubules; these last join and establish communications with the collecting tubules derived from the ultimate ramifications of the diverticulum from the Wolffian duct. The mesoderm around the tubules becomes condensed to form the connective tissue of the kidney. The ureter opens at first into the hind-end of the Wolffian duct; after the sixth week it separates from the Wolffian duct, and opens independently into the part of the cloaca which ultimately becomes the bladder (Fig. 1108).

The secretory tubules of the kidney become arranged into pyramidal masses or lobules (Fig. 1109), and the lobulated condition of the kidneys exists for some time after birth, while traces of it may be found even in the adult. The kidney of the ox and many other animals remains lobulated throughout life.

The Urinary Bladder.—The bladder is formed partly from the entodermal cloaca and partly from the ends of the Wolffian ducts; the allantois takes no share in its formation. After the separation of the rectum from the dorsal part of the cloaca (p. 1215), the ventral part becomes subdivided into three portions: (1) an anterior **vesico-urethral portion**, continuous with the allantois—into this portion the Wolffian ducts open; (2) an intermediate narrow channel, the **pelvic portion**; and (3) a posterior **phallic portion**, closed externally by the urogenital membrane. The second and third parts together constitute the **urogenital sinus**. The vesico-urethral portion absorbs the ends of the Wolffian ducts and the associated ends of the renal diverticula, and these give rise to the trigone of the bladder and part of the prostatic urethra. The remainder of the vesico-urethral portion forms the body of the bladder and part of the prostatic urethra; its apex is prolonged to the umbilicus as a narrow canal, which later is obliterated and becomes the middle umbilical ligament (urachus).

The Prostate.—The prostate arises between the third and fourth months as a series of solid diverticula from the epithelium lining the urogenital sinus and vesicourethral part of the cloaca. These buds arise in five distinct groups, grow rapidly in length and soon acquire lumina. Eventually the prostatic urethra and ejaculatory ducts are embedded in a five-lobed gland the parts of which are called the median, anterior, posterior and lateral lobes. The lateral lobes are the largest. There are no distinct dividing lines between the parts of the formed gland, and the divisions are important only because of their individual peculiarities in disease processes. **Skene's ducts** in the female urethra are regarded as the homologues of the prostatic glands.

The **bulbo-urethral glands of Cowper** in the male, and **greater vestibular glands of Bartholin** in the female, also arise as diverticula from the epithelial lining of the urogenital sinus.

The External Organs of Generation (Fig. 1110).—As already stated (page 1215), the cloacal membrane, composed of ectoderm and entoderm, originally reaches from

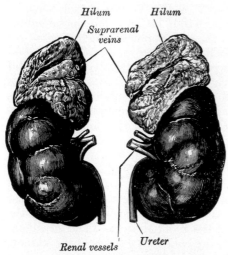

FIG. 1109.—The kidneys and suprarenal glands of a new-born child. Anterior aspect.

the umbilicus to the tail. The mesoderm extends to the midventral line for some distance behind the umbilicus, and forms the lower part of the abdominal wall; it ends below in a prominent swelling, the **cloacal tubercle.** Behind this tubercle the urogenital part of the cloacal membrane separates the ingrowing sheets of mesoderm.

The first rudiment of the penis (or clitoris) is a structure termed the **phallus**; it is derived from the phallic portion of the cloaca which has extended on to the end and sides of the under surface of the cloacal tubercle. The terminal part of the phallus representing the future glans becomes solid; the remainder, which is hollow, is converted into a longitudinal groove by the absorption of the urogenital membrane.

In the female a deep groove forms around the phallus and separates it from the rest of the cloacal tubercle, which is now termed the **genital tubercle.** The sides of the genital tubercle grow backward as the **genital swellings**, which ultimately form the labia majora; the tubercle itself becomes the mons pubis. The labia minora arise by the continued growth of the lips of the groove on the under surface of the phallus; the remainder of the phallus forms the clitoris.

In the male the early changes are similar, but the pelvic portion of the cloaca undergoes much greater development, pushing before it the phallic portion. The genital swellings extend around between the pelvic portion and the anus, and form a scrotal area; during the changes associated with the descent of the testes this area is drawn out to form the scrotal sacs. The penis is developed from the phallus. As in the female, the urogenital membrane undergoes absorption, forming a channel on the under surface of the phallus; this channel extends only as far forward as the corona glandis.

The **corpora cavernosa** of the penis (or clitoris) and of the urethra arise from the mesodermal tissue in the phallus; they are at first dense structures, but later vascular spaces appear in them, and they gradually become cavernous.

The **prepuce** in both sexes is formed by the growth of a solid plate of ectoderm into the superficial part of the phallus; on coronal section this plate presents the shape of a horseshoe. By the breaking down of its more centrally situated cells the plate is split into two lamellæ, and a cutaneous fold, the prepuce, is liberated and forms a hood over the glans. Adherent prepuce is not an adhesion really, but a hindered central desquamation.

The Urethra.—As already described, in both sexes the phallic portion of the cloaca extends on to the under surface of the cloacal tubercle as far forward as the apex. At the apex the walls of the phallic portion come together and fuse, the lumen is obliterated, and a solid plate, the **urethral plate**, is formed. The remainder of the phallic portion is for a time tubular, and then, by the absorption of the urogenital membrane, it establishes a communication with the exterior; this opening is the **primitive urogenital ostium**, and it extends forward to the corona glandis.

In the female this condition is largely retained; the portion of the groove on the clitoris broadens out while the body of the clitoris enlarges, and thus the adult urethral opening is situated behind the base of the clitoris.

In the male, by the greater growth of the pelvic portion of the cloaca a longer urethra is formed, and the primitive ostium is carried forward with the phallus, but it still ends at the corona glandis. Later it closes from behind forward. Meanwhile the urethral plate of the glans breaks down centrally to form a median

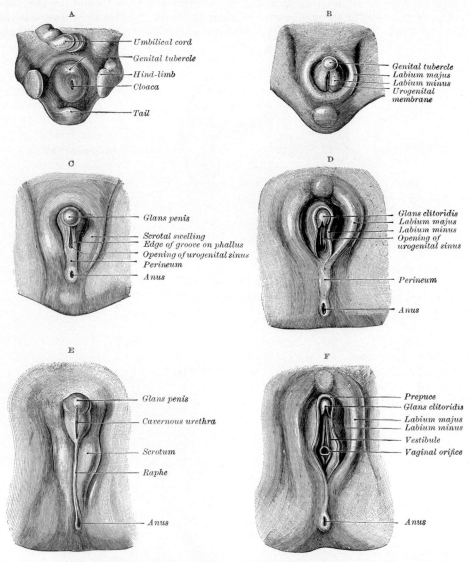

Fig. 1110.—Stages in the development of the external sexual organs in the male and female. (Drawn from the Ecker-Ziegler models.)

groove continuous with the primitive ostium. This groove also closes from behind forward, so that the external urethral opening is shifted forward to the end of the glans.

THE URINARY ORGANS.

The urinary organs comprise the **kidneys**, which produce the urine, the **ureters**, or ducts, which convey urine to the **urinary bladder**, where it is for a time retained; and the **urethra**, through which it is discharged from the body.

The Kidneys (Renes).

The **kidneys** are situated in the posterior part of the abdomen, one on either side of the vertebral column, behind the peritoneum, and surrounded by a mass of fat and loose areolar tissue. Their upper extremities are on a level with the upper border of the twelfth thoracic vertebra, their lower extremities on a level with the third lumbar. The right kidney is usually slightly lower than the left, probably

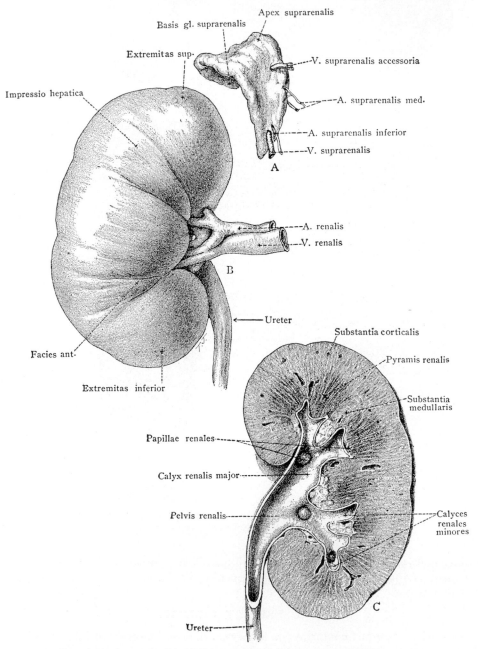

Fig. 1111.—The right kidney and suprarenal gland. A.—Suprarenal gland. B.—Kidney, surface view. C.—Kidney, longitudinal section showing pelvis. (Eycleshymer and Jones.)

due to the presence of the liver. The long axis of each kidney is directed downward and lateralward; the transverse axis backward and lateralward.

Each kidney is about 11.25 cm. in length, 5 to 7.5 cm. in breadth, and rather more than 2.5 cm. in thickness. The left is somewhat longer, and narrower, than the right. The weight of the kidney in the adult male varies from 125 to 170 gm., in the adult female from 115 to 155 gm. The combined weight of the two kidneys in proportion to that of the body is about 1 to 240. The kidneys in the new-born are about three times as large in proportion to the body weight as in the adult.

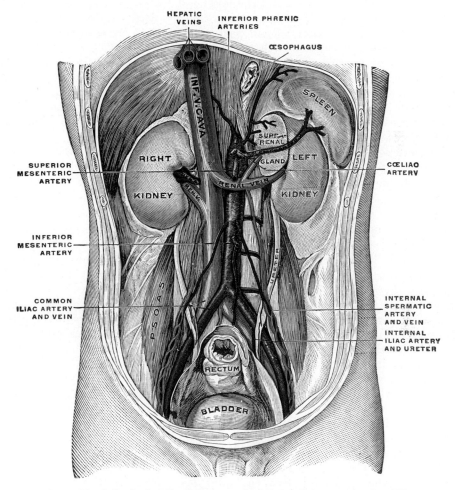

Fig. 1112.—Posterior abdominal wall, after removal of the peritoneum, showing kidneys, suprarenal capsules, and great vessels. (Corning.)

The kidney has a characteristic form, and presents for examination two surfaces, two borders, and an upper and lower extremity.

Relations.—The **anterior surface** (*facies anterior*) (Fig. 1114) of each kidney is convex, and looks forward and lateralward. Its relations to adjacent viscera differ so completely on the two sides that separate descriptions are necessary.

Anterior Surface of Right Kidney.—A narrow portion at the upper extremity is in relation with the right suprarenal gland. A large area just below this and involving about three-fourths of the surface, lies in the renal impression on the inferior surface of the liver, and a narrow but somewhat variable area near the medial border is in contact with the descending part of the duodenum. The lower part of the anterior surface is in contact laterally with the right colic flexure, and medially, as a rule, with the small intestine. The areas in relation with the liver and small intestine are covered by peritoneum; the suprarenal, duodenal, and colic areas are devoid of peritoneum.

Anterior Surface of Left Kidney.—A small area along the upper part of the medial border is in relation with the left suprarenal gland, and close to the lateral border is a long strip in contact with the renal impression on the spleen. A somewhat quadrilateral field, about the middle of the anterior surface, marks the site of contact with the body of the pancreas, on the deep surface of which are the lienal vessels. Above this is a small triangular portion, between the suprarenal and splenic areas, in contact with the postero-inferior surface of the stomach. Below the pancreatic area the lateral part is in relation with the left colic flexure, the medial with the small intestine. The areas in contact with the stomach and spleen are covered by the peritoneum of the omental bursa, while that in relation to the small intestine is covered by the peritoneum of the general cavity; behind the latter are some branches of the left colic vessels. The suprarenal, pancreatic, and colic areas are devoid of peritoneum.

The **Posterior Surface** (*facies posterior*) (Fig 1115).—The posterior surface of each kidney is directed backward and medialward. It is imbedded in areolar and fatty tissue and entirely devoid of peritoneal covering. It lies upon the diaphragm, the medial and lateral lumbocostal arches, the Psoas major, the Quadratus lumborum, and the tendon of the Transversus abdominis, the subcostal, and one or two of the upper lumbar arteries, and the last thoracic, iliohypogastric, and ilioinguinal nerves. The superior extremity of the right kidney rests upon the twelfth rib, the left usually on the eleventh and twelfth. The diaphragm separates the kidney from the pleura, which dips down to form the phrenicocostal sinus, but frequently the muscular fibers of the diaphragm are defective or absent over a triangular area immediately above the lateral lumbocostal arch, and when this is the case the perinephric areolar tissue is in contact with the diaphragmatic pleura,

Borders.—The **lateral border** (*margo lateralis; external border*) is convex, and is directed toward the postero-lateral wall of the abdomen. On the left side it is in contact at its upper part, with the spleen.

The **medial border** (*margo medialis; internal border*) is concave in the center and convex toward either extremity; it is directed forward and a little downward. Its central part presents a deep longitudinal fissure, bounded by prominent overhanging anterior and posterior lips. This fissure is named the **hilum,** and transmits the vessels, nerves, and ureter. Above the hilum the medial border is in relation with the suprarenal gland; below the hilum, with the ureter.

Extremities.—The **superior extremity** (*extremitas superior*) is thick and rounded, and is nearer the median line than the lower; it is surmounted by the suprarenal gland, which covers also a small portion of the anterior surface.

The **inferior extremity** (*extremitas inferior*) is smaller and thinner than the superior and farther from the median line. It extends to within 5 cm. of the iliac crest.

The relative position of the main structures in the hilum is as follows: the vein is in front, the artery in the middle, and the ureter behind and directed downward. Frequently, however, branches of both artery and vein are placed behind the ureter.

Renal Fascia (*fascia renalis*) (Figs. 1116, 1119).—The kidney and its vessels are imbedded in a mass of fatty tissue, termed the adipose capsule or *perirenal fat*, which is thickest at the margins of the kidney and is prolonged through the hilum into the renal sinus. The kidney and the adipose capsule together are enclosed in a specialized lamination of the subserous fascia called the renal fascia. It occupies a position between the internal investing layer of deep fascia (transversalis, endo-abdominal fascia) and the stratum of subserous fascia associated with the intestine and its blood vessels (Fig. 1117). In forming the renal fascia, the subserous fascia

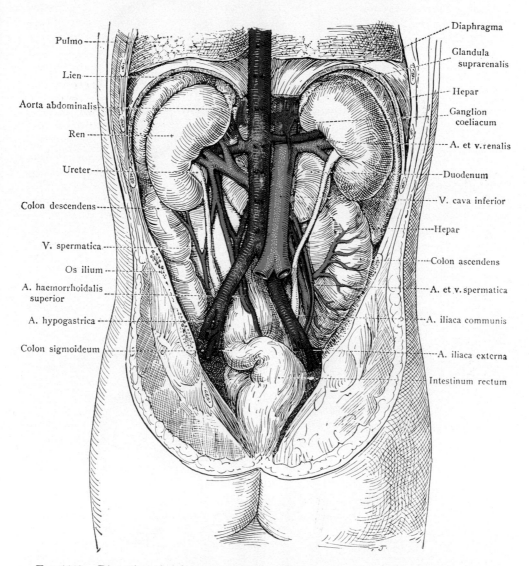

FIG. 1113.—Dissection of abdominal viscera, dorsal view showing relations of the kidneys.
(After Corning's Topographischen Anatomie in Eycleshymer and Jones.)

of the lateral abdominal wall splits into two fibrous lamellæ near the lateral border of the kidney (Fig. 1119). Both lamellæ extend medially, the anterior one over the ventral surface of the kidney, the posterior one over the dorsal surface. The anterior lamella continues over the renal vessels and aorta to join the similar mem-brane of the other side. The posterior lamella also continues across the middle line but lies deep to the aorta, and is there more adherent to the underlying deep

fascia than in the region of the kidney.   The renal fascia is connected to the fibrous
tunic of the kidney by numerous trabeculæ, which traverse the adipose capsule,
and are strongest near the lower end of the organ.   Behind the fascia renalis is a

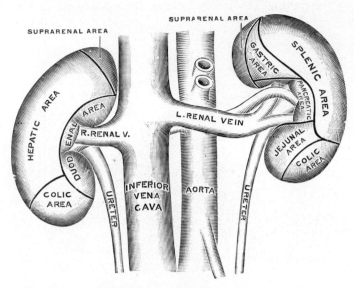

Fig. 1114.—The anterior surfaces of the kidneys, showing the areas of contact
of neighboring viscera.

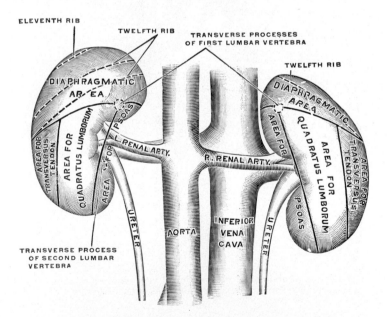

Fig. 1115.—The posterior surfaces of the kidneys, showing areas of relation to the parietes.

considerable quantity of fat, which constitutes the *paranephric body* (*pararenal fat*).

Fixation of the Kidney.—The kidneys are not rigidly fixed to the abdominal
wall and, since they are in contact with the diaphragm, move with it during respira-

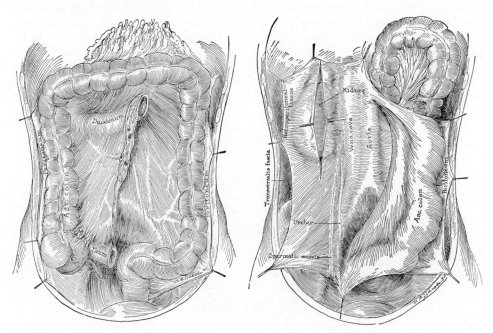

FIG. 1116.—Visceral and parietal peritoneum associated with large intestine. Small intestine and mesentery removed. (Tobin, courtesy of Anat. Record.)

FIG. 1117.—Peritoneum associated with ascending colon dissected free and displaced to expose the deeper stratum of subserous fascia associated with kidney and great vessels. (Tobin, courtesy of Anat. Record.)

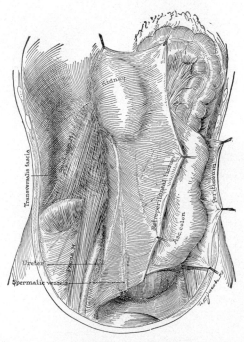

FIG. 1118.—Deeper stratum of subserous fascia dissected free and displaced to expose the transversalis fascia. (Tobin, courtesy of Anat. Record.)

tion. They are held in position by the renal fascia described above and by the large renal arteries and veins. That the adipose capsule and the paranephric fat body play an important part in holding the kidney in position is indicated by the occurrence of a condition called movable kidney in emaciated individuals (see page 1337).

General Structure of the Kidney.—The kidney is invested by a fibrous tunic or capsule which forms a firm, smooth covering to the organ. The tunic can be easily stripped off, but in doing so numerous fine processes of connective tissue and

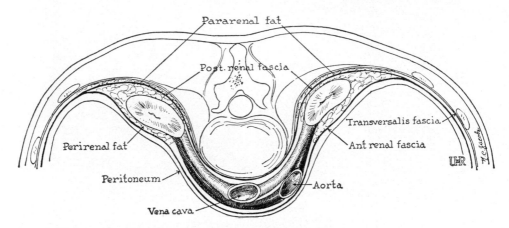

FIG. 1119.—Transverse section, showing relations of renal fascia. (Tobin, courtesy of Anat. Rec.)

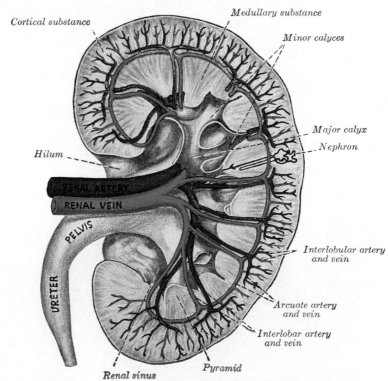

FIG. 1120.—Diagram of a vertical section through the kidney. Nephron and blood vessels greatly enlarged.

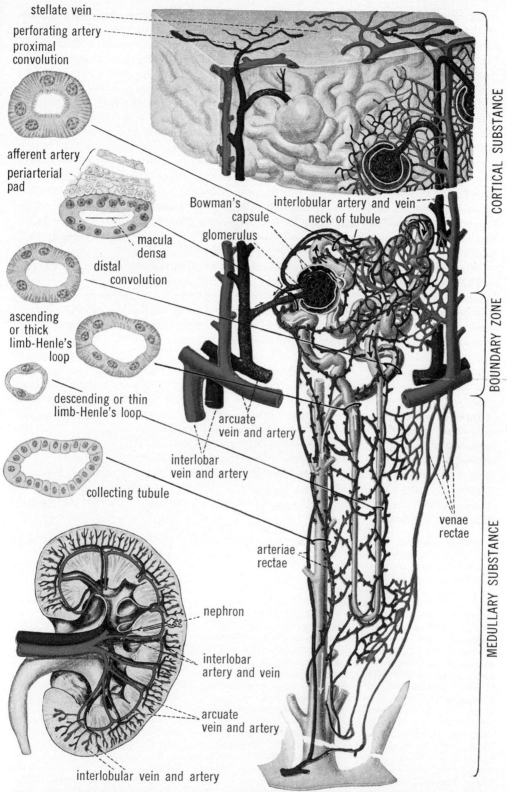

stellate vein

perforating artery

proximal convolution

afferent artery

periarterial pad

macula densa

distal convolution

ascending or thick limb-Henle's loop

descending or thin limb-Henle's loop

collecting tubule

Bowman's capsule

glomerulus

interlobular artery and vein
neck of tubule

arcuate vein and artery

interlobar vein and artery

nephron

interlobar artery and vein

arcuate vein and artery

interlobular vein and artery

arteriae rectae

venae rectae

CORTICAL SUBSTANCE

BOUNDARY ZONE

MEDULLARY SUBSTANCE

Fig. 1121.—Diagram of a portion of kidney lobule illustrating a nephron, typical histological sections of the various divisions of a nephron, and the disposition of the renal vessels. The section of the collecting tubule is reproduced at a lower magnification than the divisions of the nephron.

small bloodvessels are torn through. When the capsule is stripped off, the surface of the kidney is found to be smooth and of a deep red color. In infants fissures extending for some depth may be seen on the surface of the organ, a remnant of the lobular construction of the gland. If a vertical section of the kidney be made from its convex to its concave border, it will be seen that the hilum expands into a central cavity, the **renal sinus**, this contains the upper part of the renal pelvis and the calyces, surrounded by some fat in which are imbedded the branches of the renal vessels and nerves. The renal sinus is lined by a prolongation of the fibrous tunic, which is continuous with the covering of the pelvis of the kidney around the lips of the hilum. The **minor renal calyces,** from four to thirteen in number, are cup-shaped tubes, each of which embraces usually one but occasionally two or more of the renal papillæ; they unite to form two or three short tubes, the major calyces, and these in turn join to form a funnel-shaped sac, the **renal pelvis.** Spirally arranged muscles surround the calyces which may have a milking action on these tubes, thereby aiding the flow of urine into the renal pelvis. As the pelvis leaves the renal sinus it diminishes rapidly in caliber and merges insensibly into the ureter, the excretory duct of the kidney.

The kidney is composed of an internal **medullary** and an external **cortical substance.**

The **medullary substance** (*substantia medullaris*) consists of a series of striated conical masses, termed the **renal pyramids.** They vary from eight to eighteen in number and have their bases directed toward the circumference of the kidney, while their apices converge toward the renal sinus, where they form prominent papillæ projecting into the lumina of the minor calyces.

The **cortical substance** (*substantia corticalis*) is reddish brown in color and soft and granular in consistence. It lies immediately beneath the fibrous tunic, arches over the bases of the pyramids, and dips in between adjacent pyramids toward the renal sinus. The parts dipping in between the pyramids are named the **renal columns** (Bertini), while the portions which connect the renal columns to each other and intervene between the bases of the pyramids and the fibrous tunic are called the **cortical arches** (Fig. 1120). If the cortex be examined with a lens, it will be seen to consist of a series of lighter-colored, conical areas, termed the radiate part, and a darker colored intervening substance, which from the complexity of its structure is named the convoluted part. The rays gradually taper toward the circumference of the kidney, and consist of a series of outward prolongations from the base of each renal pyramid.

Minute Anatomy.—The **renal tubules** (Fig. 1121), of which the kidney is for the most part made up, commence in the cortical substance, and after pursuing a very circuitous course through the cortical and medullary substances, finally end at the apices of the renal pyramids by open mouths, so that the fluid which they contain is emptied, through the calyces, into the pelvis of the kidney. If the surface of one of the papillæ be examined with a lens, it will be seen to be studded over with minute openings, the orifices of the renal tubules, from sixteen to twenty in number, and if pressure be made on a fresh kidney, urine will be seen to exude from these orifices. The tubules commence in the cortex and renal columns as the **renal corpuscles** or **Malpighian bodies.** They are small rounded masses, deep red in color, varying in size, but averaging about 0.2 mm. in diameter. Each of these bodies is composed of two parts: a central glomerulus of vessels, and a double walled membranous envelope, the **glomerular capsule** (*capsule of Bowman*), which is the invaginated-pouch-like commencement of a renal tubule.

The **glomerulus** is a tuft of non-anastomosing capillaries, among which there is a scanty amount of connective tissue. This capillary tuft is derived from an arteriole, the *afferent vessel*, which enters the capsule, generally at a point opposite to that at which the capsule joins the tubule. (Fig. 1121.) Upon entering the capsule the afferent arteriole divides into from 2 to 10 primary branches, which in turn subdivide into about 50 capillary loops which generally do not anastomose. These loops are from 300 to 500μ in length. The capillaries join to form the efferent arteriole, which leaves Bowman's capsule adjacent to the afferent vessel, the latter generally being the larger of the two. The total surface area of the capillaries of all glomeruli is about 1 square meter. For a variable distance before the afferent arteriole enters the glomerulus the muscle cells of the media adjacent to the distal convolution of its own nephron are modified, appearing as relatively large afibrillar cells. This structure is said to present evidence of glandular activity. At times it appears partially to invest the artery in a nest-like group of cells embedded in a delicate fibrillar network. It is variously known as the **juxtaglomerular apparatus** (Goormagtigh), the **Polkissen** (Zimmerman) and the **periarterial pad** (Edwards). Its exact function has not been determined; neither is it known whether or not all afferent arteries contain it, but it is common in man. The efferent arteriole has only circular, smooth muscle fibers in its wall, which may be a means of regulating glomerular blood pressure. The **Malpighian** or **Bowman's capsule,** which surrounds the glomerulus, consists of a double-walled sac. The outer wall (parietal layer) is continuous with the inner wall (visceral layer) at the points of entrance and exit of the afferent and efferent vessels respectively. The cavity between the two layers is continuous with the lumen of the proximal convoluted tubule. The parietal layer is smooth. The visceral layer covers the glomerulus and dips in between the capillary loops, almost completely surrounding each one. Both layers of the capsule consist of flattened epithelial cells which have a basement membrane. This covers the outer surface of the parietal layer and is continuous with that of the tubule cells. The basement membrane of the visceral layer is in contact with the glomerular capillaries. Microdissection experiments of living glomeruli show them to lie in a gelatinous matrix. The walls of the capillaries, the overlying cells of the visceral layer of the capsule and the gelatinous matrix are now thought to constitute a filter mechanism through which non-protein constituents of the blood plasma can enter the tubule.

A **renal tubule,** beginning with the capsule of Bowman as it surrounds the glomerulus and ending where the tubule joins the excretory duct or collecting tubule, constitutes a **nephron**—the structural and functional unit of the kidney. There are about 1,250,000 of these units in each kidney.

A tubule presents during its course, many changes in shape and direction, and is contained partly in the medullary and partly in the cortical substance. At its junction with the glomerular capsule it exhibits a somewhat constricted portion, which is termed the **neck.** Beyond this the tubule becomes convoluted, and pursues a considerable course in the cortical substance constituting the **proximal convoluted tube.** The convolutions disappear as the tube approaches the medullary substance in a more or less spiral manner. Throughout this portion of its course the renal tubule is contained entirely in the cortical substance, and presents a fairly uniform caliber. It now enters the medullary substance, suddenly becomes much smaller, quite straight, and dips down for a variable depth into the pyramids, constituting the thin or **descending limb of Henle's loop.** Bending on itself, it forms what is termed the **loop of Henle** and ascending it becomes suddenly enlarged, forming the thick or **ascending limb of Henle's loop,** which enters the cortical substance where it again becomes dilated, and tortuous. It is now called the **distal convoluted tubule.** The terminal part of the ascending limb of Henle's loop crosses in contact with or sometimes lies parallel to the afferent arteriole of its own glomerulus. The turns of the distal convoluted tubule into which it merges lie among the coils of the proximal portion of the nephron and terminate in a narrow part which enters a collecting tubule.

The **straight** or **collecting tubes** commence in the radiate part of the cortex, where they receive the curved ends of the distal convoluted tubules. They unite at short intervals with one another, the resulting tubes presenting a considerable increase in caliber, so that a series of comparatively large tubes passes from the bases of the rays into the renal pyramids. In the medulla the tubes of each pyramid converge to join a central tube (*duct of Bellini*) which finally opens on the summit of one of the papillæ; the contents of the tube are therefore discharged into one of the minor calyces.

Structure of the Renal Tubules.—The various parts of the nephron present quite different cellular appearances and these appearances vary depending upon the functional state of the cells. The proximal convoluted tubule is about 14 mm. long and 59μ in diameter. It is composed of one layer of large cuboidal cells with central spherical nuclei. The cells dovetail laterally with one another and the lateral cell limits are rarely seen. The distal ends of the cells bulge into the lumen and are covered by a brush border. The cytoplasm is abundant and coarsely granular. Parallel striations in the cytoplasm perpendicular to the basement membrane are due to mitochondria.

The transition between the epithelium of the proximal convoluted tubule and the thin segment is abrupt. The thin segment may be absent in nephrons beginning near the surface of the kidney. It is composed of squamous cells with pale-staining cytoplasm and flattened nuclei. The epithelial change from the descending limb to the ascending or thick limb is also quite abrupt. The cells become cuboidal and deeper-staining, with perpendicular striations in the basal parts but without distinct cell boundaries or brush borders. At about the junction of the ascending limb with the distal convoluted tubule the nephron comes into contact with the "Polkissen" of its own afferent arteriole. Here the epithelium of the tubule is greatly modified, having high cells and crowded nuclei. This constitutes the **macula densa** or epithelial plaque, the function of which is unknown. Transition to the tortuous distal convoluted tubule is gradual. This segment of the nephron is about 5 mm. long and 35μ in diameter. The cells are lower and the lumen larger than in the proximal tubule. They do not have a brush border and the boundaries are fairly distinct. The distal convoluted tubule merges into a short connecting segment which joins the collecting or excretory tubule.

The collecting tubules have a typical epithelium which is quite different from that in the various portions of the nephron. In the smallest tubes the cells are cuboidal and distinctly outlined with round nuclei and clear cytoplasm. As the tubules become larger the cells are higher, finally becoming tall columnar in the ducts of Bellini. The columnar epithelium becomes continuous with the cells covering the surface of the papillæ.

The length of the nephron varies from 30 to 38 mm., while the length of the collecting tubules is estimated at from 20 to 22 mm.

The Renal Bloodvessels.—The kidney is plentifully supplied with blood by the renal artery, a large branch of the abdominal aorta. Before entering the kidney substance the number and disposition of the branches of the renal artery exhibit great variation. In most cases the renal artery divides into two primary branches, a larger anterior and a smaller posterior. The anterior branch supplies exclusively the anterior or ventral half of the organ and the posterior supplies the posterior or dorsal part. Therefore there is a line (Bröedel's line) in the long axis of the lateral border of the kidney which passes between the two main arterial divisions and in which there are no large vessels, a feature which is utilized to minimize hemorrhage when nephrotomy is done. The primary branches subdivide and diverge until they come to lie on the anterior and posterior aspects respectively of the calyces. Further subdivisions occur which enter the kidney substance and run between the pyramids. These are known as **interlobar arteries.** When these vessels reach the corticomedullary zone they make more or less well defined arches over the bases of the pyramids and are then called **arcuate arteries.** These vessels give off a series of branches called **interlobular** arteries. The interlobular arteries and the terminal parts of the arcuate vessels run vertically and nearly parallel towards the cortex and periphery of the kidney. The interlobular arteries may terminate as (1) an afferent glomerular artery to one or more glomeruli; (2) in a capillary plexus around the convoluted tubules in the cortices without relation to the glomerulus, therefore a nutrient artery, and (3) as a perforating capsular vessel. Divisions classified under (2) must be regarded as exceptional. The most important and numerous branches of the interlobular arteries are the afferent glomerular vessels. These break up into capillary loops, the glomerulus, within Bowman's capsule. The loops unite to form the efferent arteriole. The efferent glomerular vessel forms a plexus about the convoluted tubule and part of Henle's loop and sends one or more branches toward the pelvis, the **arteria recta,** which supplies the collecting tubules and loops of Henle. The arteriæ rectæ are derived chiefly from the efferent arterioles of glomeruli located in the boundary zone. They are frequently known as **arteriæ rectæ spuriæ** to distinguish them from a few straight vessels arising directly from the arcuate or interlobular arteries without relation to glomeruli and hence called **arteriæ rectæ veræ.** It is likely that the so-called arteriæ rectæ veræ were once derived from an efferent glomerular vessel but that the glomerulus atrophied, thus giving them the appearance of true nutrient branches from the arcuate or interlobular arteries. No arteriæ rectæ are derived from the vessels of the cortical zone. It has not been determined whether or not there are anastomoses between the capillaries of adjacent nephrons. However, there is free anastomosis between the branches of the arteriæ rectæ. The arteriæ rectæ or straight arteries surround the limbs of Henle and pass down between the straight collecting tubules, where they form terminal plexuses around the tubes. This plexus drains into the **venæ rectæ** which in turn carry the blood to the interlobular veins, thence into the arcuate veins, then into the interlobar veins and finally into the renal veins, which discharge into the inferior vena cava. It will be noted that the chief renal arteries have counterparts in the venous system. All veins from the dorsal half of the kidney cross to the ventral half between the minor calyces to join the ventral collecting veins before leaving the kidney. Whatever arterial anastomoses there are within the kidney occur post glomerular, the renal arteries and their branches therefore being terminal as far as the arteriæ rectæ. An exception to this condition is found in cases in which arterio-venous anastomoses have been described. These connections have been found in three locations; between the arteries and veins of the sinus renalis, between the subcapsular vessels and between the interlobular arteries and veins. In the latter position particularly arterial blood could reach the tubules of the nephron by retrograde flow through the veins. The constancy with which this type of anastomosis occurs or its rôle in the circulation of the kidney has not been accurately determined. Anastomosis between veins is very rich. The perforating capsular vessels, the terminations of interlobular arteries, form connections with non-renal vessels in the fat which surrounds the kidney. They frequently drain into the subcapsular or **stellate veins,** which in turn drain into the interlobular veins.

The **lymphatics** of the kidney are described on page 805.

Nerves of the Kidney.—The nerves of the kidney, although small, are about fifteen in number. They have small ganglia developed upon them, and are derived from the renal plexus, which is formed by branches from the celiac plexus, the lower and outer part of the celiac ganglion and aortic plexus, and from the lesser and lowest splanchnic nerves. They communicate with the spermatic plexus, a circumstance which may explain the occurrence of pain in the testis in affections of the kidney. They accompany the renal artery and its branches, and are distributed to the bloodvessels and to the cells of the urinary tubules.

Connective Tissue (*intertubular stroma*). — Although the tubules and vessels are closely packed, a small amount of connective tissue, continuous with the fibrous tunic, binds them firmly together and supports the bloodvessels, lymphatics, and nerves.

Variations.—Malformations of the kidney are not uncommon. There may be an entire absence of one kidney, but, according to Morris, the number of these cases is "excessively small": or there may be congenital atrophy of one kidney, when the kidney is very small, but usually healthy in structure. These cases are of great importance, and must be duly taken into account when nephrectomy is contemplated. A more common malformation is where the two kidneys are fused together. They may be joined together only at their lower ends by means of a thick mass of renal tissue, so as to form a horseshoe-shaped body, or they may be completely united, forming a disk-like kidney, from which two ureters descend into the bladder. These fused kidneys are generally situated in the middle line of the abdomen, but may be displaced as well. In some mammals, *e. g.*, ox and bear, the kidney consists of a number of distinct lobules; this lobulated condition is characteristic of the kidney of the human fetus, and traces of it may persist in the adult. Sometimes the pelvis is duplicated, while a double ureter is not very uncommon. In some rare instances a third kidney may be present.

One or both kidneys may be misplaced as a congenital condition, and remain fixed in this abnormal position. They are then very often misshapen. They may be situated higher, though this is very uncommon, or lower than normal or removed farther from the vertebral column than usual; or they may be displaced into the iliac fossa, over the sacroiliac joint, on to the promontory of the sacrum, or into the pelvis between the rectum and bladder or by the side of the uterus. In these latter cases they may give rise to very serious trouble. The kidney may also be displaced as a congenital condition, but may not be fixed; it is then known as a *floating kidney*. It is believed to be due to the fact that the kidney is completely enveloped by peritoneum which then passes backward to the vertebral column as a double layer, forming a mesonephron which permits movement. The kidney may also be misplaced as an acquired condition; in these cases the kidney is mobile in the tissues by which it is surrounded, moving with the capsule in the perinephric tissues. This condition is known as *movable kidney*, and is more common in the female than in the male. It occurs in badly nourished people, or in those who have become emaciated from any cause. It must not be confounded with the *floating kidney*, which is a congenital condition due to the development of a mesonephron. The two conditions cannot, however, be distinguished until the abdomen is opened or the kidney explored from the loin. Accessory renal arteries entering one or another or both poles of the kidney instead of at the hilum are fairly common.

The Ureters.

The **ureters** are the two tubes which convey the urine from the kidneys to the urinary bladder. Each commences within the sinus of the corresponding kidney as a number of short cup-shaped tubes, termed **calyces**, which encircle the renal papillæ. Since a single calyx may enclose more than one papilla the calyces are generally fewer in number than the pyramids—the former varying from seven to thirteen, the latter from eight to eighteen. The calyces join to form two or three short tubes, and these unite to form a funnel-shaped dilatation, wide above and narrow below, named the **renal pelvis**, which is situated partly inside and partly outside the renal sinus. It is usually placed on a level with the spinous process of the first lumbar vertebra.

The **Ureter Proper** varies in length from 28 to 34 cm., the right being about 1 cm. shorter than the left. It is a thick-walled narrow tube which is directly continuous near the lower end of the kidney with the tapering extremity of the renal pelvis. It is not of uniform caliber, varying from 1 mm. to 1 cm. in diameter. It runs downward and medialward on the Psoas major muscle and, entering the pelvic cavity, finally opens into the fundus of the bladder.

The **abdominal part** (*pars abdominalis*) lies behind the peritoneum on the medial part of the Psoas major imbedded in the subserous fascia, and is crossed obliquely by the internal spermatic vessels. It enters the pelvic cavity by crossing either the termination of the common, or the commencement of the external, iliac vessels.

At its origin the *right* ureter is usually covered by the descending part of the duodenum, and in its course downward lies to the right of the inferior vena cava, and is crossed by the right colic and ileocolic vessels, while near the superior aperture of the pelvis it passes behind the lower part of the mesentery and the terminal part of the ileum. The *left* ureter is crossed by the left colic vessels, and near the superior aperture of the pelvis passes behind the sigmoid colon and its mesentery.

The **pelvic part** (*pars pelvina*) runs at first downward on the lateral wall of the pelvic cavity, along the anterior border of the greater sciatic notch and under cover of the peritoneum. It lies in front of the hypogastric artery medial to the obturator nerve and the obturator, inferior vesical, and middle hemorrhoidal arteries. Opposite the lower part of the greater sciatic foramen it inclines medialward, and reaches the lateral angle of the bladder, where it is situated in front of the upper end of the seminal vesicle, here the ductus deferens crosses to its medial side, and the vesical veins surround it. Finally, the ureters run obliquely for about 2 cm. through the wall of the bladder and open by slit-like apertures into the cavity of the viscus at the lateral angles of the trigone. When the bladder is distended the openings of the ureters are about 5 cm. apart, but when it is empty and contracted the distance between them is diminished by one-half. Owing to their oblique course through the coats of the bladder, the upper and lower walls of the terminal portions of the ureters become closely applied to each other when the viscus is distended, and, acting as valves, prevent regurgitation of urine from the bladder. There are three points in the course of the ureter where it normally undergoes constriction: (1) at the ureteropelvic junction, average diameter 2 mm.; (2) at the place where it crosses the iliac vessels, 4 mm., and (3) where it joins the bladder, 1 to 5 mm. Between these points the abdominal ureter averages 10 mm. in diameter and the pelvic ureter 5 mm.

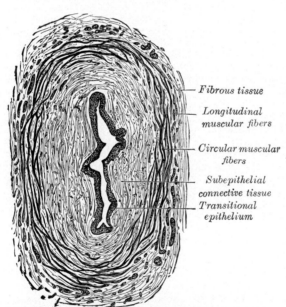

Fibrous tissue

Longitudinal muscular fibers

Circular muscular fibers

Subepithelial connective tissue

Transitional epithelium

Fig. 1122.—Transverse section of ureter.

In the **female,** the ureter forms, as it lies in relation to the wall of the pelvis, the posterior boundary of a shallow depression named the **ovarian fossa,** in which the ovary is situated. It then runs medialward and forward on the lateral aspect of the cervix uteri and upper part of the vagina to reach the fundus of the bladder. In this part of its course it is accompanied for about 2.5 cm. by the uterine artery, which then crosses over the ureter and ascends between the two layers of the broad ligament. The ureter is distant about 2 cm. from the side of the cervix of the uterus.

Structure (Fig. 1122).—The ureter is composed of three coats: **fibrous, muscular,** and **mucous coats.**

The **fibrous coat** (*tunica adventitia*) is continuous at one end with the fibrous tunic of the kidney on the floor of the sinus; while at the other it is lost in the fibrous structure of the bladder.

In the renal pelvis the **muscular coat** (*tunica muscularis*) consists of two layers, longitudinal and circular: the longitudinal fibers become lost upon the sides of the papillæ at the extremities of the calyces; the circular fibers may be traced surrounding the medullary substance in the same situation. In the ureter proper the muscular fibers are very distinct, and are arranged in three layers: an external longitudinal, a middle circular, and an internal, less distinct than the other two, but having a general longitudinal direction. According to Kölliker this internal layer is found only in the neighborhood of the bladder.

The **mucous coat** (*tunica mucosa*) is smooth, presenting only a few longitudinal folds which become effaced by distension. It is continuous with the mucous membrane of the bladder below, while it is prolonged over the papillæ of the kidney above. Its epithelium is of a transitional character, and resembles that found in the bladder (see Fig. 1129). It consists of several layers of cells, of which the innermost—that is to say, the cells in contact with the urine— are somewhat flattened, with concavities on their deep surfaces into which the rounded ends of the cells of the second layer fit. These, the intermediate cells, more or less resemble columnar epithelium, and are pear-shaped, with rounded internal extremities which fit into the concavities of the cells of the first layer, and narrow external extremities which are wedged in between the cells of the third layer. The external or third layer consists of conical or oval cells varying in number in different parts, and presenting processes which extend down into the basement membrane. Beneath the epithelium, and separating it from the muscular coats, is a dense layer of fibrous tissue containing many elastic fibers.

Vessels and Nerves.—The **arteries** supplying the ureter are branches from the renal, internal spermatic, hypogastric, and inferior vesical.

The **nerves** are derived from the inferior mesenteric, spermatic, and pelvic plexuses. The lower one-third of the ureter contains nerve cells which are probably incorporated in vagus efferent chains. The afferent supply of the ureter is contained in the eleventh and twelfth thoracic and first lumbar nerves. The vagus supply to the ureter probably also has afferent components.

Variations.—The upper portion of the ureter is sometimes double; more rarely it is double the greater part of its extent, or even completely so. In such cases there are two openings into the bladder. Asymmetry in these variations is common.

The Urinary Bladder (Vesica Urinaria; Bladder) (Fig. 1123).

The **urinary bladder** is a musculomembranous sac which acts as a reservoir for the urine; and as its size, position, and relations vary according to the amount

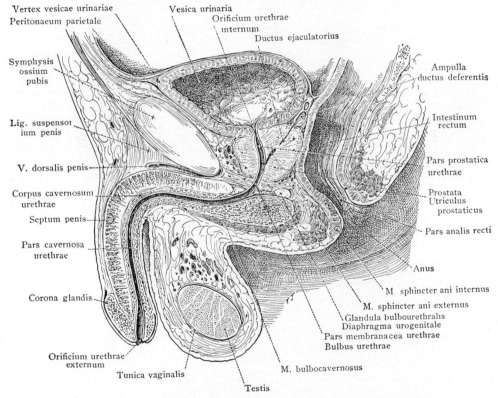

Fig. 1123.—Median sagittal section through male pelvis, viewed from left side. (Eycleshymer and Jones.)

of fluid it contains, it is necessary to study it as it appears (*a*) when *empty*, and (*b*) when *distended*. In both conditions the position of the bladder varies with the condition of the rectum, being pushed upward and forward when the rectum is distended.

The Empty Bladder.—When hardened *in situ*, the empty bladder has the form of a flattened tetrahedron, with its vertex tilted forward. It presents a fundus, a vertex, a superior and an inferior surface. The **fundus** (Fig. 1141) is triangular in shape, and is directed downward and backward toward the rectum, from which it is separated by the rectovesical fascia, the vesiculæ seminales, and the terminal portions of the ductus deferentes. The **vertex** is directed forward toward the upper part of the symphysis pubis, and from it the middle umbilical ligament is continued upward on the back of the anterior abdominal wall to the umbilicus. The peritoneum is carried by it from the vertex of the bladder on to the abdominal wall to form the middle umbilical fold. The **superior surface** is triangular, bounded on either side by a lateral border which separates it from the inferior surface, and

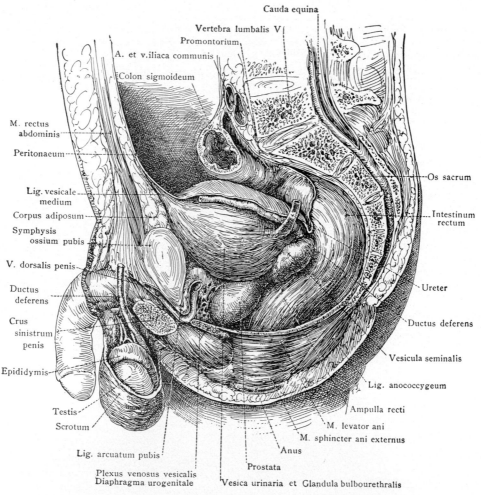

FIG. 1124.—Male pelvic organs and perineum seen from left side after removal of left pelvic wall Bladder and rectum moderately distended. (Eycleshymer and Jones.)

behind by a posterior border, represented by a line joining the two ureters, which intervenes between it and the fundus. The lateral borders extend from the ureters to the vertex, and from them the peritoneum is carried to the walls of the pelvis. On either side of the bladder the peritoneum shows a depression, named the **para-**

vesical fossa (Fig. 1153). The superior surface is directed upward, is covered by peritoneum, and is in relation with the sigmoid colon and some of the coils of the small intestine. When the bladder is empty and firmly contracted, this surface is convex and the lateral and posterior borders are rounded; whereas if the bladder be relaxed it is concave, and the interior of the viscus, as seen in a median sagittal section, presents the appearance of a V-shaped slit with a shorter posterior and a longer anterior limb—the apex of the V corresponding with the internal orifice of the urethra. The **inferior surface** is directed downward and is uncovered by peritoneum. It may be divided into a posterior or prostatic area and two infero-lateral surfaces. The prostatic area is somewhat triangular: it rests upon and is in direct continuity with the base of the prostate; and from it the urethra emerges. The infero-lateral portion of the inferior surface is directed downward and lateralward and is separated from the symphysis pubis by the prevesical fascial cleft (cavum Retzii).

When the bladder is empty it is placed entirely within the pelvis, below the level of the obliterated hypogastric arteries, and below the level of those portions of the ductus deferentes which are in contact with the lateral wall of the pelvis; after they cross the ureters the ductus deferentes come into contact with the fundus of the bladder. As the viscus fills, its fundus, being more or less fixed, is only slightly depressed; while its superior surface gradually rises into the abdominal cavity, carrying with it its peritoneal covering, and at the same time rounding off the posterior and lateral borders.

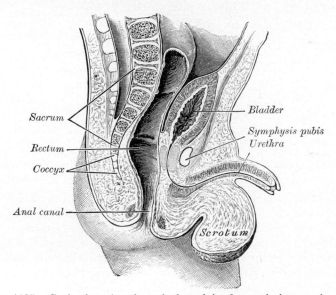

Sacrum

Rectum

Coccyx

Anal canal

Bladder

Symphysis pubis
Urethra

Scrotum

FIG. 1125.—Sagittal section through the pelvis of a newly born male child.

The Distended Bladder.—When the bladder is moderately full it contains about 0.5 liter and assumes an oval form; the long diameter of the oval measures about 12 cm. and is directed upward and forward. In this condition it presents a postero-superior, an antero-inferior, and two lateral surfaces, a fundus and a summit. The **postero-superior surface** is directed upward and backward, and is covered by peritoneum: behind, it is separated from the rectum by the rectovesical excavation, while its anterior part is in contact with the coils of the small intestine. The **antero-inferior surface** is devoid of peritoneum, and rests, below, against the pubic bones, above which it is in contact with the back of the anterior abdominal wall. The lower parts of the lateral surfaces are destitute of peritoneum, and are in contact with the lateral walls of the pelvis. The line of peritoneal reflection from the lateral surface is raised to the level of the obliterated hypogastric artery. The **fundus** undergoes little alteration in position, being only slightly lowered. It exhibits, however, a narrow triangular area, which is separated from the rectum merely by the rectovesical fascia. This area is bounded below by the prostate, above by the rectovesical fold of peritoneum, and laterally by the ductus deferentes. The ductus deferentes frequently come in contact with each other above the prostate, and under such circumstances the lower part of the triangular area is obliterated. The line of reflection of the peritoneum from the rectum to the bladder appears to undergo little or no change when the latter is distended; it is situated about 10 cm. from the anus. The **summit** is directed upward and forward above the point of attachment of the middle umbilical ligament, and hence the peritoneum which follows the ligament, forms a pouch of varying depth between the summit of the bladder, and the anterior abdominal wall.

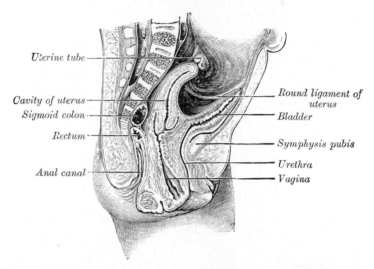

Fig. 1126.—Sagittal section through the pelvis of a newly born female child.

The Bladder in the Child (Figs. 1125, 1126).—In the newborn child the internal urethral orifice is at the level of the upper border of the symphysis pubis; the bladder therefore lies relatively at a much higher level in the infant than in the adult. Its anterior surface "is in contact with about the lower two-thirds of that part of the abdominal wall which lies between the symphysis pubis and the umbilicus" (Symington). Its fundus is clothed with peritoneum as far as the level of the internal orifice of the urethra. Although the bladder of the infant is usually described as an abdominal organ, Symington has pointed out that only about one-half of it lies above the plane of the superior aperture of the pelvis. Disse maintains that the internal urethral orifice sinks rapidly during the first three years, and then more slowly until the ninth year, after which it remains stationary until puberty, when it again slowly descends and reaches its adult position.

The Female Bladder (Fig. 1127).—In the female, the bladder is in relation behind with the uterus and the upper part of the vagina. It is separated from the anterior surface of the body of the uterus by the vesicouterine excavation, but below the level of this excavation it is connected to the front of the cervix uteri and the upper part of the anterior wall of the vagina by areolar tissue. When the bladder is empty the uterus rests upon its superior surface. The female bladder is said by some to be more capacious than that of the male, but probably the opposite is the case.

Ligaments.—The bladder is held in position by ligamentous attachments at its inferior portion or base, that is, near the exit of the urethra, and at the vertex. The remainder of the wall, enclosed in subserous fascia, is free to move during the expansion and contraction of filling and emptying.

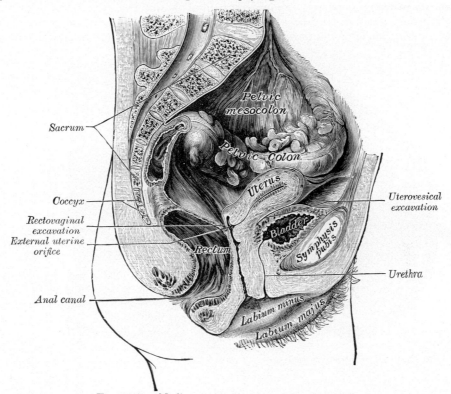

FIG. 1127.—Median sagittal section of female pelvis.

The base of the bladder is attached to the internal investing layer of deep fascia on the pubic bone by strong fibrous bands which may contain muscle fibers, the **Pubovesicales.** In the male, because the prostate is firmly bound to the bladder in this region, these attachments are between the prostate and pubic bone rather than directly to the bladder, and are named the **medial** and **lateral puboprostatic ligaments** (see page 476). In the female the attachments are directly between bladder and pubis and are therefore called the **pubovesical ligaments.**

The base of the bladder is secured posteriorly to the sides of the rectum and the sacrum by condensations of the subserous fascia underlying the sacrogenital folds. They are called the **rectovesical ligaments**, or, since they may contain smooth muscle bundles, the **Rectovesicales** muscles.

The **middle umbilical ligament** is a fibrous or fibromuscular cord, the remains of the urachus (page 1323), which extends from the vertex of the bladder to the umbilicus. It is broad at its attachment to the bladder and becomes narrow as it nears the umbilicus.

In addition to these fibrous or true ligaments, there are a series of folds, where the peritoneum is reflected from the bladder to the abdominal wall, called **false ligaments of the bladder.** Anteriorly there are three folds: the **middle umbilical fold** on the middle umbilical ligament, and two **lateral umbilical folds** on the obliterated hypogastric arteries. The reflections of the peritoneum on to the side wall of the pelvis form the **lateral false ligaments**, while the **sacrogenital folds** constitute **posterior false ligaments.**

Interior of the Bladder (Fig. 1128).—The mucous membrane lining the bladder is, over the greater part of the viscus, loosely attached to the muscular coat, and appears wrinkled or folded when the bladder is contracted: in the distended condition of the bladder the folds are effaced. Over a small triangular area, termed the **trigonum vesicæ**, immediately above and behind the internal orifice of the urethra, the mucous membrane is firmly bound to the muscular coat, and is always smooth. The anterior angle of the trigonum vesicæ is formed by the internal orifice of the

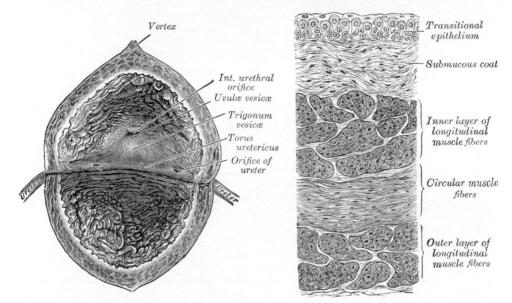

Fig. 1128.—The interior of bladder

Fig. 1129.—Vertical section of bladder wall.

urethra: its postero-lateral angles by the orifices of the ureters. Stretching behind the latter openings is a slightly curved ridge, the **torus uretericus**, forming the base of the trigone and produced by an underlying bundle of non-striped muscular fibers. The lateral parts of this ridge extend beyond the openings of the ureters, and are named the **plicæ uretericæ**; they are produced by the terminal portions of the ureters as they traverse obliquely the bladder wall. When the bladder is illuminated the torus uretericus appears as a pale band and forms an important guide during the operation of introducing a catheter into the ureter.

The **orifices of the ureters** are placed at the postero-lateral angles of the trigonum vesicæ, and are usually slit-like in form. In the contracted bladder they are about 2.5 cm. apart and about the same distance from the internal urethral orifice; in the distended viscus these measurements may be increased to about 5 cm.

The **internal urethral orifice** is placed at the apex of the trigonum vesicæ, in the most dependent part of the bladder, and is usually somewhat crescentic in form; the mucous membrane immediately behind it presents a slight elevation, the **uvula vesicæ**, caused by the middle lobe of the prostate.

Structure (Fig. 1129).—The bladder is composed of the four coats: **serous, muscular, submucous, and mucous coats.**

The **serous coat** (*tunica serosa*) is a partial one and is derived from the peritoneum. It invests the superior surface and the upper parts of the lateral surfaces, and is reflected from these on to the abdominal and pelvic walls.

The **muscular coat** (*tunica muscularis*) consists of three layers of unstriped muscular fibers: an external layer, composed of fibers having for the most part a longitudinal arrangement; a middle layer, in which the fibers are arranged, more or less, in a circular manner; and an internal layer, in which the fibers have a general longitudinal arrangement (Fig. 1130).

The *fibers of the external layer* arise from the posterior surface of the body of the pubis in both sexes (*musculi pubovesicales*), and in the male from the adjacent part of the prostate and its capsule. They pass, in a more or less longitudinal manner, up the inferior surface of the bladder, over its vertex, and then descend along its fundus to become attached to the prostate in the male, and to the front of the vagina in the female. At the sides of the bladder the fibers are arranged obliquely and intersect one another. This layer has been named the **Detrusor urinæ muscle.**

The *fibers of the middle circular layer* are very thinly and irregularly scattered on the body of the organ, and, although to some extent placed transversely to the long axis of the bladder, are for the most part arranged obliquely. Toward the lower part of the bladder, around the internal urethral orifice, they are disposed in a thick circular layer, forming the **Sphincter vesicæ**, which is continuous with the muscular fibers of the prostate.

The *internal longitudinal layer* is thin, and its fasciculi have a reticular arrangement, but with a tendency to assume for the most part a longitudinal direction. Two bands of oblique fibers, originating behind the orifices of the ureters, converge to the back part of the prostate, and are inserted by means of a fibrous process, into the middle lobe of that organ. They are the **muscles of the ureters**, described by Sir C. Bell, who supposed that during the contraction of the bladder they serve to retain the oblique direction of the ureters, and so prevent the reflux of the urine into them.

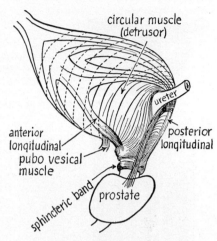

FIG. 1130.—Diagram of the muscle of the bladder (after McCrea).

The **submucous coat** (*tela submucosa*) consists of a layer of areolar tissue, connecting together the muscular and mucous coats, and intimately united to the latter.

The **mucous coat** (*tunica mucosa*) is thin, smooth, and of a pale rose color. It is continuous above through the ureters with the lining membrane of the renal tubules, and below with that of the urethra. The loose texture of the submucous layer allows the mucous coat to be thrown into folds or *rugæ* when the bladder is empty. Over the trigonum vesicæ the mucous membrane is closely attached to the muscular coat, and is not thrown into folds, but is smooth and flat. The epithelium covering it is of the transitional variety, consisting of a superficial layer of polyhedral flattened cells, each with one, two, or three nuclei; beneath these is a stratum of large club-shaped cells, with their narrow extremities directed downward and wedged in between smaller spindle-shaped cells, containing oval nuclei (Fig. 1129). The epithelium varies according as the bladder is distended or contracted. In the former condition the superficial cells are flattened and those of the other layers are shortened; in the latter they present the appearance described above. There are no true glands in the mucous membrane of the bladder, though certain mucous follicles which exist, especially near the neck of the bladder, have been regarded as such.

Vessels and Nerves.—The **arteries** supplying the bladder are the superior, middle, and inferior vesical, derived from the anterior trunk of the hypogastric. The obturator and inferior gluteal arteries also supply small visceral branches to the bladder, and in the female additional branches are derived from the uterine and vaginal arteries.

The **veins** form a complicated plexus on the inferior surface, and fundus near the prostate, and end in the hypogastric veins.

The **lymphatics** are described on page 806.

The **nerves** of the bladder are (1) fine medullated fibers from the third and fourth sacral nerves, and (2) non-medullated fibers from the hypogastric plexus. They are connected with ganglia in the outer and submucous coats and are finally distributed, all as non-medullated fibers, to the muscular layer and epithelial lining of the viscus.

Variations.—A defect of development, in which the bladder is implicated, is known under the name of *extroversion of the bladder*. In this condition the lower part of the abdominal wall and the anterior wall of the bladder are wanting, so that the fundus of the bladder presents on the abdominal surface, and is pushed forward by the pressure of the viscera within the abdomen, forming a red vascular tumor on which the openings of the ureters are visible. The penis, except the glans, is rudimentary and is cleft on its dorsal surface, exposing the floor of the urethra, a condition known as *epispadias*. The pelvic bones are also arrested in development.

The Male Urethra (Urethra Virilis) (Fig. 1131).

The **male urethra** extends from the internal urethral orifice in the urinary bladder to the external urethral orifice at the end of the penis. It presents a double curve in the ordinary relaxed state of the penis (Fig. 1123).

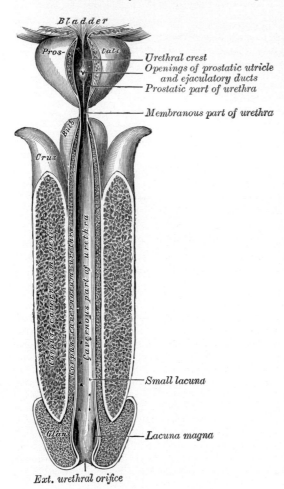

FIG. 1131.—The male urethra laid open on its anterior (upper) surface.

Its length varies from 17.5 to 20 cm.; and it is divided into three portions, the **prostatic, membranous**, and **cavernous**, the structure and relations of which are essentially different. Except during the passage of the urine or semen, the greater part of the urethral canal is a mere transverse cleft or slit, with its upper and under surfaces in contact; at the external orifice the slit is vertical, in the membranous portion irregular or stellate, and in the prostatic portion somewhat arched.

The **prostatic portion** (*pars prostatica*), the widest and most dilatable part of the canal, is about 3 cm. long, It runs almost vertically through the prostate from its base to its apex, lying nearer its anterior than its posterior surface; the form of the canal is spindle-shaped, being wider in the middle than at either extremity, and narrowest below, where it joins the membranous portion. A transverse section of the canal as it lies in the prostate is horseshoe-shaped, with the convexity directed forward.

Upon the posterior wall or floor is a narrow longitudinal ridge, the **urethral crest** (*verumontanum*), formed by an elevation of the mucous membrane and its subjacent tissue. It is from 15 to 17 mm. in length, and about 3 mm. in height. On either side of the crest is a slightly depressed fossa, the **prostatic sinus**, the floor of which is perforated by numerous apertures, the **orifices of the prostatic ducts** from the lateral lobes of the prostate; the ducts of the middle lobe open behind the crest. At the forepart of the urethral crest, below its summit, is a median elevation, the **colliculus seminalis**, upon or within the margins of which are the orifices of the prostatic utricle and the slit-like openings of the ejaculatory ducts. The **prostatic utricle** (*sinus pocularis*) forms a cul-de-sac about 6 mm. long, which runs upward and backward in the substance of the prostate behind the middle lobe. Its walls are composed of fibrous tissue, muscular fibers, and mucous membrane, and numerous small glands open on its inner surface. It was called by Weber the **uterus masculinus**, from its being developed from the united lower ends of the atrophied Müllerian ducts, and therefore homologous with the uterus and vagina in the female.

The **membranous portion** (*pars membranacea*) is the shortest, least dilatable, and, with the exception of the external orifice, the narrowest part of the canal. It extends downward and forward, with a slight anterior concavity, between the apex of the prostate and the bulb of the urethra, perforating the urogenital diaphragm about 2.5 cm. below and behind the pubic symphysis. The hinder part of the urethral bulb lies in apposition with the superficial layer of the urogenital diaphragm, but its upper portion diverges somewhat from this fascia: the anterior wall of the membranous urethra is thus prolonged for a short distance in front of the urogenital diaphragm; it measures about 2 cm. in length, while the posterior wall which is between the two fasciæ of the diaphragm is only 1.25 cm. long.

The membranous portion of the urethra is completely surrounded by the fibers of the Sphincter urethræ membranaceæ. In front of it the deep dorsal vein of the penis enters the pelvis between the transverse ligament of the pelvis and the arcuate pubic ligament; on either side near its termination are the bulbourethral glands.

The **cavernous portion** (*pars cavernosa; penile or spongy portion*) is the longest part of the urethra, and is contained in the corpus cavernosum urethræ. It is about 15 cm. long, and extends from the termination of the membranous portion to the external urethral orifice. Commencing below the superficial layer of the urogenital diaphragm it passes forward and upward to the front of the symphysis pubis; and then, in the flaccid condition of the penis, it bends downward and forward. It is narrow, and of uniform size in the body of the penis, measuring about 6 mm. in diameter; it is dilated behind, within the bulb, and again anteriorly within the glans penis, where it forms the **fossa navicularis urethræ.**

The **external urethral orifice** (*orificium urethræ externum; meatus urinarius*) is the most contracted part of the urethra; it is a vertical slit, about 6 mm. long, bounded on either side by two small labia.

The lining membrane of the urethra, especially on the floor of the cavernous portion, presents the orifices of numerous mucous glands and follicles situated in the submucous tissue, and named the **urethral glands** (*Littré*). Besides these there are a number of small pit-like recesses, or **lacunæ**, of varying sizes. Their orifices are directed forward, so that they may easily intercept the point of a catheter in its passage along the canal. One of these lacunæ, larger than the rest, is situated on the upper surface of the fossa navicularis; it is called the **lacuna magna.** The bulbo-urethral glands open into the cavernous portion about 2.5 cm. in front of the inferior fascia of the urogenital diaphragm.

Structure.—The urethra is composed of mucous membrane, supported by a submucous tissue which connects it with the various structures through which it passes.

The **mucous coat** forms part of the genito-urinary mucous membrane. It is continuous with the mucous membrane of the bladder, ureters, and kidneys; externally, with the integument covering the glans penis; and is prolonged into the ducts of the glands which open into the urethra, *viz.*, the bulbo-urethral glands and the prostate; and into the ductus deferentes and vesiculæ seminales, through the ejaculatory ducts. In the cavernous and membranous portions the mucous membrane is arranged in longitudinal folds when the tube is empty. Small papillæ are found upon it, near the external urethral orifice; its epithelial lining is of the columnar variety except near the external orifice, where it is squamous and stratified.

The submucosa has a characteristic structure. It is composed of a thick stroma of connective tissue very rich in elastic fibers. These fibers connect freely with the spongy tissue of the penis which prevents ready removal of the mucosa in this region. However, in the membranous and prostatic portions, which change but little during erection, the urethra is quite free and may on dissection be stripped readily.

Congenital defects of the urethra occur occasionally. The one most frequently met with is where there is a cleft on the floor of the urethra owing to an arrest of union in the middle line. This is known as *hypospadias*, and the cleft may vary in extent. The simplest and by far the most common form is where the deficiency is confined to the glans penis. The urethra ends at the point where the extremity of the prepuce joins the body of the penis, in a small valve-like opening. The prepuce is also cleft on its under surface and forms a sort of hood over the glans.

There is a depression on the glans in the position of the normal meatus. This condition produces no disability and requires no treatment. In more severe cases the cavernous portion of the urethra is cleft throughout its entire length, and the opening of the urethra is at the point of junction of the penis and scrotum. The under surface of the penis in the middle line presents a furrow lined by a moist mucous membrane, on either side of which is often more or less dense fibrous tissue stretching from the glans to the opening of the urethra, which prevents complete erection taking place. Great discomfort is induced during micturition, and sexual connection is impossible. The condition may be remedied by a series of plastic operations. The worst form of this condition is where the urethra is deficient as far back as the perineum, and the scrotum is cleft. The penis is small and bound down between the two halves of the scrotum, so as to resemble an hypertrophied clitoris. The testes are often retained. The condition of parts, therefore, very much resembles the external organs of generation of the female, and many children the victims of this malformation have been brought up as girls. The halves of the scrotum, deficient of testes, resemble the labia, the cleft between them looks like the orifice of the vagina, and the diminutive penis is taken for an enlarged clitoris. There is no remedy for this condition.

A much more uncommon form of malformation is where there is an apparent deficiency of the upper wall of the urethra; this is named *epispadias*. The deficiency may vary in extent; when it is complete the condition is associated with extroversion of the bladder. In less extensive cases, where there is no extroversion, there is an infundibuliform opening into the bladder. The penis is usually dwarfed and turned upward, so that the glans lies over the opening. Congenital stricture is also occasionally met with, and in such cases multiple strictures may be present throughout the whole length of the cavernous portion.

The Female Urethra (Urethra Muliebris) (Fig. 1127).

The **female urethra** is a narrow membranous canal, about 4 cm. long, extending from the internal to the external urethral orifice. It is placed behind the symphysis pubis, imbedded in the anterior wall of the vagina, and its direction is obliquely downward and forward; it is slightly curved with the concavity directed forward. Its diameter when undilated is about 6 mm. It perforates the fasciæ of the urogenital diaphragm, and its external orifice is situated directly in front of the vaginal opening and about 2.5 cm. behind the glans clitoridis. The lining membrane is thrown into longitudinal folds, one of which, placed along the floor of the canal, is termed the **urethral crest.** Many small urethral glands open into the urethra. The largest of these are the paraurethral glands (Skene) the ducts of which open just within the urethral orifice.

Structure.—The urethra consists of three coats: **muscular, erectile,** and **mucous.**

The **muscular coat** is continuous with that of the bladder; it extends the whole length of the tube, and consists of circular fibers. In addition to this, between the superior and inferior fasciæ of the urogenital diaphragm, the female urethra is surrounded by the Sphincter urethræ membraneceæ, as in the male.

A **thin layer of spongy erectile tissue,** containing a plexus of large veins, intermixed with bundles of unstriped muscular fibers, lies immediately beneath the mucous coat.

The **mucous coat** is pale; it is continuous externally with that of the vulva, and internally with that of the bladder. It is lined by stratified squamous epithelium, which becomes transitional near the bladder. Its external orifice is surrounded by a few mucous follicles.

THE MALE GENITAL ORGANS (ORGANA GENITALIA VIRILIA).

The male genitals include the **testes,** the **ductus deferentes,** the **vesiculæ seminales,** the **ejaculatory ducts,** and the **penis,** together with the following accessory structures, *viz.,* the **prostate** and the **bulbourethral glands.**

The Testes and Their Coverings (Figs. 1132, 1133).

The **testes** are two glandular organs, which produce the semen; they are suspended in the scrotum by the spermatic cords. At an early period of fetal life the testes are contained in the abdominal cavity, behind the peritoneum. Before birth they descend to the inguinal canal, along which they pass with the spermatic cord, and, emerging at the subcutaneous inguinal ring, descend into the scrotum, becoming invested in their course by coverings derived from the serous, muscular, and fibrous layers of the abdominal parietes, as well as by the scrotum.

The **coverings of the testes** are, the

Skin	Cremasteric layer
Dartos tunic }Scrotum	Internal spermatic fascia.
External spermatic fascia.	Tunica vaginalis.

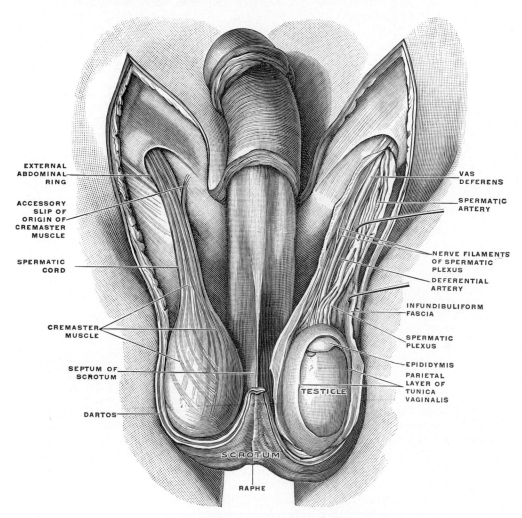

FIG. 1132.—The scrotum. The penis has been turned upward, and the anterior wall of the scrotum has been removed. On the right side, the spermatic cord, the infundibuliform fascia, and the Cremaster muscles are displayed; on the left side, the infundibuliform fascia has been divided by a longitudinal incision passing along the front of the cord and the testicle, and a portion of the parietal layer of the tunica vaginalis has been removed to display the testicle and a portion of the head of the epididymis, which are covered by the visceral layer of the tunica vaginalis. (Toldt.)

The **Scrotum** is a cutaneous pouch which contains the testes and parts of the spermatic cords. It is divided on its surface into two lateral portions by a ridge or **raphé,** which is continued forward to the under surface of the penis, and backward, along the middle line of the perineum to the anus. Of these two lateral portions the left hangs lower than the right, to correspond with the greater length of the left spermatic cord. Its external aspect varies under different circumstances: thus, under the influence of warmth, and in old and debilitated persons, it becomes elongated and flaccid; but, under the influence of cold, and in the young and robust, it is short, corrugated, and closely applied to the testes.

The scrotum consists of two layers, the **integument** and the **dartos tunic.**

The **Integument** is very thin, of a brownish color, and generally thrown into folds or rugæ. It is provided with sebaceous follicles, the secretion of which has a peculiar odor, and is beset with thinly scattered, crisp hairs, the roots of which are seen through the skin.

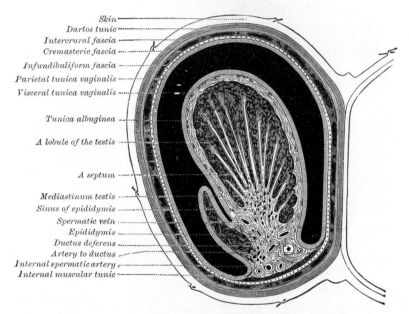

Skin
Dartos tunic
Intercrural fascia
Cremasteric fascia
Infundibuliform fascia
Parietal tunica vaginalis
Visceral tunica vaginalis
Tunica albuginea
A lobule of the testis
A septum
Mediastinum testis
Sinus of epididymis
Spermatic vein
Epididymis
Ductus deferens
Artery to ductus
Internal spermatic artery
Internal muscular tunic

Fig. 1133.—Transverse section through the left side of the scrotum and the left testis. The sac of the tunica vaginalis is represented in a distended condition. (Diagrammatic.) (Delépine.)

The **Dartos Tunic** (*tunica dartos*) contains a thin layer of non-striped muscular fibers, continuous, around the base of the scrotum, with the two layers of the superficial fascia of the groin and the perineum; it sends inward a septum, which divides the scrotal pouch into two cavities for the testes, and extends between the raphé and the under surface of the penis, as far as its root.

The dartos tunic is closely united to the skin externally, but is separated from the subjacent parts by a distinct fascial cleft, upon which it glides with the greatest facility. It contains no fat and is highly vascular.

The **Tunica Vaginalis** is described with the testes.

The **External Spermatic Fascia** (*intercrural or intercolumnar fascia*) is a thin membrane prolonged downward over the cord and testis. It is continuous, at the subcutaneous inguinal ring, with the deep fascia covering the aponeurosis of the Obliquus externus abdominis (fascia innominata of Gallaudet) and is therefore part of the external investing fascia of the body. It is separated from the enclosing dartos by a fascial cleft (page 473).

The **Cremasteric Layer** consists of the scattered bundles of the Cremaster connected into a continuous membrane by the cremasteric fascia. It forms the *middle* *spermatic layer* and corresponds to the Obliquus internus abdominis and its fasciæ (page 459).

The **Internal Spermatic Fascia** (*infundibuliform fascia; tunica vaginalis communis*) is a thin membrane, often difficult to separate from the preceding, but more easily separated from the cord and testis which it encloses. It is continuous at the internal inguinal ring with the transversalis fascia (page 464).

Vessels and Nerves.—The **arteries** supplying the coverings of the testes are: the superficial and deep external pudendal branches of the femoral, the superficial perineal branch of the internal pudendal, and the cremasteric branch from the inferior epigastric. The **veins** follow the course of the corresponding arteries. The **lymphatics** end in the inguinal lymph nodes. The **nerves** are the ilioinguinal and lumboinguinal branches of the lumbar plexus, the two superficial perineal branches of the internal pudendal nerve, and the pudendal branch of the posterior femoral cutaneous nerve.

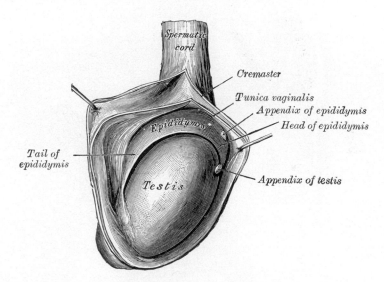

Fig. 1134.—The right testis, exposed by laying open the tunica vaginalis.

The **Inguinal Canal** (*canalis inguinalis*) is described on page 467.

The **Spermatic Cord** (*funiculus spermaticus*) (Fig. 1135) extends from the abdominal inguinal ring, where the structures of which it is composed converge, to the back part of the testis. In the abdominal wall the cord passes obliquely along the inguinal canal, lying at first beneath the Obliquus internus, and upon the fascia transversalis; but nearer the pubis, it rests upon the inguinal and lacunar ligaments, having the aponeurosis of the Obliquus externus in front of it, and the inguinal fàlx behind it. It then escapes at the subcutaneous ring, and descends nearly vertically into the scrotum. The left cord is rather longer than the right, consequently the left testis hangs somewhat lower than the right.

Structure of the Spermatic Cord.—The spermatic cord is composed of arteries, veins, lymphatics, nerves, and the excretory duct of the testis. These structures are connected together by the **innermost spermatic fascia** which is continuous with the subserous fascia of the abdomen at the internal inguinal ring, and are invested by the layers brought down by the testis in its descent.

The **arteries of the cord** are: the internal and external spermatics; and the artery to the ductus deferens.

The *internal spermatic artery*, a branch of the abdominal aorta, escapes from the abdomen at the abdominal inguinal ring, and accompanies the other constituents of the spermatic cord along the inguinal canal and through the subcutaneous inguinal ring into the scrotum. It then descends to the testis, and, becoming tortuous, divides into several branches, two or three of which accompany the ductus deferens and supply the epididymis, anastomosing with the artery of the ductus deferens: the others supply the substance of the testis.

The *external spermatic artery* is a branch of the inferior epigastric artery. It accompanies the spermatic cord and supplies the coverings of the cord, anastomosing with the internal spermatic artery.

The *artery of the ductus deferens*, a branch of the superior vesical, is a long, slender vessel, which accompanies the ductus deferens, ramifying upon its coats, and anastomosing with the internal spermatic artery near the testis.

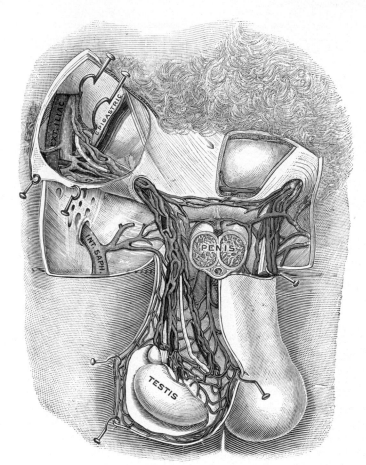

Fig. 1135.—Spermatic veins and spermatic cord. (Testut.)

The **spermatic veins** (Fig. 1135) emerge from the back of the testis, and receive tributaries from the epididymis: they unite and form a convoluted plexus, the **plexus pampiniformis**, which forms the chief mass of the cord; the vessels composing this plexus are very numerous, and ascend along the cord in front of the ductus deferens; below the subcutaneous inguinal ring they unite to form three or four veins, which pass along the inguinal canal, and, entering the abdomen through the abdominal inguinal ring, coalesce to form two veins. These again unite to form a single vein, which opens on the right side into the inferior vena cava, at an acute angle, and on the left side into the left renal vein, at a right angle.

The **lymphatic vessels** are described on page 807.

The **nerves** are the spermatic plexus from the sympathetic, joined by filaments from the pelvic plexus which accompany the artery of the ductus deferens.

The scrotum forms an admirable covering for the protection of the testes. These bodies, lying suspended and loose in the cavity of the scrotum and surrounded by serous membrane, are capable of great mobility, and can therefore easily slip about within the scrotum and thus avoid injuries from blows or squeezes. The skin of the scrotum is very elastic and capable of great distension, and on account of the looseness and amount of subcutaneous tissue, the scrotum becomes greatly enlarged in cases of edema, to which this part is especially liable as a result of its dependent position.

The **Testes** are suspended in the scrotum by the spermatic cords. They average 4 to 5 cm. in length, 2.5 cm. in breadth, and 3 cm. in the antero-posterior diameter. The weight of one gland varies from 10.5 to 14 gm. Each testis is of an oval form (Fig. 1134), compressed laterally, and having an oblique position in the scrotum; the upper extremity is directed forward and a little lateralward; the lower, backward and a little medialward; the anterior convex border looks forward and downward, the posterior or straight border, to which the cord is attached, backward and upward.

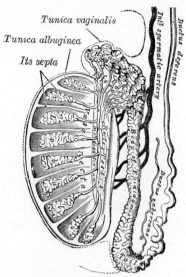

The anterior border and lateral surfaces, as well as both extremities of the organ, are convex, free, smooth, and invested by the visceral layer of the tunica vaginalis. The posterior border, to which the cord is attached, receives only a partial investment from that membrane. Lying upon the lateral edge of this posterior border is a long, narrow, flattened body, named the **epididymis**.

The **epididymis** consists of a central portion or **body;** an upper enlarged extremity, the **head** (*globus major*); and a lower pointed extremity, the **tail** (*globus minor*), which is continuous with the ductus deferens, the **duct of the testis.** The head is intimately con-

Fig. 1136.—Vertical section of the testis, to show the arrangement of the ducts.

nected with the upper end of the testis by means of the efferent ductules of the gland; the tail is connected with the lower end by cellular tissue, and a reflection of the tunica vaginalis. The lateral surface, head and tail of the epididymis are free and covered by the serous membrane; the body is also completely invested by it, excepting along its posterior border; while between the body and the testis is a pouch, named the **sinus of the epididymis** (*digital fossa*). The epididymis is connected to the back of the testis by a fold of the serous membrane.

Appendages of the Testis and Epididymis.—On the upper extremity of the testis, just beneath the head of the epididymis, is a minute oval, sessile body, the **appendix of the testis** (*hydatid of Morgagni*); it is the remnant of the upper end of the Müllerian duct. On the head of the epididymis is a second small stalked appendage (sometimes duplicated); it is named the **appendix of the epididymis** (*pedunculated hydatid*), and is usually regarded as a detached efferent duct.

The testis is invested by three tunics: the **tunica vaginalis, tunica albuginea,** and **tunica vasculosa.**

The **Tunica Vaginalis** (*tunica vaginalis propria testis*) is the serous covering of the testis. It is a pouch of serous membrane, derived from the saccus vaginalis of the peritoneum, which in the fetus preceded the descent of the testis from the abdomen into the scrotum. After its descent, that portion of the pouch which extends from the abdominal inguinal ring to near the upper part of the gland becomes obliterated; the lower portion remains as a closed sac, which invests the testis, and may be described as consisting of a **visceral** and a **parietal lamina.**

The **visceral lamina** (*lamina visceralis*) covers the greater part of the testis and epididymis, connecting the latter to the testis by means of a distinct fold. From the posterior border of the gland it is reflected on to the internal surface of the scrotal coverings.

The **parietal lamina** (lamina parietalis) is more extensive than the visceral, extending upward for some distance in front and on the medial side of the cord, and reaching below the testis. The inner surface of the tunica vaginalis is smooth, and covered by a layer of mesothelial cells. The interval between the visceral and parietal laminæ constitutes the cavity of the tunica vaginalis.

The obliterated portion of the saccus vaginalis may generally be seen as a fibrocellular thread lying in the loose areolar tissue around the spermatic cord; sometimes this may be traced as a distinct band from the upper end of the inguinal canal, where it is connected with the peritoneum, down to the tunica vaginalis; sometimes it gradually becomes lost on the spermatic cord. Occasionally no trace of it can be detected. In some cases it happens that the pouch of peritoneum does not become obliterated, but the sac of the peritoneum communicates with the tunica vaginalis. This may give rise to one of the varieties of oblique inguinal hernia (page 1357). In other cases the pouch may contract, but not become entirely obliterated; it then forms a minute canal leading from the peritoneum to the tunica vaginalis.

The **Tunica Albuginea** is the fibrous covering of the testis. It is a dense membrane, of a bluish-white color, composed of bundles of white fibrous tissue which interlace in every direction. It is covered by the tunica vaginalis, except at the points of attachment of the epididymis to the testis, and along its posterior border, where the spermatic vessels enter the gland. It is applied to the tunica vasculosa over the glandular substance of the testis, and, at its posterior border, is reflected into the interior of the gland, forming an incomplete vertical septum, called the **mediastinum testis** (*corpus Highmori*).

The **mediastinum testis** extends from the upper to near the lower extremity of the gland, and is wider above than below. From its front and sides numerous imperfect septa (*trabeculæ*) are given off, which radiate toward the surface of the organ, and are attached to the tunica albuginea. They divide the interior of the organ into a number of incomplete spaces which are somewhat cone-shaped, being broad at their bases at the surface of the gland, and becoming narrower as they converge to the mediastinum. The mediastinum supports the vessels and ducts of the testis in their passage to and from the substance of the gland.

The **Tunica Vasculosa** is the vascular layer of the testis, consisting of a plexus of bloodvessels, held together by delicate areolar tissue. It clothes the inner surface of the tunica albuginea and the different septa in the interior of the gland, and therefore forms an internal investment to all the spaces of which the gland is composed.

Structure.—The glandular structure of the testis consists of numerous lobules. Their number, in a single testis, is estimated by Berres at 250, and by Krause at 400. They differ in size according to their position, those in the middle of the gland being larger and longer. The lobules (Fig. 1136) are conical in shape, the base being directed toward the circumference of the organ, the apex toward the mediastinum. Each lobule is contained in one of the intervals between the fibrous septa which extend between the mediastinum testis and the tunica albuginea, and consists of from one to three, or more, minute convoluted tubes, the **tubuli seminiferi**. The tubules may be separately unravelled, by careful dissection under water, and may be seen to commence either by free cecal ends or by anastomotic loops. They are supported by loose connective tissue which contains here and there groups of "interstitial cells" containing yellow pigment granules. The total number of tubules is estimated by Lauth at 840, and the average length of each is 70 to 80 cm. Their diameter varies from 0.12 to 0.3 mm. The tubules are pale in color in early life, but in old age they acquire a deep yellow tinge from containing much fatty matter. Each tubule consists of a basement layer formed of laminated connective tissue containing numerous elastic fibers with flattened cells between the layers and covered externally by a layer of flattened epithelioid cells. Within the basement membrane are epithelial cells arranged in several irregular layers, which are not always clearly separated, but which may be arranged in three different groups (Fig. 1138). Among these cells may be seen the **spermatozoa** in different stages of development. (1) Lining the basement membrane and forming the outer zone is a layer of cubical cells, with small nuclei; some of these enlarge to become **spermatogonia.** The nuclei of some of the spermatogonia may be seen to be in process of indirect division (*karyokinesis*, page 21), and in consequence of this daughter cells are formed, which constitute the second zone. (2) Within this first layer are to be seen a number of larger polyhedral cells, with clear nuclei, arranged in two or three layers; these are the **intermediate cells** or **spermatocytes.** Most of these cells are in a condition of karyokinetic division, and the cells which result from this division form those of the next layer, the **spermatoblasts** or **spermatids.** (3) The third layer of cells consists of the spermatoblasts or spermatids, and each of these, without further subdivision, becomes a **spermatozoön.** The spermatids are small polyhedral cells, the nucleus of each of which contains half the usual number of chromosomes. In addition to these three layers of

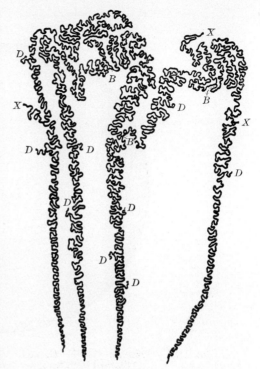

FIG. 1137.—Four seminiferous tubules from human testis showing anastomosing loops. *B*, branching or fork; *D*, diverticulum; *X*, broken end. (Johnson, Anat. Rec., 1934; courtesy of Wistar Institute.)

cells others are seen, which are termed the **supporting cells** (*cells of Sertoli*). They are elongated and columnar, and project inward from the basement membrane toward the lumen of the tube. As development of the spermatozoa proceeds the latter group themselves around the inner extremities of the supporting cells. The nuclear portion of the spermatid, which is partly imbedded in the supporting cell, is differentiated to form the head of the spermatozoön, while part of the cell protoplasm forms the middle piece and the tail is produced by an outgrowth from the double centriole of the cell. Ultimately the heads are liberated and the spermatozoa are set free. The structure of the spermatozoa is described on page 24.

In the apices of the lobules, the tubules become less convoluted, assume a nearly straight course, and unite together to form from twenty to thirty larger ducts, of about 0.5 mm. in diameter, and these, from their straight course, are called **tubuli recti** (Fig. 1136).

The **tubuli recti** enter the fibrous tissue of the mediastinum, and pass upward and backward, forming, in their ascent, a close net-work of anastomosing tubes which are merely channels in the fibrous stroma, lined by flattened epithelium, and having no proper walls; this constitutes the **rete testis.** At the upper end of the mediastinum, the vessels of the rete testis terminate in from twelve to fifteen or twenty ducts, the **ductuli efferentes;** they perforate the tunica albuginea, and carry the seminal fluid from the testis to the epididymis. Their course is at first straight; they then become enlarged, and exceedingly convoluted, and form a series of conical masses, the **coni vasculosi,** which together constitute the head of the epididymis. Each cone consists of a single convoluted duct, from 15 to 20 cm. in length, the diameter of which gradually decreases from the testis to the epididymis. Opposite the bases of the cones the efferent vessels open at narrow intervals into a single duct, which constitutes, by its complex convolutions, the body and tail of the epididymis. When the convolutions of this tube are unravelled, it measures upward of 6 meters in length; it increases in diameter and thickness as it approaches the ductus deferens. The convolutions are held together by fine areolar tissue, and by bands of fibrous tissue.

The tubuli recti have very thin walls; like the channels of the rete testis they are lined by a single layer of flattened epithelium. The ductuli efferentes and the tube of the epididymis have

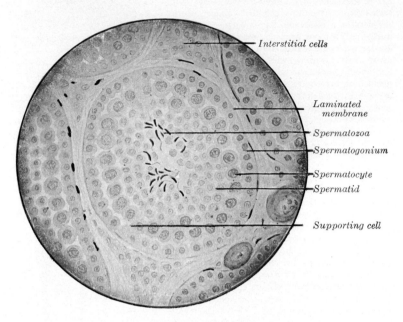

FIG. 1138.—Transverse section through a seminiferous tubule of a human testis. Stained with hematoxyline and eosin.   × 350.

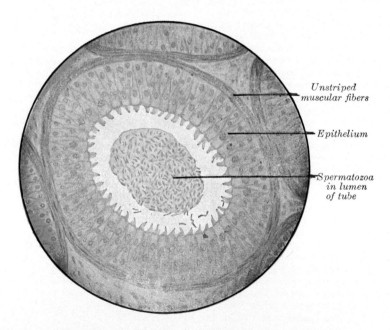

FIG. 1139.—Transverse section through the tube of the human epididymis. Stained with hematoxylin and eosin.   × 350.

walls of considerable thickness, on account of the presence in them of muscular tissue, which is principally arranged in a circular manner. These tubes are lined by columnar ciliated epithelium (Fig. 1139).

Variations.—The testis, developed in the lumbar region, may be arrested or delayed in its transit to the scrotum (*cryptorchism*). It may be retained in the abdomen; or it may be arrested at the abdominal inguinal ring, or in the inguinal canal; or it may just pass out of the subcutaneous inguinal ring without finding its way to the bottom of the scrotum. When retained in the abdomen it gives rise to no symptoms, other than the absence of the testis from the scrotum; but when it is retained in the inguinal canal it is subjected to pressure and may become inflamed and painful. The retained testis is probably functionally useless; so that a man in whom both testes are retained (*anorchism*) is sterile, though he may not be impotent. The absence of one testis is termed *monorchism*. When a testis is retained in the inguinal canal it is often complicated with a congenital hernia, the funicular process of the peritoneum not being obliterated. In addition to the cases above described, where there is some arrest in the descent of the testis, this organ may descend through the inguinal canal, but may miss the scrotum and assume some abnormal position. The most common form is where the testis, emerging at the subcutaneous inguinal ring, slips down between the scrotum and thigh and comes to rest in the perineum. This is known as *perineal ectopia testis*. With each variety of abnormality in the position of the testis, it is very common to find concurrently a congenital hernia, or, if a hernia be not actually present, the funicular process is usually patent, and almost invariably so if the testis is in the inguinal canal.

The testis, finally reaching the scrotum, may occupy an abnormal position in it. It may be inverted, so that its posterior or attached border is directed forward and the tunica vaginalis is situated behind.

Fluid collections of a serous character are very frequently found in the scrotum. To these the term *hydrocele* is applied. The most common form is the ordinary *vaginal hydrocele*, in which the fluid is contained in the sac of the tunica vaginalis, which is separated, in its normal condition, from the peritoneal cavity by the whole extent of the inguinal canal. In another form, the *congenital hydrocele*, the fluid is in the sac of the tunica vaginalis, but this cavity communicates with the general peritoneal cavity, its tubular process remaining pervious. A third variety, known as an *infantile hydrocele*, occurs in those cases where the tubular process becomes obliterated only at its upper part, at or near the abdominal inguinal ring. It resembles the vaginal hydrocele, except as regards its shape, the collection of fluid extending up the cord into the inguinal canal. Fourthly, the funicular process may become obliterated both at the abdominal inguinal ring and above the epididymis, leaving a central unobliterated portion, which may become distended with fluid, giving rise to a condition known as the *encysted hydrocele of the cord*.

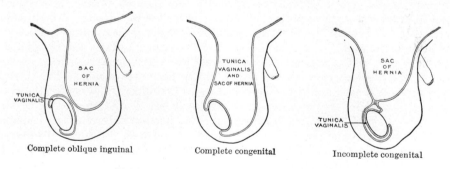

Complete oblique inguinal — Complete congenital — Incomplete congenital

Fig. 1140.—Varieties of oblique inguinal hernia.

Congenital Hernia.— There are some varieties of oblique inguinal hernia (Fig. 1140) depending upon congenital defects in the saccus vaginalis, the pouch of peritoneum which precedes the descent of the testis.

Normally this pouch is closed before birth, closure commencing at two points, *viz.*, at the abdominal inguinal ring and at the top of the epididymis, and gradually extending until the whole of the intervening portion is converted into a fibrous cord. From failure in the completion of this process, variations in the relation of the hernial protrusion to the testis and tunica vaginalis are produced; these constitute distinct varieties of inguinal hernia, *viz.*, the hernia of the funicular process and the complete congenital variety. Mitchell states that of 40 still-born infants examined, 7 showed complete obliteration of the saccus vaginalis on both sides, 12 showed sacs completely patent on both sides, and 21 exhibited all intermediate degrees of obliteration.

Where the saccus vaginalis remains patent throughout, the cavity of the tunica vaginalis communicates directly with that of the peritoneum. The intestine descends along this pouch into the cavity of the tunica vaginalis which constitutes the sac of the hernia, and the gut lies in contact with the testis. Though this form of hernia is termed *complete congenital*, the term does not imply that the hernia existed at birth, but merely that a condition is present which may allow of the descent of the hernia at any moment. As a matter of fact, congenital herniæ frequently do not appear until adult life. Where the processus vaginalis is occluded at the lower point only, *i. e.*, just above the testis, the intestine descends into the pouch of peritoneum as far as the testis, but is prevented from entering the sac of the tunica vaginalis by the septum which has formed between it and the pouch. This is known as *hernia into the funicular process* or *incomplete congenital hernia;* it differs from the former in that instead of enveloping the testis it lies above it.

The Ductus Deferens (Vas Deferens; Seminal Duct).

The **ductus deferens**, the excretory duct of the testis, is the continuation of the canal of the epididymis. Commencing at the lower part of the tail of the epididymis it is at first very tortuous, but gradually becoming less twisted it ascends along the posterior border of the testis and medial side of the epididymis, and, as a constituent of the spermatic cord, traverses the inguinal canal to the abdominal inguinal ring (Fig. 447). Here it separates from the other structures of the cord, curves around the lateral side of the inferior epigastric artery, and ascends for about 2.5 cm. in front of the external iliac artery (Fig. 580). It is next directed backward and slightly downward, and, crossing the external iliac vessels obliquely, enters the pelvic cavity, where it lies between the peritoneal membrane and the lateral wall of the pelvis, and descends on the medial side of the obliterated umbilical artery and the obturator nerve and vessels. It then crosses in front of the ureter, and, reaching the medial side of this tube, bends to form an acute angle, and runs medialward and slightly forward between the fundus of the bladder and the upper end of the seminal vesicle (Fig. 1141). Reaching the medial side of the seminal vesicle, it is directed downward and medialward in contact with it, gradually approaching the opposite ductus. Here it lies between the fundus of the bladder and the rectum, where it is enclosed, together with the seminal vesicle, in a sheath derived from the rectovesical portion of the subserous fascia. Lastly, it is directed downward to the base of the prostate, where it becomes greatly narrowed, and is joined at an acute angle by the duct of the seminal vesicle to form the ejaculatory duct, which traverses the prostate behind its middle lobe and opens into the prostatic portion of the urethra, close to the orifice of the prostatic utricle. The ductus deferens presents a hard and cord-like sensation to the fingers, and is of cylindrical form; its walls are dense, and its canal is extremely small. At the fundus of the bladder it becomes enlarged and tortuous, and this portion is termed the **ampulla**. A small triangular area of the fundus of the bladder, between the ductus deferentes laterally and the bottom of the rectovesical excavation of peritoneum above, is in contact with the rectum.

Ductuli Aberrantes.—A long narrow tube, the **ductulus aberrans inferior** (*vas aberrans of Haller*), is occasionally found connected with the lower part of the canal of the epididymis, or with the commencement of the ductus deferens. Its length varies from 3.5 to 35 cm., and it may become dilated toward its extremity; more commonly it retains the same diameter throughout. Its structure is similar to that of the ductus deferens. Occasionally it is found unconnected with the epididymis. A second tube, the **ductulus aberrans superior,** occurs in the head of the epididymis; it is connected with the rete testis.

Paradidymis (*organ of Giraldés*).—This term is applied to a small collection of convoluted tubules, situated in front of the lower part of the cord above the head of the epididymis. These tubes are lined with columnar ciliated epithelium, and probably represent the remains of a part of the Wolffian body.

Structure.—The ductus deferens consists of three coats: (1) an **external** or **areolar coat;** (2) a **muscular coat** which in the greater part of the tube consists of two layers of unstriped muscular fiber: an outer, longitudinal in direction, and an inner, circular; but in addition to these, at the commencement of the ductus, there is a third layer, consisting of longitudinal fibers, placed internal to the circular stratum, between it and the mucous membrane; (3) an **internal** or **mucous coat,** which is pale, and arranged in longitudinal folds. The mucous coat is lined by columnar epithelium which is non-ciliated throughout the greater part of the tube; a variable portion of the testicular end of the tube is lined by two strata of columnar cells and the cells of the superficial layer are ciliated.

The Seminal Vesicles (Vesiculæ Seminales) (Fig. 1141).

The **vesiculæ seminales** are two lobulated membranous pouches, placed between the fundus of the bladder and the rectum, which secrete a fluid to be added to the secretion of the testes. Each sac is somewhat pyramidal in form, the broad end being directed backward, upward and lateralward. It is usually about 7.5 cm. long, but varies in size, not only in different individuals, but also in the same individual on the two sides. The **anterior surface** is in contact with the fundus of the bladder, extending from near the termination of the ureter to the base of the

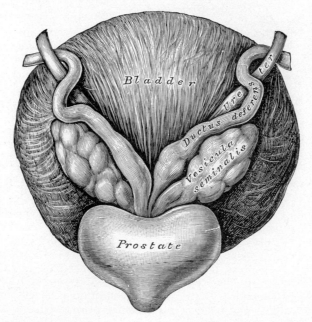

Fig. 1141.—Fundus of the bladder with the vesiculæ seminales.

prostate. The **posterior surface** rests upon the rectum, from which it is separated by the rectovesical fascia. The **upper extremities** of the two vesicles diverge from each other, and are in relation with the ductus deferentes and the terminations of the ureters, and are partly covered by peritoneum. The **lower extremities** are pointed, and converge toward the base of the prostate, where each joins with the corresponding ductus deferens to form the ejaculatory duct. Along the medial margin of each vesicle runs the ampulla of the ductus deferens.

Each vesicle consists of a single tube, coiled upon itself, and giving off several irregular cecal diverticula; the separate coils, as well as the diverticula, are connected together by fibrous tissue. When uncoiled, the tube is about the diameter of a quill, and varies in length from 10 to 15 cm.; it ends posteriorly in a cul-de-sac; its anterior extremity becomes constricted into a narrow straight duct, which joins with the corresponding ductus deferens to form the ejaculatory duct.

Structure.—The vesiculæ seminales are composed of three coats: an **external** or **areolar coat;** a **middle** or **muscular coat** thinner than in the ductus deferens and arranged in two layers, an outer longitudinal and inner circular; an **internal** or **mucous coat,** which is pale, of a whitish brown color, and presents a delicate reticular structure. The epithelium is columnar, and in the diverticula goblet cells are present, the secretion of which increases the bulk of the seminal fluid.

Vessels and Nerves.—The **arteries** supplying the vesiculæ seminales are derived from the middle and inferior vesical and middle hemorrhoidal. The **veins** and **lymphatics** accompany the arteries. The **nerves** are derived from the pelvic plexuses.

The Ejaculatory Ducts (Ductus Ejaculatorii) (Figs. 1123, 1142).

The **ejaculatory ducts** are two in number, one on either side of the middle line. Each is formed by the union of the duct from the vesicula seminalis with the ductus deferens, and is about 2 cm. long. They commence at the base of the prostate, and run forward and downward between its middle and lateral lobes, and along the sides of the prostatic utricle, to end by separate slit-like orifices close to or just within the margins of the utricle. The ducts diminish in size, and also converge, toward their terminations.

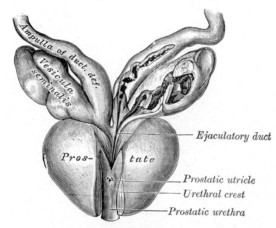

FIG. 1142.—Vesiculæ seminales and ampullæ of ductus deferentes, seen from the front. The anterior walls of the left ampulla, left seminal vesicle, and prostatic urethra have been cut away.

Structure.—The coats of the ejaculatory ducts are extremely thin. They are: an **outer fibrous layer,** which is almost entirely lost after the entrance of the ducts into the prostate; a **layer of muscular fibers** consisting of a thin outer circular, and an inner longitudinal, layer; and **mucous membrane.**

The Penis.

The **penis** is attached to the front and sides of the pubic arch and contains the greater part of the urethra. In the flaccid condition it is cylindrical in shape, but when erect assumes the form of a triangular prism with rounded angles, one side of the prism forming the dorsum. It is composed of three cylindrical masses of cavernous tissue bound together by fibrous tissue and covered with skin. Two of the masses are lateral, and are known as the **corpora cavernosa penis;** the third is median, and is termed the **corpus cavernosum urethræ** (Figs. 1144, 1146).

The integument covering the penis is remarkable for its thinness, its dark color, its looseness of connection with the deeper parts of the organ, and its absence of adipose tissue. At the root of the penis it is continuous with that over the pubes, scrotum, and perineum. At the neck it leaves the surface and becomes folded upon itself to form the **prepuce** or **foreskin.** The internal layer of the prepuce is directly continuous, along the line of the neck, with the integument over the glans. Immediately behind the external urethral orifice it forms a small secondary reduplication, attached along the bottom of a depressed median raphé, which extends from the meatus to the neck; this fold is termed the **frenulum** of the prepuce. The integument covering the glans is continuous with the urethral mucous membrane at the orifice; it is devoid of hairs, but projecting from its free surface are a number of small, highly sensitive papillæ. Scattered glands are present on the neck of the penis and inner layer of the prepuce, the **preputial glands** (Tyson). They secrete a sebaceous material of very peculiar odor, which probably contains casein, and readily undergoes decomposition; when mixed with discarded epithelial cells it is called smegma.

The prepuce covers a variable amount of the glans, and is separated from it by a potential space—the **preputial space**—which presents two shallow fossæ, one on either side of the frenulum.

Fascia.—The **superficial fascia of the penis** is directly continuous with that of the scrotum, and like it, contains a **dartos** tunic with its layer of scattered smooth muscle

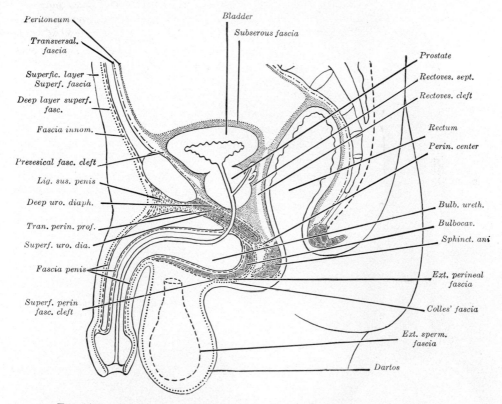

FIG. 1143.—Fasciæ of pelvis and perineum in median sagittal section. Diagram.

cells. It is not divisible into a superficial and deep layer and contains no adipose tissue. A fascial cleft between the superficial and deep fasciæ gives the skin great movability.

The **deep fascia of the penis** (*Buck's fascia*) (Fig. 1143) forms a tubular invest-ment for the shaft of the penis as far anteriorly as the corona glandis. Posteriorly, it invests the crura and bulb and is firmly attached with them to the ischiopubic rami and superficial layer of the urogenital diaphragm. At the anterior or distal extremities of the Bulbocavernosus and Ischiocavernosi, it splits into a superficial and deep lamina; the superficial lamina covers the superficial surface of these muscles as the external perineal fascia of the perineum (page 477); the deep lamina is the continuation of the proper deep fascia of the penis (Buck's fascia). A septum of fascia extends inward between the corpora cavernosa penis and the corpus caver-nosum urethræ providing separate tubular investments for these columns of erectile tissue.

86

Clinical Considerations: The deep fascia of the penis (Buck's fascia) encloses the organ in a strong capsule. An abscess, a hematoma, or an extravasation of urine from rupture of the penile urethra would be confined to the penis by this envelope. A rupture of the urethra in its membranous portion, however, would allow urine to enter the fascial cleft which is between the deep and superficial fasciae and which is continuous with the cleft in the scrotum, under Colles' fascia, and under Scarpa's fascia (see pages 473, 478).

Corpora Cavernosa Penis (Fig. 1144).—The anterior three fourths of these two cylindrical masses of erectile tissue are intimately bound together and make up the greater part of the shaft of the penis. At the pubic symphysis, however, their posterior portions diverge from each other as two gradually tapering structures called the **crura.**

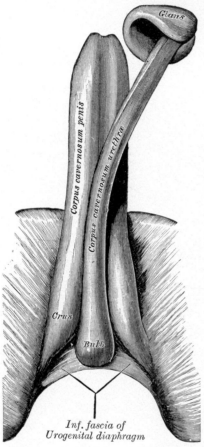

The corpora retain a uniform diameter in the shaft and terminate anteriorly in a bluntly rounded extremity approximately 1 cm. from the end of the penis, being embedded in a cap formed by the glans penis.

The corpora cavernosa penis are surrounded by a strong fibrous envelope consisting of superficial and deep fibers. The superficial fibers are longitudinal in direction, and form a single tube which encloses both corpora; the deep fibers are arranged circularly around each corpus, and form by their junction in the median plane the **septum of the penis.** This is thick and complete behind, but is imperfect in front, where it consists of a series of vertical bands arranged like the teeth of a comb; it is therefore named the **septum pectiniforme.** A shallow groove which marks their

Fig. 1144.—The constituent cavernous cylinders of the penis. The glands and anterior part of the corpus cavernosum urethræ are detached from the corpora cavernosa penis and turned to one side.

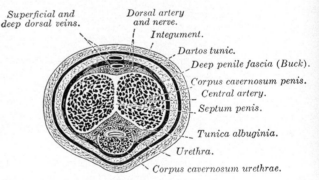

Fig. 1145.—Transverse section of the penis.

junction on the upper surface lodges the deep dorsal vein of the penis, while a deeper and wider groove between them on the under surface contains the corpus cavernosum urethræ.

Each **crus penis,** the tapering posterior portion of a corpus cavernosum penis, terminates just in front of the tuberosity of the ischium in a bluntly pointed process; anteriorly, before it meets its fellow, it presents a slight enlargement, the bulb of the corpus cavernosum penis. The crus is firmly bound to the ramus of the ischium and pubis and is enclosed by the fibers of the Ischiocavernosus muscle.

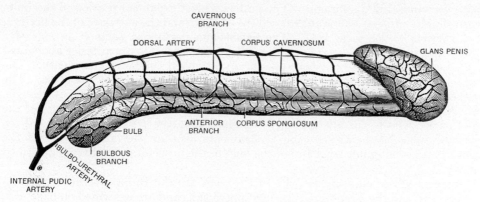

FIG. 1146.—Diagram of the arteries of the penis. (Testut.)

The **Corpus Cavernosum Urethræ** (*corpus spongiosum*) (Fig. 1144) is the part of the penis which contains the penile urethra. Its middle portion, in the shaft of the penis, is a uniform cylinder somewhat smaller than a corpus cavernosum penis. At each end it is markedly expanded, the anterior extremity forming the glans penis, the posterior the bulbus urethræ. Between the expansions, it lies in the groove on the under surface of the concorpora cavernosa penis.

The **glans penis** is the anterior end of the corpus cavernosum urethræ expanded into an obtuse cone very similar to the cap of a mushroom. It is moulded over and securely attached to the blunt extremity of the corpora cavernosa penis, and extends farther over their dorsal than their ventral surfaces. Its periphery is larger in diameter than the shaft, projecting in a rounded border, the **corona glandis**. Proximal to the corona is a constriction forming the **retroglandular sulcus** and the **neck of the penis**. At the summit of the glans is the slit-like external orifice of the urethra.

FIG. 1147.—Veins of the penis. (Testut.)

The **bulbus urethræ** is the conical enlargement of the posterior 4 or 5 cm. of the corpus cavernosum urethræ. It is just superficial to the urogenital diaphragm, the superficial fascia of which is blended with its fibrous capsule and is called the ligament of the bulb. It is enclosed by the fibers of the Bulbocavernosus.

The urethra enters the corpus cavernosum urethræ 1 or 2 cm. from the posterior extremity of the bulb by piercing the dorsal surface, *i. e.*, the surface which is blended with the urogenital diaphragm.   The posterior most expanded portion of the bulb, accordingly, projects backward toward the anus beyond the entrance of the urethra.

Ligaments. —(See page 454).   The **ligamentum fundiforme penis** is an extensive thickening of the deep layer of superficial fascia (Scarpa's) of the anterior abdominal wall just above the pubis where it is firmly attached to the rectus sheath.   The fibrous bands extend down to the dorsum and sides of the root of the penis.   The **suspensory ligament of the penis,** shorter than the above, is a strong fibrous triangle, derived from the external investing deep fascia, which attaches the dorsum of the root of the penis to the inferior end of the linea alba, the symphysis pubis, and the arcuate pubic ligament.   Serving as ligaments also are the attachments of the crura to the ischiopubic rami and of the bulb to the urogenital diaphragm described above.

Muscles.—The voluntary muscles of the penis are the Bulbocavernosus, Ischiocavernosus, and the Transversus perinei superficialis and are described on page 478.

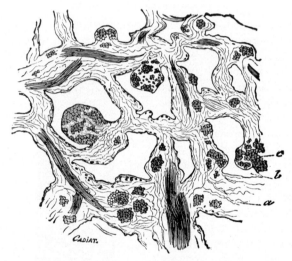

Fig. 1148.—Section of corpus cavernosum penis in a non-distended condition. (Cadiat.)   *a.* Trabeculæ of connective tissue, with many elastic fibers and bundles of plain muscular tissue, some of which are cut across (*c*).   *b.* Blood sinuses.

Structure of the Penis.—From the internal surface of the fibrous envelope, tunica albuginea, of the corpora cavernosa penis, as well as from the sides of the septum, numerous bands or cords are given off, which cross the interior of these corpora cavernosa in all directions subdividing them into a number of separate compartments, and giving the entire structure a spongy appearance (Fig. 1148).   These bands and cords are called **trabeculæ,** and consist of white fibrous tissue, elastic fibers, and plain muscular fibers.   In them are contained numerous arteries and nerves.

The component fibers which form the trabeculæ are larger and stronger around the circumference than at the centers of the corpora cavernosa; they are also thicker behind than in front.   The interspaces or cavernous spaces (blood sinuses) on the contrary, are larger at the center than at the circumference, their long diameters being directed transversely.   They are filled with blood, and are lined by a layer of flattened cells similar to the endothelial lining of veins.

The fibrous envelope of the corpus cavernosum urethræ is thinner, whiter in color, and more elastic than that of the corpora cavernosa penis.   The trabeculæ are more delicate, nearly uniform in size, and the meshes between them smaller than in the corpora cavernosa penis: their long diameters, for the most part, corresponding with that of the penis.   The external envelope or outer coat of the corpus cavernosum urethræ is formed partly of unstriped muscular fibers, and a layer of the same tissue immediately surrounds the canal of the urethra.   The corpus cavernosum urethræ with its expanded end the glans penis may be readily dissected free, since it is not so firmly attached to the corpora cavernosa penis as are they to each other.

Under cerebral or spinal stimuli the supply of arterial blood to the blood sinuses or interspaces is increased. This increase in size of sinuses in turn produces compression of the deep veins of the penis due to the elasticity of Buck's fascia. Erection is therefore a mechanical engorgement of the blood sinuses.

Vessels and Nerves.—Most of the blood to the penis is supplied by the internal pudendal artery, a branch of the hypogastric artery. The **arteries** supplying the cavernous spaces are the deep arteries of the penis and branches from the dorsal arteries of the penis, which perforate the fibrous capsule, along the upper surface, especially near the forepart of the organ. On entering the cavernous structure the arteries divide into branches, which are supported and enclosed by the trabeculæ. Some of these arteries end in a capillary net-work, the branches of which open directly into the cavernous spaces; others assume a tendril-like appearance, and form convoluted and somewhat dilated vessels, which were named by Müller **helicine arteries.** They open into the spaces, and from them are also given off small capillary branches to supply the trabecular structure. They are bound down in the spaces by fine fibrous processes, and are most abundant in the back part of the corpora cavernosa (Fig. 1145).

The blood from the cavernous spaces is returned by a series of **veins**, some of which emerge in considerable numbers from the base of the glans penis and converge on the dorsum of the organ to form the deep dorsal vein; others pass out on the upper surface of the corpora cavernosa and join the same vein; some emerge from the under surface of the corpora cavernosa penis and receiving branches from the corpus cavernosum urethræ, wind around the sides of the penis to end in the deep dorsal vein; but the greater number pass out at the root of the penis and join the prostatic plexus. Batson has demonstrated that the deep dorsal vein of the penis has connection with the vertebral veins, hence it is possible to have metastases from cancerous involvement of the pelvic viscera or external genitalia make their way to the vertebræ or even to the skull and brain without going through the heart and lungs. Pyogenic organisms may be transported by the same route. (See page 751).

The **lymphatic vessels of the penis** are described on page 806.

The **nerves** are derived from the pudendal nerve and the pelvic plexuses. On the glans and bulb some filaments of the cutaneous nerves have Pacinian bodies connected with them, and, according to Krause, many of them end in peculiar end-bulbs.

The Prostate (Prostata; Prostate Gland). (Figs. 1123, 1124, 1149.)

The **prostate** is a firm, partly grandular and partly muscular body, which is placed immediately below the internal urethral orifice and around the commencement of the urethra. It is situated in the pelvic cavity, below the lower part of the symphysis pubis, above the deep layer of the urogenital diaphragm, and in front of the rectum, through which it may be distinctly felt, especially when enlarged. It is about the size of a chestnut and somewhat conical in shape, and presents for examination a **base**, an **apex**, an **anterior**, a **posterior**, and two **lateral surfaces.**

The **base** (*basis prostatæ*) is directed upward, and is applied to the inferior surface of the bladder. The greater part of this surface is directly continuous with the bladder wall; the urethra penetrates it nearer its anterior than its posterior border.

The **apex** (*apex prostatæ*) is directed downward, and is in contact with the deep layer of the urogenital diaphragm.

Surfaces.—The **posterior surface** (*facies posterior*) is flattened from side to side and slightly convex from above downward; it is separated from the rectum by its sheath and the important Denonvilliers' fascia, which corresponds in origin and fate to the processus vaginalis in the inguinal region. It is distant about 4 cm. from the anus. Near its upper border there is a depression through which the two ejaculatory ducts enter the prostate. This depression serves to divide the posterior surface into a lower larger and an upper smaller part. The upper smaller part constitutes the **middle lobe** of the prostate and intervenes between the ejaculatory ducts and the urethra; it varies greatly in size, and in some cases is destitute of glandular tissue. The lower larger portion sometimes presents a shallow median furrow, which imperfectly separates it into a **right** and a **left lateral lobe**: these form the main mass of the gland and are directly continuous with each other behind the urethra. In front of the urethra they are connected by a band which is named the **isthmus**: this consists of the same tissues as the capsule and is devoid of glandular substance.

The **anterior surface** (*facies anterior*) measures about 2.5 cm. from above downward but is narrow and convex from side to side. It is placed about 2 cm. behind the pubic symphysis, from which it is separated by a plexus of veins and a quantity of loose fat. It is connected to the pubic bone on either side by the puboprostatic ligaments. The urethra emerges from this surface a little above and in front of the apex of the gland.

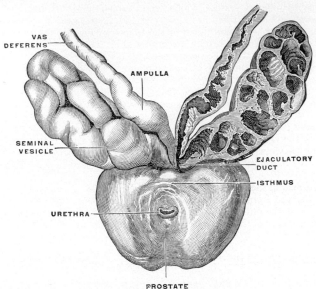

Fig. 1149.—Prostate with seminal vesicles and seminal ducts, viewed from in front and above. (Spalteholz.)

The **lateral surfaces** are prominent, and are covered by the anterior portions of the Levatores ani, which are, however, separated from the gland by a plexus of veins.

The prostate measures about 4 cm. transversely at the base, 2 cm. in its anteroposterior diameter, and 3 cm. in its vertical diameter. Its weight is about 20 gm. It is held in its position by the puboprostatic ligaments; by the deep layer of the urogenital diaphragm, which invests the prostate and the commencement of the membranous portion of the urethra; and by the anterior portions of the Levatores ani, which pass backward from the pubis and embrace the sides of the prostate. These portions of the Levatores ani, from the support they afford to the prostate, are named the **Levatores prostatæ**.

The prostate is perforated by the urethra and the ejaculatory ducts (Fig. 1142). The urethra usually lies along the junction of its anterior with its middle third. The ejaculatory ducts pass obliquely downward and forward through the posterior part of the prostate, and open into the prostatic portion of the urethra.

Structure.—The prostate is immediately enveloped by a thin but firm fibrous capsule distinct from that derived from the subserous fascia, and separated from it by a plexus of veins. This capsule is firmly adherent to the prostate and is structurally continuous with the stroma of the gland, being composed of the same tissues, *viz.*: non-striped muscle and fibrous tissue. The substance of the prostate is of a pale reddish-gray color, of great density, and not easily torn. It consists of glandular substance and muscular tissue.

The **muscular tissue** according to Kölliker, constitutes the proper stroma of the prostate; the connective tissue being very scanty, and simply forming between the muscular fibers, thin trabeculæ, in which the vessels and nerves of the gland ramify. The muscular tissue is arranged as follows: immediately beneath the fibrous capsule is a dense layer, which forms an investing sheath for the gland; secondly, around the urethra, as it lies in the prostate, is another dense layer of circular fibers, continuous above with the internal layer of the muscular coat of the bladder, and blending below with the fibers surrounding the membranous portion of the urethra. Between these two layers strong bands of muscular tissue, which decussate freely, form meshes in which the glandular structure of the organ is imbedded. In that part of the gland which is situated in front of the urethra the muscular tissue is especially dense, and there is here little or no gland tissue; while in that part which is behind the urethra the muscular tissue presents a wide-meshed structure, which is densest at the base of the gland—that is, near the bladder— becoming looser and more sponge-like toward the apex of the organ.

The **glandular substance** is composed of numerous follicular pouches the lining of which frequently shows papillary elevations. The follicles open into elongated canals, which join to form from twelve to twenty small excretory ducts. They are connected together by areolar tissue, supported by prolongations from the fibrous capsule and muscular stroma, and enclosed in a delicate capillary plexus. The epithelium which lines the canals and the terminal vesicles is of the columnar variety. The prostatic ducts open into the floor of the prostatic portion of the urethra, and are lined by two layers of epithelium, the inner layer consisting of columnar and the outer of small cubical cells. Small colloid masses, known as **amyloid bodies** are often found in the gland tubes.

Vessels and Nerves.—The **arteries** supplying the prostate are derived from the internal pudendal, inferior vesical, and middle hemorrhoidal. Its veins form a plexus around the sides and base of the gland; they receive in front the dorsal vein of the penis, and end in the hypogastric veins. The **nerves** are derived from the pelvic plexus.

Bulbourethral Glands (Glandulæ Bulbourethrales; Cowper's Glands). (Fig. 1123.)

The **bulbourethral glands** are two small, rounded, and somewhat lobulated bodies, of a yellow color, about the size of peas, placed behind and lateral to the membranous portion of the urethra, between the two layers of the fascia of the urogenital diaphragm. They lie close above the bulb, and are enclosed by the transverse fibers of the Sphincter urethræ membranaceæ.

The excretory duct of each gland, nearly 2.5 cm. long, passes obliquely forward beneath the mucous membrane, and opens by a minute orifice on the floor of the cavernous portion of the urethra about 2.5 cm. in front of the urogenital diaphragm.

Structure.—Each gland is made up of several lobules, held together by a fibrous investment. Each lobule consists of a number of acini, lined by columnar epithelial cells, opening into one duct, which joins with the ducts of other lobules outside the gland to form the single excretory duct.

THE FEMALE GENITAL ORGANS (ORGANA GENITALIA MULIEBRIA).

The female genital organs consist of an internal and an external group. The **internal organs** are situated within the pelvis, and consist of the **ovaries**, the **uterine tubes**, the **uterus**, and the **vagina**. The **external organs** are placed below the urogenital diaphragm and below and in front of the pubic arch. They comprise the **mons pubis**, the **labia majora et minora pudendi**, the **clitoris**, the **bulbus vestibuli**, and the **greater vestibular glands**.

The Ovaries (Ovaria).

The **ovaries** are homologous with the testes in the male. They are two nodular bodies, situated one on either side of the uterus in relation to the lateral wall of the pelvis, and attached to the back of the broad ligament of the uterus, behind and below the uterine tubes (Fig. 1150). The ovaries are of a grayish-pink color, and present either a smooth or a puckered uneven surface. They are each about 4 cm. in length, 2 cm. in width, and about 8 mm. in thickness, and weigh from 2 to 3.5 gm. Each ovary presents a lateral and a medial surface, an upper or tubal and a lower or uterine extremity, and an anterior or mesovarian and a posterior free border. It lies in a shallow depression, named the **ovarian fossa**, on the lateral wall of the pelvis; this fossa is bounded above by the external iliac vessels, in front by the obliterated umbilical artery, and behind by the ureter. The exact position of the ovary has been the subject of considerable difference of opinion, and the description here given applies to the ovary of the nulliparous woman. The ovary becomes displaced during the first pregnancy, and probably never again returns

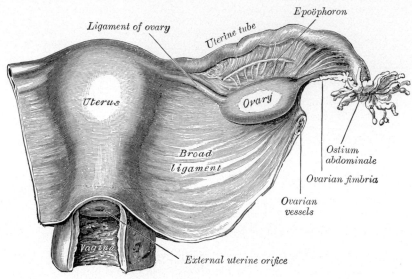

FIG. 1150.—Uterus and right broad ligament, seen from behind. The broad ligament has been spread out and the ovary drawn downward.

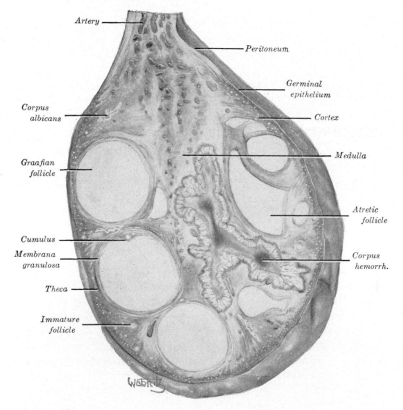

FIG. 1151.—Section through ovary of 23-year-old woman. Lightly stained with hematoxylin. × 5.

to its original position. In the erect posture the long axis of the ovary is vertical. The *tubal extremity* is near the external iliac vein; to it are attached the ovarian fimbria of the uterine tube and a fold of peritoneum, the **suspensory ligament of the ovary,** which is directed upward over the iliac vessels and contains the ovarian vessels. The *uterine end* is directed downward toward the pelvic floor, it is usually narrower than the tubal, and is attached to the lateral angle of the uterus, immediately behind the uterine tube, by a rounded cord termed the **ligament of the ovary,** which lies within the broad ligament and contains some non-striped muscular fibers. The *lateral surface* is in contact with the parietal peritoneum, which lines the ovarian fossa; the *medial surface* is to a large extent covered by the fimbriated extremity of the uterine tube. The *mesovarian border* is straight and is directed toward the obliterated umbilical artery, and is attached to the back of the broad ligament by a short fold named the **mesovarium.** Between the two layers of this fold the bloodvessels and nerves pass to reach the hilum of the ovary. The *free border* is convex, and is directed toward the ureter. The uterine tube arches over the ovary, running upward in relation to its mesovarian border, then curving over its tubal pole, and finally passing downward on its free border and medial surface.

Epoöphoron (*parovarium; organ of Rosenmüller*) (Fig. 1150). — The epoöphoron lies in the mesosalpinx between the ovary and the uterine tube, and consists of a few short tubules (**ductuli transversi**) which converge toward the ovary while their opposite ends open into a rudimentary duct, the **ductus longitudinalis epoöphori**(*duct of Gartner*).

Paroöphoron. — The paroöphoron consists of a few scattered rudimentary tubules, best seen in the child, situated in the broad ligament between the epoöphoron and the uterus. The ductuli transversi of the epoöphoron and the tubules of the paroöphoron are remnants of the tubules of the Wolffian body or mesonephros; the ductus longitudinalis epoöphori is a persistent portion of the Wolffian duct. In the fetus the ovaries are situated, like the testes, in the lumbar region, near the kidneys, but they gradually descend into the pelvis (page 1320).

Structure (Fig. 1151).—The surface of the ovary is covered by a layer of columnar cells which constitutes the **germinal epithelium of Waldeyer.** This epithelium which is in linear continuity with the peritoneum gives to the ovary a dull gray color as compared with the shining smoothness of the peritoneum; and the transition between the squamous epithelium of the peritoneum and the columnar cells which cover the ovary is usually marked by a line around the anterior border of the ovary. The ovary consists of a number of vesicular ovarian follicles imbedded in the meshes of a stroma or frame-work.

The **stroma** is a peculiar soft tissue, abundantly supplied with bloodvessels, consisting for the most part of spindle-shaped cells with a small amount of ordinary connective tissue. These cells have been regarded by some anatomists as unstriped muscle cells, which, indeed, they most resemble; by others as connective-tissue cells. On the surface of the organ this tissue is much condensed, and forms a layer (**tunica albuginea**) composed of short connective-tissue fibers, with fusiform cells between them. The stroma of the ovary may contain interstitial cells resembling those of the testis.

Vesicular Ovarian Follicles (*Graafian follicles*).—Upon making a section of an ovary, numerous round transparent vesicles of various sizes are to be seen; they are the follicles, or ovisacs containing the ova. Immediately beneath the superficial covering is a layer of stroma, in which are a large number of minute vesicles, of uniform size, about 0.25 mm. in diameter. These are the follicles in their earliest condition, and the layer where they are found has been termed the **cortical layer.** They are especially numerous in the ovary of the young child. After puberty, and during the whole of the child-bearing period, large and mature, or almost mature follicles are also found in the cortical layer in small numbers, and also "corpora lutea," the remains of follicles which have burst and are undergoing atrophy and absorption. Beneath this superficial stratum, other large and more or less mature follicles are found imbedded in the ovarian stroma. These increase in size as they recede from the surface toward a highly vascular stroma in the center of the organ, termed the **medullary substance** (*zona vasculosa of Waldeyer*). This stroma forms the tissue of the hilum by which the ovary is attached, and through which the bloodvessels enter: it does not contain any follicles.

The larger follicles (Fig. 1152) consist of an external fibrovascular coat, connected with the surrounding stroma of the ovary by a net-work of bloodvessels; and an internal coat, which consists of several layers of nucleated cells, called the **membrana granulosa**. At one part of the mature follicle the cells of the membrana granulosa are collected into a mass which projects into the cavity of the follicle. This is termed the **discus proligerus** or **corona radiata**, and in it the ovum is imbedded. The follicle contains a transparent albuminous fluid.

The development and maturation of the follicles and ova continue uninterruptedly from puberty to the end of the fruitful period of woman's life, while their formation commences before birth. Before puberty the ovaries are small and the follicles contained in them are disposed in a comparatively thick layer in the cortical substance; here they present the appearance of a large number of minute closed vesicles, constituting the early condition of the follicles; many, however, never attain full development, but shrink and disappear. At puberty the ovaries enlarge and become more vascular, the follicles are developed in greater abundance, and their ova are capable of fecundation. The follicles are supposed to secrete hormones necessary for the estrus cycle and which stimulate the growth of the uterus and mammary glands during pregnancy.

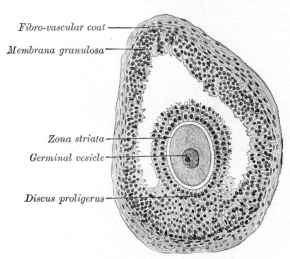

Fibro-vascular coat

Membrana granulosa

Zona striata

Germinal vesicle

Discus proligerus

FIG. 1152.—Section of vesicular ovarian follicle of cat. × 50.

Discharge of the Ovum.—The follicles, after attaining a certain stage of development, gradually approach the surface of the ovary and burst; the ovum surrounded by its corona radiata and the fluid contents of the follicle are liberated on the exterior of the ovary, and carried into the uterine tube.

Corpus Luteum.—After the discharge of the ovum the lining of the follicle is thrown into folds, and vascular processes grow inward from the surrounding tissue. In this way the space is filled up and the corpus luteum formed. It consists at first of a radial arrangement of yellow cells with bloodvessels and lymphatic spaces, and later it merges with the surrounding stroma. The corpora lutea give off secretions or hormones: (1) which are necessary for the implantation and normal development of the fetilized egg; (2) which stimulate the growth of the mammary gland and (3) which inhibit ovulation during pregnancy.

Vessels and Nerves.—The **arteries** of the ovaries and uterine tubes are the ovarian from the aorta. Each anastomoses freely in the mesosalpinx, with the uterine artery, giving some branches to the uterine tube, and others which traverse the mesovarium and enter the hilum of the ovary. The **veins** emerge from the hilum in the form of a plexus, the **pampiniform plexus**; the ovarian vein is formed from this plexus, and leaves the pelvis in company with the artery. The **nerves** are derived from the hypogastric or pelvic plexus, and from the ovarian plexus, the uterine tube receiving a branch from one of the uterine nerves.

The Uterine Tube (Tuba Uterina [Fallopii]; Fallopian Tube; Oviduct).
(Figs. 1150, 1153, 1156).

The **uterine tubes** convey the ova from the ovaries to the cavity of the uterus. They are bilateral, extending from the side of the pelvis to the superior lateral angle of the uterus. Each one is suspended by a mesenteric peritoneal fold, called the **mesosalpinx**, which comprises the upper free margin and adjacent movable portion of the broad ligament. Each tube is about 10 cm. long, and consists of three portions: (1) the **isthmus**, or medial constricted third; (2) the **ampulla**, or intermediate dilated portion, which curves over the ovary; and (3) the **infundibulum** with its **abdominal ostium**, surrounded by **fimbriæ**, one of which, the **ovarian fimbria** is attached to the ovary. The uterine tube is directed lateralward as far as the uterine pole of the ovary, and then ascends along the mesovarian border of the ovary to the tubal pole, over which it arches; finally it turns downward and ends in relation to the free border and medial surface of the ovary. The uterine opening is minute, and will only admit a fine bristle; the abdominal opening is somewhat larger. In connection with the fimbriæ of the uterine tube, or with the broad ligament close to them, there are frequently one or more small pedunculated vesicles. These are termed the **appendices vesiculosæ** (*hydatids of Morgagni*).

Structure.—The uterine tube consists of three coats: **serous, muscular,** and **mucous.** The **external** or **serous coat** is peritoneal. The **middle** or **muscular coat** consists of an external longitudinal and an internal circular layer of non-striped muscular fibers continuous with those of

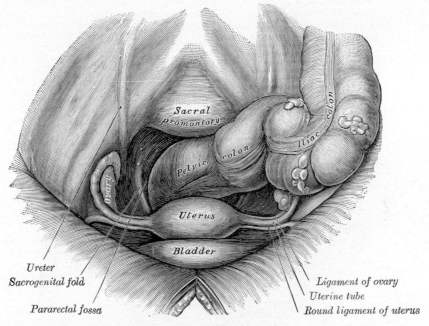

FIG. 1153.—Female pelvis and its contents, seen from above and in front.

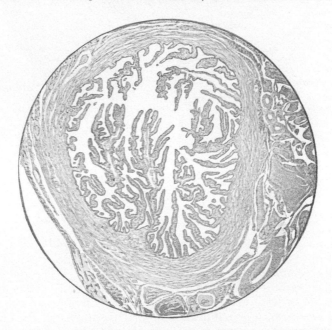

FIG. 1154.—Transverse section of a human uterine tube (ampulla). Stained with hematoxylin and eosin. × 15.

the uterus. The **internal** or **mucous coat** is continuous with the mucous lining of the uterus, and, at the abdominal ostium of the tube, with the peritoneum. It is thrown into longitudinal folds, which in the ampulla are much more extensive than in the isthmus. The lining epithelium is columnar and ciliated. This form of epithelium is also found on the inner surface of the fimbriæ, while on the outer or serous surfaces of these processes the epithelium gradually merges into the mesothelium of the peritoneum.

Fertilization of the ovum is believed (page 25) to occur in the tube, and the fertilized ovum is then normally passed on into the uterus; the ovum, however, may adhere to and undergo development in the uterine tube, giving rise to the commonest variety of *ectopic gestation*. In such cases the amnion and chorion are formed, but a true decidua is never present; and the gestation usually ends by extrusion of the ovum through the abdominal ostium, although it is not uncommon for the tube to rupture into the peritoneal cavity, this being accompanied by severe hemorrhage, and needing surgical interference.

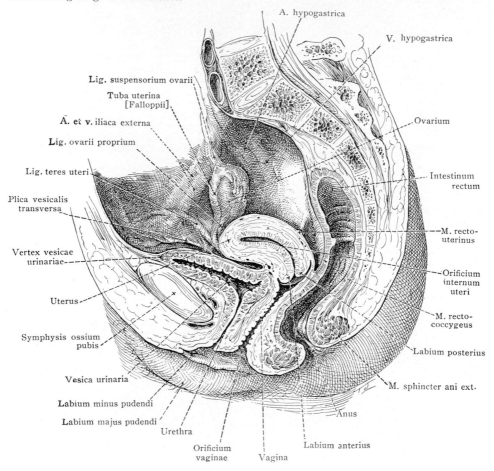

Fig. 1155.—Median sagittal section of female pelvis. The bladder is empty, the uterus and vagina slightly dilated. (Eycleshymer and Jones.)

The Uterus (Womb) (Figs. 1150, 1153, 1155).

The **uterus** is a hollow, thick-walled, muscular organ situated between the bladder and rectum. Into its upper part the uterine tubes open, one on either side, while below, its cavity communicates with that of the vagina. When the ova are discharged from the ovaries they are carried to the uterine cavity through the uterine tubes. If an ovum be fertilized it imbeds itself in the uterine wall and is normally retained in the uterus until prenatal development is completed, the uterus undergoing changes in size and structure to accommodate itself to the needs of the growing embryo (see page 48). After parturition the uterus returns almost to its former condition, but traces of its enlargement remain. It is necessary, therefore, to describe as the type-form the adult virgin uterus, and then to consider the modifications which are effected as a result of pregnancy.

In the virgin state the uterus is flattened antero-posteriorly and is pyriform in shape, with the apex directed downward and backward. It lies between the bladder in front and the pelvic or sigmoid colon and rectum behind, and is completely within the pelvis, so that its base is below the level of the superior pelvic aperture.

The long axis of the uterus usually lies approximately in the axis of the superior pelvic aperture, but as the organ is freely movable its position varies with the state of distention of the bladder and rectum. Except when much displaced by a fully distended bladder, it forms a forward angle with the vagina, since the axis of the vagina corresponds to the axes of the cavity and inferior aperture of the pelvis.

The uterus measures about 7.5 cm. in length, 5 cm. in breadth, at its upper part, and nearly 2.5 cm. in thickness; it weighs from 30 to 40 gm. It is divisible into two portions. On the surface, about midway between the apex and base, is a slight constriction, known as the **isthmus**, and corresponding to this in the interior is a narrowing of the uterine cavity, the **internal orifice** of the uterus. The portion above the isthmus is termed the **body**, and that below, the **cervix**. The part of the body which lies above a plane passing through the points of entrance of the uterine tubes is known as the **fundus**.

Body (*corpus uteri*). — The body gradually narrows from the fundus to the isthmus.

The **vesical** or **anterior surface** (*facies vesicalis*) is flattened and covered by peritoneum, which is reflected on to the bladder to form the vesicouterine excavation. The surface lies in apposition with the bladder.

The **intestinal** or **posterior surface** (*facies intestinalis*) is convex transversely and is covered by peritoneum, which is continued down on to the cervix and vagina. It is in relation with the sigmoid colon, from which it is usually separated by some coils of small intestine.

The **fundus** (*fundus uteri*) is convex in all directions, and covered by peritoneum continuous with that on the vesical and intestinal surfaces. On it rest some coils of small intestine, and occasionally the distended sigmoid colon.

The **lateral margins** (*margo lateralis*) are slightly convex. At the upper end of each the uterine tube pierces the uterine wall. Below and in front of this point the round ligament of the uterus is fixed, while behind it is the attachment of the ligament of the ovary. These three structures lie within a fold of peritoneum which is reflected from the margin of the uterus to the wall of the pelvis, and is named the **broad ligament.**

Cervix (*cervix uteri; neck*).—The cervix is the lower constricted segment of the uterus. It is somewhat conical in shape, with its truncated apex directed downward and backward, but is slightly wider in the middle than either above or below. Owing to its relationships, it is less freely movable than the body, so that the latter may bend on it. The long axis of the cervix is therefore seldom in the same straight line as the long axis of the body. The long axis of the uterus as a whole presents the form of a curved line with its concavity forward, or in extreme cases may present an angular bend at the region of the isthmus.

The cervix is about 1 inch long. The vagina is attached obliquely around the center of the periphery of the cervix. This attachment divides the cervix into two parts, an upper or supravaginal portion and a lower or vaginal portion.

The **supravaginal portion** (*portio supravaginalis* [*cervicis*]) is separated *in front* from the bladder by fibrous tissue (**parametrium**), which extends also on to its *sides* and lateralward between the layers of the broad ligaments. The uterine arteries reach the margins of the cervix in this fibrous tissue, where they cross over the ureters. The ureters, on either side, run downward and forward in the parametrium about 2 cm. from the cervix. *Posteriorly*, the supravaginal cervix is covered by peritoneum, which is prolonged below on to the posterior vaginal wall, when it is reflected on to the rectum, forming the rectouterine excavation. It is in relation with the rectum, from which it may be separated by coils of small intestine.

The **vaginal portion** (*portio vaginalis [cervicis]*) of the cervix projects free into the anterior wall of the vagina between the anterior and posterior fornices. On its rounded extremity is a small, depressed, somewhat circular aperture, the **external os** (*orificium externum uteri*), through which the cavity of the cervix communicates with that of the vagina. The external orifice is bounded by two lips, an anterior

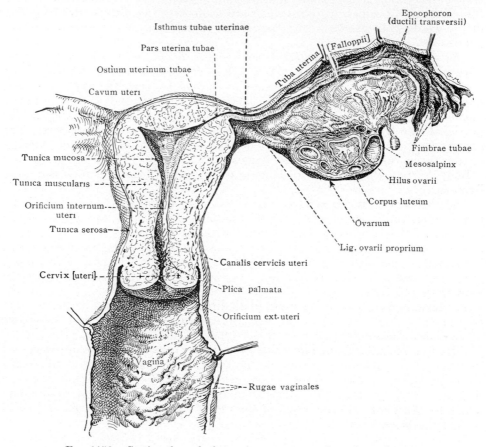

FIG. 1156.—Section through the vagina, uterus, uterine tube and ovary.
(Eycleshymer and Jones.)

and a posterior, of which the anterior is the shorter and thicker, although, on account of the slope of the cervix, it projects lower than the posterior. Normally, both lips are in contact with the posterior vaginal wall.

Interior of the Uterus (Fig. 1156).—The cavity of the uterus is small in comparison with the size of the organ.

The **Cavity of the Body** (*cavum uteri*) is a mere slit, flattened antero-posteriorly. It is triangular in shape, the base being formed by the internal surface of the fundus between the orifices of the uterine tubes, the apex by the **internal os** (*orificium internum uteri*) through which the cavity of the body communicates with the canal of the cervix.

The **Canal of the Cervix** (*canalis cervicis uteri*) is somewhat fusiform, flattened from before backward, and broader at the middle than at either extremity. It communicates above through the internal orifice with the cavity of the body, and below through the external orifice with the vaginal cavity. The wall of the canal presents an anterior and a posterior longitudinal ridge, from each of which proceed a number of small oblique columns, the **palmate folds**, giving the appearance of branches from the stem of a tree; to this arrangement the name **arbor vitæ uterina** is applied. The folds on the two walls are not exactly opposed, but fit between one another so as to close the cervical canal.

The total length of the uterine cavity from the external orifice to the fundus is about 6.25 cm.

Ligaments.—The principal ligaments of the uterus are the **broad ligaments**, the **round ligaments**, the **uterosacral ligaments**, and the **cardinal ligaments** (*ligamenta transversalia colli*). In addition to these, there are certain peritoneal folds which are called ligaments: the **vesicouterine**, **rectouterine**, and **sacrogenital ligaments**.

The **broad ligaments** (*ligamentum latum uteri*) are two thin fibrous sheets, covered on both surfaces with peritoneum, which extend from each side of the uterus to the lateral wall of the pelvis. The uterus and these lateral extensions together form a septum across the cavity of the pelvis, dividing it into an anterior or **vesicouterine** and a posterior or **rectouterine fossa**. The broad ligament is thicker at its inferior pelvic attachment than toward its free border. Between the two peritoneal sheets or *leaves of the ligament* are (1) the parametrium, (2) blood vessels and nerves, (3) the uterine tubes, (4) the ureter, (5) the round ligaments, and (6) the vestigial epoöphoron and paroöphron. The ovary might be listed as (7) but it is suspended from rather than contained in the broad ligament.

The **parametrium** is the extension of the subserous connective tissue of the uterus laterally into the broad ligament. The name has been applied also to the whole broad ligament below the attachment of the ovary, but according to the B.N.A. the latter is the **mesometrium**. It contains scattered smooth muscle bundles, is anchored to the lateral pelvic wall, and is continuous with the cardinal ligament of the intrapelvic fascia.

The **uterine artery** of each side enters the base of the broad ligament at the latter's attachment to the lateral wall of the pelvis and traverses the pelvis between the two leaves close to their reflection on to the pelvic floor. It crosses the ureter just before it reaches the cervical portion of the uterus and in the parametrium it follows the lateral border of the uterus up to the isthmus of the uterine tube. It follows the tube laterally and anastomoses with the ovarian artery. The **ovarian artery** crosses the external iliac vessels in a vertical direction and enters the most superior lateral portion of the broad ligament, enclosed in a more or less fibrous cord, the **infundibulopelvic ligament** (*ligamentum suspensorium ovarii*). It follows the attached border of the ovary and anastomoses with the uterine artery.

The superior free border of the broad ligament is occupied by the **uterine tube** except at its lateral extremity where it forms a rounded band, attaching the infundibulum of the tube to the lateral wall of the pelvis. This band, named the infundibulopelvic ligament or suspensory ligament of the ovary, also encloses the ovarian vessels as they enter the broad ligament. The upper portion of the broad ligament, extending down as far as the attachment of the ovary, is called the **mesosalpinx**. It is less fixed than the rest of the ligament and affords a movable mesenteric support for the tube.

The **ureter** crosses the attached inferior border of the broad ligament obliquely, as it courses along the pelvic floor toward the base of the bladder. It comes to within 1 or 2 cm. of the internal os of the uterus at this point and lies close to the uterine artery, between the latter and the pelvic diaphragm.

The round ligaments are described below.

The epoöphoron and paraoöphoron (page 1317) lie in the mesosalpinx.

The **ovary** is secured to the posterior surface of the broad ligament by a mesenteric attachment, the **mesovarium,** derived from the posterior leaf. It does not lie, therefore, between the leaves of the broad ligament. Folds of the posterior leaf at each end of the ovary cover the infundibulopelvic ligament (*ligamentum suspensorium ovarii*) and the **ligamentum ovarii proprium.**

The **round ligament** (*ligamentum teres uteri*) is a flattened band attached to the superior part of the lateral border of the uterus just below and anterior to the isthmus of the uterine tube. It traverses the pelvis between the leaves of the broad ligament but causes a prominent folding of the anterior leaf only. It reaches the pelvic wall lateral to the lateral vesicoumbilical fold, ascends over the external iliac vessels and inguinal ligament, and penetrates the abdominal wall through the internal inguinal ring. It passes through the inguinal canal and its constituent fibers spread out to help form the substance of the labia majora. In the fetus, the peritoneum is prolonged in the form of a tubular process for a short distance into the inguinal canal beside the ligament. This process is called the **canal of Nuck.** It is generally obliterated in the adult, but sometimes remains pervious even in advanced life. It is analogous to the saccus vaginalis, which precedes the descent of the testis.

The **cardinal ligament** (*ligamentum transversum colli,* [Mackenrodt]) is a fibrous sheet of the subserous fascia embedded in the adipose tissue on each side of the lower cervix uteri and vagina. To form it, the fasciæ over the anterior and posterior walls of the vagina and cervix come together at the lateral border of these organs, and the resulting sheet extends across the pelvic floor as a deeper continuation of the broad ligament. As the sheet reaches the lateral portion of the pelvic diaphragm, it forms anterior and posterior extensions which are attached to the internal investing layer of deep fascia (supra-anal fascia) on the inner surface of the Levator ani, Coccygeus and Piriformis. This attachment is commonly visible as a white line 2 or 3 cm. below the arcus tendineus of the Levator ani, and is called the **arcus tendineus of the pelvic fascia** (see page 471). The anterior extension is continuous with the tissue supporting the bladder. The posterior extension blends with the uterosacral ligaments. The vaginal arteries cross the pelvis in close association with this ligament, giving it additional substance and support, and bundles of smooth muscle may be imbedded in it.

The **uterosacral ligament** is a prominent fibrous band of subserous fascia which takes a curved course along the lateral wall of the pelvis from the cervix uteri to the sacrum. It is a posterior continuation of the tissue which forms the cardinal ligament. It is attached to the deep fascia and periosteum of the sacrum and contains a bundle of smooth muscle named the **Rectouterinus.** The ligaments on the two sides project out from the wall as crescentic shelves which narrow the diameter of the cavity in front of the lower rectum and mark it off as the cul-de-sac of Douglas.

The **vesicouterine fold** or **anterior ligament** is the reflection of peritoneum from the anterior surface of the uterus, at the junction of the cervix and body, to the posterior surface of the bladder.

The **rectovaginal fold** or **posterior ligament** is the peritoneum reflected from the wall of the posterior fornix of the vagina on to the anterior surface of the rectum.

The **sacrogenital** or **rectouterine folds** (*plica rectouterina* [Douglas]) are two crescentic folds which cover the uterosacral ligaments.

The **rectouterine excavation** (*excavatio rectouterina; cavum Douglasi; pouch or cul-de-sac of Douglas*) is a deep pouch formed by the most inferior or caudal portion of the parietal peritoneum. Its anterior boundary is the supravaginal cervix and posterior fornix of the vagina; posterior, the rectum, and lateral, the sacrogenital folds covering the uterosacral ligaments.

Support of the Uterus—The principal support of the uterus is the pelvic diaphragm, especially the Levator ani and its investing layers of fascia, and unless it is intact the other structures are unable to carry out their supporting function. The uterus is held in its proper position within the pelvis by its attachment to the vagina and by the cardinal, broad, and uterosacral ligaments. The blood vessels reinforce these ligaments. The round ligaments and the peritoneal folds are of relatively slight importance as mechanical supports. The padding of adipose tissue about the ligaments and organs, in well nourished individuals, is an important element of support also. There is a great variation in the size and development of the supporting structures in different individuals, and they may be thickened or strengthened in response to physiological and pathological changes.

Position of the uterus.—The form, size, and situation of the uterus vary at different periods of life and under different circumstances.

In the fetus and infant the uterus is contained in the abdominal cavity, projecting beyond the superior aperture of the pelvis (Fig. 1157). The cervix is considerably larger than the body.

At puberty the uterus is pyriform in shape, and weighs from 14 to 17 gm. It has descended into the pelvis, the fundus being just below the level of the superior aperture of this cavity. The palmate folds are distinct, and extend to the upper part of the cavity of the organ.

The position of the uterus *in the adult* is liable to considerable variation. With the bladder and rectum empty the body of the uterus is nearly horizontal when the individual is standing. The fundus is about 2 cm. behind the symphysis pubis and slightly cephalic to it. The uterus and vagina are at an angle of about 90° with each other. The external os is half way between the spines of the ischia. As the bladder fills, the uterus is bent back toward the sacrum.

During menstruation the organ is enlarged, more vascular, and its surfaces rounder; the external orifice is rounded, its labia swollen, and the lining membrane of the body thickened, softer, and of a darker color.

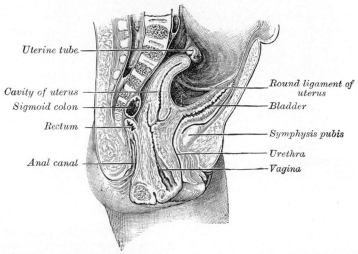

Fig. 1157.—Sagittal section through the pelvis of a newly born female child.

During pregnancy the uterus becomes enormously enlarged, and in the eighth month reaches the epigastric region. The increase in size is partly due to growth of preëxisting muscle, and partly to development of new fibers.

After parturition the uterus nearly regains its usual size, weighing about 42 gm.; but its cavity is larger than in the virgin state, its vessels are tortuous, and its muscular layers are more defined; the external orifice is more marked, and its edges present one or more fissures.

In old age the uterus becomes atrophied, and paler and denser in texture; a more distinct constriction separates the body and cervix. The internal orifice is frequently, and the external orifice occasionally, obliterated, while the lips almost entirely disappear.

Structure.—The uterus is composed of three coats: an **external** or **serous,** a **middle** or **muscular,** and an **internal** or **mucous.**

The **serous coat** (*tunica serosa*) is derived from the peritoneum; it invests the fundus and the whole of the intestinal surface of the uterus; but covers the vesical surface only as far as the junction of the body and cervix. In the lower fourth of the intestinal surface the peritoneum, though covering the uterus, is not closely connected with it, being separated from it by a layer of loose cellular tissue and some large veins.

The **muscular coat** (*tunica muscularis, myometrium*) forms the chief bulk of the substance of the uterus. In the virgin it is dense, firm, and of a grayish color, and cuts almost like cartilage. It is thick opposite the middle of the body and fundus, and thin at the orifices of the uterine tubes. It consists of bundles of unstriped muscular fibers, disposed in a thick, felt-like structure, intermixed with areolar tissue, bloodvessels, lymphatic vessels, and nerves. Muscle fibers are continued on to the uterine tube, the round ligament, and the ligament of the ovary: some passing at each side into the broad ligament, and others running backward from the cervix into the uterosacral ligaments. During pregnancy the muscular tissue becomes more prominently developed, the fibers being greatly enlarged.

The **mucous membrane** (*tunica mucosa, endometrium*) (Fig. 1158) is smooth, and closely adherent to the subjacent muscular tissue. It is continuous through the fimbriated extremity of the uterine tubes, with the peritoneum; and, through the external uterine orifice, with the lining of the vagina.

In the body of the uterus the mucous membrane is smooth, soft, of a pale red color, lined by a single layer of high columnar ciliated epithelium, and presents, when viewed with a lens, the orifices of numerous tubular follicles, arranged perpendicularly to the surface. The structure of the corium differs from that of ordinary mucous membranes, and consists of an embryonic nucleated and highly cellular form of connective tissue in which run numerous large lymphatics. In it are the tube-like **uterine glands.**

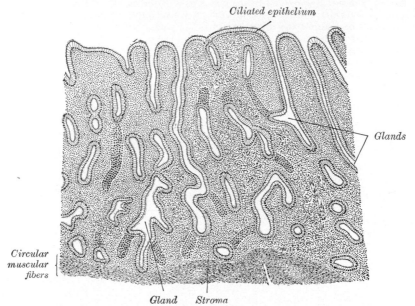

Ciliated epithelium

Glands

Circular muscular fibers

Gland　Stroma

Fig. 1158.—Vertical section of mucous membrane of human uterus. (Sobotta.)

In the cervix the mucous membrane is sharply differentiated from that of the uterine cavity. It is thrown into numerous oblique ridges, which diverge from an anterior and posterior longitudinal raphé. In the upper two-thirds of the canal, the mucous membrane is provided with numerous deep glandular follicles, which secrete a clear viscid alkaline mucus; and, in addition, extending through the whole length of the canal is a variable number of little cysts, which have become occluded and distended with retained secretion. They are called the **ovula Nabothi.** The mucous membrane covering the lower half of the cervical canal presents numerous papillæ. The epithelium of the upper two-thirds is cylindrical and ciliated, but below this it loses its cilia, and gradually changes to stratified squamous epithelium close to the external orifice. On the vaginal surface of the cervix the epithelium is similar to that lining the vagina, *viz.*, stratified squamous.

Vessels and Nerves.—The **arteries** of the uterus are the uterine, from the hypogastric; and the ovarian, from the abdominal aorta (Fig. 582). They are remarkable for their tortuous course in the substance of the organ, and for their frequent anastomoses. The termination of the ovarian artery meets that of the uterine artery, and forms an anastomotic trunk from which branches are given off to supply the uterus, their disposition being circular. The **veins** are of large size, and correspond with the arteries. They end in the uterine plexuses. In the impregnated uterus the arteries carry the blood to, and the veins convey it away from, the intervillous space of the placenta (see page 48). The **lymphatics** are described on page 807. The **nerves** are derived from the hypogastric and ovarian plexuses, and from the third and fourth sacral nerves. Afferent fibers from the uterus enter the spinal cord solely through the eleventh and twelfth thoracic nerves.

The Vagina (Fig. 1155, 1156).

The **vagina** extends from the vestibule to the uterus, and is situated behind the bladder and in front of the rectum; it is directed upward and backward, its axis forming with that of the uterus an angle of over 90°. Its walls are ordinarily in contact, and the usual shape of its lower part on transverse section is that of an H, the transverse limb being slightly curved forward or backward, while the lateral limbs are somewhat convex toward the median line; its middle part has the appearance of a transverse slit. Its length is 6 to 7.5 cm. along its anterior wall, and 9 cm. along its posterior wall. It is constricted at its commencement, dilated in the middle, and narrowed near its uterine extremity; it surrounds the vaginal portion of the cervix uteri, its attachment extending higher up on the posterior than on the anterior wall of the uterus. To the recess behind the cervix the term **posterior fornix** is applied, while the smaller recesses in front and at the sides are called the **anterior** and **lateral fornices.**

Relations.—The **anterior surface** of the vagina is in relation with the fundus of the bladder, and with the urethra. Its **posterior surface** is separated from the rectum by the rectouterine excavation in its upper fourth, and by the rectovaginal fascia in its middle two-fourths; the lower fourth is separated from the anal canal by the perineal body. As the terminal portions of the ureters pass forward and medialward to reach the fundus of the bladder, they run close to the lateral fornices of the vagina, and as they enter the bladder are slightly in front of the anterior fornix.

Structure.—The vagina consists of an **internal mucous lining** and a **muscular coat** separated by a layer of erectile tissue.

The **mucous membrane** (*tunica mucosa*) is continuous above with that lining the uterus. Its inner surface presents two longitudinal ridges, one on its anterior and one on its posterior wall. These ridges are called the **columns of the vagina** and from them numerous transverse ridges or rugæ extend outward on either side. These rugæ are divided by furrows of variable depth, giving to the mucous membrane the appearance of being studded over with conical projections or papillæ; they are most numerous near the orifice of the vagina, especially before parturition The epithelium covering the mucous membrane is of the stratified squamous variety. The submucous tissue is very loose, and contains a plexus of large veins, together with smooth muscular fibers derived from the muscular coat. It contains a number of mucous crypts, but no true glands.

The **muscular coat** (*tunica muscularis*) consists of two layers: an external longitudinal, which is by far the stronger, and an internal circular layer. The longitudinal fibers are continuous with the superficial muscular fibers of the uterus. The strongest fasciculi are those attached to the rectovesical fascia on either side. The two layers are not distinctly separable from each other, but are connected by oblique decussating fasciculi, which pass from the one layer to the other. In addition to this, the vagina at its lower end is surrounded by a band of striped muscular fibers, the **Bulbocavernosus** (see page 479).

External to the muscular coat is a layer of connective tissue, containing a large plexus of bloodvessels.

The **erectile tissue** consists of a layer of loose connective tissue, situated between the mucous membrane and the muscular coat; imbedded in it is a plexus of large veins, and numerous bundles of unstriped muscular fibers, derived from the circular muscular layer. The arrangement of the veins is similar to that found in other erectile tissues.

The External Genital Organs (Partes Genitales Externæ Muliebres)
(Fig. 1159).

The **external genital organs** of the female are: the **mons pubis**, the **labia majora et minora pudendi**, the **clitoris**, the **vestibule of the vagina**, the **bulb of the vestibule**, and the **greater vestibular glands**. The term **pudendum** or **vulva**, as generally applied, includes all these parts.

The **Mons Pubis** (*commissura labiorum anterior; mons Veneris*), the rounded eminence in front of the pubic symphysis, is formed by a collection of fatty tissue beneath the integument. It becomes covered with hair at the time of puberty.

The **Labia Majora** (*labia majora pudendi*) are two prominent longitudinal cutaneous folds which extend downward and backward from the mons pubis and form the lateral boundaries of a fissure or cleft, the **pudendal cleft** or **rima**, into which the vagina and urethra open. Each labium has two surfaces, an outer, pigmented and covered with strong, crisp hairs; and an inner, smooth and beset with large sebaceous follicles. Between the two there is a considerable quantity of areolar tissue, fat, and a tissue resembling the dartos tunic of the scrotum, besides vessels, nerves, and glands. The labia are thicker in front, where they form by their meeting the **anterior labial commissure**. Posteriorly they are not really joined, but appear to become lost in the neighboring integument, ending close to, and nearly parallel with, each other. Together with the connecting skin between them, they form the **posterior labial commissure** or posterior boundary of the pudendum. The labia majora correspond to the scrotum in the male.

The **Labia Minora** (*labia minora pudendi; nymphæ*) are two small cutaneous folds, situated between the labia majora, and extending from the clitoris obliquely downward, lateralward, and backward for about 4 cm. on either side of the orifice of the vagina, between which and the labia majora they end; in the virgin the posterior ends of the labia minora are usually joined across the middle line by a fold of skin, named the **frenulum of the labia** or **fourchette**. Anteriorly, each labium minus divides into two portions: the upper division passes above the clitoris to

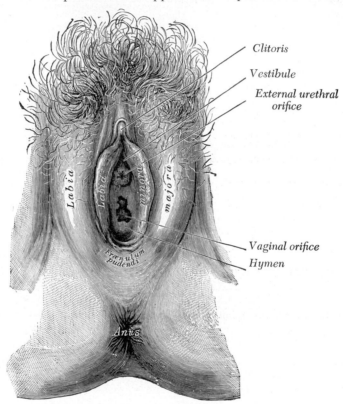

Fig. 1159.—External genital organs of female. The labia minora have been drawn apart.

meet its fellow of the opposite side, forming a fold which overhangs the glans clitoridis, and is named the **preputium clitoridis**; the lower division passes beneath the clitoris and becomes united to its under surface, forming, with the corresponding structure of the opposite side, the **frenulum of the clitoris**. On the opposed surfaces of the labia minora are numerous sebaceous follicles.

The **Clitoris** is an erectile structure, homologous with the penis. It is situated beneath the anterior labial commissure, partially hidden between the anterior ends of the labia minora. It consists of two corpora cavernosa, composed of erectile tissue enclosed in a dense layer of fibrous membrane, united together along their medial surfaces by an incomplete fibrous pectiniform septum; each corpus is connected to the rami of the pubis and ischium by a crus; the **free extremity** (*glans clitoridis*) is a small rounded tubercle, consisting of spongy erectile tissue, and highly sensitive. The clitoris is provided like the penis, with a suspensory ligament, and with two small muscles, the Ischiocavernosi, which are inserted into the crura of the clitoris.

The Vestibule (*vestibulum vaginæ*).—The cleft between the labia minora and behind the glans clitoridis is named the **vestibule of the vagina**: in it are seen the urethral and vaginal orifices and the openings of the ducts of the greater vestibular glands.

The **external urethral orifice** (*orificium urethræ externum; urinary meatus*) is placed about 2.5 cm. behind the glans clitoridis and immediately in front of that of the vagina; it usually assumes the form of a short, sagittal cleft with slightly raised margins.

The **vaginal orifice** is a median slit below and behind the opening of the urethra; its size varies inversely with that of the **hymen**.

The **hymen** is a thin fold of mucous membrane situated at the orifice of the vagina; the inner edges of the fold are normally in contact with each other, and the vaginal orifice appears as a cleft between them. The hymen varies much in shape. When stretched, its commonest form is that of a ring, generally broadest posteriorly; sometimes it is represented by a semilunar fold, with its concave margin turned toward the pubes. Occasionally it is cribriform, or its free margin forms a membranous fringe. It may be entirely absent, or may form a complete septum across the lower end of the vagina; the latter condition is known as an **imperforate hymen**. It may persist after copulation, so that its presence cannot be considered a sign of virginity. When the hymen has been ruptured, small rounded elevations known as the **carunculæ hymenales** are found as its remains. Between the hymen and the frenulum of the labia is a shallow depression, named the **navicular fossa**.

The **Bulb of the Vestibule** (*bulbus vestibuli; vaginal bulb*) is the homologue of the bulb and adjoining part of the corpus cavernosum urethræ of the male, and consists of two elongated masses of erectile tissue, placed one on either side of the vaginal orifice and united to each other in front by a narrow median band termed the **pars intermedia**. Each lateral mass measures a little over 2.5 cm. in length. Their posterior ends are expanded and are in contact with the greater vestibular glands; their anterior ends are tapered and joined to one another by the pars intermedia; their deep surfaces are in contact with the superficial layer of the urogenital diaphragm; superficially they are covered by the Bulbocavernosus.

The **Greater Vestibular Glands** (*glandulæ vestibularis majores* [*Bartholini*]; *Bartholin's glands*) are the homologues of the bulbo-urethral glands in the male. They consist of two small, roundish bodies of a reddish-yellow color, situated one on either side of the vaginal orifice in contact with the posterior end of each lateral mass of the bulb of the vestibule. Each gland opens by means of a duct, about 2 cm. long, immediately lateral to the hymen, in the groove between it and the labium minus

Mammary Gland; (Mamma Breast)

The mammary gland is an accessory of the reproductive system in function, since it secretes milk for nourishment of the infant, but structurally and developmentally it is closely related to the integument. It reaches its typical exquisite development in women during the early childbearing period but is present only in a rudimentary form in infants, children, and men.

In the adult nullipara, each mamma forms a discoidal, hemispherical, or conical eminence on the anterior chest wall, extending from the second to the sixth or seventh rib, and from the lateral border of the sternum into the axilla. It protrudes 3 to 5 cm. from the chest wall, and its cephalocaudal diameter, approximately 10 to 12 cm., is somewhat less than its transverse diameter. Its average weight is 150 to 200 gm., increasing to 400 or 500 gm. during lactation. The left mamma is generally slightly larger than the right.

The glandular tissue forms fifteen or twenty lobes arranged radially about the nipple, each lobe having its own individual excretory duct. The glandular tissue does not occupy the entire eminence called the breast; a variable but considerable amount of adipose tissue fills out the stroma between and around the lobes. The central portion is predominantly glandular, the peripheral predominantly fat. The connective tissue stroma in many places is concentrated into fibrous bands which course vertically through the substance of the breast, attaching the deep layer of the superficial fascia to the corium of the skin. These bands are known as **suspensory ligaments of the breast** or **Cooper's ligaments.** The entire breast is contained within the superficial fascia. The deep surface is separated from the underlying external investing layer of deep fascia by a fascial cleft which allows considerable mobility. The deep surface of the breast is concave, molded over the anterior chest wall mostly in contact with the pectoral fascia, but laterally with the axillary and serratus anterior fascia, and inferiorly it may reach the Obliquus externus and Rectus abdominis.

The **Mammary Papilla** (*papilla mammæ*) or **Nipple** projects as a small cylindrical or conical body, a little below the center of each breast at about the level of the fourth intercostal space. It is perforated at the tip by fifteen or twenty minute openings, the apertures of the lactiferous ducts. The characteristic skin of the nipple, pigmented, wrinkled, and roughened by papillæ, extends outward on the surface of the breast for 1 or 2 cm. to form the **areola.** The color of the nipple and areola in nulliparæ varies from rosy pink to brown, depending on the complexion of the individual. During the second month and progressing through pregnancy, the skin becomes darker and the areola becomes larger. Following lactation the pigmentation diminishes but is never entirely lost and may be used to differentiate nulliparous from parous individuals.

The **areola** (*areola mammæ*) is made rough by the presence of numerous large sebaceous glands which produce small elevations of its surface. These **areolar glands** (*glands of Montgomery*) secrete a lipoid material which lubricates and protects the nipple during nursing. The subcutaneous tissue of the areola contains circular and radiating smooth muscle bundles which cause the nipple to become erect in response to stimulation.

Development.—The primordium of the mamma is first recognizable during the sixth week of intrauterine life as a bandlike thickening of the ectoderm of the anterolateral body wall. It extends from the axilla to the inguinal region and is called the **milk line.** The thickening of the ectoderm pushes into the subcutaneous mesoderm as it enlarges. After the eighth week, only the portion of the ridge destined to become mamma is identifiable. During the remainder of fetal life the epithelial cells proliferate, gradually forming buds and cords of cells projecting into the subcutaneous tissue, and by birth, in both sexes, little more than the main ducts have formed. The glands remain in this infantile condition in the male.

Adolescent Hypertrophy.—In the female there is but slight change from the infantile condition until the approach of puberty. At this time the mamma enlarges due to an increase in glandular tissue, particularly the ducts, and to a deposit of adipose tissue. The mammary papilla and areola enlarge, increase slightly in pigmentation, acquire smooth muscle and become sensitive. After the onset of the menses, with each period there is a change in the mamma. In the premenstrual phase there is a vascular engorgement, increase in the glands, and enlargement of their lumina. During the postmenstrual phase the gland regresses and then remains in an inactive stage until the next premenstrual phase.

Hypertrophy of Pregnancy.—Visible enlargement of the breast begins after the second month of pregnancy and is accompanied by increased pigmentation and enlargement of the papilla, areola, and areolar glands. The duct system develops first, reaching its completion during the first six months; the acini and secreting portion follow during the last three months. The adipose tissue is almost completely replaced by parenchyma.

The secretion from the mammary gland during the first two or three days after parturition is thin and yellowish and is called **colostrum**. The secretion of true milk begins on the third or fourth day and continues through the nursing period.

Involution after Lactation.—At the termination of nursing, the gland gradually regresses by loss of the glandular tissue; the ducts and acini return to their former size and number, and the interstices are filled with adipose tissue. There is a slight decrease in size of the breast as a whole and it tends to become more flabby and pendulous than the nulliparous breast. The pigmentation of the nipple and areola decrease but do not entirely disappear.

Menopausal Involution.—At the end of the childbearing period, the mammæ regress and the glandular tissue reverts toward the infantile condition. The adipose tissue disappears more slowly, especially in obese individuals, but eventually a senile atrophy occurs which leaves the mamma a shriveled pendulous fold of skin.

Hormonal Relationships.—The hypertrophy of puberty and the cyclic engorgements accompanying menstruation are responses to variations in the concentration of the ovarian sex hormones from the follicles and corpora lutea. The hypertrophy of pregnancy is in response to increase in the corpus luteum hormone. The presence of the ovary is necessary only during the first part of pregnancy; later, the hormones are supplied by the placenta. Lactation is a response to the lactogenic hormone of the hypophysis, but is influenced by the nervous system through the stimulus of suckling. Suppression of the ovarian hormones after the menopause results in the involution. Quite frequently the mammary glands in the newborn of both sexes secrete a fluid called "witches milk", under the influence of the hormones passed through the placenta from the maternal circulation.

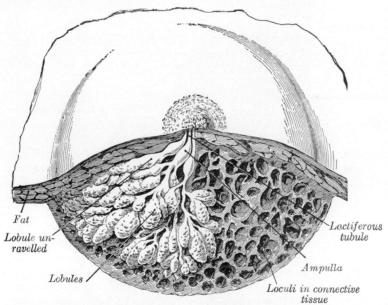

Fat

Lobule un-ravelled

Lobules

Lactiferous tubule

Ampulla

Loculi in connective tissue

Fig. 1160.—Dissection of the lower half of the mamma during the period of lactation. (Luschka.)

Structure (Figs. 1160, 1161).—The mamma consists of gland tissue; of fibrous tissue, connecting its lobes; and of fatty tissue in the intervals between the lobes. The gland tissue, when freed from fibrous tissue and fat, is of a pale reddish color, firm in texture, flattened from before backward and thicker in the center than at the circumference. The subcutaneous surface of the mamma presents numerous irregular processes which project toward the skin and are joined to it by bands of connective tissue. It consists of numerous lobes, and these are composed of lobules, connected together by areolar tissue, bloodvessels, and ducts. The smallest lobules consist of a cluster of rounded alveoli, which open into the smallest branches of the lactiferous ducts: these ducts unite to form larger ducts, and these end in a single canal, corresponding with one of the chief subdivisions of the gland. The number of excretory ducts varies from fifteen to twenty; they are termed the **tubuli lactiferi.**

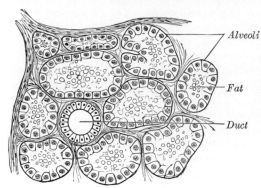

FIG. 1161.—Section of portion of mamma.

They converge toward the areola, beneath which they form dilatations or **ampullæ,** which serve as reservoirs for the milk, and, at the base of the papillæ, become contracted, and pursue a straight course to its summit, perforating it by separate orifices considerably narrower than the ducts themselves. The ducts are composed of areolar tissue containing longitudinal and transverse elastic fibers; muscular fibers are entirely absent; they are lined by columnar epithelium resting on a basement membrane. The epithelium of the mamma differs according to the state of activity of the organ. In the gland of a woman who is not pregnant or suckling, the alveoli are very small and solid, being filled with a mass of granular polyhedral cells. During pregnancy the alveoli enlarge, and the cells undergo rapid multiplication. At the commencement of lactation, the cells in the center of the alveolus undergo fatty degeneration, and are eliminated in the first milk, as **colostrum corpus**

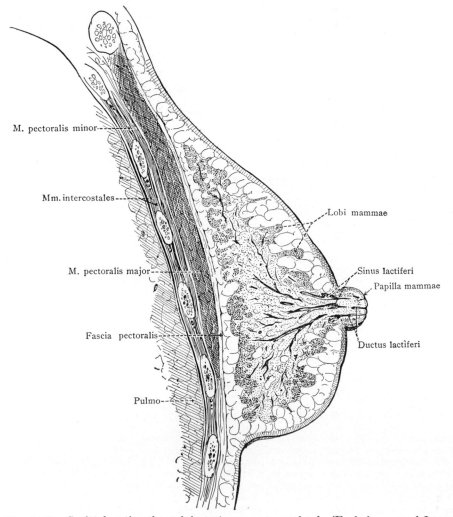

FIG. 1162.—Sagittal section through lactating mammary gland. (Eycleshymer and Jones.)

cles. The peripheral cells of the alveolus remain, and form a single layer of granular, short columnar cells, with spherical nuclei, lining the basement membrane. The cells during the state of activity of the gland, are capable of forming, in their interior, oil globules, which are then ejected into the lumen of the alveolus, and constitute the milk globules. When the acini are distended by the accumulation of the secretion the lining epithelium becomes flattened.

The **fibrous tissue** invests the entire surface of the mamma. Bands of fibrous tissue traverse the gland and connect the overlying skin to the underlying pectoral fascia. These constitute the ligaments of Cooper.

The **fatty tissue** covers the surface of the gland, and occupies the interval between its lobes. It usually exists in considerable abundance, and determines the form and size of the gland. There is no fat immediately beneath the areola and papilla.

Vessels and Nerves.—The **arteries** supplying the mammæ are derived from the thoracic branches of the axillary, the intercostals, and the internal mammary. The **veins** describe an anastomotic circle around the base of the papilla, called by Haller the **circulus venosus.** From this, large branches transmit the blood to the circumference of the gland, and end in the axillary and internal mammary veins. The **lymphatics** are described on page 808. The **nerves** are derived from the anterior and lateral cutaneous branches of the fourth, fifth, and sixth thoracic nerves.

Variations.—Independent of the physiological variations, conditions of underdeveloped breasts (*hypomastia*), hypertrophy, and inequality on the two sides are quite common. Variations in position, cephalically or caudally, are not infrequent, as might be expected from the method of embryological development. Absence of the breast, *amastia*, is very rare; an increase in the number of mammæ, **polymastia**, is not as rare. The supernumerary mammæ occur somewhere along the milk line in most instances, but other locations have been reported. Not infrequently they secrete milk during normal periods of lactation. When only the nipples of the supernumerary mammæ are present the condition is **polythelia;** the extra nipples occur along the milk line in the majority of cases and are found in males, though less frequently than in females.

Racial variations may be due to genetic influences which cause the discoidal, hemispherical pear-shaped, or conical forms to predominate. On the other hand, they may be due to intentional practices such as suppressing development by tight bandages at adolescence or tremendously elongating them by manipulation to make nursing convenient for an infant strapped on the back.

Gynecomastia is a condition in which the mammæ of a male are enlarged. In pseudogynecomastia the increase is due to adipose tissue. In the true gynecomastia, to some extent the epithelial tissue but more especially the firmer connective tissue elements are involved. It probably has a background of endocrine dysfunction but this is not clearly understood.

REFERENCES

URINARY SYSTEM

DEVELOPMENT AND ANOMALIES

ANSON, B. J., J. W. PICK, and E. W. CAULDWELL. 1942. The anatomy of commoner renal anomalies: Ectopic and horseshoe kidneys. J. Urol., *47*, 112–132.

EDWARDS, J. G. 1951. The development of the efferent arteriole in the human metanephros. Anat. Rec., *109*, 495–502.

WATERMAN, A. J. 1940. Growth and differentiation of kidney tissue of the rabbit embryo in omental grafts. J. Morph., *67*, 369–385.

WELLS, L. J., and E. T. BELL. 1946. Functioning of the fetal kidney as reflected by stillborn infants with hydroureter and hydronephrosis. Arch. Path., *42*, 274–276.

WHARTON, L. R., JR. 1949. Double ureters and associated renal anomalies in early human embryos. Contr. Embryol. Carneg. Instn, *33*, 105–112.

KIDNEY

BOYER, C. C. 1956. The vascular pattern of the renal glomerulus as revealed by plastic reconstruction from serial sections. Anat. Rec., *125*, 433–442.

CAMERON, G., and R. CHAMBERS. 1938. Direct evidence of function in kidney of an early human fetus. Amer. J. Physiol., *123*, 482–485.

DALTON, A. J. 1951. Structural details of some of the epithelial cell types in the kidney of the mouse as revealed by the electron microscope. J. nat. Cancer Inst., *11*, 1163–1185.

DAVIES, J. 1954. Cytological evidence of protein absorption in fetal and adult mammalian kidneys. Amer. J. Anat., *94*, 45–72.

EDWARDS, J. G. 1956. Efferent arterioles of glomeruli in the juxtamedullary zone of the human kidney. Anat. Rec., *125*, 521–530.

KIRKMAN, H. 1950. A comparative morphological and cytochemical study of globule leucocytes (Schollenleukocyten) of the urinary tract and of possibly related cells. Amer. J. Anat., *86*, 91–131.

MOODY, R. O., and R. G. VAN NUYS. 1940. The position and mobility of the kidneys in healthy young men and women. Anat. Rec., *76*, 111–133.

PEASE, D. C., and R. F. BAKER. 1950. Electron microscopy of the kidney. Amer. J. Anat., *87*, 349–389.

SMITH, H. W. 1951. The Kidney: Structure and Function in Health and Disease. Oxford Univ. Press, New York. xxii + 1049 pages.

SMITH, H. W. 1956. Principles of Renal Physiology. Oxford University Press, New York. x + 237 pages.

SULKIN, N. M. 1949. Cytologic studies of the remaining kidney following unilateral nephrectomy in the rat. Anat. Rec., *105*, 95–111.

ZWEMER, R. L., and R. M. WOTTON. 1944. Fat excretion in the guinea pig kidney. Anat. Rec., *90*, 107–114.

BLADDER

FRIEDMAN, N. B., and H. KUHLENBECK. 1950. Adenomatoid tumors of the bladder reproducing renal structures (nephrogenic adenomas). J. Urol., *64*, 657–670.

HEIMBERGER, R. F. 1949. The sacral innervation of the human bladder. Arch. Neurol. Psychiat., *62*, 686–688.

LANGWORTHY, O. R., and E. L. MURPHY. 1939. Nerve endings in the urinary bladder. J. comp. Neurol., *71*, 487–509.

MEYER, R. 1946. Normal and abnormal development of the ureter in the human embryo—A mechanistic consideration. Anat. Rec., *96*, 355–371.

SIMON, H. E., and N. A. BRANDEBERRY. 1946. Anomalies of the urachus: Persistent fetal bladder. J. Urol., *55*, 401–408.

TROTTER, M., and J. C. FINERTY. 1948. An anomalous urinary bladder. Anat. Rec., *100*, 259–269.

WESSON, M. B. 1950. Anatomy, physiology, embryology, and congenital abnormalities of the bladder. In Cyclopedia of Medicine, Surgery, and Specialties. F. A. Davis Co., Philadelphia. Vol. 2, 211–229.

FASCIA

BAUMANN, J. A. 1945. Développement et anatomie de la loge rénale chez l'homme. Acta Anat., *1*, 15–65.

CONGDON, E. D., and J. N. EDSON. 1941. The cone of renal fascia in the adult white male. Anat. Rec., *80*, 289–313.

TOBIN, C. E. 1944. The renal fascia and its relation to the transversalis fascia. Anat. Rec., *89*, 295–311.

TOBIN, C. E., and J. A. BENJAMIN. 1945. Anatomical and surgical restudy of Denonvilliers' fascia. Surg. Gynec. Obstet., *80*, 373–388.

BENJAMIN, J. A., and C. E. TOBIN. 1951. Abnormalities of the kidneys, ureters, and perinephric fascia: Anatomic and clinical study. J. Urol., *65*, 715–731.

NERVES AND VESSELS

ANSON, B. J., E. W. CAULDWELL, J. W. PICK, and L. E. BEATON. 1947. The blood supply of the kidney, suprarenal gland, and associated structures. Surg. Gynec. Obstet., *84*, 313–320.

EDWARDS, J. G. 1940. The vascular pole of the glomerulus in the kidney of vertebrates. Anat. Rec., *76*, 381–389.

HARMAN, P. J., and H. DAVIES. 1948. Intrinsic nerves in the mammalian kidney. I. Anatomy in mouse, rat, cat and macaque. J. comp. Neurol., *89*, 225–243.

McCORMACK, L. J., and B. J. ANSON. 1950. The arterial supply of the ureter. Quart. Bull. Northw. Univ. med. Sch., *24*, 291–294.

MITCHELL, G. A. G. 1950. The nerve supply of the kidneys. Acta Anat., *10*, 1–37

MITCHELL, G. A. G. 1951. The intrinsic renal nerves. Acta Anat., *13*, 1–15.

PEIRCE, E. C., 2ND. 1944. Renal lymphatics. Anat. Rec., *90*, 315–335.

PICK, J. W., and B. J. ANSON. 1940. The renal vascular pedicle. J. Urol., *44*, 411–434.

RONSTROM, G. N. 1947. Incidence of single and multiple renal arteries in Negroes. Amer. J. phys. Anthrop., n. s. *5*, 485–490.

WILMER, H. A. 1941. The arrangement of the capillary tuft of the human glomerulus. Anat. Rec., *80*, 507–518.

REPRODUCTIVE SYSTEM

GENERAL

ALLEN, E., C. H. DANFORTH, and E. A. DOISY. 1939. Sex and Internal Secretions. Williams & Wilkins, Baltimore, 2nd Ed. xxxvi + 1346 pages.

BLANDAU, R. J., and D. L. ODOR. 1949. The total number of spermatozoa reaching various segments of the reproductive tract in the female albino rat at intervals after insemination. Anat. Rec., *103*, 93–109.

BULLOUGH, W. S. 1951. Vertebrate Sexual Cycles. Methuen & Co., London (John Wiley & Sons, N. Y.). viii + 117 pages.

BURROWS, H. 1949. Biological Actions of Sex Hormones. 2nd Ed. Cambridge Univ. Press, London. xiv + 616 pages.

CREW, F. A. E. 1954. Sex Determination, 3rd Ed. John Wiley and Sons, Inc., New York. vii + 68 pages.

CORNER, G. W. 1942. The Hormones in Human Reproduction. Princeton Univ. Press, Princeton. xix + 265 pages.

FARRIS, E. J. 1950. Human Fertility and Problems of the Male. Author's Press, Inc., Palisades Park, N. J. xvi + 211 pages.

HOOKER, C. W. 1946. Reproduction. Ann. Rev. Physiol., *8*, 467–498.

MARKEE, J. E. 1951. Physiology of reproduction. Ann. Rev. Physiol., *13*, 367–396.

MITCHELL, G. A. G. 1938. The innervation of the ovary, uterine tube, testis and epididymis. J. Anat. (Lond.), *72*, 508–517.

REYNOLDS, E. L., and P. GROTE. 1948. Sex differences in the distribution of tissue components in the human leg from birth to maturity. Anat. Rec., *102*, 45–53.

STIEVE, P. H. 1952. Der Einfluss des Nervensystems auf Bau and Tätigkeit der Geschlechtsorgane des Menshen. Georg Thieme Verlag, Stuttgart. vii + 191 pages.

DEVELOPMENT AND ANOMALIES

DEY, F. L. 1943. Genital changes in female guinea pigs resulting from destruction of the median eminence. Anat. Rec., *87*, 85–90.

EVERETT, N. B. 1943. Observational and experimental evidences relating to the origin and differentiation of the definitive germ cells in mice. J. exp. Zool., *92*, 49–91.

GILLMAN, J. 1948. The development of the gonads in man, with a consideration of the role of fetal endocrines and the histogenesis of ovarian tumors. Carnegie Contr. Embryol. Carneg. Instn., *32*, 83–131.

GOLDBERG, M. B., and A. F. MAXWELL. 1948. Male pseudohermaphroditism proved by surgical exploration and microscopic examination. A case report with speculations concerning pathogenesis. J. clin. Endocr., *8*, 367–379.

HAMLETT, G. W. D. 1935. Primordial germ cells in a 4.5-mm. human embryo. Anat. Rec., *61*, 273–279.

HOLYOKE, E. A. 1949. The differentiation of embryonic gonads transplanted to the adult omentum in the albino rat. Anat. Rec., *103*, 675–699.

HOOKER, C. W., and L. C. STRONG. 1944. Hermaphroditism in rodents, with a description of a case in the mouse. Yale J. Biol. Med., *16*, 341–351.

PATTON, W. H. G. 1948. A case of true hermaphrodism in an adult African. Anat. Rec., *101*, 479–485.

PRICE, D. 1947. An analysis of the factors influencing growth and development of the mammalian reproductive tract. Physiol. Zoöl., *20*, 213–247.

WARREN, H. S. 1954. Agenesis of the external genitalia with report of two cases. Anat. Rec., *118*, 165–174.

YOUNG, H. H. 1937. Genital Abnormalities, Hermaphroditism and Related Adrenal Diseases. Williams & Wilkins, Baltimore. 649 pages.

MALE REPRODUCTIVE SYSTEM

BURNS, R. K. 1945. Bisexual differentiation of the sex ducts in opossums as a result of treatment with androgen. J. exp. Zool., *100*, 119–140.

CALABRISI, P. 1956. The nerve supply of the erectile cavernous tissue of the genitalia in the human embryo and fetus. Anat. Rec., *125*, 713–724.

CHRISTENSEN, G. C. 1954. Angioarchitecture of the canine penis and the process of erection. Amer. J. Anat., *95*, 227–262.

CONGDON, E. D. and J. M. ESSENBERG. 1955. Subcutaneous attachments of the human penis and scrotum. A study of 55 series of gross sections. Amer. J. Anat., *97*, 331–358.

DEYSACH, L. J.   1939.   The comparative morphology of the erectile tissue of the penis with especial emphasis on the probable mechanism of erection.   Amer. J. Anat., *64*, 111–131.

FARRIS, E. J.   1950   Human Fertility and Problems of the Male.   Author's Press, Inc., Palisades Park, N. J.   xvi + 211 pages.

FOX, W.   1956.   Seminal receptacles of snakes.   Anat. Rec., *124*, 519–540.

HAMILTON, J. B.   1942.   Male hormone stimulation is prerequisite and an incitant in common baldness.   Amer. J. Anat., *71*, 451–480.

HAMILTON, J. B.   1946.   A secondary sexual character that develops in men but not in women upon aging of an organ present in both sexes.   Anat. Rec., *94*, 466–467.

HAMILTON, J. B.   1948.   The role of testicular secretions as indicated by the effects of castration in man and by studies of pathological conditions and the short lifespan associated with maleness. Recent Progr. Hormone Res., *3*, 257–322.

HAMILTON, J. B. and S. L. LEONARD.   1938.   The effect of male hormonal substance upon the testes and upon spermatogenesis.   Anat. Rec., *71*, 105–117.

HAMILTON, J. B. and J. M. WOLFE.   1938.   The effect of male hormone substances upon birth and prenatal development in the rat.   Anat. Rec., *70*, 433–440.

KINDRED, J. E.   1952.   The histopathologic changes in the testes of rats intravenously injected with a nitrogen mustard, tris (beta-chloroethyl) amine.   J. exp. Zool., *121*, 225–293.

KUNTZ, A. and R. E. MORRIS, JR.   1946.   Components and distribution of the spermatic nerves and the nerves of the vas deferens.   J. comp. Neurol., *85*, 33–44.

MACDONALD, J. D.   1950.   Some cytochemical characteristics of certain intranuclear inclusion bodies in the epithelium of the human vas deferens.   Anat. Rec., *106*, 327–343.

PFEIFFER, C. A. and A. KIRSCHBAUM.   1943.   Relation of interstitial cell hyperplasia to secretion of male hormone in the sparrow.   Anat. Rec., *85*, 211–227.

RUKSTINAT, G. J. and R. J. HASTERLIK.   1939.   Congenital absence of the penis.   Arch. Path. (Chicago), *27*, 984–993.

TOBIN, C. E. and J. A. BENJAMIN.   1944.   Anatomical study and clinical consideration of the fasciæ limiting urinary extravasation from the penile urethra.   Surg. Gynec. Obstet., *79*, 195–204.

WELLS, L. J.   1943.   Descent of the testis; anatomical and hormonal considerations.   Surgery, *14*, 436–472.

WESSON, M. B.   1945.   The value of Buck's and Colles' fasciæ.   J. Urol., *53*, 365–372.

WILLIAMS, R. G.   1949.   Some responses of living blood vessels and connective tissue to testicular grafts in rabbits.   Anat. Rec., *104*, 147–161.

WILLIAMS, D. D.   1958.   A histological study of the effects of subnormal temperature on the testis of the fowl.   Anat. Rec., *130*, 225–242.

WISLOCKI, G. B.   1950.   Cytochemical reactions of human spermatozoa and seminal plasma. Anat. Rec., *108*, 645–661.

FEMALE REPRODUCTIVE SYSTEM

OVARY, OVA, OVULATION

BASSETT, D. L.   1943.   The changes in the vascular pattern of the ovary of the albino rat during the estrous cycle.   Amer. J. Anat., *73*, 251–291.

DUKE, K. L.   1947.   The fibrous connective tissue of the rabbit ovary from sex differentiation to maturity.   Anat. Rec., *98*, 507–525.

EVERETT, J. W.   1945.   The microscopically demonstrable lipids of cyclic corpora lutea in the rat.   Amer. J. Anat., *77*, 293–323.

EVERETT, J. W.   1956.   Functional corpora lutea maintained for months by autografts of rat hypophyses.   Endocrinology, *58*, 786–796.

EVERETT, N. B.   1942.   The origin of ova in the adult opossum.   Anat. Rec., *82*, 77–91.

ESSENBERG, J. M.   1949.   The response of germ cells to gonadotropic hormones in x-ray injured ovaries of young white mice.   West. J. Surg., *57*, 61–66.

FARRIS, E. J.   1946.   The time of ovulation in the monkey.   Anat. Rec., *95*, 337–345.

GREEN, J. A.   1957.   Some effects of advancing age on the histology and reactivity of the mouse ovary.   Anat. Rec., *129*, 333–348.

HILL, R. T., E. ALLEN, and T. C. KRAMER.   1935.   Cinemicrographic studies of rabbit ovulation. Anat. Rec., *63*, 239–245.

LANGMAN, L., and H. S. BURR.   1942.   Electrometric timing of human ovulation.   Amer. J. Obstet. Gynec., *44*, 223–230.

MARVIN, H. N.   1947.   Diestrus and the formation of corpora lutea in rats with persistent estrus, treated with desoxycorticosterone acetate.   Anat. Rec., *98*, 383–391.

MOSSMAN, H. W.   1938.   The homology of the vesicular ovarian follicles of the mammalian ovary with the coelom.   Anat. Rec., *70*, 643–655.

PANKRATZ, D. S.   1938.   Some observations on the graafian follicles in an adult human ovary. Anat. Rec., *71*, 211–219.

Pincus, G. 1939. The comparative behavior of mammalian eggs *in vivo* and *in vitro*. IV. The development of fertilized and artificially activated rabbit eggs. J. exp. Zool., *82*, 85–129.

Russell, W. L., and P. M. Douglass. 1945. Offspring from unborn mothers. Proc. nat. Acad. Sci. Wash., *31*, 402–404.

Sawyer, C. H., and J. E. Markee. 1950. The differential mechanisms by which picrotoxin and copper acetate induce ovulation in the rabbit. Endocrinology, *46*, 177–190.

Watzka, M. 1957. Weibliche Genitalorgan: Das Ovarium. In Handbuch der mikroskopischen Anatomie des Menschen (von Möllendorff). Springer-Verlag, Berlin. Vol 7, pt. 3, iv + 178 pages.

Uterus Menstruation

Alden, R. H. 1942. The oviduct and egg transport in the albino rat. Anat. Rec., *84*, 137–169.

Alden, R. H. 1945. Implantation of the rat egg. I. Experimental alteration of uterine polarity. J. exp. Zool., *100*, 229–235.

Bartelmez, G. W. 1953. Factors in the variability of the menstrual cycle. Anat. Rec., *115*, 101–120.

Barton, D. S. 1940. A study of temperature and electric potentials in the menstrual cycle. Yale J. Biol. Med., *12*, 503–523.

Bo, W. J. 1956. The relationship between vitamin A deficiency and estrogen in producing uterine metaplasia in the rat. Anat. Rec., *124*, 619–628.

Ford, D. H. 1956. A study of the changes in vaginal alkaline phosphatase activity during the the estrous cycle in adult and in young "first-estrous" rats. Anat. Rec., *125*, 261–278.

Gardner, W. U. 1955. Localization of strain differences in vaginal sensitivity to estrogens. Anat. Rec., *121*, 297–298.

Hamlett, G. W. D. 1939. Reproduction in American monkeys. I. Estrous cycle, ovulation and menstruation in Cebus. Anat. Rec., *73*, 171–187.

Jarcho, J. 1946. Malformations of the uterus; review of the subject, including embryology, comparative anatomy, diagnosis and report of cases. Amer. J. Surg., *71*, 106–166.

Langman, L., and H. S. Burr. 1941. An electrometric study of uterine activity. Amer. J. Obstet. Gynec., *42*, 59–67.

Markee, J. E. 1940. Menstruation in intraocular endometrial transplants in the rhesus monkey. Contr. Embryol. Carneg. Instn., *28*, 221–308.

Papanicolaou, G. N., H. F. Traut, and A. A. Marchetti. 1948. The Epithelia of Woman's Reproductive Organs. The Commonwealth Fund, New York. vi + 53 pages.

Reynolds, S. R. M. 1949. Physiology of the Uterus. 2nd Ed. Hoeber, New York. xxii + 611 pages.

Reynolds, S. R. M. 1946. The relation of hydrostatic conditions in the uterus to the size and shape of the conceptus during pregnancy: A concept of uterine accommodation. Anat. Rec., *95*, 283–296.

Female Pelvis and Fasciæ

Caldwell, W. E., H. C. Moley, and D. A. D'Esopo. 1940. The more recent conceptions of the pelvic architecture. Amer. J. Obstet. Gynec., *40*, 558–565.

Curtis, A. H., B. J. Anson, and F. L. Ashley. 1942. Further studies in gynecological anatomy and related clinical problems. Surg. Gynec. Obstet., *74*, 709–727.

Curtis, A. H., B. J. Anson, F. L. Ashley, and T. Jones. 1942. The blood vessels of the female pelvis in relation to gynecological surgery. Surg. Gynec. Obstet., *75*, 421–423.

Davies, J. W. 1935. The preperitoneal layer—its gynecological application. Surg. Gynec. Obstet., *60*, 941–945.

Greulich, W. W., and H. Thomas. 1944. The growth and development of the pelvis of individual girls before, during, and after puberty. Yale J. Biol. Med., *17*, 91–97.

Power, R. M. H. 1944. The exact anatomy and development of the ligaments attached to the cervix uteri. Surg. Gynec. Obstet., *79*, 390–396.

Thoms, H., and W. W. Greulich. 1940. A comparative study of male and female pelvis. Amer. J. Obstet. Gynec., *39*, 56–62.

Uhlenhuth, E. 1953. Problems in the Anatomy of the Pelvis. J. B. Lippincott Co., Philadelphia. xiv + 206 pages.

Mammæ

Agate, F. J., Jr. 1952. The growth and secretory activity of the mammary glands of the pregnant rhesus monkey (Macaca mulatta) following hypophysectomy. Amer. J. Anat., *90*, 257–284.

Anson, B. J., R. R. Wright, and J. A. Wolfer. 1939. Blood supply of the mammary gland, with surgical considerations. Surg. Gynec. Obstet., *69*, 468–473.

CHOLNOKY, T. DE. 1939. Supernumerary breast. Arch. Surg., *39*, 926–941.

DEMPSEY, E. W., H. BUNTING, and G. B. WISLOCKI. 1947. Observations on the chemical cytology of the mammary gland. Amer. J. Anat., *81*, 309–341.

KARSNER, H. T. 1946. Gynecomastia. Amer. J. Path., *22*, 235–315.

MALINIAC, J. W. 1943. Arterial blood supply of the breast. Arch. Surg., *47*, 329–343.

ROMANO, S. A., and E. M. MCFETRIDGE. 1938. The limitations and dangers of mammography by contrast mediums. J.A.M.A., *110*, 1905–1910.

THOREK, M. 1942. Plastic Surgery of the Breast and Abdominal Wall. Charles C Thomas, Springfield. xiii + 446 pages.

WILLIAMS, W. L. 1942. Normal and experimental mammary involution in the mouse as related to the inception and cessation of lactation. Amer. J. Anat., *71*, 1–41.

WILLIAMS, W. L. 1945. The effects of lactogenic hormone on post parturient unsuckled mammary glands of the mouse. Anat. Rec., *93*, 171–183.

THE ENDOCRINE GLANDS

THE **endocrine glands** or **ductless glands** (*glandulae sine ductibus*) are grouped together because of their common characteristic of not having ducts and of discharging their specific secretions, called hormones, into the blood stream.

The **hormones** are chemical messengers, and although they are carried by the blood stream to all parts of the body, only certain organs or types of cells are able to respond to their stimulation. The specific organ which does respond to a particular hormone is called its **target organ.** There are a number of hormones beside the ones secreted by the endocrine glands described in this chapter. For example, the islands of Langerhans in the pancreas secrete insulin; the gonads, androgens and estrogens; and the mucous membrane of the gastro-intestinal tract, secretin. These structures are described in other chapters.

The endocrine glands included in this chapter are the thyroid and parathyroid glands, the hypophysis or pituitary gland, the suprarenal gland, and the paraganglia. The pineal gland is included because it is ductless although its endocrine activity is not established. The thymus was at one time classed with the ductless glands but is now included in the lymphatic system.

THE THYROID GLAND

Development.—The thyroid gland is developed from a median diverticulum of the ventral wall of the pharynx which appears about the fourth week on the summit of the tuberculum impar, but later is found in the furrow immediately behind the tuerculum (Fig. 996). It grows downward and backward as a tubular duct, which bifurcates and subsequently subdivides into a series of cellular cords, from which the isthmus and lateral lobes of the thyroid gland are developed. The connection of the median diverticulum with the pharynx is termed the **thyroglossal duct**; its continuity is subsequently interrupted, and it undergoes degeneration, its upper end being represented by the foramen cecum of the tongue, and its lower by the pyramidal lobe of the thyroid gland.

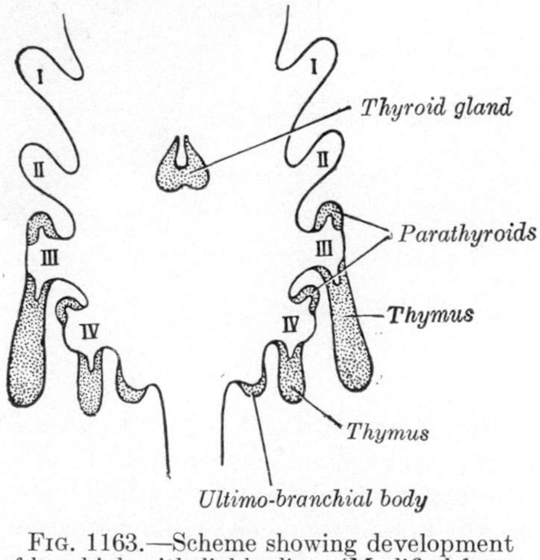

The **thyroid gland** (*glandula thyreoidea*) (Fig. 1164) is a highly vascular organ, situated at the front of the neck. It consists of right and left lobes connected across the middle line by a narrow portion, the isthmus. Its weight is somewhat variable, but is usually about 30 grams. It is slightly heavier in women and it becomes enlarged during pregnancy.

The **lobes** (*lobuli gl. thyreoideæ*) are conical in shape, the apex of each being

FIG. 1163.—Scheme showing development of brachial epithelial bodies. (Modified from Kohn.) *I, II, III, IV.* Branchial pouches.

directed upward and lateralward as far as the junction of the middle with the lower third of the thyroid cartilage; the base looks downward, and is on a level with the fifth or sixth tracheal ring. Each lobe is about 5 cm. long; its greatest width is about 3 cm., and its thickness about 2 cm. The **lateral** or **superficial surface** is convex, and covered by the skin, the superficial and deep fasciæ, the Sternocleidomastoideus, the superior belly of the Omohyoideus, the Sternohyoideus and Sternothyreoideus, and beneath the last muscle by the visceral layer of the deep fascia, which forms a capsule for the gland. The **deep** or **medial surface** is moulded over the underlying structures, viz., the trachea, the Constrictor pharyngis inferior and

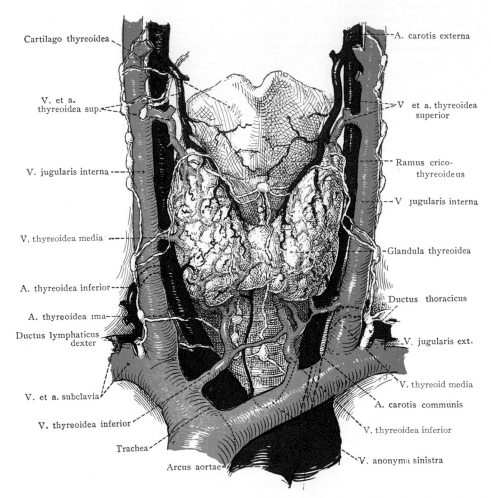

Cartilago thyreoidea

A. carotis externa

V. et a. thyreoidea sup.

V et a. thyreoidea superior

V. jugularis interna

Ramus cricothyreoideus

V jugularis interna

V. thyreoidea media

Glandula thyreoidea

A. thyreoidea inferior

Ductus thoracicus

A. thyreoidea ima

Ductus lymphaticus dexter

V. jugularis ext.

V. thyreoid media

V. et a. subclavia

A. carotis communis

V. thyreoidea inferior

V. thyreoidea inferior

Trachea

V. anonyma sinistra

Arcus aortae

FIG. 1164.—Blood supply of the thyroid gland, viewed from in front. The thoracic duct and principal lymphatics are also shown. (Ecyleshymer and Jones.)

posterior part of the Cricothyreoideus, the esophagus (particularly on the left side of the neck), the superior and inferior thyroid arteries, and the recurrent nerves. The **anterior border** is thin, and inclines obliquely from above downward toward the middle line of the neck, while the **posterior border** is thick and overlaps the common carotid artery, and, as a rule, the parathyroids.

The **isthmus** (isthmus gl. thyreoideæ) connects together the lower thirds of the lobes; it measures about 1.25 cm. in breadth, and the same in depth, and usually covers the second and third rings of the trachea. Its situation and size present, however, many variations. In the middle line of the neck it is covered by the skin and fascia, and close to the middle line, on either side, by the Sternothyreoideus.

Across its upper border runs an anastomotic branch uniting the two superior thyroid arteries; at its lower border are the inferior thyroid veins. Sometimes the isthmus is altogether wanting.

A third lobe, of conical shape, called the **pyramidal lobe**, frequently *arises* from the upper part of the isthmus, or from the adjacent portion of either lobe, but most commonly the left, and ascends as far as the hyoid bone. It is occasionally quite detached, or may be divided into two or more parts.

A fibrous or muscular band is sometimes found attached, above, to the body of the hyoid bone, and below to the isthmus of the gland, or its pyramidal lobe. When muscular, it is termed the **Levator glandulæ thyreoideæ.**

Small detached portions of thyroid tissue are sometimes found in the vicinity of the lateral lobes or above the isthmus; they are called **accessory thyroid glands** (*glandulæ thyreoideæ accessoriæ*).

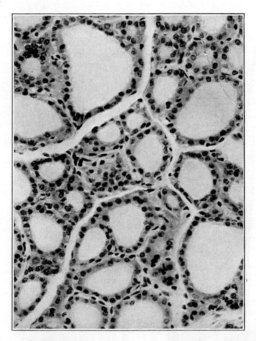

Fig. 1165.—Thyroid gland of a rat. (Kenyon, Am. J. Path.)

Structure.—The thyroid gland is invested by a thin capsule of connective tissue, which projects into its substance and imperfectly divides it into masses of irregular form and size. When the organ is cut into, it is of a brownish-red color, and is seen to be made up of a number of closed vesicles, containing colloid, and separated from each other by intermediate connective tissue (Fig. 1165.)

The thyroid follicles (acini, vesicles) of the adult are closed sacs of inconstant shape and size. They are normally of microscopic dimensions, although macroscopically visible in colloid goiter. The follicles located peripherally may be larger than those centrally placed. The cuboidal epithelium of the normal thyroid rests directly on the delicate connective tissue surrounding the follicle. No basement membrane can be seen. The capillaries and lymphatics are thus in close contact with the secretory epithelium of the gland. The follicle normally is filled with colloid which contains the active principle of the gland, thyroxin. The thyroid epithelium may secrete this hormone directly into the colloid filled lumen of the follicle where it is stored, or the hormone may be secreted directly into the capillaries. The stored colloid may be absorbed and liberated into the capillaries.

The hormone, thyroxin, requires iodine for its elaboration and is normally obtained in adequate amounts in the diet. Proper functioning of the thyroid gland and normal histological structure is dependent upon the adequacy of available iodine. The thyroid itself is activated or regulated by another hormone, the thyrotrophic hormone of the anterior pituitary gland. Removal of the thyroid results in a marked reduction of the oxidative processes of the body. This lowered metabolic rate is characteristic of hypothyroidism. In infancy and childhood the thyroid gland is essential to normal growth of the body.

Vessels and Nerves (Fig. 1166).—The **arteries** supplying the thyroid gland are the superior and inferior thyroids and sometimes an additional branch (thyroidea ima) from the innominate artery or the arch of the aorta, which ascends upon the front of the trachea. The arteries are remarkable for their large size and frequent anastomoses. The **veins** (Fig. 1164) form a plexus on the surface of the gland and on the front of the trachea; from this plexus the superior, middle, and inferior thyroid veins arise; the superior and middle end in the internal jugular, the inferior in the innominate vein. The capillary blood vessels form a dense plexus in the connective tissue around the vesicles, between the epithelium of the vesicles and the endothelium of the lymphatics, which surround a greater or smaller part of the circumference of the vesicle. The **lymphatic vessels** run in the interlobular connective tissue, not uncommonly surrounding the arteries which they accompany, and communicate with a net-work in the capsule of the gland; they may contain colloid material. They end in the thoracic and right lymphatic trunks. The **nerves** are derived from the middle and inferior cervical ganglia of the sympathetic.

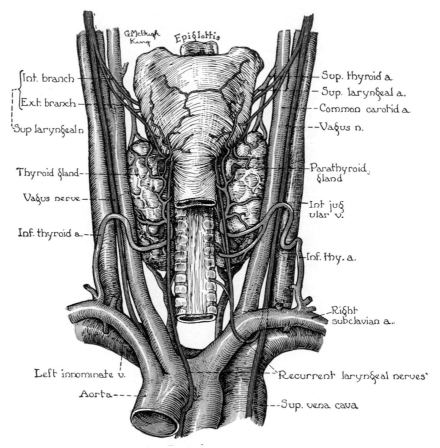

Fig. 1166.—Posterior view of larynx, trachea, thyroid, and parathyroids. Relations of thyroid arteries and laryngeal nerves are shown. (Nordland; Surgery, Gynecology and Obstetrics.)

THE PARATHYROID GLANDS (Fig. 1166).

Development.—The parathyroid bodies are developed as outgrowths from the third and fourth branchial pouches (Fig. 1163).

Anatomy.—The parathyroid glands are small brownish-red bodies, situated as a rule between the posterior borders of the lateral lobes of the thyroid gland and its capsule.

They differ from it in structure, being composed of masses of cells arranged in a more or less columnar fashion with numerous intervening capillaries. They measure on an average about 6 mm. in length, and from 3 to 4 mm. in breadth, and usually present the appearance of flattened oval disks. They are divided, according to their situation, into **superior** and **inferior**. The superior, usually two in number, are the more constant in position, and are situated, one on either side, at the level of the lower border of the cricoid cartilage, behind the junction of the pharynx and esophagus. The inferior, also usually two in number, may be applied to the lower edge of the lateral lobes, or placed at some little distance below the thyroid gland, or found in relation to one of the inferior thyroid veins.

In man, they number four as a rule; fewer than four were found in less than 1 per cent. of over a thousand persons (Pepere), but more than four (five or six) in over 33 per cent of 122 bodies examined by Civalleri. In addition, numerous minute islands of parathyroid tissue may be found scattered in the connective tissue and fat of the neck around the parathyroid glands proper, and quite distinct from them.

Structure.—Microscopically the parathyroids consist of intercommunicating columns of cells supported by connective tissue containing a rich supply of blood capillaries. Most of the cells are clear, but some, larger in size, contain oxyphil granules. Vesicles containing colloid have been described as occurring in the parathyroid.

The parathyroids secrete a hormone, parathyrin or parathormone, necessary for calcium metabolism. The tetany which follows parathyroidectomy can be relieved by feeding or injecting calcium salts or parathyroid extracts.

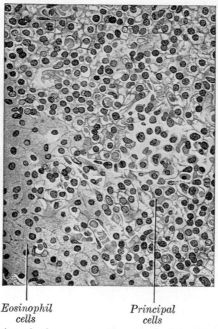

Eosinophil
cells

Principal
cells

Fig. 1167.—Section of a human parathyroid gland to show principal and eosinophil cells. × 250.

HYPOPHYSIS CEREBRI OR PITUITARY GLAND

Development.—The hypophysis has a dual origin which corresponds to the two distinct parts of the adult gland. At an early embryonic stage, about the fourth week, when the neural tube and the primitive digestive tube are still in close proximity, outgrowths or diverticula from both tubes come in contact with each

other to form the primordium of the hypophysis. The part from the neural tube
is in the diencephatic floor, the region of the hypothalamus, (Figs. 692, 694) and
is called the **infundibular process**. The part from the alimentary tube is from the
portion of the future pharynx developed from ectoderm, the stomodaeum, and is
known as **Rathe's pouch** (Fig. 999). The infundibular process retains a connection
with the hypothalamus as the stalk, preserves some resemblance to neural tissue,
and becomes the *neural lobe*. The cells of Rathe's pouch become adherent to the
infundibular process and grow partly around it, forming the *pars tuberalis*. The
remainder of the pouch forms a double layered cup and the connection with the
pharynx gradually disappears. The rostral portion of the cup thickens greatly
and becomes the glandular anterior lobe or *pars distalis*. The other layer of the

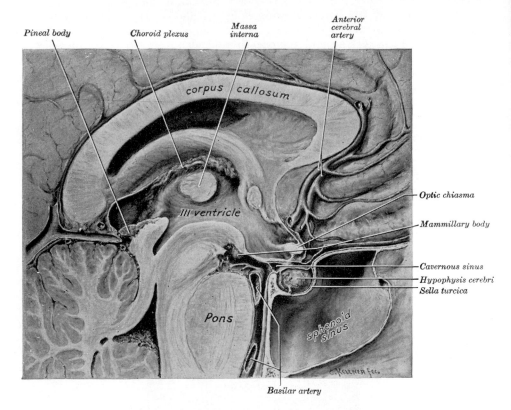

Pineal body   Choroid plexus   Massa   Anterior
                                             interna   cerebral
                                                            artery

corpus callosum

III ventricle

Optic chiasma

Mammillary body

Cavernous sinus
Hypophysis cerebri
Sella turcica

Pons

sphenoid sinus

Basilar artery

Fig. 1168.—The hypophysis cerebri in position.

cup remains adherent to the neural lobe, thickens but little, and develops into the
pars intermedia. The cavity of the original diverticulum eventually disappears
except for the vestigial lumen, in the form of one or more narrow vesicles of variable
length in the pars intermedia.

The **Hypophysis Cerebri** or **Pituitary Gland** is couched in the sella turcica or hypophyseal fossa of the body of the sphenoid bone. It is attached to the hypothalamus
by the **stalk** or **infundibulum**. After the brain has been removed from the cranial
cavity, the cut end of the stalk is visible protruding through a hole in the diaphragma sellæ (Fig. 801). The latter is a shelf of dura mater stretching between
the clinoid processes and covering over the sella turcica. In a median sagittal section the two principal portions of the gland are visible because of a difference in
color. The **posterior lobe** is pale corresponding to the overlying brain with which it

is continuous; the **anterior lobe** is somewhat larger and darker, due to its greater vascularity. The more detailed subdivisions of the gland can only be seen satisfactorily with a microscope.

The hypophysis is a small gland, 1.2 to 1.5 cm in its greatest diameter which is from side to side; its rostrocaudal diameter is approximately 1 cm, and its thickness is 0.5 cm. Its weight in an adult male is from 0.5 to 0.6 gms but varies according to the stature rather than the weight of an individual. It is larger in women, and since there is a slight increase during pregnancy, in a multipara it may weigh as much as 1 gm.

Relations.—Many important structures lie in close proximity to the hypophysis (Fig. 801, 1168). The internal carotid artery emerges from the dural covering of the cavernous sinus immediately lateral to it. The intercavernous and circular sinuses are enclosed in the diaphragma sellæ above it. The optic nerves, chiasma, and optic tracts lie between it and the bulk of the brain. In skulls with large sphenoid sinuses, the hypophysis may be separated from this air space only by a

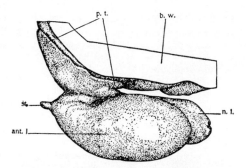

Fig. 1169.—Model of hypophysis and adjacent brain wall from a thirty-day embryo, viewed from the left side. × 25. *b. w.*, brain wall; *p. t.*, pars tuberalis; *st.*, stalk; *ant. l.*, anterior lobe; *n. l.*, neural lobe. (Atwell, Am. J. Anat.; courtesy of Wistar Institute.)

thin plate of bone and the dural lining of the sella. The practical importance of these relations is emphasized in patients with tumors of the hypophysis. They may compress the caroitd arteries or the optic nerves causing changes in the retina known as choked disks which are visible with the opthalmoscope.

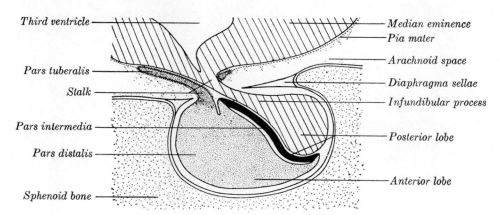

FIG. 1170.—Diagrammatic median sagittal section of the hypophysis cerebri or pituitary gland. (Atwell, Amer. J. Anat., '18.)

Structure.—The hypophysis is divided into two parts, on the basis of both morphology and function, the **glandular portion** or **adenohypophysis** and the **neural portion** or **neurohypophysis.** There is, however, some overlapping which is best shown in a table: (from Harris '55 after Rioch, Wislocki and O'Leary '40).

Adenohypophysis.—The **anterior lobe** or **pars distalis** is composed of cords of epithelial cells richly supplied with sinusoidal capillaries. The epithelial cells are of two main types, those that are colored by various stains, the **chromophiles,** and those that remain pale or unstained, the **chromophobes.** The chromphiles in turn are of two kinds, those whose granules take up acid dyes, named **acidophiles,** and those that take up basic dyes, the **basophiles.** The basophiles can again be subdivided into beta and delta types by their coloration with certain dyes. There is no definite pattern of distribution of the two chromophiles, either in different parts of the gland or within individual cords. The chromophobes are smaller than the chromophiles, less discrete, and tend to accumulate in the center of cords and clumps. The lack of mitotic division in the hypophysis and certain experimental observations indicate that the chromophiles undergo cycles of secretory activity in which they discharge their specific granules and pass through a resting stage in the form of chromophobes.

MAJOR DIVISIONS AND SUBDIVISIONS OF THE MAMMALIAN HYPOPHYSIS

Adenohypophysis {	Lobus glandularis {	1. Pars distalis 2. Pars tuberalis 3. Pars intermedia	Anterior lobe
Neurohypophysis {	Lobus nervosus (neural lobe)	1. Infundibular process	Posterior lobe
	Infundibulum (neural stalk) {	1. Infundibular stem 2. Median eminence of the tuber cinereum	Neural stalk together with sheath of portions of lobus glandularis, designated as hypophyseal stalk

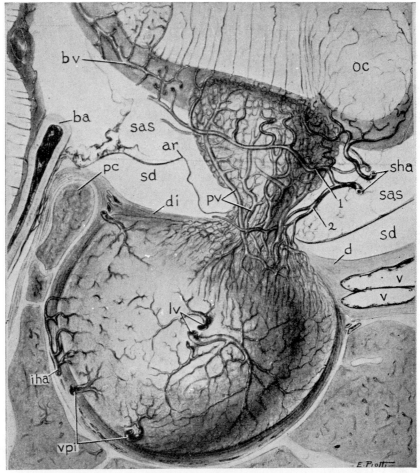

FIG. 1171.—Schematic drawing of the hypophysis of the adult rhesus monkey. *ar*, arachnoid membrane; *ba*, basilar artery; *bv*, basilar vein; *d*, dura; *di*, sellar diaphragm; *iha*, inferior hypophyseal artery; *lv*, lateral hypophyseal veins; *oc*, optic chiasma; *pc*, posterior clinoid process; *pv*, portal venules; *sas*, subarachnoid space; *sd*, subdural space; *sha*, superior hypophyseal arteries (1, branches to hypophyseal stalk; 2, branches to anterior lobe); *v*, dural veins; *vpi*, veins of infundibular process. (Wislocki, Pituitary Gland, Assn. for Research in Nervous and Mental Diseases, Williams & Wilkins.)

The **pars intermedia** is composed of a thin layer of epithelial cells between the neural lobe and the pars distalis. It encloses the remnants of the vestigial lumen of Rathke's pouch which appear as vesicles containing a "colloid" resembling that of the thyroid gland in histological preparations but having no relation to it chemically. The lining cells also may be ciliated.

Neurohypophysis.—The neurohypophysis is composed of the neural portion of the posterior lobe, the ifundibulum or stalk, and the median eminence of the tuber cinereum. All parts have a similar histological structure. The specific cell is the **pituicyte** which bears some resemblance to the neuroglial cells of the brain. They contain occasional droplets of lipid material and yellow pigment granules, but their secretory nature has not been established.

The **pars tuberalis** is a layer of cuboidal cells covering the stalk and neighboring area. It is richly supplied with arterial blood.

Blood supply.—The **arteries** to the hypophysis are the superior hypophyseal arteries from the internal carotid or posterior communicating arteries and the inferior hypophyseal arteries which are also branches of the internal carotid but traverse the cavernous sinus. The branches of the superior arteries supply the stalk and adjacent parts of the anterior lobe. The branches of the inferior arteries supply the posterior lobe. The blood supply of the pars distalis is mainly through a **portal system** of veins. The blood from the capillaries of the pars tuberalis and adjacent stalk collect into veins which pass along the stalk and break up into the numerous sinusoidal capillaries of the pars distalis (Harris '55).

The **veins** of the hypophysis are the lateral hypophyseal veins which drain into the cavernous and intercavernous sinuses.

Nerves.—The pars distalis has no specific innervation. Fibers from the superior cervical ganglion of the sympathetic system have been traced along the blood vessels but have not been conclusively associated with the glandular cells (Green '51).

The neurohypophysis is supplied by fibers from the supraoptic and paraventricular nuclei of the hypothalamus. The neurones of these nuclei contain granules of **neurosecretion** both in their cell bodies and axones. Experimental evidence indicates that the hormones extracted from the neurohypophysis originate from these neurosecretions and are merely stored in the gland. The path of these axones and their neurosecretion is known as the **hypothalamo-hypophyseal tract** (Palay '53).

Function.—The hypophysis supplies a number of hormones. Among those of the anterior lobe are a growth hormone, somatotrophin, affecting general body growth; a thyrotrophic hormone acting on the thyroid gland; an adrenocorticotrophic hormone (ACTH) acting on the suprarenal cortex; two gonadotrophic hormones, one stimulating ovarian follicles (FSH) and another stimulating the lutein cells (LH), and a hormone (prolactin) promoting milk secretion by the mammary gland. Attempts to associate the specific types of cells with the elaboration of these hormones have not been conclusive. Tumors of the gland composed of acidophils, however, are found in patients with a tremendous overgrowth of various parts of the body in a condition called acromegaly, and their absence is notable in pituitary dwarfs.

From the neurohypophysis two hormones have been extracted: oxytocin (Pituitrin) stimulates the contraction of smooth muscle and is sometimes used in obstetrical practice to make the uterus contract; the antidiuretic principle or vasopressin inhibits diuresis by the kidneys and also raises the blood pressure. As mentioned above, it is doubtful that the neural lobe elaborates these hormones. A lack of the antidiuretic principle in patients produces a condition called diabetes insipidus.

THE SUPRARENAL OR ADRENAL GLAND

The suprarenal gland in man and other mammals is a combination of two distinct glands which remain independent in fishes and other more primitive vertebrates. The two organs in the human gland are fused together but remain distinct and identifiable as the cortex and medulla of the adult gland.

Development.—The **cortex** of the suprarenal gland is first recognizable in an embryo of the sixth week as a groove in the *coelom* at the base of the mesentery near the cephalic end of the mesonephros. The cells at the bottom of the groove proliferate rapidly to form a mass in the mesenchyme extending toward the aorta. During the seventh and eighth weeks the cells become arranged into cords with dilated blood spaces between, the connection with the coelomic mesothelium is lost, and a capsule of connective tissue encloses the gland. During the remainder of fetal development the cortical tissue is composed of two zones, an outer zone of more undifferentiated cells and an inner zone of cell cords which appear to be differentiated and active in secretion. After birth the inner zone atrophies and the outer zone is differentiated into the three zones of the adult gland.

The **medulla** of the suprarenal gland is developed from cells of the *neural crest* which migrate ventrally along with the cells which form the sympathetic ganglia. These cells later detach themselves from the ganglia and become small knots of glandular cells scattered along the vertebral column. During the seventh and eighth weeks a large group of the neural cells, migrating along the suprarenal vein, invades the cortex, thus establishing the primordium of the suprarenal medulla. These glandular cells of sympathetic origin contain a substance, probably the precursor of the specific secretion, epinephrin, which is colored brown by chromic acid. This has given them their name of chromaffin or pheochrome cells. Many of the small masses of chromaffin cells mentioned above persist throughout life and are given the name paraganglia.

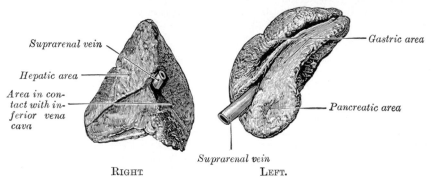

FIG. 1172.—Suprarenal glands viewed from the front.

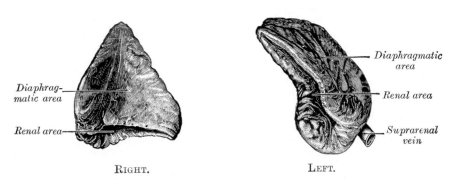

FIG. 1173.—Suprarenal glands viewed from behind.

The **suprarenal gland** (*glandula suprarenalis; adrenal gland*) (Figs. 1095, 1111) as the name suggests, is located at the cephalic pole of each of the two kidneys. They are quite different in shape on the two sides (Figs. 1172, 1173). The right gland resembles a pyramid, or the cocked hat of colonial days; the left is semilunar in form and tends to be slightly the larger. The length and width vary from 3 to 5 cm and the thickness 4 to 6 mm. The average weight is 3.5 to 5 gms.

Relations.—The **right suprarenal** is situated behind the inferior vena cava and right lobe of the liver, and in front of the diaphragm and upper end of the right kidney. The *anterior surface* looks forward and lateralward, and has two areas: a medial, narrow, and non-peritoneal, which lies behind the inferior vena cava; and a lateral, somewhat triangular, in contact with the liver. The upper part of the latter surface is devoid of peritoneum, and is in relation with the bare area of the liver near its lower and medial angle, while its inferior portion is covered by peritoneum, reflected onto it from the inferior layer of the coronary ligament; occasionally the duodenum overlaps the inferior portion. A little below the apex, and near the anterior border of the gland, is a short furrow termed the **hilum**, from which the suprarenal vein emerges to join the inferior vena cava. The *posterior surface* is divided into upper and lower parts by a curved ridge: the upper, slightly convex, rests upon the diaphragm; the lower, concave, is in contact with the upper end and the adjacent part of the anterior surface of the kidney.

The **left suprarenal** is crescentic in shape, its concavity being adapted to the medial border of the upper part of the left kidney. Its *anterior surface* has two areas: an upper one, covered by the peritoneum of the omental bursa, which separates it from the cardiac end of the stomach, and sometimes from the superior extremity of the spleen; and a lower one, which is in contact with the pancreas and lienal artery, and is therefore not covered by the peritoneum. On the anterior surface, near its lower end, is a furrow or hilum, directed downward and forward, from which the suprarenal vein emerges. Its *posterior surface* presents a vertical ridge, which divides it into two areas; the lateral area rests on the kidney, the medial and smaller on the left crus of the diaphragm.

The surface of the suprarenal gland is surrounded by areolar tissue containing much fat, and closely invested by a thin fibrous capsule, which is difficult to remove on account of the numerous fibrous processes and vessels entering the organ through the furrows on its anterior surface and base.

Accessory suprarenals (*glandulae suprarenales accessoriae*) are of frequent occurrence in the connective tissue near the main gland, but may occur near the testis or the ovary where small groups of embryonic cells might have migrated with the mesonephros, especially in certain hermaphroditic conditions. They are usually small round bodies composed of cortical cells. Larger ones may have the cortical zones represented and, more rarely, contain central medullary tissue.

Structure.—The suprarenal gland consists of two portions, an outer **cortex** taking up the greater part of the organ and an inner **medulla** (Fig. 1174). In the fresh condition the outer cortex is a deep yellow color, the inner part a dark red or brown, and the medulla a pale pink. At the transition between the cortex and medulla, there is no connective tissue barrier and the cords of the two types of cells are intermingled for a short distance.

The **cortical portion** (*substantia corticalis*) consists of a fine connective-tissue net-work, in which is imbedded the glandular epithelium. The epithelial cells are polyhedral in shape and possess rounded nuclei; many of the cells contain coarse granules, others lipoid globules. Owing to differences in the arrangement of the cells, three distinct zones can be made out: (1) the **zona glomerulosa,** situated beneath the capsule, consists of cells arranged in rounded groups, with here and there indications of an alveolar structure; the cells of this zone are very granular, and stain deeply. (2) The **zona fasciculata**, continuous with the zona glomerulosa, is composed of columns of cells arranged in a radial manner; these cells contain finer granules and in many instances globules of lipoid material. (3) The **zona reticularis,** in contact with the medulla, consists of cylindrical masses of cells irregularly arranged; these cells often contain pigment granules which give this zone a darker appearance than the rest of the cortex.

The **medullary portion** (*substantia medullaris*) is extremely vascular, and consists of large chromaffin cells arranged in a network. The irregular polyhedral cells have a finely granular cytoplasm that is probably concerned with the secretion of epinephrin. In the meshes of the cellular network are large anastomosing venous sinuses (sinusoids) which are in close relationship with the chromaffin or medullary cells. In many places the endothelial lining of the blood sinuses is in direct contact with the medullary cells. Some authors consider the endothelium absent in places and here the medullary cells are directly bathed by the blood. This intimate relationship between the chromaphil cells and the blood stream undoubtedly facilitates the discharge of the internal secretion into the blood. There is a loose meshwork of supporting connective tissue containing non-striped muscle fibers. This portion of the gland is richly supplied with non-medullated nerve fibers, and here and there sympathetic ganglia are found.

Vessels and Nerves.—The suprarenals are highly vascular organs. The arteries are numerous and of comparatively large size. These arteries are derived from the aorta and the inferior phrenic and the renal arteries. Three sets of branches penetrate the capsule, one of which breaks up in capillaries which supply the capsule. The second set breaks up into capillaries which supply the cell cords of the cortex and empty into veins in the medulla. The third set of arteries which enter the cortex traverse the cortex to supply the medulla only and break up in the sinusoids of the medulla. Venous blood from the capsule is collected into veins of the capsule. Blood from the two other sets of arteries is gathered into the central vein in the medulla which emerges at the hilum as the suprarenal vein. On the right side this vein opens into the inferior vena cava, on the left into the left renal vein.

Lymphatics accompany the large bloodvessels and end in the lumbar nodes.

The **nerves** are exceedingly numerous, and are derived from the celiac and renal plexuses. They enter the lower and medial part of the capsule, traverse the cortex, and end around the cells of the medulla. They have numerous small ganglia in the medullary portion of the gland.

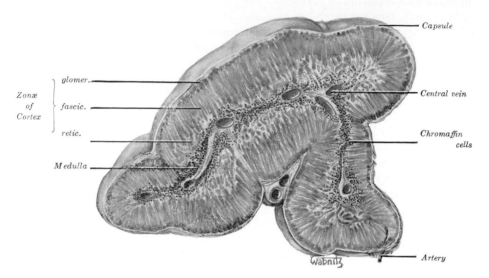

Fig. 1174.—Section through suprarenal gland of adult cadaver. Lightly stained with hematoxylin. × 5.

Function.—The adrenal medulla gives off an internal secretion, epinephrin (adrenalin) which has definite sympathomimetic actions such as causing a constriction of arterioles, acceleration of the heart rate, contraction of the radial muscle of the iris. In man an injection of the drug epinephrin hydrochloride results in a rise in systolic blood pressure, pulse rate, an increase in the minute volume of the heart and in volume of respiration. These effects are transitory and disappear after one or two hours. A rise in blood sugar, lactic acid and in the basal metabolic rate follows injection of this drug. This is due to an increased enzymatic breakdown of glycogen in liver and in muscle. The action of epinephrin is of brief duration, the hormone being rapidly inactivated in the body (Cori).

The adrenal cortex elaborates one or more hormones essential to maintenance of life. Various fractions serve in the maintenance of physiological "steady states," in regulation of the distribution of water and electrolytes and in many aspects of carbohydrate metabolism, and muscular efficiency. Research in this field is very active.

Paraganglia, Glomera, and "Glands" or "Bodies."

The various structures which have been given these names are for the most part small, difficult to demonstrate, and frequently misnamed. The following is an attempt to sort them out and to give their appropriate names and synonyms.

Paraganglia (*chromaffin bodies, chromaphil bodies,* and *pheochrome bodies*)

The **paraganglia** are small groups of chromaphil cells connected with the ganglia of the sympathetic trunk and the ganglia of the celiac, renal, suprarenal, aortic and hypogastric plexuses. They are sometimes found in connection with the ganglia of other-sympathetic plexuses.

The **Aortic Bodies** or **Lumbar Paraganglia** (*corpora para-aortica, glands or organs of Zuckerkandl*)

The **aortic glands** or **bodies** are the largest of these groups of chromaphil cells and measure in the newborn about 1 cm. in length. They lie one on either side of the aorta in the region of the inferior mesenteric artery. They decrease in size with age and after puberty are only visible with the microscope. Other groups of chromaphil cells have been found associated with the sympathetic plexuses of the abdomen independently of the ganglia.

Glomus Coccygeum (Coccygeal Gland or Body; Luschka's Gland).

The **glomus coccygeum** is placed in front of, or immediately below, the tip of the coccyx. It is about 2.5 mm. in diameter and is irregularly oval in shape; several smaller nodules are found around or near the main mass.

It consists of irregular masses of round or polyhedral cells of each mass being grouped around a dilated sinusoidal capillary vessel. Each cell contains a large round or oval nucleus, the protoplasm surrounding which is clear, and is not stained by chromic salts. It is not a chromaffin paraganglion and since its structure is not like that of the chemoreceptors (carotid bodies) its function is unknown (Hollinshead '42).

The **glomus caroticum** or **carotid body** is not a paraganglion but a chemoreceptor and is described on page 940.

The **glomus aorticum** is better named the **cardio-aortic body** or glomus aorticum supracardiale and is a chemoreceptor similar to the carotid body, page 941.

REFERENCES

Endocrine Glands and Endocrinology

Greulich, W. W., R. I. Dorfman, H. R. Catchpole, C. I. Solomon, and C. S. Culotta. 1942. Somatic and endocrine studies of puberal and adolescent boys. Monogr. Soc. Res. Child Developm., 7, 1–85.

Hollinshead, W. H. 1952. Anatomy of the endocrine glands. Surg. Clin. N. Amer., 32, 1115–1140.

Talbot, N. B., E. H. Sobel, J. W. McArthur, and J. D. Crawford. 1952. Functional Endocrinology from Birth through Adolescence. Harvard University Press, Cambridge. xxx + 638 pages.

Wilkins, L. 1950. The Diagnosis and Treatment of Endocrine Disorders in Childhood and Adolescence. Charles C Thomas, Springfield. xx + 384 pages.

Suprarenal Gland

Anson, B. J., E. W. Cauldwell, J. W. Pick, and L. E. Beaton. 1947. The blood supply of the kidney, suprarenal gland, and associated structures. Surg. Gynec. Obstet., 84, 313–320.

Bourne, G. H. 1949. The Mammalian Adrenal Gland. Oxford University Press, London. vii + 239 pages.

Crowder, R. E. 1957. The development of the adrenal gland in man, with special reference to origin and ultimate location of cell types, and evidence in favor of the "cell migration" theory. Contr. Embryol. Carneg. Instn., 36, 193–210.

Hartman, F. A., R. A. Knouff, and G. A. Howard. 1954. Response of the pelican adrenal to various stimuli. Anat. Rec., 120, 469–494.

Swinyard, C. A. 1940. Volume and cortico-medullary ratio of the adult human suprarenal gland. Anat. Rec., 76, 69–79.

Swinyard, C. A. 1943. Growth of the human suprarenal glands. Anat. Rec., 87, 141–150.

Uotila, U. U. 1940. The early embryological development of the fetal and permanent adrenal cortex in man. Anat. Rec., 86, 183–203.

Wotton, R. M., and R. L. Zwemer. 1943. A study of the cytogenesis of cortico-adrenal cells in the cat. Anat. Rec., 86, 409–416.

MACFARLAND, W. E., and H. A. DAVENPORT. 1941. Adrenal innervation. J. comp. Neurol., *75*, 219–233.

MEDULLA

BENNETT, H. S. 1941. Cytological manifestations of secretion in the adrenal medulla of the cat. Amer. J. Anat., *69*, 333–381.

CORI, C. F., and A. D. WELCH. 1941. The Adrenal Medulla. In: Glandular Physiology and Therapy. Am. Med. Assn., Chicago, 307–326.

EULER, U. S. VON. 1951. Hormones of the sympathetic nervous system and the adrenal medulla. Brit. med. J., *1*, 105–108.

FREEMAN, N. E., R. H. SMITHWICK, and J. C. WHITE. 1934. Adrenal secretion in man. Amer. J. Physiol., *107*, 529–534.

HOLLINSHEAD, W. H. 1940. Chromaffin tissue and paraganglia. Quart. Rev. Biol., *15*, 156–171.

CORTEX

BAKER, D. D., and R. N. BAILLIF. 1939. Role of capsule in suprarenal regeneration studied with aid of colchicine. Proc. Soc. exp. Biol. and Med., *40*, 117–121.

CAREY, M. M., E. P. VOLLMER, R. L. ZWEMER, and D. L. SPENCE. 1951. Decrease of adrenal ascorbic acid and cholesterol in the rat and guinea pig, following large doses of glutathione Amer. J. Physiol., *164*, 770–773.

CLAUSEN, H. J. 1940. The atrophy of the adrenal cortex following the administration of large amounts of progesterone. Endocrinology, *27*, 989–993.

DOUGHERTY, T. F., and A. WHITE. 1945. Functional alterations in lymphoid tissue induced by adrenal cortical secretion. Amer. J. Anat., *77*, 81–116.

EVERETT, N. B. 1949. Autoplastic and homoplastic transplants of the rat adrenal cortex and medulla to the kidney. Anat. Rec., *103*, 335–347.

FLEXNER, L. B., and A. GROLLMAN. 1939. The reduction of osmic acid as an indicator of adrenal cortical activity in the rat. Anat. Rec., *75*, 207–221.

HOERR, N. L. 1936. Histological studies on lipins. II. A cytological analysis of the liposomes in the adrenal cortex of the guinea pig. Anat. Rec., *66*, 317–342.

JONES, I. C. 1957. The Adrenal Cortex. Cambridge University Press, New York. x + 316 pages.

KNOUFF, R. A., J. B. BROWN, and B. M. SCHNEIDER. 1941. Correlated chemical and histological studies of the adrenal lipids. I. The effect of extreme muscular activity on the adrenal lipids of the guinea pig. Anat. Rec., *79*, 17–38.

SALMON, T. N., and R. L. ZWEMER. 1941. A study of the life history of cortico-adrenal gland cells of the rat by means of trypan blue injections. Anat Rec., *80*, 421–429.

WILLIAMS, R. G. 1947. Studies of adrenal cortex: Regeneration of the transplanted gland and the vital quality of autogenous grafts. Amer. J. Anat., *81*, 199–231.

ZWEMER, R. L., and R. TRUSZKOWSKI. 1937. The importance of corticoadrenal regulation of potassium metabolism. Endocrinology, *21*, 40–49.

HYPOPHYSIS

BLOUNT, R. F. 1945. The interrelationship of the parts of the hypophysis in development. J. exp. Zool., *100*, 79–101.

CRAFTS, R. C., and B. S. WALKER. 1947. The effects of hypophysectomy on serum and storage iron in adult female rats. Endocrinology, *41*, 340–346.

ETKIN, W. 1943. The developmental control of pars intermedia by brain. J. exp. Zool., *92*, 31–47.

CRAFTS, R. C., and H. A. MEINEKE. 1958. Erthropoietic changes in cortisone-growth hormone treated hypophysectomized rats as related to changes in oxygen need induced by various doses of thyroxin. Anat. Rec., *131*, 465–474.

DUNCAN, D. 1956. An electron microscope study of the neurohypophysis of a bird, Gallus domesticus. Anat. Rec., *125*, 457–472.

GREEN, H. T. 1957. The venous drainage of the human hypophysis cerebri. Amer. J. Anat., *100*, 435–470.

GREEN, J. D. 1951. The comparative anatomy of the hypophysis, with special reference to its blood supply and innervation. Amer. J. Anat., *88*, 225–311.

HARRIS, G. W. 1951. Neural control of the pituitary gland: I. The neurohypophysis; II. The adenohypophysis. Brit. Med. J., *2*, 559–564, 627–634.

HARRIS, G. W. 1955. Neural control of the pituitary gland. Edward Arnold, Ltd., London; The Williams & Wilkins Co., Baltimore. ix + 298 pages.

HEGRE, E. S. 1946. The developmental stage at which the intermediate lobe of the hypophysis becomes determined. J. exp. Zool., *103*, 321–333.

HOUSE, E. L. 1943. The development of the hypophysis of the ox. Amer. J. Anat., *73*, 1–25.

HUNT, T. E. 1949. Mitotic activity in the hypophysis of the rat during pregnancy and lactation. Anat. Rec., *105*, 361–373.

HUNT, T. E. 1951. The effect of hypophyseal extract on mitotic activity of the rat hypophysis. Anat. Rec., *111*, 713–725.

IFFT, J. D. 1953. The effect of superior cervical ganglionectomy on the cell population of the rat adenohypophysis and on the estrous cycle. Anat. Rec., *117*, 395–404.

MARKEE, J. E., C. H. SAWYER, and W. H. HOLLINSHEAD. 1946. Activation of the anterior hypophysis by electrical stimulation in the rabbit. Endocrinology, *38*, 345–357.

MARKEE, J. E., C. H. SAWYER, and W. H. HOLLINSHEAD. 1948. Adrenergic control of the release of luteinizing hormone from the hypophysis of the rabbit. Recent Prog. Hormone Res., *2*, 117–131.

McCONNELL, E. M. 1953. The arterial blood supply of the human hypophysis cerebri. Anat. Rec., *115*, 175–203.

McNARY, W. F., JR. 1957. Progressive cytological changes in the hypophysis associated with endocrine interaction following exposure to cold. Anat. Rec., *128*, 233–254.

RASMUSSEN, A. T. 1936. The Proportions of the Various Subdivisions of the Normal Adult Human Hypophysis Cerebri, etc. In: Res. Publ. Ass. nerv. ment. Dis., The Pituitary Gland. Williams & Wilkins, Baltimore, 118–150.

RASMUSSEN, A. T., and T. RASMUSSEN. 1952. The hypophysis cerebri of Bushman, the gorilla of Lincoln Park Zoo, Chicago. Anat. Rec., *113*, 325–347.

SAWYER, C. H. 1947. Cholinergic stimulation of the release of melanophore hormone by the hypophysis in salamander larvæ. J. exp. Zool., *106*, 145–179.

SHANKLIN, W. M. 1951. The histogenesis and histology of an integumentary type of epithelium in the human hypophysis. Anat. Rec., *109*, 217–231.

WISLOCKI, G. B. 1938. The Vascular Supply of the Hypophysis Cerebri of the Rhesus Monkey and Man. In: Res. Publ. Ass. nerv. ment. Dis., The Pituitary Gland. Williams & Wilkins, Baltimore, 48–68.

WOLFE, J. M. 1946. Effects of progesterone on the cells of the anterior hypophysis of the rat. Amer. J. Anat., *79*, 199–239.

THYROID

BROOKHAVEN SYMPOSIA IN BIOLOGY No. 7. 1955. The Thyroid. Brookhaven National Laboratory, Upton, New York. vii + 271 pages.

CARPENTER, E., and T. RONDON-TARCHETTI. 1957. Differentiation of embryonic rat thryoid *in vivo* and *in vitro*. J. exp. Zool., *136*, 393–418.

HUNT, T. E. 1944. Mitotic activity in the thyroid gland of female rats. Anat. Rec., *90*, 133–138.

NORLAND, M. 1930. The larynx as related to surgery of the thyroid based on an anatomical study. Surg. Gynec. & Obstet., *51*, 449–459.

PLAGGE, J. C. 1943. Effects of hypotonic solutions upon the living thryoid gland. Anat. Rec., *87*, 345–353.

RAMSAY, A. J., and G. A. BENNETT. 1943. Studies on the thyroid gland. I. The structure, extent and drainage of the "lymph-sac" of the thyroid gland (Felis domestica). Anat. Rec., *87*, 321–339.

RICHTER, K. M. 1944. Some new observations bearing on the effect of hyperthyroidism on genital structure and function. J. Morph., *74*, 375–393.

WELLER, G. L., JR. 1933. Development of the thyroid, parathyroid and thymus glands in man. Contr. Embryol. Carneg. Instn., *24*, 93–139.

WILLIAMS, R. G. 1944. Some properties of living thyroid cells and follicles. Amer. J. Anat., *75*, 95–119.

PARATHYROID

BAKER, B. L. 1942. A study of the parathyroid glands of the normal and hypophysectomized monkey (Macaca mulatta). Anat. Rec., *83*, 47–73.

DeROBERTIS, E. 1940. The cytology of the parathyroid gland of rats injected with parathyroid extract. Anat. Rec., *78*, 473–495.

FLEISCHMANN, W. 1951. Comparative Physiology of the Thyroid and Parathyroid Glands. Charles C Thomas, Springfield. v + 78 pages.

NORRIS, E. H. 1937. The parathyroid glands and the lateral thyroid in man: Their morphogenesis, histogenesis, topographic anatomy and prenatal growth. Contr. Embryol. Carneg. Instn., *26*, 247–294.

NORRIS, E. H. 1946. Anatomical evidence of prenatal function of the human parathyroid glands. Anat. Rec., *96*, 129–141.

RAYBUCK, H. E. 1952. The innervation of the parathyroid glands. Anat. Rec., *112*, 117–123.

PINEAL

CLAUSEN, H. J., and B. MOFSHIN. 1939. The pineal eye of the lizard (Anolis carolinensis) (a). a, photoreceptor as revealed by oxygen consumption studies. J. cell. comp. Physiol., *14*, 29–41.
SULLENS, W. E., and M. D. OVERHOLSER. 1941. Pinealectomy in successive generations of rats. Endocrinology, *28*, 835–839.

INDEX TO BIBLIOGRAPHIES

A

Abbott, L. C., 403
Abrams, G. D., 1313
Adams, E. C., 59
Adams, W. E., 714
Adamstone, F. B., 948
Adelmann, H. B., 1151
Agate, F. J., Jr., 1389
Alden, R. H., 1389
Alexander, H. L., 1206
Alexander, W. F., 1091, 1313
Allen, E., 1387, 1388
Allen, J. M., 56
Allen, L., 819
Allen, W. F., 945, 947
Allison, A. C., 947
Altmann, F., 1152
Altschul, R., 773
Alvarado, F., 1314
Anderson, F. D., 945
Anderson, R. H., 60
Andrew, N. V., 1164
Andrew, W., 1164
Angel, J. L., 402
Angulo, A. W., 772, 1206
Anson, B. J., 563, 565, 566, 600, 713, 714, 772, 820, 1088, 1089, 1090, 1091, 1152, 1206, 1312, 1313, 1314, 1385, 1386, 1389, 1403
Argyris, T. S., 1164
Ariëns-Kappers, J., 944
Armstrong, P. B., 599
Armstrong, W. G., 1088
Arnold, J. S., 319
Ashley, F. L., 714, 1090, 1389
Ashley, G. T., 563
Ashton, E. H., 402
Atwood, R. P., 945
Auer, J., 712, 771
Avery, G., 320
Awaya, K., 819
Axford, M., 1090

B

Baba, M. A., 563
Babcock, M. J., 1165
Bacon, R. L., 599
Baggenstoss, A. H., 772
Bailey, C. P., 715
Baillif, R. N., 819
Baird, J. A., 600
Baker, B. L., 773, 819, 1164, 1313, 1405
Baker, D. D., 565, 1404
Baker, R. C., 944, 1090
Baker, R. F., 1313, 1386
Baillif, R. N., 1404
Balankura, K., 819
Balo, J., 772
Barbour, E. P., 319
Barnard, J. W., 946
Barnicot, N. A., 1164
Baron, M. A., 1312
Barr, M. L., 56, 948
Barrett, O., Jr., 600
Barron, D. H., 599
Barry, A., 599, 713, 1089
Bartelmez, G. W., 773, 1389
Barton, D. S., 1389
Basmajian, J. V., 319

Bassett, D. L., 118, 1388
Bast, T. H., 1152
Batson, O. V., 772
Bauer, W., 402
Baumann, J. A., 1386
Beach, F. A., 946
Beaton, L. E., 563, 772, 1089, 1313, 1386, 1403
Becker, F., 1151
Becker, R. F., 1090, 1151
Becker, V., 1314
Bedbrook, G. M., 1090
Benjamin, J. A., 565, 566, 1386, 1388
Bell, E. T., 1385
Bell, R. H., 713, 820
Belloco, P., 565
Bencosme, S. A., 1314
Bennett, G. A., 563, 1312, 1405
Bennett, H. S., 773, 1404
Benninghoff, A., 118
Berry, C. M., 945, 947
Best, R. R., 819, 1313
Bertram, L. F., 948
Bevelander, G., 319, 1165
Bierman, H. R., 818
Billenstien, D. C., 946
Birbeck, M. S. C., 1164
Birch, C., 773
Birnbaum, G. L., 1206
Birrell, J. H. W., 948
Bishop, G. H., 946, 1090
Bishop, W. E., 1206
Black, B. M., 403
Blair, J. B., 819, 1313
Blalock, A., 601, 715
Blandau, R. J., 56, 59, 1387
Bloom W., 773
Blount, R. F., 1404
Blunck, C. F. J., 1091
BO., W. J., 1389
Boas, E. P., 713
Boas, N F., 713
Bodemer, C. W., 1151
Bodian, D., 948
Botar, J., 1090
Bourne, G. H., 1403
Boving, B. G., 60
Bowie, D. J., 1313
Boyd, J. D., 56
Boyden, E. A., 1206, 1314
Boyer, C. C., 1385
Brachet, J., 56
Bradley, K. C., 1090
Braeucker, W., 1090
Braitenberg, V., 945
Brandeberry, N. A., 1386
Brandt, W., 600
Brantigan, O. C., 403, 772
Bremer, J. L., 771
Brenner, C., 947
Brightman, M. W., 320
Brizzee, K. R., 946
Brodman, K., 947
Brody, H., 947
Brookhaven Symposia in Biology No. 7, 1405
Brown, F. R., 1090
Brown, J. B., 1404
Brown, J. O., 945
Brown, J. W., 944
Brown, S., 772
Browning, H. C., 772

Bruesch, S. R., 1088
Buchanan, A. R., 403, 944, 945
Bucy, P. C., 947
Budinger, J. M., 563
Bueker, E. D., 944, 948
Bullough, W. S., 1387
Bunting, H., 1390
Burch, G. E., 600, 601, 773, 1151
Burdette, W. J., 601
Burge, R. E., 1313
Burns, R. K., 1387
Burr, H. S., 944, 947, 1088, 1388
Burrows, H., 1387
Butcher, E. O., 1164
Butler, H. W., 712, 819, 1312
Byron, R. L., Jr., 818

C

Calabrisi, P., 1387
Calder, J. W., 772
Cameron, D. A., 402
Cameron, G., 1385
Campbell, J. B., 1089
Carey, J. H., 947
Carey, J. M., 1313
Carey, M. M., 1404
Carpenter, E., 1405
Carpenter, M. B., 945
Carpenter, W. F., 403
Carr, B. W., 713
Carvalho Pinto, V. A. De., 1089
Casey, E. J., 1152
Catchpole, H. R., 1403
Caudwell, E. W., 563, 713, 714, 1088, 1385, 1386, 1389, 1403
Cauna, N., 948
Chambers, R., 773, 1385
Chambers, W. W., 945
Chandler, S. B., 565, 713
Chang, M. C., 59, 60
Chan-Nao, L., 949
Charles, C. M., 403
Chase, H. B., 1165
Chase, R. E., 713, 600, 714, 772
Cholnoky, T. De, 1390
Chouke, K. S., 565, 772
Chow, K. L., 1151
Chow, M., 320
Christensen, G. C., 1387
Christensen, K., 1090
Clara, M., 715
Clare, M. H., 946, 1090
Clark, E. L., 319, 773, 819, 1164
Clark, E. R., 319, 773, 819, 949, 1164
Clark, S. L., 599
Clark, W. E. L., 18, 946, 949
Clausen, H. J., 714, 1404, 1406
Cleveland, H., 600
Cobb, W. M., 600
Cohen, J., 402
Cohn, S. A., 1312
Cole, W. V., 948
Comer, R. D., 563
Conel, J. L., 944
Congdon, E. D., 565, 712, 1386, 1387
Conn, L. C., 772
Cooley, D. A., 601, 715
Cooper, A. R., 118, 565
Cooper, S., 1151
Cooperband, S. R., 60

(1407)

Copenhaver, W. M., 599, 600
Cori, C. F., 1404
Corbin, K. B., 402, 1088, 1089
Corner, G. W., 59, 1387
Cossar, D. R., 1089
Costen, J. B., 1090
Coulombre, A. J., 1152
Courtice, F. C., 819
Coventry, M. B., 402
Cowley, R. A., 1090
Cox, H. T., 1164
Crafts, R. C., 773, 1404
Crawford, E. S., 715
Crawford, J. D., 1403
Crelin, E. S., 320, 714, 1152
Creech, O., Jr., 715
Crew, F. A. E., 1387
Crosby, E. C., 946
Crowder, R. E., 1403
Culotta, C. S., 1403
Cummins, H., 1164
Curry, J. L., 600
Curtis, D. H., 1090, 1389

D

Dalton, A. J., 56, 1385
Danes, B., 1205
Danforth, C. H., 1387
D'Angelo, C., 948
Daniel, P. M., 715, 1151
Danielli, J. F., 56
Danziger, S., 59
Daseler, E. H., 772
Davenport, H. A., 1404
Davies, D. V., 402
Davies, H., 1386
Davies, J. W., 565, 1385, 1389
Davila, J. C., 601
Davis, C. L., 598
Davis, L., 1090
De Bakey, M. E., 715
De Garis, C. F., 402, 600, 713, 714, 772, 1312
Dekaban, A., 946
Dempsey, E. W., 59, 1152, 1390
Dempsher, J., 1089
De Palma, A. F., 403
De Robertis, E., 1152, 1405
Derson, H., 714
D'Esopo, D. A., 1389
DeTakats, G., 1090
Detwiler, S. R., 944, 1089, 1152
Devasch, L. J., 1388
Dey, F. L., 1387
Dixon, F. W., 819
Doisy, E. A., 1387
Donald, D. E., 601
Dorfman, R. I., 1403
Doubilet, H., 1088
Dougherty, T. F., 1404
Douglass, B. E., 772
Doumanian, A., 403
Downey, H., 773
Drinker, C K., 1206
Dry, T. J., 600
DuBois, F. S., 1088
Du Brul, E. L., 319
Duggins, O. H., 1165
Duke, K. L., 1388
Duncan, D., 948, 1090, 1404
Duntley, S. Q., 1164
Duryee, W. R., 60
Dykes, J., 563

E

Earle, K. M., 945
Eastwick, H. L., 60, 564
Edmonds, H. W., 713
Edson, J. N., 565, 1386
Edwards, E. A., 772, 1090, 1164
Edwards, J. E., 599, 600, 601

Edwards, J. G., 772, 1385, 1386
Edwards, L. F., 713, 1090, 1152
Effler, D. B., 601
Ehrlich, E., Jr., 1091
Elchos, T., 715
Elftman, H., 56
Eliasson, S. G., 945
Erickson, E. E., 600
Essenberg, J. M., 713, 1387, 1388
Etkin, W., 1404
Euler, U. S. von, 1091, 1404
Evans, F. G., 319, 320
Evans, T. H., 714, 1313
Everett, J. W., 59, 946, 1388
Everett, N. B., 599, 1387, 1388, 1404

F

Fales, D. E., 599
Farris, E. J., 1387, 1388
Fawcett, D. W., 56, 60, 319
Felix, M. D., 56
Fenart, F., 1089
Fenn, W. E., 715
Ferner, H., 1314
Ferriman, D. G., 1165
Fichtelius, K. E., 818
Findlay, C. W., Jr., 1206
Finerty, J. C., 1089, 1386
Fish, H. S., 565
Fishman, I. Y., 1151
Fleischmann, W., 1405
Flexner, J. B., 60, 944
Flexner, L. B., 944, 1404
Flyger, G., 947
Foerster, O., 1089
Foley, J. O., 1088, 1091
Ford, C. E., 56
Ford, D. H., 948, 1389
Fox, C. A., 946
Fox, M. H., 60, 600, 713
Fox, W., 1388
Franchi, C. M., 1152
Francis, C. C., 319, 320, 402
Franklin, K. J., 772
Freeman, J. A., 773
Freeman, L. W., 947, 1090
Freeman, N. E., 818, 1091, 1404
Friedman, N. B., 1386
Friedman, S. M., 772, 1313
Frontera, J. G., 947
Fuber, J. F., 1206
Furuta, W. J., 319, 819

G

Gallaudet, B. B., 564
Gamble, J. L., 819
Gardner, E., 319, 402, 403
Gardner, J. H., 946, 1091, 1164, 1312
Gardner, W. D., 772
Gardner, W. U., 1389
Garn, S. M., 1312
Garner, C. M., 948
Garrett, F. D., 1089
Gay, A. J., Jr., 563
Gaylin, G. J., 715
Genis-Galvez, J. M., 819, 1152
George, R., 563
George, W. C., 59
Geren, B. B., 948
Ghormley, R. K., 402
Gilbert, E. F., 600
Gilbert, P. W., 1152
Gilfillan, R. S., 818
Gillette, R., 320
Gillilan, L. A., 945
Gillman, J., 1387
Giovacchini, R. P., 1312
Gitlin, G., 1089
Gless, P., 947

Glover, R. P., 601
Goetz, R. H., 599
Goldberg, M. B., 1387
Goldsmith, J. B., 712
Goldstein, M. S., 319
Goss, C. M., 60, 563, 598, 599, 600, 713
Gould, S. E., 600
Grafflin, A. L., 1314
Granger, B., 1313
Graves, G. O., 944, 1152
Gray, D. J., 319, 320, 402, 563
Gray, H. K., 1312
Grayson, J., 565
Green, H. T., 1404
Green, J. A., 1388
Green, J. D., 946
Greenberg, S. R., 1091
Greenblatt, C. L., 60
Gregg, D. E., 713
Gregg, R. L., 1206
Gregoire, C., 820
Greig, H. W., 563, 713
Greulich, W. W., 319, 320, 1389, 1403
Grodinsky, M., 564, 565
Grollman, A., 1404
Gross, L., 600, 713
Gross, R. E., 601, 715
Grote, P., 1387
Groves, L. K., 601
Grunt, J. A., 1090
Guth, L., 1088, 1151

H

Haber, J. J., 1313
Haines, R. W., 402, 403
Hale, A. R., 1164
Haley, J. C., 1313
Hall, E. K., 564, 599
Halpern, B. N., 819
Hambley, W. C., 1312
Hamerton, J. L., 56
Hamilton, H. L., 56
Hamilton, J. B., 60, 1165, 1388
Hamilton, W. J., 56
Hamlett, G. W. D., 60, 1387, 1389
Hammond, S., 818, 945, 1092, 1313
Hard, W. L., 1313, 1314
Hardesty, I., 1088
Harman, P. J., 947, 1386
Harris, A. J., 1091
Harris, G. W., 1404
Harris, W., 1089
Harris, W. H., 402
Harrison, F., 1088, 1089
Harrison, J. M., 947
Harrison, R. G., 56, 60, 944, 947
Harshbarger, D. E., 601
Hart, V. L., 403
Hartman, C. G., 59, 60
Hartman, F. A., 1403
Hartmann, J. F., 948
Hasterlik, R. J., 1388
Harvey, H. T., 1314
Harvey, S. C., 947
Hawkins, R. K., 1313
Hayes, M. A., 565, 773
Hayhow, W., 948
Healy, J. E., Jr., 1313
Hegre, E. S., 1405
Heimberger, R. F., 1386
Hellerman, L., 944
Hering, H. E., 948
Herrmann, F., 1165
Hertig, A. T., 59
Hess, A., 948
Hess, W. R., 946
Hessert, E. C., 1206
Heuser, C. H., 59, 60

Heymans, C., 1088
Hibbs, R. G., 599, 773
Hill, R. T., 1388
Hill, W. C. O., 599
Hinsch, G. W., 56
Hinsey, J. C., 402, 1089
Hjelmquist, U. B. E., 947
Hoerr, N. L., 319, 819, 829, 948, 1404
Hoffman, H. H., 948, 1088, 1091
Hogg, I. D., 944, 1089
Holcomb, G. R., 403
Hollingshead, W. H., 772, 948, 1091, 1313, 1403, 1404, 1405
Holtzer, H., 320
Holyoke, E. A., 564, 565, 818, 819, 1312, 1313, 1387
Hooker, C. W., 1387
Horowitz, S. L., 320, 402
Hörstadius, S., 944
House, E. L., 1312, 1405
Howard, G. A., 1403
Huber, J. F., 713
Huelke, D. F., 713, 1089
Hughes, E. S. R., 320, 1090
Humphrey, T., 945
Hunt, T. E., 563, 946, 1313, 1405
Huntington, G. S., 771, 818, 1312
Hutchinson, R. C., 1164, 1312
Hyde, J. E., 945

I

Ifft, J. D., 1405
Ingalls, N. W., 59
Ingle, D. J., 819
Ingram, W. R., 945, 946
Inman, V. T., 403
Issidorides, M., 948

J

Jackson, C. L., 1206
Jackson, R. G., 1088
Jacobs, M. H., 1205
Jacobson, H. G , 1314
Jacobson, L. F., 1313
James, T. N., 600, 601
James, T. W., 1088
Jamieson, R. W., 1091, 1089
Jansen, J., Jr., 947
Jarcho, J., 1389
Jaynes, J., 946
Jee, W. S. S., 319
Jett, H. H., 772
Jiminez-Castellanos, J., 947
Jit, I., 713, 1313, 1314
Johnson, P. L., 319, 1165
Johnson, F. E., 1314
Johnson, R. J., 599
Johnston, E. V., 1314
Johnston, T. B., 118
Johnstone, A. S., 1312
Jones, I. C., 1404
Jones, O. P., 773
Jones, T. F., 118, 565, 1090, 1389
Jonnesco, T., 1091
Joy, E. A., 1152
Judice, R. C., 1089

K

Kaada, B. R., 947
Kaliszewski, B. F., 1089
Kampmeier, O., 118, 818
Kanavel, A. B., 564
Kann, F., 563
Kaplan, E. B., 118, 403, 564, 565
Kantounis, S., 948
Karasawa, K., 820
Karsner, H. T., 1390
Kasahara, M., 1089
Katzberg, A. A., 1164

Kaylor, C. T., 598
Keegan, J. J., 1089
Keen, E. N., 599
Keen, J. A., 772
Kelikian, H., 403
Keller, R., 1165
Kellgren, J. H., 1090
Kellner, C. E., 1089
Kelly, K. H., 818
Kennedy, J. A., 599
Kenyon, 1165
Kernohan, J. W., 402
Kerr, A. T., 1089
Kerr, E. N., 599
Kessler, W. H., 1088
Kimmel, D. L., 60, 945, 949, 1089
Kindred, J. E., 59, 1151, 1312, 1388
King, B. T., 1206
King, J. E., 1151
King, T. S., 714
Kingsbury, B. F., 820
Kirgis, H. D., 1091
Kirklin, J. W., 601
Kirkman, H., 1314, 1386
Kirschbaum, A., 1388
Kisner, W. H., 1091
Klassen, K. P., 715
Klüver, H., 947
Knapp, B. I., 820
Knese, K. H., 18
Knisely, M. H., 819
Knisely, W. H., 772
Knouff, R. A., 1403, 1404
Kohn, K., 1206
Kolff, W. J., 601
Koop, C. E., 1164
Kopech, G., 56
Kopsch, F., 118, 944
Koski, K., 1312
Kousda, T., 948
Kownacki, V. P., 1206
Krahl, V. E., 319, 320, 1206
Kramer, T. C., 598, 599, 1388
Krieg, W. J. S., 944, 946, 947
Krogman, W., 320
Kropp, B. N., 714
Krumbhaar, E. B., 819
Kugel, M. A., 600, 713
Kuhlenbeck, H., 946, 1386
Kuntz, A., 1090, 1091, 1152, 1314, 1388

L

Lachmann, E., 403, 1206, 1313
Lacroix, P., 319
Lacy, P. E., 1314
Lancaster, W. B., 1152
Landis, E. M., 773
Landsmeer, J. M. F., 403, 563
Langman, L., 1388, 1389
Langworthy, O. R., 945, 1386
Laing, P. G., 403
Lanier, R. R., Jr., 320
Larsell, O., 945, 1088, 1206
Larsen, R. D., 565
Larson, S. J., 820
Lasker, G. W., 320, 714
Lasner, J., 1090
Lassek, A. M., 945
Latimer, H. B., 320, 599
Latta, J. S., 1314
Lauer, E. W., 947
La Velle, A., 948
Lawrence, M., 1152
Lebrow, M., 320
Lee, F. C., 565
Lee, I. N., 714
Lee, M. M. C., 1164
Lemmon, W. M., 715
Lerche, W., 1312
Letterman, G. S., 320

Lev, M., 600
Lewis, A. B., 1312
Lewis, E., 1090
Lewis, F. T., 818
Lewis, W. H., 56, 59, 60
Li, C. R., 819
Licata, R. H., 598
Liechty, J. D., 713
Lindsay, H. A., 948
Lippincott, S. W., 918
Lissner, H. R., 320
Lobitz, W. C., Jr., 1165
Locksley, H. B., 948
Low, F. N., 714, 773, 1152, 1206
Lowrance, E. W., 319, 320
Lyon, M., 947

M

Macchi, G., 947
MacDonald, J. C., 1388
MacFarland, W. E., 1404
MacGregor, J. W., 772
Mackenzie, D. W., Jr., 819
Madden, J. L., 1313
Magoun, H. W., 946
Mahaley, Jr., M. S., 772
Maier, H. C., 714, 1206
Maliniac, J. W., 1390
Mall, R. P., 319
Mahorner, H., 1091
Mann, I. C., 1152
Manter, J. T., 403, 563
Marchetti, A. A., 1389
Mardfin, D. F., 320
Markee, J. E., 1151, 1387, 1389, 1405
Marrazzi, A. S., 1091
Martin, C. P., 565
Martinez, W. V., 601
Marvin, H. N., 1388
Massopust, L. C., 772
Matoltsy, A. G., 1164
Maxwell, A. F., 1387
Mayer, F. E., 600
Mayer, L. L., 1088
Maynard, E. A., 947
Mayo, C. W., 1313
McAfee, D. K., 714
McArthur, J. W., 1403
McClure, C. F. W., 771
McConnell, E. M., 1405
McCormack, L. J., 714, 1088, 1386
McCotter, R. E., 1088
McCulloch, W. S., 947
McDonald, J. J., 713, 714, 1091
McFarlane, J. A., 772
McFetridge, E. M., 1390
McGregor, I. A., 1165
McKay, D. G., 59
McKim, J. S., 714
McMahon, R. A., 600, 1091
McNamara, D. G., 601
McNary, W. F., Jr., 1405
McNutt, C. W., 772
McQuitty, J. T., 1164
McVay, C. B., 563, 566
Meader, R. D., 1314
Mednick, L. W., 320
Meineke, H. A., 1404
Menkin, M. F., 60
Mercer, E. H., 1164
Meredith, J. M., 1088
Merrillees, N. C. R., 948
Merz, A. L., 320
Metz, G E., 1089
Meyer, R., 1386
Meyers, C. E., 948
Michaelson, E. C., 1152
Michels, N. A., 714, 715, 819, 1312, 1314
Midlo, C., 1164

Miller, H., 714
Miller, J. M., 1313
Miller, M. R., 1089
Miller, R. A., 563, 565, 566, 714, 1206
Miller, R. N., 946
Miller, W. S., 1206
Ming-Tzu, P., 714
Mitchell, G. A., 945, 1091, 1313, 1386, 1387
Moffat, D. B., 712
Moffett, B. C., 1088
Mofshin, B., 1406
Moley, H. C., 1389
Montagna, W., 1164, 1165
Moody, P. O., 1386
Moore, K. L., 56
Morehouse, A., 1091
Morgan, E. H., 565
Morris, E. D., 712
Morris, R. E., Jr., 1388
Morton, D. J., 402, 403
Moseley, H. F., 403
Moser, R. H., 601
Moss, M. L., 320
Mossman, H. W., 56, 1388
Moyer, E. K., 60, 949, 1089
Muller Botha, G. S., 1313
Mulholland, J. H., 1088
Munger, B. L., 1314
Murphy, E. L., 1386
Murray, M. F., 56
Murray, M. R., 564
Musgrove, J. E., 715

N

Nadas, A. S., 600
Nakai, K., 60
Newell, F. W., 1151
Newman, W. F., 319
Nicholas, J. S., 56
Nilges, R. G., 947
Nishimura, H., 60
Nishimura, K., 600
Noback, C. R., 319
Noback, G. J., 712
Noer, R. J., 1313
Nomura, S., 1091
Nonidez, J. F., 1312
Nonidez, J. N., 1091
Norland, M., 1405
Norris, E. H., 820, 1405
Norrish, R. E., 1092

O

Odgers, P. N. B., 598
Odland, G. F., 1164
Odor, D. L., 56, 59, 1378
O'Leary, J. L., 946
Oliver, R. K., 1088
Olsen, L. L., 714
Omura, K., 773
Ongley, P. A., 600
Opdyke, D. L., 714
O'Rahilly, R., 319, 714
Oram, V., 1314
Osogoe, B., 773, 819
Overholser, M. D., 1406
Ozanics, V., 1152

P

Padget, D. H., 712, 763, 772
Paff, G. H., 599
Painter, T. S., 56
Palade, G. E., 58, 773
Palay, S. L., 56
Pankratz, D. S., 1388
Papanicolaou, G. N., 1389
Parkhurst, H. T., 820
Pastore, P. N., 1088

Patek, P. R., 819
Patten, B. M., 56, 599, 945
Patton, W. H. G., 1387
Payne, F., 59
Peale, A. R., 60
Pearson, A. A., 1091
Pease, D. C., 947, 1386
Peck, H. M., 820
Peden, J. K., 1313
Pedersen, H. E., 1091
Peele, T. L., 947
Penfield, W., 947, 948
Pepper, H. R., 1088
Pepper, O. H. P., 20
Perez Casas, A., 1314
Perkins, R., 715
Person, A. A., 945, 1088
Peterson, R. R., 320
Petrakis, N. K., 818
Peyton, W. T., 946
Pfeiffer, C. A., 1388
Phillips, J. H., 773
Pick, J., 714, 1091, 1385, 1386, 1403
Pierce, E. C., 819
Peirce, E. C., 2nd, 1386
Pincus, G., 1389
Pines, J., 945
Pisha, B. V., 1165
Plagge, J. C., 1405
Pogogeff, I. A., 564
Policard, A., 1206
Pollak, O. J., 773
Polley, E. H., 1090
Pollock, L. J., 1090
Pomerat, C. M., 1205
Poppel, M. H., 1314
Poppelier, G., 772
Popper, H. P., 1314
Porter, K. R., 56, 563
Posch, J. L., 565
Potts, T. K., 1091
Power, R. M. H., 1389
Poynter, C. W. M., 713, 714
Price, D., 1387
Prichard, M. M., 715
Prince, J. H., 1152
Pyle, S. I., 319, 320

Q

Quiring, D. P., 715

R

Radigan, L. R., 1090
Ralston, H. J., 1089
Ramon y Cajal, S., 947
Ramsay, A. J., 1405
Randall, W. C., 1091
Ranson, M., 946
Ranson, S. W., 945
Rappaport, A. M., 1314
Rasmussen, A. T., 944, 946, 947, 1405
Ray, L. J., 563, 1165
Raybuck, H. E., 1164, 1406
Read, W. T., 715
Reed, A. F., 945
Reed, B. P., 56
Reed, C. I., 56
Reemtsma, K., 600
Reger, J. F., 948
Rehman, I., 712
Reimann, A. F., 563, 772
Reinertson, R. P., 1165
Reinhardt, W. O., 819
Renyi-Vamos, F., 819
Reyer, R. W., 1152
Reynolds, E. L., 1387
Reynolds, S. R. M., 1389
Richardson, K. C., 1091
Richens, C. A., 1152, 1314

Richmond, T. E., 1206
Richter, K. M., 1405
Richter, M., 1206
Riesen, A. H., 1151
Rioch, D. McK., 947
Rives, J. D., 565, 1312
Robb, J. S., 598, 600
Robertson, G. G., 319
Robertson, J. D., 948
Robinson, B. E., 403
Robinson, D. S., 819
Robinson, G. B., 1088
Robinson, R. A., 402
Robuck, J. D., Jr., 772
Roche, M. B., 320
Rock, J., 59, 60
Rodriguez, A. L., 819
Rogers, L. C., 118
Romano, S. A., 1390
Rondon-Tarchetti, T., 1405
Ronstrom, G. N., 715, 1386
Roofe, P. G., 1089
Ropes, M. W., 402
Rose, J. M., 1205
Rosen, M. D., 1206
Rosen, S., 1088
Ross, L. L., 948
Roston, J. B., 403
Roth, C. B., 60
Rothman, S., 1164
Rouviere, H., 118, 819
Rowe, G. G., 320
Rowe, L. C., 1088
Rukstinat, G. J., 1388
Rumble, C. T., 1313
Russell, W. L., 1389
Rusted, I. E., 599
Ruth, E. B., 402

S

Sabin, F. R., 818
Saccomanno, G., 1091
Salmon, T. N., 1404
Sarnat, B. G., 402, 1206
Sauer, M. E., 1312, 1313
Saunders, R. L., 320
Saunders, J. B. deC. M., 403, 1312
Sawin, P. B., 713, 772
Sawyer, C. H., 946, 1389, 1405
Schaeffer, E. M., 1091
Schaefer, J. H., 1314
Schaefter, J. B., 1206
Schaffner, 1314
Scharrer, E., 715
Scheifley, C. H., 599
Schmitt, F. O., 948
Schneider, B. M., 1404
Schneider, C. L., 403
Schneider, L. A., 772
Schnitzlein, H. N., 1088, 1091, 1313
Schofield, N. D., 713
Schour, I., 320
Schroy, P. C., 1313
Schültz, R. L., 947
Schrechter, A. E., 1091
Schuknecht, H. F., 1152
Schunke, G. B., 403
Schutz, H., 946
Schwadron, L., 1088
Schwarzacher, H. G., 948
Schwegler, R. A., Jr., 1314
Selby, C. C., 1164
Senior, H. D., 713
Sensenig, E. C., 319, 948
Shaffer, S. A., 1091
Shafiroff, G. P., 1088
Shah, M. A., 1313
Shaner, R. F., 60, 599, 600, 713, 772

Shanklin, W. M., 948, 1405
Shapiro, H. H., 320, 402, 1312
Sheehan, D., 948, 1088, 1091
Shettles, L. B., 59
Shields, T. W., 713
Shryock, E. H., 1312
Shiller, W. R., 320
Shrewsbury, M. M. Jr., 819
Shumacker, H. B., 1090
Sicher, H., 319
Siekert, R. G., 1206, 1312
Simer, P. H., 1206
Simmonds, W. J., 819
Simmons, B. S., 599
Simon, H. E., 1386
Sinclair, J. G., 599, 600, 713
Sinesi, S. J., 1164
Singer, E., 564
Singer, M., 944
Skinner, H. A., 18
Slager, R. F., 715
Smelser, G. K., 1152
Smith, A., 773
Smith, C., 820
Smith, C. A., 1152
Smith, D. B., 1091
Smith, E. I., 1312
Smith, H. W., 1386
Smith, R. D., 403, 563
Smith, R. W., 1314
Smithwick, R. H., 1404
Smythe, M. Q., 600
Snook, T., 820
Sobel, E. H., 1403
Solomon, C. I., 1403
Specht, N. W., 1312
Spector, B., 1152
Spector, W. S., 18
Spemann, H., 60
Spence, D. L., 1404
Sprague, J. M., 945, 1088, 1089, 1312
Spurling, R. G., 402
Stalker, L. K., 1313
Stalzer, R. C., 1091
Stebbins, T. A., 713
Stein, M. R., 402
Sterling, J. A., 1314
Stern, K., 946
Stewart, T. D., 320
Stieve, P. H., 1387
Stillwell, D. L., 319, 1089, 1090
Stohr, P., Jr., 1091
Stone, L. W., 1152
Stotler, W. A., 600, 946, 1091
Strayer, L. M., 402
Streeter, G. L., 60
Strong, L. C., 1387
Strong, L. H., 948, 1206, 1312
Sulkin, N. M., 1091, 1386
Sullens, W. E., 1406
Sullivan, W. E., 564
Sulzberger, M. B., 1165
Sunderland, S., 320, 563, 600, 948, 1089, 1090, 1152, 1165
Sweet, W. H., 948
Swigart, L. L., 713, 1089, 1312
Swigart, R. H., 563
Swinyard, C. A., 1091, 1403
Szentágothai, J., 946

Szepsenwol, J., 564
Szinay, Gy., 819

T

Takase, B., 1091
Takashi, M., 948
Talbot, N. B., 1403
Tandler, J., 599
Taussig, J., 1164
Tebo, H. G., 320
Telford, I. R., 320, 1312
Thomas, H., 1389
Thomas, L. B., 1206
Thomas, P. K., 1165
Thorek, M., 1390
Tobin, C. E., 565, 566, 714, 1206, 1386, 1388
Tomasch, J., 947
Toncray, J. E., 946
Töndury, G., 118
Traut, H. F., 1389
Triepel, H., 18
Trotter, M., 320, 403, 715, 1165
Truex, R. C., 402, 599, 600, 601, 772, 1089
Turman, W. G., 598
Trumble, H. C., 1092
Truszkowski, R., 1404
Turner, R. S., 949

U

Uhlenhuth, E., 1389
Uotila, U. U., 1403

V

Vakaet, L., 772
Valdez-Dapena, M. A., 56
Van Cleave, C. D., 772
Van Nuys, R G., 1386
Van Scott, E. J., 1165
Vann, H. M., 714
Venning, P., 320
Vermeire, P., 772
Villiger, E., 946
Vollmer, E. P., 1404
von Bonin, G., 947, 1313
Voshell, A. F., 403

W

Waine, H., 402
Waits, W. J., 1164
Waldo, C. M., 60
Walsch, H., 945
Walker, A. E., 946
Walker, B. S., 1404
Walker, W. J., 600, 601
Wallis, T. E., 56
Walls, E. W., 600
Walter, L. E., 1090
Ward, J. W., 945
Ware, P. F., 715
Warkany, J., 60
Warren, H. S., 1387
Warshaw, L. J., 600
Warwick, R., 945, 946
Washburn, S. L., 320, 566

Waterman, A. J., 1385
Watts, J. W., 947
Watzka, M., 1389
Weathersby, H. T., 714
Webber, R. H., 1092
Weber, H. H., 564
Weber, J., 1313
Wedum, B. G., 600
Welch, A. D., 1404
Weller, G. L., Jr., 1405
Wells, J. C., 565
Wells, L. J., 563, 1206, 1385, 1388
Wesson, M. B., 566, 1386, 1388
Wever, E. G., 1152
Wharton, L. R., Jr., 1385
Whipple, A. A., 819
White, A., 1404
White, J. C., 1404
White, L. P., 818
White, P. D., 600
Whitesell, F. B., Jr., 1312
Widran, J., 600
Wiglesworth, F. W., 714
Wilde, C. E., 945
Wilkins, L., 1403
Williams, D. D., 1388
Williams, G. D., 1164
Williams, R. G., 1404, 1405
Williams, W. L., 563, 1314, 1388, 1390
Willius, F. A., 600
Wilmer, H. A., 1386
Wilson, J. G., 60
Winborne, L. W., 949
Wintersteiner, M. P., 819
Wintrobe, M. M., 773
Wislocki, G. B., 60, 1388,14 05
Wiswell, O. B., 320
Wittmaack, K., 1152
Wolf, G. A., Jr., 1092
Wolfe, J. M., 60, 1388, 1405
Wolfer, J. A., 1389
Wolstenholme, G. E., 59
Woodburne, R. T., 713, 714, 946
Woolf, D., 1152
Woollard, H. H., 1092
Woolsey, C. N., 946
Wotton, R. M., 1386, 1403
Wrette, M., 1092
Wright, R. R., 563, 564, 600, 1389
Wright-Smith, R. J., 600

Y

Yakovlev, P. I., 944
Yanitelli, S., 565
Yeager, G. H., 1090
Yntema, C. L., 945, 1092, 1152
Yoffey, J. M., 819
Young, H. H., 1387

Z

Zariquiey, M. O., 1206
Zitrin, A., 946
Zuckerman, S., 402
Zugibe, F. T., 1152
Zweifach, B. W., 773
Zwemer, R. L., 1386, 1403, 1404

SUBJECT INDEX

Italics Indicate Latin Terms.

A

ABDOMEN, 1253
  apertures in walls, of, 1253
  boundaries of, 1253
  fascia of. 453
    triangular, 456
  lymph nodes of, 796
  regions of, 1253
  surface anatomy of, 81
Abdominal aorta, 669
  surface markings of, 85
  aortic plexus, 1085
  muscles, 446
  ring, external, 455
    inguinal, 466
    internal, 466
  viscera, surface markings of, 87
  wall, lymphatic vessels of, 799
Abducent nerve, 973
  composition and central connections of, 916
Abduction of joints, 324
Abductor digiti quinti muscle
    (foot), 556
    (hand), 523
  hallucis muscle, 555
  indicis muscle, 524
  minimi digiti muscle, 523, 556
  pollicis brevis muscle, 521
    longus muscle, 509
Accelerator urinæ muscle, 479
Accessory hemiazygos vein, 749
  nerve, 994
    composition and central connections of, 920
  obturator nerve, 1040
  olivary nuclei, 852
  organs of digestive tube, 1207
    of eye, 1114
  pancreatic duct, 1307
  part of parotid gland, 1239
  processes, 137
  pudendal artery, 690
  sinuses of nose, 1175
  spleens, 814
  thyroid glands, 1393
Acetabular fossa, 264
  notch, 264
Acetabulum, 264
Acoustic meatus, external, 164,
    203, 1128
    development of, 1123
    internal, 175, 200
  nerve, 981, 1150
    composition and central connections of, 917
    development of, 1126
    nuclei of, 918, 981
Acromioclavicular joint, 354
  surface anatomy of, 105
Acromion, 232
Acromiothoracic artery, 655
Adam's apple, 1176
Adductor brevis muscle, 535
  canal, 698
    surface anatomy of, 118
  hallucis muscle, 558
    obliquius muscle, 558
  longus muscle, 534
  magnus muscle, 535

Adductor minimus muscle, 535
  pollicis muscle, 522
    obliquius transversus muscle,
      523
  tubercle, 273
Adipose capsule of kidney, 1328
Adminiculum lineæ albæ, 463
Adrenal gland, 1399
Afferent vessels of kidney, 1334
After-birth, 52
Agger nasi, 218
Aggregated lymphatic nodules,
    1282
Agminated follicles, 1282
Air cells, ethmoidal, 211, 1175
    mastoid, 198
  sinuses of nose, 1175
Ala cinerea, 869, 920
  nasi, 1169
  of ethmoid, 210
  of sacrum, 141
  of vomer, 226
  ossis ilii, 259
Alar cartilages of nose, 1170
  lamina, 822
Alcock's canal, 475
Alimentary canal, 1207
  lymphatic capillaries in, 778
Allantois, development of, 55
Alveolar arch, 218
  arteries, 630, 631
  border of mandible, 181
  nerves, 967, 972
  process of maxilla, 218
Alveoli, formation of, 1229
Alveus, 906
Amacrine cells of retina, 1110
Amerloblasts, 1226
Amitosis, 24
Ammons' horn, 906
Amnion, development of, 32, 53
Amniotic cavity, 32
Amphiarthroses, 322
Ampulla, ampullæ, of ductus deferens, 1358
  of rectum, 1289
  of semicircular canal, 1141
  of tubuli lactiferi, 1384
  of uterine tube, 1370
  of Vater, 1307
Amygdala, 899
Amygdaloid nucleus, 899, 911
Anal canal or anal part of rectum,
    1290
    development of, 1215
    lymphatic vessels of, 804
    membrane of, 1215
    valves of, 1291
  fascia, 473
Anaphase of mitosis, 23
Anatomoses of arteries, 603
    around elbow-joint, 659
      knee-joint, 706
    crucial, 702
Anastomotic branch of inferior
    gluteal artery, 692
Anastomotica magna of brachial
    artery, 659
    of femoral artery, 703
Anatomical neck of humerus, 235
Anconæus muscle, 508

Angiology, 567
Angle of Louis, 76
  of mandible, 182
  of pubis, 263
  of rib, 154
  of sternum, 152
  sacrovertebral, 137
  subscapular, 231
Angular artery, 622
  gyrus, 886
  movement, 324
  vein, 725
Ankle bone, 294
  of child aged ten years, x-ray of,
    113
Ankle-joint, 390
  movements of, 393
  relations of tendons and vessels
    to, 392
  surface anatomy of, 117
Annular ligament, 411
  of ankle, 551
  of radius, 364
  of wrist, anterior, 514
    posterior, 514
Annulus fibrosus [of intervertebral
    fibrocartilage], 328
  inguinalis abdominis, 466
    subcutaneus, 456
  ovalis, 587
  tendineus communis [*eye*], 1115
Anococcygeal body, 1291
  nerves, 1057
  raphè, 469
Ansa hypoglossi, 1009
  lenticularis, 878
Antebrachial cutaneous nerve,
    dorsal, 1030
    lateral, 1020
    medial, 1020
  fascia, 499
Antecubital fossa, 657
Anterior annular ligament, ankle,
    551
    wrist, 511
  calcaneoastragaloid ligament,
    393
  cerebral artery, 637
  choroidal artery, 639
  circumflex artery, 655
  commissure, 907
  common ligament, vertebral,
    326
  communicating artery, 637
  condyloid foramen, 188
  costotransverse ligament, 340
  costovertebral ligament, 340
  crural nerve, 1042
  humeral circumflex artery, 68
  inferior tibiofibular ligament,
    389
  intercostal arteries, 650
  interosseous artery, 665
    nerve, 1023
  ligament, knee, 381
    wrist, 366
  peroneal artery, 710
  pillar of fauces, 1241
  pulmonary nerve plexus, 993
  radial carpal artery, 661
  radioulnar ligament, 366

Anterior, superior dental nerve, 967
  ligament, costotransverse, 340
  tibiofibular, 389
  talotibial ligament, 391
  temporal artery, 627
  tibial nerve, 1053
  ulnar carpal artery, 665
  recurrent artery, 663
Antibrachial. *See* Antebrachial.
Antihelix, 1126
Antitragicus muscle, 1128
Antitragus, 1126
Antrum cardiacum, 1272
  of Highmore, 215, 1175
  pyloric, 1273
  tympanic, 199, 1133
Anus, 1207, 1215
  lymphatic vessels of, 804
Aorta, 613
  abdominal, 669
    branches of, 669
  arch of, 616
    branches of, 617
    peculiarities of, 617
  ascending, 613
  descending, 610, 613, 666
  thoracic, 666
    branches of, 666
    rami mediastinales, 667
    pericardiaci, 666
  transverse, 616
Aortæ, dorsal, 605
  primitive, 568
  ventral, 605
Aortic arches, 605
  development of 605
  bodies, 941
  hiatus, 450
  isthmus, 609, 617
  lymph nodes, 798
  opening of heart, 591
  plexus of sympathetic, 1085
  receptors, 941
  semilunar valves, 592
  septum, 575
  sinuses, 592, 614
  spindle, 617
  valve, 592
  vestibule, 591
Aorticorenal ganglion, 1084
Aperture; *Apertura*, anterior nasal, 167, 177
  in wall of abdomen, 1253
  pelvis [minoris] inferior, 267
    superior, 266
  tympanica canaliculi chordæ, 1130
Apex cordis, 584
  of fibula, 287
  of heart, 584
  linguæ, 1230
  of nose, 1170
  ossis sacri, 141
  prostatæ, 1365
  pulmonis, 1197
Aponeurosis, 306, 440
  epicranial, 413
  lumbar, 440
  lumbocostal, 440
  of obliquus externus, 455
  palatine, 1244
  palmar, 514
  pharyngeal, 1251
  plantar, 554
  suprahyoid, 432
Apparatus digestorius, 1207
  juxtaglomerular, 1335
  lacrimalis, 1121
  respiratorius, 1167
  urogenitalis, 1315
Appendage auricular, left, 590

Appendage, auricular right; 586
  of testis, 1353
Appendices epiploicæ, 1284
  vesiculosæ, 1284
Appendicular artery, 679
  skeleton, 119
Appendix, of epididymis, 1353
  of ventricle of larynx, 1183
  surface anatomy of, 89
  testis, 1353
  vermiform, 1285
  xiphoid, 152
Aqueduct, cerebral, 881
  cochleæ, 200
  Fallopii, 200, 975
  of cochlea, 162, 209
  of Sylvius, 881
  vestibuli, 200, 1140
Aqueous humor, 1112
Arachnoid, 927
  granulations, 191, 735
  villi, 928
Arachnoidea encephali, 927
  spinalis, 927
Arantii, corpus, 592
Arbor vitæ [of cerebellum], 864
  uterina, 1375
Arch or arches, alveolar, 218
  aortic, 605, 616
  axillary muscle, 486
  branchial or visceral, 39
  carotid, 605
  crural, deep, 466
  glossopalatine, 1241
  hyoid, 41
  lumbocostal, lateral, 450
    medial, 450
  mandibular, 40
  of aorta, 616
  of atlas, 129
  of fauces, 1210, 1241
  of foot, 401
  palmar deep, 662
    superfficial, 665
  pharyngopalatine, 1241
  plantar, 711
  pubic, 267
  superciliary, 159, 193
  vertebral, 126
    articulations of, 329
  zygomatic, 165
Archipallium, 830
Architecture of femur, 275
Arcuate artery, 709, 1336
  fibers, 856
  ligaments of diaphragm, 450
  line of ilium, 258
  popliteal ligament, 381
Arcus aortæ, 616
  cartilaginis cricoideæ, 1177
  glossopalatinus, 1241
  lumbocostalis lateralis [Halleri], 450
    medialis [Halleri], 450
  pharyngopalatinus, 1241
Area acustica, 869
  auditory, 892
  cribrosa media, 200
    superior, 200
  facialis, 200
  motor, 888
  olfactory, 904
  oval, of Flechsig, 844
  parolfactoria, 911
  pericardial, 78
  piriform, 908
  postrema, 869
  preoptic, 880
  speech, 891
  striate, 891
  vestibularis, 869
  visual physic, 892
Areas of cerebral cortex, 888

Areola of mamma, 1382
Areolar glands, 1382
Arm bone, 235
  fascia of, 496
  muscles of, 496
    development of, 405
Arnold's nerve, 990
Arrectores pilorum muscle, 1161
Arterioles, 767
Artery or Arteries, *Arteria* or *Arteriæ*, abdominal aorta, 669
  accessory meningeal, 629
    pudendal, 690
  acromiothoracic, 655
  alveolar, 630
  anastomoses of, 603
  anastomotic branch of inferior gluteal, 692
  anastomotica magna, of brachial, 659
    of femoral, 703
  angular, 624
  anomyna, 617
  anterior cerebral, 637
    choroidal, 639
    ciliary, 637
    communicating, 637
    humeral circumflex, 656
    inferior cerebellar, 645
    meningeal, 634
    spinal, 645
    tympanic, 629
  aorta, 613
    abdominal 699
    arch of, 605
    ascending, 613
    descending, 666
    thoracic, 666
  appendicular, 679
  arcuate, 709, 1336
  articular, of knee, 705
  ascending cervical, 647
    palatine, 623
    pharyngeal, 626
  auditiva, interna, 646
  auditory, 646
    internal, 646
  auricular, anterior, 628
    deep, 629
    of occipital, 625
    posterior, 626
  axillary, 653
  azygos, of knee, 705
    of vagina, 688
  basilar, 645
  brachial, 656
  brachiocephalic, 617
  bronchial, 666, 1204
  buccal, 630
  buccinator, 630
  bulbar, 645
  bulbi urethræ, 691
  calcaneal, 710
  calcarine, 646
  canalis pterygoidei, 631, 634
  capsular, middle, 682
  caroticotympanic, 633
  carotid, common, 618
    external, 619
    internal, 631
  carpal, dorsal, 662
    palmar, 662, 665
    radial, 661
    ulnar, 665
  cavernous, 634
  cecal, 679
  celiac, 669
  central, of retina, 636, 1098, 1111
  centralis retinæ, 636
  cerebellar, 645
  cerebral, anterior, 637
    hemorrhage, 638

Artery, cerebral, middle, 638
  posterior, 646
  cervical, ascending, 647
    deep, 652
    superficial, 648
    transverse, 652
  cervicalis profunda, 652
  choroidal, 639, 646
  ciliary, 637
  circle of Willis, 640
  circumflex, femoral, 702
    humeral, 656
    iliac, 699
  coccygeal of inferior gluteal, 692
  cochlear, 1151
  colic, 679
  comes nervi phrenici, 650
  common carotid, 618
    iliac, 684
    interosseous, 664
  communicating, anterior, 637
    of dorsalis pedis, 709
    posterior, 639
  coronary, of heart, 615
  costocervical trunk, 652
  cremasteric, 694
  cricothyroid, 621
  cystic, 674
  deep auricular, 629
    brachial, 656
    epigastric, 694
    external pudendal, 700
    femoral, 701
    iliac circumflex, 695, 699
    lingual, 622
    palmar arch, 662
      branch of ulnar, 665
    plantar, 709
    temporal, 630
  dental, inferior, 630
    superior, 630
  descending aorta, 666
    branch of occipital, 625
    palatine, development of, 631
  digital, foot, 711
    hand, 666
    palmar, 666
  dorsal carpal of radial, 661
    of ulnar, 665
    interosseous, 664
    metacarpal, 662
    nasal, 636
    of penis, 691
  dorsales linguæ, 622
  dorsalis hallucis, 709
    pedis, 708
    ramus plantaris profundus, 709
    scapulæ, 655
  epigastric, deep or inferior, 694
    superficial, 699
    superior, 649, 650
  esophageal, of aorta, 667
    of inferior thyroid, 646
  ethmoidal, 635
  external carotid, 619
    iliac, 694
    maxillary, 622
    plantar, 711
    pudendal, 700
    spermatic, 694
  facial, 622
    transverse, 627
  femoral, 695
    circumflex, 702
  fibular, of foot, 708
  frontal, 636
  gastric, 672, 673
  gastroduodenal, 673
  gastroepiploic, 673
  genicular, 703, 705
  genus media, 705

Artery, *genus inferiores*, 705
  genus superiores, 705
  suprema, 703
  glandular, submaxillary, 623
  gluteal, 691, 693
  helicine, 1365
  hemorrhoidal, inferior, 690
    middle, 687
    superior, 680
  hæmorrhoidalis, inferior, 691
    media, 686
    superior, 680
  hepatic, 672
  highest genicular, 703
    intercostal, 650
    thoracic, 655
  humeral circumflex, 656
  hyoid, 621
  hypogastric, 577, 579, 686
    obliterated, 686
  hypophyseal, 634
  ileal, of ileocolic, 679
  ileocolic, 679
  iliac circumflex, 695, 699
    common, 684
    external, 694
    internal, 685
  iliolumbar, 692
  inferior alveolar, 630
    articular, of knee, 706
    cerebellar, 646
    dental, 630
    epigastric, 694
    genicular, 705
    gluteal, 691
    hemorrhoidal, 690
    labial, 623
    laryngeal, 647
    mesenteric, 680
    pancreaticoduodenal, 678
    phrenic, 683
    profunda, 657
    thyroid, 646
    tympanic, 627
    ulnar collateral, 658
    vesical, 687
  infrahyoid, 621
  infraorbital, 630
  infrascapular, 655
  innominate, 617
  intercostal, 667, 668
    branches of internal thoracic, 650
    superior, 652
  interlobular, of kidney, 1336
  internal auditory, 646
    carotid, 631
      x-ray of, 67
    iliac, 685
    mammary, 649
    maxillary, 628
    palpebral, 635
    plantar, 711
    pudendal or pudic, 689, 691
    spermatic, 682
    thoracic, 649
  interosseous, anterior, 665
    common, 664
    dorsal, 665
    palmar, 662
    posterior, 665
    volar, 665
  intestinal, 678
  labial, 623
  lacrimal, 634
  laryngeal, inferior, 647
    superior, 621
  lateral calcaneal, 711
    femoral circumflex, 702
    nasal, 624
    palpebral, 634
    sacral, 692
    tarsal, 709

Artery, lateral thoracic, 655
  left colic, 681
    gastric, 672
  lienal, 674
  lingual, 621
    deep, 622
  long, thoracic, 655
  lumbar, 683
  malleolar, 708
    internal, 708
  mammary, external, 655
    internal, 649
  masseteric, 630
  maxillary, external, 622
    internal, 628
    pterygoid branches, 630
  medial palpebral, 635
    tarsal, 709
  median, 665
  mediastinal, from aorta, 667
    from internal mammary, 649
  medidural, 629
  medullary, 645
  meningeal, accessory, 629
    anterior, 634
    middle, 629
    of ascending pharyngeal, 626
    of occipital, 625
    of vertebral, 645
    small, 629
  mesenteric, inferior, 680
    superior, 678, 1283
  metacarpal, 662
  metatarsal, 708
  middle capsular, 682
    cerebral, 638
    collateral, 658
    genicular, 705
    hemorrhoidal, 687
    meningeal, 629
    sacral, 683
    suprarenal, 682
    vesical, 687
  musculophrenic, 649, 650
  mylohyoid, 630
  nasal, 636
    dorsal, 636
    lateral, 624
  nasopalatine, 631
  nutrient, of femur, 703
    of fibula, 710
    of humerus, 658, 659
    of tibia, 711
  obturator, 688
  occipital, 625
  of brain, 640
  of corpus cavernosum, 691
  of ductus deferens, 687
  of head and neck, 618
  of labyrinth, 1151
  of lower extremity, 695
  of penis, 689, 691
  of pterygoid canal, 631, 634
  of semilunar ganglion, 634
  of trunk, 666
  of upper extremity, 641
  ophthalmic, 634
  ovarian, 682
  palatine, ascending, 623
    descending, 631
    of ascending pharyngeal, 627
  palmar arch, deep, 662
    superficial, 665
    carpal, 661
    digital, common, 666
    interosseous, 665
    metacarpal, 662
    proper, 666
  volaris indicis radialis, 662
  palpebral, 634, 635
  pancreatic, of lienal, 675
  pancreatica magna, 677
  pancreaticoduodenal, 675, 678

Artery, perforating, of foot, 710
  of hand, 662
  of internal mammary, 650
  of thigh, 701
pericardiacophrenic, 650
pericardial, 650
perineal, 691
  superficial, 691
peroneal, 710
  anterior, 710
pharyngeal, ascending, 626
  of internal maxillary, 631
phrenic, inferior, 683
  superior, 669
plantar, deep, 709
  lateral (external), 711
  medial (internal), 711
  metatarsal, 711
pontine, 646
popliteal, 704
posterior alveolar, 630
  auricular, 626
  cerebral, 645
  communicating, 639
  dental, 630
  humeral circumflex, 655
  inferior cerebellar, 645
  interosseus, 665
  meningeal, from vertebral, 645
  scapular, 648
  scrotal, 691
  spinal, 645
  superior alveolar, 630
  tibial, 709
prevertebral, 627
princeps cervicis, 625
  hallucis, 709
  pollicis, 662
profunda brachii, 657
  cervicalis, 652
  femoris, 701
  lingua, 622
  penis, 691
pudendal external, 700
  internal, 689
    in female, 691
    in male, 689
pudic external, 700
  internal, 689
pulmonary, 611
pyloric, 673
radial, 660
  collateral, 658
  recurrent, 661
radialis indicis, 662
ranine, 622
rectæ, 1336
recurrent, interosseous, 665
  of hand, 661
  radial, 661
  tibial, 708
  ulnar, 663
renal, 682
retroduodenal, 673
right colic, 679
  coronary, 615
  gastric, 675
  gastroepiploic, 673
sacral, lateral, 692
  middle, 683
scapular circumflex, 655
  posterior, 647
  transverse, 647
sciatic, 691
scrotal, posterior, 691
seventh segmental, 609
short ciliary, 637
  gastric, 677
sigmoid, 681
spermatic, 682
  external, 695
  internal, 682

Artery, sphenopalatine, 631
spinal, 643
splenic, 674
sternal, 650
sternocleidomastoid, 621, 625
striate, 638
structure of, 765
stylomastoid, 626
subclavian, 609, 641
subcostal, 668
sublingual, 622
submaxillary, 623
submental, 623
subscapular, 655
superficial cervical, 648
  epigastric, 699
  external pudendal, 700
  iliac circumflex, 699
  palmar arch, 665
  temporal, 627
superior articular of knee, 705
  cerebellar, 646
  epigastric, 649, 650
  gluteal, 693
  hemorrhoidal, 681
  intercostal, 652
  labial, 623
  laryngeal, 621
  mesenteric, 678
  pancreatico-duodenal, 673
  phrenic, 669
  profunda, 657
  thoracic, 655
  thyroid, 621
  tympanic, 629
  ulnar collateral, 658
  vesical, 687
suprahyoid, 622
supraorbital, 634
suprarenal, 682
  inferior, 682
  middle, 682
  superior, 683
suprascapular, 647
sural, 705
tarsal, 709
temporal, 627
  deep, 630
  middle, 628
  superficial, 627
testicular, 682
thoracic, 666
  aorta, 666
  axis, 655
  highest, 654
  lateral, 655
  superior, 655
thoracoacromial, 655
thoracodorsal, 655
thyrocervical trunk, 646
thyroid axis, 646
  inferior, 646
  superior, 621
  thyroidea ima, 618
tibial, anterior, 706
  posterior, 709
  recurrent, 708
tonsillar, 623
tracheal, 647
transverse cervical, 652
  facial, 627
  perineal, 691
  scapular, 647
transversa colli, 647
  ramus ascendens, 648
    descendens, 648
tunica adventitia, 765
  intima, 765
  media, 765
tympanic, 627, 629
ulnar, 662
  collateral, 659
  recurrent, 663

Artery, umbilical, 577
  in fetus, 686
urethral, 691
  bulb, 691
uterine, 687
vaginal, 688
vasa aberrantia, 657
  brevia, 677
  intestini tenuis, 678
vertebral, 609, 643
vesical, 687
vestibular, 1151
Vidian, 631, 634
Arthrodia, 324
Articular arteries, 705
  capsules, 325, 334
  cartilage, 306
  disk of acromioclavicular joint, 354
    of distal radioulnar joint, 366
    of sternoclavicular joint, 353
    of temporomandibular joint, 336
  lamella of bone, 313
  meniscus, 336
  process of vertebræ, 127
  tubercle of temporal bone, 160, 196
Articulation or Articulations, 321
  acromiclavicular, 354
  amphiarthroses, 322
  ankle, 390
  atlantoöccipital, 334
  atlas with axis or epistropheus, 331
    with occipital bone, 334
  by reciprocal reception, 323
  calcaneocuboid, 395
  calcaneus and astragalus, 396
    with cuboid, 397
  capitulorum, 337
  carpometacarpal, 371
  cartilages of ribs with each other, 343
  classification of, 322
  condyloid, 323
  costocentral, 337
  costochondral, 341
  costosternal, 341
  costotransverse, 340
  costovertebral, 337
  coxal, 374
  cubiti, 360
  cuboideonavicular, 399
  cuneocuboid, 399
  cuneonavicular, 398
  development, 321
  diarthroses, 322
  digitorum manus, 374
    pedis, 401
  digits, 374, 401
  elbow, 360
  ellipsoidea, 323
  genu, 380
  gomphosis, 322
  hip, 374
  humeral, 356
  immovable, 322
  intercarpal, 369
  interchondral, 343
  intercuneiform, 399
  intermetacarpal, 372
  intermetatarsal, 400
  intertarsal, 393
  knee, 380
  lower extremity, 374
  mandible, 335
  metacarpophalangeal, 372
  metatarsophalangeal, 401
  movable, 322
  movements, of, 324
  navicular with cuneiform bones, 398

Articulation, pelvis, 345
　with vertebral column, 345
　phalanges of foot, 401
　　of hand, 374
　pubic bones, 349
　　symphysis, 349
　radiocarpal, 366
　radioulnar, 364
　　distal, 366
　　proximal, 364
　sacrococcygeal symphysis, 348
　sacroiliac, 345
　sacrum and coccyx, 347
　scapuloclavicular, 354
　schindylesis, 322
　sellaris, 323
　shoulder, 356
　sternoclavicular, 105, 352
　sternocostal, 341
　sternum, 343
　sutura, 322
　symphysis, 322
　　pubis, 349
　synarthroses, 322
　synchondrosis, 322
　syndesmosis, 322
　talocalcaneal, 393
　talocalcaneonavicular, 394
　talocrural, 390
　tarsometatarsal, 399
　tarsus, 393
　temporomandibular, 335
　tibiofibular, 389
　tibiotarsal, 390
　trochoidea, 323
　trunk, 326
　upper extremity, 352
　vertebral arches, 324
　　bodies, 326
　　column, 326
　　　with cranium, 334
　　　with pelvis, 345
　wrist, 366
Aryepiglottic fold, 1182
Aryepiglotticus muscle, 1186
Arytænoideus muscles, 1185
Arytenoid cartilages, 1178
　glands, 1187
　swellings, 1167
Ascending aorta, 613
　cervical artery, 647
　colon, 1287
　lumbar vein, 749
　oblique muscle, 458
　palatine artery, 623
　pharyngeal artery, 626
　ramus of ischium, 262
　　of os pubis, 263
Association fibers of cerebral
　hemispheres, 895
Asterion, 192
Astragalus, 294
Astrocytes, 934
Atlantoöccipital articulation,
　334
Atlas, 129
Atria, Atrium dextrum, 586
　muscle bundles of, 594
　of bronchi, 1204
　of heart, left, 586
　　primitive, 572
　　right, 586
　　sinistrum, 590
　of nasal fossa, 1170
Atrial canal, 572
Atrioventricular bundle of His,
　596
　canal, 572
　node, 595
　opening, left, 588
　　right, 589
Atrium dextrum, 586
　sinistrum, 590

Attic or epitympanic recess, 199
　1130
Attolens aurem muscle, 1127
Attrahens aurem muscle, 1127
Auditory artery, 646
　internal, 646
　canal, external, 1128
　meatus, external, 1128
　nerve, 981
　ossicles, 119, 1136
　　development of, 1136
　pit, 1122
　plate, 1122
　tube, 1135
　　cartilaginous portion of, 1135
　　cushion of, 1135
　　isthmus of, 1135
　　osseous portion of, 1135
　　pharyngeal ostium, 1248
　　tonsil of, 1135
　　torus tubarius, 1135
　vesicle, 1123
Auerbach's plexus, 1284
Auricle, or Auricula of ear, 1122
　cartilage of, 1127
　development of, 1122
　of heart, 586
　　dextra, 586
　　left, 590
　　right, 586
　　sinistra, 590
　ligaments of, 1127
　muscles of, 1127
　vessels and nerves of, 1128
Auricular appendage, left, 590
　　right, 586
　artery, anterior, 628
　　deep, 629
　　posterior, 626
　lymph nodes, 784
　muscles, 1153
　nerve, anterior, 1007
　　great, 1007
　　of vagus, 990
　　posterior, 1007
　surface of ilium, 259
　　of sacrum, 139
　tubercle of Darwin, 1126
　vein, posterior, 727
Auriculotemporal nerve, 970
Auris interna, 1139
Auscultation, triangle of, 486
Autonomic ganglia of nerves,
　1062, 1065
　　structure, 937
　nervous system, 833, 1060
　　development, 833
A–V node, 595
Axes of pelvis, 267
Axial filament of spermatozoön,
　26
　skeleton, 119
Axilla, 652
　fascia of, 486
Axillary arch muscle, 486
　artery, 653
　　surface markings of, 108
　lymph nodes, 793
　nerve, 1016
　sheath, 490, 653
　vein, 745
Axis, 131
　celiac, 669
　of lens, 1114
　optic, 1122
　thoracic, 655
　thyroid, 646
　vertebra, 131
Axis-cylinders, 931
Axon of nerve cell, 931
Azygos arteries of vagina, 688
　artery, articular, 705
　uvulæ muscle, 1246

Azygos, vein, 749

B

Back, bones of, surface markings
　of, 75
　muscles of, 438
　　surface markings of, 76
Baillarger, band of, 887
Ball-and-socket joint, 323
Band, iliotibial, 530
　moderator, 590
　of Giacomini, 906
Bare area of liver, 1260
Bartholin, duct, of, 1241
　glands of, 1323, 1381
Basal ganglia, 898
　lamina, 822
　plate, 822
　ridge, or cingulum of teeth,
　1221
　vein, 734
Base of heart, 584
　of sacrum, 139
　of skull, inferior surface, 159
　　upper surface of, 172
Basihyal of hyoid bone, 185
Basilar artery, 645
　crest, 1147
　membrane, 1148
　part of occipital bone, 189
　plexus of veins, 740
　sinus, 740
Basilic vein, 743
　median, 744
Basion, 162
Basis cerebri, 882
　cordis, 584
　ossis sacri, 139
　pedunculi, 870
　prostratæ, 1365
　pulmonis, 1197
Basivertebral veins, 750
Basket cells of cerebellum, 865
Bechterew, nucleus of, 861
Bed of stomach, 1273
Bell, nerve of, 1010
Bellini, duct of, 1335
Bertin, ligament of, 376
Betz, giant cells of, 889
Biceps brachii muscle, 497
　femoris muscle, 541
　flexor cubiti muscle, 497
Bicipital fascia, 498
　groove, 236
　ridges, 236
Bicuspid teeth, 1222
　valve, 590
Bigelow, Y-shaped ligament of,
　375
Bile capillaries, 1304
　ducts, 1304, 1305
　lymphatic capillaries in, 779
　structure of, 1306
Bipolar cells of retina, 1110
Biventer cervicis muscle, 443
Bladder, 1339
　gall, 1305
　urinary, 1339
　　abnormalities of, 1345
　　development of, 1345
　　distended, 1339, 1341
　　empty, 1339, 1340
　　female, 1342
　　in child, 1342
　　interior of, 1344
　　ligaments of, 1343
　　lymphatic vessels of, 805
　　structure of, 1344
　　trigone of, 1344
　　vessels and nerves of, 1345
Blandin, glands of, 1237
Blastocyst, 29

Blastopore, 34
Blood, composition of, 769
  corpuscles, 769
  course of, in adult, 577
    in fetus, 577
  islands, 52, 604
  plasma, 769
  platelets, 770
Body or Bodies anococcygeal, 1291
  aortic, 941
  cavities, development of, 37
  ciliary, 1104
  coccygeal, 1403
  geniculate, 877
  Malpighian, of kidney, 1334
    of penis, 1360
    of spleen, 1360
    of stomach, 1273
    of uterus, 1373
    of vertebra, 126
  olivary, 848
  perineal, 477, 1291
  pineal, 878
  pituitary, 1395
  polar, 25
  quadrigeminal, 869
  restiform, 864
  thyroid, 1391
  trapezoid, 863
Body stalk, 32, 36, 53
Bone or Bones, ankle, 294
  arm, 235
  astragalus, 294
  atlas, 129
  axis, 131
  bloodvessels of, 312
  breast, 149
  calcaneus, 289
  calf, 287
  canaliculi of, 314
  cancellous tissue of, 310
  capitate, 253
  carpal, 248
  cells, 314
  chemical composition of, 314
  clavicle, 227
  coccyx, 141
  collar, 227
  compact tissue of, 310
  cranial, 186
  cuboid, 296
  cuneiform, of carpus, 249
    of tarsus, 297
  development of, 315
  ear, 1136
  elbow, 241
  epistropheus, 131
  ethmoid, 209
  facial, 216
  femur, 269
  fibula, 287
  finger, 256
  foot, 289
  frontal, 193
  formation of, 310
  hamate, 254
  Haversian canals of, 313
    systems of, 312
  hip, 258
  humerus, 235
  hyoid, 185
  ilium, 258
  incus, 1137
  inferior maxillary, 179
    nasal conchæ, 225
  innominate, 258
  intracartilaginous, 315
  intramembranous, 315
  ischium, 261
  lacrimal, 220
    lesser, 220
  lacunæ of, 314

Bone, lamellæ of, 313
  lingual, 185
  lower extremity, 258
    jaw, 179
  lunate, 249
  lymphatics of. 312
  malar, 220
  malleus, 1136
  mandible, 179
  marrow of, 311
  maxillæ, 214
  medullary artery of, 312
    membrane of, 310
  metacarpal, 254
  metatarsal, 299
  minute anatomy of, 312
  multangular, greater, 252
    lesser, 252
  nasal, 213
  navicular, of carpus, 249
    of tarsus, 297
  nerves of, 312
  nutrient artery of, 312
  occipital, 186
    of hand, 248
  os calcis, 289
    coxæ, 258
    magnum, 253
  ossification of, 315
  palate, 222
  palatine, 222
  parietal, 190
  patella, 282
  pelvic, 265
  periosteum of, 310
    lymphatic capillaries in, 775
  phalanges of foot, 302
    of hand, 257
  pisiform, 252
  pubis, 263
  radius, 246
  ribs, 153
  sacrum, 137
  scaphoid, of foot, 297
    of hand, 249
  scapula, 230
  semilunar, 249
  sesamoid, 304
  shin, 282
  sphenoid, 222
  sphenoidal conchæ, 208
  stapes, 1137
  sternum, 149
  structure and physical proper-
    ties of, 310
  subperiosteal, 315
  sutural, 213
  talus, 294
  tarsal, 289
  temporal, 195
  thigh, 269
  tibia, 282
  trapezoid, 252
  triangular, 250
  turbinated, 225
  ulna, 241
  unciform, 254
  upper extremity, 227
    jaw, 214
  veins of, 312
  vertebra prominens, 132
  vertebræ, cervical, 128
    coccygeal, 137
    lumbar, 135
    sacral, 137
    thoracic, 132
  vessels of, 312
  vomer, 226
  Wormian, 213
  zygomatic, 220
Bony landmarks of abdomen, 83
  of back, 75
  of lower extremity, 110

Bony landmarks, of upper extremity, 100
Bowman, capsule of, 1334, 1335
  membrane of, 1103
Brachia or Brachium conjunctiva
  of cerebellum, 865
  of corpora quadrigemina, 870
  pontis, 865
Brachial artery, 656
  surface marking of, 108
  cutaneous nerve, lateral, 1030
    medial, 1020
    posterior, 1020
  fascia, 496
  plexus, 1011
  veins, 745
Brachialis anticus muscle, 498
Brachiocephalic artery, 617
  veins, 746
Brachioradialis muscle, 505
Brain, arteries of, 640
  commissures of, 832, 878, 907
  development of, 825
  divisions of, 825
  dura of, 924
  meninges of, 924
  pathways from, to spinal cord, 858
  pia of, 926
  sensory pathways from spinal
    cord to, 856
  surface markings of, 68
  veins of, 733
  ventricles of, 899
Branchial arches, 39
  development of, 40
  grooves, 39
Breast bone, 149
Breasts or mammæ, 1381
  development of, 1382
Bregma, 158
Bregmatic fontanelle, 177
Bridge of nose, 1169
Brim of pelvis, 265
Broad ligaments of uterus, 1266, 1373
Broca, area, 891
  diagonal band of, 905, 911
  gyrus of, 885
Broedel's line, 1336
Bronchi, 1188
  divisions of, 1199
  eparterial, 1189
  hyparterial, 1189
  intrapulmonary, 1202
  left, 1189, 1199, 1201
  lymphatic capillaries in, 778
  right, 1189, 1201
  segmental, 1200
Bronchial arteries, 666, 1204
  nerves, 993
  veins, 749, 1204
Bronchomediastinal lymphatic
  trunks, 784
Bronchopulmonary segments, 1200
Bronchus dexter, 1189
  sinister, 1189
Brunner's glands, 1282
Buccæ, 1218
Buccal artery, 630
  branches of facial nerve, 980
  cavity, 1215
  fat pad, 422
  glands, 1218
  long nerve, 969
  nerve, 969
Buccinator artery, 630
  muscle, 420
  nerve, 969
Bucco-nasal membrane, 44
Buccopharyngeal fascia, 422, 428
  fat pad, 428

Buccopharyngeal, membrane, 44
Buck's fascia, 1362
Bulb, eye, 1095
  hair, 1159
  internal jugular vein, 729
  olfactory, 907
  of posterior cornu, 900
  spinal, 847
  urethral, 1363
  vaginal, 1381
  of vestibule, 1381
Bulbar arteries, 645
Bulbocavernosus muscle, 479
Bulbourethral glands of Cowper,
  1323, 1367
Bulboventricular loop, 572
  sulcus, 572
Bulbus cordis, 572
  oculi, 1095
  olfactorius, 904
  urethræ, 1363
  vestibuli, 1381
Bulla ethmoidalis, 177, 1172
Bundle of His, 596
  medial forebrain, 880
  of Vicq d'Azyr, 876
  oval, 826
Burdach, tract of, 843
Burns' space, 430
Bursa, omental, 1266
  development of, 1214
  pharyngeal, 1249
  prepatellar, 533
Bursæ, 326, 409
  beneath glutæus maximus, 537
  near knee-joint, 386
  shoulder-joint, 358
  synovial, 326

C

Calamus scriptorius, 853, 869
Calcaneal arteries, 711
  lateral, 711
  medial, 711
  sulcus, 292
  tuberosity, 292
Calcaneo-astragaloid articulation,
  393
  ligaments, 393
Calcaneo-cuboid ligaments, 396
  surface anatomy of, 115
Calcaneo-navicular ligaments,
  397
Calcaneo-tibial ligament, 391
Calcaneus, 289
Calvar avis, 883
Calcarine arteries, 646
  fissure, 883
Calf bone, 287
Calleja, islands of, 908
Callosal convolution, 905
  fissure, 905
Calyces, renal, 1334, 1337
Camper, fascia of, 453
Canal or Canals, adductor, 695
  Alcock's, 475, 1056
  alimentary, 1207
  alveolar, 165, 215
  anal, 1290
  atrial, 572
  auditory, external, 1126
  carotid, 162, 200
  central, of spinalis cord, 842
  cervical of uterus, 1375
  condyloid, 175, 188
  craniopharyngeal, 209
  ethmoidal, 194, 211
  femoral, 696
  Haversian, of bone, 313
  Hunter's, 695, 698
  hypoglossal, 188
  incisive, 159, 219

Canal, inguinal, 466, 1342
  lacrimal, 1122
  mandibular, 181
  nasolacrimal, 177
  neural, 35
  neurenteric, 35
  of Huguier, 197, 987, 1131
  of Nuck, 1322, 1376
  of Petit, 1113
  of Schlemm, 1099
  pharyngeal, 159, 166
  pterygoid, 159, 166
  pterygopalatine, 166, 215, 223
  sacral, 141
  semicircular, 1141
    membranous, 1144
  spermatic, 466
  spiral, of modiolus, 1143
  vertebral, 141, 147
Canaliculi of bone, 314
  dental, 1224
Canaliculus, inferior tympanic,
  162, 201
  innominatus of Arnold, 206
  mastoid, 162
Canalis centralis cochleæ, 200
  cervicis uteri, 1375
  reuniens [of Hensen], 1144, 1146
  semicircularis lateralis, 1141
    posterior, 1141
    superior, 1141
Cancellous tissue of bone, 314
Canine eminence, 214
  fossa, 214
  teeth, 1222
Caninus muscle, 418
Canthi of eyelids, 1118
Capillaries, 767
  bile, 1304
  lymphatic, 775
  structure of, 767
Capitate bone, 253
Capitulum, humeri, 239
  mallei, 1136
  stapedis, 1137
Capsula articularis, See Individual joints.
  externa, 899
  extrema, 899
  interna, 899
  lentis, 1113
  vasculosa lentis, 1097
Capsular artery, middle, 682
Capsule, adipose, of kidney, 1332
  adrenal, 1400
  external, 899
  internal, 899
  lens, 1113
  of Bowman, 1334, 1335
  of Glisson, 1368, 1301
  of Tenon, 1117
Caput cæcum coli, 1284
  femoris, 269
  fibulæ, 287
  humeri, 235
  pancreatis, 1308
  tali, 296
Cardiac ganglion of Wrisberg,
  1084
  glands of stomach, 1277
  muscular tissue, 597
  nerves, cervical, 991
    from sympathetic, 1072
    from vagus, 991
    thoracic, 991
  notch, 1199
  orifice of stomach, 1272
  plexus of nerves, 1083
  veins, 724
Cardinal veins, 718
Carotico-clinoid foramen, 174,
  208
  ligament, 209

Caroticotympanic artery, 633
  nerve, 1068
Carotid arch, 605
  development of, 605
  artery, common, 618
    external, 619
      surface markings, 71
    internal, 631
      x-ray of, 67
  body, 940
  canal, 162, 200
  ganglion, 981
  groove, 174
  nerve, internal, 1067
  nerves from glossopharyngeal,
    984
  plexus, 1067
  sheath, 431
  sinus, 631, 941
  triangles, 71, 619
Carpal arteries from radial, 661
  from ulnar, 662
  bones, 248
  net-work, 661
Carpometacarpal articulations,
  371
Carpus, 248
  articulations of, 369
  ossification of, 258
  surface form of, 115
Cartilage or Cartilages, articular,
  306
  arytenoid, 1178
  auricula, 1126
  corniculate, 1179
  costal, 157, 308
  cricoid, 70, 1177
  cuneiform, 1179
  epiglottic, 1179
  epiphyseal, 315
  ethmovomerine, 227
  hyaline, 306
  intrathyroid, 1177
  lacunæ, 307
  laryngeal, 1176
  lateral nasal, 1170
  Meckel's, 40, 182
  of nose, 1169
  of Santorini, 1179
  of Wrisberg, 1179
  pinna, 1127
  septum of nose, 1170
  sesamoid, 1170
  temporary, 315
  tracheal, 1190
  thyroid, 1176
  vomeronasal, 1172
  white fibro-, 306, 308
Cartilagines alares minores, 1170
Cartilago alaris major, 1170
  crus laterale, 1170
    mediale, 1170
  auriculæ, 1126
  cricoidea, 1177
  epiglottica, 1179
  nasi lateralis, 1170
  septi nasi, 1170
  thyreoidea, 1176
  triticea, 1180
Caruncula lacrimalis, 1121
Carunculæ hymenales, 1381
Cauda equina, 838
  helicis, 1127
  pancreatis, 1309
Caudate lobe of liver, 1298, 1300
  nucleus, 898
  process of liver, 1298
Cavernous arteries, 634
  nerves of penis, 1087
  plexus, 1068
  portion of urethra, 1347
  sinuses, 739
  nerves in, 1068

Cavernous. spaces of penis, 1362
Cavity or Cavities, body or celom, 37
  buccal, 1216
  cotyloid, 264
  glenoid, 234
  of lesser pelvis, 266
  mediastinal, 1194
  nasal, 175, 1170
  mouth proper, 1216
  oral, 1216
  pericardial, 581
  peritoneal, 1258
  pleural, 1191
  of septum pellucidum, 907
  sigmoid, of radius, 247
    of ulna, 244
  subarachnoid, 928
  subdural, 925
  thorax, 1194
  tympanic, 1130
    mucous membranes of, 1138
  uterus, 1374
Cavum conchæ, 1126
  laryngis, 1181
  Meckelii, 960
  nasi, 175,
  oris, 1216
    proprium, 1216
  Retzii, 1341
  subarachnoidea, 927
  tympani, paries carotica, 1133
    labyrinthica, 1133
    mastoidea, 1133
  tympanum, 1130
    paries jugularis, 1130
    membranacea, 1130
    tegmentalis, 1130
  uteri, 1374
Cecal arteries, 679
  fossæ, 1271
Cecum, 1284
  lymphatic vessels of, 804
Celiac artery, 669
  axis, 669
  branches of vagus nerve, 994
  ganglion, 1084
  plexus, 1084
Cell or Cells, animal, 21
  basket, of cerebellum, 865
  Betz, 887
  bone, 314
  centroaciner, 1311
  chromaffin, 1401
  definition of, 21
  division of, 21, 22
    by mitosis, 23
  enamel, 1227
  fat, 306
  fundus glands, 1276
  germ, 22
  giant, 314
    of Betz, 887
  Golgi, 887
  gustatory, 1094
  mass, inner, 22
  membrane, 21
  mitral, 907
  nerve, 930
  nucleus of, 21
  of Claudius, 1150
  of Deiters, 1150
  of Hensen, 1150
  of Paneth, 1282
  olfactory, 1094
  Purkinje, 865
  Sertoli, 1355
  sheath, 825
  spinal ganglion, 931
  reproduction of, 21
  structure of, 21
  tufted, 907
Cellulæ ethmoidales, 1175

Celom, 35, 37
Cement of teeth, 1224
  formation of, 1228
Centers of ossification, 315
  visual, 912
Central artery of retina, 636, 1098
  canal of medulla spinalis, 842
  cells of fundus glands, 1276
  fissure, 883
  gray stratum of cerebral aqueduct, 870
  lobe, 887
  nervous system, 821, 826
  sulcus, 883
  tendinous point of perineum, 477
  tendon of diaphragm, 450
Centroacinar cells of Langerhans, 1311
Centrosome, 21
Cephalic flexure of embryonic brain, 825
  portion of sympathetic system, 1067
  veins, 742
    accessory, 742
Ceratohyal of hoid bone, 186
Cerebellar arteries, 646
  peduncles, 865
  tract, of Flechsig, 844
  veins, 735
Cerebellum, 863
  brachia conjunctiva, 865
  pontis, 865
  development of, 828
  fibræ propriæ, 865
  gray substance of, 865
  lobes of, 863
  nucleus dentatus, 867
  peduncles of, 864
  structure of, 865
  vermis of, 863
  white substance of, 864
Cerebral aqueduct, 881
  arteries, anterior, 637
    middle, 638
    posterior, 645
  cortex, nerve cells of, 887
    fibers of, 887
    structure of, 887
    types of, 887
  fissure, lateral, 882
  hemispheres, 881
    borders of, 882
    cingulum of, 895
    fibers of, association, 895
      commissural, 892
      projection, 892
      transverse, 892
    fissures of, 882
    gray substance of, 882
    gyri of, 883
    lobes of, 883
    poles of, 882
    structure of, 887
    sulci of, 882, 883
    surfaces of, 882
    white substance of, 892
  nerves, 951. See Cranial nerves.
  peduncles, 828
  veins, 735
  ventricles, 867, 881, 899
Cerebrospinal fasciculus, 846
  fibers of internal capsule, 899
  fluid, 928
  nerves, structure of, 930
Ceruminous glands, 1130
Cervical artery, ascending, 647
  deep, 652
  superficial, 648
  transverse, 652
  branch of cardiac nerves, 991
  of facial nerve, 981

Cervical, enlargement of spinal cord, 837
  fascia, 426
  ganglia, 1070, 1071
  lymph nodes, 789
  muscles, lateral, 432
  nerve, cutaneous or transverse, 1008
  nerves, 1001, 1005
    divisions of, anterior, 1005
      posterior, 1008
  pleura, 1191
  plexus, 1005
    branches of, 1006
  portion of sympathetic, 1070
  rib, 132, 158
  veins, 728
  vertebræ, 128
Cervicalis ascendens muscle, 442
Cervix uteri, 1399
  portic supravaginalis, 1399
    vaginalis, 1400
  of uterus, 1399
Chambers of eye, 1106
Chassaignac's tubercle, 70
Check ligaments, 335
  of eye, 1117
Cheeks, 1218
Chest, 147
Chiasma, optic, 879
Chiasmatic groove, 174, 204
Choanæ, 44, 159, 175, 177, 1172
Chondrin, 310
Chondrocranium, 122
Chondroepitrochearis muscle, 491
Chrondroglossus muscle, 1235
Chondromucoid, 310
Chondrosternal ligament, 341
  intra-articular, 342
Chondroxiphoid ligaments, 343
Chorda obliqua, 364
  tympani nerve, 972
Chordæ tendineæ, 589
  Willisi, 735
Chorioidea, 1103
  lamina choriocapillaris, 1104
  vasculosa, 1104
Chorion, 30
  development of, 47
  frondosum, 49
  læve, 49
Chorionic villi, 48
Choroid artery, 639
  coat of eyeball, 1103
Choroid fissure, 831, 904
  plexuses of fourth ventricle, 867
    of lateral ventricle, 903
    of third ventricle, 882
    development, 829
Choroidal artery, anterior, 639
  posterior, 646
  fissure, eye, 1097
Chromaffin cells, 1401
Chromaphil and cortical systems, 1397
  development of, 1397
Chromatolysis, 943
Chromosomes, 21, 25
Chyle, 775
Chyliferous vessels, 775
Cilia, 1118
Ciliaris muscle, 1104
Ciliary arteries, 637
  body, 1104
  ganglion, 958
  glands, 1118
  muscle, 1104
  nerves, 959
  processes, 1104
Cingulate gyrus, 844
  sulcus, 883
Cingulum of cerebral hemisphere, 895

Cingulum of teeth, 1221
Circle, arterial, of Willis, 640
Circular folds of small intestine, 1280
  sinus, 740
  sulcus, 883
Circulation, beginning of, 576
  in fetus, 577
  of blood in adult, 567
Circulus arteriosus major, 637
  minor, 637
  venosus [mammæ], 1385
Circumduction, 325
Circumferential fibrocartilage, 309
Circumflex arteries, femoral, 702
  humeral, 656
  iliac, 695, 699
  nerve, 1018
Circumvallate papillæ, 1232
Cisterna basalis, 928
  cerebellomedullaris, 927
  chiasmatis, 927
  chyli, 784
  fossæ cerebri lateralis, 927
  interpeduncularis, 927
  magna, 928
  pontis, 927
  venæ magnæ cerebri, 927
Cisternæ, subarachnoid, 928
Clarke's column, 841, 844
Claudius, cells of, 1150
Claustrum, 899
Clava, 849
Clavicle, 227
  ossification of, 229
  pecularīties of, in sexes, 229
  structure of, 229
  surface anatomy of, 100
Clavipectoral fascia, 487
Cleavage lines, skin, 1158
Cleft palate, 179
Cleidohyoideus muscle, 434
Clinging fibers of cerebellum, 867
Clinoid processes, anterior, 174, 207
  middle, 174, 204
  posterior, 174, 204
Clitoris, 1380
  frenulum of, 1380
  glans of, 1380
  nerves of, 1057
  prepuce of, 1380
Clivus of sphenoid, 205
Cloaca, ectodermal, 1215
  entodermal, 1215
  pelvic portion of, 1323
  phallic portion of, 1323
  vesicourethral portion of, 1323
Cloacal duct, 1215
  membrane, 1215
  tubercle, 1324
Cloquet, lymph nodes of, 795
Clunial nerves, 1004
Coccygeal arteries, 692
  body, 1403
  cornua, 143
  gland, 1403
  nerve, division, of anterior, 1057
    posterior, 1004
  plexus, 1057
  vertebræ, 126
Coccygeus muscle, 470
Coccyx, 126, 141
  ossification of, 145
Cochlea, 1142
  aqueduct of, 200
  cupula of, 1142
  hamulus laminæ spiralis, 1143
  helicotrema of, 1142, 1143
  lamina spiralis ossea, 1143
  modiolus of, 1142

Cochlea, scalæ of, 1143
  spiral canal of, 1143
    lamina of, 1143
  vessels of, 1151
Cochlear artery, 1151
  nerve, 917, 981, 1151
  nuclei, 918
  root of acoustic nerve, 981
Cochleariform process, 202, 1135
Cog-tooth of malleus, 1136
Colic arteries of ileocolic, 679
  left, 681
  middle, 680
  right, 679
  flexures, right and left, 1284
  impression, 1296
  valve, 1285
Collar bone, 227
Collateral circulation, 603
  fissure, 883
  ganglia, 1065
Collecting tubes of kidney, 1335
Colles, fascia of, 262, 454, 478, 1362
Colliculus of arytenoid cartilage, 1206
  facialis, 869
  inferior, 873
  nervi optici, 1109
  superior, 872
Collum anatomicum humeri, 236
  femoris, 270
  mallei, 1136
  tali, 296
Coloboma, 1097
Colon, 1287
  ascending, 1287
  descending, 1287
  iliac, 1288
  left or splenic flexure of, 1287
  pelvic, 1288
  right or hepatic flexure of, 1287
  sigmoid, 1288
  structure of, 1291
  surface, anatomy of, 92
  transverse, 1287
  tunica mucosa, 1291
    muscularis, 1291
    serosa, 1292
  vessels and nerves of, 1293
Colored lines of Retzius, 1224
  or red corpuscles, 769
Colorless corpuscles, 768
Colostrum, 1383
  corpuscles, 1384
Columella, 43
Cclumna or *Columnæ carneæ*, 589
  nasi, 1168
  of Clarke, 841
  of fornix, 907
  of spinal cord, 839
    anterior, 841
    dorsal, 841
    lateral, 842
    posterior, 841
    ventral, 841
  of vagina, 1379
  rectal, or Morgagni, 1291
  renal, 1334
  vertebral, 126
Comma-shaped fasciculus, 844
Commissura labiorum anterior, 1380
  palpebrarum lateralis, 1118
    medialis, 1118
Commissural fibers of cerebral hemispheres, 892
Commissure of brain, anterior, 832, 907
  posterior, 878
  habenular, 878
  hippocampal, 905
  of corpus callosum, 832

Commissure of labia majora, 1380
  of spinal cord, 839
  palpebral, 1118
Common bile duct, 1304, 1306
  lymphatics of, 805
  carotid artery, 618
  dental germ, 1226
  iliac arteries, 684
    lymph nodes, 797
    veins, 758
  interosseous artery, 664
  ligament, 326
  peroneal nerve 1047
Communicans fibularis nerve, 1053
  tibialis nerve, 1051
Communicantes cervicales nerves, 1009
  rami, 1000, 1065
Communicating artery, anterior, 637
  from doralis pedis, 709
  posterior, 639
Compact tissue of bone, 310
Comparison of bones of hand and foot, 303
Complexus muscle, 443
Composition and central connections of cranial nerves, 910
  of spinal nerves, 921
Compressor naris muscle, 417
Concha (conchæ) of auricula, 1126
  nasal, inferior, 225
    middle, 212
    superior, 212
  sphenoidal, 208
Conchal crest, 215, 223
Condyle (condyles) of mandible, 182
  occipital, 188
  of femur, 274
  of tibia, 283, 284
Condyloid articulation, 323
  canal, 175, 188
  foramen, anterior, 188
  fossa, 162, 188
  process of mandible, 182
Cones of retina, 1111
Confluence of sinuses, 188, 739
Coni vasculosi, 1355
Conjoined tendon of internal oblique and transversus muscles, 460
Conjugate diameter of pelvis, 266
Conjunctiva, 1119
  bulbar portion, 1120
  caruncle lacrimal, 1121
  fornix, 1120
  lacus lacrimalis, 1121
  palpebral portion, 1119
  plica semilunaris, 1120
Connective tissues, 305
  extraperitoneal, 467
Conoid ligament, 354
  tubercle, 228
Constriction, duodenopyloric, 1273
Constrictor *pharyngis inferior* muscle, 1249
  medius muscle, 1249
  superior muscle, 1249
  urethræ muscles, 480, 482
Conus arteriosus, 588
  elasticus [larynx], 1181
  medullaris, 836
Convoluted tubes of kidney, 1335
Convolutions of brain, 882
Cooper, ligament of, 458, 1382
Copula, 1209
Cor, 583
Coracoacromial ligament, 358
Coracobrachialis muscle, 496

Coracoclavicular fascia, 488
  ligament, 354
Coracohumeral ligament, 358
Coracoid process, 234
  tuberosity, 228
Cord, gangliated, 1065
  spermatic, 1351
  spinal, 826
  umbilical, 53
  vocal, 1182
Corium or cutis vera, 1155
  layers of, 1156
  stratum papillare, 1156
    reticulare, 1156
Cornea, 1099, 1102
  structure of, 1102
Corneal corpuscles, 1103
  endothelium, 1103
  epithelium, 1103
  spaces, 1103
Corniculate cartilages, 1179
Cornu or Cornua, ammonis, 906
  anterius, 841, 900
  inferior, 900
  lateralis, 842
  majora [os hyoidei], 185
  minora [os hyoidei], 186
  of coccyx, 143
  of hyoid bone, 185
  of lateral ventricles, 900
  of sacrum, 138
  of spinal cord, 841
  of thyroid cartilage, 1176, 1177
  posterius, 841, 900
Corona glandis, 1363
  radiata [brain], 893
  [ovum], 24
Coronal suture, 158, 163
Coronary arteries, 615
  of stomach, 672
  artery of heart, 615
  ligament of liver, 1301
  of knee, 384
  plexuses, 1084
  sinus, 574, 724
  opening of, 587
  sulcus of heart, 583
  veins of heart, 724
  of stomach, 764
Coronoid fossa, 239
  process of mandible, 182
  of ulna, 241
Corpora cavernosa, penis, 1324, 1362
  bulbs of, 1363
  crura of, 1362
  mammillaria, 878
  quadrigemina, 828, 869
    brachia of, 870
    structure of, 870
Corpus Arantii, 590
  amygdaloideum, 899
  callosum, 892
    development of, 832
    genu of, 892
    rostrum of, 892
    splenium of, 892
  cavernosum, artery to, 691
    urethræ, 1362, 1363
  ciliare, 1104
  femoris, 273
  fibulæ, 287
  geniculatum laterale, 877
    mediale, 877
  Highmori, 1354
  humeri, 236
  incudis, 1137
  luteum, 1370
  luysii, 878
  maxillæ, 214
  medullare, 864
  ossis hyoidei, 185
    ilii, 258

Corpus ossis ischii, 261
    pubis, 263
  pancreatis, 1309
  papillare [corium], 1155
  penis, 1362
  pineale, 878
  radii, 246
  sphenoidale, 204
  spongiosum, 1363
  sterni, 152
  striatum, 898
  tali, 295
  tibiæ, 284
  trapezoideum, 863
  ulnæ, 244
  uteri, 1373
  vertebræ, 127
  vitreum, 1112
Corpuscles, blood, 769
  genital, 939
  Golgi and Mazzoni, 939
  Grandry, 939
  granular, 315
  Hassall, 817
  Herbst, 939
  Pacinian, 939
  renal, 1334
  Ruffini, 939
  tactile, 939
  Wagner and Meissner, 939
Corrugator cutis ani muscle, 482
  supercilii muscle, 417
Cortex of cerebellum, 865
  of cerebrum, 888
  of kidney, 1334
  of lymph nodes, 781
  of suprarenal, 1401
Corti, ganglion of, 1140, 1151
Cortical arches of kidney, 1334
  arterial system of brain, 640
  portion of suprarenal gland, 1401
  substance of kidney, 1334
  of lens, 1114
Costæ, 153
Costal cartilages, 157, 1309
  element or process, 129
  groove, 154
  pleura, 1191
  tuberosity, 229
Costocentral articulation, 337
Costocervical trunk, 652
Costochondral articulations, 343
Costocoracoid ligament, 491
  membrane, 491
Costocoracoideus muscle, 491
Costomediastinal sinus, 79, 1193
Costosternal articulations, 341
Costotransverse articulations, 340
  ligaments, 340
Costovertebral articulations, 337
  ligament, anterior, 340
Costoxiphoid ligament, 343
Cotyledons, 52
Cotyloid cavity, 264
  ligament, 264
Cowper's glands, 1323, 1367
Coxal articulation, 374
  movements of, 379
  muscles in relation to, 379
Cranial arachnoid, 927
  bones, 186
  dura mater, 925
  fossa, anterior, 172
    middle, 173
    posterior, 175
  nerves, 834
    abducent, 973
    accessory, 994
    acoustic, 981
    composition and central con-
      nections of, 910
    development of, 834

Cranial nerves, eighth, 917
  eleventh, 994
  facial, 974
  fifth, 915, 986
  first, 910
  fourth, 960
  glossopharyngeal, 981
  hypoglossal, 921, 995
  ninth, 919
  oculomotor, 957
  olfactory, 955
  optic, 956
  outline of, 952, 953
  second, 956
  seventh, 916, 974
  sixth, 916
  tenth, 920, 986
  third, 957
  trigeminal, 960
  trochlear, 960
  twelfth, 995
  vagus, 986
  parasympathic nerves, 1061
  pia mater, 926
  sympathetics, 1067
Cranium, 61, 158
  bones of, 61, 186
  development of, 122
  membranous, 122
Cremaster muscle, 459, 1350
Cremasteric artery, 694
  fascia, 459
Crescents of Gianuzzi, 1241
Crest or Crests, basilar, 1147
  conchal, 215, 223
  ethmoidal, 217, 224
  frontal, 194
  iliac, 259
  incisor, 219
  infratemporal, 163, 206
  internal occipital, 175, 188
  intertrochanteric, 271
  lacrimal, 218, 220
  nasal, 219, 223
  neural, 35, 824, 833
  obturator, 263
  pubic, 263
  right atrial, 586
  sphenoidal, 205
  supramastoid, 196
  terminal, 586
  tibial, 284
  of tubercles of humerus, 236
  urethral, in female, 1348
    in male, 1346
Cribriform fascia, 528
  plate of ethmoid, 209
Cricoarytænoideus lateralis
    muscle, 1185
  posterior muscle, 1185
Cricoarytenoid ligament, 1181
Cricoid cartilage, 1177
Cricothyreoideus muscle, 1185
Cricothyroid artery, 621
  ligament, middle, 1181
  membrane, 1181
Cricotracheal ligament, 1180
Crista arcuata [arytehoid car-
    tilage], 1178
  colli costæ, 153
  falciformis, 200
  galli, 210
  supraventricularis, 590
  terminalis, 586
  vestibuli, 1140
Crossed pyramidal tract, 846
Crown of a tooth, 1220
Crucial anastomosis, 702
  ligaments, 383
Cruciate crural ligament, 551
  eminence of occipital bone, 188
  ligament of atlas, 333
  of knee, 383

Crura of diaphragm, 450
  of fornix, 907
  of penis, 1362
  of stapes, 1137
  of subcutaneous inguinal ring, 456
Crural arch, deep, 466, 695
  fascia, 543
  ligament, transverse, 554
  nerve, anterior, 1042
  septum, 696
  sheath, 695
Crureus muscle, 533
Crus, cerebri, 870
  commune [semicircular canals], 1141
  fornicis, 907
Crusta or pes of cerebral peduncle, 870
  petrosa of teeth, 1225
    formation of, 1228
Cruveilhier, glenoid ligaments of 373, 401
  fascia, 472
Crypts of Lieberkühn, 1282
Crystalline lens, 1113
  cortical substance of, 1114
  development of, 1097
  nucleus of, 1114
Cuboid bone, 296
Cuboideonavicular articulation, 399
Cul de sac of Douglas, 1260, 1376
Cumulus oöphorus, 24
Cuneate nucleus, 851
  tubercle, 849
Cuneiform bone of carpus, 251
  of tarsus, first, 297
    second, 298
    third, 298
  cartilages, 1179
  tubercle, 1182
Cuneocuboid articulation, 399
Cuneonavicular articulation, 398
Cuneus, 885
Cup, optic, 1097
Cupula of cochlea, 1142
  of pleura, 1191
Curvatura ventriculi major, 1273
  minor, 1273
Curvatures of stomach, 1273
Curved lines of ilium, 259
Curves of vertebral column, 145
Cushion of auditory tube, 1249
  of epiglottis, 1179
Cushions, endocardial, 575
Cusps of bicuspid valve, 592
  of tricuspid valve, 589
Cuspus dorsales, 589
  septalis, 589
  ventrales, 589
Cutaneous cervical nerve, 1008
  nerve, external, 1040
    internal, 1020, 1043
    lesser, 1020
    middle, 1042
  nerves, of abdomen, 1037
    of back, 998
    of face, 974
    of foot, 1052
    of lower limb, 1040
    of neck, 1006, 1008
    of thorax, 1034
    of upper limb, 1030
Cuticle, 1153, 1161
Cuticula dentis, 1228
Cutis plate, 119
  vera or corium, 1155
Cutting teeth, 1221
Cuvier, ducts of, 718
Cymba conchæ, 1126
Cystic artery, 674
  duct, 1306

Cystic, vein, 765
Cytoplasm, 21
Cytotrophoblast, 46

D

DACRYON, 170
Dartos tunic, 1350
Darwin, auricular tubercle of, 1126
Decidua, 50
  basalis, 50
  capsularis, 50
  development of, 50
  parietalis, 50
  placentalis, 50
  stratum compactum of, 51
    spongiosum of, 51
  vera, 50
Deciduous teeth, development 1223
Decussation of brachium conjunctiva, 874
  of lemniscus, 856
  of optic nerves, 957
  pyramidal, 847
  sensory, 856
Deep abdominal ring, 470
  artery of penis, 689, 691
  auricular artery, 629
  cerebral veins, 733
  cervical artery, 652
    fascia, 426
    lymph nodes, 789
    vein, 731
  crural arch, 466, 695
  epigastric artery, 694
    vein, 756
  external pudendal artery, 700
    fascia, 407
  femoral artery, 702
  iliac circumflex artery, 702
    vein, 756
  lingual artery, 622
  muscles of back, 438
  palmar arch, 662
  peroneal nerve, 1053
  petrosal nerve, 977
  plantar artery, 709
  Sylvian vein, 734
  temporal arteries, 630
    nerves, 969
  transverse fascia of leg, 543, 546
Degeneration, Wallerian, 943
Degenerative changes in nerve tissue, 932
Deglutition, 1245
Deiters, cells of, 1150
  nucleus of, 860
Deltoid ligament, 391
  tuberosity, 237
Deltoideus muscle, 493
Demilunes of Heidenhain, 1241
Demours, membrane of, 1103
Dendrites, 930
Dendrons, 930
  of nerve cells, 930
Dens, or *Dentes*, 1220
  canini, 1222
  decidui, 1223
  incisivi, 1222
  molares, 1222
  odontoid process of axis, 131
  permanentes, 1221
  præmolares, 1222
  serotinus, 1222
Dental artery, inferior, 630
  posterior, 630
  canaliculi, 1224
  formulæ, 1220
  furrow, 1226
  germs, 1226
  lamina, 1226

Dental nerve, inferior, 972
  pulp, 1223
  sac, 1228
Dentate fascia, 906
  gyrus, 906
  ligament, 927
Denticulate ligament, 927
Dentin, 1224
  formation of, 1228
  intertubular, 1224
  secondary, 1225
Dentinal canaliculi, 1224
  fibers, 1224
  matrix, 1224
  sheath of Neumann, 1224
  tubules, 1224
Depressor alæ nasi muscle, 418
  anguli oris muscle, 419
  labii inferioris muscle, 419
  septi muscle, 418
Dermic coat of hair follicle, 1160
Dermis, 1155
Descemet, membrane of, 1103
Descendens cervicalis nerve, 1009
  hypoglossi nerve, 996, 1009
Descending aorta, 666
  colon, 1287
  oblique muscle, 454
  palatine artery, 623
  process of lacrimal bone, 220
  ramus of hypoglossal nerve, 996
    of ischium, 262
    of os pubis, 263
Descent of testis, 1320
Detrusor urinæ muscle, 1345
Development of body cavities, 37
  of chorion, 48
  of embryo, 32
  of nervous system, 821
Diagonal band of Broca, 905
Diameters of pelvis, 266, 267
Diaphragm, 449
  lymphatic vessels of, 809
  muscles of, 450
  pelvic, 469
  urogenital, 475
Diaphragma sellæ, 925
Diaphragmatic lymph nodes, 808
  pleura, 1191
Diaphysis, 318
Diarthroses, 322
Diencephalon, 874
  development of, 828, 829
Digastric fossa, 198
  nerve from facial, 979
  triangle, 72
Digastricus muscle, 432
Digestion, organs of, 1207
Digestive apparatus, 1207
  development of, 1207, 1210
  tube, 1207
  surface markings of, 87
Digital arteries of hand, 666
  fossa of epididymis, 1353
  of femur, 270
  nerves of lateral plantar, 1052
    of medial plantar, 1052
    of median, 1023
    of musculocutaneous, 1021
    of ulnar, 1029
    radial, 1031
  veins of foot, 754
    of hand, 742
Digits, articulations of, 374
Dilatator naris anterior muscle, 418
  posterior muscle, 418
  pupillæ muscle, 1107
  tubæ muscle, 1135
Diploic veins, 733
Direct cerebellar fasciculus, 844
  pyramidal tract, 846

Discus articularis, 336
Disk, interpubic, 349
  optic, 1109
Diverticulum ilei, 1280
  Meckel's, 55, 1280
Division of cells, 21
Dorsal aortæ, 609
  artery of penis, 689, 691
  carpal artery, of radial, 661
    of ulnar, 665
  ligament, 514
  fissure of medulla oblongata, 847
  interossei muscles, 524, 559
  interosseous artery, 664
    nerve, 1031
  lamina, 822
  mesogastrium, 1212
  metacarpal arteries, 662
    veins, 742
  nasal artery, 636
  nerve of penis, 1057
  pulmonary nerves, 993
  spinal artery, 645
  veins of penis, 758
  venous arch of foot, 752
    net-work of hand, 742
  vestibular nucleus, 860
Dorsalis hallucis artery, 709
  pedis artery, 708
    branches of, 709
    surface markings of, 118
  scapulæ artery, 655
Dorsoepitrochlearis brachii muscle, 486
Dorsomedian fissure of medulla oblongata, 847
Dorsum ilii, 259
  linguæ, 1231
  nasi, 1169
  of tongue, 1231
  sellæ, 174, 204
Douglas, pouch or Cul de sac of, 1260
Drum, ear, 1130
Duct or Ducts, accessory pancreatic, 1309
  cloacal, 1215
  common bile, 1304, 1306
  cystic, 1303, 1306
  ejaculatory, 1348, 1360
  frontonasal, 177, 195
  hepatic, 1304
  lacrimal, 1121, 1122
  lactiferous, 1384
  liver, 1304
  lymphatic right, 784
  Müllerian, 1316
  nasolacrimal or nasal, 1122
  of Bartholin, 1241
  of Bellini, 1335
  of bulbourethral glands, 1367
  of Cuvier, 718
  of Gärtner, 1369
  of Rivinus, 1240
  of Santorini, 1310
  of Wirsung, 1309
  pancreatic, 1309
  parotid, 1239
  pronephric, 1315
  prostatic, 1346
    orifices of, 1346
  semicircular, 1144
  seminal, 1358
  Skene's, 1323
  Stensen's, 1239
  sublingual, 1240
  submaxillary, 1240
  thoracic, 782
  thyroglossal, 1231, 1391
  vitelline, 36, 1211
  Warton's, 1240
  Wolffian, 1315

Ductless glands, 1391
  chromophil and cortical systems, 1400
  parathyroid, 1394
  pineal body, 878
  suprarenals, 1399
  thyroid, 1391
Ductuli aberrantes [testis], 1358
  efferentes [testis], 1355
  transversi [epoöphoron], 1369
Ductus arteriosus, 579
  choledochus, 1306
  cochlearis, 1146
  deferens, 1358
    ampulla of, 1358
  endolymphaticus, 1140, 1144
  longitudinalis epoophori, 1369
  pancreaticus [Wirsungi], 1309
  utriculosaccularis, 1144
  venosus, 723
    development of, 577
    fossa for, 1299
    obliterated, 762
Duodenal fossæ, 1270
  glands, 1282
  impression, 1296
Duodenojejunal flexure, 1280
  fold, 1270
  fossa, 1270
Duodenomesocolic fold, 1270
Duodenopyloric constriction, 1273
Duodenum, 1278
  lymphatic vessels of, 803
  suspensory ligament, 1279
  muscle of, 1279
  surface anatomy of, 88
  vessels and nerves of, 1280
Dura mater, cranial, 925
  arteries of, 629
  endosteal layer of, 925
  meningeal layer of, 925
  processes of, 925
  veins of, 735
  encephali, 925
  spinal, 925
  spinalis, 925
  venous sinuses of, 735
Dural sinuses, 735

E

Ear, 1122
  auricula of, 1126
  cochlea, 1142
  development of, 1122
  external, 1126
    muscles of, 1127
  internal, or labyrinth, 1139
  meatus acusticus externus, 1126
  membranous labyrinth, 1149
  middle, 1123, 1130
  osseous labyrinth, 1139
  pinna of, 1126
  semicircular canals of, 1149
  surface anatomy of, 66
  tympanic cavity of, 1130
    mucous membrane of, 1138
    muscles of, 1138
    ossicles of, 1136
    vessels and nerves of, 1138
  vestibule of, 1140
Ectoderm, 30
Ectodermal cloaca, 1215
Ectoplasm, 21
Edinger-Westphal nucleus of midbrain, 914
Eighth nerve, 917
Ejaculator urinæ muscle, 479
Ejaculatory ducts, 1348, 1360
Elastic fibrocartilage, 306
  laminæ of cornea, 1103

Elastic membrane of larynx, 1180
Elbow, adult, frontal view, x-ray of, 99
  bone, 241
  of child aged eleven years, frontal view, x-ray of, 101
    ten years, lateral view, x-ray of, 101
Elbow joint, 360
  anastomoses around, 659
  movements of, 363
  surface anatomy of, 102, 106
    markings of, 102, 106
  vessels and nerves of, 363
Eleventh nerve, 920
Ellipsoidea, 323
Embryo, development of, 32
  growth of, 35, 56,
Embryology, 21-58
  allantois, 55
  amnion, 32, 53
Embryonic disk, 32
Eminence, canine, 214
  cruciate, occipital bone, 188
  frontal, 159, 163, 193
  hypothenar, 511
  iliopectineal, 260
  intercondyloid, of tibia, 283
  medial, of rhomboid fossa, 869
  parietal, 158, 163, 192
  pyramidal, of tympanic cavity, 1133
  thenar, 511
Eminentia arcuata, 199
  pyramidalis, 1133
Emissary veins, 740
Enamel cells, 1227
  droplet, 1228
  epithelium, 1227
  fibers or prisms, 1224
  of teeth, 1224
    formation of, 1228
  organ, 1227
Enarthrosis, 324
Encephalon, 828
Endbrain, 828
End-bulbs of Krause, 939
End-plates, motor, of Kühne, 943
Endocardial cushions, 575
Endocardium, 581
  primitive, 568
Endocrine glands, 1391
Endoplasm, 21
Endolymph, 1144
Endomysium, 562
Endoneurium, 936
Endosteal layer of dura mater, 925
Endosteum, 310
Endothelium of blood vessels, 765
  corneal, 1102
  of lymphatic vessels, 669
Enlargements of spinal cord, 837
Ensiform appendix, 152
Entodermal cloaca, 1215
Eosinophil corpuscles, 769
Eparterial bronchus, 1189
Ependymal layer, 821
Epicardium, 579
Epicondyles of femur, 274
  of humerus, 239
Epicranial aponeurosis, 413
Epicranius muscle, 413
Epidermic coat of hair follicle, 1159
Epidermis, development of, 1153
  structure of, 1153
Epididymis, 1353
  appendix of, 1353
Epidural space, 925
Epigastric artery, deep inferior, 694

Epigastric artery, deep inferior, surface markings of, 95
  superficial, 699
  superior, 650
  lymph nodes, 797
  region, 1254
  vein, deep, 756
    inferior, 756
Epiglottis, 1179
  tubercle or cushion of, 1179
Epimysium, 562
Epineurium, 936
Epiotic center of temporal bone, 203
Epiphyses, See Individual bones.
Epiphyseal cartilage, 315
Epiphysis, 878
Epiploic foramen, 1258, 1267
Epistropheus, 131, 144
Epithalamus, 829, 877
  ganglion habenulæ, 878
  pineal body, 878
  posterior commissure, 878
  trigonum habenulæ, 878
Epithelium, enamel, 1255
  germinal, 1319
  stratified of cornea, 1099
Epitrochleoanconæus muscle, 502
Epitympanic recess, 1130
Eponychium, 1158
Epoöphoron, 1317, 1369
Equator of lens, 1114
Erector clitoridis muscle, 481
  penis muscle, 480
  spinæ or *sacrospinalis* muscle, 440
Eruption of teeth, 1229
Esophageal arteries, 647, 667
  glands, 1252
  hiatus in diaphragm, 450
  nerves, 993
  plexus, 993
Esophagus, 1251
  abdominal portion of, 1252
  cervical portion of, 1251
  lymphatic vessels of, 812
  nerves of, 1252
  structure of, 1252
  tela submucosa, 1252
  thoracic portion of, 1251
  tunica mucosa, 1252
    muscularis, 1252
  vessels of, 1252
  x-ray of, during passage of a barium meal, 79
Ethmoid bone, 209
  articulations of, 213
  crest, 217, 223
  cribriform plate of, 209
  foramina, 170
  horizontal lamina of, 210
  labyrinth of lateral mass of, 211
  lamina papyracea of, 211
    perpendicularis, 211
  perpendicular plate of, 210
  uncinate process of, 211
  vertical plate, 210
Ethmoidal arteries, 635
  canals, 194
  cells, 211, 1172
  notch, 194
  process of inferior nasal concha, 224
  sinuses, 211
  spine, 173, 204
Ethmovomerine cartilage, 227
Eustachian tube, 1135
  valve, 587
Excavation, rectouterine, 1260
  retrovesical, 1260
  vesicouterine, 1260

Extensor carpi radialis accessorius muscle, 506
  brevis muscle, 506
  intermedius muscle, 506
  longus muscle, 506
  carpi ulnaris muscle, 508
  coccygis muscle, 444
  digiti quinti proprius muscle, 507
  digitorum brevis muscle, 553
  communis muscle, 506
  longus muscle, 544
  hallucis brevis muscle, 553
  longus muscle, 544
  indicis proprius muscle, 510
  minimi digiti muscle, 507
  ossis metacarpi pollicis muscle, 509
  metatarsi hallucis muscle, 544
  pollicis brevis muscle, 510
  longus muscle, 509
  primi internodii pollicis muscle, 510
  secundi internodii pollicis muscle, 510
Exterior of skull, 158
External acoustic meatus, 164, 1125, 1128
  arcuate ligament, 451
  auditory canal, 1128
    meatus, 1128
  calcaneal artery, 711
  calcaneo-astragaloid ligament, 393
  canthus of eyelids, 1118
  circumflex artery, thigh, 702
  cutaneous nerve, thigh, 1042
  geniculate body, 877
  genitalia, female, 1347
    male, 1348
  inguinal ring, 457
  intercostal muscles, 447
  jugular vein, 74
  lateral ligament, 335, 362, 369
  ligament of malleus, 1163
  malleolar artery, 708
  mammary artery, 655
  oblique muscle, 454
  organs of generation, 1348, 1379
  plantar artery, 711
    nerve, 1052
  popliteal nerve, 1052
  pterygoid muscle, 425
    nerve, 969
  pudic arteries, 700
  respiratory nerve of Bell, 1015
  saphenous vein, 752
  semilunar fibrocartilage, 384
  spermatic artery, 694
    fascia, 1350
    nerve, 1038
  sphincter ani muscle, 482
Extraspinal veins, 750
Extremity, lower, arteries of, 118, 695
  articulations, 115
  bones of, 110, 247
  joints, 374
  lymphatics, 794
  muscles of, 117, 526
  nerves of, 118
  topographic anatomy of, 110
  veins of, 118, 743
  upper, arteries, 108, 657
  articulations, 105
  bones of, 100, 227
  lymphatics, 792
  muscles, 106, 483
  topographic anatomy, 100
  veins of, 108, 742
Extrinsic muscles of tongue, 1234

Eye, 1095
  accessory organs of, 1114
  bulb of, 1095
  anterior chamber, 1099, 1106
    pole, 1095
  aqueous humor, 1112
  canal of Schlemm, 1099
  chambers of, 1107
  choroid, 1099, 1103
  ciliary body, 1104
    muscle, 1099
    processes, 1099
  cornea, 1099, 1102
  crystalline lens, 1097, 1113
    spatia zonularis, 1113
    suspensory ligament, 1113
  development of, 1096
  iris, 1105
    nerves of, 956
  optic axis, 1096
  orbiculus ciliaris, 1104
  posterior chamber, 1106
    pole, 1096
  pupil, 1105
  pupillary membrane, 1097, 1107
  refracting media, 1112
  retina, 1097, 1108
    central artery, 1111
    fovea centralis, 1109
    layers of, 1109
    macula lutea, 1109
    optic disc, 1109
    ora serrata, 1109
    par ciliaris, 1097, 1109, 1111
      iridica, 1097, 1109, 1111
    pigmented layer, 1109
    proper, 1109
    rods and cones, 1171
    supporting frame-work of, 1111
  sclera, 1099, 1100
  tapetum, 1104
  tunic, fibrous, 1100
    nervous, 1100
    uvea, 1103
    vascular, 1103
  vascular tunic of, 1103
  vessels, 1114
  vitreous body, 1099, 1112
  zonula ciliaris, 1099, 1113
  capsule of Tenon, 1117
  conjunctiva, 1119
  development of, 1096
    central artery of retina, 1098
    hyaloid artery, 1097
    lens vesicle, 1097
    optic cup, 1097
      nerve, 1097
      stalk, 1096
      vesicle, 1096
    pupillary membrane, 1097, 1107
  fascia bulbi, 1117
  muscles, extrinsic, 416, 417
    intrinsic, 416, 417
  surface anatomy, 65
  tarsal glands of, 1119
  tunics of, 1099
Eyeball. *See* Eye, bulb of.
Eyebrows, 1118
Eyelashes, 1118
Eyelids, 1118
  canthus of, 1118
  development of, 1099
  muscles of, 416
  structure of, 1118
  surface anatomy of, 65
  tarsi of, 1118
Eye-teeth, 1222

F

FACE, bones of, 213
development of, 42
lymphatics of, 784
surface anatomy of, 61
Facial artery, 622
surface markings of, 62
transverse, 627
bones, 213
canal, hiatus of, 199
prominence of, 1133
lymph nodes, 784
nerve, 974
composition and central connections of, 916
sympathetic efferent fibers of, 1061
vein, anterior, 726
common, 727
deep, 727
posterior, 727
transverse, 727
Facies convexa cerebri, 882
dorsalis sacri, 138
pelvina sacri, 137
Falciform ligament of liver, 1259, 1300
margin of fossa ovalis, 530
process of sacrotuberous ligament, 348
Fallopian tubes, 1370
Fallopius, aqueduct of, 1133
False ligaments of bladder, 1343
pelvis, 265
ribs, 153
vocal cords, 1182
Falx aponeurotica inquinalis, 460
cerebelli, 925
cerebri, 925
Fascia or Fasciæ, 407
abdomen, 453
triangular, 456
anal, 471
ankle, 551
antebrachial, 499
arm, 496
axillary, 489
bicipital, 498
brachial, 496
buccopharyngeal, 423, 428
Buck's, 1361, 1362, 1365
Camper's, 453
cervical, 426
clavipectoral, 487
Colles', 262, 453, 478, 1362
colli, 426
coracoclavicular, 488
cremasteric, 459
cribrosa, 528
cruris, 543
dartos, 1361
deep, 407
of penis, 1361
of deltoideus, 492
Denonvilliers', 1365
dentate, 910
dorsal, of foot, 553
external spermatic, 1350
Gallaudet's, 454
forearm, 499
hand, 511
iliaca, 526
iliopectineal, 527
infraspinata, 494
infundibuliform, 465, 1351
innermost spermatic, 1351
innominata, 454, 1260, 1350
intercolumnar, 1350
intercostal, 447
intercrural, 457, 1350
internal spermatic, 1351
lata, 528

Fascia lata, falciform margin of, 530
fossa ovalis of, 530
iliotibial tract or band of, 530
leg, 543
deep, transverse, 543
lumbar, 440
lumbodorsal, 438
masseteric, 422
middle spermatic, 1352
obturator, 470
orbital, 1118
palmar, 514
parotideomasseteric, 422
pectoral, 487
pelvic, 470
penile, 1361
perineal, 471
piriformis, 470
plantar, 554
pretracheal, 431
prevertebral, 430
psoas and iliacus, 526, 527
rectovesical, 1365
renalis, 1320
Scarpa's, 453
Sibson's, 430, 1192
spermatic, external, 458, 1350
innermost, 1351
internal, 1351
middle, 1350
subscapular, 487
superficial, 407, 426, 528
of penis, 1357
supraspinatus, 493
temporal, 422
thigh, 528
thoracic region, 446, 487
transversalis, 464, 1253, 1329
triangular, of abdomen, 456
upper extremity, 483
urogenital diaphragm, 480, 481, 1346
region, 478
vertebral, 430
Fasciculus, cerebrospinal, 923
cerebrospinalis anterior, 858
lateralis, 858
comma-shaped, 844
cuneatus, 843
gracilis, 843
lateral cerebrospinal, 858
proper, 846
spinothalamic, 845
lateralis proprius, 844
of Lissauer, 845
longitudinal inferior, 895
medial, 859, 872
superior, 895
mammillo-thalamic, 880
occipitofrontal, 895
olivospinal, 846
perpendicular, 895
posterior proper, 844
retroflexus of Meynert, 911
rubrospinal, 846, 872
spinocerebellar, dorsal, 844, 864
ventral, 845
spinoölivary, 846
spinotectal, 845
spinothalamic, 845
tectospinal, 846
uncinate, 895
ventral spinothalamic, 845, 846
vestibulospinal, 846
Fasciola cinerea, 832, 905
Fauces, arches or pillars of, 1210, 1241
isthmus of, 1241
muscles of actions of, 1244
Female genital organs, 1367
bulb of vestibule, 1381

Female genital organs, carunculæ hymenales, 1381
clitoris, 1380
development of, 1315
epoöphoron, 1369
fourchette, 1380
glands of Bartholin, 1381
hymen, 1381
labia majora, 1379
minora, 1380
mons pubis, 1370
navicular fossa, 1381
ovaries, 1367
uterine tubes, 1370
uterus or womb, 1372
vagina, 1378
vestibule, 1381
greater vestibular glands, 1381
x-ray of, 97
urethra, 1348
Femoral artery, 695
surface marking of, 118
canal, 696
circumflex arteries, 702
cutaneous nerve, anterior, 1042
lateral, 1039
posterior, 1047
fossa, 696
nerve, 1042
ring, 696
septum, 696
sheath, 695
triangle, 695, 697
vein, 755
Femur, 269
architecture of, 275
inner, of upper, 275
of distal portion, 280
ossification of, 282
surface anatomy of, 112
Fenestra cochleæ, 1133
ovalis, 1133
rotunda, 1133
vestibuli, 1133, 1140
Fertilization of ovum, 28
Fetal circulation, 577
membranes, development of, 32
Fetus, circulation in, 576
foramen ovale in, 573
vascular system in, peculiarities of, 576
Fibers, arcuate, 851
collagenous, 325
commissural, 892
dentinal, 1224
dorsal root, 921
intercolumnar, 456
intercrural, 456
intrafusal, 939
nerve, 931
non-medulated, 932
of muscle, 561
of Purkinje, 596
of Tomes, 1224
olfactory projection, 906
pain and temperature, 922
preganglionic, 1061
projection, 892
reticular, 306
somatic efferent, 923
sustentacular, of Müller, 1111
touch and pressure, 921
Fibræ pontis profundæ, 861
superficiales, 861
propriæ [cerebellum], 865
Fibrocartilage, 306
circumferential, 309
connecting, 309
interarticular, 309
intervertebral, 327
semilunar, of knee, 383, 384
stratiform, 309

Fibrocartilage, yellow or elastic, 306
white, 306, 308
Fibrocartilaginous lamina, inter-pubic, 349
Fibrous capsule of Glisson, 1301
joint, 325
rings of heart, 593
sheaths of flexor tendons of fingers, 503
of toes, 555
tunic of kidney, 1332
Fibula, 287
nutrient artery of, 710
ossification of, 289
surface form of, 115
Fibular artery, 708
collateral ligament of knee-joint, 382
Fifth metacarpal bone, 256
metatarsal bone, 301
nerve, 915
Filiform papillæ of tongue, 1233
Filum terminale, 837
Fimbriæ of uterine tube, 1370
Fingers, bones of, 254
First cuneiform bone, 297
dorsal metacarpal artery, 662
bone, 299
metatarsal artery, 708
bone, 299
nerve, 955
Fissure or Fissures, Fissura, antitragohelicina, 1127
calcarina, 883
cerebellar, 863
development of, 828
cerebral, 882
calcarine, 883
callosal, 906
central, 883
collateral, 883
development of, 833
hippocampal, 906
lateral, 882
longitudinal, 882
parietoöccipital, 883
transverse, 904
cerebri lateralis [Sylvii], 882
longitudinalis, 882
choroidal, 904, 1097
cingulate, 883
circuminsular, 883
collateralis, 883
dentate, 906
Glaserian, 197, 1131
hippocampi, 832, 906
longitudinal, 882
of liver, 1299
of lungs, 1199
of Rolando, 883
of Sylvius, 882
orbital, inferior, 163, 171
superior, 170, 174, 207
parietoöccipitalis, 883
petroöccipital, 162, 175
petrosphenoidal, 162
petrotympanic, 160, 197, 1131
prima [cerebellum], 828, 865
pterygoid, 208
pterygomaxillary, 165
secunda [cerebellum], 828
sphenomaxillary, 163, 165
tympanomastoid, 161
vestibular, 1143
Fixation of kidney, 1330
muscles, 412
Flechsig, cerebellar tract of, 844, 845
oval area of, 844
Flexor accessorius muscle, 556
brevis minimi digiti muscle, 523, 558
carpi radialis muscle, 501

Flexor carpi ulnaris muscle, 501
digiti quinti brevis muscle of foot, 558
of hand, 523
digitorum brevis muscle, 555
longus muscle, 548
profundus muscle, 502
sublimis muscle, 502
hallucis brevis muscle, 556
longus muscle, 548
longus digitorum muscle, 548
pollicis brevis muscle, 521
longus muscle, 503
Flexure, cervical, 825
colic, left, 1284
right, 1284
hepatic, 1287
pontine, 825
sigmoid, 1284, 1288
splenic, 1287
ventral cephalic, 825
Floating ribs, 153
Floor of fourth ventricle, 869
Fluid, cerebrospinal, 928
Fold or Folds, aryepiglottic, 1181, 1182
duodenojejunal, 1270
gastropancreatic, 1267
glossoepiglottic, 1179
ileocecal, 1271
of Treves, 1271
malleolar, 1132
rectouterine, 1375
rectovesical, 1264
sacrogenital, 1264
salpingopalatine, 1249
salpingopharyngeal, 1249
transverse, of rectum, 1290
umbilical, 1343
uterus, palmate of, 1375
ventricular, of larynx, 1182
vestigial of Marshall, 575, 581
vocal, of larynx, 1182
Follicle of hair, 1159
Follicles, agminated, 1282
Graafian, or vesicular ovarian, 1369
Fontana, spaces of, 1101
Fontanelles, 177
Foot, arches of, 401
fascia of, 553
muscles of, 553
ossification of bones of, 302
phalanges of, articulations of, 401
skeleton of, 290, 291
surface anatomy of, 113
x-ray of, 113
Foramen or Foramina, carotico-clinoid, 174, 208
cecum of frontal bone, 194
of medulla oblongata, 847
of tongue, 1209, 1231
condyloid anterior, 188
epiploic, 1214, 1258, 1267
ethmoidal, 170
incisive, 159, 219
infraorbital, 168, 214
interventricular, 901
intervertebral, 127
jugular, 162, 175
lacerum, 162, 174
magnum, 162, 175, 186, 189
mandibular, 181
mastoid, 163, 166, 175, 198
mental, 169, 180
obturator, 265
of Huschke, 203
of Luschka, 868
of Majend, 868
of Monro, 901
of Scarpa, 159, 219
of Stenson, 159, 219

Foramen of Thebesius, 587
of Vesalius, 174, 206
of Winslow, 1214, 1258, 1267
optic, 174, 204, 208
ovale of heart, 573
of sphenoid, 160, 165, 206
palatine, 159
parietal, 158, 191
rotundum, 166, 174, 206
sacral, 137, 138
sciatic, 348
singulare, 200
sphenopalatine, 166, 223
spinosum, 160, 174, 206
sternal, 152
stylomastoid, 161, 201
supraorbital, 167, 171, 194
supratrochlear, 239
thyroid, 265
transversarium, 127
vena-caval, 450
venarum minimarum, 587
vertebral, 126
zygomaticofacial, 168, 221
zygomaticoörbital, 222
zygomaticotemporal, 163, 221
Forceps, anterior, 895
posterior, 895
Forearm, fascia of, 499
muscles of, 499
Fore-brain, 874
development of, 33, 828
Foregut, 36, 1207
Forel, tegmental field of, 878
Foreskin, 1360
Formation reticular, 855, 870
of spinal cord, 842
Fornix of brain, 896
body of, 907
crura of, 907
development of, 832
pillars of, 907
of conjunctiva, 1119
Fossa or Fossæ, acetabular, 264
antecubital, 657
canine, 214
cecal, 1271
cochlearis, 1140
condyloid, 162, 188
coronoid, 239
cranial anterior, 172
middle, 173
posterior, 175
digastric, 198
digital, of epidermis, 1353
of femur, 270
duodenal, 1270
duodenojejunal, 1270
femoral, 696
for ductus venosus, 1299
for gall-bladder, 1300
for inferior vena cava, 1300
for umbilical vein, 1299
glenoid, 197
hypophyseos, 174, 204
ileocecal, 1271
iliac, 259
incisive, 169, 180, 214
incudis, 1133
infraspinatous, 232
infratemporal, 164
intercondyloid, of femur, 274
of tibia, 283
interpeduncular, 869
intersigmoid, 1272
ischiorectal, 473
jugular, 200
lacrimal, 169, 194
mandibular, 160, 164, 197
mastoid, 197
nasal, 1170
navicularis [urethae], 1347
[vulva], 1381

Fossa of liver, 1296
  of Rosenmüller, 1247, 1249
  of skull, anterior, 172
    middle, 173
    posterior, 175
  occipital, inferior, 175
  olecranon, 239
  ovalis, of fascia lata, 530
    of heart, 587
  ovarian, 1266
  pararectal, 1264
  paravesical, 1266
  pericecal, 1271
  peritoneal, 1269
  popliteal, 703
  pterygoid, 208
  pterygopalatine, 166
  radial, 239
  retrocecal, 1272
  retroperitoneal, 1269
  rhomboid, 850, 869
  sagittal, of liver, 1298
  scaphoid, 159, 208
  sphenomaxillary, 166
  subarcuate, 200
  subscapular, 230
  supraspinatous, 231
  supratonsillar, 1242
  Sylvian, 833
  temporal, 163
  trochanteric, 270
  vermian, 188
  vesicæ felleæ, 1300
Fountain decussation of Meynert,
  873
Fourchette, 1380
Fourth metacarpal bone, 255
  metatarsal bone, 301
  nerve, 915
  ventricle, 868
    floor of, 868
Fovea capitis femoris, 269
  centralis retinæ, 1109, 1111
    structure of, 1111
  dentis, 129
  inguinal, lateral, 465
    medial, 465
  of rhomboid fossa, 869
  trochlear, 169
Free nerve-endings, 1151
Frenula of colic valve, 1285
Frenulum of clitoris, 1380
  linguæ, 1231
  of labia minora, 1380
  of lips, 1217
  of prepuce, 1360
  veli, 869
Frontal air sinus, 195, 1175
  artery, 636
  bone, 193
    articulations of, 195
    orbital or horizontal part of,
      194
    ossification of, 195
    squama of, 193
    structure of, 195
  crest, 173, 194
  eminences, 159, 163, 193
  gyri, 883
  lobe, 883
  nerve, 962
  operculum, 883
  process of maxilla, 217
  sulci, 883
  suture, 159, 167, 193
  vein, 725
Frontalis muscle, 414
Frontoethmoidal suture, 173
Frontonasal duct, 195
  process, 42
Frontopontile fibers, 889
Frontosphenoidal process of zygomatic bone, 221

Fundiform ligament of penis,
  1364
Fundus, oculi, 1108
  stomach, 1276
    glands, 1276
  tympani, 1130
  uteri, 1373
Fungiform papillæ of tongue,
  1232
Funiculi of medulla spinalis, 843
Funiculus separans, 869
  spermaticus, 1351
Furrow dental, 1226
  naso-optic, 44, 1009
Fusiform gyrus, 886

G

Galea aponeurotica, 415
Galen, veins of, 735
Gall-bladder, 1304
  fossa for, 1300
  lymphatic capillaries in, 779
  vessels of, 805
  structure of, 1304
Gangliated cord, 1065
Ganglion or Ganglia, 824, 936
  aorticorenal, 1079
  autonomic, 833, 937
  basal, 898
  cardiac, of Wrisberg, 1084
  carotid, 1067
  celiac, 1079
  central, 1065
  cervical, 1070, 1072
  cervicale inferius, 1072
    medius, 1071
    superius, 1070
  cervicothoracic, 1074
  ciliary, 958
  collateral, 1065
  Gasserian, 960
  geniculate, 975
  habenulæ, 878
  interpeduncular, 872
  jugular, 982, 987
  Langley's, 1241
  lenticular, 958
  Meckel's, 960
  nodosum, 987
  of Corti, 1143, 1151
  of glossopharyngeal, 981
  of Scarpa, 981, 1150
  of Wrisberg, 1084
  ophthalmic, 958
  otic, 984
  petrous, 982
  phrenicum, 1085
  pterygopalatine, 976, 1062
  ridge or neural crest, 35, 824
  semilunar, of trigeminal nerve,
    960
  semilunare [Gasseri], 960
  sensory, 936
  sphenopalatine, 976, 1062
  spinal, 997
  spiral, of cochlea, 1142, 1151
  splanchnicum, 1076
  stellate, 1074
  submandibular, 979
  superior, of glossopharyngeal,
    982
  sympathetic mesenteric, 1085
  thoracic, 1075
  thyroid, 1072
  trigeminal, 960
  terminale, 954
  vagus, 987
  vertebral, 1072
  vestibular, 981
Ganglionic layer of retina, 1109
  ridge, 35
Gärtner, duct of, 1317, 1369

Gasserian ganglion, 960
Gaster, 1272
Gastric arteries, short, 677
  artery, left, 672
    right, 674
  glands, 1277
  impression, 1298
  lymph nodes, 799
  nerves from vagus, 994
  plexuses from sympathetic,
    1087
    from vagus, 994
  veins, short, 763
Gastrocnemius muscle, 545
Gastrocolic ligament, 1260, 1261
  omentum, 1268
Gastroduodenal artery, 673
Gastroepiploic arteries, 677
  lymph node, right, 799
  veins, 764
Gastrohepatic omentum, 1267
Gastrolienal ligament, 813, 1266
Gastropancreatic fold, 1267
Gastrophrenic ligament, 1273
Gemellus inferior muscle, 540
  superior muscle, 540
Gemmules of nerves, 930
Genes, 25
Genicular arteries, 703, 705
Geniculate bodies, 912
  ganglion of facial nerve, 975
Geniculum of facial nerve, 975
Genioglossus muscle, 1235
Geniohyoglossus muscle, 1235
Geniohyoideus muscle, 434
Genital cord, 1317, 1320
  glands, development, 1317
  organs of female, 1367
    external, 1379
    of male, 1348
    external, 1379
  ridge, 1317
  swellings, 1324
  tract in female, x-ray of, 97
  tubercle, 1324
Genitocrural nerve, 1038
Genitofemoral nerve, 1038
Gennari, band of, 891
Genu of corpus callosum, 892
  of internal capsule, 899
Gerlach, tubal tonsil of, 1135
Germ cells centers of lymph
  nodule, 781
  dental, 1226
  layers, 30
Germinal epithelium, 1319, 1369
Giacomini, band of, 906
Giant cells, 314
  of Betz, 889
Gianuzzi, crescents of, 1241
Gill-clefts, 40
Gimbernat's ligament, 456
Gingivæ, 1218
Ginglymus, 323
Giraldes, organ of, 1358
Girdle of inferior extremity, 227
  pelvic, 227
  shoulder, 227
  superior extremity, 227
Glabella, 159, 167
Gladiolus, 152
Gland or Glands, accessory of
  mouth, 1241
  part of parotid, 1239
  aortic, 940, 1402
  areolar, mammæ, 1382
  arytenoid, 1187
  buccal, 1218
  bulbourethral, 1367
  cardiac, 1277
  ceruminous, 1130
  ciliary, 1118
  coccygeal, 1493

Glands, Cowper's, 1323, 1367
ductless, 1391
duodenal, 1282
endocrine, 1391
esophageal, 1252
fundic, 1275
gastric, 1275
genital, 1317
intestinal, 1282
labial, 1218
lacrimal, 1121
larynx, 1187
lingual, 1237
mammary, 1381
Meibomian, 1119
molar, 1218
mucous, of tongue, 1237
of Bartholin, 1323, 1381
of Blandin, 1237
of Brunner, 1282
of eye, 1119
of Littré, 1347
of Luschka, 1403
of Montgomery, 1382
of Nuhn, 1237
of Pacchioni, 928
parathyroid, 1394
parotid, 1237
Peyer's, 1282
pituitary, 1395
preputial, 1361
prostate, 1365
pyloric, 1277
salivary, 1237
sebaceous, 1161
serous, of tongue, 1237
sublingual, 1240
submaxillary, 1239
sudoriferous, 1163
suprarenal, 1399
sweat, 1163
tarsal, 1119
thymus, 816
thyroid, 1391
tongue, 1237
trachoma, 1121
urethral, 1347
uterine, 1378
vestibular, greater, 1323, 1381
Glans clitoridis, 1381
penis, 1363
Glaserian fissure, 197, 1131
Glenohumeral ligaments, 358
Glenoid cavity, 234
fossa, 197
ligament of Cruveilhier, 373, 401
of shoulder, 358
Glenoidal labrum of hip-joint, 377
of shoulder-joint, 358
Gliding joints, 323
Glisson's capsule, 1268, 1302
Globular processes of His, 43
Globus major [epididymis], 1353
minor [epididymis], 1353
pallidus, 898
Glomus aorticum, 940, 1403
caroticum, 1403
coccygeum, 1403
Glossoepiglottic folds, 1179, 1230
Glossopalatine arch, 1241
nerve, 975
Glossopalatinus muscle, 1235
Glossopharyngeal nerve, 919, 951, 981
composition and central connections of, 919
Glottis respiratoria, 1183
vocalis, 1183
rima of, 1183
Glutæus maximus muscle, 536
medius muscle, 537
minimus muscle, 538

Gluteal artery, inferior, 691
superior, 693
lines of ilium, 259
muscles, 536
nerves, 1047
tuberosity, 273
veins, 757
Golgi bodies, 19
cells of, 887
organs of, 939,
Golgi and Mazzoni, corpuscles of, 939
Goll, tract of, 843
Comphosis, 322
Gowers, tract of, 845
Graafian follicles, 24, 1369
structure of, 1369
Gracile nucleus, 851
Gracilis muscle, 533
Grandry, tactile corpuscles of, 939
layer of dentin, 1224
Granulations, arachnoid, 928
Gray commissures of medulla spinalis, 839
substance of cerebellum, 865
of cerebral hemispheres, 887
of cortex, 882
of medulla oblongata, 851
Great or Greater auricular nerve, 970
cardiac nerve, 1071
vein, 724
cavernous nerve, 1087
cerebral vein, 735
curvature of stomach, 1273
longitudinal fissure, 882
multangular bone, 252
occipital nerve, 1002
omentum, 1257, 1268
palatine foramen, 159
pelvis, 265
peritoneal sac, 1258
sacrosciatic ligament, 347
saphenous vein, 752
sciatic foramen, 347
notch, 262
sigmoid cavity, 244
splanchnic nerve, 1076, 1078
superficial petrosal nerve, 976
transverse fissure of brain, 904
trochanter, 270
vestibular glands, 1323, 1381
wings of sphenoid, 206
Groove, auriculoventricular, 583
bicipital, 236
carotid, 174, 205
chiasmatic, 174, 204
costal, 154
infraorbital, 169, 215
intertubercular, of humerus, 236
lacrimal, 170, 215
musculospiral, 237
mylohyoid, 181
neural, 35
obturator, 265
occipital, 161, 198
olfactory, 173
optic, 204
primitive, 33
pterygopalatine, 208
vertebral, 143
Growth of embryo, 35, 56
Gubernaculum dentis, 1229
testis, 1321
Gudden, commissure of, 957
mammillo-tegmental bundle of, 880
Gullet, 1251
Gums, 1218
Gustatory calculi, 1094
cells, 1095

Gustatory hair, 1095
pore, 1095
Gynecomastia, 1385
Gyre, Gyrus or Gyri, of brain, 883
angular, 886
central anterior, 884
posterior, 886
cingulate, 885
dentate, 832, 906
frontal, 884
fusiform, 885
hippocampal, 886
lingual, 885
marginal, 886
medifrontal, 884
occipital, 885
of Broca, 885
of insula, 887
olfactory, 905
orbital, 884
precentral, 883
precuneus, 886
quadrate, 886
straight, 885
subcallosal, 832, 911
superior parietal lobule, 886
supracallosal, 832, 905, 906
supramarginal, 886
temporal, 885
uncus, 886, 905

H

HABENULAR commissure, 878
Hair, 1158
bulb, 1160
cells of spiral organ of Corti, 1149
cuticle of, 1153
follicle of, 1159
gustatory, 1095
olfactory, 1094
root of, 1159
scapus or shaft of, 1159
structure of, 1159
Haller, vas aberrans of, 1358
Hamate bone, 254
Hamstring muscles, 541
Hamulus of hamate bone, 254
lacrimal, 220
laminæ spiralis, 1143
pterygoid, 159
Hand, *x*-ray of, 103
and wrist of child aged eleven years, *x*-ray of, 104
two-and-a-half years, *x*-ray of, 105
fascia of, 511
phalanges of, articulations of, 374
skeleton of, 248
surface anatomy of, 104, 105
Hard palate, 1218
Hare-lip, 179
Harrison's sulcus, 158
Hassall, corpuscles of, 817
Haustra, 1282
Haversian canals of bone, 312, 313
systems of bone, 312
Head, arteries of, 618
lymphatics of, 784
muscles of, 406
development of, 406
veins of, 725
x-ray of, 64
Hearing, organ of, 1122
Heart, 567
apex of, 584
arteries of, 615
atrioventricular bundle of His, 596
node, 595

Heart, atrium, left, 584
right, 586
base of, 584
component parts of, 583
conduction system of, 594
congenital malformations of, 598
development of, 568
endocardium, 581
fibrous rings of, 592
lymphatic capillaries of, 779
vessels of, 812
marginal veins of, 724
muscular structure of, 590, 594
nerves of, 598
size and weight of, 579
skeleton of, 592
structure of, 597
surface marking of, 80
trigonum fibrosum, 592
valves of, 78, 589
development of, 576
veins of, 724
ventricle, left, 591
right, 587
ventricular septum of, 592
wall, 579
Heidenhain, demilunes of, 1241
Helicine arteries, 1365
Helicis major muscle, 1128
minor muscle, 1128
Helicotrema, 1142
Helix, 1126
Hemal nodes, 782
Hemiazygos vein, 749
accessory, 749
Hemispheres, cerebellar, 863
cerebral, 882
Hemolymph nodes, 782
Hemorrhoidal artery, inferior, 690
middle, 687
superior, 681
nerve, inferior, 1056
plexuses of nerves, 1087
vein, inferior, 757
middle, 757
superior, 764
venous plexus, 757
Henle, loop of, 1335
Henle's layer of hair follicle, 1160
Hensen, canalis reuniens of, 1144, 1146
node of, 34
stripe of, 1150
supporting cells of, 1150
Hepar, 1294
capsula fibrosa [Glissoni], 1301
facies inferior, 1296
posterior, 1296
superior, 1296
margo anterior, 1298
tunica serosa, 1302
Hepatic artery, 672, 1302
branches of vagus nerve, 994
cells, 1302
cylinders, 1301
duct, 1303
flexure of colon, 1287
lymph nodes, 799
plexus, 1085
sinusoids, 1301, 1303
veins, 762, 1301, 1303
Hepatoduodenal ligament, 1260, 1268
Hepatogastric ligament, 1260, 1268
Hepatorenal ligament, 1301
Hernia, congenital, complete, 1357
incomplete, 1358
into funicular process, 1358
Herophilus, torcular of, 733

Hesselbach, interfoveolar ligament of, 465
triangle of, 96
Hiatus, aortic, 450
esophageal, 451
of facial canal, 199
semilunaris, 177, 1172
Highest intercostal artery, 652
veins, 747
nuchal line, 187
thoracic artery, 655
Highmore, antrum of, 215, 1175
Hilum of kidney, 1328
of lung, 1198
of suprarenal, 1401
Hindbrain, development of, 35, 825
Hindgut, 36, 1207
Hinge joint, 323
Hip bone, 258
articulations of, 265
ossification of, 265
structure of, 265
surface anatomy of, 110
Hipjoint, 374
movements of, 379
muscles in relation with, 379
surface marking of, 110
Hippocampal commissure, 907
fissure, 832, 886
formation, 905
gyrus, 886
Hippocampus, 832, 905, 909
His, atrioventricular bundle of, 596
globular processes of, 43
Horizontal cells of retina, 1110
part of palatine bone, 222
semicircular canal, 1141
Houston's valves of rectum, 1290
Howship's lacunæ, 312
Huguier, canal of, 197, 978, 1131
Humeral articulation, 356
bursæ in relation to, 358
movements of, 359
vessels and nerves of, 359
circumflex arteries, 656
Humerus, 235
ossification of, 240
structure of, 239
surface anatomy of, 100
Humor, aqueous, 1112
Hunter's canal, 695, 698
Huschke, auditory teeth of, 1147
foramen of, 203
Huxley's layer of hair follicle, 1160
Hyaline cartilage, 306
Hydatid of Morgagni, 1317, 1353, 1371
pedunculated, of epididymis, 1353
Hymen, 1381
Hyoepiglottic ligament, 1180
Hyoglossal membrane, 1237
Hyoglossus muscle, 1235
Hyoid arch, 41
arteries, 621
bone, 185
body of, 185
cornua of, 185
ossification of, 186
Hyothyroid ligaments, 1180
membrane, 1179
Hypochondriac regions, 1254
Hypochordal bar or brace, 120
Hypogastric artery, 685
branches of, 686
in fetus, 685
obliterated, 686
variations in, 686
lymph nodes, 798
plexus, sympathetic, 1082, 1086

Hypogastric region, 1254
vein, 757
zone, 1254
Hypoglossal canal, 188
nerve, 70, 921, 972
composition and central connections of, 921
nucleus of, 921
Hypophyseal artery, 634
fossa, 204
Hypophysis cerebri, 1395
development of, 1396
function of, 1399
named parts, 1396, 1397
structure of, 1397
Hypothalamus, 829, 878
corpora mammillaria, 878
hypophysis or pituitary body, 879, 1395
infundibulum, 878
optic chiasma, 879
subthalamic tegmental region, 878
tuber cinerum, 878
Hypothenar eminence, 511
fascial compartment, 517
muscles, 523

I

ILEOCECAL fold, 1271
fossæ, 1271
valve, 1285
Ileocolic artery, 679
lymph nodes, 801
Ileum, 1280
lymphatic vessels of, 803
Iliac arteries, common, 684
surface markings of, 1365
external, 684, 694
surface markings of, 1365
internal, 685
circumflex artery, deep, 695
superficial, 699
vein, deep, 756
superficial, 755
colon, 1287
fascia, 526
fossa, 259
lymph nodes, 797
spines, 260
tuberosity, 259
vein, common, 758
external, 755
internal, 757
Iliacus muscle, 528
fascia of, 526
Iliocapsularis muscle, 528
Iliococcygeus muscle, 470
Iliocostalis cervicis muscle, 442
dorsi muscle, 442
lumborum muscle, 442
Iliofemoral ligament, 375
Iliohypogastric nerve, 1037
Ilioinguinal nerve, 1037
Iliolumbar artery, 692
ligament, 345
vein, 760
Iliopectineal eminence, 260
fascia, 527
Iliosacralis muscle, 470
Iliotibial band or tract, 530
trochanteric ligament, 376
Ilium, 258
ala of, 259
body of, 258
crest of, 259
dorsum of, 259
gluteal lines of, 259
spines of, 259
Imbedding or implantation of ovum, 30
Immovable articulations, 322

Implantation, 30
Impression, colic, 1296
  duodenal, 1296
  gastric, 1296
  renal, 1296
  rhomboid, 229
  suprarenal, 1296
  trigeminal, 199
Incisive bone, 219
  canals, 159, 219
  foramen, 159, 219
  fossa, 169, 214
  teeth, 1221
Incisor crest, 219
  teeth, 1221
Incisura angularis, 1273
  apicis cordis, 584
  cardiaca, 1273
  fastigii, 828
  radialis, 244
  temporalis, 885
  trochlearis, 244
Incremental lines of Salter, 1224
Incus, 1137
  crus breve, 1137
    longum, 1137
  development of, 1123
  ligaments of, 1137
Inferior alveolar artery, 630
  articular arteries, knee, 705
  calcaneonavicular ligament,
    397
  cerebellar peduncles, 864
  constrictor muscle, 1249
  dental artery, 630
    nerve, 972
  epigastric vein, 756
  fascia of urogenital diaphragm,
    475
  ganglion, 982
  labial artery, 623
  laryngeal nerve, 991
  longitudinal sinus, 735
  oblique muscle, 1115
  profunda artery, 658
  pubic ligament, 349
  quadrigeminal body, 872
  sagittal sinus, 735
  striate veins, 734
  tarsal plate, 1118
  thyroarytenoid ligaments, 1182
  turbinated bone, 225
  vesical artery, 687
  vocal cords, 1182
Infracostales muscles, 447
Infraglenoid tuberosity, 233
Infrahyoid artery, 621
  muscles, 434
Infraorbital artery, 630
  canal, 215
  foramen, 168, 214
  groove, 169, 215
  plexus of nerves, 968
Infrapatellar pad of fat, 385
Infrascapular artery, 655
Infraspinatous fascia, 494
  fossa, 232
  muscle, 494
Infrasternal notch, 76
Infratemporal crest, 163, 206
  fossa, 164
  surface of maxilla, 214
Infratrochlear nerve, 963
Infundibuliform fascia, 465,
  1351
Infundibulopelvic ligament, 1375
Infundibulum of brain, 878
  of ethmoid bone, 177, 212, 1172
Inguinal aponeurotic falx, 460
  canal, 466, 1351
  ligament, 456
    reflected, 456
  lymph nodes, 794

Inguinal regions, 1253
  ring, abdominal, 466
    subcutaneous, 456
Inion, 166
Inlet of pelvis, 266
Innominate artery, 617
  bone, 258
  fascia, 454
  veins, 746
Inscriptions, tendinous, of rectus
  abdominis, 461
Insertion of muscles, 562
Insula, 887
  circular sulcus of, 883
  development of, 833
  gyri of, 887
  opercula of, 885
Integument, 1153
Interarticular chondrosternal
  ligament, 342
  costocentral ligaments, 340
  fibrocartilages, 327
  sternocostal ligaments, 342
Intercalated discs, 597
Intercapitular veins, 745, 754
Intercarpal articulations, 369
  movements of, 370
Intercavernous sinuses, 740
Intercellular biliary passages,
  1303
Intercentral ligaments, 326
Interchondral ligaments, 343
Interclavicular ligament, 353
Interclinoid ligament, 209
Intercolumnar fascia, 1350
  fibers, 456
Intercondyloid eminence of tibia,
  274
  fossa of femur, 274
  of tibia, posterior, 282
Intercostal arteries from aorta,
  667
  highest, 650
  from internal mammary, 650
  superior, 650
  fasciæ, 447
  lymph nodes, 808
  membranes, 447
  muscles, 447
  nerves, 1033
  spaces, 153
  veins, 747
Intercostales externi muscles, 447
  interni muscles, 447
Intercostobrachial nerve, 1034
Intercrural fascia, 454, 1350
  fibers, 456
Intercuneiform articulations, 399
Interfoveolar ligament of Hesselbach, 465
Interglobular spaces, 1224
Interior of bladder, 1344
  of larynx, 1181
  of skull, 171
  of uterus, 1374
Interlobular arteries of kidney,
  1336
Intermetacarpal articulations,
  372
Intermetatarsal articulations, 400
Internal abdominal ring, 466
  acoustic meatus, 200
  arcuate ligament, 450
  calcaneal arteries, 711
  calcaneo-astragaloid ligament,
    394
  calcaneo-navicular ligament,
    397
  canthus of eyelids, 1118
  capsule of brain, 899
  carotid artery, 67, 69
  circumflex artery, 702
  cutaneous nerve, arm, 1020

Internal cutanenous nerve, lesser,
  1020
  geniculate body, 912
  iliac artery, 685
    lymph nodes, 798
    vein, 757
  intercostal muscles, 447
  jugular vein, 74
  lateral ligament, elbow, 362
    mandible, 336
    wrist, 368
  malleolar artery, 708
  mammary artery, 649
    lymph nodes, 808
  maxillary lymph nodes, 786
  oblique muscle, 458
  palpebral arteries, 635
  plantar artery, 711
    nerve, 1051
  popliteal nerve, 1050, 1052
  pterygoid muscle, 424
  pudendal artery, 689
    veins, 757
  pudic artery, 689
    nerve, 1055
    veins, 757
  respiratory nerve of Bell, 1010
  saphenous nerve, 1043
    vein, 752
  semilunar fibrocartilage, 384
  sphincter ani muscle, 482
Interossei muscles of foot, 559
  of hand, 524
Interosseous arteries, 664, 665
  ligament, 341
  membrane of forearm, 364
    of leg, 389
  nerve, dorsal or posterior, 1031
    volar or anterior, 1023
  volaris primus muscle, 525
Interparietal bone, 190
Interpeduncular fossa, 869
  ganglion, 872
Interphalangeal articulations,
  374, 401
Interpleural space, 1195
Interpubic disk, 349
  fibrocartilaginous lamina, 349
Intersegmental septa, 119
Intersigmoid fossa, 1272
Interspinal ligaments, 330
Interspinales muscles, 444
Intertarsal articulations, 393
Intertragic notch, 1126
Intertransversales muscles, 444
Intertransverse ligaments, 330
Intertrochanteric crest, 271
  line, 271
Intertubercular plane, 1253
Intertubular dentin, 1224
Intervenous tubercle, 587
Interventricular foramen, 901
  septum, 592
Intervertebral fibrocartilages, 327
  foramina, 127
  veins, 751
Intervillous space, 47
Intestinal arteries, 678
  glands, 1282
  villi, 1282
Intestine, development of, 1211
  large, 1284
    x-ray of, after barium enema,
      91
  lymphatic nodules of, 1283
  lymphatics of, 805
  small, 1278
    lymphatic vessels of, 805
    structure of, 1280
    vessels and nerves of, 1283
  surface markings of, 88
Intestinum cæcum, 1284
  crassum, 1284

Intestiuum ileum, 1280
  jejunum, 1280
  rectum, 1289
  tenue, 1278
    tela submucosa, 1282
    tunica mucosa, 1282
      muscularis, 1282
    serosa, 1282
Intra-articular ligament, 340
Intracartilaginous ossification, 316
Intra-epithelial plexus of cornea, 1103
Intrafusal fasciculi, 1156
Intrajugular process, 188
Intralobular veins, 1303
Intramembranous ossification, 315
Intrapulmonary bronchi, 1202
Intraspinal veins, 750
Intrathyroid cartilage, 1177
Intrinsic muscles of tongue. 1235
  spinal reflex paths, 924
Intumescentia cervicalis, 837
Iris, 1105
Ischiocapsular ligament, 374
Ischiocavernosus muscle, 480, 481
Ischiorectal fossa, 473
Ischium, 261
  body of, 261
  rami of, 262
  spine of, 262
  tuberosity of, 262
Island of Reil, 887
Islands, blood, 52, 576
  of Calleja, 908
  of Langerhans, 1311
Isocortex, layers of, 887
Isthmus, aortic, 609, 617
  faucium, 1216, 1241
  glandula thyreoidea, 1391
  of external acoustic meatus, 1128
  of limbic lobe, 886
  of thyroid gland, 1391
  of uterine tube, 1370
  rhombencephali, 825
Iter chordæ anterius, 1131
  posterius, 1131
Ivory of teeth, 1224

J

JACOB'S membrane, 1111
Jacobson, nerve of, 983, 1139
  vomeronasal organs of, 45, 1172
Jejunum, 1280
  lymphatic vessels of, 803
Joints. See Articulations.
  development of, 317
Jugular foramen, 162, 175
  fossa, 200
  ganglion of glossopharyngeal nerve, 982
    of vagus nerve, 987
  nerve, 1070
  notch, 151, 188
  process, 162, 188
  surface of temporal bone, 201
  tubercle, 189
  vein, anterior, 728
    external, 728
    internal, 729
      bulb of, 729
    posterior external, 74, 728
    surface markings of, 74
Jugum sphenoidale, 209
Juxtaglomerular apparatus, 1335

K

KARYOKINESIS, 23
Keith and Flack, node of, 595

Kerkring, valves of, 1280
Kidney, 1326
  artery of, 682
  calyces of, 1334
  development of, 1326
  fascia of, 1328
  fixation of, 1330
  hilum of, 1328
  lymphatic capillaries in, 779
    vessels of, 805
  Malpighian corpuscle, 1334
  medullary substance of, 1334
  minute anatomy of, 1334
  nerves of, 1336
  paranephric body, 1330
  relations of, 1376
  renal artery, 682
  structure of, 1332
  surface marking of, 94
  tubules of, 1335
  veins of, 762, 1336
  weight and dimensions of, 1326
Knee-cap, 282
  x-ray, 109, 112
Knee-joint, 380
  bursæ of, 386
  movements of, 387
  surface anatomy of, 109, 112
Krause, end-bulbs of, 939
Kühne, motor end-plates of, 943

L

LABBE, posterior anastomotic vein of, 734
Labia majora, 1380
  minora, 1381
  oris, 1217
Labial arteries, 623
  commissures, 1380, 1381
  glands, 1218
  grooves, 1208
Labiodental lamina, 1226
Labrum glenoidale, 358, 377
Labyrinth, membranous, 1144
  vessels of, 1151
  osseous, 1139
Labyrinthus ethmoidalis, 211
Lacertus fibrosus, 498,
Lacinate ligament, 551
Lacrimal apparatus, 1121
  artery, 634
  bone, 220
  canals, 1122
  caruncula, 1121
  crest, anterior, 218
    posterior, 170
  ducts or canals, 1122
    ampullæ of, 1122
  fossa, 169, 194, 218
  gland, 1122
  groove, 170, 215
  hamulus, 220
  nerve, 962
  notch, 215
  papilla, 1118
  process of inferior nasal concha, 225
  punctum, 1118
  sac, 1099, 1121, 1122
  tubercle, 218
Lacteals, 775
Lactiferous ducts, 1384
Lacuna magna [of urethra], 1347
Lacunæ of bone, 313
  of cartilage, 307
  of urethra, 1347
  venous, 735
Lacunar ligament, 456
Lacus lacrimalis, 1118, 1121
Lagena, 1146
Lambda, 158

Lambdoidal suture, 158, 166, 189
Lamellæ of bone, 313
  articular, 307
Lamina basalis, 1104
  alar, 822
  cartilaginis cricoideæ, 1177
  choriocapillaris, 1103
  cribrosa ethmoidalis, 210
    scleræ, 1101
  dental, 1226
  dorsal or alar, 822
  elastic, of cornea, 1103
  fibrocartilaginea interpubica, 349
  ganglionaris, of isocortex, 887
  granularis, 887
  horizontales, 222
  labiodental, 1226
  lingual, 1226
  medullary, 875
  multiformis, 887
  nasal, 43
  of vertebræ, 127
  perpendicularis, 210, 211
  pyramidalis, 887
  reticular, 1150
  spiral, of cochlea, 1143
  spiralis ossea, 1143
  terminalis, 879, 882, 907
  vasculosa, 1103
  ventral or basal, 822
  zonalis, 887
Langerhans, centro-acinar cells of, 1311
  islands of, 1311
Langer's lines, 1157
Langley's ganglion, 1241
Large deep petrosal nerve, 976
  intestine, 1284
    cecum, 1284
    colic valve, 1285
    colon, 1287
      ascending, 1287
      descending, 1287
      iliac, 1288
      sigmoid or pelvic, 1288
      transverse, 1287
    rectum, 1289
    x-ray of, 91
Laryngeal artery, inferior, 647
  superior, 621
  nerves, 990
    inferior, 991
    recurrent, 991
    superior, 990
  part of pharynx, 1248
  prominence, 1176
  saccule, 1183
  sinus, 1183
Larynx, 1176
  cartilages of, 1176
  conus elasticus of, 1181
  elastic membrane of, 1180
  glands of, 1187
  interior of, 1181
  ligaments of, 1179
  lymphatic vessels of, 789, 1187
  mucous membrane of, 1187
  muscles of, 1185
    actions of, 1187
  nerves of, 1187
  rima glottidis of, 1183
  surface marking of, 70
  ventricle of, 1095, 1183
  vessels of, 1187
  vestibule of, 1181
  vocal cords of, 1182
Lateral cartilages, nose, 1170
  cerebrospinal fasciculus, 846
  crioarytenoid muscle, 1185
  hyothyroid ligament, 1179
  mesoderm, 33
  nasal cartilage, 1170

Lateral olfactory gyrus, 830, 905
	stria, 905
	sinuses of dura, 738
	spinothalamic fasciculus, 845
	thyrohyoid ligament, 1179
	vertebral muscles, 436
Latissimus dorsi muscle, 485
Layer of rods and cones, 1111
Layers of cerebral cortex, 887
Least splanchnic nerve, 1078
Left atrium, 590
	auricle, 590
	auricular appendage, 590
	coronary plexus, 1084
	vein, 724
	lobe of liver, 1300
	ventricle, 591
Leg, fascia of, 543
	deep transverse, 546
	muscles of, 543
	development of, 405
Lemniscus, lateral, 873
	medial, 873
	spinal, 873
Lens, capsule of, 1113
	vascular, 1097
	changes produced in, by age,
		1114
	crystalline, 1097, 1113
	development of, 1097
	equator of, 1114
	poles of, 1114
	structure of, 1114
	suspensory ligament of, 1113
	vesicle, 1097
Lenticular ganglion, 958
	process of incus, 1137
Lentiform nucleus, 831, 898
Lesser cavernous nerve, 1087
	curvature of stomach, 1273
	lacrimal bone, 220
	multangular bone, 252
	omentum, 1267
	pelvis, 266
	peritoneal sac, 1260, 1266
	sac or omental bursa of peri-
		toneum, 1258
		boundaries of, 1266
	sciatic foramen, 348
		notch, 262
	sigmoid cavity, 244
	splanchnic nerve, 1079
	trochanter, 271
	tubercle, 237
	tuberosity, 237
Leucocytes, 770
Levator anguli oris muscle, 418
	scapulæ muscle, 487
	ani muscle, 469
	claviculæ muscle, 487
	glandulæ thyreoideæ muscle,
		1393
	menti muscle, 419
	palati muscle, 1245
	palpebræ superioris muscle,
		958, 1114
	prostatæ muscle, 469
	scapulæ muscle, 487
	veli palatini muscle, 1245
Levatores costarum muscles, 448
Lieberkühn, crypts of, 1282
Lien, 812
	accessorius, 814
	extremitas inferior, 813
		superior, 813
	facies diaphragmatica, 813
		gastrica, 813
		renalis, 813
	margo anterior, 813
		posterior, 813
Lienal artery, 674
	plexus of nerves, 1085
	vein, 763

Ligament or Ligaments, Ligamen-
	tum, Ligamenta, acromiocla-
	vicular, 325, 354
	alar, 335
	ankle, 390
	annular of ankle, 551
		of radius, 364
		of stapes, 1138
		of wrist, 514
	anterior, ankle, 389
		inferior, 389
		longitudinal, 326
		superior, costotransverse,
			340
		tibiofibular, 389
		wrist, 366
	apical odontoid, 335
	arcuate, 450
		popliteal, 381
		gastrolienal, 813
		phrenicolienal, 813
	arteriosum, 579
	atlantoaxial, 331
	atlantoöccipital, 334
	bifurcated, 375
	bladder, 1343
	broad, of uterus, 1375
	calcaneo-astragaloid, 393
	calcaneo-cuboid, 395
	calcaneo-fibular, 392
	calcaneo-navicular, plantar,
		397
	calcaneo-tibial, 391
	capsular. See individual joints.
	cardinal, 1375, 1376
	carotico-clinoid, 209
	carpo-metacarpal, 371
	carpus, 369, 370
	central, of spinal cord, 927
	check of atlas, 335
		of eye, 1117
	chondrosternal, 341
		intra-articular, 342
	chondroxiphoid, 343
	common, anterior, 326
		posterior, 327
	conoid, 354
	Cooper's, 458, 487, 1382
	coracoacromial, 355
	coracoclavicular, 354
	coracohumeral, 358
	coronary, of knee, 384
	coronary, of knee, 384
		of liver, 1259, 1301
	costocoracoid, 491
	costotransverse, 340, 341
	costovertebral, anterior, 340
	costoxiphoid, 343
	cotyloid, 264
	cricoarytenoid, posterior, 1181
	cricotracheal, 1180
	cruciate, crural, 551
		of atlas. 333
		of knee, 383
	cuboideonavicular, 399
	deltoid, of ankle-joint, 391
	dentate, 927
	denticulatum, 927
	dorsal carpal, 514
		radiocarpal, 367
		radioulnar, 366
	elbow, 360
	falciform, of liver, 1259, 1300
	fibular collateral, of knee-joint,
		382
	fundiform, of penis, 1364
	gastrocolic, 1260, 1261
	gastrolienal, 1266
	gastrophrenic, 1273
	Gimbernat's, 456
	glenohumeral, 358
	glenoid, 358
		of Cruveilhier, 373, 401

Ligament, glenoid of shoulder-
	joint, 358
	glenoidal labrum of hip-joint
		377
		of shoulder-joint, 358
	Henle's, 460
	hepatoduodenal, 1260, 1268
	hepatogastric, 1260, 1268
	hepatorenal, 1259, 1301
	Hesselbach's, 465
	hip-joint, 374
	hyoepiglottic, 1180
	hyothyroid, 1180
	iliofemoral, 375
	iliolumbar, 345
	iliotrochanteric, 376
	inferior transverse of scapula,
		356
	infundibulopelvic, 1375
	inguinal, 456
		reflected, 456
	interarticular, of ribs, 340
		sternocostal, 342
	intercarpal, 369
	intercentral, 326
	interchondral, 343
	interclavicular, 353
	interclinoid, 209
	intercuneiform, 399
	interfoveolar, 465
	intermetacarpal, 372
	intermetatarsal, 400
	interosseous, ankle, 394
	interphalangeal, foot, 401
		hand, 374
		wrist, 369
	interpubic fibrocartilaginous
		lamina, 349
	interspinal, 330
	interspinous, 330
	intertarsal, 393
	intertransverse, 330, 348
	intra-articular, 340
	ischiocapsular, 376
	knee-joint, 380
	lacinate, 551
	lacunar, 456
	lateral atlantoöccipital, 334
		external, ankle, 392
			elbow, 362
			mandible, 335
			wrist, 369
		internal, 335, 362, 369
			of uterus, 1375
	left triangular, of liver, 1260
		vena caval, 581
	long plantar, 396
	lumbocostal, 440
	medial palpebral, 416
	metacarpophalangeal, 372
	metatarsophalangeal, 401
	middle cricothyroid, 1181
	mucosum of knee, 385
	oblique cord, 364
		popliteal, 381
	occipitoaxial, 334
	odontoid, 335
	orbicular, 364
		of auricula or pinna, 1127
		of Bertin, 376
		of Bigelow, 375
		of larynx, 1179
		of Mackenrodt, 1376
		of malleus, 1137
		of neck of rib, 341
		of pinna or auricula, 1127
		of ossicles, 1137
		of Treitz, 1279
		of Zinn, 1115
		ovarian, 1369
		palmar, 309, 372
		palpebral, 1119
		pectinate, of iris, 1103

Ligament, pelvic, 345
  pericardiosternal, 581
  pericardiovertebral, 581
  pericardiophrenic, 581
  phrenicocolic, 1269
  phrenicopericardiac, right, 759
  plantar, long, 396
  posterior, tibiofibular, 389
    cricoarytenoid, 1181
    inferior, 389
    longitudinal, 327
    of knee, 381
    sacroiliac, 346
    superior, tibiofibular, 389
  Poupart's, 456
  pterygomandibular, 421
  pterygospinous, 209, 423
  pubic, 349
  pubocapsular, 376
  pubofemoral, 376
  pulmonary, 1193
  quadrate, 364
  radial collateral, of elbow-joint, 362
    of wrist-joint, 369
  radiate, 340
    sternocostal, 341
  radiocarpal-joint, 366
  radioulnar, 366
  reflected inguinal, 456
  rhomboid, 353
  right triangular of liver, 1260
  round, hip-joint, 377
    of liver, 1300
    of uterus, 1376
  sacrococcygeal, 348
  sacroiliac, 346, 347
  sacrosciatic, 347
  sacrospinous, 347
  sacrotuberous, 347
  scapular, 356
  shoulder-joint, 356
  sphenomandibular, 336
  spinoglenoid, 356
  spiral, of ductus cochlearis, 1147
  stellate, 340
  sternoclavicular, 352
  sternocostal, 341
  sternopericardiac, 581
  sternal, 343
  structure of, 325
  stylohyoid, 432
  stylomandibular, 337
  stylomaxillary, 337
  subpubic, 349
  superficial transverse of fingers, 516
  superior transverse of scapula, 356
  suprascapular, 356
  supraspinal, 329
  supraspinous, 329
  suspensory, of axilla, 489
    of eye, 1118
    of lens, 1113
    of mamma, 487
    of ovary, 1369
    of penis, 1364
  sutural, 317
  talocalcaneal, 393, 394
  talofibular, 391
  talonavicular, dorsal, 395
  talotibial, 391
  tarsometatarsal, 399
  tarsus, 393
  temporomandibular, 335
  tendo oculi, 417
  teres, of hip, 376
    of liver, 1301
    of uterus, 1376
  thyroarytenoid, inferior, 1182
  thyroepiglottic, 1181

Ligament, thyrohyoid, 1179
  tibial collateral, of knee-joint, 382
  tibiofibular, 389
  tibionavicular, 391
  transversalis colli uteri, 137
  transverse acetabular, 3775
    carpal, 511
    crural, 551
    humeral, 358
    inferior, tibiofibular, 389
    of knee, 384
    metacarpal, 372
    metatarsal, 400
    pelvic, 477
    scapula, 356
    trapezoid, 354
    triangular, of liver, 1259, 1301
    of perineum, 477
    of tubercle of rib, 341
  ulnar collateral of elbow-joint, 362
    of wrist-joint, 257
  umbilical, 1343
  uterine, 1375
  utero-sacral, 1376
  ventricular, of larynx, 1182
  vertebral, 326
  vesical, 1343
  volar carpal, 511
    metacarpophalangeal, 372
    radiocarpal, 366
    radioulnar, 366
  of Wrisberg, 384
  Y-shaped, of Bigelow, 375
Ligamenta accessoria plantaria, 401
  auricularia [Valsalva], 1127
  *fasium [ossis metacarp.] dor-
    salia*, 372
  interossea, 372
  [ossis metatars.] dorsalia, 399
    intercssea, 400
    plantaria, 399
  collateralia metatarsophalangea, 401
  cuneometatarsea interossea, 400
  flava (ligmenta subflavia), 329
  navicularicuneiformia dorsalia, 398
    plantaria, 398
  suspensoria [of mammæ], 487
  vocales, 1182
Ligamentous action of muscles, 326
Ligamentum arcuatum pubis, 349
  arteriosum, 611
  capituli costæ interarticulare, 340
    radiatum, 340
  *capitulorum [ossis metacarpal-
    ium] transversum*, 372
  carpi dorsale, 511
    transversum, 511
    volare, 511
  collaterale carpi radiale, 369
    ulnare, 368
    fibulare, 382
    radiale, 362
    tibiale, 382
    ulnare, 362
  colli costæ, 341
  costoclaviculare, 353
  cricothyreoideum medium, 1181
  incudis posterius, 1138
    superius, 1138
  latum pulmonis, 1193
    uteri, 1375
  longitudinale anterius, 326
    posterius, 327
  malleoli lateralis anterius, 389
    posterius, 389
  nuchæ, 330

Ligamentum patellæ, 381
  popliteum obliquum, 381
  teres femoris, 376
    hepatis, 1259, 1301
    uteri, 1375
  transversum, 377
    atlantis, 331
    cruris, 551
    genu, 384
    scapulæ inferius, 356
      superius, 356
  tuberculi costæ, 341
  venosum, 1299
Ligature of arteries. See each artery.
Limbs, development of, 45
Limen insulæ, 831, 887, 905
Line or Lines, *Linea* or *Liniæ*,
    alba, 463
  arcuate, of ilium, 259
  aspera, 273
  cleavage, 1157
  colored, of Retzius, 1224
  curved, of ilium, 259
  gluteal, of ilium, 259
  iliopectineal, 259, 263
  incremental, of Salter, 1224
  intercondyloid, 274
  intertrochanteric, 271
  Langer's, 1157
  mylohyoid, 180
  nuchal, 162, 187
  oblique, of fibula, 288
    of mandible, 180
    of radius, 247
  of Schreger, 1224
  quadrata, 273
  pectineal, femur, 273
    ilium, 259, 263
  popliteal, of tibia, 285
  semicircularis, 463
  semilunares, 464
  spiral, of femur, 271
  splendens, 927
  temporal, 159, 163, 191
  tension, 1157
Lingua, 1230
  apex, 1230
  dorsum, 1231
  facies inferior, 1231
  musculi, 1235
  papillæ, 1231
  radix, 1230
  tunica mucosa, 1236
Lingual artery, 621
  deep, 622
  surface markings of, 74
  bone, 185
  branches of glossopharyngeal nerve, 983
  gyrus, 885
  lamina, 1226
  lymph nodes, 786
  nerve, 972
  papillæ, 1232
  tonsil, 1231, 1236
  veins, 730
Lingula of mandible, 181
  of sphenoid, 174, 205
Lip, hare, 179
  tympanic, 1147
  vestibular, 1147
Lips, 1217
Liquor sanguinis, 769
Lissauer, fasciculus of, 845
  tract of, 845
Littré, urethral glands of, 1347
Liver, 1294
  arteries of, 1301
  bare area of, 1297
  bile ducts of, 1303
    common, 1303
    cystic, 1304

Liver, development of, 1301
  excretory apparatus of, 1304
  fixation of, 1301
  fossæ of, 1298
  gall-bladder, 1305
  hepatic artery, 672, 1302
    cells, 1302
    duct, 1302, 1303
    veins, 762, 1303
  ligaments of, 1300
  lobes of, 1300
  lobules of, 1302
  longitudinal fissures of, 1298
  lymphatic capillaries in, 779
    vessels of, 805
  nerves of, 1301
  portal vein, 762, 1303
  structure of, 1302
  surface markings of, 92
  surfaces of, 1296
  transverse fissure of, 577
  vessels of, 1301
  veins of, 1303
Lobe or Lobes, *Lobus* of cerebellum, 863
  of cerebral hemisphere, 883
    frontal, 883
    insula, 887
    occipital, 884
    parietal, 886
    precuneus, 886
    quadrate, 886, 1300
    quadratus, 1300
    temporal, 885
  of liver, 1300
  of lung, 1199
  of thyroid gland, 1391
  of liver, 1302
  paracentral, 886
  parietal, 886
  Spigelian, 1300
Lobules or *Lobuli* of auricula, 1126
  hepatis, 1302
  of testes, 1350
Lockwood, tendon of, 1115
Locus cæruleus, 869
  caudatus, 1300
Long buccal nerve, 969
  calcaneocuboid ligament, 396
  ciliary nerves, 963
  external lateral ligament, knee, 382
  or internal saphenous nerve, 1043
  plantar ligament, 396
  saphenous nerve, 1043
    vein, 752
  subscapular nerve, 1014
  thoracic artery, 655
    nerve, 1014
Longissimus capitis muscle, 442
  cervicis muscle, 442
  dorsi muscle, 442
Longitudinal fasciculus, inferior, 896
  superior, 896
  fissure, cerebral, 882
    great, 893
    of liver, 1298
  sinuses, 735, 737
  striæ, lateral and medial, 893
  sulci of heart, 584
Longitudinalis linguæ inferior muscle, 1236
  superior muscle, 1235
Longus capitis muscle, 436
  colli muscle, 436
Loop of Henle, 1335
Lower extremity, arteries of, 695
  articulations of, 374
  bones of, 258
  lymphatic nodes of, 794

Lower extremity, lymphatic vessels of, 795
  muscles of, 526
  surface anatomy of, 110
    markings of, 115
  veins of, 752
  jaws, bones of, 179
  lateral cartilage, nose, 1170
Lower, tubercle of, 587
Lumbar aponeurosis, 440
  arteries, 683
  enlargement of spinal cord, 837
  lymph nodes, 798
  nerves, anterior, 1003
    posterior, 1003
  plexus of nerves, 1036
  regions of abdomen, 1253
  triangle, 486
  vein, ascending, 749, 751
  veins, 751
  vertebræ, 126, 135, 144
Lumbocostal aponeurosis, 440
  arch, 450
  ligament of rib, 340
Lumbodorsal fascia, 438
Lumboinguinal nerve, 1039
Lumbosacral plexus, 1036
  trunk, 1036
Lumbricales muscles of foot, 556
  of hand, 524
Lunate bone, 249
  surface of acetabulum, 265
Lung-buds, 1167
Lungs, 1196
  development of, 1167
  fissures and lobes of, 1199
  lymphatics of, 812
  nerves of, 1205
  root of, 1201
  structure of, 1202
  surface markings of, 78
  vessels of, 1204
Lunulæ of nails, 1158
  of semilunar valves, 590
Luschka, formina of, 868, 930
  gland of, 1403
Lymph Node or Nodes, 780
  abdominal, 796
  aortic, 798
  auricular, 784
  axillary, 793
  buccinator, 785
  cervical, 789
  capsule, 781
  cortex of, 780
  deltoideopectoral, 792
  diaphragmatic, 808
  epigastric, 797
  facial, 784, 785
  gastric, 799
  hepatic, 799
  hilum of, 780
  hypogastric, 798
  ileocolic, 801
  iliac, 797
  infraorbital, 785
  inguinal, 794, 795
  intercostal, 808
  internal mammary, 808
  lingual, 786
  lumbar, 798
  mastoid, 784
  maxillary, 785
  mediastinal, 810
  medulla, 781
  mesenteric, 799, 801
  mesocolic, 801
  obturator, 798
  occipital, 784
  of Cloquet, 795
  of head, 784
  of lower extremity, 794

Lymph nodes of neck, 784, 789
  of Rosenmüller, 795
  of thorax, 808
  of upper extremity, 792, 793
  pancreaticoduodenal, 801
  pancreaticolienal, 801
  pararectal, 801
  paratracheal, 790
  parietal, 797, 808
  parotid, 785
  pelvic, 796
  popliteal, 794
  preauricular, 784
  retropharyngeal, 786
  sacral, 798
  sinuses, 781
  splenic, 801
  Stahr, middle gland of, 789
  sternal, 808
  structure of, 781
  subinguinal, 795
  submaxillary, 789
  submental, 789
  suprahyoid, 789
  supramandibular, 785
  supratrochlear, 792
  tibial, anterior, 794
  of tongue, 787
  tracheobronchial, 811
  visceral, of abdomen and pelvis, 796, 799
Lymphatic capillaries, 775
  distribution of, 775
  duct, right, 811
  nodules, aggregated, 1282
    solitary, 1282
  of spleen, 814
  system, 775
  trunks, bronchomediastinal, 784, 811
    intestinal, 784
    jugular, 784
    lumbar, 784
    subclavian, 784
  vessels, 312, 779
    of abdominal viscera, 801
      wall, 796
    of anal canal and anus, 804
    of auricula and external acoustic meatus, 786
    of bladder, 805
    of cecum, 804
    of colon, 804
    of common bile-duct, 805
    development of, 779
    of diaphragm, 809
    of ductus deferens, 807
    of duodenum, 803
    of esophagus, 812
    of external genitals, 799
    of face, 786
    of gall-bladder, 805
    of gluteal region, 804
    of heart, 812
    of ileum, 803
    of jejunum, 803
    of kidney, 805
    lacteals, 803
    of larynx, 789
    of liver, 805
    of lower extremity, 794
    of lungs, 812
    of mamma, 809
    of mouth, 787
    of nasal cavities, 787
    of neck, 789
    of ovary, 807
    of palatine tonsil, 787
    of pancreas, 805
    of pelvic viscera, 799
    of pelvis, 796, 799
    of penis, 807
    of perineum, 799

Lymphatic vessels of pharynx, 789, 791
  of pleura, 812
  of prostate, 806
  of rectum, 804
  of reproductive organs, 807
  of scalp, 786
  of small intestine, 802
  of spleen, 805
  of stomach, 803
  of suprarenal glands, 805
  of testes, 807
  of thoracic viscera, 872
    wall, 809
  of thymus, 812, 816
  of thyroid gland, 791
  of tongue, 787
  of upper extremity, 792
  of ureter, 806
  of urethra, 807
  of urinary organs, 805
  of uterine tube, 807
  of uterus, 808
  of vagina, 808
  of vermiform process, 804
  of vesculæ seminales, 807
  structure of, 780
Lymphocyte, 770
Lymphoglandulæ, 780
Lyra of fornix, 907

M

MACEWEN, suprameatal triangle of, 197
Mackenrodt, ligament of, 1376
Macroglia, 934
Macrophages, 311, 781, 1157, 1303
Macula acustica sacculi, 1144
  utriculi, 1144
  cribrosa media, 1140
    superior, 1140
  lutea, 1109, 1111
  structure of, 1111
Magendie, foramen of, 868, 930
Malar bone, 220
  process of maxilla, 217
Male genital organs, 1348
  bulbourethral glands, 1367
  ductus deferens, 1358
  ejaculatory duct, 1360
  epididymis, 1353
  penis, 1360
  prostate, 1365
  seminal vesicles, 1359
  testes and their coverings, 1348
  pronucleus, 28
  urethra, 1346
Malleolar arteries, 708
  folds, 1132
  sulcus, 287
Malleolus, lateral, 289
  medial, 286
Malleus, 1137
  development of, 1123
  ligaments of, 1137
Malpighian bodies of spleen, 815
  corpuscles of kidney, 1335
Mammæ, 1381
  development of, 1382
  hypertrophy of, 1382
  lymphatic vessels of, 809
  nerves of, 1385
  papilla or nipple of, 1382
  structure of, 1383
  vessels of, 1385
Mammary arteries, external, 655
  internal, 649
  gland, 1381
  internal lymph node, 808
  veins, internal, 747

Mammillary bodies, 911
  process, 137
Mandible, 179
  angle of, 182
  articulations of, 183, 335
  body of, 179
  changes in, due to age, 183
  condyloid process of, 182
  coronoid process of, 182
  ossification of, 182
  ramus of, 181
  symphysis of, 180
Mandibular arch, 40
  branches of facial nerve, 981
  canal, 181
  foramen, 181
  fossa, 164, 197
  nerve, 968
  notch, 182
Manubrium of malleus, 1136
  of sternum, 150
Margin, supraorbital, 193
Marginal artery, gyrus, 640
  veins of foot, 752
  of heart, 724
Marrow of bone, 311
Marshall, oblique vein of, 575, 582, 722, 725
  vestigial fold of, 575, 581, 725
Massa intermedia, 829, 875
Masses, lateral, of atlas, 130
Masseter muscle, 422
Masseteric artery, 630
  fascia, 422
  nerve, 969
Mastication, muscles of, 422
Masticatory nerve, 951
Mastoid canaliculus, 162, 201
  cells, 199
  foramen, 163, 166, 198
  fossa, 197
  lymph nodes, 784
  notch, 161, 198
  portion of temporal bone, 203
  process, 198
Matrix of nail, 1158
Maturation of ovum, 25
Maxilla, 214
  articulations of, 219
  changes in, due to age, 219
  ossification of, 215
Maxillary antrum, 215, 1175
  external artery, 622
  internal, 628
  lymph nodes internal, 786
  nerve, 964
  process of inferior nasal concha, 225
  of palatine bone, 223
  of zygomatic bone, 222
  processes of fetus, 41, 44
  sinus, 214, 215
  tuberosity, 215
  vein, internal, 727
Meatus or Meatuses, acusticus externus, 1128
    cartilagineus, 1128
    externus, osseous, 1129
  auditory, external, 164, 203, 1128
    internal, 175, 975, 1150
  external acoustic, 164, 203, 1128
  internal acoustic, 175, 975, 1150
  of ear, 1128
  of nose, 177, 1172
  urinary, 1381
Mechanism of pelvis, 350
  of respiration, 451
  of thorax, 343
Meckel's cartilages, 40, 182
  diverticulum, 55, 1280

Meckel's ganglion, 976
Media, refracting, of eye, 1112
Medial geniculate body, 877, 912
  lemniscus, 858
  longitudinal fasciculus, 872
  olfactory gyrus, 905
    stria, 905
  tarsal arteries, 709
  wall of nasal cavity, 1172
Median antebrachial vein, 744
  basilic vein, 744
  nerve, 1021
Mediastinal arteries from aorta, 667
  from internal mammary, 650
  lymph nodes, 810
  pleura, 1191
Mediastinum, 1194
  testis, 1354
Medidural artery, 629
Medulla, adrenal, 1401
  of hair, 1161
  oblongata, 846
    arcuate fibers of, 851
    development of, 825
    fasciculus cuneatus, 851
      gracilis, 851
    fissures and sulci of, 847
    formatio reticularis, 855
    gray substance of, 851
    olive of, 848
    pyramid of, 858
    restiform bodies of, 859
    structure of, 850
    white substance of, 856
  spinalis, (spinal cord), 836
    central canal of, 842
    columns of, 841
    development of, 821
    enlargements of, 837
    fissures of, 837
    gray commissures of, 839
      substance of, 839
    ligamentum denticulatum, 927
    meninges of, 924
    neuroglia of, 933
    posterior column of, 839
    sulci of, 837
    veins of, 751
    white commissure of, 842
  suprarenal, 1400
Medullary artery of bone, 312
  lamina, 875
  segments of nerves, 932
  sheath of nerve-fibers, 932
  spaces of bone, 318
  substance of kidney, 1334
    of lymph node, 781
    of ovaries, 1369
    of suprarenal, 1400
  velum, 867
Medullated nerve-fibers, 932
Megakaryocytes, 311
Meibomian glands, 1119
Meiosis, 25
Meissner's plexus, 1284
  tactile corpuscles, 939
Membrane or membranes, *Membrana, anal*, 1215
  arachnoid, 927
  atlantoöccipital, 334
  basilar, 1148
  bones, 126
  of brain and spinal cord, 924
  Bowman's, 1103
  bucconasal, 44
  cell, 21
  cloacal, 1215
  costocoracoid, 491
  criothyroid, 1181
  Demours', 1103
  Descemet's, 1103
  elastic, of larynx, 1181

Membrane, fenestrated, 765
  fetal, development of, 46
  glanulosa [of Graafian follicle],
    1370
  hyaloid, 1097
  hyoglossal, 1237
  hyothyroid, 1179
  intercostal, 447
  interosseous, of forearm, 364
    of leg, 389
  Jacob's, 1111
  limiting, retina, 1111
  medullary, of bone, 126
  Nasmyth's, 1228
  nuclear, 22
  obturator, 538
  pharyngeal, 1207
  pupillary, 1097, 1107
  Reissner's, 1146
  synovial, 325
  tectoria [of atlas and occipital
    bone], 335
  tectorial, of ductus cochlearis,
    1150
  thyrohyoid, 1180
  tympanic, 1131
  vestibular, 1146
  vitelline, 28
Membranous cochlea, 1146
  cranium, 122
  labyrinth, 1144
  portion of urethra, 1347
  semicircular canals, 1144
  vertebral column, 120
Meningeal artery, accessory, 629
    anterior, 629
    from ascending pharyngeal,
      626
    from occipital, 625
    from vertebral, 645
    middle, 629
      surface marking of, 69
    posterior, 627
  branch of spinal nerve, 1001
  layer of dura mater, 925
  nerve, 965
    from hypoglossal, 996
    from maxillary, 968
Meninges of brain and medulla
  spinalis, 826
Menisci, 383
  of knee-joint, 383
Meniscus, articular, 336
Menstrual age of fetus, 55
Mental foramen, 169, 180
  nerve, 972
  protuberance, 180
  spines, 180
  tubercle, 180
Mentalis muscle, 419
Mentohyoideus muscle, 432
Mescencephalon, 828, 869
Mesenchyme, 37, 568
Mesenteric arteries, 678, 680
  lymph nodes, 801
  plexuses of nerves, 1085
  veins, 764
Mesenteries, 1266, 1267
  mesentery proper, 1269
  sigmoid mesocolon, 1260, 1269
  transverse mesocolon, 1269
Mesenteriole of vermiform
  process, 1285
Mesenterium, 1269
Mesocardium, arterial, 581
  venous, 581
Mesocolic lymph nodes, 801
Mesocolon, sigmoid, 1264, 1269
  transverse, 1269
Mesoderm, 32
  extraembryonic, 32
  formation of, 32
  splanchnic, 568

Mesogastrium, 1211
Mesometrium, 1375
Mesonephros, 1316
Mesorchium, 1317, 1320
Mesosalpinx, 1375
Mesothelium, 1258
Mesovarium, 1317, 1369
Metacarpal arteries, 662
  bones, 254
    articulations of, 256
    characteristics of, 255
    ossification of, 258
Metacarpophalangeal articula-
  tions, 372
Metacarpus, 254
Metaphase of mitosis, 23
Metatarsal arteries, 709
  bones, 299
    characteristics of, 299
    surface anatomy of, 115
  veins, 754
Metatarsophalangeal articula-
  tions, 401
Metatarsus, 299
  ossification of, 302
Metathalamus, 877
Metencephalon, 825
Metopic suture, 193
Meynert, fasciculus retroflexus of,
  911
  fountain decussation of, 873
Microgliocytes, 935
Midbrain, 35, 869
  development of, 828
  nuclei of, 870
Microglia, 935
Midcarpal joint, 370
Middle capsular artery, 682
  cerebellar peduncles, 865
  constrictor muscle, 1249
  costotransverse ligament, 341
  cutaneous nerve, thigh, 1043
  dental nerve, 967
  subscapular nerve, 1017
  superior alveolar nerve, 967
  suprarenal artery, 682
  thyrohyoid ligament, 1179
  tibiofibular ligament, 389
  vesical artery, 687
Milk line, 1382
  teeth, 1223
Mitochondria, 21
Mitosis, 23
Mitral orifice, 591
  valve, 591
Moderator band, 590
Modiolus of cochlea, 1142
Molar glands, 1218
  teeth, 1222
Molecular layer of cortex of cerebellum, 865
  of cerebrum, 887
Monakow, rubrospinal fasciculus
  of, 846, 923
Monro, foramen of, 881, 901
Mons pubis, 84, 1367, 1379
  Veneris, 1379
Monticulus, 863
Morgagni, hydatid of, 1317, 1353,
  1371
  rectal columns of, 1291
  sinus of, 1250
Morula, 29
Moss fibers, 867
Motor areas of cerebral cortex,
  888
Motor end-plates, 943
  nerves, 943
  neurons, lower and upper, 923
  tract, 923
Mouth, 1214
  development of, 1207
  lymphatics of, 787

Mouth, mucous membrane of,
  1218
  muscles of, 418
Movable articulations, 322
Movements admitted in joints,
  324
Mucous glands of tongue, 1237
  sheaths. See Synovial.
Müller, orbitals muscle of, 1117
  sustentacular fibers of, 1111
Müllerian duct, 1316
  eminence, 1317
Multangular bones, 252
Multicuspid teeth, 1222
Multifidus muscle, 443
  spinæ muscle, 443
Muscle or Muscles, abdominal,
  453
  action of, 411
  anal region, 471
  anterior crural, 543
    femoral, 528
    vertebral, 436
  anterolateral of abdomen, 453
  arm, 496
  of auricula or pinna, 415, 1127
  axillary arch, 486
  back, 438
    surface markings of, 75, 76
  bundles of atria, 594
    of ventricles, 594
  cardiac, 597
  cervical, 426
  constrictors of pharynx, 1249
    urethræ, 480, 482
  development of, 405
  diaphragm, 449
  dorsal antebrachial, 505
  external sphincter ani, 482
  eyelid, 416
  fasciculi of, 562
  fibers of, 561
  fixation, 412
  foot, 553
  forearm, 499
  form of, 405
  gluteal region, 536
  hamstring, 541
  hand, 511
  head, 406, 412
    development of, 406
  hypothenar, 523
  iliac region, 526
  insertion of, 562
  intercostal, 447
  intermediate volar, 524
  internal sphincter ani, 482
  interosseous, dorsal, 559
    of foot, 559
    of hand, 524
    palmaris, 521
    plantar, 559
  intracostal, 447
  laryngeal, 1185
  lateral cervical, 431
    crural, 550
    vertebral, 436
  leg, 543
    development of, 406
  lower extremity, 526
  lumbrical of foot, 556
    of hand, 524
  mastication, 422
  medial femoral, 533
  mouth, 418
  neck, 425
  nerves and vessels of, 562
  nose, 417
  oblique of abdomen, 453
    inferior of eye, 1115
    superior of eye, 1115
  ocular, 1114
  omohyoid, 435

Muscle, orbitals of H. Müller, 1117
  origin of, 562
  palate, 1244
  pelvic, 468
  perineal, deep transverse, 482
    superficial transverse, 480
  of perineum, 471
  pharynx, 1248
  of pinna or auricula, 1127
  plantar first layer, 554
    fourth layer, 559
    second layer, 556
    third layer, 557
  plate, 119
  posterior crural, 545
    femoral, 541
  scalp, 413
  shoulder-girdle, development of, 406
  striated (striped), 405
    structure of, 559
  suboccipital, 445
  superficial cervical, 426
  suprahyoid, 432
  suspensory, of duodenum, 1279
  synergetic, 412
  tendons of, 407
  thenar, 520
  thigh, 528
  thoracic, 446
    surface anatomy of, 76
  tongue, 1234
  trachelomastoid, 442
  trunk, 438
  tympanic cavity, 1138
  upper extremity, 483
  ureters, 1345
  urogenital region (female), 480 (male), 478
  uvula, 1246
  ventrolateral, of neck, development of, 406
  volar antebrachial, 500
Musculus or *Musculi, Musculi, abductor, hallucis,* 555
  digiti quinti (pedis), 556
    [*manus*], 523
  indicis, 523
  minimi digiti, 523
  pollicis, 521
    brevis, 521
    longus, 510
  accelerator urinæ, 479
  accessorius, 442
    of foot, 556
  adductor brevis, 535
    hallucis, 558
    longus, 534
    magnus, 535
    minimus, 535
    obliquus transversus, 558
    pollicis obliquus, 522
    transversus, 523
  anconæus, 508
  antitragicus, 1127
  arrectores pilorum, 1161
  articularis cubiti, 499
    genu or subcrureus, 533
  aryepiglotticus, 1185
  arytænoideus, 1185
  attollens aurem, 1127
  attrahens aurem, 1127
  auricularis, 1127
  azygos uvulæ, 1246
  biceps, 497
    brachii, 497
    femoris, 541
    flexor cubiti, 497
  biventer cervicis, 443
  brachialis, 498
    anticus, 498
  brachioradialis, 505

Musculus, buccinator, 420
  bulbocavernosus, 479, 480
  canius, 418
  cervicalis ascendens, 442
  chondroepitrochlearis, 491
  chondroglossus, 1235
  ciliaris, 1106
  cleidohyoideus, 434
  coccygeus, 470
  complexus, 443
  compressor naris, 417
  constrictor pharnygis inferior, 1249
    medius, 1249
    superior, 1249
    urethræ, 482, 1347
  coracobrachialis, 497
  corrugator, 417
    cutis ani, 1293
    supercilii, 417
  costocoracoideus, 491
  cremaster, 459
  cricoarytænoideus, 1185
  cricothyroideus, 1185
  crureus, 533
  deltoideus, 493
  depressor alæ nasi, 418
    anguli oris, 419
    labii inferioris, 419
    septi, 418
  detrusor urinæ, 1345
  digastricus, 432
  dilator naris, 418
    pupillæ, 1107
  dorsoepitrochlearis brachii, 486, 499
  ejaculator urinæ, 479
  epicranius, 413
  epitrocheoanconæus, 502
  erector clitoridis, 481
    penis, 480
    spinæ, 440
  extensor carpi radialis accessorius, 506
    brevior, 506
    brevis, 506
    intermedius, 506
    longior, 506
    longus, 506
    ulnaris, 508
    hallucis brevis, 553
    longus, 544
    coccygis, 444
    digiti quinti proprius, 507
    digitorum brevis, 553
    communis, 506
    longus, 544
    indicis proprius, 510
    minimi digiti, 507
    ossis metacarpimetatarsi, pollicies hallucis, 544
    pollicis brevis, 510
    longus, 510
    primi internodii pollicuis, 510
    proprius hallucis, 544
    secundi internodii pollicus, 510
  flexor accessorius, 556
    brevis minimi digiti, 523, 558
    carpi radialis, 501
    ulnaris, 501
    digiti quinti brevis [pedis], 558
    [*manus*], 523
    digitorum brevis, 555
    longus, 548
    profundus, 502
    sublimis, 502
    hallucis brevis, 557
    longus, 548
    pollicis brevis, 521
    lohgus, 504
  frontalis, 414
  gastrocnemius, 545

Musculus, gemellus, 540
  inferior, 540
  superior, 540
  genioglossus, 1235
  geniohyoglossus, 1235
  geniohyoideus, 434
  glossopalatinus, 1239, note, 1241, 1246
  glutæus maximus, 536
    medius, 537
    minimus, 538
  gracilis, 533
  helicis major, 1128
    minor, 1128
  hyoglossus, 1235
  iliacus, 528
    minor, 528
  iliocapsularis, 528
  iliococcygeus, 469
  iliocostalis, 440
    cervicis, 442
    dorsi, 442
    lumborum, 442
  iliosacralis, 470
  incisivus labii, 420
  infraspinatus, 494
  intercostales, 447
    externi, 447
    interni, 447
  interossei dorsales manus, 524
    palmaris, 525
    pedis, 559
    plantares, 557
  interosseus palmaris primus, 521, 525
  interspinales, 444
  intertransversales, 444
  ischiocavernosus, 480, 481
  latissimus dorsi, 485
  levator anguli oris, 418
    scapulæ, 487
    ani, 469
    claviculæ, 487
    glandulæ thyreoideæ, 1393
    labii superioris, 418
    menti, 419
    palati, 1245
    palpebræ superioris, 1114
    prostatæ, 469
    scapulæ, 487
    veli palantini, 1245
  levatores costarum, 448
  lingualis, 1236
  longissimus capitis, 442
    cervicis, 442
    dorsi, 442
  longitudinalis linguæ, 1235
  longus capitis, 436
    colli, 436
  lumbricales [manus], 524, 556
    [pedis], 556
  masseter, 424
  mentalis, 419
  mentohyoideus, 432
  multifidus spinæ, 443
  mylohyoideus, 433
  nasalis, 417
  nasolabialis, 420
  obliquus auriculæ, 1128
    capitis inferior, 445, 454
    superior, 445
    externus abdominis, 454
    inferior oculi, 445, 454
    internus abdominis, 459
    superior oculi, 1115, 1116
  obturator externus, 540
    internus, 539
  occipitalis, 414
  occipitofrontalis, 414
  omohyoideus, 435
  opponens digiti quinti [manus], 523
    [pedis], 558
  minimi aigiti, 523

Musculus, opponens, pollicis, 521
  orbicularis oculi, 417
    oris, 420
    palpebrarum, 416
  ossiculorum auditus, 1138
  palatoglossus, note, 1235, note,
    1246
  palatopharyngeus, 1246
  palmaris brevis, 523
    longus, 501
  papillares, 591
  pectinati [of left auricle], 591
    [of right auricle], 586
  pectineus, 534
  pectoralis major, 490
    minimus, 491
    minor, 491
  peronæus accessorius, 551
    brevis, 550
    longus, 550
    quartus, 551
    quinti digiti, 551
    tertius, 545
  peroneocalcaneus externus, 551
    internus, 548
  peroneocuboideus, 551
  peroneotibialis, 548
  pharyngopalatinus, 1247
  piriformis, 538
  pisiannularis, 524
  pisimetacarpus, 524
  pisiuncinatus, 524
  plantaris, 546
  platysma, 425
  popliteus, 547
    minor, 548
  procerus, 417
  pronator quadratus, 505
    teres, 500
  psoas, major, 527
    nubirm 528
    parvus, 528
  pterygoideus externus, 425
    internus, 424
  pubococcygeus, 469
  puborectalis, 469
  pubovesicales, 1343
  pyramidalis, abdominis, 462
    nasi, 418
  quadratus femoris, 532, 540
    labii, 418
    lumborum, 467
    menti, 419
    plantæ, 556
  quadriceps extensor femoris, 532
  recti [of eyeball], 1115
  rectovesicales, 1343
  rectus abdominis, 460
    capitis anterior, 436
      lateralis, 436
      posterior, 445
    anticus, 436
    posticus, 445
    inferior oculi, 1115
    lateralis oculi, 1114
    medialis oculi, 1114
    femoris, 532
    superior, oculi, 1115
  retrahens aurem, 1127
  rhomboideus major, 486
    minor, 486
    occipitalis, 486
  risorius, 419
  rotatores, 444
    spinæ, 444
  sacrospinalis, 440
  salpingopharyngeus, 1251
  sartorius, 530
  scalenus anterior, 437
    anticus, 437
    medius, 437
    pleuralis, 438
    posterior, 437

Musculus, scalenus, posticus, 437
  semimembranosus, 542
  semispinalis capitis, 443
    cervicis, 443
    colli, 443
    dorsi, 443
  semitendinosus, 542
  serratus anterior, 492
    magnus, 492
    posterior, inferior, 449
      superior, 448
    posticus, 448
  soleus, 546
  sphincter ani externus, 482
    internus, 482
    pupillæ, 1107
    recti, 482
    urethræ membranaceæ, 480
    vaginæ, 480
    vesicæ, 1345
  spinalis capitis, 443
    cervicis, 443
    colli, 443
    thoracis, 442
  splenius capitis, 440
    cervicis, 440
    colli, 440
  stapedius, 1136
  sternalis, 491
  sternoclavicularis, 492
  sternocleidomastoideus, 431
  sternohyoideus, 434
  sternomastoideus, 431
  steonothyroideus, 434
  styloglossus, 1235
  stylohyoideus, 433
  stylopharyngeus, 1250
  subanconæus, 499
  subclavius, 492
  subcostales, 447
  subcrureus, 533
  subscapularis, 493
  supinator, 508
    brevis, 508
    longus, 505
  supraclavicularis, 432
  supracostalis, 447
  supraspinatus, 494
  suspensorius, duodeni, 1279
  temporalis, 424
  temporparietales, 415
  tensor faciæ latæ, 538
    palati, 1245
    tarsi, 416
    tympani, 1138
    veli palatini, 1245
  teres major, 495
    minor, 495
  tibiofacialis anterior, 543
  thyreoarytænoideus, 1186
  thyreoepiglotticus, 1187
  thyroarytenoideus, 1186
  thyreohyoideus, 434
  tibialis anterior, 543
    anticus, 543
    posterior, 549
  trachealis, 1191
  tragicus, 1128
  transversalis, 460
    cervicis, 442
  transversus abdominis, 459
    auriculæ, 1128
    linguæ, 1236
    menti, 419
    nuchæ, 415
    pedis, 558
    perinæi, 478, 480
      profundus, 480, 482
      superficialis [in female],
        478
      [in male], 478
    thoracis, 448
  trapezius, 485

Musculus, triangularis, 419
    sterni, 448
  triceps brachii, 498
    extensor cubiti, 498
    suræ, 546
  uvulæ, 1246
  vastus externus, 532
    intermedius, 533
    internus, 533
    lateralis, 532
    medialis, 533
  ventricularis, 1187
  verticalis linguæ, 1246
  vocalis, 1186
  zygomaticus, 418
    major, 418
Muscular fibers of heart, 594
  process of arytenoid cartilage,
    1179
  tissue, cardiac, 596
  triangle, 435, 1126
Musculocutaneous nerve of arm,
    1020
  of leg, 1053
Musculophrenic artery, 649
Musculospiral groove, 237
  nerve, 1030
Myelencephalon, 825
Myelinated nerve fibers, 825
Mylohyoid artery, 630
  groove, 181
  line, 180
  muscle, 433
  nerve, 972
Myocæl, 35, 119
Myocardium, 580
  primitive, 570
Myofibrillæ, 561
Myology, 405
Myometrium, 1376

N

Nails, 1158
Nares, 1168
Nasal aperture, anterior, 175, 177
  artery, 636
    lateral, 624
  bones, 213
    articulations of, 214
    ossification of, 214
  cartilages, 1170
  cavity, 175, 1170
  concha, inferior, 225
    middle, 212
    superior, 212
  crest, 219, 223
  duct, 1122
  fossa, 175, 1170
    arteries of, 1174
    lymphatic capillaries in, 787
    mucous membrane of, 1173
    nerves of, 1174
    veins of, 1174
    vessels of, 1174
    vestibule of, 1170
  laminæ, 43
  meatus, 1172
  mucous membrane, 1173
  nerve from ophthalmic, 963
  notch of frontal bone, 194
    of maxilla, 214
  part of frontal bone, 194
    of pharynx, 1247
  process of frontal bone, 194
    of maxilla, 218
  processes of fetus, 43
  septum, 176
  sinuses, 1175
  spine, anterior, 167, 214, 219
    of frontal bone, 194
    posterior, 159, 222
Nasalis muscle, 417
Nasion, 167, 194

Nasmyth's membrane, 1228
Nasociliary nerve, 959
Nasofronta, vein, 739
Nasolabialis muscle, 420
Nasolacrimal canal, 177
  duct, 1099, 1122
Nasoöptic furrow, 44, 1099
Nasopalatine nerve, 966
Nasopharynx, 1247
Nasus externus, 1168
Navicular bone of carpus, 249
  of tarsus, 297
  fossa, 1381
Neck, lymph nodes of, 784, 789
  vessels of, 791
  muscles of, 426
    development of, 405
  surface anatomy of, 69
  triangles of, 71
  veins of, 725
Neopallium, 831
  roots, 997
Nerve or Nerves, or abducent, 916
  accessory, 994
  acoustic, 917, 1150
  alveolar, 967, 972
  anococcygeal, 1057
  anterior crural, 1042
    interosseous, 1023
    superior alveolar, 967
    thoracic, 1015
    tibial, 1053
  antebrachial cutaneous, 1020
  Arnold's, 990
  auditory, 981
  auricular, 1007
    great, of auriculotemporal, 970
    of vagus, 990
    posterior, 979
  auriculotemporal, 970
  axillary, 1014
  brachial cutaneous, lateral, 1019
    medial, 1020
    posterior, 1030
  bronchial, 993
  buccal, long, 969
    of facial, 980
  buccinator, 967
  cardiac, sympathetic, 1071
    thoracic, 991
    vagus, 1017
  caroticotympanic, 1068, 1139
  carotid of glossopharyngeal, 984
  cavernous, of penis, 1087
  celiac, of vagus, 994
  cells, 930
    of cerebellar cortex, 865
    of cerebral cortex, 887
    of spinal cord, 930
  cerebral, 951. See Cranial.
  cerebrospinal, structure of, 931
  cervical, 1001, 1005
    cutaneous, 1008
    divisions of, 1001, 1005
    of facial, 981
    transverse, 1008
  chorda tympani, 978, 1139
  ciliary, 958
  of clitoris, 1057
  coccygeal, division of, 1004, 1045
  cochlear, 917, 1151
  cone of, origin of, 931
  cranial, 834, 951
    abducent, [6th], 973
    accessory, [11th], 994
    acoustic, [8th], 981
    composition and central connections of, 910

Nerve, cranial facial, [7th], 974
    glossopharyngeal, [9th], 981
    hypoglossal, [12th], 995
    oculomotor, [3rd], 957
    olfactory, [1st], 955
    optic, [2nd], 956
    trigeminal [5th], 915
    trochlear, [4th], 915
    vagus, [10th], 986
  crural, anterior, 1042
  cutaneous cervical, 1008
    external, thigh, 1041
    internal, forearm, 1020
      lesser, thigh, 1043
      middle, thigh, 1042
  deep branch of radial, 1030
    of ulnar, 1029
    peroneal, 1053
    petrosal, 977
    temporal, 969
  descending ramus of hypoglossal, 996
  development of, 821
  digastric, from facial, 979
  digital, of lateral plantar, 1052
    of medial plantar, 1052
    of median, 1023
    of radial, 1029
    of superficial peroneal, 1053
    of ulnar, 1028
  dorsal antebrachial cutaneous, 1030
    branch of ulnar, 1028
    cutaneous, foot, 1052, 1053
    digital, 1028
    of penis, 1057
    scapular, 1015
  of dura mater, 965
  dural, 990
  eighth, 8th, 917
  eleventh, 11th, 994
  endings, 937
  end-organs of, 937
  epineurium of, 936
  esophageal, 993
  ethmoidal, 963
  external carotid, 1070
    nasal, 966
    plantar, 1052
    popliteal, 1052
    pterygoid, 969
    saphenous, 1043
    spermatic, 1038
  facial, 916, 1061
  fasciculi, 843
  femoral, 1042
    cutaneous, anterior, 1042
      lateral, 1041
      posterior, 1047
  fibers, 931
    of cerebral cortex, 892
  medullated, 931
    myelinated, 931
    neurilemma, 932
    non-medullated, 936
    primitive sheath, 932
  fifth, 5th, 915
  first, 1st, 955
  fourth, 4th, 915
  frontal, 962
  ganglia of, 936
    autonomic, 937
    parasympathetic, 1062
    sensory, 936
    sympathetic, 1065
  gastric branches of vagus, 994
  gemmula of, 930
  genitocrural, 1038
  genitofemoral, 1038
  glossopalatine, 975
  glossopharyngeal, 919
  gluteal, 1047
  great auricular, 1007

Nerve, greater occipital, 1002
    splanchnic, 1076
    superficial petrosal, 976, 984
  hemorrhoidal inferior, 1056
  hepatic branches of vagus, 994
  hypoglossal, 921, 995
  iliohypogastric, 1037
  ilioinguinal, 1037
  incisive, 972
  inferior dental, 972
  infraorbital, 964
  infrapatellar, 1043
  infratrochlear, 963
  intercostal, 1033
  intercostobrachial, 1034
    carotid 1070
    cutaneous of arm, 1020
    popliteal, 1050
    saphenous, 1043
  interosseous, dorsal, 1031
    volar, 1023
  Jacobson's, 983, 1139
  jugular, 1070
  labial posterior, 1056
    superior, 968
  lacrimal, 962
  laryngeal, 991
  laryngopharyngeal of sympathetic, 1071
  lateral antebrachial cutaneous, 1019
    brachial cutaneous, 1019
    femoral cutaneous, 1040
    plantar, 1052
    sural cutaneous, 1053
  lesser splanchnic, 1079
  lingual, 972
    of glossopharyngeal, 986
  long ciliary, 958
    saphenous, 1043
    subscapular, 1017
    thoracic, 1015
  lowest splanchnic, 1079
  lumbar, divisions of, 1003, 1036
  lumboinguinal, 1039
  lumbosacral trunk, 1036
  mandibular, 968
    of facial, 981
  masseteric, 969
  maxillary, 964
    inferior, 968
  medial antebrachial cutaneous, 1020
    brachial cutaneous, 1020
    plantar, 1050
    sural cutaneous, 1053
  median, 1021
  meningeal, 965
    middle, 965
    of hypoglossal, 996
    of maxillary, 965
    of vagus, 990
  mental, 972
  middle superior alveolar, 967
  motor, 943
  musculocutaneous of arm, 1021
    of leg, 1053
  musculospiral, 1029
  myelinated, 935
  mylohyoid, 972
  nasal, of ophthalmic, 963
    from sphenopalatine, 966
  nasociliary, 963
  nasopalatine, 966
  ninth, 981
  obturator, 1040
    accessory, 1040
  occipital greater, 1002
    smaller, 1006
    third, 1002
  oculomotor, 911, 1061, 1068
  of Hering, 984
  of pterygoid canal, 976
  of spleen, 816

Nerve of taste, 1095
of tongue, 1236
of urethral bulb, 1056
of Wrisberg, 1020
olfactory, 955
ophthalmic, 961
optic, 911
orbital, 965
palatine, 966
palmar cutaneous, of median, 1028
of ulnar, 1028
palpebral, inferior, 968
parasympathetic, cranial, 1061
sacral, 1063
perforating cutaneous, 1049
peripheral, 935
termination of, 937
perineal, 1056
perineurium of, 936
peroneal, 1052
deep, 1053
superficial, 1053
petrosal, deep, 977, 1070
external, 1070
greater superficial, 976
large, deep, 977
superficial, 976
smaller superficial, 1139
pharyngeal, of glosso-
pharyngeal, 986
of sphenopalatine, 967
of vagus, 990
phrenic, 1010
plantar, 1052
plexus of. See Plexus.
annular, 1103
aortic abdominal, 1085
Auerbach's, 1282, 1284
brachial, 1011
cardiac, 1075, 1083
carotid, 1067
cavernous, 1068
celiac, 1084
cervical, 1005
posterior, 1002, 1005, 1007, 1008
coccygeal, 1057
corneal, 1103
coronary, 1084
esophageal, 991, 993
gastric, 994, 1085
hemorrhoidal, 1087
hepatic, 1085
hypogastric, 1086
infraorbital, 968
lienal, 1085
lumbar, 1003, 1036
lumbosacral, 1036
Meissner's, 1282, 1284
mesenteric, 1085
myenteric, 1282, 1284
plexus, ovarian, 1085
parotid, 971
patellar, 1040, 1043
pelvic, 1087
pharyngeal, 986, 991, 1071
phrenic, 1010, 1085
prostatic, 1087
pudendal, 1055
pulmonary, 993
renal, 1085
sacral, 1004, 1045
solar, 1084
spermatic, 1085
splenic, 1085
subsartorial, 1043
submucosal, intestine, 1284
suprarenal, 1085
tonsillar, 986
tympanic, 984
uterine, 1087
vaginal, 1087

Nerve, plexus of, vesical, 1087
pneumogastric, 986
popliteal, 1050, 1052
posterior scrotal, 1056
to pterygoideus externus, 969
internus, 968
pterygopalatine, 967
pudendal, 1056
inferior, 1047
pudic, internal, 1056
pulmonary, 993
radial, 1029
rami communicantes, gray and white, 1065
recurrent, laryngeal, 991
respiratory, of Bell, 1010, 1015
roots, 839, 997
sacral, 1004, 1041
saphenous, 1043
sciatic, 1047, 1049
scrotal, posterior, 1056
second, 2nd, 911
seventh, 7th, 916
short ciliary, 958
sixth, 6th, 916
smaller occipital, 1006
spermatic, external, 1038
sphenopalatine branches of maxillary, 965
spinal, 1001
accessory, 994
composition and central connections of, 921
development of, 824
divisions of, 1001, 1004
roots of, 839, 997
structure of, 997
splanchnic, 1076, 1078
stato-acoustic, 917
to stapedius, 978
stylohyoid, 979
subscapular, 1017
to subclavius, 1015
suboccipital, 1001, 1005
superficial branch of radial, 1030
of ulnar, 1029
superior labial, 968
supraäcromial, 1008
supraclavicular, 1015
supraorbital, 962
suprascapular, 1015, 1017
suprasternal, 1008
supratrochlear, 962
sural, 1053
cutaneous, lateral, 1053
medial, 1053
sympathetic, 1061
temporal, deep, 969
of facial, 979
temporomalar, 965
tenth, 10th, 986
terminations of, 937
third, 3rd, 912
thoracic, divisions of, 1002, 1031
thoracodorsal, 1017
thyrohyoid, 997
tibial, 1050
anterior, 1053
tissue, degenerative changes in, 943
tonsillar, 986
transverse cervical, 1008
trifacial, 960
trigeminal, 915, 960
trochlear, 915
twelfth, 12th, 995
tympanic of glossopharyngeal, 983
ulnar, 1024
collateral, 1029
unmyelinated, 936

Nerve, vagus, 920
vestibular, 981, 1150
vidian, 976
volar digital, 1023
interosseous, 1023
vomeronasal, 954
zygomatic, 965
of facial, 951
zygomaticofacial, 965
zygomaticotemporal, 965
Nervi auriculares anteriores, 971
clunium inferiores, 1047
communicantes cervicales, 1009
hypoglossi, 1009
ethmoidales, 963
lumbales, 1036
anteriores, 1036
magnocellularis of von Monakow, 855
spinales, 997
rami anteriores, 1004
posteriores, 1001
terminalis, 951
thoracales, 1002
anteriores, 1031
Nervous system, 821
autonomic, 833, 1060
cranial, 951
central, 821
cranial, 1061
development of, 821
histology of, 930
parasympathetic, 1061
peripheral, 951
sacral, 1061
sympathetic, 1063
thoracolumbar, 1063
Nervus ramus externus, 994
internus, 994
canalis pterygoidei, 976
clunium inferior medialis, 1049
communicans fibularis, 1053
cutaneus antebrachii dorsalis, 1030
lateralis, 1019
medialis, 1020
brachii medialis, 1020
posterior, 1030
colli, 1008
femoralis lateralis, 1039
posterior, 1047
descendens cervicalis, 1009
hypoglossi, 996
dorsalis clitoridis, 1057
penis, 1057
scapulæ, 1015
facialis, 974
rami buccales, 980
temporales, 979
zygomatici, 980
ramus colli, 981
digastricus, 979
marginalis mandibulæ, 981
stylohyoideus, 979
femoralis, 1042
frontalis, 962
furcalis, 1036
ganglion petrosum, 982
superius, 986
rami linguales, 986
pharyngei, 986
tonsillares, 986
ramus stylopharyngeus, 986
glossopharyngeus, 919
hæmorrhoidalis inferior, 1056
hypoglossus, 921
ramus descendens, 996
thyreohoideus, 997
intermedius [of Wrisberg], 974
ischiadicus, 1049
maxillaris, 964

*Nervus maxillaris ramus alveolaris
    superior anteriores*, 966
    medius, 966
    meatus auditorii externi, 971
    oculomotorius, 912
    olfactorius, 955
    ophthalmicus, 961
    opticus, 911
    spinosus, 968
        ramus cutaneus palmaris,
        1028
            dorsalis manus, 1028
            profundus, 1029
            superficialis, 1029
            ulnaris, 1024
            volaris manus, 1028
    supratrochlaris, 962
    tentorii, 962
    trigeminus, 860
    trochlearis, 960
    terminalis, 951
    vagus, 920
        rami bronchiales, 993
            cardiaci, 991
            cœliaci, 994
            gastrici, 994
            hepatici, 994
            œsophagei, 993
        ramus auricularis, 990
            laryngeus, 990
                inferior, 991
                superior, 990
            meningeus, 990
            pharyngeus, 990
    Vidii, 976
Net-work, carpal, 661
    malleolar, 708
Neumann, dentinal sheath of,
    1224
Neural arch, 127
    canal, 35
    crest, 35, 824, 833
    folds, 35
    groove, 35
    tube, 35
Neuroblasts, 821, 825
Neurocentral synchondrosis, 144
Neuroglia, 933
Neurolemma, 932
Neurology, 821
Neuromeres, 824, 838
Neuromuscular spindles, 939
Neuron theory, 931
Neurons, 930
    motor, 923
Neurotendinous spindles, 939
Neurtrophilic corpuscles, 770
Ninth nerve, 919
Nipple or papilla of mamma, 1382
Nissl's granules, 930
Node or Nodes, atrioventricular,
    595
    hemal, 782
    hemolymph, 782
    lymph, 780
    primitive, 33
    of Keith and Flack, 595
    of Ranvier, 932
    of Tawara, 595
    sinoatrial, 595
Noduli lymphatici aggregati, 1282
Nodulus corpus Arantii, 590
Non-medullated nerve fibers, 936
Norma basalis, of skull, 159
    frontalis, 167
    lateralis, 162
    occipitalis, 166
    verticalis, 158
Normal stomach, *x*-ray of after a
    barium meal, 90
Nose, 1168
    accessory sinuses of, 1175
    alar cartilages of, 1170

Nose, arteries of, 1170
    cartilage of septum of, 1169
    cartilaginous frame-work of,
    1169
    cavities of, 1169
    development of, 42
    external, 1168
    fossæ, 1170
    lateral cartilage of, 1170
    lymphatics of, 787
    mucous membrane of, 1173
    muscles of, 417, 1170
    nerves of, 1170
    veins of, 1170
Notch, acetabular, 264
    cardiac, 1199
    ethmoidal, 194
    intertragic, 1126
    jugular, 188
    lacrimal, 215
    mandibular, 182
    mastoid, 161
    nasal, of frontal, 194
        of maxilla, 214
    parietal, 198
    preoccipital, 885
    presternal, 151
    of Rivinus, 1131
    scapular, 232
    sciatic, 261, 262, 267
    semilunar, of ulna, 244
    sphenopalatine, 225
    superior thyroid, 1176
    supraorbital, 167, 171, 194
    ulnar, or radius, 247
    umbilical, of liver, 1298
    vertebral, 130
Notochord, 34
Nuchal fascia, 438
    ligament, 330
    line, 162, 187
Nuck, canal of, 1322
Nuclear fragmentation, 24
    layer of cerebellar cortex, 866
    layers of retina, 1109, 1110
Nucleated sheath of Schwann,
    932
Nucleoli, 20
Nucleoplasm, 67
Nucleus or Nuclei, 21
    abducens nerve, 916
    accessory cuneate, 851
        nerve, 920, 994
    accumbens, 908
    alae cinereae, 853, 920
    ambiguus, 853
    amygdaloid, 899, 911
    arcuatus, 855
    autonomic, 914
    of Bechterew, 861
    of Cajal, 871
    caudate, 898
    cell, 21
    of cochlear nerve, 917
    cuneatus, 851
    of Darkscheivitsch, 870
    Deiter's, 860
    dentatus [of cerebellum], 867
    dorsal motor, vagus, 853
    dorsalis, 841
    of Edinger-Westphal, 914
    emboliformis, 867
    facial nerve, 859, 917
    fastigii, 867
    globosus, 867
    of glossopharyngeal nerve, 919
    gracilis, 851
    hypoglossal nerve, 853, 921
    hypothalmic, 879
    intercalatus, 855, 880
    interpeduncularis, 872
    interpositus, 867
    interstitial of Cajal, 871

Nucleus, *lacrimalis*, 917
    lateral reticular, 855
    lentiform, 898
    of lens, 1114
    of Luys, 878
    magnocellularis, 855
    mammillary, 880
    of medial longitudinal fascicu-
    lus, 871
    of mesenchephalic root of V,
    870
    motor of V, 859, 915
    of olfactory nerve, 910
    olivaris inferior, 851
    olivaris superior, 860
    olivary, 851, 860
    of oculomotor nerve, 870, 912,
    914
    of optic nerve, 911
    of origin of motor nerves, 961
    paraventricularis, 880
    pontis, 861
    of Perlia, 870
    of posterior commissure, 878
    prepositus, 856
    pulposus, 121
    of Ramon y Cajal, 871
    red, 871
    reticularis thalami, 877
    ruber, 872
    salivatorius, 917, 920
    of Schwalbe, 860
    semilunaris thalami, 876
    sensorius superior n. V, 859
    sensory, 915, 974
    sensory of V, 859, 915
    of spinal tract of V, 853, 859
    of Staderini, 855
    statoäcusticus, 860, 917
    supraöptic, 880
    of tegmentum of pons, 859
    of thalamus, 875
    tractus solitarius, 855
    trapezoid, 863
    of trigeminal nerve, 870
    trochlearis, 870
    tuberales, 881
    vagus nerve, 853, 920
    ventralis posterolateralis, 877
        posteromedialis, 876
    of vestibular nerve, 860, 919
    Von Monakow, 855
Nuel, space of, 1150
Nuhn, glands of, 1237
Nutrient artery of bone, 312
    of femur, 703
    of fibula, 710
    of humerus, 658
    of tibia, 711
    foramen of fibula, 287
Nymphæ, 1389

O

OBELION, 159
Obex, 867
Oblique cord, 364
    ligament, 364
    line of fibula, 288
        of mandible, 180
        of radius, 247
    muscle of abdomen, 454, 458
        of eye, inferior, 1115
            superior, 1115
    popliteal ligament, 381
    ridge of clavicle, 228
    sinus of pericardium, 581
    vein of left atrium, 581, 725
        of Marshall, 581, 725
Obliquus auriculæ muscle, 1127
    capitis inferior muscle, 445
        superior muscle, 445

Obliquus externus abdominis
     muscle, 454
  inferior muscle, 445
     nerve, 958
  internus abdominis muscle, 458
  occuli infer or muscle, 1115
     superior muscle, 1115
  superior muscle, 445
Obliterated ductus anteriosus,
     579, 611
  venosus, 762
  hypogastric artery, 685
  umbilical vein, 762, 1258
Obturator artery, 688
  crest, 263
  externus muscle, 540
  fascia, 470
  foramen, 265
  groove, 265
  internus muscle, 539
  membrane, 538
  nerve, 1040
     accessory, 1040
  tubercle, 265
  vein, 757
Occipital artery, 625
  bone, 186
     articulations of, 190
     basilar part of, 189
     lateral parts of, 188
     ossification of, 190
     squama of, 187
     structure of, 190
  condyles, 188
  crest, internal, 175, 188
  fossæ, 175
  groove, 161, 198
  lobe, 884
  lymph nodes, 784
  nerve, 1006
  protuberance, 162, 163, 187,
     188
  sinus, 739
  sulcus, 885
  triangle, 73, 435
  vein, 727
Occipitalis muscle, 414
Occipitoaxial ligaments, 335
Occipitofrontal fasciculus, 896
Occipitofrontalis muscle, 414
Occipitomastoid suture, 163, 166,
     175
Ocular bulb, 1095
  muscles, 1114
Oculomotor nerve, 912, 1061
  autonomic nucleus of, 914
  composition and central con-
     nections of, 912
  proprioceptive fibers in, 914
  somatic nucleus of, 914
Odontoblasts, 1223, 1228
Odontoid ligaments, 335
  process of axis, 131
Olecranon, 241
  fossa, 239
  process, 241
Olfactory areas, 42
  bulb, 904
     structure of, 907
  cells, 907, 1094
  fila, 1094
  groove, 173
  gyrus, 830, 905
  hairs, 1094
  mucous membrane, 1094
  nerves, 910, 1094
     composition and central con-
        nections of, 910
     development of, 830
  pathways, 911
  pits, 42
  projection fibers, 905, 911
  stria, 905, 911

Olfactory sulcus, 884
  tract, 904
  trigone, 905
  tubercle, 905
Oligodendrocytes, 935
Oligodendroglia, 935
Oliva, 848
Olive, 848
Olivary body, 848
  nucleus, 826, 851
Olivocerebellar fibers, 844
Olivospinal fasciculus, 846
Omental bursa, 1260, 1266
  recess, 1267
Omentum, gastrocolic, 1268
  gastrohepatic, 1267
  greater, 1268
  lesser, 1267
  small, 1267
Omohyoid muscle, 435
Oocyte, primary, 25
  secondary, 25
Opening or Openings, aortic, in
     diaphragm, 450
  atrioventricular, 589, 591
  caval, in diaphragm, 451
  esophageal, in diaphragm, 451
  in roof of fourth ventricle, 868
  of aorta in left ventricle, 591
  of coronary sinus, 587
  of inferior vena cava, 587
  of pulmonary artery, 590
     veins, 590
  of superior vena cava, 587
  saphenous, 530
Opercula of insula, 833, 883, 885
Ophthalmic artery, 634
  ganglion, 958
  nerve, 961
  veins, 739
Opisthion, 162
Opisthotic center of temporal
     bone, 203
Opponens digiti quinti muscle,
     523
  minimi digiti muscle, 523
  pollicis muscle, 521
Optic axis, 1096
  chiasma, 879, 912, 957, 1097
  commissure, 912
  cup, 828, 1097
  disk, 1109
  foramen, 174, 204, 956
  groove, 204
  nerve, 911, 1097
     composition and central con-
        nections of, 911
  radiations, 877, 895, 899
  stalk, 828, 1096
  thalamus, 874
  tracts, 879, 912, 957, 1097
  vesicle, 828, 1096
Ora serrata, 1109, 1111
  part of pharynx, 1247
Orbicular ligament, 364
Orbicularis oculi muscle, 416
  lacrimal part, 416
     orbital part, 416
     palpebral part, 416
  oris muscle, 419
  palpebrarum muscle, 416
Orbiculus ciliaris muscle, 1104
Orbit, 169
  relation of nerves in, 973
Orbital fascia, 1118
  fissures, 163, 174, 177, 207, 222
  gyri, 883
  nerve, 965
  operculum, 883
  plates, 198
  process of palatine bone, 224
     of zygomatic bone, 221
  septum, 1119

Orbital sulcus, 883
  vein, 725
Orbitosphenoids, 207
Organ or Organs, enamel, 1227
  genital, of female, 1367
  oculi accessoria, 1114
  of Corti, 1148
  of digestion, 1207
  of female, 1367
  of Giraldes, 1358
  of Golgi, 939
  of hearing, 1122
  of male, 1348
  of Rosenmüller, 1317, 1369
  of sight, 1095
  of smell, 1093
  of taste, 1094
  of the senses, 1093
  spiral, of Corti, 1148
  urinary, 1325
  urogenital, 1315
  vomero-nasal of Jacobson, 45,
     1172
Orifice or Orifices, atrioventric-
     ular, 588, 591
  cardiac, of stomach, 1272
  mitral, 591
  of mouth, 1215
  of ureters, 1344
  of uterus, 1374
  pyloric, of stomach, 1273
  urethral, 1344, 1347, 1384
  vaginal, 1381
Origin of muscles, 411
Os acetabuli, 265
  calcis, 289
  capitatum, 253
  coccygis, 141
  coxæ, 258
     articulations of, 265
     ossification of, 265
     structure of, 265
  cuboideum, 296
  cuneiforme intermedium, 298
     laterale, 298
     mediale, 297
  ethmoidale, 209
  external of uterus, 1374
  frontale, 193
  hamatum, 254
  hyoideum, 185
  ilii, 258
  incisivum, 219
  innominatum, 258
  internal of uterus, 1374
  ischii, 261
  lacrimale, 220
  lunatum, 249
  magnum, 253
  metacarpale, 255
  naviculare pedis, 306
  occipitale, 186
  palatinum, 222
  parietale, 190
  pisiforme, 252
  pubis, 263
  sacrum, 137
  scaphoidium, 249
  sphenoidale, 204
     alæ majores, 206
     minores, 207
  temporale, 195
  trapezoideum, 252
  trigonum, 296
  triquetrum, 251
  zygomaticum, 221
Ossa carpi, 248
  cranii, 186
  extremitatis, 258
  faciei, 213
  metacarpalia, 255
  metatarsalia, 299
  nasalia, 213

Ossa sesamoidea, 304
  tarsi, 289
Ossein, 315
Ossicles, auditory, 1136
  ligaments of, 1137
Ossicula auditus, 1136
Ossification,. See individual bones.
Osteoblasts, 311
Osteoclasts, 316, 1229
Osteodentin, 1225
Osteogenetic fibers, 315
Osteology, 119
Ostia of paranasal sinuses, 1175
Ostium, abdominal, of uterine
   tube, 1370
  of eustachian tube, 1135
  maxillare, 177, 1172
  pharyngeal, of auditory tube,
   1248
  primitive urogenital, 1324
  primum [heart], 513
  secundum [heart], 573
Otic ganglion, 984
Otoconia, 1146
Outlet of pelvis, 266
Ova, primitive, 1320
Oval bundle, 824
Ovarian arteries, 682
  follicle, 24
  fossa, 1266, 1367
  plexus of nerves, 1087
  veins, 761
Ovaries, 1367
  descent of, 1322
  development of, 1319
  ligaments of, 1369
   vessels of, 807
  medullary substance of, 1369
  nerves of, 1370
  structure of, 1369
  vesicular or Graafian follicles
   of, 1369
  vessels of, 1370
Oviduct, 1370
Ovula Nabothi, 1378
Ovum, 24
  corona radiata of, 24
  discharge of, 1370
  fertilization of, 27
  germinal spot of, 24
   vesicle of, 24
  imbedding of, 28
  implantation of, 28
  maturation of, 25
  segmentation of, 28
  size of, 24
  zona pellucida of, 24

P

PACCHIONIAN bodies, 928
Pacinian corpuscles, 939
Pain, impulses of, 922
Palatal process of maxilla, 218
Palate, 1218
  arches of, 129
  bone, 222
  cleft, 179
  development of, 41
  hard, 1218
  soft, 1219
Palatine aponeurosis, 1244
  artery, ascending, 623
   pharyngeal, 626
   descending, 631
  bone, 222
   articulations of, 225
   horizontal part of, 222
   orbital process of, 224
   ossification of, 225
   pyramidal process or tuber-
    osity of, 223
   sphenoidal process of, 225

Palatine bone, vertical part of,
   223
  foramen, 159
  muscles, 1244
  nerves, 966
  process of maxilla, 218
  processes of fetus, 44
  tonsils, 1242
  uvula, 1219
  velum, 1219
Palatoglossus muscle, 1235, note,
  1246
Palatopharyngeus muscle, 1246
Palatum, 1218
  durum, 1218
  molle, 1219
Palmar aponeurosis, 514
  arch, deep, 662
   superficial, 665
  cutaneous branch of median
   nerve, 1023
   of ulnar nerve, 1028
  fascia, 514
  interossei muscles, 525
  interosseous arteries, 665
  ligaments, 369, 372
  nerves of ulnar, 1028
Palmaris brevis muscle, 523
  longus muscle, 501
Palmate folds of uterus, 1375
Palpebræ, 1118
Palpebral arteries, 634, 635, 636
  commissures or canthi, 1128
  fissure, 1118
  ligament, 1119
   medial, 417
  nerves from maxillary, 968
  raphé, lateral, 417
Pampiniform plexus of spermatic
   veins, 761
Pancreas, 1308
  accessory duct of, 1310
  arteries, 677
  body of, 1308
  development of, 1309
  duct of, 1310
  head of, 1308
  lymphatic vessels of, 805
  neck of, 1309
  nerves of, 1312
  structure of, 1311
  surface marking of, 93
  tail of, 1309
  uncinate process of, 1308
  veins, 764
  vessels of, 1311
Pancreatica magna artery, 673
Pancreaticoduodenal arteries,
   673, 678
  lymph nodes, 803
  veins, 764
Pancreaticolienal lymph nodes,
   801
Paneth, cells of, 1282
Papilla, lacrimal, 1118
  mammæ, 1382
Papillæ, circumvallate, 1232
  conial, 1233
  filiform, 1233
  fungiform, 1232
  of skin, 1156
  of tongue, 1332
  simplices, 1234
  vallatæ, 1232
Papillary layer of skin, 1156
  process, 1298
Paracentral lobule, 886
Paradidymis, 1358
Parallel striæ of Retzius, 1224
Paramastoid process, 189
Parametrium, 1373
Paranephric body, 1330
Pararectal fossa, 1264

Pararectal lymph nodes, 801
Pararenal fat, 1330
Parasympathetic motor root, 959
  nerves, cranial, 1061
   sacral, 1063
Parathyroid glands, 1394
  development of, 1394
  structure of, 1395
Paravesical fossa, 1266
Parietal bone, 190
  cells of fundic glands, 1277
  eminence, 158, 163, 191
  foramen, 158, 191
  lobe, 886
   gyri of, 886
  notch, 198
  operculum, 886
  pleura, 1191
  pericardium, 581
  peritoneum, 1258
  veins, emissary, 741
Parietomastoid suture, 166, 175
Parietoöccipital fissure, 883
Parietotemporal artery, 639
Parolfactory area, 906
Paroöphoron, 1317, 1369
Parotid duct, 1237
  gland, 1237
   accessory part of, 1237
   nerves of, 1239
   structure of, 1238, 1239
   surface marking of, 64
   vessels of, 1239
  lymph nodes, 785
  plexus, 975
Parotideomasseteric fascia, 422
Parovarium, 1369
Pars ciliaris retinæ, 1104, 1109,
   1111
  functionales, 51
  iridica retinæ, 1107, 1109, 1111
Parumbilical veins, 765
Patella, 282
  articulation of, 283
  movements of, 387
  ossification of, 283
  structure of, 282
  surface anatomy of, 115
Patellar plexus, 956, 959
  retinacula, 1381
  surface of femur, 275
Pectinate ligament of iris, 1103
Pectineal line, 273
Pectineus muscle, 534
Pectiniforme septum, 1362
Pectoralis major muscle, 490
  minimus muscle, 491
  minor muscle, 491
Pedicles of a vertebra, 127, 128
Peduncle or Peduncles, cerebellar,
   864
  cerebral, 859
  olivary, 851
Pelvic colon, 1288
  diaphragm, 469
   fascia of, 470, 475
  girdle, 227
  muscles, 468
  plexuses, 1087
  portion of sympathetic system,
   1078, 1082
Pelvis, 265
  articulations of, 345
  axes of, 267
  boundaries of, 265, 267
  brim of, 265
  cavity of lesser, 266
  diameters, 266, 267
  greater or false, 265
  in fetus, 269
  inferior aperture, 267
  inlet of, 266
  lesser or true, 266

Pelvis, ligaments of, 346
linea terminalis of, 265
lymph nodes of, 796
major, 265
male and female, differences between, 268
mechanism of, 350
minor, 266
outlet of, 267
position of, 268
renal, 1334
superior aperture, 267
x-ray of, 109
Penis, 1360
body of, 1362
bulb, 1363
corona glandis, 1363
corpora cavernosa, 1360, 1362
corpus cavernosum urethræ, or *corpus spongiosum*, 1360, 1363
crura of, 1362
deep artery of, 689, 691
dorsal artery of, 689, 691
veins of, 758
fascia, 1361, 1362
fundiform ligament of, 1364
foreskin of, 1360
glands, 1361
glans, 1363
lymphatic vessels of, 807
muscles of, 478
nerves of, 1365
prepuce of, 1360
septum pectiniforme, 1362
structure of, 1364
suspensory ligament of, 1364
Perforated substance, 869, 905
Perforating arteries from internal mammary, 650
from profunda femoris, 702
of hand, 662
cutaneous nerve, gluteal, 1049
Pericardiacophrenic artery, 650
Pericardial arteries, 650, 666
cavity, 581
fold, 39
pleura, 1191
Pericardium, 581
nerves of, 1011
oblique sinus of, 581
parietal, 580
reflections, 581
relations of, 581
serous, 581
transverse sinus of, 581
vessels of, 650
vestigial fold of, 582
visceral, 579
Pericecal folds, 1271
fossæ, 1271
Perichondrium, 306
Perikaryon, 930
Perilymph, 1140, 1144
Perineal artery, 691
body, 1291
branch of fourth sacral nerve, 1047
fat, 1328
muscles, 478, 480
nerve, 1056
Perineum, boundaries of, 471
central tendinous point of, 477
fascia of, 471
lymphatic vessels of, 799
muscles of, 478
Perineurium, 936
Periorbita, 1118
Periosteum, 310
Peripheral end-organs, 937
nerves, 935
nervous system, 951
organs of special senses, 1094

Periscleral lymph space, 1117
Peritoneal cavity, 1258
fossæ or recesses, 1269
sacs, 1258, 1260, 1266
Peritoneum, 1258
epiploic foramen of, 1267
greater sac of, 1258
lesser sac of, 1260
ligaments of, 1267
lymphatic capillaries in, 778
main cavity or greater sac of, 1258
mesenteries, 1269
omenta, 1266
omental bursa of, 1266
parietal portion of, 1258
visceral portion of, 1258
Perlia, nucleus of, 870, 914
Permanent teeth, 1220
development of, 1229
Peronæus accessorius muscle, 551
brevis muscle, 550
longus muscle, 550
quartus muscle, 551
quinti digiti muscle, 551
tertius muscle, 545
Peroneal artery, 710
muscles, 550
nerves, 1052
retinacula, 551
septa, 543
Peroneocalcaneus externus muscle, 551
internus muscle, 548
Peroneocuboideus muscle, 551
Peroneotibialis muscle, 548
Perpendicular fasciculus, 896
line of ulna, 245
plate of ethmoid, 210
Pes or base of cerebral peduncle, 870
Petit, canal of, 1113
triangle of, 486
Petroöccipital fissure, 162
Petrosal nerve, deep, 976
large deep, 977
superficial, 976
superficial, greater, 976
smaller, 1139
process, 205
sinuses, 730, 740
Petrosphenoidal fissure, 162
Petrosquamous sinus, 739
suture, 199, 201
Petrotympanic fissure, 160, 197, 1131
Petrous ganglion, 982
portion of temporal bone, 199
Peyer's patches, 1282
Phalanges digitorum manus, 257
pedis, 302
of foot, 302
of hand, 257
ungual, 302
Pharyngeal aponeurosis, 1251
artery, ascending, 627
bursa, 1249
grooves, 39
membrane, 1207
nerve from glossopharyngeal, 983
from sphenopalatine, 978
from vagus, 987
ostium of auditory tube, 1248
plexus of nerves, 984, 987, 993
pouches, 39
recess, 1247
tonsil, 1249
tubercle, 160, 189
veins, 730
Pharyngopalatine arch, 1241
Pharyngopalatinus muscle, 1246
Pharynx, 1247

Pharynx, aponeurosis of, 1251
development of, 1251
laryngeal part of, 1249
mucous coat of, 1251
muscles of, 1249
nasal part of, 1248
oral part of, 1249
structure of, 1251
Philtrum, 420
Phrenic arteries, 669, 683
nerve, 1010
plexus of nerves, 1085
veins, 747, 762
Phrenicocolic ligament, 1269
Phrenicocostal sinus, 79, 1193
Phrenicolienal ligament, 813
Phrenicopericardiac ligament, 759
Pia of brain, 926
of cord, 926
mater, cranial, 927
encephali, 926
spinalis, 927
Pigment of iris, 1107
of skin, 1155
Pigmented layer of retina, 1107
Pili, 1158
Pillars of Corti, 1149
of external abdominal ring, 457
of fauces, 1224, 1241
Pineal body, 878
recess, 882
Pinna, 1126
cartilage of, 1127
ligaments of, 1127
Piriform lobe, 830
Piriformis muscle, 538
fascia of, 470
Pisiannularis muscle, 524
Pisiform bone, 252
Pisimetacarpus muscle, 524
Pisiuncinatus muscle, 524
Pisohamate ligament, 369
Pisometacarpal ligament, 369
Pits, olfactory, 42
Pituitary body, 1395
gland, 1395
Pivot-joint, 323
Placenta, 46, 51
circulation through, 52
cotyledons of, 52
development of, 46
fetal portion of, 51
maternal portion of, 51
separation of, 52
Plane, intertubercular, 1253
subcostal, 1254
transpyloric, 1253
Plantar aponeurosis, 554
arch, 711
arteries, 711
cutaneous venous arch, 752
digital veins, 754
fascia, 554
interossei muscles, 559
ligament, long, 395
metatarsal arteries, 711
nerves, 1052
Plantaris muscle, 546
Planum nuchale, 166, 187
occipitale, 166, 187
Plate or Plates, cribriform of ethmoid, 209
orbital or frontal, 194
perpendicular, of ethmoid, 210
pterygoid, of sphenoid, 208
tarsal, 1118
Platelets of blood, 770
Platysma muscle, 70, 426
Pleura, 1191
cavity of, 1191
cervical, 1191
costal, 1191

Pleura, cupula of, 1191
  diaphragmatic, 1191
  lymphatic vessels of, 812
  mediastinal, 1191
  nerves of, 1193
  parietal, 1191
  pericardial, 1191
  pulmonary, 1191
  reflections of, 1191
  structure of, 1193
  surface markings of, 79
  vessels of, 1193
Plexiform layers of retina, 1110
Pleuropericardial fold, 39
Pleuroperitoneal fold, 39
Plexus, choroid, of fourth ventricle, 867
  of lateral ventricle, 903
  of third ventricle, 882
  of nerves, annular, 1103
    aortic abdominal, 1085
    Auerbach's, 1282, 1284
    autonomic, 1082
    brachial, 1011
    cardiac, 1083
    cavernous, 1068
    celiac, 1084
    cervical, 1005, 1009, 1011
      posterior, 1001, 1005, 1006, 1008
    coccygeal, 1057
    corneal, 1103
    coronary, 1084
    esophageal, 991, 993
    gastric, 994, 1085
    hemorrhoidal, 1087, 1294
    hepatic, 1085
    hypogastric, 1086
    infraorbital, 967
    internal carotid, 1067
    lienal, 1085
    lumbar, 1036
    lumbosacral, 1036
    Meissner's, 1282, 1284
    mesenteric, 1085
    myenteric, 1282, 1284
    ovarian, 1085
    parotid, 971
    patellar, 1040, 1043
    pelvic, 1087
    pharyngeal, 986, 987, 1071
    phrenic, 1085
    prostatic, 1087
    pudendal, 1055
    pulmonary, 993
    renal, 1085
    sacral, 1045
    solar, 1084
    spermatic, 1085
    splenic, 1085
    submucosal, 1284
    subsartorial, 1043
    suprarenal, 1085
    tympanic, 1138
    uterine, 1087
    vaginal, 1087
    vesical, 1087
  of veins, basilar, 740
    hemorrhoidal, 757
    pterygoid, 727
    pudendal, 758
    uterine, 758
    vertebral, 750
    vesical, 758
    vesicoprostatic, 758
Plica or Plicæ, circulares]*Kerkringi*], 1280
  fimbriata [tongue], 1231
  gubernatrix, 1321
  lacrimalis [*Hasneri*], 1122
  semilunaris [conjunctiva], 1120, 1121
    [tonsil], 1242

Plica sublingualis, 1240
  triangularis [tonsil], 1242
  ureteric, 1344
  vascularis, 1321
  ventriculareæ [larynx], 1182
  vesicalis transversa, 1266
  vocales, 1182
Pneumogastric nerve, 986
Polar bodies or polocytes, 25
Poles of cerebral hemispheres, 882
  of eyeball, 1095
  of lens, 1114
Polkissen, 1335
Polymorphonuclear leucocytes, 770
Pons Varolii, 859
  development of, 825
  hepatis, 1299
  structure of, 859
Ponticulus [auricula], 1127
  nuclei, 862
Pontine arteries, 646
Poplitea. artery, 703
    surface marking of, 118
  fossa or space, 703
  line of tibia, 285
  lymph nodes, 194
  nerves, 1050, 1052
  surface of femur, 273
  vein, 754
Popliteus muscle, 547
  minor, 548
Pore, gustatory, 1094
Porta hepatis, 577, 1299
Portal vein, 762
Postanal gut, 1215
Postaxial borders of limbs, 46
Postcentral sulcus, 886
Posterior alveolar artery, 630
  basis bundle, 844
  calcaneo-astragaloid ligament, 393
  circumflex humeral artery, 656
  column of spinal cord, 841
  common ligament, 327
  costotransverse ligament, 341
  cricoarytenoid muscle, 1185
  deep cervical vein, 731
  dental artery, 630
  humeral circumflex artery, 656
  inferior tibiofibular ligament, 389
  interosseous artery, 665
    nerve, 1031
  pillar of fauces, 1241
  proper fasciculus, 844
  pulmonary nerves, 993
  radial carpal artery, 661
  radioulnar ligament, 366
  root of spinal nerves, 839
  sacrosciatic ligament, 347
  scapular artery, 648
    nerve, 1014
  scrotal nerves, 1056
  spinal artery, 645
  superior alveolar artery, 630
  talotibial ligament, 391
  temporal artery, 628
  tibiofibular ligament, 367, 381
  ulnar carpal artery, 665
    recurrent artery, 663
  vertebral vein, 731
Posterolateral ganglionic arteries, 646
Posteromedial ganglionic arteries, 646
Postsphenoid part of sphenoid, 209
Pouch of Douglas, 1260, 1375
  of Prussak, 1138
  Rathke's, 1396
Pouches, pharyngeal, 39
Poupart's ligament, 456

Præputium clitoridis, 1380
  penis, 1360
Preaortic portion of duodenum, 1279
Preauricular lymph nodes, 784
  point, 61
  sulcus of ilium, 259
Preaxial borders of limbs, 46
Precentral gyrus, 886
  sulcus, 882
Precuneus lobule, 886
Preganglionic fibers, 1061
Premolar teeth, 1222
Prepatellar bursa, 386
Prepuce of clitoris, 1380
  of penis, 1360
    development of, 1324
Preputial glands, 1361
  space, 1361
Presphenoid, 209
Presternal notch, 151
Pretracheal fascia, 431
Prevertebral artery, 627
  fascia, 430
Prevesical facial cleft, 1341
Previsceral cleft, 431
Primary spermatocytes, 27
  villi, 51
Primitive aortæ, 575
  atrium, 572
  choanæ, 44
  costal arches, 121
  groove, 33
  gut, 36
  jugular veins, 720
  node, 33
  olfactory lobe, 830
  ova, 1320
  palate, 44
  pericardial, 37
  segments, 35, 119
  streak, 33
  urogenital ostium, 1324
  ventricle of heart, 570
Princeps cervicis artery, 625
  pollicis artery, 662
Prismata adamantina, 1224
Process or Processes, alveolar, 218
  articular, of vertebræ, 127
  axis-cylinder, 931
  ciliary, 1104
  clinoid, 174, 204, 207
  condyloid, of mandible, 182
  coracoid, 234
  coronoid, of mandible, 182
    of ulna, 241
  costal, 129
  descending, of lacrimal, 221
  dura mater, 925
  frontal, of maxilla, 217
  frontonasal, 42
  frontosphenoidal, of zygomatic, 221
  globular, of His, 43
  inferior nasal concha, 225
  intrajugular, 188
  jugular, 162, 188
  lateral nasal, 42
  lenticular, of incus, 1137
  malar, of maxilla, 217
  mastoid, 198
  maxillary, of inferior nasal concha, 226
    of palatine bone, 223
    of zygomatic bone, 222
  muscular, or arytenoid, 1179
  nasal, of frontal bone, 194
    of maxilla, 217
  odontoid, of axis or epistropheus, 131
  orbital, of palatine bone, 224
    of zygomatic bone, 221
  palatal, of maxilla, 218

Process, palatine, of maxilla, 21
  papillary, of liver, 1298
  paramastoid, 189
  petrosal, 205
  phalangeal, of Corti's rods,
    1150
  pterygoid, of sphenoidal bone,
    208
  pyramidal, of palatine bone,
    159, 223
  septal cartilage of nose, 1170
    turbinated, 208
  sphenoidal, of palatine bone,
    225
  spinous, of ilium, 260
    of vertebræ, 127
  styloid, of fibula, 287
    of radius, 248
    of temporal bone, 161, 203
    of ulna, 246
  temporal, of zygomatic, 222
  transverse, of vertebræ, 129,
    131
  trochlear, of calcaneus, 293
  uncinate, of ethmoid, 211
  vaginal, of sphenoid, 208
    of temporal, 201, 203
  vermiform, 1285
  vertebræ, 135, 137
  vocal, of arytenoid, 1179
  xiphoid, 152
  zygomatic, of frontal, 194
    of maxilla, 217
    of temporal bone, 196
Processus condylaris, 182
  mastoideus, 198
  styloideus, 203
Proctodeum, 1215
Prodentin, 1228
Profunda, 657
  brachii artery, 657
  cervicalis artery, 652
  femoris artery, 701
    surface markings of, 108
    vein, 755
  linguæ artery, 622
Projection fibers of cerebral hemispheres, 892
Prominence of aqueduct of
  Fallopius, 1133
  of facial canal, 1133
  laryngeal, 1176
Promontorium, 1133
Promontory of tympanic cavity,
  1133
Pronator quadratus muscle, 505
  teres muscle, 500
Pronephric duct, 1315
Pronephros, 1315
Pronucleus, female, 28
  male, 28
Proötic center of temporal bone,
  203
Prophase or karyokinesis, 23
Prosencephalon, 35, 828, 874
Prostate, 1365
  development of, 1366
  gland, 1365
  lobes of, 1365
  lymphatic vessels of, 806
  nerves of, 1367
  structure of, 1366
  vessels of, 1367
Prostatic ducts, orifices of, 1346
  plexus of nerves, 1087
  portion of urethra, 1346
  sinus, 1346
  utricle, 1346
Protoplasmic process of nerve
  cells, 934
Protuberance, mental, 180
  occipital, 162, 163, 187, 188
Prussak, pouch of, 1138

Psalterium, 907
Psoas magnus muscle, 527
  major muscle, 527
    fascia covering, 526
  minor muscle, 528
  parvus muscle, 528
Pterion, 163
  ossicle, 213
Pterotic center of temporal bone,
  203
Pterygoid canal, 159, 166, 976
  fissure, 208
  fossa of sphenoid, 208
  hamulus, 159, 208
  muscles, 425
  nerve, external, 969
  plates, 208
  plexus of veins, 727
  processes of sphenoid, 208
  tubercle, 208
Pterygoideus externus muscle, 425
  internus muscle, 425
Pterygomandibular ligament, 421
  raphé, 421
Pterygomaxillary fissure, 165
Pterygopalatine canal, 215
  fossa, 166, 222
  ganglion, 976, 1062
  groove, 208
  nerve, 967
Pterygospinous ligament, 209,
  423
Pubic arch, 267
  bones, articulation of, 349
  ligaments, 349
  region, 1255
  tubercle or spine, 263
  vein, 756
Pubis, 263
  angle of, 263
  body of, 263
  crest of, 263
  iliopectineal eminence of, 263
  obturator crest of, 263
  rami of, 263
  symphysis of, 349
  tubercle or spine of, 263
Pubocapsular ligament, 375, 376
Pubococcygeus muscle, 469
Pubofemoral ligament, 376
Puboprostatic ligament, 476, 1343
Puborectalis muscle, 469
Pubovesical ligaments, 1343
Pubovesicales muscles, 1343
Pudendal artery, accessory, 690
  internal, in female, 691
    in male, 689
  cleft or rima, 1379
  nerve, 1055
    inferior, 1056
  plexus, nervous, 1055
    venous, 758
  veins, internal, 757
Pudendum, 1379
Pudic arteries, 689
  nerve, internal, 1056
  veins, internal, 751
Pulmonary artery, 611
    opening in right ventricle,
      590
  ligaments, 1193
  nerves, 993
  pleura, 1191
  semilunar valves, 590
  trunk, 611
  veins, 717
    openings of, in left atrium,
      590
Pulmones, 1196
  facies costalis, 1197
    mediastinalis, 1198
  margo anterior, 1199
    inferior, 1199

Pulmones, margo posterior, 1199
Pulp cavity of teeth, 1223
  dental, 1223
  of spleen, 815
Pulpa lienis, 815
Pulvinar, 875
Puncta lacrimalia, 1118, 1122
Pupil, 1103
  congenital atresia of, 1098
Pupillary membrane, 1097
Purkinje, cells of, 867
  fibers of, 596
Putamen, 898
Pyloric antrum, 1301
  artery, 673
  glands, 1277
  orifice of stomach, 1273
  part of stomach, 1273
  valve, 1275
  veins, 764
Pyramid or Pyramids, 1133
  of medulla oblongata, 847
  of temporal bone, 199
  of vestibule, 1140
  renal, 1334
Pyramidal cells of cerebral cortex,
  889
  decussation, 847
  eminence of tympanic cavity,
    1133
  lobe of thyroid gland, 1393
  process of palatine bone, 223
  tracts, 923
Pyramidalis muscle, 462
  nasi muscle, 417
Pyramis medullæ obolngatæ, 847

Q

QUADRATE lobe of liver, 1300
  lobule, 886
Quadratus femoris muscle, 540
  labii inferioris muscle, 418
    superioris muscle, 418
  lumborum muscle, 467
    fascia covering, 467
  menti muscle, 419
  plantæ muscle, 556
Quadriceps extensor muscle, 532
  femoris muscle, 532
Quadrigeminal bodies, 869, 872

R

RADIAL artery, 660
  branches of, 661
  peculiarities of, 661
  recurrent, 661
  surface marking of, 108
  fossa, 239
  nerve, 1029
  sulcus, 237
  tuberosity, 246
Radialis indicis artery, 662
Radiate ligament, 340
  sternocostal ligaments, 341
Radices arci vertebræ, 127
Radiocarpal articulation, 366
  movements of, 369
Radiohumeral joint, surface
  anatomy of, 106
Radioulnar articulations, 106,
  364
  ligaments, 364
  union, middle, 364
Radius, 246
  ossification of, 248
  structure of, 248
  surface anatomy of, 104
Radix linguæ, 1230
  longa, 959
  pili, 1159
  pulmonis, 1201

Rami of ischium, 262
  of pubis, 263
Ramus of mandible, 181
Ranine artery, 622
  vein, 730
Ranvier, nodes of, 932
Raphé, anococcygeal, 482
  lateral palpebral, 417
  of medulla, 826
  of palate, 1219
  of scrotum, 1349
  pterygomandibular, 421
Rathke's pouch, 1396
Receptaculum chyli, 784
Receptor organs, 938
Recess or Recesses, or *Recessus*
    ellipticus, 1140
  epitympanic, 1130
  infundibuli, 882
  intersigmoideus, 1272
  lateral, of fourth ventricle, 867
  nasopalatine, 1172
  omental, 1267
  optic, 882
  peritoneal, 1269
  pharyngeal, 1247, 1249
  pineal, 882
  sacciformis, 366
  sphæricus, 1140
  sphenoethmoidal, 177, 1172
  suprapinealis, 882
  of Tröltsch, 1138
Rectal ampulla, 1289
  columns ot Morgagni, 1291
Rectococcygeal muscles, 1292
Rectouterine excavation, 1260, 1376
  folds, 1376
Rectovesical excavation, 1260
  folds, 1264
  layer of pelvic fascia, 1358
Rectovesical muscles, 1343
Rectum, 1289
  ampulla of, 1289
  anal part of, 1290
  development of, 1215
  Houston's valves of, 1290
  lymphatic vessels of, 804
  relations of, 1290
Rectus abdominis muscle, 460
    sheath of, 461
  capitis anterior muscle, 436
    anticus major muscle, 436
      minor muscle, 436
  capitis lateralis muscle, 436
    posterior major muscle, 445
      minor muscle, 445
  femoris muscle, 532
    inferior nerve, 958
    medialis nerve, 958
  muscles of eyeball, 1115
Recurrent artery, interosseous, 665
  radial, 661
  tibial, 708
  ulnar, 663
  branches from deep volar arch, 662
  laryngeal nerve, 991
  nerve, 991
Red corpuscles, 769
  nucleus, 872
Reflected inguinal ligament, 456
Reflections of pleuræ, 1191
Refracting media of eye, 1112
Regions of abdomen, 1253
Reil, island of, 887
Reissner, vestibular membrane
  of, 1146
Renal arteries, 682
  calyces, 1334
  columns, 1334
  corpuscles, 1334

Renal fascia, 1328
  impression, 1296
  pelvis, 1296
  plexus, 1085
  pyramids, 1334
  sinus, 1334
  tubules, 1334, 1335
  veins, 762
  vessels, afferent and efferent, 1336
Renes, 1326
Reproduction of cells, 21
Reproductive system, female, 1367
  male, 1348
Respiration, mechanism of, 451
Respiratory apparatus, 1167
  development of, 1167
  nerve of Bell, 1010, 1015
  system, 1167
Restform bodies of medulla, 850, 864
Rete canalis hypoglossi, 741
  foraminis ovalis, 742
  testis, 1355
Retia venosa vertebrarum, 750
Reticular formation, 842, 855, 870
  lamina, 1150
  layer of skin, 1157
Retina, 1108
  central artery of, 636
  development of, 1098
  fovea centralis, 1109
  layers of, 1109
  macula lutea, 1109
  membrana limitans, 1111
  ora serrata, 1109
  structure of, 1109
  supporting frame-work of, 1111
Retinacula of hip-joint, 375
  patellar, 381
  peroneal. 553
Retrahens aurem muscle, 1127
Retroglandular sulcus of penis, 1363
Retroperitoneal fossæ, 1269
Retropharyngeal lymph nodes, 786
  space, 430
Retzius, colored lines of, 1224
  space of, 1341
Rhinal fissure, external, 830
Rhinencephalon, 904, 907
  development of, 830
  gyrus of, 911
Rhodopsin, 1109
Rhombencephalon, 35, 825
  development of, 825
Rhombic lip, 826
Rhomboid fossa, 869
  impression, 229
  ligament, 353
Rhomboideus major muscles, 486
  minor muscle, 486
  occipitalis muscle, 486
Ribs, 153
  common characteristics of, 153
  development of, 121
  false, 153
  floating or vertebral, 153
  ossification of, 157
  peculiar, 156
  structure of, 157
  true, 153
  vertebrochondral, 153
  vertebrosternal, 153
Ridge, ganglion, 35, 824
  supracondylar, 237
  trapezoid or oblique, 228
Ridges, bicipital, 236
Right atrium, 586
  auricle, 586
  auricular appendix, 586

Right coronary artery, 615
  plexus, 1084
  veins, 724
  gastroepiploic lymph nodes, 799
  ventricle, 587
Rima glottidis, 1181, 1183
  of mouth, 1216
  palpebrarum, 1118
  pudendal, 1379
Ring or Rings, abdominal, 457, 465
  femoral, 696
  fibrous, of heart, 593
  subcutaneous inguinal, 456
  tympanic, 203
Risorius muscle, 419
Rivinus, ducts of, 1240
  notch of, 1131
Rod-bipolars of retina, 1111
Rod-granules of retina, 1110
Rods and cones, layer of, 1111
  of Corti, 1148
  of retina, 1111
Rolando, fissure of, 883
  substantia gelatinosa of, 841
  tubercle of, 849
Root of lung, 1201
  of penis, 1360
Root sheaths of hair, 1160
Roots of spinal nerves, 967, 997
  of teeth, 1220
Rosenmüller, fossa of, 1247, 1249
  lymph node of, 795
  organ of, 1317, 1369
Rostrum of corpus callosum, 892
  sphenoidal, 206
Rotary joint, 323
Rotation, movement of, 323
Rotatores muscles, 444
  spinæ muscle, 444
Round ligament of hip-joint, 376
  of liver, 1301
  of uterus, 1376
Rubrospinal fasciculus, 923
Ruffini, corpuscles of, 939
Russell, Risien, hook bundle of, 865

S

Sac, dental, 1227
  lacrimal, 1122
  of peritoneum, 1258, 1260
Saccule, laryngeal, 1183
  of vestibule, 1144
Sacculus, 1144
Saccus lacrimalis, 1122
  vaginalis, 1321
Sacral arteries, lateral, 692
  artery, middle, 683
  canal, 141
  cornua, 138
  crest, 138
  foramina, 137, 138
  groove, 138
  lymph nodes, 798
  nerves, division of, 1004, 1047
  parasympathetic nerves, 1063
  plexus, 1045
  sympathetics, 1063
  tuberosity, 139
  veins, 757, 759
Sacrococcygeal ligaments, 348
Sacrogenital folds, 1264, 1376
Sacroiliac articulation, 345
  ligaments, 346, 347
Sacrosciatic ligaments, 347
Sacrospinalis muscle, 440
Sacrovertebral angle, 137
Sacrum, 127, 137
  ala of, 141
  apex, of, 141

Sacrum articulations of, 141
  auricular surface of, 139
  base of, 139
  ossification of, 144
  structure of, 141
  variations of, 151
Saddle-joint, 324
Sagittal fossa of liver, 1298
  sinuses, 735, 737
  sulcus, 188, 191, 194
  suture, 158, 166
Salivary glands, 1237
  development of, 1208
  parotid, 1237
  structure of, 1238
  sublingual, 1237
  submaxillary, 1237
Salpingopalatine fold, 1249
Salpingopharyngeal fold, 1249
Salpingopharyngeus muscle, 1249
Salter, incremental lines of, 1224
Santorini, cartilages of, 1179
  duct of, 1310
Saphenous nerves, 1043
  opening, 530
  veins, 752, 753
Sarcolemma, 561
Sarcoplasm, 561, 597
Sarcosomes, 597
Sartorius muscle, 530, 561
Scala media [cochlea], 1146
  tympani, 1143
  vestibuli, 1143
Scalene tubercle, 156
Scalenus anterior muscle, 437
  anticus muscle, 437
  medius muscle, 437
  pleuralis muscle, 438
  posterior muscle, 437
  posticus muscle, 437
Scalp, lymphatic vessels of, 786
  muscle of, 413
  skin of, 413
Scapha, 1126
Scaphoid bone, ankle, 297
  wrist, 249
  fossa of sphenoid, 159, 208
Scapula, 230
  acromion of, 232
  coracoid process of, 234
  glenoid cavity of, 234
  ligaments of, 355
  ossification of, 235
  spine of, 232
  structure of, 244
  surface anatomy of, 100
Scapular arteries, 647
  circumflex artery, 655
  nerve, posterior, 1014
  notch, 232
Scapuloclavicular articulation, 354
Scapus or shaft of hair, 1161
  pili, 1161
Scarpa, fascia of, 453
  foramina of, 159, 219
  ganglion of, 981, 1150
  triangle of, 697
Schwalbe, nucleus of, 860
Schindylesis, 322
Schlemm, canal of, 1099
Schreger, lines of, 1224
Schwann, sheath of, 825, 932
Sciatic artery, 691
  foramen, 348
  nerves, 1046, 1049
  notch, 262
  veins, 757
Sclera, 1099
Sclero-corneal junction, 1101
Sclerotogenous layer, 119
Sclerotome, 119
Scrotal arteries, posterior, 691

Scrotal nerves, posterior, 1056
Scrotum, 1349
  dartos tunic of, 1350
  integument of, 1350
  nerves of, 1351
  raphé of, 1349
  vessels of, 1351
Sebaceous glands, 1161
Sebum cutaneum, 1161
Second cuneiform bone, 298
  metacarpal bone, 255
  metatarsal bone, 300
  nerve, 956
Secondary areolæ of bone, 316
  dentin, 1224
  oöcytes, 25
  spermatocytes, 27
  tympanic membrane, 1133
Segmentation, nucleus, 28, 824
  of fertilized ovum, 28, 824
Segments, primitive, 35
  spinal, 838
Sella turcica, 174, 204
Semicanalis m. tensoris tympani, 202, 1135
  tubæ auditivæ, 202, 1135
Semicircular canals, 1140, 1141
  ducts, 1144
Semilunar artery, 634
  bone, 249
  fibrocartilages of knee, 384
  ganglion of abdomen, 1085
  of trigeminal nerve, 960
  notch of ulna, 244
  valves, 576
Semimembranosus muscle, 542
Seminal duct, 1358
  vesicles, 1359
Semispinalis capitis muscle, 443
  cervicis muscle, 443
  colli muscle, 443
  dorsi muscle, 443
Semitendinosus muscle, 542
Sensations, peripheral termina-
    tions of nerves of, 937
Senses, special organs of, 1093
Sensory decussation, 856
  ganglia of nerves, 836, 997
  nerve terminations, 938
  pathways from spinal cord to
    brain, 844
  roots, 839
Septum, aortic, 575
  canalis musculotubarii, 202,
    1135
  crural, 696
  femorale, 696
  inferius of heart, 575
  interatrial, 587
  intermedium, 573
  interventricular, 575, 592
  lucidum, 901
  mobile nasi, 1170
  nasal, 175, 176
  orbital, 1119
  pectiniforme penis, 1361
  pellucidum, 832, 901
  primum, 573
  secundum, 573
  spurium, 574
  tongue, 1237
  transversum, 38, 573
  of semicircular ducts, 1144
  urorectal, 1215
  ventricular, 590, 592
  ventriculorum, 592
Serous glands of tongue, 1237
  membrane, pericardium, 581
  peritoneum, 1258
  pleura, 1202
Serratus anterior muscle, 492
  magnus muscle, 492
  posterior inferior muscle, 449

Serratus posterior superior
  muscle, 448
  posticus muscles, 448
Sertoli, cells of, 1355
Sesamoid bones, 304
  cartilages, 1170
Seventh, 7th, nerve, 916
Shaft of hair, 1161
Sheath or Sheaths, carotid, 431
  crural, 695
  dentinal, of Neumann, 1224
  femoral, 695
  flexor tendons of fingers, 503
  of toes, 555
  rectus abdominis muscle, 460
  of Schwann, 825, 932
  synovial of tendons around
    ankle, 552
  in front of wrist, 512
  on back of wrist, 513
  tendon, fibrous, 516
  synovial, 513
Shin bone, 283
Short calcaneocuboid ligament,
    397
  gastric veins, 764
  plantar ligament, 397
  saphenous vein, 754
Shoulder blade, 230
  of child aged six years, x-ray of,
    100
  girdle, 227
  muscles of, 492
  development of, 406
  x-ray of, 98
Shoulder-joint, 356
  bursæ near, 358
  movements of, 359
  vessels and nerves of, 359
Sibson's fascia, 430, 1192
Sight, organ of, 1095
Sigmoid arteries, 681
  cavity of radius, 247
  of ulna, 244
  colon, 1288
  flexure of colon, 1287, 1288
  mesocolon, 1260, 1264, 1269,
    1288
  sinus, 738
  sulcus, 198
Sinoatrial node, 594, 595
Sinus or Sinuses, air, 69
  aortic, 592, 615
  basilar, 740
  carotid, 631
  cavernous, 740
  cervicalis, 41
  circular, 740
  confluence of, 188, 739
  coronarius, 587
  coronary, 575, 722
  costomediastinal, 1193
  dura mater, 735
  epididymis, 1353
  external jugular vein, 728
  frontal, 194, 1175
  intercavernous, 740
  laryngeal, 1183
  lateral, 738
  longitudinal, 735, 737
  maxillary, 215
  of Morgagni, 1250
  occipital, 739
  of nose, 1175
  paranasal, 1175
  pericardial, 581
  oblique, 581
  transverse, 581
  petrosal, 740
  petrosquamous, 739
  phrenicocostal, 1193
  piriformis, 1249
  pocularis, 1346

Sinus prostatic, 1346
　renal, 1328, 1334
　rhomboidalis, 35
　sagittal, 735, 737
　scleræ, 1099
　septum, 573, 574
　sigmoid, 738
　sphenoidal, 205, 1175
　sphenoparietal, 739
　straight, 737
　tentorial, 737
　tonsillaris, 1242
　transverse, 738, 740
　urogenital, 1323
　Valsalva, 592
　venarum, 586
　venosus, 572, 722
Sinusoids of Minot, 722, 1303
Sixth, 6th, nerve, 916
Skeleton, development of, 119
Skene's duct, 1323
Skin, 1153
　appendages of, 1158
　　hairs, 1158
　　nails, 1158
　　sebaceous glands, 1161
　　sudoriferous glands, 1163
　　sweat glands, 1163
　arteries of, 1158
　cleavage lines, 1157, 1158
　corium or cutis vera, 1156
　development of, 1153
　epidermis or cuticle, 1153
　furrows of, 1153
　Langer's lines, 1157
　lymphatic capillaries in, 776
　nerves of, 1158
　pappillary layer of, 1156
　reticular layer of, 1157
　stratum corneum, 1155
　　granulosum, 1154
　　lucidum, 1155
　　mucosum, 1154
　true, 1155
Skull, 158
　lateral view, *x*-ray of, 64
　development of, 122
　differences in, due to age, 177
　exterior of, 158
　fossa of, 172-174
　interior of, 171
　norma basalis, 159
　　frontalis, 167
　　lateralis, 162
　　occipitalis, 166
　　verticalis, 158
　sexual differences in, 179
　surface anatomy of, 61
　upper surface of base of, 172
Skull-cap, inner surface of, 171
Small cardiac vein, 724
　cavernous nerves, 1087
　intestine, 1278
　　and stomach, *x*-ray of, 87
　　circular folds of, 1280
　　duodenum, 1278
　　glands of, 1282
　　ileum, 1280
　　jejunum, 1280
　　lymphatic nodules of, 1282
　　　vessels of, 803
　　Meckel's, diverticulum of, 1280
　　mucous membrane of, 1282
　　muscular coat of, 1282
　　nerves of, 1284
　　Peyer's patches of, 1282
　　serous coat of, 1282
　　submucous coat of, 1282
　　valvulæ conniventes of, 1280
　　vessels of, 1283
　　villi of, 1281
　occipital nerve, 1006

Small saphenous vein, 754
　sciatic nerve, 1047
　wings of sphenoid, 207
Smaller occipital nerve, 1006
Smallest cardiac veins, 725
Smell, organ of, 1093
Soft palate, 1218
　aponeurosis of, 1244
　arches or pillars of, 1219
　muscles of, 1244
Solar plexus, 1084
Sole of foot, muscles of, first layer, 554
　　fourth layer, 559
　　second layer, 556
　　third layer, 559
Soleus muscle, 548
Solitary cells of medulla spinalis, lymph nodules, 1282
Somatic fibers of spinal nerves, 917
　layer of mesoderm, 32
Somatopleure, 35
Somites, 35, 571
Space or spaces, Burns', 430
　corneal, 1102
　Fontana's, 1101
　intercostal, 153
　interglobular, of teeth, 1224
　interpleural, 1193
　middle palmar, 519
　Nuel's, 1150
　popliteal, 703
　preputial, 1361
　prevesical, 1341
　retropharyngeal, 430
　retropubic, 1341
　Retzius', 1341
　subarachnoid, 928
　suprasternal, 430
　Tenon's, 1100
　thenar, 519
Spatia zonularia, 1113
Speech area, 891
Spermatic artery, internal, 682
　canal, 466
　cord, 1351
　　structure of, 1351
　　fascia, external, 458, 1350
　　　middle, 459, 1350
　　　innermost, 1351
　　　internal, 466, 1351
　　nerve, 1038
　　plexus of nerves, 1085
　　veins, 761, 1352
Spermatids, 27, 1355
Spermatoblasts, 1355
Spermatocytes, 27, 1355
Spermatogonia, 27, 1355
Spermatozoön, 26, 1355
　formation of, 1355
Sphenoethmoidal recess, 177, 1172
　suture, 173
Sphenofrontal suture, 163, 173
Sphenoid bone, 204
　body of, 204
　pterygoid processes of, 208
　wings of, 206, 207
Sphenoidal air sinuses, 205, 1175
　conchæ, 208
　crest, 205
　process of palatine bone, 225
　　of septal cartilage of nose 1170
　rostrum, 206
　spine, 159, 206
　turbinated processes, 208
Sphenomandibular ligament, 336, 425
Sphenomaxillary fissure, 163, 165
　fossa, 166

Sphenopalatine artery, 631
　foramen, 166, 177, 224
　ganglion, 976, 1062
　nerves, 965
　notch, 224, 225
Sphenoparietal sinus, 739
　suture, 174
Sphenosquamosal suture, 163
Sphenozygomatic suture, 163
Sphincter ani externus muscle, 482
　internus muscle, 482
　pupillæ muscle, 1107
　recti muscle, 482
　urethræ membranaceæ muscle, 480, 482
　vaginæ muscle, 480
　vesicæ, 1345
Spigelian lobe of liver, 1300
Spina angularis, 160, 206
　helicis, 1127
　scapulæ, 232
Spinal accessory nerve, 994
　arachnoid, 927
　arteries, 645
　column, 126
　cord, 836
　　cauda equina, 838
　　central canal, 842
　　columns, 841
　　commissures, 839, 842
　　conus medullaris, 836
　　development of, 821
　　enlargements of, 837
　　fasciculi, 843
　　filum terminale, 837
　　fissures, 837
　　funiculi, 843
　　gray substance of, 839
　　horns of, 841
　　meninges, 924
　　motor pathways, 844
　　nerve roots of, 839
　　neuroglia, 933
　　nuclei, 841
　　neuromeres, 838
　　reticular formation, 842
　　segments, 838
　　sensory pathways, 843
　　sulci, 837
　　substantia gelatinosa (of Rolando), 841
　　terminal ventricle, 842
　　tract of, 842
　　white substance of, 842
　ganglia, 824, 997
　lemniscus, 853
　nerves, 1004
　　afferent (sensory) fibers of, 1000
　　autonomic fibers of, 1000
　　composition and central connections of, 921
　　connections with sympathetic, 1000
　　development of, 824
　　divisions of, 1001, 1004
　　fibers of, 1002
　　parasympathetic fibers of, 1001
　　points of emergence of, 997
　　radix dorsalis, 839
　　　ventralis, 839
　　roots of, 967, 997
　　size and direction of, 997
　　somatic efferent fibers of, 917
　　structure of, 1000
　　sympathetic fibers of, 1000
　segments, 838
Spinalis capitis muscle, 443
　cervicis muscle, 443
　colli muscle, 443

Spinalis dorsi muscle, 442
  thoracis muscle, 442
Spindle, neuromuscular, 939
  neurotendinous, 939
Spine or Spines, ethmoidal, 173,
    204
  frontal bone, 194
  iliac, 260, 261
  ischial, 262
  mental, 180
  nasal, 159, 167, 214, 219, 222
  pubic, 263
  scapular, 232
  sphenoidal, 160, 206
  suprameatal, 164, 203
  tibial, 283
  trochlear, 194
Spinoglenoid ligament, 356
Spinoölivary fasciculus, 845
Spinotectal fasciculus, 845, 915
Spinothalamic fasciculus, 845
Spinous process, vertebra, 127
Spiral canal of modiolus, 1143
  ligament, 1147
  line of femur, 271
  organ of Corti, 1148
  thread of spermatozoön, 27
Splanchnic fibers of spinal nerves,
    1001
  layer of mesoderm, 32
  nerves, 1078
Splanchnopleure, 35
Spleen, 812
  accessory, 814
  bloodvessels of, 815
  development of, 813
  lymphatic nodules of, 815
    vessels, of, 801
  Malpighian bodies of, 815
  nerves of, 816
  relations of, 813
  size and weight of, 815
  structure of, 814
  supernumerary, 814
  surface marking of, 94
  surfaces of, 813
  trabeculæ of, 814
Splenial center of ossification, 183
Splenic artery, 674
      distribution of, 815
  cells, 815
  flexure of colon, 1287
  lymph nodes, 801
  plexus, 1085
  pulp, 815
  vein, 763
Splenium of corpus callosum, 892
Splenius capitis muscle, 440
  cervicis muscle, 440
  colli muscle, 440
Spongioblasts, 821, 825
Spring ligament, 398
Spur of malleus, 1136
Squama, frontal, 193
  occipital, 187
Squamosal suture, 163
Stalks, optic, 828, 1096
Stapedius muscle, 1138
Stapes, 1137
  annular ligament of, 1138
  development of, 1123
Stato-acoustic nerve, 917
Stellate ligament, 340
  veins of kidney, 1336
Stensen, duct of, 1239
  foramina of, 159, 219
Stephanion, 163
Sternal angle, 76, 152
  end of clavicle, 229
  foramen, 152
  lymph nodes, 808
  plate, 121
Sternalis muscle, 491

Sternebræ, 150
Sternoclavicular articulation, 352
  surface anatomy of, 105
Sternoclavicularis muscle, 492
Sternocleidomastoid artery, 621,
    625
Sternocleidomastoideus muscle,
    70, 431
Sternocostal articulations, 341
  ligaments, 341
  surface of heart, 585
Sternohyoideus muscle, 434, 1010
Sternomastoid artery, 621, 625
  muscle, 431
Sternopericardiac ligaments, 581
Sternothyroideus muscle, 434, 1010
Sternum, 149
  articulations of, 153, 343
  development of, 121
  ossification of, 152
Stomach, 1272
  and small intestines, x-ray of,
    87
  atonic, after a barium meal,
    x-ray of, 90
  bed, 1273
  body of, 1273
  cardiac glands of, 1277
    orifice of, 1272
  component parts of, 1272
  curvatures of, 1272
  development of, 1210
  duodenopyloric constriction of,
    1273
  fundus of, 1273
    glands of, 1276
  incisura angularis, 1273
  interior of, 1274
  lymphatic vessels of, 803
  mucous membrane of, 1275
  muscular coat of, 1277
  nerves of, 1278
  normal, x-ray of, after a barium
    meal, 90
  openings of, 1272
  position of, 1274
  pyloric antrum, 1273
    glands, 1276
    orifice, 1273
    valve, 1275
  serous coat of, 1277
  shape and position of, 1274
  structure of, 1275
  subdivisions of, 1273
  sulcus intermedius, 1273
  surface marking of, 87
  surfaces of, 1272
  teeth, 1222
  vessels of, 1278
Stomodeum, 36, 1207
Stratiform fibrocartilage, 309
Stratum cinereum, 872
  compactum [decidua], 52
  corneum, 115
  germinativum, 1154
  granulosum, 1154
  intermedium [choroid], 1104
  lemnisci, 872
  lucidum, 1155
  moleculare, 865, 910
  mucosum, 1154
  opticum [retina], 1109
    [superior colliculus], 872
  papillare, 1156
  profundum, 871
  reticulare, 1156
  spongiosum [decidua], 52
  zonale, 872
Streak, primitive, 33
Stria, longitudinal, 893
  medullaris, 869
  olfactory, 905, 911
  terminalis, 911

Striate arteries, 638
  veins, inferior, 734
Striated muscle, 405, 559
  lymphatic capillaries in,
    779
Stripe of Hensen, 1150
Striped muscle, 405, 559
Stroma of iris, 1107
  of kidney, 1337
  of ovary, 1369
Styloglossus muscle, 1235
Stylohyal part of styloid process,
    203
Stylohyoid ligament, 433
  nerve, from facial, 979
Stylohyoideus muscle, 433
Styloid process of fibula, 287
  of radius, 248
  of temporal bone, 161, 203
  of ulna, 246
Stylomandibular ligament, 337,
    428
Stylomastoid artery, 626
  foramen, 161, 201
Stylomaxillary ligament, 337
Stylopharyngeus muscle, 1250
Subanconeus muscle, 499
Subarachnoid cavity, 928
  cisternæ, 928
  septum, 927
  space, 928
Subarcuate fossa, 200
Subcallosal gyrus, 905, 911
Subcardinal veins, 719
Subclavian arteries, 641
  first part, 641
    second portion of, 642
    surface anatomy of, 74
    third portion of, 642
  triangle, 74, 435
  vein, 745
Subclavius muscle, 492
Subcostal arteries, 668
  zone, 1254
Subcostales muscles, 447
Subcrureus or articularis genu
  muscle, 533
Subcutaneous inguinal ring, 456
Subdural cavity, 925
Subepithelial plexus of cornea,
    1103
Subfrontal gyre, 886
Subinguinal lymph nodes, 795
Sublingual artery, 622
  gland, 1240
Sublobular veins, 1302
Submandibular artery, 623
  duct, 1239
  ganglion, 979
  gland, 1239
    surface markings of, 72
  lymph nodes, 785
  triangle, 72, 432
Submental artery, 623
  lymph nodes, 789
  triangle, 432
Submucosa, plexus of, 1284
Suboccipital muscles, 445
  triangle, 445, 643
Subperiosteal ossification, 316
Subperitoneal connective tissue,
    467
Subpleural mediastinal plexus,
    650
Subpubic ligament, 349
Subsartorial plexus, 1043
Subscapular angle, 231
  artery, 655
  fascia, 493
  fossa, 230
  nerves, 1017
Subscapularis muscle, 493
Subserous fascia, 407, 1258

Substantia adamantina, 1224
  eburnea, 1224
  ferruginea, 869
  gelatinosa centralis, 842
    of Rolando, 841
  grisea centralis, 839, 870
  nigra, 870
  ossea, 1225
  propria (cornea), 1102
  reticularis, 842, 855, 870
Subthalamic tegmental region, 878
Suctorial pad, 422
Sudoriferous glands, 1163
Sulci and fissures of cerebral hemisphere, 882
  of cerebellum, 863
  of medulla oblongata, 847
  of spinal cord, 837
Sulcus, anterior longitudinal, of heart, 584
  antihelicis transversus, 1127
  arteriæ vertebralis, 130
  calcaneal, 292
  central, 883
  centralis [Rolandi], 883
  cingulate, 883
  circular, 883
  coronary, of heart, 583
  frontal, 883
  hypothalamic, 829, 880
  intermedius [stomach], 1273
  interventricularis, 584
  intraparietal, 886
  lateral cerebral, 882
  limitans [rhomboid fossa], 821, 869
  malleolar, 289
  median, of rhomboid fossa, 869
    of tongue, 1231
  occipital, 884
  olfactory, 884
  orbital, 884
  paramedial, 906
  postcentral, 886
  posterior longitudinal, of heart, 584
  preauricular, of ilium, 259
  precentral, 883
  radial, 237
  retroglandular, 1363
  sagittalis, 188, 191, 194
  sigmoid, 198
  spirales, 1147
  subparietal, 886
  tali, 295
  temporal, 885
  terminal, or right atrium, 586
    of tongue, 1231
  tubæ auditivæ, 162, 207
  tympanic, 202, 1130, 1132
Supercilia, 1118
Superciliary arches, 159, 163, 167, 193
Superficial cervical artery, 648
  lymph nodes, 789
  muscle, 426
  nerve, 1008
  epigastric artery, 699
  external pudendal artery, 700
    pudic artery, 700
  iliac circumflex artery, 699
  long plantar ligament, 396
  palmar arch, 665
  perineal artery, 691
  peroneal nerve, 1053
  Sylvian vein, 734
  temporal artery, 627
    vein, 727
  transverse ligament of fingers, 516
    perineal muscle, 478, 480
  volar artery, 665

Superficialis volæ artery, 661
Superior articular arteries, 705
  calcaneocuboid ligament, 395
  cerebellar peduncles, 864
  colliculus, 872, 912, 915
  constrictor muscle, 1249
  dental nerve, 967
  epigastric artery, 650
  intercostal artery, 652
  lingualis muscle, 1263
  longitudinal sinus, 735
  maxillary nerve, 964
  medullary velum, 867
  nasal concha, 212
  nuchal line, 187
  oblique muscle, 1115
  orbital fissure, 170, 174, 207
  pancreaticoduodenal artery, 673, 678
  petrosal sinus, 740
  profunda artery, 657
  sagittal sinus, 735
  semicircular canal, 1141
  tarsal plate, 1118
  thoracic artery, 655
  tibiofibular articulation, 389
  tympanic artery, 629
  ulnar collateral artery, 658
  vesical artery, 687
  vocal cords, 1182
Supernumerary spleen, 814
Supinator brevis muscle, 508
  longus muscle, 505
  muscle, 508
Supporting cells of Hensen, 1150
  of Sertoli, 1355
  frame-work of retina, 1111
Suppressor zones, 890
Supra-acromial nerves, 1008
Supracallosal gyrus, 905
Supraclavicular branches of brachial plexus, 1014
  nerves, 1008
Supraclavicularis muscle, 432
Supracondylar process, 241
Supraglenoid tuberosity, 234
Suprahyoid aponeurosis, 432
  artery, 622
  lymph nodes, 789
  muscles, 432
  triangle, 73, 432
Supramarginal gyrus, 886
Supramastoid crest, 196
Suprameatal spine, 164, 203
  triangle, 164
Supraorbital artery, 634
  foramen, 167, 171, 194
  margin, 193
  nerve, 962
  notch, 167, 171, 194
  vein, 725
Suprarenal arteries, 682, 683
  glands, 1399
    functions of, 1402
    lymphatic vessels of, 1401
    nerves of, 1401
    structure of, 1401
    vessels of, 1401
  impression, 1298
  plexus, 1085
  veins, 762
Suprascapular artery, 647
  ligament, 356
  nerve, 1015
Supraspinal ligament, 329
Supraspinatous fascia, 493
  fossa, 231
  muscle, 498
Supraspinous ligament, 329
Suprasternal nerves, 1008
  space, 430
Supratonsillar fossa, 1242

Supratrochlear foramen, 239
  nerve, 962
Sural arteries, 705
  cutaneous nerve, lateral, 1053
    medial, 1049
Sural nerve, 1049
Surface anatomy and surface markings of abdomen, 81
  accessory nerve, 74
  acromioclavicular joint, 105
  adductor canal, 118
  ankle-joint, 113, 117
  anterior jugular vein, 73
    tibial artery, 118
  aorta, abdominal, 96
  appendix vermiformis, 89
  axillary artery, 108
  back, 75
  bones of abdomen, 85
    of back, 75
    of cranium, 61
    of lower extremity, 110
    of neck, 69
    of thorax, 76, 83
    of upper extremity, 100, 104
  brachial artery, 108
    plexus, 74, 108
  brain, 69
  calcaneus, 115
  carpal bones, 104
  caruncula lacrimalis, 65
  cecum, 89
  celiac artery, 96
  cervical cutaneous nerve, 73
  clavicle, 100
  colon, ascending, 92
    descending, 92
    iliac, 92
    transverse, 92
  common carotid artery, 74
    peroneal nerve, 118
  cranium, 61
  deep peroneal nerve, 1053
  deltoideus muscle, 107
  diaphragm, 80
  digestive tube, 87
  dorsalis pedis artery, 118
  duodenum, 88
  ear, 66
  elbow-joint, 101
  esophagus, 71
  external carotid artery, 74
    jugular vein, 74
    maxillary artery, 64
  eye, 65
    nerve, 65, 74
  femoral artery, 118
    triangle, 117
  femur, 110
  fibula, 115
  fissures of brain, 69
  fold of groin, 82
  frontal sinus, 69
  gall-bladder, 93
  head and neck, 61
  heart, 80
    coronary sulcus, 80
    longitudinal sulcus, 80
    orifices of, 80
  Hesselbach's triangle, 96
  hip-bones, 110
  hip-joint, 110
  humerus, 100
  hyoid bone, 70
  ileocolic junction, 88
  iliac arteries, 96
    inferior, epigastric artery, 95
  infrasternal notch, 76
  inguinal rings and canal, 84
  internal carotid artery, 69
    jugular vein, 71, 74

Surface anatomy, internal mammary artery, 80
intestines, 88
joints of fingers, 106
foot, 115
jugular notch, 78
veins, 74
kidneys, 94
knee-joint, 112, 115
lacrimal puncta, 65
sac, 65
larynx, 70
lateral ventricle of brain, 69
latissimus dorsi, 82, 106
left common carotid artery
linea alba, 82
semilunaris, 82
lingual artery, 72
liver, 92
lower extremity, 110
lungs, 78
mamma, 76
maxillary sinus, 69
mesenteric arteries, 96
metacarpal bones, 104
metatarsal bones, 115
metatarso-phalangeal joint, 106
middle meningeal artery, 69
muscles of abdomen, 81, 82
of arm, 106
of back 75
of buttock, 117
of foot, 117
of forearm, 106
of hand, 107
of head and neck, 64, 70
of leg, 117, 118
of thigh, 117
of thorax, 76
neck, 69
triangles of, 71
occipital artery, 72
palmar or volar arches, 108
palpebral fissure, 65
pancreas, 93
patella, 115
pectorales muscles, 106
pelvis, 109
perineum, 96
nerves, 118
phalanges of foot, 115
of hand, 105
phrenic nerve, 74
pleuræ, 79
plica semilunaris, eye, 65
popliteal artery, 118
fossa, 118
posterior tibial artery, 118
profunda brachii artery, 108
femoris artery, 118
pupil, 66
radial artery, 108
radiohumeral joint, 106
radioulnar joints, 106
radius, 101
Reid's base line, 64
renal arteries, 96
scapula, 100
serratus anterior muscle, 82 106
shoulder-joint, 106
spleen, 94
sternal angle, 76
sternoclavicular joint, 105
sternocleidomastoideus muscle, 70, 73
stomach, 87
subclavian artery, 74, 108
subdural and subarachnoid cavities, 76
submaxillary gland, 73
supraclavicular nerves, 73, 74

Surface anatomy, synovial sheaths around ankle, 118
of wrist and hand, 105
talus, 115
tarsus and foot, 115
temporomandibular joint, 61
tendinous inscriptions of rectus abdominis, 460
thorax, 76
tibia, 115
tibial artery, 118
trachea, 70
transverse sinus, 66, 69
trapezius, 106
triangles of neck, 71
tympanic antrum, 66
membrane, 66
ulna, 104
nerve, 108
umbilicus, 82
upper extremity, 100
ureters, 95
urogenital organs, female, 98
male, 97
vena cava, 93
vermiform process, 89
vertebral column, 75
viscera, 87
volar or palmar arches, 108
wrist and hand, 106
wrist-joint, 106
Suspensory ligament, axilla, 489
breast, 487, 1382
eye, 1117
lens, 1113
ovary, 1369, 1376
penis, 1364
Sustentacular fibers of Müller, 1111
Sustentaoulum lienis, 1269
talare, 292, 293
Sutura dentata, 322
harmonia, 323
limbosa, 323
notha, 323
serrata, 323
squamosa, 323
vera, 322
Sutural bones, 213
Suture, coronal, 158, 163, 192
frontal, 159, 193
frontoethmoidal, 173
lambdoidal, 158, 173, 189, 192
metopic, 193
occipitomastoid, 163
parietomastoid, 163
petroöccipital, 162
petrosquamous, 199, 201
sagittal, 158
sphenoethmoidal, 173
sphenofrontal, 163, 173
sphenoparietal, 163, 174
sphenopetrosal, 174
sphenosquamosal, 163, 174
sphenozygomatic, 163
squamosal, 163
zygomaticofrontal, 163
zygomaticotemporal, 163
Sweat glands, 1163
Sylvian fissure, 833
fossa, 833
veins, 734
Sylvius, aqueduct of, 881
fissure of, 882
Sympathetic fibers of spinal nerves, 1000
nerves, 1061
connections with spinal nerves, 1000, 1066
nervous system, development of, 883
cephalic portion of, 1067

Sympathetic nervous system, cervical portion of, 1070
pelvic portion of, 1082
thoracic portion of, 1074
plexuses, 1082
trunks, 1065
Symphysis of mandible, 180
ossium pubis, 349
pubis, 349
sacrococcygea, 348
Synarthroses, 322
Synchondrosis, 322
neurocentral, 144
Syncytiotrophoblast, 46
Syndesmology, 317. *See* Joints and Ligaments.
Syndesmosis, 322
tibiofibularis, 389
Synovia, 325
Synovial bursæ, 326, 409
cavity, 325
fluid, 325
membrane, 325. *See also* Individual Joints.
sheaths, 326
of tendons around ankle, 551
on back of wrist, 513
on front of wrist, 512
Systemic circulation, 603
veins, 723

T

TACTILE corpuscles of Golgi and Mazzoni, 939
of Pacini, 939
of Ruffini, 939
of Wagner and Meissner, 939
Tænia coli, 1284
of fourth ventricle, 867
of muscular coat of large intestine, 1284
pontis, 867
thalami, 875
ventriculi quarti, 867
Talocalcaneal articulation, 393
Talocalcaneonavicular articulation, 394
Talocrural articulation, 390
Talofibular ligaments, 392
Talonavicular joint, 394
Talotibial ligaments, 391
Talus, 294, 303
Tapetum of choroid of eye, 1104
of corpus callosum, 895
Tarsal arteries, 709
bones, 289
glands, 1119
plates, 1118
Tarsi of eyelids, 1118
Tarsometatarsal articulations, 399
Tarsus, 289
articulations of, 393
inferior, eye, 393, 1118
ossification of, 302
superior, eye, 1118
synovial membranes of, 400
Taste fibers, 917, 920
nerves of, 1095
organ of, 1094
Taste-buds, 1094, 1237
Tectorial membrane of ductus cochlearis, 1150
Tectospinal fasciculus, 924
Teeth, 1220
bicuspid, 1222
canine, 1222
cement or crusta petrosa of, 1225
crown of, 1221, 1222
cutting, 1221

Teeth deciduous, 1223
  dental canaliculi of, 1224
  dentin of, 1224
  development of, 1225
  enamel of, 1224
  eruption of, 1229
  eye, 1222
  incisive, 1221
  incisors, 1221
  ivory of, 1224
  milk, 1223
  molar, 1222
  multicuspid, 1222
  necks of, 1220, 1222
  permanent, 1221
    successional, 1229
    superadded, 1229
  premolar, 1220
  pulp cavity of, 1223
  roots of, 1220, 1221
  stomach, 1221
  structure of, 1223
  substantia adamantina of, 1224
    eburnea of, 1224
    ossea of, 1225
  temporary, 1223
  wisdom, 1222
Tegmen tympani, 199, 1130
Tegmental part of pons, 859
Tegmentum, 852
Tela chorioidea [fourth ventricle],
    832, 880
  [third ventricle], 880
Telencephalon, 828, 880
Telophase of karyokinesis, 23
Temperature, impulses of, 922
Temporal arteries, 627, 630
  bone, 195, 203
    articulations of, 203
    mastoid portion of, 198
    ossification of, 203
    petrous portion of, 199
    pyramid of, 199
    squama of, 195
    tympanic part of, 202
  fascia, 422
  fossa, 163
  gyri, 885
  lines, 159, 163, 192
  lobe, 885
  muscle, 422
  nerves of auriculotemporal, 970
    of facial, 979
  operculum, 885
  pole, 882
  process of zygomatic bone, 221
  veins, 727
Temporalis muscle, 424
Temporary teeth, 1223
Temporomalar nerve, 971
Temporomandibular articulation,
    335
Temporomaxillary vein, 727
Tendinous arch of pelvic fascia,
    469
  inscriptions of rectus abdominis
    muscle, 461
  levator ani muscle, 469
Tendo Achillis, 546
  calcaneus, 546
  oculi, 417
Tendon or Tendons, 411
  back of wrist, relations of, 513
  central, of diaphragm, 450
  conjoined, of internal oblique
    and transversalis muscles,
    460
  of conus arteriosus, 593
  front of wrist, 512
  superior, of Lockwood, 1115
  of Zinn, 1115
Tendril fibers of cerebellum, 867
Tendon, capsule of, 1117

Tension lines, 1157
Tensor fasciæ latæ muscles, 538
  palati muscle, 1245
  tarsi muscle, 416
  tympani muscle, 1138
    semicanal for, 202, 1135
  veli palatini muscle, 1245
Tenth, 10th nerve, 920
Tentorial sinus, 737
Tentorium cerebelli, 925
Teres major muscle, 495
  minor muscle, 495
Terminal crest of right atrium,
    586
  sulcus of right, atrium, 586
  vein, 735
  ventricle, 842
Testis or Testes, 1320, 1348
  appendages of, 1353
  appendix of, 1353
  coni vasculosi of, 1355
  coverings of, 1348
  descent of, 1320
  ductuli efferentes, 1355
  ductus deferens, 1358
  gubernaculum, 1321
  lobules of, 1354
  lymphatic capillaries of, 779
    vessels of, 807
  mediastinum, 1354
  rete, 1355
  structure of, 1354
  tubuli recti, 1355
    seminiferi, 1354
  tunica albuginea, 1354
    vaginalis, 1353
    vasculosa, 1353, 1354
Thalamus, 829, 874
  geniculate bodies, 877
  intermediate mass of, 829, 875
  massa intermedia, 875
  nuclei of, 876
  pulvinar, 875
  structure of, 875
  surfaces of, 874
Thebesius, foramina of, 725
  valve of, 587, 724
  veins of, 725
Thenar eminence, 511
  facial cleft, 519
    compartment, 517
  muscles, 520
  space, 519
Thigh bone, 269
  fascia lata of, 528
    superficial, 528
  muscles of, 528
Third cuneiform bone, 298
  metacarpal bone, 255
  metatarsal bone, 301
  nerve, 957
  trochanter, 273
  ventricle of brain, 881
Thoracic aorta, 666
  arteries, 655
  axis, 655
  cardiac nerves, 991
  duct, 782
  nerves, divisions of, 1002, 1014,
    1031
  portion of gangliated cord, 1074
  vertebræ, 126, 132
Thoracoacromial artery, 655
Thoracodorsal artery, 655
  nerve, 1017
Thoracoepigastric vein, 753
Thoracolumbar sympathetics,
    1063
Thorax, 147
  boundaries of, 148
  cavity of, 1191
  lymph nodes, 808
  lymphatic vessels of, 809

Thorax, mechanism of, 343
  muscles of, 446
    surface anatomy of, 76
  openings of, 148, 149
  skeleton of, 147
  surface anatomy of, 76
  x-ray of heart and diaphragm,
    anterior view, 82
Thumb, carpometacarpal articu-
    lation of, 371
Thymus, 816
  glands, 816
  lymphatic vessels of, 812
  nerves of, 818
  structure of, 817
  vessels of, 818
Thyreoarytænoideus muscle, 1186
Thyreohyoideus muscle, 434
Thyreoidea ima artery, 618
Thyroarytenoid ligaments, 1182
  muscle, 1186
Thyrocervical trunk, 646
Thyroepiglottic ligament, 1179
  muscle, 1187
Thyroglossal duct, 1231, 1391
Thyrohyals of hyoid bone, 185
Thyrohyoid ligaments, 1179
  membrane, 1179
  muscle, 434
Thyroid arteries, 621
  axis, 646
  body, 1391
  cartilage, 1176
  foramen, 265
  gland, 1391
    isthmus of, 1391, 1392
    lobes of, 1391
    lymphatic vessels of, 792
    nerves of, 1394
    pyramidal lobe of, 1393
    structure of, 1393
    vessels of, 1394
  notch, superior, 1176
  veins, 730, 747
Thyroids, accessory, 1393
Tibia, 283
  nutrient artery of, 711
  ossification of, 287
  surface anatomy of, 115
Tibial artery, anterior, 706
    surface marking of, 118
  posterior, 709
    surface marking of, 118
  recurrent, 708
  collateral ligament of knee-
    joint, 382
  nerve, 1053
    anterior, 1053
  surfaces of femur, 275
  beins, 754
Tibialis anterior muscle, 543
  anticus muscle, 543
  posterior muscle, 549
Tibiofascialis muscle, 544
Tibiofibular articulation, 389
  ligament, middle, 389
  syndesmosis, 389
Tibionavicular ligament, 391
Tibiotarsal articulation, 390
Tissues, connective, 305
Tomes' fibers, 1224
Tongue, 1209, 1230
  dorsum of, 1231
  frenulum of, 1231
  glands of, 1237
  lymph node of, 787
  lymphatic vessels of, 787
  mucous membrane of, 1236
  muscles of, 1234
    actions of, 1236
  nerves of, 1236
  papillæ of, 1231
  septum of, 1237

Tongue structure of, 1236
  vessels of, 1237
Tonsil, of cerebellum, 863
  lingual, 1231, 1243
  palatine, 1209, 1242
    lymphatic vessels of, 878
    nerves of, 1244
    structure of, 1244
    vessels of, 1244
  pharyngeal, 1249
  tubal, 1135
Tonsillæ intestinales, 1282
  palatinæ, 1242
Tonsillar artery, 623
  nerves from glossopharyngeal, 986
  sinus, 1242
Torcular Herophili, 188, 739
Torus of auditory tube, 1249
  uretericus, 1344
  uterinus, 1266
Touch fibers, 922
Trabeculæ carneæ, 589, 591
  of penis, 1364
  of spleen, 814
  of testis, 1354
Trachea, 1188
  lymphatic capillaries in, 778
  nerves of, 1191
  relations of, 1189
  structure of, 1190
  surface anatomy of, 70
  vessels of, 1191
Tracheal artery, 647
Trachealis muscle, 1191
Trachelomastoid muscle, 442
Tracheobronchial lymph nodes, 811
Trachoma glands, 1121
Tracts or Tractus, auditory, 899, 918
  of Burdach, 843
  cerebelloreticular, 864
  cerebellorubral, 865
  cerebrospinal, 846, 923
  comma, of Schultze, 844
  corticobulbar, 870, 899
  corticospinal, 846, 870, 899, 923
  cuneatus, 843
  dentatorubral, 876
  dorsolateral, 845, 922
  fastigiobulbar, 865
  fibræ pontis, 861
    propriæ, cerebellum, 865
  of Flechsig, 844
  forebrain bundle, medial, 881, 911
  of Goll, 843
  of Gowers, 845, 865, 923
  gracilis, 843
  of Gudden, 880, 911
  iliotibialis, 530
  interfascicularis, 844
  lemniscus, lateral, 870, 873, 915, 918
    medial, 858, 862, 873, 877, 922
    spinal, 853
  trigeminal, 915
  trigeminothalamic, 873, 916
  of Lissauer, 845, 922
  longitudinal fasciculus, medial, 859, 862, 872, 912, 915, 916, 917
    posterior, 912, 920
  mammillotegmental, 880, 911
  mammillothalamic, 876, 880, 911
  mesencephalicus V, 860
  olfactorius, 904
  olfactory, 904, 910
  olivocerebellar, 864

Tracts olivospinal, 846
  optic, 870, 880, 912, 915, 947
    radiation, 899, 912, 915
  opticus, 957
  oval area of Flechsig, 844
  of Phillipe-Gombault, 844
  pontocerebellar, 865
  proprius, dorsalis, 844
    lateralis, 846
    ventralis, 846
  pyramid, 858
  pyramidal, aberrant, 863, 870, 916, 917, 921
    crossed, 846, 921, 923
    direct, 846
  reticulospinal, 847, 917
  reticulothalamic, 876
  retroflexus of Meynert, 911
  rubrospinal, 846, 873, 923
  septomarginal, 844
  solitarius, 826, 855, 917, 919, 920
  spinocerebellar, 844, 858, 862, 864, 865, 923
  spinotectal, 845, 915
  spinothalamic, 845, 846, 858, 862, 877, 922
  spiralis foraminosus, 200
  sulcomarginal, 947, 919
  tectobulbar, 872, 912, 915
  tectospinal, 847, 858, 872, 912, 915, 924
    of tegmentum, central, 852
  thalamoölivary, 852, 862, 873
  trapezoid body, 863, 918
  trigeminal, secondary, 876
    mesencephalic, 860, 916
    spinal, 853, 916
  uncinate bundle of Russell, 865
  vestibulocerebellar, 864
  vestibulospinal, 846, 919, 924
    of Vicq D'Azyr, 876, 880, 911
Tragicus muscle, 1128
Tragus, 1126
Transpyloric plane, 1253
Transversa colli artery, 652
Transversalis cervicis muscle, 442
  colli artery, 652
  fascia, 464
  muscle, 459
Transverse acetabular ligament
  of hip-joint, 377
  aorta, 616
  carpal ligament, 511
  cervical artery, 646
    nerve, 1008
  colon, 1287
  crural ligament, 551
  facial artery, 627
    vein, 727
  fissure of brain, 833
    of liver, 1299
  folds of rectum, 1291
  ligament, atlas, 333
    humeral, 358
    fingers, 521
    knee, 384
    metacarpal, 372
    metatarsal, 400
    pelvis, 477
  ligaments of scapula, 356
  lingualis muscle, 1236
  mesocolon, 1260, 1269, 1287
  occipital sulcus, 885
  portion of duodenum, 1279
  process of a vertebra, 127
  scapular artery, 647
  sinus, 175, 738
    of pericardium, 581
  temporal gyri, 885
Transversus abdominis muscle, 459

Transversus auriculæ muscle, 1128
  linguæ muscle, 1236
  menti muscle, 419
  nuchæ muscle, 415
  pedis muscle, 558
  perinæi muscles, 478
    profundus muscle in female, 482
      in male, 480
    superficialis muscle, 478, 480
      in female, 480
      in male, 478
  thoracis muscle, 448
Trapezium, 252
Trapezius muscle, 485
Trapezoid body, 863, 919
  bone, 252
  ligament, 354
  nucleus, 863
  ridge, 228
Treitz, ligament of, 1279
Treves, bloodless fold of, 1271
Triangle or Triangles, of auscultation, 486
  carotid, 71, 432, 435
  cervical, 71, 426, 432
  digastric, 72
  femoral, 697
  Hesselbach's, 95
  lumbar, 485
  muscular, 71, 435
  neck, 71, 426
  occipital, 73, 435
  of Petit, 486
  of Phillipe-Gombault, 844
  of vagus nerve, 869
  Scarpa's, 697
  subclavian, 73, 435
  submaxillary, 72, 432
  submental, 432
  suboccipital, 445, 643
  suprahyoid, 73, 432
  suprameatal, 64, 164, 197, 4?7
Triangular articular disk, 366
  bone, 249
  fascia of abdomen, 456
  ligament, 477
    of liver, 1259
Triangularis muscle, 419
  sterni muscle, 448
Triceps brachii muscle, 498
  extensor cubiti muscle, 498
  muscle, 498
  suræ muscle, 546
Tricuspid valve, 589
Trifacial nerve, 960
Trigeminal nerve, 915, 960
  composition and central connections of, 915
  ganglion (Gasser), 960
  impression for, 199
  mandibular division, 968
  maxillary division, 964
  ophthalmic division, 961
  referred pain in, 973
  semiulunar ganglion, 960
  spinal tract of, 916
Trigone, olfactory, 905
Trigonum femorale, 697
  fibrosum 593
    dentrum, 593
    sinistrum, 593
  habenulæ, 878
  hypoglossa, 853, 869, 995
  olfactorium, 905
  vesicæ, 1344
Trochanter, greater, 270
  lesser, 271
  third, 272
Trochanteric fossa, 270
Trochlea of humerus, 239

Trochlear fovea, 169, 194
  nerve, 915, 960
    composition and central con-
      nections of, 915
    nuclei of, 870
  process of calcaneus, 293
  spine, 194
Trochoid joint, 323
Trolard, anastomotic vein of, 734
Troltsch, recess of, 1138
Trophoblast, 29
True pelvis, 266
  skin, 1155
  vocal cords, 1182
Truncus arteriosus, 575
  costocervicalis, 652
  pulmonis, 611
  sympathicus, 1065
  thyreocervicalis, 646
Trunk, arteries of, 666
  articulations of, 326
  costocervical, 652
  muscles of, 438
  thyrocervical, 646
Tube, auditory, 1135
  digestive, 1207
  Eustachian, 1135
  Fallopian, 1370
  neural, 44
  uterine, 1370
Tuber cinereum, 849, 878
  frontale, 193
  omentale [liver], 1296
    [pancreas], 1309
  parietale, 191
Tubercle, adductor, 273
  anterior, 129
  articular, of temporal bone,
    160, 196
  auricular, of Darwin, 1126
  conoid, 228
  cuneate, 849
  cuneiform, 1182
  of epiglottis, 1179
  of femur, 271
  greater, 236
  of humerus, 235
  lesser, 236
  intervenous, 587
  jugular, 189
  lacrimal, 218
  of Lower, 587
  mental, 180
  obturator, 265
  olfactory, 907
  peroneal, 293
  pharyngeal, 160, 189
  posterior, 130
  pubic, 263
  pyterygoid, 208
  of rib, 154
  of Rolando, 849
  scalene, 156
Tuberculum acusticum, 869
  articularis, 196
  impar, 1209
  intervenosum, 587
  majus [humeri], 236
  minus [humeri], 236
  nuclei cuneati, 849
  gracilis, 849
  sellæ, 174, 204
Tuberosity, calcaneal, 292
  coracoid, 229
  costal, 230
  of cuboid, 296
  deltoid, 237
  of fifth metatarsal bone, 301
  gluteal, 273
  greater, 236
  iliac, 259
  infraglenoid, 233
  ischial, 262

Tuberosity, lesser, 236
  maxillary, 215
  of navicular bone, 297
  of palatine bone, 223
  radial, 246
  supraglenoid, 234
  tibial, 283
  ulna, 244
Tubuli lactiferi, 1384
  recti [testis], 1355
  seminiferi, 1354
Tubule, renal, 1334, 1335
Tunica adventitia, 765
  albuginea [ovary], 1369
    [testis], 1354
  conjunctiva bulbi, 1120
  dartos, 1350
  elastica externa, 765
  fibrosa oculi, 1100
  fibrous, of kidney, 1330
  intima, 765
  media, 765
  serosa, 1258, 1277
  vaginalis, 1351, 1353
    *communis [testis et funiculi
      spermatici],* 1351
    propria testis, 1353
  vasculosa [testis], 1354
    oculi, 1103
Tunics of eyeball, 1100, 1103
Tunnel of Corti, 1149
Turbinated bone, 225
  processes, sphenoidal, 208
Twelfth, 12th nerve, 921
Tympanic antrum, 199
  artery, 629
    from ascending pharyngeal,
      627
    from internal maxillary, 628
  canaliculus, inferior, 162, 201
  cavity, 1130
    arteries of, 1138
    attic or epitympanic recess
      of, 1130
    carotid or anterior wall of,
      1133
    jugular wall or floor of, 1130
    labyrinthic or median wall
      of, 1133
    mastoid or posterior wall of,
      1133
    membranous or lateral wall
      of, 1130
    mucous membrane of, 1138
    muscles of, 1138
    nerves of, 1138
    ossicles of, 1135
    tegmental wall or roof, 1130
    vessels of, 1138
  lip, 1147
  membrane, 66, 1131
  nerve (Jacobson's), 983, 1130
  plexus, 984, 1130
  ring, 203
  sulcus, 202, 1130, 1132
Tympanohuyal part of temporal
  bone, 203
Tympanomastoid fissure, 161
Tympanum, 1130

U

Ulna, 241
  ossification of, 246
  structure of, 246
  surface anatomy of, 104
Ulnar artery, 662
  collateral artery, 658
  recurrent artery, 663
  nerve, 1024
  notch of radius, 247
Ultimo-branchial bodies, 1391

Umbilical arteries in fetus, 577
  cord, 53
  folds, 1343
  fossa of liver, 1298
  notch of liver, 1298
  veins, 55,579, 723
    obliterated, 762, 1259
  vesicle, 55
  vessels 55
  zone, 1254
Umbilicus, 53, 82, 86
Umbo of membrana tympani,
  1132
Unciform bone, 254
Uncinate fasciculus, 895
Uncus, 886
Ungual phalanges, 257, 302
Ungues, 1158
Upper extremity, bones of, 227
  jaw, 214
Urachus, 1323
Ureter, 1337
  arteries of, 1339
  lymphatic vessels of, 806
  muscles of, 1344
  nerves of, 1339
  orifices of, 1344
  x-ray of, pelves and minor cal-
    yces, 92
Urethra, development of, 1324
  female, 1348
  male, 1346
    crest or verumontanum of,
      1346, 1348
  lymphatic vessels of, 807
  muliebris, 1348
  virilis, 1346
Urethral artery, 691
  bulb, 1347
  crest, in female, 1348
    in male, 1246
  glands, 1347
  orifices, 1344, 1381
  plate, 1324
Urinary bladder, 1339
  abnormalities of, 1345
  female, 1342
  ligaments of, 1343
  male, 1339
  meatus, 1381
  organs, 1325
Urogenital apparatus, 1315
  diaphragm, 476
  fold, 1316
  organs, 1315
  ostium, primitive, 1324
  sinus, 1323
Urorectal septum, 1215
Uterine artery, 687
  glands, 1378
  plexus of nerves, 1087
  plexuses of veins, 758
Uterosacral ligaments, 1376
Uterus, 1370, 1372
  in adult, 1377
  cervix of, 1373
    during menstruation, 1377
    pregnancy, 1377
  in fetus, 1377
  form, size and situation of, 1377
  fundus of, 1373
  interior of, 1374
  isthmus of, 1373
  ligaments of, 1375
  lymphatic capillaries of, 809
    vessels of, 808
  masculinus, or prostatic
    utricle, 1346
  nerves of, 1346
  in old age, 1377
  palmate folds of, 1375
  after parturition, 1377
  position of, 1377

Uterus at puberty, 1377
  virgin state of, 1373
Utricle, prostatic, 1346
  of vestibule, 1144
Utriculus, 1144
Uvea, 1103
Uvula of cerebellum, 863
  palatine, 1219
  vesicæ, 1344

V

VAGINA, 1378, 1379
  lymphatic vessels of, 808
Vaginæ mucosæ, 326
Vaginal artery, 688
  bulb, 1381
  orifice, 1381
  plexus of nerves, 1087
  plexuses of veins, 758
  process of sphenoid bone, 208
  of temporal bone, 201
Vagus nerve, 920, 986
  cardiac nerves, 991
  composition and central con-
    nections of, 920
  jugular ganglion, 987
  laryngeal nerves, 990
  nodosa ganglion, 987
Valleculæ of tongue, 1179
Valsalva, sinuses of, 592
Valve or Valves, anal, 1291
  aortic, 592
  bicuspid, 591
  colic, 1285
  of coronary sinus, 587
  Eustachian, 587
  of heart, 589
    development of, 576
  Houston's, 1290
  ileocecal, 1285
  of inferior vena cava, 587, 759
  Kerkring's, 1280
  lymphatics, 781
  mitral, 591
  pulmonary, 590
  pyloric, 1275
  right and left venous, 575
  semilunar aortic, 576
  Thebesian, 587, 724
  triscupid, 589
  of veins, 769
Valvula bicuspidalis, 591
  foraminis ovalis, 590
  sinus coronarii [*Thebesii*], 587
  tricuspidalis, 589
  venæ cavæ infreioris, 587
Valvulæ conniventes, 1280
Vas, Vasa aberrans of Haller, 1358
  aberrantia [from branchial
    artery], 657
  deferens, 1358
  gastrica brevia, 677
  intestini tenuis, 678
  spirale, 1148
  vasorum [arteries], 767
    [veins], 769
Vascular capsule of lens, 1097
  system, changes in, at birth,
    576
  development of, 568, 604,
    718
  peculiarities in fetus, 576
  tunics of eye, 1103
Vastus externus muscle, 532
  intermedius muscle, 532, 533
  internus muscle, 533
Vastus lateralis muscle, 532
  medialis muscle, 533
Vater, ampulla of, 1307
Vein or Veins, of abdomen, 751
  accessory hemiazygos, 718, 749
  anastomotic, of Labbé, 734

Vein angular, 725
  auditory, 1151
  auricular, 727
  axillary, 745
  azygos, 719, 749
  basal, 734
  basilic, 743
    median, 744
  basivertebral, 750
  brachial, 745
  brachiocephalic, 721, 746
  of brain, 733
  bronchial, 749, 1204
  cardiac, 724, 725
  cardinal, 718
  cephalic, 742
    accessory, 742
  cerebellar, 735
  cerebral, 733, 735
  choroid, 735
  coats of, 768
  common facial, 726
    iliac, 758
  coronary, 724
    of stomach, 764
  cystic, 765
  deep cerebral, 734
    cervical, 731
    epigastric, 756
    facial, 727
    femoral, 754
    forearm, 745
    hand, 744
    lower extremity, 754
    upper extremity, 744
  development of, 718
  digital, of foot, 752
    of hand, 742
  diploic, 733
  dorsal digital, 752
    metacarpal, 742, 745
    of penis, 758
  emissary, 735, 740
  epigastric, 756
  extraspinal, 750
  facial, 725, 726
  femoral, 754
  frontal, 725
  of Galen, 734
  gastroepiploic, 764
  gluteal, 757
  of hand, 742, 744
  of head and neck, 725
  of heart, 724
  hemiazygos, 718, 749
  hemorrhoidal, 757, 764
  hepatic, 762
  hypogastric, 757
  iliac, 718, 755, 758
  inferior vena cava, 720, 759
  innominate 720, 746
  intercapitular, 742
  intercostal, highest, 718, 747
  interlobular, of kidney, 1336
  intervertebral, 751
  intralobular, of liver, 1303
  intraspinal, 750
  jugular, 728, 729
    anterior, 728
    external, 728
    internal, 729
    posterior, 728
    primitive, 718
  labial, 726
  lateral sacral, 757
  of Labbé, posterior anasto-
    motic, 734
  of left atrium, 725
  lienal or splenic, 763
  lingual, 730
  of lower extremity, 751
  lumbar, 759
    ascending, 749, 760

Vein mammary, internal, 747
  marginal, of foot, 752
    of heart, 724
  maxillary, internal, 727
  median antebrachial, 744
    basilic, 744
  of medulla spinalis, 751
  mesenteric, 764
  metatarsal, 754
  nasofrontal, 739
  of neck, 725, 727
  oblique, of left atrium [Mar-
    shalli], 575, 582, 722, 725
  obturator, 757
  occipital, 727
  ophthalmic, 735, 739
  orbital, 725
  ovarian, 761
  palpebral, 727
  pancreatic, 764
  pancreaticoduodenal, 764
  parumbilical, 765
  of pelvis, 751
  penis, dorsal of, 758
  peroneal, 754
  pharyngeal, 730
  phrenic, inferior, 762
    superior, 747
  plantar, 754
  plexus of, basilar, 740
    hemorrhoidal, 757
    prostatic, 758
    pterygoid, 727
    pudendal, 757
    uterine, 758
    vaginal, 758
    vertebral, 750
    vesical, 758
    vesicoprostatic, 758
  popliteal, 754
  portal, 717, 762
  posterior of left ventricle, 725
  precardinal, 718
  primitive jugular, 718
  profunda femoris, 755
  pubic, 756
  pudendal, internal, 757
  pudic, 757
  pulmonary, 723
  pyloric, 764
  ranine, 730
  renal, 762, 1345
  sacral, 757, 759
  saphenous, 752, 753
  sciatic, 757
  short gastric, 764
  spermatic, 761
  of spinal cord, 751
  splenic or lienal, 763
  striate, inferior, 734
  structure of, 768
  subcardinal, 719
  subclavian, 745
  sublobular, of liver, 1302
  superficial, 717
    of lower extremity, 752
    of upper extremity, 742
  superior cerebral, 734
    mesenteric, 764
    phrenic, 747
    sagittal, 735
    supracardinal, 719
    testicular, 719
    vena cava, 747
  supraorbital, 725
  suprarenal, 762
  Sylvian, 734
  systemic, 723
  temporal, 727
  temporomaxillary, 727
  terminal, 735
  Thebesian, 725
  thoraco-epigastric, 753

Vein of thorax, 746
  thyroid, inferior, **747**
    middle, 730
    superior, 730
  tibial, 754
  transverse facial, 727
  Trolard, great anastomotic of, 734
  umbilical, 723
    obliterated, 762, 1299
  of upper extremity, 742
  valves of, 769
  vena azygos major, 749
    minor, 747
    cava, inferior, 759
      superior, 747
  vertebral, 730
    column, 749
  visceral, 722
  vitelline, 722
  volar, 742, 744
Velamentous insertion of umbilical cord, 52
Velum interpositum, 880
  medullary, 867
  palatine, 1219
Vena or *Venæ advehentes*, 723
  anonyma dextra, 746
    sinistra, 742
  basivertebrales, 750
  brachiales, 745
  bronchiales, 749
  cava inferior, 574, 587, 718
    superior, 574, 587, 720, 747
  caval foramen in diaphragm, *cerebelli*, 735
  cerebri internæ [Galeni], 735
  cervicalis profunda, 731
  circumflexa ilii profunda, 756
  cordis, 724
    media, 725
    minimæ, 587
    parva, 724
  corporis striati, 735
  gastricæ breves, 764
  magna [*Galeni*], 735
    cubiti, 742
    portæ, 762
  posterior ventriculi sinistri, 725
  profunda femoris, 755
  revehentes, 723
  saphena magna, 752
    parva, 754
  stellatæ [kidney], 1336
  vorticosæ, 1101, 1104
Venous arches, 752
  lacunæ of dura mater, 735
  mesocardium, 581
  plexus, hemorrhoidal, 757
    ovarian, 761, 1370
    pampiniform, 761, 1352
    pharyngeal, 730
    pterygoid, 727
    pudendal, 757
    spermatic, 761, 1352, 1370
    uterine, 758
    vaginal, 758
    vesical, 758
  sinuses, 717, 735
    of dura mater, 735
  valves, right and left, 574
Ventral aorta, development of, 604
  cochlear nucleus, 918
  fissure of medulla oblongata, 847
  lamina, 822
  mesogastrium, 1211, 1215
  pulmonary nerves, 993
  spinothalamic fasciculus, 845,
Ventricle, terminal, of medulla spinalis, 842

Ventricles, of brain, 867, 881, 899
  x-ray of, injected with air, 66
  of heart, 587, 591
  of larynx, 1181, 1183
Ventricular folds of larynx, 1182
  ligament of larynx, 1182
  septum, 592
Ventriculus, 1272
  dexter, 587
  laryngis [*Morgagni*], 1183
  lateralis, 899
  quartus, 867
  sinister, 591
  tertius, 880
Ventromedian fissure of medulla oblongata, 847
Vermian fossa, 188
Vermiform process or appendix, 804, 1285
Vermis of cerebellum, 863
Vertebra prominens, 132
Vertebræ, 126
  cervical, 126, 128
  coccygeal, 126, 137
  ligaments of, 326, 329
  lumbar, 135
  muscles, lateral, 436
  sacral, 137
  thoracic, 132
Vertebral arch, 126
  arches, articulations of, 329
  artery, 643
  canal, 141, 147
  column, 126, 145
    articulations of, 326
    surface form of, 75
    veins of, 750
  fascia, 430
  foramen, 126, 133
  groove, 146
  notches, 127
  ribs, 153
  veins, 730
  venous plexuses, 750
Vertical part of palatine bone, 223
Verticalis linguæ muscle, 1236
Vesica fellea, 1305
  urinaria, 1339
Vesical artery, 687
  plexus of nerves, 1087
    of veins, 758
  auditory, 1123
  lens, 1097
  optic, 828, 1096
  umbilical, 36
Vesicoprostatic plexus of veins, 758
Vesicouterine excavation, 1260
Vesiculæ seminales, 1359
Vesicular ovarian follicles, 1369
Vestibular arteries, 1151
  bulb, 1381
  fissure, 1143
  ganglion, 1150
  glands, greater, 1381
  lip, 1147
  membrane, 1146
  nerve, 919, 1150
    composition and central connections of, 919
    nuclei of, 860, 919
Vestibule, of internal ear, 1140
  of larynx, 1181
  of mouth, 1216
  of nasal cavity, 1170
  of omental bursa, 1267
  of vagina, 1381
Vestibulospinal fasciculus, 846
Vestibulum, 1140
Vestigal fold of Marshall, 575, 581, 725
  of pericardium, 581
Vibrissæ, 1168

Vicq d'Azyr, bundle of, 876, 911
Vidian artery, 631, 634
  canal, 208
Villi, arachnoid, 928
  of chorion, 50
  of intestine, 1281
Viscera, surface anatomy of, 87
Visceral arches, 40
  nervous system, 1057
  receptors, 940
Visual area of cortex, 891
  centers, 912
  purple, 1109
Visuopsychic, area, 892
Visuosensory area, 891
Vitelline circulation, 722
  duct, 36, 1211
  membrane, 28
  veins, 722
Vitellus, 24
Vitreous body of eye, 1099, 1112
Vocal cords, 1182
  folds, 1182
  process of arytenoid cartilage, 1179
Vocalis muscle, 1186
Voice, organ of, 1176
Volar arches, 665
  surface markings of, 106
  branch of ulnar nerve, 1029
  carpal artery, 665
    ligament, 511
    net-work, 665
  digital arteries, 666
    nerves, 1023
  interosseous artery, 665
    nerve, 1023
  metacarpal arteries, 662
    veins, 745
  venous arches, 745
Volaris indicis radialis artery, 662
Vomer, 226
Vomeronasal cartilage, 1173
  nerve, 956
  organs, 45, 954
Vulva, 1379

W

WAGNER and Meissner, corpuscles of, 939
Waldeyer, germinal epithelium of, 1369
  odontoblasts of, 1223
  zona vasculosa of, 1369
Wallerian degeneration, 943
Wharton's duct, 1240
  jelly, 54
White fibrocartilage, 309
  nerve-fibers, 842
  rami communicantes, 1001, 1065
Willis, circle of, 640
Windpipe, 1188
Winslow, foramen of, 1214, 1258, 1267
Wirsung, duct of, 1309
Wisdom teeth, 1222
Wolffian body, 1316
  duct, 1315
  tubules, 1316
Womb, 1372
Wormian bones, 213
Wrisberg, cardiac ganglion of, 1084
  cartilages of, 1179
  ligament of, 384
  nerve of, 1020
  nervus intermedius of, 974
Wrist and hand of child, *x*-ray of, 104, 105
Wrist-joint, 366
  surface anatomy of, 104

Wrist-joint, tendons of, 513

X

X CHROMOSOMES, 26
Xiphoid appendix, 152
    process, 76, 152

Y

Y CHROMOSOMES, 26
Yellow elastic tissue, 325
Yolk-sac, 32, 54
Yolk-stalk 36, 54

Y-shaped cartilage of acetabulum, 264
    ligament of Bigelow, 375

Z

ZINN, ligament or tendon of, 1115
    zonule of, 1113
Zona incerta, 878
    pellucida, 24
    vasculosa of Waldeyer, 1369
Zones of abdomen, 1254
Zonula ciliaris, 1099, 1113
Zonule of Zinn, 1113
Zygomatic arch, 165

Zygomatic bone, 220
    branch of facial nerve, 980
    nerve, 965
    process of frontal bone, 194
        of maxilla, 217
        of temporal bone, 196
Zygomaticofacial foramen, 168, 221
    nerve, 965
Zygomaticofrontal suture, 163
Zygomaticoörbital foramina, 222
Zygomaticotemporal foramen, 163, 221
    nerve, 965
    suture, 163
Zygomaticus muscle, 418